OFFICIAL
METHODS OF ANALYSIS

OF THE

ASSOCIATION OF OFFICIAL
ANALYTICAL CHEMISTS

WILLIAM HORWITZ, Editor

PETER CHICHILO and HELEN REYNOLDS, ASSOCIATE EDITORS

———

ELEVENTH EDITION, 1970

———

PUBLISHED BY THE
ASSOCIATION OF OFFICIAL ANALYTICAL CHEMISTS
PO Box 540, BENJAMIN FRANKLIN STATION
WASHINGTON, DC 20044

Composed by
Monotype Composition Company, Inc.
Baltimore, Maryland

Printed and bound by
George Banta Company, Inc.
Menasha, Wisconsin

Preface to Eleventh Edition

INTRODUCTION

With this edition, AOAC's *Official Methods of Analysis* marks its fiftieth year. Every 5 years since 1920 the Association has published the analytical methods resulting from its efforts in applying analytical science to consumer protection in the areas of agricultural commodities and public health. Prior to 1920 the AOAC methods were issued as Bulletins of the Department of Agriculture, Bureau of Chemistry. Like its predecessors, this edition incorporates all previously published methods considered in current use, as well as those developed or revised during the past 5-year period.

The Association of Official Analytical Chemists (more familiarly known as the AOAC) was established in 1884 by Federal and State agricultural chemists, with the full support of commercial chemists. Until 1965, it was called the Association of Official Agricultural Chemists. While the immediate concern of the founders was to develop uniform and accurate methods for the analysis of fertilizers, they laid the foundation for the continuing development of analytical methods in other areas. Through the years the Association diversified its studies until they now embrace over 500 topics in the broad fields of agriculture, foods, drugs, cosmetics, the environment, and the health and welfare of man and animals. The ever-widening scope of the Association's activities culminated in a change in name in 1965 from "Agricultural Chemists" to "Analytical Chemists." This edition of *Official Methods of Analysis* is the first to be published under the present name.

OBJECTIVE

The objective of this book is to provide both research and regulatory chemists with reliable methods of analysis for determining the composition of commodities subject to legal control. This reliability must be demonstrated by a published study showing the reproducibility of the method in the hands of professional analysts. Adherence to this basic requirement has resulted in a compendium of methods of analysis which has been accorded preferred status in Federal and State courts, and which is generally referred to in Federal and State regulations and governmental and commercial specifications for foods and agricultural commodities. The demonstrated reliability of AOAC methods has prompted their use wherever a need for analysis arises in research or surveillance activities.

DEVELOPMENT AND VALIDATION OF AOAC METHODS

The methods in this compilation were developed and tested by the cooperative efforts of AOAC members in their professional capacities as staff scientists of Federal, State, provincial, and municipal regulatory agencies; experiment stations, colleges, and universities; industry, consulting laboratories, and similar institutions. The methods were approved by government scientists acting in their official capacities. The Association has traditionally sought and obtained participation from industry scientists, who become Associate members by virtue of cooperating in the methods development program.

The central figure in the method study is the Associate Referee, an experienced scientist who is appointed to study a problem area under a process predetermined by the Association. The unique aspect of this process is the required collaborative study. Having reviewed the problem area, devised or adapted a method, tested it, and found it successful in his own laboratory, the Associate Referee proceeds with the collaborative study. This entails recruiting qualified analysts from six or more laboratories (government, industrial, or academic) to test the proposed method, using samples and detailed instructions prepared by the Associate Referee. The collaborators submit their results to the Associate Referee who prepares a report and evaluation for his General Referee, a specialist in the problem area. The latter reviews and evaluates the entire study and makes his recommendations to the appropriate Subcommittee. Each Subcommittee is composed of four experienced and qualified members who make the final recommendation to the Association at its annual meeting. Regardless of the recommendations of the Associate Referee, General Referee, or the Subcommittee, a method does not become official until the Association has voted to adopt it. Only active (official) members may vote on adoption of methods.

When a method is adopted for the first time it is published as *Official First Action*. This designation serves notice that final adoption is pending, and permits an opportunity for any further study that may be deemed appropriate.

Methods that have performed successfully for at least 1 year may be raised to the status of *Official Final Action* after recommendation by the appropriate General Referee and Subcommittee and an affirmative vote of the Association.

A few methods are adopted as *Procedures*. Such methods are generally sorting or screening methods or well-established types of examinations, or auxiliary operations, such as sampling or preparation of a sample, which may not have been subjected to collaborative study.

STYLE, FORM, TERMS

The AOAC editorial style for the publication of methods has evolved over the years to include the following essentials:

(1) A standardized format which follows the flow of laboratory operations.

(2) Use of the imperative form of the verb.

(3) Use of standardized definitions, terminology, and style.

(4) Extensive use of cross references to identical reagents, apparatus, and methods elsewhere in the book.

(5) Free use of abbreviations and simplifications, and elimination of practically all articles (a, an, the) and many prepositions (of, for).

These conventions, along with surplus methods, have again permitted publication of the entire collection of methods within a single volume.

Methods are divided into sections for ease in execution and cross reference. The number of sections depends on the complexity of the method. A relatively simple method may only need "Apparatus," "Reagents," and "Determination." In a complex method, "Determination" may be further supplemented by "Preparation of Sample," "Extraction," "Preparation of Standard Curve," "Calculations," and similar steps. A method incorporating a novel technic may be introduced by a section on "Principles."

For satisfactory application of the methods, users of the Book must read the "Definitions of Terms and Explanatory Notes." This introduction provides the principles which have been used consistently throughout the volume, particularly with respect to reagents and apparatus, and which are primarily responsible for economy in the use of space. The definitions given in this section are those generally accepted in the field of analytical chemistry; however, there are some that are peculiar to *Official Methods*. New to this section is a list of names and addresses of companies repeatedly referenced as suppliers of apparatus and reagents, and also a list of commonly used trade names.

Two changes of older units and symbols were adopted to conform to the S. I. System (Systeme International d'Unites) of metric units as follows:

New		*Old*	
Unit	Symbol	Unit	Symbol
micrometer	μm	micron	μ
nanometer	nm	millimicron	mμ

HIGHLIGHTS OF THE ELEVENTH EDITION

Range of new methods and participation.—Basically the organizational framework of this edition parallels that of the previous issue, and the broad areas covered are the same. Two hundred and forty-nine new methods have been added. In relation to the broad categories, the new methods are distributed as follows: Foods and feeds 50%; drugs and vitamins 23%; agricultural materials 12%; extraneous materials 9%; microbiological methods 2%; and color additives, cosmetics, microchemical methods, and radioactivity 4%.

With reference to organizational participation, the Food and Drug Administration developed or validated 50% of these methods, industrial firms 29%, State and university laboratories 8%, U.S. Department of Agriculture 5%, Internal Revenue Service 3%, and other U.S. and Canadian Government agencies 5%. An increasing number of methods are now being obtained through cooperation with other professional organizations, both national and international.

New challenges of multiresidue multiproduct methods.—Especially deserving of mention are two new multiresidue multiproduct methods developed after years of research to meet a universal need in connection with monitoring pesticide levels in the general food supply. One of these methods couples advances in gas chromatography with procedures evolved from the extraction and cleanup technics developed for use with the paper chromatographic method of the previous edition. This method has been validated for 12 chlorinated pesticides on 33 crops, dairy products, and vegetable oils, and for 7 phosphated pesticides on 2 crops. The other method (sweep codistillation) is applicable to determination of 6 phosphated pesticides on 7 crops. The development and validation of these complex schemes is a significant achievement with considerable potential for further development.

First AOAC polarographic methods; increasing use of gas chromatographic and atomic absorption spectrophotometric methods.—Although polarography is now almost a classical technic, polarographic methods appear in the book for the first time for the determination of fumaric acid as a direct food additive and for the determination of organophosphorus pesticide residues. Gas chromatographic methods have shown remarkable growth. They are included for the first time in the chapters on "Pesticide Formulations," "Beverages: Distilled Liquors," "Coffee and Tea," "Eggs and Egg Products," "Flavors," "Food Additives: Direct," "Drugs in Feeds," "Pesticide Residues," "Cosmetics," and "Vitamins." Interest in metals has been revitalized by the advent of atomic absorption spectrophotometry. New methods for metals appear in the chapters on "Beverages: Distilled Liquors," "Fish and Other Marine Products," "Animal Feed," and "Metals and Other Elements as Residues in Foods."

International dimension.—In carrying out its objective of developing uniform methods of analysis, the AOAC maintains joint committees and liaison with and representation in numerous scientific and legislative groups. Noteworthy in this connection is the progress being made through cooperation with international scientific organizations. Details for sampling, fat, and salt methods in the "Dairy Products" chapter have been adopted after agreement among the International Dairy Federation, the International Organization for Standardization, and the AOAC. Similarly, methods for pH, total nitrogen, and fat in the "Cacao" chapter have been agreed upon by AOAC and Office International du Cacao et du Chocolat. Methods for diquat and paraquat were developed by the Collaborative Pesticide Analytical Committee (CPAC, based in Europe) and were studied collaboratively by the AOAC. A method for thiram, developed and studied by CPAC, also appears in the "Pesticide Formulations" chapter. A number of international standards now being considered for acceptance by governments as a result of the work of the Joint FAO/WHO Food Standards Program—Codex Alimentarious Commission, utilize or refer to AOAC methods.

Refinements in this volume.—Many refinements were made in incorporating the new methods and revisions, including establishment of new chapters, reorganization of others, and changes in chapter titles and arrangements. Only the most important changes are mentioned here.

A completely new area of concern to food analysts was unfolded by the discovery of the aflatoxins only a decade ago. This field has been the subject of such active research during the past five years that a new, integrated chapter has been established. It is noteworthy for its extensive treatment of sample preparation, calibration of standards, applications to specific susceptible commodities, and confirmation by derivative and bioassay technics. In anticipation of further developments in related fields, provision has been made for other mold-derived toxins and for plant and marine toxins in this chapter on "Natural Poisons."

The methods for food additives have been reorganized and are now in one or another of three newly established chapters: "Food Additives: Direct," "Food Additives: Indirect," or "Drugs and Feed Additives in Animal Tissues." "Food Additives: Direct" includes most of the methods in the deleted chapter on "Preservatives and Artificial Sweeteners," plus the antioxidant portion of the "Fats and Oils" chapter. "Food Additives: Indirect" includes the extractability methods for polymers and a new method for polynuclear hydrocarbons in foods. "Drugs and Feed Additives in Animal Tissues," a

relatively new study area, with 4 methods at present, is expected to grow rapidly.

The former chapter on "Pesticides" is now "Pesticide Formulations" to clearly differentiate it from "Pesticide Residues."

The "Grain and Stock Feeds" chapter, which includes pet food, has been given a more meaningful title, "Animal Feed," and now appears at the beginning of the Food Section.

The chapter on "Enzymes" is deleted, because most of the methods are primarily for specific foods and are now in the chapters on "Cereals" and "Vegetable Products, Processed." The only true determination of an enzyme (papain) as an ingredient rather than as an index of deterioration or processing has been placed in the new chapter, "Food Additives: Direct." This does not mean that enzyme studies have been discontinued; on the contrary, a new Referee has planned a broadened program in this area.

The former lengthy chapter on "Metals, Other Elements, and Residue in Foods," has been replaced by two chapters: "Metals and Other Elements as Residues in Food," covering inorganic materials, and "Pesticide Residues," covering organic materials. The latter chapter is further subdivided into general and specific methods.

Chapter 46 on Safety.—This chapter was prepared by a permanent Committee on Safety appointed to advise on how to avoid laboratory accidents and related matters. The chapter identifies serious hazards in the use of certain reagents, apparatus, and technics and suggests measures which the analyst can take to preclude or protect against these hazards. Specific hazards which appear in the individual methods are cross referenced to this chapter. Obviously not all possible hazards could be identified in this initial review.

Treatment of "surplus" methods.—Forty-three methods judged to be infrequently used were designated surplus when the 10th edition was issued. At that time, it was announced that in future issues these methods would be published by title only unless interested scientists advised the Association of a current use for them. As a result of responses received, 8 of these methods are republished in full with the surplus designation removed. The remaining 35, plus 16 others subsequently declared immediate surplus by the Association, appear as surplus methods by title only. The 10th edition should be consulted if a need for these methods arises. Seventy-six additional methods have been marked for surplus status in this edition. Laboratories which utilize these methods and desire that they be retained in the next edition should notify the Association. Particular attention is directed to the surplus status of the time-honored Gutzeit method for arsenic residues.

Reference tables.—There are two new reference

tables: "Density of sucrose solutions at 0–100°C and 0–70% in mg/ml" and "Volume factors for thermal expansion of sucrose solutions up to 100°C."

The Munson-Walker table is deleted in favor of the later Hammond table for calculating various sugars from weights of copper. The Domke table of apparent specific gravity of sucrose solutions was deleted because more recent data are given in the Plato table, **47.008.**

Tables associated with surplus methods or otherwise judged to be used infrequently are marked with the surplus designation and will be treated accordingly in the next issue unless the Association is advised of a continuing need.

Registry numbers.—The Chemical Abstracts Service Registry Number is included in the index following each compound for which a method is given. This is a unique number for that compound and permits entry into the chemical information retrieval system of the Chemical Abstracts Service.

OUTLOOK

The growth, diversification, and ever widening horizon of the Association's activity is expected to continue. New products and new areas of concern emerge continually and more advanced technics and more sophisticated instruments are being applied to analytical problems. It is inevitable that the analytical chemist will be faced with more numerous and more complex problems in the future. To meet the many challenges ahead, the Association is always on the alert to strengthen its manpower resources. Experienced scientists are invited to participate in the AOAC program. Those interested should contact the Executive Secretary.

Cooperation with other organizations will continue to be a primary goal. The Association welcomes all opportunities for joint ventures with other organizations in the national as well as the international area.

Finally, the Association seeks the cooperation of all users of *Official Methods of Analysis* in keeping it attuned to the times. Users' comments are invited on all aspects of this Book. Comments of reviewers, both published and privately submitted, have been particularly helpful.

ACKNOWLEDGMENTS

A massive cooperative effort has made possible another issue of *Official Methods of Analysis*. Credit is due to:

1. Associate Referees and their collaborators for developing and testing the individual methods;
2. General Referees for guidance, reviews, and evaluations in particular areas of study;
3. Subcommittee members for evaluation and advisory services;
4. Staff members of the Association for coordination of the overall activity, and the tremendous task of compiling, organizing, editing, and proofreading the overall product;
5. Volunteer proofreaders and those who provided clerical assistance.

It is estimated that over 2500 individuals were directly or indirectly involved in this work during the past five years. The Association is deeply indebted to each of them, and expresses its sincere appreciation for their help in fostering this unrivaled treatise of laboratory-tested analytical methods.

WILLIAM HORWITZ
Executive Director
Association of Official
Analytical Chemists

Washington, D.C.
May 17, 1970

Preface to First Edition

"In presenting this revision of the official and tentative methods of analysis of the Association of Official Agricultural Chemists, it is appropriate to give a brief statement of the organization of the Association, its purpose, and the procedure by which the methods are adopted.

"Membership in the Association is institutional and includes the State Departments of Agriculture, the State Agricultural Colleges and Experiment Stations, the Federal Department of Agriculture, and the Federal, State, and City offices charged with the enforcement of food, feed, drug, fertilizer, insecticide and fungicide control laws.

"The Association was founded at Philadelphia, Pa., September 9, 1884, by the following representative agricultural chemists of that time, the organization being the result of a series of informal meetings held the immediately preceding years:

"Prof. H. W. Wiley, Chemist of the Department of Agriculture, Washington, D.C.

Mr. Clifford Richardson, Assistant Chemist of the Department of Agriculture, Washington, D.C.

Mr. Philip E. Chazal, State Chemist of South Carolina.

Dr. Chas. W. Dabney, Jr., State Chemist of North Carolina.

Dr. W. J. Gascoyne, State Chemist of Virginia.

Dr. E. H. Jenkins, Connecticut Experiment Station.

Prof. John A. Meyers, State Chemist of Mississippi.

Prof. H. C. White, State Chemist of Georgia.

Mr. C. DeGhequier, Secretary National Fertilizer Association.

Dr. Schumann, Dr. Lehmann, Mr. Gaines and others."

Contents

Illustrations

Definitions of Terms and Explanatory Notes

Reagents

(1) Term "H_2O" means distilled water, except where otherwise specified, and except where the water does not mix with the detn, as in "H_2O bath."

(2) Term "alcohol" means 95% ethanol by vol. Alcohol of strength x% may be prepd by dilg x ml 95% alcohol to 95 ml with H_2O. Absolute alcohol is 99.5% by vol. Formulae of specially denatured alcohols used as reagents are as follows:

SDA No.		
	100	parts alcohol plus
1	5	wood alcohol
2-B	0.5	benzene or rubber hydrocarbon solv.
3-A	5	MeOH
12-A	5	benzene
13-A	10	ether
23-A	10	acetone
30	10	MeOH

(3) Term "ether" means ethyl ether, peroxide-free by following test: To 10 ml ether in small, clean g-s cylinder previously rinsed with the ether, add 1 ml freshly prepd 10% KI soln. Shake, and let stand 1 min. No yellow color should be present in either layer.

(4) Reagents listed below, unless otherwise specified, have approx. strength stated and conform in purity with Recommended Specifications for Analytical Reagent Chemicals of American Chemical Society:

	Assay
Sulfuric acid..............	95.0–98.0% H_2SO_4
Hydrochloric acid..........	36.5–38.0% HCl
Nitric acid................	69.0–71.0% HNO_3
Fuming nitric acid.........	$\geq$90% HNO_3
Acetic acid................	$\geq$99.7% $HC_2H_3O_2$
Hydrobromic acid..........	47.0–49.0% HBr
Ammonium hydroxide.......	28–30% NH_3
Phosphoric acid...........	$\geq$85% H_3PO_4

Where no indication of diln is given, reagent is of concn given above.

(5) All other reagents and test solns, unless otherwise described in text, conform to requirements of American Chemical Society. Where such specifications have not been prepd, use highest grade reagent. When anhyd. salt is intended, it is so stated; otherwise the crystd product is meant.

(6) Unless otherwise specified, phenolphthalein (phthln) used as indicator is 1% alc. soln; Me orange is 0.1% aq. soln; Me red is 0.1% alc. soln.

(7) Directions for stdzg reagents are given in Chapter **45.**

(8) Unusual reagents not mentioned in reagent sections or cross referenced, other than common reagents normally found in laboratory, are italicized first time they occur in method.

(9) Com. prepd reagent solns must be checked for applicability to specific method. They may contain undeclared buffers, preservatives, chelating agents, etc.

(10) In expressions $(1 + 2)$, $(5 + 4)$, etc., used in connection with name of reagent, first numeral indicates vol. reagent used, and second numeral indicates vol. H_2O. For example, HCl $(1 + 2)$ means reagent prepd by mixing one vol. HCl with two vols H_2O. When one of reagents is solid, expression means parts by wt, first numeral representing solid reagent and second numeral H_2O. Solns for which the solv. is not specified are aq. solns.

(11) In making up solns of definite percentage it is understood that x g substance is dissolved in H_2O and dild to 100 ml. Altho not theoretically correct, this convention will not result in any appreciable error in any of methods given in this book.

(12) All calcns are based on table of international atomic weights, **47.001.**

Apparatus

(13) Burets, vol. flasks, and pipets conform to following Federal specifications (available from General Services Admin., Federal Supply Service, Washington, DC 20406):

Buret	NNN-B-00789a	May 19, 1965
Flask, vol.	NNN-F-00289b	Aug 29, 1967
Pipet, vol.	NNN-P-00395b	May 31, 1968
Pipet, measuring	NNN-P-00350b	Aug 30, 1967

See also NBS Circular 602, "Testing of Glass Volumetric Apparatus" (Superintendent of Documents, US Government Printing Office, Washington, DC 20402).

(14) Standard taper ($\bar{\mathbb{S}}$) glass joints may be used instead of stoppers where the latter are specified or implied for connecting glass app.

(15) Sieve designations, unless otherwise specified, are those described in Federal Specification RR-S-366d, June 21, 1966 (available from General Services Admin.). The designation "'100-mesh' (or other number) powder (material, etc.)" means material

ground to pass thru std sieve No. 100 (or other number). The corresponding international std and US std sieves are given in following table:

Designation (Nominal Sieve Opening)

International Standard (ISO)	US Standard		
	inches	mm	No.
	0.500	12.7	½''
11.2 mm	0.438	11.2	7/16''
8.00	0.312	8.00	5/16''
5.66	0.223	5.66	3½
4.00	0.157	4.00	5
2.83	0.111	2.83	7
	0.0937	2.38	8
2.00	0.0787	2.00	10
1.41	0.0555	1.41	14
1.00	0.0394	1.00	18
	0.0331	0.841	20
707 μm	0.0278	0.707	25
	0.0234	0.595	30
500	0.0197	0.500	35
	0.0165	0.420	40
250	0.0098	0.250	60
177	0.0070	0.177	80
	0.0059	0.149	100
125	0.0049	0.125	120
88	0.0035	0.088	170
	0.0029	0.074	200
63	0.0025	0.063	230

(16) Term "paper" means filter paper, unless otherwise specified.

(17) Term "high-speed blender" designates mixer with 4 canted, sharp-edge, stainless steel blades rotating at the bottom of 4-lobe jar at 10,000–12,000 rpm. Suspended solids are reduced to fine pulp by action of blades and by lobular shape of the container, which swirls suspended solids into blades. Waring Blendor, or equiv., meets these requirements.

(18) "Flat-end rod" is glass rod with one end flattened by heating to softening in flame and pressing vertically on flat surface to form circular disk with flat bottom at end.

(19) Designation and pore diam. range of fritted glassware are: extra coarse, 170–220 μm; coarse, 40–60; medium, 10–15; fine, 4–5.5.

(20) Unless otherwise indicated, temps are expressed as degrees Centigrade.

Standard Operations

(21) Operations specified as "wash (rinse, ext, etc.) with two (three, four, etc.) 10 ml (or other quantity) portions H_2O (or other solv.)" mean that the operation is to be performed with indicated vol. of solv. and repeated with same vol. of solv. until number of portions required have been used.

(22) Definitions of terms used in methods involving spectrophotometry are those given in JAOAC 37, 54(1954). The most important principles and definitions are:

(a) More accurate instrument may be substituted for less accurate instrument (e.g., spectrophtr may replace colorimeter) where latter is specified in method.

(b) *Absorbance(s)* (*A*).—Neg. logarithm to base 10 of ratio of transmittance (*T*) of sample to that of ref. or std material. Other names that have been used for quantity represented by this term are optical density, extinction, and absorbancy.

(c) *Absorptivity(ies)* (*a*).—Absorbance per unit concn and cell length. $a = A/bc$, where b is in cm and c in g/L, or $a = (A/bc) \times 1000$, if c is in mg/L. Other names that have been used for this or related quantities are extinction coefficient, specific absorption, absorbance index, and $E_{1cm}^{1\%}$.

(d) *Transmittance(s)* (*T*).—Ratio of radiant power transmitted by sample to radiant power incident on sample, when both are measured at same spectral position and with same slit width. Beam is understood to be parallel radiation and incident at right angles to plane parallel surface of sample. If sample is soln, solute transmittance is quantity usually desired and is detd directly as ratio of transmittance of soln in cell to transmittance of solv. in an equal cell. Other names that have been used for this quantity are transmittancy and transmission.

(e) *Standardization.*—Spectrophtr may be checked for accuracy of wavelength scale by ref. to Hg lines: 239.95, 248.3, 253.65, 265.3, 280.4, 302.25, 313.16, 334.15, 365.43, 404.66, 435.83, 546.07, 578.0, and 1014.0 nm. To check consistency of absorbance scale prep. soln of 0.0400 g K_2CrO_4/L 0.05N KOH and det. absorbance at following wavelengths in 1 cm cell: 230 nm, 0.171; 275, 0.757; 313.2, 0.043; 375, 0.991; 400, 0.396. See "Standards for Checking the Calibration of Spectrophotometers," Letter Circular LC-1017, reissued Jan 1967, NBS.

(23) Common safety precautions are given in Chapter 46.

Editorial Conventions

(24) For sake of simplicity, abbreviations Cl and I instead of Cl_2 and I_2 are used for chlorine and iodine. Similar abbreviations have been used in other cases. The same abbreviation may also be used for the ion where no ambiguity will result.

(25) Reagents and apparatus referenced with only a letter, e.g. (c), will be found in the reagent or apparatus section of that method.

(26) To conserve space, most of the articles and some prepositions have been eliminated.

(27) The names and addresses of manufacturers and suppliers, and trade names of frequently mentioned materials, are furnished below solely as a matter of identification and convenience, without implication of approval, endorsement, or certification. The same products available from other suppliers or other brands from other sources may serve equally well if proper tests indicate their use is satisfactory.

Manufacturers and Suppliers

Ace Glass, Inc., PO Box 688, 1430 N. West Blvd, Vineland, NJ 08360

Allied Chemical Corp., Specialty Chemicals Division, PO Box 405, Morristown, NJ 07960

American Cyanamid Co., Agricultural Division, PO Box 400, Princeton, NJ 08540

American Instrument Co., 8030 Georgia Ave, Silver Spring, MD 20910

(ATCC) American Type Culture Collection, 12301 Parklawn Dr, Rockville, MD 20852

Analabs, Inc., 80 Republic Dr, North Haven, CT 06473

Applied Science Laboratories, Inc., PO Box 440, State College, PA 16801

Atlas Chemicals Industries, Inc., Chemicals Division, Wilmington, DE 19899

Baird-Atomic, Inc., 33 University Rd, Cambridge, MA 02138

J. T. Baker Chemical Co., 222 Red School Ln, Phillipsburgh, NJ 08865

Barber-Colman Co., 1300 Rock St, Rockford, IL 61101

Beckman Instruments, 2500 Harbor Blvd, Fullerton, CA 92634

Brinkmann Instruments, Inc., Cantiague Rd, Westbury, NY 11590

Burdick & Jackson Laboratories, Inc., 1953 S. Harvey St, Muskegon, MI 49442

Calbiochem, 3625 Medford St, Los Angeles, CA 90063

Carborundum Co., PO Box 423, Niagara Falls, NY 14302

Cenco Instrument Corp., 2600 S. Kostner Ave, Chicago, IL 60623

Coleman Instruments, 42 Madison St, Maywood, IL 60153

Corning Glass Works, Laboratory Products Dept., Corning, NY 14830

Difco Laboratories, 920 Henry St, Detroit, MI 48201

Dohrmann Instrument Co., 1062 Linda Vista Ave, Mountain View, CA 94040

Dow Chemical Co., Agricultural Dept., PO Box 1706, Midland, MI 48640

Dow Corning Corp., Midland, MI 48640

Eastman Kodak Co., Eastman Organic Chemicals, 343 State St, Rochester, NY 14650

Fischer & Porter Co., County Line Rd, Warminster, PA 18974

Fisher Scientific Co., 711 Forbes Ave, Pittsburgh, PA 15219

Floridin Co., 3 Penn Center, Pittsburgh, PA 15235

GAF Corp., 140 W. 51st St, New York, NY 10020

Hamilton Co., PO Box 307, Whittier, CA 90608

Hess & Clark Laboratories, 7th and Orange Sts, Ashland, OH 44805

Hoffmann-La Roche, Inc., Nutley, NJ 07110

Johns-Manville Products Corp., 22 E. 40th St, New York, NY 10016

K&K Laboratories, Inc., 121 Express St, Engineers Hill, Plainview, NY 11803

Kimble Products, Owens-Illinois, Toledo, OH 43601

Kontes Glass Co., Spruce St, Vineland, NJ 08360

Eli Lilly & Co., 740 S. Alabama St, Indianapolis, IN 46206

Mallinckrodt Chemicals Works, 2nd & Mallinckrodt Sts, St. Louis, MO 63160

Matheson Coleman & Bell, 2909 Highland Ave, Norwood, OH 45212

Merck & Co., Inc., Rahway, NJ 07065

Miles Laboratories, Inc., Elkhart, IN 46514

(NBS) National Bureau of Standards, Washington, DC 20234

(NF) National Formulary, American Pharmaceutical Association, 2215 Constitution Ave, Washington, DC 20037

New York Laboratory Supply Co., 76 Varick St, New York, NY 10013

Nutritional Biochemicals Corp., 26201 Miles Rd, Cleveland, OH 44128

Perkin-Elmer Corp., Norwalk, CT 06852

Phillips Petroleum Co., Bartlesville, OK 74003

Rohm & Haas Co., Independence Mall West, Philadelphia, PA 19105

(S&S) Schleicher & Schuell, Inc., 543 Washington St, Keene, NH 03431

Salsbury Laboratories, Charles City, IA 50616

Sargent-Welch Scientific Co., N. Linder Ave, Skokie, IL 60076

Scientific Glass Apparatus Co., 735 Broad St, Bloomfield, NJ 07003

Scientific Products, Inc., 1210 Leon Pl, Evanston, IL 60201

Shell Chemical Co., Agricultural Chemicals Division, 110 W. 51st St, New York, NY 10020

G. Frederick Smith Chemical Co., 867 McKinley Ave, PO Box 23344, Columbus, OH 43223

Arthur H. Thomas Co., Vine St at 3rd, PO Box 779, Philadelphia, PA 19105

Ultra-Violet Products, Inc., 5114 Walnut Grove Ave, San Gabriel, CA 91778

Union Carbide Corp., 270 Park Ave, New York, NY 10017

Uniroyal Chemical, Elm St, Naugatuck, CT 06770

(USDA) U.S. Department of Agriculture, Office of Information, Washington, DC 20250

(USP) United States Pharmacopeial Convention, Inc., 4630 Montgomery Ave, Bethesda, MD 20014

Velsicol Chemical Corp., 341 E. Ohio St, Chicago, IL 60611

Wallerstein Co., 125 Lake Ave, Staten Island, NY 10303

Winthrop Laboratories, 90 Park Ave, New York, NY 10016

Trade Names

Amberlite. Ion exchange resins. Rohm and Haas Co.

Anakrom. Gas chromatography supports. Analabs, Inc.

Celite. Diatomaceous products. Johns-Manville Products Corp.

Chromosorb. Chromatographic supports and packings. Johns-Manville Products Corp.

Dowex. Ion exchange resins. Dow Chemical Co.

Florisil. Chromatographic adsorbents. Floridin Co.

Gas-Chrom. Gas chromatography solid supports. Applied Science Laboratories, Inc.

Hyflo Super-Cel. Diatomaceous products. Johns-Manville Products Corp.

(28) The following abbreviations, many of which conform with those of *Chemical Abstracts*, are used. In general, principle governing use of periods after abbreviations is that period is used where final letter of abbreviation is not the same as final letter of word it represents. Periods are not used with units, except inch(es) and gallon(s).

Abbreviation	Word
a	absorptivity(ies)
A	absorbance(s) thruout (not restricted to formulas); not absorption. A' is used for std or blank; subscript numerals usually denote wavelengths in nm
Ac	CH_3CO- (acetyl, not acetate)
ACS	American Chemical Society
addn	addition
addnl	additional
alc.	alcoholic (not alcohol)
alk.	alkaline (not alkali)
alky	alkalinity
amp	ampere(s)
amt	amount
anhyd.	anhydrous
AOCS	American Oil Chemists' Society
app.	apparatus
approx.	approximate(ly)
aq.	aqueous
ASTM	American Society for Testing and Materials
atm.	atmosphere, atmospheric
av.	average (except as verb)
bp	boiling point
ca	about, approximately
calc.	calculate
calcd	calculated
calcg	calculating
calcn	calculation
Cat. No.	Catalog Number
centrf.	centrifuge
centrfd	centrifuged
centrfg	centrifuging
Chap.	chapter
chromatgc	chromatographic
chromatgd	chromatographed
chromatgy	chromatography
Ci	curie(s)
cm	centimeter(s)
compd	compound
com.	commercial(ly)

Abbreviation	Word
conc.	concentrate (as verb or noun)
concd	concentrated
concg	concentrating
concn	concentration
contg	containing
cpm	counts per minute
cryst.	crystalline (not crystallize)
crystd	crystallized
crystg	crystallizing
crystn	crystallization
cu in.	cubic inch(es)
dc	direct current
det.	determine
detd	determined
detg	determining
detn	determination
diam.	diameter
diat. earth	diatomaceous earth
dil.	dilute
dild	diluted
dilg	diluting
diln	dilution
distd	distilled
distg	distilling
distn	distillation
DMF	N,N-dimethylformamide
EDTA	ethylenedinitrilotetraacetic acid (or -tetraacetate)
e.g.	for example
elec.	electric, electrical
equiv.	equivalent
est.	estimate
estd	estimated
estg	estimating
estn	estimation
Et	ethyl
EtOH	ethanol (the chemical entity C_2H_5OH)
evap.	evaporate
evapd	evaporated
evapg	evaporating
evapn	evaporation
ext	extract
extd	extracted
extg	extracting
extn	extraction
Fig.	figure (illustration)
fl oz	fluid ounce(s) (29.57 ml)
fp	freezing point
g	gram(s)
gal.	gallon(s) (3.785 L)
GLC	gas-liquid chromatography
g-s	glass-stoppered
HOAc	acetic acid (not HAc)
hr	hour(s)
ht	height
id	inner diameter
in.	inch(es) (2.54 cm)

Abbreviation	Word	Abbreviation	Word
inorg.	inorganic	ppb	parts per billion $(1/10^9)$
insol.	insoluble	ppm	parts per million $(1/10^6)$
IR	infrared	ppt	precipitate
JAOAC	Journal of the Association of Official Analytical Chemists (after 1965)	pptd	precipitated
		pptg	precipitating
		pptn	precipitation
	Journal of the Association of Official Agricultural Chemists (before 1966)	Pr	propyl
		prep.	prepare
		prepd	prepared
kg	kilogram(s)	prepg	preparing
L	liter(s)	prepn	preparation
lb	pound(s) (453.6 g)	psi	pounds per square inch
liq.	liquid	pt	pint(s) (473 ml)
m	meter(s); milli—as prefix	qt	quart(s) (946 ml)
m	molal	qual.	qualitative(ly)
M	molar (as applied to concn; not molal)	quant.	quantitative(ly)
		®	Trademark name—(Registered)
ma	milliampere (cf amp)	r-b	round-bottom (flask)
max.	maximum	ref.	reference
mech.	mechanical(ly)	resp.	respectively
Me	methyl	rpm	revolutions per minute
MeOH	methyl alcohol	sat.	saturate
mg	milligram(s)	satd	saturated
min	minute(s)	satg	saturating
min.	minimum	satn	saturation
mixt.	mixture	SDF	special denatured formula (applied to alcohol)
ml	milliliter(s)		
mm	millimeter(s)	sec	second(s)
mp	melting point	sep.	separate(ly)
$m\mu$	millimicron $(10^{-6}$ mm); use nanometer (nm) $(10^{-9}$ m)	sepd	separated
		sepg	separating
mv	millivolt	sepn	separation
N	normal (as applied to concn); in equations, normality of titrating reagent	sol.	soluble
		soln	solution
		solv.	solvent
n	refractive index	sp gr	specific gravity (apparent density)
NBS	National Bureau of Standards	spectrophtr	spectrophotometer
neg.	negative	spectrophtric	spectrophotometric(ally)
neut.	neutral	sq	square
neutze	neutralize	std	standard
neutzd	neutralized	stdzd	standardized
neutzg	neutralizing	stdze	standardize
neutzn	neutralization	stdzg	standardizing
NF	National Formulary	stdzn	standardization
ng	nanogram $(10^{-9}$ g)	T	transmittance
nm	nanometer $(10^{-9}$ m); formerly $m\mu$	tech.	technical
No.	number	temp.	temperature
-OAc	acetate (cf Ac)	titr.	titrate
od	outer diameter	titrn	titration
org.	organic	titrg	titrating
oxidn	oxidation	TLC	thin layer chromatography
oz	ounce(s) (28.35 g)	USDA	United States Department of Agriculture
p	pico (10^{-12}) as prefix		
par.	paragraph	USP	United States Pharmacopeia
pet ether	petroleum ether	UV	ultraviolet
phthln	phenolphthalein	v	volt(s)
pos.	positive	v/v	both components measured by vol.
powd	powdered (as adjective)	vac.	vacuum

Abbreviation	Word
vol.	volume; also volumetric when used with flask
w/w	both components measured by wt
wt	weight
μ	micron (0.001 mm); use micrometer (μm) (10^{-6} m)
μg	microgram(s) (10^{-6} g)
μl	microliter(s) (10^{-6} L)
μm	micrometer (10^{-6} m); formerly μ
'	foot (feet) (1' = 30.48 cm)
"	inch(es) (1" = 2.54 cm)
/	per
%	per cent (parts per 100); percentage
>	more than; greater than; above; exceeds (use with numbers only)
<	less than; under; below (use with numbers only)
≦, ⩽	not more than, not greater than, equal to or less than

Abbreviation	Word
≧, ⩾	not less than, equal to or greater than, equal to or more than, at least
⊤	standard taper
⊤	standard taper spherical joint

(29) ★ This symbol indicates a method which is in or is being considered for "surplus" status. Such methods are satisfactory methods, having been subjected to collaborative studies and review. They are thought not to be in current use for various reasons: The purpose for which they were developed no longer exists; the product for which they were developed no longer is marketed; they have been replaced by other methods; etc. These methods retain their official status but are carried in this or next edition only by ref. Any laboratory using these methods and who wishes the text retained or reprinted in next edition must so notify the AOAC. Cards for this purpose will be found under back cover.

Official Methods of Analysis
OF THE
ASSOCIATION OF OFFICIAL ANALYTICAL CHEMISTS

---

1. Agricultural Liming Materials (1)

1.001 Sampling—Procedure
(*Caution: See* **46.036**.)

Take sample representative of lot or shipment, avoiding disproportionate quantity of surface or of any modified or damaged zone, as follows:

(**a**) *Burnt or lump lime, in bulk.*—Collect composite sample of ≥ 10 shovelfuls/car, with proportionate quantities from smaller lots, taking each shovelful from different part of lot or shipment. Immediately crush to pass 2″ diam. circular opening, mix thoroly and rapidly, reduce composite to ca 5 lb sample by riffling or quartering, and place in labeled, dry, airtight container.

(**b**) *Hydrated lime and ground burnt lime, in bags.*—Select 10 bags from different parts of each lot or shipment of 20 tons or less and 1 addnl bag for each addnl 5 tons. From each bag selected withdraw core from top to bottom with sampling tube. Combine cores, mix thoroly and rapidly, reduce composite to ca 2 lb by riffling or quartering, and place in dry, air-tight container.

(**c**) *Ground limestone and ground marl, in bags.*— Proceed as in (**b**).

(**d**) *Ground limestone, ground burnt lime, ground marl, and slag, in bulk.*—With slotted sampling tube, withdraw samples to full sampler depth from 10 points in lot or shipment, and proceed as in (**b**), beginning "Combine cores, . . ."

1.002 Mechanical Analysis—Procedure
(*Caution: See* **46.036**.)

If entire sample is not to be dried, obtain lesser portions by riffling or quartering. Dry at 110° to constant wt and cool to room temp.

Obtain 90–150 g dry sample by riffling or quartering. Break any agglomerates formed during drying by rolling dry sample with hard rubber roller on hard rubber mat or by equally effective means that does not result in crushing the limestone. Quant. transfer weighed sample to 8″ diam. std sieve or set of sieves (e.g., Nos. 10, 20, 40, 60, 80, and 100 or other appropriate combination).

Sieve by lateral and vertical motion accompanied by jarring action. Continue ≥ 5 min or until addnl 3 min of sieving time fails to change results of any sieve fraction by 0.5% of total sample wt. Avoid overloading any sieve when assaying closely sized materials.

Det. wt of each sieve fraction and report as % of total sample wt.

1.003 Preparation of Sample—Procedure

Reduce dried sample, **1.002**, to quantity sufficient for analysis and grind ≥ 0.5 lb reduced sample in mortar, ball mill, or other mech. app. to pass No. 60 sieve. Mix thoroly, and store in air-tight container.

Neutralizing Value—Official Final Action
(Uncorrected for sulfide content)

1.004   *Reagents*

(**a**) *Sodium hydroxide std soln.*—0.25N. Prep. and stdze as in **45.033–45.037**.

(**b**) *Hydrochloric acid std soln.*—0.5N. Stdze against (**a**), using phthln.

1.005 *Indicator Titration Method*

Place 0.5 g burnt or hydrated lime (1 g ground limestone or ground marl), prepd as in **1.003**, in 250 ml erlenmeyer; add 50 ml HCl std soln and boil *gently* 5 min. Cool, and titr. excess acid with NaOH std soln, using phthln. For burnt and hydrated lime report as % CaO; for limestone and marl report as % CaCO₃ equivalence.

% $CaCO_3$ equivalence of sample = 2.5 × (ml HCl − ml NaOH/2).

1.006 *Potentiometric Titration Method*
(Applicable to liming materials contg large amt of ferrous Fe or coloring matter, but not to silicate materials)

Proceed as in **1.005** thru "Cool, . . ." Transfer to 250 ml beaker and insert glass and calomel electrodes of pH meter, buret contg 0.25N NaOH, and mech. stirrer. Stir at moderate speed to avoid splash. Deliver NaOH rapidly to pH 5, then dropwise until soln attains pH 7 and remains constant 1 min while stirring. (If end point is passed, add, from 1 ml Mohr pipet, just enough 0.5N HCl to bring pH to <7, and back-titr. slowly to pH 7.) Add ml of excess acid, if used, to initial 50 ml in calcg. Report as % CaCO₃ equivalence as in **1.005**.

1.007 Approximate Proportions of Calcium and Magnesium in Magnesic Limestone

Slightly acidify titrd soln, **1.005** or **1.006**, transfer to 250 ml vol. flask, and dil. to vol. Det. Ca in 50 ml aliquot as in **7.076**, beginning "dil. to ca 100 ml . . ." Subtract its CaCO₃ equivalence from total CaCO₃ equivalence, **1.005** or **1.006**, and assign difference as CaCO₃ equivalence of the Mg content of the limestone.

Caustic Value (2)—Official Final Action

1.008   *Apparatus (Figure 1:1)*

Use 500 ml Pyrex erlenmeyer, *A*, and fritted glass filter (Corning Glass Works No. 39535, 30F), *F*. Connect filter to siphon tube *B* with thick-wall rubber tubing. Use receiving flasks *M* and *N* calibrated to *deliver* 50 and 100 ml, resp. *S* is suction flask.

1.009   *Determination*

Transfer portion of sample, **1.003**, to weighing bottle and det. wt bottle and contents in atm. of min. moisture and CO₂ content. With polished, narrow-point spatula calibrated to hold ca 1.5 g, withdraw charge to be used and det. exact wt by difference. In-

sert charge directly into dry flask, *A*, fitted with tight rubber stopper.

Prep. *sucrose soln immediately before use* by placing 25 g granulated sucrose in measuring flask calibrated to *deliver* 500 ml. Dissolve sucrose with cold *CO₂-free* H₂O and dil. to vol. Holding both erlenmeyer contg charge and flask contg sucrose soln in slightly inclined position, insert neck of sucrose soln flask short distance into erlenmeyer, and carefully transfer sucrose soln with synchronized rotary motion of both flasks to prevent granulation of lime. Stopper erlenmeyer securely, agitate, and add, if desired, quantity of clean dry beads. Completely dissolve uncoated caustic lime by six 1 min agitations at 2 or 3 min intervals. Crush any solid particles not disintegrated by inverting flask to trap particles between stopper and neck of flask and carefully twisting stopper. Let stand 15 min and filter as follows:

Connect filter cone *F* with siphon *B* and close stopcock *D*. Connect receiving flasks, apply suction, and quickly connect erlenmeyer *A* contg lime soln with stopper *E*. Open stopcock *C* and filter 25–50 ml soln. Close *C* and open *D* to release suction. Remove *M* and replace with similar dry flask. Close *D*, open *C*, and continue filtration until both *M* and *N* are filled at least to marks. To disconnect system, close stopcock *C*, and gently press down outlet of flask *M* and then outlet of flask *N*, to remove any excess liq. above marks. Let intermediate connection empty, open stopcock *D*, and remove *M* and *N*. Titr. first 50 ml, or pilot aliquot, of filtered soln with 0.5N HCl,

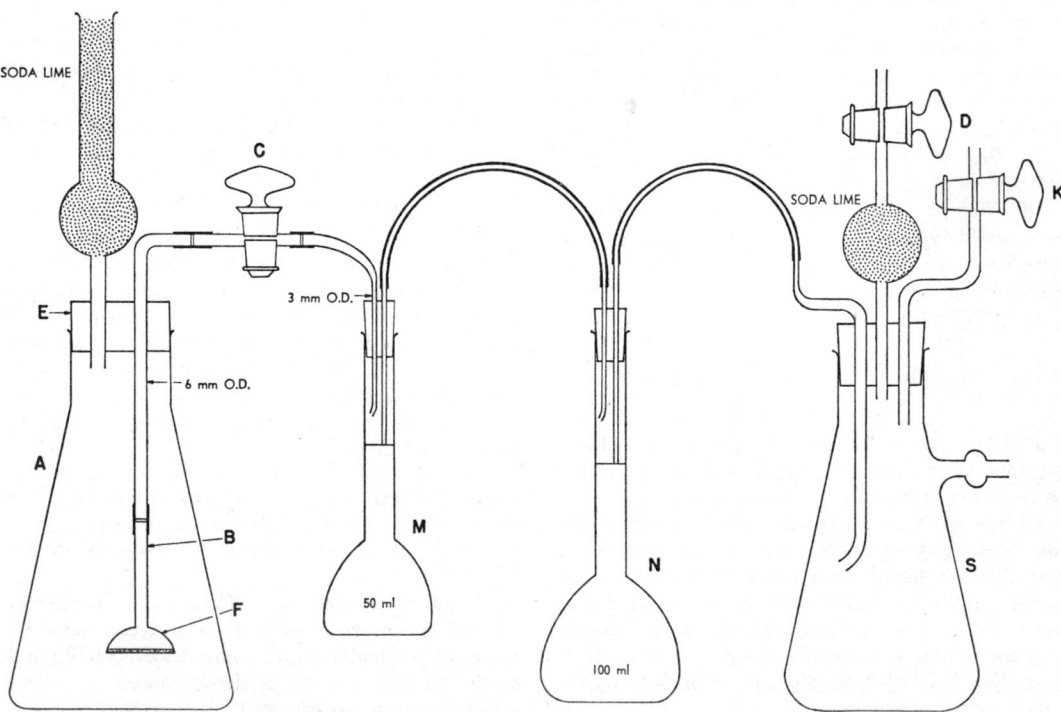

FIG. 1:1—Apparatus for automatic filtration and measurement of lime solutions

using phthln. To covered 200 ml beaker add twice vol. 0.5N acid required for this titrn, add second (100 ml) aliquot of filtered soln to this acid and phthln, and complete titrn.

Calc. caustic value of sample as: $X = 7V/W$, in which X = % active CaO; V = ml 0.5N acid used/100 ml lime soln; and W = g sample.

1.010 Carbon Dioxide—Official Final Action

Proceed as in 2.107–2.108, using 3 g burnt or hydrated lime (0.5–1.0 g limestone or marl) prepd as in 1.003. Report as % $CaCO_3$.

CALCIUM SILICATE SLAGS

1.011 Neutralizing Value (3)—Official Final Action

(Uncorrected for sulfide content)

(a) *Blast furnace slag.*—Transfer 0.5 g sample, ground to pass No. 80 sieve, to 250 ml erlenmeyer. Wash down with small portions H_2O and add 35 ml 0.5N HCl while swirling. Heat to gentle boil over burner, *agitating suspension continuously* until bulk of sample dissolves. Boil 5 min and cool to room temp.; then dil. with CO_2-free H_2O to ca 150 ml and add 1 ml *30% H_2O_2* and 5 drops bromocresol green, 2.129(d). Back-titr. with 0.5N NaOH, adding first 15 ml rapidly and titrg dropwise thereafter, vigorously agitating contents of stoppered flask after each addn, until indicator tint matches or slightly exceeds that of pH 5.2 phthalate buffer soln, 45.011, of like vol. and indicator concn, after 2–3 sec agitation.

(b) *Rock phosphate reduction furnace slag.*—Transfer 0.5 g sample to 250 ml beaker. Wash down with small portions H_2O and add, stirring continuously, 50 ml HOAc (1 + 4). Heat to boiling and boil 5 min, stirring frequently. Evap. to dryness on steam bath. Add 20 ml of the HOAc, dil. to 150 ml, and heat to boiling; add NH_4OH (1 + 1) to distinct yellow of Me red. Digest ca 10 min on hot plate. Filter by gravity thru 9 cm paper, catching filtrate in 100 × 50 mm lipped Pyrex crystg dish; wash beaker 3 times and paper 5 addnl times with neut. 0.5N NH_4OAc. Evap. filtrate on hot plate. Adjust heat so bubbles breaking thru viscous surface film are released gently to avoid spattering. (To expedite dehydration, repeat treatments with 25 ml hot H_2O and evapn 2 or 3 times.) Continue heating residue on hot plate until no HOAc odor remains. Heat addnl 10 min at full heat of hot plate; then ignite 10 min in muffle at 550°. Cool, wet residue with 15 ml H_2O, place watch glass over dish, and add 25 ml 0.5N HCl thru lip of dish. Heat 5 min over burner at gentle simmer. Rinse watch glass, filter suspended matter on 9 cm paper, catching filtrate in 250 ml erlenmeyer, and wash dish and filter 3 times with hot H_2O. Titr. excess acid with 0.5N NaOH to distinct yellow of Me red. Net acid used × 5 = neutzg value of slag in terms of % $CaCO_3$ equivalence.

Sulfide Sulfur (4)—Official Final Action

(*Note:* $CdSO_4$ is toxic; *see also* 46.084.)

1.012 Reagents

(a) *Zinc dust.*—Low in Pb.

(b) *Absorbent.*—Dissolve 20 g $CdSO_4 \cdot 2\frac{2}{3}H_2O$ in H_2O and dil. to 1 L. Adjust to pH 5.6 potentiometrically or colorimetrically. If colorimetrically, match sep. 50 ml aliquot to buffer of same pH, 45.011.

(c) *Sodium hydroxide std soln.*—0.1N. Prep. and stdze as in 45.033–45.037.

(d) *Std acid.*—0.1N HCl. Stdze against std alkali, (c), using Me red.

(e) *Methyl red indicator.*—Dissolve 0.2 g Me red in 100 ml alcohol.

1.013 Apparatus

Fit 250 ml erlenmeyer with 2-hole No. 5.5 stopper. Insert thru stopper 60 ml separator with stem drawn out to 2 mm and bent upward at tip, adjusting separator so stem is $\frac{1}{4}''$ from bottom of flask. Also insert thru stopper 6 mm glass outlet tube. Connect with amber rubber tubing to inlet of 25 × 150 mm tube half filled with H_2O and heated to near boiling before and during detn. Connect in series 2 addnl tubes of same size, each contg 25 ml absorbent soln and held in 600 ml beaker filled with cold H_2O.

1.014 Determination

Charge absorbent tubes with absorbent soln and heat H_2O tube to gentle boiling. Weigh 1 g slag, ground to pass No. 80 sieve, into evolution flask, add 1 g Zn dust, and wash down sides with 5–10 ml H_2O; mix contents with flat-end rod and connect flask to app. Add 50 ml HCl (1 + 4) to separator and let acid flow into reaction flask while swirling contents. If necessary, apply pressure to transfer acid and close stopcock while a little of the acid is still above it. Heat until boiling starts; then regulate to maintain active but not too vigorous boiling for 10 min. Swirl flask frequently after adding acid and for first 5 min of boiling. To disconnect, hold inlet in first absorbent tube firmly with one hand and quickly pull off rubber tubing with other hand without pinching.

Filter CdS suspension by gravity on 9 cm paper into 250 ml erlenmeyer and wash with H_2O to vol. of 100 ml. Add 4 drops Me red soln and agitate vigorously while titrg slowly with 0.1N NaOH to exact tint of *ref. soln* (50 ml absorbent soln dild to 100 ml, with identical indicator concn, in 250 ml erlenmeyer). If end point is passed so that $Cd(OH)_2$ ppts, add 1–2 ml 0.1N HCl, let stand until ppt disappears, and complete titrn dropwise, agitating vigorously. Net ml 0.1N NaOH/2 = % $CaCO_3$ equivalence of sulfide S in sample.

ml 0.1N NaOH × 0.0016 = g sulfide S/detn; g sulfide S × 100 = % sulfide S.

ELEMENTARY ANALYSIS
Gravimetric Methods

1.015 Preparation of Sample Solution by Acid Digestion (5)—Official Final Action

(*Caution: See* **46.019**, **46.026**, and **46.028**.)

Prep. samples as in **1.003**, preferably in agate mortar. Grind silicates to pass No. 100 sieve and dry all samples at 105°.

Weigh 2 g limestone or 0.5 g silicate. If sample contains org. matter, transfer to Pt crucible and place in cold furnace. Raise temp. gradually to 1000° and hold 15 min. Transfer sample to 400 ml beaker and, if ignited, moisten cautiously with H_2O. Add 10 ml HNO_3 and evap. on hot plate at low heat until mixt. becomes pasty. Cool, and add 10 ml H_2O and 20 ml 60% $HClO_4$. Boil to heavy fumes of $HClO_4$, cover, and fume slowly until soln is colorless or slightly yellow (5–10 min). Do not evap. to dryness. Cool to <100° and add 50 ml H_2O. Filter thru Whatman 41H or finer paper into 250 ml vol. flask. *Wash thoroly with hot H_2O to remove all traces of $HClO_4$.* Reserve filtrate and washings for prepn of *Sample Solns A and B*, **1.016**(a) and (b).

1.016 Silica (5)—Official Final Action

(*See* also **1.040–1.042**.)

(*Caution: See* **46.025** and **46.028**.)

Transfer paper with SiO_2 to uncovered Pt crucible and heat gently with low flame until paper chars without flame. Partially cover crucible and cautiously burn C. Finally cover completely and heat with blast lamp or in furnace at 1150–1200°. Cool in desiccator and weigh. Repeat to constant wt (*A*). Treat with ca 1 ml H_2O, 2 drops H_2SO_4 (1 + 1), and 10 ml HF. Cautiously evap. to dryness in hood. Heat 2 min at 1050–1100°, cool in desiccator, and weigh (*B*). $A - B$ = g SiO_2 in sample. g $SiO_2 \times$ 0.4674 = g Si.

(a) *Sample Soln A.*—(0.008 g limestone or 0.002 g silicate/ml.) Fuse residue from Si detn with 0.5 g Na_2CO_3 by heating covered crucible 10 min over Meker burner. Cool, fill crucible ⅔ full with H_2O, and add 2 ml 60% $HClO_4$ dropwise, with stirring. Warm if necessary to dissolve melt. Add to filtrate and washings reserved for prepn of *Sample Soln A* in **1.015**. Dil. to 250 ml with H_2O.

(b) *Sample Soln B.*—(0.00016 g limestone or 0.00004 g silicate/ml.) Dil. 10 ml *Sample Soln A* to 500 ml with H_2O.

1.017 Oxides of Iron, Aluminum, Phosphorus, and Titanium (6)—Official Final Action

(Alternatively, Fe, Al, Mn, P, and Ti may be detd colorimetrically as in **1.024–1.039**.)

To 125 ml aliquot *Soln A* from **1.016**(a), add 10 ml HCl and few drops Me red indicator; heat to gentle boiling and add NH_4OH (1 + 1) until ppt forms and indicator just changes to distinct yellow. Boil ≤2 min and filter rapidly. Wash ppt 6–8 times with hot 2% NH_4NO_3 soln. Return ppt and filter to original beaker, add 10 ml HCl, and macerate filter with policeman. Dil. with H_2O, heat to dissolve ppt, dil. to ca 200 ml, and reppt as above. Wash thoroly with the hot NH_4NO_3 soln until Cl-free. Combine first and second filtrates and save for Ca and Mg detns.

Place ppt in Pt crucible and dry. Ignite gently to oxidize C, heat to bright red ca 10 min, cool in desiccator, and weigh in covered crucible as Fe_2O_3, Al_2O_3, P_2O_5, and TiO_2.

1.018 Calcium (6)—Official Final Action

Conc. combined filtrates and washings from **1.017** to ca 50 ml; make slightly alk. with NH_4OH (1 + 1); while still hot, add satd $(NH_4)_2C_2O_4$ soln dropwise as long as any ppt forms, and then enough excess to convert Mg salts also to oxalate. Heat to boiling, let stand ≥3 hr, decant clear soln thru filter, pour 15–20 ml hot H_2O on ppt, and again decant clear soln thru filter. Dissolve any ppt remaining on filter by washing with hot HCl (1 + 9) into original beaker, wash 6 times with hot H_2O, and then reppt boiling hot, by adding NH_4OH and a little satd $(NH_4)_2C_2O_4$ soln. Let stand as before, filter thru same filter, and wash with hot H_2O until Cl-free. Reserve filtrates and washings from both pptns for detn of Mg, **1.020**.

Complete detn by one of following methods and report as % CaO:

(a) Ignite ppt in crucible either over S-free blast or in elec. furnace at 950° to constant wt, cool in desiccator, and weigh as CaO.

(b) Incinerate filter over low flame, mix ignited ppt with finely pulverized and dried mixt. of equal parts of $(NH_4)_2SO_4$ and NH_4Cl, and drive off excess sulfate by carefully heating upper portion of crucible. Complete ignition, cool in desiccator, and weigh as $CaSO_4$.

(c) Perforate apex of cone; wash CaC_2O_4 ppt into beaker used for pptn; then wash filter with hot H_2SO_4 (1 + 4) and titr. at 85–90° with 0.1N $KMnO_4$.

Magnesium (7)—Official Final Action

1.019   Reagent

Phosphate soln.—Dissolve 100 g $(NH_4)_2HPO_4$ in hot H_2O, dil. to 1 L, and add 5 ml $CHCl_3$.

1.020   Determination

To combined filtrates and washings, **1.018**, add 2 ml 1M citric acid, 100 ml NH_4OH, and 50 ml alcohol. Then add 25 ml of the phosphate soln, with constant stirring, and let stand 12–24 hr. Filter, wash twice with NH_4OH (1 + 9), and dissolve ppt in HNO_3 (1 + 4), washing soln into original beaker to vol. of 100–150 ml. Add 1/10 vol. NH_4OH and 2 drops of the phosphate soln. Stir vigorously and let stand ≥ 3 hr. Filter thru gooch, wash with NH_4OH $(1 + 9)$, moisten filter with *satd soln of NH_4NO_3 made slightly ammoniacal*, ignite, and weigh as $Mg_2P_2O_7$. Report as % MgO. Correct wt $Mg_2P_2O_7$ for co-pptd $Mn_2P_2O_7$ by detg Mn as in **33.035.**

EDTA Titration Methods
Calcium and Magnesium (8)—Official
Final Action

(Not applicable to samples with high phosphate content or contg <2% Mg)

(*Caution: See* **46.050.**)

1.021 *Reagents*

(a) *Buffer soln.*—pH 10. Dissolve 67.5 g NH_4Cl in 200 ml H_2O, add 570 ml NH_4OH, and dil. to 1 L.

(b) *Potassium hydroxide-potassium cyanide soln.*— Dissolve 280 g KOH and 66 g KCN in 1 L H_2O.

(c) *Potassium cyanide soln.*—2%. Dissolve 2 g KCN in 100 ml H_2O.

(d) *Eriochrome black T indicator soln.*—Dissolve 0.2 g indicator (Eastman Kodak P6361 or equiv.) in 50 ml MeOH contg 2 g hydroxylamine.HCl. Store ≤ 1 month.

(e) *Magnesium std solns.*—0.25 and 1.00 mg/ml. Dissolve 0.25 and 1.00 g Mg turnings in HCl $(1 + 10)$ and dil. each to 1 L with double distd H_2O.

(f) *Calcium std soln.*—1 mg/ml. Dissolve 2.4973 g $CaCO_3$, primary std grade, previously dried 2 hr at 285°, in HCl $(1 + 10)$. Dil. to 1 L with double distd H_2O.

(g) *Calcein indicator.*—Grind together 1 g indicator, 10 g charcoal (Norite A is satisfactory), and 100 g KCl. (Indicator is described in Anal. Chem. **28**, 882 (1956), and is available from G. Frederick Smith Chemical Co.)

(h) *Disodium dihydrogen EDTA std solns.*—*(1)* *0.4%.*—Dissolve 4 g Na_2H_2EDTA in 1 L H_2O. Stdze against std Ca and Mg solns. *(2)* *0.1%.*— Prep. as in *(1)*, using 1 g Na_2H_2EDTA, and stdze against std 0.25 mg/ml Mg soln.

1.022 *Standardization*

(a) *For calcium.*—Pipet 10 ml std Ca soln into 300 ml erlenmeyer and add 10 ml H_2O. Add 10 ml KOH-KCN soln and ca 35 mg calcein indicator. Using magnetic stirrer and artificial light, titr. with 0.4% EDTA std soln to disappearance of all green. Titr. 3 or more aliquots and use av. to calc. titer Ca soln = 10/ml EDTA soln.

(b) *For magnesium.*—Pipet 10 ml 0.25 and 1.00 mg/ml std Mg solns into 300 ml erlenmeyers and add 100 ml H_2O. Add 5 ml pH 10 buffer, 2 ml 2% KCN soln, and 10 drops eriochrome black T indicator. Using magnetic stirrer and artificial light, titr. with 0.1 and 0.4% EDTA std solns, resp., until color changes permanently from wine red to pure blue. Titr. 3 or more aliquots and use av. to calc. titer Mg soln = 2.5/ml EDTA soln, or 10/ml EDTA soln, resp.

1.023 *Determination*

Dry sample at 110° to constant wt and cool to room temp. Grind to pass thru No. 60 or 80 sieve and mix thoroly. Accurately weigh ca 0.5 g into 250 ml beaker, add 20 ml HCl $(1 + 1)$, and evap. to dryness on hot plate. Dissolve residue in 5 ml HCl $(1 + 10)$, dil. to ca 100 ml with H_2O, and digest over low flame 1 hr. Cool, transfer to 200 ml vol. flask, dil. to vol., mix, and let settle or filter.

(a) *For calcium.*—Pipet 10 ml aliquot into 300 ml erlenmeyer and titr. as in **1.022(a)**, observing end point thru soln and away from light. % Ca = (Titer EDTA std soln for Ca) × ml EDTA std soln × 2/g sample.

(b) *For magnesium.*—(For agricultural limestones contg >4% Mg.) For Ca + Mg pipet 10 ml aliquot into 300 ml erlenmeyer and titr. with 0.4% EDTA soln as in **1.022(b)**. % Mg = (Titer EDTA std soln for Mg) × [(ml EDTA std soln in Ca + Mg titrn) − (ml EDTA std soln in Ca titrn)] × 2/g sample.

(c) *For magnesium.*—(For agricultural limestones contg 2–4% Mg.) Pipet 10 ml aliquot (0.5–1.0 mg Mg) into 300 ml erlenmeyer and add exact quantity of 0.4% EDTA soln required for Ca detn. Titr. with 0.1% EDTA soln as in **1.022(b)**. % Mg = (Titer EDTA std soln for Mg) × ml EDTA std 0.1% soln × 2/g sample.

Colorimetric Methods (9)—Official First Action

Det. Al, Fe, Mn, P, and Ti in solns prepd by $HClO_4$ digestion, **1.015–1.016**, or NaOH fusion, **1.024.** Det. Si only in soln prepd by NaOH fusion.

Carry reagent blanks thru detn with stds and samples. Treat aliquots of blank soln (corresponding to aliquot sizes of sample solns taken for analysis) as in *Determination* for appropriate element and correct values for samples accordingly.

1.024 Preparation of Sample Solution by Sodium Hydroxide Fusion

Prep. samples as in **1.003**, preferably in agate mortar. Grind samples to pass No. 100 sieve and dry at 105°.

(a) *Sample Soln A.*—(0.005 g limestone or 0.002 g silicate/ml.) Place 0.5 g limestone or 0.2 g silicate in 75 ml Ni crucible. If sample contains org. matter, place uncovered crucible in cold furnace, raise temp. gradually to 900°, and hold 15 min. Remove crucible from furnace and let cool. Mix 0.3 g KNO_3 with sample and add 1.5 g NaOH pellets. Cover crucible with Ni cover and heat 5 min at dull redness over gas flame. (Do not fuse in furnace.) Remove from flame and swirl melt around sides. Cool, add ca 50 ml H_2O, and warm to disintegrate fused cake. Transfer to 150 ml beaker contg 15 ml 5N $HClO_4$ $(1(60\%) + 1)$. Scrub crucible and lid with policeman, and wash any residue into beaker. Transfer to 100 ml vol. flask and dil. to vol. (*Sample Soln A*). (This soln is acidic and is normally clear and free of insol. matter. Occasionally particles of oxidized Ni from crucible appear.

When this occurs, let particles settle before taking aliquots.)

(b) *Sample Soln B.*—(0.00015 g limestone or 0.00004 g silicate/ml.) Dil. 15 ml limestone *Sample Soln A* or 10 ml silicate *Sample Soln A* to 500 ml with H_2O.

Aluminum

1.025   *Reagents*

(a) *Aluminum std solns.*—(1) *Stock soln.*—100 µg Al/ml. To 0.1000 g pure Al metal in 30 ml beaker, add 6 ml HCl (1 + 1). Cover with watch glass and warm gently until Al completely dissolves. Dil. to 1 L with H_2O. (2) *Working soln.*—4 µg Al/ml. Dil. 20 ml stock soln to 500 ml.

(b) *Aluminon soln.*—Dissolve sep. in H_2O: 0.5 g NH_4 aurintricarboxylate in 100 ml; 10 g acacia (gum arabic) in 200 ml; and 100 g NH_4OAc in 400 ml. Filter acacia soln. Add 56 ml HCl to NH_4OAc soln and adjust pH to 4.5 with HCl or NH_4OH. Combine 3 solns and dil. to 1 L with H_2O.

(c) *Antifoam soln.*—Disperse 0.03 g silicone defoamer (Dow Corning Corp. Antifoam A) in 100 ml H_2O.

(d) *Thioglycollic acid soln.*—Dil. 1 ml $HSCH_2COOH$ to 100 ml with H_2O.

1.026   *Preparation of Standard Curve*

Transfer aliquots of std soln contg 0, 4, 20, 40, 60, and 80 µg Al to 100 ml vol. flasks and proceed as in **1.027**. Prep. std curve by plotting $\%T$ against µg Al on semilog paper.

1.027   *Determination*

Use *Sample Soln A* for limestones contg <0.2% or silicates contg <0.8% Al and adjust pH of aliquot to 4.5 with NH_4OH. For materials contg greater concns of Al, use *Sample Soln B* and omit pH adjustment.

Transfer aliquot (20 ml or less contg <80 µg Al) of *Sample Soln A* or *B* to 100 ml vol. flask. Dil. to 20 ml with H_2O. Add 2 ml thioglycollic acid soln, 0.5 ml antifoam soln, and 10 ml aluminon soln. Place flask in boiling H_2O 20 min (250 ml beaker contg 125 ml H_2O holds 100 ml vol. flask conveniently). Remove flask from H_2O and let cool ca 30 min. Dil. to 100 ml with H_2O. Read $\%T$ at 525 nm against 0 µg Al soln (prepd for std curve) set at 100% T. Det. µg Al from std curve. Calc. % Al in sample.

Iron

1.028   *Reagents*

(a) *Iron std solns.*—(1) *Stock soln.*—100 µg Fe/ml. Dissolve 0.1000 g pure Fe metal in 5 ml 2N HCl and dil. to 1 L with H_2O. (2) *Working soln.*—5 µg Fe/ml. Dil. 25 ml stock soln to 500 ml.

(b) *2,4,6-Tripyridyl-s-triazine (TPTZ) soln.*—(Available from G. Frederick Smith Chemical Co.) Dissolve 0.500 g TPTZ in few drops HCl and dil. to 1 L with H_2O.

(c) *Hydroxylamine hydrochloride soln.*—Dissolve 50 g $NH_2OH.HCl$ in H_2O. Add 10 ml TPTZ soln and 0.5 g $NaClO_4.H_2O$, and dil. to 500 ml with H_2O. Transfer to separator, add 25 ml nitrobenzene, and shake several min. Let phases sep. and discard lower nitrobenzene phase contg Fe. Repeat extn 2 or 3 times.

(d) *Acetate buffer soln.*—Dissolve 164 g anhyd. NaOAc in H_2O. Add 115 ml HOAc, 10 ml $NH_2OH.HCl$ soln, 0.05 g TPTZ, and 1 g $NaClO_4.H_2O$, and dil. to 1 L with H_2O. Transfer to separator, add 25 ml nitrobenzene, and shake several min. Let phases sep. and discard lower nitrobenzene phase. Repeat extn 3 or 4 times.

1.029   *Preparation of Standard Curve*

Treat aliquots of std soln contg 0, 5, 50, and 100 µg Fe as in **1.030**. Prep. std curve by plotting $\%T$ against µg Fe on semilog paper.

1.030   *Determination*

Use *Sample Soln A* (≤5 ml) for limestones contg <0.05% or silicates contg <0.2% Fe and *Sample Soln B* for materials contg greater concns of Fe.

Transfer aliquot (<100 µg Fe) of *Sample Soln A* or *B* to 100 ml vol. flask. Add 3 ml $NH_2OH.HCl$ soln and 10 ml TPTZ soln. Add NH_4OH dropwise until Fe derivative remains violet on mixing. Add 10 ml buffer soln and dil. to 100 ml. Read $\%T$ at 593 nm against 0 µg Fe soln (prepd for std curve) set at 100% T. Det. µg Fe from std curve. Calc. % Fe in sample.

Manganese
*(Caution: See **46.026** and **Acids**, Chap. **46**.)*

1.031   *Reagents*

(a) *Manganese std soln.*—50 µg Mn/ml. Dissolve 0.0500 g pure Mn metal in 20 ml 0.5N H_2SO_4 and dil. to 1 L with H_2O.

(b) *Acid mixture.*—Add 800 ml HNO_3 and 200 ml H_3PO_4 to H_2O and dil. to 2 L.

1.032   *Preparation of Standard Curve*

Treat aliquots of std soln contg 0, 50, 100, 300, and 500 µg Mn as in **1.033**. Prep. std curve by plotting $\%T$ against µg Mn on semilog paper.

1.033   *Determination*

Transfer aliquot (<500 µg Mn) of *Sample Soln A* to 150 ml beaker. Add 25 ml acid mixt. and 0.3 g KIO_4. Bring to boil and keep near boiling temp. 10 min after color develops. Let cool, transfer to 50 ml vol. flask, dil. to vol., and mix. Read $\%T$ at 525 nm against 0 µg Mn soln (prepd for std curve) set at 100% T. Det. µg Mn from std curve. Calc. % Mn in sample.

Phosphorus

(Do not clean glassware with detergents contg P.)

1.034   *Reagents*

(a) *Phosphorus std solns.*—(1) *Stock soln.*—100 μg P/ml. Dissolve 0.4393 g KH_2PO_4 in H_2O and dil. to 1 L. (2) *Working soln.*—5 μg P/ml. Dil. 25 ml stock soln to 500 ml.

(b) *Ammonium molybdate soln.*—Dissolve 20 g $(NH_4)_6Mo_7O_{24}.4H_2O$ in 500 ml H_2O. Add 285 ml H_2SO_4, cool, and dil. to 1 L with H_2O.

(c) *Hydrazine sulfate soln.* — Dissolve 2 g $N_2H_4.H_2SO_4$ in H_2O and dil. to 1 L.

1.035   *Preparation of Standard Curve*

Treat aliquots of std soln contg 0, 5, 50, and 75 μg P as in **1.036**. Prep. std curve by plotting $\%T$ against μg P on semilog paper.

1.036   *Determination*

Transfer aliquot ($\leq$15 ml contg <75 μg P) of *Sample Soln A* to 100 ml vol. flask. Add 5 ml NH_4 molybdate soln and mix. Add 5 ml $N_2H_4.H_2SO_4$ soln, dil. to 70 ml with H_2O, and mix. Place flask in boiling H_2O 9 min. Remove, *cool rapidly*, and dil. to vol. Read $\%T$ at 827 nm against 0 μg P soln (prepd for std curve) set at 100% T. Det. μg P from std curve. Calc. % P in sample.

Titanium

1.037   *Reagents*

(a) *Titanium std solns.*—(1) *Stock soln.*—100 μg Ti/ml. Place 0.1668 g TiO_2 and 2 g $K_2S_2O_7$ in Pt crucible. Heat covered crucible gently at first and then to dull redness for ca 15 min. Dissolve melt in 50 ml H_2SO_4 (1 + 1) and dil. to 1 L with H_2O. (2) *Working soln.*—5 μg Ti/ml. Dil. 25 ml stock soln to 500 ml.

(b) *Acetate buffer soln.*—pH 4.7. Dissolve 41 g anhyd. NaOAc in H_2O, add 30 ml HOAc, and dil. to 1 L.

(c) *Disodium-1,2-dihydroxybenzene-3,5-disulfonate (Tiron) soln.*—Dissolve 4 g Tiron in H_2O and dil. to 100 ml.

1.038   *Preparation of Standard Curve*

Treat aliquots of std soln contg 0, 5, 50, and 75 μg Ti as in **1.039**, but do not add dithionite to stds. Prep. std curve by plotting $\%T$ against μg Ti on semilog paper.

1.039   *Determination*

Transfer aliquot (<75 μg Ti) of *Sample Soln A* to 50 ml beaker. Dil. to ca 25 ml with H_2O. Add 5 ml Tiron soln and then NH_4OH (1 + 9) dropwise until soln is neut. to Congo red paper. (Tiron soln must be added before pH is adjusted.) Transfer to 50 ml vol. flask, add 5 ml buffer soln, dil. to vol. with H_2O, and mix thoroly. Add 25 mg dithionite ($Na_2S_2O_4$) and dissolve with min. agitation (to avoid reappearance of blue). Read $\%T$ at 410 nm, within 15 min after adding dithionite, against 0 μg Ti soln (prepd for std curve) set at 100% T. Det. μg Ti from std curve. Calc. % Ti in sample.

Silicon

(Clean all glassware with HCl (1 + 1).)

1.040   *Reagents*

(a) *Silicon std soln.*—20 μg Si/ml. Place 0.0428 g pure SiO_2 in 75 ml Ni crucible and treat as in **1.024**(a), but dil. with H_2O to 1 L instead of 100 ml.

(b) *Tartaric acid soln.*—Dissolve 50 g tartaric acid in H_2O and dil. to 500 ml. Store in plastic bottle.

(c) *Ammonium molybdate soln.*—Dissolve 7.5 g $(NH_4)_6Mo_7O_{24}.4H_2O$ in 75 ml H_2O, add 10 ml H_2SO_4 (1 + 1), and dil. to 100 ml with H_2O. Store in plastic bottle.

(d) *Reducing soln.*—Dissolve 0.7 g Na_2SO_3 in 10 ml H_2O. Add 0.15 g 1-amino-2-naphthol-4-sulfonic acid and stir until dissolved. Dissolve 9 g $NaHSO_3$ in 90 ml H_2O, add to first soln, and mix. Store in plastic bottle.

1.041   *Preparation of Standard Curve*

Treat aliquots of std soln contg 0, 20, 100, and 200 μg Si as in **1.042**. Prep. std curve by plotting $\%T$ against μg Si on semilog paper.

1.042   *Determination*

Transfer 10 ml *Sample Soln B* to 100 ml vol. flask (*use Sample Soln A* for limestones contg <0.2% Si) and add 1 ml NH_4 molybdate soln with swirling. Mix well, and let stand 10 min. Add 4 ml tartaric acid soln with swirling, and mix well. Add 1 ml reducing soln with swirling, dil. to vol., mix well, and let stand $\geq$30 min. Read $\%T$ at 650 nm against 0 μg Si soln (prepd for std curve) set at 100% T. Det. μg Si from std curve. Calc. % Si in sample.

SELECTED REFERENCES

(1) JAOAC 7, 252(1924).

(2) Ind. Eng. Chem. 20, 312(1928); JAOAC 11, 153 (1928); 14, 283(1931).

(3) JAOAC 27, 74, 532(1944); 28, 310(1945); 31, 71(1948).

(4) JAOAC 31, 715(1948).

(5) JAOAC 46, 603(1963); 47, 1019(1964).

(6) U.S. Geol. Survey Bull. 700, p. 106; Ind. Eng. Chem. 9, 1114(1917).

(7) Washington, "Chemical Analysis of Rocks," 3rd Ed., 1919, p. 181.

(8) JAOAC 45, 1(1962); 46, 611(1963); 50, 190 (1967).

(9) JAOAC 47, 1019(1964).

2. Fertilizers[*]

Sampling—Official Final Action

2.001 *Solid Fertilizers (1)*

(a) *Bagged fertilizers.*—Use slotted single or double tube, or slotted tube and rod, with solid cone tip at one end. Take sample as follows: Lay bag horizontally and remove core diagonally from end to end. From lots of 10 bags or more, take core from each of 10 bags. When necessary to sample lots of <10 bags, take 10 cores but at least 1 core from each bag present. For small packages (≤10 lb) take 1 entire package as sample.

(b) *Bulk fertilizers, including railroad car-size lots.*—Use trier of design represented in Table 2:1.

Table 2:1   Trier specifications

Trier	Length, in.	od in.	id in.	Compartments No.	Size, in.
Missouri	59	1⅛	⅞	8	3
552 Grain[a]	63	1⅜	1⅛	11	3½
Missouri "D"[b]	52	1¼	1	1	45

Triers available from:
[a] Seedboro Equipment Co., 618 W. Jackson Blvd, Chicago, IL 60606.
[b] American Tool and Die, Inc., 1105 Maple St, West Des Moines, IA 50265.

Draw 10 vertical cores distributed in std concentric sampling pattern (Fig. 2:1) of such design that each core represents approx. equal fractions of lot.

Bulk shipments may be sampled at time of loading or unloading by passing National Plant Food Institute type sampling cup, Fig. 2:2 (mouth dimensions: width ¾″, length 16″, or as long as max. diam. of stream), thru entire stream of material as it drops from belt or chute. Make sampling such as to assure

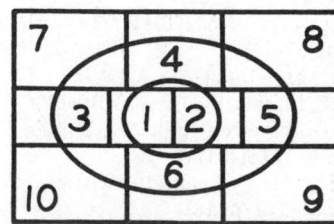

FIG. 2:1—Sampling pattern

≥10 equal-timed-spaced passes thruout transfer operation. Stream samples are not applicable unless uniform continuous flow of fertilizer is maintained for >3 min while lot is being sampled.

(c) *Preparation of sample.*—Place composite sample in airtight container and deliver entire sample to laboratory. If composite sample is reduced in field, use riffle.

FIG. 2:2—Sampling cup

2.002 *Liquid Fertilizers (2)*
(In Absence of Free Ammonia)

(a) *Clear solns.*—(Mixed liqs and N solns.) Secure sample directly from mixing vat, storage tank, or delivery tank after thoro mixing. Take sample from surface or thru direct tap. Flush direct tap, or delivery line and faucet, and collect sample in glass or polyethylene container. Alternatively, lower sample container into well mixed material thru port in top of tank and let fill. Seal container tightly.

(b) *Fluid fertilizers with suspended material.*—(Salt suspensions and slurries.) Agitate material in storage until thoroly mixed (15 min usually adequate) before taking sample. Sample directly as in (a), or use 500 ml Missouri or Indiana sampling bottle, Fig. 2:3. Lower sampling bottle from top opening to bottom of tank and raise slowly while filling. Transfer to sample bottle and seal tightly.

Alternatively, secure sample from tap on recirculation line after agitating *and* recirculating simultaneously until thoroly mixed. Draw sample while recirculating. If recirculation line is attached to manifold delivery line, allowing cross-contamination, pump ca 1′ or 500 gal. into temporary storage tank, then sample from recirculation line as above or delivery line. Transfer to sample bottle and seal tightly.

---

[*] Methods so marked are surplus methods. *See* "Definitions of Terms and Explanatory Notes," item (29).

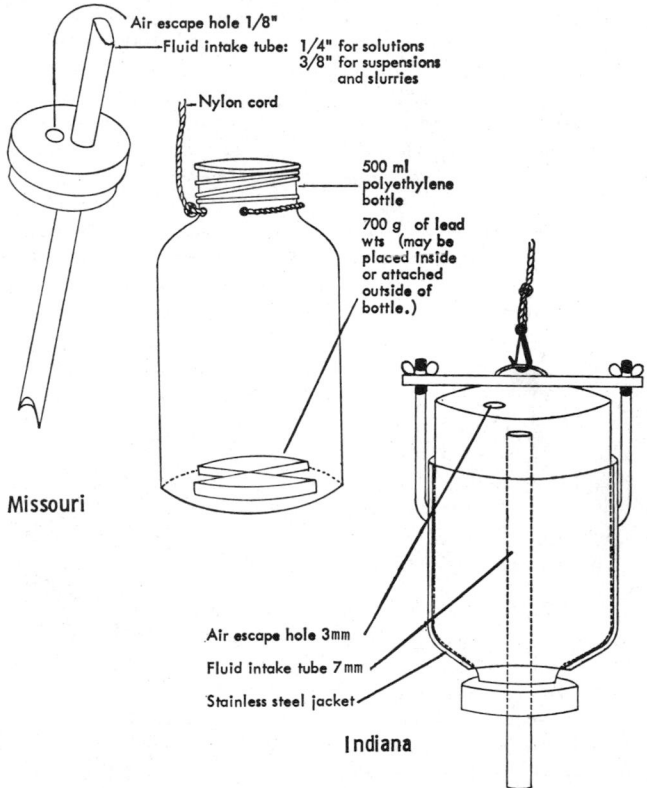

FIG. 2:3—Missouri and Indiana weighted restricted-fill fluid fertilizer sampling bottles designed to fill while being lowered (and raised) in storage tanks

Ammoniacal Solutions (3)

2.003   *Apparatus*

(a) *Container.*—Polyethylene reagent-form bottle with buttress-type cap, 1 qt capacity.

(b) *Sample flow control apparatus.*—Construct from following fittings: $1\frac{1}{2} \times \frac{1}{4}''$ reducing bushing; $\frac{1}{4}''$ tee; $\frac{1}{4}''$ nipple 12–18″ long (length not critical); two $\frac{1}{4}''$ stainless steel, blunt-nose needle valves with hose connections (Hoke No. 328). All fittings except valves can be either Al or stainless steel. (*See* Fig. 2:4.)

Attach valves directly to tee which is then attached to reducing bushing thru nipple. To both valves attach $\frac{1}{4}''$ id Tygon tubing (Hoke No. 314A hose connection), 12″ length to sample valve and sufficient length to vent valve to reach disposal area or container. To free end of sample tubing attach 3″ length of $\frac{1}{4}''$ glass or stainless steel tubing inserted thru No. 4 rubber stopper. To exit end of metal tube attach addnl 6″ length of Tygon tubing. Make certain all connections are tight. App. can be attached directly to tank cars, but requires addnl coupling, which varies with installation, to attach to storage tanks. $1\frac{1}{2}''$ "quick coupler" (Ever-Tite Coupling Co., 254 W. 54th St, New York, NY 10019) suffices in most cases.

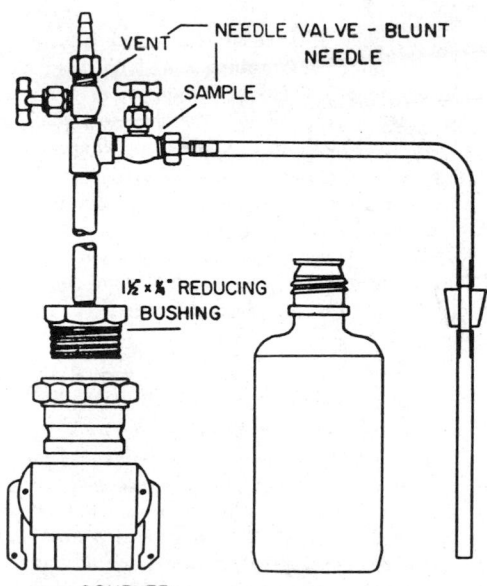

FIG. 2:4—Sampling apparatus for ammoniacal solutions, including "quick coupler" for attaching to storage tanks

2.004   *Sampling*

Prep. sample bottle in laboratory by adding ca 500 ml H_2O, replacing cap, and weighing accurately (± 0.1 g). Attach sampling app. to car or tank and, with sample valve closed, flush line thru vent valve. Partially collapse sample bottle, insert sample tube with stopper, and seat tightly. With sample tube dipping below surface of H_2O in bottle, throttle vent valve to maintain small flow of soln and partially open sample valve, collecting ca 100 ml sample. (Bottle should not expand to full size during this time.) Close sample valve, remove sample tube, partially collapse bottle, and cap tightly. Reweigh (± 0.1 g) and calc. wt sample. Cool to 20°, transfer to 1 or 2 L vol. flask, dil. to vol. with H_2O, mix thoroly, and take aliquots for analysis.

Anhydrous Ammonia (3)

(*Caution:* Use extreme care in handling anhyd. NH_3. Suitable gas mask and rubber gloves are required. *See* **46.032**.)

2.005   *Sampling*

Use sample tube of thermal shock-resistant glass calibrated to contain 100 ml and graduated in 0.05 ml subdivisions up to 0.5 ml. (DuPont special oil centrf. tube or ASTM long-form oil tube is satisfactory.) Flush line and fill tube to 100 ml mark with sample in such manner that condensing moisture will not enter sample tube. (Skirt attached to end of sample line will drain moisture away.)

2.006   *Water and Nitrogen*

Immediately close sample tube with tight-fitting rubber stopper into which is inserted tight-fitting piece of 0.25″ id glass tubing 2–3″ long, bent at its exit from outer end of stopper to let gases escape but to exclude entrance of moisture or moisture-laden air. Place in H_2O bath at approx. air temp. and let NH_3 evap. When temp. of sample tube is ca that of bath, remove tube, wipe outer surface, and det. vol. of residue.

% H_2O in sample = ml residue $\times$ C, where C = 0.74, 0.70, or 0.66 for pressures in original containers of 100, 150, or 200 psi, resp.

$$\% N = (100 - \% H_2O) \times 0.8224.$$

2.007 Preparation of Sample (4)—Official Final Action

Reduce gross sample to quantity sufficient for analysis or grind ≥ 0.5 lb of reduced sample without previous sieving. For fertilizer materials and moist fertilizer mixts, grind to pass sieve with 1 mm circular openings, or No. 20 sieve; for dry mixts that tend to segregate, grind to pass No. 40 sieve. Grind as rapidly as possible to avoid loss or gain of moisture during operation. Mix thoroly and store in tightly stoppered bottles.

2.008 ★ **Mechanical Analysis of Bone,** ★ **Tankage, and Basic Slag (5)— Official Final Action**

Transfer 100 g original bone or tankage or 10 g basic slag to sieve with circular openings 0.5 mm diam., and sift. Break lumps with soft rubber pestle if material tends to cake. Weigh coarse portion remaining on sieve. Det. fine portion by difference.

Mechanical Analysis of Phosphate Rock (6)— Official Final Action

2.009   *Apparatus*

(a) *Water pressure control.*—See Fig. 2:5. Connect valve, *A*, std pressure gage, *B*, and aerator, *C*, with $\frac{3}{8}$″ diam. pipe.

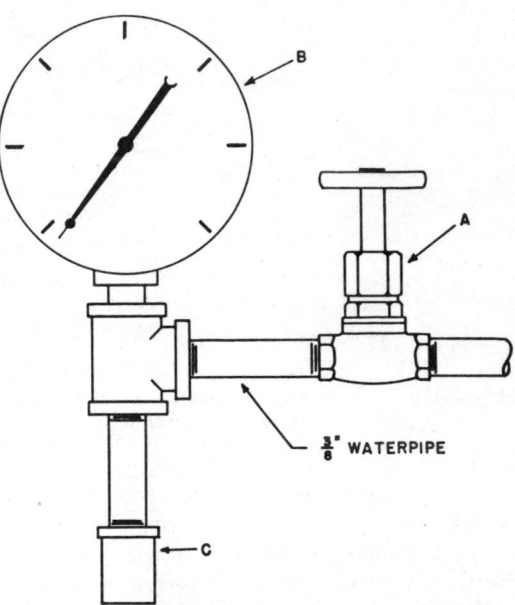

FIG. 2:5—Apparatus for control of water pressure

(b) *Sieves.*—Nos. 100 and 200, bronze or stainless steel cloth, checked against certified sieves. Sieves 8″ diam. and 2″ in depth to sieve cloth are recommended for both wet and dry sieving, but other sizes may be used if detd to be suitable under conditions of method. (Other sieves in U.S. series may be used, with precaution to ensure complete sepn of sample into desired fractions.)

(c) *Sieve shaker.*—Ro-Tap, Syntron, or other suitable machine.

2.010   *Reagent*

Dispersing agent.—Dissolve 36 g Na hexametaphosphate and 8 g Na_2CO_3 in H_2O and dil. to 1 L.

2.011   *Determination*

(a) *Ground phosphate rock.*—Place 100 g sample on No. 200 sieve and wash with moderate stream of tap H_2O at max. gage pressure of 4 lb until H_2O

passing sieve is clear, with care to avoid loss of sample by splashing. Dry material remaining on sieve at 105° and transfer to No. 100 sieve in series with No. 200 sieve of same diam. and depth. Shake 8 min in mech. shaker. Det. % sample passing No. 100 sieve by subtracting wt of material retained on that sieve from 100. Det. % sample passing No. 200 sieve by subtracting sum of wts of material retained on that sieve and on No. 100 sieve from 100.

(b) *Soft phosphate with colloidal clay.*—Add 100 g sample to rapidly stirred soln of 50 ml dispersing agent and 450 ml tap H_2O, with care to avoid contact of unwetted material with shaft of stirrer and side of beaker. Stir 5 min after addn of sample is completed. Transfer slurry to No. 200 sieve and proceed as in (a).

2.012   Total Water—Official Final Action

(Not applicable to samples that yield volatile substances other than H_2O at drying temp.)

Heat 2 g sample, **2.007**, 5 hr in oven at 99–101°. In case of $NaNO_3$, $(NH_4)_2SO_4$, and K salts, heat to constant wt at 129–131°. Report % loss in wt as H_2O at temp. used.

FREE WATER
Vacuum-Desiccation Methods (7)
2.013   *Method I—Official Final Action*

Place 2 g prepd sample, **2.007**, in tared weighing dish. (Weigh extremely hygroscopic or damp materials by difference in covered dishes.) Dry sample at 25–30° (precise results depend on as constant a temp. as possible) in vac. desiccator over anhyd. $Mg(ClO_4)_2$, P_2O_5, or BaO, under ≥ 20 or $\leq 22''$ vac. (8–10" absolute pressure) 16–18 hr. Reweigh, and report % loss in wt as free H_2O.

2.014   *Method II—Official First Action*

Weigh 2 g prepd sample, **2.007**, into tared glass weighing dish. Dry sample 2 hr±10 min at 50±1.5° in oven under vac. of 19–21" (absolute pressure 9–11"). (Temp. control within specified limits thruout oven chamber is essential.) Maintain vac. by passing desiccated air thru chamber. Cool dried sample in desiccator and reweigh. Report % loss in wt as free H_2O.

2.015   ★ Acid-Insoluble Ash (8)— ★
Official Final Action

Transfer 2 g sample to 400 ml beaker. Add 100 ml HCl (1 + 4), cover with watch glass, and immerse 30 min in steam or hot H_2O bath (98–100°), keeping liq. level in beaker below that of H_2O in bath. Stir at 10 min intervals, and after 30 min remove from bath and filter thru 11 or 12.5 cm medium paper, transferring insol. residue to filter with stream of H_2O. Fold paper contg residue, place in porcelain crucible, and ignite in muffle furnace 1 hr at 800°. Cool, transfer contents of crucible to original beaker with 50 ml HCl (1 + 4), cover, and again immerse in steam or

hot H_2O bath 30 min, stirring occasionally. After 30 min, remove from bath and filter thru weighed gooch contg acid-washed asbestos mat on filter paper disk. Wash insol. residue several times with H_2O, dry crucible 1 hr at 125°, cool in desiccator, and weigh. Calc. net increase in wt crucible to % acid-insol. ash.

PHOSPHORUS
Total Phosphorus
2.016   *Reagent*

Magnesium nitrate soln.—Dissolve 950 g P-free $Mg(NO_3)_2.6H_2O$ in H_2O and dil. to 1 L.

2.017   *Preparation of Solution—*
Official Final Action
(Caution: See **46.019, 46.026, 46.028, 46.030,** *and* **46.069.***)*

Treat 1 g sample by (a), (b), (c), (d), or (e), as indicated. Cool soln, transfer to 200 or 250 ml vol. flask, dil. to vol., mix, and filter thru dry filter.

(a) *Materials containing small quantities of organic matter.*—Dissolve in 30 ml HNO_3 and 3–5 ml HCl, and boil until org. matter is destroyed (30 min for liqs and suspensions).

★**(b)** *Fertilizers containing much Fe or Al phosphate, and basic slag.*★—Dissolve in 15–30 ml HCl and 3–10 ml HNO_3.

(c) *Organic material like cottonseed meal alone or in mixtures.*—Evap. with 5 ml of the $Mg(NO_3)_2$ soln, ignite, and dissolve in HCl.

★**(d)** *Materials or mixtures containing large quantities of organic matter.*★—(With cottonseed meal and similar materials it is best to add first ca 5 ml HNO_3 and then the H_2SO_4.) Add 20–30 ml H_2SO_4 to sample in 200 ml flask. Let mixt. digest, at gentle heat if necessary, until violence of reaction is over. Add 2–4 g $NaNO_3$ or KNO_3, boil, and add addnl small amt nitrate after soln is nearly colorless, or add nitrate in small portions from time to time. When soln is colorless, cool, add 150 ml H_2O, and boil few min.

(e) *All fertilizers.*—Boil gently 30–45 min with 20–30 ml HNO_3 in suitable flask (preferably Kjeldahl for samples contg large amts of org. matter) to oxidize all easily oxidizable matter. Cool and add 10–20 ml 70–72% $HClO_4$. Boil very gently until soln is colorless or nearly so and dense white fumes appear in flask. Do not boil to dryness at any time (Danger!). (With samples contg large amts of org. matter, temp. should be raised to fuming point, ca 170°, over period of at least 1 hr.) Cool slightly, add 50 ml H_2O, and boil few min.

Spectrophotometric Molybdovanadophosphate Method (9)—Official Final Action

(Not applicable to materials yielding colored solns or solns contg ions other than orthophosphate which form colored complexes with molybdovanadate. Not recommended for basic slag.)

2.018   *Apparatus*

Photometer.—Beckman Instruments, Inc. Model DU spectrophtr with stray light filter and matched 1 cm absorption cells. With other photometers analyst must det. suitability for use and conditions for satisfactory performance. Means for dispelling heat from light source is desirable.

2.019   *Reagents*

(a) *Molybdovanadate reagent.*—Dissolve 40 g NH_4 molybdate.$4H_2O$ in 400 ml hot H_2O and cool. Dissolve 2 g NH_4 metavanadate in 250 ml hot H_2O, cool, and add 450 ml 70% $HClO_4$. (*Caution: See* **46.028**(a) *and* (d).) Gradually add molybdate soln to vanadate soln with stirring, and dil. to 2 L.

(b) *Phosphate std soln.*—Prep. solns of pure, dry (2 hr at 105°) KH_2PO_4 (52.15% P_2O_5) contg 0.4–1.0 mg P_2O_5/ml in 0.1 mg increments. Prep. fresh solns contg 0.4 and 0.7 mg P_2O_5/ml weekly.

2.020   *Preparation of Standard Curve*

· Pipet 5 ml aliquots of 7 std phosphate solns (2–5 mg P_2O_5/aliquot) into 100 ml vol. flasks and add 45 ml H_2O. Then, within 5 min for entire series, add 20 ml molybdovanadate reagent by buret or pipet, dil. to vol. and mix. Let stand 10 min.

Select 2 absorption cells (std and sample cells) and fill both with 2 mg std. Set spectrophtr to 400 nm and adjust to zero A with std cell. Sample cell must check zero A within 0.001 unit; otherwise read A difference for sample cell and correct subsequent readings. (Choose cell showing pos. A against other as sample cell so that this pos. A is always subtracted.) Using sample cell, det. A of other stds with instrument adjusted to zero A for 2 mg std. After each detn empty and refill cell contg 2 mg std, to avoid error that might arise from temp. changes. Plot A against concn in mg P_2O_5/ml std soln.

2.021   *Preparation of Solution*

Treat 1 g sample as in **2.017**(a), (b), (c), (d), or (e), preferably (e) when these acids are suitable solv. (Soln should be free of N oxides and NOCl.)

(a) For P_2O_5 content up to 5%, dil. to 250 ml.

(b) For P_2O_5 content >5%, dil. to such vol. that 5 or 10 ml aliquot contains 2–5 mg P_2O_5.

2.022   *Determination*

Pipet, into 100 ml vol. flasks, 5 ml aliquots of std phosphate solns contg 2 and 3.5 mg P_2O_5/aliquot, resp., and develop color as in **2.020**. Adjust instrument to zero A for 2 mg std, and det. A of 3.5 mg std. (It is essential that the A of latter std be practically identical with corresponding value on std curve.)

(a) *Samples containing up to 5% P_2O_5.*—Pipet, into 100 ml vol. flask, 5 ml sample soln, **2.021**(a), and 5 ml std phosphate soln contg 2 mg P_2O_5. Develop color and det. A concurrently with and in same

manner as for std phosphate solns in preceding par., with instrument adjusted to zero A for 2 mg color std. Read P_2O_5 content of soln from std curve. With series of sample solns, empty and refill cell contg 2 mg std after each detn.

% P_2O_5 in sample = $100 \times [(\text{mg } P_2O_5 \text{ from std curve} - 2)/20]$.

(b) *Samples containing more than 5% P_2O_5.*—Pipet 5 or 10 ml sample soln, **2.021**(b), into 100 ml vol. flask. Without adding std phosphate soln, proceed as in (a).

% P_2O_5 in sample = $100 \times (\text{mg } P_2O_5 \text{ from std curve/mg sample in aliquot})$.

Gravimetric Quinolinium Molybdophosphate Method (10)—Official Final Action

2.023   *Reagents*

(Store solns in polyethylene bottles.)

(a) *Citric-molybdic acid reagent.*—Dissolve 54 g 100% molybdic anhydride (MoO_3) and 12 g NaOH with stirring in 400 ml hot H_2O, and cool. Dissolve 60 g citric acid in mixt. of 140 ml HCl and 200 ml H_2O, and cool. Gradually add molybdic soln to citric acid soln with stirring. Cool, filter, and dil. to 1 L. (Soln may be green or blue; color deepens on exposure to light.) If necessary, add 0.5% $KBrO_3$ soln dropwise until green color pales. Store in dark.

(b) *Quinoline soln.*—Dissolve 50 ml *synthetic* quinoline, with stirring, in mixt. of 60 ml HCl and 300 ml H_2O. Cool, dil. to 1 L, and filter.

(c) *Quimociac reagent.*—Dissolve 70 g Na molybdate.$2H_2O$ in 150 ml H_2O. Dissolve 60 g citric acid in mixt. of 85 ml HNO_3 and 150 ml H_2O, and cool. Gradually add molybdate soln to citric acid-HNO_3 mixt. with stirring. Dissolve 5 ml synthetic quinoline in mixt. of 35 ml HNO_3 and 100 ml H_2O. Gradually add this soln to molybdate-citric acid-HNO_3 soln, mix, and let stand 24 hr. Filter, add 280 ml acetone, dil. to 1 L with H_2O, and mix.

2.024   *Preparation of Solution*

Treat 1 g sample as in **2.017**, dilg to 200 ml.

2.025   *Determination*

Pipet, into 500 ml erlenmeyer, aliquot contg ≤25 mg P_2O_5 and dil. to ca 100 ml with H_2O. Continue by one of the following methods:

(a) Add 30 ml citric-molybdic acid reagent and boil gently 3 min. (Soln must be ppt-free at this time.) Remove from heat and swirl carefully. Immediately add 10 ml quinoline soln from buret with continuous swirling. (Add first 3–4 ml dropwise and remainder in steady stream.) Or:

(b) Add 50 ml quimociac reagent, cover with watch glass, place on hot plate in well-ventilated hood, and boil 1 min.

After treatment by (a) or (b), cool to room temp., swirl carefully 3–4 times during cooling, filter into gooch with glass fiber filter paper previously dried at

250° and weighed, and wash with five 25 ml portions of H_2O. Dry crucible and contents 30 min at 250°, cool in desiccator to constant wt, and weigh as $(C_9H_7N)_3H_3[PO_4.12MoO_3]$. Subtract wt reagent blank. Multiply by 0.03207 to obtain wt P_2O_5 (or by 0.01400 for P). Report as % P_2O_5 (or % P).

Alkalimetric Quinolinium Molybdophosphate Method (11)—Official First Action

2.026 Reagents

(a) *Quimociac reagent.*—See **2.023**(c).

(b) *Sodium hydroxide std soln.*—(1 ml = 1 mg P_2O_5.) Dil. 366.32 ml 1N NaOH, **45.033–45.037**, to 1 L with H_2O.

(c) *Nitric acid std soln.*—Prep. HNO_3 soln equiv. to concn of (b) and stdze by titrg against (b), using phthln. (For greater precision, use HNO_3 soln corresponding to 1/5 concn of (b).)

(d) *Citric acid.*—10% (w/v).

(e) *Indicators.*—(1) *Thymol blue soln.*—0.1%. Add 2.2 ml 0.1N NaOH to 0.1 g thymol blue and dil. to 100 ml with 50% alcohol. (2) *Phenolphthalein.*—0.1%. Dissolve 0.1 g phthln in 100 ml 50% alcohol. (3) *Mixed indicator.*—Mix 3 vols (1) and 2 vols (2).

2.027 Preparation of Sample Solution

Treat 1 g sample as in **2.017**, first par. and (a) or (e).

2.028 Determination

(a) *Precipitation.*—Transfer aliquot contg ≤30 mg P_2O_5 and ≤5 ml concd acid to 500 ml erlenmeyer, add 20 ml citric acid soln, and adjust to ca 100 ml. Add 60 ml quimociac reagent to prepd sample soln, immediately cover with watch glass, and place on medium temp. hot plate. After soln comes to boil, move to cooler portion of hot plate and boil gently 1 min. Let cool until flask can be handled comfortably with bare hand.

(b) *Filtration and washing.*—Prep. pulped-paper pad ca ¼″ thick on perforated porcelain disk in funnel by adding 2 or more approx. equal increments of H_2O suspension of pulped paper and sucking dry with vac. between addns. Swirl flask, pour contents onto filter, and wash flask with five ca 15 ml portions H_2O, adding washings to funnel. Immediately after funnel has emptied, wash down sides with ca 15 ml H_2O to remove residual acetone, which causes excessively fast drying and later lump formation if allowed to evap. Wash with 3 addnl 15 ml portions H_2O, letting funnel empty between addns. Keep drying of ppt to min. Using only jet of H_2O, transfer ppt and pad to pptn flask and break up pad with jet of H_2O. Do not smear ppt against funnel or flask.

(c) *Titration.*—Titr. with std NaOH soln and add 3–5 ml excess. Add 1 ml mixed indicator and titr. with std HNO_3 soln to grey-blue end point. If overtitrd (greenish-yellow), add addnl excess std NaOH soln and titr. to grey-blue.

(d) *Blank.*—Det. blank on all reagents, adding known quantity (1–2 mg) of P_2O_5. Use 1 + 9 dilns of std NaOH and HNO_3 for titrn and subtract theoretical titer equiv. to P_2O_5 added from experimental titer. Calc. difference equiv. to 0.3663N NaOH and subtract this blank from all sample detns.

Calc. and report as % P_2O_5.

Alkalimetric Ammonium Molybdophosphate Method (12)—Official First Action

2.029 Reagents

(a) *Molybdate soln.*—Dissolve 100 g MoO_3 in mixt. of 144 ml NH_4OH and 271 ml H_2O. Cool, and pour soln slowly, stirring constantly, into cool mixt. of 489 ml HNO_3 and 1148 ml H_2O. Keep final mixt. in warm place several days or until portion heated to 40° deposits no yellow ppt. Decant soln from any sediment and keep in g-s vessels.

(b) *Acidified molybdate soln.*—To 100 ml molybdate soln, (a), add 5 ml HNO_3. Filter immediately before use.

(c) *Sodium hydroxide std soln.*—Dil. 324.03 ml 1N alkali, carbonate-free, **45.033–45.037**, to 1 L. (100 ml of this soln should neutze 32.40 ml 1N acid; 1 ml = 1 mg or 1% P_2O_5 on basis of 0.1 g sample.) For basic slag, stdze against std phosphate material of ca same composition as sample being examined. (Since burets in constant use may become so corroded as to increase their capacity, test them at least annually.)

(d) *Std acid soln.*—Prep. soln of HCl or of HNO_3, corresponding to concn of (c) or to ½ this concn, and stdze by titrn against (c), using phthln.

2.030 Preparation of Solution

(a) Treat 1 g sample as in **2.017**(a), (b), (c), (d), or (e), preferably (a) when these acids are suitable solv.

(b) Proceed as in **2.017**(a), (b), (c), or (e), preferably (a) when these acids are suitable solv. Add 25 ml *10% $BaCl_2$ soln* to hot digestate, boil ca 2 min, cool, dil. to 200 ml, mix, filter thru dry filter, and continue as in **2.031**(b).

2.031 Determination

(a) Prep. sample soln as in **2.030**(a). Pipet, into beaker or flask, aliquot corresponding to 0.4 g sample for P_2O_5 content of sample <5%; 0.2 g for 5–20%; 0.1 g for >20%. Add 5–10 ml HNO_3, depending on method of soln (or equiv. in NH_4NO_3); then add NH_4OH until ppt that forms dissolves only slowly on vigorous stirring, dil. to 75–100 ml, and adjust to 25–30°. If sample does not give ppt with NH_4OH as test of neutzn, make soln slightly alk. to litmus paper with NH_4OH and then slightly acid with HNO_3 (1 + 3). Add 20–25 ml acidified molybdate soln for P_2O_5 content <5%; 30–35 ml for 5–20%; and enough acidified molybdate soln to insure complete pptn for >20%. Place soln in shaking or stirring app. and agitate 30 min at room temp.;

decant *at once* thru filter and wash ppt twice by decanting with 25–30 ml portions H_2O, agitating thoroly and allowing to settle. Transfer ppt to filter and wash with cold H_2O until filtrate from 2 fillings of filter yields pink color on adding phthln and 1 drop of the std alkali. Transfer ppt and filter to beaker or pptg vessel, dissolve ppt in small excess of the std alkali, add few drops of phthln, and titr. with std acid. Report as % P_2O_5.

(b) Prep. soln as in **2.030(b)**. Proceed as in **2.031(a)** to diln to 75–100 ml. Heat in H_2O bath to 45–50°, add acidified molybdate soln at rate of 75 ml /100 mg P_2O_5 present, and let mixt. remain in bath 30 min, stirring occasionally. Decant *at once* thru filter, wash, and titr. as in **2.031(a)**.

(c) *Not applicable to superphosphates and other fertilizers containing sulfate or to solns prepd with aid of sulfuric acid.*—Prep. sample soln as in **2.030(a)**. Proceed as in **2.031(b)**.

Water-Soluble Phosphorus

2.032 Preparation of Solution—
Official Final Action

Place 1 g sample on 9 cm filter and wash with small portions H_2O until filtrate measures ca 250 ml. Let each portion pass thru filter before adding more and use suction if washing would not otherwise be complete within 1 hr. If filtrate is turbid, add 1–2 ml HNO_3, dil. to 250 ml, and mix.

2.033 Gravimetric Quinolinium
Molybdophosphate Method—
Official Final Action

Pipet aliquot contg $\leq$25 mg P_2O_5 into 500 ml erlenmeyer. Dil., if necessary, to 50 ml, add 10 ml HNO_3 $(1 + 1)$, and boil gently 10 min. Cool, dil. to 100 ml, and proceed as in **2.025(b)**.

2.034 Alkalimetric Quinolinium
Molybdophosphate Method—
Official First Action

Pipet aliquot contg $\leq$30 mg P_2O_5 into 500 ml erlenmeyer. Dil., if necessary, to 50 ml, add 10 ml HNO_3 $(1 + 1)$, boil gently 10 min, cool, and proceed as in **2.028**, beginning "add 20 ml citric acid soln . . ."

2.035 Spectrophotometric
Molybdovanadophosphate Method—
Official First Action

Adjust concn according to **2.021(a)** or **(b)** and proceed as in **2.022**.

2.036 Alkalimetric Ammonium
Molybdophosphate Method—
Official First Action

Pipet, into beaker or flask, aliquots of soln corresponding to 0.4 g sample for P_2O_5 content of sample <5%, 0.2 g for 5–20%, or 0.1 g for >20%, and dil. to 50 ml, if necessary. Add 10 ml HNO_3 $(1 + 1)$ and

boil gently 10 min. Cool, nearly neutze with NH_4OH, dil. to 60–75 ml, and proceed as in **2.031(a)**, beginning "Add 20–25 ml acidified . . ."

Citrate-Insoluble Phosphorus (13)—
Official Final Action

2.037   *Reagents*

(a) *Ammonium citrate soln (12).*—Should have sp gr of 1.09 at 20° and pH of 7.0 as detd electrometrically.

Dissolve 370 g cryst. citric acid in 1.5 L H_2O and nearly neutze by adding 345 ml NH_4OH (28–29% NH_3). If concn of NH_3 is <28%, add correspondingly larger vol. and dissolve citric acid in correspondingly smaller vol. H_2O. Cool, and check pH. Adjust with NH_4OH $(1 + 7)$ or citric acid soln to pH 7. Dil. soln, if necessary, to sp gr of 1.09 at 20°. (Vol. will be ca 2 L.) Keep in tightly stoppered bottles and check pH from time to time. If pH has changed from 7.0, readjust.

(b) *Other reagents and solns.*—See **2.016, 2.019, 2.023,** or **2.029.**

2.038   *Determination*

(a) *Acidulated samples, mixed fertilizers, and materials containing water-soluble compounds.*—After removing H_2O-sol. P_2O_5, **2.032**, transfer filter and residue, within 1 hr, to 200 or 250 ml flask contg 100 ml NH_4 citrate soln previously heated to 65°. Close flask tightly with smooth rubber stopper, shake vigorously until paper is reduced to pulp, and relieve pressure by removing stopper momentarily. Continuously agitate stoppered flask in constant temp. app. at exactly 65°. (Action of app. should be such that dispersion of sample in citrate soln is continually maintained and entire inner surface of flask and stopper is continually bathed with soln.)

Exactly 1 hr after adding filter and residue, remove flask from app. and immediately filter by suction as rapidly as possible thru Whatman No. 5 paper or equiv., using buchner or ordinary funnel with Pt or other cone. Wash with H_2O at 65° until vol. filtrate is ca 350 ml, allowing time for thoro draining before adding more H_2O. If material is one that yields cloudy filtrate, wash with *5% NH_4NO_3 soln.* Det. P_2O_5 in citrate-insol. residue by one of following methods:

(1) Dry paper and contents, transfer to crucible, ignite until all org. matter is destroyed, and digest with 10–15 ml HCl until all phosphate dissolves; or (2) treat wet filter and contents as in **2.017(a), (c), (d),** or **(e)**. Dil. soln to 250 ml, or other suitable vol., mix well, filter thru dry paper, and det. P_2O_5 as in **2.022, 2.025,** or **2.031.**

(b) *Nonacidulated samples.*—Place 1 g sample (ground to pass No. 40 sieve in case of Ca metaphosphate) on dry 9 cm paper. Without previous washing with H_2O, proceed as in **(a)**. If sample contains much org. matter (bone, fish, etc.), dissolve residue insol. in NH_4 citrate as in **2.017(c), (d),** or **(e)**.

**2.039 Alkalimetric Quinolinium
Molybdophosphate Method (14)—
Official First Action**

Treat 1 g sample by **2.038**(a) or (b). Transfer aliquot of citrate-insol. P_2O_5 contg ≤ 5 ml concd acid to 500 ml erlenmeyer. Add 20 ml 10% citric acid soln and dil. to 100 ml with H_2O. Continue as in **2.028**(a), beginning "Add 60 ml quimociac reagent ..."

**2.040 Citrate-Soluble Phosphorus—
Official Final Action**

Subtract sum of H_2O-sol. and citrate-insol. P_2O_5 from total P_2O_5 to obtain citrate-sol. P_2O_5.

Available Phosphorus

**2.041 Indirect Method—Official
Final Action**

Subtract citrate-insol. P_2O_5 from total P_2O_5 to obtain available P_2O_5.

Direct Method—Official Final Action

2.042   Reagents

(*Caution: See* **46.026, 46.028, 46.030,** and **Acids,** Chap. 46.)

(a) *Nitric-perchloric acid mixture.*—Add 300 ml 70% $HClO_4$ to 700 ml HNO_3.

(b) *Ternary acid mixture.*—Add 20 ml H_2SO_4 to 100 ml HNO_3, mix, and add 40 ml 70% $HClO_4$.

(c) *Modified molybdovanadate reagent.*—Prep. as in **2.019**(a) except use 250 ml 70% $HClO_4$ instead of 450 ml.

2.043   Preparation of Solution

(a) *Acidulated samples, mixed fertilizers, and materials containing water-soluble compounds.*—(*1*) *Without filtration of citrate digestate.*—Place 1 g sample on 9 cm paper and wash by gravity with twelve 10 ml portions H_2O into 500 ml vol. flask. Let each portion pass thru filter before adding more. Let paper drain thoroly, remove, and rinse funnel with 10 ml H_2O. Treat H_2O-insol. residue with NH_4 citrate soln as in **2.038**(a). Exactly 1 hr after adding filter and residue, remove flask from app. and transfer contents to flask contg H_2O-sol. fraction. Cool to room temp. immediately, dil. to vol., mix thoroly, and let stand at least 2 hr before removing aliquot.

(*2*) *With filtration of citrate digestate.*—If desired, wash by gravity into 500 ml Kohlrausch flask contg 5 ml HNO_3 (1 + 1), catching filtrate from insol. residue, **2.038**(a), in the Kohlrausch flask contg H_2O-sol. fraction, and wash residue until vol. soln in flask is ca 500 ml. Cool, dil. to 500 ml, and mix.

(b) *Nonacidulated samples.*—Place 1 g sample (ground to pass No. 40 sieve in case of Ca metaphosphate) on dry 9 cm paper. Without previous washing with H_2O, proceed as in (a)(*1*) or (*2*). If (*2*) is used, wash residue until vol. soln is ca 350 ml. Cool, dil. to 500 ml, and mix.

**2.044 Alkalimetric Quinolinium
Molybdophosphate Method (14)—
Official First Action**

Treat 1 g sample by appropriate modification of **2.043**. Transfer aliquot contg ≤ 30 mg P_2O_5 and ≤ 10 ml NH_4 citrate soln, **2.037**(a), to 500 ml erlenmeyer. Dil., if necessary, to 50 ml, add 10 ml HNO_3 (1 + 1), and boil gently 10 min. Cool, dil. to 100 ml, and continue as in **2.028**(a), beginning "Add 60 ml quimociac reagent..."

**2.045 Spectrophotometric
Molybdovanadophosphate Method
(15)—Official Final Action**

(Not applicable to materials yielding colored solns or solns contg ions other than orthophosphate which form colored complexes with molybdovanadate. Not recommended for basic slag.)

Prep. std curve as in **2.020**, using photometer, **2.018**.

Pipet, into 100 ml vol. flasks, 5 ml aliquots std phosphate solns contg 2 and 3.5 mg P_2O_5/aliquot, **2.019**(b), resp., add 2 ml 70% $HClO_4$, and develop color as in **2.020**. Adjust instrument to zero A for 2 mg std and det. A of 3.5 mg std. (A of latter must be practically identical with corresponding value on std curve.)

Prep. sample as in **2.043**.

(a) *Samples containing up to 5% P_2O_5.*—Pipet 10 ml sample soln into 125 ml erlenmeyer, and treat by one of following methods (*Caution: See* **46.019, 46.026,** and **46.028**):

(*1*) Add 5 ml 20% $NaClO_3$ soln and 10 ml HNO_3-$HClO_4$ mixt., **2.042**(a). Boil gently until greenish-yellow color disappears (ca 20 min), cool, and add 2 ml HCl. After vigorous reaction subsides, evap. to fumes of $HClO_4$, and fume 2 min.

(*2*) Add 5 ml ternary acid mixt., **2.042**(b), swirl, boil gently 15 min, and digest at 150–200° until clear white salt or colorless soln remains. Evap. to white fumes and continue heating 5 min.

Cool, add 15 ml H_2O, and boil 5 min. Transfer to 100 ml vol. flask, dil. to 50 ml, swirl, and cool to room temp. Add 5 ml std phosphate soln contg 2 mg P_2O_5 and 20 ml modified molybdovanadate soln, **2.042**(c). Dil. to 100 ml, and continue as in **2.022**(a).

(b) *Samples containing more than 5% P_2O_5.*—Dil. soln to such vol. that 5–10 ml aliquot contains 2–5 mg P_2O_5. Digest as in (a)(*1*) or (*2*). Without adding std phosphate soln, continue as in (a).

**2.046 Gravimetric Quinolinium
Molybdophosphate Method (16)—
Official Final Action**

(a) *Solns containing no organic phosphorus.*—Prep. sample as in **2.043**. Pipet, into 500 ml erlenmeyer, aliquot contg ≤ 25 mg P_2O_5 and ≤ 10 ml original NH_4 citrate. Dil., if necessary, to ca 50 ml, add 10 ml HNO_3 (1 + 1), and boil gently 10 min. Cool, dil. to 150 ml, and proceed as in **2.025**(a) or (b).

(b) *Solns containing organic phosphorus.*—(*Caution: See* **46.019, 46.026,** and **46.028.**) Select aliquot as in (a). Add 10 ml 20% NaClO₃ and 10 ml HNO₃-HClO₄ mixt., **2.042**(a). Boil vigorously until greenish-yellow color disappears (usually ca 30 min), cool, and add 2 ml HCl. After vigorous reaction subsides, evap. to white fumes, and continue heating 5 min. Cool, and proceed as in **2.025**(a) or (b).

2.047 Alkalimetric Ammonium Molybdophosphate Method (17)— Official First Action

(a) *Solns containing no organic phosphorus.*— Pipet, into suitable vessel, aliquot contg ≤25 mg P₂O₅ and ≤10 ml original NH₄ citrate. Add 10 ml HNO₃ (1 + 1) and boil gently 15 min. Cool, add 15 ml soln contg 10 g NH₄NO₃, add NH₄OH until ppt that forms dissolves only slowly on vigorous stirring, and dil. to 75–100 ml. Slowly add 45 ml acidified molybdate soln, **2.029**(b), place in 50° bath, and agitate continuously 45 min. Continue as in **2.031**(a), beginning, "decant *at once*..."

(b) *Solns containing organic phosphorus.*—Proceed as in **2.046**(b) thru fuming 5 min. Cool, add 15 ml soln contg 10 g NH₄NO₃, and continue as in **2.031**(a), beginning, "then add NH₄OH until ppt that forms..."

NITROGEN

2.048 ★ Detection of Nitrates— ★ Official Final Action

Mix 5 g sample with 25 ml hot H₂O, and filter. To 1 vol. of this soln add 2 vols H₂SO₄, free from HNO₃ and oxides of N, and let cool. Add few drops *concd FeSO₄ soln* in such manner that fluids do not mix. If nitrates are present, junction at first shows purple, afterwards brown, or if only minute quantity is present, reddish color. To another portion of soln add 1 ml *1% NaNO₃ soln* and test as before to det. whether enough H₂SO₄ was added in first test.

Total Nitrogen

(Provide adequate ventilation in laboratory and do not permit accumulation of exposed Hg.)

2.049 Reagents—Official Final Action

(a) *Sulfuric acid.*—93–98% H₂SO₄, N-free.

(b) *Mercuric oxide or metallic mercury.*—HgO or Hg, reagent grade, N-free.

(c) *Potassium sulfate (or anhydrous sodium sulfate).*—Reagent grade, N-free.

(d) *Salicylic acid.*—Reagent grade, N-free.

(e) *Sulfide or thiosulfate soln.*—Dissolve 40 g com. K₂S in 1 L H₂O. (Soln of 40 g Na₂S or 80 g Na₂S₂O₃.5H₂O in 1 L may be used.)

(f) *Sodium hydroxide.*—Pellets or soln, nitrate-free. For soln, dissolve ca 450 g solid NaOH in H₂O, cool, and dil. to 1 L. (Sp gr of soln should be 1.36 or higher.)

(g) *Zinc granules.*—Reagent grade.

(h) *Zinc dust.*—Impalpable powder.

(i) *Methyl red indicator.*—Dissolve 1 g Me red in 200 ml alcohol.

(j) *Hydrochloric or sulfuric acid std soln.*—0.5N, or 0.1N when amt of N is small. Prep. as in **45.012** or **45.040.**

(k) *Sodium hydroxide std soln.*—0.1N (or other specified concn). Prep. as in **45.033–45.035.**

Stdze each std soln with primary std, Chap. **45,** and check one against the other. Test reagents before use by blank detn with 2 g sugar, which insures partial reduction of any nitrates present.

Caution: Use freshly opened H₂SO₄ or add dry P₂O₅ to avoid hydrolysis of nitriles and cyanates. Ratio of salt to acid (wt:vol.) should be ca 1:1 at end of digestion for proper temp. control. Digestion may be incomplete at lower ratio; N may be lost at higher ratio. Each g fat consumes 10 ml, and each g carbohydrate 4 ml, H₂SO₄ during digestion.

2.050 Apparatus—Official Final Action

(a) *For digestion.*—Use Kjeldahl flasks of hard, moderately thick, well-annealed glass with total capacity ca 500–800 ml. Conduct digestion over heating device adjusted to bring 250 ml H₂O at 25° to rolling boil in ca 5 min or other time as specified in method. To test heaters, preheat 10 min if gas or 30 min if elec. Add 3–4 boiling chips to prevent superheating.

(b) *For distillation.*—Use 500–800 Kjeldahl or other suitable flask, fitted with rubber stopper thru which passes lower end of efficient scrubber bulb or trap to prevent mech. carryover of NaOH during distn. Connect upper end of bulb tube to condenser tube by rubber tubing. Trap outlet of condenser in such way as to ensure complete absorption of NH₃ distd over into acid in receiver.

2.051 Improved Kjeldahl Method for Nitrate-Free Samples (18)— Official Final Action

(*Caution: See* **46.030** and **46.065.**)

Place weighed sample (0.7–2.2 g) in digestion flask. Add 0.7 g HgO or 0.65 g metallic Hg, 15 g powd K₂SO₄ or anhyd. Na₂SO₄, and 25 ml H₂SO₄. If sample >2.2 g is used, increase H₂SO₄ by 10 ml for each g sample. Place flask in inclined position and heat gently until frothing ceases (if necessary, add small amt of paraffin to reduce frothing); boil briskly until soln clears and then ≥30 min longer (2 hr for samples contg org. material).

Cool, add ca 200 ml H₂O, cool below 25°, add 25 ml of the sulfide or thiosulfate soln, and mix to ppt Hg. Add few Zn granules to prevent bumping, tilt flask, and add layer of NaOH (usually 25 g solid reagent or enough soln to make contents strongly alk.) without agitation. (Thiosulfate or sulfide soln may be mixed with the NaOH soln before addn to flask.) Immediately connect flask to distg bulb on condenser, and, with tip of condenser immersed in std acid and 5–7 drops indicator in receiver, rotate flask to mix contents thoroly; then heat until all NH_3 has distd (at least 150 ml distillate). Remove receiver, wash tip of condenser, and titr. excess std acid in distillate with std NaOH soln. Correct for blank detn on reagents.

2.052 Improved Kjeldahl Method for Nitrate-Containing Samples— Official Final Action

(Not applicable to liqs or to materials with high Cl:NO_3 ratio; *Caution: See* **46.030** and **46.065.**)

Place weighed sample (0.7–2.2 g) in digestion flask. Add 40 ml H_2SO_4 contg 2 g salicylic acid. Shake until thoroly mixed and let stand, with occasional shaking, 30 min or more; then add (*1*) 5 g $Na_2S_2O_3.5H_2O$ or (*2*) 2 g Zn dust (as impalpable powder, not granulated Zn or filings). Shake and let stand 5 min; then heat over low flame until frothing ceases. Turn off heat, add 0.7 g HgO (or 0.65 g metallic Hg) and 15 g powd K_2SO_4 (or anhyd. Na_2SO_4), and boil briskly until soln clears, then ≥30 min longer (2 hr for samples contg org. material).

Proceed as in second par. of **2.051.**

Comprehensive Nitrogen Method (19)— Official First Action

(Applicable to all fertilizer samples; *Caution: See* **46.030** and **46.079.**)

2.053 Reagents

(a) *Chromium metal.*—100 mesh, low N (Fisher Scientific Co. No. C-318 or Sargent-Welch Scientific Co. No. SC11432 are satisfactory).

(b) *Alundum.*—Norton 14X (Arthur H. Thomas Co.).

(c) *Dilute sulfuric acid.*—Slowly add 625 ml H_2SO_4 to 300 ml H_2O. Dil. to ca 1 L and mix. After cooling, dil. to 1 L with H_2O and mix. Avoid absorption of NH_3 from air during prepn, particularly if stream of air is used for mixing.

(d) *Sodium thiosulfate or potassium sulfide soln.*— 160 g $Na_2S_2O_3.5H_2O/L$ or 80 g K_2S/L.

For other reagents, *see* **2.049.**

2.054 Determination

Place 0.2–2.0 g sample contg ≤60 mg nitrate N in 500–800 ml Kjeldahl flask and add 1.2 g Cr powder. Add 35 ml H_2O or, with liqs, lesser amt to make total vol. of liq. 35 ml. Let stand 10 min with occasional gentle swirling to dissolve all nitrate salts. Add 7 ml HCl and let stand ≥30 sec but ≤10 min.

Place flask on preheated burner with heat input set at 7.0–7.5 min boil test, **2.050**(a). After heating 3.5 min, remove from heat and let cool.

Add 22 g K_2SO_4, 1.0 g HgO, and few granules Alundum. Add 40 ml dil. H_2SO_4, (c). (If adequate ventilation is available, 25 ml H_2SO_4 may be added instead of dil. H_2SO_4. If org. matter which consumes large amt of acid exceeds 1.0 g, add addnl 1.0 ml H_2SO_4 for each 0.1 g org. matter in excess of 1.0 g.)

Place flask on burners set at 5 min boil test. (Preheated burners reduce foaming with most samples. Cut back heat input if foam fills ≥⅔ of bulb of flask. Use variable heat input until this phase is past.) Heat at 5 min boil test until dense white fumes of H_2SO_4 clear bulb of flask. Digestion is now complete for samples contg ammoniacal, nitrate, and urea N. For other samples, swirl flask gently and continue digestion 60 min more.

Proceed as in **2.051**, second par., substituting **2.053**(d) for **2.049**(e).

Raney Powder Method (19)— Official First Action

(Applicable to all fertilizer samples; *Caution: See* **46.030** and **46.079.**)

2.055 Reagents

(a) *Raney catalyst powder No. 2813.*—50% Ni, 50% Al (W. R. Grace and Co., Raney Catalyst Division, 819 Hamilton National Bank Building, Chattanooga, TN 37402). *Caution:* Raney catalyst powders react slowly in water or moist air to form alumina; avoid prolonged contact with air or moisture during storage or use.

(b) *Sulfuric acid-potassium sulfate soln.*—Slowly add 200 ml H_2SO_4 to 625 ml of H_2O and mix. Without cooling, add 106.7 g K_2SO_4 and continue stirring until all salt dissolves. Dil. to ca 1 L and mix. Cool, dil. to 1 L with H_2O, and mix. Avoid absorption of NH_3 from air during prepn particularly if stream of air is used for mixing.

For other reagents, see **2.049.**

2.056 Determination

Place 0.2–2.0 g sample contg ≤42 mg nitrate N in 500–800 ml Kjeldahl flask (800 ml flask is preferred with samples which foam considerably, especially orgs). Add 1.7 g Raney catalyst powder, 3 drops *tributyl citrate*, and 150 ml H_2SO_4-K_2SO_4 soln. If org. matter exceeds 0.6 g, add addnl 2.5 ml of this soln for each 0.1 g of org. matter in excess of 0.6 g.

Swirl to mix sample with acid and place flask on cold burner. If burner has been in use, turn off completely at least 10 min before placing flask on burner. After flask is on burner, set heat input to 5 min boil test. When sample starts boiling, reduce heat to pass 10 min boil test. After 10 min, raise flask to vertical position and add 0.7 g HgO and 15 g K_2SO_4. (Contents of Kel-Pak No. 5 (Matheson Scientific, 1850 Greenleaf Ave, Elk Grove Village, IL 60007) without plastic container may be used.) Replace flask in inclined position and increase heat to 4–5 min boil test. (Cut back heat input if foam fills ≥⅔ of bulb of flask. Use variable heat input until this phase is past.) Heat at 4–5 min boil test until dense white fumes of H_2SO_4 clear bulb of flask. Digestion is now complete for samples contg only ammoniacal, nitrate, and urea N. For other samples, swirl flask gently and continue digestion another 30 min.

Proceed as in **2.051**, second par. If 800 ml Kjeldahl flasks have been used, add 300 instead of 200 ml H_2O.

Ammoniacal Nitrogen

2.057 Magnesium Oxide Method— Official Final Action

(Not applicable in presence of urea)

Place 0.7–3.5 g, according to NH_3 content of sample, in distn flask with ca 200 ml H_2O and 2 g or more *carbonate-free MgO*. Connect flask to condenser by Kjeldahl connecting bulb, distill 100 ml liq. into measured quantity of std acid, **2.049**(j), and titr. with std NaOH soln, **2.049**(k), using Me red, **2.049**(i).

2.058 ★ Formaldehyde Titration ★ Method—Official Final Action

(Applicable to NH_4NO_3 and $(NH_4)_2SO_4$)

Weigh 7.003 or 14.007 g sample and dil. to 250 or 500 ml. Pipet 25 or 50 ml into 300–500 ml erlenmeyer (ca 1.5 g may be rapidly weighed and washed directly into flask). Add ca 1 ml 37% HCHO soln for each 0.1 g sample in aliquot. Dil. to 150–200 ml and let stand 5 min. Titr. with 0.25–0.50N NaOH, **2.049**(k), using 5 drops phthln, until there is no perceptible color change at point of contact, or until proper shade of pink persists. (If electrometric titrn is preferred, titr. to ca pH 8.6.) Det. blank on HCHO soln.

% ammoniacal N = net ml NaOH × normality × 1.4007/wt sample.

Nitrate and Ammoniacal Nitrogen

2.059 ★ Ferrous Sulfate-Zinc-Soda ★ Method—Official Final Action

(Not applicable in presence of org. matter, Ca cyanamide, and urea)

Place 0.35, 0.5, or 0.7 g sample in 600–700 ml flask and add 200 ml H_2O, 5 g powd. Zn, 1–2 g $FeSO_4.7H_2O$, and 50 ml NaOH soln (sp gr 1.33). Connect flask with distg app., distill, collect distillate in usual way in std acid, **2.049**(j), and titr. with std NaOH soln, **2.049**(k), using Me red, **2.049**(i). In analysis of nitrate salts dissolve 3.5 or 5.0 g in H_2O, dil. to 250 ml, and use 25 ml aliquot.

2.060 Devarda Method (20)— Official Final Action

(Not applicable in presence of org. matter, Ca cyanamide, and urea)

Place 0.35 or 0.5 g sample in 600–700 ml flask and add 300 ml H_2O, 3 g *Devarda alloy* (Cu 50, Al 45, Zn 5), and 5 ml NaOH soln (42% by wt), pouring latter down side of flask so that it does not mix at once with contents. By means of Davisson (J. Ind. Eng. Chem. **11**, 465(1919)) or other suitable scrubbing bulb that will prevent passing over of any spray, connect with condenser, tip of which always extends beneath surface of std acid in receiving flask. Mix contents of

distg flask by rotating. Heat slowly at first and then at rate to yield 250 ml distillate in 1 hr. Collect distillate in measured quantity of std acid, **2.049**(j), and titr. with std NaOH soln, **2.049**(k), using Me red, **2.049**(i).

Nitrate Nitrogen

2.061 Robertson Method (21)— Official Final Action

(Applicable in presence of Ca cyanamide and urea; *Caution: See* **46.030** and **46.065**.)

(a) Det. total N as in **2.052**.

(b) Det. H_2O-insol. N as in **2.064**, but use 2.5 g sample. Dil. filtrate to 250 ml.

(c) Det. ammoniacal N in 50 ml filtrate as in **2.057**.

(d) Place another 50 ml portion filtrate in 500 ml Kjeldahl flask and add 2 g $FeSO_4.7H_2O$ and 20 ml H_2SO_4. (If total N is >5%, use 5 g $FeSO_4.7H_2O$.) Digest over hot flame until all H_2O is evapd and white fumes appear, and continue digestion at least 10 min to drive off nitrate N. If severe bumping occurs, add 10–15 glass beads. Add 0.65 g Hg, or 0.7 g HgO, and digest until all org. matter is oxidized. Cool, dil., add the K_2S soln, and complete detn as in **2.051**. Before distn add pinch of mixt. of Zn dust and granular "20-mesh" Zn to each flask to prevent bumping.

Total N (a) − H_2O-insol. N (b) = H_2O-sol. N.
H_2O-sol. N − N obtained in (d) = nitrate N.

2.062 Jones Modification of Robertson Method (21)—Official Final Action

(Applicable when H_2O-sol. N need not be detd; *Caution: See* **46.030** and **46.065**.)

Weigh 0.5 g sample into Kjeldahl flask, add 50 ml H_2O, and rotate gently. Add 2 g $FeSO_4.7H_2O$ and rotate. Add 20 ml H_2SO_4. Digest over hot flame. When H_2O evaps and white fumes appear, add 0.65 g Hg and proceed as in **2.051**. Cool, dil., and distill as usual. Total N − N thus found = nitrate N.

2.063 ★ Water-Insoluble Nitrogen in ★ Cyanamide (22)— Official Final Action

Weigh 2 g finely ground sample and place in mortar. Gradually add ca 70 ml H_2O while stirring with pestle, and grind thoroly. Transfer mixt. to beaker, washing out mortar with H_2O. Filter on 11 cm paper. When all cyanamide has been transferred to paper, wash with addnl 250 ml H_2O, draining each portion before adding more H_2O. Transfer paper and residue to digestion flask. Det. N in residue as in **2.051**.

2.064 Water-Insoluble Nitrogen— Official Final Action

(*See* **2.069**(a) and (b) for urea-formaldehyde or mixts contg such compds.)

Place 1 or 1.4 g sample in 50 ml beaker, wet with alcohol, add 20 ml H_2O, and let stand 15 min, stirring occasionally. Transfer supernatant to 11 cm Whatman No. 2 paper in 60° long-stem funnel 2.5″ diam., and wash residue 4 or 5 times by decanting with H_2O at room temp. (20–25°). Finally transfer all residue to filter and complete washing until filtrate measures 250 ml. Det. N in residue as in 2.051.

★ Nitrogen Activity ★

2.065 Removal of Water-Soluble Nitrogen— Official Final Action

(a) *Mixed fertilizers.*—See 2.058, 10th ed.

(b) *Raw materials,*—See 2.058, 10th ed.

2.066 Water-Insoluble Organic Nitrogen Soluble in Neutral Permanganate— Official Final Action

See 2.059, 10th ed.

2.067 Water-Insoluble Organic Nitrogen Distilled from Alkaline Permanganate (23)—Official Final Action

See 2.060–2.061, 10th ed.

Nitrogen Activity Index (AI) of Urea-Formaldehyde Compounds (24)— Official Final Action
(Applicable to urea-formaldehyde compds and mixts contg such compds)

2.068 *Reagent*

Phosphate buffer soln.—Dissolve 14.3 g KH_2PO_4 and 91.0 g K_2HPO_4 in H_2O and dil. to 1 L. Dil. 100 ml of this soln to 1 L (pH 7.5).

2.069 *Determination*

(a) Crush sample (do not grind) to pass No. 20 sieve.

(b) Det. cold H_2O-insol. N (*WIN*) as in 2.064, keeping temp. at 25±2°. Stir at 5 min intervals during 15 min standing.

(c) Det. hot H_2O-insol. N (*HWIN*) in phosphate buffer soln as follows: Place accurately weighed sample contg 0.1200 g *WIN* in 200 ml tall form beaker. Add ca 0.5 g $CaCO_3$ to mixed fertilizers contg urea-CH_2O compds. From supply of boiling buffer soln, add 100 ml from graduate to sample, stir, cover, and immerse *promptly* in boiling H_2O bath so that liq. in beaker is below H_2O level in bath. Maintain bath at 98–100°, checked with thermometer, and stir at 10 min intervals. After exactly 30 min, remove beaker from bath and filter promptly thru 15 cm Whatman No. 12 fluted paper. If filtration takes >4 min, discard detn. Repeat detn, adding, with stirring, 1 g Celite filter-aid just before removing beaker from bath, and filter.

Wash insol. residue completely onto paper with boiling H_2O and continue washing until total vol. used is 100 ml. Complete washing before filtrate becomes cloudy or its temp. drops to <60°. Det. total N (*HWIN*) in wet paper and residue as in 2.051, using 35 ml H_2SO_4 when $CaCO_3$ has been added.

$$\text{Activity index } (AI) = (\%WIN - \%HWIN) \times 100 / \%WIN$$

Urea (25)—Official Final Action

2.070 *Reagent*

Neutral urease soln.—Use fresh com. 1% urease soln, or dissolve 1 g urease powder in 100 ml H_2O, or shake 1 g jack bean meal with 100 ml H_2O 5 min. Transfer 10 ml soln to 250 ml erlenmeyer, dil. with 50 ml H_2O, and add 4 drops Me purple (available from Fisher Scientific Co.). Titr. with 0.1N HCl to reddish-purple; then back-titr. to green with 0.1N NaOH. From difference in ml, calc. amt 0.1N HCl required to neutze remainder of soln (usually ca 2.5 ml/100 ml), add this amount of acid, and shake well.

Verify enzyme activity of urease source periodically. Discard any source which does not produce soln capable of hydrolyzing 0.1 g urea/20 ml soln.

2.071 *Determination*

Weigh 10±0.01 g sample and transfer to 15 cm Whatman No. 12 fluted filter paper. Leach with ca 300 ml H_2O into 500 ml vol. flask. Add 75–100 ml satd $Ba(OH)_2$ soln to ppt phosphates. Let settle and test for complete pptn with few drops satd $Ba(OH)_2$ soln. Add 20 ml 10% Na_2CO_3 soln to ppt excess Ba and any sol. Ca salts. Let settle and test for complete pptn. Dil. to vol., mix, and filter thru 15 cm Whatman No. 12 fluted paper. Transfer 50 ml aliquot (equiv. to 1 g sample) to 200 or 250 ml erlenmeyer and add 1–2 drops Me purple. Acidify soln with 2N HCl and add 2–3 drops excess. Neutze soln with 0.1N NaOH to first change in color of indicator. Add 20 ml neutral urease soln, close flask with rubber stopper, and let stand 1 hr at 20–25°. Cool flask in ice-H_2O slurry and titr. at once with 0.1N HCl to full purple; then add ca 5 ml excess. Record total vol. added. Back-titr. excess HCl with 0.1N NaOH to neut. end point.

% Urea = (ml 0.1N HCl − ml 0.1N NaOH) × 0.3003/wt sample.

2.072 Slow-Release Nitrogen (26)— Official Final Action

Weigh 20 g unground sample into 600 ml Berzelius tall-form, lipless beaker. Add 150 ml H_2O at boiling temp., after bubbling ceases. Without further heating, place on magnetic stirrer with ⅜ × 1½″ Teflon-covered stirring bar, cover, and stir exactly 30 min at speed to produce good agitation without bouncing of bar. Immediately decant supernatant thru Whatman No. 4 paper into 200 ml vol. flask. (For fertilizers difficult to filter, transfer contents of beaker to 150 ml centrf. tubes immediately after 30 min stirring, centrf., and decant supernatant into 200 ml vol. flask.) Rinse beaker and residue with H_2O, swirl, and decant supernatant thru paper into vol. flask. Cool to room temp. and dil. to vol. with H_2O.

Det. N in 10 ml aliquot by **2.051** for nitrate-free and **2.052** for org. and nitrate-contg fertilizers, and calc. % N in filtrate. Det. total % N in sep. portion ground sample by **2.051** or **2.052**, resp.

% Slow-release N = % total N − % N in filtrate.

Biuret (27)—Official First Action

2.073   *Reagents*

(a) *Alkaline tartrate soln.*—Dissolve 40 g NaOH in 500 ml H_2O, cool, add 50 g $NaKC_4H_4O_6 \cdot 4H_2O$, and dil. to 1 L. Let stand 1 day before use.

(b) *Copper sulfate soln.*—Dissolve 15 g $CuSO_4$ $.5H_2O$ in CO_2-free H_2O and dil. to 1 L.

(c) *Biuret std soln.*—1 mg/ml. Dissolve 100 mg reagent grade biuret in CO_2-free H_2O and dil. to 100 ml.

(d) *Ion exchange resin.*—Fill 50 ml buret with 30 cm column of Amberlite IR120(H) resin on glass wool plug. Regenerate column after each use by passing 100 ml H_2SO_4 (1 + 9) or HCl (1 + 4) thru column at ca 5 ml/min and then washing with H_2O until pH of effluent is >6.

2.074   *Preparation of Standard Curve*

Transfer series of aliquots, 2–50 ml, of std biuret soln to 100 ml vol. flasks. Adjust vol. to ca 50 ml with CO_2-free H_2O, add 1 drop Me red, and neutze with $0.1N$ H_2SO_4 to pink color. Add with swirling 20 ml alk. tartrate soln and then 20 ml $CuSO_4$ soln. Dil. to vol., shake 10 sec, and place in H_2O bath 15 min at $30 \pm 5°$. Also prep. reagent blank. Set A of each soln against blank at 555 nm (instrument with 500–570 nm filter is also satisfactory) with 2–4 cm cell. Plot std curve.

2.075   *Determination*

(a) *In urea.*—Continuously stir 2–5 g sample in 100 ml ca 50° H_2O 30 min. Filter and wash into 250 ml vol. flask, and dil. to vol. Transfer 25 ml aliquot to 100 ml vol. flask and proceed as in **2.074**.

(b) *In mixed fertilizers.*—Continuously stir 10–20 g sample in 150 ml ca 50° H_2O 30 min. Filter and wash into 250 ml vol. flask, and dil. to vol. Transfer 25 ml aliquot to column, (d), and adjust flow to 4–5 ml/min. Receive eluate in 100 ml beaker. When liq. level falls to top of resin bed, wash with two 25 ml portions H_2O. To eluate and washings add 2 drops Me red and then $1N$ NaOH to yellow color. Add $0.1N$ H_2SO_4 until soln just turns pink, transfer to 100 ml vol. flask, and dil. to vol. with CO_2-free H_2O. Transfer 50 ml aliquot to 100 ml vol. flask and proceed as in **2.074**.

POTASSIUM

★ *Lindo-Gladding Method (28)—* ★
Official Final Action

2.076   *Reagents*

(a) *Ammonium chloride soln.*—Dissolve 100 g NH_4Cl in 500 ml H_2O, add 5–10 g pulverized K_2PtCl_6, and shake at intervals 6–8 hr. Let mixt. settle overnight and filter. (Residue may be used to prep. fresh supply.)

(b) *Platinum soln.*—Use Pt soln contg equiv. of 0.05 g Pt (0.105 g H_2PtCl_6)/ml. 1 ml = 0.024 g K_2O.

(c) *Diglycol stearate soln.*—Dissolve 20 g diglycol stearate, tech., in 1 L benzene-alcohol (1 + 1).

(d) *Acid-alcohol.*—Mix 200 ml alcohol with 20 ml HCl and cool to room temp.

2.077   *Preparation of Solution*

(a) *Mixed fertilizers.*—Place 2.5 g sample, or factor wt 2.430 g, in 250 ml vol. flask, and add 125 ml H_2O and 50 ml satd $(NH_4)_2C_2O_4$ soln; add 1 ml diglycol stearate soln if needed to prevent foaming. Boil 30 min, add slight excess of NH_4OH, and after cooling, dil. to 250 ml. Mix, and pass thru dry filter.

(b) *Potassium salts (potassium chloride and sulfate, potassium-magnesium sulfate, and kainit).*—Dissolve 2.5 g, or factor wt 2.430 g, and dil. to 250 ml without adding NH_4OH and $(NH_4)_2C_2O_4$. When interfering substances such as NH_3, Ca, Al, etc., are present, proceed as in (a).

(c) *Organic materials (cottonseed meal, tobacco stems, etc.).*—For total K, sat. 10 g sample with H_2SO_4 and ignite in muffle at *low red heat* (625–650°) to destroy org. matter. Add little HCl, warm slightly to loosen mass from dish, transfer to 500 ml vol. flask, add NH_4OH and satd $(NH_4)_2C_2O_4$ soln, cool, dil. to 500 ml, mix, pass thru dry filter, and proceed as in **2.078**(a).

(d) *Ashes from wood, cotton hulls, etc.*—Boil 10 g sample with 300 ml H_2O 30 min, and while hot add slight excess of NH_4OH and then enough satd $(NH_4)_2C_2O_4$ soln to ppt all Ca present. Cool, dil. to 500 ml, mix, pass thru dry filter, and proceed as in **2.078**(a).

(e) *Potassium nitrate or potassium and sodium nitrate.*—If impure, proceed as in (a); if pure enough, proceed as for K salts, (b), except evap. aliquot to dryness in porcelain dish with 2 ml HCl (if Pt dish is used, add H_2SO_4 instead) and take up with H_2O and few drops HCl, before adding Pt soln.

2.078   *Determination*

(a) *Mixed fertilizers.*—In ca 100 ml quartz, SiO_2, or Pt dish, evap. nearly to dryness 25 or 50 ml aliquot of soln, **2.077**(a), (c), or (d), to which is added enough K-free $1N$ NaOH (1–2 ml) to prevent formation of free H_3PO_4 during ignition; add 1 ml H_2SO_4 (1 + 1) and 6–8 granules of granulated *sugar*, evap. to dryness, and ignite to white ash at low temp. (The

H_2SO_4 may be added after evapn to dryness and before ignition.) Maintain dull red heat (600–650°) until residue is perfectly white. Dissolve residue in hot H_2O, using at least 20 ml/100 mg K_2O present, and add few drops HCl and then excess Pt soln. Evap. on H_2O bath to thick paste, avoiding exposure to NH_3. Treat residue with ca 6 ml acid-alcohol soln. (Temp. of wash solns should be <30°.) After 15 min filter on gooch or on medium fritted crucible (Pyrex M porosity), and wash ppt thoroly with alcohol, both by decanting and on filter, continuing washing after filtrate is colorless (75 ml is usually enough). Wash 5 or 6 times with 10 ml portions NH_4Cl soln to remove impurities from ppt. Wash again thoroly with alcohol and dry ppt 30 min at 100°. Cool and weigh. Wash K_2PtCl_6 thru crucible with hot H_2O; then wash all H_2O from crucible with alcohol, and dry crucible and residue 30 min at 100°. Cool, reweigh, and calc. wt difference to K_2O. If factor wt and 50 ml aliquot (contg 0.486 g sample) are used, multiply wt by 40 to obtain % K_2O.

(b) *Potassium chloride.*—Acidify 50 ml soln prepd as in **2.077**(b) with few drops HCl, add excess Pt soln, and evap. to thick paste. Treat residue as in (a). If NH_4OH and $(NH_4)_2C_2O_4$ are used in prepg soln, ignite and complete detn as in (a).

(c) *Potassium sulfate, potassium-magnesium sulfate, and kainit.*—Acidify 50 ml soln prepd as in **2.077**(b) with few drops HCl and add excess Pt soln. Evap. mixt. and proceed as in (a), but use 25 ml portions NH_4Cl soln. If NH_4OH and $(NH_4)_2C_2O_4$ are used in prepg soln, ignite and complete detn as in (a), but use 25 ml portions NH_4Cl soln.

To convert K_2PtCl_6 to KCl use factor 0.3068; to K_2SO_4, 0.3586; to K_2O, 0.1938.

★ *Wet-Digestion Method (29)*— ★
Official Final Action

2.079 *Preparation of Solution*

Proceed as in **2.077**(a).

2.080 *Determination*

Place 50 ml aliquot soln (or 25 ml aliquot and 25 ml H_2O, if sample contains >20% K_2O) in 500 ml Kjeldahl flask. Add 10 ml HNO_3 and *silica granule* (ca 1 cm long, previously weighed along with prepd gooch or medium porosity fritted Pyrex crucible). Boil 2 min and add 10 ml HCl. Boil down to ca 25 ml, and add 5 ml HCl and excess Pt soln. Boil down to 10–15 ml, rotating flask occasionally, and then add 5 ml HCl. Reduce heat and boil down to 3–5 ml (depending on amt of ppt), rotating flask frequently near end of evapn. Remove flask from heat and swirl to dissolve any sol. residue on walls. Cool, and immediately add 25 ml alcohol to wash down neck of flask. Chill under tap, swirl, and let stand at least 5 min. Decant into weighed crucible and transfer ppt and granule with aid of stream of alcohol. Wash 5–6 times with 10 ml portions NH_4Cl soln, **2.076**(a), to

remove Mg and Na salts from ppt. Wash again thoroly with alcohol and dry ppt 30 min at 100°. Weigh and subtract wt crucible plus silica granule. $K_2PtCl_6 \times 0.1938 = K_2O$.

★ *Recovery of Platinum (30)—Procedure* ★

2.081 *Recovery from Alcohol Washings*

(a) Let NH_4Cl washings run into flask contg alcohol washings. Let $(NH_4)_2PtCl_6$ settle, decant supernatant, and save residue. Reduce as in **2.082**(a) or (b).

(b) Evap. alcohol waste in porcelain dish on steam bath or elec. hot plate. (Piece of filter paper in dish prevents most of Pt from sticking to dish.) Filter on buchner and wash reduced Pt. Transfer to porcelain dish and ignite at ca 700° in muffle ca 20 min. Digest reduced Pt in porcelain dish on steam bath with several portions HCl (1 + 3). Repeat until soln is colorless. Wash well with H_2O until test with $AgNO_3$ shows no Cl. Digest with few portions HNO_3 (1 + 4), wash, dry, and weigh.

(c) Acidify alcohol waste with HCl. Add either "20-mesh" Zn, or Al in stick or sheet form (for 75–150 ml acid use 10–20 g metal), and let stand until all Pt is reduced. Filter, ignite at 700°, and proceed as in (b).

2.082 *Recovery from K_2PtCl_6 Salt*

(a) Dissolve K_2PtCl_6 in 20 parts or more hot H_2O, acidify with HCl, and reduce with either "20-mesh" Zn or Al in sheet or stick form. Filter and ignite as in **2.081**(b).

(b) Dissolve K_2PtCl_6 in H_2O and ppt as $(NH_4)_2PtCl_6$ with NH_4Cl. Let stand several hr, filter on buchner with suction, and wash with alcohol. Transfer to porcelain dish and ignite in muffle, first ca 20 min at ca 200° and finally 30 min at ca 700°.

(c) Dissolve K_2PtCl_6 in 20 parts or more boiling H_2O. Add *Na formate* slowly (pinch at time), stirring well at each addn. (Use great care to control excessive foaming with resultant loss of Pt.) Reduction is complete when soln becomes colorless. If supernatant does not become colorless, test for complete reduction as follows:

Pipet 25 ml into 250 ml beaker, and add few drops HCl and small amt KI soln. Red color indicates presence of unreduced Pt (or other oxidant such as HNO_3).

Filter reduced Pt and ignite as in **2.081**(b).

2.083 *Preparation of Platinum Solution*

Dissolve Pt from **2.081** or **2.082** in porcelain dish on steam bath with 3 parts HCl and 1 part HNO_3. Evap. with addns of HCl 3 times to remove excess HNO_3, and then with H_2O 3 times to remove excess HCl, but do not evap. below ¼ original vol. Filter, and dil. to calcd vol. Evap. and test 10 ml portion, or portion equiv. to 1 g Pt, for material insol. in 80%

alcohol. If impurities are evident, reduce soln again, purify Pt, and redissolve. To det. concn of soln, evap. 2 ml in porcelain dish with ca 0.5 g excess of K_2SO_4. Add alcohol and wash K_2PtCl_6 as in **2.078**. (Soln may be prepd so that 1 ml = 1% K_2O in 1 g sample.)

Flame Photometric Method (31)—
Official Final Action
(*Caution: See* **46.007**.)

2.084   *Reagents and Apparatus*

(a) *Ammonium oxalate soln.*—Dissolve 40 g $(NH_4)_2C_2O_4$ in 1 L H_2O.

(b) *Methyl red indicator.*—Dissolve 0.2 g Me red in 100 ml alcohol.

(c) *Dilute nitric acid.*—Reagent grade (1 + 10).

(d) *Anion exchange resin.*—Amberlite IR-4B (Fisher Scientific Co.); Duolite A-7 or Duolite A-41 (Diamond Shamrock Chemical Co., PO Box 829, Redwood City, CA 94064); Permutit-S (Permutit Co., E49 Midland Ave, Paramus, NJ 07652); or equiv.

(e) *Potassium nitrate or potassium chloride.*—Recrystallize reagent grade salt twice from H_2O and dry 5 hr at 105°.

(f) *Ion exchange column.*—Made from 12″ length of std wall glass tubing, 2.5 cm od; one end closed by 1-hole No. 4 rubber stopper thru which is inserted 2-way stopcock or glass tubing connected to rubber tubing and compressor clamp. Do not let stopcock tubing protrude above stopper. Choose stopper large enough so that there is no space between stopper vertex and column wall. Alternatively use glass chromatgc tube 12″ × 19 mm id with stopcock or valve at bottom to control flow rate (such as Scientific Glass Apparatus Co. No. C-4225).

Place glass wool plug in bottom of column, close valve, and add H_2O to ht of 4″. Transfer portion of resin to 200 ml beaker and suspend in H_2O. Transfer slurry to column and adjust ht of packed resin to 8″, draining excess H_2O until 1″ head remains. Regenerate resin after 10 successive aliquots have passed thru, except Amberlite IR-4B which can be used for 20 aliquots. For Na, regenerate after 5 aliquots have passed thru.

2.085   *Preparation of Resin*

Place ca 450 g resin in 4 L beaker and add 2 L 5% NaOH. Stir 30 min with elec. stirrer. Let resin settle, and decant NaOH soln. Repeat treatment with 5% NaOH twice, decanting NaOH soln after final treatment. Add 2 L H_2O to resin, stir few min, let resin settle, and decant wash H_2O. Repeat 3–4 times. Resin is now in free base form. Regenerate to NO_3 form by treating 3 times with 5% HNO_3, in same manner as with NaOH soln. Wash resin with H_2O until washings reach pH 2 or above by backwashing in column or by stirring and decanting in large beaker. Store resin under H_2O in stoppered bottle.

2.086   *Preparation of Solution*

(a) *Mixed fertilizers and potassium-magnesium sulfate.*—Weigh 1.5058 g sample into 250 ml vol. flask (500 ml flask if sample contains >30% K_2O), add 125 ml H_2O and 50 ml $(NH_4)_2C_2O_4$ soln, and boil 30 min. Cool, dil. to vol., mix, and pass thru dry filter.

(b) *Potassium chloride and sulfate.*—Dissolve 1.5058 g in H_2O and dil. to 500 ml.

2.087   *Preparation of Standard Curve*

Dissolve 1.2931 g KNO_3 (or 0.9535 g KCl) in H_2O and dil. to 500 ml (1000 ppm K). Prep. std solns by diln covering range 0–80 ppm K at intervals not >10 ppm, adding appropriate amt $LiNO_3$ if internal std instrument is to be used. Prep. std curve of emission against concn, adjusting instrument so that 50 ppm K gives reading near mid-scale. Atomize portions of std solns until readings for series are reproducible.

2.088   *Determination*

(a) *Mixed fertilizers, potassium sulfate, and potassium-magnesium sulfate.*—Transfer 10 ml aliquot of sample soln to 250 ml beaker. Add 1 drop Me red and neutze with HNO_3 (1 + 10). Adjust H_2O level in column to top of resin and quant. transfer aliquot to column. Open stopcock to give flow rate of 2 drops/sec, collecting effluent in 250 ml vol. flask. Wash aliquot into resin with 2–3 small portions H_2O. Collect 50–75 ml effluent; then open stopcock and collect addnl 100 ml by pouring H_2O into column, making certain that H_2O level does not fall below top of resin bed. Dil. to vol. and mix (if internal std instrument is used, add required amt $LiNO_3$ before dilg to vol.). Atomize portions of sample several times to obtain reliable av. reading for each soln. Det. ppm K from std curve. (Temp. of std and sample solns must not differ by >2°.) Calc. % K_2O as follows:

$$0\text{–}30\%: \qquad \text{ppm K}/2 = \% \, K_2O$$
$$>30\%: \qquad \text{ppm K}/1 = \% \, K_2O$$

(b) *Potassium chloride.*—Proceed as in (a) but omit neutzn and resin treatment.

2.089   *Instrument and Procedure*
                              Performance Test

Weigh 1.5058 g K acid phthalate (primary std) and transfer to 250 ml vol. flask. Add ca 0.5 g $(NH_4)_2HPO_4$ and proceed as in **2.086**(a), beginning "add 125 ml H_2O . . ." Calcd % K_2O = 23.0.

Volumetric Sodium Tetraphenylboron
Methods—Official Final Action
Method I (32)

2.090   *Reagents*

(a) *Formaldehyde soln.*—37%.

(b) *Sodium hydroxide soln.*—20%. Dissolve 20 g NaOH in 100 ml H_2O.

(c) *Sodium tetraphenylboron (STPB) soln.*—Approx. 1.2%. Dissolve 12 g $NaB(C_6H_5)_4$ in ca 800 ml

H_2O. Add 20–25 g $Al(OH)_3$, stir 5 min, and filter (Whatman No. 42 paper or equiv.) into 1 L vol. flask. Rinse beaker sparingly with H_2O and add to filter. Collect entire filtrate, add 2 ml 20% NaOH, dil. to vol. with H_2O, and mix. Let stand 48 hr and stdze. Adjust so that 1 ml STPB = 1% K_2O. Store at room temp.

(d) *Benzalkonium chloride (BAC) soln.*—Approx. 0.625%. Dil. 38 ml 17% Zephiran chloride (Winthrop Laboratories; also available at local pharmacies as benzalkonium chloride) to 1 L with H_2O, mix, and stdze. Cetyltrimethylammonium bromide may be substituted for Zephiran chloride. If other concn is used, adjust vol.

(e) *Clayton Yellow (Titan Yellow; Colour Index No. 19540)*.—0.04%. Dissolve 40 mg in 100 ml H_2O.

2.091   *Standardization of Solutions*

(a) *BAC soln.*—To 1.00 ml STPB soln in 125 ml erlenmeyer, add 20–25 ml H_2O, 1 ml 20% NaOH, 2.5 ml HCHO, 1.5 ml 4% $(NH_4)_2C_2O_4$, and 6–8 drops indicator, (e). Titr. to pink end point with BAC soln, using 10 ml semimicro buret. Adjust BAC soln so that 2.00 ml = 1.00 ml STPB soln.

(b) *Sodium tetraphenylboron soln.*—Dissolve 2.500 g KH_2PO_4 in H_2O in 250 ml vol. flask, add 50 ml 4% $(NH_4)_2C_2O_4$ soln, dil. to vol. with H_2O, and mix. (It is not necessary to bring to boil.) Transfer 15 ml aliquot (51.92 mg K_2O, 43.10 mg K) to 100 ml vol. flask; add 2 ml 20% NaOH, 5 ml HCHO, and 43 ml STPB reagent. Dil. to vol. with H_2O, mix *thoroly*, let stand 5–10 min, and pass thru dry filter. Transfer 50 ml aliquot of filtrate to 125 ml erlenmeyer, add 6–8 drops of indicator, (e), and titr. excess reagent with BAC soln. Calc. titer as follows:

$F = 34.61/(43\ \text{ml} - \text{ml BAC}) = \%\ K_2O/\text{ml}$ STPB reagent. Factor F applies to all fertilizers if 2.5 g sample is dild to 250 ml and 15 ml aliquot is taken for analysis. If results are to be expressed as K rather than as K_2O, substitute 28.73 for 34.61 in calcg F.

2.092   *Determination*

Place 2.5 g sample (1.25 g if K_2O >50%) in 250 ml vol. flask, add 50 ml 4% $(NH_4)_2C_2O_4$ and 125 ml H_2O, and boil 30 min. (If org. matter is present, add 2 g K-free C before boiling.) Cool, dil. to vol. with H_2O, mix, and pass thru dry filter or let stand until clear. Transfer 15 ml aliquot of sample soln to 100 ml vol. flask and add 2 ml 20% NaOH and 5 ml HCHO. Add 1 ml std STPB soln for each 1% K_2O expected in sample plus addnl 8 ml excess to ensure complete pptn. Dil. to vol. with H_2O, mix *thoroly*, let stand 5–10 min, and pass thru dry filter (Whatman No. 12 or equiv.). Transfer 50 ml filtrate to 125 ml erlenmeyer, add 6–8 drops of indicator, (e), and titr. excess reagent with std BAC soln.

% K_2O in sample = (ml STPB added − ml BAC) × F, where F = % K_2O/ml STPB reagent. (Multiply by 2 if 1.25 g sample was used.)

Method II (33)—Official Final Action

(For use with sample prepd for available P detn)

2.093   *Reagents*

See **2.090**(a), (b), (c), (d), and (e).

2.094   *Standardization of Solutions*

(a) *Benzalkonium chloride.*—In 125 ml erlenmeyer, add 2.5 ml neut. NH_4 citrate soln, **2.037**(a), 15–20 ml H_2O, 4 ml HCHO, and 2.5 ml 20% NaOH soln. Swirl; then add 4.00 ml STPB soln and 6–8 drops indicator, (e). Titr. to pink end point with BAC soln, using 10 ml semimicro buret. Adjust BAC soln so that 2.00 ml = 1.00 ml STPB soln.

(b) *Sodium tetraphenylboron soln.*—Dissolve 1.4447 g primary standard KH_2PO_4 in H_2O in 500 ml vol. flask, add 100 ml neut. NH_4 citrate soln, **2.037**(a), dil. to vol. with H_2O, and mix. Transfer 25 ml aliquot (25.00 mg K_2O, 20.75 mg K) to 100 ml vol. flask; add 8 ml HCHO and 5 ml 20% NaOH, swirl, and add 25 ml STPB reagent. Dil. to vol. with H_2O, mix *thoroly*, let stand 5–10 min, and pass thru dry filter. Transfer 50 ml aliquot of filtrate to 125 ml erlenmeyer, add 6–8 drops indicator, **2.090**(e), and titr. excess reagent with BAC soln. Calc. titer as follows:

$F = 25$ mg $K_2O/(25$ ml STPB − ml BAC) = mg K_2O/ml STPB reagent. If results are to be expressed as K rather than K_2O, substitute 20.75 for 25 in calcg F.

2.095   *Preparation of Sample*

Prep. as in **2.043**.

2.096   *Determination*

Transfer 25 ml aliquot of sample soln to 100 ml vol. flask. (If org. matter is present, treat 100 ml portion with 1 g K-free C and filter before transferring aliquot.) Add 8 ml HCHO *first* and then 5 ml 20% NaOH soln, and wash down sides of flask with H_2O. Swirl and add 1 ml STPB for each 1.5 mg K_2O expected in sample aliquot plus addnl 8 ml excess to ensure complete pptn. Dil. to vol. with H_2O, mix *thoroly*, let stand 5–10 min, and pass thru dry filter (Whatman No. 12 or equiv.). Transfer 50 ml aliquot filtrate to 125 ml erlenmeyer, add 6–8 drops indicator, **2.090**(e), and titr. excess reagent with std BAC soln.

% K_2O in sample = (ml STPB added − ml BAC) × F × 2.

Calcn applies to all fertilizers if 1 g sample is dild to 500 ml and 25 ml aliquot is taken for analysis.

OTHER ELEMENTS

Minor Nutrients by Atomic Absorption Spectrophotometry (34)—Official Final Action

(*Caution: See* **46.006.**)

2.097   *Apparatus*

Atomic absorption spectrophotometer.—Several com. models are available. Since each design is somewhat different, with varying requirements of light source, burner flow rate, and detector sensitivity, only general outline of operating parameters is given in Table **2.098.** Operator must become familiar with settings and procedures adapted to his own app. and use table only as guide to concn ranges and flame conditions.

2.098   *Operating Parameters*

Element	Wave-length, Å	Flame	Range μg/ml	Remarks
Ca	4227	Rich Air-C_2H_2	2–20	1% La, 1% HCl
	4227	Rich N_2O-C_2H_2	2–20	Requires special burner
Cu	3247	Air-C_2H_2	2–20	
Fe	2483	Rich Air-C_2H_2	2–20	
Mg	2852	Rich Air-C_2H_2	0.2–2	May need La
Mn	2795	Air-C_2H_2	2–20	
Zn	2138	Air-C_2H_2	0.5–5	

2.099   *Standard Solutions*

(Do not use <2 ml pipets or <25 ml vol. flasks. Automatic diln app. may be used. Prep. std solns in 0–20 μg range fresh daily.)

(**a**) *Calcium solns.*—(*1*) *Stock soln.*—25 μg Ca/ml. Dissolve 1.249 g $CaCO_3$ in min. amt 3N HCl. Dil. to 1 L. Dil. 50 ml to 1 L. (*2*) *Working std solns.*—0, 5, 10, 15, and 20 μg Ca/ml contg 1% La and ca 1% HCl. To 25 ml vol. flasks add 0, 5, 10, 15, and 20 ml Ca stock soln. Add 5 ml La stock soln and dil. to 25 ml.

(**b**) *Copper stock soln.*—1000 μg Cu/ml. Dissolve 1.000 g pure Cu metal in min. amt HNO_3 and add 5 ml HCl. Evap. almost to dryness and dil. to 1 L with 0.1N HCl.

(**c**) *Iron stock soln.*—1000 μg Fe/ml. Dissolve 1.000 g pure Fe wire in ca 30 ml 6N HCl with boiling. Dil. to 1 L.

(**d**) *Lanthanum stock soln.*—50 g La/L ca 5% HCl. Dissolve 58.65 g La_2O_3 (99.99%, Alfa Inorganics, 8 Congress St, Beverly, MA 01915, or equiv.) in 250 ml HCl, adding acid slowly. Dil. to 1 L.

(**e**) *Magnesium stock soln.*—1000 μg Mg/ml. Place 1.000 g pure Mg metal in 50 ml H_2O and slowly add 10 ml HCl. Dil. to 1 L.

(**f**) *Manganese stock soln.*—1000 μg Mn/ml. Dissolve 1.582 g MnO_2 in ca 30 ml 6N HCl. Boil to remove Cl and dil. to 1 L.

(**g**) *Zinc stock soln.*—1000 μg Zn/ml. Dissolve 1.000 g pure Zn metal in ca 10 ml 6N HCl. Dil. to 1 L.

(**h**) *Other std solns.*—Dil. aliquots of solns (**b**), (**c**), (**e**), (**f**), and (**g**) with 0.5N HCl to make at least 4 std solns of each element within range of detn.

2.100   *Preparation of Sample Solutions*

(*Caution: See* 46.019, 46.025, *and* 46.028.)

(**a**) *Inorganic materials and mixed fertilizers.*—Dissolve 1.00 g well-ground sample in 10 ml HCl in

150 ml beaker. Boil and evap. soln nearly to dryness on hot plate. *Do not bake residue.* Redissolve residue in 20 ml 2N HCl, boiling gently if necessary. Filter thru fast paper into 100 ml vol. flask, washing paper and residue thoroly with H_2O. Measure absorption of soln directly, or dil. with 0.5N HCl to obtain solns within ranges of instrument. If Ca is to be detd, add enough La stock soln to make final diln 1% La (i.e., 5 ml La to 25 ml flask, 20 ml to 100 ml flask, etc.).

(**b**) *Fertilizers containing organic matter (tankage, corncobs, cottonseed hulls, etc.).*—Place 1.00 g sample in 150 ml beaker (Pyrex, or equiv.). Char on hot plate and ignite 1 hr at 500° with muffle door propped open to allow free access of air. Break up cake with stirring rod and dissolve in 10 ml HCl as in (**a**).

(**c**) *Fertilizers containing fritted trace elements.*—Dissolve 1.00 g or less well-ground sample in 5 ml $HClO_4$ and 5 ml HF. Boil and evap. to dense $HClO_4$ fumes. Dil. carefully with H_2O, filter, and proceed as in (**a**). Alternatively, dissolve sample in 10 ml HCl, 5 ml HF, and 10 ml MeOH. Evap. to dryness. Add 5 ml HCl and evap. Repeat HCl addn and evapn. Dissolve residue as in (**a**). (Normally Pt ware should be used; Pyrex or other glassware may be used if Na, K, Ca, and Fe are not to be detd.)

2.101   *Determination*

(P interferes in Ca and may interfere in Mg detn with air-C_2H_2 burners. Eliminate interference by adding La stock soln to std and sample solns so that final dilns contain 1% La. P does not interfere in Ca detn when N_2O-C_2H_2 burner is used.)

Set up instrument as in table, **2.098,** or previously established optimum settings for app. to be used. Secondary or less sensitive lines (Gatehouse, B. M., and Willis, J. B., Spectrochim. Acta **17,** 710 (1961)) may be used to reduce necessary diln if desired. Read at least 4 std solns within analytical range before and after each group of 6–12 samples. Flush burner with H_2O between samples, and re-establish 0 absorption point each time. Prep. calibration curve from av. of each std before and after sample group. Read concn of samples from plot of absorption against μg/ml.

2.102   *Calculations*

% Element = (μg/ml) × (F/sample wt) × 10^{-4}.

$$F = \text{ml original diln} \times \text{ml final diln/ml aliquot, if original 100 ml vol. is dild.}$$

Acid-Soluble Boron (35)—Official Final Action

2.103   *Apparatus*

Use high sensitivity glass electrode pH meter for titrn. (Quinhydrone electrode system or similar assemblies may also be used.) Use assembly with burets, electrodes, and mech. stirrer, arranged for convenient use with 250 ml beaker. Use ordinary 50 ml burets for the 0.025N NaOH and 0.02N HCl.

2.104   *Reagents*

(**a**) *Boric acid std soln.*—Dissolve 1 g H_3BO_3 in H_2O and dil. to 1 L. 1 ml = 0.1748 mg B.

(b) *Sodium hydroxide std soln.*—CO_2-free, ca 0.025N. Stdze as follows: Pipet 25 ml std H_3BO_3 soln into 250 ml beaker, add 3.0 g NaCl, acidify to Me red, dil. to 150 ml, boil to expel CO_2, cool, and titr. potentiometrically as in **2.105**. Det. blank by repeating titrn, substituting 25 ml H_2O for H_3BO_3 soln. Calc. B equivalence as follows:

$$mg\ B/ml = 4.369/[(ml\ NaOH\ soln) - (ml\ blank)].$$

Protect from atm. CO_2 by soda-lime tubes or other suitable means.

(c) *Methyl red indicator.*—Dissolve 0.1 g Me red in 50 ml alcohol, dil. to 100 ml with H_2O, and filter if necessary.

2.105 *Determination*

Weigh sample within 1 mg (1.0 g for up to 0.45% B, smaller samples for above that content) and place in 250 ml beaker. Add ca 50 ml H_2O and 3 ml HCl. Heat to boiling and keep hot until carbonates are decomposed. Keep soln hot but do not boil during following phosphate removal:

Add *10% Pb(NO₃)₂ soln*, usually 10 ml, or 1 ml for each 1.2% P_2O_5 if P_2O_5 content is known to be >12%. Add $NaHCO_3$, little at time, until soln approaches neutrality (often observed by formation of white ppt in addn to insol. matter already present). Add few drops Me red and continue adding $NaHCO_3$ gradually until *just* alk. to Me red (yellow or very slightly orange). Keep mixt. hot but not boiling (H_2O bath or steam bath is best) 30 min, adding addnl small amts of $NaHCO_3$ if needed to keep same indicator color. (If indicator is bleached by nitrate present, add more; if color is obscured by org. matter, use external spot tests to follow neutzn.) After neutzn and heating, 40–50 ml soln should remain.

Filter soln into 250 ml beaker and wash solids thoroly with hot H_2O. Acidify filtrate with few drops HCl and boil briefly to expel most of CO_2. Neutze hot soln with 0.5N NaOH, and reacidify with 0.5N HCl, using 0.3–0.5 ml excess. Dil. to ca 150 ml and boil gently few min to expel remaining CO_2. Cool to room temp. in running H_2O. Roughly neutze mixt., using CO_2-free 0.5N NaOH, and place beaker in titrn assembly with electrodes and stirrer immersed. Start stirrer and adjust pH to exactly 6.30 by adding 0.025N NaOH or 0.02N HCl as required. (When properly adjusted, pH should be steady; drifting usually is due to incomplete removal of CO_2.) When reading of pH 6.30 is steady, read 0.025N NaOH buret, add 20 g *mannitol* or cryst. D-*sorbitol*, and titr. with 0.025N NaOH to pH 6.30. (Conveniently done with slidewire type instrument by opening pH meter circuit when mannitol is added, leaving scale setting at 6.30, closing circuit again when indicator color shows that end point is being approached, and carefully adding std NaOH soln until galvanometer needle returns to zero. With practice, somewhat slow approach to equilibrium, characteristic of glass electrode, can be anticipated so as not to overrun end

point.) When end point is reached, again read buret. Correct quantity of std NaOH soln used by reagent blank detd by repeating detn with all reagents but without sample. Calc. B content by following formula:

$$\% B = (ml\ NaOH\ soln\ in\ detn - ml\ blank) \times (mg\ B/ml\ NaOH\ soln)/(10 \times g\ sample)$$

2.106 Water-Soluble Boron (35)— Official Final Action

(Not applicable in presence of >5% urea or urea-formaldehyde resins)

Weigh 2.5 g sample into 250 ml beaker. Add 125 ml H_2O, boil gently ca 10 min, and filter hot thru Whatman No. 40 paper, or equiv., into 400 ml beaker. Wash solids well with 6 washings hot H_2O and dil. to ≥200 ml with H_2O. Heat filtrate just to boiling. Add 15 ml 10% $BaCl_2$ soln to ppt sulfates and phosphates, and add powd $Ba(OH)_2$, cautiously with stirring, until just alk. to phthln, avoiding large excess. Boil in open beaker ≥60 min to expel NH_3. (Samples colored by org. matter should be boiled longer.) If necessary, add H_2O to keep vol. to ≥150 ml. Add and stir 1–2 teaspoonfuls Filter-Cel or other inert filtering aid, and filter with suction thru packed paper pads into 500 ml Pyrex erlenmeyer. Wash ppt 6 times with hot boiled H_2O. (Avoid too large wash vols which increase vol. in flask to point of dangerous bumping in next step.)

Make filtrate just colorless to phthln with HCl (1 + 5), add Me red, and make just pink with the acid. Add 5 or 6 boiling stones and stirring rod, cover with watch glass, and boil 5 min to remove CO_2. Cool in cold H_2O while covered. Wash cover glass, stirrer, and sides of flask. Titr. to yellow of Me red with *std 0.05N NaOH*, **45.033–45.037**. Add 20 g D-*mannitol* and 1 ml or more phthln, shake, and wash down sides of flask. Titr. to pink end point. Det. blank in exactly same manner as sample. 1 ml 0.05N NaOH = 0.000540 g B or 0.00477 g $Na_2B_4O_7.10H_2O$. Or, (Titer − blank) × factor = lb $Na_2B_4O_7.10H_2O$/ton (factor = 3.807 for 0.05N NaOH).

★ Carbonate Carbon (36)— ★ Official Final Action

2.107 *Apparatus and Reagents*

Knorr alkalimeter with CO_2 absorption train.—Fill guard tube of alkalimeter with Ascarite. Connect upper end of condenser to absorption train consisting of 5 or 6 U-shape, g-s drying tubes (or equiv.) joined in series. Charge first tube with H_2SO_4 and second with Ag_2SO_4-H_2SO_4 soln (10 g Ag_2SO_4 in 100 ml H_2SO_4) to remove acidic gases other than CO_2. Charge third tube with $Mg(ClO_4)_2$ to absorb H_2O. Fill inlet ⅔ of fourth and succeeding tubes with Ascarite to absorb CO_2, and outlet ⅓ of each tube with $Mg(ClO_4)_2$. Connect last tube in train with aspirating bottle or suction source.

Condition app. daily before use, and also when freshly filled tube is placed in train, by aspirating air at rate of 2–3 bubbles/sec thru dry alkalimeter assembly and absorption train until CO_2 absorption tubes attain constant wt (usually 20–30 min). Use similarly packed tare and std procedure for wiping tubes with dry, lint-free cloth before each weighing.

2.108   *Determination*

Transfer 2 g sample to dry alkalimeter flask. Momentarily open stopcocks of first 2 CO_2 absorption tubes to air to equalize pressure, weigh tubes sep., and place in position in train. With assembled alkalimeter connected to absorption train, adjust rate of aspiration of air thru system to ca 2 bubbles/sec. Close funnel stopcock, remove alkalimeter guard tube, fill funnel with 50 ml HCl (1 + 4), and replace guard tube. Open funnel stopcock and let acid run slowly into flask, taking care that evolution of gas is so gradual as not to materially increase flow thru tubes. After all acid is added, agitate alkalimeter assembly to insure complete dispersion of sample in acid soln. Continue aspiration, gradually heat contents of flask to boiling, and boil 2–3 min after H_2O begins to condense. Discontinue heating and continue aspiration 15–20 min or until app. cools. Remove, equalize internal and external pressure, and reweigh absorption tubes.

Increase in wt = wt CO_2. (Material increase in wt of second tube usually indicates exhaustion of first tube, but may result from too rapid evolution of CO_2 in relation to aspiration rate.) Report % (by wt) CO_2 in sample.

Water-Soluble Chlorine (37)— Official Final Action

2.109   *Reagents*

(a) *Silver nitrate std soln.*—Dissolve ca 5 g recrystd $AgNO_3$ in H_2O and dil. to 1 L. Stdze against pure, dry NaCl and adjust so that 1 ml soln = 0.001 g Cl.

(b) *Potassium chromate indicator.*—See **45.029**(b).

2.110   *Determination*

Place 2.5 g sample on 11 cm filter paper and wash with successive portions of boiling H_2O until washings total nearly 250 ml, collecting filtrate in 250 ml vol. flask. Cool, dil. to vol. with H_2O, and mix well. Pipet 50 ml into 150 ml beaker, add 1 ml K_2CrO_4 indicator, and titr. with std $AgNO_3$ soln until red color of Ag_2CrO_4 is permanent.

Acid-Soluble Calcium (38)— Official Final Action

2.111 *Method I*

Weigh 2.5 g sample into 250 ml vol. flask, add 30 ml HNO_3 and 10 ml HCl, and boil 30 min. Cool, dil. to vol., mix, and filter if necessary. Transfer 25 ml aliquot to beaker and dil. to 100 ml. Add 2 drops

bromophenol blue, **6.018**(f). Add NH_4OH (1 + 4) until indicator changes from yellow to green (not blue). If overrun, bring back with HCl (1 + 4). (This gives pH of 3.5–4.0.) Dil. to 150 ml, bring to boil, and add 30 ml satd hot $(NH_4)_2C_2O_4$ soln slowly, stirring constantly. If color changes from green to blue or yellow again, adjust to green with the HCl. If yellow, adjust with NH_4OH to green. Digest on steam bath 1 hr, or let stand overnight, and cool to room temp. Filter supernatant thru quant. paper, gooch, or fritted glass filter, and wash ppt thoroly with NH_4OH (1 + 50). Place paper or crucible with ppt in original beaker and add mixt. of 125 ml H_2O and 5 ml H_2SO_4. Heat to 70° or above and titr. with 0.1N $KMnO_4$ until first slight pink appears. Correct for blank and calc. to Ca.

2.112 ★ *Method II* ★

Place CaC_2O_4 and filter paper from **2.123** in beaker in which pptn was made and dissolve and titr. as in **2.111**.

Cobalt (39)—Official Final Action
(Caution: See **46.026, 46.028,** *and* **Acids,** *Chap. 46.)*

2.113   *Reagents*

(Use H_2O free of interfering elements. Check by shaking 2 drops 0.01% dithizone in CCl_4 with 10 ml H_2O. CCl_4 phase should remain green.)

(a) *Ternary acid mixt.*—See **2.042**(b).

(b) *Ammonium hydroxide.*—Use fresh stock. (Reagent becomes contaminated with heavy metals on prolonged storage in glass.)

(c) *Isoamyl acetate.*—Distd.

(d) *2-Nitroso-1-naphthol.*—0.05% soln. Dissolve 0.05 g 2-nitroso-1-naphthol in 8 drops 1N NaOH and 1 ml H_2O. Add 50–60 ml H_2O and 6.5–7 ml NH_4OH, and dil. to 100 ml with H_2O. Divide into 2 ca equal parts and wash each part twice in 100 ml centrf. tube with 20 ml isoamyl acetate. Shake 30 sec and centrf. after each addn. (It may be necessary to remove part of aq. phase to ensure complete removal of foreign matter at interface.)

(e) *Cobalt std solns.*—(1) *Stock soln.*—200 μg Co/ml. Dissolve 0.0808 g $CoCl_2.6H_2O$ in H_2O and dil. to 100 ml. (2) *Std soln.*—2 μg Co/ml. Dil. 1 ml stock soln to 100 ml with H_2O.

2.114   *Determination*

Slowly add 20 ml ternary acid mixt. to 2.00 g pulverized, mixed fertilizer in 150 ml beaker. Cover with watch glass and digest on steam bath overnight. Transfer to hot plate and heat covered until dense white fumes appear. (At this point HNO_3 will have been expelled. Take care not to lose significant amts of $HClO_4$.) Dil. sample contg undissolved residue with H_2O, transfer to 50 ml vol. flask, and dil. to vol. Transfer to 100 ml centrf. tube and centrf. 5 min at 2000 rpm. Transfer aliquot, contg 2–5 μg Co, to 50 ml g-s centrf. tube. Add 10 ml 20% *diammonium citrate soln* and 2 drops phthln indicator. Adjust pH carefully to distinct pink with NH_4OH (1 + 1) and add successively 1 ml 10% $Na_2S_2O_3$ *soln*, 2 ml 2-nitroso-1-naphthol soln, and 5 ml isoamyl acetate. (Only isoamyl acetate addn requires high level of precision.) Shake mixt. 5 min and let sep. Centrf., if necessary. Draw off and discard aq. phase thru glass capillary tube attached to vac. pump. Wash isoamyl acetate phase with two 5 ml portions $1N$ NaOH and one 5 ml portion $1N$ HCl. Shake 5 min after each addn, let layers sep., and draw off and discard aq. phase. Centrf. 2 min at 1500 rpm and measure A or %T at 530 nm with isoamyl acetate as ref. Det. Co from calibration curve relating A or log %T to Co content of std solns contg 0, 2, 4, and 5 μg Co.

Iron (40)—Official Final Action

(*Note:* Diphenylamine may be harmful. *Caution:* See **46.079** and **46.084**.)

2.115 *Reagents*

(a) *Diphenylamine soln.*—Dissolve 1 g in 100 ml H_2SO_4.

(b) *Diphenylamine sulfonate soln.*—Dissolve 0.5 g in H_2O in 100 ml vol. flask and dil. to vol.

(c) *Potassium dichromate std solns.*—$0.1N$ and $0.01N$. Prep. $0.1N$ $K_2Cr_2O_7$ as in **45.025**. Prep. $0.01N$ soln by dilg 100 ml $0.1N$ soln to 1 L.

(d) *Mercuric chloride saturated soln.*—Shake $HgCl_2$ with H_2O and let settle.

(e) *Stannous chloride soln.*—Dissolve 20 g $SnCl_2.2H_2O$ in 20 ml HCl, warming gently. Add 20 ml H_2O and dil. to 100 ml with HCl (1 + 1). Keep warm until clear; then add few granules Sn.

2.116 *Preparation of Sample Solution*

(a) *Suitable for all fertilizers.*—Treat 1 g as in **2.017**(e), using 15 ml $HClO_4$. Hold $\geq$1 hr at ca 170° to remove HNO_3 completely. Dil. to 200 ml.

(b) *Suitable for soluble salts and oxides.*—Dissolve 1 g in 10 ml HCl, warming gently. Dil. to 200 ml.

2.117 *Reduction*

Heat aliquot of sample soln (100 ml and 50 ml, resp., for samples contg <0.5 and 0.5–4.0% Fe) to boiling. Add few drops diphenylamine sulfonate soln, and add $SnCl_2$ soln from dropping bottle until violet color is discharged; then add 2 drops excess. Usually 1–6 drops are required. Larger quantity may be used with samples contg large amt of Fe.) If reduction does not take place, discard and proceed as follows with second aliquot:

Add few granules Zn, boil few min, and either filter off excess Zn, washing with hot H_2O, or let Zn dissolve. Heat to boiling and finish reduction with $SnCl_2$ and diphenylamine sulfonate indicator as before. Add 10 ml HCl (1 + 1). Adjust vol. to 75–110 ml with H_2O. Cool rapidly in cold H_2O. Add 10 ml satd

$HgCl_2$ soln, swirl gently, add 5 ml H_3PO_4, and titr. immediately. (Small amt of HgCl must ppt to ensure complete reduction.)

2.118 *Titration*

Add 1 drop diphenylamine indicator by pipet (no more; excess will interfere with end point if amt of Fe is small). Titr. with $0.01N$ $K_2Cr_2O_7$ soln. Since end point may be difficult to see with very small amt Fe, approach end point slowly, allowing few sec for color to develop. Titr. to permanent blue (sometimes green with very small amt Fe). For samples contg >4% Fe, use $0.1N$ $K_2Cr_2O_7$ for titrn. 1 ml $0.1N$ $K_2Cr_2O_7$ = 0.00558 g Fe; 1 ml $0.01N$ = 0.000558 g Fe.

Acid-Soluble Magnesium— Official Final Action

EDTA Titration Method (41)

(Applicable to samples contg $\leq$0.25% Mn or Zn)

2.119 *Reagents*

Use reagents **1.021**(a), (b), (c), (d), (f) (1 ml = 1 mg Ca, equiv. to 0.6064 mg Mg), (g), (h) (stdzd as in **2.120**), and in addn:

(a) *Triethanolamine soln.*—(1 + 1).

(b) *Potassium ferrocyanide soln.*—Dissolve 4 g $K_4Fe(CN)_6.3H_2O$ in 100 ml H_2O.

2.120 *Standardization*

Pipet 10 ml Ca std soln into 300 ml erlenmeyer. Add 100 ml H_2O, 10 ml KOH-KCN soln, 2 drops triethanolamine soln, 5 drops $K_4Fe(CN)_6$ soln, and 15$\pm$1 mg calcein indicator. Immediately place flask on magnetic or other mech. stirrer in front of daylight fluorescent light and white background. While stirring, titr. with EDTA soln to disappearance of all fluorescent green and until soln remains pink. Titr. 3 or more aliquots. From av., calc. Ca titer in mg/ml EDTA soln. Ca titer × 0.6064 = Mg titer in mg/ml.

2.121 *Preparation of Solution*

(*Caution:* See **46.019** and **46.028**.)

(a) *Organic materials.*—Weigh 1 g sample into 250 ml boiling flask or erlenmeyer. Add 5 ml HCl and 10 ml HNO_3, and boil on hot plate or over low flame until easily oxidized org. matter is destroyed (ca 15 min). Cool, add 5 ml $HClO_4$, 70–72%, and heat to appearance of copious fumes and momentary cessation of boiling, but not to dryness. Cool, and transfer to 250 ml beaker with ca 100 ml H_2O. Continue with pH adjustment, as in **2.122**.

(b) *Inorganic materials and mixed fertilizers.*—Weigh 1 g sample into 250 ml beaker. Add 5 ml HCl and 10 ml HNO_3. Cover with watch glass and heat on asbestos mat on hot plate nearly to dryness (ca 30 min). If soln remains colored from org. residues, cool, add 5 ml $HClO_4$, 70–72%, and continue heating to copious fumes and momentary cessation of boiling, but not to dryness.

2.122   *Determination*

Cool prepd soln to room temp. Wash watch glass and inside of beaker to ca 100 ml with H_2O. Using pH meter with glass electrode and mech. stirring, adjust to ca pH 3 with 30% KOH soln and finally to pH 4.0 with 10% KOH soln. Add $FeNH_4(SO_4)_2$ soln, 5 ml for sample <7% P_2O_5, 10 ml for sample 7–15% P_2O_5, 15 ml for sample 16–30% P_2O_5, and proportionate quantities for samples >30% P_2O_5. Adjust to pH 5.0 with KOH solns as above, or with HCl (1 + 4) if pH is >5.0. Cool to room temp. and transfer to 250 ml vol. flask with H_2O. Dil. to vol. with H_2O and mix. Let stand until ppt settles. Disturbing ppt as little as possible, filter enough soln for aliquots required for titrn thru dry 11 cm fluted paper, Whatman No. 1, or equiv.

Pipet two equal aliquots contg <15 mg Ca plus Mg (usually 25 ml) into two 300 ml erlenmeyers and dil. each to 100 ml with H_2O. To one (titrn A for Ca plus Mg) add 5 ml pH 10 buffer soln, 2 ml KCN soln, 2 drops triethanolamine soln, 5 drops $K_4Fe(CN)_6$ soln, and 8 drops eriochrome black-T indicator. Titr. immediately with EDTA soln, stirring and lighting as in **2.120**. Color changes are wine red, purple, dark blue, to clear pure blue end point, becoming green if overtitrd.

To second aliquot (titrn B for Ca) add 10 ml KOH-KCN soln, 2 drops triethanolamine soln, 5 drops $K_4Fe(CN)_6$ soln, and 15±1 mg calcein indicator. Titr. immediately with EDTA soln as in **2.120**.

(Titrn A − Titrn B) × Mg titer EDTA × 100/ mg sample in aliquot = % Mg.

Titrn B × Ca titer EDTA × 10/mg sample in aliquot = % Ca.

2.123   ★ *Gravimetric Method (42)—* ★ *Official Final Action*

Weigh 2.5 g sample into 250 ml vol. flask, add 30 ml HNO_3 and 10 ml HCl, and boil 30 min. Cool, dil. to vol., and mix. Transfer aliquot of clear soln contg ≤12 mg Mg to beaker, partially neutze with NH_4OH, and add few drops Me red. Add NH_4OH until soln is yellow, then HCl until barely pink. Add 10 ml satd $(NH_4)_2C_2O_4$ soln for each 50 ml soln, adjust to pH 5.0 (faint pink) by addn of HCl (1 + 4) or NH_4OH (1 + 4), boil few min, cool, and again adjust to pH 5.0, adding more Me red if necessary. Stir thoroly and let soln stand until ppt settles.

Filter thru 11 cm paper fine enough to retain CaC_2O_4 and wash 10 times with hot H_2O. (Ppt may be used for Ca detn, **2.112**.) Evap. filtrate to ca 100 ml and add 5 ml *10% citric acid soln* and enough NH_4OH to make alk. to *bromothymol blue* indicator (0.1 g bromothymol blue dissolved in 1.6 ml 0.1N NaOH and dild to 25 ml with H_2O). Add 5 ml *10% $(NH_4)_2HPO_4$ soln*. Stir vigorously until ppt forms. Add 15 ml NH_4OH and let stand at least 2 hr,

stirring frequently. If only small quantities of Mg are present and no ppt forms during stirring or after adding the 15 ml NH_4OH, let stand overnight.

Transfer ppt to small filter or filtering crucible. Wash with NH_4OH (1 + 9), and ignite slowly in crucible at temp. <900° (preferably in muffle with pyrometric control) until C is burned and then 1–2 hr at 950–1000°. Cool in desiccator and weigh as $Mg_2P_2O_7$.

Residue consists of $Mg_2P_2O_7$ and possibly $Mn_2P_2O_7$ and $Ca_3(PO_4)_2$. Correct for Mn as follows:

Dissolve residue in 10 ml H_2SO_4 (1 + 9), transfer to 250 ml erlenmeyer, and add 50 ml HNO_3 (1 + 3) and 2 ml H_3PO_4. Heat nearly to bp, and add 0.3 g KIO_4 with swirling. Hold 30–60 min at 90–100° or until color development is complete. Cool, and dil. to convenient vol. In another flask contg same quantities of reagents treated similarly, match color by adding *std $KMnO_4$ soln*, or compare with std $KMnO_4$ soln in colorimeter. From vol. $KMnO_4$ soln required, or reading of colorimeter, calc. wt $Mn_2P_2O_7$ in residue. Subtract this wt from total wt, and regard difference as $Mg_2P_2O_7$ which contains 21.84% Mg.

2.124   ★ *Volumetric Method—Official* ★ *Final Action*

Filter ppt of $MgNH_4PO_4$ from **2.123** thru asbestos pad on gooch. Remove excess NH_3 by washing with soln of equal vols alcohol and H_2O (6–10 washings). Quant. transfer pad and ppt to beaker with H_2O (ca 50 ml). Add enough 0.1N H_2SO_4 from buret to dissolve ppt, and add small excess. Titr. excess acid with 0.1N NaOH, using *mixed indicator* (0.02 g neutral red and 0.2 g bromocresol green dissolved in 100 ml alcohol) as indicator. Color change is orange-gray to beginning of blue end point (pH 4.4). Stdze 0.1N NaOH with the acid, using mixed indicator. 1 ml 0.1N acid = 0.00122 g Mg. Correct for blank from reagents.

If Mn is present, add 1 ml H_2SO_4 to soln from above titrn, and transfer to 200 ml vol. flask. Dil. to vol., mix, and pipet 50 ml clear soln into beaker. Add 5 ml H_3PO_4, heat nearly to bp with stirring or swirling, add 0.3 g KIO_4 for each 15 mg Mn, and hold 30–60 min at 90–100°, or until color development is complete. Dil. to measured vol. contg ≤20 ppm Mn and compare with $KMnO_4$ std soln in colorimeter.

Correct previous titrn, or calcd wt of Mg, for Mn present, taking account of dilns.

2.125   Water-Soluble Magnesium (42)— Official Final Action

(a) *In potassium-magnesium sulfate, magnesium sulfate, and kieserite.*—Weigh 1 g sample into 250 ml vol. flask, add 200 ml H_2O, and boil 30 min. Cool, dil. to vol. with H_2O, and mix. Transfer to beaker aliquot of clear soln contg <12 mg Mg. Dil. to ca 100 ml with H_2O and proceed as in (b), beginning "**Add ca 1 g NH_4Cl . . .**"

(b) *In other materials, including mixed fertilizers.*— Weigh 1 g sample into 500 ml vol. flask, add 350 ml H_2O, and boil 1 hr. Cool, dil. to vol., mix, and filter if necessary. Transfer to beaker aliquot contg <12 mg Mg, usually 200 ml. Add ca 1 g NH_4Cl for each 100 ml and few drops Me red, and acidify with HCl. Proceed as in **2.123**, line 4, beginning "partially neutze with NH_4OH . . ."

(c) *By EDTA method.*—Transfer aliquot soln prepd as in **(a)** or **(b)** to beaker and det. Mg as in **2.122**, using HCl or KOH to adjust pH.

Acid-Soluble Manganese—Official Final Action

2.126   *Colorimetric Method (43)*

(Applicable to samples contg $\leq 5\%$ Mn)

Place 1 g sample in 200 ml wide-neck vol. flask or 250 ml beaker. Add 10 ml H_2SO_4 and 30 ml HNO_3. Heat gently until brown fumes diminish; then boil 30 min. If org. matter is not destroyed, cool, add 5 ml HNO_3, and boil. Repeat process until no org. matter remains, and boil until white fumes appear. Cool slightly, and add 50 ml H_3PO_4 (1 + 9). Boil few min. Cool, dil. to 200 ml in vol. flask, mix, and let stand to allow pptn of $CaSO_4$.

Pipet 50 ml clear soln into beaker. Heat nearly to bp, with stirring or swirling, add 0.3 g KIO_4 for each 15 mg Mn present, and hold 30–60 min at 90–100°, or until color development is complete. Cool, and dil. to measured vol. that will provide satisfactory concn for colorimetric measurement by instrument chosen (usually <20 ppm Mn). Compare in colorimeter against std $KMnO_4$ soln, **7.092**, or in spectrophtr at 530 nm. Calc. to Mn.

★   *Bismuthate Method (44)*   ★

2.127   *Reagents*

(a) *Sodium bismuthate powder.*—80% $NaBiO_3$, contg $\leq 0.0005\%$ Mn and $\leq 0.002\%$ Cl.

(b) *Potassium permanganate std soln.*—0.0910N. Dissolve 2.876 g $KMnO_4$ in H_2O and dil. to 1 L. 1 ml = 1 mg Mn. Stdze as in **45.027**.

(c) *Ferrous sulfate std soln.*—0.0910N. Dissolve 25.3 g $FeSO_4 \cdot 7H_2O$, 25 ml H_2SO_4, and 25 ml H_3PO_4 in H_2O and dil. to 1 L. 1 ml = 1 mg Mn. Stdze with $KMnO_4$ near time of actual use. Place measured portion ca equiv. to max. quantity of Mn to be detd in erlenmeyer contg 200 ml cold H_2SO_4 (3 + 97), and titr. with $KMnO_4$ std soln.

2.128   *Determination*

To 1 g sample in erlenmeyer (preferably 300 ml), add 5–10 ml HNO_3 and 7 ml H_2SO_4. Evap. on hot plate to white fumes. Add few drops HNO_3, again evap. to white fumes, and repeat until org. matter is destroyed. Cool. Add 100 ml H_2O, 10 ml HNO_3, and just enough $NaBiO_3$ to give strong permanganate color, or if quantity of Mn is small, slight excess of

$NaBiO_3$. Boil gently 2–3 min. If permanganate color or MnO_2 disappears, cool somewhat, and repeat bismuthate treatment. (Permanent permanganate color or persistence of MnO_2 indicates sufficient excess of bismuthate.) Add *satd $NaHSO_3$ soln* dropwise while stirring until Mn compds are reduced and soln clears. Avoid large excess. Boil gently 2–3 min. Cool to room temp., and dil. to ca 100 ml. If soln contains <40 mg Mn, proceed with detn; if >40 mg Mn, transfer to 200 ml vol. flask, add 5 ml H_2SO_4 and 10 ml HNO_3, cool, dil. to vol., and mix. Pipet aliquot contg ≤ 40 mg Mn into erlenmeyer and dil. to 100 ml with soln contg 5 ml H_2SO_4 and 10 ml HNO_3 in 100 ml.

Before continuing, prep. suction filters of asbestos washed with H_2SO_4 (3 + 97) and then with H_2O. (Glass filter tubes with perforated porcelain disks to support asbestos and connected with suction flask are satisfactory. Mn soln must not contact rubber.) Then complete detn without interruption. To Mn soln at 20–30° add at least 0.25 g $NaBiO_3$ for each 10 mg Mn. Swirl contents of flask 1 min, add 100 ml H_2O, and mix. Filter with suction thru prepd filter and wash with cold H_2SO_4 (3 + 97) until washings show no pink tint. Disconnect suction flask, and add $FeSO_4$ std soln from buret until permanganate color disappears; then add at least 10% excess with 1 ml as min. excess. Titr. excess $FeSO_4$ with $KMnO_4$ std soln to faint pink. From $KMnO_4$ equivalence of ml $FeSO_4$ soln used, subtract the $KMnO_4$ used in backtitrn. Calc. % Mn in sample from difference.

Copper—Official Final Action

★   *Long Volumetric Method (45)*   ★

2.129   *Reagents*

(a) *Sodium thiosulfate std soln.*—0.03N. Prep. daily by dilg 0.1N soln, **45.038–45.039**. 1 ml 0.03N $Na_2S_2O_3$ = 1.906 mg Cu.

(b) *Potassium iodide soln.*—Dissolve 50 g KI in H_2O and dil. to 100 ml.

(c) *Starch soln.*—Mix ca 1 g sol. starch with enough cold H_2O to make thin paste, add 100 ml boiling H_2O, and boil ca 1 min while stirring.

(d) *Bromocresol green indicator.*—Dissolve 0.1 g tetrabromo-*m*-cresolsulfonphthalein in 1.5 ml 0.1N NaOH, and dil. to 100 ml with H_2O.

2.130   *Determination*

Weigh 2 g if sample contains <5% Cu; if $\geq 5\%$, weigh enough to furnish little under 0.1 g Cu. Place sample in 300 ml erlenmeyer, and add 5–10 ml HNO_3 and 7.0 ml H_2SO_4. Digest on hot plate to dense white fumes. If soln darkens owing to org. matter, cool somewhat, add little more HNO_3, and digest again to dense white fumes, repeating if necessary until org. matter appears to be destroyed. Cool, and add 25–30 ml H_2O. Boil 1 min, remove from hot plate, and stir occasionally ca 15 min. Filter into 250 ml erlenmeyer and wash filter and residue with 6 small portions hot H_2O. Cool to room temp. and dil. to 100 ml.

Pass H_2S (*Caution: See* **46.059**) thru soln in erlenmeyer 10–15 min. Prep. wash soln by dilg 10 ml H_2SO_4 to 1 L and satg with H_2S. Filter sample soln thru paper of fine texture and wash paper and ppt with 7 small portions of the wash soln, keeping funnel covered with watch glass as much as possible. Reserve for Zn detn.

Place paper and ppt in glazed porcelain crucible and ignite at dull red heat until C is completely destroyed. Blow H_2S out of pptn flask and wash the CuS from H_2S delivery tube into flask with *Br-H_2O*. Add 5 ml HNO_3 to CuO in cold crucible and warm until CuO dissolves. (This may require 10 min, after which disregard insol. specks.) Wash soln into pptn flask with H_2O and dil. to 35 ml.

Add excess Br-H_2O and few glass beads. Boil until excess Br is entirely expelled and vol. is < 30 ml. Cool slightly and cautiously add NH_4OH until mixt. is distinctly alk. Boil until odor of NH_3 is very faint. Add 5 ml HOAc and boil 1 min more. Cool to room temp. and dil. to 25–30 ml. Add 2 ml KI soln and titr. with std $Na_2S_2O_3$ soln to light yellow. Add ca 1 ml cold starch soln and continue titrn to disappearance of starch-I color. Calc. quantity of Cu in sample soln.

2.131   Short Volumetric Method (46)

Place 2 g sample in 300 ml erlenmeyer and add 10 ml HNO_3 and 5 ml H_2SO_4. Digest on hot plate to white fumes. If soln darkens, owing to org. matter, cool slightly, add little more HNO_3, and digest again to white fumes, repeating operation if necessary until org. matter appears to be destroyed. Cool, add 50 ml H_2O, boil ca 1 min, and cool to room temp.

Add bromocresol green, then NH_4OH until indicator changes to light green (pH 4). Cool again to room temp., and if indicator changes back to more acid color, add NH_4OH dropwise until indicator becomes light green again, avoiding excess. Add 2 g NH_4HF_2 (Toxic. *Caution: See* **46.084**), mix well, and let stand ca 5 min. Add 8–10 g KI, mix well, and titr. with std $Na_2S_2O_3$ soln to light yellow. Add ca 1 ml starch soln and continue titrg slowly until color is nearly same as just before addn of the KI and becomes no darker on standing 20 sec. Report as % Cu.

Sodium (31)—Official Final Action

2.132   Reagents and Apparatus

Use reagents and app. of **2.084**, and in addn: *Sodium chloride.*—ACS. Dry 2 hr at 105°.

2.133   Preparation of Solution

Prep. soln as in **2.086**(a), using 2.5 g sample (< 4% Na) or 1.25 g (4–20% Na).

2.134   Preparation of Standard Curve

Proceed as in **2.087**, using 1.2716 g NaCl, range of diln 0–40 ppm Na, intervals ≤ 5 ppm, and midscale for 25 ppm Na.

2.135   Determination

Transfer 25 ml sample soln (< 4% Na) or 10 ml (4–20% Na) into 150 ml beaker. Add 1 drop Me red indicator, **2.084**(b), and proceed as in **2.088**(a), beginning "and neutze with HNO_3 (1 + 10)."

Det. ppm Na from std curve, **2.134**. Calc. % Na as follows:

$$0–4\ \%: \qquad \text{ppm Na}/10 = \% \text{ Na}$$
$$4–20\%: \qquad \text{ppm Na}/2\ = \% \text{ Na}$$

Zinc
2.136   Gravimetric Method (47)—
Official First Action
(For samples contg ≥ 0.1% Zn)

For samples contg < 0.20% Zn, weigh 10 g or just enough to furnish 4 mg Zn; for samples contg 0.20% Zn or more, weigh 2 g. Treat samples as in **2.130** thru sepn of CuS. Evap. combined filtrate and washings to ca 100 ml. If soln is darker than light yellow or light green, add excess of satd $KMnO_4$ soln and heat to boiling, adding more $KMnO_4$ soln if necessary to maintain excess. Add *6% SO_2 soln* until Mn is reduced, then excess of 1–2 ml, and continue evapn to ca 80 ml. Cool, and add 5 ml *40% citric acid soln* and 2 drops bromophenol blue, **3.007**(c). Add NH_4OH to slight change of indicator color, and cool to room temp. Adjust to pH 3.0 by adding NH_4OH or H_2SO_4 (1 + 1) dropwise. (For comparison, place 100 ml *0.05% citric acid soln*, pH 3.0, in another 250 ml erlenmeyer and add 2 drops of the bromophenol blue soln.)

Pass rapid stream of H_2S (*Caution: See* **46.059**) thru sample soln 45 min. Prep. wash soln contg 0.5 g citric acid/L and sat. with H_2S. Filter sample soln thru fine ashless paper. Use rubber policeman to loosen ppt sticking to flask and delivery tube, and wash ppt onto filter with jet of wash soln. Wash paper and ppt 7 more times with small amts of wash soln, keeping funnel covered with watch glass as much as possible. Place paper and ppt in Pt crucible that has been ignited and weighed with cover. Ignite in uncovered crucible at low temp., preferably in muffle, until paper is oxidized; then 1 hr at 950–1000°. Place cover on crucible while hot, cool in desiccator contg H_2SO_4, and weigh as ZnO. Report as Zn.

2.137   Colorimetric Method (48)—
Official First Action
(For samples contg < 4% Zn)

To 2.5 g sample in Kjeldahl flask add ca 10 ml HNO_3 and exactly 10 ml H_2SO_4. Boil down to white fumes. If soln darkens owing to org. matter, add little more HNO_3 and boil down again to white fumes, repeating if necessary until org. matter is destroyed. Cool, and add 100 ml H_2O. Boil 3–5 min, and cool to room temp. Filter with suction thru mat of filter paper pulp. Wash out flask, and wash filter at least 5 times with dil. H_2SO_4 (5 + 995). Dil. filtrate with H_2O to 250 ml in vol. flask. Dil. this soln to such vol. that 10 ml aliquot contains ca 20 μg Zn. Pipet 10 ml aliquot into flask and det., by titrn, vol. $1N$ NH_4OH required to neutze to Me red. Using another 10 ml aliquot, proceed as in **3.043–3.046**, adding detd vol. $1N$ NH_4OH after adding 40 ml Soln A, **3.041**(1).

Total Sulfur (49)—Official Final Action
2.138 *Reagents*

(a) *Barium chloride soln.*—10%. Dissolve 100 g $BaCl_2.2H_2O$ in 900 ml H_2O and filter thru Whatman No. 42 paper, or equiv. 1 ml = 14 mg S.

(b) *Bromine in carbon tetrachloride.*—10%. Add 10 g Br to 90 g reagent grade CCl_4. Stir until homogeneous. Store in g-s bottle. (*Caution: See* **46.047** and **46.049.**)

2.139 *Determination*

Weigh sample contg 50–150 mg S into 250 ml beaker, and add 20 ml 10% Br in CCl_4, (b). Mix by swirling beaker at 5 min intervals during 30 min. Add 15 ml HNO_3 and mix as before. Evap. to 1–2 ml on warm hot plate. Add 15 ml HCl and 10 ml H_2O. Evap. just to dryness on warm hot plate or steam bath. Add 10 ml HCl and 50 ml H_2O, heat to boiling, boil 5 min, and filter thru Whatman No. 42 paper, or equiv. Wash paper with ten 20 ml portions hot H_2O.

Heat filtrate to boiling. Add 5–6 drops 10% $BaCl_2$ soln, (a). After 1 min, add dropwise quantity of $BaCl_2$ soln equiv. to expected S content plus 5 ml excess. Digest at gentle boil 1 hr. Remove from hot plate and let ppt settle 15–20 min. Filter immediately thru prepd gooch, previously ignited and weighed. Wash with hot H_2O until 10 ml wash H_2O shows no ppt with 3 ml 1% $AgNO_3$. Dry and ignite at 800° to constant wt. Cool in desiccator over $MgClO_4$ and weigh. % S = g $BaSO_4$ × 0.1374 × 100/g sample.

2.140 Free Sulfur (50)—Official Final Action
(*Caution: See* **46.011, 46.047, 46.048,** and **46.049.**)

Ext 1 g sample with CS_2 in Soxhlet app., letting extn thimble drain at least 12 times. Transfer ext to 250 ml beaker. Evap. CS_2 in draft at room temp. Heat in oven 20 min at 60–70°; then cool to room temp. Add 10 ml satd soln of Br in CCl_4, cover, and let stand ca 30 min, stirring several times. Add 15 ml HNO_3, cover, and let stand ca 30 min, stirring several times. Evap. on hot plate to ca 5 ml. Add 20 ml HCl and evap. to ca 5 ml. Add ca 50 ml H_2O, filter, and wash with 2% HCl. Add 2 drops bromophenol blue, **6.018**(f), and then NH_4OH to first color change. Add HCl dropwise until distinctly acid, then 5 drops excess; dil. to 150 ml, heat to boiling, and add 10% $BaCl_2$ soln, **2.138**(a), dropwise until ca 50% excess is present. Cover beaker and digest on steam bath at

least 1 hr. Cool to room temp. and filter thru asbestos on gooch previously ignited at 500° and weighed. Wash 10 times with hot H_2O. Ignite in muffle at 500° at least 20 min. Cool in desiccator and weigh as $BaSO_4$. Calc. as S as in **2.139.**

★ Acid-Forming or Nonacid-Forming ★ Quality (51)—Official Final Action
2.141 *Reagents*

(a) *Mixed indicator.*—Weigh 0.1 g bromocresol green and 0.02 g Me orange into agate mortar, triturate, and slowly add 2 ml $0.1N$ NaOH. Dil. to 100 ml with H_2O.

(b) *Sodium carbonate-sucrose soln.*—Dissolve 106 g Na_2CO_3, or 286 g $Na_2CO_3.10H_2O$, and 50 g sucrose in H_2O. Dil. to 1 L. Pipet 10 ml into 250 ml erlenmeyer, carefully add 30 ml $1N$ HCl, and boil gently few min to remove CO_2. Titr. with $0.5N$ NaOH as below.

ml $0.5N$ NaOH used in titrg = soln blank.

2.142 *Determination*

If fertilizer mixt., ground as in **2.007**, contains <30% of sum [total N + available P_2O_5 + H_2O-sol. K_2O], weigh 1 g sample into 100 or 150 ml porcelain or Pyrex beaker. If sum is ≥30, use 0.5 g, and for salts of Na or K use 0.25 g. With pipet or buret add 10 ml Na_2CO_3-sucrose soln, and mix thoroly with sample, except for unmixed nitrate salts or for mixed fertilizers contg considerable nitrate N. (Nitrate salts and mixed fertilizers contg considerable nitrate N should not be treated with sucrose. Instead, use 10 ml Na_2CO_3 soln prepd as in **2.141**(b) but without sucrose and add 0.25 g C black directly to and mixed with weighed sample.) Place in sand bath to depth of mixt. in beaker and evap. to complete dryness. (To avoid loss by spattering, use cone of ashless filter paper folded so that base will just slip into beaker and touch sides all around, with apex cut off to form vent ca 3 mm diam.) Place beakers in furnace heated to ca 250°, and raise temp. gradually to and hold at 575–600° (dull red) 1 hr. (It is not necessary that all C be removed.) Remove beaker and cool. Add 50 ml H_2O, cover with watch glass, and add 30 ml $1N$ HCl thru lip of beaker. After effervescence ceases, place covered beaker on hot plate or steam bath and hold just below bp 1 hr. Titr. by one of following methods:

(a) *With mixed indicator.*—Filter soln thru paper disk, or pad of asbestos that has been digested with $1N$ HCl and washed acid-free with H_2O, using gooch and suction. Wash with hot H_2O. To clear filtrate (ca 100 ml) add 0.4 ml of the mixed indicator, and titr. to light green (until green definitely predominates over yellow; pH 4.3). (Duplicate soln of fertilizer ash displaying max. acid color for this indicator may be used as comparison to det. first change. Titrn is conveniently carried out on white porcelain plate, with artificial daylight bulb placed at convenient angle above and back of plate.)

(b) *With glass electrode.*—Cool to room temp., and without filtering titr. soln in 150 ml beaker with 0.5N NaOH to pH 4.3, using glass electrode app., or other means of electrometric titrn, and continuous stirrer. Make blank titrn, **2.141**(b), using glass electrode.

Subtract algebraically ml 0.5N NaOH used in titrns from blank, **2.141**(b). For 1 g sample multiply result by 50; 0.5 g sample, by 100; 0.25 g sample, by 200. Pos. values represent excess base in ash expressed as lb $CaCO_3$/ton fertilizer. Neg. values represent excess acidity in same terms.

% N found (**2.052**) × 35.7 is considered acid-forming power of the N in terms of equiv. lb $CaCO_3$/ton fertilizer, and is given neg. sign in calcg net acid-base balance.

% citrate-insol. P_2O_5 (**2.038**) × 28.2 = alky equiv. to 2 of the 3 Ca atoms of $Ca_3(PO_4)_2$, expressed as lb $CaCO_3$/ton fertilizer. Correct net balance for fertilizer for this basicity, assumed to be relatively inactive in soil, by giving value neg. sign.

Algebraic sum of acid-base balance of ash and corrections for N and citrate-insol. P_2O_5 is net balance of fertilizer expressed as lb $CaCO_3$/ton. If neg., fertilizer is considered acid-forming; if pos., nonacid-forming.

PEAT (52)—OFFICIAL FIRST ACTION
(Moss, humus, and reed-sedge types)

2.143   *Preparation of Sample*
Place representative field sample on square rubber sheet, paper, or oil cloth. Reduce sample to quantity required by quartering and place in moisture proof container. *Work rapidly to prevent moisture losses.*

Moisture
2.144   *Method I*
Mix sample thoroly and place 10–12 g in ignited and weighed (with fitted heavy duty Al foil cover) Vycor or porcelain evapg dish, ≥75 ml capacity. Crush soft lumps with spoon or spatula. Cover immediately with Al foil cover and weigh to nearest mg. Dry, uncovered, 16 hr at 105°. Remove from oven, cover tightly, cool, and weigh. % Moisture (report to nearest 0.1%) = (g as-received sample − g oven-dried sample) × 100/g as-received sample.

2.145   *Method II*
(Use when pH, N, fiber, etc., are to be detd.)
Mix thoroly and weigh 100–300 g representative sample, **2.143,** and spread evenly on large flat pan. Crush soft lumps with spoon or spatula and let come to moisture equilibrium with room air ≥24 hr. Stir occasionally to maintain max. air exposure of entire sample. When wt is constant, calc. loss in wt as % moisture removed by air drying. Grind representative portion air-dried sample 1–2 min in high-speed blender; use for moisture, ash, and N detns.

Mix air-dried, ground sample and weigh, to nearest mg, equiv. of 10 g sample on as-received basis (g

air-dried sample equiv. to 10.0 g as-received sample = 10.0 − [(10.0 × % moisture removed)/100]). Place weighed sample in ignited and weighed (with fitted heavy duty Al foil cover) Vycor or porcelain evapg dish and proceed as in **2.144.** % Moisture (report to nearest 0.1%) = (10.0 − g oven-dried sample) × 10.0.

2.146   *Ash*
Place uncovered (retain cover for weighing) Vycor or porcelain dish contg dried sample from moisture detn in muffle. Gradually bring to 550° and hold until completely ashed. Cover with retained Al foil cover, cool, and weigh. % Ash (report to nearest 0.1%) = g ash × 100/g as-received sample taken for moisture detn. (If moisture Method II was used, g as-received sample = 10.0.)

2.147   *Organic Matter*
% Org. matter = 100.0 − (% moisture + % ash).

Water Capacity and Volumes (53)
2.148   *Apparatus*
Dispensing apparatus.—2 dispensing burets, 250 ml in 1 ml subdivisions, ±2 ml tolerance, pinchcock type; 1-hole No. 6 rubber stopper; straight polyethylene drying tube with serrated rubber tubing fittings, 150 mm long, ¾″ od, ⅝″ id (Cenco Instrument Corp. No. 14782–2); and stainless steel screen circle, ca 16 mesh and 28.7 mm diam.

Assemble dispensing app. as follows: Discard serrated rubber tubing fittings from polyethylene drying tube and use tube only. Center stainless steel screen on one end of tube and seal. (Soldering iron is useful.) Adjust length of tube to match convenient graduation of buret; then scallop end without screen to allow for water drainage, and insert into dispensing buret with screen side up.

2.149   *Preparation of Sample*
See **2.143.**

2.150   *Determination*
Det. moisture content on sep. sample by Method I or II, **2.144** or **2.145.**

Weigh buret fitted with plastic tube and screen. Working rapidly to prevent moisture losses, mix sample thoroly, place on top of No. 4 screen, and shake until sieving is complete. Use only portion that has passed thru sieve for detn. Firmly pack buret with 10″ of 4 mesh sample as follows: Attach rubber stopper to delivery end of buret. Add ca 20 ml portions, *firmly* tapping 3 times vertically from ht of 6″ on rubber stopper, for final ht of 10″. (This will ensure that ht of final wet vol. is 7.5–10″.) Remove stopper; weigh buret to nearest g. Position buret to use sink as drain. Place H_2O source (5 gal. bottle) equipped with siphon device above level of buret. Connect clamped rubber tubing of siphon device to buret with glass tubing (ca 5″ long, constricted at one end) inserted into one-hole rubber stopper *fitting tightly* into top of buret. Attach rubber tubing with pinch clamp to delivery end of buret. Open both clamps and pass H_2O thru sample ≥ 24 hr, maintaining water reservoir over sample at all times. (Moss-type samples may float but gradually settle as sample becomes wet.) After initial soaking, regulate H_2O flow thru column by adjusting screw clamp at delivery end of buret. (In-flow of H_2O should be ca equal to out-flow; flow of ca 1 drop/sec is suitable.) When sample is *supersatd*, close both clamps and let sample settle in H_2O ca 5 min. Top surface of sample should be as level as possible.

Raise buret and replace rubber tubing on delivery end of buret with 250 ml dispensing buret filled with H_2O, using rubber stopper for connection. Connect two burets tightly, *with no air leaks*. Remove siphon device and open outlet clamps of both burets to empty. (Suction created is equiv. to ca 15″ H_2O. Check for air leaks to ensure that std suction is exerted on sample. It is important to remove excess H_2O as described.) Measure ht of wet peat. Ht should be 7.5–10″. Record vol. in ml and weigh buret, plastic tube with screen, and wet peat to nearest g.

Wet sample again as above ≥ 1 hr, drain by suction, record vol., and weigh. Repeat until consistent results are obtained.

2.151   *Calculations*

Saturated Volume Weights, g/ml

As-received = g as-rec. sample/ml wet vol.

Oven-dried = g dried sample/ml wet vol., where g dried sample = g as-rec. sample × [(100 − % moisture)/100].

Wet = g wet sample/ml wet vol.

Water-Holding Capacity, %

(a) Weight basis:

As-received = [(g wet sample − g as-rec. sample) × 100]/g as-rec. sample

Oven-dried = [(g wet sample − g dried sample) × 100]/g dried sample

(b) Volume basis:

Water vol., % = [(g wet sample − g dried sample) × 100]/(ml wet vol. × 1.0)

Dry Peat Volume

Dry peat vol., % = (g dried sample × 100)/(ml wet vol. × 1.4)

Air Volume

Air vol., % = 100 − (% water vol. + % dry peat vol.)

SELECTED REFERENCES

(1) JAOAC **12**, 97(1929); **33**, 424(1950); **38**, 108, 541(1955); **50**, 190, 382(1967); **51**, 445(1968).

(2) JAOAC **52**, 592(1969).

(3) JAOAC **42**, 500(1959).

(4) JAOAC **12**, 98(1929); **24**, 253(1941).

(5) JAOAC **3**, 95(1917).

(6) JAOAC **40**, 711(1957).

(7) JAOAC **46**, 582(1963); **47**, 32, 1040(1964).

(8) JAOAC **38**, 413(1955).

(9) JAOAC **41**, 517(1958).

(10) Z. Anal. Chem. **189**, 243(1962); JAOAC **45**, 40, 201, 999(1962); **46**, 579(1963).

(11) Z. Anal. Chem. **189**, 243(1962); JAOAC **45**, 40, 999(1962); **49**, 1201(1966); **52**, 587(1969).

(12) USDA Div. Chem. Bull. **56**, 36(1898); JAOAC **47**, 420(1964).

(13) JAOAC **5**, 443, 460(1922); **6**, 384(1923); **14**, 182(1931); **19**, 269(1936); **22**, 254(1939); **42**, 512(1959).

(14) JAOAC **52**, 587(1969).

(15) JAOAC **44**, 233(1961).

(16) JAOAC **46**, 570(1963); **47**, 420(1964).

(17) JAOAC **44**, 229(1961); **47**, 420(1964).

(18) JAOAC **33**, 100(1950); **38**, 56(1955).

(19) JAOAC **53**, 450(1970).

(20) Chem. Ztg. **16**, 1952(1892); JAOAC **6**, 391 (1923); **15**, 267(1932).

(21) JAOAC **13**, 208(1930); **15**, 267(1932).

(22) JAOAC **18**, 62, 218(1935); **19**, 68, 279(1936).

(23) JAOAC **13**, 215(1930).

(24) JAOAC **38**, 436(1955); **44**, 245(1961).

(25) Ind. Eng. Chem., Anal. Ed. **7**, 259(1935); JAOAC **41**, 637(1958); **42**, 494(1959).

(26) JAOAC **48**, 1105(1965); **49**, 206(1966); **50**, 191(1967).

(27) JAOAC **43**, 499(1960).

(28) JAOAC **18**, 237, 260, 281(1935); **19**, 302(1936).

(29) Anal. Chem. **21**, 984(1949); JAOAC **35**, 674 (1952); **36**, 649(1953).

(30) JAOAC **28**, 782(1945).

(31) J. Agr. Food Chem. **3**, 48(1955); JAOAC **41**, 533(1958); **48**, 398(1965); **51**, 446, 857(1968).

(32) Anal. Chem. **29**, 1044(1957); **30**, 1882(1958); JAOAC **41**, 533(1958); **43**, 472(1960).

(33) JAOAC **52**, 384, 566(1969).

(34) JAOAC **48**, 406, 1100(1965); **50**, 191, 401 (1967); **51**, 446, 847(1968).

(35) JAOAC **32**, 422(1949); **33**, 132(1950); **36**, 623 (1953); **38**, 407(1955).

(36) JAOAC **38**, 413(1955).

(37) JAOAC **11**, 34, 201(1928); **16**, 69(1933).

(38) JAOAC **24**, 302(1941).

(39) Anal. Chem. **30**, 1153(1958); JAOAC **48**, 412 (1965); **52**, 382(1969).

(40) JAOAC **50**, 192, 397(1967); **52**, 382(1969).

(41) JAOAC **47**, 450(1964); **49**, 206(1966).

(42) JAOAC **20**, 252(1937); **22**, 270(1939); **23**, 249 (1940); **24**, 268(1941); **25**, 326(1942).

(43) JAOAC **23**, 249(1940).

(44) JAOAC **24**, 268(1941).

(45) JAOAC **24**, 305(1941).

(46) JAOAC **25**, 77, 352(1942).

(47) JAOAC **25**, 77, 361(1942).

(48) JAOAC **25**, 78(1942).

(49) JAOAC **47**, 436(1964).

(50) JAOAC **25**, 348(1942).

(51) JAOAC **19**, 284(1936); **22**, 289(1939).

(52) JAOAC **50**, 192, 394(1967).

(53) JAOAC **51**, 1296(1968); **52**, 384(1969).

3. Plants

3.001 Sampling (1)—Official Final Action

When more than one plant is sampled, include enough plants in sample to insure that it adequately represents av. composition of entire lot of plants sampled. (This number depends upon variability in composition of the plants.) Det. details of sampling by purpose for which sample is taken.

3.002 Preparation of Sample (1)— Official Final Action

(a) *For mineral constituents.*—Thoroly remove all foreign matter from material, especially adhering soil or sand, but to prevent leaching, avoid excessive washing. Air- or oven-dry as rapidly as possible to prevent decomposition or wt loss by respiration, grind, and store in tightly stoppered bottles. If results are to be expressed on fresh wt basis, record sample wts before and after drying. When Cu, Mn, Zn, Fe, Al, etc. are to be detd, avoid contaminating sample by dust during drying and from grinding and sieving machinery.

(b) *For carbohydrates.*—Thoroly remove all foreign matter and rapidly grind or chop material into fine pieces. Add weighed sample to enough hot redistd alcohol to which enough pptd CaCO₃ has been added to neutze acidity, using enough alcohol so that final concn, allowing for H₂O content of sample, is ca 80%. Heat nearly to bp on steam or H₂O bath 30 min, stirring frequently. (Samples may be stored until needed for analysis.)

3.003 Moisture—Official Final Action— See 7.003, 7.007, or 7.008

3.004 Ash—Official Final Action—*See* 31.012–31.013; 7.010

3.005 Sand and Silica—Official Final Action

Ignite 10–50 g sample in flat-bottom Pt dish in muffle, at 500–550°, until residue is white or nearly so. (Pt dishes must be used with caution in ashing plant materials high in Fe; for such materials, use well-glazed porcelain crucibles and run blank detn.) Moisten with 5–10 ml HCl, boil ca 2 min, evap. to dryness, and heat on steam bath 3 hr to render SiO₂ insol. Moisten residue with 5 ml HCl, boil 2 min, add ca 50 ml H₂O, heat on H₂O bath few min, filter thru hardened paper, and wash thoroly. To this filtrate add filtrate and washings from alkali-sol. SiO₂ detn (b) and dil. to 200 ml. Designate as *Soln A.*

(a) *Sand.*—Wash residue from filter into Pt dish and boil ca 5 min with ca 20 ml satd Na₂CO₃ soln; add few drops 10% NaOH soln, let mixt. settle, and

decant thru ignited and weighed gooch. Boil residue in dish with another 20 ml portion Na₂CO₃ soln and decant as before. Repeat process. Transfer residue to gooch and wash thoroly, first with hot H₂O, then with little HCl (1 + 4), and finally with hot H₂O until Cl-free. Dry filter and contents, ignite at 500–550°, and weigh as sand. Confirm by microscopic examination.

(b) *Alkali-soluble SiO₂.*—Combine alk. filtrate and washings from (a), acidify with HCl, evap. to dryness, add 5 ml HCl, again evap., and dehydrate by heating 2 hr at 110–120°. Moisten residue with 5–10 ml HCl, boil ca 2 min, add ca 50 ml H₂O, and heat on H₂O bath 10–15 min. Filter thru ashless filter or ignited and weighed gooch, wash with hot H₂O, ignite at 500–550°, and weigh as SiO₂. Add filtrate to Soln A.

METALS

3.006 Iron and Aluminum (2)— Official Final Action
(*Caution: See* 46.030.)

Take aliquot of Soln A, **3.005**, contg enough Fe and Al to form ca 40 mg Fe- and AlPO₄. Add few drops HNO₃, Br-H₂O, or H₂O₂ to oxidize Fe. If soln does not already contain excess phosphate, add 0.5 g (NH₄)₂HPO₄, stir until dissolved, and dil. to 50 ml with H₂O. Add few drops thymol blue soln, **34.097** (g), and then add NH₄OH until soln just turns yellow. Add 0.5 ml HCl and 25 ml 25% NH₄OAc soln, and stir. Let stand at room temp. until ppt settles (ca 1 hr). Filter, and wash 10 times with hot 5% NH₄NO₃ soln. Ignite at 500–550° and weigh as FePO₄ and AlPO₄.

Fuse ignited ppt in Pt crucible with ca 4 g mixt. of equal parts Na₂CO₃ and K₂CO₃. When fusion is complete, let crucible cool, add 5 ml H₂SO₄, and heat until copious fumes of SO₃ are evolved. Cool, transfer to flask, add H₂O, and digest until soln is clear. Reduce Fe with Zn, cool, and titr. with 0.1N KMnO₄. Correct for blank and calc. as % Fe or % Fe₂O₃. Calc. to FePO₄ and subtract from total Fe- and AlPO₄ to obtain AlPO₄. Correct for blank and report as Al₂O₃.

Methods for Iron Only

Colorimetric Method (3)—Official Final Action
3.007 **Reagents**

(a) *Acetic acid.*—2M. Dil. 120 g HOAc to 1 L with H₂O.

(b) *Ammonium citrate soln.*—1%. Dissolve 1 g NH₄ citrate in H₂O and dil. to 100 ml.

(c) *Bromophenol blue indicator.*—0.04%. Grind 0.1 g bromophenol blue in mortar with 3 ml 0.05N NaOH, transfer to vol. flask, and dil. to 250 ml with H_2O.

(d) *Buffer solns:*

(1) pH 3.5.—Mix 6.4 ml 2M NaOAc with 93.6 ml 2M HOAc and dil. to 1 L.

(2) pH 4.5.—Mix 43 ml 2M NaOAc with 57 ml 2M HOAc and dil. to 1 L.

(e) *Hydroquinone soln.*—Dissolve 1 g hydroquinone in 100 ml pH 4.5 buffer, (d)(*2*). Keep in refrigerator, and discard when any color develops.

(f) *o-Phenanthroline soln.*—Dissolve 1 g o-phenanthroline.H_2O in H_2O, warming if necessary, and dil. to 400 ml.

(g) *Sodium acetate soln.*—2M. Dissolve 272 g NaOAc.$3H_2O$ in H_2O and dil. to 1 L.

(h) *Iron std soln.*—1 mg/ml. Dissolve 1 g electrolytic Fe in 50 ml 10% H_2SO_4, warming if necessary to hasten reaction. Cool, and dil. to 1 L with H_2O.

3.008   *Preparation of Sample*

(*Caution: See* **46.011, 46.025,** and **46.030.**)

Use Soln A, **3.005,** or if Soln A is not available, weigh samples of finely ground plant material (1–5 g, depending on Fe content) into porcelain crucibles with smooth inner surfaces, and ash overnight at 500–550° in muffle. Cool, add 5 ml HCl (1 + 1), and heat on steam bath 15 min to dissolve Fe and to hydrolyze pyrophosphate. Filter into 100 ml vol. flask. Transfer insol. residue to filter and wash 5 times with 3 ml portions hot HCl (1 + 100), then with hot H_2O until washings are Cl-free. Ignite paper and any remaining C in Fe-free Pt crucible. Cool, add 2 drops H_2SO_4 and 1 ml HF, and carefully evap. to SO_3 fumes. Cool, add few drops HCl (1 + 1), and warm. Filter and wash as before into same vol. flask, dil. to vol., and mix.

3.009   *Determination*

Pipet identical aliquots of Soln A, **3.005,** or sample soln, **3.008,** into 25 ml vol. flask and into test tube or small erlenmeyer. Add 5 drops bromophenol blue indicator to aliquot in test tube, and titr. with 2M NaOAc soln until color matches that of equal vol. of pH 3.5 buffer contg same quantity of indicator. Add 1 ml hydroquinone soln and 2 ml o-phenanthroline soln to aliquot in vol. flask, and adjust pH to 3.5 by adding same vol. NaOAc soln found necessary for aliquot in test tube. If turbidity develops upon adjusting pH of aliquot in test tube, add 1 ml NH_4 citrate soln to vol. flask before adding the NaOAc soln. Dil. to vol., mix, and let stand 1 hr for complete color development. Det. Fe colorimetrically.

Select aliquot contg quantity of Fe suitable for range of colorimeter to be used.

For photoelec. colorimeter, this quantity depends on light filter (470–520 nm) and thickness of cells used. No. 430 dark-shade, blue-green, Corning Glass Works glass filter ca 12.5 mm thick (obtained by using 2 molded filters of half this thickness) is satisfactory, and when used with 1 cm cells in Cenco-Sheard-Sanford photelometer (Cenco Instrument Corp.), reliable range is 0.02–0.1 mg Fe/25 ml soln.

For spectrophtr, prep. curve relating T or A to mg Fe in 25 ml by treating series of solns contg varying quantities of Fe that cover usable range of instrument exactly as described for unknowns, detg their respective readings, and plotting these against corresponding concns of Fe. H_2O may be used as ref., and blanks detd to correct for quantity Fe in reagents used, or blank soln itself may be made basis of comparison.

For visual colorimeter, range of 0.2–0.5 mg Fe/25 ml is suggested. Prep. series of stds covering this range simultaneously with unknowns and compare each unknown with std that does not vary >25% from it in concn.

3.010   *Titrimetric Method (4)—*
      Official Final Action

Take appropriate aliquot of Soln A or of soln prepd as in **3.008,** and oxidize Fe by adding soln of $KMnO_4$ (1 + 1000) dropwise until very faint permanganate color persists. Add 5 ml 10% NH_4CNS and titr. with *dil. $TiCl_3$ soln* until red color disappears. (To prep. appropriate $TiCl_3$ soln, boil 5–10 ml 20% $TiCl_3$ with 50 ml HCl few min, cool, and dil. to 1 L. Stdze against std Fe soln, keep in dark in well-filled container, and restdze each time it is used, or every few hr when many detns are being made. Discard when decomposition is indicated by loss of color and increased titer against std.)

Calcium—Official Final Action

3.011   *Macro Method (5)*

Transfer aliquot of Soln A, **3.005,** to 200 ml beaker, add H_2O if necessary to vol. of 50 ml, heat to boiling, and add 10 ml satd $(NH_4)_2C_2O_4$ soln and drop Me red, **2.049**(i). Almost neutze with NH_4OH and boil until ppt is coarsely granular. Cool, add NH_4OH (1 + 4) until color is faint pink (pH 5.0), and let stand ≥4 hr. Filter, and wash with H_2O at room temp. until filtrate is oxalate-free. (Reserve filtrate and washings for Mg detn, **3.013.**)

Break point of filter with Pt wire, and wash ppt into beaker in which Ca was pptd, using stream of hot H_2O. Add ca 10 ml H_2SO_4 (1 + 4), heat to ca 90°, add ca 50 ml hot H_2O, and titr. with 0.05N $KMnO_4$. Finally add filter paper to soln and complete titrn.

3.012   *Micro Method (6)*

Weigh 2 g sample into small crucible and ignite in muffle at 500–550°. Dissolve ash in HCl (1 + 4) and transfer to 100 ml beaker. Add 5 ml HCl and evap. to dryness on steam bath to dehydrate SiO_2. Moisten residue with 5 ml HCl, add ca 50 ml H_2O, heat few min on steam bath, transfer to 100 ml vol. flask, cool quickly to room temp., dil. to vol., shake, and filter, discarding first portion of filtrate.

Pipet 15 ml aliquot into conical-tip centrf. tube contg 2 ml satd $(NH_4)_2C_2O_4$ soln and 2 drops Me red, **2.049**(i). Add 2 ml HOAc $(1 + 4)$, rotating tube to mix contents thoroly. Add NH_4OH $(1 + 4)$, while intermittently rotating tube, until soln is faintly alk.; then add few drops of the HOAc from dropper until color is faint pink (pH 5.0). (It is important at this point to rotate tube so that last bit of liq. in conical tip has required color.) Let stand ≥ 4 hr; then centrf. 15 min. (Ppt should be in firm lump in tip of tube.) Remove supernatant, using suction device, Fig. 3:1, taking care not to disturb ppt. Wash ppt by adding 2 ml NH_4OH $(1 + 49)$, rotating tube to break up ppt. (It may be necessary to jar tube sharply.) Centrf. 10 min, again remove supernatant, and wash with re-agent as before. Repeat washing of ppt 3 times.

After last supernatant has been removed, add 2 ml H_2SO_4 $(1 + 4)$ to tube, break up ppt as before, heat on steam bath to 80–90°, and titr. in tube with 0.02N $KMnO_4$, rotating liq. during titrn to attain proper end point. If tube cools to $<60°$ during titrn, as indi-cated by slow reduction of $KMnO_4$, reheat in steam bath few min and complete titrn. Perform blank on identical quantity H_2SO_4 in similar tube heated to same temp. to det. quantity $KMnO_4$ soln necessary to give end point color. Subtract this value from buret reading. 1 ml 0.02N $KMnO_4$ = 0.000400 g Ca. Report as % Ca.

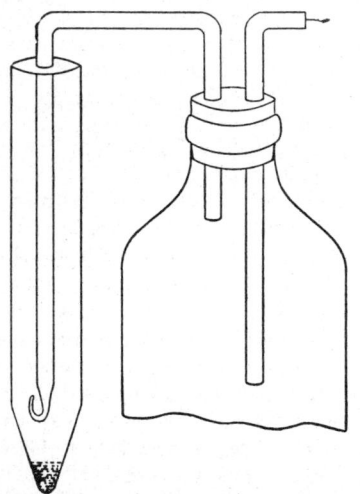

FIG. 3:1—Suction device used in micro method for determining calcium

3.013 Magnesium (7)—Official Final Action
(Caution: See **46.011** *and* **46.026**.*)*

To combined filtrate and washings from Ca detn, **3.011**, add 30 ml HNO_3 and evap. to dryness to de-compose NH_4 salts. Take up with 5 ml HCl and dil. to ca 100 ml with H_2O. Add 5 ml *10% Na citrate soln*

and 10 ml *10% $(NH_4)_2HPO_4$ soln*, or enough to ppt all the Mg. Add NH_4OH $(1 + 4)$ with constant stir-ring (using policeman) until soln is faintly alk. and ppt forms; then add 25 ml NH_4OH, stir vigorously until ppt is granular, and keep in cool place over-night. Filter, and wash free from Cl with cold NH_4OH $(1 + 10)$. Ignite in muffle at 500–550° until all C is oxidized, then at 900–950° ca 4 hr to form $Mg_2P_2O_7$. Cool, and weigh as $Mg_2P_2O_7$. (If sample is excessively high in Mn, dissolve ignited ppt in HNO_3, det. Mn as in **3.014**, and correct $Mg_2P_2O_7$ for $Mn_2P_2O_7$.) Report as % Mg.

3.014 Manganese (8)—Official Final Action

To aliquot of Soln A, **3.005**, contg 0.2–0.5 g ash, add 15 ml H_2SO_4 and evap. to ca 30 ml. Add 5–10 ml HNO_3 and continue evapn. (Do not evap. until dense fumes appear, because $Fe_2(SO_4)_3$ then dis-solves with difficulty. HNO_3 may be present, but not HCl.) Add H_2O, little at time, heat until Fe salts dissolve, and dil. to ca 150 ml. Add 0.3 g KIO_4, or its equiv. in HIO_4, in small portions, boil few min or until color of $KMnO_4$ shows no further increase in intensity, and let cool.

Prep. std as follows: To vol. H_2O equal to sample add 15 ml H_2SO_4 and enough pure $Fe(NO_3)_3$, free from Mn, to equal ca quantity of Fe in sample. Add measured quantity of 0.1N $KMnO_4$ until color is slightly darker than sample, then add 0.3 g KIO_4, and boil few min. When cool, transfer sample and std to 250 ml vol. flasks and dil. to vol. with H_2O. (If color is weak, it may be necessary to dil. to <250 ml.) Compare colors in colorimeter. (Photoelec. colorimeter with 525–550 nm filter may be used.) Report as % Mn.

3.015 Sodium and Potassium—
Official Final Action

Moisten 1–10 g sample with H_2SO_4 $(1 + 10)$, dry in oven, and ignite in muffle at 500–550° to destroy org. matter. Heat residue on steam bath with 2–5 ml HCl and ca 50 ml H_2O. Transfer to beaker and add NH_4OH dropwise until ppt formed requires several sec to dissolve, thus leaving soln only faintly acid. Heat nearly to boiling, and add NH_4OH to ppt all Fe, Al, etc. Boil in covered beaker ca 1 min; remove, and if no NH_3 is detected by smelling, continue addn, dropwise, until it can be detected. Stir and without letting ppt settle, pour on filter. Wash im-mediately with hot H_2O, effecting rapid filtration by directing fine jet around edge of ppt to cut it free from paper. Wash ppt several times, return to orig-inal beaker, dissolve with few drops HCl, and warm. Reppt Fe, Al, and P_2O_5 with NH_4OH as above; filter, and wash until free from Cl.

Evap. combined filtrates and washings to dryness, heat at $<450°$ until NH_4 salts are expelled, and dis-solve in hot H_2O. Add 5 ml satd $Ba(OH)_2$ soln, heat to boiling, let settle few min, and det. if pptn is com-plete by adding more $Ba(OH)_2$ soln to little clear liq.

When no further ppt is produced, filter and wash thoroly with hot H_2O.

Heat filtrate to boiling and add NH_4OH $(1 + 4)$ and 10% $(NH_4)_2CO_3$ soln to complete pptn of Ba, Ca, etc. Let stand short time on H_2O bath, filter, and wash ppt thoroly with hot H_2O. Evap. filtrate and washings to dryness, expel NH_4 salts by heating at $<450°$, treat with little hot H_2O, and add few drops of the dil. NH_4OH, 1 or 2 drops of the $(NH_4)_2CO_3$ soln, and few drops satd NH_4 oxalate soln. Let stand few min on H_2O bath and set aside few hr. Filter, evap. to complete dryness on H_2O bath, and heat at $\leq 500°$ until all NH_4 salts are expelled and residue is nearly or quite white. Dissolve in min. amt H_2O, filter into weighed Pt dish, add few drops HCl, evap. to dryness on H_2O bath, heat at $\leq 500°$, cool in desiccator, and weigh as KCl + NaCl. Repeat heating to constant wt.

Sodium and/or Potassium

Flame Photometric Method (9)— Official Final Action

3.016   *Reagents*

(a) *Potassium stock soln.*—1000 ppm K. Dissolve 1.907 g dry KCl in H_2O and dil. to 1 L.

(b) *Sodium stock soln.*—1000 ppm Na. Dissolve 2.542 g dry NaCl in H_2O and dil. to 1 L.

(c) *Lithium stock soln.*—1000 ppm Li. Dissolve 6.108 g LiCl in H_2O and dil. to 1 L. (Needed only if internal std method of evaluation is to be used.)

(d) *Ammonium oxalate stock soln.*—0.24N. Dissolve 17.0 g $(NH_4)_2C_2O_4$.H_2O in H_2O and dil. to 1 L.

(e) *Extracting solns.*—(*1*) *For potassium.*—For internal std method dil. required vol. LiCl stock soln to 1 L; otherwise use H_2O. (*2*) *For sodium.*—To 250 ml NH_4 oxalate stock soln add required vol. LiCl stock soln (if internal std method is used) and dil. to 1 L. If internal std requirements are same for both Na and K detns, this reagent may be used as common extg soln.

3.017   *Preparation of Standard Solutions*

Dil. appropriate aliquots of stock solns to prep. series of stds contg K and/or Na in stepped amts (including 0) to cover instrument range, and Li and NH_4 oxalate (if required) in same concns as in corresponding extg solns. (If common extg soln is used, 1 set of stds contg both K and Na suffices.)

3.018   *Sample Extraction*

Transfer weighed portion of finely ground and well mixed sample to erlenmeyer of at least twice capacity of vol. of extg soln to be used. Add measured vol. extg soln, stopper flask, and shake vigorously at frequent intervals during at least 15 min. Filter thru dry, fast paper. If paper clogs, pour contents onto addnl fresh paper and combine filtrates. Use filtrate for detn.

Note: Do not make exts more concd than required for instrument because there is tendency toward incomplete extn as ratio of sample wt to vol. extg soln increases. Prep. sep. exts for K and Na when their concns in sample differ greatly. For K, use wt sample ≤ 0.1 g/50 ml extg soln; for low Na concns, use ≥ 1.0 g/50 ml extg soln; and for higher concns, prep. weaker exts by reducing ratio of sample to extg soln rather than by dilg stronger exts.

3.019   *Determination*
(*Caution: See* **46.007.**)

Rinse all glassware used in Na detn with dil. HNO_3, followed by several portions H_2O. Protect solns from air-borne Na contamination.

Operate instrument according to manufacturer's instructions. Permit instrument to reach operating equilibrium before use. Atomize portions of std solns toward end of warm-up period until reproducible readings for series are obtained.

Run stds, covering concn range of samples involved, at frequent intervals during atomization of series of sample solns. Repeat this operation with both std and sample solns enough times to result in reliable av. reading for each soln. Plot analysis curves from readings of stds, and calc. $\%$ K and/or Na in samples.

Potassium—Official Final Action

3.020   *Platinic Chloride Method*

Dissolve residue of mixed chlorides, **3.015,** in few ml H_2O, acidify with few drops HCl, and add excess H_2PtCl_6 soln, **2.076(b).** Evap. on H_2O bath to thick paste; treat residue repeatedly with 80% alcohol, decanting thru weighed gooch or other form of filter; transfer ppt to filter; and wash with 80% alcohol until filtrate is colorless. Dry 30 min at $100°$ and weigh. $K_2PtCl_6 \times 0.1609 = K$. If Na is desired, calc. K to KCl and subtract this from the KCl + NaCl, **3.015.**

3.021   *Perchloric Acid Method (10)*
(*Caution: See* **46.028.**)

Prep. sample as in **3.015,** up to point where heavy metals have been removed and Na and K are in form of chlorides. (Sulfates must be absent.) Add 3–5 ml 60% $HClO_4$. Evap. to dryness, dissolve in hot H_2O, and again evap. to dryness. Heat to $350°$, cool, and weigh, if combined perchlorates are desired. Add 10–20 ml anhyd. *EtOAc-n-butanol* $(1 + 1)$. Digest near bp several min. Decant into gooch. Wash once or twice by decanting with few ml of the EtOAc-butanol mixt. Dissolve in min. amt H_2O, evap. to dryness, and ext as before. Filter, and wash several times with 1 ml of the EtOAc-butanol mixt. Dry in oven at $110°$ several min and heat 15 min at $350°$. Cool and weigh. $KClO_4 \times 0.2822 = K$. Calc. Na by difference.

3.022   *Rapid Method for Potassium Only*

Proceed as in **3.015** thru "and if no NH_3 is detected ... until it can be detected." Add few ml satd $(NH_4)_2CO_3$ soln, let stand few hr, filter, and wash with hot H_2O until Cl-free. Conc. to small vol., transfer to Pt evapg dish, evap. to drive off excess NH_3, add 0.5 ml H_2SO_4 $(1 + 1)$, evap., ignite by swirling dish over free flame, and proceed as in **3.020**.

Sodium Only
Uranyl Acetate Method (11)—
Official Final Action

3.023 *Reagent*

Magnesium uranyl acetate soln:

(**a**) *Uranyl acetate soln.*—To 85 g $UO_2(OAc)_2.2H_2O$ in 1 L vol. flask add 60 g HOAc and H_2O to ca 900 ml. Heat to dissolve, cool, and dil. to vol. with H_2O. (*Caution: See* **46.083.**)

(**b**) *Magnesium acetate soln.*—To 500 g $Mg(OAc)_2.4H_2O$ in 1 L vol. flask add 60 g HOAc and H_2O to ca 900 ml. Heat to dissolve, cool, and dil. to vol. with H_2O.

Reheat (**a**) and (**b**) sep. to ca 70° until all salts dissolve. Mix 2 solns at this temp. and let cool to ca 30°. Place vessel contg mixed reagent in H_2O at 20°, and hold at 20° 1–2 hr, or until slight excess of salts has crystd out. Filter thru dry filter into dry bottle.

3.024 *Determination*

Moisten 1–10 g sample with H_2SO_4 $(1 + 10)$, dry in oven, and ignite in muffle at 500–550° to destroy org. matter. Heat residue on steam bath with 2–5 ml HCl, add ca 40 ml H_2O, and heat to boiling. Add enough 5% $CaCl_2$ soln to ensure pptn of all phosphates. Ppt phosphates by making slightly alk. with NH_4OH. Filter, and evap. to 5 ml or less if no salts sep. Cool, add 100 ml Mg uranyl acetate soln, place mixt. in H_2O bath at 20°, and either stir vigorously 45 min or let stand 24 hr at this temp. Filter with suction, and wash with *alcohol satd with Na-Mg-uranyl acetate*. Dry 30 min at 105–110°, cool, and weigh. Wt Na-Mg-uranyl acetate $\times$ 0.0153 = wt Na.

Cobalt—Official Final Action
(*Caution: See* **46.001, 46.011, 46.040, 46.049,** and **46.068.**)

Nitrosocresol Method (12)

3.025 *Reagents*

(Make all distns in Pyrex stills with $\overline{\mathbb{S}}$ joints. Store reagents in g-s Pyrex bottles.)

(**a**) *Redistilled water.*—Distill twice, or pass thru column of ion exchange resin (IR-100A, H-form, or equiv.) to remove heavy metals.

(**b**) *Hydrofluoric acid.*—Reagent grade, 48%. Procurement in vinyl plastic bottles is advantageous.

(**c**) *Perchloric acid.*—Reagent grade, 60%. No further purification necessary.

(**d**) *Hydrochloric acid.*—$(1 + 1)$. Add equal vol. reagent grade concd HCl to distd H_2O and distill.

(**e**) *Ammonium hydroxide.*—$(1 + 1)$. Distill concd NH_4OH into equal vol. redistd H_2O.

(**f**) *Ammonium hydroxide.*—0.02N. Add 7 ml of the NH_4OH $(1 + 1)$ to 2.5 L redistd H_2O.

(**g**) *Carbon tetrachloride.*—Distill over CaO, passing distillate thru dry, acid-washed filter paper. Used CCl_4 may be recovered as in **3.040(a)**.

(**h**) *Dithizone.*—Dissolve 0.5 g dithizone in 600–700 ml CCl_4 (tech. grade is satisfactory). Filter into 5 L separator contg 2.5–3.0 L 0.02N NH_4OH, shake well, and discard CCl_4 layer. Shake with 50 ml portions redistd CCl_4 until CCl_4 phase as it seps is pure green. Add 1 L redistd CCl_4 and acidify slightly with the HCl $(1 + 1)$. Shake the dithizone into CCl_4 layer and discard aq. layer. Store in cool, dark place, preferably in refrigerator.

(**i**) *Ammonium citrate soln.*—40%. Dissolve 800 g citric acid in 600 ml distd H_2O, and, while stirring, slowly add 900 ml NH_4OH. Reaction is exothermic and care must be taken to prevent spattering. Adjust pH to 8.5 if necessary. Dil. to 2 L and ext with 25 ml portions dithizone soln until aq. phase stays orange and CCl_4 remains predominantly green. Then ext soln with CCl_4 until all orange is removed.

(**j**) *Hydrochloric acid.*—0.1N. Dil. 16.6 ml of the HCl $(1 + 1)$ to 1 L with redistd H_2O.

(**k**) *Hydrochloric acid.*—0.01N. Dil. 100 ml of the 0.1N HCl to 1 L with redistd H_2O.

(**l**) *Sodium hydroxide soln.*—1N. Dissolve 40 g NaOH in 1 L redistd H_2O.

(**m**) *Borate buffer.*—pH 7.8. Dissolve 20 g H_3BO_3 in 1 L redistd H_2O. Add 50 ml 1N NaOH and adjust pH if necessary. Equal vols borate buffer and 0.01N HCl should give soln of pH 7.9.

(**n**) *Borate buffer.*—pH 9.1. To 1 L borate buffer, pH 7.8, add 120 ml 1N NaOH and adjust pH if necessary.

(**o**) *Skellysolve B.*—Essentially *n*-hexane. Purify by adding 20–30 g silica gel/L, let stand several days, and distill. Available from Skelly Oil Co., Solvents Division, Kansas City, MO 64141.

(**p**) *Cupric acetate soln.* — Dissolve 10 g $Cu(OAc)_2.H_2O$ in 1 L redistd H_2O.

(**q**) *o-Nitrosocresol soln.*—Dissolve 8.4 g anhyd. $CuCl_2$ and 8.4 g $NH_2OH.HCl$ in 900 ml H_2O. Add 8 ml *m*-cresol (Eastman Kodak Co., practical grade) and stir vigorously while slowly adding 24 ml 30% H_2O_2. Stir with mech. stirrer 2 hr at room temp. (Standing for longer periods results in excessive decomposition.) Add 25 ml HCl and ext *o*-nitrosocresol with four 150 ml portions Skellysolve B, (**o**), in large separator. Then add addnl 25 ml HCl and again ext with four 150 ml portions Skellysolve B. Wash combined Skellysolve B exts twice with 50–100 ml portions 0.1N HCl and twice with 50–100 ml portions redistd H_2O. Shake *o*-nitrosocresol soln with successive 50–100 ml portions 1% $Cu(OAc)_2$ soln until aq. phase is no longer deep blood-red. When light purple is evident, extn is complete. Discard Skellysolve B phase, acidify aq. soln of Cu salt with 25 ml HCl, and ext reagent with two 500 ml portions of the Skellysolve B; wash twice with 150–200 ml portions 0.1N HCl and several times with 150–200 ml portions redistd H_2O. Store *o*-nitrosocresol soln in refrigerator at ca 4°. Reagent is stable 6 months or more.

(r) *Sodium o-nitrosocresol soln.*—Ext 100 ml o-nitrosocresol by shaking with two 50 ml portions borate buffer, pH 9.1, in separator. (If this is carried out as 2 extns, resulting reagent is more concd. It is important that total vol. o-nitrosocresol soln equal total vol. buffer.)

(s) *Cobalt std solns.*—(1) *Stock soln.*—Heat $CoSO_4 \cdot 7H_2O$ in oven at 250–300° to constant wt (6–8 hr). Weigh exactly 0.263 g of the $CoSO_4$ and dissolve in 50 ml redistd H_2O and 1 ml H_2SO_4. Dil. to 1 L. (2) *Working soln.*—0.5 μg/ml. Transfer 5 ml stock soln to 1 L vol. flask and dil. to vol. with redistd H_2O.

(t) *Hydroxylamine acetate buffer.*—pH 5.1±0.1. Dissolve 10 g $NH_2OH \cdot HCl$ and 9.5 g anhyd. NaOAc in 500 ml redistd H_2O.

3.026 Apparatus

(a) *Platinum dishes.*—Approx. 70 ml; for ashing.

(b) *Automatic dispensing burets.*—100 ml; type that can be fitted to ordinary 5 lb reagent bottle and filled by means of aspirator bulb is most convenient.

(c) *Wooden separator rack.*—Twelve 125 ml separator size is convenient for dithizone extns. Rack is fitted across top with removable bar padded with sponge rubber so all 12 separators can be shaken as unit.

(d) *Racks.*—Consisting of 2″ × 2″ × 25″ wooden bars with holes drilled at close intervals to take 50 ml centrf. tubes fitted with No. 13 ₹ glass stoppers. To make these tubes, ream out necks of heavy-wall Pyrex centrf. tubes (Rockefeller Institute type) with ₹ C rod and grind to take ₹ stopper. Place tubes upright in one section, and place other section (fitted with sponge rubber disks ½″ thick in bottom of holes) across their tops. Fasten 2 sections at ends with removable rubber connectors made from ordinary tubing of convenient size, so that any number of tubes can be shaken as unit. Use these tubes for reaction of Co with nitrosocresol, extn of complex into Skellysolve B, and washing of Skellysolve B soln.

(e) *Shaking machine.*—Mech. shaker giving longitudinal stroke of 2″ at ca 180 strokes/min; use to make dithizone extns and to ext Co complex, or shake by hand.

(f) *Colorimeter.*—Suitable for measuring T at ca 345 nm. (Colorimeter described by Ellis and Brandt (Anal. Chem. **21**, 1546(1949)) and Coleman Instruments, 42 Madison St, Maywood, IL 60153, Model 11 or 14 spectrophtr, using null-point method, are satisfactory. With Model 11 instrument, calibration curve deviates slightly from linearity, but region between 0 and 1 μg Co approaches straight line.) Use matched pair of Pyrex absorption cells at least 5 cm long. (American Instrument Co. Cat. No. 5-997, Style D, horizontal, with neck for cork or rubber stopper is satisfactory; od 13 mm, length 5 cm, and capacity ca 3 ml.)

3.027 Cleaning of Glassware

Clean 120 ml Pyrex separators for dithizone extns by initially soaking 30 min in hot HNO_3 and rinsing several times with H_2O. As added precaution, shake with several portions dithizone in CCl_4. After use, clean by rinsing with H_2O, drain, and stopper to avoid contamination. It is not necessary to clean every time with acid. Repeat HNO_3 cleaning if blanks are unusually high.

Clean 50 ml g-s Pyrex centrf. tubes by soaking 30 min in HNO_3 followed by several rinsings in H_2O.

Completely submerge pipets in cylinder of H_2SO_4-$K_2Cr_2O_7$ cleaning soln overnight, rinse several times with H_2O, and suspend upright in rack to dry.

Wash all other glassware thoroly in detergent and rinse well with tap H_2O followed by dip in H_2SO_4-$K_2Cr_2O_7$ cleaning soln. Rinse off cleaning soln with tap H_2O followed by several distd H_2O rinses.

Clean Pt by scrubbing with sea sand followed by boiling in HCl (1 + 2) 30 min, and rinse several times with H_2O.

3.028 Preparation of Sample

See 3.002(a). Oven-dry all plant material 48 hr and prep. for ashing by either of following methods:

(a) Grind material in Wiley mill equipped with stainless steel sieve, mix thoroly by rolling, and sample by quartering.

(b) Using stainless steel shears, cut material by hand fine enough for convenient sampling.

3.029 Ashing of Samples
(*Caution: See* **46.011, 46.025,** and **46.028.**)

Weigh 6 g dry plant tissue into clean Pt dish. Cover with Pyrex watch glass and place in cool muffle; heat slowly to 500° and hold at this temp. overnight. Remove sample and cool. Wet down ash carefully with fine stream redistd H_2O. From dispensing buret slowly add 2–5 ml $HClO_4$, dropwise at first to prevent spattering. Add ca 5 ml HF, evap. on steam bath, transfer to sand bath, and keep at medium heat until fuming ceases.

Cover with Pyrex watch glass, return to partially cooled muffle, heat gradually to 600°, and keep at this temp. 1 hr. Remove sample and cool. Add 5 ml HCl (1 + 1) and ca 10 ml redistd H_2O. Replace cover glass and warm on steam bath to dissolve. (Usually clear soln essentially free of insol. material is obtained.) Transfer sample to 50 ml vol. flask, washing dish several times with redistd H_2O, dil. to vol., and mix thoroly. (Pt dishes can ordinarily be used several times between sand and acid cleanings.)

3.030 Dithizone Extraction
(*Caution: See* **46.011(b), 46.028(a)** and **(d),**
and **46.049.**)

Transfer suitable aliquot (2–3 g dry material) to 120 ml separator (use petroleum jelly as stopcock lubricant). Add 5 ml NH_4 citrate soln and 1 drop phthln; adjust to pH 8.5 with NH_4OH $(1 + 1)$. If ppt forms, add addnl NH_4 citrate. Add 10 ml dithizone in CCl_4 and shake 5 min. Drain CCl_4 phase into 100 ml beaker. Repeat as many times as necessary, using 5 ml quantities of dithizone soln and shaking 5 min each time. Extn is complete when aq. phase remains orange and CCl_4 phase remains predominantly green. Then add 10 ml CCl_4, shake 5 min, and combine with CCl_4 ext. Final 10 ml CCl_4 should be pure green. If not, extn was incomplete and must be repeated.

Add 2 ml $HClO_4$ to combined CCl_4 exts, cover beaker with Pyrex watch glass, and digest on hot plate until colorless. Remove cover glass and evap. slowly to dryness. (If sample is heated any length of time at high temp. when dry, losses of Co may occur. Heat only enough to evap. completely to dryness. If free acid remains, it interferes with next step where pH control is important.)

Add 5 ml $0.01N$ HCl to residue. Heat slightly to assure soln. If Cu is to be detd, transfer with redistd H_2O to 25 ml vol. flask, and dil. to vol. Transfer 20 ml aliquot to 50 ml g-s centrf. tube or 60 ml separator and reserve remainder for Cu detn, **3.039.** If Cu is not to be detd, transfer entire acid soln with redistd H_2O to centrf. tube or separator.

3.031   *Determination*

Add 5 ml borate buffer, pH 7.8, and 2 ml freshly prepd Na *o*-nitrosocresol soln to sample soln. Add exactly 5 ml Skellysolve B and shake 10 min. Remove aq. phase by moderate suction thru finely-drawn glass tube. To Skellysolve B layer add 5 ml $Cu(OAc)_2$ soln and shake 1 min to remove excess reagent. Again remove and discard aq. phase. Wash Skellysolve B by shaking 1 min with 5 ml redistd H_2O, removing aq. layer as before; finally shake Skellysolve B 1 min with 5 ml hydroxylamine-NaOAc buffer to reduce Fe. Transfer Skellysolve B soln of the Co complex to 5 cm absorption cell and read in photoelec. colorimeter, using Corning Glass Works std thickness filters Nos. 5860 and 4308, or light band as close as possible to point of max. A, 360 nm.

3.032   *Blanks and Standards*

With each set of detns include ashing blank and Co stds of 0.0, 0.5, and 1.0 μg. Beer's law holds for this range. T of 0.0 μg point should be $>90\%$. If below, repurify *o*-nitrosocresol by transferring alternately to aq. phase as Cu salt and to Skellysolve B phase as free compd after acidifying aq. phase. Ashing blank should have T <2–3% lower than reagent blank.

It is also advisable to include std sample with each set of samples to detect contamination or unusual losses of Co in method. Com. buckwheat flour contg 0.05 ppm Co has proved satisfactory for this purpose.

3.033   *Calculations*

Express results in terms of ppm Co, based upon dry wt of sample.

(μg Co/ml dithizone aliquot)

$$\times \text{(ml total soln/g dry sample)} = \text{ppm Co.}$$

Value for μg Co is obtained from curve minus ashing blank.

Nitroso-R-Salt Method (13)
3.034   *Reagents*

Those listed in **3.025** and following:

(a) *Nitroso-R-salt soln.*—0.2%. Dissolve 2 g powd nitroso-R-salt (Eastman Kodak Co., No. 1124) in redistd H_2O, **3.025(a)**, and dil. to 1 L.

(b) *Dilute nitric acid.*—$(1 + 1)$. Dil. HNO_3 with equal vol. H_2O and redistill in Pyrex app. Store in Pyrex bottles.

(c) *Bromine water.*—Satd soln of Br in redistd H_2O, **3.025(a)**.

(d) *Citric acid soln.*—0.2N. Use special reagent grade Pb-free citric acid.

3.035   *Preparation and Ashing of Samples*

Proceed as in nitrosocresol method, **3.028–3.029,** thru "(Usually clear soln essentially free of insol. material is obtained.)" except use 10 g instead of 6 g dry plant tissue.

3.036   *Dithizone Extraction*

Transfer entire soln to 120 ml separator, and proceed as in **3.030,** thru "If free acid remains . . . pH control is important.)" Dissolve in 1 ml citric acid soln, transfer to 25 ml vol. flask, and dil. to vol. with redistd H_2O, **3.025(a)**.

3.037   *Determination*

Transfer suitable aliquot (ca 8 g dry material) of citric acid soln, **3.036,** to 50 ml beaker. Evap. to 1–2 ml. Add 3 ml borate buffer, **3.025(n)**, and adjust pH to 8.0–8.5 with NaOH (check externally with phenol red). (Vol. ≤ 5 ml.) Add 1 ml nitroso-R-salt soln *slowly with mixing.* Boil 1–2 min and add 2 ml dil. HNO_3. Boil 1–2 min, add 0.5–1.0 ml Br-H_2O, cover with watch glass, and let stand warm 5 min. Boil 2–3 min to remove excess Br (use effective fume removal device). Cool, and dil. to 10 or 25 ml (depending on length of light path in absorption cell). Transfer to cell and read at 500 nm within 1 hr. Prep. stds contg 0.5, 1, 2, 3, and 4 μg Co and add 1 ml citric acid soln, **3.034(d)**, to each. Proceed as for unknowns, beginning "Evap. to 1–2 ml."

Copper (13)—Official Final Action
3.038   *Reagents*

Those listed in **3.025** and following:

(a) *Sodium diethyldithiocarbamate soln.*—0.1%. Freshly prepd in redistd H_2O, **3.025(a)**.

(b) *Copper std soln.*— 1 µg/ml. Dissolve 0.3929 g $CuSO_4.5H_2O$ in redistd H_2O, **3.025**(a), add 5 ml H_2SO_4, dil. to 1 L, and mix. Take 10 ml aliquot, add 5 ml H_2SO_4, dil. to 1 L, and mix.

3.039 **Determination**

Transfer aliquot (0.5–1 g dry material) from soln obtained from **3.030** or **3.036** to 125 ml separator. Add 2 ml NH_4 citrate soln, 1 drop phthln, 5 ml Na diethyldithiocarbamate soln, and NH_4OH (1 + 1), **3.025**(e), until pink. Add 10 ml CCl_4 and shake 5 min. Drain CCl_4, centrf. 5 min, transfer to absorption cell, and read with filters (Corning Glass Works) 3389 and 5113, or at 430 nm.

Prep. std curve with 1, 5, 10, 15, and 20 µg Cu treated as above.

Zinc—Official Final Action
Mixed Color Method (14)

3.040 **Reagents**

(Redistill all H_2O from Pyrex glass. Treat all glassware with HNO_3 (1 + 1) or fresh chromic acid cleaning soln. Rinse repeatedly with ordinary distd H_2O and finally with Zn-free H_2O.)

(a) *Carbon tetrachloride.*—Use ACS grade without purification. If tech. grade is used, dry with anhyd. $CaCl_2$ and redistill in presence of small quantity CaO. (Used CCl_4 may be reclaimed by distn in presence of NaOH (1 + 100) contg small amts of $Na_2S_2O_3$, followed by drying with anhyd. $CaCl_2$ and fractional distn in presence of small amts of CaO.) (*Caution: See* **46.011**(b) *and* **46.049**.)

(b) *Zinc std solns.*—(1) *Stock soln.*—1 mg/ml. Place 0.25 g pure Zn in 250 ml vol. flask. Add ca 50 ml H_2O and 1 ml H_2SO_4; heat on steam bath until all Zn dissolves. Dil. to vol. and store in Pyrex vessel. (2) *Working soln.*—10 µg/ml. Dil. 10 ml stock soln to 1 L. Store in Pyrex vessel.

(c) *Ammonium hydroxide soln.*—1N. With all-Pyrex app. distill NH_4OH into H_2O, stopping distn when half has distd. Dil. distillate to proper concn. Store in g-s Pyrex vessel.

(d) *Hydrochloric acid.*—1N. Displace HCl gas from HCl in glass flask by slowly adding equal vol. H_2SO_4 from dropping funnel that extends below surface of the HCl. Absorb displaced HCl gas by conducting it thru delivery tube to surface of H_2O in receiving flask (no heat is necessary). Dil. to proper concn. Use of 150 ml each of HCl and H_2SO_4 will yield 1 L purified HCl soln of concn >1N.

(e) *Diphenylthiocarbazone (dithizone) soln.*—Dissolve 0.20 g dithizone in 500 ml CCl_4, and filter to remove insol. matter. Place soln in g-s bottle or large separator, add 2 L 0.02N NH_4OH (40 ml 1N NH_4OH dild to 2 L), and shake to ext dithizone into aq. phase. Sep. phases, discard CCl_4 phase, and ext ammoniacal soln of dithizone with 100 ml portions CCl_4 until CCl_4 ext is pure green. Discard CCl_4 phase after each extn. Add 500 ml CCl_4 and 45 ml 1N HCl, and shake to ext dithizone into CCl_4. Sep. phases and

discard aq. phase. Dil. CCl_4 soln of dithizone to 2 L with CCl_4. Store in brown bottle in dark, cool place.

(f) *Ammonium citrate soln.*—0.5M. Dissolve 226 g $(NH_4)_2HC_6H_5O_7$ in 2 L H_2O. Add NH_4OH (80–85 ml) until soln has pH of 8.5–8.7. Add excess dithizone soln (aq. phase is orange-yellow after phases have been shaken and sepd), and ext with 100 ml portions CCl_4 until ext is full green. Add more dithizone if necessary. Sep. aq. phase from CCl_4 and store in Pyrex vessel.

(g) *Carbamate soln.*—Dissolve 0.25 g Na diethyldithiocarbamate in H_2O and dil. to 100 ml with H_2O. Store in refrigerator in Pyrex bottle. Prep. fresh after 2 weeks.

(h) *Dilute hydrochloric acid.*—0.02N. Dil. 100 ml 1N HCl to 5 L.

3.041 **Preparation of Solutions**

To reduce measuring out reagents and minimize errors due to variations in composition, prep. 3 solns in appropriate quantities from reagents and store in Pyrex vessels, taking care to avoid loss of NH_3 from Solns A and B. Discard solns after 6–8 weeks because Zn increases slowly with storage. Det. std curve for each new set of reagents. Following quantities of Solns A and B and 2 L dithizone soln are enough for 100 detns:

(1) *Soln A.*—Dil. 1 L 0.5M NH_4 citrate and 140 ml 1N NH_4OH to 4 L.

(2) *Soln B.*—Dil. 1 L 0.5M NH_4 citrate and 300 ml 1N NH_4OH to 4.5 L. Just before using, add 1 vol. carbamate soln to 9 vols NH_3-NH_4 citrate soln to obtain vol. of Soln B immediately required.

Note: If Zn-free reagents have been prepd, they can be used to test chemicals for Zn. Certain lots of NH_4OH and HCl are sufficiently free of Zn to be used without purification.

3.042 **Ashing**

Ash 5 g finely ground, air-dried plant material in Pt dish in elec. muffle at 500–550°. Include blank detn. Moisten ash with little H_2O; then add 10 ml 1N HCl (more if necessary) and heat on steam bath until all substances sol. in HCl are dissolved. Add 5–10 ml hot H_2O. Filter off insol. matter on **7 cm paper** (Whatman No. 42 or equiv. previously washed with two 5 ml portions hot 1N HCl, then washed with hot H_2O until free of HCl), and collect filtrate in 100 ml vol. flask. Wash filter with hot H_2O until washings are not acid to Me red. Add 1 drop Me red, **2.049**(i), to filtrate in 100 ml flask; neutze with 1N NH_4OH and add 4 ml 1N HCl. Cool, and dil. to vol. with H_2O.

3.043 **First Extraction**
(Sepn of dithizone complex-forming metals from ash soln)

Pipet aliquot of ash soln contg ≤30 µg Zn into 125 ml Squibb separator. Add 1 ml 0.2N HCl for each 5 ml ash soln <10 ml taken, or 1 ml 0.2N NH_4OH for each 5 ml >10 ml taken. (10 ml aliquot is usually satisfactory in analysis of plant materials.) Add 40 ml Soln A and 10 ml dithizone reagent. Shake vigorously 30 sec to ext from aq. phase the Zn and other dithizone complex-forming metals that may be present; then let layers sep. At this point excess of dithizone (indicated by orange or yellow-orange aq. phase) must be present. If excess dithizone is not present, add more reagent until, after shaking, excess is indicated. Shake down the drop of CCl_4 ext from surface, and drain CCl_4 ext into second separator as completely as possible without letting any aq. layer enter stopcock bore. Rinse down CCl_4 ext from surface of aq. layer with 1–2 ml clear CCl_4; then drain this CCl_4 into second separator without letting aq. phase enter stopcock bore. Repeat rinsing process as often as necessary to flush ext completely into second separator. Add 5 ml clear CCl_4 to first separator, shake 30 sec, and let layers sep. (CCl_4 layer at this point will appear clear green if metals that form dithizone complexes have been completely extd from aq. phase by previous extn.) Drain CCl_4 layer into second separator and flush ext down from surface and out of separator as directed previously. If last ext does not possess distinct clear color, repeat extn with 5 ml clear CCl_4 and flushing-out process until complete extn of dithizone complex-forming metals is assured; then discard aq. phase.

3.044   Second Extraction
(Sepn of Cu by extn of Zn into 0.02N HCl)

Pipet 50 ml 0.02N HCl into separator contg CCl_4 soln of metal dithizonates. Shake vigorously 1.5 min, and let layers sep. Shake down drop from surface of aq. phase, and as completely as possible drain CCl_4 phase contg all Cu as dithizonate, without letting any aq. phase, which contains all the Zn, enter stopcock bore. Rinse down CCl_4 ext from surface of aq. phase, and rinse out stopcock bore with 1–2 ml portions clear CCl_4 (same as in first extn) until all traces of green dithizone have been washed out of separator. Shake down drop of CCl_4 from surface of aq. phase, and drain CCl_4 as completely as possible without letting any aq. phase enter stopcock bore. Remove stopper from separator and lay it across neck until small amt of CCl_4 on surface of aq. phase evaps.

3.045   Final Extraction
(Extn of Zn in presence of carbamate reagent)

Pipet 50 ml Soln B and 10 ml dithizone soln into 50 ml 0.02N HCl soln contg the Zn. Shake 1 min and let phases sep. Flush out stopcock and stem of separator with ca 1 ml CCl_4 ext; then collect remainder in test tube. Pipet 5 ml ext into 25 ml vol. flask, dil. to vol. with clear CCl_4, and det. T of dild soln with photoelec. colorimeter equipped with Sextant Green (Corning Glass Works No. 401) or equiv. filter, with max. T ca 525 nm. (*Caution:* Protect final ext from sunlight as much as possible and read within 2 hr.)

Det. Zn present in aliquot from curve relating T and concn, correct for Zn in blank, and calc. % Zn in sample.

3.046   Standard Curve
Obtain data for std curve by detg T values for each of series of solns contg known quantities Zn. To prep. these Zn solns, place 0, 5, 10, 15, 20, 25, 30, and 35 ml Zn working std soln in 100 ml vol. flasks. To each flask add 1 drop Me red and neutze with 1N NH_4OH; then add 4 ml 1N HCl and dil. to vol. Proceed exactly as for ash solns, beginning with first extn, and using 10 ml aliquots of each of the Zn solns. (The 10 ml aliquots contain 0, 5, 10, 15, 20, 25, 30, and 35 μg Zn, resp.) Construct std curve by plotting μg Zn against T on semilog paper.

Single Color Method (15)
3.047   Reagents
See 3.040–3.041 plus following:

(a) *Dilute dithizone soln.*—Dil. 1 vol. dithizone soln, 3.040(e), with 4 vols CCl_4.

(b) *Carbamate soln.*—Dissolve 1.25 g Na diethyldithiocarbamate in H_2O and dil. to 1 L. Store in refrigerator and prep. fresh after long periods of storage.

(c) *Dilute ammonium hydroxide.*—Dil. 20 ml 1N NH_4OH, 3.040(c), to 2 L.

3.048   Ashing
Weigh 2 g sample finely ground plant material into suitable crucible (well-glazed porcelain, Vycor, or Pt), include crucible for blank detn, and heat in muffle at 500–550° until ashing is complete. Cool, moisten ash with little H_2O, add 10 ml 1N HCl (more if necessary to ensure excess of acid), and heat on steam bath until all sol. material dissolves. Add few ml hot H_2O and filter thru quant. paper into 200 ml vol. flask. Wash paper with hot H_2O until washings are not acid to Me red. Add 2 drops Me red soln to filtrate, neutze with 1N NH_4OH, add exactly 3.2 ml 1N HCl, dil. to vol. with H_2O, and mix.

3.049   Formation of Zinc Dithizonate
(Removal of interferences and sepn of excess dithizone)

Pipet aliquot of ash soln contg ≤15 μg Zn into 125 ml amber glass separator. (25 ml aliquot is usually satisfactory.) If necessary to use different vol., add 0.4 ml 0.2N HCl for each 5 ml less, or 0.4 ml 0.2N NH_4OH for each 5 ml more, than 25 ml taken. If <25 ml of the soln is taken, add H_2O to 25 ml.

Add 10 ml dithizone reagent, 3.040(e), to aliquot in separator and shake vigorously 1 min. Let layers sep. and discard CCl_4 layer. Add 2 ml CCl_4 to aq. soln, let layers sep., and discard CCl_4. Repeat this rinsing once. Then add 5 ml CCl_4, shake vigorously 15 sec, let layers sep., and discard CCl_4. Rinse once more with 2 ml CCl_4 as above. Discard CCl_4 layer and let CCl_4 remaining on surface of soln in funnel evap. before proceeding.

Add 40 ml NH_4 citrate Soln A, **3.041**(1), 5 ml carbamate soln, **3.047**(b), and 25 ml dil. dithizone reagent, **3.047**(a). Add carbamate and dithizone reagents accurately from pipet or buret. Shake vigorously 1 min. Let layers sep. and draw off aq. layer thru fine tip glass tube connected to aspirator with rubber tubing. To remove excess dithizone from CCl_4 layer, add 50 ml $0.01N$ NH_4OH and shake vigorously 30 sec.

3.050 Determination

Dry funnel stem with pipestem cleaner and flush out with ca 2 ml of the Zn dithizonate soln. Collect adequate portion of remaining soln in 25 ml erlenmeyer, or other suitable container, and stopper tightly. (Amber glass containers are convenient, but colorless glassware will suffice if solns are kept in dark until T readings are made.)

Measure T of each soln against CCl_4 with photoelec. colorimeter equipped with light filter with max. T near 535 nm. (Sextant Green Corning Glass Works filter No. 4010 is suitable.) Correct for Zn in blank detns. Calc. quantity Zn present in soln from curve relating concn and T.

3.051 Standard Curve

Into 200 ml vol. flasks place 0, 2, 4, 6, 8, 10, 12, and 14 ml, resp., Zn working std soln. To each flask add 2 drops Me red soln, neutze with $1N$ NH_4OH, add 3.2 ml $1N$ HCl, and dil. to vol. with H_2O. Pipet 25 ml aliquots of each of these solns, contg 0, 2.5, 5, 7.5, 10, 12.5, 15, and 17.5 μg Zn, resp., into amber glass separators, and proceed as for ash solns, **3.049**, beginning with second par. Det. T of each soln and plot values against corresponding quantities Zn on semilog paper.

Molybdenum (16)—Official Final Action

3.052 Apparatus

Photoelectric colorimeter or spectrophotometer.—Capable of isolating band at ca 465 nm. (Cenco-Sheard-Sanford Photelometer equipped with Corning Glass Works filter No. 502 with max. T at 440–460 nm and 1 cm cells of 10 ml capacity is suitable.)

3.053 Reagents

(a) *Amyl alcohol.*—Reagent grade isoamyl alcohol (3-methyl-1-butanol), bp 128–132°.

(b) *Dilute hydrochloric acid.*—(1) *20% soln.*—Dil. concd HCl to ca 20% HCl. (2) *6N soln.*—Stdze to second decimal place.

(c) *Iron std soln.*—100 μg/ml. Dissolve 0.7022 g $Fe(NH_4)_2(SO_4)_2.6H_2O$ in H_2O, add 1 ml H_2SO_4, and dil. to 1 L.

(d) *Molybdenum std soln.*—100 μg/ml. Dissolve 0.0920 g $(NH_4)_6Mo_7O_{24}.4H_2O$ in H_2O and dil. to 500 ml. Prep. more dil. solns as required.

(e) *Potassium thiocyanate soln.*—20%. Dissolve 50 g KCNS in H_2O and dil. to 250 ml.

(f) *Sodium fluoride saturated soln.*—Add 200 ml H_2O to ca 10 g NaF. Stir until satd and filter.

(g) *Stannous chloride soln.*—(1) *20% soln.*—Weigh 10 g $SnCl_2.2H_2O$ into beaker, add 10 ml 20% HCl, (b)(1), and heat until completely dissolved. Cool, add granule of metallic Sn, dil. to 50 ml with H_2O, and store in g-s bottle. (2) *0.8% wash soln.*—Dil. 4 ml 20% soln to 100 ml with H_2O.

3.054 Determination

(*Caution: See* **46.019, 46.026,** *and* **46.028.**)

Weigh 1–5 g finely ground sample, contg ≤ 35 μg Mo, into 200 ml tall-form Pyrex beaker. To 1, 2, or 5 g samples add 10, 15, or 35 ml HNO_3, resp. Include 2 beakers for blanks. Cover beaker with cover glass, and let stand ca 15 min; then heat cautiously on steam bath or hot plate at ca 100°, avoiding frothing over top. If froth approaches cover glass, remove beaker from heat until frothing subsides; then continue heating. Digest, usually ca 2 hr, until most of solids disappear.

Cool to room temp. If contents should go to dryness, add few ml HNO_3. Add 6 ml 70–72% $HClO_4$, cover beaker, place on hot plate, and gradually raise temp. so that contents boil vigorously but do not bump. Continue heating until digestion is complete as indicated by liq. becoming colorless or pale yellow. If necessary, make repeated addns of HNO_3 and $HClO_4$ and continue to digest until C is completely oxidized.

After digestion is complete, place cover glass slightly to one side of top of beaker, or replace it with Speedyvap cover glass or similar device, and evap. just to dryness or until residue appears only slightly moist. Remove beaker from hot plate, and cool. Wash down sides of beaker and underside of cover glass with few ml H_2O, return to hot plate, and boil few min. Remove from hot plate, cool, and again rinse sides of beaker and cover glass with small amt H_2O.

Add 2 drops Me orange and neutze with NH_4OH. Add $6N$ HCl, dropwise with stirring, until soln is just acid; then add 8.2 ml excess to give final concn of ca 3% HCl. Add 2 ml satd NaF soln, and 1 ml Fe soln, if sample contains <100 μg Fe.

Transfer soln to 125 ml separator and dil. to 50 ml with H_2O. Add 4 ml 20% KCNS soln, mix thoroly, and add 1.5 ml 20% $SnCl_2$ soln. Mix again, and from buret or pipet, add exactly 15 ml isoamyl alcohol. Stopper separator and shake vigorously 1 min, let phases sep., and drain and discard aq. layer. Ext into alcohol without delay, since colored complex is somewhat unstable in aq. soln.

Add 25 ml freshly prepd 0.8% $SnCl_2$ wash soln, and shake gently 15 sec. Let phases sep., and drain and discard aq. layer. Transfer isoamyl alcohol soln to tube of suitable size, and centrf. 5 min at ca 2000 rpm to remove H_2O droplets. If alcohol layer does not appear to be optically clear, recentrf. Stopper tubes to prevent evapn, if T readings cannot be made immediately.

Compare unknown solns with isoamyl alcohol at ca 465 nm in a photoelec. colorimeter or spectrophtr, and make appropriate corrections in T readings for Mo in blanks. Obtain Mo concn from calibration curve relating T (or A) readings to concns of series of solns of known Mo content.

Prep. calibration curve for instrument used, as follows: Dil. 25 ml std Mo soln to 500 ml to obtain soln contg 5.0 μg/ml. Place aliquots of this soln contg 0, 5, 10, 15, 20, 25, 30, and 35 μg Mo, resp., into 200 ml tall-form beakers and carry them thru entire procedure, beginning with digestion with HNO_3 and $HClO_4$. Plot T (or A) readings against corresponding Mo concns.

NONMETALS
Arsenic—Official Final Action
3.055   *Preparation of Solution*
See **25.008.**

3.056   *Determination*
Proceed as in **25.009–25.010,** or take aliquot and det. as in **6.012,** beginning "add 3 ml H_2SO_4 ..."

Sulfur—Official Final Action
Sodium Peroxide Method (17)
(*Caution: See* **46.035.**)

3.057   *Preparation of Solution*
Place 1.5–2.5 g sample in ca 100 ml Ni crucible and add 5 g anhyd. Na_2CO_3. Mix thoroly, using Ni or Pt rod, and moisten with ca 2 ml H_2O. Add Na_2O_2, ca 0.5 g at time, mixing thoroly after each addn, and continue until mixt. becomes nearly dry and quite granular (ca 5 g Na_2O_2). Place crucible over S-free flame or elec. hot plate and heat carefully, stirring occasionally, until contents are fused. (If material ignites, detn is worthless.)

After fusion, remove crucible, let cool somewhat, and cover hardened mass with more Na_2O_2 to depth of ca 5 mm. Heat gradually and finally with full flame until fusion again takes place, rotating crucible occasionally to bring any particles adhering to sides into contact with oxidizing material. Continue heating 10 min after fusion is complete. Cool somewhat, place warm crucible and contents in 600 ml beaker, and carefully add ca 100 ml H_2O. After initial violent action ceases, wash material out of crucible, make slightly acid with HCl (adding small portions at time), transfer to 500 ml vol. flask, cool, dil. to vol., and filter.

3.058   *Determination*
Dil. aliquot of prepd soln to ca 200 ml with H_2O and add HCl until ca 0.5 ml free acid is present. Heat to boiling and add 10 ml 10% $BaCl_2$ soln dropwise with constant stirring. Continue boiling ca 5 min, and let stand 5 hr or longer in warm place. Decant thru ashless paper or ignited and weighed gooch. Add 15–20 ml boiling H_2O to ppt, transfer to filter, and wash with boiling H_2O until filtrate is Cl-free. Dry ppt and filter, ignite, and weigh as $BaSO_4$. Wt ppt $\times$ 0.1374 = S.

Magnesium Nitrate Method (18)
3.059   *Preparation of Solution*
Weigh 1 g sample into large porcelain crucible. Add 7.5 ml $Mg(NO_3)_2$ soln, **2.016,** so that all material comes in contact with soln. (It is important that enough $Mg(NO_3)_2$ soln be added to ensure complete oxidn and fixation of the S present. For larger samples and for samples with high S content, proportionally larger amts of this soln must be used.) Heat on elec. hot plate (180°) until no further action occurs. Transfer crucible while hot to muffle and let it remain at low heat ($\leq$500°) until charge is thoroly oxidized. (No black particles should remain. If necessary, break up charge and return to muffle.) Remove crucible from muffle and let cool. Add H_2O; then HCl in excess. Bring soln to boil, filter, and wash thoroly. If preferred, transfer soln to 250 ml vol. flask before filtering and dil. to vol. with H_2O.

3.060   *Determination*
Dil. entire filtered soln, **3.059,** to 200 ml, or take 100 ml aliquot of the measured vol., dil. to 200 ml, and proceed as in **3.058.**

Phosphorus (19)—Official Final Action
3.061   *Macro Method*
(**a**) *For samples exceedingly high in P and low in Ca and Mg (certain seeds, grains, etc.)*—Prep. soln as in **3.059,** or evap. filtrate and washings from S detn, **3.058,** to 50 ml, and proceed as in **2.031** or **8.027.**

(**b**) *For other samples.*—Take 50 ml aliquot of Soln A, **3.005,** and proceed as in **2.031** or **8.027.**

Micro Method (20)
3.062   *Reagents*
(**a**) *Phosphorus std soln.*—0.025 mg P/ml. Dissolve 0.4394 g pure dry KH_2PO_4 in H_2O and dil. to 1 L. Dil. 50 ml of this soln to 200 ml.

(**b**) *Ammonium molybdate soln.*—Dissolve 25 g NH_4 molybdate in 300 ml H_2O. Dil. 75 ml H_2SO_4 to 200 ml and add to NH_4 molybdate soln.

(**c**) *Hydroquinone soln.*—Dissolve 0.5 g hydroquinone in 100 ml H_2O, and add 1 drop H_2SO_4 to retard oxidn.

(**d**) *Sodium sulfite soln.*—Dissolve 200 g Na_2SO_3 in H_2O, dil. to 1 L, and filter. Either keep this soln well stoppered or prep. fresh each time.

3.063   *Preparation of Solution*
To 1 or 2 g sample in small porcelain crucible add 1 ml $Mg(NO_3)_2$ soln, **2.016,** and place on steam bath.

After few min cautiously add few drops HCl, taking care that gas evolution does not push portions of sample over edge of crucible. Make 2 or 3 further addns of few drops HCl while sample is on bath so that as it approaches dryness it tends to char. If contents become too viscous for further drying on bath, complete drying on hot plate. Cover crucible, transfer to cold muffle, and ignite 6 hr at 500°, or until even gray ash is obtained. (If necessary, cool crucible, dissolve ash in little H_2O or alc.-glycerol, evap. to dryness, and return uncovered to muffle 4–5 hr longer.) Cool, take up with HCl (1 + 4), and transfer to 100 ml beaker. Add 5 ml HCl and evap. to dryness on steam bath to dehydrate SiO_2. Moisten residue with 2 ml HCl, add ca 50 ml H_2O, and heat few min on bath. Transfer to 100 ml vol. flask, cool immediately, dil. to vol., mix, and filter, discarding first portion of filtrate.

3.064 *Determination*

To 5 ml aliquot filtrate in 10 ml vol. flask add 1 ml NH_4 molybdate soln, rotate flask to mix, and let stand few sec. Add 1 ml hydroquinone soln, again rotate flask, and add 1 ml Na_2SO_3 soln. (Last 3 addns may be made with Mohr pipet.) Dil. to vol. with H_2O, stopper flask with thumb or forefinger, and shake to mix thoroly. Let stand 30 min, and compare immediately in colorimeter with 2 ml std KH_2PO_4 soln treated simultaneously and identically. (With either unknown or std set at 25.0 mm, readings within 10 mm, *i.e.*, range of 20 mm, are accurate. If concn of P in unknown set is outside this range, it may be brought nearer to that of std by dilg filtrate, ashing smaller or larger sample, making filtrate to smaller or larger vol., or using smaller aliquot. Photoelec. colorimeter equipped with filter with max. T at 625–675 nm may be used instead of visual instrument.) Report as % P.

Gravimetric Quinoline Molybdate Method (21)—Official First Action

3.065 *Preparation of Solution*

Weigh accurately ca 2 g plant sample in porcelain dish, and add 7.5 ml $Mg(NO_3)_2$ soln, **2.016.** Dry in oven 2 hr at 110–115° (or until dry). Ignite carefully over Fisher burner, or equiv., until bubbling and smoking cease. Complete ashing in furnace 4 hr at 550–600°. Dissolve ash in few ml HCl (2 + 1) and evap. to dryness on steam bath. Take up residue in 10–15 ml HCl (1 + 9) and filter thru coarse paper into 200 ml vol. flask. Wash paper thoroly with H_2O and let filtrate cool to room temp. Dil. to vol. with H_2O.

3.066 *Determination*

Pipet 40 ml aliquot into 300 or 500 ml erlenmeyer and proceed as in **2.025.**

Chlorine (22)—Official Final Action

(If bromides or iodides are present in significant amts, correct results accordingly.)

3.067 *Preparation of Solution*

First verify complete retention of Cl in each kind of material by trial, since losses can occur, especially with samples high in carbohydrates, if insufficient Na_2CO_3 is present during ignition, or in any case if excessive temp. is used.

Moisten 5 g sample in Pt dish with 20 ml 5% Na_2CO_3 soln, evap. to dryness, and ignite as thoroly as possible at ≤500°. Ext with hot H_2O, filter, and wash. Return residue to Pt dish and ignite to ash; dissolve in HNO_3 (1 + 4), filter, wash thoroly, and add this soln to H_2O ext.

3.068 *Gravimetric Method*

To prepd soln, **3.067,** add 10% $AgNO_3$ soln, avoiding more than slight excess. Heat to boiling, protect from light, and let stand until ppt coagulates. Filter on weighed gooch, previously heated to 140–150°, and wash with hot H_2O, testing filtrate to prove excess of $AgNO_3$. Dry AgCl at 140–150°, cool, and weigh. Report as % Cl.

Volumetric Method I (23)

(Since limit of accuracy of this titrn is considered to be ±0.2 mg Cl, accuracy of 1.0% requires samples contg ≥20 mg.)

3.069 *Reagents*

(a) *Silver nitrate std soln.*—1 ml = 0.00355 g Cl. Prep. soln slightly stronger than $0.1N$, stdze as in **45.032,** and adjust to exactly $0.1N$.

(b) *Ammonium or potassium thiocyanate std soln.*—$0.1N$. Prep. soln slightly stronger than $0.1N$, stdze as in **45.031(b),** and adjust to exactly $0.1N$.

(c) *Ferric indicator.*—Satd soln of $FeNH_4(SO_4)_2$ $.12H_2O$.

(d) *Nitric acid.*—Free from lower oxides of N by dilg usual pure acid with ca ¼ vol. H_2O, and boiling until perfectly colorless.

3.070 *Determination*

To prepd soln, **3.067,** add known vol. std $AgNO_3$ soln in slight excess. Stir well, filter, and wash AgCl ppt thoroly. To combined filtrate and washings add 5 ml ferric indicator and few ml HNO_3, and titr. excess Ag with thiocyanate std soln to permanent light brown. From ml $AgNO_3$ used, calc. quantity of Cl.

Volumetric Method II (24)

3.071 *Reagents*

(a) *Potassium iodide std soln.*—1 ml = 1 mg Cl. Weigh 4.6824 g pure (ACS) KI, dried to constant wt at 105–150°, dissolve in H_2O, and dil. to 1 L.

(b) *Silver nitrate stock soln.*—Approx. $0.3N$. 1 ml = ca 10 mg Cl. Dissolve 48 g $AgNO_3$ in H_2O, filter, and dil. to 1 L.

(c) *Silver nitrate std soln.*—Dil. 100 ml reagent (b) to ca 900 ml and adjust by stdzg against reagent (a) so that 1 ml = 1 mg Cl.

(d) *Chloride-free starch indicator.*—For each 100 ml final soln take 2.5 g sol. starch and make to paste with cold H_2O. Stir out lumps, add 25–50 ml more cold H_2O, and stir or shake 5 min. Centrf., decant, and discard liq. Repeat extn 3 times and finally transfer residue to flask contg proper amt of boiling H_2O. Stir again, heat to boil, cover with small beaker, and cool under tap, shaking occasionally.

(e) *Dilute sulfuric acid.*—Add 35 ml H_2SO_4 to each 1 L H_2O, boil 5–10 min, and cool to room temp.

(f) *Iodine indicator.*—To ca 20 g I in 500 ml g-s bottle add 400 ml dil. H_2SO_4, (e), and shake 10 min. Decant and discard first soln, since it may contain iodides. Repeat process and store soln in small g-s bottles.

(g) *Potassium permanganate soln.*—Dissolve 60 g $KMnO_4$ in 400 ml warm H_2O (ca 50°) and dil. to 1 L.

(h) *Potassium sulfate-copper sulfate mixture.*—Thoroly mix 16 parts K_2SO_4 and 1 part $CuSO_4$.$5H_2O$.

(i) *Wash soln.*—Mix 980 ml H_2O and 20 ml HNO_3.

3.072   *Determination*
(*Caution: See* 46.019, 46.026, *and* 46.080.)

Weigh sample contg 10–40 mg Cl into beaker. (If >4 g is taken, use proportionately more HNO_3 and $KMnO_4$ soln.) Add 10 ml $0.3N$ $AgNO_3$ and stir until sample is thoroly soaked with soln, adding little H_2O or warming if necessary. Add 25 ml HNO_3, stir, add 5 ml $KMnO_4$ soln, and stir until frothing stops. Place mixt. in H_2O bath or on hot plate and keep just below boiling. Stir, and wash down sides of beaker at intervals with min. amt of H_2O. After 20 min, or when reaction stops, add addnl $KMnO_4$ soln, little at time, until color begins to fade slowly. Dil. to ca 125 ml with boiling H_2O and heat 10 min longer. (Beaker may stand in bath or on hot plate until ready to filter.)

Filter while hot thru Whatman No. 5, or equiv. paper, with suction as follows: Place disk of 30-mesh stainless steel wire gauze or No. 40 filter cloth in bottom of 3″ Hirsch funnel. Fold 9 cm paper over bottom of No. 11 rubber stopper, shaping it to funnel by making 9–10 folds up side of stopper. Place paper in funnel and apply strong suction. Wet paper and keep wet while fitting into funnel so as to avoid double thicknesses of paper. Wash paper thoroly, first with H_2O and then with wash soln. Discard washings and rinse out flask. Decant thru filter and transfer ppt and sample residue to filter. If filtrate is not turbid, or if it is only slightly opalescent, wash ppt thoroly, applying wash soln very gently, but keeping strong suction on filter. If combined filtrate and washings are clear, test for Ag. If turbid, re-heat and pass thru filter, repeating until clear, and finally

wash as above. If filtrate does not give definite test for Ag, repeat detn on smaller sample.

Place paper and contents in Kjeldahl flask and add such amts of K_2SO_4-$CuSO_4$ mixt. and H_2SO_4 as would be appropriate for protein detn on same kind and amt of sample, and digest similarly. (For 2 g grass, 8 g sulfate mixt. and 20 ml acid are enough.) When digest is cool, add 175 ml H_2O, boil 5–10 min, and cool to room temp. Titr. the Ag_2SO_4 in Kjeldahl flask with std KI, using 5 ml starch indicator and 30 ml I indicator. (Add latter just before titrn.) Rinse neck of flask after each addn of KI when near end point and titr. until soln stays blue after shaking. If <30 mg Cl is present, add starch and I solns at beginning. If larger but unknown amt is present, add 2 ml starch and 10 ml I indicator at beginning and titr. until approach of end point is seen. Shake vigorously to coagulate ppt, add rest of starch and I solns, and proceed to end point. If known large amt is present, titr. to within 2 ml of end point, shake as above, add indicator reagents, and continue titrn. If end point is overrun, add 5 ml std $AgNO_3$ soln and titr. again.

Blank detns are not necessary after testing reagents. If blank made by using pure sugar as sample is >0.05 mg, examine filter paper, distd H_2O, and various reagents for Cl.

3.073 Selenium (25)—Official Final Action
(Applicable to materials contg >2 ppm Se)
(*Caution: See* 46.011, 46.019, 46.026, 46.030,
46.047, *and* 46.081.)

Grind air-dried sample and carefully prep. uniform subsample. Prep. mixt. of 50 ml H_2SO_4 and 100 ml HNO_3 in 600 ml beaker. Add 5 g powd sample to acid mixt. slowly, with stirring, restricting temp. of mixt. to ≤80°. When first vigorous reaction is over, warm gently with occasional stirring until evolution of NO_2 fumes ceases. Warm at ≤120° until liq. darkens slightly. Transfer liq. to distg flask equipped with short condenser, thistle safety tube, and ⦛ connections, Fig. 3:2. Add 100 ml *HBr contg 2 ml Br*. Warm gently 15 min and distill into 100 ml erlenmeyer contg 5 ml H_2O. Have outlet of distg tube submerged. If, on gentle warming, drop of Br does not collect beneath H_2O in receiver, add 2 ml Br to distg flask thru thistle tube and repeat gentle warming. Distill 60 ml into receiver. To distillate add 25 ml H_2O and cool in ice-H_2O. Pass slow stream of SO_2 into distillate until Br is removed. Add 0.25 g $NH_2OH.HCl$, warm on steam bath 15 min at 80°, and let stand overnight at room temp. Se appears at bottom of erlenmeyer as rose-pink ppt. Modify further treatment according to amt of ppt.

(a) *Precipitate not greater than 0.5 mg.*—Filter Se ppt thru small asbestos gooch with suction. If small amt of oily material accompanies pptd Se, wash pad with 10 ml alcohol and then with 10 ml H_2O. Redissolve pptd Se from pad with 10 ml 48% HBr which has been made bright red by addn of Br. Collect filtrate by suction in 25 ml vol. flask and wash pad

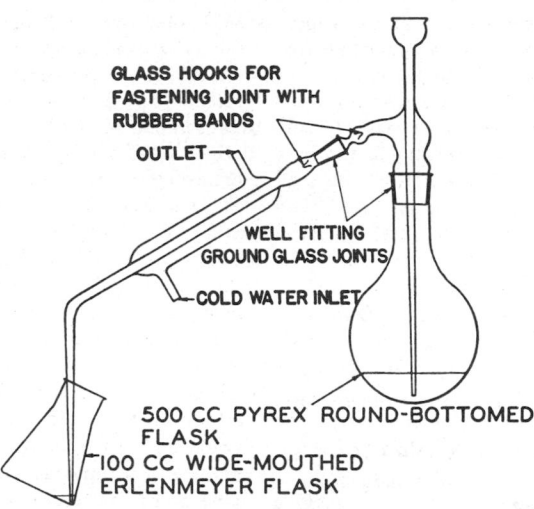

FIG. 3:2—Apparatus for distilling selenium

with 2 portions H_2O. Decolorize filtered soln with SO_2 and add 1 ml soln contg *100 mg $NH_2OH.HCl$ and 25 mg gum arabic/ml*. Dil. to vol. with H_2O. Transfer flask to steam bath and heat 30 min at 80°; cool to room temp., shake vigorously, and transfer contents to 50 ml Nessler tube.

Before final pptn of Se in vol. flask, prep. series of stds in 25 ml vol. flasks by addn of 0.01, 0.02, 0.05, 0.1, 0.2, 0.5, and 0.7 mg Se as Na_2SeO_4. Ppt these stds after addn of HBr, Br, H_2O, $NH_2OH.HCl$, and gum arabic, and treat precisely as sample is treated. Compare sample with std in any suitable color comparator and det. quantity of Se. Express results as ppm air-dried sample.

(b) *Precipitate below 1 ppm (established by preceding determination) and for greater precision.*—Distill 10 g sample with HBr, as above, after preliminary acid treatment. When distn is complete, replace sample in distn flask with second acid-digested 10 g sample; add distillate from first distn, 50 ml addnl HBr, 2–4 ml Br, and 22 ml H_2SO_4. Let stand and repeat distn as often as necessary to integrate minute amt of Se until amt adequate for measurement is obtained.

(c) *Initial precipitate in excess of 0.5 mg.*—Redissolve washed ppt in HBr, colored with Br as in (a). Transfer dissolved material to 100 ml beaker and dil. with 20% HBr to 50 ml. Ppt with SO_2 and add 0.25 g $NH_2OH.HCl$. Warm on steam bath 15 min, and let stand overnight at room temp. Filter on weighed gooch, dry 4 hr at 85°, and weigh. (Use balance sensitive to at least 0.05 mg.)

Fluorometric Method (26)—
Official First Action

(*Caution: See* 46.008, 46.019, 46.026, and 46.028.)

3.074 *Apparatus*

(a) *Micro-Kjeldahl flasks.*—30 ml Pyrex, ca 170 mm total length with ℣ 12/18 outer joint at mouth.

(b) *Air condensers.*—10 × 140 mm Pyrex tubes with ℣ 12/18 inner joint.

(c) *Micro-Kjeldahl digestion unit with glass fume duct.*—Fit rack to hold flasks and attached air condensers in nearly upright position during early stages of digestion. Use in fume hood.

(d) *Fluorometer.*—Capable of illuminating sample at 369 nm and measuring fluoresced light at 525 nm. Turner Associates, 2524 Pulgas Ave, Palo Alto, CA 94303, Model 110 fluorometer equipped with GE F4T4 lamp, No. 7–60 primary filter, and No. 58 secondary filter is satisfactory.

3.075 *Reagents*

Use deionized H_2O distd in glass for prepg solns and dilns.

(a) *Nitric acid.*—Redistd in glass.

(b) *Hydroxylamine-ethylenediaminetetraacetic acid soln.*—Add ca 20 ml H_2O to 1.9 g EDTA (acid form). Slowly add ca $5N$ NH_4OH with stirring until EDTA just dissolves. Some excess NH_4OH is not harmful. Dissolve 6 g $NH_2OH.HCl$ in 100 ml H_2O. Combine solns and dil. to 250 ml with H_2O.

(c) *Cresol red indicator.*—Dissolve 0.1 g cresol red in 10 ml H_2O and 1 drop 50% NaOH soln. Dil. to 50 ml with H_2O.

(d) *Selenium std soln.*—0.3 µg Se/ml. Add 10 ml HNO_3 to 30.0 mg Se (purity ≥99%) and warm to dissolve. Dil. to 100 ml with H_2O, mix well, and transfer exactly 1 ml to micro Kjeldahl flask. Add 2 ml 70% $HClO_4$ and 1 glass bead. Boil gently to $HClO_4$ fumes and cool. Add 1 ml H_2O and 1 ml HCl $(1 + 4)$; heat 30 min in boiling H_2O bath. Transfer to 1 L vol. flask and dil. to vol. with ca $1N$ HCl. Store in all-glass container. Soln is stable several months at room temp.

(e) *2,3-Diaminonaphthalene (DAN) soln.*—Prep. soln in semidarkened room or in room with only yellow light at time of detn. Protect from light and prep. fresh for each set of detns. Add 50 ml ca 0.1N HCl to 0.05 g DAN (available from K&K Laboratories, Inc.). Place in 50° H_2O bath in dark 15 min. Cool to ca room temp. and ext twice with 10 ml decalin, shaking vigorously each time and discarding decalin. Filter thru paper satd with H_2O. For >8 detns, prep. larger quantity.

(f) *Decalin.*—Eastman Kodak No. 1905 decahydronaphthalene, or equiv.

3.076 *Preparation of Samples*

Grind air-dried samples to pass No. 18 or finer sieve. Cut fresh or wet samples finely with scissors or knife, or grind in food chopper to assure representative sample.

Some plants (e.g., *Astragalus bisulcatus, A. racemosus, Stanleya bipinnata,* and *Oonopsis condensata*) contain Se in volatile form that is lost during drying. Analyze these plants without drying. With usual agricultural crops, this is not a problem if drying is performed at 60–70°.

3.077 *Preparation of Fluorometric Blanks and Standard*

(a) *Blank.*—Place 1 ml H_2O in micro Kjeldahl flask. (For samples contg <0.1 ppm, carry 10 ml HNO_3 as blank thru entire detn.)

(b) *Std.*—Place 1.0 ml std Se soln in micro Kjeldahl flask.

Add 2 ml 70% $HClO_4$ to each flask and continue as in detn, beginning "Mix contents of flasks ..."

3.078 *Determination*

(a) *Samples containing <4 ppm selenium.*— Weigh ≤1 g sample (air-dried wt basis) contg ≤0.4 μg Se into micro Kjeldahl flask. Add 1 glass bead previously cleaned with HNO_3. Add 10 ml HNO_3 and let stand at room temp. ≥4 hr. (Use 5 ml HNO_3 for samples <0.5 g.) Affix air condenser and place flask in nearly upright position on micro Kjeldahl digestion unit. Heat ca 15 min at low flame and then increase heating until HNO_3 condenses in lower part of air condenser. Heat 10 min longer, turn off burner, and let cool 5 min. Wash down sides of flask with 2 ml 70% $HClO_4$ thru air condenser. Swirl flask and continue refluxing 15 min. Remove air condenser and continue heating, drawing off fumes in fume duct, until $HClO_4$ fumes appear and then 15 min longer. Cool, add 1 ml H_2O, and again heat to $HClO_4$ fumes and 1–2 min longer. Cool and add 1 ml H_2O.

Mix contents of flasks and add 1 ml HCl (1 + 4) to each. Place in boiling H_2O bath 30 min. Cool to ca room temp.

To each flask add 5 ml NH_2OH-EDTA soln and 2 drops cresol red indicator. Neutze to yellow with ca 5N NH_4OH and add HCl (1 + 4) to orange-pink. *From this point, perform all manipulations in semidarkened room or room with yellow light only.* Prep.

DAN soln, add 5 ml to each flask, and dil. to neck with ca 0.1N HCl. Mix and place in 50° H_2O bath in dark 25 min.

Remove flasks from H_2O bath and cool to ca room temp. in pan of H_2O. Pour solns into 125 ml separators with Teflon stopcocks and contg 10.0 ml decalin. Shake vigorously ≥30 sec, let stand ca 1 min, and drain and discard lower layer. Wash decalin twice by shaking vigorously ≥15 sec with 25 ml ca 0.1N HCl. (VirTis, Rt 208, Gardiner, NY 12525, Extractomatic shaker with 100 ml separators may be substituted. When used, shake ext 5 min and wash 1 min periods.) Transfer decalin layer into 12 ml centrifuge tubes and centrf. 2 min at moderate speed. Pour decalin soln into fluorometer tubes, zero fluorometer against decalin, and read all tubes at 525 nm within 5 min. Correct std and unknown readings for blank. Ppm Se = 0.3 × sample reading/std reading × g sample.

(b) *Samples containing >4 ppm selenium.*— Proceed as in (a) thru "Place in boiling H_2O bath 30 min. Cool to ca room temp." Dil. digest to adequate vol. and take aliquot contg ca 0.3 μg Se for detn. Alternatively, digest sample in 10 vols HNO_3 2 hr on steam bath. Dil. to definite vol., and carry appropriate aliquot thru detn. Latter method is especially applicable when proper sampling requires large sample. Do not dil. decalin soln contg piazselenol, as this introduces errors.

Boron (27)—Official Final Action
Quinalizarin Method

3.079 *Reagents*

(a) *Dilute sulfuric acid.*—0.36N. Dil. 10 ml H_2SO_4 to 1 L.

(b) *Calcium hydroxide saturated soln.*—Filter before use.

(c) *Quinalizarin soln.*—Dissolve 45 mg quinalizarin in 1 L 95–96% H_2SO_4.

(d) *Boron std soln.*—0.5 mg B/ml. Dissolve 2.860 g H_3BO_3 and dil. to 1 L with H_2O. Prep. working stds by further diln with H_2O.

3.080 *Determination*

Place 1.00–2.00 g dry, ground plant material in Pt or SiO_2 dish. Add 5 ml satd $Ca(OH)_2$ soln and dry at 105°. Carefully drive off volatile material over burner, ash in muffle 1 hr at 600°, and cool. Add exactly 10 or 15 ml 0.36N H_2SO_4, break up ash with glass rod, stir gently, and filter. Transfer 2 ml filtrate to colorimeter tube, add an exact quantity (e.g., 15 ml) quinalizarin reagent, stopper tube, and mix by swirling gently. Let tube stand at room temp. 24 hr (or until both unknowns and stds have cooled to same temp). Shake tube again immediately before reading in photoelec. colorimeter (620 nm filter).

Adjust colorimeter to 100% T with blank soln prepd as above but using 2 ml H_2O in place of sample soln. Prep. std curve with series of stds contg 0.5 to 10 μg B/ml.

OTHER CONSTITUENTS
Sugars (28)—Official Final Action

3.081 *Preparation of Solution*

(a) *General method.*—Prep. fresh sample as in **3.002(b)**. Pour alc. soln thru filter paper or extn thimble, catching filtrate in vol. flask. Transfer insol. material to beaker, cover with 80% alcohol, warm on steam bath 1 hr, let cool, and again pour alc. soln thru same filter. If second filtrate is highly colored, repeat extn. Transfer residue to filter, let drain, and dry. Grind residue so that all particles will pass thru 1 mm sieve, transfer to extn thimble, and ext 12 hr in Soxhlet app. with 80% alcohol. Dry residue and save for starch detn. Combine alc. filtrates and dil. to vol. at definite temp. with 80% alcohol.

For dried materials, grind samples finely, and mix well. Weigh sample into beaker, and continue as above, beginning "cover with 80% alcohol ..."

(b) *Applicable when starch is not to be determined.*—Prep. fresh sample as in **3.002(b)**, but boil on steam bath 1 hr. Decant soln into vol. flask, and comminute solids in high-speed blender with 80% alcohol. Boil blended material on steam bath 0.5 hr, cool, transfer to vol. flask, dil. to mark with 80% alcohol at room temp., filter, and take aliquot for analysis.

Grind dry material to pass No. 20 sieve or finer, transfer weighed sample to vol. flask, and add 80% alcohol and enough CaCO₃ to neutze any acidity. Boil 1 hr on steam bath, cool, adjust vol. at room temp. with 80% alcohol, filter, and take aliquot for analysis.

3.082 *Clarification with Lead*

Place aliquot alc. ext in beaker on steam bath and evap. off alcohol. Avoid evapn to dryness by adding H_2O if necessary. When odor of alcohol disappears, add ca 100 ml H_2O and heat to 80° to soften gummy ppts and break up insol. masses. Cool to room temp. and proceed as in (a) or (b):

(a) Transfer soln to vol. flask, rinse beaker thoroly with H_2O, and add rinsings to flask. Add enough satd neut. $Pb(OAc)_2$ soln to produce flocculent ppt, shake thoroly, and let stand 15 min. Test supernatant with few drops of the $Pb(OAc)_2$ soln. If more ppt forms, shake and let stand again; if no further ppt forms, dil. to vol. with H_2O, mix thoroly, and filter thru dry paper. Add enough solid Na oxalate to filtrate to ppt all the Pb, and refilter thru dry paper. Test filtrate for presence of Pb with little solid Na oxalate.

(b) Add twice min. amt of satd neut. $Pb(OAc)_2$ soln required to cause complete pptn, as found by testing portion of supernatant with few drops dil. Na oxalate soln. Let mixt. stand only few min; then filter into beaker contg estd excess of Na oxalate crystals. Let Pb ppt drain on filter and wash with cold H_2O until filtrate no longer gives ppt in oxalate soln. Assure excess of oxalate by testing with 1 drop $Pb(OAc)_2$. Filter and wash pptd Pb oxalate, catching filtrate and washings in vol. flask. Dil. to vol. with H_2O and mix.

3.083 *Clarification with Ion-Exchange Resins (29)*

Place aliquot alc. ext, **3.081**, in beaker and heat on steam bath to evap. alcohol. Avoid evapn to dryness by adding H_2O. When odor of alcohol disappears, add ca 15–25 ml H_2O and heat to 80° to soften gummy ppts and break up insol. masses. Cool to room temp. Prep. thin mat of Celite on filter paper in buchner or on fritted glass filter and wash until H_2O comes thru clear. Filter sample thru Celite mat, wash mat with H_2O, dil. filtrate and washings to appropriate vol. in vol. flask, and mix well.

Place 50.0 ml aliquot in 250 ml erlenmeyer; add 2 g *Amberlite IR-120(H)* analytical grade cation and 3 g *Duolite A-4(OH)* anion ion exchange resins. Let stand 2 hr with occasional swirling. Take 5 ml aliquot de-ionized soln and det. reducing sugars as glucose as in **31.055**.

Glucose

3.084 *Micro Method—Official Final Action—See 31.055*

Fructose (30)—Official Final Action

3.085 *Reagents*

(a) *Glucose oxidase preparation.*—Add slowly, stirring constantly, 100 ml H_2O to 5 g glucose oxidase prepn ("Dee-O," Miles Laboratories, Inc., Elkhart, IN 46514). Stir ca 1 min and centrf. or filter to obtain clear soln. Add ca 1 ml CHCl₃ and refrigerate. Soln is stable at least 1 month.

(b) *McIlvaine's citrate-phosphate buffer.*—Dissolve 214.902 g $Na_2HPO_4.12H_2O$ and 42.020 g citric acid in H_2O and dil. to 1 L.

3.086 *Determination*

To suitable aliquot add ¼ its vol. of buffer to give pH ca 5.8. Add 30% as much glucose oxidase prepn as estd glucose content (for 500 mg glucose add 150 mg glucose oxidase, *i.e.*, 3 ml soln), and few drops 30% H_2O_2 (omit if Somogyi method is to be used in detn). Let stand overnight at room temp.

Det. fructose by Somogyi micro method, **31.055**, or by Munson-Walker method, **31.039–31.040**, using table below. Check equivs in range of interest, using pure fructose as std, and make appropriate corrections.

Abbreviated Munson and Walker Table for Calculating Fructose

(*From Official and Tentative Methods of Analysis, AOAC, 5th Ed., 1940*)

Cuprous Oxide mg	Fructose mg	Cuprous Oxide mg	Fructose mg
10	4.5	300	148.6
50	23.5	350	174.9
100	47.7	400	201.8
150	72.2	450	229.2
200	97.2	490	253.9
250	122.7	—	—

Reducing Sugars—Official Final Action

3.087 *Munson-Walker General Method—*
See 31.039

3.088 *Quisumbing-Thomas Method—*
See 31.049

Sucrose—Official Final Action

3.089 *Hydrochloric Acid Inversion*

Using aliquot of cleared soln, **3.082**, proceed as in **7.059**.

3.090 *Invertase Inversion*

(1) *For plants giving hydrolysis end point within 2 hours.*—Pipet aliquot of cleared soln, **3.082**, into 400 ml Pyrex beaker and make slightly acid to Me red with HOAc. Add 3 drops 1% soln of *Wallerstein Co. red label invertase.* Let mixt. stand at room temp. 2 hr. Add reagents as in **31.049** or **31.036**, and det. reducing power. Calc. results as invert sugar. Deduct reducing power of original soln, also expressed as invert sugar, and multiply difference by 0.95.

(2) *For plants giving slower hydrolysis end point.*—Place aliquot of soln, **3.082**, in small vol. flask. Make slightly acid to Me red with HOAc. Add 3 drops 1% soln of *Wallerstein Co. red label invertase* and few drops toluene. Stopper flask and let stand overnight or longer at room temp. Dil. to vol. with H_2O and use aliquot for reducing power as above. Results may include some other carbohydrates slowly hydrolyzed by invertase.

3.091 **Ether Extract—Official Final Action—**
See 7.048

3.092 **Crude Fiber—Official Final Action—**
See 7.053–7.057

3.093 **Total Nitrogen—Official Final Action—**
See 2.052

3.094 **Nitrogen (Nitrate-Free Samples)—**
Official Final Action—See 2.051

Starch (31)—Official Final Action

3.095   *Reagents*

(a) *Iodine-potassium iodide soln.*—Grind 7.5 g I and 7.5 g KI with 150 ml H_2O, dil. to 250 ml, and filter.

(b) *Alcoholic sodium chloride soln.*—Mix 350 ml alcohol, 80 ml H_2O, and 50 ml 20% NaCl soln, and dil. to 500 ml with H_2O.

(c) *Alcoholic sodium hydroxide soln.*—0.25N. Mix 350 ml alcohol, 100 ml H_2O, and 25 ml 5N NaOH, and dil. to 500 ml with H_2O.

(d) *Dilute hydrochloric acid.*—0.7N. Dil. 60 ml HCl to 1 L with H_2O.

(e) *Somogyi phosphate sugar reagent.*—Dissolve 56 g anhyd. Na_2HPO_4 and 80 g Rochelle salt in ca 1 L H_2O, and add 200 ml 1.00N NaOH. Then slowly add, with stirring, 160 ml 10% $CuSO_4.5H_2O$ soln. Dissolve 360 g anhyd. Na_2SO_4 in this soln, transfer to 2 L vol. flask, and add exactly 200 ml 0.1N KIO_3 soln (3.5760 g/L). Dil. to vol., mix well, let stand several days, and filter thru dry paper into dry flask, discarding first 50 ml filtrate. Store reagent at 20–25°. It is 0.01N with respect to KIO_3; 5.00 ml is equiv. to 10 ml 0.005N $Na_2S_2O_3$.

Det. glucose factor of reagent as follows: Accurately weigh 150 mg NBS glucose into 1 L vol. flask, dissolve in H_2O, dil. to vol., and mix well. Transfer 5 ml aliquot to 25 × 200 mm Pyrex test tube, add exactly 5 ml Somogyi reagent, stopper with size 00 crucible, and heat (together with several blanks contg 5 ml H_2O and 5 ml reagent) exactly 15 min in boiling H_2O bath. Titr. as in **3.096**. From difference between blank and std titrns, calc. mg glucose equiv. to 1 ml exactly 0.005N $Na_2S_2O_3$. Effective range for detn is 0.05–1.0 mg glucose in 5 ml aliquot.

(f) *Sodium thiosulfate std soln.*—0.005N. Dissolve 2.73 g $Na_2S_2O_3.5H_2O$ in H_2O and dil. to 2 L. Stdze daily as follows: Add 1 ml KI soln, (g), and 3 ml 1.5N H_2SO_4 to 5 ml Somogyi sugar reagent. Let stand 5 min, and titr. with $Na_2S_2O_3$ soln, adding starch indicator, **36.062(b)**, just before end point.

(g) *Potassium iodide soln.*—2.5%. Stabilize with little Na_2CO_3.

3.096   *Determination*

Select sample as in **3.001**, remove all foreign matter, dry, and grind to pass No. 80 sieve. Weigh accurately 0.1–1.0 g powd sample contg ca 20 mg starch into Pyrex test tube, 25 × 150 mm. Add ca 200 mg fine sand and 5 ml H_2O, and mix well with stirring rod to wet sample. Heat tube in boiling H_2O bath 15 min to gelatinize starch. Cool to room temp., and place in 22–25° bath. Add 5 ml 60% $HClO_4$ rapidly with constant agitation. Grind tissue against lower wall of tube with stirring rod for ca min at time. Repeat grinding frequently during 30 min; then without delay transfer quant. to 100 ml vol. flask with H_2O. Add 3 ml 5% uranyl acetate soln to ppt protein, dil. to vol. with H_2O, mix well, and centrf. portion of mixt. Pipet 10 ml clear supernatant into 25 × 150 mm test tube. Add ca 100 mg Celite, 5 ml 20% NaCl soln, and 2 ml I-KI reagent, and mix well. Let stand overnight, centrf., and decant supernatant.

Wash. starch-I ppt by suspending it in 5 ml alc. NaCl soln, centrf., and decant supernatant. Add 2 ml alc. NaOH soln to packed ppt. Gently shake and tap tube until ppt is no longer blue. (Do not use stirring rod; allow ample time for complex to decompose.) Wash walls of tube with 5 ml alc. NaCl soln, centrf. liberated starch, and wash with 5 ml alc. NaCl soln as before. Add 2 ml 0.7N HCl to ppt. Stopper tube loosely with size 00 crucible, and heat

2.5 hr in boiling H_2O bath. (Bath should have cover with holes to accommodate tubes; holes not occupied by tubes must be covered.) Cool, and transfer quant. to 25 ml vol. flask. Add drop phenol red, **45.009,** and neutze with $1N$ NaOH. Discharge color with *0.1N oxalic acid*, dil. to vol., and mix well. Transfer 5 ml aliquot to 25×200 ml Pyrex test tube, add exactly 5 ml Somogyi reagent, and stopper tube with size 00 crucible. Heat together with several blanks contg 5 ml H_2O and 5 ml Somogyi reagent in vigorously boiling H_2O bath exactly 15 min. Remove tube from bath and cool to 25–30°. Add 1 ml 2.5% KI soln down wall of tube without agitation and then add 3 ml $1.5N$ H_2SO_4 rapidly with agitation. After all Cu_2O dissolves, titr. soln with $0.005N$ $Na_2S_2O_3$, adding starch indicator, **36.062(b),** just before end point is reached. Treat blank solns similarly.

% starch = [50(ml blank − ml sample)
$\qquad \times$ 0.90/mg sample] $\times$ (N/0.005)
$\qquad \times$ G $\times$ 100

where $50 = $ diln factor, $0.90 = $ factor glucose to starch, $N = $ actual normality $Na_2S_2O_3$ soln, and $G = $ mg glucose equiv. to 1 ml $0.005N$ $Na_2S_2O_3$.

Lignin (*32*)—Official Final Action
Direct Method
3.097 *Preparation of Sample*

Grind sample in mill to pass No. 80 sieve and dry at 105°. Ext weighed sample (5–10 g) 30 hr in Soxhlet app. with alcohol-benzene soln (32 parts alcohol and 68 parts benzene by wt). Dry material in oven to free it from solvs and place in flask of suitable size. Add 150 ml H_2O/g sample, and reflux 3 hr. Filter mixt. while still hot, preferably thru weighed fritted glass crucible, and transfer extd material to flask. Add 1% HCl (111 g concd HCl + 3890 ml H_2O) in proportion of 150 ml acid soln/g plant material, and reflux 3 hr. Filter mixt. while still hot thru fritted glass crucible previously used, wash with H_2O until acid-free, dry at 105°, and weigh. Calc. % total loss due to successive extn with alcohol-benzene soln, hot H_2O, and 1% HCl. (With samples not especially rich in carbohydrates and proteins, extn with hot H_2O may be omitted.)

3.098 *Apparatus*

App., Fig. 3:3, consists of: (1) 1500 ml bottle, *A*, to which is attached by 2-hole rubber stopper 250 ml dropping funnel, *C*, having lower end of stem bent as illustrated and placed close to bottom of *A*; (2) Drechsel gas-washing bottle, *D*; (3) 3 Pyrex test tubes, 38×300 mm diam., *G*, *G'*, *G''*, connected in parallel by device, *O*, and immersed in wooden box, *L*, filled with crushed ice, *H*; and (4) bottle contg H_2O for absorption of excess HCl, *K*. *G*, *G'*, and *G''* are provided with 2-hole rubber stoppers; glass tube with right angle bend extends thru 1 hole nearly to bottom of test tube, and similar tube extending ca 10 mm into test tube passes thru other hole. Rubber connections and stopcocks for regulating flow of gas are provided as indicated in diagram. *A* is filled with ca 500 ml H_2SO_4 and *C* with HCl; HCl flowing thru stopcock *B* into *A* generates HCl gas, which is dried by H_2SO_4 in *D*, and flows into *G*, *G'*, and *G''* contg samples and fuming HCl reagent.

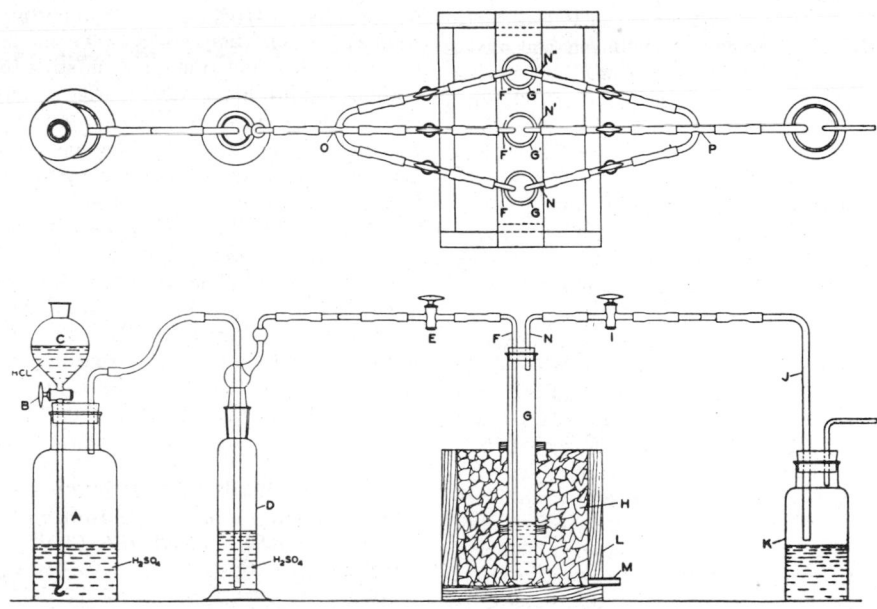

FIG. 3:3—Apparatus for determining lignin

3.099   *Reagent*

Fuming hydrochloric acid.—(*Caution: See* **46.031.**) Density 1.212–1.223 at 15°. To 500 g NaCl in 1 L g-s Pyrex distg flask, add cold soln of 250 ml H_2O in 450 ml H_2SO_4. Connect side tube of distg flask to glass tube passing thru H_2SO_4 wash bottle, and connect outlet tube of H_2SO_4 wash bottle to another glass tube, immersed in flask contg 3 L HCl. Surround flask contg HCl with crushed ice. Heat distg flask with small flame and pass HCl gas into acid soln until it attains sp gr of 1.212–1.223 at 15°. Keep reagent refrigerated at 0° or below. If only few detns are to be made, prep. correspondingly smaller quantity.

3.100   *Determination*

Weigh three 1 g samples of extd and dried sample in weighing bottle and place in 3 large test tubes, *G*, *G′*, and *G″*. Add 20 ml of the reagent to each tube, using this acid to wash down any particles clinging to sides. When all material is wet with reagent, add addnl 30 ml reagent. Add ca 3 drops *capryl alcohol* to minimize foaming. Place test tubes, *G*, *G′*, and *G″*, in wooden box, *L*, and surround with crushed ice. Lubricate tubes *F*, *F′*, and *F″* with drop of glycerol so that they move easily thru holes in rubber stoppers. Lead dry HCl gas from generator into reaction mixts thru tubes *F*, *F′*, and *F″* (*F′* and *F″* are shown in top view), which reach nearly to bottom of tubes *G*, *G′*, and *G″*. Regulate flow of gas thru reaction mixts in *G*, *G′*, and *G″* by stopcocks shown in top view, continuing passage of gas 2 hr. (At first rather slow stream of gas passes in, but during last 15 min, flow is fairly rapid.)

After reaction period discontinue flow of gas, and disconnect long tubes *F*, *F′*, and *F″* and outlet tubes of test tubes *G*, *G′*, and *G″* from *O* and *P*. Pull tubes *F*, *F′*, and *F″* just above surface of reaction mixt., and close with short pieces of rubber tubing having one end plugged with short piece of glass rod. Similarly close off outlet tubes, *N*, *N′* and *N″*. Place tubes contg reaction mixt. in cold room or refrigerator (8–10°) for 24 hr.

Transfer contents of *G*, *G′*, and *G″* to 1 L erlenmeyers, taking care to remove any material adhering either on inside or outside of tubes *F*, *F′*, and *F″*. Dil. reaction mixts to 500 ml with H_2O. Connect flasks to reflux condensers and boil 1 hr. Prep. 3 gooches in usual manner, dry at 105°, and weigh. Ignite one of weighed crucibles, *X*, on Bunsen burner, cool in desiccator, and reweigh. Let contents of flasks cool to room temp. and filter thru weighed gooches. Wash ppts collected in gooches with hot H_2O, dry at 105°, and weigh in weighing bottles. Ignite crude lignin in crucible *X* over Bunsen flame and det. wt ash. Place one of other 2 gooches in wide-neck Kjeldahl flask and det. % N in crude lignin as in **2.051.** If methoxyl in lignin is to be detd, collect ppt from one of flasks in dried (105°) fritted glass crucible and proceed as in **42.037.**

Wt lignin = wt crude lignin − wt ash − wt crude protein (N × 6.25). Calc. % lignin in original dry unextd material.

3.101   *Indirect Method (33)*

Ext 1 g sample with alcohol-benzene (1 + 2) 4 hr in Soxhlet or comparable app. (extn vessel may be either coarse porosity Alundum or paper thimble, closed at top with filter paper or plug of cotton). Wash sample in thimble with suction, using 2 small portions alcohol followed by 2 small portions ether. Heat at 45° in nonsparking oven to drive off ether, and transfer sample to 250 ml wide-mouth erlenmeyer. Add 40 ml *1% soln of pepsin in 0.1N HCl*, wetting sample well by adding small portion reagent, stirring or shaking thoroly, and finally washing down sides of flasks with remaining soln. Incubate at 40° overnight.

Add 20–30 ml hot H_2O and filter, using filter stick. (Filter sticks are made with Pyrex fritted glass disk, 30 mm diam, medium porosity. Thin layer of preashed diat. earth (Hyflo Super-Cel, or similar filter-aid) is sucked onto disk from H_2O suspension. This is usually enough for easy filtration; if not, add extra Super-Cel to material being filtered. Some sticks filter slowly with some samples. It is advisable to obtain more than needed and discard slow-filtering ones. It is conveneint to arrange filter sticks in set of 12 attached to vac. manifold by rubber tubing.)

Repeat washing twice and then wash residue into flask by forcing 7–8 ml 5% (w/w) H_2SO_4 downward thru filter stick, using air pressure. Wash stick further with the H_2SO_4, finally adding enough to bring total vol. to ca 150 ml. Reflux vigorously on hot plate 1 hr, adding H_2O occasionally to maintain original vol. Filter off acid. Wash residue with three 20–30 ml portions hot H_2O, two 15–20 ml portions alcohol, and two 15 ml portions ether. Leave vac. on few min to dry residue, and transfer from stick to flask by tapping and brushing. Heat to drive off any residual ether. If disk formed upon drying is difficult to break up into finely divided state (sometimes in case of immature plant samples), disperse residue in ether in flask and then boil off ether on steam bath. Add 20 ml 72% (w/w) H_2SO_4 at 20° to residue and hold 2 hr at 20°, stirring occasionally. Add 125 ml H_2O, filter, wash once with 20 ml hot H_2O, and filter again. Wash residue from filter stick and reflux as before 2 hr, using 150 ml 3% (w/w) H_2SO_4. Filter residue onto gooch with asbestos pad and wash with hot H_2O until acid-free. Dry at 105–110° and det. lignin by loss in wt on ignition at 600°.

PIGMENTS

Chlorophyll—Official Final Action

Photoelectric Colorimetric Method for Total Chlorophyll Only (34)

3.102   *Apparatus*

(a) *Mortar and pestle.*—Deep glass mortar ca 4″ id with well-defined lip.

(b) *Photoelectric colorimeter.*—Calibrate for chlorophyll, using plant ext as in **3.104** and light filters with max. T near 660 nm. (Combination of Corning Glass Works H. R. light filters Nos. 243 and 396 is suitable.)

(c) *Wash bottles.*—Type fitted with rubber bulb, permitting operation with one hand.

(d) *High-speed blender.*—Waring Blendor or equiv. (Vessels similar to No. 3, shown in JAOAC **25**, 583(1942), possess advantages over original blender container.)

3.103 Reagents

(a) *Acetone.*—(*1*) Undild acetone and (*2*) 85% soln by vol. Com. acetone, tech. grade, is satisfactory.

(b) *Quartz sand.*—Acid-washed and dried.

3.104 Determination

(*Caution: See* **46.004, 46.040,** *and* **46.046.**)

Select field material carefully to ensure representative sample. Remove representative portion from field sample, and if fresh, cut finely with hand shears and mix as thoroly as possible. Grind dried material in mill and mix thoroly.

Weigh 1–5 g into mortar and add small quantity (ca 0.1 g) $CaCO_3$ or Na_2CO_3. Macerate tissue with pestle, add quartz sand, and grind short time; then add 85% acetone, little at time, and continue grinding until tissue is finely ground. Transfer mixt. to funnel, filter with suction, and wash residue with 85% acetone. Return residue to mortar with more 85% acetone and grind again. Filter and wash as before. Repeat procedure until tissue is devoid of any green, and washings are colorless. (It is advisable to grind residue at least once with undild acetone and then to add enough H_2O at end to bring acetone concn to 85%. High-speed blender may be used instead of mortar to macerate and ext tissue (*see* **3.107**), but each investigator should satisfy himself that device used exts tissue completely.) When extn is complete, transfer filtered ext to vol. flask of appropriate size and dil. to vol.

Measure T of soln with photoelec. colorimeter, and read quantity of chlorophyll present from curve relating T and concn. Express chlorophyll values as mg/g tissue, or in other convenient manner.

Calibrate photoelec. colorimeter as follows: Ext sample of fresh, green leaf material with 85% acetone, filter, wash residue, and dil. ext to vol. as above. Make series of dilns of ext and measure T of original and of each of dild solns with instrument in same manner as when chlorophyll prepn is being used as calibration std. Transfer aliquot of original ext to ether and evaluate total chlorophyll spectrophtric as in **3.107**(b) and (c). From value thus obtained, calc. chlorophyll content of original ext and that of each of dild solns, and construct curve relating concn of chlorophyll with T or A.

Spectrophotometric Method for Total Chlorophyll and the a and b Components (35, 36)

3.105 Apparatus

Use app. in **3.102** (except photoelec. colorimeter), plus following:

(a) *Scrubbing tubes for washing ether solns.*—Open tubes of ca 20 mm diam. to one end of each of which is sealed tube of smaller diam. drawn to fine jet at lower end.

(b) *Spectrophotometer.*—Capable of isolating spectral region of ca 3 nm near 660 nm with negligible stray radiation. Tubulated cells with tightly fitting glass stoppers are recommended for work with ether.

3.106 Reagents

Those listed in **3.103** and following:

Ether.—Com. grade is satisfactory without further purification.

3.107 Determination

(Wash glassware with concd Na_3PO_4 soln to remove traces of acid that may decompose chlorophyll.)

(a) *Extraction of chlorophyll from tissue.*—Select and prep. sample as in **3.104.** Disintegrate weighed portion (2–10 g, depending on chlorophyll content) of fresh plant tissue in blender cup that contains small quantity (ca 0.1 g) $CaCO_3$, or by use of mortar as in **3.104.** After tissue is thoroly disintegrated, filter ext thru buchner fitted with quant. paper. Wash residue with 85% acetone, **3.103**(a), and if necessary, use little ether to remove last traces of pigment. If extn is incomplete, return residue and paper to blender container with more 85% acetone and repeat extn. Filter and wash, as directed previously, into flask contg first filtrate. Transfer filtrate to vol. flask of appropriate size and dil. to vol. with 85% acetone.

Pipet aliquot of 25–50 ml into separator contg ca 50 ml ether. Add H_2O carefully until it is apparent that all fat-sol. pigments have entered ether layer. Drain and discard H_2O layer. Place separator contg ether soln in upper rack of support. Add ca 100 ml H_2O to second separator placed in rack below first. Set scrubbing tube in place, and let ether soln run thru it to bottom of lower separator and rise in small droplets thru the H_2O. When all soln has left upper separator, rinse it and scrubbing tube with little ether added from medicine dropper. Place scrubbing tube in upper separator and exchange its place in support with separator now contg ether soln. Drain and discard H_2O in upper separator, add similar portion of fresh H_2O to lower separator, and repeat washing process. Continue washing ether soln until all acetone is removed (5–10 washings). Then transfer ether soln to 100 ml vol. flask, dil. to vol., and mix.

(b) *Spectrophotometric measurements.*—Add ca teaspoonful anhyd. Na_2SO_4 to 60 ml reagent bottle, and fill it with ether soln of pigment. When this soln is optically clear, pipet aliquot into another dry bottle and dil. with enough dry ether to cause $\log_{10} I_0/I$ value (A) to fall between 0.2 and 0.8 at wavelength to be used. (Most favorable value is near 0.6 at 660 nm, since such soln yields satisfactory value at 642.5 nm.)

Fill 2 clean g-s absorption cells with dry ether from pipet and polish outside surfaces of each, first with cotton wet with alcohol and then with dry cotton. Place cells in instrument, and det. whether each gives same galvanometer deflection. If not, clean again or select cells that do, and do this daily. Empty one cell, fill it with the dried ether soln, and place in instrument. Adjust entrance and exit slits until spectral region isolated is 3–4 nm at 660.0 nm.

Det. whether instrument is in proper adjustment for wavelength by taking readings thru solv. and soln at intervals of 1 nm from 658–665 nm. Calc. $\log_{10} I_0/I$ value for each wavelength at which readings were taken. Highest value should be at 660.0 nm; if not, adjust instrument until it is, or make 660.0 nm readings at wavelength setting that gave highest value. In case of grating instrument, apply same correction at 642.5 nm; however, with prism instrument, correction at 642.5 nm must be obtained from wavelength calibration curve for particular instrument in use. Calibrate instrument for wavelength in this way often enough to insure that it remains in proper adjustment. Take I_0 and I readings at 660.0 and 642.5 nm (or corrected settings) for each unknown soln.

(c) *Calculation of chlorophyll concentration.*—Calc. $\log_{10} I_0/I$ values for each of readings made, substitute them in following simplified equations, and solve for total chlorophyll and each of a and b components as follows:

equation holds in case of chlorophylls a and b at given wavelength:

$$(4) \qquad (\log_{10} I_0/I)_{observed} = (\log_{10} I_0/I)_a + (\log_{10} I_0/I)_b.$$

If 1 cm cell is used, this equation may be expressed as:

$$(5) \qquad (\log_{10} I_0/I)_{observed} = a_a c_a + a_b c_b.$$

Concns of chlorophylls a and b in given ether soln can now be calcd by equation (5) as follows:

(a) Det. $\log_{10} I_0/I$ values for soln at 2 different wavelengths (660.0 and 642.5 nm have been found advantageous for this purpose).

(b) Select from table proper absorptivities corresponding to wavelengths used.

(c) Substitute observed $\log_{10} I_0/I$ value and absorptivities in equation (5) for each of the 2 wavelengths used as illustrated for 660.0 and 642.5 nm in equations (6) and (7). Solve these 2 equations simultaneously for 2 unknowns, the concns of chlorophylls a and b.

$$(6) \quad \log_{10} I_0/I \text{ (at 660.0 nm)} = 102c_a + 4.50c_b.$$

$$(7) \quad \log_{10} I_0/I \text{ (at 642.5 nm)} = 16.3c_a + 57.5c_b.$$

Equations (1), (2), and (3) were derived in this way.

Criterion for accuracy of chlorophyll values detd by spectrophtric method is agreement between analytical results as detd from measurements at different wavelengths. It has been demonstrated by Comar and Zscheile (36) that measurements at 660.0 and 642.5 nm are convenient for routine analysis; however, readings may be made at other wavelengths to check these values. Absorptivities for chlorophylls a and b in ether soln that may be used for this purpose are presented in Table 3:1:

$$(1) \qquad \text{Total chlorophyll (mg/L)} = 7.12 \log_{10} \frac{I_0}{I} \text{ (at 660.0 nm)} + 16.8 \log_{10} \frac{I_0}{I} \text{ (at 642.5 nm)}.$$

$$(2) \qquad \text{Chlorophyll } a \text{ (mg/L)} = 9.93 \log_{10} \frac{I_0}{I} \text{ (at 660.0 nm)} - 0.777 \log_{10} \frac{I_0}{I} \text{ (at 642.5 nm)}.$$

$$(3) \qquad \text{Chlorophyll } b \text{ (mg/L)} = 17.6 \log_{10} \frac{I_0}{I} \text{ (at 642.5 nm)} - 2.81 \log_{10} \frac{I_0}{I} \text{ (at 660.0 nm)}.$$

3.108 Supplementary Information

Factors involved in spectrophtric analysis of chlorophyll system have been discussed in detail by Comar and Zscheile (36). These authors used Beer's law in form:

$$c = (\log_{10} I_0/I)/al,$$

where I_0 is intensity of light transmitted by solv.-filled cell; I is intensity of light transmitted by soln-filled cell; c is concn of chlorophyll (g/L); a is absorptivity; and l is thickness of soln layer in cm.

Since, at given wavelength, observed $\log_{10} I_0/I$ value of soln having 2 components represents sum of $\log_{10} I_0/I$ values of each of components, following

Table 3:1 Absorption constants used in analysis (after Comar and Zscheile (36))

Wavelength nm	Absorptivities (for Ether Solns)	
	Chlorophyll a	Chlorophyll b
660.0	102	4.50
642.5	16.3	57.5
600.0	9.95	9.95
581.0	8.05	8.05
568.0	7.11	7.11
613.0	15.6	8.05
589.0	5.90	10.3

These values may be used for calcns as follows:

(a) Values for total chlorophyll and % composition may be calcd from A at 660.0 and 642.5 nm as described.

(b) Check values for total chlorophyll may be calcd from A at intersection points 600.0, 581.0, and 568.0 nm.

(c) Check values for % composition may be calcd from A for each of points 613.0 and 589.0 nm in combination with value of total concn obtained from (a) or (b).

3.109 Carotenes—Official Final Action
See 39.014–39.023

TOBACCO
Moisture (37)—Official Final Action
3.110 *Apparatus*

(a) *Drying oven.*—Forced-draft, regulated to 99.5±0.5°. Suggested dimensions: $19 \times 19 \times 19''$. Approx. oven settings: fresh air intake vent ⅕ open; air control damper ¼ open; air exhaust vent ⅛ open.

(b) *Moisture dish.*—Al, diam. 45–65 mm, depth 20–45 mm, with tight fitting cover.

3.111 *Determination*

Accurately weigh ca 5 g sample (ground to pass 1 mm or finer screen) into weighed moisture dish and place uncovered dish in oven.

Do not exceed 1 sample/10 sq in. shelf space, and use only 1 shelf. Dry 3 hr at 99.5±0.5°. Remove from oven, cover, and cool in desiccator to room temp. (ca 30 min). Reweigh to nearest 1 mg and calc. % moisture.

Chlorides (33)—Official Final Action
Potentiometric Method
3.112 *Reagent*

Silver nitrate std soln.—0.1N. Stdze against KCl as in sample analysis.

3.113 *Apparatus*

(a) *pH meter.*—Leeds and Northrup, Sumneytown Pike, N. Wales, PA 18051, Beckman Instruments, or equiv., equipped with Ag and glass electrodes, Beckman Nos. 1261 and 1190-42, resp., or equiv.

(b) *Buret.*—10 ml, graduated in 0.05 or 0.02 ml, preferably reservoir type.

3.114 *Determination*

Accurately weigh ca 2 g tobacco, ground to pass No. 40 sieve, into 250 ml electrolytic beaker. Add 100 ml H_2O, small amt at first to thoroly wet tobacco; then remainder. Let stand at least 5 min at room temp., stirring intermittently. Pipet 5 ml HNO_3 (1 + 9) into mixt. and insert clean electrodes. Start magnetic stirrer and continue stirring thruout titrn at rate that produces vigorous agitation without spattering. Titr. with std 0.1N $AgNO_3$ soln to potential previously established as equivalence point.

Det. equivalence point potential graphically by making several titrns on one or more tobacco samples. Recheck occasionally, and redet. when either electrode is replaced. Record vol. of titrant and calc.

% Cl = ml $AgNO_3$ × normality × 3.5453/g sample.

Nitrogen (39)—Official Final Action
Kjeldahl Method for Samples Containing Nitrates
(For nitrate-free samples omit salicylic acid and thiosulfate treatment.)

3.115 *Reagents*

See **2.049** and the following:

(a) *Sodium hydroxide-thiosulfate soln.*—Dissolve 500 g NaOH pellets and 40 g $Na_2S_2O_3 \cdot 5H_2O$ in H_2O and dil. to 1 L.

(b) *Indicators.*—(1) Dissolve 1 g Me red in 200 ml alcohol; *or* (2) prep. mixed indicator by dissolving 0.8 g Me red and 0.2 g methylene blue in 500 ml alcohol.

3.116 *Apparatus*

See **2.050.**

3.117 *Determination*

Place weighed sample (1–2 g) in digestion flask. Add vol. H_2SO_4 (contg 2 g salicylic acid/40 ml) corresponding to wt sample (35 ml for 1 g, 40 ml for 2 g for NO_3-contg samples; 20 and 25 ml, resp., for NO_3-free samples). Shake until thoroly mixed; let stand ≥30 min with occasional shaking; then add 5 g $Na_2S_2O_3 \cdot 5H_2O$. Shake, let stand 5 min, and heat carefully until frothing ceases. Turn off heat, add 0.7 g HgO (or metallic Hg) and 15 g K_2SO_4, and boil briskly 1–1.5 hr after soln clears.

Cool, add ca 200 ml H_2O, cool to ca room temp., and add few Zn granules. Tilt flask and carefully add 50 ml NaOH-thiosulfate soln without agitation. Immediately connect flask to distn bulb on condenser whose tip is immersed in 50 ml std 0.1N acid in receiving flask. Then rotate digestion flask carefully to mix contents. Heat until at least 150 ml distillate collects, and titr. excess acid with std base, using Me red or mixed indicator. Correct for blank detn on reagents.

Potassium (40)—Official Final Action
3.118 *Reagents*

(a) *Potassium std solns.*—(1) *Stock std soln.*—1000 ppm K. See **3.016**(a). (2) *Working std solns.*—Place 0, 5, 10, 15, 20, 25, and 30 ml stock soln in seven 1 L vol. flasks, add 40 ml 3N HCl to each, and dil. to vol. with H_2O.

(b) *Diatomaceous earth.*—Celite 545, acid-washed.

3.119 *Apparatus*

(a) *Flame photometer.*—Natural gas-air fuel, or equiv., adequate for K analysis.

(b) *Chromatographic tube.*—20 × 150 mm with coarse fritted disk.

3.120   Preparation of Sample Solution

Accurately weigh ca 0.5 g tobacco dust into ca 40 ml weighing dish. Add ca 1 g of the Celite and mix intimately with spatula. Transfer quant. thru powder funnel into chromatgc tube. Add addnl Celite thru funnel into tube until 1″ layer accumulates on top of sample-Celite mixt. Compact sample and Celite by tapping tip of tube on table top, and insert tip of tube into neck of 1 L vol. flask. Add 40 ml 3N HCl into tube by pipet or dispenser, washing down sides of tube, and let elute into vol. flask. When liq. level reaches top of Celite, add 25 ml H_2O to tube and let elute. Add second 25 ml portion H_2O, let elute normally, or force thru rapidly with compressed air. Rinse tip of tube into vol. flask, dil. to vol. with H_2O, and mix well.

3.121   Determination

Det % T for sample eluate and K stds as specified in instruction manual of flame photometer used. *See* also **3.019.**

Prep. calibration curve and det. ppm K of unknown sample from curve.

% K = ppm K × 0.1/g sample.
% K_2O = ppm K × 0.1205/g sample.

Total Alkaloids (As Nicotine)
Distillation Method (41)—
Official Final Action

3.122   Apparatus

(a) *Distillation apparatus.*—500 ml Kjeldahl flask fitted with inlet tube for steam, trap bulb, and condenser; Griffith still (Tobacco Sci. **1**, 130(1957), available from Lab Glass, Inc., PO Box 5067, Kingsport, TN 37663); or other suitable steam distn app.

(b) *Spectrophotometer.*—Beckman Instruments Model DU or other instrument capable of accurately measuring A in 200–300 nm range, equipped with 1 cm quartz cells.

3.123   Reagents

(a) *Alkali-salt soln.*—Dissolve 300 g NaOH in 700 ml H_2O and sat. with NaCl.

(b) *Silicotungstic acid soln (for gravimetric determination).*—Dissolve 120 g $SiO_2.12WO_3.26H_2O$ in H_2O and dil. to 1 L. (Soln should be clear and free from green color.)

3.124   Standardization

(*Caution:* Nicotine is very toxic. Avoid contact with skin and eyes. *See* **46.011** and **46.015.**)

Purify best grade of nicotine com. available by successive vac. distns until center cuts from 2 successive distns have same a at 259 nm (ca 34.3). Accurately weigh ca 0.2 g purified nicotine; dissolve in and dil. to 1 L with ca 0.05N HCl. Dil. 10 ml aliquot of this soln to 100 ml with ca 0.05N HCl. Det.

A at 259 nm and calc. $a = A/c × b$, where c is concn of nicotine in g/L and b is cell length in cm.

3.125   Distillation

Accurately weigh 2–5 g tobacco sample and transfer to distn flask or app. (If final detn of nicotine is gravimetric, use sample contg at least 0.1 g alkaloids; if spectrophtric, use sample of at least 2 g.) (If Griffith still is used, use 0.05–0.2 g sample.) Place 25 ml HCl (1 + 4) in receiver (1 L vol. flask is desirable) and place receiver so that condenser tube dips into acid. (With Griffith still, use 10 ml HCl (1 + 4) in 250 ml vol. flask.) Add 50 ml alkali-salt soln to distn flask so that sample is rinsed into bottom of flask. (With Griffith still, use 5 ml alkali-salt soln.) If large vol. of liq. is required for proper function of still, add more alkali-salt soln; do not dil. Connect flask to app. immediately and steam distill with as rapid current of steam as can be condensed efficiently. Effluent condensate should not be above room temp. Apply heat to distn flask from burner, mantle, or other heat source to keep vol. in flask approx. constant. Collect ca 900 ml condensate (or distill addnl 100 ml after condensate shows' no nicotine by silicotungstic acid test). (With Griffith still, collect 225 ml.) Dil. distillate to vol.

3.126   Determination

(a) *Spectrophotometric.*—Dil. aliquots of distillate (if necessary) with 0.05N HCl so that A at 259 nm is 0.5–0.8 and read A at 236, 259, and 282 nm. Calc. corrected $A'_{259} = 1.059 × $ [observed $A_{259} − \frac{1}{2}(A_{236} + A_{282})$] after correcting all observed A values to original distillate vol. basis. Concn, c, of alkaloids as nicotine in g/L is given by $c = A'_{259}/a × b$, where a is absorptivity at 259 nm, and b is cell length in cm. Calc. % alkaloid (as nicotine) = $c × $ vol. distillate (L) × 100/g sample.

(b) *Gravimetric.*—Det. alkaloids in distillate as in **6.103,** but double amt of silicotungstic acid specified, i.e., 2 ml/each 10 mg alkaloids expected.

Cundiff-Markunas Method (41)—
Official Final Action

(Total alkaloids (as nicotine), tertiary alkaloids (as nicotine), and secondary alkaloids (as nornicotine).)

3.127   Reagents

(a) *Benzene-chloroform soln.*—Mix equal parts by vol. of benzene and $CHCl_3$ and sat. with H_2O.

(b) *Sodium hydroxide soln.*—36%. Dissolve 500 g NaOH in H_2O and dil. to 1 L.

(c) *Dilute acetic acid.*—5%. Dil. 50 ml HOAc to 1 L with H_2O.

(d) *Crystal violet indicator.*—Dissolve 0.5 g crystal violet in 100 ml HOAc.

(e) *Perchloric acid std soln.*—0.025N. Add 4.7 ml 72% $HClO_4$ to freshly opened 5 lb bottle HOAc and mix. (*Caution: See* **46.022** and **46.028(a)** and **(d).**) Stdze as follows: Accurately weigh 0.1 g KH phthalate (NBS) into 125 ml erlenmeyer, add 50 ml HOAc, and heat to dissolve. Cool, add 2 drops indicator, and titr. to blue-green end point. Perform blank titrn on 50 ml HOAc and 2 drops indicator soln, and correct vol. of titrant.

$$N = \frac{\text{wt KH phthalate} \times 4.896}{\text{ml HClO}_4}$$

3.128 *Determination*

Accurately weigh 2.5 g finely ground tobacco into 250 ml erlenmeyer. Add 15 ml 5% HOAc and swirl until tobacco is thoroly wetted. Pipet 100 ml benzene-CHCl$_3$ soln into flask, and then 10 ml 36% NaOH soln. Stopper flask tightly and shake 20 min, using wrist-action shaker. Add 4.5–5 g (2 teaspoonfuls) Filter-Cel, mix, and filter most of benzene layer thru Whatman No. 2 paper into second flask. If filtrate has any turbidity, add 2–2.5 g (1 teaspoonful) addnl Filter-Cel and refilter thru Whatman No. 2 paper. Filtrate must be clear.

Pipet 25 ml aliquots of filtrate into each of two 125 ml erlenmeyers. Pass stream of air over surface of soln in first flask 5 min, add 2 drops indicator, and titr. to green end point with 0.025N HClO$_4$. Add 1.0 ml Ac$_2$O to second flask and let stand at least 15 min. Add 25 ml HOAc and 2 drops indicator, and titr. to blue-green end point with 0.025N HClO$_4$. Take first appearance of blue-green thruout soln as end point. For each series of analyses perform blank titrns and correct respective vols of titrant.

Calc. % alkaloids as follows: % total alkaloids (as nicotine) = $V_1 \times N \times 32.45/$wt sample; % tertiary alkaloids (as nicotine) = $(2V_2 - V_1) \times N \times 32.45/$wt sample; % secondary alkaloids (as nornicotine) = $2(V_1 - V_2) \times N \times 29.64/$wt sample; where V_1 = vol. titrant for nonacetylated aliquot; V_2 = vol. titrant for acetylated aliquot; and N = normality HClO$_4$.

Menthol (42)—Official Final Action
Colorimetric Method

3.129 *Principle*

Menthol is sepd from cigarette tobacco filler by distn and detd spectrophtric, after reaction with *p*-dimethylaminobenzaldehyde.

3.130 *Apparatus and Reagents*

(a) *Distillation apparatus.*—See Fig. 3:4.

(b) *Spectrophotometer.*—With matched cells; capable of measuring A at 550 nm.

(c) *Menthol std soln.*—1 mg/ml. Accurately weigh 100 mg USP *l*-menthol into 100 ml vol. flask, add alcohol to dissolve, and dil. to vol. with alcohol.

(d) *DMAB color reagent.*—Dissolve 0.5 g *p*-dimethylaminobenzaldehyde (Eastman Kodak, white label) in 100 ml H$_2$SO$_4$ (1.6 + 1).

3.131 *Preparation of Calibration Curve*

Prep. dil. stds by pipeting aliquots contg 0, 3, 4, 6, 8, and 10 mg menthol into 100 ml vol. flasks and dilg

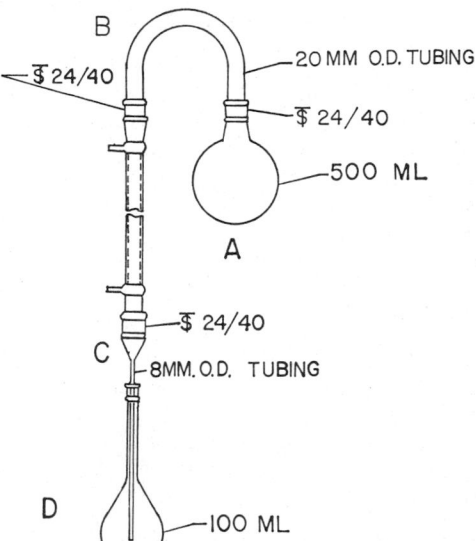

FIG. 3:4—Distillation apparatus; see *Determination* for explanation of symbols

to vol. with alcohol (1 + 1). Pipet 1 ml each dil. std into 10 ml test tube, add 5 ml color reagent, mix, and place in boiling H$_2$O bath *exactly* 2 min. Cool in tap H$_2$O, and within 15 min det. A at 550 nm, using reagent blank for 0 A setting of spectrophtr.

Prep. calibration curve by plotting A against menthol concn (mg/100 ml).

3.132 *Determination*

Accurately weigh 2.00–2.15 g cigarette filler and transfer to distn flask, A. Add 80 ml H$_2$O and few boiling stones, connect flask, A, to condenser with tube, B, attach adapter, C, to condenser, and immerse tip in 20 ml alcohol in 100 ml vol. receiving flask.

Gently heat distn flask until distn begins; then increase heat and lower receiving flask, D, so tip of adapter is no longer immersed. Distill until 20 ml distillate collects. Disconnect condenser from tube, B, and wash down condenser with alcohol, remove receiving flask, dil. distillate to ca 70 ml with alcohol, and add H$_2$O almost to vol. Mix, add alcohol to vol., and mix again.

Pipet 1 ml distillate into 10 ml test tube, add 5 ml color reagent, mix, and place in boiling H$_2$O bath *exactly* 2 min. Cool in tap H$_2$O, and within 15 min det. A at 550 nm, using "color" soln from nonmentholated tobacco carried thru detn as blank. (If nonmentholated sample corresponding to mentholated sample is not available, use reagent blank.) Use nonmentholated tobacco blank within 15 min after color development step. Fresh nonmentholated tobacco blank soln may be required during multiple sample runs.

Det. mg menthol from calibration curve. % Menthol = mg menthol/(g original sample × 10).

Gas Chromatographic Method

3.133   *Apparatus and Reagents*

(a) *Gas chromatograph.*—Equipped with flame ionization detector and thermostated injection port and column oven. Use following conditions for analysis: Column, 5′ × ⅛″ od stainless steel packed with 10% (w/w) silicone oil DC-550 on 60–80 mesh Chromosorb W; column temp. 150°; detector temp. 150°; injection port temp. 175°; N carrier gas flow rate ca 35 ml/min. Adjust H and air flows for max. sensitivity and reasonable stability.

(b) *Mechanical shaker.*—Wrist action.

(c) *Menthol-anethole std soln.*—0.250 mg menthol and 0.50 mg anethole/ml. Weigh exactly 0.5000 g tech. grade anethole and wash into 1 L vol. flask with 200 ml alcohol. Transfer 0.2500 g USP *l*-menthol to the vol. flask with enough alcohol to bring to vol. Store soln in dark g-s bottle. Do not use after 6 weeks.

(d) *Extracting soln.*—0.50 mg anethole/ml. Dissolve 1.000 g anethole in alcohol in 2 L vol. flask, dil. to vol. with alcohol, and store in dark.

3.134   *Determination of Ratio Factor*

Weigh ca 3 g nonmentholated control filler, contg all usual humectants but no menthol or anethole, into 125 ml flask fitted with rubber stopper. Pipet 50 ml std menthol-anethole soln into flask, stopper, and shake 1 hr on mech. shaker. Let solids settle 15 min and chromatograph 2 μl aliquot of supernatant. Repeat twice more to obtain total of 3 replicates of std chromatogram. For quant. results, inject both std and unknown samples by inserting 2″ needle to hilt, injecting 2 μl rapidly, and withdrawing needle at once. (Menthol elutes in ca 3 min, anethole in ca 5 min.) After ca 10 min, all other compds are eluted and new injection can be made.

Draw baselines under menthol and anethole peaks and measure peak hts in mm. Using mean peak ht of menthol and anethole from 3 std chromatograms, calc. std ratio factor of menthol to anethole as follows:

Std ratio factor = peak ht for menthol (0.25 mg/ml)/peak ht for anethole (0.50 mg/ml).

3.135   *Determination*

Accurately weigh 8–8.5 g mentholated cigarette filler and place in 250 ml erlenmeyer fitted with rubber stopper. Pipet 100 ml extg soln into flask, stopper, and shake 2 hr on mech. shaker. Let solids settle 15 min and chromatograph 2 μl aliquot of supernatant. Draw baselines under menthol and anethole peaks and measure peak hts in mm. Calc. ratio factor of unknown menthol as follows:

Ratio factor for unknown = peak ht for unknown menthol/peak ht for anethole (0.50 mg/ml).

% Menthol = (unknown ratio factor × 0.25 × 10)/(std ratio factor × g sample).

SELECTED REFERENCES

(1) Botan. Gaz. **73**, 44(1922); Proc. Am. Soc. Hort. Sci. 1927, p. 191; JAOAC **13**, 224(1930); **16**, 71(1933); **19**, 70(1936).

(2) JAOAC **11**, 203(1928); **16**, 70(1933); **19**, 70 (1936).

(3) Ind. Eng. Chem., Anal. Ed. **9**, 67(1937); **10**, 13(1938); JAOAC **25**, 555(1942); **27**, 526(1944).

(4) JAOAC **19**, 359(1936); **27**, 526(1944).

(5) J. Biol. Chem. **7**, 83(1910); JAOAC **4**, 392 (1921); **16**, 70(1933).

(6) J. Biol. Chem. **47**, 475(1921); **50**, 527, 537 (1922); JAOAC **14**, 216(1931); **16**, 71(1933); **19**, 71(1936).

(7) JAOAC **3**, 329(1920); **4**, 393(1921); **16**, 71 (1933); **19**, 71(1936).

(8) JAOAC **4**, 393(1921).

(9) JAOAC **39**, 419(1956).

(10) JAOAC **19**, 71(1936).

(11) J. Am. Chem. Soc. **51**, 1664(1929); JAOAC **19**, 71(1936).

(12) JAOAC **34**, 710(1951); **36**, 405(1953).

(13) JAOAC **36**, 405(1953).

(14) Ind. Eng. Chem., Anal. Ed. **13**, 145(1941); JAOAC **24**, 520(1941).

(15) JAOAC **36**, 397(1953).

(16) JAOAC **39**, 412(1956); **41**, 309(1958).

(17) USDA Bur. Chem. Bull. **105**, p. 151; **116**, p. 92; **137**, p. 30.

(18) JAOAC **6**, 415(1923).

(19) JAOAC **16**, 71(1933).

(20) JAOAC **14**, 216(1931); J. Biol. Chem. **59**, 255(1924).

(21) JAOAC **49**, 212, 284(1966).

(22) JAOAC **11**, 209(1928); **12**, 195(1929); **21**, 107 (1938).

(23) Sutton, "Systematic Handbook of Volumetric Analysis," 11th ed., 1924, p. 146; J. Am. Chem. Soc. **37**, 1128(1915).

(24) JAOAC **18**, 379(1935); **19**, 72(1936).

(25) JAOAC **19**, 236(1936).

(26) JAOAC **52**, 627(1969).

(27) JAOAC **41**, 304(1958).

(28) JAOAC **14**, 73, 225(1931); **15**, 71(1932).

(29) JAOAC **36**, 402(1953).

(30) JAOAC **41**, 307, 681(1958); **42**, 650(1959).

(31) Anal. Chem. **20**, 850(1948).

(32) JAOAC **15**, 124(1932); **18**, 386(1935); **19**, 107 (1936).

(33) JAOAC **32**, 288(1949).

(34) Ind. Eng. Chem., Anal. Ed. **12**, 148(1940); **15**, 524(1943).

(35) Ind. Eng. Chem., Anal. Ed. **14**, 877(1942); JAOAC **27**, 517(1944).

(36) Plant Physiol. **17**, 198(1942).

(37) JAOAC **49**, 212, 525(1966); **51**, 447(1968).

(38) JAOAC **46**, 415(1963); **47**, 177(1964).

(39) JAOAC **42**, 33, 302(1959); **47**, 177(1964).

(40) JAOAC **49**, 212, 521(1966); **51**, 448(1968).

(41) JAOAC **43**, 524(1960).

(42) JAOAC **51**, 448, 650(1968).

4. Disinfectants

Phenol Coefficient (1)—Official Final Action

(Applicable to testing disinfectants miscible with H_2O that do not exert bacteriostatic effects that cannot be neutzd by one of 3 subculture media specified, or overcome by suitable subtransfer procedures. The 95% confidence limits are ±12%.)

1. Using Salmonella typhosa

4.001   *Reagents*

(a) *Culture media.*—(1) *Nutrient broth.*—Boil 5 g beef ext (Difco), 5 g NaCl, and 10 g peptone (Anatone, peptic digest of pork tissues, excluding glands and organs, manufactured by Cudahy Laboratories, Inc., 5014 S 33rd St, Omaha, NB 68107) in 1 L H_2O 20 min, and dil. to vol. with H_2O; adjust to pH 6.8. (If colorimetric method is used, adjust broth to give dark green with bromothymol blue.) Filter thru paper, place 10 ml quantities in 20 × 150 mm test tubes, and autoclave 20 min at 121°. Use this broth for daily transfers of test cultures.

(2) *Synthetic broth.*—*Soln A:* Dissolve 0.05 g L-cystine, 0.37 g DL-methionine, 0.4 g L-arginine.HCl, 0.3 g DL-histidine.HCl, 0.85 g L-lysine.HCl, 0.21 g L-tyrosine, 0.5 g DL-threonine, 1.0 g DL-valine, 0.8 g L-leucine, 0.44 g DL-isoleucine, 0.06 g glycine, 0.61 g DL-serine, 0.43 g DL-alanine, 1.3 g L-glutamic acid.HCl, 0.45 g L-aspartic acid, 0.26 g DL-phenylalanine, 0.05 g DL-tryptophan, and 0.05 g L-proline in 500 ml H_2O contg 18 ml $1N$ NaOH. *Soln B:* Dissolve 3.0 g NaCl, 0.2 g KCl, 0.1 g $MgSO_4.7H_2O$, 1.5 g KH_2PO_4, 4.0 g Na_2HPO_4, 0.01 g thiamine.HCl, and 0.01 g niacinamide in 500 ml H_2O. Mix Solns A and B, dispense in 10 ml quantities in 20 × 150 mm tubes, and autoclave 20 min at 121°. Before using for daily transfers of test cultures, add aseptically 0.1 ml sterile 10% glucose soln per tube.

(3) *Nutrient agar.*—Dissolve 1.5% Bacto agar (Difco) in nutrient broth and adjust to pH 7.2–7.4 (blue-green with bromothymol blue) or in synthetic broth, tube, autoclave, and slant.

(4) *Subculture media.*—Use (a), (b), or (c), whichever gives lowest result. (Com. dehydrated brands made to conform with preceding specifications may be used.) With oxidizing products and products formulated with toxic compds contg certain heavy metals like Hg, (b) will usually give lowest result. With products contg cationic surface active materials, (c) will usually give lowest results.

(a) *Nutrient broth* described in (a)(1);

(b) *Fluid thioglycolate medium USP XVIII:* Mix 0.5 g L-cystine, 0.75 g agar, 2.5 g NaCl, 5.5 g glucose, 5.0 g H_2O-sol. yeast ext, and 15.0 g pancreatic digest of casein with 1 L H_2O. Heat on H_2O bath to dissolve, add 0.5 g Na thioglycolate or 0.3 ml thioglycolic acid, and adjust with $1N$ NaOH to pH 7.1 ±0.2. Reheat without boiling and filter thru moistened filter paper, if necessary, add 1.0 ml freshly prepd 0.1% Na resazurin soln, transfer 10 ml quantities to 20 × 150 mm tubes, and autoclave 20 min at 121°. Cool at once to 25° and store at 20–30°, protected from light.

(c) *"Letheen broth":* Dissolve 0.7 g lecithin (Azolectin) and 5.0 g polysorbate 80 ("Tween 80") in 400 ml hot H_2O and boil until clear. Add 600 ml soln of 5.0 g beef ext (Difco), 10.0 g peptone (Anatone, (a)(1)), and 5 g NaCl in H_2O, and boil 10 min. Adjust with $1N$ NaOH and/or $1N$ HCl to pH 7.0 ±0.2 and filter thru coarse paper; transfer 10 ml quantities to 20 × 150 mm tubes, and autoclave 20 min at 121°.

(d) *Cystine trypticase agar (BBL).*—Suspend 29.5 g in 1 L H_2O. Heat gently with frequent agitation and boil ca 1 min or until soln is complete. Transfer 10 ml quantities to 20 × 150 mm tubes, and autoclave at 12 lb pressure 15 min. Cool in upright position and store at 20–30° ≤25 days. Use for monthly transfer of stab stock cultures of *Ps. aeruginosa* PRD 10 (ATCC 15442).

(b) *Test organism.*—Hopkins strain 26 of *Salmonella typhosa* (Zopf) Weldin, FDA, ATCC No. 6539 (formerly called *Bac. typhosus* and *Eberthella typhosa*). Maintain stock culture on nutrient agar slants by monthly transfers. Incubate new stock transfer 2 days at 37°; then store at 2–5°. From stock culture inoculate tube of nutrient broth and make at least 4 consecutive daily transfers (≤30) in nutrient broth, incubating at 37°, before using culture for testing. (If only 1 daily transfer has been missed, it is not necessary to repeat the 4 consecutive transfers.) Use 22–26 hr culture of organism grown in nutrient broth at 37° in test. Shake, and let settle 15 min before using. With *Ps. aeruginosa* PRD 10, proceed as in **4.011**.

(c) *Phenol stock soln.*—5% (w/v). Weigh 50 g USP phenol, which congeals at ≥40°, in beaker. Dissolve in H_2O, rinse soln into 1 L vol. flask, and dil. to vol. Stdze with $0.1N$ KBr-$KBrO_3$ soln, **36.208,** as follows: Transfer 25 ml stock soln to 500 ml vol. flask and dil. to vol. with H_2O. Transfer 15 ml aliquot of dild soln to 500 ml I flask and proceed as in **36.209(b)**, beginning "... and add 30 ml std KBr-$KBrO_3$ soln."

Calc. % phenol in stock soln = $(30 - $ ml $0.1N$ $Na_2S_2O_3$ soln from titrn) × 0.001569 × 1333 ×

$100/1000$; where $30 =$ ml $0.1N$ KBr-KBrO$_3$ soln added, $0.001569 =$ g phenol equiv. to 1 ml $0.1N$ KBr-KBrO$_3$ soln, $1333 =$ diln factor, and $1000 =$ original vol. phenol stock soln.

If necessary, adjust stock soln to $5.00\pm0.05\%$ phenol by adding H$_2$O or phenol. Keep in well stoppered amber bottles in cool place, protected from light.

4.002   *Apparatus*

(a) *Glassware.*—1, 5, and 10 ml vol. pipets; 1, 5, and 10 ml Mohr pipets graduated to 0.1 ml or less; 100 ml g-s cylinders graduated in 1 ml divisions; Pyrex lipped test tubes, 25 × 150 mm (medication tubes); bacteriological culture tubes 20 × 150 mm (test culture and subculture tubes). Plug medication tubes with cotton wrapped in 1 layer of cheese cloth. Sterilize all glassware 2 hr in hot air oven at 180°. Loosely plug pipets with cotton at mouth and place in closed metal containers before sterilizing.

(b) *Water bath.*—Insulated, relatively deep H$_2$O bath with cover having ≥10 well-spaced holes which admit medication tubes but not their lips.

(c) *Racks.*—Any convenient style. Blocks of wood (size depending on space in incubator) with deep holes are satisfactory. Have holes well spaced to insure quick manipulation of tubes. It is convenient to have them large enough to admit medication tubes while dilns are being made.

(d) *Transfer loop.*—Make 4 mm id single loop at end of 2–3″ Pt or Pt alloy wire No. 23 B & S gage or 4 mm loop fused on 3″ shaft (available from Matthey-Bishop, Inc., Malvern, PA 19355). Fit other end in suitable holder (glass or Al rod). Bend loop at 30° angle with stem, Fig. 4:1.

4.003   *Operating Technic*

Make 1% stock diln of substance to be tested (or any other convenient diln, depending on anticipated concn) in g-s cylinder. Make final dilns, from 1% stock diln, directly into medication tubes and remove all excess >5 ml. (Range of dilns should cover killing limits of disinfectant in 5–15 min and should at same time be close enough for accuracy.) From 5% stock phenol soln make 1–90 and 1–100 dilns directly into medication tubes. Place these tubes, contg 5 ml each of final dilns of disinfectant and of phenol, and tube contg test culture in H$_2$O bath at 20° and leave 5 min. Add 0.5 ml test culture to each of dilns at time intervals corresponding to intervals at which transfers are to be made. (Thus, by time 10 tubes have been seeded at 30 sec intervals, 4.5 min has elapsed, and 30 sec interval intervenes before transference to subculture begins.) Add culture from graduated pipet large enough to seed all tubes in any one set. In using *Ps. aeruginosa* PRD 10 (ATCC 15442), proceed as in **4.011.**

In inoculating medication tubes, hold them in slanting position after removal from bath, insert pipet to just above surface of disinfectant, and run

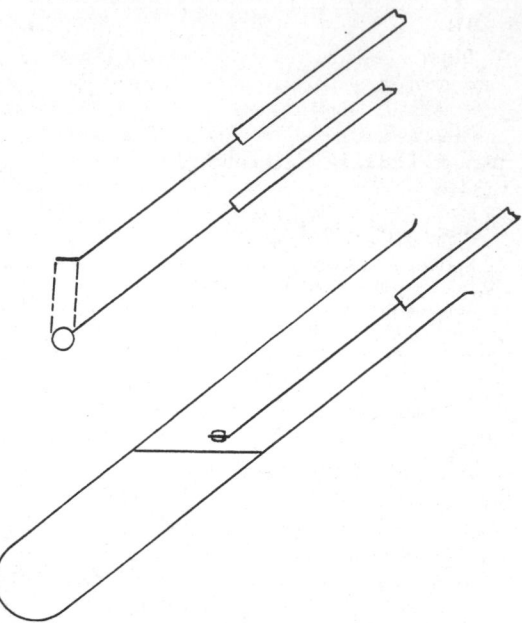

FIG. 4:1—Transfer loop and manner of using in phenol coefficient technic

in culture without letting tip touch disinfectant. After adding culture, agitate tubes gently but thoroly to insure even distribution of bacteria, and replace in bath; 5 min after seeding first medication tube, transfer 1 loopful of mixt. of culture and dild disinfectant from medication tube to corresponding subculture tube. To facilitate transfer of uniform drops of medication mixt., hold tube at 60° angle, and withdraw loop so that plane of loop is parallel with surface of liq. (Fig. 4:1). After 30 sec, transfer loopful from second medication tube to second subculture tube and continue process for each successive diln; 5 min after making first transfer, begin second set of transfers for 10 min period, and finally repeat for 15 min period.

Gently agitate medication tubes before taking each interval loop subsample for transfer to subculture medium. Before each transfer heat loop to redness in flame and flame mouth of every tube. Sterilize loop immediately after each transfer (before replugging tubes) to allow time for cooling. Use care in transferring and seeding to prevent pipet or needle from touching sides or mouth of medication tube, and see that no cotton threads adhere to inner sides or mouths of tubes. Incubate subcultures 48 hr at 37° and read results. Thoroly agitate individual subculture tubes before incubation. Macroscopic examination is usually sufficient. Occasionally 3 day incubation period, agar streak, microscopic examination, or agglutination with antityphoid serum may be necessary to det. feeble growth or suspected contamination.

4.004   *Calculation*

Express results in terms of phenol coefficient number, or highest diln killing test organism in 10 min but not in 5 min, whichever most accurately reflects germicidal value of disinfectant. Phenol coefficient is number obtained by dividing numerical value of greatest diln (denominator of fraction expressing diln) of disinfectant capable of killing *S. typhosa* in 10 min but not in 5 min by greatest diln of phenol showing same results.

Example:

	Disinfectant (X):		
Diln	5 Min	10 Min	15 Min
1–300	0	0	0
1–325	+	0	0
1–350	+	0	0
1–375	+	+	0
1–400	+	+	+

	Phenol:		
1– 90	+	0	0
1–100	+	+	+

Phenol coefficient would be $\dfrac{350}{90} = 3.89$.

Test is satisfactory only when phenol control gives one of following readings:

Phenol	5 Min	10 Min	15 Min
1– 90	+ or 0	+ or 0	0
1–100	+	+	+ or 0

If none of dilns of disinfectant shows growth in 5 min and killing in 10 min, est. hypothetical diln only when any 3 consecutive dilns show following results: first, no growth in 5 min; second, growth in 5 and 10 min but not in 15 min; and third, growth in 5, 10, and 15 min.

Example:

	Disinfectant (X):		
Diln	5 Min	10 Min	15 Min
1–300	0	0	0
1–350	+	+	0
1–400	+	+	+

	Phenol:		
1– 90	0	0	0
1–100	+	+	0

Phenol coefficient would be $\dfrac{325}{95} = 3.42$.

To avoid giving impression of fictitious accuracy, calc. phenol coefficient to nearest 0.1. Thus, in examples cited above, phenol coefficients would be reported as 3.9 and 3.4, instead of 3.89 and 3.42.

Note: It is commonly accepted criterion that disinfectants for general use be at diln equiv. in germicidal efficiency to 5% phenol against *S. typhosa* thru use of calcn 20 × *S. typhosa* coefficient to det. number of parts H_2O in which 1 part of germicide should be incorporated; however, this should be regarded as highest possible diln which could be considered for practical disinfection and is subject to confirmation by Use-Diln Method. Where this criterion is found invalid, use highest diln that will kill *S. choleraesuis* in Use-Diln Method as index to highest diln for use in practical disinfection.

4.005   *2. Using Staphylococcus aureus (1)*

Proceed as in **4.001–4.004**, except to change phenol dilns and test organisms. Use temp. of 20°. Use 22–26 hr culture of *Staph. aureus* FDA 209, ATCC No. 6538, having at 20° at least resistance indicated by following:

Phenol	5 Min	10 Min	15 Min
1–60	+ or 0	+ or 0	0
1–70	+	+	+

Note: Calc. results as in **4.004**. If conversion 20 × *Staph. aureus* coefficient is used to det. number of parts H_2O in which 1 part germicide may be incorporated to disinfect where pyogenic organisms are the objective, this diln is subject to confirmation by Use-Diln Method. Where this criterion is found invalid, use highest diln that will kill both *Staph. aureus* and *S. choleraesuis* in Use-Diln Method as index to highest diln for use in practical disinfection in hospitals, clinics, and other places where pyogenic bacteria may have special significance.

4.006   *3. Using Pseudomonas aeruginosa—*
           Official First Action

Proceed as in **4.001–4.004**. Use 22–26 hr culture of *Ps. aeruginosa* PRD 10 (ATCC 15442), having resistance to phenol at 20° at least as follows:

Phenol	5 Min	10 Min	15 Min
1–80	+ or 0	+ or 0	0
1–90	+	+	+

Use-Dilution Method (2)—
Official Final Action

(Applicable to testing disinfectants miscible with H_2O to confirm phenol coefficient results and to det. max. dilns effective for practical disinfection)

1. Using Salmonella choleraesuis

4.007   *Reagents*

(a) *Culture media.*—See **4.001**(a).

(b) *Test organism, Salmonella choleraesuis.*—(ATCC 10708). Maintain stock culture on nutrient agar slants by monthly transfers. Incubate new stock transfer 2 days at 37°; then store at 2–5°. From stock culture inoculate tube of nutrient broth and incubate at 37°. Make 3 consecutive 24 hr transfers; then inoculate tubes of nutrient broth (2 for each 10 carriers to be tested), using one loop of inoculum with each tube; incubate 48–54 hr at 37°.

(c) *Phenol.*—See **4.001**(c).

(d) *Sterile distilled water.*—Prep. stock supply of H_2O in 1 L flasks, plug with cotton, sterilize 20 min at 121°, and use to prep. dilns of medicants.

(e) *Asparagine soln.*—Make stock supply of 0.1% asparagine ("Bacto") soln in H_2O in erlenmeyer of convenient size, plug with cotton, and sterilize 20 min at 121°. Use to cover metal carriers for sterilization and storage.

(f) *Sodium hydroxide soln.*—Approx. 1N (4%). (For cleaning metal carriers before use.)

4.008   *Apparatus*

(a) *Glassware.*—As in **4.002**(a). Also: straight side Pyrex test tubes, 20 × 150 mm; 15 × 110 mm petri dishes; 100 ml, 300 ml, and 1 L erlenmeyers. Sterilize petri dishes in closed metal containers.

(b) *Water bath and racks.*—See **4.002**(b) and (c).

(c) *Transfer loops and needles.*—(1) See **4.002**(d). (2) Make 3 mm right angle bend at end of 2–3″ nichrome wire No. 18 B&S gage. Have other end in suitable holder (glass or Al rod).

(d) *Carriers.*—Polished stainless steel cylinders (penicillin cups), 8±1 mm od, 6±1 mm id, length 10±1 mm, of type 304 stainless steel, SS 18–8. (Obtainable from S. & L. Metal Products Corp., 58–29 57 Drive, Maspeth, NY 11378)

(e) *Petri dishes.*—Have available ca 6 sterile petri dishes matted with 2 layers of S&S No. 597 or Whatman No. 2, 9 cm filter paper.

4.009   *Operating Technic*

Soak ring carriers overnight in 1N NaOH, rinse with tap H_2O until rinse H_2O is neut. to phthln, then rinse twice with distd H_2O; place cleaned ring carriers in multiples of 10 in cotton plugged erlenmeyers or 25 × 150 mm cotton plugged Pyrex test tubes, cover with asparagine soln, **4.007**(e), sterilize 20 min at 121°, cool, and hold at room temp. Transfer 20 sterile ring carriers, using flamed nichrome wire hook, into 20 ml 48–54 hr nutrient broth test culture in sterile 25 × 150 mm medication tube. After 15 min contact period remove cylinders, using flamed nichrome wire hook, and place on end in vertical position in sterile petri dish matted with filter paper, **4.008**(e). Cover and place in incubator at 37° and let dry ≥20 min but ≤60 min. Hold broth culture for detn of its resistance to phenol by phenol coefficient method, **4.003**.

From 5% stock phenol soln make 1–90 and 1–100 dilns directly into medication tubes. Place tube for each diln in H_2O bath and let come to 20°. Make stock soln of germicide to be tested in sterile g-s cylinder. From this soln make 10 ml dilns to be tested, depending upon phenol coefficient found and/or claimed against *S. typhosa* at 20°, directly into each of ten 25 × 150 mm medication tubes; place the 10 tubes in H_2O bath at 20° and let come to temp. Det. diln to be tested by multiplying phenol coefficient number found and/or claimed by 20 to det. number of parts H_2O in which one part germicide is to be incorporated.

Add 0.5 ml of test culture suspension to 1–90 diln of phenol control; after 30 sec interval, add 0.5 ml to 1–100 diln of control, using sterile cotton plugged pipets. After adding culture, agitate tubes gently but thoroly to distribute bacteria evenly, and replace in bath; 5 min after seeding first medication tube, transfer 1 loopful of mixt. of culture and dild phenol from medication tube to corresponding subculture tube. After 30 sec, transfer loopful from second medication tube; 5 min after making first set of transfers begin second set of transfers for 10 min period; and finally repeat for 15 min period. Use technic of loop sampling, flaming loop and mouths of tubes and agitating medication and subculture tubes as in phenol coefficient method, **4.003**. Incubate subcultures 48 hr at 37° and read results. Resistance in 48–54 hr culture of *S. choleraesuis* should fall within range specified for 24 hr culture of *S. typhosa* in phenol coefficient method.

Add 1 contaminated dried cylinder carrier at 1 min intervals to each of the 10 tubes of use-diln of germicide to be tested. Thus, by time 10 tubes have been seeded, 9 min will have elapsed, plus 1 min interval before transfer of first carrier in series to individual tube of subculture broth. This interval is constant for each tube with prescribed exposure period of 10 min. The 1 min interval between transfers allows adequate time for flaming and cooling nichrome wire hook and making transfer in manner so as to drain all excess medication from carrier. Flame lips of medication and subculture tubes in conventional manner. Immediately after placing carrier in medication tube, swirl tube 3 times before placing it back in bath. Shake subculture tubes thoroly, incubate 48 hr at 37°, and report results as + (growth) or − (no growth) values.

Where there is reason to suspect that lack of growth at conclusion of incubation period may be due to bacteriostatic action of medicant adsorbed on carrier that has not been neutzd by subculture medium used, transfer each ring to new tube of sterile medium and reincubate for addnl 48 hr period at 37°. Where soln under test is such that material adsorbed on ring carriers and transferred into subculture medium makes it unsuitable for growth of test organism, as may be case with concd acids and alkalies, products carrying antibiotics, and wax emulsions, transfer each ring to new tube of sterile medium 30 min after initial transfer and incubate both primary and secondary subculture tubes 48 hr at 37°. Results showing no growth on all 10 carriers will confirm phenol coefficient number found. Results showing growth on any of the 10 carriers indicate phenol coefficient number to be unsafe guide to diln for use. In latter case, repeat test, using lower dilns (higher concns) of germicide under study. Max. diln of germicide which kills test organism on 10 carriers in 10 min interval represents presumed max. safe use-diln for practical disinfection.

4.010   *2. Using Staphylococcus aureus*

Proceed as in **4.009** except change phenol dilns and test organism to those specified in **4.005**. Use 48–54 hr culture of *Staph. aureus* FDA 209, ATCC No. 6538, having at least resistance specified for 24 hr culture at 20° in phenol coefficient method, **4.005**. Results showing growth on any of 10 carriers indicate that diln is too high for use in disinfecting where pyogenic bacteria must be killed. In such cases repeat test, using lower dilns (higher concns). Max. diln of germicide which kills both this test organism and *S. choleraesuis* on 10 carriers in 10 min interval represents max. presumed safe use-diln for disinfecting in hospitals, clinics, and other places where pyogenic bacteria have special significance.

Note: While killing in 10 of 10 replicates specified provides reasonably reliable index in most cases, killing in 59 out of 60 replicates is necessary for confidence level of 95%.

**4.011   3. Using Pseudomonas aeruginosa—
Official First Action**

Proceed as in **4.009.** Use 48–54 hr nutrient broth culture *Ps. aeruginosa* PRD 10 (ATCC 15442). Carry stock culture on BBL CTA (cystine trypticase agar) in stab culture incubated 48 hr at 37° and stored at 5° with transfer every 30 days. Transfer nutrient broth test cultures daily for 30-day intervals with incubation at 37°. Make fresh transfer from stock culture every 30 days. Do not shake 48–54 hr test culture but decant liq. culture aseptically, leaving pellicle behind, to obtain 20 ml culture for inoculating 20 carriers in medicant tube.

**Available Chlorine Germicidal Equivalent
Concentration (3)—Official Final Action**

(Applicable to H$_2$O-miscible disinfectants for detg available Cl germicidal equiv. concns with products offered for use as germicidal rinses for previously cleaned nonporous surfaces, especially where speed of action and capacity are essential considerations.)

4.012   *Reagents*

Use reagents specified in **4.001,** and in addn:

(a) *Sterile distilled H$_2$O.*—See **4.007**(d).

(b) *Sterile phosphate buffer soln.*—pH 8.0. Add 97.5 ml soln contg 11.61 g anhyd. K$_2$HPO$_4$ in 1 L H$_2$O to 2.5 ml soln contg 9.08 g anhyd. KH$_2$PO$_4$ in 1 L H$_2$O and autoclave 20 min at 121° in cotton plugged erlenmeyer.

(c) *NaOCl std stock soln.*—Approx. 5%. Store NaOCl stock soln in tightly closed bottle in refrigerator, and det. exact available Cl concn at frequent intervals by As$_2$O$_3$ titrn, **6.175.**

(d) *Test organisms.*—Use *S. typhosa* ATCC No. 6539 or *Staph. aureus* ATCC No. 6538 or both.

4.013   *Apparatus—See* **4.002**

4.014   *Operating Technic*

Det. resistance of test culture to phenol as in **4.001–4.005,** and use cultures with resistance specified. Prep., in sterile g-s cylinders, NaOCl solns contg 200, 100, and 50 ppm available Cl in sterile buffer soln, **4.012**(b). Transfer 10 ml of each soln to 25 × 150 mm medication tubes, place tubes in 20° H$_2$O bath, and let come to temp.

Starting with tube contg 200 ppm available Cl, add 0.05 ml test culture prepd as in **4.001**(b), shake, and return to H$_2$O bath. After 1 min make transfer to tube of appropriate subculture medium, **4.001**(a) (4), using flamed 4 mm loop. At 1.5 min, add another 0.05 ml culture to the 200 ppm Cl soln, shake, and return to bath. After addnl 1 min interval (2.5 min in test), make second subculture in same manner, and in 30 sec, or at 3 min time in test, add another 0.05 ml culture, shaking and returning to H$_2$O bath. After another 1 min interval (4 min in test) make another transfer to tube of subculture medium.

Repeat operation to give total of 10 added increments. This requires total time of 14.5 min for each soln and addn of 0.5 ml total culture with subculture at std 1 min intervals after addn of culture aliquots. At conclusion of test shake all subculture tubes and incubate 48 hr at 37°.

Repeat operation with solns contg 100 and 50 ppm available Cl. Prep. soln of germicide to be tested at concn recommended or selected for study in sterile H$_2$O in g-s graduate. Transfer 10 ml to 25 × 150 mm medication tubes, place in H$_2$O bath, and let come to temp. Repeat procedure with this soln.

To be considered equiv. in disinfecting activity to 200 ppm available Cl, unknown germicide must show absence of growth in as many consecutive tubes of subculture tube series as 200 ppm available Cl std. Det. activity equiv. to 100 and 50 ppm available Cl in same manner. *See* example below.

In this example, 25 ppm soln of germicide X could be considered equiv. to 200 ppm soln of available Cl, and 20 ppm soln equiv. to 100 ppm of available Cl, but 10 ppm soln of germicide X would not be considered equiv. in germicidal activity to 50 ppm of available Cl.

Example:

Germicide	Concn ppm Avail. Cl	Subculture Series									
		1	2	3	4	5	6	7	8	9	10
NaOCl control	200	−	−	−	−	−	+	+	+	+	+
	100	−	−	−	+	+	+	+	+	+	+
	50	−	−	+	+	+	+	+	+	+	+
Unknown (X)	25	−	−	−	−	−	+	+	+	+	+
	20	−	−	−	−	+	+	+	+	+	+
	10	−	+	+	+	+	+	+	+	+	+

− = No growth   + = growth

Draw conclusions relative to germicidal equiv. concns only when resistance of test culture to NaOCl control is such at that least 1 neg. increment is obtained at 50 ppm concn and 1 pos. increment is obtained at 200 ppm level.

Sporicidal Test (4)—Official Final Action

(Suitable for detg sporicidal activity of liq. and gaseous chemicals. Applicable to germicides for detg presence or absence of sporicidal activity against specified spore-forming bacteria in various situations and potential efficacy as sterilizing agent.)

4.015   *Reagents*

(a) *Culture media.*—(*1*) *Soil extract nutrient broth.*—Ext 1 lb garden soil in 1 L H_2O, filter several times thru S&S No. 588 paper, and dil. to vol. (pH should be ≥5.2). Add 5 g beef ext. (Difco), 5 g NaCl, and 10 g peptone (Anatone, **4.001**(a)(*1*)). Boil 20 min, dil. to vol., adjust with $1N$ NaOH to pH 6.9, and filter thru paper. Dispense in 10 ml portions into 25 × 150 mm tubes, and autoclave 20 min at 121°. Use this broth to propagate test culture of *Bacilli*.

(*2*) *Nutrient agar.*—See **4.001**(a)(*3*). Use slants of this medium to maintain stock culture of *Bacilli*.

(*3*) *Modified fluid thioglycolate medium USP XVIII.*—Prep. as in **4.001**(a)(*4*)(b), except add 20 ml $1N$ NaOH to each L before dispensing for sterilization. Use this medium to subculture spores exposed to $2.5N$ HCl. For spores exposed to unknown germicides use fluid thioglycolate medium, **4.001**(a)(*4*)(b).

(*4*) *Soil extract-egg-meat medium.*—Add 1.5 g Bacto Egg-Meat Medium dehydrated (Difco) to 25 × 150 mm tube; then add 15 ml garden soil ext, (*1*), and sterilize 20 min at 15 lb. Use this medium to propagate test cultures of *Clostridia* and maintain stock cultures of species of this genus.

(b) *Test organisms.*—Use *Bacillus subtilis*, ATCC No. 19659, or *Clostridium sporogenes*, ATCC No. 3584, for routine evaluation. Method is also applicable for use with strains of *B. anthracis, Cl. tetani,* or other spore forming species.

(c) *Dilute hydrochloric acid.*—$2.5N$. Use to det. resistance of dried spores. Stdze and adjust to $2.5N$ as in **45.013**.

4.016   *Apparatus*

(a) *Glassware.*—Bacteriological culture tubes, unflared, 25 × 150 mm; 100 ml g-s cylinders graduated in 1 ml divisions; 65 mm id funnels; supply of 15 × 110 mm petri dishes matted with 2 sheets S&S No. 597 or Whatman No. 2, 9 cm filter paper. Sterilize all glassware and matted petri dishes 2 hr in air oven at 180°.

(b) *Water bath.*—See **4.002**(b).

(c) *Racks.*—See **4.002**(c).

(d) *Transfer loop, hook, and forceps.*—See **4.008**(c).

(e) *Tissue grinder.*—Arthur H. Thomas Co., No. 4288-B, Size B, or equiv.

(f) *Suture loop carrier.*—From spool of size 3 surgical silk suture, prep. std loops by wrapping the silk around ordinary pencil 3 times, slipping coil so formed off end of pencil, and holding it firmly with thumb and index finger of left hand while passing another piece of suture through coil, knotting, and tying securely. Then shear off end of coil and knotted suture to within $\frac{1}{16}''$. This should provide overall length of ca 2.5″ of suture in 2-loop coil that can be conveniently handled in ordinary aseptic transfer procedure.

Ext loops in groups of 20 by immersion in 10 ml pet ether in stoppered, unflared test tube, shaking frequently during 30 min at room temp., and hold overnight (18–24 hr) at 2–5°. Shake, remove loops, drain, and dry.

(g) *Cylinder carriers.*—"Penicylinders," porcelain, 8±1 mm od, 6±1 mm id, 10±1 mm long. (Available from Fisher Scientific Co., Cat. No. 7-907.)

4.017   *Operating Technic*

Grow all *Bacilli* in soil ext nutrient broth and all *Clostridia* in soil ext-meat-egg medium. Inoculate 3 tubes, using 1 loop stock culture, and incubate 72 hr at 37°. Place supply of suture loops and cylinder carriers in sep. petri dishes matted with filter paper, and sterilize 20 min at 121°. Use new loops for each test and penicylinders free from chips or cracks. Filter *Cl. sporogenes* thru sterilized funnel contg moist cotton pledget into each of 3 sterile 25 × 150 mm test tubes, using same funnel. In prepg *B. subtilis* culture, pour tube of 72 hr culture into tissue grinder and macerate to break up pellicle. Filter thru sterile funnel contg moist cotton pledget into sterile 25 × 150 mm tube, repeating operation for other 2 tubes. Place 10 sterile suture loops or penicylinders into each of 3 tubes contg 10 ml filtrate from 72 hr culture of *Cl. sporogenes*, agitate, and let stand 10–15 min. Using this procedure, contaminate 35 loops or cylinders. Place contaminated suture loops or cylinders into petri dish matted with 2 layers of filter paper. Follow same procedure for *B. subtilis*.

Place the 35 suture loops or cylinders contaminated with *Cl. sporogenes* or *B. subtilis* in vac. desiccator contg $CaCl_2$ and draw vac. of 27″ Hg for 20 min. Dry 24 hr under vac. (Spores dried and held under these conditions will retain resistance 7 days or longer.)

Transfer 10 ml $2.5N$ HCl, **4.015**(c), into sterile 25 × 150 mm tube. Place tube in 20° constant temp. H_2O bath and let come to temp. Rapidly transfer 4 dried, contaminated loop or cylinder carriers to acid tube. Transfer remaining dried, contaminated suture loop or cylinder carriers to tube of thioglycolate subculture medium, **4.015**(a)(*3*), as viability control. After 2, 5, 10, and 20 min, withdraw individual loops or cylinders from acid and transfer to individual tubes of subculture medium. Rotate each tube vigorously 20 sec and resubtransfer. Incubate 21 days at 37°. Test spores should resist HCl at least 2 min, and many may resist HCl for full 20 min.

Place 10 ml disinfectant at diln recommended for use or under investigation into each of six 25 × 150 mm tubes. Place tubes in 20° H₂O bath and let come to temp. Using flamed forceps, place 5 suture loops or cylinders, contaminated with *Cl. sporogenes* or *B. subtilis* and dried 24 hr under vac., into each of the 6 tubes contg disinfectant, using 2-min intervals for seeding each tube. Five suture loops or cylinders can be placed into each tube within 5 sec. This seeding operation will take 10 min. After contact period specified for disinfectant has been achieved, remove suture loops or cylinders, using sterilized needle hook, from each tube of disinfectant to subculture medium, placing 1 suture loop or cylinder per tube. Five cylinders can be removed within each 2 min interval. Flame transfer needle hook after each carrier has been transferred to subculture medium. After completion of transfer or within 30 min after completion, resubtransfer each suture loop or cylinder to fresh tube of thioglycolate medium and incubate 21 days at 37°. If no growth is observed after 21 days, heat-shock tubes 20 min at 80° and reincubate 72 hr at 37°. Report results as + (growth) or − (no growth) values.

Dilns of unknown germicides found effective against specific spores in this test, using suture loop or penicylinder carriers, may be expected to be effective in disinfecting against same spores at equiv. time periods in practical applications. Killing in 30 of 30 trials on 1 carrier at diln and time specified is considered satisfactory evidence of desired response against single test organism when applied to carrier giving lowest result, although for confidence level of 95%, killing in 59 of 60 replicates is required. Tests with both *B. subtilis* and *Cl. sporogenes* using 30 replicates with each of the 2 carriers named to provide min. of 120 carriers are required to support unqualified sporicidal claim or to provide presumptive evidence of sterilizing activity at concn, time, and conditions specified. No more than 2 failures can be tolerated in this 120 carrier trial.

Fungicidal Test (5)—Official Final Action

(Applicable for use with H₂O-miscible type fungicides used to disinfect inanimate objects.)

Using Trichophyton interdigitale

4.018 *Test Organism*

Use as test fungus typical strain of *Trichophyton interdigitale* isolated from dermatophytosis of foot. (Strain must sporulate freely on artificial media, presence of abundant conidia being manifested by powdery appearance on surface of 10-day culture, particularly at top of agar slant, and confirmed by microscopic examination. Conidia-bearing mycelium should peel easily from surface of glucose agar. Conidia of required resistance survive 10 min exposure at 20° to phenol diln of 1:60, but not to one of 1:45. Strain No. 640, ATCC, is suitable.)

4.019 *Culture Medium*

Carry fungus on agar slants of following composition: Glucose 2%, Neopeptone (Difco) 1%, agar 2%, adjusted to pH 6.1–6.3. Use same culture medium to prep. cultures for obtaining conidial suspension, and use fluid medium of same nutrient composition (without agar) to test viability of conidia after exposure to fungicide.

4.020 *Care of Fungus Strain*

Store stock culture of fungus on glucose agar slants at 2–5°. At intervals ≤3 months, transfer it to fresh agar slants, incubate 10 days at 25–30°, and store at 2–5° until next transfer period. Do not use culture that has been kept at or above room temp. >10 days as source of inoculum for culture. (Cultures may be kept at room temp. to preserve strain and to inoculate cultures if transferred at intervals ≤10 days.)

4.021 *Preparation of Conidial Suspension*

Prep. petri dish cultures by planting inoculum at center of agar plate and incubating culture at 25–30° for 10, but ≤15 days. Remove mycelial mats from surface of 5 agar plate cultures, using sterile spatula or heavy flattened wire. Transfer to heat-sterilized glass tissue grinder (Arthur H. Thomas Co. size B) and macerate with 25 ml sterile physiological NaCl soln (0.85% NaCl), or to heat-sterilized erlenmeyer contg 25 ml sterile saline with glass beads, and shake thoroly. Filter suspension thru sterile absorbent cotton to remove hyphal elements. Est. density of conidial suspension by counting in hemacytometer and store at 2–10° as stock spore suspension (125–155 million conidia/ml) for up to 4 weeks for use in prepg test suspensions of conidia. Stdze test conidial suspensions as needed by dilg stock spore suspension with physiological NaCl soln so that it contains 5 million conidia/ml.

4.022 *Operating Technic*

Prep. dilns of fungicide. (Tests are similar to those described in **4.003**.) Place 5 ml of each fungicide soln and of phenol control solns in 25 × 150 mm test-culture tubes, arrange in order of ascending dilns, place tubes in 20° H₂O bath, and let come to temp. With graduated pipet place 0.5 ml spore suspension in first tube of fungicidal soln, shake, and immediately replace in H₂O bath; 30 sec later add 0.5 ml conidial suspension to second tube. Repeat at 30 sec intervals for each fungicidal diln. If more convenient, run test at 20 sec intervals. After 5, 10, and 15 min exposure to fungicide, remove sample from each conidia-fungicide mixt. with 4 mm loop and place in 10 ml glucose broth, **4.019**. To eliminate risk of faulty results due to possible fungistatic action, make subtransfers from the initial glucose broth subculture tubes to fresh tubes of glucose broth, using the 4 mm loop before incubation, or make initial subcultures in glucose broth contg either 0.005% Na thioglycolate, 1.5% iso-octylphenoxy-polyethoxy-ethanol, or mixt. of 0.07% lecithin (Azolectin) and 0.5% polysorbate 80 ("Tween 80"), whichever gives lowest result. Incubate inoculated tubes at 25–30°. Read final results after 10 days, altho indicative reading can be made in 4 days.

Note: Highest diln that kills spores within 10 min is commonly considered as highest diln that could be expected to disinfect inanimate surfaces contaminated with pathogenic fungi.

Germicidal and Detergent Sanitizers (6)— Official Final Action

(Suitable for detg the min. concn of germicide which can be permitted for use in sanitizing hard, nonporous surfaces. Twice this concn is min. recommended starting concn. Method also dets max. water hardness tolerances for recommended concns. Check accuracy of hard-water tolerance results with quaternaries thru use of ref. samples of known tolerance and chemical composition as control measure.)

4.023   *Reagents*

(a) *Culture media.*—(1) *Nutrient agar A.*—Boil 3 g beef ext, 5 g peptone (Bacto or equiv.; special grades must not be used), and 15 g agar in 1 L H₂O. Tube, and autoclave 20 min at 121°. Use for daily transfer of test culture. (2) *Nutrient agar B.*—Prep. as above but use 30 g agar. Use for growing test cultures in French square bottles. (3) *Nutrient agar (AOAC).*—See **4.001**(a)(3). Use for prepg stock culture slants.

(b) *Subculture media.*—(1) Use tryptone glucose ext agar (Difco), adding 25 ml stock neutralizer, (c)/L. (2) Tryptone glucose ext agar (Difco).

(c) *Neutralizer stock soln.*—Mix 40 g Azolectin (purified lecithin), 280 ml polysorbate 80 and 1.25 ml phosphate buffer, (e); dil. with H₂O to 1 L and adjust to pH 7.2. Dispense in 100 ml portions and autoclave 20 min at 121°.

(d) *Neutralizer blanks.*—For use with 200 ppm quaternary NH₄ compd or less. Mix 100 ml neutralizer stock soln, (c), 25 ml 0.25M phosphate buffer stock soln, (e), and 1675 ml H₂O. Dispense 9 ml portions into 20 × 150 mm tubes. Autoclave 20 min at 121°.

(e) *Phosphate buffer stock soln.*—0.25M. Dissolve 34.0 g KH₂PO₄ in 500 ml H₂O, adjust to pH 7.2 with 1N NaOH, and dil. to 1 L.

(f) *Phosphate buffer dilution water.*—Add 1.25 ml 0.25M phosphate buffer stock soln, (e), to 1 L H₂O and dispense in 99 ml portions. Autoclave 20 min at 121°.

(g) *Test organisms.*—Use *Escherichia coli* ATCC No. 11229 or *Staphylococcus aureus* ATCC 6538. Maintain stock cultures on nutrient agar AOAC, (a)(3), at refrigerator temp.

4.024   Resistance to Phenol of Test Cultures

Det. resistance to phenol at least every 3 months by **4.001–4.005**. Resistance of *E. coli* should be equiv. to that specified for *S. typhosa* in **4.004** and that for *Staph. aureus* equiv. to that specified for this organism in **4.005**.

4.025   *Apparatus*

(a) *Glassware.*—250 ml wide-mouth erlenmeyers; 100 ml graduated cylinder; Mohr pipets; 20 × 150 mm test tubes. Wash in strong, fresh cleaning soln, and fill and drain with H₂O at least 3 times. Sterilize at 180° in hot air oven ≥2 hr.

(b) *Petri dishes.*—Sterile.

(c) *French square bottles.*—175 ml, borosilicate.

(d) *Water bath.*—Thermostated or controlled at 25°.

4.026   Preparation of Culture Suspension

From stock culture inoculate tube of nutrient agar A, **4.023**(a)(1), and make at least 3 consecutive daily transfers (≤30), incubating transfers 20–24 hr at 35°. Do not use transfers for >30 days. If only 1 daily transfer has been missed, no special procedures are required; if 2 daily transfers are missed, repeat with 3 daily transfers.

Prep. 175 ml French square culture bottles contg 20 ml nutrient agar B, **4.023**(a)(2), autoclave 20 min at 121°, and let solidify with bottle in horizontal position. Inoculate culture bottles by washing growth from slant into 99 ml phosphate buffer diln water, **4.023**(f), and adding 2 ml of this suspension to each culture bottle, tilting back and forth to distribute suspension; then drain excess liq. Incubate 18–24 hr at 35°, agar side down. Remove culture from agar surface of 4 or more bottles, using 3 ml phosphate buffer diln water and glass beads in each bottle to suspend growth. Filter suspension thru Whatman No. 2 paper and collect in sterile tube. (Filtration may be hastened by rubbing paper gently with sterile policeman.) Stdze suspension to give av. of 10 × 10⁹ organisms/ml by diln with sterile phosphate buffer diln water, **4.023**(f).

If Lumetron colorimeter is used, dil. suspension in sterile Lumetron tube to give % T according to table:

% Light Transmission Filters, nm							Av. Bacterial Count/ml
370	420	490	530	550	580	650	
7.0	4.0	6.0	6.0	6.0	7.0	8.0	13.0 × 10⁹
8.0	5.0	7.0	7.0	7.0	8.0	9.0	11.5
9.0	6.0	8.0	8.0	8.0	9.0	10.0	10.2
10.0	7.0	9.0	9.0	9.0	11.0	11.0	8.6
11.0	8.0	10.0	10.0	10.0	12.0	13.0	7.7
13.0	9.0	12.0	12.0	12.0	13.0	15.0	6.7

If McFarland nephelometer and $BaSO_4$ stds are used, select 7 tubes of same id as that contg test culture suspension. Place 10 ml of each suspension of $BaSO_4$, prepd as indicated in table, in each tube and seal tube. Stdze suspension to correspond to No. 4 std:

Std No.	ml 2% $BaCl_2$ Soln	ml 1% H_2SO_4 (v/v) Soln	Av. Bacterial Count/ml
1	4.0	96.0	5.0×10^9
2	5.0	95.0	7.5
3	6.0	94.0	8.5
4	7.0	93.0	10.0
5	8.0	92.0	12.0
6	10.0	90.0	13.5
7	12.0	88.0	15.0

4.027 Synthetic Hard Water

Prep. *Soln A* by dissolving 31.74 g $MgCl_2$ (or equiv. of hydrates) and 73.99 g $CaCl_2$ in boiled distd H_2O and dilg to 1 L. Prep. *Soln B* by dissolving 56.03 g $NaHCO_3$ in boiled distd H_2O and dilg to 1 L. Soln A may be heat sterilized; Soln B must be sterilized by filtration. Place required amt Soln A in sterile 1 L flask and add ≥ 600 ml sterile distd H_2O; then add 4 ml Soln B and dil. to 1 L with sterile distd H_2O. Each ml Soln A will give a water equiv. to ca 100 ppm of hardness calcd as $CaCO_3$ by formula:

Total hardness as ppm $CaCO_3 = 2.495 \times$ ppm Ca $+ 4.115 \times$ ppm Mg.

pH of all test waters up to 2000 ppm hardness should be 7.6–8.0. Check prepd synthetic waters chemically for hardness at time of tests, using following method or other methods described in 12th Ed. of *Standard Methods for the Examination of Water, Sewage, and Industrial Wastes.*

4.028 Hardness Method

(a) *EDTA std soln.*—Dissolve 4.0 g Na_2H_2EDTA $.2H_2O$ and 0.10 g $MgCl_2.6H_2O$ in 800 ml H_2O and adjust by subsequent diln so that 1 ml of soln is equiv. to 1 mg $CaCO_3$ when titrd as in (b). Prep. std Ca soln (1 ml = 1 mg $CaCO_3$) by weighing 1 g $CaCO_3$, dried overnight or longer at 105°, into 500 ml erlenmeyer and adding dil. HCl thru funnel until $CaCO_3$ is dissolved. Add 200 ml H_2O, boil to expel CO_2, and cool. Add few drops Me red indicator and adjust color to intermediate orange with dil. NH_4OH or HCl as required. Transfer quant. to 1 L vol. flask and dil. to vol.

(b) *Determination.*—Dil. 5–25 ml sample (depending on hardness) to 50 ml with H_2O in erlenmeyer or casserole. Add 1 ml *buffer soln* (67.5 g NH_4Cl and 570 ml NH_4OH dild to 1 L with H_2O), 1 ml *inhibitor* (5.0 g $Na_2S.9H_2O$ or 3.7 g $Na_2S.5H_2O$ dissolved in 100 ml H_2O), and 1 or 2 drops *indicator soln* (0.5 g Chrome Black T in 100 ml 60–80% alcohol). Titr. with EDTA std soln slowly, stirring continuously, until last reddish tinge disappears from soln, adding

last few drops at 3–5 sec intervals. Hardness as mg $CaCO_3/L$ = (ml std soln $\times$ 1000)/ml sample.

4.029 Unknown Samples

Use composition declared or detd as guide to sample wt required for vol. sterile H_2O used to prep. 20,000 ppm soln. From this stock diln, transfer 1 ml into 99 ml of the water to be used in test to give concn of 200 ppm. In making transfer, fill 1 ml pipet and drain back into stock soln; then refill to correct for adsorption on glass. After mixing, discard 1 ml to provide 99 ml of the test water in **4.030.**

4.030 Operating Technic

Measure 99 ml water to be used in test, contg bactericide at concn to be tested, into chemically clean, sterile, 250 ml wide-mouth erlenmeyer and place in constant temp. bath until it reaches 25°, or at least 20 min. Prep. duplicate flasks for each germicide to be tested. Also prep. similar flask contg 99 ml sterile phosphate buffer diln water, **4.023(f)**, as "initial numbers" control.

Add 1 ml culture suspension to each test flask as follows: Whirl flask, stopping just before suspension is added, creating enough residual motion of liq. to prevent pooling of suspension at point of contact with test water. Add suspension midway between center and edge of surface with tip of pipet slightly immersed in test soln. Avoid touching pipet to neck or side of flask during addn. Transfer 1 ml portions of this exposed culture to neutralizer blanks exactly 30 and 60 sec after addn of suspension. Mix well immediately after transfer.

For "numbers control" transfer, add 1 ml culture suspension to 99 ml sterile phosphate diln water in same manner. In case of numbers control, plants need be made only immediately after adding and mixing thoroly ≤ 30 sec. (In performing test, it is advantageous to use milk pipets to add culture and withdraw samples.)

Plate from neutralizer tube to agar, using subculture medium **4.023(b)(1)** for quaternary NH_4 compds and **4.023(b)(2)** with numbers control. Where 0.1 ml portions are planted, use 1 ml pipet graduated in 0.1 ml intervals. For dilns to give countable plates, use phosphate buffer diln H_2O, **4.023(f)**. For numbers control, use following diln procedure: Transfer 1 ml exposed culture (1 ml culture suspension transferred to 99 ml phosphate buffer diln water in H_2O bath) to 99 ml phosphate buffer diln water, **4.023(f)**, (*diln A*). Shake thoroly and transfer 1 ml diln A to 99 ml phosphate buffer diln water, **4.023(f)**, (*diln B*). Shake thoroly and transfer 1 ml diln B to 99 ml phosphate buffer diln water (*diln C*). Shake thoroly and transfer four 1 ml and four 0.1 ml aliquots from diln C to individual sterile petri dishes.

For test samples, use following diln procedure: Transfer 1 ml exposed culture into 9 ml neutralizer, **4.023(d)**. Shake and transfer four 1 ml and four 0.1

ml aliquots to individual sterile petri dishes. For numbers control, use subculture medium **4.023(b)** (*2*); for tests with quaternary NH₄ compds, use medium **4.023(b)(*1*)**. Cool agar to solidify, and then invert and incubate 48 hr at 35° before counting.

4.031 Results

Results to be considered valid must meet std effectiveness: 99.999% reduction in count of number of organisms within 30 sec. Report results according to actual count and % reduction over numbers control. Counts on numbers control for germicide test mixt. should fall between 75 and 125 million/ml for % reductions to be considered valid.

4.032 Sterility Controls

(**a**) *Neutralizer.*—Plate 1 ml from previously unopened tube.

(**b**) *Water.*—Plate 1 ml from each type of water used.

(**c**) *Sterile distilled water.*—Plate 1 ml.

After counting plates, confirm that surviving organisms are *E. coli* by transfer to brilliant green bile broth fermentation tubes or lactose broth and EMB agar; confirm *Staph. aureus* by microscopic examination.

Germicidal Spray Products (*7*)— Official Final Action

(Suitable for detg effectiveness of sprays and pressurized spray products as spot disinfectants for contaminated surfaces)

4.033 Reagents

Use reagents specified in **4.001** and **4.007** except that test organism *Salmonella typhosa* is not used.

Use as test organisms *Trichophyton interdigitale* ATCC 640, prepd as in **4.021,** to which has been added 0.02 ml octylphenoxypolyethoxyethanol (Triton X100, Rohm & Haas)/10 ml suspension to facilitate spreading, *Salmonella choleraesuis* ATCC 10708, **4.007(b)**, and *Staphylococcus aureus* ATCC 6538, maintained as in **4.007(b)**.

4.034 Apparatus

Use app. specified in **4.002** and **4.008**, and in addn:

(**a**) *Capillary pipets.*—0.1 ml, graduated to deliver 0.01 ml. Sterilize in air oven 2 hr at 180°.

(**b**) *Microscope slides.*—Non-corrosive, 1 × 1″. Sterilize by placing individual slides in petri dish matted with 2 pieces 9 cm filter paper (Whatman No. 2 or equiv.) in air oven 2 hr at 180°.

(**c**) *Bacteriological culture tubes.*—Pyrex, 32 × 200 mm.

(**d**) *Metal forceps.*—Sharp points, straight, 115 mm long.

4.035 Operating Technic

Thoroly shake 48 hr nutrient broth cultures of *S. choleraesuis* and *Staph. aureus* and let settle 10 min.

With sterile capillary pipet or sterile 4.0 mm loop, transfer 0.01 ml culture onto 1 sq in. sterile test slide in petri dish and immediately spread uniformly over entire area. Cover dish immediately and repeat operation until 12 slides have been prepd for each organism. (Use 2 slides as control.) Dry all slides 30–40 min at 37°.

Spray 10 slides for specified time and distance. Hold each slide 10 min, drain off excess liq., and transfer slide to individual 32 × 200 mm tube contg 20 ml appropriate subculture medium, **4.001(a)(*4*)**, with flamed forceps. Shake culture thoroly. If broth appears cloudy after 30 min, make subculture to fresh individual tubes of subculture broth. Transfer 2 unsprayed slides, as viability controls, to individual subculture tubes in same manner.

Incubate all tubes used for primary and secondary transfers 48 hr at 37°. Read as + (growth) or − (no growth). Killing of both test organisms in 10 of 10 trials is satisfactory evidence of disinfecting action.

Det. resistance of test culture to 5 sec spraying of test slides with phenol solns, using De Vilbiss (PO Box 552, Somerset, PA 15501) No. 251 atomizer, or equiv. Results are satisfactory only when all 10 control slides with *S. aureus* sprayed with 2.0% phenol soln give neg. readings on subculture and at least 5 of 10 control slides sprayed with 1.25% phenol soln give pos. reading on subculture. With *S. choleraesuis*, all 10 control slides sprayed with 1.5% phenol soln should give neg. readings on subculture and at least 5 of 10 control slides sprayed with 0.5% phenol soln should give pos. readings on subculture. With *T. interdigitale*, 10 of 10 control slides should give neg. readings in subculture when sprayed with 1.5% phenol soln and at least 5 of 10 control slides should give pos. readings in subculture after spraying with 1.0% phenol soln.

If there is reason to believe that lack of growth in subtransfer tubes is due to bacteriostasis, inoculate all incubated subculture tubes with loop needle inoculation of respective test culture and reincubate. Growth of these inocula eliminates bacteriostasis as cause of lack of growth. If there is question as to possibility of contamination as source of growth in subculture tubes, make gram stains and/or subculture for identification, according to respective test culture.

If fungicidal activity as well as germicidal activity is involved, use test suspension of *T. interdigitale* spores, **4.021**, and prep. 12 slides, using 0.01 ml std spore suspension, spraying and subculturing exactly as above. Make subcultures in glucose broth, **4.019,** incubating 7 days at 25–30°.

Water Disinfectants for Swimming Pools (*8*)— Official Final Action

(Suitable for presumptive evidence of acceptability of products for disinfecting swimming pool water)

4.036   *Test Culture Media*

(a) *Nutrient Agar A.*—See **4.023**(a)(*1*).

(b) *Nutrient Agar B* (Trypticase Soy Agar, BBL).—See **4.037**(b).

(c) *Nutrient Agar C.*—Prep. as in **4.001**(a)(*3*).

4.037   *Subculture Media*

(a) *Tryptone glucose extract agar (Difco).*—Dissolve 24 g in 1 L freshly distd H_2O and heat to boiling to dissolve completely. Autoclave 15 min at 121°. Use for plate counts of *E. coli* survivors.

(b) *Trypticase soy agar (BBL).*—Suspend 40 g powder in 1 L H_2O. Let stand 5 min and mix thoroly. Heat gently with occasional agitation and boil ca 1 min or until soln is complete. Autoclave 15 min at 121°. Let cool and reautoclave 15 min at 121°. Use for plate counts of *S. faecalis* survivors.

(c) *Fluid thioglycolate medium (Difco).*—See **4.001**(a)(*4*)(b).

(d) *Lactose broth (Difco).*—Dissolve 19 g in 1 L H_2O. Dispense in tubes with fermentation vials in 10 ml portions. Autoclave 15 min at 121°. Use for detg presence of *E. coli* survivors.

(e) *Eosin methylene blue agar (Difco).*—Suspend 36 g in 1 L H_2O and heat to boiling to dissolve completely. Autoclave 15 min at 121°. Use for confirming *E. coli* survivors.

(f) *S-F agar (Difco).*—Dissolve 36 g in 1 L H_2O. Add 15 g agar and heat to boiling to dissolve completely. Autoclave 15 min at 121°. Use for confirming *S. faecalis* survivors.

4.038   *Neutralizer Stock Solns*

(a) *Sodium thiosulfate soln.*—Dissolve 1 g $Na_2S_2O_3$ in 1 L H_2O. Dispense in 100 ml portions and autoclave 20 min at 15 lb.

(b) *Azolectin soln.*—See **4.023**(c).

(c) *Other prepns.*—Prepns found to be suitable and necessary, depending upon nature of germicidal prepns to be studied.

4.039   *Neutralizer Blanks*

(a) *With 0.6 ppm residual chlorine or less.*—Dil. 10 ml neutralizer stock soln, **4.038**(a), with 90 ml sterile H_2O. Dispense aseptically in 9 ml portions into sterile 25 × 150 mm tubes.

(b) *With quaternary ammonium compounds and phenolic derivatives.*—Mix 10 ml neutralizer stock soln, **4.038**(b), 2.5 ml 0.25*M* phosphate buffer stock soln, **4.040**(a), and 167.5 ml H_2O. Dispense in 9 ml portions into 20 × 150 mm tubes. Autoclave 20 min at 121°.

(Use dilns of **4.038**(c) as suitable.)

4.040   *Reagents*

(a) *Phosphate buffer stock soln.*—0.25*M*. See **4.023**(e).

(b) *Phosphate buffer dilution water.*—See **4.023**(f).

(c) *Sodium thiosulfate std solns.*—(*1*) Dissolve exactly 24.820 g $Na_2S_2O_3 \cdot 5H_2O$ in H_2O and dil. to 1 L. Stdze as in **45.039** or as follows:

Dissolve 3.250 g potassium biniodate ($KIO_3 \cdot HIO_3$) in H_2O and dil. to 1 L. Dissolve ca 5 g KI in 100 ml H_2O. Add 10 ml H_2SO_4 (1 + 10) and exactly 25 ml biniodate soln. Titr. with $Na_2S_2O_3$ soln, using starch indicator, (d), near end of titrn. Record ml thiosulfate used. Normality $Na_2S_2O_3$ = (ml biniodate × 0.1)/(ml thiosulfate).

(*2*) Prep. 0.001*N* $Na_2S_2O_3$ by dilg 10 ml soln (*1*) to 1 L with H_2O.

(d) *Starch indicator soln.*—See **6.004**(f), except use few drops $CHCl_3$ instead of Hg as preservative.

(e) *Sterile phosphate buffer stock solns.*—(*1*) Dissolve 11.61 g anhyd. K_2HPO_4 in 1 L H_2O and autoclave 20 min at 121°. (*2*) Dissolve 9.08 g anhyd. KH_2PO_4 in 1 L H_2O and autoclave 20 min at 121°.

(f) *NaOCl stock soln.*—Approx. 5%. Store NaOCl stock soln in tightly closed bottle in refrigerator and det. exact available Cl at frequent intervals by As_2O_3 titrn, **6.176**.

(g) *Test organism.*—Use *Escherichia coli* ATCC 11229 and *Streptococcus faecalis* PRD. Maintain, by monthly transfer, stock cultures of *E. coli* on *Nutrient Agar C*, and *S. faecalis* on *Nutrient Agar B*; store at 4–5°.

4.041   *Apparatus*

(a) *Glassware.*—500 ml wide-mouth erlenmeyers; 100 ml graduated cylinders; Mohr pipets; milk pipets; 20 × 150 mm tubes; Board of Health tubes; 200, 500, 1000 ml vol. flasks. Wash in strong, fresh cleaning soln, and fill and drain with H_2O at least 3 times. Heat ≥2 hr at 180° in hot air oven.

(b) *Petri dishes.*—Sterile.

(c) *Water bath.*—Thermostated or controlled at 20 or 25°.

4.042   *Preparation of Culture Suspension*

From stock culture inoculate tube Nutrient Agar A for *E. coli* and Nutrient Agar B for *S. faecalis;* make at least 3 consecutive daily transfers (≤30), incubating transfer 20–24 hr at 35–37°. Do not transfer for >30 days. If only one daily transfer has been missed, no special procedures are required; if 2 daily transfers are missed, repeat with 3 daily transfers. Remove culture from agar surface, using 5 ml phosphate buffer diln water, **4.040**(b). Transfer culture suspension to sterile centrf. tube and centrf. 1–2 min at speed necessary to settle agar particles. Transfer supernatant to another sterile centrf. tube and centrf. to obtain complete sepn of cells. Discard supernatant and resuspend cells in 5 ml buffer diln water. With *S. faecalis*, centrf., discard supernatant, and resuspend cells in 5 ml buffer diln water 2 addnl times. Finally, stdze suspension to give av. of 2.0×10^8 organisms/ml by diln with sterile phosphate diln water.

If Lumetron is used, dil. suspension in sterile Lumetron tube to give $\% T$ according to table:

	% Light Transmission, Filter nm						Av. Bacterial Count, ml
	370	420	490	530	580	650	
E. coli	90	88	89	88	91	92	2.0×10^8
S. faecalis	86	82	85	85	87	89	2.0×10^8

Make serial diln plate count of each culture suspension before use, using phosphate buffer diln water, **4.040(b)**, and subculture medium, **4.037(a)**, with *E. coli* and **(b)** with *S. faecalis*. Incubate diln plates in inverted position 48 hr at 35–37°. Use Quebec Colony Counting Chamber and report results in terms of number of bacteria/ml suspension. Count of 2.0×10^8 is desired so that 1 ml test culture suspension + 199 ml test soln will provide soln contg 1 million organisms/ml. Permitted variation in test culture suspension is +500,000 and −100,000/ml of the 200 ml test soln. Use actual count for calcg zero time count in later tests.

4.043   *Determining Chlorine Demand of Freshly Distilled Test Water*

Place 200 ml H_2O in each of five 500 ml erlenmeyers. To flasks 1–5, resp., add 0.025, 0.05, 0.075, 0.1, and 0.15 ml of 200 ppm available Cl prepd from NaOCl soln, **4.040(f)**. Shake each flask, and let stand several min. Add crystal KI and 1 ml HOAc, and swirl. Add 1 ml starch soln, **4.040(d)**. Flask showing perceptible blue indicates Cl demand has been satisfied.

4.044   *Operating Technic*

Place ca 600 ml freshly sterilized distd H_2O in 1 L vol. flask. Add ca 1.5–3.0 ml K_2HPO_4 buffer, **4.040(e)(1)**, and 0.5 ml KH_2PO_4, **4.040(e)(2)**, and dil. to 900 ml. Add enough NaOCl from suitable diluent of std stock soln, **4.040(f)**, to satisfy Cl demand of 1 L test H_2O, **4.043**, and to provide ca 0.6 ppm residual available Cl. Dil. to vol. (Example: If Cl demand of H_2O is 0.1 ppm, add 3.5 ml of 200 ppm soln of available Cl made from std stock NaOCl soln, **4.040(f)**, and dil. to vol. This should provide soln with ca 0.6 ppm residual available Cl at pH 7.5 ±0.1.) Transfer 199 ml of this test soln to each of three 500 ml erlenmeyers and place in H_2O bath at either 20 or 25°. Let come to temp.

To first flask, add 1 ml boiled distd H_2O and det. residual available Cl as follows: Add small crystal KI and 1 ml HOAc; then add 1 ml starch soln, **4.040(d)**. Blue soln indicates presence of Cl. Titr. with $0.001N$ $Na_2S_2O_3$, **4.040(c)(2)**, until color disappears. ml $0.001N$ $Na_2S_2O_3 \times 0.1773 =$ ppm residual available Cl. This represents available Cl at 0 time in test. Result should be ≥ 0.58 but ≤ 0.62.

To remaining flasks add 1 ml each of test culture suspension, **4.042**, as follows: Swirl flask, stopping just before suspension is added, to create enough centrifugal motion to prevent pooling of suspension at point of contact with test H_2O. Add suspension midway between center and edge of liq. surface, immersing tip of pipet slightly below surface of H_2O. Avoid touching pipet to neck or side of test flask during operation.

From one of these 2 flasks transfer 1 ml aliquots to neutralizer blanks, **4.039(a)**, after intervals of 0.5, 1, 2, 3, 4, 5, and 10 min. Shake neutralizer blank thoroly immediately after adding sample. Prep. serial diln plate counts from neutralizer blanks, using phosphate buffer diln H_2O, **4.040(b)**, and subculture medium, **4.037(a)** for *E. coli* and **(b)** for *S. faecalis*.

After prepg diln plate counts, inoculate 5 lactose broth tubes, **4.037(d)**, with 1.0 ml aliquots from each neutralizer blank tube for each time interval when *E. coli* is used as the test organism, and 5 thioglycollate broth tubes, **4.037(c)**, with 1.0 ml aliquots from each neutralizer blank tube for each time interval when *S. faecalis* is test organism.

Incubate all diln plates in inverted position and subculture tubes 48 hr at 37°. Use Quebec Colony Counting Chamber in reading diln plates and report results in terms of number of surviving bacteria/ml test H_2O. Absence of colony growth on diln plates and absence of growth in all 5 lactose or thioglycollate tubes, as case may be, is necessary to show complete kill of test organism.

Immediately after transferring 10 min interval sample from second flask to neutralizer blank tube, remove third flask from H_2O bath and det. residual available Cl exactly as specified for first flask. Results should represent residual available Cl present at 10 min exposure interval. To be acceptable, concn of available Cl in this flask should be >0.4 ppm. Results in Cl control test described above should show complete kill of *E. coli* and *S. faecalis* within 0.5 min.

With unknown sample, prep. 2 flasks contg 199 ml each of soln at concn recommended or to be studied, using Cl demand-free, unbuffered, freshly distd H_2O previously prepd in 1 L vol. flask where Cl demand, as detd above, has been satisfied by addn of NaOCl soln. Place flasks in H_2O bath at 20 or 25°; let come to temp. Inoculate one flask with 1 ml std test culture suspension of *E. coli* and other with 1 ml std test culture suspension of *S. faecalis*. Subculture at exactly same time intervals and in same manner used with NaOCl control except vary composition of neutralizer blank depending upon nature of chemical or mixt. of chemicals under investigation. For example, mixt. of Cl-contg chemical and quaternary NH_4 compd would require special neutralizer blank prepd by using both neutralizer stock solns, **4.038(a)** and **(b)**.

Where no concn of chemical under study has been recommended and objective of study is to det. concn of unknown necessary to provide result equiv. to that obtained with Cl control std, use series of three or four 500 ml flasks contg 199 ml of varying concns of chemical and 1 ml stdzd culture suspension with each test organism. Report results as log (number of survivors) at each time interval both for Cl controls and various concns of unknown under test.

Lowest concn of unknown germicide or germicidal mixt. providing results equiv. to those obtained with NaOCl as Cl std is considered lowest concn which could be expected to provide acceptable disinfecting activity in swimming pool water.

Tuberculocidal Activity (9)— Official Final Action

(Suitable for detg max. tuberculocidal diln of disinfectants used on inanimate surfaces)

I. Presumptive In Vitro Screening Test Using Mycobacterium smegmatis

4.045 *Reagents*

(a) *Test organism.* — *Mycobacterium smegmatis* (PRD No. 1) (available from Pesticides Regulation Div., ARS, USDA, Research Center, Beltsville, MD 20705). Maintain on nutrient agar slants by monthly transfers. Incubate new stock transfer 2 days at 37°, then store at 2–5°. From stock culture inoculate tubes of Proskauer-Beck broth, incubate 48 hr in slanting position, carry 30 days, using 48 hr transfers, and use these 48 hr cultures to start test cultures. Inoculate 1 or 2 tubes of Proskauer-Beck broth. Incubate 6–7 days at 37°. Incubate tubes 48 hr in slanting position to provide max. surface aeration and then in upright position 4–5 days. Add 1.5 ml sterile 2.0% Bacto-Gelatin soln and homogenize culture with sterilized glass tissue grinder (Arthur H. Thomas Co., Size B). Adjust to 20% T at 650 nm with sterile Proskauer-Beck broth for use in testing.

(b) *Culture media.*—(*1*) *Modified Proskauer-Beck broth.*—Dissolve 2.5 g KH₂PO₄ [K_2HPO_4], 5.0 g asparagine, 0.6 g MgSO₄.7H₂O, 2.5 g Mg citrate, 20.0 ml glycerine, 0.0046 g FeCl₃, and 0.001 g ZnSO₄.7H₂O in 1 L H₂O. Adjust to pH 7.2–7.4 with 1N NaOH. Filter thru paper, place 10 ml aliquots in individual 20 × 150 mm tubes, and sterilize 20 min at 121°. Use for propagating 48 hr test starter cultures and 6–7 day test cultures.

(*2*) *Subculture media.*—Use (*1*) with addn of suitable neutzg agents such as purified lecithin (Azolectin) or Na thioglycolate, where necessary.

(*3*) *Nutrient agar.*—Prep. as in **4.001**(a)(*3*). Use to maintain stock culture.

(*4*) *Sterile distilled water.*—See **4.007**(d).

4.046 *Apparatus*

(a) *Glassware, water bath, transfer loops and needles, and petri dishes.*—See **4.008**(a), (b), (c), and (e).

(b) *Carriers.*—See **4.016**(g).

4.047 *Operating Technic*

Transfer 20 sterile penicylinder carriers, using flamed nichrome wire hook, into 20 ml 6–7 day homogenized stdzd broth culture, **4.045**(a), in sterile 25 × 150 mm medicant tube. After 15 min contact period, remove cylinders and place on end in vertical position in sterile petri dish matted with filter paper, **4.008**(e). Cover and place in incubator at 37° and let dry ≥20 min but ≤60 min. This will provide dried test carriers in groups of 20 in individual petri dishes. With each group of 20 carriers, add 1 dried cylinder at 30 sec intervals to each of 20 tubes contg 10 ml diln of germicide to be tested (at 20° in H₂O bath). Flame lips of medicant and subculture tubes. Immediately after placing carrier in medicant tube, swirl tube 3 times before placing it back in H₂O bath. (Thus, by time 20 tubes have been seeded, 9 min and 30 sec has elapsed, leaving 30 sec interval prior to subculturing series at 10 min exposure for each carrier. The 30 sec interval between transfers allows adequate time for flaming and cooling transfer hook and making transfer in manner so as to drain all excess medicant from carrier.) Transfer carrier to 10 ml subculture media, **4.045**(b)(*2*). Shake all subculture tubes thoroly and incubate 12 days at 37°. Report results as + (growth) or − (no growth). Where there is reason to suspect that results may be affected by bacteriostatic action of medicant carried over in subculture tubes, use suitable neutralizer in subculture media.

Make at least 30 carrier exposures at each of 3 relatively widely spaced dilns of germicide under test between no response and total response diln levels. Calc. % of carriers on which organism is killed at each diln. Using log % probit paper (3 cycle logarithmic normal No. 32.376, Codex Book Co., Inc., Norwood, MA 02062), locate % kill points on diln lines employed (log scale). Draw best fitting straight line thru these 3 points and extend to intercept 99% kill line. Read diln line (log scale) at point of intercept. This is presumed 95% confidence end point for product. (Do not use presumptive test organism for checking validity of this presumptive end point.)

II. Confirmative In Vitro Test for Determining Tuberculocidal Activity

4.048 *Reagents*

(a) *Culture media.*—(*1*) *Modified Proskauer-Beck medium.*—Prep. as in **4.045**(b)(*1*), and in addn, place 20 ml aliquots in 25 × 150 mm tubes. Use 10 ml portions for daily transfers of test cultures and 20 ml portions for subculturing porcelain cylinders.

(*2*) *Middlebrook 7H9 Broth Difco A.*—Dissolve 4.7 g in 900 ml H₂O contg 2 ml glycerol and 15.0 g agar. Heat to boiling to dissolve completely. Distribute in 180 ml portions and autoclave 15 min at 121°. To each 180 ml sterile medium at 45°, add 20 ml Middlebrook ADC Enrichment (Difco) under aseptic conditions and distribute in 10 ml portions in sterile 20 × 150 mm tubes. Slant. Use to maintain test culture.

(*3*) *Middlebrook 7H9 Broth Difco B.*—Dissolve 4.7 g in 900 ml H₂O contg 2 ml glycerol and 1.0 g agar. Heat to boiling to dissolve completely. Distribute in

18 ml portions in 25 × 150 mm tubes, and autoclave 15 min at 121°. To each 18 ml sterile medium at 45° add 2 ml Middlebrook ADC Enrichment under aseptic conditions. Use to subculture for survival.

(4) *Kirchners Medium Difco.*—Dissolve 13.1 g in 1000 ml H_2O contg 20 ml glycerol and heat to boiling to dissolve completely. Distribute in 18 ml portions in 25 × 150 mm tubes and autoclave 15 min at 121°. To each 18 ml sterile medium at 50–55° add 2 ml Middlebrook ADC Enrichment under aseptic conditions. Use to subculture for survival.

(5) *TB Broth Base Difco (without polysorbate 80).*—Dissolve 11.6 g in 1000 ml H_2O contg 50 ml glycerol and 1.0 g agar. Heat to boiling to dissolve completely. Distribute in 18 ml portions in 25 × 150 mm tubes, and autoclave 15 min at 121°. To each 18 ml sterile medium at 50° add 2 ml Dubos Medium Serum (Difco) under aseptic conditions. Use to subculture for survival.

(b) *Test organism.*—*Mycobacterium tuberculosis* var. *bovis* (BCG) (available from Research Foundation, 70 W Hubbard St, Chicago, IL 60610). Maintain stock cultures on culture medium (a)(2) by monthly or 6 weeks transfer. Incubate new stock transfer 15–20 days at 37° until sufficient growth is indicated; then store at 2–5°. From stock culture inoculate tube of culture medium (a)(1) and incubate 21–25 days at 37°. Shake gently once daily for 9 days; then allow to remain quiescent until 21–25th day. Make daily transfers from 21 day cultures. Transfer culture to heat-sterilized glass tissue grinder, grind, and dil. with culture medium (a)(1) to give 10% T at 650 nm. Use to inoculate porcelain cylinders used in test. Tests will be satisfactory only when organism is killed on all 10 carriers by aq. phenol (1 + 50) and shows survival after exposure to aq. phenol (1 + 75) control.

(c) *Sterile distilled water.*—See **4.007**(d).

(d) *Sterile normal horse serum without preservative.*—Difco Laboratories or Microbiological Associates, 4733 Bethesda Ave, Bethesda, MD 20014.

4.049   *Apparatus*

(a) *Glassware, water bath, transfer loops and needles, and petri dishes.*—See **4.008**(a), (b), (c), and (e).

(b) *Carriers.*—See **4.016**(g).

4.050   *Operating Technic*

Soak ring carriers overnight in 1*N* NaOH; rinse with tap H_2O and then with distd H_2O until distd H_2O is neut. to phthln; then rinse twice with distd H_2O. Place clean ring carriers in multiple of 10 or 20 in capped erlenmeyer or 20 × 150 mm tubes. Autoclave 20 min at 121°, cool, and hold at room temp. Transfer 10 sterile ring carriers, using flamed wire hook, into enough (ca 15–20 ml) 21–25 day stdzd test culture, **4.048**(b), in 25 × 150 mm medication tube. After 15 min contact period, remove cylinders,

using flamed wire hook, and place on end in vertical position in sterile petri dish matted with filter paper, **4.008**(e). Cover, place in incubator at 37°, and let dry ≥20 min and ≤60 min.

Let 10 tubes contg 10 ml use-diln germicide sample to be tested come to 20° in H_2O bath and add 1 contaminated cylinder carrier at either 30 sec or 1 min intervals to each tube. Immediately after placing carrier in medication tube contg sample of use-diln germicide, swirl tube 3 or 4 times before placing it back in bath. (Thus, by time 10 tubes have been seeded, 9 min will have elapsed, plus 1 min interval before transfer of first carrier in series to individual tube of 10 ml serum, **4.048**(d), if 1 min intervals are used. This interval is constant for each tube with prescribed exposure period of 10 min. Interval between transfers allows adequate time for flaming and cooling wire hook and making transfer in manner so as to drain all excess medication from carrier.) Transfer carrier to 10 ml serum, **4.048**(d), after exactly 10 min contact. Shake tube contg carrier in serum thoroly and place carrier in tube contg 20 ml broth, **4.048**(a)(1). From same tube take 2 ml portions serum and place in any two of the subculture media, **4.048**(a)(3), (4), (5). Repeat this with each of the 10 carriers. Incubate 1 tube of each subculture medium with 2 ml sterile serum as control. Where there is reason to suspect that germicide to be tested may possess bacteriostatic action, use suitable neutralizer in lieu of serum. Shake each subculture tube thoroly, incubate 60 days at 37°, and report results as + (growth) or − (no growth). If no growth or only occasional growth is observed in subculture, incubate addnl 30 days before making final reading. Max. diln of germicide which kills test organism on the 10 carriers, and no growth in each of the 2 ml aliquots for 2 extra media, represents max. safe use-diln for practical tuberculocidal disinfection.

SELECTED REFERENCES

(1) J. Roy. Sanit. Inst. **24**, 424(1903); Am. J. Public Health **3**, 575(1913); U.S. Dept. Agr. Circ. **198** (1931); JAOAC **32**, 408(1949); **38**, 465(1955); Soap Chem. Specialties **34**, No. 10, 79(1958).

(2) J. Bact. **49**, 526(1945); Am. J. Vet. Research **9**, 104(1948); JAOAC **36**, 466(1953).

(3) Soap Sanit. Chemicals **27**, No. 2, 133(1951); JAOAC **38**, 274(1955); **40**, 755(1957).

(4) JAOAC **36**, 480(1953); **39**, 480(1956); **40**, 759 (1957); **49**, 701(1966).

(5) Arch. Dermatol. and Syphilol. **28**, 15(1933); J. Bact. **42**, 225(1941); **47**, 102(1944); JAOAC **37**, 616(1954); **38**, 274(1955).

(6) Am. J. Public Health **38**, 1405(1948); J. Milk and Food Technol. **19**, 183(1956); Federal Register **21**, 7020(1956); JAOAC **41**, 541(1958).

(7) JAOAC **44**, 422(1961); **50**, 763(1967); Soap Chem. Specialties **38**(2), 69(1962).

(8) JAOAC **47**, 540(1964); **48**, 640(1965).

(9) JAOAC **48**, 635(1965).

5. Hazardous Substances

PREPARATIONS CONTAINING PHENOL

Phenol

Method I (1)—Official Final Action

(Applicable to com. cresols, saponified cresol solns, coal tar dips and disinfectants, and to kerosene solns of phenols in absence of salicylates or β-naphthol)

5.001 *Reagents*

(Caution: See 46.026 and 46.065.)

(a) *Dilute nitric acid.*—Aerate HNO_3 until colorless and dil. 1 vol. with 4 vols H_2O

(b) *Millon reagent.*—To 2 ml Hg in 200 ml erlenmeyer under hood, add 20 ml HNO_3. After first violent reaction, shake as needed to disperse Hg and maintain action. After ca 10 min, when action practically ceases even in presence of undissolved Hg, add 35 ml H_2O, and if basic salt seps, add enough dil. HNO_3 to dissolve it. Add 10% NaOH soln dropwise with thoro mixing until curdy ppt that forms after adding each drop no longer redissolves but disperses as permanent turbidity. Add 5 ml dil. HNO_3 and mix well. Prep. fresh daily.

(c) *Phenol std soln.*—Dissolve weighed quantity pure phenol (congealing point $\geq 40°$) in enough H_2O to make $\geq 1\%$ soln. On day it is to be used, dil. to make 0.025% aq. soln (final std).

(d) *Formaldehyde soln.*—Dil. 2 ml 37% HCHO soln to 100 ml with H_2O.

(e) *Methyl orange indicator.*—0.5% aq. soln.

5.002 *Apparatus*

(a) *Nessler cylinders.*—50 ml tall form, matched.

(b) *Test tubes.*—Approx. 180 × 20 mm, with rubber stoppers, marked at 25 ml.

(c) *Water bath for heating test tubes.*—Beaker contg disk of wire gauze raised ca 1″ from bottom may be used.

5.003 *Preparation of Sample*

(a) *Commercial cresol.*—Weigh by difference ca 2.5 g sample into 250 ml vol. flask, dissolve in 10 ml 10% NaOH soln, and dil. to vol. with H_2O.

(b) *Saponified cresol solns, coal tar dips and disinfectants, kerosene solns of phenols, etc.*—Weigh by difference ca 5 g sample (or use 5 ml and calc. wt from density) into 250 ml vol. flask and dil. to mark with H_2O. With products consisting largely of kerosene, bring H_2O level to mark and take aliquots from aq. portion only.

5.004 *Determination*

Transfer 5 ml aliquot prepd soln to 200 ml vol. flask and promptly dil. to ca 50 ml. Add 1 drop Me orange, **5.001**(e), and then dil. HNO_3 until soln is practically neut. Dil. to vol. and shake well.

Place 5 ml dild soln in each of 2 marked test tubes; in each of 2 addnl test tubes place 5 ml std phenol soln. Flow 5 ml Millon reagent down side of each tube, mix, and place tubes in boiling H_2O bath; continue boiling exactly 30 min, cool immediately and thoroly by immersion in bath of cold H_2O at least 10 min, and add 5 ml dil. HNO_3 to each tube.

Mix well and add 3 ml HCHO soln to one of each pair of tubes. Dil. all tubes to 25 ml mark with H_2O, stopper, shake well, and let stand overnight. (Tubes contg HCHO fade to yellow; others show orange or red color.)

Pipet 20 ml from each of the 2 phenol tubes to 100 ml vol. flasks; add 5 ml dil. HNO_3 to each, dil. to vol., and mix. (Red flask contains "phenol std," yellow flask "phenol blank.") Transfer these solns to burets. Pipet 10 ml of each sample soln into Nessler tubes. (The orange or red constitutes the "unknown" and the yellow the "sample blank." Mark each Nessler tube distinctly to avoid confusion.) Add to "sample blank" tube measured quantity of "phenol std" and add same vol. "phenol blank" to "unknown." Agitate thoroly (aided by insertion of rubber stoppers, if necessary), and compare colors. When tubes are brought to match, each ml phenol std used = 1% phenol if sample weighing exactly 5 g was used, or 2% if exactly 2.5 g was used.

Note.—Take following precautions: Pair of phenol tubes provides enough final solns to assay several unknowns, but all the latter must have accompanied phenol solns thruout entire process with identical reagents and treatment. If end point is inadvertently overrun it is possible to work back to it, but since mistakes may be made in this operation it is better to repeat comparison on fresh portions from original tubes. Too much delay in matching tubes must be avoided after titrn is started, otherwise excess HCHO present in blanks may have time after mixing to affect intensity of red color. Millon reagent is dangerously poisonous and should not be transferred with ordinary pipet and mouth suction unless protective trap is used.

5.005 *Method II (2)—Official Final Action*

(Applicable to detn of phenol in presence of salicylates)

Weigh by difference 10 g sample into separator (or use 10 ml and calc. wt from density of sample). Add 50 ml kerosene and ext with three 100 ml portions H_2O. Filter aq. exts thru wet filter into 500 ml vol. flask, dil. to vol. with H_2O, and proceed as in **5.004**.

When tubes are brought to match, each ml phenol std used = 1% phenol if sample weighing exactly 10 g was used.

SODA LYE

Carbonate and Hydroxide (3)—
Official Final Action

5.006   *Determination*

Weigh ca 10 g sample from weighing bottle, dissolve in CO_2-free H_2O, and dil. to definite vol. Titr. aliquot with $0.5N$ HCl, **45.012–45.013**, using Me orange, **5.001**(e), and note total alky found. Transfer equal aliquot to vol. flask and add enough 10% $BaCl_2$ soln to ppt all carbonate, avoiding any unnecessary excess. Dil. to vol. with CO_2-free H_2O, stopper, shake, and let stand. When liq. clears, pipet off one-half and titr. with the $0.5N$ HCl, using phthln; ml $0.5N$ acid required for this titrn $\times 2 =$ ml $0.5N$ acid equiv. to NaOH present in original aliquot. Difference between this figure and ml $0.5N$ HCl required for total alky = ml $0.5N$ acid equiv. to Na_2CO_3 present in aliquot. Calc. % Na_2CO_3 and NaOH.

SELECTED REFERENCES

(*1*) USDA Bull. **1308**, p. 17; JAOAC **13**, 160(1930).
(*2*) Ind. Eng. Chem., Anal. Ed. **1**, 232(1929).
(*3*) Sutton "Systematic Handbook of Volumetric Analysis," 10th ed., p. 61 (1911).

6. Pesticide Formulations [★]

GENERAL METHODS

6.001 Sampling—Procedure

(*Caution: See* **46.041.**)

Examine shipping cases closely for code numbers, different labels, and other pertinent information. Give special attention to products subject to deterioration.

Caution: Use care in sampling and transporting toxic materials to avoid personal injury and contamination of transportation facilities in case of breakage. When dealing with rodenticides and weed-killers, avoid mutual contamination with other products during transportation.

Mark each sample container according to laboratory requirements.

(a) *Small package retail units.*—Take one unopened unit (1 lb if dry, 1 pt if liq.), except take min. of 2 units of small baits in cake form. Size of sample is governed by composition of material and analytical methods.

(b) *Large package dry products (25 lb or more).*—Sample unopened containers, using trier long enough to reach bottom of container by inserting into container at one edge or corner and probing diagonally toward opposite edge or corner. Take cores by code or batch number. Analyze cores from same code or batch number as composite or individually. Clean trier thoroly after sampling each batch.

Store samples in air-tight glass, metal, plastic, or cardboard containers.

(c) *Large package liquid products (5 gallons or more).*—Use glass, plastic tubing, or stainless steel trier with plunger, or rubber tubing for certain materials. Store samples in glass or containers of other noncorrosive material with screw top caps lined with Teflon or other inert material. Plastic containers may be used only for carefully selected products.

6.002 Preparation of Sample— Official Final Action

Thoroly mix all samples before analysis. Det. H_2O-sol. As on samples as received, without further pulverization or drying. In case of lye, NaCN, or KCN, weigh large quantities in weighing bottles and analyze aliquots of their aq. solns.

6.003 Moisture—Official Final Action

(Applicable to Paris green, powd Pb arsenate, Ca arsenate, Mg arsenate, Zn arsenite, powd Bordeaux mixt., and Bordeaux mixt. with arsenicals)

★ Methods so marked are surplus methods. *See* "Definitions of Terms and Explanatory Notes," item (29).

Dry 2 g to constant wt at 105–110° and report loss in wt as moisture.

Total Arsenic—Official Final Action

Hydrazine Sulfate Distillation Method (1)

(Nitrates do not interfere. Applicable to detn of total As in Paris green, Pb arsenate, Ca arsenate, Zn arsenite, Mg arsenate, and Bordeaux mixt. with arsenicals)

6.004 *Reagents*

(a) *Arsenious oxide std soln.*—0.1 or 0.05N. *See* **45.005–45.006.**

(b) *Iodine std soln.*—0.1 or 0.05N. *See* **45.019–45.020.**

(c) *Bromate std soln.*—0.1 or 0.05N. Dissolve ca 2.8 or 1.4 g $KBrO_3$ in boiled H_2O and dil. to 1 L. Stdze as follows: Pipet 25 ml aliquots of the As_2O_3 soln, (a), into 500 ml erlenmeyers. Add 15 ml HCl, dil. to 100 ml, heat to 90°, and titr. with the $KBrO_3$ soln, using 10 drops Me orange, (g). Do not add indicator until near end of titrn, and agitate soln continuously to avoid local excess of $KBrO_3$ soln. Add $KBrO_3$ soln very slowly near end point; at end point soln changes from red to colorless.

(d) *Hydrazine sulfate-sodium bromide soln.*—Dissolve 20 g $N_2H_4.H_2SO_4$ and 20 g NaBr in 1 L HCl $(1 + 4)$.

(e) *Sodium hydroxide soln.*—Dissolve 400 g NaOH in H_2O and dil. to 1 L.

(f) *Starch indicator.*—Mix ca 2 g finely powd. potato starch with cold H_2O to thin paste; add ca 200 ml boiling H_2O, stirring constantly, and immediately discontinue heating. Add ca 1 ml Hg, shake, and let soln stand over the Hg.

(g) *Methyl orange indicator.*—0.05%. Dissolve 0.5 Me orange in H_2O and dil. to 1 L.

6.005 *Apparatus (Figure 6:1)*

Set 500 ml distn flask on metal gauze that fits over circular hole in heavy sheet of asbestos board, which in turn extends out far enough to protect sides of flask from direct flame of burner. First receiving flask holds 500 ml and contains 40 ml H_2O; second holds 500 ml and contains 100 ml H_2O. Vol. in first flask should be ≤40 ml, otherwise compd of As may sep. that is difficult to dissolve without danger of loss of $AsCl_3$. Keep both flasks cool by placing in pan of circulating H_2O, or contg H_2O and ice.

6.006 *Determination*

(*Caution: See* **46.041** and **46.078.**)

Weigh sample contg ≤0.4 g As and transfer to distg flask. Add 50 ml $N_2H_4.H_2SO_4$-NaBr soln,

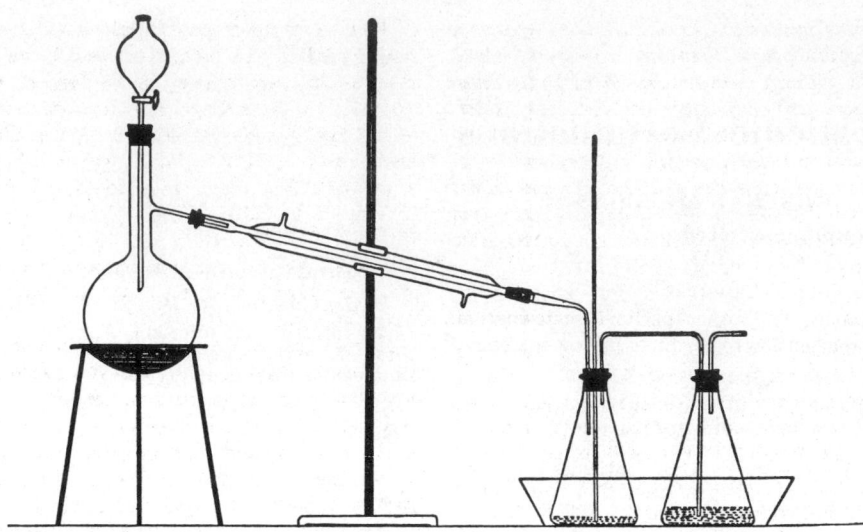

FIG. 6:1—Apparatus for distilling arsenious chloride

close flask with stopper that carries funnel tube, and connect side tube with condenser. Boil 2–3 min, add 100 ml HCl from dropping funnel, and distill until vol. in distg flask is reduced to ca 40 ml; add 50 ml more HCl and continue distn until vol. is again reduced to ca 40 ml. Wash down condenser, transfer contents of receiving flasks to 1 L vol. flask, dil. to vol., mix thoroly, and proceed as in (a) or (b):

(a) Pipet 200 ml aliquot into erlenmeyer and nearly neutze with NaOH soln, using few drops phthln, and keeping soln well cooled. If neut. point is passed, add HCl until again slightly acid. Neutze with NaHCO₃, add 4–5 g excess, and add std I soln from buret, shaking flask continuously until yellow color disappears slowly from soln. Add 5 ml starch indicator and keep adding std I soln dropwise until blue color is permanent.

(b) Pipet 200 ml aliquot into erlenmeyer and titr. with KBrO₃ soln, (c), beginning "heat to 90° ..."

Calc. % As. Report as As_2O_3 or As_2O_5, according to whether As is present in trivalent or pentavalent form. If condition of arsenic is unknown, report as As.

Iodimetric Method (2)
(Applicable in presence of sulfides, sulfites, thiosulfates, and large quantities of S or org. matter)

6.007   *Reagent*

Sodium thiosulfate soln.—Dissolve 13 g crystd $Na_2S_2O_3.5H_2O$ in H_2O and dil. to 1 L.

See **6.004** for other reagents and solns and **6.005** for app.

6.008   *Determination*
(*Caution: See* **46.041** and **46.078**.)

Weigh sample contg ≤0.4 g As and transfer to distg flask. Add 50 ml $N_2H_4.H_2SO_4$-NaBr soln,

6.004(d), and distill as in **6.006**. Make distillate to vol. in 1 L vol. flask, mix thoroly, and transfer 200 ml aliquot to 400 ml Pyrex beaker or porcelain casserole. Add 10 ml HNO_3 and 5 ml H_2SO_4, evap. to sirupy consistency on steam bath, and then heat on hot plate until white fumes of H_2SO_4 appear. Cool, and wash into 500 ml erlenmeyer. If vol. H_2SO_4 is appreciably lessened by fuming, add enough H_2SO_4 to make total vol. ca 5 ml. Dil. to 100–150 ml, add 1.5 g KI, and boil until vol. is reduced to ca 40 ml. Cool soln under running H_2O, dil. to 100–150 ml, and add $Na_2S_2O_3$ soln, **6.007,** dropwise until I color just disappears. Nearly neutze H_2SO_4 with NaOH soln, **6.004**(e), finish neutzn with NaHCO₃, add 4–5 g excess, and titr. with std I soln as in **6.006**(a). From ml std soln used calc. % As in sample. Report as As_2O_3, As_2O_5, or As as in **6.006**.

Ion Exchange Method (3)—Official Final Action
(Applicable to inorg. arsenates and arsenites)

6.009   *Apparatus*

Ion exchange column.—Use Allihn filter tube 10 × 2.7 cm od with coarse filter disk. Attach piece of rubber tubing to bottom of filter tube and regulate flow with Hoffman clamp. To tube add aq. slurry of Dowex 50WX8, 50–100 mesh, using resin bed vol. of 12 ml, and place 500 ml separator above tube.

Regenerate resin bed before each run by first backwashing column few min with H_2O; then elute with 350 ml 2N HCl followed by 200 ml H_2O at 20 ml/ min.

6.010   *Preparation of Sample*
(*Caution: See* **46.041**.)

Weigh 200 mg sample (100 mg if As content is >30%) into 150 ml beaker, add 7 ml HNO_3, and bring to boil. Add 3 ml 2N $KBrO_3$ and evap. to dryness, avoiding spattering. Backwash and regenerate resin during this evapn. Dissolve cooled residue in 2 ml $6N$ HCl without heat and add 8 ml H_2O. Filter into separator, and wash filter with three 10 ml portions H_2O. (If residue dissolves completely in 2 ml $6N$ HCl, omit filtration, and dil. directly to 40 ml.) Pass soln thru resin column at 20 ml/min and collect eluate in 250 ml erlenmeyer. Wash separator and column with 20 and 40 ml portions of H_2O into same erlenmeyer.

6.011 *Determination*

Add 50 ml HCl to eluate to make $4N$. Add 1 g $NaHCO_3$, 0.2 g at time, swirling constantly. Add 1 g KI, stopper, and swirl until all KI dissolves. After 5 min, titr., without starch indicator, with $0.05N$ $Na_2S_2O_3$, **45.038–45.039,** to disappearance of I. (Recognition of end point is facilitated by making titrn on porcelain stand. In presence of starch, reaction between I and $Na_2S_2O_3$ is retarded, so appreciable quantity of $Na_2S_2O_3$ reacts with acid. End point becomes indistinct if >30 ml $Na_2S_2O_3$ is used in titrn.) 1 ml $0.05N$ $Na_2S_2O_3 = 1.873$ mg As.

Water-Soluble Arsenic— Official Final Action

(Applicable to detn of H_2O-sol. arsenic in Pb arsenate, Ca arsenate, Zn arsenite, Mg arsenate, and Bordeaux mixt. with arsenicals)

6.012 *Determination*
(*Caution: See* **46.041.**)

To 2 g original sample if powder, or 4 g if paste, in 1 L Florence flask, add 1 L recently boiled H_2O that has been cooled to 32°. Stopper flask and place in constant temp. H_2O bath at 32°. Digest 24 hr, shaking hourly 8 hr during this period. Filter thru dry filter. If filtrate is not clear, refilter thru buchner contg paper and enough Filter-Cel coating to give clear soln. Discard first 50 ml.

Transfer 250–500 ml *clear* filtrate to erlenmeyer, add 3 ml H_2SO_4, and evap. on hot plate. When vol. is ca 100 ml, add 1 g KI, and continue boiling until vol. is ca 40 ml. Cool, dil. to ca 200 ml, and add $Na_2S_2O_3$ soln, **6.007,** dropwise, until I color is exactly removed. (Avoid use of starch indicator at this point.) Neutze with $NaHCO_3$, add 4–5 g excess, titr. with std I soln, shaking flask continuously, until yellow disappears slowly, add 5 ml starch indicator, **6.004(f),** and continue titrn to permanent blue. Correct for quantity of std I soln necessary to produce same color, using same reagents and vol. From ml std I soln used, calc. % H_2O-sol. As in sample.

6.013 Lead (4)—Official Final Action
(Applicable to such prepns as Bordeaux-Pb arsenate, Bordeaux-Zn arsenite, Bordeaux-Paris green, and Bordeaux-Ca arsenate)

(*Caution: See* **46.026, 46.031, 46.041, 46.047, 46.059,** and **46.078.**)

Weigh 1 g powd. sample and transfer to beaker. Add 5 ml *HBr* (ca 1.38 sp gr) and 15 ml HCl, and evap. to dryness to remove As. Repeat treatment; add 20 ml HCl, and again evap. to dryness. Add 25 ml $2N$ HCl to residue, heat to boiling, filter immediately to remove SiO_2, and wash with boiling H_2O to vol. of 125 ml. See that all $PbCl_2$ is in soln before filtering; if it will not dissolve completely in 25 ml $2N$ acid, add 25 ml more and dil. filtrate to 250 ml. Pass in H_2S until pptn is complete. Filter, and wash ppt thoroly with $0.5N$ HCl satd with H_2S. Save filtrate and washings for Zn detn.

Transfer paper with sulfides of Pb and Cu to 400 ml Pyrex beaker and completely oxidize all org. matter by heating on steam bath with 4 ml H_2SO_4 and ca 20 ml *fuming HNO₃* in covered beaker. Evap. on steam bath, and then completely remove HNO_3 by heating on hot plate until copious white fumes of H_2SO_4 appear. Cool, add 2–3 ml H_2O, and again heat to fuming. Cool, add 50 ml H_2O and 100 ml alcohol, and let stand several hr (preferably overnight). Filter thru gooch, previously washed with H_2O, then with *acidified alcohol* (100 parts H_2O, 200 parts alcohol, and 3 parts H_2SO_4), and finally with alcohol, and dried at 200°. Wash ppt of $PbSO_4$ in crucible ca 10 times with acidified alcohol, and then with alcohol, to remove H_2SO_4.

Dry at 200° to constant wt, keeping crucible covered to prevent loss from spattering. From wt $PbSO_4$, calc. % Pb in sample, using factor 0.6832.

Copper (4)—Official Final Action

(Applicable to such prepns as Bordeaux-Pb arsenate, Bordeaux-Zn arsenite, Bordeaux-Paris green, and Bordeaux-Ca arsenate)

(*Caution: See* **46.019** and **46.026.**)

6.014 *Electrolytic Method*

Evap. filtrate and washings from $PbSO_4$ pptn, **6.013,** to fuming; add few ml *fuming HNO₃* to destroy org. matter, and continue evapn to ca 3 ml. Take up with ca 150 ml H_2O, add 5 ml HNO_3, and filter if necessary. Wash into 250 ml beaker, adjust vol. to 200 ml, and electrolyze, using rotating anode and weighed gauze cathode with current of 2–3 amp. After all Cu has apparently deposited (ca 30 min), add 15–20 ml H_2O to electrolyte and continue electrolysis few min. If no further deposition occurs on newly exposed surface of electrode, wash with H_2O without breaking current either by siphoning or quickly replacing beaker with electrolyte successively with 2 beakers of H_2O. Interrupt current, rinse cathode with alcohol, dry few moments in oven, and weigh. Calc. % Cu in sample.

6.015 *Volumetric Thiosulfate Method*
(*Caution: See* **46.019** and **46.026.**)

Proceed as in **6.014** to point at which filtrate and washings from $PbSO_4$ pptn are treated with fuming HNO_3 and evapd to vol. of ca 3 ml. Take up in ca 50 ml H_2O, add NH_4OH in excess, and boil to expel excess NH_3, as shown by color change in liq. and partial pptn. Add 3–4 ml HOAc $(4 + 1)$, boil 1–2 min, cool, add 10 ml 30% KI soln, and titr. with std $Na_2S_2O_3$ soln, **31.041**, until brown color becomes faint. Add starch indicator, **6.004**(f), and continue titrn cautiously until blue color due to free I entirely disappears. From ml std $Na_2S_2O_3$ soln used, calc. % Cu in sample.

Zinc (5)—Official Final Action

(Applicable to such prepns as Bordeaux-Pb arsenate, Zn arsenite, Bordeaux-Zn arsenite, Bordeaux-Paris green, and Bordeaux-Ca arsenate)

6.016   *Reagent*

Mercury-thiocyanate soln.—(*Caution: See* **46.065.**) Dissolve 27 g $HgCl_2$ and 30 g NH_4SCN in H_2O and dil. to 1 L.

6.017   *Determination*

(*Caution: See* **46.059.**)

Conc. filtrate and washings from sulfide pptn, **6.013,** by gentle boiling to ca 50 ml, and continue evapn on steam bath to dryness. Dissolve residue in 100 ml H_2O contg 5 ml HCl, and add 35–40 ml Hg-thiocyanate soln with vigorous stirring. Let stand ≥ 1 hr with occasional stirring. Filter thru weighed gooch, wash with H_2O contg 20 ml Hg-thiocyanate soln/L, and dry to constant wt at 105°. Calc. to % Zn, using factor 0.1312.

Note: Some Fe is usually present and during Zn detn should be in ferrous condition. In pptg sulfides pass H_2S into soln long enough to reduce Fe as well as to ppt Cu and Pb. $ZnHg(SCN)_4$ ppt normally is white, and occluded $Fe(SCN)_3$ should not give more than faint pink color.

Total Fluorine—Official Final Action

Lead Chlorofluoride Method (6)

6.018   *Reagents*

(a) *Fusion mixture.*—Mix 30 g· anhyd. Na_2CO_3 with 40 g anhyd. K_2CO_3.

(b) *Lead chlorofluoride wash soln.*—Dissolve 10 g $Pb(NO_3)_2$ in 200 ml H_2O, dissolve 1 g NaF in 100 ml H_2O and add 2 ml HCl, and mix these 2 solns. Let ppt settle and decant. Wash ppt 4 or 5 times with 200 ml H_2O by decanting, and then add ca 1 L cold H_2O to ppt and let stand 1 hr or longer, with occasional stirring. Filter and use clear filtrate. (Prep. more wash soln as needed by adding more H_2O to ppt of PbClF and stirring.)

(c) *Silver nitrate std soln.*—0.1 or 0.2N. Stdze as in **45.032.**

(d) *Potassium or ammonium thiocyanate std soln.*—0.1N. Stdze by comparing with std $AgNO_3$ soln under same conditions as in detn.

(e) *Ferric indicator.*—To cold satd Cl-free $FeNH_4(SO_4)_2.12H_2O$ soln add enough colorless HNO_3 to bleach brown color.

(f) *Bromophenol blue indicator.*—Grind 0.1 g powder with 1.5 ml 0.1N NaOH and dil. to 25 ml.

6.019   *Determination*

(a) *Samples difficult to decompose such as cryolite, and others that contain Al or appreciable quantities of siliceous material.*—Mix 0.5 g sample (or less if necessary to contain 0.01–0.10 g F) with 5 g fusion mixt. and 0.2–0.3 g *powd.* SiO_2, cover with 1 g fusion mixt., and heat to fusion over Bunsen burner. (Use of blast lamp is unnecessary since it is preferable not to heat much beyond melting temp. If much Al is present, uniform, clear, liq. melt cannot be obtained; particles of white solid will sep. in melt. Cooled melt should be colorless, or at least should not have more than gray color.)

Leach cooled melt with hot H_2O and when disintegration is complete, filter into 400 ml beaker. Return insol. residue to Pt dish with jet of H_2O, add 1 g Na_2CO_3, dil. to 30–50 ml, and boil few min, disintegrating any lumps with flat-end rod. Filter thru same paper, wash thoroly with hot H_2O, and adjust vol. of filtrate and washings to ca 200 ml. Add 1 g ZnO dissolved in 20 ml HNO_3 $(1 + 9)$, boil 2 min, stirring constantly, filter, and wash thoroly with hot H_2O. During this washing return gelatinous mass to beaker 3 times and thoroly disintegrate in wash soln because proper washing of this ppt on filter is difficult. (Mass can easily be returned to beaker by rotating funnel above beaker while cutting ppt loose from paper with jet of wash soln.)

Add 2 drops bromophenol blue indicator to filtrate, and with cover glass almost entirely over beaker add HNO_3 $(1 + 4)$ until color just changes to yellow. Make soln slightly alk. with 10% NaOH soln, and with cover glass on beaker, boil gently to expel CO_2. Remove from burner; add the HNO_3 until color just changes to yellow and then 10% NaOH until color just changes to blue; then add 3 ml *10% NaCl soln.* (Vol. of soln at this point should be ca 250 ml.)

Add 2 ml HCl $(1 + 1)$ and 5 g $Pb(NO_3)_2$ and heat on steam bath. As soon as $Pb(NO_3)_2$ is in soln, add 5 g NaOAc, stir vigorously, and digest on steam bath 30 min with occasional stirring. Let stand overnight, filter, and wash ppt, beaker, and paper once with cold H_2O, then 4 or 5 times with PbClF wash soln, and then once more with cold H_2O.

Transfer ppt and paper to beaker in which pptn was made, stir paper to pulp, add 100 ml HNO_3 $(5 + 95)$, and heat on steam bath until ppt dissolves. (5 min is ample to dissolve ppt. If sample contains appreciable quantity of sulfates, ppt will contain $PbSO_4$, which will not dissolve. In such case heat 5–10 min with stirring and consider PbClF to be dissolved.) Add slight excess 0.1N or 0.2N $AgNO_3$, digest on steam bath 30 min, and cool to room temp., protecting from light; filter, wash with cold H_2O, and det. $AgNO_3$ in filtrate by titrn with std thiocyanate soln, using 10 ml ferric indicator. Subtract amt of

AgNO$_3$ found in filtrate from that originally added. Difference is amt required to combine with Cl in the PbClF; from this difference calc. % F in sample on basis that 1 ml 0.1N AgNO$_3$ = 0.00190 g F.

(b) *Water-soluble fluorides in presence of organic matter.*—In presence of up to 50% org. matter such as flour, pyrethrum, tobacco powder, and derris or cubé powders, which readily decompose without addn of powd. SiO$_2$ and contain little or no sulfates, Al, or siliceous compds, mix 0.5 g sample (or less if necessary to contain 0.01–0.1 g F) with 5 g fusion mixt., cover with 1 g fusion mixt., and heat to fusion over Bunsen burner. Leach cooled melt with hot H$_2$O, and when disintegration is complete, filter into 600 ml beaker. Wash thoroly with hot H$_2$O and proceed as in (a), third par.

In presence of >50% org. matter or org. matter that is impractical to free without preliminary ashing, such as apple peel and pulp, transfer enough sample to Pt crucible to be representative of mixt. and to contain 0.01–0.1 g F. Add 15 ml H$_2$O and enough *F-free CaO* (0.3–0.4 g) to make mixt. distinctly alk. to phthln, mix with glass rod, and evap. to dryness on steam bath and in oven at 105°. Ignite at low heat, preferably in muffle ($\leq$600°), until org. matter is thoroly charred. Pulverize, with glass rod, any lumps present in charred ash, mix with 5 g of the fusion mixt., and proceed as in (a), first par., beginning "cover with 1 g fusion mixt. . . ."

(c) *Water-soluble samples in absence of organic matter and appreciable quantities of sulfates or Al salts.*—In absence of org. matter or other interfering substances, fusion may be omitted and detn made on aliquot of aq. soln contg 0.01–0.1 g F, as in (a), third par.

In presence of Al, as in samples contg Na$_2$SiF$_6$ and KAl(SO$_4$)$_2 \cdot 12$H$_2$O, transfer sample to 400 ml beaker, dissolve in 150 ml hot H$_2$O, add 6 g fusion mixt., and boil. Add 1 g *ZnO* dissolved in 20 ml HNO$_3$ (1 + 9), boil 2 min with constant stirring, filter into 500 ml vol. flask, and wash thoroly with hot H$_2$O. Cool to room temp. and dil. to vol. Transfer 200 ml aliquot contg 0.01–0.10 g F to 600 ml beaker and proceed as in (a), third par.

(d) *Sodium and Mg fluosilicates, or samples containing >5% sulfates in absence of Al and B, with or without moderate quantities of organic matter.*—With large amts of Na$_2$SiF$_6$ and some other more volatile fluosilicates, *e.g.*, MgSiF$_6$, where there is possibility of some F being evolved as SiF$_4$ before fusion is effected, or in samples contg appreciable amts of sulfates, distill F as in **6.023,** and det. F in distillate as follows: Add several drops bromophenol blue indicator, make alk. with NaOH, and adjust vol. to ca 250 ml by gently boiling down vol. from 400 to 250 ml. Proceed as in (a), third par., beginning "Remove from burner; . . ."

Notes: These methods give accurate results for 0.01–0.10 g F. Below 0.01 g, results tend to be slightly low, and above 0.10 g, slightly high. Con-venient sample to fuse is one contg 0.07–0.08 g F; too large sample may result in incomplete fusion. Large amts of B compds and alkali salts retard or prevent complete pptn of PbClF. B has greater effect when amt of F is large than when it is small. In methods described B has little effect, and it may be disregarded in analysis of insecticides if quantity of F to be pptd is $\leq$0.03 g. With some prepns contg Na$_2$B$_4$O$_7$ or H$_3$BO$_3$, where it is difficult to obtain representative mixt. when extremely small sample (0.1 g) is used for analysis, take larger sample and ppt PbClF from aliquot of fusion soln. Quantity of alkali carbonates specified in fusion and in washing of insol. residue is not large enough to cause low results. If sample contains S, remove it with CS$_2$ and det. F on air-dried residue, allowing in calcns for % S removed. (*Caution: See* **46.039, 46.040,** and **46.048.**)

Modified Travers Method (7)
(Applicable in absence of B, Al, and large amts of pyrethrum powder)

6.020 *Reagents*

(a) *Alcoholic potassium chloride soln.*—Dissolve 60 g KCl in 400 ml H$_2$O, add 400 ml alcohol, and test with phthln; if soln is not neut., adjust to exact neutrality by adding NaOH or HCl soln.

(b) *Sodium hydroxide std soln.*—0.2N. Prep. and stdze as in **45.033–45.036.**

6.021 *Determination*

Treat 0.5 g sample in small beaker with 20–25 ml H$_2$O. Add 0.3 g finely divided *pptd SiO$_2$* and few drops Me orange. Add HCl dropwise until soln assumes apparently permanent pink; then add 2 ml excess, cover beaker with watch glass, and boil 1 min. Cool to room temp., add 4 g KCl, and stir until KCl dissolves. Add 25 ml alcohol and let stand 1 hr, stirring frequently. Filter thru gooch contg disk of filter paper covered with medium pad of asbestos. Wash ppt with alc. KCl soln until one washing does not destroy color made by 1 drop 0.2N NaOH and phthln (usually 3–4 washings). Transfer crucible and contents to 400 ml beaker, add 100 ml recently boiled H$_2$O and 1–2 ml phthln, heat, and titr. with std NaOH soln. Finish titrn with the F soln actively boiling. Calc. % F (1 ml 0.2N NaOH = 0.0057 g F).

Distillation Method (8)
(Applicable to H$_2$O-sol. or H$_2$O-insol. insecticides in absence of gelatinous SiO$_2$, B, and Al)

6.022 *Reagents*

(a) *Sodium alizarin sulfonate indicator.*—Dissolve 0.1 g Na alizarin sulfonate in 200 ml H$_2$O.

(b) *Thorium nitrate soln.*—Approx. 0.05N. Stdze in terms of g F/ml by titrg F obtained by distn from std NaF, as in **6.023.** In stdzg for use with **6.023**(b) add 5 ml satd KMnO$_4$ soln in addn to other reagents in distn flask.

6.023 *Determination*

(a) *In absence of organic matter.*—Weigh sample contg ca 0.09 g F, and with aid of little H$_2$O transfer

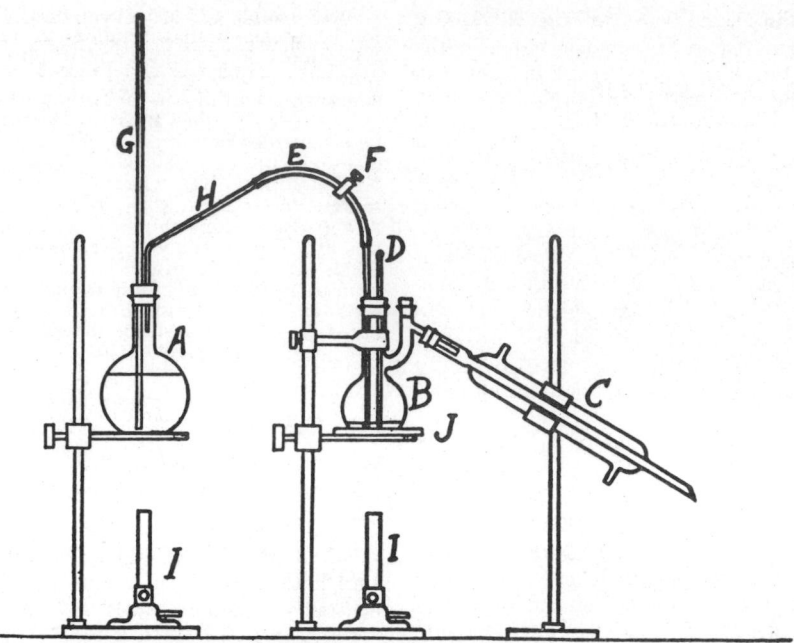

FIG. 6:2—Apparatus for determining fluorine

to 250 ml Claisen distn flask contg 12 glass beads. Adjust to ca 30 ml and close flask with 2-hole rubber stopper, thru which pass thermometer and 4 mm glass tube, both of which extend into soln. (The 4 mm glass tube extends ca 5 cm above rubber stopper and by means of rubber tube, E, connects still with 1 L Florence flask contg H_2O for steam generation. Flask is equipped with steam discharge, H, and pressure tube, G. See Fig. 6:2.)

Bring H_2O in steam generating flask to bp with pinchcock, F, in release tube open. Connect distg flask to condenser, and add 25 ml H_2SO_4 thru top of 4 mm tube, using pipet or special funnel. With pinchcock, F, open, connect rubber tubing to 4 mm tube. Light burner under Claisen flask. Regulate flow of steam by adjusting burner flames and pinchcock, F, so that vol. of soln is held constant and temp. in flask, B, is kept at 145–150°. Continue distn until 400 ml distillate collects. Dil. to 500 ml in vol. flask, transfer 50 ml aliquot to tall-form 150 ml beaker, and add 5 drops indicator, 6.022(a). Adjust acidity with 1% NaOH soln and HCl (1 + 249) until pink just disappears. Add 2 ml of the HCl, and titr. with $0.05N$ $Th(NO_3)_4$ to permanent pink, using buret graduated in 0.05 ml.

(b) *In presence of organic matter.*—(*Caution: See* **46.019, 46.030,** and **46.080.**) In presence of moderate amts of org. matter transfer sample contg ca 0.09 g F and contg ≤0.2 g org. matter, with aid of little H_2O, to 250 ml Claisen distn flask contg 12 glass beads. Add 5 ml satd $KMnO_4$ soln, adjust to ca 30 ml, and proceed as in (a), beginning "close flask with 2-hole rubber stopper, . . ."

In presence of large amts of org. matter, transfer sample to medium-size Pt dish, add 15 ml H_2O and enough *F-free CaO* to make mixt. distinctly alk. to phthln, mix with glass rod, and evap. to dryness on steam bath and in oven at 105°. Ignite at low heat, preferably in muffle ($\leq600°$), until org. matter is thoroly charred. Pulverize any lumps present in charred ash with glass rod, transfer to 250 ml Claisen distn flask by brushing, and finally wash out dish with 30 ml H_2SO_4 (1 + 9). Except to add 22 ml instead of 25 ml H_2SO_4, proceed as in (a), par. 2.

Note: If coating of pptd SiO_2 forms on inside of distn flask, remove by treatment with hot concd alkali soln, as it is capable of retaining F during distn of some samples and giving it up, at least in part, in later distns.

Fluorine Present as Sodium Fluosilicate— Official Final Action
(B, CaO, and alum absent)

6.024   *Reagents*

Alcoholic potassium chloride and sodium carbonate soln.—Dissolve 1.0 g Na_2CO_3 in 100 ml alc. KCl reagent, 6.020(a).

For other reagent *see* **6.020.**

6.025   *Determination*

Weigh 1 g sample into Pt dish, and add rapidly, with continuous stirring, 50 ml of the alc. KCl-Na_2CO_3 reagent. Do not let soln become acid, and if necessary, use more reagent to insure alky. Continue stirring until all sol. portions of sample dissolve. Proceed as in **6.021,** beginning: "Filter thru gooch . . ."

Calc. % Na_2SiF_6 (1 ml 0.2N NaOH = 0.009403 g Na_2SiF_6).

★ PARIS GREEN ★
(*Caution: See* **46.041.**)

6.026 Moisture—Official Final Action—
See **6.003**

6.027 Total Arsenic—Official Final Action—
See **6.006**

Total Arsenious Oxide—Official Final Action
(Following methods det. only As present in trivalent form (As_2O_3) and Sb present in trivalent form (Sb_2O_3) in absence of ferrous and cuprous salts.)

Method I (9)
6.028   *Reagents*
See **4.028**, 10th ed.

6.029   *Determination*
Iodometric titrn. See **4.029**, 10th ed.

6.030 Method II (10)
Bromate titrn. See **4.030**, 10th ed.

6.031 Water-Soluble Arsenious Oxide—Official Final Action
Iodometric titrn. See **4.031**, 10th ed.

Total Copper—Official Final Action
6.032 Electrolytic Method
See **4.032**, 10th ed.

6.033 Volumetric Thiosulfate Method (11)
See **4.033**, 10th ed.

LEAD ARSENATE
(*Caution: See* **46.041** and **46.078.**)

6.034 Moisture—Official Final Action
(a) *Powder.*—Dry 2 g to constant wt at 105–110° and report loss in wt as H_2O.
(b) *Paste.*—Proceed as in (a), using 50 g. Grind dry sample to fine powder, mix well, transfer small portion to sample bottle, and again dry 1–2 hr at 105–110°. Use this anhyd. material to det. total Pb and total As.

Total Arsenic—Official Final Action
6.035 Method I—See 6.006

6.036 Method II (12)
(Not applicable in presence of Sb)
Dissolve 1 g powd. sample with HNO_3 (1 + 4) in porcelain casserole or evapg dish, add 5 ml H_2SO_4, and heat on hot plate to copious evolution of white fumes. Cool, add little H_2O, and again evap. until white fumes appear, to assure removal of last trace

of HNO_3. Wash into 200 ml vol. flask with H_2O, cool, dil. to vol., and filter thru dry filter. Transfer 100 ml filtrate to erlenmeyer and proceed as in **6.012**, beginning "add 1 g KI, ..." From ml std I soln used, calc. % total As as As_2O_3.

6.037 Total Arsenious Oxide (13)—Official Final Action
Weigh 2 g powd sample and transfer to 200 ml vol. flask, add 100 ml H_2SO_4 (1 + 6), and boil 30 min. Cool, dil. to vol., shake thoroly, and filter thru dry filter. Nearly neutze 100 ml filtrate with NaOH soln, **6.004**(e), using few drops phthln. If neut. point is passed, make acid again with the dil. H_2SO_4. Continue as in **6.012**, beginning "Neutze with $NaHCO_3$, ..." From ml std I soln used calc. % As_2O_3.

Total Arsenic Oxide (14)—Official Final Action
6.038   *Reagents*
(a) *Potassium iodide soln.*—Dissolve 20 g KI in H_2O and dil. to 100 ml.
(b) *Thiosulfate std soln.*—0.05N. Prep. daily by dilg 0.1N soln, **45.038–45.039**. 1 ml 0.05N $Na_2S_2O_3$ = 2.873 mg As_2O_5.

6.039   *Determination*
Weigh 0.5 g powd sample and transfer to erlenmeyer. Add 25–30 ml HCl and evap. to dryness on steam bath. Add 50 ml HCl and if necessary to effect soln, heat on steam bath, keeping flask covered with watch glass to prevent evapn of acid. Cool to 20–25°, add 10 ml of the KI soln and 50 ml (or more if necessary to produce clear soln) 25% NH_4Cl soln, and immediately titr. liberated I with std $Na_2S_2O_3$ soln. When color becomes faint yellow, dil. with ca 150 ml H_2O and continue titrn carefully, dropwise, until colorless, using starch indicator, **6.004**(f), near end point. From ml $Na_2S_2O_3$ soln used, calc. % As_2O_5.

6.040 Water-Soluble Arsenic—Official Final Action
Proceed as in **6.012**, and calc. results as As_2O_5.

6.041 Total Lead (15)—Official Final Action
In 600 ml beaker on hot plate heat 0.5 g powd sample and ca 25 ml HNO_3 (1 + 4). Filter to remove any insol. residue. Dil. to at least 400 ml, heat nearly to boiling, and add NH_4OH to slight pptn, then HNO_3 (1 + 9) to redissolve ppt, adding 1–2 ml excess. Into this soln, kept almost boiling, pipet 50 ml hot 10% K_2CrO_4 soln, stirring constantly. Decant while hot thru weighed gooch, previously heated to 140–150°, and wash several times by decanting and then on filter with boiling H_2O until washings are colorless. Dry $PbCrO_4$ at 140–150° to constant wt. From wt $PbCrO_4$, calc. % Pb, using factor 0.6411. ($PbCrO_4$ ppt may contain small quantity $PbHAsO_4$, which will cause slightly high results, but this error rarely is > 0.1–0.2%.)

CALCIUM ARSENATE
(Caution: See 46.041.)

**6.042 Moisture—Official Final Action—
See 6.003**

**6.043 Total Arsenic—Official Final Action—
See 6.006**

**6.044 Total Arsenious Oxide (16)—
Official Final Action**

(a) *Not applicable in presence of nitrates.*—Weigh 1 g sample, transfer to 500 ml erlenmeyer, and dissolve in 100 ml HCl (1 + 3). Heat to 90° and titr. with std $KBrO_3$ soln, **6.004**(c), using 10 drops Me orange, **6.004**(g). From ml std $KBrO_3$ soln used, calc. % As_2O_3.

(b) *Applicable in presence of small quantities of nitrates.*—Proceed as in (a) except to titr. at room temp.

**6.045 Water-Soluble Arsenic—
Official Final Action**

Proceed as in **6.012**, and calc. results as As_2O_5. (In testing Ca arsenate by this method, low value for H_2O-sol. As is not assurance against plant injury when using this product.)

Total Calcium (16)—Official Final Action
6.046   *Reagents*

(a) *Ammonium oxalate soln.*—Dissolve 40 g $(NH_4)_2C_2O_4.H_2O$ in 1 L H_2O.

(b) *Potassium permanganate std soln.*—0.1N. Prep. and stdze as in **45.026–45.027**.

6.047 *Method I*

Dissolve 2 g sample in 80 ml HOAc (1 + 3), transfer to 200 ml vol. flask, dil. to vol., and filter thru dry filter. Transfer 50 ml aliquot to beaker, dil. to ca 200 ml, heat to boiling, and ppt Ca with $(NH_4)_2C_2O_4$ soln. Let beaker stand 3 hr on steam bath, filter, and wash ppt with hot H_2O. Dissolve ppt in 200 ml H_2O contg 25 ml H_2SO_4 (1 + 4), heat to ca 70°, and titr. with std $KMnO_4$ soln. From ml $KMnO_4$ soln used, calc. % Ca.

6.048 *Method II*

(Not applicable in presence of Pb.
Caution: See **46.041** and **46.078**.)

Weigh 2 g sample, transfer to beaker, add 5 ml *HBr* (ca 1.38 sp gr) and 15 ml HCl, and evap. to dryness under hood to remove As. Repeat treatment, add 20 ml HCl, and again evap. to dryness. Take up with H_2O and little HCl, filter into 200 ml vol. flask, wash, and dil. to vol. Transfer 50 ml aliquot to beaker, add 10 ml HCl and few drops HNO_3, boil, and make slightly alk. with NH_4OH. Let stand few min and filter. Dissolve ppt in HCl (1 + 4), reppt, filter thru same paper, and wash

with hot H_2O. To combined filtrates and washings add 20 ml HOAc (1 + 3) and adjust to ca 200 ml. Heat to boiling, ppt with $(NH_4)_2C_2O_4$ soln, and let stand 3 hr on steam bath. Filter, and wash with hot H_2O. Ignite at 950°, and weigh as CaO; or dissolve ppt in 200 ml H_2O contg 25 ml H_2SO_4 (1 + 4), heat to ca 70°, and titr. with std $KMnO_4$ soln. From wt CaO or ml $KMnO_4$ soln used calc. % Ca.

★ ZINC ARSENITE ★
(Caution: See 46.041.)

**6.049 Moisture—Official Final Action—
See 6.003**

6.050 Total Arsenic—Official Final Action
Proceed as in **6.006** and calc. as As_2O_3.

Total Arsenious Oxide—Official Final Action
6.051 *Method I (16)*
Bromate titrn. *See* **4.051**, 10th ed.

6.052 *Method II*
Iodometric titrn. *See* **4.052**, 10th ed.

**6.053 Water-Soluble Arsenic—
Official Final Action**
Proceed as in **6.012**, and calc. results as As_2O_3.

6.054 Total Zinc (16)—Official Final Action
Gravimetric method. *See* **4.054**, 10th ed.

★ COPPER CARBONATE ★
Copper—Official Final Action
6.055 *Electrolytic Method*
See **4.055**, 10th ed.

6.056 *Volumetric Thiosulfate Method*
See **4.056**, 10th ed.

COPPER NAPHTHENATE
(Caution: See 46.041.)

Copper (17)—Official First Action
6.057 *Titrimetric Method*

Accurately weigh sample contg ca 0.2 g Cu into dry g-s flask. Add 5 ml pet ether to concd products. Add 100 ml H_2O, 1.5 g NH_4HF_2, and 5–10 g KI. Stopper and shake vigorously until reaction is complete (usually ca 2 min). Wash stopper and sides of flask with H_2O and titr. with std 0.1N $Na_2S_2O_3$ (stdzd against Cu) to light brown. Add starch indicator, **6.004**(f), titr. almost to end point, add 2 g KSCN, shake to dissolve, and complete titrn to starch end point.

6.058 *Electrolytic Method*

Accurately weigh sample contg ca 0.2 g Cu into 200 ml separator. Add 50 ml pet ether and 25 ml

HNO₃ (1 + 4), and shake 2 min. Drain aq. phase into 250 ml beaker and save. Wash pet ether twice with 15 and 10 ml HNO₃ (1 + 4), and combine acid exts. Neutze with NH₄OH, acidify with 6 ml H₂SO₄ and 4 ml HNO₃, and proceed as in **6.014,** beginning "adjust vol. to 200 ml, . . ." using current of ca 0.5 amp during first 10 min and 1.5–2.0 amp for ca 20 min.

BORDEAUX MIXTURE
(*Caution: See* **46.041.**)

6.059   Moisture—Official Final Action

(a) *Powder.*—Dry 2 g to constant wt at 105–110°. Report loss as H₂O.

(b) *Paste.*—Heat ca 100 g in oven at 90–100° until dry enough to powder readily and note loss in wt. Powder this partially dried sample and det. remaining H₂O in 2 g as in (a). Det. CO₂ as in **6.061,** both in original paste and in partially dried sample. Calc. total H₂O by following formula:

$$M = a + \frac{(100 - a)(b + c)}{100} - d,$$

where M = % total H₂O in original paste; a = % loss in wt of original paste during first drying; b = % loss in wt of partially dried paste during second drying; c = % CO₂ remaining in partially dried paste after first drying; and d = % total CO₂ in original paste.

Carbon Dioxide (*18*)—Official Final Action
6.060   *Apparatus*

Use 200 ml erlenmeyer with 2-hole stopper; in one hole fit dropping funnel with stem extending almost to bottom of flask, and thru other hole pass outlet of condenser that is inclined upward at 30° angle from horizontal. Connect upper end of condenser with CaCl₂ tube, which in turn connects with double U-tube filled in middle with pumice fragments, previously satd with *20% CuSO₄.5H₂O soln* and subsequently dehydrated, and with CaCl₂ at either end. Connect 2 weighed U-tubes to absorb CO₂, first filled with porous soda-lime, and second, ⅓ with soda-lime and ⅔ with CaCl₂, placing the CaCl₂ at exit end of train. Attach Geissler bulb, partly filled with H₂SO₄, to last U-tube to show rate of gas flow, and connect aspirator with Geissler bulb to draw air thru app. Connect absorption tower filled with soda-lime to mouth of dropping funnel to remove CO₂ from air entering app.

6.061   *Determination*

Weigh 2 g powder or 10 g paste into the erlenmeyer and add ca 20 ml H₂O. Attach flask to app., omitting the 2 weighed U-tubes, and draw CO₂-free air thru app. until it displaces original air. Attach weighed U-tubes as in **6.060,** close stopcock of dropping funnel, pour into it 50 ml HCl (1 + 4), reconnect with soda-lime tower, and let acid flow into erlenmeyer,

slowly if there is much CO₂, rapidly if there is little. When effervescence diminishes, place low Bunsen flame under flask and start flow of H₂O thru condenser, letting slow current of air flow thru app. at same time. Maintain steady but quiet boiling and slow air current thru app. Boil few min after H₂O begins to condense, remove flame, and continue air flow at ca 2 bubbles/sec until app. is cool. Disconnect weighed absorption tubes, cool in balance case, and weigh. Increase in wt = CO₂.

Copper—Official Final Action
6.062   *Electrolytic Method*
(Also applicable to CuCO₃ and CuSO₄)

Dissolve powd sample contg 0.2–0.25 g Cu in 45 ml HNO₃ (1 + 4). Filter if necessary, dil. to 200 ml, and electrolyze as in **6.014.**

6.063   *Volumetric Thiosulfate Method*

Dissolve 2 g powd sample in ca 25 ml HNO₃ (1 + 4), dil. to 50 ml, add NH₄OH in excess, and heat. Without removing ppt that has formed, boil off excess NH₃, add 3–4 ml HOAc, cool, add 10 ml 30% KI soln, and titr. as in **6.015,** beginning "titr. with std Na₂S₂O₃ soln, . . ."

★   BORDEAUX MIXTURE WITH   ★
PARIS GREEN
(*Caution: See* **46.041.**)

6.064   Moisture—Official Final Action—
See 6.059

6.065   Carbon Dioxide—Official Final Action—
See 6.061

6.066   Total Arsenic—Official Final Action

Proceed as in **6.006,** using 2 g sample, and calc. results as As₂O₃.

6.067   Total Arsenious Oxide—
Official Final Action

Iodometric titrn. *See* **4.067,** 10th ed.

6.068   Water-Soluble Arsenious Oxide—
Official Final Action

Iodometric titrn. *See* **4.068,** 10th ed.

Copper—Official Final Action

6.069   *Electrolytic Method I—See* **6.014**

6.070   *Electrolytic Method II*
(*Short Method*)

See **4.070,** 10th ed.

6.071   *Volumetric Thiosulfate Method—*
See 6.015

★ BORDEAUX MIXTURE WITH ★ LEAD ARSENATE
(Caution: See 46.041.)

6.072   Moisture—Official Final Action— See 6.059

6.073   Carbon Dioxide—Official Final Action— See 6.061

6.074   Total Arsenic—Official Final Action

Proceed as in **6.006**, using 2 g sample, and calc. results as As_2O_5.

6.075   Water-Soluble Arsenic— Official Final Action

Proceed as in **6.012** and calc. results as As_2O_5.

Copper—Official Final Action
6.076   *Electrolytic Method—See 6.014*

6.077   *Volumetric Thiosulfate Method— See 6.015*

6.078   Lead—Official Final Action—*See 6.013*

Lead and Copper—Official Final Action
6.079   *Electrolytic Method (19)*

(Caution: See 46.026, 46.047, and 46.078.)
See 4.079–4.080, 10th ed.

BORDEAUX MIXTURE WITH CALCIUM ARSENATE
(Caution: See 46.041.)

6.080   Moisture—Official Final Action— See 6.059

6.081   Carbon Dioxide—Official Final Action— See 6.061

6.082   Total Arsenic—Official Final Action

Proceed as in **6.006**, using 2 g sample, and calc. results as As_2O_5.

6.083   Water-Soluble Arsenic— Official Final Action

Proceed as in **6.012** and calc. results as As_2O_5.

Copper—Official Final Action
6.084   *Electrolytic Method I—See 6.014*

6.085   *Electrolytic Method II—See 6.070*

6.086   *Volumetric Thiosulfate Method— See 6.015*

★ SODIUM AND POTASSIUM ★ CYANIDES
(Caution: See 46.050.)

6.087   Cyanide (20)—Official Final Action

$AgNO_3$ titrn. *See* **4.088–4.089**, 10th ed. *(Caution: See 46.084.)*

Chloride (21)—Official Final Action
6.088   *Method I*

Pptn with $AgNO_3$ and thiocyanate back-titrn. *See* **4.090–4.091**, 10th ed.

6.089   *Method II*

Distn, pptn with $AgNO_3$, and thiocyanate back-titrn. *See* **4.092**, 10th ed.

★ CALCIUM CYANIDE ★
6.090   Cyanide (22)—Official Final Action

$AgNO_3$ titrn. *See* **4.093–4.094**, 10th ed.

Chloride (22)—Official Final Action
6.091   *Method I*

See **4.095**, 10th ed.

6.092   *Method II (23)*

See **4.096**, 10th ed.

SOAP
Moisture (23)
6.093   *Toluene Distillation Method— Official Final Action*

Weigh ca 20 g sample into 300–500 ml flask; add 50 ml toluene (tech. grade is satisfactory); and, to prevent foaming, add ca 10 g lump rosin (do not use powd). Distill into Dean and Stark type distg tube receiver and continue distn until no more H_2O collects in receiver. Cool contents of tube to room temp., read vol. H_2O under toluene in tube, and calc. % H_2O.

6.094   Potassium and Sodium (24)— Official Final Action

Dissolve ca 5 g sample in H_2O, decompose with HCl (1 + 4), filter off H_2O, and wash fat with cold H_2O. Det. both K and Na in filtrate as in **3.015** and **3.020** or **3.016–3.019**.

MINERAL OILS
Unsulfonated Residue (25)— Official Final Action
6.095   *Reagent*

(Caution: See 46.030 and 46.031.)

Fuming 38N sulfuric acid.—In tared g-s bottle (2.5 L acid bottle is convenient) mix fuming H_2SO_4 (free from N oxides) (A) with H_2SO_4 (B) to obtain mixed acid (C), contg slightly >82.38% total SO_3. Depending on strength of fuming acid available, use following proportions of 2 acids: 100 parts A (15–

20% free SO_3) to 50 parts B; 100 parts A (20–30% free SO_3) to 75 parts B; and 100 parts A (50% free SO_3) to 140 parts B. Mix thoroly (considerable heat is generated), let cool, and again weigh to det. amt mixed acid obtained. Det. exact strength of mixed acid (C) and also of reserve supply of acid (B) as follows:

Pour ca 50 ml into small beaker and fill ca 10 ml weighing bulb or pipet by slight suction, wiping off outside of bulb with moist, then with dry, cloth. Weigh on analytical balance and let acid flow slowly down sides of neck of 1 L vol. flask into ca 200 ml cold H_2O. (The sizes of bulb and flask give final soln ca 0.5N.) When bulb has drained, wash all traces of acid into flask, taking precautions against loss of SO_3 fumes. Dil. to vol. and titr. from buret with std alkali, using same indicator as used in stdzg. Calc. SO_3 content of both acids, and add calcd amt of reserve acid (B) to amt of mixed acid (C) on hand to bring C to 82.38% total SO_3 (equiv. to 100.92% H_2SO_4). After adding required amt of B, again analyze mixed acid to make certain it is of proper concn (±0.15% H_2SO_4). Keep acid in small bottles or in special dispenser bottle (*26*) to prevent absorption of H_2O from air.

6.096   *Determination*

Pipet 5 ml sample into 6″ Babcock cream bottle, **16.115**(a), either 9 g 50% or 18 g 30% type. To reduce viscosity of heavy oils, warm pipet after initial drainage by passing it several times thru flame; then drain thoroly. If greater accuracy is desired, weigh measured sample and calc. exact vol. from wt and sp gr. Slowly add 20 ml 38N H_2SO_4, gently shaking or rotating bottle and taking care that temp. does not rise above 60°. Cool in ice-H_2O if necessary. When mixt. no longer develops heat on shaking, agitate thoroly, place bottle in H_2O bath, and heat 10 min at 60–65°, keeping contents of bottle thoroly mixed by shaking vigorously 20 sec at 2 min intervals. Remove bottle from bath and add H_2SO_4 until oil is in graduated neck. Centrf. 5 min (or longer if necessary to obtain constant vol. of oil) at 1200–1500 rpm. Read vol. of unsulfonated residue from graduations on neck of bottle and, to convert to ml, multiply reading from 9 g 50% bottle by 0.1 and reading from 18 g 30% bottle by 0.2. From result obtained calc. % by vol. unsulfonated residue.

MINERAL OIL-SOAP EMULSIONS
Water (*27*)

6.097 *Toluene Distillation Method—*
Official Final Action

Weigh ca 25 g sample and proceed as in **6.093**, except use less rosin.

6.098 Total Oil (*28*)—Official Final Action

Weigh ca 10 g sample into Babcock cream bottle, **16.115**(a). Dil. with ca 10 ml hot H_2O and add 5–10 ml H_2SO_4 (1 + 1). Heat in hot H_2O bath ca 5 min to hasten sepn of oil, add enough satd NaCl soln to bring oil layer within graduated neck of bottle, centrf. at 1200 rpm 5 min, and let cool. Read vol. of oil layer, det. density, and from these values calc. wt and %. From this % value deduct % fatty acids (and phenols if present), detd sep., to obtain % oil.

6.099 Soap (*27*)—Official Final Action

(Error will result if apparent molecular wt of fatty acids varies appreciably from that of oleic acid.)

Weigh 20 g sample into separator, add 60 ml pet ether, and ext mixt. once with 20 ml and 4 times with 10 ml 50% alcohol. Break emulsion if necessary by letting 1 or 2 ml 20% NaOH soln run down wall of separator. Then gently swirl separator and let stand few min. Drain alc. layers and wash successively thru pet ether contained in 2 other separators. Combine alc. exts in beaker and evap. on steam bath to remove alcohol. Dissolve residue in ca 100 ml H_2O made alk. with NaOH. Transfer to separator, acidify with HCl or H_2SO_4, ext 3 times with ether, and wash ether exts twice with H_2O. Combine ether exts, evap. in weighed beaker on steam bath, and weigh as fatty acids. From wt fatty acids calc. % soap in sample as Na or K oleate.

6.100 Unsulfonated Residues—
      Official Final Action

Using 5 ml of the recovered oil, **6.098**, proceed as in **6.096**.

6.101 Ash (*29*)—Official Final Action

Evap. 10 g sample, or more if necessary, in Pt dish. Ignite, and leach charred mass with H_2O. Ignite residue, add leachings, evap. to dryness, ignite, and weigh. From this wt calc. % ash. Test ash for Cu, Ca, CaF_2, etc.

TOBACCO AND TOBACCO PRODUCTS

Nicotine
(*Note:* Nicotine is very toxic. Avoid contact with skin.)

Silicotungstic Acid Method (30)—
Official Final Action
(Includes nornicotine)

6.102   *Reagent*

Silicotungstic acid soln.—Dissolve 120 g silicotungstic acid ($4H_2O.SiO_2.12WO_3.22H_2O$ or SiO_2 $.12WO_3.26H_2O$) in H_2O and dil. to 1 L. (Acid should be white or pale yellow crystals, free from green color; soln should be free from cloudiness and green color. Of the several silicotungstic acids, $4H_2O.SiO_2.10WO_3.3H_2O$ and $4H_2O.SiO_2.12WO_3$ $.20H_2O$ do not give cryst. ppts with nicotine and should not be used.)

6.103 *Determination*

Weigh sample contg preferably 0.1–1.0 g nicotine. If sample contains very little nicotine (ca 0.1%), do not increase amt to point where it interferes with distn. Wash with H_2O into 500 ml Kjeldahl flask, and if necessary add little paraffin to prevent frothing and few small pieces pumice to prevent bumping. Add 10 g NaCl and 10 ml NaOH soln (30% by wt) and close flask with rubber stopper thru which passes stem of trap bulb and inlet tube for steam. Connect trap bulb to well-cooled condenser, lower end of which dips below surface of 10 ml HCl $(1 + 4)$ in suitable receiving flask. Steam distill rapidly. When distn is well under way heat flask to reduce vol. of liq. as far as practicable without bumping or excessive sepn of insol. matter. Distill until few ml distillate shows no cloud or opalescence when treated with drop silicotungstic acid soln and drop HCl $(1 + 4)$. Confirm alky of residue in distn flask with phthln.

Adjust distillate, which may total 1000–1500 ml, to convenient vol. (soln may be concd on steam bath without loss of nicotine), mix well, and pass thru dry filter if not clear. Test distillate with Me orange to confirm acidity. Pipet aliquot contg ca 0.1 g nicotine into beaker (if samples contain very small amts of nicotine, aliquot contg as little as 0.01 g nicotine may be used). To each 100 ml liq., add 3 ml HCl $(1 + 4)$ and 1 ml silicotungstic acid for each 0.01 g nicotine supposed to be present. Stir thoroly and let stand overnight at room temp. Before filtering, stir ppt to see that it settles quickly and is in cryst. form. Filter on either ashless paper or gooch and wash with HCl $(1 + 1000)$ at room temp. Continue washing for 2 or 3 fillings of filter after no more opalescence appears when few ml fresh filtrate is tested with few drops nicotine distillate. In case of paper, transfer paper and ppt to weighed Pt crucible, dry carefully, and ignite until all C is destroyed. Finally heat over Meker burner ≤10 min. Wt residue × 0.1141 = wt nicotine in aliquot. In case of gooch, dry in oven 3 hr at 105° and weigh. Wt residue × 0.1012 = wt nicotine in aliquot.

DERRIS AND CUBÉ POWDER

Rotenone

Crystallization Method (31)— Official Final Action

(*Caution: See* **46.049** *and* **46.084**.)

6.104 *Reagents*

(a) *Purified rotenone.*—Dissolve rotenone in boiling CCl_4; cool in refrigerator or ice bath at 0–10° until pptn of rotenone-CCl_4 solvate stops. Filter thru buchner and wash once or twice with ice-cold CCl_4. Conc. filtrate, crystallize, and filter as before. Transfer cryst. residue to beaker, add ca twice their vol. alcohol, and heat nearly to boiling. (Crystals need not dissolve completely.) Cool to room temp., filter thru

buchner, and draw air thru cryst. residue until most alcohol is removed. Remove rotenone from funnel, dry in air, and finally heat 1 hr at 105°. Mp, detd in Pyrex, of purified material should be 163–164°. (Mother liquors may be concd and rotenone-CCl_4 solvate allowed to crystallize. Cryst. material may be used for further purification, or kept for prepn of wash solns or for seeding to induce crystn in detn.)

(b) *Rotenone-CCl_4 solvate.*—Ppt rotenone from CCl_4 soln, filter by suction, and dry in air.

(c) *Rotenone-CCl_4 wash soln.*—Sat. CCl_4 at 0°, and keep at 0° during use.

(d) *Alcohol saturated with rotenone at room temp.*

(e) *Charcoal, activated.*—Norit-A neutral, USP reagent, or equiv.

6.105 *Preparation of Solution*

(a) Weigh 30 g (if sample contains >7% rotenone, use quantity to give 1.0–1.5 g rotenone in 200 ml aliquot) finely powd root and 10 g of the C into 500 ml g-s erlenmeyer. Add 300 ml $CHCl_3$, measured at known room temp.; fasten stopper securely and place flask on shaking machine. Agitate vigorously ≥4 hr, preferably interrupting shaking with overnight rest (or flask may be shaken continuously overnight). Filter mixt. rapidly into suitable flask, using fluted paper without suction and keeping funnel covered with watch glass to avoid evapn loss. Stopper flask and adjust temp. of filtrate to that of original $CHCl_3$.

(b) *Alternative extraction method.*—If sample has ratio of rotenone to total ext of >0.4, use amt contg 1.0–1.5 g rotenone and successively ext 4 times with $CHCl_3$, using 300 ml $CHCl_3$ and 4 hr agitation for the first extn as in (a) and 200 ml and 2 hr each for other extns. Filter after each extn and return marc to flask for extn with fresh solv. Finally combine exts, evap. almost to dryness, and use entire ext to det. rotenone.

(c) *Extraction method for formulations containing 0.75–1.0% rotenone with or without sulfur and/or pyrethrins.*—Weigh two 50 g portions sample into sep. 500 ml g-s erlenmeyers. Add 5 g of the C and 300 ml $CHCl_3$, measured at known room temp., to each. Stopper and continue as in (a).

6.106 *Determination*

(*Caution: See* **46.011**, **46.018**, **46.046**, **46.049**, *and* **46.056**.)

Pipet 200 ml soln, **6.105** (or entire soln if alternative extn, (b), is used), into 500 ml Pyrex erlenmeyer and distill until ca 25 ml remains. (For formulations, **6.105**(c): In absence of S, combine the 2 exts in one of the erlenmeyers. In presence of S, remove all $CHCl_3$ on steam bath in air current, avoiding prolonged heating. Add 35 ml acetone to each residue and boil gently on steam bath to dissolve all resins. Remove from steam bath, stopper tightly, and hold 2 hr at 0–5°. Filter both acetone solns thru same 15 ml capacity, medium porosity, fritted glass buchner into single 500 ml erlenmeyer. Rinse and wash with acetone at 5°. Remove acetone as $CHCl_3$ was removed above.)

Evap. almost to dryness on steam bath in current of air. Remove remainder of solv. under reduced pressure, heating cautiously on steam bath when necessary to hasten evapn. (Suction may be applied directly to flask if stopper with vent is used to release pressure, so that excessive vac. may be avoided. Use flasks with slightly convex bottoms; do not use flasks below av. wt.) Dissolve ext in 15 ml hot CCl_4 and again, in similar manner, remove all solv. Repeat with another 10–15 ml portion hot CCl_4. (This treatment removes all $CHCl_3$ from resins. $CHCl_3$ ext is usually completely sol. in CCl_4; if small amts of insol. material are present, purification described later will eliminate them.)

Dissolve residue in ca 10 ml hot CCl_4 and transfer quant. with hot CCl_4 to 50 ml erlenmeyer marked at 25 ml. Adjust vol. to 25 ml by evapg on steam bath or by adding CCl_4. Cool flask in ice bath several min, stopper flask, and swirl until crystn is apparent. Seed with few crystals of rotenone-CCl_4 solvate if necessary to induce crystn. If at this stage only small amt of cryst. material seps, add accurately weighed quantity of purified rotenone, 6.104(a), estd to be enough to assure that final result, expressed as pure rotenone, is ≥1 g. Then warm to dissolve completely, and again induce crystn. At same time prep. satd soln of rotenone in CCl_4, 6.104(c), for washing. Place flasks contg ext and washing soln in ice bath capable of holding temp. at 0°, and let stand overnight. (Store ice bath in refrigerator to keep ice from melting too rapidly.)

After 17–18 hr in ice bath, rapidly filter ext thru weighed gooch fitted with filter paper disk, removing flask from ice bath only long enough to pour each fraction of ext into crucible. Rinse cryst. residue from flask and wash under suction once with the ice-cold satd rotenone-CCl_4 wash soln. (≤12–15 ml soln should be used for rinsing and washing.) Continue suction ca 5 min; then dry to constant wt at 40° (ca 1 hr). Wt obtaincd is crude rotenone-CCl_4 solvate.

Break up contents of crucible with spatula, mix thoroly, and weigh 1.000 g into 50 ml erlenmeyer. Add 10 ml alcohol previously satd with rotenone at room temp., swirl flask few min, stopper tightly, and set aside ≥4 hr, preferably overnight, at same temp. Filter on weighed gooch fitted with filter paper disk. Rinse crystals from flask and wash under suction with alcohol satd with rotenone at temp. of recrystn (ca 10 ml usually required). Continue suction 3–5 min and then dry crucible at 105° to constant wt (ca 1 hr).

Multiply g residue by g total crude rotenone-CCl_4 solvate, and add 0.07 g to product as correction for rotenone held in soln in the 25 ml CCl_4 used in crystn. If any pure rotenone was added, subtract its wt from value obtained. This gives wt pure rotenone contained in aliquot of ext.

Note: Most important precaution in using this method is to keep temp. of CCl_4-rotenone wash soln and crucibles as near 0° as possible. Keep wash soln surrounded by crushed ice except when actually being used. In warm weather keep crucibles in refrigerator until ready to use.

Ultraviolet Method (32)—Official First Action
6.107   *Standardization*

Prep. solns of purified rotenone, 6.104(a), in alcohol contg 3 different concns between 3 and 10 µg/ml. A curves of solns should be smooth with max. at 294 nm and min. at 257 nm. Read against alcohol blank, using as narrow slit width as possible. Record A of each std soln at 284, 294, and 304 nm. From these values, calc. av. absorptivity, a, at each wavelength specified: $a = A/bc$, where b is cell length (cm) and c is concn in g/L. Record absorptivities as a_{284}, a_{294}, and a_{304}.

6.108   *Determination*
(Caution: See 46.011 and 46.046.)

Accurately weigh sample contg 50–60 mg rotenone and transfer to 125 ml ℥ erlenmeyer. Add magnetic stirring bar, and pipet in 100 ml acetone. Stopper, and stir at fast speed 10 min. Filter thru rapid paper, Whatman No. 31 or equiv., and pipet 1 ml aliquot filtrate into 100 ml ℥ vol. flask. Remove solv. with current of clean air while heating in 60° H_2O bath. Avoid prolonged heating. Add 50 ml alcohol and warm slightly to dissolve resins. Cool to room temp. and dil. to vol. with alcohol. Stopper and mix thoroly.

Using same slit widths as for stdzn, record A at 284 (A_{284}), 294 (A_{294}), and 304 nm (A_{304}).

$$\% \text{ Rotenone} = [(2A_{294} - A_{284} - A_{304})/b(2a_{294} - a_{284} - a_{304}] \times (100/\text{mg sample per ml})$$

Infrared Method (33)—Official First Action
6.109   *Standardization*

Prep. std solns of pure rotenone, 6.104(a), in $CHCl_3$ at concns of 5, 10, 15, and 20 mg/ml. Scan each std soln from 7.0 to 8.0 µm at speed of 6 min/µm and scale of 10 cm/µm, using 0.1 mm cell and accurately matching cell filled with $CHCl_3$ as ref. Scan each in duplicate. Obtain av. A of each concn, using 7.57 µm as base point and 7.65 µm as peak. Plot A against concn.

6.110   *Determination*

Weigh sample contg 250–300 mg rotenone into 25 × 200 mm culture tube. Add 1–2 g anhyd. Na_2SO_4, 2 g activated charcoal, and 50 ml $CHCl_3$ by pipet. Close securely with Teflon-lined screw cap and tumble end over end at ca 35 rpm 1 hr. Filter thru medium paper, avoiding evapn losses. Transfer 20 ml aliquot to 50 ml erlenmeyer and evap. on steam bath with current of air. Transfer residue to 10 ml g-s vol. flask and dil. to vol. with $CHCl_3$. Stopper, and mix thoroly.

Scan from 7.0 to 8.0 μm, using 0.1 mm cell and matched cell filled with CHCl₃ as ref. Det. *A* by baseline method from 7.57 to 7.75 μm and peak at 7.65 μm, using same scanning speed and scale expansion as in stdzn.

Calc. % rotenone from std curve and wt sample in final diln.

6.111   Total Ether Extract— Official Final Action

(*Caution: See* **46.009, 46.039, 46.054,** and **46.070(b).**)

Ext 5 g finely powd. root with ether 48 hr in Soxhlet or other efficient extn app. Conc. ext and filter off any insol. material present. Receive filtrate in tared beaker, evap. ether on steam bath, and dry in oven at 105° to constant wt.

PYRETHRINS
Mercury Reduction Method (34)— Official Final Action

(*Caution: See* **46.039, 46.054, 46.070,** and **46.073.**)

6.112   *Reagents*

(a) *Deniges reagent.*—Mix 5 g yellow HgO with 40 ml H₂O, and, while stirring, slowly add 20 ml H₂SO₄; then add addnl 40 ml H₂O and stir until all dissolves. Test for absence of mercurous Hg by adding few drops of (b) to 10 ml and titrg with (c) as in **6.114,** beginning "Add 50 ml previously prepd and cooled dil. HCl ..."

(b) *Iodine monochloride soln.*—Dissolve 10 g KI and 6.44 g KIO₃ in 75 ml H₂O in g-s bottle; add 75 ml HCl and 5 ml CHCl₃, and adjust to faint I color (in CHCl₃) by adding dil. KI or KIO₃ soln. If much I is liberated, use stronger soln of KIO₃ than $0.01M$ at first, making final adjustment with $0.01M$ soln. Keep in dark and readjust when necessary.

(c) *Potassium iodate std soln.*—$0.01M$. Dissolve 2.14 g pure KIO₃, previously dried at 105°, in H₂O and dil. to 1 L. 1 ml soln = 0.0057 g pyrethrin I and needs no further stdzn.

(d) *Alcoholic sodium hydroxide soln.*—$1.0N$. Dissolve 40 g NaOH in alcohol and dil. to 1 L with alcohol.

(e) *Petroleum ether.*—Aromatic-free, bp range 30–60°.

(f) *Ethyl ether.*—Peroxide-free, reagent grade.

6.113   *Preparation of Sample*

(a) *Pyrethrum powder.*—Ext sample contg 40–150 mg total pyrethrins in Soxhlet or other efficient extn app. 7 hr with pet ether. After extn is complete, evap. pet ether to ca 40 ml, stopper flask, and place in refrigerator at 0±0.5° overnight. Filter cold ext thru cotton plug satd with cold pet ether, in stem of funnel, collecting filtrate in 250 ml erlenmeyer. Wash with three 15 ml portions cold pet ether. Evap. filtrate and washings on H₂O bath, using air current, until <1 ml solv. remains.

Add 15–20 ml 0.5N alc. NaOH to evapd ext, connect to reflux condenser, and boil gently 1–1.5 hr. Transfer to 600 ml beaker and add enough H₂O to bring vol. to 200 ml. Add few glass beads, or preferably use boiling tube, and boil down to 150 ml. Transfer to 250 ml vol. flask and add 1 g Filter-Cel and 10 ml 10% BaCl₂ soln. Do not shake before dilg to vol. Dil. to vol., mix thoroly, filter off 200 ml, neutze with H₂SO₄ (1 + 4), using 1 drop phthln, and add 1 ml excess. (If necessary to hold soln overnight at this point, leave in alk. condition.)

(b) *Pyrethrum extracts in mineral oil.*—Weigh or measure sample contg 40–150 mg total pyrethrins, add 50 ml pet ether and 1 g Filter-Cel, and place in refrigerator at 0±0.5° overnight. Filter thru gooch into 300 ml erlenmeyer and wash with three 15 ml portions cold pet ether. Evap. filtrate and washings on H₂O bath, using air current, until <1 ml solv. remains.

Add 20 ml 1N alc. NaOH, or more if necessary, to ext, connect to reflux condenser, and boil gently 1–1.5 hr. Transfer to 600 ml beaker and add enough H₂O to make aq. layer 200 ml. If >20 ml alc. NaOH soln was used, add enough H₂O so that all alcohol is removed when vol. is reduced to 150 ml. Add few glass beads, or preferably use boiling tube, and boil aq. layer down to 150 ml. Transfer to 500 ml separator and drain aq. layer into 250 ml vol. flask. Wash oil layer once with H₂O and add wash H₂O to aq. portion. If slight emulsion still persists after draining aq. layer and washings, add 2–3 ml 10% BaCl₂ soln, but do not shake vigorously after adding BaCl₂ because reversed emulsion difficult to sep. may form. To aq. soln in 250 ml flask add 1 g Filter-Cel and 10 ml or more of the BaCl₂ soln. Swirl gently and let stand 30 min. Dil. to vol., mix thoroly, and filter off 200 ml. Test filtrate with BaCl₂ soln to see if enough has been added to obtain clear soln. Neutze with H₂SO₄ (1 + 4), using 1 drop phthln, and add 1 ml excess. (If necessary to hold soln overnight at this point, leave in alk. condition.)

6.114   *Determination of Pyrethrin I*

Filter acid soln from **6.113**(a) or (b) thru 7 cm paper, coated lightly with suspension of Filter-Cel in H₂O, on buchner, and wash with three 15 ml portions H₂O. Transfer to 500 ml g-s separator and ext with two 50 ml portions pet ether. Shake each ext at least 1 min, releasing pressure if necessary by inverting separator and carefully venting thru stopcock. Let layers sep. at least 5 min or until aq. layer is clear before draining and re-extn. Reserve aq. layer for pyrethrin II detn. Do not combine pet ether exts but wash each in sequence with same three 10 ml portions H₂O, and filter pet ether exts thru small cotton plug into clean 250 ml separator. Wash separators and cotton in sequence with 5 ml pet ether. Ext combined pet ether solns with 5 ml 0.1N NaOH, shaking vigorously at least 1 min. Let layers sep. at least 5 min before draining aq. layer into 100 ml beaker. Wash pet ether with addnl 5 ml portion 0.1N NaOH and with 5 ml H_2O, adding washings to beaker. Add 10 ml Deniges reagent and let stand in complete darkness 1 hr at $25\pm2°$.

Add 20 ml alcohol and ppt HgCl with 3 ml satd NaCl soln. Warm to ca 60° and let stand several min until ppt coagulates and settles. Filter thru small paper, transferring all ppt to paper, and wash with 10 ml or more hot alcohol. Wash with 2 or more 10 ml portions hot $CHCl_3$ and place paper and contents in 250 ml g-s erlenmeyer. Add 50 ml previously prepd and cooled dil. HCl $(3+2)$. Add 5 ml $CHCl_3$ or CCl_4 and 1 ml freshly adjusted ICl soln, and titr. with 0.1M KIO_3 soln, shaking vigorously ≥30 sec after each addn, until no I color remains in $CHCl_3$ or CCl_4 layer. Take as end point when red color disappears from solv. layer and does not return within 1–3 min. From ml std KIO_3 soln used in titrn and blank on Deniges reagent, calc. % pyrethrin I. (Reactions:

$$2HgCl_2 + 4ICl = 4HgCl_2 + 2I_2$$
$$2I_2 + KIO_3 + 6HCl = KCl + 5ICl + 3H_2O$$

Addn of ICl does not change vol. relationship between mercurous Hg and KIO_3 soln, and aids in detg end point in titrn of small amts of Hg.)

Note: Chrysanthemum monocarboxylic acid reacts with Deniges reagent to form series of colors beginning with phthln red, which gradually changes to purple, then to blue, and finally to bluish green. Color reaction is very distinct with 5 mg monocarboxylic acid, and amts as low as 1 mg can usually be detected. Therefore no pyrethrin I should be reported if color reaction is neg.

With samples contg much perfume or other saponifiable ingredients, it may be necessary to use as much as 50 ml 1N alc. NaOH. When lethanes are present, after washing HgCl ppt with alcohol and $CHCl_3$, wash once more with alcohol and then several times with hot H_2O.

6.115   Determination of Pyrethrin II (35)

If necessary, filter aq. residue from pet ether extn thru gooch. Conc. filtrate to ca 50 ml and transfer to 500 ml g-s separator. Wash beaker with three 15 ml portions H_2O. Acidify with 10 ml HCl and sat. with NaCl. (Acidified aq. layer must contain visible NaCl crystals thruout following extns.)

Ext with 50 ml ether, drain aq. layer into second separator, and ext again with 50 ml ether. Continue extg and draining aq. layer, using 35 ml for third and fourth extns. Shake each ext ≥1 min, releasing pressure, if necessary, by inverting separator and carefully venting thru stopcock. Let layers sep. at least 5 min or until aq. layer is clear before subsequent draining and extn. Combine ether exts, drain, and wash with three 10 ml portions satd NaCl soln. Filter ether exts thru cotton plug into 500 ml erlenmeyer and wash separator and cotton with addnl 10 ml ether. Evap. ether on H_2O bath and remove any fumes of HCl with air current and continued heating ≤5 min. Dry 10 min at 100°.

Treat residue with 75 ml boiling H_2O and filter thru 9–11 cm Whatman No. 1, or equiv., paper. Wash flask and paper with five 20 ml portions boiling H_2O or until filtrate from final wash is neut. to litmus. Add 1–2 drops phthln and rapidly titr. with 0.02N NaOH (1 ml = 0.00374 g pyrethrin II). Check normality of 0.02N NaOH on same day sample is titrd.

FORMALDEHYDE
Formaldehyde in Solutions—
Official Final Action
Hydrogen Peroxide Method (36)

6.116   *Reagents*

(a) *Sulfuric acid std soln.*—1N. Prep. and stdze as in **45.040–45.042**.

(b) *Sodium hydroxide std soln.*—1N. Stdze against (a), using litmus or bromothymol blue indicator. 1 ml = 30.03 mg HCHO.

(c) *Hydrogen peroxide soln.*—Com., contg ca 3% H_2O_2. If acid, neutze with NaOH, (b), using litmus or bromothymol blue indicator.

(d) *Litmus indicator.*—Soln of purified litmus of such concn that 3 drops gives distinct blue color to 50 ml H_2O.

(e) *Bromothymol blue indicator.*—Dissolve 1 g bromothymol blue in 500 ml alcohol, 50% by vol.

6.117   *Determination*

Pipet 50 ml 1N NaOH soln into 500 ml erlenmeyer and add 50 ml of the H_2O_2. Add weighed amt sample (ca 3 g) from weighing pipet, letting point of pipet reach nearly to liq. in flask. Place funnel in neck of flask and heat on steam bath 5 min, shaking occasionally. Remove from bath, wash funnel with H_2O, cool to room temp., and titr. excess NaOH with std acid, using bromothymol blue or litmus. (Cool flask before titrn to obtain sharp end point with litmus.) From ml 1N NaOH used and wt sample, calc. % HCHO according to following equation

$$NaOH + HCHO + H_2O_2 = HCOONa + 2H_2O.$$

If HCHO soln contains appreciable free acid, titr. sep. portion and calc. acidity as % HCOOH. Correct for this acidity in calcg % HCHO.

6.118   Cyanide Method (37)
(Applicable only to dil. solns)

Treat 15 ml 0.1N $AgNO_3$, **45.028–45.030**, with 6 drops HNO_3 $(1+1)$ in 50 ml vol. flask, add 10 ml *KCN soln* (3.1 g in 500 ml H_2O), dil. to vol., shake well, filter thru dry filter, and titr. 25 ml filtrate with 0.1N NH_4SCN, **45.003–45.004**, as in **3.070**. Acidify another 15 ml portion 0.1N $AgNO_3$ with 6 drops of the dil. HNO_3 and treat with 10 ml of the KCN soln to which has been added measured quantity of sample (wt calcd from sp gr) contg ≤25 mg HCHO. Dil. to 50 ml, filter, and titr. 25 ml aliquot with the 0.1N

NH4SCN for excess of Ag as before. Difference between ml NH4SCN used in these 2 titrns × 2 = ml 0.1N NH4SCN corresponding to KCN used by the HCHO. Calc. % HCHO present. 1 ml 0.1N NH4SCN = 3.003 mg HCHO.

6.119 Formaldehyde in Seed Disinfectants (38)—Official Final Action

(Applicable to detn of HCHO absorbed in inert carrier, e.g., bentonite, talc, charcoal, sawdust)

Weigh ca 5 g sample contg 0.3–0.5 g HCHO in weighing bottle and transfer to 800 ml Kjeldahl flask. Add 25 ml H2O and 12 ml H2SO4 (1 + 4). Steam distill rapidly, passing vapors thru condenser with delivery end dipping into 25 ml H2O in 500 ml vol. flask. Collect ca 450 ml distillate, keeping vol. in distg flask nearly constant with aid of small flame. After distn, wash delivery tube, and dil. distillate to vol. with H2O.

Into each of two 200 ml vol. flasks measure 20 ml 0.1N AgNO3. To each flask add 12 drops HNO3 (1 + 1) and 30 ml H2O. To one of flasks add slowly, with constant shaking, 30 ml *KCN soln* (3.1 g in 1 L H2O). Dil. to vol., shake well, and filter thru dry filter. To 100 ml filtrate add 3 ml HNO3 and 5 ml FeNH4(SO4)2 indicator, 6.018(e), and titr. with 0.1N KCNS.

Pipet 25 ml HCHO distillate into small beaker contg 30 ml of the KCN soln, mix well, and add slowly, with constant shaking, to second flask contg the acidified AgNO3 soln. Dil. to vol. with H2O, filter, acidify 100 ml filtrate with 3 ml HNO3, and titr. with the KCNS soln, using FeNH4(SO4)2 indicator.

Difference between ml KCNS soln used in these 2 titrns × 2 = ml 0.1N KCNS equiv. to HCHO. Calc. % HCHO present. 1 ml 0.1N KCNS = 3.003 mg HCHO.

LIME SULFUR SOLUTIONS AND DRY LIME SULFUR

Soluble Sulfur (39)—Official Final Action

(Use low S reagents)

6.120   *Preparation of Sample*

(a) *Solns.*—Accurately weigh ca 10 g soln, transfer to 250 ml vol. flask, and immediately dil. to vol. with recently boiled and cooled H2O. Mix thoroly and either take necessary aliquots in individual pipets in min. time for detns or transfer to small bottles, filling them completely and avoiding contact of soln with air as much as possible. Stopper bottles, seal with paraffin, and store in dark, cool place.

(b) *Dry lime-sulfur.*—Thoroly stir 5 g sample with ca 50 ml H2O in 250 ml beaker. Let settle and decant thru paper into 250 ml vol. flask. Repeat extn with H2O until filtrate is colorless and ca 200 ml is obtained. Transfer residue to paper, wash with hot H2O, cool to room temp., and dil. to vol. Dry residue 1.5 hr at 105°, and reserve for free S and sulfite S

detns in residue, if desired. (Ext S from dry residue with CS2 (*Caution: See* 46.039, 46.040, and 46.048), evap. on steam bath or in air current, dry 15 min at 105°, weigh, and calc. % S.)

Prep. soln in min. time and keep beaker and funnel covered as much as possible.

6.121   *Determination*

With clean, dry pipet transfer 10 ml prepd soln, 6.120(a) or (b), to 250 ml beaker. Partially cover with cover glass and add 2–3 g Na2O2 in small portions, with stirring, from tip of spatula. Continue adding Na2O2 until all S appears to be oxidized to sulfate (yellow color disappears). Add slight excess Na2O2, completely cover beaker with cover glass, and heat on steam bath, stirring occasionally, 15–20 min.

Wash off cover glass and sides of beaker, acidify with HCl (1 + 4), and filter if necessary. Dil. to 150–200 ml, heat to boiling, and add 10% BaCl2 soln (11 ml/1 g BaSO4), with constant stirring, at such rate that ca 4 min is required to add necessary amt. Let stand until clear and cool, filter thru quant. paper, wash until Cl-free, ignite carefully, and heat to constant wt over Bunsen burner. Calc. % S from wt BaSO4, using factor 0.1374.

Thiosulfate Sulfur (39)—Official Final Action
6.122   *Reagent*

Ammoniacal zinc chloride soln.—Dissolve 50 g ZnCl2 in ca 500 ml H2O, add 125 ml NH4OH and 50 g NH4Cl, and dil. to 1 L.

6.123   *Determination*

To 50 ml H2O in 200 ml vol. flask add 50 ml prepd soln, 6.120(a) or (b). Add slight excess of the ammoniacal ZnCl2 soln and dil. to vol. Complete detn as rapidly as possible. Shake thoroly and filter thru dry filter. To 100 ml filtrate add few drops Me orange or Me red, 6.004(g) or 2.049(i), and exactly neutze with 0.1N HCl. Titr. neut. soln with 0.05N I, 6.004(b), using few drops starch indicator, 6.004(f). From ml I soln used, calc. % thiosulfate S present. (Factor of I soln in terms of As2O3 × 1.296 = equiv. in thiosulfate S.)

Sulfide Sulfur—Official Final Action
6.124   *Zinc Chloride Method* (39)

To 10–15 ml H2O in small beaker add 10 ml aliquot prepd soln, 6.120(a) or (b). Calc. quantity of ammoniacal ZnCl2 soln, 6.122, necessary to ppt all S in aliquot and add slight excess. Stir thoroly, filter, wash ppt twice with cold H2O, and transfer paper and ppt to beaker in which pptn was made. Cover with H2O, disintegrate paper with glass rod, and add ca 3 g Na2O2, keeping beaker well covered with watch glass. Warm on steam bath with frequent shaking until all S is oxidized to sulfate, adding more Na2O2 if necessary. Acidify slightly with HCl

$(1 + 4)$, filter to remove shreds of paper, wash thoroly with hot H_2O, and det. S in filtrate as in **6.121.**

6.125 Indirect Method

Difference between soluble S and sum of thiosulfate S and sulfate S = sulfide S.

6.126 Sulfate Sulfur—Official Final Action

Slightly acidify soln from **6.123** with HCl $(1 + 4)$ and heat to boiling. Add slowly, with constant stirring, slight excess 10% $BaCl_2$ soln, boil 30 min, let stand overnight, and filter. Calc. S from wt $BaSO_4$, and report as % sulfate S.

6.127 Total Calcium (39)— Official Final Action

To 25 ml prepd soln, **6.120**(a) or (b), add 10 ml HCl, evap. to dryness on steam bath, treat with H_2O and few ml HCl $(1 + 4)$, warm until all $CaCl_2$ dissolves, and filter to remove S and any SiO_2 present. Dil. filtrate to 200–250 ml, heat to boiling, add few ml NH_4OH in excess, and then add excess satd $(NH_4)_2C_2O_4$ soln. Continue boiling until pptd CaC_2O_4 assumes well defined granular form, let stand 1 hr, filter, and wash few times with hot H_2O. Ignite at 950° in Pt crucible to constant wt (CaO) and calc. % Ca.

ANT POISONS AND RODENTICIDES

6.128 ★ Alpha-Naphthylthiourea (40)— ★ Official First Action

(*Caution: See* **46.039, 46.041,** and **46.046.**)

N detn. *See* **4.132,** 10th ed.

6.129 Thallous Sulfate (41)— Official Final Action

(*Caution: See* **46.019, 46.026, 46.031,** and **46.041.**)

Weigh sample contg 0.1–0.15 g Tl_2SO_4 (usually 10 g), transfer to 800 ml Kjeldahl flask, and add 25 ml H_2SO_4 followed by 5–10 ml HNO_3. After first violent reaction ceases, heat until white fumes of H_2SO_4 appear. Add few drops *fuming* HNO_3 and continue heating and adding HNO_3 until org. matter is destroyed, as shown by colorless or light yellow soln. Cool, add 10–15 ml H_2O, again cool, and wash contents of flask into 400 ml beaker, continuing washing until vol. is 60–70 ml. Boil several min to remove all HNO_3, cool, and filter into 400 ml beaker. Wash with hot H_2O until vol. in beaker is 175 ml, neutze with NH_4OH, and then slightly acidify with H_2SO_4 $(1 + 4)$. Add 1 g $NaHSO_3$ to insure reduction of thallic to thallous state. Heat to boiling, add 50 ml *10% KI soln*, stir, and let stand overnight. Filter thru tight gooch contg 2 disks S&S 589 white ribbon paper covered by medium pad of asbestos. Wash 4 or 5 times with 10 ml portions *1% KI soln*, and finally with absolute alcohol. Dry to constant wt at 105°

(1–1.5 hr), and weigh as TlI. From this wt, calc. % Tl as Tl_2SO_4, using factor 0.7619.

Warfarin (3-(α-Acetonylbenzyl)-4-hydroxy Coumarin) (42)—Official Final Action

(Applicable to baits contg ca 0.025% and to concs contg ca 0.5% warfarin. Not applicable to pelleted baits or baits consisting of cracked corn treated with alc. warfarin soln and aq. sugar soln, and then dried.)

6.130 Reagents

(a) *Sodium pyrophosphate soln.*—1%. Dissolve 5 g $Na_4P_2O_7 \cdot 10H_2O$ in 500 ml H_2O.

(b) *Petroleum ether, purified.*—Ext 200 ml pet ether with three 20 ml portions 1% $Na_4P_2O_7$ soln.

(c) *Warfarin std soln.*—10 μg/ml. Dissolve 100 mg pure warfarin (available from WARF Institute, PO Box 2037, Madison, WI 53701) in 100 ml 1% $Na_4P_2O_7$ soln. Dil. 10 ml to 100 ml with 1% $Na_4P_2O_7$ soln, and dil. 10 ml of second soln to 100 ml with 1% $Na_4P_2O_7$ soln.

6.131 Determination

Weigh 10 g sample (0.025%) or 0.600 g (0.5%) into 125 ml g-s flask or 100 ml centrf. tube and add 50 ml Et ether from pipet. Stopper tightly and shake on shaking machine ca 30 min. Transfer 5 or 10 ml to centrf. tube (or centrf. directly), stopper, and centrf. 5 min at high speed or until clear. Take precautions to avoid evapn of ether.

Pipet 10 ml 1% $Na_4P_2O_7$ soln into g-s 16 × 150 mm test tube and add 2 ml centrfd ether ext from pipet. Stopper and shake vigorously 2 min. Centrf. at high speed until aq. layer is clear. Draw off ether layer, including any emulsion that remains, using fine-tip glass tube attached to aspirator. Add ca 2 ml Et ether, shake vigorously, centrf., and completely draw off ether layer. Repeat ether extn, and then ext twice with purified pet ether in same manner.

Prep. blank soln similarly, using 2 ml ether instead of 2 ml ether ext.

Det. A of aq. soln in 1 cm silica cell at 308 nm against blank soln in Beckman spectrophtr, model DU, or equiv. Det. A' (ca 0.46), of the std warfarin soln against 1% $Na_4P_2O_7$ soln.

$$\% \text{ Warfarin} = (A/A') \times 0.025 \text{ (for baits)}$$
$$\text{or} \times 0.417 \text{ (for concs).}$$

FUMIGANTS

Fumigant Mixtures (43)—Official First Action

(Applicable to org. components of CS_2, CCl_4, $(CH_2)_2Cl_2$, and $(CH_2)_2Br_2$ mixts. *Precautions:* Handle with care in hood or well-ventilated area. Mixts are volatile, poisonous, and sometimes flammable and may be fatal if inhaled or swallowed. They cause skin and eye irritation. In case of contact, immediately remove contaminated clothing and flush affected area with copious amts of H_2O. Do not reuse clothing until free of contamination. Do not use containers or equipment of Al, Mg, or their alloys.)

6.132 *Principle*

Components are detd by GLC. Peak area of each component is measured and compared to stds of same fumigant mixt. Precision of method is ±0.6% for each component.

6.133 *Sampling*

Obtain representative 1 L sample from container. Sample bulk containers by means of weighted bottle, lowered toward bottom and raised at such rate that it is ¾ full when withdrawn. Sample drums or small containers with thief or thru tap or valve located so that sample comes from well below surface. Prevent contamination of product or sample.

Place sample in clean, dry, and solv. vapor-tight, glass bottle of such size that it is nearly filled (not above shoulder) by sample. Vapor-tight g-s bottles or screw cap bottles with Sn-foil lined caps are satisfactory. Store samples at low temp. Cool sample to <18° before opening for analysis.

6.134 *Apparatus*

(a) *Gas chromatograph.*—Beckman Instruments GC-2, or equiv. Operating conditions: Column temp., 110°; injection port temp., 200°; flow rate, 80 ml He/min.

(b) *Recorder.*—0.05–1.05 mv, full scale response. Ball and disk integrator may be used.

(c) *Syringe.*—Hamilton Co. 10 μl No. 701N, or equiv.

(d) *Column.*—4′ stainless steel, ¼″ od, 0.194″ id, packed with reagent **6.135**(a). Max. temp. is 160°. Other columns can be used but chromatgc conditions and sample size must be adjusted in accordance with column requirements. One such column is: 10′ stainless, ³⁄₁₆″ od, 0.12″ id, packed with 20% by wt *N,N*-bis-(2-cyanoethyl) formamide on Chromosorb W, acid-washed, 80–100 mesh. Columns are available from com. suppliers. Criterion for use is emergence of each component of mixt. of CS_2, CCl_4, $(CH_2)_2Cl_2$, and $(CH_2)_2Br_2$ as sep. peak.

6.135 *Reagents*

(a) *Column packing.*—30% by wt tricresyl phosphate on Chromosorb P, 30–60 mesh.

(b) *Carbon disulfide std.*—ACS.

(c) *Carbon tetrachloride std.*—ACS.

(d) *Ethylene dichloride std.*—Purified 1,2-dichloroethane, available from laboratory supply houses, or use center cut of fractionation of com. product.

(e) *Ethylene dibromide (1,2-dibromoethane) std.*—Purified or distd as in (d).

6.136 *Preparation of Standards*

Prep. fresh stds just before analysis which approximate expected composition, by wt, of fumigant mixt. Place proper wt of each component in 25 ml g-s vol. flask and mix well. Do not make to vol. Cool CS_2 to prevent loss.

Carefully fill weighed 10 ml vol. flask to mark with prepd std and weigh. Use this wt to det. g/5 μl values for each component of std.

6.137 *Determination*

Purge column thoroly at 110° before use. Establish 0 base line at full sensitivity. Inject 5 μl std fumigant mixt. into chromatograph. Attenuate successively so that each peak is at max. % of chart scale. (If instrument other than Beckman GC-2 is used, adjust sample size and attenuation, if necessary.) Repeat injection. Detd area for each component, corrected for any base line drift, should differ by ≤1%. Order of elution from column is: CS_2, CCl_4, $(CH_2)_2Cl_2$, and $(CH_2)_2Br_2$. Total analysis time is ca 21 min.

Inject 5 μl sample into chromatograph. Det. corrected area of each component from chromatogram, or note integrator reading.

g Component = $S \times C/B$, where S = wt component in std, B = area for component in std, and C = area for component in sample. Perform calcn for each component in sample.

% Component = g component in sample × 100/ sum of g components in sample.

Last equation is not applicable in presence of unmeasured contaminants.

HERBICIDES

Potassium Cyanate (44)—Official Final Action
(Caution: See 46.041.)

6.138 *Reagent*

Wash soln.—Satd aq. soln of hydrazodicarbamide, $NH_2CONHNHCONH_2$. Prep. by mixing some KCNO and semicarbazide.HCl, $NH_2CONHNH_2$ .HCl, in H_2O, filter, and wash ppt with H_2O. Transfer ppt to flask, add small amt H_2O, shake vigorously, and filter. (Solubility of ppt in H_2O is ca 1 part in 6600.)

6.139 *Determination*

Transfer sample contg 0.2–0.5 g KCNO to 100 ml beaker, add 20 ml wash soln and 1 g semicarbazide .HCl, and let stand 24 hr. Filter hydrazodicarbamide on gooch or fine fritted glass crucible, wash with 10 ml wash soln, and dry at 100° to constant wt. Wt residue × 0.6869 = KCNO.

Amitrole (3-Amino-s-triazole) (45)—
Official First Action
(Caution: See 46.018 and 46.041.)

6.140 *Preparation of Sample Solution*

(a) *50% Dry powder formulation.*—Transfer 10.000 g sample to 100 ml g-s vol. flask, using powder funnel. Add 50 ml N,N-dimethylformamide (DMF). Shake 2–3 min to dissolve amitrole. (Undissolved amitrole is powder and can be differentiated visually from inerts which are usually crystals.) Let settle and carefully decant supernatant into 100 ml vol.

flask. Repeat extn of residue with three 15 ml portions DMF, letting settle each time before decanting into vol. flask. Dil. combined exts to vol. with DMF and shake well. Filter 40–50 ml thru fritted glass filter of medium porosity. Pipet 25 ml into 400 ml beaker contg 50 ml H_2O.

(b) *90% Dry powder formulation.*—Dissolve 1.0000 g sample in 100 ml H_2O in 400 ml beaker.

(c) *Aqueous amitrole.*—Pipet 5 ml sample into 400 ml beaker contg 50 ml H_2O.

6.141 *Determination*

Adjust sample soln or dild aliquot to pH 1.8 with 0.5N HCl. Stir mech. and titr. with 0.5 ml increments 0.5N NaOH to pH 3.5–4.0. (Use Beckman Model G pH meter, or equiv., equipped with glass-calomel electrode system, and stdzd at pH 4.0 and 7.0 with buffers **45.007**(c) and (d).) Add 0.5N NaOH rapidly to pH 6.5 and then dropwise to pH 7.5 (second inflection point). Plot pH against ml 0.5N NaOH and det. first inflection point (occurs at pH 2.5–2.9).

% Amitrole by wt = $(B - A) \times 0.5 \times 8.408/C$, where A = ml 0.5N NaOH required to titr. to first inflection point; B = ml 0.5N NaOH required to titr. to pH 7.5; and C = 2.5 for 50% dry powder formulation, (a), g sample for 90% dry powder formulation, (b), and 5.0 $\times$ sp gr sample for aq. amitrole, (c).

lb Amitrole in aq. amitrole/U.S. gal. = % amitrole $\times$ sp gr $\times$ 8.32/100.

Dimethyl 2,3,5,6-Tetrachloroterephthalate (Dacthal) (46)—Official First Action

(Caution: See **46.011, 46.018, 46.039, 46.040, 46.041, 46.045, 46.046,** and **46.048.**)

Gas Chromatographic Method

(Note: Under conditions specified, other pesticides or ingredients may interfere with GLC analysis, e.g., aldrin has same retention time as Dacthal. Aldrin and Dacthal may be sepd at 170° column temp.)

6.142 *Apparatus*

Gas chromatograph.—6′ × ⅛″ id stainless steel column contg 10% UC-98 (Applied Science Laboratories, Inc.) on 80–100 mesh silanized Diatoport S (Hewlet-Packard Co., Rt 41, Avondale, PA 19311). Conditions (applicable to Hewlet-Packard F&M Model 5750)—temps: column 200°; injection port 240°; flame ionization detector 260°; H, air, and He carrier flows, 115, 600, and 25 ml/min, resp.; chart speed 0.25″/min; attenuation 4×; range setting 10^2 (10^{-10} amp full scale).

6.143 *Determination*

(a) *Benzene extraction.*—Grind granular product. Weigh portion contg ca 300–400 mg Dacthal into Whatman extn thimble (33 × 80 mm). Cover with glass wool. Place thimble in medium Soxhlet extractor; add 150–175 ml benzene and 3 glass beads. Ext 6

hr. Quant. transfer ext to 400 ml beaker and evap. to ca 5 ml on steam bath with dry air current; remove and evap. to dryness with air current. Add ca 150 ml acetone and let stand until soln is complete (white, flakey crystals may indicate incomplete soln; soln may be hastened by placing flask in ultrasonic cleaner). Filter soln thru glass wool into 200 ml vol. flask. Wash beaker with acetone, transfer washings to vol. flask, and dil. to vol.

(b) *Alternative acetone extraction.*—Substitute acetone for benzene in extn. Proceed as in (a) thru "Ext 6 hr." Continue with "Filter soln thru glass wool ..."

Inject duplicate 5 μl sample soln into gas chromatograph. Compare peak ht or peak area to std curve to det. % hexachlorobenzene (HCB) and Dacthal.

6.144 *Preparation of Standard Curve*

(a) *Dacthal std solns.*—Weigh 0.5 g Dacthal (available from Diamond Shamrock Chemical Co., 300 Union Commerce Bldg, Cleveland, OH 44115) into 100 ml vol. flask, add ca 90 ml acetone (soln is rapid), and dil. to vol. Pipet 5, 10, and 15 ml into sep. 25 ml vol. flasks and dil. to vol. with acetone.

(b) *Hexachlorobenzene (HCB) std solns.*—Weigh 0.5 g ref. grade HCB into 100 ml vol. flask, add 90 ml benzene, and dil. to vol. with benzene. Pipet 1, 2, and 3 ml into sep. 25 ml vol. flasks and evap. to dryness with current of dry air. Add 20 ml acetone to each flask and dil. to vol. with acetone.

Inject 5 μl each dild HCB and Dacthal std at least twice. Prep. curve of peak area or ht against concn for Dacthal and peak ht against concn for HCB.

Infrared Method

6.145 *Preparation of Sample*

Grind granular product. Weigh sample contg 200–500 mg Dacthal into Whatman extn thimble. Proceed as in **6.143** thru "... evap. to dryness with air current." Add 25 ml CS_2, allow ca 30 min for complete soln, and quant. transfer to 50 ml vol. flask with CS_2, filtering sample thru glass wool. Dil. to vol.

6.146 *Preparation of Standard Solution*

Weigh 1.25 g Dacthal into 100 ml vol. flask. Add ca 90 ml CS_2 (soln may be hastened by placing flask in ultrasonic cleaner) and dil. to vol. Pipet 10, 15, and 20 ml into sep. 25 ml vol. flasks and dil. to vol.

6.147 *Determination*

Set spectrophtr at optimum operating condition. Use 0.5 mm KBr (or NaCl) matched cells. Fill ref. cell with CS_2. Transfer dild stds to other cell and scan slowly from 1100 to 900 cm^{-1}. Repeat with samples. Construct baseline from 1030 to 925 cm^{-1} and draw line from midpoint of absorption max. at 964 cm^{-1} to intersect baseline. Compute ΔA at 964 cm^{-1} at point of intersection for stds and sample.

Prep. ΔA-concn curve for std; Beer's law is obeyed over concn range 2–15 mg std Dacthal/ml. Calc. % Dacthal from std curve.

Dicamba (3,6-Dichloro-*o*-anisic Acid; 2-Methoxy-3,6-dichlorobenzoic Acid) (47)— Official First Action

6.148 *Apparatus*

Infrared spectrophotometer.—With BaF_2 cells, 0.025 mm, and matched NaCl cells, 0.2 mm.

6.149 *Reagents*

(a) *Acetone.*—Spectral grade.

(b) *Dimethylamine (DMA) soln.*—60% (w/w).

(c) *Dicamba std.*—Ref. grade (Velsicol Chemical Corp.).

6.150 *Preparation of Sample*

(Sample wts are for cell thicknesses specified. For other cells, adjust wts to yield peak between 30 and 60% T.)

(a) *Aqueous solns of DMA salt (4 lb/gal.).*—Pipet, using same pipet as for std, 5.00 ml sample soln into tared 25 ml vol. flask and weigh sample. Dil. to vol. with acetone. (Use this soln directly in 0.025 mm BaF_2 cell.)

(b) *Solns of DMA salt (other concentrations).*— Prep. as in (a), adjusting sample size to yield 2.4 g dicamba/25 ml.

(c) *Technical dicamba.*—Weigh 0.2±0.005 g sample into tared 25 ml vol. flask and dil. to vol. with CS_2.

6.151 *Preparation of Standard*

(a) *Liquid formulations.*—(*1*) *Aqueous solns of DMA salt (4 lb/gal.):* Weigh 11.98±0.02 g dicamba std into tared 50 ml beaker. Add 5 ml H_2O and 4 ml 60% DMA. Adjust pH to 7.0 by titrg with 60% DMA soln, using magnetic stirrer and pH meter. (All solids should be dissolved at this time.) Rinse each pH electrode with two 1 ml H_2O rinses (4 ml total), collecting rinses in the 50 ml beaker. Cool soln to room temp. and transfer to tared 25 ml vol. flask. Rinse beaker twice with H_2O, collecting rinses in flask. Dil to vol. with H_2O and mix thoroly. Weigh flask and contents to det. total wt of soln. Pipet 5.0 ml std formulation into tared 25 ml vol. flask, weigh, and dil. to vol. with acetone.

(*2*) *Aqueous solns of DMA salt (other concns):* Prep. as in (a)(*1*), adjusting dicamba content to required concn.

(b) *Technical dicamba.*—Weigh 0.2±0.005 g dicamba std into tared 25 ml vol. flask and dil. to vol. with CS_2.

6.152 *Determination*

(a) *Liquid formulations.*—Record spectra of std and sample between 1070 and 930 cm^{-1} (9.3–10.7

μm), using BaF_2 cell. Use air in ref. beam. Obtain A at 1012 cm^{-1} (9.89 μm), using horizontal baseline tangent to min. between 1020 and 1070 cm^{-1} (9.4–9.7 μm) as ref.

(b) *Technical formulations.*—Record spectra of std and sample from 1100 to 930 cm^{-1} (9.1–10.7 μm), using NaCl cells. Use CS_2 in ref. cell. Obtain A at 1012 cm^{-1} (9.89 μm), using horizontal baseline tangent to min. between 1075 and 1035 cm^{-1} (9.3–9.66 μm).

6.153 *Calculations*

(a) *Liquid formulations.*—Dicamba, lb/gal. = $(A_{sample} \times C)/A_{std}$, where C = lb std/gal. = (g std $\times$ % purity of std $\times$ 8.35)/25.

% Dicamba by wt = $(A_{sample} \times F)/($g sample/25 ml$)$, where F = [(g std/25 ml) $\times$ % purity of std]/ A_{std}.

(b) *Technical dicamba.*—% Dicamba by wt = $(A_{sample} \times F)/$g sample, where F = (g std $\times$ % purity of std)/A_{std}.

6.154   2,4-Dichlorophenoxyacetic Acid (2,4-D) (48)—Official Final Action

(*Caution: See* **46.041, 46.054,** and **46.070(b)**.)

(a) *In preparations of free acid with no insoluble carrier.*—Weigh 1 g sample into 250 ml erlenmeyer, dissolve in 75 ml neut. alcohol, and titr. with 0.1N NaOH, using 5 drops bromothymol blue, **6.185(a)**. (5 drops phthln may be substituted, provided this indicator has been used to stdze the alkali.) 1 ml 0.1N NaOH = 0.0221 g 2,4-dichlorophenoxyacetic acid.

(b) *In herbicides containing free acid and insoluble carrier.*—Weigh sample contg 1 g of the acid into 250 ml beaker, add 25 ml 1N NaOH and 50 ml H_2O, warm and stir 15 min to dissolve acid, and cool to room temp. Filter thru paper into 250 ml separator and wash any insol. matter, collecting washings in separator. Neutze contents of separator with 10% H_2SO_4, add 10 ml excess, and ext with two 75 ml portions ether. Combine ether exts in separator, wash free from H_2SO_4 with three 10 ml portions H_2O, and filter thru cotton plug, previously satd with ether, into 400 ml beaker. Rinse separator with ether, and filter rinsings thru the cotton into beaker. To contents of beaker add 25 ml H_2O and few boiling chips, evap. on steam bath until ca 25 ml ether remains, and remove balance of ether at room temp. in air current. To residual aq. soln add 100 ml neut. alcohol and titr. with 0.1N NaOH as in (a).

(c) *In herbicides containing salts of 2,4-D.*—Weigh sample equiv. to ca 1 g free acid and dissolve in 50 ml H_2O. If insol. carrier is present, filter thru paper and wash residue. Transfer clear soln to 250 ml separator, and proceed as in (b), beginning "Neutze contents of separator . . ."

Total Chlorine in Compounds of 2,4-D and 2,4,5-Trichlorophenoxyacetic Acid (2,4,5-T) in Liquid Herbicides—Official Final Action

Parr Bomb-Boric Anhydride Method (49)

(*Caution: See* **46.013, 46.035,** and **46.041.**)

6.155 *Reagents*

Boric anhydride.—Eastman Kodak Co. or Fisher Scientific Co. material has been found satisfactory; or prep. by heating H_3BO_3 at 120–220° ca 2 weeks.

6.156 *Preparation of Sample*

(a) *Esters.*—To 2.5 g B_2O_3 in 42 ml Parr bomb, elec. ignition type, add, from small weighing buret, ca 0.2–0.6 g sample (0.030–0.034 g Cl is convenient). Never take sample >0.6 g. Samples from 0.4 to 0.6 g will burn intensely without accelerator. When sample is <0.4 g add 99% isopropanol as accelerator so that total org. matter approaches 0.5 g, but do not use >0.25 g isopropanol. (Intense burn of sample is required for total Cl recovery.)

(b) *Amine salts.*—Weigh ca 0.5 g sample from weighing bottle or buret into cup of 42 ml Parr elec. ignition bomb. Add 5–10 drops NaOH soln (1 + 1), avoiding excess which makes residue difficult to break up, to decompose amine radical and make Na salt. Place in oven 30–60 min at 100°. Cool cup, add 0.2 ml 99% isopropanol, break up softened residue, and add 2.5 g B_2O_3.

6.157 *Determination*

Thoroly mix mixt. in cup with thin stirring rod. Measure 15 g *calorimetric grade* Na_2O_2 with std measuring dipper, add small portion to contents of bomb, and stir. Add balance of Na_2O_2, and thoroly mix by stirring with rod. Withdraw rod and brush free of adhering particles. Quickly cut or break off lower 1.5″ of rod and imbed in fusion mixt. Prep. head by heating fuse wire momentarily in flame and immersing it in small quantity *sucrose*. (1 mg sucrose is enough to start combustion.) Assemble bomb and ignite in usual manner.

Place ca 100 ml H_2O in 600 ml beaker and heat nearly to boiling. After cooling bomb, dismantle and dip cover into the hot H_2O to dissolve any fusion mixt. on underside. Wash cover with fine jet of H_2O, catching washings in beaker. With tongs, lay fusion cup on side in same beaker of hot H_2O, covering it immediately with watch glass. After fused material dissolves, remove cup and rinse with hot H_2O, cool soln, add several drops phthln, neutze with HNO_3, and add 5 ml excess. Det. Cl by Volhard method, **6.223**(a), or by electrometric titrn, **6.223**(c).

Det. blank which includes all reagents used. Cl × 3.117 = 2,4-D acid; ×2.402 = 2,4,5-T acid.

Diquat (6,7-Dihydrodipyrido (1,2-*a*:2′, 1′-*c*) Pyrazidiinium Ion) (50)—Official First Action

AOAC-CIPAC Method

6.158 *Reagents*

(a) *Acetate buffer soln.*—pH 4.05. Dissolve 10.88 g $NaOAc.3H_2O$ in H_2O, add 19 ml HOAc, dil. to 2 L with H_2O, and mix.

(b) *Diquat std solns.*—(1) *Stock soln.*—0.2 mg diquat/ml. Prep. stock soln by dissolving 0.1968 g pure diquat dibromide monohydrate ($C_{12}H_{12}N_2Br_2$ $.H_2O$, molecular wt 362.1; 50.87% cation; available from Chevron Chemical Co., 940 Hensley St, Richmond, CA 94804) in buffer soln, dil. to 500 ml with buffer soln, and mix. (2) *Working soln.*—0.02 mg diquat/ml. Dil. 10.0 ml stock soln to 100 ml with buffer soln. Prep. dild stds fresh as required.

6.159 *Determination*

Transfer, using buret, 10.0, 20.0, and 30.0 ml std diquat soln, contg 0.2, 0.4, and 0.6 mg diquat, resp., to three 100 ml vol. flasks, dil. each soln to vol. with buffer soln, and mix. Measure A of stds at 310 nm in 1 cm silica cell, with buffer soln as ref., and draw calibration curve relating A to mg diquat.

Accurately weigh portion (w g) of well mixed sample contg ca 0.5 g diquat, transfer to 250 ml vol. flask, dil. to vol. with buffer soln, and mix (*Soln A*). Transfer 10.0 ml Soln A to 200 ml vol. flask, dil. to vol. with buffer soln, and mix (*Soln B*). Transfer 5.0 ml Soln B to 100 ml vol. flask, dil. to vol. with buffer soln, and mix (*Soln C*).

Measure A of Soln C at 310 nm in 1 cm silica cell, with buffer soln as ref. Read diquat content of Soln C (y mg) directly from the prepd calibration curve or calc. diquat content by interpolation.

$$\% \text{ Diquat, w/w} = 100 \, y/w.$$

Paraquat (1,1′-Dimethyl-4,4′-bipyridinium Ion) (50)—Official First Action

AOAC-CIPAC Method

6.160 *Reagents*

(a) *Sodium dithionite.*—1% soln in 0.1N NaOH. (Sodium dithionite, $Na_2S_2O_4.2H_2O$, is also called sodium hydrosulfite and sodium hyposulfite.) Do *not* keep soln >3 hr; solid is unstable in presence of moisture. Store solid in small air-tight bottles in vac. desiccator.

(b) *Paraquat std soln.*—0.25 mg paraquat/ml. Dry analytical std (available from Chevron Chemical Co., 940 Hensley St, Richmond, CA 94804) to constant wt at 100–120° before weighing (paraquat salts are hygroscopic). Dissolve 0.1728 g paraquat dichloride (72.40% cation) in H_2O, dil. to 500 ml with H_2O, and mix. Prep. soln fresh as required.

6.161 *Preparation of Standard Curve*

Pipet 50 ml std soln into 250 ml vol. flask, dil. to vol. with H_2O, and mix. Pipet 5, 10, 15, and 20 ml aliquots of this dild std soln into sep. 100 ml vol. flasks. (When dild to vol. these solns contain 2.5, 5.0, 7.5, and 10.0 μg paraquat/ml, resp.) Proceed as in **6.163**. Plot A against μg paraquat/ml at final diln.

6.162   *Preparation of Sample*

Accurately weigh portion well mixed sample contg ca 0.25 g paraquat. Transfer to 500 ml vol. flask, dil. to vol. with H_2O, and mix well (*Soln A*). Pipet 10 ml Soln A into 100 ml vol. flask, dil. to vol. with H_2O, and mix well (*Soln B*). Pipet 10 ml Soln B into 100 ml vol. flask and proceed as in **6.163**.

6.163   *Determination*

(Complete analysis of one soln before adding dithionite to next soln.)

Add 10 ml Na dithionite soln to one 100 ml vol. flask and dil. to vol. with H_2O. Mix by inverting end-over-end three times at such speed that air bubble travels from one end to other; do *not* shake flask vigorously, as this tends to cause fading of color due to oxidn. Immediately measure A of soln at 600 nm, using reagent blank (no paraquat) to set the 100% T or for ref. side for dual beam instruments. Similarly, treat each flask in turn, completing color measurement without delay before adding dithionite to next soln.

% Paraquat = (μg/ml from std curve) × 5/g sample.

Sodium Salt of Dalapon (2,2-Dichloropropionic Acid) (51)—Official Final Action

(*Caution: See* **46.041**.)

6.164   *Apparatus*

(a) *Reflux apparatus.*—250 ml erlenmeyer connected thru ⑤ 35/25 ball joint to reflux condenser.

(b) *Filtering apparatus.*—60 ml, medium porosity fritted glass funnel attached to glass filter bell, 11 cm od, 18 cm high, with bottom gasket and slide valve.

6.165   *Reagents*

(a) *Mercuric-cupric nitrate soln.*—(*Caution: See* **46.065**.) Dissolve 100.0 g yellow HgO and 60 g $Cu(NO_3)_2 \cdot 3H_2O$ in 500 ml $3.100 \pm 0.003N$ HNO_3, measured from vol. flask, in 1 L vol. flask, dil. to vol. with H_2O, and filter.

(b) *Potassium iodide soln.*—Dissolve 150 g KI in H_2O, dil. to 1 L, and make neut. to phthln.

6.166   *Determination*

Accurately weigh sample contg 0.11–0.22 g Na salt of 2,2-dichloropropionic acid, transfer to erlenmeyer of reflux app., and add 100 ml Hg-Cu nitrate soln. Add some boiling chips, attach condenser, and reflux 15 min. Cool in H_2O bath. Filter thru filtering app., washing flask and ppt acid-free with H_2O from wash bottle. Discard filtrate and washings, and

place 250 ml narrow-mouth erlenmeyer in filtering bell.

Add 50 ml KI soln to erlenmeyer to dissolve any remaining ppt, transfer to funnel, and stir until ppt dissolves. Draw soln into narrow-mouth erlenmeyer with vac. Wash flask and funnel with ≤50 ml KI soln from wash bottle, adding washings to filtrate. Add few boiling chips to filtrate and boil 1 min. Cool in H_2O bath. Titr. immediately with 0.1N HCl, using phthln.

% 2,2-Dichloropropionic acid = ml 0.1N HCl × 0.003899 × 100/g sample.

% Na salt 2,2-dichloropropionic acid = ml 0.1N HCl × 0.004499 × 100/g sample.

Sodium Trichloroacetate (52)— Official Final Action

(*Caution: See* **46.011, 46.039, 46.041,** and **46.070**.)

6.167   *Apparatus*

Reflux apparatus.—250 ml erlenmeyer attached thru ⑤ 24/40 joint to 50 cm water-cooled condenser.

6.168   *Reagent*

Dioxane.—Freshly distd.

6.169   *Determination*

Dissolve 25 g sample in H_2O and dil. to 100.0 ml. Pipet aliquot (usually 10 ml), titrg ca half that of blank, into 250 ml refluxing flask, add 1 drop Me red, and neutze with ca 1N H_2SO_4 to distinct orange-pink. pH is 5.3–5.5; usually <0.15 ml is required. If soln is acid, titr. with ca 1N NaOH. Add 25.00 ml 1N H_2SO_4, 35 ml dioxane, and few glass beads. Boil vigorously under reflux at least 60 min. Cool, add 2 drops Me red, and titr. with std 1N NaOH to sharp change from orange to yellow end point. Perform blank detn, omitting sample.

% Na trichloroacetate = Net ml 1N acid × 0.1854 × 100/g sample in aliquot.

Volatility of Ester Forms of Hormone-Type Herbicides—Official Final Action

6.170   *Material*

(a) *Paper bags.*—No. 20 to open with flat bottom. Close with paper clips.

(b) *Filter paper.*—7 cm diam.

(c) *Bacteriological loop.*—0.01 ml. Wash with acetone after each application or heat to cherry red in flame.

(d) *Test plants.*—Actively growing tomato seedlings 2.5–3″ high in 3–4″ pots.

(e) *Formulation to be tested.*—Use 0.01 ml aliquot of 4 lb/gal. formulation or equiv. vol. of other concns.

(f) *High and low volatile ester stds.*—Use butyl ester of 2,4-D as high volatile ester and tetrahydrofurfural ester of 2,4-D as low volatile ester with same wt of acid/gal. as formulations to be tested.

6.171 — *Operating Technic*

Open bags with flat bottom and place plant toward one side on bottom of bag. Apply 0.01 ml of formulation to middle of filter paper by means of bacteriological loop, and for controls, apply 0.01 ml solv. only. Place treated paper in bottom of bag. Do not touch treated part of paper against plant, sides of bag, or pot. Close bag by folding top, secure with clips, and let stand 24 hr at 85–110°F.

Use 3 plants per treatment and 3 for controls. Repeat test on another day.

Remove plants from bag, let stand 24 hr, and read curvature (stem bending, epinasty) response. (Fold and discard used bags to prevent contamination.) Rate plants according to scale 1 to 6. (*See* Fig. 6:3.) To detect small differences between low volatile esters, or differences between 2,4-D and 2,4,5-T types, hold plants 7 days after treatment to allow time for modified leaves or stem lesions to develop. Absence of such responses indicates that formulation was a low volatile 2,4,5-T ester.

ORGANIC MERCURIAL SEED DISINFECTANTS
Mercury

6.172 ★ *Volatilization Method (53)—* ★ *Official Final Action*

See **4.150–4.151**, 10th ed. (*Caution: See* **46.041** and **46.065**.)

6.173 *Precipitation Method (53)— Official Final Action*

(*Caution: See* **46.041, 46.048,** and **46.059**.)

Place 0.5–2.0 g sample, depending on amt of Hg present, in 200 ml erlenmeyer connected thru ⸎ joint to air condenser. Add 10 ml H_2SO_4, connect flask to condenser, and rotate so acid will wet entire sample. Add 3–5 ml *30% H_2O_2* dropwise thru condenser tube, and rotate flask to mix. After active reaction subsides, heat over low flame 15–20 min, add

addnl 5 ml H_2O_2, and continue heating until all org. matter is destroyed (indicated by clear soln), adding more H_2O_2 if necessary. Remove flask from heat, let cool, wash down condenser, and transfer contents to beaker, filtering if necessary. Dil. to ca 200 ml and destroy excess H_2O_2 by titrn with *3% $KMnO_4$ soln*. Ppt the Hg with H_2S, filter thru weighed gooch, and dry at 105–110°. Ext dried ppt with CS_2 to remove any pptd S, again dry, and weigh. HgS × 0.8622 = Hg.

SODIUM HYPOCHLORITE SOLUTIONS (54)
Sodium Hypochlorite

Arsenious Oxide Titration Method— Official Final Action

6.174 — *Reagents*

(**a**) *Arsenious oxide std soln.*—0.1N. Prep. as in **45.005–45.006**, using 2.473 g As_2O_3.

(**b**) *Iodine std soln.*—Prep. as in **45.019**. Stdze against (**a**).

6.175 — *Determination*

Transfer 20 ml sample to 1 L vol. flask and dil. to vol. Pipet 50 ml aliquot of mixt. into 200 ml erlenmeyer. Add excess As_2O_3 soln and then decided excess $NaHCO_3$. Titr. excess As_2O_3 with std I soln, using starch soln, **6.004**(f), or the I as its own indicator. Subtract vol. I soln, corrected to 0.1N, from vol. As_2O_3 soln used, and from this value and sp gr of soln, calc. % NaOCl. 1 ml 0.1N As_2O_3 = 0.003722 g NaOCl.

6.176 Available Chlorine— Official Final Action

Calc. % available Cl from titrn, **6.175**. 1 ml 0.1N As_2O_3 = 0.003545 g available Cl.

6.177 Chloride Chlorine—Official Final Action

Pipet 50 ml aliquot prepd soln, **6.175**, into 200 ml erlenmeyer and add slight excess As_2O_3 soln,

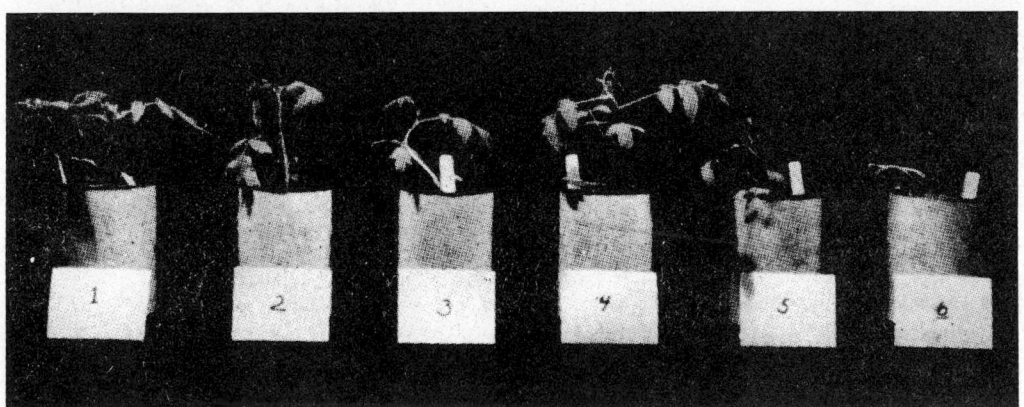

FIG. 6:3—Response scale of test plants to ester forms of hormone-type herbicides

6.174(a), calcd from NaOCl titrn; add slight excess HNO₃, neutze with *CaCO₃*, and titr. with 0.1N AgNO₃, **45.028–45.030**, using K₂CrO₄ soln, **45.029** (b), or the Ag₃AsO₄ formed in soln, as indicator. Det. blank on reagents and correct for any Cl found. From this corrected titrn and sp gr of sample, calc. % Cl. From this value subtract ½ the % available Cl. Difference = % chloride Cl.

6.178   Sodium Hydroxide (55)— Official Final Action

Stdze pH meter equipped with calomel and glass electrodes, using std pH 6.9 buffer soln, **45.007**(d).

Place 50 ml 10% BaCl₂.2H₂O soln and 30 ml 3% H₂O₂ soln in 250 ml beaker. Neutze to pH 7.5 with ca 0.1N NaOH, using pH meter. Add 10 ml sample from pipet, stir vigorously 1 min, and titr. to pH 7.5 with stdzd 0.1N HCl, using pH meter.

$$\% \text{ NaOH} = \frac{\text{ml HCl} \times \text{normality} \times 4.0}{\text{ml sample} \times \text{sp gr}}$$

6.179   ★   Carbon Dioxide—   ★ Official Final Action

Evolution into std Ba(OH)₂ soln. *See* **4.158–4.159**, 10th ed.

CALCIUM HYPOCHLORITE AND BLEACHING POWDER (54)

Available Chlorine

6.180   *Arsenious Oxide Titration Method— Official Final Action*

Weigh 5–10 g thoroly mixed sample into porcelain mortar, add 30–40 ml H₂O, and triturate to smooth cream (high-test Ca(OCl)₂ will dissolve readily and not form a cream). Add more H₂O, stir well with pestle, and let insol. residue settle few moments. Pour mixt. off into 1 L vol. flask, add more H₂O, and thoroly triturate sample and pour off as before. Repeat operation until all material is transferred to flask. Rinse mortar and pestle, catch wash H₂O in flask, dil. to vol., and mix. Without letting material settle, pipet 25–50 ml aliquot into 200 ml erlenmeyer. Add excess std As₂O₃ soln, **6.174**(a), and then decided excess of NaHCO₃. Titr. excess As₂O₃ with std I soln, **6.174**(b), using starch soln, **6.004**(f), or I as its own indicator. Subtract vol. I soln, corrected to 0.1N, from vol. As₂O₃ soln used, and calc. % available Cl. 1 ml 0.1N As₂O₃ = 0.003545 g available Cl.

CHLORAMINE T (54)

Active Chlorine

Arsenious Oxide Titration Method— Official Final Action

6.181   *Determination*

Transfer 0.5 g sample to 300–500 ml erlenmeyer, dissolve in 50 ml H₂O, and add excess of std As₂O₃ soln, **6.174**(a), and 5 ml H₂SO₄ (1 + 4). Add decided excess NaHCO₃ and titr. excess As₂O₃ with std I soln, **6.174**(b), using starch soln, **6.004**(f), or I as its own indicator. From this titrn calc. active Cl in sample. 1 ml 0.1N As₂O₃ soln = 0.001773 g active Cl. (To convert active Cl to available Cl, multiply active Cl by 2.)

6.182   Total Chlorine—Official Final Action

Dissolve 0.5 g sample in 50 ml H₂O in erlenmeyer and add slight excess of the std As₂O₃ soln as calcd from active Cl titrn, **6.181**. Add 5 ml HNO₃ (1 + 4), neutze with *CaCO₃*, and titr. with std AgNO₃, **45.028–45.030**, using K₂CrO₄, **45.029**(b), as indicator. Det. blank on reagents and correct for any Cl found. From corrected titrn calc. % total Cl in sample. 1 ml 0.1N AgNO₃ = 0.003545 g Cl. If total Cl exceeds active Cl, NaCl is indicated.

6.183   Sodium—Official Final Action

Weigh 0.5 g sample in SiO₂ or porcelain dish and add ca 25 ml H₂O and 3–5 ml H₂SO₄ (1 + 4). Evap. to sirupy consistency on steam bath and finally to dryness on hot plate. Ignite at full heat of Bunsen burner, cool, and weigh as Na₂SO₄. (Residue should be completely sol. in H₂O and should show no turbidity with NH₄OH and (NH₄)₂CO₃.) Test for Na in flame. If residue meets these tests it may be considered pure Na₂SO₄. From wt residue, calc. % Na in sample.

QUATERNARY AMMONIUM COMPOUNDS

Chloride—Official Final Action

6.184   *Potentiometric Titration Method*

Transfer sample contg 30–35 mg Cl to 600 ml beaker, dil. to 200 ml with H₂O, and add 5 ml HNO₃ (1 + 1). Add just enough acetone to dissolve ppt that forms and titr. with 0.1N AgNO₃, using potentiometric titrimeter (Fisher Titrimeter, or equiv.). Calc. % Cl (1 ml 0.1N AgNO₃ = 3.545 mg Cl) and equiv. % quaternary NH₄ salt.

Adsorption Indicator Method

6.185   *Reagents*

(a) *Bromothymol blue indicator.*—Dissolve 1 g indicator in 500 ml 50% alcohol.

(b) *Dichlorofluorescein soln.*—0.1%. Dissolve 100 mg indicator in 100 ml 70% alcohol.

6.186   *Determination*

Transfer sample contg 30–140 mg Cl (usually ca 1 g quaternary NH₄ salt) into 300 ml erlenmeyer, dil. to 75 ml with H₂O, and add 25 ml isopropanol. Neutze if necessary with HOAc (1 + 9), using 1 drop bromothymol blue (pH 4–6). Add 10 drops dichlorofluorescein, and titr. with 0.1N AgNO₃, avoiding direct sunlight. Ppt becomes red at end point and may flocculate just before end point. Calc. % Cl and equiv. % quaternary NH₄ salt.

ORGANIC INSECTICIDES AND OTHER PESTICIDES

Aldrin, Dieldrin, and Endrin—Official Final Action

Total Chlorine by Sodium Biphenyl Reduction Method (56)

6.187 *Principles*

Org. halogen compds are decomposed by Na biphenyl and liberated halide ion is titrd by Volhard method or potentiometrically after extn with H_2O from reaction medium. Applicable to detn of aldrin, dieldrin, or endrin in dusts, granules, wettable powders, emulsifiable concs, and solns in absence of other org. Cl-contg compds. More than trace amts of H_2O and appreciable amts of org. compds contg labile H cause excessive consumption of Na biphenyl. Interference of S is avoided, when present, by special treatment.

6.188 *Reagents*

(a) *Dilute nitric acid.*—6% by wt. Add 60 ml HNO_3 to 945 ml H_2O.

(b) *Sodium biphenyl reagent.*—30% w/w. (*Caution: See* **46.034** and **46.038**.) Place 300 ml dry toluene and 58 g Na in dry 2 L 3-neck flask equipped with adjustable speed sealed stirrer, inlet for N, and reflux condenser. With stirrer off, and with slow stream of N passing thru flask, warm until refluxing begins and Na is entirely melted. Agitate vigorously until Na is finely dispersed; then cool to <10°. Remove reflux condenser and add 1.25 L anhyd. ethylene glycol dimethyl ether. Add 390 g biphenyl with moderate stirring and with slow stream of N passing thru flask. Reaction should begin within few min, indicated by blue or green color which gradually darkens to black. Maintain temp. at <30° with oil bath or other cooling medium not involving hazard should flask contg Na break. Reaction should be complete in 1 hr. Reagent protected from moisture and air has useful life of 1–2 months at 25°.

(Premixed reagent, packed in 15 ml vials, each enough for 1 detn, is available from Southwestern Analytical Chemicals, PO Box 485, Austin, TX 78767.)

(c) *Toluene.*—Nitration grade, Cl-free.

6.189 *Preparation of Sample*

(*Caution: See* **46.041** and **46.084**.)

(a) *Technical products.*—Accurately weigh ca 0.1 g sample into 125 ml separator contg 25–30 ml toluene. Cautiously add 10–14 g Na biphenyl reagent, mix by swirling, and let stand 5 min. If soln is not dark green, add addnl 10–14 g reagent. (Dieldrin and endrin require 15 min reaction time after final addn of reagent.)

Destroy excess reagent by dropwise addn of H_2O, shaking frequently between addns, until green color is completely removed. Then slowly add 25 ml dil. HNO_3, with intermittent swirling. Stopper separator,

and mix with gentle rocking motion, venting occasionally. Avoid vigorous shaking during this first extn.

Let sep., rinse stopper and walls of separator with H_2O, and drain aq. phase into 250 ml g-s erlenmeyer. Re-ext reaction mixt. with two 25 ml portions dil. HNO_3, shaking vigorously. Add aq. exts to erlenmeyer and det. Cl.

(b) *Emulsifiable concentrates and oil spray solns.*—Mix thoroly and weigh sample contg 0.05–0.08 g Cl into 250 ml separator contg 25–30 ml toluene. Proceed as in (a), beginning "Cautiously add . . ."

(c) *Dusts, granules, and wettable powders.*—Weigh sample contg 0.1–0.15 g active ingredient in paper Soxhlet extn thimble, place in extn app., and ext with ca 150 ml acetone in 300 ml flask 3 hr. Evap. ext to dryness on steam bath, dissolve residue in few ml toluene, and quant. transfer to 250 ml separator, using 25–30 ml toluene. Continue as in (a), beginning "Cautiously add . . ."

If S is brought into soln by decomposition of emulsifiers or other compds such as org. thiophosphates, remove as follows: Add 30% NaOH soln to acid soln in erlenmeyer until alk. to phthln, and add 1 ml excess. Add 5 ml 30% H_2O_2, heat to boiling on hot plate, and boil ca 10 min. Let cool slightly, cautiously add 5 ml more 30% H_2O_2, and boil again ca 10 min. Cool, and add small flake (ca 0.05 g) *hydrazine sulfate* to remove last traces of H_2O_2. Neutze with dil. HNO_3 to phthln and add 2–3 ml excess.

6.190 *Determination*

(a) *Colorless solns.*—To acid aq. soln add 30 ml H_2O, 10 ml nitrobenzene, 3 ml ferric indicator, **6.018(e)**, and, from buret, 0.4–0.6 ml 0.05N KCNS. Swirling constantly, titr. with 0.1N $AgNO_3$ until red is discharged, and add 2–5 ml excess. Stopper flask tightly and shake vigorously 15 sec. Without refilling buret, titr. slowly with the 0.05N KCNS until end point approaches. Stopper flask, shake vigorously 20–30 sec, and continue titrn until 1 drop produces distinct reddish color which does not fade on swirling or vigorous shaking.

(b) *Colored solns or chloride in presence of bromide and/or iodide.*—To acid aq. soln add 30 ml H_2O, transfer to 400 ml beaker, adjust vol. to 200–250 ml, and add 0.5 g $Ba(NO_3)_2$. Titr. with 0.1N $AgNO_3$ potentiometrically, with stirring, using cell system of either glass ref. electrode and Ag indicating electrode or Ag-AgCl electrode system, electronic voltmeter, and 10 ml buret.

(c) *Blank determination.*—Det. blank on all reagents by adding 10–14 g Na biphenyl reagent to 25 ml toluene and continuing as in **6.189(a)**.

6.191 *Calculations*

% Aldrin, dieldrin, or endrin = (net ml $AgNO_3$ − ml blank) × normality × 35.45 × F/(10 × g sample), where F is 1.61 for aldrin, 1.81 for dieldrin, and 1.74 for endrin.

(For most accurate results, det. factor F for specific batch of tech. pesticide used in formulation. Toxicant content is stenciled on drum. Calc. $F = P/C$, where P = purity (toxicant content as stenciled on drum), and C = % Cl by wt.)

Infrared Method (56)

6.192   *Principles*

Dieldrin and endrin in dusts, granules, wettable powders, emulsifiable concs, and solns are purified on adsorbent columns. Hexachloro-epoxy-octahydro-endo,exo-dimethanonaphthalene (HEOD) content of the purified dieldrin or of tech. dieldrin is detd by IR A, using baseline technic, and dieldrin is calcd assuming 85% HEOD content. Endrin content of purified or tech. endrin is detd as hexachloro-epoxy-octahydro-endo,endo-dimethanonaphthalene similarly.

Aldrin is extd from dusts, wettable powders, and inorg. fertilizers on adsorbent column. Hexachloro-hexahydro-endo,exo-dimethanonaphthalene (HHDN) content of the ext or of tech. aldrin is detd by IR A, using baseline technic, and aldrin is calcd assuming 95% HHDN content. Method is not applicable to emulsifiable concs or granules contg petroleum hydrocarbon solvs or to mixts contg other common pesticides or adjuvants that absorb in same wavelength region as HHDN.

6.193   *Apparatus*

Infrared spectrophotometer.—With sealed liq. cells with NaCl windows, having optical path length of ca 0.1 mm (dieldrin and endrin) and 0.2 mm (aldrin).

6.194   *Reagents*

(a) *Chromatographic solvent A.*—Mix 1 vol. $CHCl_3$ with 19 vols hexane.

(b) *Chromatographic solvent B.*—Mix 1.5 vols acetone with 98.5 vols chromtgc solvent A.

(c) *Extraction solvent.*—Mix 1 vol. acetone with 19 vols CS_2.

6.195   *Preparation of Standard Solutions*

(Recrystd 99+% ref. stds are available from Shell Chemical Co.)

(a) *HEOD std soln for dieldrin.*—Weigh accurately ca 100, 200, 300, 400, 500, and 600 mg std hexachloro-epoxy-octahydro-endo,exo-dimethanonaphthalene (HEOD) into 10 ml vol. flasks, dissolve in CS_2, and dil. to vol. Concns will be 1, 2, 3, 4, 5, and 6 g/100 ml, resp.

(b) *Std soln for endrin.*—Accurately weigh ca 50, 100, 150, 200, 300, and 400 mg std hexachloro-epoxy-octahydro-endo,endo-dimethanonaphthalene (endrin) into 10 ml vol. flasks, dissolve in CS_2, and dil. to vol. Concns will be 0.5, 1.0, 1.5, 2.0, 3.0, and 4.0 g/100 ml. resp.

(c) *HHDN std soln for aldrin.*—Accurately weigh ca 100, 150, 200, 250, 300, and 350 mg std hexachloro-endo,exo-dimethanonaphthalene (HHDN) into 10 ml vol. flasks, dissolve in CS_2, and dil. to vol. Concns will be 1.0, 1.5, 2.0, 2.5, 3.0, and 3.5 g/100 ml, resp.

6.196   *Preparation of Standard Curve*

Fill 0.1 mm cell (0.2 mm for aldrin) with most dil. of stds solns, using hypodermic syringe. Adjust spectrophtr to optimum settings for gain, slit width, response, speed, and drum drive. Make duplicate scans of CS_2 soln over scanning range indicated in table and repeat with each of other std solns at same instrument settings.

For each of scans of the 6 std solns of each compd, draw line between baseline points indicated in table. Draw perpendicular from zero radiation line thru absorption peak to baseline and measure distance from 0 line to peak, P, and to baseline P_0. Calc. A ($= \log P_0/P$) and plot as ordinate against concn in g/100 ml as abscissa.

Since std curve intersects abscissa at pos. concn value, method is not applicable to concns below this value.

Peak wavelengths given in table are characteristic for low concns and they shift at higher concns. P is always detd as distance from 0 line to point of max. absorption.

6.197   *Characteristic Wavelength Points for Infrared Determination of Dieldrin, Endrin, and Aldrin, μm*

Compound	Scanning Range	Baseline Points	Peak at Low Concn
HEOD	11.59–12.18	11.64, 12.18	11.80
Endrin	11.43–12.04	11.50, 11.97	11.76
HHDN	11.79–12.24	11.85, 12.24	12.01

6.198   *Preparation of Sample*

(*Caution: See* **46.011, 46.041, 46.046, 46.056,** *and* **46.061.**)

(a) *Dusts and wettable powders.*—Transfer 3–20 g sample, depending on concn (75–0.5%), weighed to nearest 0.01 g, to chromatgc tube contg 25–50 mm (ca 5.5 g) Hyflo Super-Cel. (For finely divided dieldrin or endrin powder, use 3 g activated C instead of Super-Cel.) Tamp or vibrate column slightly to settle contents. Place 250 ml wide-mouth erlenmeyer or 500 ml evapg dish under tip of column.

Working in well ventilated hood, add 50 ml portions extn solv. to column (if S is present, ext with acetone instead of extn solv.), letting solv. percolate thru column between addns, until 150 ml ext collects. Rinse tip of column with addnl 10 ml extn solv.

Evap. solv. almost to dryness on steam bath under N. Dry HEOD or HHDN residues 15 min at 75°; dry endrin in vac. oven 15 min at 30° and 10 mm pressure. (Extd endrin may no longer be associated with its inhibitors. Residue must not be exposed to elevated temps and must be dissolved promptly to avoid decomposition.)

Cool residue and dissolve in few ml CS_2. Quant. transfer to vol. flask of such size (5–100 ml) to give optimum concn of 3 g HEOD, 2 g endrin, or 2 g HHDN/100 ml, dil. to vol. with CS_2, and mix thoroly. If soln is cloudy from H_2O, add little NaCl, shake, and let settle.

(b) *Granules containing dieldrin or endrin.*—Slurry 40 g Florisil in 200 ml beaker with 100 ml hexane. Transfer to chromatgc column with stream of hexane from wash bottle. Eliminate any bubbles or voids by vibration or agitation. Let hexane drain until only 2–3 mm layer remains above surface of column. Add small layer of Na_2SO_4 to top of column.

Transfer 2–10 g finely ground sample, depending on concn (10–1%), to prepd column. Rinse down column walls with three 10 ml portions chromatgc solv. A, letting each portion enter column before adding next. Add 170 ml chromatgc solv. A, let percolate thru column, and discard.

Flow 10 ml chromatgc solv. B gently down walls of tube, avoiding disturbing surface of adsorbent. After solv. sinks into column, repeat washing with 2 addnl 10 ml portions. Add 220 ml chromatgc solv. B and let flow at rate of 2–5 ml/min, collecting effluent in 500 ml wide-mouth erlenmeyer or evapg dish. Evap. solv. to dryness on steam bath, avoiding spattering, and proceed as in (a), using 5–10 ml vol. flask.

(c) *Emulsifiable concentrates and solns.*—Weigh 1.5 g dieldrin conc. (1.5 lb/gal.), 1.0 g endrin conc. (1.6 lb/gal.), or 30.0 g 0.5% dieldrin soln, and add 5 ml hexane. Transfer to prepd column and proceed as in (b).

(d) *Technical materials.*— Transfer sample contg 1.75–4.00 g dieldrin, 1.50–3.00 g endrin, or 1.00–2.00 g aldrin, weighed to 0.01 g, to 100 ml vol. flask. Dissolve in CS_2 and dil. to vol. with CS_2.

6.199 *Determination*

Fill same 0.1 mm cell (0.2 mm for aldrin) used for prepn of std curve with sample soln. Make duplicate scans, and calc. A and mean A as in prepn of std curve. From appropriate std curve obtain g HEOD, endrin, or HHDN/100 ml sample soln, W.

% dieldrin = $W \times V \times 1.175/S$;
% endrin = $W \times V/S$;
% aldrin = $W \times V \times 1.053/S$;

where V = ml sample soln; S = g sample; 1.175 and 1.053 = conversion factors HEOD to dieldrin and HHDN to aldrin, resp.

Technical Allethrin (57)—
Official First Action
(Caution: See 46.041.)

6.200 *Principles*

Allethrin reacts quant. with ethylenediamine to form chrysanthemum monocarboxylic acid which is detd by titrn with std NaOMe in pyridine. Chrysan-

themum monocarboxylic acid, anhydride, and acid chloride interfere quant. and are detd independently.

6.201 *Reagents*

(a) *Absolute alcohol.*—SDF No. 2-B is satisfactory.

(b) *Methanolic hydrochloric acid std soln.*—0.1N. Dil. 17 ml HCl (1 + 1) to 1 L with anhyd. MeOH. Stdze against std 0.1N NaOH, using phthln. If used at temp., T, different from that at which stdzd, T_0, calc. corrected normality = $N[1-0.001(T - T_0)]$.

(c) *Sodium methylate std soln.*—0.1N in pyridine. Transfer 50 ml 2N NaOMe (*Caution: See 46.038*) to 1 L bottle contg 75 ml anhyd. MeOH and dil. to 1 L with redistd pyridine. Stdze against NBS benzoic acid, using pyridine as solv. and thymolphthalein, (i), as indicator. Dispense from 50 ml automatic buret with vents connected to Ascarite tubes. Stdze daily against std methanolic HCl, (b).

(d) *Methanolic potassium hydroxide std soln.*—0.02N.

(e) *Morpholine soln.*—Transfer 8.7 ml redistd morpholine to 1 L bottle and dil. to 1 L with anhyd. MeOH. Fit bottle with 2-hole rubber stopper; thru 1 hole insert 20 ml pipet so that tip extends below surface of liq., and thru other hole insert short piece of glass tubing to which is attached aspirator bulb.

(f) *Ethylenediamine.*—Redistd com. grade contg <3% H_2O. Dispense from automatic buret with vents connected to Ascarite tubes.

(g) *Dimethyl yellow-methylene blue mixed indicator.*—Dissolve 1 g dimethyl yellow (*p*-dimethylaminoazobenzene) and 0.1 g methylene blue in 125 ml anhyd. MeOH.

(h) *α-Naphtholbenzein indicator.*—1% alc. soln.

(i) *Thymolphthalein indicator.*—1% pyridine soln.

6.202 *Determination of Chrysanthemum Monocarboxylic Acid Chloride*

Add 8–10 drops mixed indicator, (g), to ca 150 ml anhyd. MeOH and add 0.1N HCl, (b), dropwise until soln appears reddish-brown by transmitted light. Add 0.02N KOH, (d), dropwise until appearance of first green. Transfer 25 ml to each of three 125 ml g-s erlenmeyers, reserving 1 flask as ref. color for end point. Into each of other flasks add 1.5–2.5 g sample from weighing pipet, swirling flask while adding sample. Within 5 min, titr. with 0.02N KOH, (d), to first green end point, using blank as ref. color. Calc. milliequiv. chrysanthemum monocarboxylic acid chloride/g sample, $C = A \times N/g$ sample, where A = ml N normal KOH required; $C \times 18.67$ = % chrysanthemum monocarboxylic acid chloride.

6.203 *Determination of Chrysanthemum Monocarboxylic Acid*

Transfer 25 ml anhyd. alcohol to each of two 125 ml g-s erlenmeyers, add 8–9 drops α-naphtholbenzein indicator, and cool to 0° in ice bath. Neutze by adding 0.02N NaOH dropwise to bright green end point.

To each flask add 1.5–2.5 g sample from weighing pipet. Immediately titr. with 0.02N NaOH, **45.035,** to first bright green end point. Calc. milliequiv. chrysanthemum monocarboxylic acid and acid chloride/g sample: $D = A \times N/g$ sample, where A = ml N normal NaOH required; $(D - C) \times 16.82$ = % chrysanthemum monocarboxylic acid.

6.204   Determination of Chrysanthemum Monocarboxylic Anhydride

Pipet 20 ml morpholine soln, (**e**), into each of four 250 ml erlenmeyers, using same pipet. Fill pipet by exerting pressure in bottle with aspirator bulb. Reserve 2 flasks for blanks; into each of other flasks add 1.5–2.5 g sample from weighing pipet. Swirl flasks and let samples and blanks stand at room temp. 5 min. Add 4–5 drops mixed indicator, (**g**), to each flask and titr. with 0.1N HCl, (**b**), until color changes from green to faint red when viewed by transmitted light. Calc. milliequiv. chrysanthemum monocarboxylic anhydride/g sample: $E = (B - A) \times N/g$ sample, where A = ml N normal HCl required for sample, and B = ml N normal HCl required for blank; $(E - 2C) \times 31.84$ = % chrysanthemum monocarboxylic anhydride.

6.205   Determination of Allethrin

Add sample contg 0.8–1.1 g allethrin to each of two 250 ml erlenmeyers from weighing pipet. To each of 2 flasks as blanks and to samples add 25 ml ethylenediamine, (**f**), with swirling. Let samples and blanks stand 2 hr at 25±2°. Wash down sides of flasks with 50 ml redistd pyridine. To each flask add 6–10 drops thymolphthalein indicator, (**i**), and titr. with 0.1N NaOMe, (**c**), to first permanent blue-green end point. (With colorless samples, first blue end point may be used.) Calc. milliequiv. allethrin/g sample: $F = (A - B) \times N/g$ sample, where A = ml N normal NaOMe required for sample, and B = av. ml N normal NaOMe required for blank; $(F + C - D - E) \times 30.24$ = % allethrin.

Carbaryl (1-Naphthyl N-methylcarbamate) (58)—Official First Action

(*Caution: See* **46.018, 46.040,** and **46.056.**)

6.206   Apparatus and Reagents

(**a**) *Infrared spectrophotometer.* — Perkin-Elmer Corp., Model 21, or equiv. Operator must adapt conditions to his instrument. CHCl$_3$ solns contg 6 mg carbaryl/ml should give peak ht ca 0.30 A units at 8.94 μm; 2.4 mg/ml CHCl$_3$, ca 0.36 at 5.75 μm.

(**b**) *Carbaryl std solns.*—(*1*) 6 mg/ml. Transfer 600 mg carbaryl (99.66%, available from Union Carbide Corp.) to 100 ml vol. flask, dil. to vol. with CHCl$_3$, and mix. (*2*) 2.4 mg/ml. Pipet 10 ml std soln *1* into 25 ml vol. flask, dil. to vol. with CHCl$_3$, and mix.

6.207   Extraction

(**a**) *5% Carbaryl dust.*—Transfer weighed sample contg 0.3 g carbaryl to 300 ml g-s erlenmeyer. Add 50 ml CHCl$_3$ with pipet, stopper, and shake 30 min on shaking machine. Transfer to 50 ml centrf. tube, stopper, and centrf. 5 min at 1500 rpm. Use supernatant for detn.

(**b**) *50% Carbaryl dust, 50% wettable powder, or 85% sprayable powder.*—Transfer weighed sample contg 0.3 g carbaryl to 50 ml vol. flask. Add ca 30 ml CHCl$_3$ and swirl to dissolve carbaryl. Dil. to vol. with CHCl$_3$ and shake vigorously 2 min. Transfer to 50 ml centrf. tube and proceed as in (**a**).

6.208   Determination

(**a**) *At 8.94 μm.*—Transfer sample soln to NaCl cell and scan. If Perkin-Elmer Model 21 spectrophtr is used, set instrument as follows: cell, 0.5 mm compensated with CHCl$_3$; range 8.5–9.5 μm; resolution, 960 (program); speed, 2; gain, adjusted (ca 5). Repeat scan with std soln *1*. Measure A of carbaryl peak at 8.94 μm, using baseline from 8.8 to 9.3 μm.

% Carbaryl = $A \times B' \times 100/(A' \times B)$, where A and A' = absorbance of sample and std, resp., at 8.94 μm and B and B' = mg sample and mg std/ml, resp.

(**b**) *At 5.75 μm.*—Pipet 10 ml sample soln into 25 ml vol. flask, dil. to vol. with CHCl$_3$, and mix. Transfer soln to NaCl cell and scan. If Perkin-Elmer Model 21 spectrophtr is used, set instrument as follows: cell, 0.5 mm compensated with CHCl$_3$; range, 5.3–6.1 μm; resolution, 960 (program); speed, 2; gain, adjusted (ca 5). Repeat scan with std soln *2*. Measure A of carbaryl peak at 5.75 μm, using baseline from 5.3 to 6.1 μm.

Calc. % carbaryl as in (**a**), using A at 5.75 μm.

Technical Chlordane
Total Chlorine Method (59)— Official Final Action

(*Caution: See* **46.011, 46.018, 46.038, 46.039, 46.040, 46.041,** and **46.045.**)

6.209   Standardization of Standard Solutions

(**a**) *Sodium chloride std soln.*—0.1N. Dissolve 5.845 g NaCl, previously dried 2 hr at 105°, in H$_2$O, and dil. to 1 L in vol. flask.

(**b**) *Silver nitrate std soln.*—0.1N. Prep. as in **45.028.** To 250 ml g-s erlenmeyer add 15.00 ml 0.1N NaCl, (**a**), 50 ml H$_2$O, 10 ml HNO$_3$ (1 + 1), boiled to expel oxides of N, and 25.00 ml of the AgNO$_3$ soln. Add 3 ml nitrobenzene, stopper, and shake vigorously 15 sec. Add 5 ml ferric indicator, **6.018(e)**, and back-titr. with 0.1N KCNS, (**c**), to reddish-brown end point. (Potentiometric titrn using Ag indicator electrode and Ag-AgCl or glass ref. electrode may be substituted for indicator method, but must be used in both stdzn and detn.)

(**c**) *Potassium thiocyanate std soln.*—0.1N. Prep.

and titr. against AgNO₃ soln, (b), as in **45.031(b)**. Calc. F = ml AgNO₃ soln/ml KCNS soln.

Normality AgNO₃ soln = ml NaCl soln × 0.1000 /(ml AgNO₃ soln − ml KCNS soln × F).

6.210 Preparation of Sample

(a) *Emulsifiable concentrate formulations.*—Accurately weigh sample contg 0.5±0.05 g tech. chlordane into 50 ml vol. flask, dissolve, and dil. to vol. with toluene. Transfer 5 ml aliquot to 125 ml separator, add 15 ml or g Na biphenyl reagent, **6.188**(b), and swirl. If soln is not dark green, add more reagent. Let stand 3 min and add 3–5 ml H₂O dropwise. With stopper removed, swirl soln gently to decompose excess reagent. Add 25 ml H₂O, stopper, and mix with gentle rocking motion. (Do not shake vigorously.) Let layers sep. and drain lower aq. layer into 250 ml erlenmeyer. Re-ext solv. layer with two 25 ml portions 3N HNO₃ and combine aq. solns in erlenmeyer.

(b) *Dusts, granular impregnates, and wettable powders.*—Accurately weigh sample contg 0.5±0.05 g tech. chlordane into Soxhlet extn thimble. Ext with 80 ml benzene in Soxhlet app. 1 hr. Transfer to 100 ml vol. flask, washing with several 3 ml portions benzene. Dil. to vol. with benzene and transfer 10 ml aliquot to 125 ml separator. Proceed as in (a).

6.211 Determination

Add 15.00 ml 0.1N AgNO₃ and 3 ml nitrobenzene to erlenmeyer, stopper, and shake vigorously 15 sec. Rinse stopper, add 5 ml ferric indicator, **6.018**(e), and back-titr. with 0.1N KCNS to reddish-brown end point. (Designate ml KCNS as D.)

Det. blank on reagents by pipetting 5 ml toluene into 125 ml separator, add 15 ml or g Na biphenyl reagent, and proceed as in **6.210**(a), thru combining aq. solns in erlenmeyer. Add 15.00 ml 0.1N NaCl, 25.00 ml 0.1N AgNO₃, and 3 ml nitrobenzene, and proceed as above. Calc. blank correction factor, C = ml KCNS used in stdzn of AgNO₃ − ml KCNS used in blank detn.

% Chlorine = [15 − ($C + D$) × F] × normality AgNO₃ × 3.545/g sample.

% Tech. chlordane = % Cl × 1.56.

Colorimetric Method (60)— Official Final Action

(Method is empirical; all conditions must be reproduced exactly to attain good precision. Temp., reaction time, and vol. of reagents affect color intensity.)

6.212 Apparatus

(a) *Constant temperature bath.*—Capable of maintaining 100±1° and holding twelve 20 × 150 mm test tubes.

(b) *Cuvets.*—10 or 2 mm light path (available from Pyrocell Mfg. Co., 91 Carver Ave, Westwood, NJ 07675).

(c) *Spectrophotometer.*—Capable of accepting cuvets, (b).

6.213 Reagents

(a) *Methanol.*—90% (by vol.).

(b) *Methanol-benzene.*—Mix 7 vols MeOH with 3 vols benzene.

(c) *Diethanolamine.*—Purify by vac. distn at ca 20 mm Hg and take middle fraction. (*Caution: See* **46.011** and **46.015**.)

(d) *Diethanolamine-KOH soln (Davidow reagent).*—Mix 1 vol. reagent (c) with 2 vols 1.0N KOH in MeOH.

(e) *Chlordane std solns.*—1.5, 2.5, and 3.5 mg/ml. Ref. grade (available from Velsicol Chemical Corp.). Dissolve tech. chlordane in reagent (b). Discard stds after 2 weeks.

6.214 Preparation of Sample

(a) *Liquid formulations.*—Transfer weighed sample contg 200–300 mg tech. chlordane to 100 ml graduated cylinder and dil. to 100 ml with MeOH-benzene.

(b) *High concentration solid formulations (10% chlordane or more).*—Treat as in (a) and shake vigorously several min. Let settle 1 hr.

(c) *Low concentration solid formulations (less than 10% chlordane).*—Transfer weighed sample contg 200–300 mg tech. chlordane to Soxhlet and ext 1 hr with pentane. (*Caution: See* **46.039** and **46.074**.) Evap. pentane on steam bath and transfer ext to 100 ml g-s graduated cylinder. Dil. to 100 ml with MeOH-benzene.

6.215 Determination

Pipet 2 ml aliquot prepd sample to 20 × 150 mm test tube. Add No. 8 grit SiC boiling chip and 2 ml Davidow reagent, and place in 100° constant temp. bath. Remove after exactly 45 min and cool immediately in beaker of cold H₂O. Transfer to 10 ml vol. flask and dil. to vol. with 90% MeOH. Transfer aliquot of soln to 2 mm cuvet and read A at 550 nm within 15 min with 90% MeOH as ref. (Comparable results are obtained by dilg soln to 50 ml and using cuvet of 1 cm light path.)

Treat 2 ml each std soln with each set of samples. (Read 1 std soln before samples, 1 after half the samples are read, and 1 after last sample is read.)

6.216 Calculations

Calc. absorptivity (a) for each of 3 stds as follows, and use av. in subsequent calcns (expected a is ca 0.25): $a = A'/W$, where A' = A std soln and W = mg tech. chlordane (2 × concn std soln in mg/ml).

% Tech. chlordane in sample = A × 5000/(a × mg sample) where A = A sample soln and a = av. absorptivity.

Hexachlorocyclopentadiene (HEX)
(61)—Official Final Action

(Applicable to tech. chlordane, but not to formulations)

6.217   *Reagent*

*Hexachlorocyclopentadiene (HEX) std solns.—Stock soln.—*0.1 g/100 ml. Weigh 0.1000 g hexachlorocyclopentadiene ref. std (available from Velsicol Chemical Corp.) in 100 ml vol flask, dil. to vol. with MeOH, and shake to dissolve. *Std soln 1.—*0.005 g/100 ml. Dil. 5 ml stock soln to 100 ml with MeOH. *Std soln 2.—*0.002 g/100 ml. Dil. 2 ml stock soln to 100 ml with MeOH.

Method I

6.218   *Calibration*

With MeOH in both ref. and sample cells (matched 1 cm silica), adjust 0 and 100% settings on UV spectrophtr at 324 nm. Empty sample cell, rinse several times with, and then fill with, *Std Soln 1*, and read *A*. Empty sample cell, rinse with MeOH, then rinse and fill with *Std Soln 2*, and read *A*. Calc. *A* factor, *K*, for each std soln = (g std HEX/100 ml)/*A*. Average the two *K* values.

6.219   *Determination*

Weigh 0.5 g sample in 100 ml vol. flask, dil. to vol. with MeOH, and shake to dissolve. Proceed as in **6.218**, treating sample soln in same manner as stds.

% HEX in sample = (*A* of sample soln × 100 × *K*)/(g sample/100 ml).

6.220   *Method II*

(Includes corrections for other components of chlordane which absorb at 324 nm.)

Proceed as in **6.218–6.219**, except det. *A* of all solns at 300, 324, and 350 nm. Settings of 0 and 100% must be repeated at 300, 324, and 350 nm for *A* readings at those points. Calc. K = (g std HEX/100 ml)/$[A_{324} - 0.5(A_{300} + A_{350})]$.

% HEX in sample = $[A_{324} - 0.5(A_{300} + A_{350})]$ × 100 × *K*/(g sample/100 ml).

Dichlorodiphenyltrichloroethane
(1,1,1-Trichloro-2,2-Bis(p-Chlorophenyl) Ethane) (DDT)

Total Benzene-Soluble Chlorine Method (62)

(Applicable in absence of other org. Cl compds. Use H_2O_2 and isoamyl alcohol-ether extn method on dispersible powders or sprays that contain surface active agents or other ingredients that react with $AgNO_3$. *Caution: See* **46.034, 46.039, 46.040, 46.041,** and **46.045.**)

6.221   *Reagents*

(a) *Benzene.*—Thiophene- and Cl-free.

(b) *Metallic sodium.*—Ribbons or small pieces.

(c) *Decolorizing carbon.*—Test for presence of Cl by heating with HNO_3 (1 + 4), filtering, and adding $AgNO_3$ soln to filtrate. If Cl is present, wash with the HNO_3 until washings are Cl-free.

Note: Run blank on all reagents, limiting 0.1N $AgNO_3$ to 5 ml.

6.222   *Preparation of Solution*

(a) *In technical grade DDT.*—Weigh sample contg ca 1 g DDT and transfer to 250 ml vol. flask. Dissolve sample in 10 ml benzene; then dil. to vol. with *99% isopropanol.* Transfer 25 ml aliquot to 250–500 ml ₮ erlenmeyer. (Direct weighing of sample may be substituted, provided it does not introduce error >0.1%.)

Add 2.5 g Na and shake to mix sample with isopropanol. Do not add Na thru top of condenser or get Na on ground glass joints. Connect flask to reflux condenser and boil gently ≥30 min, shaking occasionally. Eliminate excess Na by cautiously adding 10 ml 50% isopropanol thru condenser at rate of 1–2 drops/sec. Disconnect condenser, add 60 ml H_2O, boil soln ca 30 min to expel isopropanol, and proceed as in **6.223**(a), (b), (c), or (d).

(b) *In dusting mixtures containing DDT in absence of organic matter.*—Weigh sample contg ca 0.75 g DDT, transfer to 100–200 ml vol. flask, and add exactly 100 ml benzene. Shake until DDT dissolves and soln is well mixed. Let settle and transfer 10 ml aliquot to 250–500 ml ₮ erlenmeyer.

Evap. on steam bath to remove most of benzene. (Do not evap. to dryness, as DDT may decompose with loss of HCl.) Add 25 ml *99% isopropanol* and proceed as in (a), second par.

If free S is present, proceed as in (f), beginning "Then add 5 ml *30% H_2O_2* . . ."

(c) *In dusting mixtures in presence of organic matter (coloring matter, plant resins, etc.).*—Weigh sample contg ca 0.75 g DDT, transfer to 100–200 ml vol. flask, and add 0.5–1.0 g decolorizing C and exactly 100 ml benzene. Shake until DDT dissolves and soln is well mixed. Filter into narrow-neck flask thru fast qual. paper without suction, keeping funnel covered with watch glass to avoid evapn loss. Transfer 10 ml aliquot to 250–500 ml ₮ erlenmeyer. Proceed as in (b), second par. Before detg Cl remove org. matter as follows:

Cool, add 2 or 3 drops phthln, and neutze by adding HNO_3 (1 + 1) dropwise; then 10 ml excess. Cool, if necessary, to room temp., transfer contents of flask and aq. washings to small separator, and shake with 15 ml *isoamyl alcohol-ether* (1 + 1). Drain aq. layer into second separator and ext again with 15 ml of the isoamyl alcohol-ether mixt. Drain aq. layer into 250 ml beaker. Wash the 2 exts successively with 10 ml H_2O, and repeat second washing with addnl 10 ml H_2O. Combine aq. wash solns with aq. soln in beaker. Det. Cl by one of following methods:

(*1*) Proceed as in **6.223**(a), beginning "Add slight excess 0.1N $AgNO_3$ . . ."

(*2*) Proceed as in **6.223**(b), beginning "Add 0.1N $AgNO_3$ . . ."

(3) Proceed as in **6.223(c)**, beginning "Cool flask to room temp. ...."

(4) Add 2 or 3 drops phthln to sample, make alk. by adding 1*N* NaOH, and proceed as in **6.223(d)**, beginning "transfer contents to Pt dish."

(d) *In mineral oil sprays in absence of organic matter (plant extractive material, organic thiocyanates).* —Transfer weighed sample contg 0.065–0.075 g DDT to 250–500 ml $\overline{S}$ flask. Add 25 ml *99% isopropanol* and proceed as in **(a)**, second par.

Note: If DDT content is <2%, use isoamyl alcohol-ether extn, **(c)**, second par., to remove excess oil.

Proceed as in **6.223(a)**, **(b)**, **(c)**, or **(d)**.

(e) *In mineral oil sprays in presence of organic matter (plant extractive material from pyrethrum or derris and/or cubé.)*—Proceed as in **(d)**, using isoamyl alcohol-ether extn, **(c)**, to remove excess oil.

(f) *In mineral oil sprays in presence of organic thiocyanates with or without plant extractive material.* —Transfer sample contg 0.065–0.075 g DDT to 250–500 ml $\overline{S}$ erlenmeyer. Add 25 ml *99% isopropanol* and proceed as in **(a)**, second par. thru "add 60 ml H_2O, ..." Then add 5 ml *30% H_2O_2*, few drops at time, thru top of condenser, heat mixt. in flask to boiling, and boil 15 min. Add addnl 5 ml H_2O_2 and again boil 15 min. Add 15 ml more H_2O_2, disconnect reflux condenser, and boil 15–30 min to expel isopropanol. Proceed as in **(c)**, second par.

(g) *In emulsions (solvent, emulsifier, and water).*— Weigh well mixed sample contg ca 0.75 g DDT in weighing bottle. Wash into 100 ml vol. flask and dil. to vol. with *isopropanol*. Transfer 10 ml aliquot to 250–500 ml $\overline{S}$ erlenmeyer. Expel isopropanol and H_2O on steam bath in air current. If drops of H_2O still remain, add 10 ml isopropanol and repeat evapn. Add 25 ml 99% isopropanol and proceed as in **(a)**, second par.

Note: If S is brought into the soln as by decomposition of emulsifier, proceed as in **(f)**, beginning "Then add 5 ml *30% H_2O_2* ...."

6.223   *Determination*

(a) Cool flask and transfer contents to 250 ml beaker. Add 2–3 drops phthln and neutze with HNO_3 (1 + 1); then add 10 ml excess. Add slight excess 0.1*N* AgNO₃, **45.032**, and coagulate pptd AgCl by digesting on steam bath 30 min, stirring frequently. Cool, filter thru fast qual. paper, and wash thoroly with H_2O. Add 5 ml satd Fe alum soln, **6.018(e)**, and det. excess AgNO₃ in filtrate by titrn with 0.1*N* KCNS, **45.031(b)**. Subtract quantity AgNO₃ found in filtrate from that originally added. Difference is that required to combine with Cl in the DDT. 1 ml 0.1*N* AgNO₃ = 0.003545 g Cl. Cl × 2 = DDT.

(b) Cool flask, add 2–3 drops phthln soln, and neutze with HNO_3 (1 + 1); then add 10 ml excess. Add 0.1*N* AgNO₃ from buret in excess of amt necessary to ppt all Cl; then add 5 ml *nitrobenzene* and 0.5 g $Fe_2(SO_4)_3$ and swirl flask to coagulate ppt. Backtitr. excess AgNO₃ with 0.1*N* KCNS to faint pink. Cross-titr. with both std solns, crossing end point in each direction to assure results. Calc. % DDT as in **(a)** from quantity of AgNO₃.

(c) Cool flask, add 2–3 drops phthln, neutze with HNO_3 (1 + 1), and add 6 ml excess. Cool flask to room temp. and transfer contents to 400 ml beaker. (Vol. should be 200–250 ml.) Titr. Cl with 0.1*N* AgNO₃ potentiometrically, using Ag-AgCl electrodes (Fisher Titrimeter or equiv.). Calc. % DDT as in **(a)**.

Note: When this method is used, decolorizing C step in **6.222(c)**, and isoamyl alcohol-ether extn in **6.222(c)**, **(d)**, and **(e)**, may be omitted.

(d) Cool flask and transfer contents to Pt dish. Evap. to dryness and ignite as thoroly as possible at temp. not exceeding dull red (ca 525°). Ext with hot H_2O, filter, and wash. Return residue to Pt dish and ignite to ash; dissolve in HNO_3 (1 + 4), filter from any insol. residue, wash thoroly, and add this soln to aq. ext. Add 0.1*N* AgNO₃, avoiding more than slight excess. Heat to boiling, protect from light, and let stand until ppt coagulates. Filter on weighed gooch, previously heated to 140–150°, and wash with hot H_2O, testing filtrate to prove excess of AgNO₃. Dry AgCl at 140–150°, cool, and weigh. Calc. % Cl and from this calc. % DDT as in **(a)**.

Note: Det. blank on all reagents, limiting 0.1*N* AgNO₃ to 5 ml.

Infrared Method (63)
(Caution: See 46.041.)

6.224   *Reagent*

DDT std soln.—Weigh 0.250 g tech. DDT (ESA Pesticide Reference Standard Technical DDT available from City Chemical Corp., 132 West 22nd St, New York, NY 10011) into 50 ml vol. flask or g-s container and add exactly 25 ml CS₂. If sample to be analyzed contains S, add wt of S expected in portion of sample to be taken for analysis. Shake to dissolve and add small amt of anhyd. Na₂SO₄. Centrf. portion of soln if it is not clear.

6.225   *Determination*

Weigh sample contg ca 0.25 g DDT into 50 ml vol. flask and add exactly 25 ml CS₂ and small amt of anhyd. Na₂SO₄. Let stand ≥30 min with occasional shaking. Transfer portion to g-s test tube and centrf. short time. Transfer to NaCl cell and scan with Perkin-Elmer Model 21 spectrophtr, or equiv., using following settings and conditions: cell, 0.5 mm; no compensation; balance instrument without cells in place; region, 8.5–10.5 μm; resolution, 960 (Program); speed, 4; filter, out; gain, adjusted.

Scan std soln in same manner.

Measure A of DDT peak at 9.83 μm with baseline from 9.4 μm to 10.2 μm, and calc. % DDT.

2,2-Dichlorovinyl Dimethyl Phosphate (DDVP) (64)—Official First Action

Method I

(Applicable to sand/sugar base fly bait contg ca 0.5% and 4 lb/gal. DDVP emulsifiable concs. *Caution: See* 46.041.)

6.226   *Apparatus*

(a) *Infrared spectrophotometer.*—Capable of recording in region 2–15 μm. Slit width must be adjustable to give signal-to-noise ratio of ca 100 to 1; with sealed liq. absorption cell, NaCl windows, and 0.2 mm path length.

(b) *Hypodermic syringe.*—Luer type, glass, 1.0 ml. Use 18 gage (Stubbs), 2″ slip-on needle.

6.227   *Reagents*

(a) *2,2-Dichlorovinyl dimethyl phosphate.*—Use std DDVP of known purity. (Available from Shell Chemical Co.)

(b) *Adsorbent clay.*—Diat. earth. (Hyflo Super-Cel.)

6.228   *Calibration of Apparatus*

Into each of five 10 ml vol. flasks, weigh, to nearest 0.1 mg, 25, 75, 100, 150, and 200 mg DDVP std, and dil. to vol. with CHCl₃. Calibration solns contain ca 2.5, 7.5, 10, 15, and 20 g DDVP/L.

Fill sealed liq. absorption cell with CHCl₃, adjust spectrophtr to optimum settings, and scan over 10.7–9.9 μm. Without changing settings, fill cell in turn with each of prepd calibration solns, starting with most dil., and scan each soln over 10.7–9.9 μm.

For each scan, construct baseline thru absorption min. at ca 10.0 μm parallel to 0 radiation line. Draw perpendicular to 0 radiation line thru absorption max. of calibration soln at ca 10.2 μm and measure radiant power P_0 (at 10.0 μm) and P (at 10.2 μm), in any convenient units but keeping same units thruout. Calc. A as log (P_0/P). Repeat calcns, using absorption min. at ca 10.5 μm as ref. point.

Subtract A of cell and CHCl₃ obtained above from A of cell and calibration solns. Plot net A of DDVP as ordinate against g/L DDVP as abscissa for each ref. point (10.0 and 10.5 μm).

6.229   *Preparation of Sample Solution*

(a) *Sand/sugar base fly baits.*—Prep. 25 × 400 mm extn column by adding enough adsorbent clay to make layer 2″ high when gently packed. Place 250 ml vol. flask under outlet. Accurately weigh sample contg 0.2–1.0 g DDVP. Transfer sample to extn column with CHCl₃, and rinse sample container with CHCl₃.

Working in well-ventilated hood, add 50 ml CHCl₃ to column. Using stirring device, vigorously agitate sample and top half of adsorbent layer to form slurry with solv. Withdraw stirring device, and rinse it and column with addnl CHCl₃ from wash

bottle. Let solv. percolate thru column until level is few mm above clay-sample layer.

Add ca 50 ml CHCl₃ to column, agitate sample and clay with stirrer as above, and let solv. percolate thru column until upper level approaches clay-sample layer. Repeat with two addnl 50 ml portions CHCl₃. When solv. ht has diminished to 2–3 mm, rinse column with three 10 ml portions CHCl₃, letting each portion enter clay layer before adding next. Let column drain and rinse outlet tip with CHCl₃, collecting rinse in 250 ml vol. flask.

Transfer CHCl₃ eluate to evapg dish (125 mm diam.) marked at 40–50 ml. Evap. on steam bath to 40–50 ml. Remove dish and continue evapn at room temp. to 10–15 ml. Using CHCl₃, quant. transfer to vol. flask of such size to give DDVP concn of ca 0.5–1.0 g/100 ml when soln is dild to vol.

(b) *Emulsifiable concentrates.*—Weigh enough sample, to nearest 0.2 mg, to give ca 1 g DDVP/100 ml CHCl₃ when dild to vol. in 10, 25, or 50 ml vol. flask.

6.230   *Determination*

Dil. CHCl₃ soln of DDVP to vol. with CHCl₃, mix thoroly, and fill calibrated liq. absorption cell with sample soln. Using same instrument settings as for calibration, scan sample soln over 10.7–9.9 μm.

Examine spectra for possible interference and use appropriate absorption min. as ref. point. (If solvs or other ingredients interfere at one of ref. points, use alternative ref. point.) For example, β-naphthol, often used as stabilizer in fly baits, exts with CHCl₃ and absorbs at ca 10.5 μm, requiring use of 10.0 μm ref. point.

Calc. A of sample soln as in 6.228.

From calcd A, read DDVP concn from calibration curve, relating A to concn in g/L of soln. Calc. DDVP as follows:

DDVP, % by wt = [(g DDVP/L) × ml sample soln]/(10 × g sample).

Method II (65)

(Applicable to ca 0.5% (w/w) spray soln and ca 1.0% (w/w) cattle spray in hydrocarbon solvs)

6.231   *Apparatus*

Infrared spectrophotometer.—Double beam instrument with specifications as in 6.226(a).

6.232   *Reagents*

2,2-Dichlorovinyl dimethyl phosphate. — See 6.227(a).

6.233   *Preparation of Compensating Solvent*

Transfer ca 30 ml sample to 125 ml separator and ext (2–3 min per extn) with 4 ca 30 ml portions 0.5N NaOH. Dry DDVP-free hydrocarbon phase by passing it thru 2–3 g anhyd. Na₂SO₄. Reserve dried solv. for prepn of DDVP std soln and as compensating solv. in ref. cell.

6.234 *Determination*

Prep. std DDVP soln in compensating solv. that approximates (on wt basis) DDVP content of sample. Calc. DDVP content of std soln to nearest 0.01% by wt.

After detg optimum instrument parameters for compensation technic, scan std soln over 9.9–10.7 μm (1010–935 cm^{-1}) region with ref. cell contg compensating solv. in ref. beam of spectrophtr. Scan sample against compensating solv. in same manner.

From differential spectra, det. A of DDVP at 10.2 μm (980 cm^{-1}) of std, A', and sample, A, measured from baseline drawn between minima near 10.0 and 10.6 μm. Calc. DDVP as follows:

DDVP, % by wt = % DDVP in std $\times A/A'$.

Vapona, % by wt = DDVP, % by wt/0.93.

Dodine (n-Dodecylguanidine acetate) (66)—Official First Action

(*Caution: See* **46.022, 46.028(a)** and **(d)**, and **46.041.**)

6.235 *Reagents*

(a) *Perchloric acid.*—0.05N. Dissolve 4.2 ml 72% HClO$_4$ in HOAc and dil. to 1 L with HOAc. Stdze as follows: Accurately weigh 0.200 g HKC$_8$H$_4$O$_4$ into 250 ml erlenmeyer. Dissolve in 20 ml HOAc by gently heating flask on hot plate. Add 80 ml Ac$_2$O and 8 drops metanil yellow indicator. Place erlenmeyer contg bar on magnetic stirrer and titr. with HClO$_4$ to first definite red (magenta). Titr. reagent blank and correct sample titer. Calc.

normality = $0.200/(0.20422 \times$ net ml HClO$_4$)

(b) *Metanil yellow.*—0.20%. Dissolve 0.200 g metanil yellow powder in 100 ml MeOH.

(c) *Potassium acid phthalate.*—Primary (NBS) std HKC$_8$H$_4$O$_4$.

6.236 *Determination*

Accurately weigh sample contg ca 0.600 g dodine into 250 ml erlenmeyer. Add 10 ml HOAc followed by 90 ml Ac$_2$O. Mix by swirling flask 5 min. Filter slurry with vac. thru large, medium porosity fritted glass buchner into 250 ml vac. flask. Wash erlenmeyer and residue in funnel with two 10 ml portions HOAc-Ac$_2$O (10 + 90). Place vac. flask contg bar on magnetic stirrer, add 8 drops metanil yellow indicator to flask, and titr. soln with stdzd ca 0.05N HClO$_4$ to first definite red (magenta). Titr. reagent blank and correct sample titer. Calc.

% dodecylguanidine acetate
= (net ml HClO$_4 \times$ normality $\times$ 28.75)/g sample

Heptachlor—Official Final Action

Active Chlorine Method (59)

6.237 *Reagents*

(a) *Dilute acetic acid.*—80%. Dil. 800 ml HOAc to 1 L with H$_2$O.

(b) *Silver nitrate-acetic acid std soln.*—Dissolve 17 g AgNO$_3$ in 200 ml H$_2$O, add 56 ml HNO$_3$ (1 + 1), and dil. to 1 L with HOAc. Stdze potentiometrically by adding 25 ml of this soln to 600 ml beaker contg 250 ml 80% HOAc. Immerse glass and Ag electrodes in soln and stir with magnetic stirrer. Titr. with 0.1N NaCl soln, **6.209(a)**, to end point (max. change in emf/ml NaCl soln). Normality AgNO$_3$ = ml NaCl $\times$ normality NaCl/ml AgNO$_3$.

6.238 *Preparation of Sample*

(a) *Emulsifiable concentrate formulations.*—Accurately weigh sample contg 0.3±0.05 g heptachlor in 250 ml erlenmeyer. Dissolve in 50 ml HOAc, and pipet in 25 ml 0.1N AgNO$_3$, **(b)**. Attach reflux condenser and reflux 1 hr.

(b) *Granular and dust formulations.*—(*Caution: See* **46.039, 46.041,** and **46.074.**) Accurately weigh sample contg 0.3±0.05 g heptachlor into 80 × 25 mm Soxhlet extn thimble. Ext 2 hr with *pentane* (*Skellysolve A*) and transfer ext to 250 ml erlenmeyer. Attach short reflux column such as 3-ball Snyder or 12″ Vigreaux to flask and evap. to dryness on steam bath. (Results will be low if reflux column is not used.) Rinse down column with 50 ml HOAc into flask, pipet in 25 ml 0.1N AgNO$_3$, **(b)**, attach reflux condenser, and reflux 1 hr.

6.239 *Determination*

Rinse tip of condenser or column with H$_2$O and cool soln to room temp. Transfer quant. to 600 ml beaker, rinsing with four 10 ml portions 80% HOAc. Immerse glass and Ag electrodes in soln and stir with magnetic stirrer. Titr. with 0.1N NaCl soln, **6.209(a)**, to end point.

% Heptachlor = 37.33 $\times$ (25 $\times$ normality AgNO$_3$ soln − ml NaCl soln $\times$ normality NaCl soln)/g sample.

Gas Chromatographic Method (67)

6.240 *Apparatus*

(a) *Gas chromatograph.*—Equipped with H flame ionization detector; capable of accepting glass column and glass-lined sample introduction system or on-column injection. Use following instrumental conditions for analysis: column temp. 175°; detector temp. 175–190°; sample introduction system temp. 190°; N carrier gas pressure 30 psig; recorder chart speed 2.5 cm/min.

(b) *Glass-stoppered tubes.*—Approx. 25 and 75 ml capacity.

(c) *Microliter syringe.*—10 μl, Hamilton Co., 701-N.

6.241 *Reagents*

(a) *Heptachlor.*—Ref. grade (Velsicol Chemical Corp.).

(b) *Aldrin.*—Ref. grade (Velsicol Chemical Corp. or Shell Chemical Co.).

6.242   *Preparation of Column*

To 9.5 g 100–120 mesh Gas Chrom Q in vac. flask add 0.50 g Versilube F-50 (available from Applied Science Labs) dissolved in 50 ml CH₂Cl₂. Shake slurry well to wet solid thoroly. Connect flask to H₂O aspirator and evap. solv. with frequent shaking. When solids appear dry, complete drying by placing flask in steam bath and connecting to vac. pump until ca 4 mm pressure is attained. Remove flask from steam bath and let cool under vac.

Fill 5′ × ⅛″ od (0.067″ id) Pyrex glass tube with this packing, using vac. pump and gentle tapping. Plug ends of column with glass wool. Condition column 24 hr in 190° oven while purging with N. Let column cool while still purging with N; then install in chromatograph.

6.243   *Preparation of Sample*

(a) *Liquids.*—Weigh sample contg ca 750 mg heptachlor into 75 ml g-s vial and add 500 mg ref. grade aldrin. Add 75 ml fresh CS₂, stopper, and shake vigorously 2 min.

(b) *Solids.*—Transfer weighed sample contg ca 750 mg heptachlor to Soxhlet and ext 2 hr with 75 ml pentane. Let cool, add 500 mg ref. grade aldrin to soln, and swirl.

6.244   *Calibration*

Weigh 0.2500 g ref. grade heptachlor and 0.1670 g ref. grade aldrin into 25 ml g-s flask. Dissolve in 25 ml CS₂. Chromatograph this soln under conditions given in **6.240**(a). Analyze this calibration mixt. 5 times to obtain accurate response correction factor. (On new column, it is sometimes desirable to inject several 5 µl aliquots of std soln to condition column before use.)

6.245   *Determination*

Let instrument equilibrate as in **6.240**(a). Inject ca 1 µl sample soln at sensitivity setting such that ht of heptachlor peak is ca ¾ full scale. For each analysis, allow 10–12 min for heptachlor related components to elute. Components and approx. retention times in min are: heptachlor 4.5, aldrin 5.9, chlordene 3.1, and γ-chlordane 9.9.

6.246   *Calculations*

Calc. area of heptachlor and aldrin peaks by multiplying peak ht in mm by width of peak at half ht in mm. Alternatively, use integrator. Calc. response correction factor (f, ca 0.82) for each of the 5 std injections as follows:

f = (area of heptachlor peak × mg aldrin × purity of aldrin)/(area of aldrin peak × mg heptachlor × purity of heptachlor).

Average 5 replicates and use av. to calc. % heptachlor in samples.

% Heptachlor = (area of heptachlor peak × mg aldrin × purity of aldrin × 100)/(area of aldrin peak × mg sample × f).

Hexachlorocyclohexane ("Benzene Hexachloride") (BHC), Gamma Isomer (Lindane)

Partition Chromatographic Method (68)— Official Final Action

(*Caution: See* **46.009, 46.011, 46.039, 46.040, 46.041,** and **46.054.**)

6.247   *Apparatus*

(a) *Partition column.*—Column and O type reduction valve are shown in Fig. 6:4. Construct column of heavy-wall Pyrex tubing ca 3.5 mm thick, 90 cm long × 2.5 cm diam. Seal coarse porosity fritted

FIG. 6:4—Partition column and solvent evaporator

glass disk in place and attach No. 18/9 ℥ joint 5 cm below disk. Supply pressure from laboratory supply line. (Column available from Scientific Glass Aparatus Co.; specify Cat. No. JC 1800 constructed from heavy rather than std wall tubing.)

(b) *Solvent evaporator.*—Fig. 6.4. Fractions are evapd to dryness under reduced pressure at 60°, with aid of H_2O pump. Solv. is recovered in trap consisting of Kjeldahl flask immersed in mixt. of NaCl and ice.

(c) *Melting point apparatus.*—Use Thiele mp app. equipped with mech. stirrer. App. shown in Fig. 34:5, or Hershberg modification (69) (available from Ace Glass, Inc., Cat. No. 7686) is suitable.

(d) *Thermometer.*—Precision grade, meeting NBS specifications; partial immersion; range 90–120° in 0.2° subdivisions. Calibrated by, or calibrated against thermometer checked by, NBS.

(e) *Melting point tubes.*—1–2 mm capillary tubes of uniform wall thickness and diam.

6.248 Reagents

(a) *n-Hexane.*—Com. grade, distd before use.

(b) *Nitromethane.*—Reflux com. grade material 4 hr and distill. No visible residue is left after evapn of 10 ml purified material.

(c) *Silicic acid.*—Use Mallinckrodt reagent grade (for chromatgy) which meets following requirements: When column prepd as in 6.250 is used for detn on sample contg known amt of γ-isomer, flow rate and packing characteristics should be similar to those of an H_2SiO_3 known to be satisfactory, and recovery of γ-BHC should be within ±3% of the γ-BHC content.

(d) *Dye soln.*—Dissolve 25 mg D&C Violet No. 2 (1-hydroxy-4-p-toluino-anthraquinone) in 50 ml mobile solv. and store in g-s bottle. (Available from Allied Chemical Corp.)

(e) *Mobile solvent.*—Satd soln nitromethane in n-hexane. Vigorously shake 2 L n-hexane with excess nitromethane in g-s bottle. Decant mobile solvent from nitromethane as needed.

6.249 Preparation of Sample

(a) *Powders with >10% γ-BHC.*—Crush and thoroly mix sample with mortar and pestle. Weigh enough sample into tared 125 ml erlenmeyer to provide ca 0.2 g γ-isomer after extg and aliquoting. Add 25 ml mobile solv., heat just to boiling on steam bath, and cool to room temp., shaking occasionally. Decant and ext thru buchner with ca 34 mm medium porosity fritted disk into 100 ml Kohlrausch flask, with gentle suction. Re-ext residue in flask, using 10 ml mobile solv. Wash residue and flask with five 10 ml portions cold mobile solv., decanting each wash thru buchner. (Extn may also be performed in filter-beaker such as Cat. No. JM 2770 of Scientific Glass App. Co., filtering into 100 ml vol. flask.) Add 2 ml dye soln and dil. to vol. with mobile solv.

(b) *Dusts containing <10% γ-BHC.*—Weigh enough sample to provide 1.75–2.00 g γ-isomer. Transfer to Soxhlet extractor and ext overnight with ether. Evap. most of ether on steam bath and evap. remainder at room temp. under vac. Ext γ-isomer from residue with mobile solv. as in (a).

6.250 Preparation of Column
(Caution: See **46.004** and **46.061**.)

Transfer 100±0.5 g H_2SiO_3 to high-speed blender, add 300 ml mobile solv., and with mixing, add 55 ml nitromethane. After mixing 15–30 sec, pour mixt. into column thru glass funnel. Stir slurry with long glass stirring rod to displace air bubbles. Wash down sides of column with few ml mobile solv. and apply 5 lb pressure to pack column and force out excess solv.; tap column gently to aid packing. When boundary between solv. and H_2SiO_3 remains stationary, release pressure cautiously, pipet out most of excess solv., and reapply pressure until ca 3 mm solv. remains above adsorbent.

6.251 Determination
(Caution: See **46.015** and **46.018**.)

Pipet 10 ml aliquot of sample soln onto column by letting it flow slowly down inside of column without disturbing surface of the H_2SiO_3. Wash down side of column with 2 ml of the mobile solv. and force soln into column by applying 2–3 lb pressure, releasing pressure when all solv. has entered column. Add 10 ml mobile solv. and force into column. Release pressure and slowly add mobile solv. to within 3–5″ from top of column. Apply enough pressure to force solv. thru column at 3–4 ml/min. Just before last trace of dye leaves column, begin to collect 10 ml fractions, alternately using two 10 ml graduated cylinders. Transfer each fraction to 125 ml erlenmeyer and evap. to dryness, using solv. evaporator. (Evap. fractions without boiling; if boiling begins, raise flask momentarily from H_2O bath.)

Appearance of γ-isomer upon evapn is recognized by its tendency to cover bottom of flask as white residual film with typical crystal formation. When first residue of γ-isomer is recognized, begin to collect 10 ml fractions until all γ-isomer is obtained (usually no more than 8 fractions). Dissolve residue in each flask with 5 ml n-hexane and transfer to weighed flask, rinsing flasks successively with 5 ml portions n-hexane. Evap. solv., using solv. evaporator. Evacuate flask ca 20 min at room temp. with vac. pump. (There is little danger in evacuating 125 ml erlenmeyer; larger size erlenmeyer, however, is likely to collapse under vac.) Release vac., wipe with clean, moist towel, and let stand 5 min. Weigh, and calc. % γ-benzene hexachloride in original sample.

6.252 Melting Point Determination of the Gamma Fraction

Dissolve residue in min. amt of acetone and transfer quant. to 10 ml beaker. Evap. acetone at

40°, using filtered air stream. Scrape residue from beaker for mp detn. (Beaker may be set on piece of solid CO_2 to ensure prepn of finely powd product.) Place material in agate mortar and mix thoroly with pestle.

Select 2 clean, dry capillary tubes and fill with sample. Be sure material is well packed into bottom of tube to ensure max. contact between sample and wall of tube. Insert tubes and thermometer bulb in Thiele tube so that samples and thermometer bulb touch. Start stirrer and heater, and adjust heating rate at 1°/min at 90°. Continue heating until sample melts or reaches 106°. Reduce heating rate to 0.5°/min and continue heating until sample melts.

Sample mp is corrected temp. of bath when last solid disappears into the clear melt. If mp is <108°, check result by IR method, 6.253–6.256.

Infrared Spectrophotometric Method (70)— Official Final Action

(Applicable to tech. BHC. *Caution: See* 46.018, 46.041, and 46.048.)

6.253 *Apparatus*

Infrared spectrometer.—With matched pair of liq. absorption cells, 0.5–1.1 mm thick.

6.254 *Calibration of Cells*

Det., in spectrometer, difference between deflections of the 2 cells filled with CS_2. Plainly mark one cell to be used as sample cell for reading I. Correct values of I_0 obtained with other cell by adding or subtracting difference between cells and refer to this as cell factor F. Check factor every 10–14 days.

6.255 *Preparation of Standards and Working Curves*

Obtain α, β, γ, and δ isomers of BHC, either by fractional crystn from tech. material or as sepd materials, and recrystallize several times from solvs that have been redistd from all-glass app. Recrystallize from following solvs until mps by capillary tube method become constant: α isomer from benzene followed by MeOH (mp ca 158°); β isomer from toluene (mp ca 210.5°, sealed capillary); γ isomer from MeOH (mp ca 113°); and δ isomer from CCl_4 followed by $CHCl_3$ (mp ca 138.5°).

Confirm purity of each isomer as follows: Evap. to dryness enough mother liquor from last crystn to yield at least 1 g dissolved solids, grind residue, and dry overnight in evacuated desiccator. Weigh and dissolve in enough CS_2 to make 4 g/100 ml soln. Prep. corresponding soln of recrystd isomer as std. Compare solns of residue and std in spectrometer at wavelength points used for analysis of other isomers. Consider purity of isomer satisfactory if A of residue soln is not significantly greater than that of std at these points.

Prep. working curves of the isomers by detg T of their solns in CS_2 at various concns as in 6.256. Calc. A and plot against concn in g/L.

6.256 *Determination*

Reduce sample of tech. BHC to ca 2 g by grinding and quartering, and dry 24 hr *in vacuo* at room temp. Weigh 1.5000 g dried material into 50 ml vol. flask and dil. to vol. with CS_2 (equiv. to 30 g/L). Shake vigorously to dissolve (β isomer is not completely sol. and will settle out). Pipet 25 ml of this sample soln into another 50 ml vol. flask and again dil. to vol. with CS_2 (equiv. to 15 g/L). Fill sample cell with the concd soln for reading I, and fill blank cell with CS_2, place in spectrometer, and read T in duplicate at following wavelengths:

	Wavelength (μm)
Alpha	12.58
Beta	13.46
Gamma	14.53
Delta	13.22
Epsilon	13.96

Average duplicates for calcns. Repeat readings with dil. soln (15 g/L) at α and γ wavelengths. Calc. A of each of isomers at the various wavelengths from T measurements by equation:

$$\text{Log } \frac{(F \times I_b) - (F \times I_b \times \% \, Sct)}{I_s - (F \times I_b \times \% \, Sct)} = A,$$

where F = cell factor, I_b = reading of blank cell, $\% \, Sct$ = % scatter, I_s = reading of sample cell, and A = absorbance.

Obtain approx. concns from working curves, 6.255. Correct A at each wavelength for absorption of interfering components. (Altho β isomer has low solubility in CS_2, this isomer interferes with δ analytical point; therefore det. A of β isomer in CS_2 at this point and apply as correction.) Since these new values are overcorrected, make repeated evaluations until successive values are constant, within desired precision.

★ Radioactive Tracer Method (71)— ★ Official First Action

6.257 *Principles*

Method is based on addn of pure γ isomer labeled with radioactive ^{36}Cl to sample of BHC contg unknown amount of γ isomer. Detn of decrease in radioactivity from std level to dild level, on pure weighable γ fraction recovered from mixt., is measure of γ isomer content of sample. Isolation of pure γ material need not be quant.

(Technic can be applied to BHC samples having wide range of γ content. Wt of unknown sample to be analyzed should be increased or decreased according to its estd γ content, so that ratio of labeled γ added to ordinary γ in sample will approximate ratio used in this method.)

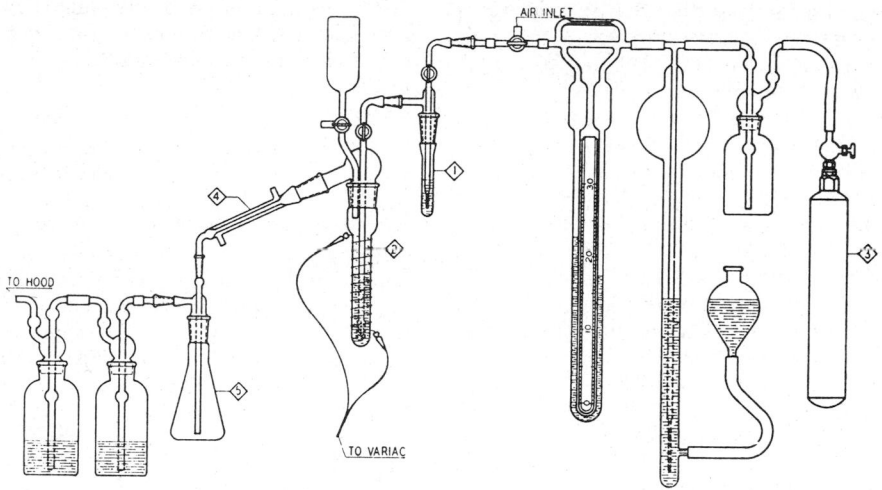

FIG. 6:5—Chlorination apparatus

6.258   *Preparation of Labeled Gamma*
                                      Isomer Standard

(*Caution: See* **46.011, 46.039, 46.040,
46.045,** and **46.047.**)

Radioactive chlorination of C_6H_6 is based on rapid
establishment of exchange equilibrium between Cl
and Cl-ion in aq. soln. Inactive Cl bubbled thru
radioactive HCl becomes active by exchange; transfer of radioactive ^{36}Cl into Cl phase is near quant.

Place 15 ml C_6H_6 in benzene reaction tube (2, Fig.
6:5). By means of 4 ml pipet to which is attached
hypodermic syringe, place 4 ml aq. *radioactive 0.2N
HCl* contg 12 microcuries ^{36}Cl in Cl-exchange tube
(1, Fig. 6:5).

Pass ordinary *Cl from cylinder* (3, Fig 6:5) 30 min
thru system up to tube contg radioactive HCl in
order to displace all air from system. Open stopcock
above radioactive HCl tube and bubble ordinary Cl
into the HCl 6 min at rate of 0.1 g/min. Radioactive
Cl, along with excess ordinary Cl, passes into benzene reaction tube and dissolves in the benzene.

Then place 150 watt lamp 3″ from center of C_6H_6
tube and let it remain there until yellow-green disappears, when reaction is complete. Introduce stream
of air thru bubbler in benzene tube, apply heat to
coil, and distill C_6H_6. Air stream will flush vapors
thru condenser. Dry cake of ca 1 g crude labeled
BHC in 75° vac. oven to remove traces of C_6H_6.

Ext γ isomer from cake with 2 ml *n*-hexane satd
with *nitromethane* by heating to bp and stirring
vigorously. Decant ext into 50 ml beaker and repeat
extn. Wash spent cake with 2 ml cold *n*-hexane and
combine with previous exts. Evap. solv., using heat
lamp placed ca 6″ above beaker, to obtain γ oil.

Add 3.5 g pure unlabeled γ isomer to γ oil. Dissolve mixt. in 16 ml alcohol (SDF No. 3A is satisfactory) by heating and stirring. Cool to 20° with
constant stirring. Let slurry stand in bath 15 min

after crystals appear. Filter, and wash with alcohol.
Mp of dried crystals is 112.0–112.8°.

Repeat recrystn at least twice to remove all traces
of isomers other than γ. Dry final crystals 3 hr at 70°
in vac. oven to obtain labeled std.

6.259   *Isolation of Gamma Isomer*

Weigh 120±5 mg (to 0.1 mg) of labeled std into
tared 15 × 50 mm shell vial and add 1000±5 mg (to
0.1 mg) tech. grade BHC sample.

Add 1.2 ml *perchloroethylene*, place cap (can be
made from 5 ml beaker cut in half) on vial, and insert
vial into well of 115° perchloroethylene heating bath
(1, Fig. 6:6). Let vial remain in bath 15 min, stirring
occasionally. (Not all of crude sample necessarily
dissolves.) Cool mixt. in 20° H_2O bath (3, Fig. 6:6) 30
min, occasionally stirring to allow crystn of isomers
other than γ. Leave cap on during crystn.

Tare 15 × 50 mm shell vial and place in Niederl-
Niederl sulfur filtration app. (2, Fig. 6:6). Filter

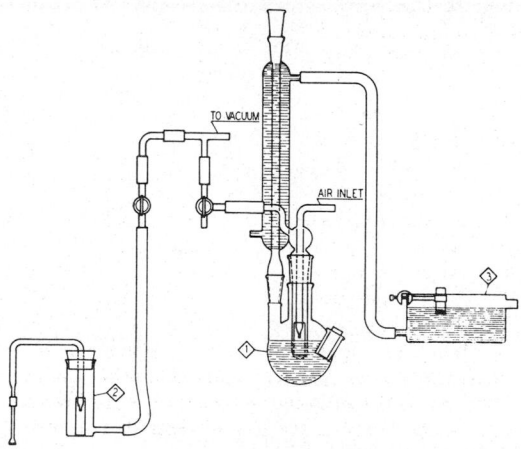

FIG. 6:6—Sample isolation apparatus

supernatant from crystals thru filter stick into tared vial. Wash crystals by adding 0.3 ml perchloroethylene and cooling to 20° while stirring. Filter wash into vial contg original filtrate.

Place vial contg filtrate and wash in evapn tube inserted in top of heating bath and evap. solv., using air stream directed at surface of soln and adjusted to avoid splashing. Most of perchloroethylene will evap. in 30 min. Weigh residue, which is γ oil. Usual yield is 300–450 mg.

Crystallize γ oil by dissolving in 0.8 ml of *1,4-dioxane* and *n-butyl alcohol* (1 + 1)/g of mixt. while heating and stirring until soln is homogeneous. Cool 15 min at 20° in H_2O bath; then scratch walls of vial to induce crystn. After crystals appear, let slurry stand in bath 10 more min; then filter in Niederl-Niederl filtration app. Wash crystals with ca 5 drops cooled *n*-butyl alcohol. Mp of crystals is 100–112° after drying 30 min in 75° vac. oven.

Recrystallize material from *n*-butyl alcohol, using ca 4 ml solv./g crystals, by dissolving and then cooling to 20° as before. Filter, wash with ca 3 drops *n*-butyl alcohol, and dry 30 min in 75° vac. oven. Repeat recrystn, using 3 ml alcohol/g (SDF No. 3A alcohol is satisfactory). Dry crystals in 75° vac. oven 2 hr. Usual yield ca 50 mg; mp 112.0–112.8°. If mp is not in this range, repeat recrystn.

6.260   *Counting*

Use thin-wall, glass, liq.-jacketed counting tube (25 mg/sq cm, 10 ml capacity) for soln counting. (Counting tube, Fig. 6:7, is available as Model J. T., N. Wood Counter Lab., 5491 Blackstone Ave, Chicago, IL 60615.)

Take background count before counting sample, filling counter tube with same solv. used to dissolve sample. Subtract this value from count of both sample and std.

Weigh, to 0.1 mg, isolated pure γ sample into 12 ml snap cap vial, add 10.0 ml acetone, and shake until sample dissolves. Transfer soln slowly into counter tube with hypodermic syringe (take care not to subject thin glass wall to too sudden pressure changes or tube will break) and count ca 15,000 total counts, noting time. Wash out tube 3 times with fresh acetone, and siphon dry. Check background again in 10 min to make sure tube is decontaminated. Similarly prep. soln of 50 mg std and count to same approx. total count as sample, noting time.

Calc. mg γ BHC in sample, $X = R(B - C)/C$, where R = mg radioactive std added to sample; B = specific activity of std, *i.e.*, cpm of std/mg std counted; and C = specific activity of isolated sample, *i.e.*, cpm of isolated sample/mg sample counted.

Note: Before radioactive compds are made or purchased, authorization for their use must be obtained from Atomic Energy Commission, to insure that proper precaution will be observed in handling these materials.

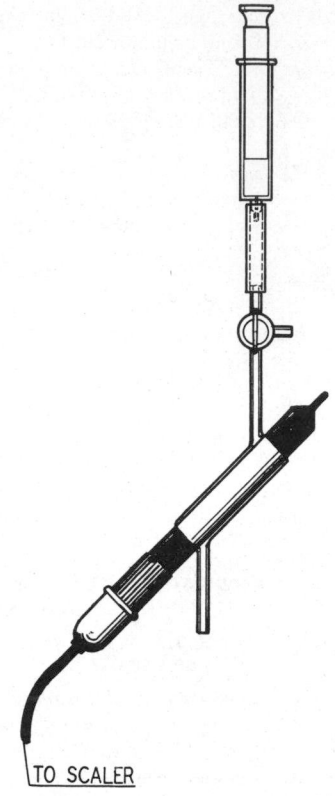

TO SCALER

FIG. 6:7—Counting apparatus

Malathion
(*Caution: See* **46.018, 46.040, 46.041,** and **46.043.**)

Infrared Spectrophotometric Method (72)—Official Final Action

(Applicable to dusts, dust base concs, and wettable powders where malathion is only active ingredient. Other extractable org. materials such as dispersing agents, emulsifiers, and solvs may interfere and should be tested for interference. S does not interfere.)

6.261   *Apparatus*

Infrared spectrophotometer.—Capable of making measurements in 11–13 μm region. Both single beam and double beam instruments such as Beckman Instruments IR-5 (both as single beam and double beam instrument) and Perkin-Elmer Corp., Models 21 and 112, are suitable. Use 0.5 mm cell for 4–10% dusts and 0.1 mm for 25–50% products.

6.262   *Reagents*

(a) *Malathion.*—Purified material; available from American Cyanamid Co.

(b) *Malathion std soln.*—Accurately weigh 0.2–0.25 g purified malathion (for 4–10% dusts) or 1.2–1.25 g (for 25–50% dust base concs and wettable powder) into 2 oz wide-mouth bottle fitted with screw cap (vinylite liner). Add 25 ml acetonitrile from pipet or buret and shake well.

(c) *Acetonitrile.*—Essentially transparent in 11–13 μm region. (Matheson Coleman & Bell acetonitrile, bp 80–82°, has been found satisfactory.)

6.263   *Preparation of Sample Solution*

Accurately weigh 5 g sample (for 4–5% dust or 25% dust base conc. or wettable powder) or 2.5 g (for 10% dust or 50% dust base conc.). Transfer quant. to 2 oz wide-mouth bottle fitted with screw cap (vinylite liner). Add 25 ml acetonitrile from pipet or buret and shake well ca 2 min. Filter thru No. 12 Whatman folded paper into g-s flask, and stopper. (If diluent readily seps from acetonitrile, filtering may be omitted.)

6.264   *Determination*

Fill suitable cell, using hypodermic syringe, with appropriate std soln and obtain IR spectra from 11.0 to 13.0 μm. (When using single beam instrument, adjust to give 80% T at 11.45 μm with cell in position.) Using same instrument settings, scan sample solns in same manner.

Measure distances Y and X for both sample and std, where X is distance from 0 line to peak at 12.2 μm, and Y is distance from 0 line to base line at 11.45 μm valley. Calc. A of each soln as follows: $A = \log (Y/X)$.

$$\% \text{ Malathion} = (A_{sample}/A_{std})(\text{wt std/wt sample}) \times \% \text{ purity of std.}$$

Colorimetric Method (73)—
Official First Action

6.265   *Principles*

Malathion, S-(1,2-dicarbethoxyethyl) O,O-dimethylphosphorodithioate, is decomposed by alkali in alcohol to Na O,O-dimethylphosphorodithioate, Na fumarate, and alcohol. Na O,O-dimethylphosphorodithioate is converted to cupric complex sol. in cyclohexane with formation of intense yellow compd whose intensity is proportional to concn of O,O-dimethylphosphorodithioic acid and which is measured colorimetrically at 420 nm.

Ferric reagent is added to oxidize materials which would reduce cupric to cuprous ions. With phosphorodithioic acid, cuprous ions form colorless complex which is apparently more stable than yellow cupric complex.

Method is applicable to emulsifiable liqs and wettable powders and dusts, including those contg S. Captan and carbaryl interfere. Before application of method to mixts, effect of unfamiliar components should be specifically detd.

6.266   *Reagents*

(a) *Malathion reference std.*—See **6.262**(a).

(b) *Acetonitrile.*—Bp 80–82°. Pass thru column of silica gel, discarding yellow first portions of eluate

and collecting colorless eluate. pH of 10% aq. soln should be 5–7.

(c) *Anhydrous alcohol.*—SDF 2B or 3A is suitable.

(d) *Cyclohexane.*—Practical grade.

(e) *Sodium hydroxide soln.*—Approx. 0.5N. Dissolve 4 g NaOH in 200 ml H_2O.

(f) *Ferric reagent.*—Dissolve 4.0 g $FeCl_3.6H_2O$ in 160 ml HCl and dil. to 500 ml with H_2O. Dil. 25 ml of this soln to 1 L with H_2O.

(g) *Copper sulfate soln.*—Dissolve 1.5 g $CuSO_4$.$5H_2O$ in 100 ml H_2O.

6.267   *Preparation of Standard Solutions*

Vol. changes of alc. solns with temp. are appreciable. Bring each soln to vol. just before proceeding to next step.

(a) *Std soln A.*—Accurately weigh into 5 or 10 ml beaker 1.00±0.02 g malathion ref. std. Transfer quant. to 1 L vol. flask with anhyd. alcohol. Dil. with anhyd. alcohol to ca 5 ml below mark and let stand to selected temp. Record temp., dil. to vol. with anhyd. alcohol, and mix well. Soln is stable 2 weeks. Adjust to recorded temp. before withdrawing aliquots.

(b) *Std soln B.*—Pipet 15 ml aliquot *Std Soln A* into 250 ml vol. flask. Add 2.5 ml acetonitrile and dil. with anhyd. alcohol to ca 5 ml below mark. Hold until sample for analysis is ready for final diln. At that time, dil. with anhyd. alcohol to vol. and mix well.

6.268   *Preparation of Sample*

(If >1 sample soln is prepd for assay, dil. all final sample and std solns to ca 5 ml below mark as prepd. Dil. all solns to vol. at same time.)

(a) *Emulsifiable concentrates.*—Accurately weigh, into 5 or 10 ml beaker, sample contg 1.00±0.02 g malathion. Transfer quant. to 1 L vol. flask with anhyd. alcohol, dil. to vol., and mix well. Immediately pipet 15 ml aliquot into 250 ml vol. flask. Add 2.5 ml acetonitrile, dil. with anhyd. alcohol to vol., and mix well.

(b) *Wettable powders and dusts.*—Accurately weigh sample contg 0.30±0.02 g malathion and transfer quant. to 4 oz bottle. From pipet or buret add 50 ml acetonitrile. Cap bottle tightly and shake vigorously 2–3 min manually or on reciprocating shaker. Let solids settle 3–5 min. If necessary, centrf. 2–3 min at 1500–2000 rpm. Immediately pipet 25 ml aliquot supernatant into 250 ml vol. flask. Dil. with anhyd. alcohol to vol. and mix well. Immediately pipet 25 ml aliquot dild soln into 250 ml vol. flask, dil. with anhyd. alcohol to vol., and mix well.

6.269   *Determination*

Carry std thru analysis with sample. Perform entire analysis without interruption.

Pipet 25 ml aliquots std and sample solns into sep. 250 ml separators. Add 2±0.1 ml 0.5N NaOH and mix well by swirling gently (do not shake) 5–10 sec.

Let stand 120 ± 10 sec. Add 75 ± 1 ml ferric reagent and mix well by swirling 10 sec. Let stand 5 min.

Transfer cyclohexane, measured from 50 ml vol. flask, to each separator. Let flasks drain 1 min. Handle each std and sample sep., carrying each thru to completion without interruption.

Add 2.0 ± 0.1 ml Cu reagent and immediately shake separator exactly 1 min. (Cu malathion complex is unstable in aq. phase. Add Cu reagent from fast delivery Mohr pipet and start shaking with practically no delay. Delay of only 15 sec results in 4% lower A; losses up to 40% result after 2 min delay.)

Let phases sep. As soon as sepn occurs, discard aq. phase. Let little solv. rinse stem of separator; then transfer clear solv. phase into small beaker for transfer to cell or transfer directly into cell. (Manipulate phase sepn of both std and sample solns similarly.) Measure A of yellow soln within 5 min at 420 nm against cyclohexane. A of std and sample solns should be within 10% of each other.

% Malathion = $(A_{sample}/A_{std}) \times$ (g std/g sample) $\times$ % purity of std ($\times 0.3$). Factor 0.3 applies only to wettable powders and dusts.

Organic Thiocyanates
Thiocyanate Nitrogen in Livestock or Fly Sprays (74)—Official Final Action
(*Caution: See* **46.041**.)

6.270   *Reagents*

(a) *Strong potassium polysulfide soln.*—Dissolve 180 g KOH in 120 ml H_2O. Sat. 100 ml of this soln with H_2S (ca 42 g) (*Caution: See* **46.059**) while cooling. Add remaining 100 ml KOH soln and 80 g S. Shake until dissolved.

(b) *Mixed sulfide soln.*—To 100 ml (a) add 50 g $Na_2S.9H_2O$, 30 g KOH, and 200 ml H_2O.

(c) *Sodium bisulfite.*—$Na_2S_2O_5$ or $NaHSO_3$.

(d) *Copper sulfate soln.*—20% aq. soln $CuSO_4$ $.5H_2O$.

(e) *Wash soln.*—To 300 ml H_2O add 1 ml H_2SO_4 $(1+4)$, 1 g (c), 10 ml (d), and 12 g Na_2SO_4, and pass SO_2 into soln for 10 min.

6.271   *Preparation of Sample*

Weigh sample preferably contg ca 0.03 g thiocyanate N into 250 ml g-s erlenmeyer. (If % is very low, do not unduly increase amt of sample without correspondingly increasing amt of mixed sulfide soln used; 20–25 g fly spray is usually enough.) Add 35 ml mixed sulfide soln and shake vigorously at room temp. 10 min, during which time reaction is nearly completed. Heat to 70° on steam bath, carefully releasing pressure resulting from heating, shake 15 min at 70°, and cool.

Removal of petroleum oil.—Transfer mixt. to separator with ca 200 ml H_2O. Add 50 ml pet ether, shake, and drain aq. layer into 600 ml beaker. Wash

pet ether layer with two 10 ml portions H_2O, adding washings to main soln. (If emulsions form during washing, break by acidifying with H_2SO_4 $(1+4)$.) Drain aq. layer and wash pet ether layer with H_2O as above. Discard pet ether layer.

6.272   *Determination*

Dil. combined aq. soln to ca 300 ml and neutze with H_2SO_4 $(1+4)$, using litmus paper as outside indicator. Add 2 ml H_2SO_4 $(1+4)$, bring mixt. to boil quickly, and boil 8 min to remove H_2S. Cool. If fatty acids or oils are present, transfer to separator, ext with pet ether, and return aq. phase to original beaker. Filter thru small buchner and transfer filtrate to beaker. Neutze to litmus paper with 10% KOH soln and add 1 ml H_2SO_4 $(1+4)$. Add 1 g Na bisulfite and stir until dissolved. Add excess (ca 15 ml) $CuSO_4$ soln and pass SO_2 into soln 10 min.

Let pptd CuCNS settle 2 hr, and filter with suction thru 2″ buchner coated with layer of asbestos, upon which is placed No. 42 Whatman paper or equiv., second layer of asbestos, layer of diatomite, and finally third layer of asbestos. If filtrate is not clear, centrf. soln at 2000 rpm 10–15 min, and pour thru filter again. Wash filter and ppt once or twice with wash soln, continue suction until filter pad is dry, and transfer to 800 ml Kjeldahl flask. (Filter pad may be folded in filter paper together with bits of moist filter paper used to wipe out buchner, and whole placed in Kjeldahl flask.) Add few glass beads, 35 ml H_2SO_4, 10 g K_2SO_4, and ca 0.7 g HgO or 0.65 g Hg. (*Caution: See* **46.030** and **46.065**.) Digest until colorless, then 15 min more. Det. N as in **2.051**, second par. Perform blank analysis on paper, filter pad, and reagents.

Parathion—Official Final Action
(*Caution: See* **46.041**.)

Volumetric Method (75)
(Applicable to tech. parathion)

6.273   *Apparatus*

(a) *Photoelectric colorimeter.*—Equipped with filter to give max. T between 400 and 450 nm. Spectrophtr set at 405 nm may also be used.

(b) *Potentiometer.*—Beckman Instruments, or equiv. Equipped with adapter for outside Pt and calomel electrodes. Dead-stop end point equipment may also be used.

6.274   *Reagents*

(a) *Zinc dust.*—Low in Fe.

(b) *Sulfanilic acid.*—Anhyd. recrystd material. Check purity by N detn.

(c) *p-Nitrophenol.*—Mp 112–113°.

(d) *Sodium nitrite std soln.*—$0.1N$. Stdze weekly. Accurately weigh 0.4–0.45 g of the sulfanilic acid into 400 ml tall beaker. Add 80 ml H_2O, 10 ml HCl, 30 ml HOAc, and 5 g NaBr. Place electrodes and mech. stirrer in reaction mixt. and titr. with the 0.1N NaNO₂. Add in 5 ml portions until within 1 ml of calcd end point; then add NaNO₂ soln in 0.1 ml portions until max. rise in potential is obtained. At first, 3–5 min is required for potential to become constant; as end point is approached, especially after 0.1 ml addns, reaction should be complete within 1 min. As alternative, dead-stop end point technic may be used (75), or following spot test, adding NaNO₂ soln in 4 drop portions near end point: Dip glass rod into soln being titrd and touch rod quickly to piece of KI-starch paper, (e). End point is reached when intense blue-black color appears immediately and can be obtained repeatedly during 1 min period without further addn of NaNO₂.

Normality NaNO₂ soln = g sulfanilic acid × 1000/ml NaNO₂ × 173.2.

(e) *Starch iodide paper.*—Triturate 10 parts starch with 200 parts H_2O, bring to boil, and add 1 part KI. Impregnate strips of filter paper with this soln, dry, and preserve in g-s bottles.

6.275 Preparation of Standard Curve of p-Nitrophenol

Accurately weigh 100 mg p-nitrophenol, transfer to 1 L vol. flask, and dil. to vol. with 0.1N NaOH. Transfer 2, 4, 6, 8, 10, and 20 ml aliquots of this soln to 100 ml vol. flasks and dil. each soln to vol. with 0.1N NaOH. Read A of each soln in photoelec. colorimeter (400–450 nm) or spectrophtr (405 nm) against H_2O as ref. Plot A against concn in mg/ml.

6.276 Separation of Parathion and p-Nitrophenol

Using weighing pipet, accurately weigh 0.6–0.9 g sample into 100 ml ether in 250 ml separator. Ext ether soln with four (or until ext is colorless) 20 ml portions chilled 1% Na_2CO_3 soln, collecting combined aq. layers in 200 ml vol. flask. Transfer ether layer to 400 ml tall beaker, rinsing separator with small portions ether.

6.277 Determination of p-Nitrophenol

Add 20 ml 1N NaOH to combined aq. exts and dil. to vol. with H_2O. Measure A of soln as in **6.275** and read concn p-nitrophenol in mg/ml from std curve.

$$\% \ p\text{-Nitrophenol} = \frac{(\text{mg/ml}) \times 200 \times 100}{1000 \times \text{g sample}}$$

6.278 Determination of Parathion

(*Caution: See* **46.011, 46.039,** and **46.054.**)

Add 35 ml HOAc-HCl mixt. (9 + 1) to ether soln, **6.276.** Add 2 g Zn dust, cover beaker with watch glass, and heat soln gently on steam bath 45 min, or until most of ether evaps and soln is colorless. Add 30 ml HCl and heat 10 min longer to complete soln of Zn dust. Wash down beaker and watch glass with H_2O. Filter reduced mixt. thru paper and rinse

beaker thoroly with H_2O. Dil. to 125 ml and cool to room temp. Add 5 g NaBr (or KBr) and titr. with 0.1N NaNO₂ as in **6.274(d).** % Parathion = ml NaNO₂ × normality × 29.13/g sample.

6.279 Dust Preparations and Wettable Powders

Transfer weighed sample to thimble and ext with 150 ml ether in Soxhlet app. 1 hr. Transfer ether ext to 250 ml separator, and sep. p-nitrophenol and parathion as in **6.276.** Det. sample size by parathion concn as follows: 10%, 6.75 g; 15% 4–5 g; 25%, 2.5–3.5 g.

6.280 Emulsifiable Concentrates

Accurately weigh sample contg 0.6–0.9 g parathion into 400 ml tall beaker. Heat on steam bath 30 min, passing gentle stream of air over surface of sample to hasten evapn. Cool to room temp., and wash into 250 ml separator with 150 ml ether. Ext ether soln with four (or until ext is colorless) 10 ml portions chilled 1% Na_2CO_3 soln, adding 2 g anhyd. Na_2SO_4 each time. Collect combined aq. layers in 200 ml vol. flask for detn of p-nitrophenol as in **6.277,** and collect ether layer in 400 ml tall beaker for detn of parathion as in **6.278.**

Colorimetric Method (76)
(Applicable to dusts and wettable powders)

6.281 Principle

Parathion is extd with alcohol and hydrolyzed with KOH to form K p-nitrophenate which is detd colorimetrically.

6.282 Preparation of Standard Curve

Weigh 60 mg reagent grade p-nitrophenol into 100 ml vol. flask, dissolve in alcohol, and dil. to vol. with alcohol. Pipet 10 ml into 100 ml vol. flask and dil. to vol. with alcohol. Prep. p-nitrophenol stds contg 0.3, 0.18, and 0.06 mg/100 ml by pipetting 5, 3, and 1 ml aliquots, resp., of second diln into sep. 100 ml vol. flasks, adding from pipet 5 ml *1N KOH in 50% alcohol*, and dilg to vol. with 50% alcohol. Measure A at 405 nm in 1 cm Corex cells against 50% alcohol and plot A against concn.

6.283 Preparation of Sample

Weigh sample contg ca 10 mg parathion into 250 ml g-s flask. Pipet in 100 ml alcohol and shake occasionally during 10 min. Filter ca 25 ml into g-s container.

6.284 Determination of Free p-Nitrophenol

Pipet 10 ml aliquot of above soln into 100 ml vol. flask and dil. to vol. with 50% alcohol. Add 5 drops 1N KOH in 50% alcohol, and measure A at 405 nm within 2 min against 50% alcohol. Calc. free p-nitrophenol.

6.285   *Determination of Parathion*

Pipet 5 ml filtered soln into 125 ml g-s flask, pipet in 5 ml 1*N* KOH in 50% alcohol, and add glass beads to prevent bumping. Reflux at least 30 min. Cool, and transfer to 100 ml vol. flask with 50% alcohol. Dil. to vol. with 50% alcohol and measure *A* as in **6.282.** Calc. parathion, using std curve, dilns, and factor: Parathion = *p*-nitrophenol/0.478. Correct for free *p*-nitrophenol.

Phorate (Thimet®) (O,O-Diethyl S-(Ethylthio)methyl Phosphorodithioate (77)—Official Final Action

(Applicable to analysis of 5 and 10% granules. Presence of other pesticides and extractable org. materials such as dispersing agents, emulsifiers, and solvs requires testing for interference.)

6.286   *Apparatus*

(a) *Infrared spectrophotometer.*—Capable of measurement in 7.9–8.6 μm range; with 0.5 mm cell.

(b) *Chromatographic tube.*—15 × 450 mm with stopcock or Ultramax valve (Fischer & Porter Co. Cat. No. 274–001 or 274–100).

6.287   *Reagents*

(a) *Phorate reference std.*—Purified (obtainable from American Cyanamid Co.).

(b) *Phorate std soln.*—Accurately weigh by difference from Smith or Lunge pipet 1.0–1.1 g ref. std phorate into 250 ml beaker contg 45 ml acetonitrile. Reserve for detn.

(c) *Cyclohexane.*—Practical grade.

(d) *Acetonitrile.*—Practical grade, bp 82–84°.

6.288   *Preparation of Sample Solution*

(*Caution: See* **46.011, 46.040,** *and* **46.043.**)

Accurately weigh 20±0.01 g sample of 5% granular material (10±0.01 g for 10%). Place small glass wool plug in bottom of chromatgc tube, transfer sample to tube, and gently tap sides with spatula or rod to settle contents. Place 250 ml beaker under column. Add 50 ml acetonitrile to column and let solv. percolate thru at rate of 40–50 drops/min until flow stops. Place beakers contg std (from **6.287**(b)) and sample solns in shallow H_2O bath at 30–35° and evap. under gentle stream of air until odor of acetonitrile is no longer detectable. (Sample solns on evapn will change from clear to cloudy and then to residue of 2 layers.) Treat residue with four 5 ml and one 4 ml portions cyclohexane, quant. transferring cyclohexane layers to 25 ml vol. flask. (Keep cyclohexane-immiscible layer in beaker during each extn.) Dil. to vol. with cyclohexane.

6.289   *Determination*

Using hypodermic syringe, fill 0.5 mm cell with prepd std soln, and obtain IR spectrum from 7.9 to 8.6 μm. (With single beam instrument, adjust to give 75% *T* at 8.2 μm with cell contg std soln in posi-

tion.) Using same instrument settings, treat prepd sample solns similarly.

Draw baseline from inflection points 8.10 to 8.48 μm. Draw perpendicular from 0 radiation line thru absorption peak, and measure distance from 0 to baseline (*Y*) and from 0 to absorption peak (*X*) in same units. Calc. $A = \log (Y/X)$ for sample (*A*) and std (*A′*).

$$\% \text{ Phorate} = (A/A') \times (\text{wt std/wt sample}) \times \% \text{ purity of std.}$$

Piperonyl Butoxide (78)— Official Final Action

(*Caution: See* **46.041.**)

6.290   *Apparatus*

Photoelectric colorimeter.—Klett-Summerson, or equiv. equipped with narrow band-pass interference type filter with *T* range ca 625–635 nm. (Filter is available from: Baird-Atomic Inc.; Bausch and Lomb Optical Co., Rochester, NY 14602; Farrand Optical Co., Inc., Bronx Blvd and East 238th St, New York, NY 10070; and Photovolt Corp., 95 Madison Ave, New York, NY 10016.) Spectrophtr set at wavelength in range 625–635 nm may also be used.

6.291   *Reagents*

(a) *Purified tannic acid.*—Purify as follows: To 20 g tannic acid (USP reagent grade) add 100 ml EtOAc (99%) and stir mech. ca 1 hr. Filter by suction thru fritted glass funnel, and wash residue with three 5 ml portions EtOAc. To combined filtrate and washings add 2 g finely powd Darco G-60 (or equiv. decolorizing C), and stir mech. ca 0.5 hr. Filter by gravity thru double thickness Whatman No. 1 (or equiv.) paper into graduated dropping funnel. Wash residue several times with EtOAc until vol. of filtrate and washings is ca 125 ml. Place dropping funnel over 1 L, 3-neck, r-b flask, equipped with mech. stirrer, and with vigorous agitation in flask add filtrate dropwise to 5 times its vol. of toluene. Purified tannic acid is pptd immediately.

Filter by suction thru fritted glass funnel, and wash product thoroly with toluene, stirring solids with toluene to assure complete removal of EtOAc. Continue suction until practically all toluene is removed. Dry purified tannic acid in vac. oven at ca 40°, and place in tightly stoppered bottle.

(b) *Tannic acid reagent.*—Completely dissolve exactly 0.025 g purified tannic acid in 20 ml HOAc by shaking at room temp. Add 80 ml H_3PO_4 and mix thoroly. Prep. fresh daily. Store tightly stoppered as it is hygroscopic.

(c) *Purified piperonyl butoxide.*—Purify by low pressure fractional distn of tech. product. (*Caution: See* **46.015.**) Also available from FMC Corp., Organic Chemicals Div., PO Box 1616, Baltimore, MD 21203.

(d) *Piperonyl butoxide std soln.*—50 μg/0.1 ml. Weigh exactly 1.000 g purified piperonyl butoxide into 100 ml vol. flask. (Hypodermic syringe and needle are convenient for adding sample to flask.) Dil. to vol. with deodorized kerosene and mix well. Pipet 10 ml of this soln into 200 ml vol. flask. Dil. to vol. with deodorized kerosene and mix well. This soln is stable for several months. If std is to be used with sample contg pyrethrum, add enough pyrethrum ext to std before initial diln to give ratio piperonyl butoxide to pyrethrins similar to sample.

6.292   *Preparation of Sample*

Accurately weigh sample contg 0.5–1.5 g piperonyl butoxide into tared 100 ml vol. flask, dil. to vol. with deodorized kerosene, and mix well. Pipet 10 ml into 200 ml vol. flask, dil. to vol. with deodorized kerosene, and mix well.

6.293   *Determination*

Pipet 0.1 ml (from 1 ml pipet graduated in 0.1 ml) sample soln into 18 × 150 mm test tube. Add exactly 5 ml tannic acid reagent and shake vigorously 1 min. Treat std and blank, consisting of 0.1 ml deodorized kerosene, simultaneously in same manner.

Place test tubes in test-tube basket and place in vigorously boiling H_2O bath 5 min. Remove basket and let tubes cool to room temp. Transfer solns to colorimeter tubes and read, against H_2O, using 625–635 nm filter or setting. (After cooling to room temp. there is no appreciable change in A for several hr.)

Subtract A of deodorized kerosene from readings of both sample and std.

Mg piperonyl butoxide = $A_{sample} \times 0.05/A_{std}$.

Sabadilla Alkaloids (79)—
Official Final Action
(In dust formulations)

6.294   *Determination*
(*Caution: See* **46.011, 46.040,** and **46.056.**)

Weigh 10 g mixed 50% sabadilla dust (or corresponding quantity of lesser concn) into 500 ml g-s erlenmeyer. Add exactly 300 ml ether-$CHCl_3$ (3 + 1), and shake 5 min. Make alk. with 10 ml NH_4OH and shake 2 hr on shaking machine. Let stand overnight; then shake 1 hr.

Filter, avoiding evapn. Place 200 ml aliquot in 500 ml separator, acidify with H_2SO_4 (3 + 97), and shake; withdraw small amt of aq. layer and test with litmus paper, returning soln to separator. Add 50 ml of the dil. H_2SO_4 and shake. Let sep. and transfer acid ext to second 500 ml separator. Add 50 ml pet ether to acid ext and shake. Let layers sep. and transfer acid ext to third separator. Repeat extn of soln in first separator with two 50 ml portions of the dil. H_2SO_4, using same 50 ml pet ether in second separator for washing. Collect acid exts in third separator.

Make acid exts alk. to phthln with NH_4OH. Ext with three 50 ml portions $CHCl_3$. Wash each $CHCl_3$ ext by shaking gently with same 100 ml portion H_2O in fourth separator. (If emulsion forms, add small amt of anhyd. Na_2SO_4.)

Filter each $CHCl_3$ ext thru cotton into weighed 250 ml flask. Evap. $CHCl_3$ on steam bath. Add few ml alcohol, and evap. again. Dry 1 hr at 100° and weigh sabadilla alkaloids. Calc. % total alkaloids.

6.295   *Qualitative Test*

Add 1–2 ml H_2SO_4 to few mg of residue, **6.294.** Presence of sabadilla alkaloids is indicated by yellow that gradually becomes intensely red with greenish fluorescence.

Sulfoxide (n-Octyl Sulfoxide of Isosafrole)
(80)—Official First Action

6.296   *Principle*

Sulfoxide is sepd from solvs, emulsifiers, pyrethrins, and other insecticides by silicic acid column chromatgy with successive eluting solns: $CHCl_3$, 2% acetone in $CHCl_3$, and 10% acetone in $CHCl_3$. Sulfoxide is removed in last eluate and is detd by UV spectrophotometry.

6.297   *Apparatus*

(a) *Spectrophotometer.*—Beckman Instruments, model DU quartz spectrophtr with 1.0 sq. cm silica cells, or equiv.

(b) *Chromatographic tube with sealed-in fritted disk.*—20 mm id, 400 mm total length (Scientific Glass Apparatus Co., No. C-4189).

6.298   *Reagents*

(a) *Acetone in chloroform.*—2% (v/v) and 10% (v/v).

(b) *Silicic acid.*—Mallinckrodt Chemical Works, No. 2847, 100 mesh, dried overnight at 120°.

6.299   *Preparation of Column*

Combine 45 g silicic acid with 110 ml $CHCl_3$ in beaker. Stir with glass rod and pour slurry into chromatgc tube. Do not rinse beaker or add more $CHCl_3$. Apply 5–7 lb air pressure to top of column until $CHCl_3$ level is just above surface of silicic acid.

6.300   *Preparation of Sample*

Accurately weigh sample contg 0.750–1.00 g tech. sulfoxide into 25 ml vol. flask. (For formulations contg <5.0% tech. sulfoxide, use 20 g sample.) Dil. to vol. with $CHCl_3$, and mix.

6.301   *Chromatography*

Pipet 5 ml dild sample onto column. Apply 5–7 lb pressure to force sample into silicic acid. Release pressure, add $CHCl_3$ as needed, and re-apply pressure. Collect 100 ml $CHCl_3$ eluate and discard.

Change receiver and elute with 2% acetone soln

under pressure as before. Collect 240–250 ml eluate and discard.

Change receiver and elute under pressure with 10% acetone soln, collecting 200 ml in 1 L beaker. Collection time for each fraction is ca 60–90 min.

6.302   Determination

Evap. 10% acetone eluate to dryness on steam bath. Do not overheat. Remove beaker when CHCl$_3$ odor cannot be detected. Cool to room temp. Quant. transfer residue in beaker to 100 ml vol. flask with alcohol, and dil. to vol. Dil. 1 ml soln to 100 ml with alcohol. Read A at 256 and 288 nm.

Calc. $\Delta A = A_{288} - A_{256}$. % Sulfoxide $= \Delta A \times 5000/(\text{g sample} \times 10.795)$.

Tetraethylpyrophosphate (TEPP)
(81)—Official Final Action
(Caution: See 46.041.)

6.303   Reagents

(a) *Indicator.*—0.1% aq. soln Me red or chlorophenol red.

(b) *Amberlite IR-4B(OH) (free base form) resin.*—Analytical grade. Amberlite IR-45, Dowex 3, or equiv. are satisfactory.

6.304   Preparation of Resin Column

Screen resin to remove particles <30-mesh. Slurry 30 g screened resin with H$_2$O, and pour into 100 ml buret contg small plug of glass wool at bottom. Wash resin column with 150 ml 3% NaOH soln at flow rate of ca 5 ml/min and then rinse with H$_2$O until effluent is acid to phthln, adjusting stopcock of buret so flow rate is ca 25 ml/min. Wash with aq. acetone (1 + 3) to displace H$_2$O. Column is now ready for use.

Notes: Because channeling may result if column runs dry, keep liq. level ca 1″ above resin bed at all times. Because resin tends to pack in column as it adsorbs acidic material, expand resin bed after each detn before adding new sample by back-washing with acetone (1 + 3) as follows: Connect large funnel to tip of buret with rubber hose, and add the dil. acetone from funnel until liq. level reaches top of buret; let resin settle, and then let soln flow from buret until surface is 1″ above resin bed. Column is now ready to receive next sample.

After 8–10 samples have passed thru column, regenerate resin by repeating original treatment with 3% NaOH soln, H$_2$O, and acetone (1 + 3). Washing with dil. acetone must be continued until effluent is colorless.

6.305   Determination

(a) *In purified or technical grades of tetraethylpyrophosphate not mixed with solvent, emulsifying agent, etc.*—From 5–10 ml weighing buret weigh by difference, to nearest mg, 2.5 g sample (1.0 g if tetraethylpyrophosphate content is >50%) into 50 ml

acetone (1 + 3) in 125 ml separator. Mix by swirling, and let soln stand 15 min at 25±2°. Run soln thru resin column by gravity at ca 25 ml/min, and catch effluent in 250 ml vol. flask. Wash separator and column with three 50 ml portions acetone (1 + 3), collecting washings in same flask. Dil. combined effluent to vol. with H$_2$O, mix, and transfer 100 ml aliquot to 250 ml beaker. Add 50 ml 0.1N NaOH to contents of beaker, stir well, let stand 30 min at room temp., and back-titr. with 0.1N HCl, using pH meter (or indicator, 6.303(a), if pH meter is not available). Calc. % tetraethylpyrophosphate $=$ Net ml 0.1N NaOH $\times$ 3.67/wt sample taken.

(b) *In formulations of tetraethylpyrophosphate containing organic solvent and emulsifying agent.*—Proceed as in (a), except filter acetone soln thru 1″ cotton plug in cylindrical funnel (1″ diam., 3″ long) before adding it to column if oil seps from soln. Pass acetone washings successively thru separator, cylindrical funnel, and resin column as in (a). (Cotton plug absorbs oil.)

Dithiocarbamates
(Caution: See 46.041.)

Carbon Disulfide Evolution Method (82)—
Official Final Action

(Applicable only to concs or formulations free from interfering substances.)

6.306   Principle

Dithiocarbamates decompose on heating in acid medium. Evolved CS$_2$ is passed thru Pb(OAc)$_2$ soln traps to remove H$_2$S and SO$_2$ formed from sample impurities. Washed CS$_2$ is reacted with methanolic KOH, and xanthate formed is titrd with I soln.

6.307   Apparatus

Carbon disulfide evolution apparatus.—See Fig. 6:8. Available from Scientific Glass Apparatus Co.

6.308   Reagent

Methanolic potassium hydroxide.—2N. Dissolve 112 g KOH pellets in 500 ml anhyd. MeOH, filter thru cotton, and add addnl 500 ml anhyd. MeOH.

6.309   Determination

Add 20 ml 10% Pb(OAc)$_2$ soln to each Pb(OAc)$_2$ trap and pipet 50 ml 2N MeOH-KOH soln into MeOH-KOH absorber (Fig. 6:8). (Absorber must be dry at time of addn.) Add 50 ml H$_2$SO$_4$ (1 + 4) to reaction flask and heat acid to boiling. Adjust aspiration rate to ≤1 bubble/sec thru MeOH-KOH soln, using stopper in reaction flask.

Weigh ≤5 g sample (contg 0.1–0.3 g dithiocarbamates) into small filter paper cone and fold cone to prevent sample loss. Remove stopper from reaction flask, insert wrapped sample, and immediately stopper flask. Adjust air flow if necessary and maintain steady, moderate boil. Do not let acid soln enter

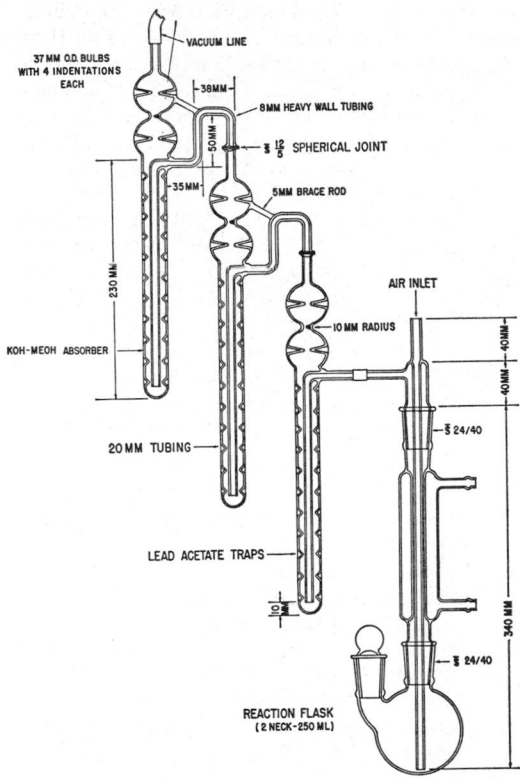

FIG. 6:8—Carbon disulfide evolution apparatus

air inlet tube. Some dust formulations react vigorously and require special care to prevent ejection of hot acid. As reaction proceeds, adjust system so that rates of boiling and aspiration are almost in equilibrium, producing only very slow rate of bubbling thru MeOH-KOH soln. Continue boiling 1.5 hr. Disconnect MeOH-KOH absorber and rinse contents into 500 ml erlenmeyer, using ca 250 ml H_2O. (To remove absorber contents, apply slight air pressure to top of absorber and force soln thru side arm. Rinse 4 times with ca 25 ml H_2O, forcing out rinse H_2O in same manner with air pressure.)

Add 3 drops phthln, and titr. with 30% HOAc until red just disappears. Immediately titr. with $0.1N$ I; near end point, add 5 ml starch indicator soln, **6.004(f),** and titr. to faint but definite color change.

Det. blank (usually 0.1–0.2 ml $0.1N$ I) by dilg 50 ml MeOH-KOH soln with 250 ml H_2O, neutzg with 30% HOAc, and titrg as above.

Calc. % dithiocarbamate = (Sample titrn − blank) × (I normality) × (equiv. wt dithiocarbamate)/(g sample × 10).

Equiv. wts (½ mol. wts) of zineb, maneb, ziram, nabam, and (⅓ mol. wt) ferbam are 137.87, 132.65, 152.91, 128.18, and 138.82, resp.

Thiram
(Bis(dimethylthiocarbamoyl)disulfide)
(Tetramethylthiuram Disulfide)

Collaborative Pesticides Analytical Committee (CPAC) Method (83)—Official First Action

6.310 *Principles*

Thiram is decomposed by boiling with mixed mineral acids to $Me_2NH \cdot HCl$, CS_2, and carbonyl sulfide. The gaseous mixt. is carried by air stream thru $CdSO_4$ scrubber to remove H_2S, and then into absorption system contg MeOH-KOH soln. Mixed xanthate monothiocarbonate soln is neutzd and titrd with std aq. I.

Method is not specific for thiram. Sep. characterization test, **29.154,** must be made.

6.311 *Apparatus*

Assembly and operating conditions.—Assemble app. as shown in Fig. 6:9 with 30 ml $CdSO_4$ soln in first absorber, 25 ml KOH soln in second absorber, and 5 ml in each bubbler. Turn on condenser H_2O and maintain H_2O bath surrounding $CdSO_4$ scrubber at 70–80° thruout test. Keep main KOH absorber at <25° by immersion in beaker of cold H_2O. Absorber must be dry or rinsed with MeOH before adding KOH soln. Air bleed must reach nearly to bottom of digestion flask. Make all joints gas-tight, using small amts of H_3PO_4, petrolatum, or silicone grease.

Check app. for absorber leaks and efficiency periodically, using pure Na diethyldithiocarbamate. Recoveries should be 99–101%. Check purity of Na diethyldithiocarbamate by dissolving ca 0.5 g, accurately weighed, in 100 ml H_2O and titrg directly with $0.1N$ I, using ca 2% starch soln as indicator. 1 ml $0.1N$ I = 0.02253 g Na diethyldithiocarbamate. % Na diethyldithiocarbamate = 2.253 × ml $0.1N$ I/g sample.

6.312 *Reagents*

(a) *Acid mixture.*—Dissolve 2.5 g ZnO in 100 ml dil. HOAc (1 + 1).

(b) *Cadmium sulfate soln.*—Dissolve 18.5 g $3CdSO_4 \cdot 8H_2O$ in 100 ml H_2O.

(c) *Potassium hydroxide soln.*—2N in MeOH and contg <1 ppm Cu or Fe.

(d) *Iodine std soln.*—0.1N. Stdze as in **45.020.**

6.313 *Determination*

Accurately weigh and transfer sample contg ca 0.3 g thiram to digestion flask, using small amt H_2O, if necessary. Assemble air bleed and dropping funnel, Fig. 6:9, and add 20 ml acid mixt. thru funnel. Connect app. to controlled aspiration (vac. or compressed air) so that ca 3 bubbles/sec pass thru absorbers. After sample is evenly dispersed, heat and reflux 30 min at moderate rate. Turn off cooling H_2O and flush condenser and first absorber with steam from flask ≤1 min. Remove burner and disconnect

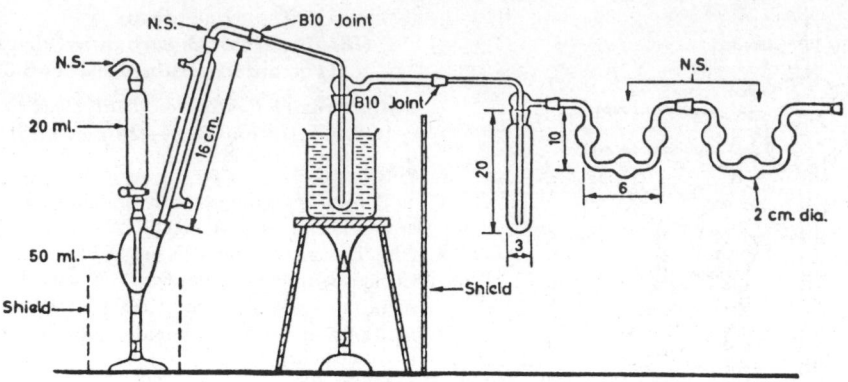

FIG. 6:9—Absorption system for thiram. Dimensions in cm;
N.S. = nonstandard; B/10 = ⨂ 10/30

train. Wash contents of KOH absorber and bubblers into 600 ml beaker with 300–400 ml H_2O, add 1–2 drops phthln, just neutze with HOAc (1 + 9) from buret, and add 3 drops excess. With continual stirring, titr. immediately (preferably within 1 min as decomposition of mixed xanthate/monothiocarbonate soln is extremely rapid under acidic conditions) with $0.1N$ I (t ml), using ca 2% starch soln as indicator. Det. blank in same manner, omitting sample (b ml). 1 ml $0.1N$ I = 0.01202 g thiram.

% Thiram = 1.202 $(t - b)$/g sample.

SELECTED REFERENCES

(1) Ind. Eng. Chem. **14**, 207(1922); JAOAC **5**, 33, 402(1922); **6**, 313(1923).
(2) JAOAC **7**, 313(1924).
(3) Anal. Chem. **22**, 1066(1950); JAOAC **46**, 672 (1963).
(4) JAOAC **5**, 398(1922).
(5) J. Am. Chem. Soc. **40**, 1036(1918); JAOAC **5**, 398(1922).
(6) J. Research Natl. Bur. Standards **3**, 581(1929); JAOAC **25**, 670(1942); **27**, 74(1944); **28**, 72 (1945).
(7) Compt. rend. **173**, 714, 836(1921); JAOAC **14**, 253(1931).
(8) J. Am. Chem. Soc. **55**, 1741(1933); Ind. Eng. Chem., Anal. Ed. **5**, 7(1933); **9**, 551(1937); **11**, 21(1939); JAOAC **21**, 459(1938).
(9) Ind. Eng. Chem. **1**, 208(1909); JAOAC **3**, 158 (1917).
(10) JAOAC **5**, 34(1921).
(11) J. Am. Chem. Soc. **24**, 1082(1902).
(12) USDA Bur. Chem. Bull. **105**, p. 167.
(13) JAOAC **3**, 332(1920).
(14) JAOAC **3**, 333(1920).
(15) USDA Bur. Chem. Bull. **137**, p. 40; **152**, p. 68.
(16) JAOAC **5**, 33(1921); 392(1922).
(17) JAOAC **47**, 253(1964).
(18) Fresenius, "Quantitative Chemical Analysis," Trans. 6th German Ed., 1906, amplified and revised, Vol. 2, 1180; U.S. Geol. Survey Bull. **700**, p. 218.
(19) JAOAC **15**, 289(1932); **17**, 62(1934).
(20) JAOAC **10**, 27(1927).
(21) JAOAC **10**, 28(1927).
(22) JAOAC **10**, 29(1927).
(23) JAOAC **9**, 27(1926).
(24) USDA Bur. Chem. Circ. **10**, p. 7.
(25) JAOAC **10**, 30, 124(1927); **11**, 35(1928).
(26) USDA Bull. **898**, p. 48.
(27) JAOAC **9**, 28(1926).
(28) USDA Bur. Chem. Bull. **105**, p. 165.
(29) JAOAC **9**, 29(1926).
(30) USDA Bur. Animal Ind. Bull. **133**.
(31) Ind. Eng. Chem., Anal. Ed. **10**, 19(1938); JAOAC **21**, 148(1938); **22**, 408(1939); **24**, 70 (1941); **43**, 376(1960).
(32) JAOAC **42**, 96(1959); **46**, 668(1963).
(33) JAOAC **44**, 580(1961); **46**, 668(1963).
(34) Contrib. Boyce Thompson Inst. **8**, No. 3, 175 (1936); Ind. Eng. Chem., Anal. Ed. **10**, 5 (1938); JAOAC **43**, 354(1960).
(35) Soap **10**, No. 5, 89(1934); JAOAC **43**, 354 (1960); **46**, 664(1963).
(36) Ber. **31**, 2979(1898); J. Am. Chem. Soc. **27**, 1183(1905); USDA Bur. Chem. Bull. **99**, p. 30; **132**, p. 49; **137**, p. 47.
(37) Z. anal. Chem. **36**, 18(1897); USDA Bur. Chem. Bull. **132**, p. 49.
(38) Ind. Eng. Chem., Anal. Ed. **3**, 357(1931); JAOAC **25**, 80, 668(1942).
(39) JAOAC **3**, 353(1920).
(40) JAOAC **31**, 366(1948).
(41) JAOAC **22**, 411(1939); **25**, 79(1942); **28**, 72 (1945).
(42) JAOAC **36**, 634(1953); **43**, 365(1960).
(43) JAOAC **48**, 576(1965); **49**, 207(1966).
(44) JAOAC **35**, 377(1952).
(45) JAOAC **50**, 568(1967).
(46) JAOAC **52**, 1287(1969).
(47) JAOAC **51**, 1301(1968).

(48) Anal. Chem. 19, 475(1947).

(49) JAOAC 36, 378(1953); 43, 382(1960).

(50) Analyst 92, 375(1967); JAOAC 51, 1304, 1306 (1968).

(51) Anal. Chem. 31, 418(1959); JAOAC 43, 382 (1960); 45, 522(1962).

(52) Anal. Chem. 27, 1774(1955); JAOAC 43, 382 (1960); 45, 522(1962).

(53) Whitmore, "Organic Compounds of Mercury," p. 365; JAOAC 13, 156(1930).

(54) JAOAC 18, 63, 65(1935); 43, 346(1960).

(55) JAOAC 43, 346(1960).

(56) JAOAC 44, 595(1961).

(57) Anal. Chem. 25, 1207(1953); JAOAC 40, 732 (1957).

(58) JAOAC 50, 566(1967).

(59) JAOAC 45, 513(1962).

(60) JAOAC 48, 573(1965).

(61) JAOAC 49, 254(1966).

(62) JAOAC 30, 319(1947); 31, 368(1948).

(63) JAOAC 40, 286(1957); 43, 342(1960).

(64) JAOAC 47, 268(1964).

(65) JAOAC 49, 251(1966).

(66) JAOAC 52, 1292(1969).

(67) JAOAC 51, 565(1968).

(68) JAOAC 32, 684(1949); 39, 373(1956).

(69) Ind. Eng. Chem. 8, 312(1936).

(70) Anal. Chem. 19, 779(1947); Report No. 4760, May 15, 1949, Phys. Chem. Lab., Hooker Electrochemical Co., Niagara Falls, N.Y.

(71) Anal. Chem. 25, 1661(1953); JAOAC 40, 737 (1957).

(72) JAOAC 43, 360(1960).

(73) JAOAC 47, 248(1904).

(74) JAOAC 34, 677(1951).

(75) JAOAC 35, 381(1952); 36, 384(1953); Anal. Chem. 23, 1167(1951).

(76) JAOAC 43, 344(1960); 47, 242(1964).

(77) JAOAC 47, 245(1964).

(78) JAOAC 35, 771(1952); 43, 350(1960).

(79) JAOAC 43, 374(1960).

(80) JAOAC 51, 562(1968).

(81) Anal. Chem. 21, 808(1949).

(82) JAOAC 48, 562(1965).

(83) J. Sci. Food Agr. 8, 509(1964); JAOAC 49, 40 (1966); 51, 447(1968).

7. Animal Feed*

7.001 Sampling (*1*)—Procedure

Use slotted single or double tube, or slotted tube and rod, all with pointed ends.

Take at least 1 lb sample, 2 lb preferred, as follows: Lay bag horizontally and remove core diagonally from end to end. Det. number of cores as follows: From lots of 1–10 bags, sample all bags; from lots of 11 or more, sample 10 bags. Take 1 core from each bag sampled, except that for lots of 1–4 bags take enough diagonal cores from each bag to total at least 5 cores. For bulk feeds draw at least 10 cores from different regions; in sampling small containers (10 lb or less) 1 package is enough. Reduce composite sample to quantity required, preferably by riffling, or by mixing thoroly on clean oil-cloth or paper and quartering. Place sample in air-tight container.

A sample from less than these numbers of bags may be declared an official sample if guarantor agrees. For samples that cannot be representatively taken with probe described, use other sampling means.

7.002 Preparation of Sample— Official Final Action

Grind sample to pass sieve with circular openings ½₅″ (1 mm) diam. and mix thoroly. If sample cannot be ground, reduce to as fine condition as possible. Do not grind molasses feeds.

Moisture—Official Final Action
I. Drying in Vacuo at 95–100° (*2*)

7.003 *Determination*

Dry quantity of sample contg ca 2 g dry material to constant wt at 95–100° under pressure ≤100 mm Hg (ca 5 hr). For feeds with high molasses content use pressure ≤70 mm Hg. Use covered Al dish ≥50 mm diam. and ≤40 mm deep. Report loss in wt as moisture.

II. By Distillation with Toluene (*3*)

7.004 *Apparatus*

250 ml distg flask of Pyrex or other resistant glass connected by means of "distg tube receiver" to 20″ sealed-in, straight-tube Liebig condenser with delivery tube ≤⁵⁄₁₆″ in diam. as in Fig. 7:1. Receiver, dimensions shown, is made by attaching proper side tube to calibrated section of 5 ml Mohr pipet and sealing outlet. Tube is calibrated in ml by distg known quantities H_2O into graduated column, and

column of H_2O may be read to hundredths with reasonable accuracy. Clean tube and condenser with $K_2Cr_2O_7$-H_2SO_4 mixt., rinse thoroly with H_2O, then alcohol, and dry in oven to prevent undue amt H_2O from adhering to inner surfaces during detn.

7.005 *Determination*

If sample is likely to bump, add dry sand to cover bottom of flask. Add enough toluene to cover sample completely (ca 75 ml). Weigh and introduce enough sample into toluene to give 2–5 ml H_2O and connect app. as shown, Fig. 7:1. Fill receiving tube with toluene, pouring it thru top of condenser. Bring to boil and distill slowly, ca 2 drops/sec, until most of the H_2O passes over; then increase rate of distn to ca 4 drops/sec.

When all H_2O is apparently over, wash down condenser by pouring toluene in at top, continuing distn

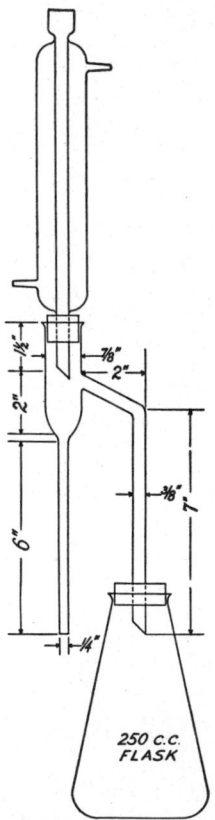

FIG. 7:1—Apparatus for determining moisture

★ Methods so marked are surplus methods. *See* "Definitions of Terms and Explanatory Notes," item (29).

short time to see whether any more H_2O distills over; if it does, repeat washing-down process. If any H_2O remains in condenser, remove by brushing down with tube brush attached to Cu wire and satd with toluene, washing down condenser at same time. (Entire process is usually completed within 1 hr.) Let receiving tube come to room temp. If any drops adhere to sides of tube, force them down, using Cu wire with end wrapped with rubber band. Read vol. H_2O and calc. to %.

III. Drying without Heat over Sulfuric Acid (4)

7.006   *Reagent*

Sulfuric acid.—Boil H_2SO_4 in large Kjeldahl flask 4 hr, close flask with stopper carrying $CaCl_2$ tube, and cool.

7.007   *Determination*

(*Caution: See* **46.015.**)

Weigh 2–5 g sample into metal dish 5–10 cm diam. with tight-fit cover. (If subsequent fat detns are to be made, fat extn cones may be used.) Mix substances that dry down to horn-like material with fat-free cotton or other suitable material. Place 200 ml of the fresh H_2SO_4 in strong, tight vac. desiccator. Place uncovered dish in desiccator and exhaust with vac. pump to pressure ≤ 10 mm Hg.

If pump is not available, place 10 ml ether in small beaker in desiccator and exhaust with H_2O filter pump. Between pump and desiccator interpose empty bottle next to desiccator and bottle of H_2O next to pump. Draw air from desiccator thru the H_2O and turn desiccator stopcock the instant H_2O begins to rise in tube leading from empty bottle.

Gently rotate desiccator 4 or 5 times during first 12 hr. After 24 hr open desiccator, causing incoming air to bubble thru H_2SO_4; place cover on dish and make first weighing. After weighing, place sample in desiccator contg fresh H_2SO_4 and exhaust as before. Rotate desiccator several times during interval and weigh again after suitable drying period. Repeat process to constant wt.

7.008   IV. Drying at 135° (5)

(Not to be used when fat detn is to be made on same sample)

Regulate elec. air oven to $135\pm2°$. Using low, covered Al dishes, **7.003**, weigh ca 2 g sample into each dish and shake until contents are evenly distributed. With covers removed, place dishes and covers in oven as quickly as possible and dry samples 2 hr. Place covers on dishes and transfer to desiccator to cool. Weigh and calc. loss in wt as H_2O.

7.009   V. In Highly Acid Milk Byproducts (6)

Add ca 2 g ZnO, freshly ignited or oven dried, to flat-bottom dish ≥ 5 cm diam. and weigh. Add ca 1 g sample and weigh quickly. Add ca 5 ml H_2O and dis-

tribute sample evenly on bottom of dish. Heat on steam bath, exposing max. surface of dish bottom to live steam until apparently dry. Heat at 98–100° in air oven 3 hr or to constant wt. Cool in desiccator; then weigh quickly. Det. wt residue. Titr acidity of sample and calc. as lactic acid, **16.022.** To compensate for H_2O formed when acid is neutzd by ZnO, add 0.1 g to residue wt for each g acid (as lactic) in weighed sample. Report % residue (corrected) as total solids.

7.010   Ash (7)—Official Final Action

Weigh 2 g sample into porcelain crucible and place in muffle furnace preheated to 600°. Hold at this temp. 2 hr with automatic control pyrometer. Transfer crucibles directly to desiccator, cool, and weigh immediately, reporting % ash to first decimal place.

NITROGEN

Qualitative Tests for Proteins (8)— Official Final Action

7.011   ★   *Biuret Test*   ★
See **22.012–22.013,** 10th ed.

7.012   ★   *Millon Test*   ★
See **22.014–22.015,** 10th ed. (*Caution: See* **46.018, 46.026,** and **46.065.**)

7.013   ★   *Glyoxylic Acid Test*   ★ (*Hopkins-Cole*)
See **22.016–22.017,** 10th ed. (*Caution:* Wear face shield and heavy rubber gloves as protection against reagent bump. *See also* **46.018** and **46.063.**)

7.014   ★   *Adamkiewicz Test*   ★
See **22.018,** 10th ed.

7.015   ★   *Xanthoproteic Test*   ★
See **22.019,** 10th ed.

Crude Protein—Official Final Action

7.016   *Kjeldahl Method (9)*

Det. N as in **2.051.** Multiply result by 6.25, or in case of wheat grains by 5.70.

Dumas Method (10)

7.017   *Principle*

N, freed by pyrolysis and subsequent combustions, is swept by CO_2 carrier into nitrometer. CO_2 is absorbed in KOH and vol. residual N is measured and converted to equiv. protein by numerical factor.

7.018   *Apparatus and Reagents*

(a) *Nitrogen analyzer and accessories.*—Consists of combustion and collection and measuring systems. Suitable instrument, Model 29A, with following accessories and reagents is available from Coleman Instruments Corp., 42 W. Madison St, Maywood, IL

60153: Al combustion boats, No. 29–412; Vycor combustion tubes, No. 29–328; CuO-Pt catalyst (CuO wire form with 2.5% Pt reforming catalyst), No. 29–160; reduced Cu wire, No. 29–120; Co_3O_4, No. 29–170; CuO powder, fines, No. 29–140; 45% KOH, No. 29–110.

(b) *Balance.*—Accurate to 0.01 mg.

(c) *Barometer.*—Hg type, readable to 0.1 mm.

7.019   *Preparation of Samples*

Grind to pass No. 30 sieve. Store in capped bottles.

7.020   *Determination*

Operate instrument in accordance with instructions of manufacturer. (Following directions apply to Coleman Model 29A Nitrogen Analyzer. Consult Operating Directions D-360B, Coleman Cat. No. 29–904, for addnl details.)

After combustion furnaces have come to thermal equilibrium, turn combustion cycle control to START and let proceed normally thru cycle. Observe indicated temp. on pyrometer of both upper and lower combustion furnaces at end of combustion portion of cycle. Furnace temps should be 850–900°. If not, adjust.

Prep. combustion tube by inserting stainless steel screen in lower end of combustion tube (end farthest from trademark). In upper end, place enough glass wool to form ¼″ plug when packed. With 7⁄16″ glass rod, drive glass wool down to stainless steel plug. Holding tube vertically, pour CuO-Pt catalyst directly from dispenser bottle into combustion tube until it reaches upper end of trademark. Tap or vibrate tube on bench until reagent settles to approx. center of trademark.

Weigh and record wt of empty Al combustion boat. Place sample in boat. Weigh and record wt of sample and combustion boat. Difference between wts is sample wt. Following sample wts in mg are guides to suitable sample sizes: bermuda grass 150–300; rice bran, wheat shorts, dehydrated alfalfa 150–250; range feed 100–200; cottonseed meal 75–150; edible soy protein 50–150. Weigh sample to nearest 0.01 mg. To avoid wt changes, record wt within 1 min after sample and boat are placed on balance. If this is impossible, weigh sample inside weighing bottle, such as Kimble No. 15165 or 15166.

Turn combustion tube to horizontal, and carefully insert loaded sample boat into open end of tube. Slide or push boat, without spilling contents, until it reaches trademark. Raise open end until tube forms 60–70° angle to horizontal. Tap or vibrate combustion tube on bench top while rotating tube between thumb and forefinger. Raise open end of tube and add vol. Co_3O_4 and vol. CuO fines equal to vol. sample. For convenient means of adding above reagents to samples, place vol. CuO fines and vol. Co_3O_4, each equal to vol. sample, in addnl combustion boat; add contents of boat, but not boat itself, to combustion tube; and rotate partially filled com-

bustion tube between thumb and forefinger while varying angle of tube 20–45° from horizontal. Continue rotating, tapping, and vibrating until sample is dispelled from boat and is thoroly mixed with oxidizing agents. Raise open end until tube forms 60–70° angle to horizontal; add CuO-Pt catalyst ca ½″ above sample boat. Tap or vibrate gently to eliminate voids. Add CuO-Pt catalyst to within ¾″ of top of tube, again tapping or vibrating gently to eliminate voids.

Install prepd combustion tube in N analyzer. Adjust 45% KOH soln meniscus to calibrating mark in nitrometer with digital readout meter. Record counter reading, R_1. (Counter reading should preferably lie between 500 and 1000 μl at this point. Vent control may be used to assist in arriving at this counter setting, if necessary.) Record syringe temp., t_1, indicated on special scale thermometer. Add 2 min more to combustion portion of cycle by turning auxiliary timer to setting 3. (Once this is done, addnl 2 min will be automatically programmed into each subsequent cycle.) Turn combustion cycle control to START. Let analyzer proceed thru its cycle. After cycle is complete and combustion cycle control has entered STAND-BY section, readjust KOH meniscus to calibration mark with digital readout counter. Record new counter reading, R_2, and syringe temp., t_2. Det. blank for instrument under same conditions as actual analysis except omit sample.

7.021   *Calculations*

(a) Record observed N vol., $V_o = R_2 - R_1$, where V_o = observed N vol. (μl), R_1 = initial counter reading, and R_2 = final counter reading.

(b) Det. corrected N vol. (in μl), $V_c = V_o - (V_b + V_t)$, where V_b = vol. blank (μl), V_t = vol. correction for temp. (μl) = $C_f(t_2 - t_1)$. C_f is obtained from **7.022** (based on final counter reading); t_2 and t_1 are in °K.

(c) Det. corrected barometric pressure, $P_c = P_o - (P_b + P_v)$, where P_o = observed barometric pressure (mm Hg), P_b = barometric temp. correction (from **7.023**), and P_v = pressure correction for vapor pressure of KOH soln (from **7.024**).

(*Note:* Empirical approximation of $(P_b + P_v)$ = 11.0 will be satisfactorily accurate for P_o between 740 and 780 mm Hg and syringe temp. between 298 and 305°K.)

(d) Calc. % N = $(P_c \times V_c \times 0.0449)/(T \times W)$, where T = final syringe temp. in °K and W = sample wt in mg.

Example:

P_o = 750.1 mm Hg at 25°C; W = 148.91 mg

	Start	Finish
Counter readings, blank	500 μl	524 μl
Counter readings, sample	524	6955

t_1 = 302.7°K, t_2 = 303.0°K, V_o = 6955 − 524 = 6431 μl

$V_c = 6431 [24 + C_f(t_2 - t_1)] = 6431 (24 + 35 \times 0.3) = 6396 \ \mu l$

$P_c = 750.1 - (3.1 \times 9.6) = 737.4$

$\% \ N = (737.4 \times 6396 \times 0.04493)/(303.0 \times 148.91) = 4.69\%$

(e) Calc. % protein = % N $\times$ 6.25, or % N $\times$ 5.70 in case of wheat grains.

7.022 *Volume correction for temperature correction factor* (C_f) ($\mu l/^\circ K$)^a

Final Counter Reading (μl)	(C_f) (Nitrometers with Check Value)
0	12
5000	29
10000	45
15000	62
20000	79
25000	95
30000	112
35000	129
40000	145
45000	162
50000	179

^{a} Vol. correction, $V_t = C_f(t_2 - t_1)$.

7.023 *Barometric temperature correction* (P_b)

Temperature, °C	P_o (mm Hg)	
	700–749	750–780
10	1.2	1.3
15	1.8	1.9
20	2.3	2.5
25	2.9	3.1
30	3.5	3.7
35	4.1	4.3

7.024 *Pressure correction* (P_v) *for vapor pressure of KOH (for practical purposes, temp. of KOH is same as syringe)*

Temperature, °K	P_v (mm Hg)
288	4.1
293	5.7
298	7.4
303	9.6
308	12.5
313	16.5

7.025 ★ Albuminoid Nitrogen— ★
Official Final Action

Pptn with Cu(OH)$_2$ and N detn. *See* **22.020–22.021**, 10th ed.

7.026 ★ Amido Nitrogen— ★
Official Final Action

% total N − % albuminoid N = % amido N.

Urea and Ammoniacal Nitrogen (11)—
Official Final Action

7.027 *Reagents*

(a) *Defoaming soln.*—Dow Corning Corp. Antifoam B Emulsion.

(b) *Urease soln.*—Prep. fresh soln by dissolving stdzd urease in H$_2$O so that each 10 ml neutzd soln will convert N of at least 0.1 g pure urea.

Standardization.—To det. alky of com. urease prepn dissolve 0.1 g in 50 ml H$_2$O and titr. with 0.1N HCl, using Me red, **2.049**(i). Add same quantity 0.1N HCl to each 0.1 g urease in prepg urease soln. To det. enzyme activity, prep. ca 50 ml neutzd 1% soln. Add different quantities of soln to 0.1 g samples pure urea and follow with enzyme digestion and distn as in detn. Calc. activity of urease prepn from quantity of this urease soln that completely converted urea, in order to permit complete recovery of N by distn.

(c) *Calcium chloride soln.*—Dissolve 25 g CaCl$_2$ in 100 ml H$_2$O.

7.028 *Determination*

Place 2 g sample in Kjeldahl flask with ca 250 ml H$_2$O. Add 10 ml urease soln, stopper tightly, and let stand 1 hr at room temp. or 20 min at 40°. Cool to room temp. if necessary. Use addnl urease soln if feed contains >5% urea (ca 12% protein equiv.). Rinse stopper and neck with few ml H$_2$O. Add 2 g or more MgO (heavy type), 5 ml CaCl$_2$ soln, and 3 ml defoaming soln, and connect flask with condenser by Kjeldahl connecting bulb. Distill 100 ml into measured quantity of std acid, **2.049**(j), and titr. with std alkali, **2.049**(k), using Me red, **2.049**(i).

Urea (12)—Official Final Action
(Applicable to animal feeds and their ingredients)

7.029 *Apparatus*

Spectrophotometer.—Instrument with max. band width 2.4 nm at 420 nm, with 1 cm cuvets.

7.030 *Reagents*

(a) *p-Dimethylaminobenzaldehyde (DMAB).*—Dissolve 16.00 g (Eastman Kodak Co. No. 95 only) in 1 L alcohol and add 100 ml HCl. Stable 1 month. Prep. new std curve with each new batch of reagent.

(b) *Zinc acetate.* — Dissolve 22.0 g Zn(OAc)$_2$ .2H$_2$O in H$_2$O, add 3 ml HOAc, and dil. to 100 ml.

(c) *Potassium ferrocyanide.*—Dissolve 10.6 g K$_4$Fe(CN)$_6$.3H$_2$O in H$_2$O and dil. to 100 ml.

(d) *Vegetable charcoal.*—Darco G60.

(e) *Phosphate buffer soln.*—pH 7.0. Dissolve 3.403 g anhyd. KH$_2$PO$_4$ and 4.355 g anhyd. K$_2$HPO$_4$ sep. in ca 100 ml portions freshly distd H$_2$O. Combine solns and dil. to 1 L with H$_2$O.

(f) *Urea std solns.*—(1) *Stock soln.*—5 mg/ml. Dissolve 5.000±0.001 g reagent grade urea in H$_2$O and dil. to 1 L with H$_2$O. (2) *Working solns.*—Pipet 2, 4, 6, 8, 10, 12, 14, 16, 18, and 20 ml stock soln into

250 ml vol. flasks and dil. to vol. with phosphate buffer. Dilns contain 0.2, 0.4, 0.6, 0.8, 1.0, 1.2, 1.4, 1.6, 1.8, and 2.0 mg urea/5 ml, resp. (3) *Reference soln.*—Use std soln contg 1.0 mg urea/5 ml as ref. std. Store at <24°. Stable 1 week.

7.031 Preparation of Standard Curve

Pipet 5 ml aliquots of working std solns into 20 × 150 mm (25 ml) test tubes and add 5 ml DMAB soln to each. Prep. reagent blank of 5 ml buffer soln and 5 ml DMAB soln. Shake tubes thoroly and let stand 10 min in H_2O bath at 25°. Read A in 1 cm cuvet at 420 nm with reagent blank at zero A. Plot A against concn urea. Plot should be straight line; if not, repeat, using new lot of DMAB.

7.032 Determination

Weigh 1.00 g ground sample into 500 ml vol. flask. Add 1 g charcoal, ca 250 ml H_2O, 5 ml $Zn(OAc)_2$ soln, and 5 ml $K_4Fe(CN)_6$ soln. Shake mech. 30 min and dil. to vol. with H_2O. Let stand until ppt settles. Decant thru Whatman No. 40 paper and collect clear filtrate. Pipet 5 ml filtrate into test tube, add 5 ml DMAB soln, and shake thoroly. Include reference std (5 ml soln (f)(3) and 5 ml DMAB soln) and reagent blank with each group of samples. Let stand 10 min in H_2O bath at 25°. Read A at 420 nm against reagent blank.

% Urea = $(1.0 \times A_{sample} \times 100)/A_{std} \times$ mg sample in aliquot.

Nitrate and Nitrite Nitrogen (13)— Official Final Action

7.033 Principle

Nitrate and nitrite are extd with Cd and Ba chloride soln. Bulk of sol. proteins are pptd in alk. soln and clarified soln is passed thru metallic Cd column, reducing nitrate to nitrite. Nitrite is measured colorimetrically. (*Caution:* Cd salts are toxic. *See* **46.084.**)

7.034 Reagents and Apparatus

(a) *Nitrate-nitrogen std solns.*—(1) *Stock soln.*— 12 μg nitrate N/ml. Dissolve 0.867 g KNO_3 in 1 L H_2O. Dil. 25 ml to 250 ml with H_2O. (2) *Working solns.*— 0.6, 1.2, 1.8, 2.4, 3.0 μg N/ml. Dil. 5, 10, 15, 20, and 25 ml stock soln to 100 ml with H_2O.

(b) *Extracting soln.*—Dissolve and dil. 50 g $CdCl_2$ + 50 g $BaCl_2$ to 1 L with H_2O. Adjust to pH 1 with HCl.

(c) *Ammonium chloride buffer soln.*—pH 9.6. Dissolve 50 g NH_4Cl in 500 ml H_2O and adjust pH with NH_4OH. Dil. to 1 L with H_2O.

(d) *Sodium hydroxide.*—2.5N. Dissolve 50 g NaOH in 500 ml H_2O.

(e) *Sulfanilamide soln.*—0.5%. Dissolve 1.25 g sulfanilamide in 250 ml HCl (1 + 1). Soln is stable 1–2 months.

(f) *Coupling reagent.*—Dissolve 0.5 g N(1-naphthyl)ethylenediamine.HCl in 100 ml H_2O.

Store in g-s dark bottle in refrigerator. Soln is stable several weeks.

(g) *Salt soln.*—Dissolve 100 g NaCl in 500 ml H_2O. Add 50 ml buffer soln, (c), and dil. to 1 L with H_2O.

(h) *Reduction column.*—25 ml buret or equiv. id chromatgc tube with stopcock and reservoir (Kontes Glass Co. Cat. No. K-420280 or Scientific Glass Apparatus Co. Cat. No. JC-1508).

7.035 Preparation of Columns

Prep. supply of metallic Cd by placing Zn rods into 500 ml 20% $CdSO_4$ soln. After reaction for 3 hr, discard soln and scrape moss-like Cd growth from Zn rods. Place Cd in high-speed blender, add 500 ml H_2O, and blend 2 sec. Wash fine metal particles with H_2O onto sieves, collecting only 20–40 mesh size. Fill reduction column with H_2O and add 2 cm plug of glass wool. Press any trapped air from glass wool as it is pushed to bottom of column with glass rod. Add Cd to depth of 10 cm, using min. of very gentle tapping. Wash column with 25 ml 0.10N HCl, two 25 ml portions H_2O, and finally 25 ml buffer, (c), dild 1 + 9. Keep column covered with salt soln, (g), when not in use.

Normally columns can be used repeatedly if kept under salt soln between analyses. When succession of highly proteinaceous or other sol. org. contg samples are treated, flow rate may decrease gradually. Repeating 25 ml 0.10N HCl treatment may restore original flow rate; if not, prep. new column. Reproducible flow rate is important. Actual rate can be 3–5 ml/min but once established, it must be identical (±0.1 ml) for samples and stds.

7.036 Preparation of Standard Curve

Prep. std curve of 3, 6, 9, 12, and 15 μg nitrate-nitrite N by pipeting 5.0 ml aliquots of working stds into 30 ml beakers. Add 5 ml buffer soln, (c), and 15 ml H_2O, mix well, and transfer quant. to reduction column, using min. H_2O. Adjust flow rate thru column to 3–5 ml/min. Just as reservoir empties, add 15 ml salt soln, (g). Collect eluate, including salt wash, in 50 ml vol. flask (total vol. of eluate should be ca 40 ml). Add 5 ml sulfanilamide reagent, (e), mix, and let stand 3 min. Add 2 ml coupling reagent (f), mix, dil. to vol. with H_2O, mix, and let stand 20 min for max. color development. Color is stable ≥2 hr. Det. A in 1 cm cells at 540 nm against reagent blank. Plot A against μg nitrate-nitrite N.

7.037 Extraction

(a) *Low level nitrate samples (grains, meals, supplements, etc.).*—Wash 5.0 g finely ground sample into 250 ml vol. flask. Add 100 ml extg soln, (b), and 100 ml H_2O, and mix. Let stand 1 hr with occasional swirling. Add 20 ml 2.5N NaOH, dil. to vol. with H_2O, mix, and filter immediately thru rapid paper. Pipet 10 ml buffer soln, (c), into 100 ml vol. flask, dil. to vol. with clear filtrate, and mix.

(b) *Dry, high level nitrate products (dried plants, hays, meals, etc.).*—Weigh 5.0 g finely ground sample into 500 ml vol. flask. Add 100 ml extg soln, (b), and 300 ml H_2O, and mix. Let stand 1 hr with occasional swirling, add 40 ml 2.5N NaOH, dil. to vol. with H_2O, mix, and filter immediately thru rapid paper. Pipet 10 ml buffer soln, (c), into 100 ml vol. flask, dil. to vol. with clear filtrate, and mix.

(c) *Grasses, silages, and other wet materials.*—Weigh 100 g sample into 1 gal. capacity high-speed blender. Add 100 ml extg soln, (b), and 800 ml H_2O, including vol. contributed by sample as detd in **7.003** or **7.004**. Homogenize 1 min, pour into 2 L beaker, and let stand 1 hr. Add 100 ml buffer soln, (c) (total vol. 1 L), mix well, and filter thru No. 42 Whatman paper, collecting portion of clear filtrate.

7.038 *Determination*

(a) *Nitrate plus nitrite nitrogen.*—Pipet 25 ml buffered sample exts, **7.037**(a) or (b), or 5 ml ext, (c), into reduction column and treat as in **7.036**, beginning, "Adjust flow rate thru column ..." Rinse column with 30 ml H_2O between samples to remove NaCl. Use portion of buffered sample exts with equiv. diln and pH as ref. soln in detg A at 540 nm. Also det. nitrate-nitrite in reagents and correct for this blank value. Calc. total nitrate-nitrite N from std curve.

(b) *Nitrite nitrogen.*—Pipet aliquot clear sample filtrate (contg <15 μg nitrite) into 50 ml vol. flask and dil. with H_2O to ca 40 ml. Mix well, add 5 ml sulfanilamide reagent, (e), mix, and let stand 3 min. Add 2 ml coupling reagent, (f), and dil. to vol. with H_2O. Mix well and let stand 20 min for max. color development. Measure A in 1 cm cells against sample ext with equiv. diln at 540 nm. Correct for nitrite reagent blank.

(c) *Nitrate nitrogen.*—Calc. by difference between (a) and (b) above.

7.039 *Calculation*

ppm NO_2 and/or NO_3 N = μg NO_3 N found × diln factor/g sample.

Diln factors for exts: **7.037**(a), 11.1; (b), 22.2; (c), 200.

Pepsin Digestibility of Animal Protein Feeds (14)—Official Final Action

7.040 *Principles*

Defatted sample is digested 16 hr with warm acid soln of pepsin under constant agitation. Insol. residue is centrfd, dried and weighed, examined microscopically, and analyzed for protein; or filtered, washed, and analyzed for protein. Method is applicable to meat scrap, meat and bone scrap, digester tankage, fish meal, whale meal, blood meal, hydrolyzed feather meal, and poultry by-product meal. It is not intended for evaluation of protein quality.

7.041 *Apparatus*

(a) *Centrifuge.*—Capable of at least 1750 rpm with 150 ml conical bottom tubes. If necessary, soln may be centrfd in 50 ml tubes.

(b) *Agitator.*—See Fig. **7:2**. Continuous, slow speed (15 rpm), end-over-end type, to operate inside incubator at 45±2° and carry 8 oz screwcap prescription bottles. Agitator (with bottles) available from David E. Sims, 716 Forrest Ave, Quincy, IL 62301. Extra bottles available from above supplier. Bottles, 8 oz GXTA Phoenix prescription; also available from Kerr Glass Mfg Co., Lancaster, PA 17604, as GXTA or CTA. Stirring or reciprocating (shaking) type agitator cannot be used because solid particles collect on sides of container and do not contact pepsin soln.

(c) *Glass fiber filter paper.*—Reeve Angel No. 934–AH, or equiv., 2.4 cm diam. For indigestible residues.

FIG. 7:2—Agitator

7.042 *Reagents*

(a) *Pepsin soln.*—0.2 % pepsin (activity 1:10,000) in 0.075N HCl. Prep. dil. HCl by dilg 6.1 ml HCl to 1 L with H_2O. Add pepsin just before use, stirring until completely dissolved.

(b) *Alcohol.*—Denatured is satisfactory.

(c) *Filter aid.*—Diat. earth type such as Hyflo Super-Cel (Johns-Manville Products Corp.).

7.043 *Extraction*

(*Caution: See* **46.011**, **46.039**, *and* **46.054**.)

Ext sample, ground in Wiley mill to pass 2 mm screen, by one of following methods:

(a) *By extraction.*—Prep. extn thimble from 11 cm Whatman No. 2 paper, or equiv., as follows: Fold paper in half; straighten paper and refold at right angles to first fold; turn paper over and repeat process with folds at 45° to original fold; while holding creased paper in one hand, place short test tube (6–8 mm smaller in diam. than extractor sample holder or cup in which thimble is to be used) at its center; fold along natural crease lines to form 4-pointed star around tube; and wrap points in same direction around tube to complete thimble.

Weigh 1.000 g sample into thimble and ext 1 hr with ether at condensation rate of 3–4 drops/sec. (If Soxhlet is used, top of thimble should extend above siphon tube to avoid loss of solid particles. If paper contg sample is totally submerged in siphon cup, sample must be completely wrapped in paper.) Observe ether ext to det. that no solid particles were carried into solv. beaker. If approx. fat content is desired, evap. ether, and dry and weigh residue. Remove paper from sample container or cup and let dry at room temp. Unfold and quant. brush defatted sample into digestion bottle, avoiding contamination by brush bristles or filter paper fibers. Proceed as in **7.044.**

(b) *By centrifuging.*—Stir 1.000 g sample thoroly with 10 ml ether in 15 ml centrf. tube and centrf. 5 min at ≥1750 rpm. Decant ether and repeat extn with three 5 ml portions ether. If approx. fat content is desired, combine ether exts, evap., dry, and weigh residue. Proceed as in **7.044.**

7.044.   *Pepsin Digestion*

Quant. transfer defatted sample to 8 oz agitator bottle. Add 150 ml freshly prepd pepsin-HCl soln, prewarmed to 42–45°. Stopper bottle, clamp in agitator, and incubate with continuous agitation 16 hr at 45°.

7.045   *Treatment of Residue*

For indigestible residue, indigestible protein, and microscopic examination of residue.—Transfer contents of agitator bottle to centrf. tube and centrf. 5 min at ≥1750 rpm. If 150 ml tube is unavailable, centrf. in 50 ml portions, collecting entire residue in same tube. Decant, rinse agitator bottle twice with 15–20 ml portions warm H_2O, and add rinse H_2O to residue in tube. Stir well, centrf., and decant wash H_2O. Wash residue once more with warm H_2O and twice with alcohol. Resuspend residue in 5–10 ml alcohol and filter quant. with gentle suction thru weighed No. 4 gooch crucible contg glass fiber filter paper. (Prep. crucible by inserting paper, washing twice with warm H_2O, and twice with alcohol with gentle suction. Dry in oven 30 min at 100–110°, cool, and weigh.) Wash indigestible residue with alcohol and suck dry. Dry in oven 30 min at 110°. Cool, weigh, and calc. indigestible residue. Examine microscopically, if desired. Quant. transfer residue and pad to Kjeldahl flask and det. crude protein by **7.016.**

For indigestible protein only.—After incubation add ca 1 g filter aid to digestion mixt. in agitator bottle. Filter quant. with gentle suction thru Whatman No. 2 paper or thru gooch with glass paper or asbestos pad. Wash 3 times with warm H_2O. Transfer paper contg moist residue to Kjeldahl flask and det. crude protein as in **7.016.**

7.046   *Calculations*

Calc. (*1*) % indigestible residue and (*2*) % indigestible protein from above on original sample basis; (*3*) calc. total protein from **7.016.** % crude protein in indigestible residue = (*2*) × 100/(*1*); % of crude protein content of sample not digested = (*2*) × 100/(*3*); % of crude protein content of sample digested = 100 − % not digested.

OTHER CONSTITUENTS
Crude Fat or Ether Extract

Use method **7.048** or **7.049** for mixed feeds other than (*1*) entirely baked and/or expanded, (*2*) entirely dried milk products, or (*3*) feeds contg urea.

Direct Method—Official Final Action
7.047   *Reagent*

Anhydrous ether.—Wash com. ether with 2 or 3 portions H_2O, add solid NaOH or KOH, and let stand until most of H_2O is abstracted from the ether. Decant into dry bottle, add small pieces of carefully cleaned metallic Na, and let stand until H evolution ceases. Keep ether, thus dehydrated, over metallic Na in loosely stoppered bottles. (*Caution: See* **46.034** *and* **46.054.**)

7.048   *Determination*

(Large quantities of H_2O-sol. components such as carbohydrates, urea, lactic acid, glycerol, and others may interfere with extn of fat; if present, ext 2 g sample on small paper in funnel with five 20 ml portions H_2O prior to drying for ether extn. *Caution: See* **46.009, 46.011,** and **46.054.**)

Ext ca 2 g sample, dried as in **7.003** or **7.007**, with anhyd. ether. Use thimble with porosity permitting rapid passage of ether. Extn period may vary from 4 hr at condensation rate of 5–6 drops/sec to 16 hr at 2–3 drops/sec. Dry ext 30 min at 100°, cool, and weigh.

7.049   *Indirect Method—Official Final Action*

Det. moisture as in **7.003** or **7.007**; then ext dried substance as in **7.048,** and dry again. Report loss in wt as ether ext.

7.050   *In Baked or Expanded Pet Food (15)—* *Official Final Action*

(To be used only on products all of which have been baked and/or expanded. Not applicable to canned, fresh, or frozen pet food. Such products should be dried at 70–100°, then ground, and drying completed by **7.003** or **7.007** followed by **7.048** or **7.049.** *Caution: See* **46.011, 46.054,** and **46.073.**)

Place 2 g ground, well-mixed sample in Mojonnier fat-extn tube, add 2 ml alcohol to prevent lumping on addn of acid, and shake to moisten all particles. Add 10 ml HCl (25 + 11), mix well, and set tube 30–40 min in H_2O bath at 70–80°, shaking frequently. Fill to within 1–2 ml of mark with alcohol and cool. (Level of liq. should be in neck of Mojonnier tube just below pouring-off level.)

Add 25 ml ether, stopper with glass, cork, Neoprene, or good quality rubber stopper thoroly cleaned with alcohol, and shake vigorously 1 min. Carefully release pressure so that no solv. is lost. Wash adhering solv. and fat from stopper back into extn tube with few ml redistd pet ether (bp <60°). Add 25 ml redistd pet ether, stopper, and shake vigorously 1 min. Let stand until upper liq. is practically clear or centrf. 20 min at ca 600 rpm. Pour as much of ether-fat soln as possible thru filter consisting of cotton pledget packed just firmly enough in funnel stem to let ether pass freely into 150 ml beaker contg several glass beads. Rinse lip of tube with few ml pet ether. Re-ext liq. remaining in tube twice, each time with only 15 ml of each ether, shaking 1 min after addn of each ether. Pour clear ether soln thru filter into same beaker as before, and wash tip of tube, stopper, funnel, and end of funnel stem with few ml of mixt. of 2 ethers (1 + 1). Evap. slowly on steam bath.

Redissolve dried fat residue in four 10 ml portions Et ether, filtering each portion thru small fat-free paper into 100 ml beaker, contg few glass beads, that has been predried at 100°, cooled in air, and then weighed against counterpoise treated similarly. Use fifth 10 ml portion ether for rinsing paper and funnel. Evap. ether on steam bath, dry in 100° oven 90 min, cool in air, and as soon as room temp. is reached, weigh against counterpoise treated similarly. Correct this wt by blank detn on reagents used.

7.051 In Dried Milk Products (16)—
Official Final Action
Proceed as in 16.156(b) and 16.157, using 8.5 ml H₂O and 1.5 ml NH₄OH.

7.052 In Fish Meal (17)—
Official First Action
(*Caution: See* 46.009, 46.011, 46.039, and 46.046.)

Weigh 4–5 g sample to nearest 0.01 g into Alundum or paper extn thimble, cover with light layer of cotton, and ext with acetone in continuous extractor 16 hr. Distill off acetone until vol. in flask is 10–15 ml, transfer to 100 ml tared beaker, washing flask free of all oil with fresh acetone, and evap. with current of warm air. (Convenient method is to place flask on warm surface, e.g., over steam radiator, in front of small elec. fan.) When no H₂O or acetone can be observed, place beaker in vac. oven at 80° and apply 24–25″ vac. 1 hr. Transfer to desiccator, cool, and weigh.

Transfer extd meal residue from thimble to 150 ml beaker. Remove any remaining solv. by heating on warm surface and then add 60 ml 4N HCl. Digest 1 hr at or near bp on hot plate, stirring occasionally with glass rod and adding H₂O as needed to maintain vol. in beaker. (Complete removal of acetone is necessary before this digestion, otherwise vaporization of solv. will carry meal particles over side of vessel onto hot plate.) Filter thru 12.5 cm fluted paper. Wash residue on filter until acid-free, using Me red on portions of filtrate to follow progress of washing. Place filter and meal in 150 ml beaker and dry 1 hr in air oven at 80–90°. Transfer filter and contents to thimble and ext 16 hr with acetone. Remove solv. and weigh ext as above. Sum of wts of exts = total fat.

Crude Fiber (18)—Official First Action
American Oil Chemists Society-Association of Official Analytical Chemists Method

7.053 Principles
Crude fiber is loss on ignition of dried residue remaining after digestion of sample with 1.25% H₂SO₄ and 1.25% NaOH solns under specific conditions. Method is applicable to grains, meals, flours, feeds, and fiber-bearing material from which fat can be extd to leave workable residue.

7.054 Reagents
(a) *Sulfuric acid soln.*—0.255N. 1.25 g H₂SO₄/100 ml.

(b) *Sodium hydroxide soln.*—0.313N. 1.25 g NaOH/100 ml, free, or nearly so, from Na₂CO₃.

(Concns of these solns must be checked by titrn.)

(c) *Prepared asbestos.*—Spread thin layer acid-washed, medium or long fiber asbestos in evapg dish and heat 16 hr at 600° in furnace. Boil 30 min with 1.25% H₂SO₄, filter, wash thoroly with H₂O, and boil 30 min with 1.25% NaOH. Filter, wash once with 1.25% H₂SO₄, wash thoroly with H₂O, dry, and ignite 2 hr at 600°.

Det. blank by treating 1.0 g prepd asbestos with acid and alkali as in detn. Correct crude fiber results for any blank, which should be negligible (ca 1 mg). Asbestos recovered from detn may be used in subsequent detns.

(d) *Alcohol.*—MeOH, isopropanol, 95% or reagent alcohol.

(e) *Antifoam.*—Dow Corning Corp. Antifoam A compd dild 1 + 4 with mineral spirits or pet ether, or H₂O-dild Antifoam A Emulsion (1 + 4). Do not use Antifoam Spray.

(f) *Bumping chips or granules.*—Broken Alundum crucibles or equiv. granules (RR Alundum 90 mesh, Norton Co., New Bond St, Worcester, MA 01606) are satisfactory.

7.055 Apparatus
(a) *Digestion apparatus.*—With condenser to fit 600 ml beaker and hot plate adjustable to temp. that will bring 200 ml H₂O at 25° to rolling boil in 15 ±2 min. (Available from Labconco Corp., 8811 Prospect Ave, Kansas City, MO 64132.)

(b) *Ashing dishes.*—Silica, Vitreosil 70 × 15 mm; or porcelain, Coors, No. 450, size 1, or equiv.

(c) *Desiccator.*—With efficient desiccant such as 4–8 mesh Drierite (CaCl₂ is not satisfactory).

(d) *Filtering device.*—With No. 200 type 304 or 316 stainless steel screen (W. S. Tyler Co., 8200 Tyler Blvd, Mentor, OH 44060), easily washed of digested residue. Either Oklahoma State filter screen (*see* Fig. 7:3; available from Labconco Corp.) or modified California polyethylene buchner (*see* Fig. 7:4; consists of 2 piece polyethylene funnel manufactured by Nalge Co., 75 Panorama Creek Drive, Rochester, NY 14625, Cat. No. 4280, 70 mm, without No. 200 screen, or equiv. Seal screen to filtering surface of funnel, using small tip soldering iron).

(e) *Suction filter.*—To accommodate filtering devices. Attach suction flask to trap in line with aspirator or other source of vac. with valve to break vac.

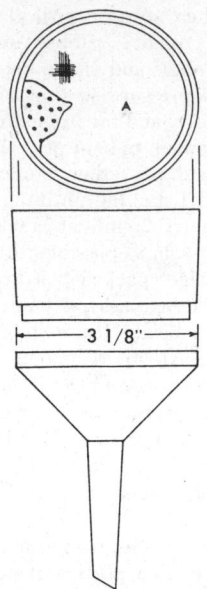

FIG. 7:4—Modified California State buchner funnel, 2-piece polyethylene, covered with 200-mesh screen, A, heat-sealed to edge of filtering surface

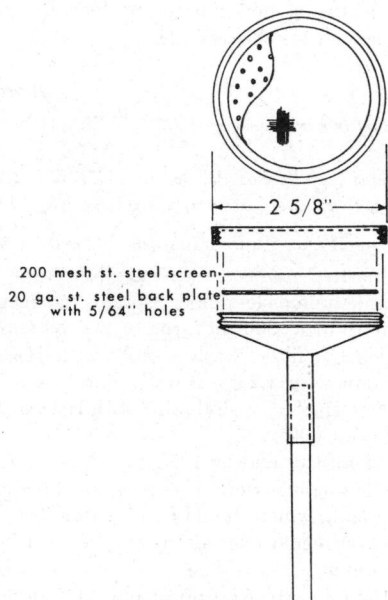

200 mesh st. steel screen
20 ga. st. steel back plate with 5/64″ holes

← 2 5/8″ →

FIG. 7:3—Oklahoma State filter screen

(f) *Liquid preheater.*—For preheating H_2O, 1.25% H_2SO_4, and NaOH solns to bp of H_2O. Convenient system, shown in Fig. 7:5, consists of sheet Cu tank with 3 coils of ⅜″ od Cu tubing, 12.5 feet long. Solder inlets and outlets where tubing passes thru tank walls. Connect to reflux condenser and fill with H_2O. Keep H_2O boiling with two 750 watt thermostatically controlled hot plates. Use Tygon for inlet leads to reservoirs of H_2O, acid, and alkali; use gum rubber tubing for outlets. Capacity of preheater adequate for 60 analyses in 8 hr.

7.056   *Preparation of Sample*

Reduce sample (riffle is suitable) to 100 g and place portion in sealed container for H_2O detn. Immediately det. H_2O. Grind remainder to uniform fineness. (Weber mill (Sargent-Welch Scientific Co.)

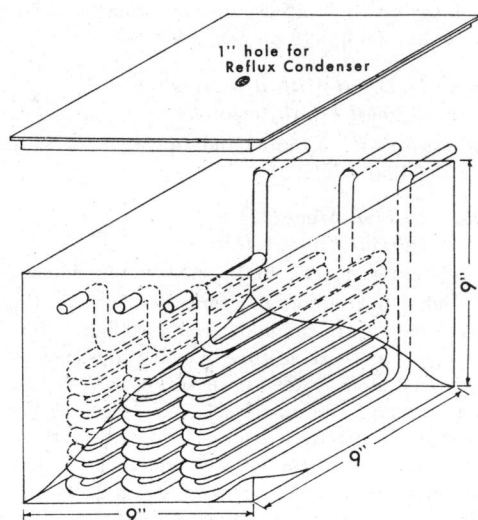

1″ hole for Reflux Condenser

9″
9″
9″

FIG. 7:5—Continuous heater for distilled water, 1.25% alkali, and 1.25% acid

with screen 0.033–0.040″, Micro mill (Pulverizing Machinery Div., Slick Industries, Summit, NJ 07901) with screen ⅟₂₅–⅟₁₆″, and Wiley mill with 1 mm screen give comparable fineness.) Since most materials lose moisture during grinding, det. H_2O on ground sample at same time sample is taken for crude fiber detn.

7.057   *Determination*

Ext 2 g ground material with ether or pet ether, **14.080.** If fat is <1%, extn may be omitted. Transfer to 600 ml beaker, avoiding fiber contamination from paper or brush. Add ca 1 g prepd asbestos, 200 ml boiling 1.25% H_2SO_4, and 1 drop dild antifoam. (Excess antifoam may give high results; use only if necessary to control foaming.) Bumping chips or granules may also be added. Place beaker on digestion app. with preadjusted hot plate and boil exactly 30 min, rotating beaker periodically to keep solids from adhering to sides. Remove beaker, and filter as in (a) or (b).

(a) *Using Oklahoma filter screen.*—Turn on suction and insert screen (precoated with asbestos if extremely fine materials are analyzed) into beaker, keeping face of screen just under surface of liq. until all liq. is removed. Without breaking suction or raising filter, add 50–75 ml boiling H_2O. After wash is removed, repeat with three 50 ml washings. (Work rapidly to keep mat from becoming dry.) Remove filter from beaker and drain all H_2O from line by raising above trap level. Return mat and residue to beaker by breaking suction and blowing back. Add 200 ml boiling 1.25% NaOH and boil exactly 30 min. Remove beaker, and filter as above. Without breaking suction, wash with 25 ml boiling 1.25% H_2SO_4 and three 50 ml portions boiling H_2O. Drain free of excess H_2O by raising filter. Lower filter into beaker and wash with 25 ml alcohol. Drain line, break suction, and remove mat by blowing back thru filter screen into ashing dish. Proceed as in last par.

(b) *Using California buchner.*—Filter contents of beaker thru buchner (precoated with asbestos if extremely fine materials are being analyzed), rinse beaker with 50–75 ml boiling H_2O, and wash thru buchner. Repeat with three 50 ml portions H_2O, and suck dry. Remove mat and residue by snapping bottom of buchner against top while covering stem with thumb or forefinger and replace in beaker. Add 200 ml boiling 1.25% NaOH and boil exactly 30 min. Remove beaker, and filter as above. Wash with 25 ml boiling 1.25% H_2SO_4, three 50 ml portions H_2O, and 25 ml alcohol. Remove mat and residue; transfer to ashing dish.

Dry mat and residue 2 hr at 130±2°. Cool in desiccator and weigh. Ignite 30 min at 600±15°. Cool in desiccator and reweigh. % Crude fiber in ground sample = C = (Loss in wt on ignition − loss in wt of asbestos blank) × 100/wt sample. % Crude fiber on desired moisture basis = C × (100 − % moisture desired)/(100 − % moisture in ground sample). Report to 0.1%.

7.058   Reducing Sugars (*19*)—
Official Final Action

Place 10 g sample in 250 ml vol. flask. If material is acid, neutze by adding 1–3 g $CaCO_3$. Add 125 ml 50% alcohol by vol., mix thoroly, and boil on steam bath or by partially immersing flask in H_2O bath at 83–87° 1 hr, using small funnel in neck of flask to condense vapor. Cool and let mixt. stand several hr, preferably overnight. Dil. to vol. with neut. 95% alcohol, mix thoroly, let settle or centrf. 15 min at 1500 rpm, and decant closely. Pipet 200 ml supernatant into beaker and evap. on steam bath to 20–30 ml. Do not evap. to dryness. Little alcohol in residue does no harm.

Transfer to 100 ml vol. flask and rinse beaker thoroly with H_2O, adding rinsings to flask. Add enough *satd neut.* Pb $(OAc)_2$ *soln* (ca 2 ml) to produce flocculent ppt, shake thoroly, and let stand 15 min. Dil. to vol. with H_2O, mix thoroly, and filter thru dry paper. Add enough anhyd. Na_2CO_3 or K oxalate to filtrate to ppt all Pb, again filter thru dry paper, and test filtrate with little anhyd. Na_2CO_3 or K oxalate to make sure that all Pb has been removed.

Proceed as in **31.039,** using 25 ml aliquot (representing 2 g sample). Express results as glucose or invert sugar.

7.059   Sucrose (*19*)—Official Final Action

Place 50 ml prepd soln, **7.058,** in 100 ml vol. flask, add piece of litmus paper, neutze with HCl, add 5 ml HCl, and let inversion proceed at room temp. as in **31.026**(c). When inversion is complete, transfer soln to beaker, neutze with Na_2CO_3, return soln to 100 ml flask, dil. to vol. with H_2O, filter if necessary, and det. reducing sugars in 50 ml soln (representing 2 g sample) as in **7.058.** Calc. results as invert sugar. [% total sugar after inversion − % reducing sugars before inversion (both calcd as invert sugar)] × 0.95 = % sucrose.

Because insol. material of grain or cattle food occupies some space in flask as originally made up, correct by multiplying all results by factor 0.97, as results of large number of detns on various materials show av. vol. of 10 g material to be 7.5 ml.

★ **Starch—Official Final Action** ★

7.060   *Direct Acid Hydrolysis*

See **8.017.** Use sample contg 2.5–3 g dry material.

7.061   *Diastase Method with Subsequent*
Acid Hydrolysis

Ext quantity of sample (ground to impalpable powder and representing 4–5 g dry material) on close texture filter with five 10 ml portions ether; wash with 150 ml alcohol, 10% by vol., and then with few ml 95% alcohol. Place residue in beaker with 50 ml H_2O and continue as in **31.110,** third par.

7.062   *In Presence of Interfering*
***Polysaccharides* (*20*)**

See **22.048,** 10th ed.

7.063   *In Condensed or Dried Milk Products—*
***Qualitative Test* (*21*)**

See **22.049,** 10th ed.

7.064 ★ Pentosans (22)— ★
Official Final Action
See **22.050–22.051,** 10th ed.

7.065 ★ Galactan—Official Final Action ★
See **22.052,** 10th ed. (*Caution: See* **46.011** and **46.026.**)

7.066 ★ Water-Soluble Acidity (23)— ★
Official Final Action
See **22.053,** 10th ed.

7.067 Ferrous Salts (24)—
Official Final Action

Moisten entire surface of sheet of white glazed paper with 10% $K_3Fe(CN)_6$ soln. Sift portion of sample thru fine sieve (No. 40) so that feed is distributed thinly over entire area. After few moments, wash off feed under slow stream of H_2O. Blue speck or spot denotes particle of ferrous salt.

7.068 Copper Salts (24)—Official Final Action

Proceed as in **7.067,** except use 10% $K_4Fe(CN)_6$ soln. Brown speck or spot denotes particle of Cu salt.

7.069 Potassium Iodide (24)—
Official Final Action

Moisten entire surface of sheet of white glazed paper with mixt. of starch indicator (3 parts) and $Br-H_2O$ (1 part). Sift portion of sample so that feed is distributed thinly over entire area. Blue spot denotes particle of iodide. If extremely small amt of KI is to be detected, modify procedure by carefully charring 10 g or more of feed, washing residue with small amt of H_2O, and evapg filtered soln in white evapg dish so that solids are concd on one small spot. When moistened with the starch indicator and $Br-H_2O$, blue color denotes presence of iodide.

Minerals in Feeds by Atomic Absorption
Spectrophotometry (25)—Official Final Action
(*Caution: See* **46.006.**)

7.070 *Apparatus*
Atomic absorption spectrophotometer.—See **2.097.**

7.071 *Operating Parameters*

See **2.098,** except use fuel-rich air-C_2H_2 flame for Ca and Mg, and ranges of operation for μg element/ml soln are: Ca 5–20, Fe 5–20, Mg 0.5–2.5, Mn 5–20, and Zn 1–5.

7.072 *Reagents*

(*See* introduction to **2.099.** Com. prepd std solns may be used.)

(a) *Calcium std solns.*—Prep. as in **2.099**(a).

(b) *Iron, magnesium, manganese, and zinc std solns.*—Prep. stock solns as in **2.099**(c), (e), (f), and (g), and dil. aliquots with 0.1–0.5N HCl to make at least 4 std solns of each element within range of detn.

7.073 *Preparation of Sample Solution*

(a) *Dry ashing.*—Ash 2–10 g sample in well-glazed porcelain dish. Start in cold furnace, bring to 550°, and hold 4 hr. Cool, add 10 ml 3N HCl, cover with watch glass, and boil gently 10 min. Cool, filter into 100 ml vol. flask, and dil. to vol. with H_2O. Subsequent dilns with 0.1–0.5N HCl may be necessary to bring sample solns into analytical range.

(b) *Wet digestion.*—Proceed as in **7.077**(a), adding 25 ml HNO_3 for each 2.5 g sample and dilg to 100 ml with H_2O. Digestion can be made at low heat on hot plate, using 600 ml beaker covered with watch glass. Subsequent dilns with 0.1–0.5N HCl may be necessary to bring sample solns into analytical range.

7.074 *Determination*
See **2.101.**

7.075 *Calculation*
See **2.102.**

Calcium—Official Final Action
7.076 *Method I (26)*
(Applicable to mineral feeds only)

Weigh 2 g finely ground sample into SiO_2 or porcelain dish and ignite in muffle to C-free ash, but avoid fusing. Boil residue in 40 ml HCl (1 + 3) and few drops HNO_3. Transfer to 250 ml vol. flask, cool, dil. to vol., and mix thoroly. Pipet 25 ml clear liq. into beaker, dil. to ca 100 ml, and add 2 drops Me red, **2.049**(i). Add NH_4OH (1 + 1) dropwise to pH 5.6, as shown by intermediate brownish-orange. If overstepped, add with dropper HCl (1 + 3) to orange. Add 2 drops HCl (1 + 3). Color should now be pink (pH 2.5–3.0), not orange. Dil. to ca 150 ml, bring to boil, and slowly add, with constant stirring, 10 ml hot satd (4.2%) soln of $(NH_4)_2C_2O_4$. If red changes to orange or yellow, add HCl (1 + 3) dropwise until color again changes to pink. Let stand overnight for ppt to settle. Filter supernatant thru quant. paper, gooch, or fritted glass filter (fine Pyrex is preferable), and wash ppt thoroly with NH_4OH (1 + 50). Place paper or crucible with ppt in original beaker, and add mixt. of 125 ml H_2O and 5 ml H_2SO_4. Heat to $\geq 70°$ and titr. with 0.1N $KMnO_4$ soln to first slight pink. Presence of paper may cause color to fade in few sec. Correct for blank and calc. % Ca.

Method II (27)
7.077 *Preparation of Solution*
(*Caution: See* **46.026** and **46.028.**)

(a) Weigh 2.5 g sample into 500 or 800 ml Kjeldahl flask. Add 20–30 ml HNO_3 and boil gently 30–45 min to oxidize all easily oxidizable matter. Cool soln somewhat and add 10 ml 70–72% $HClO_4$. Boil very gently, adjusting flame as necessary, until soln is colorless or nearly so and dense white fumes appear. Use particular care not to boil to dryness (Danger!)

at any time. Cool slightly, add 50 ml H₂O, and boil to drive out any remaining NO₂ fumes. Cool, dil., filter into 250 ml vol. flask, dil. to vol., and mix thoroly.

(b) Weigh 2.5 g finely ground sample into SiO₂ or porcelain dish and ignite as in **7.010.** Add 40 ml HCl (1 + 3) and few drops HNO₃ to residue, boil, transfer to 250 ml vol. flask, cool, dil. to vol., and mix thoroly.

7.078   *Determination*

Pipet suitable aliquot of clear soln, **7.077**(a) or (b), into beaker, dil. to 100 ml, and add 2 drops Me red, **2.049**(i). Continue as in **7.076,** beginning "Add NH₄OH (1 + 1) dropwise ..." except use 0.05N KMnO₄.

(100 ml is suitable aliquot of sample soln for grain feeds; for mineral feeds 25 ml aliquot may be taken and titrd with 0.1N KMnO₄. For suitable precision, size of sample, aliquot, and concn of KMnO₄ must be so adjusted that at least 20 ml std KMnO₄ soln is consumed.)

Soluble Chlorine
Titration Method (28)—Official Final Action
7.079   *Reagents*

(a) *Potassium chloride std soln.*—0.001 g Cl/ml. Recrystallize reagent KCl 3 times from H₂O, dry at 110°, and heat at ca 500° to constant wt. Dissolve 2.1029 g in H₂O and dil. to 1 L.

(b) *Silver nitrate soln.*—Dissolve 5 g AgNO₃ in 1 L H₂O and adjust soln so that 1 ml = 1 ml std KCl soln.

(c) *Potassium thiocyanate soln.*—Dissolve 2.5 g KSCN in 1 L H₂O and adjust so that 1 ml = 1 ml std AgNO₃ soln. Stdze as in **45.004.**

(d) *Ferric sulfate soln.*—Dissolve 60 g Fe₂(SO₄)₃ + Aq. in H₂O and dil. to 1 L.

(e) *Ferric sulfate indicator.*—To filtered 25% soln of Fe₂(SO₄)₃ + Aq. add equal vol. HNO₃.

7.080   *Determination*

Transfer 3 g sample to 300 ml erlenmeyer. Add 50 ml Fe₂(SO₄)₃ soln (accurately measured), swirling flask to prevent caking of sample and to facilitate soln of Cl. Add 100 ml (also accurately measured) NH₄OH (1 + 19). Swirl flask enough to ensure soln of Cl and thoro mixing of soln. (Very little swirling is necessary. If soln is agitated by vigorous vertical shaking, filtration will be difficult.) Let mixt. settle 10 min. Filter thru dry 11 cm Whatman No. 41 paper or equiv. Use 50 ml aliquots (⅓ of total) on samples low in Cl (0–2% Cl) and 25 ml aliquots (⅙ of total) on samples high in Cl (>2%). For mineral and other feeds contg >10% Cl, weigh 1 g and use 15 ml (¹⁄₁₀ of total).

If approx. % Cl in sample is not known, take 10 ml aliquot for trial titrn. To this add 10 ml HNO₃ and 10 ml Fe₂(SO₄)₃ indicator. Dil. to ca 50 ml. Add

0.5 ml KSCN soln and immediately add, with stirring, enough AgNO₃ soln to entirely eliminate any reddish color. From this titrn calc. vol. AgNO₃ soln necessary to ppt all Cl in aliquot to be used, adding excess equal to ca 10% total vol. necessary, altho somewhat greater excess will not affect results. Min. total of 10 ml should be used.

To sample aliquot in 250 ml beaker add 10 ml HNO₃ and 10 ml Fe₂(SO₄)₃ indicator (or 20 ml soln contg equal vols of these solns). Add, with stirring, calcd vol. AgNO₃ soln. Heat to boiling and cool to room temp., stirring enough to coagulate ppt. (Cooling may be hastened by immersion of beakers in cold H₂O.) Titr. excess AgNO₃ with KSCN. End point is indicated by first appearance of reddish tint that persists 15 sec. For accurate work use ref. soln contg all ingredients except KSCN. End point is first change in color.

Potentiometric Method (29)— Official Final Action
7.081   *Apparatus*

Potentiometer.—With Ag-AgCl reference electrode and Ag-indicating electrode (Fisher Scientific Co. Cat. No. 9–313–216 and 13–639–122, or equiv.).

7.082   *Standardization*

Weigh 125 mg dry NaCl into 400 ml beaker. Add 200 ml H₂O and 1 ml HNO₃.

Null potentiometer and titr. NaCl soln with 0.1N AgNO₃ soln. Plot ml AgNO₃ soln against mv or scale readings. Add titrant in small enough increments so that voltage end point is obvious. Use same end point for samples.

7.083   *Determination*

(a) *Samples containing less than 5% sodium chloride.*—Weigh 5.844 g sample into 400 ml beaker. Add ca 200 ml H₂O and 1 ml HNO₃. Swirl mixt. gently and let stand 10 min for complete soln of chlorides. Titr., while stirring, to same voltage end point as in **7.082.**

% NaCl = ml 0.1N AgNO₃/10.

(b) *Samples containing more than 5% sodium chloride.*—Weigh 5.844 g sample into 200 ml vol. flask. Add ca 190 ml H₂O and 1 ml HNO₃, dil. to vol. with H₂O, mix, and let stand 10 min. Transfer aliquot contg equiv. of ca 125 mg NaCl to 400 ml beaker, dil. to ca 200 ml, add 1 ml HNO₃, and titr. as in (a).

% NaCl = diln factor × ml 0.1N AgNO₃/10.

Cobalt (30)—Official Final Action
7.084   *Reagents*

(a) *Cobalt std soln.*—0.05 mg Co/ml. Do not dry; use as received. Dissolve 0.2385 g CoSO₄.7H₂O in H₂O and dil. to 1 L. This soln may be dild to suitable concn to prep. std curve.

(b) *Nitroso-R salt soln.*—Dissolve 1 g $C_{10}H_4OH$. $NO(SO_3Na)_2$ in H_2O and dil. to 500 ml.

(c) *Spekker acid.*—Mix 150 ml 85% H_3PO_4 and 150 ml H_2SO_4, and dil. to 1 L with H_2O.

(d) *Sodium acetate soln.*—Dissolve 500 g $NaOAc.3H_2O$ in H_2O and dil. to 1 L with H_2O.

7.085   *Preparation of Standard Curve*

To 1, 2, etc., up to 11 ml portions std Co soln in 100 ml vol. flasks add 2 ml Spekker acid, 10 ml nitroso-R salt soln, and 10 ml NaOAc soln. Prep. blank by using 2 ml Spekker acid and 10 ml NaOAc soln, but omitting nitroso-R salt soln. Bring blank and std solns to boil on hot plate. Add 5 ml HNO_3 and boil solns $\geq$1, but $\leq$2 min. Cool, and dil. solns to 100 ml.

7.086   *Determination*
(Caution: See **46.026** *and* **46.059.**)

Ash 2 g sample 2 hr at 600°, transfer to 200 ml vol. flask with 20 ml HCl and 50 ml H_2O, boil 5 min, cool, and dil. to vol. Let soln settle. Pipet suitable aliquot into small flask. For samples contg 0.01–0.2% Co use equiv. of 0.25 g sample. Use more or less according to Co concn expected. Max. quantity Co in sample should be 0.5 mg, since soln no longer appears to follow Beer's law above this concn.

Pass brisk current of H_2S thru soln 10 min. Filter directly into 100 ml vol. flask thru Whatman No. 40 paper. Wash with ca 50 ml *1% H_2SO_4 satd with H_2S.* Add 2 small glass beads and boil off H_2S. (Flasks must be given individual attention, as violent bumping may occur.) Shake flasks often. Add 5 ml HNO_3 and boil until nitrous fumes no longer appear. (Take care, as vol. of soln will be low and bumping and spattering may occur. At first indication of this, immediately remove from hot plate.) Small amt HNO_3 remaining will not affect result. Cool, add 2 drops phthln, and take to first faint pink with ca 30% NaOH soln. Immediately add 2 ml Spekker acid followed by 10 ml nitroso-R salt soln and 10 ml NaOAc soln. Bring to vigorous boil, carefully add 5 ml HNO_3, and boil $\geq$1 but $\leq$2 min. Cool and dil. to vol.

Compare color with std Co solns in colorimeter, using green or No. 54 filter, or in spectrophtr at 540 nm. Read color within 2 hr. Report % Co to third decimal place.

Copper (31)—Official Final Action

7.087   *Preparation of Standard Curve*

Dissolve 1.9645 g $CuSO_4.5H_2O$ in H_2O and dil. to 500 ml. (1 ml = 1 mg Cu.) Use from 1 to 10 ml of this soln to prep. set of stds in 100 ml Pyrex g-s vol. flasks. Add 4 ml HCl, dil. to 50 ml, add 5 ml *tetraethylenepentamine*, dil. to vol. with H_2O, stopper, and mix thoroly. Prep. blank, using all reagents except Cu. Filter blank and stds before reading color as in **7.088.**

7.088   *Determination*

Prep. sample soln as in **7.086**, using 8 g sample. Pipet 50 ml aliquot into 100 ml Pyrex g-s vol. flask, add 5 ml tetraethylenepentamine, dil. to vol. with H_2O, and mix thoroly. Filter and compare colors within 30 min in colorimeter (red or No. 66 filter) or read in spectrophtr at 620 nm. Report % Cu to third decimal place.

7.089   **Fluorine—Official Final Action**
See **25.029–25.035**, especially **25.033.**

Iodine in Mineral Mixed Feeds—
Official Final Action

7.090 ★ *Knapheide-Lamb Method (32)* ★
See **22.084–22.086**, 10th ed.

7.091   *Elmslie-Caldwell Method (33)*

(Not applicable to iodized mineral feeds contg little or no org. matter. *Caution: See* **46.047.**)

Place sample contg 3–4 mg I in 200–300 ml Ni dish. Add ca 5 g Na_2CO_3, 5 ml NaOH soln (1 + 1), and 10 ml alcohol, taking care that entire sample is moist. Dry at ca 100° to prevent spattering upon subsequent heating (30 min is usually enough).

Place dish and contents in furnace heated to 500° and keep at that temp. 15 min. (Ignition of sample at 500° appears to be necessary only to carbonize any sol. org. matter that would be oxidized by Br-H_2O if not so treated. Temp. >500° may be used if necessary.) Cool, add 25 ml H_2O, cover dish with watch glass, and boil gently 10 min. Filter thru 18 cm filter paper and wash with boiling H_2O, catching filtrate and washings in 600 ml beaker (soln should total ca 300 ml). Neutze to Me orange with 85% H_3PO_4 and add 1 ml excess.

Add excess Br-H_2O and boil soln gently until colorless, and then 5 min longer. Add few crystals *salicylic acid* and cool soln to ca 20°. Add 1 ml 85% H_3PO_4 and ca 0.5 g KI, and titr. I with 0.005N $Na_2S_2O_3$, adding starch soln when liberated I color is nearly gone.

Acid-Soluble Manganese (34)—
Official Final Action

7.092   *Reagent*

Potassium permanganate std soln.—500 ppm Mn. Prep. and stdze as in **45.026–45.027**, except use 1.4383 g $KMnO_4$ and 0.12 g Na oxalate. Transfer aliquot contg 20 mg Mn to beaker. Add 100 ml H_2O, 15 ml H_3PO_4, and 0.3 g KIO_4, and heat to bp. Cool, and dil. to 1 L. Protect from light. Dil. this soln contg 20 ppm Mn with H_2O (previously boiled with 0.3 g KIO_4/L) to make convenient working stds in range of concns to be compared.

7.093   *Determination*
(Caution: See **46.026** *and* **46.030.**)

Ash weighed sample, 5–15 g, at dull red heat (ca 600°) in porcelain dish. Cool, and add 5 ml H_2SO_4

and 5 ml HNO$_3$ to ash in dish or to ash transferred to beaker with 20–30 ml H$_2$O. Evap. to white fumes. If C is not completely destroyed, add further portions HNO$_3$, boiling after each addn. Cool slightly, transfer to 50 or 100 ml vol. flask, and add vol. dil. H$_3$PO$_4$ soln (8 + 92) equal to ½ vol. of flask (25 or 50 ml). Cool, dil. to vol., mix, and filter or let stand until clear.

If 50 ml flask was used, pipet 25 ml clear soln into beaker or 50 or 100 ml vol. flask and add 15 ml H$_2$O. If 100 ml flask was used, pipet 50 ml into beaker or 100 ml flask and add 30 ml H$_2$O. Heat nearly to bp, and with stirring or swirling add 0.3 g KIO$_4$ for each 15 mg Mn present. Keep 30–60 min at 90–100°, or until color development is complete. Cool, dil. to measured vol. of 50 or 100 ml, and mix. Compare with std KMnO$_4$ soln in colorimeter or in spectrophtr at 530 nm. Calc. ppm Mn.

Phosphorus

7.094 Volumetric Method (27)—
Official Final Action

Using aliquot of soln, 7.077(a), proceed as in 2.031(a). Calc. as % P.

Photometric Method (35)—
Official Final Action

7.095   *Apparatus*

Spectrophotometer.—Capable of isolating 400 nm band and accepting ≤15 mm diam. cells.

7.096   *Reagents*

(a) *Molybdovanadate reagent.*—Prep. as in 2.019 (a), except add only 250 ml 70% HClO$_4$ to NH$_4$VO$_3$ soln.

(b) *Phosphorus std solns.*—(1) *Stock soln.*—2 mg P/ml. Dissolve 8.788 g KH$_2$PO$_4$ in H$_2$O and dil. to 1 L. (2) *Working soln.*—0.1 mg P/ml. Dil. 50 ml stock soln to 1 L.

7.097   *Preparation of Standard Curve*

Transfer aliquots of working std soln contg 0.5, 0.8, 1.0, and 1.5 mg P to 100 ml vol. flasks. Treat as in **7.098,** beginning "Add 20 ml molybdovanadate reagent ...." Prep. std curve by plotting mg P against %T on semilog paper.

7.098   *Determination*

Ash 2 g sample, in 150 ml beaker, 4 hr at 600°. Cool, add 40 ml HCl (1 + 3) and several drops HNO$_3$, and bring to boil. Cool, transfer to 200 ml vol. flask, and dil. to vol. with H$_2$O. Filter, and place aliquot contg 0.5–1.5 mg P in 100 ml vol. flask. Add 20 ml molybdovanadate reagent, dil. to vol. with H$_2$O, and mix well. Let stand 10 min; then read %T at 400 nm against 0.5 mg std set at 100% T. (Use ≤15 mm diam. cells.) Det. mg P from std curve.

% P = mg P in aliquot/(g sample in aliquot × 10).

Basic Feed Microscopy (36)—
Official Final Action

7.099   *Apparatus*

(a) *Magnifier-fluorescent illuminator with desk base, 3×, or reading glass.*

(b) *Microscopes and illuminator.*—See **40.002** (1) and (n). Following are preferred:

(1) *Widefield stereoscopic microscope.*—With arm rests, flat stage (remove spring holders), optional substage illumination, inclined eyepiece, and lenses to magnify ca 7–30×, 15× optimum.

(2) *Compound microscope.*—With mech. stage, substage condenser, inclined binocular eyepiece, 3 position rotating nosepiece, lenses to magnify ca 36–400×, 120× optimum.

(3) *Microscope illuminator.*—With iris diaphragm; movable stand holder with rod to permit adjusting light source as to ht and angle for substage or direct over-stage lighting; able to hold 2 blue glass filters or 1 blue and 1 ground glass; 60–100 watt bulb.

(c) *Sieves.*—Nest of 5″ No. 10, 20, 40, 60, 80, and bottom pan.

(d) *Stages.*—Dark Co glass plates 4 × 4″ (Fisher Scientific Co. Cat. No. 13-735); or blue paper and microscope slides.

(e) *Spot plates.*—Black and white.

(f) *Forceps.*—Fine pointed, curved. If necessary, bend and grind on emery wheel for good contact of points.

(g) *Dropping bottles.*—Amber, 30 ml, as reagent dispensers.

(h) *Micro-spatula; micro-stirring rods made by drawing out glass rods; spoon.*

7.100   *Reagents*

(a) *Chloroform.*—Tech. Recover by filtration and distn.

(b) *Acetone.*—Tech.

(c) *Acetone, dilute.*—Dil. 75 ml acetone with 25 ml H$_2$O.

(d) *Dilute hydrochloric acid.*—Dil. 1 vol. HCl with 1 vol. H$_2$O.

(e) *Dilute sulfuric acid.*—Dil. 1 vol. H$_2$SO$_4$ with 1 vol. H$_2$O.

(f) *Iodine soln.*—Dissolve 0.75 g KI and 0.1 g I in 30 ml H$_2$O and add 0.5 ml HCl. Store in amber dropping bottle.

(g) *Millon reagent.*—Dissolve, by gently warming, 1 part by wt Hg in 2 parts by wt HNO$_3$. Dil. with 2 vols H$_2$O. Let mixt. stand overnight and decant supernatant. Soln contains Hg(NO$_3$)$_2$, HgNO$_3$, HNO$_3$, and some HNO$_2$. Store in g-s bottle. (*Caution: See* **46.079.**)

(h) *Molybdate soln.*—Add 100 ml 10% NH$_4$NO$_3$ soln to 400 ml molybdate soln, **2.029(a).** Use only clear supernatant to fill 30 ml amber dropping bottle. Discard and refill when crystn occurs.

(i) *Mountant I.*—Dissolve 10 g chloral hydrate in 10 ml H$_2$O and add 10 ml glycerine. Store in amber dropping bottle.

(j) *Mountant II.*—Dissolve 160 g chloral hydrate in 100 ml H_2O and add 10 ml HCl.

(k) *Silver nitrate soln.*—10%. Dissolve 10 g $AgNO_3$ in 100 ml H_2O.

7.101   Standards

(a) *Feed ingredients.*—Collect ingredients used in grain and stock feeds known to conform to definitions of Association of American Feed Control Officials as stds. Store in 4 oz bottles. To control insects, add ca 1 ml CS_2, and stopper. Become thoroly familiar with structural appearance of stds before and after treatment with org. solvs.

(b) *Weed seeds.*—Collect common weed seeds occurring in grains. Most may be found in foreign material obtained after sieving com. whole grains with U.S. Grain Testing Sieve having $\frac{5}{64}''$ triangular holes. Identify from illustration in "Identification of Crop and Weed Seeds" (USDA Handbook 219 (1963), Government Printing Office, Washington, DC 20402). Store in numbered vials. Become familiar with those weed seeds designated as prohibited and restricted noxious under state laws of individual concern. (*See* "State Noxious-Weed Seed Requirements Recognized in the Administration of the Federal Seed Act" (USDA, Consumer and Marketing Service, Grain Div., Beltsville, MD 20705).)

Identification of Vegetable Tissues
7.102   Principles

Feeds are fractionated according to particle size and cleaned where necessary for clear observation; conglomerates are disintegrated into constituents, and fractions arranged on stage suitable for microscopic examination at lowest magnification that permits identification of components when compared to std feed ingredients.

7.103   General Methods

(a) *Scratch feeds.*—Spread representative portion of sample on white paper and examine under magnifier-fluorescent illuminator at $3\times$ or with reading glass. Identify grains and weed seeds; note other foreign material, heat- and insect-damaged particles, live insects, and rodent excreta; examine for smut, ergot, and mold ("Grain Inspection Manual," USDA).

(b) *Mashes comparatively free from adhering fine particles.*—(1) *Low power microscopy.*—Arrange in nest form 3 sieves that will adequately fractionate feed according to particle size. Generally, for cattle feeds use No. 10, 20 and 40; for poultry feeds, No. 20, 40, and 60. Include bottom pan. Add ca 10 g unground feed (plastic tablespoon makes convenient scoop) to nest, and sieve thoroly. With spatula, spread portion from each sieve on $4 \times 4''$ Co glass stage and place under stereoscopic microscope. (Blue paper may also be used as stage.) Arrange illuminator

above and near stage so light strikes sample at angle of ca 45° for shadow contrast. Adjust magnification (ca $15\times$ optimum), illumination, and light filters to individual preference for clear observation. Blue light or northern daylight is preferred. Examine each fraction on stage sep. and systematically. Observe feed particles, continually probing, turning, and testing resistance to pressure with forceps. Note particle size, shape, color, resistance to pressure, texture, odor, and major structural features. Compare with stds. If desired, transfer individual particles with forceps to second glass plate for direct comparison with corresponding tissues from stds. Likewise transfer conglomerates and break up by gentle pressure with flat end of forceps. Make list of observed ingredients. Neglect trace grains which may be normal inpurities in major grains. (Consult "Official Grain Standards of the United States," USDA, for amts of "other grains" permissible as impurities in whole grains.)

(2) *High power microscopy.*—Lower illuminator and select filters so adequate blue light is reflected thru substage condenser of high power microscope. With micro-spatula, transfer little of fine sievings from bottom sieve and pan to slide, add 2 drops mountant I, stir, and disperse with micro-stirring rod. Examine microscopically ($120\times$ optimum). Compare histologically with stds. Remove slide, add 1 drop I soln, stir, and re-examine. Starch cells are stained pale blue to black; yeasts and other protein cells, pale yellow to brown. If further tissue clarification is desired, boil little of same fine sievings 1 min with ca 5 ml mountant II. Cool, transfer drop or 2 of bottom settlings to slide, cover, and examine microscopically.

(c) *Oily feeds or those containing large particles obscured by adhering fine particles.*—(Most poultry feeds and unknowns are best examined by this technic.) Place ca 10 g unground feed in 100 ml tall-form beaker and nearly fill with $CHCl_3$ (hood). Stir briefly and let settle ca 1 min. With spoon, transfer floating (org.) material to 3.5″ cover glass, drain, and dry on steam bath. Sieve, and proceed as in (b). If desired, filter, dry, suspend fine particles in $CHCl_3$, and examine microscopically (rarely necessary).

(d) *Feeds in which molasses has caused lumpiness and otherwise obscured vision.*—Place ca 10 g unground feed in 100 ml tall-form beaker. Add 75 ml 75% acetone, stir few min to dissolve molasses, and let settle. Carefully decant and repeat extn. Wash residue twice with acetone by decantation, dry on steam bath, sieve, and proceed as in (b).

(e) *Pellets or crumbles.*—Gently grind few pellets at time in mortar with pestle with enough pressure to sep. pellet into its constituents, but not to break up constituents themselves. Sieve first grind thru No. 20 sieve and return particles remaining on sieve to mortar for further grinding. Depending on nature of pellet, proceed with ground material as in (b), (c), or (d).

Identification of Animal Tissues and Major Mineral Constituents

7.104 Principles

Feeds contg animal tissues and minerals when suspended in CHCl₃ readily sep. into 2 fractions: (1) Org. fraction which floats, consisting of muscle fibers, connective tissue, dried ground organs, feather remains, hoof and horn particles, etc. from either animal or marine products, plus all vegetable tissues. (2) Mineral fraction which sinks, consisting of bones, fish scales, teeth, and minerals.

7.105 Preparation of Sample

Perform CHCl₃ flotation sepn as in 7.103(c). Collect floating material and dry on steam bath. Decant CHCl₃, collect mineral fraction, and dry on steam bath.

7.106 Identification of Animal Tissue

Examine dried floating material as in 7.103(b).

7.107 Identification of Major Mineral Constituents

Place dried mineral fraction on nest of No. 40, 60, and 80 sieves and bottom pan. Sieve and place the 4 fractions in sep. groups on same Co glass plate or blue paper stage. Examine under stereoscopic microscope at ca 15×. Animal and fish bones, fish scales, and mollusc shells are generally recognizable. Salt usually occurs in cubes which may be dyed. Calcite form of limestone occurs as rhombohedrons.

7.108 Confirmatory Tests

With forceps, place unknown particle on glass plate and break up by applying gentle pressure with flat surface. Working under stereoscopic microscope, sep. particles ca 1″ and place beside each a fractional drop of reagent solns listed by touching end of dropper to plate. Push particle into liq. with micro stirring rod and observe what occurs at interface. Follow order given until positive identification is obtained. If preferred, perform tests in black spot plate.

(a) *Silver nitrate soln.*—(1) Crystal immediately turns chalk white and slowly expands: chloride, probably salt. (2) Crystal turns yellow and yellow needles begin to grow: mono- or dibasic phosphate, generally dicalcium phosphate. (3) Sparingly sol. white needles form (Ag₂SO₄): sulfate, Mn-MgSO₄. (4) Particles slowly darken: bone.

(b) *Dilute hydrochloric acid.*—(1) Vigorous effervescence: CaCO₃. (2) Mild effervescence or none: make following tests.

(c) *Molybdate soln.*—Formation of minute yellow crystals at some distance from particle: tricalcium phosphate, either bone or rock phosphate. (All phosphates react, but mono- and dibasic phosphates have been identified with AgNO₃.)

(d) *Millon reagent.*—(1) Disintegrated particles mostly float, turn pink to red (protein), and fade in

ca 5 min: bone phosphate. (2) Particles appear to swell and disintegrate but remain on bottom: defluorinated rock phosphate. (3) Particles merely disintegrate slowly: rock phosphate.

(e) *Dilute sulfuric acid.*—Long, thin white needles slowly form on addn of drop of H₂SO₄ (1 + 1) to HCl (1 + 1) soln of particle: confirms Ca.

PRESERVATIVES

Ethoxyquin (1,2-Dihydro-6-ethoxy-2,2,4-trimethylquinoline) (37)— Official Final Action

7.109 Reagents and Apparatus

(a) *Quinine sulfate reference soln.*—1 μg/ml 0.1N H₂SO₄. Dissolve 0.100 g quinine sulfate NF XII in 1 L 0.1N H₂SO₄. Dil. 10 ml aliquot of this soln to 1 L with 0.1N H₂SO₄. Use to calibrate photofluorometer.

(b) *Ethoxyquin std solns.*—Add 100.0 mg liq. ethoxyquin to 100 ml vol. flask and dil. to vol. with pet ether (*Soln A*). Dil. 5 ml *Soln A* to 100 ml with pet ether (*Soln B*, 50 μg/ml). Dil. 5 ml *Soln B* to 100 ml with pet ether (*Soln C*, 2.5 μg/ml). Dil. 10 ml *Soln C* to 20 ml with pet ether (1.25 μg/ml) and 5 ml to 25 ml (0.50 μg/ml).

(c) *Photofluorometer.*—Equipped with primary filter passing 365 nm Hg line (Corning Glass Works No. 5874, or equiv.) and secondary filter passing 420–500 nm (Corning Glass Works 3389 + 4308, or equiv.).

7.110 Preparation of Standard Curve

Adjust photofluorometer to read 0 with pet ether and 100 with quinine sulfate ref. soln. Obtain fluorescence readings for ethoxyquin std solns contg 0–2.5 μg/ml. Plot readings against μg ethoxyquin/ml on linear paper.

7.111 Determination

Place 10±0.1 g finely ground sample in 100 ml beaker and slurry with 50 ml MeOH. Stir and let stand 10 min. Decant thru plug of glass wool into 250 ml vol. flask. Reslurry residue with two 50 ml portions MeOH, decant, and filter, combining all filtrates. Dil. to vol. with MeOH. Transfer 25 ml aliquot to 250 ml separator, add 100 ml H₂O, and mix well. Add 50 ml pet ether, stopper, and shake moderately 1 min. Let stand few min to sep. (If emulsion forms, add ca 100 mg NaCl crystals. After emulsion breaks, drain aq. lower layer into 250 ml beaker.) Transfer pet ether layer to second 250 ml separator, return aq. layer to first separator, and re-ext with two 25 ml portions pet ether.

Add 50 ml H₂O to combined pet ether exts in separator, stopper, and shake moderately. Let sep., drain lower aq. layer, and discard. Transfer pet ether layer to 100 ml vol. flask, and dil. to vol. with pet ether. Adjust photofluorometer as above and det.

fluorescence readings. Obtain μg ethoxyquin/ml from std curve. Ppm ethoxyquin = 100 × μg/ml.

If untreated feed is available, prep. std curve from series of samples contg 0 to 250 μg ethoxyquin/10 g and carried thru detn.

7.112 Drugs in Feeds—*See* Chapter 38

7.113 Molasses and Molasses Products—
***See* Chapter 31**

7.114 Cyanogenetic Glucosides—
***See* 26.062.**

7.115 Hydrocyanic Acid Formed by Hydrolysis
of Glucosides in Beans—
***See* 26.063—26.064**

SELECTED REFERENCES

(1) JAOAC 33, 424(1950); 41, 223(1958); 48, 658 (1965).
(2) JAOAC 17, 68(1934).
(3) JAOAC 8, 295(1925); 9, 30(1926).
(4) USDA Bur. Chem. Bull. 122, p. 219; 132, p. 150.
(5) JAOAC 13, 173(1930); 14, 152(1931); 17, 178 (1934); 18, 80(1935).
(6) JAOAC 36, 213(1953); 37, 98, 253(1954).
(7) JAOAC 25, 857(1942); 26, 220(1943).
(8) JAOAC 18, 81, 369(1935).
(9) JAOAC 37, 241(1954); 38, 56(1955).
(10) JAOAC 51, 766(1968).
(11) JAOAC 24, 867(1941); 25, 874(1942); 27, 494 (1944).
(12) JAOAC 50, 56(1967).
(13) JAOAC 51, 763(1968).
(14) J. Agr. Food Chem. 3, 159(1955); JAOAC 40, 606(1957); 41, 233(1958); 42, 231(1959); 43, 320(1960).
(15) JAOAC 37, 98, 250(1954); 38, 225(1955).
(16) JAOAC 15, 524(1932); 17, 190(1934); 18, 351(1935); 28, 80(1945).
(17) JAOAC 31, 98, 606(1948).
(18) JAOAC 42, 222(1959); 43, 335(1960); 44, 567 (1961); 45, 578(1962).
(19) USDA Bur. Chem. Circ. 71; JAOAC 41, 276 (1958); 42, 39(1959).
(20) J. Agr. Research 23, 995(1923); JAOAC 9, 31 (1926).
(21) JAOAC 21, 595(1938); 23, 656(1940).
(22) J. Landw. 48, 357(1900); 49, 7(1901).
(23) USDA Bur. Chem. Bull. 137, p. 152; JAOAC 30, 594(1947).
(24) JAOAC 14, 142(1931); 15, 77(1932); 23, 86 (1940); 28, 80(1945).
(25) JAOAC 51, 776(1968).
(26) JAOAC 10, 177(1927); 19, 93, 574(1936); 28, 80(1945).
(27) Ind. Eng. Chem., Anal. Ed. 7, 116, 167(1935); JAOAC 30, 606(1947); 31, 98(1948); 32, 650 (1949); 33, 162(1950); 34, 563(1951).
(28) JAOAC 26, 87(1943); 28, 80(1945).
(29) JAOAC 52, 607(1969).
(30) JAOAC 35, 79, 559(1952).
(31) Anal. Chem. 19, 325(1947); JAOAC 37, 246 (1954); 38, 222(1955).
(32) JAOAC 17, 67, 173(1934); 18, 335(1935); 38, 96(1955).
(33) JAOAC 18, 338(1935); 21, 596(1938); 23, 688 (1940); 33, 83(1950).
(34) J. Am. Chem. Soc. 39, 2366(1917); G. Frederick Smith Chemical Co. Pubs., 1, 5th ed. (1950); JAOAC 22, 78, 673(1939); 24, 865(1941); 25, 892(1942).
(35) JAOAC 48, 654(1965).
(36) JAOAC 47, 504(1964).
(37) JAOAC 44, 560(1961); 46, 306(1963); 47, 512 (1964).

8. Baking Powders and Baking Chemicals

8.001 Preparation of Sample—
Official Final Action

Remove entire sample from package, pass thru No. 20 sieve, and mix thoroly.

Total Carbon Dioxide (1)—Official Final Action
(Applicable to baking powders contg added CaCO₃)

8.002 *Reagent*

Displacement soln.—Dissolve 100 g NaCl or $Na_2SO_4.10H_2O$ in 350 ml H_2O. Add ca 1 g $NaHCO_3$ and 2 ml Me orange, **5.001**(e), and then enough H_2SO_4 (1 + 5) or HCl (1 + 2) to make just acid (decided pink). Stir until all CO_2 is removed. This soln is used in gas-measuring tube and leveling bulb and seldom needs replacement.

8.003 *Apparatus*

Chittick apparatus.—Fig. 8:1. Connect decomposition flask, A, by glass T-tube, B, provided with stopcock, C, to graduated gas-measuring tube, D, connected in turn with leveling bulb, E. For A always use 250 ml wide-mouth extn flask of Pyrex or other resistant glass fitted with 2-hole rubber stopper, thru one hole of which passes extended tip of 25 ml buret, F, and thru other, glass tube of same diam. as connecting T-tube. Use buret graduated in ml at 20°, numbered at 5 ml intervals, and fitted with extralong tip bent to pass thru rubber stopper. Connect glass tube leading from decomposition flask to T-tube with rubber tubing to permit rotation of flask. Use gas-measuring tube graduated in ml at 20° with zero mark at point 25 ml below top marking to allow for graduating upward from 0 to 25 ml and downward from 0 to 200 ml. Connect gas-measuring tube to ca 300 ml leveling bulb with long rubber tube.

(Available from Sargent-Welch Scientific Co.)

8.004 *Determination* (2)

Weigh 1.7 g prepd sample, **8.001**, into flask A, and connect flask with app., Fig. 8:1. Open stopcock C, and using leveling bulb E, bring displacement soln to 10 ml graduation above zero mark. (This 10 ml is practically equal in vol. to that of acid to be used in decomposition.) Let app. stand 1–2 min for temp. and pressure within app. to come to room conditions.

Close stopcock, lower leveling bulb somewhat to reduce pressure within app., and slowly add 10 ml H_2SO_4 (1 + 5) or HCl (1 + 2) to decomposition flask from buret F. To prevent escape of liberated

CO_2 thru acid buret into air, at all times during decomposition keep displacement soln at level lower in leveling bulb than that in gas-measuring tube. Rotate and then vigorously agitate decomposition flask to mix contents intimately. Let stand 5 min to secure equilibrium. Equalize pressure in measuring tube, using leveling bulb, and read vol. of gas in tube. Observe temp. of air surrounding app. and also barometric pressure, and multiply ml gas evolved by factor given in table **47.007** for this temp. and pressure. Corrected reading/10 = % CO_2 by wt.

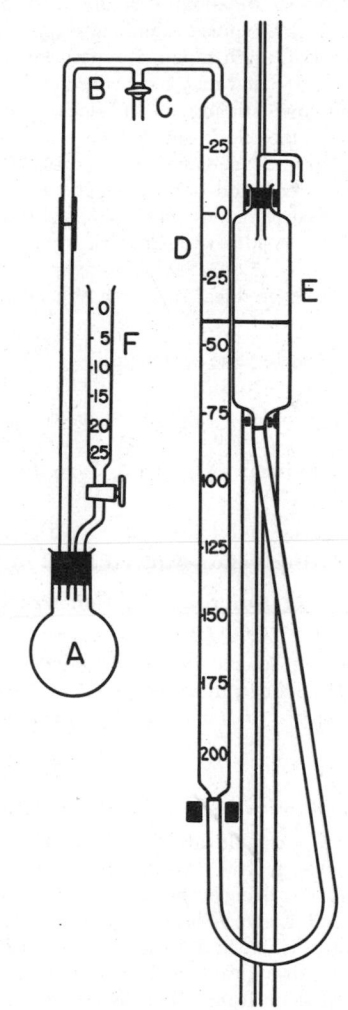

FIG. 8:1—Chittick apparatus for gasometric determination of carbon dioxide

8.005   Residual Carbon Dioxide (3)— Official Final Action

(a) *After drying on water bath.*—Place 1.7 g baking powder in clean, dry, 250 ml wide-mouth Soxhlet extn flask, A, **8.003**. Add 20 ml H_2O. Put flask *on cover* of H_2O bath (single or multiple) in which boiling H_2O is kept at constant level of 2″ below top of bath. (H_2O in bath must boil vigorously all thru detn. Opening in cover of bath must be 3″ diam. to prevent flask from touching H_2O.) Evap. contents of flask until no moisture is visible in residue or inside surface of flask. (Sample should be completely dry in 1.5–2 hr.) Leave flask on H_2O bath 2 hr more. Add 10 ml H_2O, and let stand until flask is at room temp. (ca 1 hr).

Det. CO_2 with Chittick app. as in **8.004**, using correction factors in **47.007**. Shake flask vigorously until further shaking produces no increase in reading.

(b) *After drying in oven.*—Place 1.7 g sample in clean, dry 250 ml wide-mouth Soxhlet extn flask, A, **8.003**. Tap flask to spread sample evenly on bottom. Add 10 ml H_2O with pipet. Stir with glass rod to break up powder that may have caked on bottom of flask. Wash down stirring rod and sides of flask with 10 ml H_2O. Place flask on shelf near center of air oven set at $100\pm2°$, and evap. to dryness. After 5 hr, remove from oven, add 10 ml H_2O, and cool to same temp. as air surrounding Chittick app., **8.003**. Det. CO_2 present in residue with Chittick app., using correction factors in **47.007**. Shake flask vigorously until further shaking produces no increase in reading.

8.006   Available Carbon Dioxide— Official Final Action

(Applicable to baking powders contg added $CaCO_3$)

Subtract residual CO_2, **8.005**, from total CO_2, **8.004**.

Neutralizing Value—Official Final Action

8.007   *Of Acid-Reacting Materials Other Than Phosphates*

Dissolve 1 g sample in hot H_2O and titr. with $0.2N$ NaOH, using phthln. Express result as parts $NaHCO_3$ equiv. to 100 parts of the acid-reacting material.

8.008   *Of Monocalcium Phosphate (4)*

Weigh 0.84 g sample into 375 ml casserole. Add 24 ml cold H_2O and, after stirring for moment, add 90.0 ml $0.1N$ NaOH. Bring suspension to boil in exactly 2 min, and boil 1 min. While soln is still boiling hot, add 1 drop phthln, and back-titr. with $0.2N$ HCl until all pink disappears. Boil soln 1 min, and again add $0.2N$ HCl until pink just disappears. 90 − (ml $0.2N$ HCl × 2) = neutzg value, parts $NaHCO_3$ equiv. to 100 parts of the phosphate.

8.009   *Of Anhydrous Monocalcium Phosphate (4)*

Use 100 ml $0.1N$ NaOH and stir intermittently 5 min before bringing to boil. Proceed as in **8.008**.

8.010   *Of Sodium Acid Pyrophosphate (4)*

Weigh 0.84 g sample and 20 g NaCl into 375 ml casserole, and slowly add 25 ml H_2O while stirring. Stir and crush with flat-end rod 3–5 min. Add 90.0 ml $0.1N$ NaOH and 1 drop phthln, and titr. with $0.2N$ HCl until pink disappears. If "starch filled" or 50% neutzg strength pyrophosphate is being titrd, use 70.0 ml $0.1N$ NaOH. Vol. (ml) $0.1N$ NaOH − (ml $0.2N$ HCl × 2) = neutzg value, parts $NaHCO_3$ equiv. to 100 parts Na acid pyrophosphate.

8.011   Tartaric Acid, Free or Combined (Qualitative Test) (5)— Official First Action

(Applicable in presence of phosphates)

Shake ca 5 g sample repeatedly with ca 250 ml cold H_2O in flask, and let insol. portion settle. Decant soln thru filter, and evap. filtrate to dryness. Powder residue, add few drops 1% resorcinol soln, **31.147**, and ca 3 ml H_2SO_4, and heat slowly. Tartaric acid is indicated by rose-red, discharged on diln with H_2O.

Cream of Tartar and Free Tartaric Acid in Tartrate Powders (6)—Official Final Action

Total, Combined, and Free Tartaric Acid

8.012   *Determination*

To 2.5 g sample in 250 ml vol. flask add 100 ml H_2O at ca 50°, and hold at room temp. ca 30 min, shaking occasionally. Cool, dil. to vol. with H_2O, shake vigorously, and filter thru large fluted paper. Pipet 2 portions of 100 ml each of *clear* filtrate into 250 ml beakers, and evap. to ca 20 ml. To one portion add 3.5 ml ca $1N$ KOH. Mix well, and add 2 ml HOAc. Again mix well and add 100 ml alcohol, stirring constantly. Treat other portion similarly, but use $1N$ NaOH instead of KOH. Then treat each mixt. sep. as follows: Cool to ca 15°, stir vigorously ca 1 min, and leave in refrigerator overnight. Collect ppt in gooch on thin, tightly tamped pad of asbestos. Rinse beaker with ca 75 ml ice-cold 80% alcohol, carefully washing down sides of beaker. Finally wash sides of crucible with 25 ml alcohol and suck dry. Transfer contents of crucible to original beaker with ca 100 ml hot H_2O, and titr. with $0.1N$ alkali, using phthln. Designate titer of portion treated with KOH as "A" and that treated with NaOH as "B."

8.013   *Calculations*

% total tartaric acid = 1.5(A + 0.6).
% cream of tartar = 1.88(B + 0.6).
% free tartaric acid = 1.5(A − B).

In above formulas "0.6" represents solubility of cream of tartar in reaction mixt. in terms of $0.1N$ alkali.

Free Tartaric Acid (Direct Determination)

8.014 *Reagent*

Saturated alcohol.—To ca 50 g finely powd pure cream of tartar in erlenmeyer add ca 100 ml alcohol and 100 ml H_2O, shake vigorously several min, and let stand 15 min, shaking occasionally. Filter on paper in buchner; wash with ca 200 ml alcohol (1 + 1), then with alcohol, and finally with ether. Dry at temp. of boiling H_2O. To 500 ml *absolute* alcohol add ca 5 g of the purified cream of tartar and let stand 2 hr, shaking occasionally. Properly purified cream of tartar requires ≤ 0.15 ml $0.1N$ alkali to neutze 100 ml of mixt. of 50 ml $CHCl_3$ and 150 ml of the satd alcohol.

8.015 *Determination*

Weigh 1.25 g sample into *absolutely dry* 200 ml vol. flask, add 50 ml $CHCl_3$, and let stand ca 5 min, shaking occasionally. (Discard detn if upon addn of $CHCl_3$, powder sticks to bottom of flask, indicating moisture.) Add 100 ml satd alcohol, shake ca 5 min, and let stand 30 min, shaking at frequent intervals. (It is not necessary to filter the alcohol reagent.) Dil. to vol. with the satd alcohol, shake few min, and filter thru large fluted paper. Titr. 100 ml clear filtrate with $0.1N$ alkali, using phthln. Vol. (ml) alkali used $\times 1.2 = \%$ free tartaric acid.

8.016 *Free Tartaric Acid (Qualitative Test)*

Ext 5 g sample with absolute alcohol and evap. alcohol from ext. Dissolve residue in NH_4OH (1 + 10), transfer to test tube, add good-size crystal of $AgNO_3$, and heat gently. Tartaric acid is indicated by formation of Ag mirror. (If desired, alc. ext may be tested as in **8.011**.)

Starch—Official Final Action

8.017 *Direct Acid Hydrolysis Method*

(For baking powders and baking chemicals free from Ca)

Stir 5 g sample 1 hr in 250 ml beaker with 50 ml cold H_2O. Transfer to filter and wash with 250 ml cold H_2O. Heat insol. residue 2.5 hr with 200 ml H_2O and 20 ml HCl (sp gr 1.125) in flask provided with reflux condenser. Cool, and nearly neutze with NaOH. Transfer to 250 ml vol. flask, dil. to vol., filter, and det. glucose in aliquot of filtrate as in **31.039**. Wt glucose obtained $\times 0.90 =$ wt starch (J. Am. Chem. Soc. **26**, 266(1904)).

8.018 *Indirect Method (7)*

(For baking powders and baking chemicals contg Ca)

Mix 5 g sample with 200 ml HCl (1 + 11) in 500 ml vol. flask and let mixt. stand 1 hr, shaking frequently. Filter on 11 cm hardened paper, taking care to obtain clear filtrate. Rinse flask once without at-tempting to remove all starch, and wash paper twice with cold H_2O. Carefully wash starch from paper back into flask with 200 ml H_2O. Add 20 ml HCl (sp gr 1.125) and proceed as in **8.017**. (Treatment with HCl, without dissolving starch, effectively removes Ca, which otherwise would be pptd as tartrate by alk. Cu soln.)

Aluminum

Qualitative Test (8)—Official Final Action

(In presence of phosphates)

8.019 *Reagents*

(a) *Ammonium acetate soln.*—50%. Dissolve 50 g NH_4OAc in 50 ml H_2O.

(b) *Aurintricarboxylic acid soln.*—0.1%. Dissolve 0.1 g aurintricarboxylic acid in H_2O and dil. to 100 ml.

8.020 *Detection*

Place 1 g sample in 250 ml beaker, add 5 ml ca $1N$ HCl and 20 ml H_2O, and heat until starch hydrolyzes. Add 100 ml cold H_2O, 5 ml *10% $NaNH_4HPO_4$.$4H_2O$ soln*, and 3 drops Me orange. Add NH_4OH dropwise until ppt forms or color changes; then add $1N$ HCl dropwise until ppt dissolves or color changes plus 2 or 3 drops excess. Add 5 ml aurintricarboxylic acid soln and let stand 1 min. Add 50% NH_4OAc soln dropwise until ppt forms or color changes and then 1 ml excess. Let stand 5 min, stirring occasionally, and filter. Bright red ppt on filter paper indicates presence of Al.

8.021 **Insoluble Ash and Preparation of Solution (9)—Official Final Action**

Char 5 g sample in Pt dish at heat below redness (ca 500°). Boil carbonaceous mass with HCl (1 + 2.5), filter into 500 ml vol. flask, and wash with hot H_2O. Return residue, together with paper, to Pt dish, and burn to white ash. Boil again with the dil. HCl, filter, wash, combine filtrates, and dil. to 500 ml. Incinerate residue after last filtration and weigh ash insol. in acid.

8.022 **Iron and Aluminum (9)— Official Final Action**

Draw 100 ml aliquot prepd soln. **8.021**, and sep. SiO_2 if necessary. Mix soln with excess *10% Na_2HPO_4 .$12H_2O$ soln*. Add NH_4OH until permanent ppt is obtained, then HCl dropwise until ppt dissolves. Bring soln to boil and boil 2–3 min; mix with considerable excess 50% NH_4OAc soln, **8.019**(a), and 4 ml HOAc (4 + 1). As soon as ppt of $AlPO_4$, mixed with $FePO_4$, settles, collect on filter, wash with hot H_2O, ignite, and weigh. Fuse mixed phosphates with 10 parts Na_2CO_3, dissolve in H_2SO_4 (1 + 6), reduce with Zn, and det. Fe by titrn with std $KMnO_4$ soln (1 ml = 1 mg Fe). Det. P_2O_5

in aliquot from **8.021** as in **8.027** or **2.031**. Wt mixed phosphates − wt $(Fe_2O_3 + P_2O_5)$ = wt Al_2O_3.

8.023   Calcium (9)—Official Final Action

Heat combined filtrate and washings obtained in **8.022** to 50°, and add excess satd NH_4 oxalate soln. Let stand in warm place until ppt settles, filter, wash ppt with hot H_2O, dry, and ignite over Bunsen burner and finally over blast lamp at ≥950°. Cool in desiccator and weigh as CaO.

8.024   Potassium and Sodium (9)— Official Final Action

Evap. aliquot prepd soln, **8.021**, nearly to dryness to remove excess HCl, dil., and heat to boiling. While soln is still boiling add 10% $BaCl_2 . 2H_2O$ soln as long as ppt forms, and then enough satd $Ba(OH)_2$ soln to make liq. strongly alk. After ppt settles, filter, and wash with hot H_2O; heat filtrate to boiling, add enough $(NH_4)_2CO_3$ *soln* (1 part $(NH_4)_2CO_3$ in 5 parts NH_4OH soln $(1 + 12)$) to ppt all the Ba, filter, and wash with hot H_2O. Evap. filtrate to dryness and ignite residue below redness to remove NH_4 salts. Add little H_2O and few drops $(NH_4)_2CO_3$ soln to residue. Filter into weighed Pt dish, evap., ignite below redness, and weigh mixed K and Na chlorides.

Digest residue with hot H_2O, filter thru small filter, and dil. filtrate, if necessary, to provide at least 20 ml liq. for each 100 mg K_2O. Acidify with few drops HCl and add excess Pt soln, **2.076(b)**. Evap. on H_2O bath to thick paste; treat residue repeatedly with 80% alcohol, decanting thru weighed gooch or other filter; transfer ppt to filter, and wash thoroly with 80% alcohol. Dry 30 min at 100° and weigh. Calc. K found to its equiv. of KCl and subtract result from wt mixed chlorides to obtain wt NaCl.

Phosphorus—Official Final Action

8.025   *Reagents*

(a) *Ammonium nitrate soln.*—Dissolve 100 g P-free NH_4NO_3 in H_2O and dil. to 1 L.

(b) *Magnesia mixture.*—*(1)* Dissolve 55 g crystd $MgCl_2 . 6H_2O$ in H_2O, add 140 g NH_4Cl and 130.5 ml NH_4OH, and dil. to 1 L. Or, *(2)* dissolve 55 g crystd $MgCl_2 . 6H_2O$ in H_2O, add 140 g NH_4Cl, dil. to 870 ml, and add NH_4OH to each required portion of soln just before using, at rate of 15 ml/100 ml soln.

(c) *Ammonium hydroxide soln for washing.*— $(1 + 9)$. Should contain ≥2.5% NH_3 by wt.

8.026   *Preparation of Solution*

Mix 5 g sample with little $Mg(NO_3)_2$ soln, **2.016**, dry, ignite, dissolve in HCl $(1 + 2.5)$, and dil. to definite vol. In aliquot of soln det. P_2O_5 as in **8.027** or **2.031**.

8.027   *Determination*

Pipet aliquot of prepd soln into 250 ml beaker; add NH_4OH in slight excess and barely dissolve ppt formed with few drops HNO_3, stirring vigorously. If HCl or H_2SO_4 has been used as solv., add ca 15 g cryst. NH_4NO_3 or soln contg that quantity. To hot soln add 70 ml molybdate soln, **2.029(a)**, for every 100 mg P_2O_5 present. Digest 1 hr at ca 65° and test for complete pptn of P_2O_5 by adding more molybdate soln to clear supernatant. Filter, and wash with cold H_2O or preferably with the NH_4NO_3 soln. Dissolve ppt on filter with NH_4OH $(1 + 1)$ and hot H_2O, and wash into beaker to vol. ≤100 ml. Neutze with HCl, using litmus paper or *bromothymol blue* as indicator; cool, and from buret slowly add (ca 1 drop/sec), stirring vigorously, 15 ml magnesia mixt./100 mg P_2O_5 present. After 15 min add 12 ml NH_4OH and let stand until supernatant is clear (usually 2 hr); filter, wash ppt with NH_4OH $(1 + 9)$ until washings are practically Cl-free, dry, burn at low heat, and ignite to constant wt, preferably in elec. furnace at 950–1000°; cool in desiccator, and weigh as $Mg_2P_2O_7$. Report as % P_2O_5.

8.028   *Qualitative Test—Official Final Action*

Add 10 ml H_2O to 1–2 g sample in 150 ml beaker. Make just acid with HNO_3, filter, take equal vols filtrate and NH_4 molybdate soln, **2.029(a)**, and warm at 40–50°. Yellow ppt indicates presence of phosphate.

8.029   Sulfate (10)—Official Final Action

Boil 5 g sample 1.5 hr with mixt. of 300 ml H_2O and 15 ml HCl. Filter, wash filter thoroly with hot H_2O, cool combined filtrate and washings, and dil. to 500 ml with H_2O. Det. sulfate in 100 ml aliquot as in **3.058**.

8.030   Ammonia—Official Final Action

To 2 g sample in distn flask add 300–400 ml H_2O and excess of NaOH soln $(1 + 1)$, connect with condenser, and distill into measured vol. std acid. Titr. excess acid in distillate with std alkali, using Me red.

8.031   Arsenic—Official Final Action

Place 5 g sample directly in generator, **25.007(a)**; add 10 ml H_2O, little at time to prevent foaming over, and then 15 ml As-free HCl, adding it dropwise until foaming ceases. Heat on steam bath until drop of mixt., when dild and treated with I soln, does not show blue. Then dil. to ca 30 ml with H_2O and continue as in **25.010**, beginning "add 5 ml KI reagent ...". Prep. blank and stds for comparison, using As-free HCl of same concn as that used in detn.

8.032   Fluorine—Official Final Action— See 25.029–25.035

8.033   Lead—Official Final Action— See 25.041–25.053

SELECTED REFERENCES

(1) JAOAC **6,** 453(1923).

(2) JAOAC **10,** 36(1927).

(3) JAOAC **31,** 278(1948); **32,** 83, 269(1949); **33,** 77(1950).

(4) JAOAC **33,** 77(1950); **34,** 296(1951).

(5) Ann. chim. anal. **4,** 263(1899)

(6) JAOAC **13,** 385(1930); **22,** 599(1939).

(7) Conn. Agr. Expt. Sta. Rpt. 1900 (II), p. 174.

(8) J. Am. Chem. Soc. **47,** 142(1925); JAOAC **34,** 61(1951); **35,** 57(1952).

(9) Conn. Agr. Expt. Sta. Rpt. 1900, p. 178.

(10) USDA Bur. Chem. Bull. **13** (V), p. 596; Conn. Agr. Exp. Sta. Rpt. 1900, p. 179.

9. Beverages: Distilled Liquors *

SPIRITS

9.001   Physical Examination—Procedure

Note and record following: (a) Color and depth of color; (b) odor—whisky, brandy, rum, etc., or foreign; (c) taste—whisky, brandy, rum, etc., or foreign.

Color (1)—Official Final Action

9.002 *Definition*

Whisky color units are defined as $10 \times A$ at 430 nm, measured in monochromatic light, of sample $\frac{1}{2}''$ thick which has spectral color characteristics of an av. whisky free of turbidity.

This definition applies only to A values obtained with precise spectrophtr with band width of ≤ 1 nm at 430 nm, and whose wavelength and photometer scales have been checked and corrected for inaccuracies by the methods recommended by NBS, in LC-1017, Jan. 1967.

Potassium Dichromate Calibration Method

9.003 *Preparation of Standard Curve*

Prep. solns of $K_2Cr_2O_7$ in $0.01N$ H_2SO_4 as follows:

Color Unit	g/l	Color Unit	g/l
1	0.0500	6	0.3000
2	0.1000	7	0.3500
3	0.1500	8	0.4000
4	0.2000	9	0.4500
5	0.2500	10	0.5000

Read A of these solns in spectrophtr at 430 nm against H_2O, using same size cell as used in detns. If other than $\frac{1}{2}''$ cell is used, convert reading to this size. Plot color units against A or calc. av. factor for converting instrument reading to color units if straight line is obtained.

9.004 *Determination*

Place sample, or sample dild with 50% alcohol, in cell and det. A against H_2O. Calc. color units, using factor or std curve.

Natural and Artificial Coloring Matter (Organic and Water-Soluble Color) (2)—Official Final Action

Spectrophotometric Method

9.005 *Apparatus*

(a) *Spectrophotometer.*—See 9.002.
(b) *Graduated cylinder.*—Cylindrical type of uni-

★ Methods so marked are surplus methods. *See* "Definitions of Terms and Explanatory Notes," item (29).

---

form diam., with pressed or molded base and ⊤ stopper. Distance from base to top is 285–295 mm. To contain 50 ml at 20°, graduated in 0.2 ml with each fifth mark distinguished by longer line; numbered from bottom upward at 2 ml intervals; error of graduations ≤ 0.2 ml at any point. (Available from Scientific Glass Apparatus Co., as Print No. 572391.)

9.006 *Reagents*

(a) *n-Methyl propyl ketone.*—2-Pentanone practical.
(b) *Saturated sodium chloride soln.*—USP or ACS NaCl.
(c) *Alcohol.*—MeOH, reagent grade, or alcohol, USP.

9.007 *Determination*

Pipet 20 ml whisky into cylinder, 9.005(b). Add by pipet, in order, 10 ml satd NaCl soln, 0.5 ml HCl, and 10 ml Me propyl ketone. Immediately invert 10–15 times and let layers sep. Color in lower layer indicates presence of caramel, vegetable extractives, or synthetic dye. Read vol. of org. layer within 1 hr and det. its A at 430 nm. If A is too great or if solv. layer is cloudy, dil. aliquot to known vol. with either 50% MeOH or 50% EtOH and read A.

9.008 *Calculation*

Example: If from 20 ml sample, org. layer of 16.1 ml was obtained which had A of 0.420 in 1 cm cell after diln $1 + 1$ with 50% alcohol: $(16.1 \times 0.420 \times 12.7 \times 2)/20 = 8.59$ color units (Lovibond number), where 12.7 is conversion factor to color units.

Specific Gravity (Apparent)—Official Final Action

9.009 *Apparatus*

(a) *Constant temperature water bath.*
(b) *Pycnometers.*—100 and 50 ml (Fig. 9:1).

9.010 *Calibration*

Fill thoroly cleaned pycnometer with recently distd H_2O, stopper, and immerse in constant temp. H_2O bath with bath level above graduation mark on pycnometer. After 30 min, remove stopper and with capillary tube adjust until bottom of meniscus is tangent to graduation mark. With small roll of filter paper, dry inside neck of pycnometer, stopper, and immerse in H_2O at room temp. 15 min. Remove pycnometer, dry, let stand 15 min, and weigh. Empty pycnometer, rinse with acetone, and dry thoroly in air with suction. Let empty flask come to

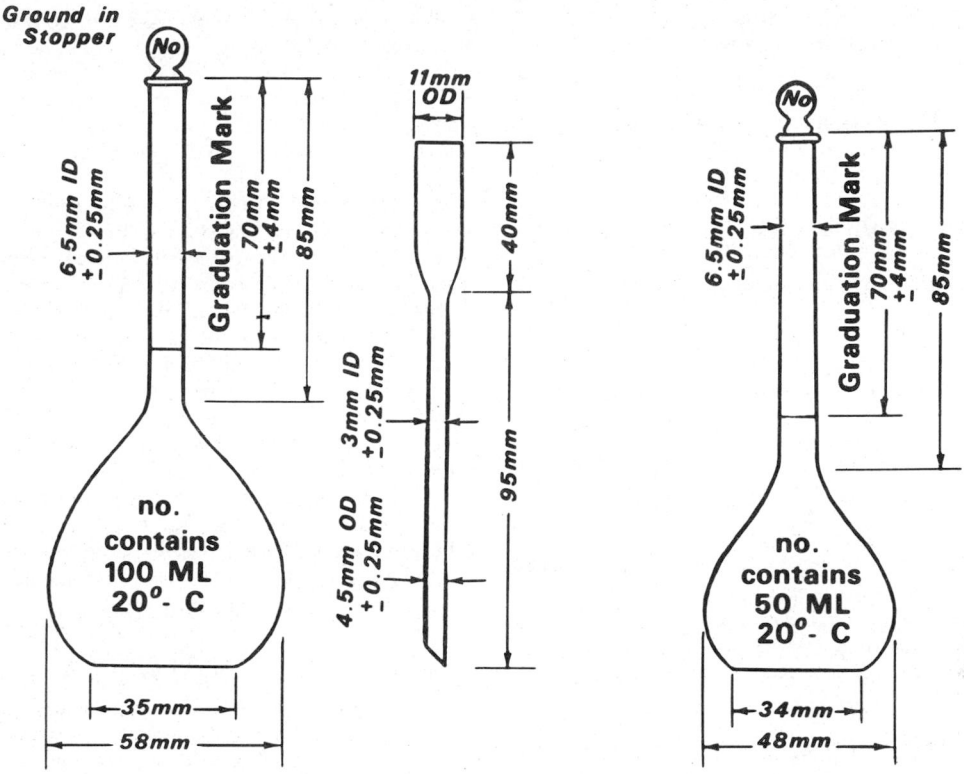

FIG. 9:1—100 ml and 50 ml pycnometers.

room temp., stopper, and weigh. Wt in air of contained H_2O = wt filled pycnometer − wt empty pycnometer.

9.011   *Determination*

Obtain wt sample as in **9.010**.

Sp gr in air = S/W, where S = wt sample, and W = wt H_2O.

Alcohol by Volume

From Specific Gravity by Pycnometer (3)—Official Final Action

9.012   *Apparatus*

Distillation apparatus.—500 ml flask, connected thru bulb (Iowa State type is convenient) to vertically assembled Liebig condenser with jacket ≥400 mm long, inner tube 9±1 mm id, with adapter. Joints may be live rubber or ⊤̅. Heat with elec. or gas-operated unit.

9.013   *Determination*

(Some samples do not require distn prior to detn, e.g., straight bourbon whisky; alcohol-H_2O mixts contg traces of volatile ingredients.)

(a) *Samples containing 60% or less alcohol by volume.*—Calibrate 100 ml pycnometer, Fig. 9:1, as in **9.010**, at one of temps specified in **47.003**. Fill clean, dry pycnometer with sample and adjust to vol. at calibration temp. as in **9.010**.

Transfer contents of pycnometer to distg flask, just previously rinsed with cold H_2O and contg few glass beads or equiv. Rinse pycnometer 3 times, using total of 25 ml cold H_2O (40 ml for cordials or wines), and add rinse H_2O to flask. Place wet pycnometer so that adapter extends just into bulb. Surround pycnometer with ice or ice-H_2O. Complete connections and pass thru H_2O-jacket rapid stream of H_2O kept at ≤25° at outlet. Distill ca 96 ml at uniform rate in ≥30 but ≤60 min, using longer times for higher percentages of alcohol. Remove and stopper pycnometer, mix distillate by swirling, and wash down with H_2O any drops that may be above graduation mark. Immerse in constant temp. bath at calibration temp. and after 30 min carefully dil. to vol., with aid of capillary tube, by adding H_2O previously boiled and cooled to same temp. Det. sp gr of distillate as in **9.011**. Obtain corresponding % alcohol by vol. from **47.003**. (This result is % alcohol by vol. at 15.56° (60°F).)

(b) *For samples containing more than 60% alcohol by volume.*—Proceed as in (a) with following changes: Calibrate 100 ml and 50 ml pycnometers, Fig. 9:1, at 15.56°, fill 50 ml pycnometer with sample, and adjust to vol. at 15.56°. Add 50 ml cold H_2O to distg flask before transfer of sample and collect distillate in 100 ml pycnometer. Adjust to vol. at 15.56°. Obtain sp gr of distillate, and from table, **47.003**, obtain % alcohol by vol. in distillate. Calc. as follows: % alcohol by vol. in sample at $15.56° = D \times W/W'$; where D = % alcohol by vol. in distillate at 15.56°; W = wt H_2O at 15.56° in 100 ml pycnometer; and W' = wt H_2O at 15.56° in 50 ml pycnometer.

From Specific Gravity by Hydrometer (4)— Official Final Action

(Applicable to spirits contg ≤600 mg ext/100 ml)

9.014 *Apparatus*

(a) *Hydrometer.*—Graduated to 0.1 or 0.2° proof, with calibration corrections.

(b) *Thermometer.*—Graduated to 0.25 or 0.5°F, with calibration corrections.

(c) *Cylinder.*—Clear glass, 2.5″ diam., 14″ high.

(d) *Metal clips.*—To hold thermometer in cylinder.

9.015 *Determination*

Clean and dry hydrometer before use. Let hydrometer, thermometer, cylinder, and sample come to room temp. Rinse cylinder, contg thermometer held in place by spring frame clip, 2 or 3 times with portion of sample. Fill cylinder to desired level with sample, holding cylinder at ca 45° angle to reduce agitation and air bubbles. (After hydrometer is inserted, liq. level should be slightly below rim of cylinder.) Place palm of hand over top of cylinder and slowly invert 3 or 4 times to equalize temps of liq. and cylinder. Wipe off any liq. on outside of cylinder. (Do not place hands on cylinder in such way as to warm liq. inside.) Insert hydrometer in liq.; then raise and lower hydrometer bulb from top to bottom 5 or 6 times to temper and distribute slight temp. changes thruout liq. Keep hydrometer bulb in liq., dry stem, and let hydrometer come to rest without wetting more than few tenths degrees of exposed stem.

Read hydrometer, then thermometer. To read hydrometer scale, place eye slightly below plane of surface of liq., and then slowly raise head, keeping eye perpendicular to hydrometer, until surface flattens from ellipse into straight line. Take point where this line intersects hydrometer scale as reading of hydrometer.

Raise hydrometer slightly above its point of rest and again let it come to rest in liq. Read hydrometer and thermometer again to verify original readings. Read hydrometer to nearest 0.02° and thermometer to nearest 0.1°. Remove and dry hydrometer. Reinvert cylinder and contents several times (with thermometer left in place) to thermally equilibrate system. Retemper hydrometer, dry stem, and again read hydrometer and thermometer. Apply calibration corrections for both hydrometer and thermometer. Calc. true % of proof from Table No. 1 of the U.S. Treasury Department Gauging Manual, 1962. Average calcd values if they agree within 0.1° proof; otherwise take addnl readings and average.

Det. ext as in **9.023** and for every 100 mg ext/100 ml add 0.4° proof to apparent proof.

9.016 From Refraction—Official Final Action

Measure 25 ml sample into distn flask, noting temp.; dil. with 100 ml H_2O, distill nearly 100 ml, dil. to vol. at same temp., and det. immersion refractometer reading. Obtain corresponding % alcohol from **47.004**.

When vol. measurements are made at temp. other than 15.56°, multiply % alcohol from **47.004** by appropriate factor from **9.017** (below).

Williams Field Test (5)—Procedure
9.018 *Apparatus*

Williams tube.—See Fig. 9:2. Available from Kimble Products as Kimble No. G3-216. Clean frequently and dry.

9.017 *Factors for calculating original alcohol content for 25 and 50 ml samples distilled to 100 ml when immersion refractometer measurements are made at 20, 25, 30, or 35°*

Alc. % by Vol. in Distillate at 15.56°	25 ml Sample				50 ml Sample			
	Temp. of Measurement				Temp. of Measurement			
	20°	25°	30°	35°	20°	25°	30°	35°
	Multiply Alcohol in Distillate by:				Multiply Alcohol in Distillate by:			
0–3.99	4.001	4.002	4.003	4.004	2.000	2.000	2.000	2.000
4–5.99	4.003	4.006	4.009	4.013	2.000	2.001	2.001	2.001
6–7.99	4.005	4.011	4.016	4.021	2.001	2.001	2.002	2.002
8–9.99	4.007	4.015	4.023	4.030	2.001	2.002	2.003	2.004
10–11.99	4.009	4.019	4.028	4.037	2.001	2.003	2.004	2.006
12–13.99	4.010	4.021	4.031	4.041	2.002	2.004	2.006	2.007
14–15.99	4.011	4.022	4.032	4.043	2.002	2.005	2.007	2.009
16–19.99	4.011	4.023	4.034	4.045	2.003	2.006	2.008	2.011
20–more	4.011	4.024	4.036	4.047	2.003	2.006	2.009	2.012

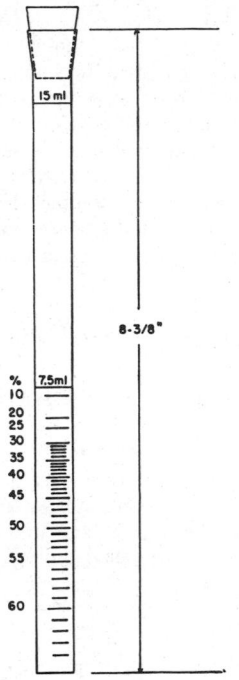

FIG. 9:2—Williams tube

9.019 *Reagent*

(a) *Dilute hydrochloric acid.*—Dil. 10 ml HCl to 100 ml with H_2O.

(b) *Solvent.*—Mix 70 ml Pentasol or isoamyl alcohol, 28 ml toluene, and 2 ml dil. HCl. Shake well until acid completely dissolves.

9.020 *Determination*

Place sample in tube, accurately adjusting bottom of meniscus to coincide with 7.5 ml mark. Remove any excess sample on sides of tube above 7.5 ml mark with swab or roll of filter paper. Add 7.5 ml solv. to 15 ml mark. Stopper tube and invert number of times to mix intimately. Stand tube upright and let sep. When sepn is complete, rotate tube to shake down globules of lower soln that adhere to sides, and stopper. When settling and drainage are complete, read % alcohol (by vol.) where meniscus between the 2 layers falls on calibration mark. Repeat operation of mixing and settling, and read again.

9.021 *Temperature Correction*

Correct for effects of temp. and alcohol concn according to Table 9:1.

Example: Indicated % alcohol from tube: 48.0% at 90°F. Correction factor from table is −1.1; 48.0 − 1.1 = 46.9%.

**9.022 Alcohol by Weight—
Official Final Action**

Accurately weigh 40–50 g sample, using clean, dry 50 ml pycnometer, Fig. 9:1, or other closed vessel. (If alcohol is 60% or less by vol., the 100 ml sample of **9.013**(a) may be weighed and used.) Transfer to 500 ml distn flask contg 50 ml H_2O and few clean glass beads or equiv. Rinse pycnometer 3 times, bringing contents of distn flask to ca 125 ml. Distill, and det. % alcohol by vol. in distillate as in **9.013**(a). Det. corresponding % alcohol by wt in distillate from table, **47.005**. Multiply result by wt distillate and divide by wt sample.

Table 9:1 Temperature (°F) correction factors

%	60°	62°	64°	66°	68°	70°	72°	74°	76°	78°
43	+0.5	+0.3	+0.2	0.0	−0.1	−0.2	−0.4	−0.5	−0.7	−0.8
43.4	+0.5	+0.4	+0.2	+0.1	0.0	−0.2	−0.3	−0.5	−0.6	−0.7
44	+0.6	+0.4	+0.3	+0.2	0.0	−0.1	−0.3	−0.4	−0.5	−0.7
45	+0.7	+0.5	+0.4	+0.3	+0.1	0.0	−0.2	−0.3	−0.4	−0.6
46	+0.8	+0.7	+0.5	+0.4	+0.2	+0.1	0.0	−0.2	−0.3	−0.5
47	+0.9	+0.8	+0.6	+0.5	+0.3	+0.2	+0.1	−0.1	−0.2	−0.4
47.5	+1.0	+0.8	+0.7	+0.5	+0.4	+0.3	+0.1	0.0	−0.2	−0.3
48	+1.1	+0.9	+0.7	+0.6	+0.4	+0.3	+0.2	0.0	−0.1	−0.2
49	+1.1	+1.0	+0.8	+0.7	+0.6	+0.4	+0.3	+0.1	0.0	−0.1
50	+1.2	+1.1	+0.9	+0.8	+0.7	+0.5	+0.4	+0.3	+0.1	0.0

%	80°	82°	84°	86°	88°	90°	92°	94°	96°	98°
43	−0.9	−1.1	−1.2	−1.4	−1.5	−1.6	−1.8	−1.9	−2.0	−2.2
43.4	−0.9	−1.0	−1.2	−1.3	−1.4	−1.6	−1.7	−1.9	−2.0	−2.2
44	−0.8	−0.9	−1.1	−1.2	−1.4	−1.5	−1.6	−1.8	−1.9	−2.1
45	−0.7	−0.8	−1.0	−1.1	−1.3	−1.4	−1.5	−1.7	−1.8	−2.0
46	−0.6	−0.7	−0.9	−1.0	−1.2	−1.3	−1.4	−1.6	−1.7	−1.8
47	−0.5	−0.6	−0.8	−0.9	−1.0	−1.2	−1.3	−1.5	−1.6	−1.7
47.5	−0.4	−0.6	−0.7	−0.8	−1.0	−1.1	−1.3	−1.4	−1.5	−1.7
48	−0.4	−0.5	−0.6	−0.8	−0.9	−1.1	−1.2	−1.3	−1.5	−1.6
49	−0.3	−0.4	−0.5	−0.7	−0.8	−1.0	−1.1	−1.2	−1.4	−1.5
50	−0.2	−0.3	−0.4	−0.6	−0.7	−0.9	−1.0	−1.1	−1.3	−1.4

9.023   Extract—Official Final Action

Weigh, or measure at 20°, 25–100 ml sample, evap. to dryness on steam bath, dry 30 min at 100°, cool in desiccator 30 min, and weigh.

9.024   Ash—Official Final Action

Proceed as in **31.012** or **31.013**, using residue from **9.023**.

Potassium
Flame Photometric Method (6)—
Official Final Action

9.025   Reagent and Apparatus

(a) *Std solns.*—Prep. as in **11.022**(a), except make final dilns, i.e., 1–10 ppm K, with 50% alcohol.

(b) *Flame spectrophotometer.*—See **11.022**(b).

9.026   Determination
(*Caution: See* **46.007**.)

Proceed as in **11.023**, except burn sample undild, or, if necessary, dild with 50% alcohol (usually 2.5–5.0 times). Calc ppm K as in **11.023**.

Sodium
Flame Photometric Method (6)—
Official Final Action

9.027   Reagent and Apparatus

(a) *Std solns.*—Prep. as in **11.024**, except make final dilns, i.e., 1–10 ppm Na, with 50% alcohol.

(b) *Flame spectrophotometer.*—See **11.022**(b).

9.028   Determination
(*Caution: See* **46.007**.)

Proceed as in **11.023**, except burn sample undild, or, if necessary, dild with 50% alcohol until %T falls within %T range of stds. Calc. ppm Na as in **11.023**.

9.029   Phosphorus—Official Final Action
—See 11.032

Copper (7)—Official Final Action
Atomic Absorption Method

9.030   Reagent

(Distill H_2O and alcohol from all-Pyrex stills into Cu-free receiver.)

Copper std solns.—(*1*) *Stock soln.*—0.2 mg/ml. Dissolve 0.393 g $CuSO_4.5H_2O$ (free from any whitish deposit) in 500 ml vol. flask contg H_2O and 2 ml H_2SO_4. Dil. to vol. and mix. (*2*) *Working soln.*—0.004 mg/ml. Prep. daily by dilg 2.00 ml stock soln to 100 ml.

9.031   Preparation of Standard Curve

To series of 50 ml vol. flasks contg 25 ml alcohol, add 0, 2, 4, 6, 10, and 12 ml Cu working std soln. Dil. nearly to mark with H_2O, mix, and cool to room temp. before dilg to vol. Stds contain 0.0, 0.16, 0.32, 0.48, 0.80, and 0.96 ppm Cu (μg/ml), resp.

9.032   Determination
(*Caution: See* **46.006**.)

Follow operating instructions supplied by atomic absorption spectrophtr manufacturer or previously established optimum settings for equipment used. Adjust instrument to zero A while aspirating blank. Read at 3247 Å $\geq$4 std solns within analytical range before and after each 6–10 samples. Prep. calibration curve from av. of each std before and after sample group. Use std curve to convert A values for samples to ppm Cu.

ZDBT Colorimetric Method

9.033   Reagents

Prep. H_2O, alcohol, and Cu stds as in **9.030**, and in addn:

Zinc dibenzyldithiocarbamate (ZDBT)-carbon tetrachloride soln.—0.2%. Dissolve 2 g ZDBT (Uniroyal Chemical or K & K Laboratories) in 1 L CCl_4 by warming in H_2O bath at <77°. Filter thru Whatman No. 41, or equiv. acid-washed paper, into dark bottle. Store in refrigerator.

9.034   Apparatus

Separators.—60 or 125 ml pear-shaped separators with Teflon stopcocks. Clean separators with hot H_2SO_4-$K_2Cr_2O_7$ cleaning soln and rinse with H_2O. Before each analysis, shake mixt. of 10 ml H_2O, 0.5 ml 6N H_2SO_4, and 10 ml ZDBT-CCl_4 soln in each separator 1 min. Clean inside of stems with cotton swab soaked in ZDBT-CCl_4 soln. Drain and rinse separators with H_2O.

9.035   Preparation of Standard Curves

(a) *80–135° proof alcoholic samples.*—To separators contg 5 ml alcohol, add 0, 0.50, 1.00, 2.00, and 3.00 ml Cu working std soln and 5, 4.5, 4, 3, and 2 ml H_2O, resp., and dil. to 10 ml. Solns in separators contain 0.0, 0.20, 0.40, 0.80, and 1.20 μg Cu/ml (ppm), resp. Treat as in **9.036**. Plot ppm Cu against A.

(b) *Aqueous samples, wines, and other low proof samples.*—Prep. as in (a) except use 5 ml H_2O instead of alcohol.

9.036   Determination

To separator contg 10 ml sample (dil. sample >135° proof to 80–135° proof) or std, add 0.5 ml 6N H_2SO_4 and 10.0 ml ZDBT-CCl_4 soln. Stopper and shake briefly; release pressure by removing stopper. Replace stopper and shake vigorously 100 times. If funnel stems are not dry, remove drops of liq. with small roll acid-washed paper (e.g., Whatman 41) to prevent draining H_2O drops into cuvet. Insert plug of fine glass wool (Corning Glass Works No. 3950) or cotton into each stem to filter out possible haze materials. Within 10–60 min, det. A of CCl_4 layer at 438 nm. Let few ml CCl_4 layer pass thru filtering medium before collecting sample in cuvet. Use CCl_4 layer from appropriate 0 ppm Cu soln (prepd as for std curve (**a**) or (**b**)) as ref. Det. Cu concn from appropriate std curve. Multiply by diln factor if sample was dild.

Iron (*8*)—Official First Action
Atomic Absorption Method

9.037 *Apparatus*

Spectrophotometer.—Perkin-Elmer Corp. 303, or equiv., with 3-slot Boling burner head, or equiv.

9.038 *Reagents*

(Use Fe-free H_2O and reagents; rinse glassware with HCl and H_2O before use.)

Iron std solns.—(*1*) *Stock soln.*—10 μg/ml. Dissolve 0.0684 g ferrous ethylenediammonium sulfate.$4H_2O$ ($FeC_2H_4(NH_3)_2SO_4.4H_2O$, G. Frederick Smith Chemical Co.) in H_2O, add 2.5 ml H_2SO_4, dil. to 1 L with H_2O, and mix thoroly. (*2*) *Working solns.*—0.0, 0.1, 0.2, 0.3, and 0.4 ppm. To 100 ml vol. flask contg 50 ml 43% alcohol, add 0, 1, 2, 3, and 4 ml stock soln and dil. each soln nearly to vol. with 43% alcohol. Mix thoroly, let cool to room temp., and adjust to 100 ml with 43% alcohol.

9.039 *Determination*

(*Caution: See* **46.006.**)

Follow manufacturer's operating instructions, using air-C_2H_2 flame with flow meter set at 9 for Perkin-Elmer 303 and Fe only (i.e., single element) tube. Set wavelength at 2483 Å and adjust spectrophtr to 0 A while aspirating blank (0.0 ppm Fe). Analyze stds before and after duplicate series of samples. Det. av. A values. Aspirate H_2O between each detn to flush burner and reset A to 0 with blank. Plot std curve of A against ppm Fe. Read ppm Fe in sample from this curve.

TPTZ Colorimetric Method

(Not applicable to brandy)

9.040 *Apparatus*

(**a**) *Spectrophotometer.* — Beckman Instruments Model DU, or equiv., or photoelec. colorimeter with suitable filter, e.g., Klett colorimeter with No. 60 filter.

(**b**) *Water bath.*—To maintain constant temp. at ca 60°.

9.041 *Reagents*

(Use Fe-free H_2O and reagents; rinse glassware with HCl and H_2O before use.)

(**a**) *Hydroxylamine hydrochloride soln.*—40%. Dissolve 10 g $NH_2OH.HCl$ in 25 ml H_2O.

(**b**) *Ammonium perchlorate soln.*—10%. Dissolve 10 g NH_4ClO_4 in 100 ml H_2O.

(**c**) *1,2-Propanediol cyclic carbonate (propylene carbonate).*—Superior grade (Matheson Coleman & Bell).

(**d**) *2,4,6-Tripyridyl-s-triazine (TPTZ) soln.*—

0.001*M*. Add 0.0781 g TPTZ (G. Frederick Smith Chemical Co.) to 100 ml H_2O contg 5 drops HCl in 250 ml vol. flask. Dil. to vol. with H_2O and filter thru coarse fritted glass funnel. Store in Fe-free glassware.

(**e**) *Sodium acetate soln.*—40%. Dissolve 48.2 g anhyd. NaOAc in 75.7 ml H_2O and 24.3 ml HCl. Add 5 ml 0.001*M* TPTZ, 5 ml 40% $NH_2OH.HCl$, 2 ml 10% NH_4ClO_4, and 10 ml propylene carbonate. Add 5 ml $CHCl_3$, shake, and discard lower layer. After 2 $CHCl_3$ extns, add 5 ml 0.001*M* TPTZ and repeat $CHCl_3$ extn. (Four extns are necessary to obtain water-white soln.) Store in Fe-free glassware.

(**f**) *Ascorbic acid solns.*—(*1*) *5%.*—Dissolve 2.5 g ascorbic acid in 25 ml H_2O and dil. to 50 ml with alcohol. Prep. fresh daily. (*2*) *5% Ascorbic acid in sodium acetate buffer.*—Dissolve 2.5 g ascorbic acid in 20 ml H_2O, add 5 ml 40% NaOAc, and dil. to 50 ml with alcohol. Prep. fresh daily.

(**g**) *Iron std solns.*—Prep. same concns as in **9.038,** but prep. 200 ml each working soln.

9.042 *Preparation of Standard Curve*

Pipet 50 ml 43% alcohol contg known amts Fe (i.e. 0 (reagent color blank), 0.1, 0.2, 0.3, and 0.4 ppm) into 5 sep. 100 ml vol. flasks. Add 2 ml 5% ascorbic acid in NaOAc buffer and 2 ml TPTZ, and heat samples 15 min in ca 60° H_2O bath.

Cool solns to room temp. and measure A of each sample on spectrophtr at 593 nm or photoelec. colorimeter with appropriate filter. Use 43% alcohol to zero colorimeter. Subtract A of reagent color blank from A of samples. Plot corrected A readings against ppm Fe to obtain std curve. (Straight line is obtained with Fe concns used.)

9.043 *Determination*

Pipet 50 ml sample into each of 2 sep. 100 ml vol. flasks and add 2 ml 5% ascorbic acid to each. Add 2 ml TPTZ to one flask and 2 ml H_2O to other (product blank). Heat 15 min in ca 60° H_2O bath. Cool solns and measure A of each soln as for std curve. Subtract A of reagent color blank (from **9.042**) and also A of product color blank from A of samples. Det. Fe concn from std curve.

Chloride (*9*)—Official Final Action

9.044 *Apparatus*

See **11.027.**

9.045 *Reagents*

See **11.028** and in addn:

(**a**) *Dilute chloride std soln.*—Dil. 50 ml chloride std soln, **11.028**(c), to 500 ml with H_2O. Alternatively, dissolve 0.2103 g KCl in H_2O and dil. to 1 L. 1 ml = 0.1 mg Cl.

(**b**) *Dilute silver nitrate std soln.*—Dil. 50 ml std soln, **11.028**(d), to 500 ml with H_2O. Alternatively, dissolve 0.4791 g $AgNO_3$ in H_2O and dil. to 1 L. 1 ml = 0.1 mg Cl.

(c) *Alcohol soln.*—Place 500 ml alcohol in 1 L vol. flask, add ca 475 ml H_2O, mix, cool to room temp., and dil. to 1 L with H_2O.

9.046   *Determination*

Det. equivalence point voltage as in **11.029** except use alcohol soln instead of H_2O to adjust vol. to 100 ml. Use std solns **11.028**(c) and (d).

Pipet 5 ml dil. std Cl soln into 250 ml beaker, and add 95 ml alcohol soln and 1.0 ml HNO_3. Titr. with dil. std $AgNO_3$ soln to predetd equivalence voltage as in **11.029**.

Pipet 100 ml distd spirits sample into 250 ml beaker, add 1.0 ml HNO_3, and titr. with dil. std $AgNO_3$ soln as above. Ppm Cl in sample = $(V_w/V_s) \times C \times 10$, where V_w = ml std $AgNO_3$ used by sample, V_s = ml std $AgNO_3$ used by std Cl soln, and C = 0.5 mg Cl in 5 ml std Cl soln used.

9.047   Total Acids—Official Final Action

Neutze ca 250 ml boiled H_2O in porcelain evapg dish ($7\frac{1}{2}''$ dish is convenient). Add 25 ml sample and titr. with $0.1N$ NaOH, using ca 2 ml phthln.

9.048   Fixed Acids—Official Final Action

Evap. 25–50 ml sample to dryness in Pt dish on steam bath and dry 30 min in oven at 100°. Dissolve and transfer residue with several portions of neut. alcohol of ca same proof as sample, using 25–50 ml in all, to porcelain dish contg ca 250 ml neutzd boiled H_2O. Titr. with $0.1N$ NaOH, using 10 ml buret graduated in 0.05 ml and ca 2 ml phthln.

9.049   Volatile Acids—Official Final Action

Volatile acids = total acids from **9.047** − fixed acids from **9.048**.

Esters and Aldehydes—Official Final Action
9.050   *Reagents*

(a) *Sodium thiosulfate std soln.*—$0.05N$. Prep. by dilg $0.1N$ soln, **45.038**.

(b) *Iodine soln.*—Approx. $0.05N$.

(c) *Sodium bisulfite soln.*—Approx. $0.05N$. (Deterioration is retarded if soln contains ca 10% alcohol; do not use after ca 1 week.)

9.051   *Preparation of Sample*

To 200 ml sample in 500 ml erlenmeyer, add ca 35 ml H_2O and few grains SiC (Carborundum). Distill slowly into 200 ml vol. flask until distillate is nearly at mark. Dil. to vol. and mix.

9.052   *Determination of Esters (10)*

Transfer 100 ml distillate to 500 ml flask, neutze free acid, add measured excess $0.1N$ NaOH, connect flask with air-cooled condenser ca 60 cm long, heat 2 hr on steam bath, let cool, and titr. excess alkali. Reject detns in which excess $0.1N$ alkali is <2 ml, or is >10 ml. Calc. esters as EtOAc. Correct for blank

detn performed on 100 ml 50% alcohol (absolute alcohol-H_2O, 1 + 1).

9.053   *Determination of Aldehyde*

Place remainder of distillate from **9.051** in 500 ml flask, add ca 100 ml H_2O and excess $NaHSO_3$ soln, and let stand ca 30 min, shaking occasionally. (Excess $NaHSO_3$ should be equiv. of ca 25 ml I soln.) Add excess I soln, and titr. this excess with std $Na_2S_2O_3$ soln. Run blank contg same quantities of I soln and bisulfite soln as used in sample. Difference between titrns in ml $Na_2S_2O_3$ soln $\times 1.1$ = mg acetaldehyde in sample.

Fusel Oil—Official Final Action
Method I (11)
9.054   *Reagents*

(a) *p-Dimethylaminobenzaldehyde (DMAB) soln.* —In 100 ml vol. flask dissolve 1 g DMAB in mixt. of 5 ml H_2SO_4 and 90 ml H_2O, and dil. to vol. with H_2O.

(b) *Isobutyl alcohol.*—Eastman Kodak Co. X-303 (highest purity for fusel oil assay).

(c) *Isoamyl alcohol.*—Eastman Kodak Co. X-18 (highest purity for fusel oil assay).

(d) *Ethyl alcohol.*—Redistd middle 50% fraction.

(e) *Synthetic std fusel oil.*—Weigh 2 g std isobutyl alcohol and 8 g std isoamyl alcohol into 1 L vol. flask and dil. to vol. with H_2O. Pipet two 10 ml portions into 100 ml vol. flasks and dil. to vol., one with H_2O and other with alcohol. Prep. working stds for products in range of 0–170 proof contg 1.0–6.0 g synthetic fusel oil/100 L by dilg 1.0–6.0 ml aliquots of aq. std soln to 100 ml with alc. soln of proof expected for dild sample when pipeted into analysis tube. Prep. similar working stds for products in range of 170–190 proof by dilg 1.0–6.0 ml aliquots of alc. std soln to 100 ml with alc. soln of proof of sample or its diln.

When 6 ml synthetic std dild with 190 proof alcohol is carried thru analysis, A should be 0.83 ± 0.03 at 530 nm.

9.055   *Preparation of Samples*

(Aged, blended and rectified products, whiskies, brandies, rums, vodka, and liqueurs require distn prior to analysis.)

Determination of true proof of sample.—Det. alcohol as in **9.013**.

For samples contg >6 g fusel oil/100 L, dil. distd sample with H_2O to concn of 2.0–5.0 g fusel oil/100 L. Dil. 5 ml brandies, rum, and blended whiskies to 100 ml; dil. 5 ml heavy brandies, rums, and straight whiskies to 250 ml.

9.056   *Determination*

Pipet 2 ml aliquots of sample or dild sample, distd, if necessary, 2 ml H_2O (for reagent blank), and 2 ml aliquots of stds into 15 × 150 mm g-s or covered test tubes. Stopper or cover tubes, and place in rack, then in ice bath. Pipet 1 ml DMAB soln into each tube, shake, and replace in ice bath for 3 min. With tubes still in ice bath, add 10 ml chilled H_2SO_4 from buret down side of tubes. Shake tubes individually and replace in ice bath for 3 min. Transfer rack of tubes from ice bath to boiling H_2O bath and boil 20 min. Transfer tubes to ice bath for 3–5 min, then to room temp. bath. Read $\%T$ of developed color of samples and stds on spectrophtr at 538–543 nm against reagent blank as ref. (Use same wavelength for both stds and unknowns.) Plot g fusel oil in std samples/100 L on linear scale as abscissa against $\%T$ as ordinate on log scale of semilog paper. Convert $\%T$ of samples to g fusel oil/100 L from std curve. If diln was used, multiply g fusel oil/100 L found by diln factor to obtain g fusel oil/100 L in original sample. Analyze 2 levels of stds with each series of unknowns.

Precision expected: Whiskies and brandies, ±5%; rum, ±8%; gin, vodka, spirits, ±0.4 g/100 L.

Method II (12)

9.057   Reagents

(a) *Color reagent.*—Dissolve 1 g Na salt of 4-hydroxybenzaldehyde-3-sulfonic acid in H_2O, dil. to vol. in 25 ml vol. flask with H_2O, and filter.

(b) *Fusel oil std solns.*—Weigh 2 g isobutyl alcohol, 9.054(b), and 8 g isoamyl alcohol, 9.054(c), into 1 L vol. flask and dil. to vol. with 50% alcohol. Dil. 0, 1, 2, 3, 5, 10, and 15 ml portions to vol. with 50% alcohol in 100 ml vol. flasks (0.0, 0.1, 0.2, 0.3, 0.5, 1.0, and 1.5 g fusel oil/L). Std soln contg 1.0 g fusel oil/L should give A of ca 0.4 at 445 nm in 9.059.

(c) *Alcohol.*—50%. Free of fusel oil (ACS).

9.058   Preliminary Distillation

Add 20 ml H_2O to 50 ml sample and distill, slowly at first, collecting ca 50 ml in 50 ml vol. flask. Dil. to vol. with H_2O. (For samples known to contain >150 g fusel oil/100 L, use 25 ml sample plus 45 ml H_2O.)

9.059   Color Development

To a dry 10 ml vol. flask, add 0.1 ml distillate from serological blow-out pipet. (Pipet should have pointed tip and should be thoroly cleaned ($K_2Cr_2O_7$-H_2SO_4 plus H_2O rinse) before use. Rinse pipet several times with distillate, and wipe end dry. Bring liq. to line while holding tip to outside surface of vol. flask. Then insert end to bottom of vol. flask and release sample. After draining pipet, hold flask at 45° angle and blow out pipet.)

Add 0.1 ml color reagent from 1 ml buret graduated in 0.01 ml; then add 2 ml H_2SO_4 from 50 ml buret. Mix, and place unstoppered flask in H_2O bath at room temp. (250 ml beaker is convenient). Bring to boil and hold 30 min. Let cool, dil. to vol. with H_2SO_4, and det. A at 445 nm against H_2O on Beckman DU spectrophtr, or equiv. instrument.

9.060   Blank and Standards

Carry 0.1 ml 50% alcohol and 0.1 ml portions of std solns thru color development. Use same 0.1 ml pipet for blank, stds, and sample. Subtract A of 50% alcohol blank from A of sample and stds.

9.061   Calibration Curve or Factor

Plot corrected A of stds against concn. (Straight line is obtained up to ca 150 g fusel oil/100 L; above this value, curve flattens. Concn of color reagent may be increased, but it is best to dil. distd sample so that A is <0.6.) Factor (A of 1.0 g fusel oil/L) may be detd from curve.

9.062   Calculations

$100A_s \times D/A_0 = $ g fusel oil/100 L, where 100 = diln of 0.1 ml sample to 10 ml in color development, A_s = corrected A of sample, A_0 = factor (A of 1 g fusel oil/L), and D = diln of sample before distn.

Higher Alcohols (n-Propyl Alcohol, Isobutyl Alcohol, and Isoamyl Alcohol) and Ethyl Acetate (13)—Official Final Action

9.063   Apparatus

(a) *Gas chromatograph.*—Equipped with flame ionization detector. (1) *Column.*—30% Carbowax 1500 (w/w) on Chromosorb W (60–80 mesh, acid-washed). Weigh 9 g Carbowax 1500 into 250 ml beaker and dissolve by stirring with H_2O on steam bath. Weigh 30 g Chromosorb W in 250 ml beaker and combine with Carbowax soln in large flat-bottom Pyrex glass baking dish or flat-bottom polyethylene container (ca 8 × 10″). Add H_2O to just cover solid support and mix thoroly. Evap. H_2O with frequent stirring in hood. (Gentle steam may be applied to hasten evapn.) After evapn of H_2O, heat coated support in 100° oven ca 2 hr.

Pack 8′ × ¼″ od Cu tubing tightly and evenly by repeated tapping, and condition in column oven at 150° with He flow rate of 150 ml/min until steady baseline is observed at attenuation 1× at operating parameters (ca 24 hr).

(2) *Approximate parameters.*—Column temp. 70° (isothermal); detector and inlet temp. 150°; He carrier flow 150 ml/min.

Optimum operating conditions vary with column and instrument, and must be detd by using std solns. Adjust parameters for max. peak sharpness and optimum sepn. With high level std, n-PrOH should give almost complete baseline sepn from EtOH.

(b) *Syringe.*—10 μl, Hamilton Co. No. 701, or equiv.

9.064   Reagents

(a) *Isobutyl alcohol.*—See 9.054(b).

(b) *Isoamyl alcohol.*—See 9.054(c).

(c) *n-Propyl alcohol.*—Redistd, reagent grade.

(d) *Ethyl acetate.*—Redistd, reagent grade.

(e) *n-Butyl alcohol.*—Redistd, reagent grade.

(f) *n-Butyl alcohol internal std solns.*—(1) *High level.*—Dil. 10 ml *n*-butyl alcohol to 100 ml with 40% alcohol. (1 ml added to 100 ml sample or std is equiv. to ca 81 g *n*-butyl alcohol/100 L.) (2) *Low level.*— Dil. 1 ml *n*-butyl alcohol to 200 ml with 95% alcohol. (1 ml added to 100 ml sample or std is equiv. to ca 4.1 g/100 L.)

(g) *n-Propyl alcohol, isobutyl alcohol, isoamyl alcohol, and ethyl acetate high level std solns.*—(1) *Stock soln.*—Accurately weigh 1 ml *n*-PrOH, 1 ml isobutyl alcohol, 2 ml isoamyl alcohol, and 1 ml EtOAc into 100 ml vol. flask and dil. to vol. with 40% alcohol. (2) *Intermediate soln.*—Dil. 10 ml stock soln to 200 ml with 40% alcohol. (3) *Working soln.*—(Approx. 40.2, 41.1, 81.2, and 45.1 g/100 L *n*-PrOH, isobutyl alcohol, isoamyl alcohol, and EtOAc, resp.) Dil. 5 ml stock soln to 100 ml with 40% alcohol. Add 1 ml high level *n*-butyl alcohol internal std soln, (f)(1), and mix. Prep. fresh weekly.

(h) *n-Propyl alcohol, isobutyl alcohol, isoamyl alcohol, and ethyl acetate low level working solns.*—(Approx. 2.0, 2.1, 4.1, and 2.3 g/100 L *n*-PrOH, isobutyl alcohol, isoamyl alcohol, and EtOAc, resp.) Dil. 5 ml high level intermediate soln, (g)(2), to 100 ml with 95% alcohol. Add 1 ml low level internal std soln, (f)(2), and mix. Prep. fresh weekly.

Prep. std soln of ca same concn as sample if latter differs grossly from appropriate (high or low level) std.

9.065   *Determination*

Make preliminary injection of 10 μl sample to det. absence of *n*-butyl alcohol. (If present, subtract its amt from total *n*-butyl alcohol (original and internal std) content.) Add 1 ml internal std soln, (f) (high or low level, depending on higher alcohol and EtOAc concn) to 100 ml sample in vol. flask, and chromatograph 10 μl aliquots of sample and std solns in triplicate.

Measure peak hts of *n*-PrOH, isobutyl alcohol, isoamyl alcohol, and EtOAc to nearest 0.05 cm and calc. peak ht ratio of each to *n*-butyl alcohol (internal std) in sample and std solns. (For more accurate detn of isoamyl alcohol, use peak areas.)

$X = H \times S/H'$, where X = concn of higher alcohol or EtOAc in sample (g/100 L); H = peak ht (or area for isoamyl alcohol) ratio of higher alcohol or EtOAc to *n*-butyl alcohol in sample; H' = peak ht (or area for isoamyl alcohol) ratio of higher alcohol or EtOAc to *n*-butyl alcohol in std; S = concn of higher alcohol or EtOAc in std (g/100 L).

Sum of isoamyl and isobutyl alcohol concns is ca equiv. to fusel oil concn as detd in **9.057–9.062**.

Furfural (14)—Official Final Action
9.066   *Reagent*

Furfural std soln.—Redistill furfural thru short packed fractionating column at atm. pressure, and collect fraction boiling at 161.2° (uncorrected).

Weigh 1 ml redistd furfural into 100 ml vol. flask and dil. to vol. with alcohol. Pipet 5 ml of this soln into 500 ml vol. flask and dil. to vol. with 50% alcohol (concn, ca 116 mg/L). Concd soln retains strength, but dil. soln does not.

9.067   *Determination*

Pipet 25 ml distd spirits into volatile acid distn flask, Fig. 9:3, with ᵀ joints and steam distill until 200 ml collects. If haze is present in distillate, dil. with known vol. alcohol. Det. A at 277 nm.

Det. A of std solns of furfural contg 0, 1, 2, 3, 4, and 5 mg furfural/L. Plot std curve or calc. av. A of 1 mg furfural/L, A' (ca 0.15). Furfural, mg/L = $(A/A') \times F$, where F is diln factor (vol. final soln on which A is detd/vol. sample).

Detection of Acetone, Other Ketones, Isopropanol, and Tertiary Butyl Alcohol— Official Final Action
9.068   *Reagent*

Mercuric sulfate soln.—Mix 5 g yellow HgO with 40 ml H_2O and add, with stirring, 20 ml H_2SO_4 and 40 ml H_2O. Stir until completely dissolved. (*Caution: See* **46.079**.)

9.069   *Determination*

To 2 ml distillate, **9.051**, add 3 ml H_2O and 10 ml $HgSO_4$ soln. Heat on boiling H_2O bath 3 min. White or yellow ppt forming within 3 min indicates presence of acetone, other ketones, or *tert*-butyl alcohol. Disregard any ppt forming after 3 min on boiling H_2O bath.

If no ppt forms, test for isopropanol as follows: Place 8 g CrO_3 in 100 ml Kohlrausch flask, and add

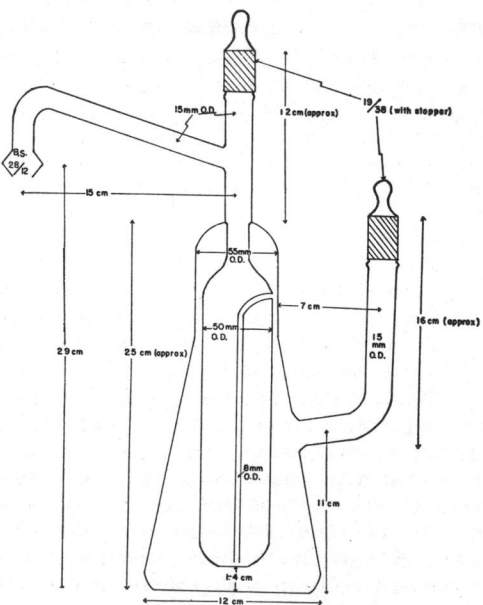

FIG. 9:3—Steam distillation flask

15 ml H_2O and 2 ml H_2SO_4. Connect flask with reflux condenser and add 5 ml sample very slowly thru condenser. Reflux 30 min; then cool and distill off 2 ml, collecting distillate in 10 ml graduated cylinder. Add 3 ml H_2O and 10 ml $HgSO_4$ soln, and proceed as above.

9.070 Sugars—Official Final Action
See Chapter 31

Methanol—Official Final Action
Chromotropic Acid Colorimetric Method (15)

9.071 *Reagents*

(a) *Potassium permanganate soln.*—Dissolve 3.0 g $KMnO_4$ and 15.0 ml H_3PO_4 in 100 ml H_2O. Prep. monthly.

(b) *Sodium salt of chromotropic acid (sodium 1,8-dihydroxynaphthalene-3,6-disulfonate) soln.*—5% aq. soln. Filter if not clear. Prep. weekly. Either acid or salt may be used.

9.072 *Purification of Chromotropic Acid*

If A of blank is >ca 0.05, purify reagent as follows:

Dissolve 10 g chromotropic acid or its salt in 25 ml H_2O. (Add 2 ml H_2SO_4 to aq. soln of salt to convert it to free acid.) Add 50 ml MeOH, heat just to boiling, and filter. Add 100 ml isopropanol to ppt free chromotropic acid. (Add more isopropanol to increase yield of purified acid.)

9.073 *Preparation of Sample*

Dil. or adjust sample to total alc. concn of 5–6%. Using 50 ml sample, distill thru simple still, collecting 40 ml distillate. Dil. to 50 ml with H_2O. (If alcohol has been detd previously, distillate may be adjusted to 5–6% alc. concn and used for this test.) If >0.05% MeOH by vol. is present, dil. to ca that concn with 5.5% alcohol. For samples contg <0.05% MeOH, measure 200 ml into efficient fractionating still, place system under total reflux 15 min, and then slowly distill at high rate of reflux (at least 20:1). Collect 10 ml distillate and dil. to 160 ml with H_2O.

9.074 *Determination*

Pipet 2 ml $KMnO_4$ soln into 50 ml vol. flask. Chill in ice bath, add 1 ml chilled dild sample, and let stand 30 min in ice bath. Decolorize with little dry $NaHSO_3$ and add 1 ml chromotropic acid soln. Add 15 ml H_2SO_4 slowly with swirling and place in hot (60–75°) H_2O bath 15 min. Cool, add enough H_2O to bring approx. to 50 ml mark, mix, and dil. to vol. with H_2O at room temp. Read A at 575 nm, using reagent blank of 5.5% alcohol treated similarly as ref. Treat *std MeOH soln* contg 0.025% by vol. MeOH in 5.5% alcohol simultaneously in same manner, and read A. (Temp. of std and sample should be within 1° since temp. affects A.)

Calc. quantity of MeOH in sample as follows: %

$MeOH = (A/A') \times 0.025 \times F$, where $A = A$ of sample, $A' = A$ of std MeOH, and F = diln factor of sample.

Example: Sample was dild 25 times; A of sample = 0.421; A of std MeOH = 0.368. Then $(0.421/0.368) \times 0.025 \times 25 = 0.715\%$.

(If color of sample is too intense, dil. with H_2SO_4-alcohol blank prepd as above. Not more than 3-fold diln is permitted, as ratio of chromotropic acid to HCHO is too low if diln is greater.)

9.075 *Immersion Refractometer Method (16)*

Det. Zeiss immersion refractometer reading at 17.5° of distillate obtained in detn of alcohol. If, on ref. to table, **9.076**, refractometer reading shows sp gr agreeing with that obtained in alcohol detn, **9.013**, it may be assumed that no MeOH is present. Low refractometer reading indicates presence of appreciable amt of MeOH. If absence from the soln of refractive substances other than H_2O and the alcohols is assured, this difference in refraction is conclusive evidence of presence of MeOH.

Addn of MeOH to alcohol decreases refractive index in direct proportion to amt added; hence quant. calcn is made by interpolation in table, **9.076**, of figures for pure alcohol and MeOH of same sp gr as sample.

Example.—Distillate has sp gr at 15.56° of 0.9625 and refractometer reading at 17.5° of 43.1. By interpolation in table, readings for alcohol and MeOH at this gravity are 65.2 and 31.7, resp., and difference is 33.5; $65.2 - 43.1 = 22.1$; $(22.1 \div 33.5) \times 100 = 66.0$, showing 66.0% of total alcohol present is MeOH.

9.076 See page 154.

Artificial Colors
(*See also* **9.005–9.008**)

9.077 *Marsh Test—Official First Action*

To 10 ml sample in 20 ml test tube add enough freshly shaken *Marsh reagent* (100 ml amyl alcohol, 3 ml H_3PO_4, and 3 ml H_2O) to nearly fill tube, and shake several times. Let layers sep. Color in lower layer indicates that sample has been colored with caramel, synthetic dye, or extractive material from uncharred white oak chips.

In absence of any color, test 10 ml in same manner, using enough fusel oil, amyl alcohol, or Pentasol to nearly fill tube and shaking several times. Deeply colored lower layer indicates synthetic dye. Det. its identity as in Chap. **34**. To confirm caramel apply one or more of following tests:

9.078 *Mathers Test—Official Final Action—* See **11.051**

9.079 ★ *Cyclohexanol Test—* ★
Official Final Action
See **9.059**, 10th ed.

9.076   *Scale readings on Zeiss immersion refractometer at 17.5°, corresponding to specific gravities of ethyl and methyl alcohol solutions*

Sp. Gr. 15.56° / 15.56°	Scale Readings			Sp. Gr. 15.56° / 15.56°	Scale Readings		
	Ethyl Alcohol	Methyl Alcohol	Differences		Ethyl Alcohol	Methyl Alcohol	Differences
1.0000	15.0	15.0	0.0	0.9720	51.5	27.0	24.5
.9990	15.8	15.3	0.5	.9710	53.0	27.5	25.5
.9980	16.6	15.6	1.0	.9700	54.6	28.1	26.5
.9970	17.5	15.9	1.6	.9690	56.1	28.7	27.4
.9960	18.5	16.2	2.3	.9680	57.6	29.2	28.4
.9950	19.4	16.5	2.9	.9670	59.1	29.6	29.5
.9940	20.4	16.9	3.5	.9660	60.6	30.1	30.5
.9930	21.4	17.2	4.2	.9650	62.0	30.6	31.4
.9920	22.5	17.5	5.0	.9640	63.3	31.0	32.3
.9910	23.6	17.9	5.7	.9630	64.6	31.5	33.1
.9900	24.7	18.2	6.5	.9620	65.8	31.9	33.9
.9890	25.9	18.6	7.3	.9610	67.0	32.4	34.6
.9880	27.1	19.0	8.1	.9600	68.1	32.8	35.3
.9870	28.4	19.5	8.9	.9590	69.2	33.3	35.9
.9860	29.6	19.9	9.7	.9580	70.2	33.7	36.5
.9850	31.0	20.4	10.6	.9570	71.2	34.1	37.1
.9840	32.4	20.8	11.6	.9560	72.1	34.5	37.6
.9830	33.8	21.3	12.5	.9550	73.0	34.9	38.1
.9820	35.2	21.8	13.4	.9540	73.8	35.3	38.5
.9810	36.7	22.3	14.4	.9530	74.6	35.6	39.0
.9800	38.3	22.8	15.5	.9520	75.4	35.9	39.5
.9790	39.9	23.4	16.5	.9510	76.2	36.2	40.0
.9780	41.5	24.0	17.5	.9500	76.9	36.5	40.4
.9770	43.1	24.5	18.6	.9490	77.6	36.8	40.8
.9760	44.8	25.0	19.8	.9480	78.3	37.0	41.3
.9750	46.5	25.5	21.0	.9470	79.0	37.3	41.7
.9740	48.2	26.0	22.2	.9460	79.7	37.6	42.1
.9730	49.8	26.5	23.3				

Scale readings are applicable only to instruments calibrated in arbitrary scale units proposed by Pulfrich, *Z. angew. Chem.*, 1899, p. 1168. According to this scale, 14.5 = 1.33300, 50.0 = 1.34650, and 100.0 = 1.36464. If instrument used is calibrated in other arbitrary units, refractive index corresponding to observed reading can be converted into equivalent Zeiss reading by referring to **47.004.**

9.080   Coal-Tar Colors
See **Chap. 34**

Tannin (17)—Official Final Action

9.081   *Reagents*

(a) *Folin-Denis reagent.*—To 750 ml H_2O add 100 g $Na_2WO_4.2H_2O$, 20 g phosphomolybdic acid, and 50 ml H_3PO_4. Reflux 2 hr, cool, and dil. to 1 L.

(b) *Sodium carbonate saturated soln.*—To each 100 ml H_2O add 35 g anhyd. Na_2CO_3, dissolve at 70–80°, and let cool overnight. Seed supersatd soln with crystal of $Na_2CO_3.10H_2O$, and after crystn filter thru glass wool.

(c) *Tannic acid std soln.*—0.1 mg/ml. Dissolve 100 mg tannic acid in 1 L H_2O. Prep. fresh soln for each detn.

9.082   *Preparation of Standard Curve*

Pipet 0 to 10 ml aliquots std tannic acid soln into 100 ml vol. flasks contg 75 ml H_2O. Add 5 ml Folin-Denis reagent and 10 ml Na_2CO_3 soln, and dil. to vol. with H_2O. Mix well and det. A after 30 min at 760 nm. Plot A against mg tannic acid/100 ml.

9.083   *Determination*

Using 1 ml sample, det. A as in **9.082** and obtain mg tannic acid/100 ml from std curve. If A is too

great, repeat detn on 1 + 4 diln of sample. Samples treated as above may be compared in Nessler tubes against freshly prepd tannic acid stds treated in same manner.

CORDIALS AND LIQUEURS

9.084   Physical Examination—Procedure

Note and record following: (a) Appearance, whether bright or turbid and presence of sediment; (b) color and depth of color; (c) odor; (d) taste.

9.085   Specific Gravity—Official Final Action —See 9.011

9.086   Alcohol—Official Final Action

(a) *By weight.*—See **9.022.**

(b) *By volume.*—See **9.013.** Use pycnometer calibrated at 15.56°.

Methanol—Official Final Action

9.087   *Preparation of Sample*

Measure sample contg 20–25 ml absolute alcohol into distg flask, add enough H_2O to make total ca 100 ml, and distill, collecting ca 50 ml distillate. To distillate add 4 g NaCl for each 10 ml H_2O and let stand several hr for complete satn.

Transfer to separator, using ca 10 ml satd NaCl soln to wash out container, and shake with 25 ml pet ether. When sepn is complete, transfer aq. soln to second separator contg 25 ml pet ether; shake, and transfer aq. soln to third separator, also contg 25 ml pet ether; shake, and when sepn is complete, drain aq. soln into 200 ml distg flask. Meanwhile add 25 ml satd NaCl soln to first separator and follow sample thru with this soln, finally adding washings to sample soln in distg flask. Repeat this operation with second 25 ml portion satd NaCl soln, finally adding this also to distg flask. Distill mixt. into 50 ml vol. flask, using suitable adapter. After 48–49 ml distills, disconnect app., fill flask to mark with H_2O, mix, and det. MeOH as in **9.074** or **9.075**.

9.088 Aldehydes—Official Final Action

Measure 100–200 ml sample into distn flask. If solid content is $\leq$25 g/100 ml, add 12.5–25 ml H_2O; if >25 g/100 ml, add 5 ml H_2O for each 10 g solid matter present; distill slowly, collecting vol. distillate equal to that of sample, and proceed as in **9.053**

9.089 Fusel Oil—Official Final Action

Using 50 ml prepd distillate, **9.088**, proceed as in **9.056, 9.059–9.062,** or **9.065.**

9.090 Total Solids—Official Final Action

(a) *From specific gravity of dealcoholized sample.*— Transfer residue from alcohol detn, **9.086**(b), to original pycnometer with H_2O, dil. to mark with H_2O at 15.56°, and mix. Adjust temp. of pycnometer and contents to 20°; adjust meniscus to mark, using capillary tube or narrow strips of filter paper to remove any excess liq. while in 20° bath. Weigh, and calc. sp gr of liq. From **47.008** det. % dry substance and corresponding sp gr at 20°/4°. Sp gr at 20°/4° $\times$ % dry substance = total solids (g/100 ml).

(b) *By evaporation.*—Fill 25 ml vol. flask with sample at 20°, and adjust meniscus, using capillary tube or narrow strips of filter paper, while flask is immersed in bath held at same temp. ca 30 min. Quant. transfer contents of flask to 100 ml vol. flask with H_2O and dil. to vol. with H_2O at convenient temp. At same temp. pipet 10 ml dild sample into dish contg sand and dry as in **31.008**. Wt residue $\times$ 40 = total solids (g/100 ml).

(c) *From refractive index of dealcoholized sample.*— Restore residue from alcohol detn to original vol. by evapg or dilg as necessary. Det. refractometer reading of soln at 20° and obtain corresponding % dry substance. From **47.008** det. sp gr corresponding to % dry substance found and multiply by % dry substance to obtain g total solids/100 ml sample. To obtain % total solids, divide total solids/100 ml by sp gr, **9.011.**

9.091 Glycerol—Official Final Action

(a) *Products containing 5 g/100 ml or less of total solids.*—See **11.010**(a) or (b).

(b) *Products containing more than 5 g/100 ml of*

total solids.—Into porcelain dish measure sample ($\leq$100 ml) contg $\leq$25 g solid matter and evap. on steam bath to remove alcohol. Transfer to 500 ml erlenmeyer, using such amt of H_2O that final vol. will be ca 100 ml, and proceed as in **11.011.**

9.092 Sucrose—Official Final Action

(a) *By polarization.*—Pipet, into evapg dish, vol. sample equiv. to 52 g as calcd from sp gr, **9.011,** and exactly neutze with 1*N* NaOH, calcg amt required from acidity, **9.099.** Evap. on steam bath to remove alcohol, transfer to 200 ml vol. flask, and proceed as in **31.025** or **31.026,** beginning "add necessary clarifying agent ..." in **31.025**(a).

(b) *By reducing sugars before and after inversion.*— Approximate sugar content of sample from total solids, **9.090,** and pipet sample contg 5–7 g sugars into porcelain dish; exactly neutze with 1*N* NaOH soln, calcg amt required from acidity, **9.099,** and evap. on steam bath to remove alcohol. Transfer to 200 ml vol. flask, clarify with neut. $Pb(OAc)_2$ soln, **31.021**(d), remove excess Pb with K oxalate, and proceed as in **31.032,** using **31.039** for detn of reducing sugars.

9.093 Ash—Official Final Action

Proceed as in **31.012** or **31.013,** using 25 ml sample.

9.094 Soluble and Insoluble Ash— Official Final Action

Using ash from **9.093,** proceed as in **31.015.**

9.095 Alkalinity of Soluble Ash— Official Final Action

Use sol. ash from **9.094,** proceed as in **31.016.**

9.096 Alkalinity of Insoluble Ash— Official Final Action

Using insol. ash from **9.094,** proceed as in **31.017.**

9.097 Phosphorus—Official Final Action

Using ash obtained in **9.093,** det. P_2O_5 as in **11.032.**

9.098 Caramel—Official Final Action— See **11.051**

9.099 Total Acidity—Official First Action

Place ca 600 ml H_2O in 800 ml beaker, add ca 1 ml phthln, and titr. to pink soln with 0.1*N* NaOH. Add 10–20 ml sample (unless this quantity gives soln such deep color that it will obscure end point, in which case 5 ml may be used) and titr. to pink comparable to that of soln before sample was added. Calc. acidity as g/100 ml sample in terms of predominating acid present in sample.

9.100 Characteristic Acids—Preparation of Sample—Procedure

Use sample contg $\leq$30 g solids and $\leq$200 mg acid to be detd, as calcd from acidity; evap. to ca 30 ml and treat as in **9.101–9.104.**

9.101 Tartaric Acid—Official Final Action

Designate as x the ml $1N$ alkali required to neutze sample, add $x + 3$ ml $1N$ NaOH, heat to ca 60°, and let stand overnight. Add $x + 6$ ml $1N$ H_2SO_4 and continue as in **22.062**, beginning "Transfer adjusted sample to 250 ml vol. flask ..."

9.102 Citric Acid—Official Final Action

Transfer adjusted sample to 250 ml vol. flask, using enough H_2O to make total vol. 70 ml, and continue as in **22.065**, beginning "Add 2 ml $1N$ HNO_3 ..."

9.103 Total Malic Acid (Laevo and Inactive)— Official First Action

Proceed as in **9.101** to obtain filtrate and washings from KH tartrate; then evap. this soln to ca 15 ml and continue as in **22.071**, beginning "Transfer with small amt H_2O ..."

9.104 Laevo-Malic Acid—Official First Action

Proceed as in **9.101** to obtain filtrate and washings from KH tartrate; then evap. to ca 5 ml on steam bath and proceed as in **22.079**, beginning "Cool, add NaOH $(1 + 1)$ ..."

9.105 Volatile Esters—Official Final Action

Measure 100–500 ml sample into distg flask and steam distil as in **12.026**, collecting vol. distillate at least twice as great as vol. alcohol contained in sample. (If detn **9.106** is to be made, use 500 ml sample.) Disconnect app. and wash out condenser with little H_2O. Add ca 1 ml phthln, and titr. to pink that persists >1 min, using $0.1N$ NaOH or KOH. Add measured excess of 25–50 ml $0.1N$ alkali to soln, reflux 1 hr, cool, and titr. excess alkali with $0.1N$ H_2SO_4. Calc. number of ml $0.1N$ alkali used in saponification of esters as EtOAc. 1 ml $0.1N$ alkali = 8.8 mg EtOAc.

9.106 ★ Gamma Undecalactone ★ (Qualitative Test) (18)— Official Final Action

(Peach and apricot cordials)

See **9.087**, 10th ed.

9.107 ★ Optical-Crystallographic ★ Properties of Hydrazino-γ-Undecalactone—Official Final Action

See **9.088**, 10th ed.

9.108 Benzaldehyde—Official Final Action

See **19.094–19.095**.

9.109 Thujone (19)—Official First Action

To 500 ml sample add 1 ml *freshly distd aniline* and 1 ml H_3PO_4, and reflux 30 min on steam bath. Distill two 100 ml portions; reject first and test second for thujone as follows:

Add 0.5 g *semicarbazide hydrochloride* and 0.6 g anhyd. NaOAc (or 1.0 g crystd salt) and let mixt. stand overnight. Distill off alcohol at min. pressure. Steam distill to remove essential oils and other volatile material; collect and reject first ca 15 ml distillate. Wash down condenser with little alcohol and with H_2O. Cool sample, add 1 ml H_2SO_4 $(1 + 1)$, and again steam distill, collecting 20 ml distillate in cylinder. Pour distillate into small separator, and add 20 ml ether, using receiver as measure. Shake and sep. ether soln. Add 10 ml 65% alcohol and let ether evap. spontaneously. After all ether evaps, note odor of residue. Odor of thujone will be apparent if ≥ 2 mg is present in soln, provided it is not masked by presence of other odoriferous substances. Make modified Legal test as follows:

To soln obtained as above, add 1 ml *10% ZnSO₄ soln* and 0.25 ml freshly prepd *aq. Na nitroprusside soln* (0.1 g/ml). Slowly, with constant stirring, add 2 ml 5% NaOH soln. Let stand 1–2 min. Add 1.5 ml HOAc and mix. Ppt of raspberry red color (resembling alcohol ppt of red fruit juice) shows presence of thujone. Neg. test is shown by similar ppt having appearance similar to that of alcohol ppt from apple jelly or other light colored fruit.

SELECTED REFERENCES

(1) JAOAC **39**, 723(1956); **41**, 118(1958).
(2) JAOAC **38**, 821(1955); **39**, 730(1956); **40**, 440 (1957).
(3) Ind. Eng. Chem., Anal. Ed. **14**, 237(1942); JAOAC **28**, 88(1945); **41**, 118(1958); **42**, 329 (1959).
(4) JAOAC **40**, 436(1957); **42**, 327(1959); **43**, 657 (1960).
(5) Ind. Eng. Chem. **18**, 841(1926); JAOAC **35**, 239(1952).
(6) JAOAC **37**, 945(1954); **46**, 299(1963); **47**, 720 (1964).
(7) JAOAC **50**, 334, 338(1967).
(8) JAOAC **53**, 12(1970).
(9) JAOAC **49**, 498(1966).
(10) JAOAC **37**, 921(1954).
(11) JAOAC **42**, 331(1959); **43**, 655(1960); **44**, 383 (1961).
(12) JAOAC **46**, 285(1963).
(13) JAOAC **51**, 915(1968).
(14) JAOAC **43**, 659(1960); **44**, 392(1961).
(15) JAOAC **41**, 121(1958); **42**, 336(1959).
(16) J. Am. Chem. Soc. **27**, 964(1905); Ind. Eng. Chem. **19**, 844(1927); JAOAC **28**, 800(1945).
(17) JAOAC **35**, 255(1952).
(18) JAOAC **16**, 420(1933); **19**, 75, 183(1936).
(19) Ann. chim. anal. **13**, 227(1908); Schweiz. Wochschr. **49**, 337, 507(1911); JAOAC **19**, 120 (1936); **20**, 69(1937).

10. Beverages: Malt Beverages and Brewing Materials*

BEER
(Unless otherwise directed, express results as % by wt.)

10.001 Preparation of Sample— Official Final Action

Remove CO_2 by transferring sample to large flask and shaking, gently at first and then vigorously, keeping temp. of beer at 20–25°. If necessary, remove suspended material by passing the CO_2-free beer thru dry filter paper.

Color

Spectrophotometric Method (Standard Reference Color Method) (1) —Official Final Action

10.002 Apparatus

Spectrophotometer.—Capable of isolating band width of ≤ 1 nm at 430 nm with wavelength and photometer scales checked and corrected for inaccuracies in accordance with instructions contained in NBS Letter Circular LC-1017 of Jan. 1967.

10.003 Preparation of Sample

Partially degas sample by opening bottle at room temp., pouring contents into 1 L erlenmeyer, and swirling gently. Avoid formation of turbidity, and conduct partial degassing and readings as rapidly as possible.

10.004 Determination

Place prepd sample in suitable cell and det. A at 430 nm and at 700 nm.

10.005 Calculations

Calc. A from thickness at which read to $\frac{1}{2}''$ $(A_{1/2})$. If $(A_{1/2 \text{ at } 430 \text{ nm}}) \times 0.039 > (A_{1/2 \text{ at } 700 \text{ nm}})$, sample is assumed "free of turbidity" and color is calcd as follows:

Beer color intensity $= 10 \times (A_{1/2 \text{ at } 430 \text{ nm}})$. If $(A_{1/2 \text{ at } 700 \text{ nm}}) > 0.039 \times (A_{1/2 \text{ at } 430 \text{ nm}})$, clarify sample by centrfg or filtering, and redet. A.

Report color intensity values to nearest 0.1 unit.

Photometric Method—Official Final Action

10.006 Apparatus

Use any com. available filter photometer or abridged spectrophtr utilizing moderately broad spectral band and having adequate sensitivity. Use light filter with peak T in range 420–450 nm (blue-violet) for max. sensitivity and precision. (Filters for wavelengths in blue or blue-green range may also be used, but result in reduced precision.) Cell should be of such size, if possible, as to give A values between 0.187 and 0.699 (20–65% T), where max. precision is achieved. Use same size cell for both color measurement and calibration.

10.007 Calibration of Photometers

Beer calibration method.—For each color intensity value for which measurements are to be made, obtain 6–8 replicate bottles of beer which are low in air content and have been pasteurized.

Det. color intensity value of the beer by averaging readings obtained for at least 2 bottles by Standard Reference Color (SRC) Method, 10.004. If these values must be obtained from another laboratory, ship bottles of beer by the fastest available method, marked to avoid rough handling.

Det. photometer reading of the beer by averaging readings obtained for at least 2 bottles with wavelength and cell as in 10.006. Calc. calibration factor in accordance with photometer instructions or prep. calibration curve by plotting A or photometer scale reading against the SRC value for sample, assuming that curve passes thru origin. This calibration will be accurate only for readings in immediate vicinity of calibration point. If it is desired to accurately measure color intensity of more than one sample or colors over range of values, calibrate photometer for each sample or use beers having colors which cover desired range. Calc. av. calibration factor or prep. av. calibration curve.

10.008 Preparation of Sample—See 10.003

10.009 Determination

Place sample in cell and det. photometer reading. Calc. color intensity value, using calibration factor or calibration curve. Report color to nearest 0.1 unit.

Total Haze after Chilling (2)— Official First Action

10.010 Reagents

(Use turbidity-free distd H_2O thruout.)

(a) Hydrazine sulfate soln.—1%. Dissolve 1.000 g hydrazine sulfate in H_2O (may require 4–6 hr) and dil. to 100 ml.

---

* Many methods in this chapter have been tested by both American Society of Brewing Chemists and Association of Official Analytical Chemists and have been adopted by both Associations. See "Methods of Analysis, A.S.B.C.," 6th rev. ed., 1958.

(b) *Stock formazin suspension.*—Dissolve 2.500 g hexamethylenetetramine (formin) in 25 ml H_2O in 125 ml erlenmeyer, pipet in 25 ml hydrazine sulfate soln, (a), and stopper flask. Formazin begins to ppt in 6–8 hr and pptn is complete within 24 hr. Prep. every 3 months.

(c) *1000 Turbidity std.*—Dil. 14.5 ml well mixed stock suspension, (b), to 1000 ml with H_2O in vol. flask. Prep. weekly. (1000 formazin turbidity units (FTU) on empirical formazin turbidity scale represents reflectance of insol. reaction products of 0.0725 g hydrazine sulfate with 0.7250 g hexamethylenetetramine dild to 1000 ml.)

(d) *Working stds for visual method.*—Prep. suitable dilns, daily, of 1000 turbidity std with H_2O. FTU stds <100 are suitable for fresh beers; higher stds may be required for older samples. Use increments of 10 FTU for stds <100 FTU; in 20 FTU increments for 100–200; and in 50 FTU increments for >200 FTU.

Visual Method

10.011   Apparatus

(a) *Clark Turbidimeter, Model T.*—Code 756. Available from Cargille Scientific Inc., 55 Commerce Rd, Cedar Grove, NJ 07009. Viewing box of same dimensions and lighting is also suitable.

(b) *Red Plexiglas sheet.*—¼″ thick, ca 1 sq ft.

(c) *Constant temperature bath.*—0±0.2°.

(d) *Ice-water bath.*—Contg few drops wetting agent.

(e) *Flint glass bottles.*—Of same dimensions as flint glass bottles contg beer test samples; or clear drinking glasses (shells), 10 oz, od ca 66 mm at bottom and 67 mm at top.

10.012   Determination

(Make comparisons with samples at 0°. Keep test samples in 0° bath when not matching turbidities.)

Place container of beer to be tested in upright position in 0° bath and hold 24 hr.

Prep. series of formazin turbidity working stds covering range of expected turbidities of test samples. Fill into flint glass bottles of same dimensions as those holding beer test samples.

If beer is in flint glass bottles, carefully remove bottle from constant temp. bath without disturbing sediment. Dip bottle into ice-H_2O bath contg few drops wetting agent to prevent fogging or accumulation of H_2O droplets on bottle while in viewing box. Place bottle of beer in viewing box between 2 bottles of formazin turbidity working stds. Compare turbidities by viewing thru red Plexiglas sheet placed 2″ in front of bottles. Change formazin stds until that working std is found which most closely matches turbidity of test sample.

If beer is not in flint glass bottles, carefully remove container from constant temp. bath and, without disturbing sediment, pour beer into clear 10 oz

drinking glass (shell) which has been pre-chilled by standing (external contact only) in ice-H_2O bath contg wetting agent. Degassing is not necessary. Use formazin turbidity working stds in identical 10 oz glasses to match turbidities as above for bottles.

Report as total haze of the beer after chilling, formazin turbidity units (FTU) of working std giving closest match. In range up to 100 FTU, report to nearest 10 FTU; 100–200, 20; >200, 50.

Nephelometric Method

10.013   Calibration

Nephelometer.—Prep. calibration curve at 580 nm or other suitable wavelength for instrument employed by use of series of working stds or dilns of 1000 turbidity std. If readout device of nephelometer is 0–100 scale of arbitrary units, set needle to indicate 0 units when cuvet is filled with turbidity-free distd H_2O and 100 units when it is filled with selected formazin turbidity std.

10.014   Determination

Place containers of beer to be tested in upright position in 0° bath and hold 24 hr.

Pre-chill nephelometer cuvet in small ice-H_2O bath contg wetting agent (external contact only). Carefully remove container of beer from bath and, without disturbing sediment, rinse and fill cuvet with test sample. Place cuvet in ice-H_2O bath contg wetting agent, and degas beer by stirring with thermometer. When beer temp. is 0°, place cuvet in sample chamber of nephelometer and det. reading. (Beer must be at 0° when taking reading.)

10.015   Calculations

Calc. FTU total haze from calibration curve or by formula: $FTU = R \times S/100$, where R = nephelometer (galvanometer scale) reading; S = FTU of formazin turbidity std used for calibration of nephelometer.

10.016 Specific Gravity—Official Final Action

Det. sp gr of prepd sample, **10.001**, at 20/20° (in air) as in **9.011**, but use pycnometers described in **10.088**(i) and **10.089**(b) or (c).

10.017 Apparent Extract— Official Final Action

Find apparent ext corresponding to sp gr detd at 20/20° from **47.009**, reporting to second decimal place.

10.018 Alcohol by Volume— Official Final Action

See **11.003**, but use pycnometers described in **10.088**(i) and **10.089**(b) or (c).

Alcohol by Weight

10.019 Specific Gravity Method— Official Final Action

See **9.022**, but use pycnometers described in **10.088**(i) and **10.089**(b) or (c).

Refractometer Method (3)— Official First Action

10.020 Apparatus

(a) *Immersion refractometer.*—Bausch & Lomb, or equiv., with prisms covering range 1.32–1.37 *n*.

(b) *Water bath.*—See **10.088**(k).

(c) *Pycnometer.*—See **10.088**(i) and **10.089**(b) or (c).

10.021 Calibration

Adjust refractometer light to give max. contrast between light and dark fields. Adjust color compensator and focus for sharp, color-free dividing line. H_2O double-distd from glass should read ca 14.50 at 20°. Read H_2O before each sample series. Rinse prism with H_2O after each sample and dry with soft tissue.

Prep. calibration curve to convert refractometer readings and sp gr detns to % alcohol by wt by analyzing beers covering alcohol range of interest by **10.019** and **10.022**. Plot results, using ordinates $(R - N)$, where R = refractometer reading ($R_{beer} - R_{water}$), $N = 1000 \times$ (sp gr $- 1.00000$), and abscissa = % alcohol by wt (**10.019**). Fit least squares line to adequate number of points to get accuracy desired. Det. equation of line and slope. Calc. % alcohol by wt by formula or read from calibration curve. % alcohol by wt $= F \times (R - N) + C$, where F = slope of calibration line, and C = constant of calibration curve equation.

10.022 Determination

Det. sp gr of decarbonated beer by **10.016**. Place refractometer cuvet contg distd H_2O and clear decarbonated beer samples in 20° H_2O bath. Place prism of refractometer in H_2O cuvet and check temp. after 15 min. Make 5 readings to nearest 0.1 scale division and average results (R_{water}). Transfer dry prism to beer sample cuvet, wait at least 1 min, make 5 readings to nearest 0.1 scale division, and average results (R_{beer}). Calc. % alcohol by wt by formula or read from calibration curve.

10.023 Real Extract—Official Final Action

(a) Evap. 75–100 ml sample (accurately weighed to 0.1 g) on H_2O bath or asbestos plate, at temp. ≤80°, to ca ⅓ original vol. Cool, make to original wt with H_2O, and det. sp gr with pycnometer at 20/20°. Det. real ext directly from **47.009**.

(b) If no anti-foam material was used in detn of alcohol, **10.018**, quant. transfer residue with hot H_2O to 100 ml vol. flask. Cool, and dil. to 100 ml at 20°. Det. sp gr at 20/20°, **10.016**, and find ext directly

from **47.009.** If 100 ml beer was taken, correct as follows:

Ext found $\times$ sp gr of dealcoholized beer

/sp gr of beer = g ext/100 g beer.

10.024 Extract of Original Wort— Official Final Action

Calc. from following formula and report to first decimal place:

$$O = \frac{(A \times 2.0665) + E}{100 + (A \times 1.0665)} \times 100, \text{ in which}$$

O = ext of orig. wort; A = % alcohol by wt (g/100 g beer); and E = % real ext, **10.023**(a) or (b).

10.025 Real Degree of Fermentation or Real Attenuation—Official Final Action

Calc. as follows and report to first decimal place:

(orig. ext − real ext) × 100/orig. ext.

10.026 Apparent Degree of Fermentation or Apparent Attenuation— Official Final Action

Calc. as follows and report to first decimal place:

(orig. ext − apparent ext) × 100/orig. ext.

Total Acidity (4)—Official Final Action

10.027 Indicator Titration Method

Bring 250 ml H_2O to boil and continue boiling 2 min. From fast flowing pipet add 25 ml beer previously decarbonated by shaking and filtering, **10.001**. After emptying pipet, continue heating 60 sec, regulating heat so that soln resumes boiling during final 30 sec. Remove from heat, stir 5 sec, and cool rapidly to room temp.

Add 0.5 ml 0.5% phthln. Titr. with 0.1N NaOH against white background. Make frequent color comparisons with sample of equal vol. and diln to which has been added approx. anticipated amt of alkali but no indicator. Titr. to first appearance of faint pink. Read buret. Add 0.2 ml more alkali; color should then be permanent, definite pinkish-red, indicative of over-titrn. Take first buret reading as end point.

Observe strictly all details of method. However, 100 ml H_2O, 10 ml beer, and 0.2 ml indicator may be used in place of amts specified above. (Use potentiometric titrn method, **10.028**, for beers of dark color which (even when dild) may not permit judging phthln end point with necessary precision.)

Report results: (a) as lactic acid, to nearest 0.01% (1 ml 0.1N alkali = 0.0090 g lactic acid); or (b) as ml 1N alkali, to nearest 0.1 ml, necessary for neutzn of 100 g beer.

10.028 Potentiometric Titration Method

Use glass-calomel electrode system. Decarbonate beer completely by shaking, **10.001**. Using 50 ml undild sample (or such quantity as best suits titrn assembly), titr. potentiometrically with 0.1N NaOH to pH 8.2. Add alkali in 1.5 ml portions to ca pH 7.6, and in 0.15 ml portions from there to pH 8.2. Make sure that complete equilibrium and good convergence are attained before reading buret at exactly pH 8.2. Report results as in **10.027.**

Precautions: Observe all details of good potentiometric technic, including following: Stdze potentiometer against fresh $0.05M$ K acid phthalate, **45.007**(c), before and after any set of titrns; read potentiometer to nearest 0.02 unit; use flexible shielding around electrode leads and motor cords; ground motor and motor cords, preferably to H_2O pipes; avoid contact between electrodes and glass beaker; use proper stirring speed to assure quick mixing but to avoid foaming which may temporarily trap some of alkali added; stop titrn at $\leq$pH 8.6 to minimize alkali contamination of glass electrode; check batteries frequently. Follow manufacturer's instructions for potentiometer used.

Hydrogen-Ion Concentration (pH)—Official Final Action

10.029   *Electrometric Method*

Det. pH of undild sample, **10.001,** using glass-calomel electrode system. Follow manufacturer's instructions for potentiometer used. Check pH meter before and after use against std K acid phthalate buffer, **45.007**(c). Observe precautions in **10.028.** Report results to nearest 0.05 pH.

10.030   Volatile Acids—Official Final Action

Using 100 ml beer, proceed as in **11.038.** Express result as HOAc, g/100 ml. 1 ml $0.1N$ alkali = 0.0060 g HOAc.

10.031   Reducing Sugars— Official Final Action

Dil. 25 ml prepd sample, **10.001,** measured at 20°, to 100 ml with H_2O at same temp. Det. reducing sugars in 25 ml of this soln by Munson-Walker method, **31.065,** or dil. 50 ml beer with H_2O to 100 ml and use Lane-Eynon method, **31.064.** Express result as g maltose/100 ml beer. For conversion to % by wt, divide results by sp gr of beer.

10.032   Dextrin—Official Final Action

To 25 ml prepd sample, **10.001,** measured at 20° in erlenmeyer, add 15 ml HCl (sp gr 1.125) and dil. to 200 ml. Attach flask to reflux condenser, and keep in boiling H_2O bath 2 hr. Cool, nearly neutze with NaOH soln (1 + 1), dil. to 250 ml, filter, and det. glucose as in **31.053.** [Glucose (g/100 ml) − (1.053 × maltose, **10.031**)] × 0.9 = g dextrin/100 ml beer.

10.033   Glycerol—Official Final Action— *See* 11.010(b)

10.034   Ash—Official Final Action

Evap. to dryness 50 ml prepd sample, **10.001,** measured at 20°. Proceed as in **31.012** or **31.013.**

10.035   Phosphorus—Official Final Action

To 50 ml prepd sample, **10.001,** measured at 20°, add 20 ml *2% $Ca(OAc)_2$ soln,* evap. to dryness, and ignite at low redness to white ash. Add 10–15 ml boiling HNO_3 (1 + 9) and det. P_2O_5 as in **2.031.** (Washing phosphomolybdate ppt with 1% KNO_3 soln instead of H_2O prevents creeping.)

10.036   Protein—Official Final Action

To 25 ml prepd sample, **10.001,** at 20° in Kjeldahl flask, add 2–3 ml H_2SO_4 and conc. to sirupy consistency. Det N as in **2.051.** % N × 6.25 = % protein.

$$\% \text{ protein} = [(\text{ml } 0.1N \text{ acid} - \text{ml } 0.1N \text{ base})$$
$$\times 1.4 \times 6.25 \times 100]/(\text{sp gr}$$
$$\times \text{ml sample} \times 1000).$$

Carbon Dioxide—Official Final Action
Manometric Method (5)

10.037   *Apparatus*

(a) *Piercing apparatus.*—(1) *For bottles.*—Consists of gas-tight packing box and fastening for adjustment over container, and hollow spike connected to accurate pressure gage and outlet valve. Check gages frequently. (2) *For cans.*—Consists of metal frame in which can is placed. Top of app., which is pressed or screwed down and locked over can top, contains hollow spike surrounded by compressible rubber sealing plug; hollow spike leads to accurate pressure gage and outlet valve. (One app., adjustable for use with both bottles and cans, may be employed.)

Notes: Piercing devices can be obtained from Zahm and Nagel Co., Inc., 74 Jewett Ave, Buffalo, NY 14214; and Micromat Co., 548 Piermont Ave, Hillsdale, NJ 07642.

For suitable manometer for calibrating gages, *see* Gray and Stone, Ind. Eng. Chem., Anal. Ed., **10,** 15 (1938). Dead wt testing unit suitable for calibration can be obtained from AMETEK/Mansfield & Green, Solon, OH 44139; Amthor Testing Instrument Co., Inc., 45 Van Sinderen Ave, Brooklyn, NY 11207; Dresser Industries, Inc., 250 E. Main St, Stratford, CT 06497, and other companies.

(b) *Absorption buret.*—(Fig. 10:1). Consists of graduated tube (one type has 0–5 ml graduated in 0.05 ml divisions, 5–15 ml in 0.1 ml, and 15–25 ml in 0.5 ml) with bulb marked at 40 ml, and closed at each end by stopcocks. Connect buret to valve of piercing app. and to leveling bulb by transparent alk.-resistant plastic or rubber tubing. (Burets are available from Zahm and Nagel Co. and Micromat Co., (a), and from New York Laboratory Supply Co.)

(c) *Leveling bulb.*—Approx. 300 ml, with support.

10.038   *Determination*

Bring samples to 25° by immersion in H_2O bath at 25°. If sample is bottle, make scratch on bottle at beer level. If sample is can, weigh unopened can.

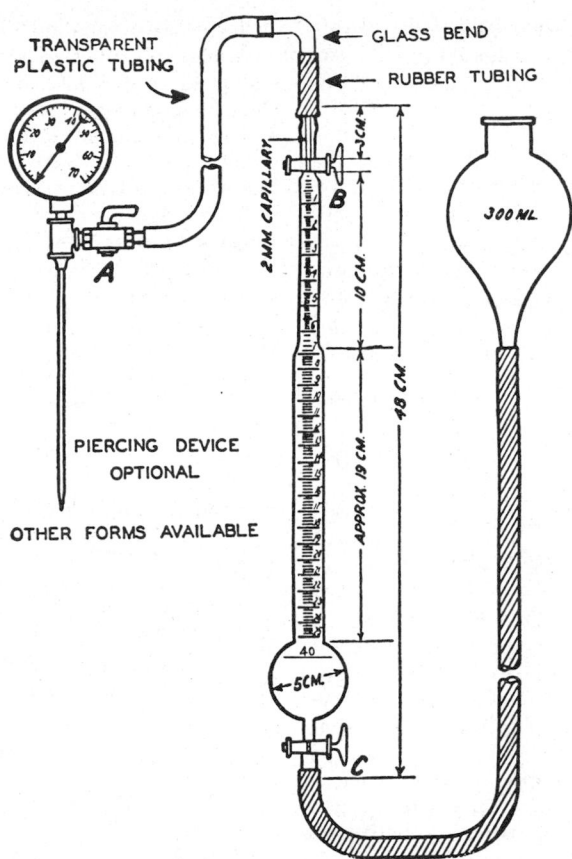

FIG. 10:1—Absorption buret (other forms available)

Fill leveling bulb and then absorption buret with 15% NaOH soln. Displace air in tubing connecting it to piercing app. completely with H_2O or NaOH soln and attach piercing device to bottle or can. Take care that no air is trapped in system that will be carried into buret during detn.

With valve of piercing device closed, pierce bottle crown or can by depressing hollow steel spike. Shake bottle or can until pressure reaches constant max. value. Stop shaking and record pressure reading. Open valve on piercing app. cautiously and let gas-foam mixt. flow into absorption buret until pressure gage reads zero. Close valve and shake or tip buret (depending on its construction) until CO_2 is absorbed and gas vol. in buret reaches max. value. Adjust leveling bottle to equalize hydrostatic pressure and read vol. of "headspace air" contained in buret.

If detn of "total air" is also desired, continue evolution of gas from bottle or can by shaking it. Absorb evolved CO_2 by swirling and shaking buret. Continue shaking and CO_2 absorption until there is no further increase in vol. of unabsorbed gas in buret. Final vol. of unabsorbed gas may be considered the "air content" or "total air" of container.

Disconnect piercing device from package and in-sert thermometer to be sure that temp. is 25°. Det. headspace vol. as follows:

(a) *Bottles.*—Fill bottle to top with H_2O and pour from it into 100 ml graduated cylinder until liq. level in bottle corresponds to scratch mark placed on it. Vol. in ml of liq. poured off is headspace vol.

(b) *Cans.*—Empty beer from can and let it drain completely. Weigh empty can. Fill empty can with H_2O and weigh. Subtract wt empty can from wt un-opened can of beer to obtain wt of beer before open-ing can. Divide beer wt by sp gr of beer to obtain vol. beer in can in ml. Subtract wt empty can from wt can filled with H_2O. Difference is wt H_2O, equiv. to vol. in ml required to fill can completely. Subtract vol. beer from vol. can to obtain headspace in can before opening. (This detn of headspace in cans is only approx. correct, due to unknown degree of bulg-ing of cans under pressure, distortion of end on open-ing or puncturing can, and difficulty of accurately defining when can is completely filled with H_2O.)

Calc. % CO_2 by wt and vol. as follows:

% CO_2 by wt = $[P - (ml$ "head-space air" $\times$ $14.7/ml$ headspace$)] \times 0.00965$, where P = absolute pressure in psi = gage pressure + 14.7.

Vols CO_2 = % CO_2 by wt $\times$ sp gr of beer/0.1976
= % CO_2 by wt $\times$ 5.0607 $\times$ sp gr of beer.

Report % by wt to second decimal, and vols CO_2 to first decimal.

Foam Collapse Rate (6)—Official Final Action
Sigma Value Method

10.039   *Apparatus*

(a) *Special foam funnel.*—Marked at 800 ml. Kontes Glass Co. drawing No. 9357B or CGW drawing No. XA-7396 (Special Apparatus Section, Corning Glass Works).

(b) *Stopwatch.*—Or clock that indicates sec.

10.040   *Determination*

Perform detn at room temp. (22–27°).

Attemperate beer in container to 25±0.5° in H_2O bath or constant temp. room.

Clean foam funnel thoroly with warm detergent soln; rinse well, first with warm H_2O and then with H_2O at ca 25°. Clamp funnel at suitable ht to ringstand and let drain 1 min.

Make foam detns immediately after draining.

Open beer container, rest side of container on funnel edge, and direct stream of beer into center of funnel, pouring smoothly to avoid entrapping air in beer. Pour until foam reaches 800 ml mark, start stopwatch, and cover funnel with 100 mm or larger watch glass. After 30 sec, open stopcock to let all beer flow out in 25–30 sec at as uniform rate as possible; open stopcock wide for last 1–2 sec until small amt of foam drains out. Immediately close stopcock, reset stopwatch to 0, and start it again. Discard drained beer.

After exactly 200 sec, let beer formed from collapsed foam flow out into 100 ml graduate at such rate that all beer drains off in 25–30 sec (total time 225–230 sec). Just as last drop of beer drains off, close stopcock and stop stopwatch. Record time in sec as "t," and ml drained beer as "b."

To collapse remaining foam, wash down inside of funnel with 2 ml isopropanol or butyl alcohol delivered from fine-point pipet. Open stopcock wide and let liq. drain into 25 ml graduate 1 min.

Record ml drained beer as "c" (ml liq. drained −2 ml defoaming agent).

10.041   *Calculations*

$$\text{Sigma value} = \frac{t}{2.303 \log \dfrac{b + c}{c}},$$

where t = time of foam collapse (225–230 sec), b = ml beer collapsed from foam in time t, c = ml beer from residual foam at time t. Report to nearest whole number.

Foam Flashing Method
10.042   *Apparatus*

(a) *Compressed carbon dioxide gas.*—Contained in steel cylinder equipped with reducing valve.

(b) *Pressure surge tank.*—Approx. 2 gal., fitted with inlet and outlet gas connections, bleeder valve, and pressure gage. (Or use ¼″ Type 10 Pressure Regulator, 3–60 psi, Lexington Control, Inc., PO Box 132, Burlington, MA 01803.)

(c) *Orifice foam flashing apparatus.*—Foam flashing orifice tube connected to stainless steel Master Volume Gage Bottle attachment seated pressure-tight on open bottle. Permits application of gas pressure to expel beer from bottle as foam. Furnished with inlet valve (No. 1) and outlet valve (No. 2), and adjustable-ht sample tube (Micromat Co., 548 Piermont Ave, Hillsdale, NJ 07642).

(d) *Graduated cylinder.*—200 ml, 4.6 cm id $\times$ 12 cm deep, graduated in 5 ml intervals to brim (Labtician Products Co., 205–09 Jamaica Ave, Hollis, NY 11423) (500 ml graduated cylinder truncated smoothly at 200 ml mark may be used).

(e) *Stopwatch.*—Or clock that indicates sec.

10.043   *Determination*

Perform detns at room temp. (22–27°).

Clean grease from equipment, and connect CO_2 cylinder, pressure surge tank, and orifice foam flashing app. in that order, with Tygon tubing. Be sure all connections are gas-tight. Set CO_2 cylinder reducing valve to 31 lb gage pressure. Replace air in pressure surge tank with CO_2. Close inlet valve (No. 1) and adjust pressure on surge tank to 29 lb, using bleeder valve to reduce excess pressure.

Attemperate bottles of beer to 25±0.5° in H_2O bath or constant temp. room.

Clean 200 ml graduate with detergent soln, rinse well with H_2O, and fill with H_2O. Let graduate drain free of H_2O 1 min; then secure graduate beneath foam flashing orifice tube in upright position with clamp and ringstand so placed that they do not interfere with reading graduations.

Open attemperated beer bottle; fit its neck to bottle attachment of orifice foam flashing app. to secure bottle in place. Raise sample tube so that it is above liq. level in headspace. Open inlet and outlet valves (No. 1 and No. 2) to flush headspace and connecting Tygon tubing with CO_2. Close valves. Bring sample tube to ca 1 cm from bottom of bottle and secure tube in this position by tightening gasket sealing nut at top of bottle attachment portion of app. Open inlet valve (No. 1). If pressure on surge tank drops, readjust to 29 lb.

With orifice tube diverted from foam receiving cylinder, open outlet valve (No. 2) and let outflowing foam go to waste for 10 sec. Then direct stream of foam into measuring cylinder by placing orifice tube at oblique angle below (tip ca ¼ in. away from) rim of inside wall of cylinder. Fill cylinder just to overflowing. Just as overflow begins, divert stream of foam out of cylinder, start stopwatch, and close outlet valve (No. 2) to stop flow of foam. After exactly 90 sec, read ml liq. beer formed from collapsed foam. Wash down cylinder walls with 2 ml isopropanol from pipet and carefully swirl liq. in cylinder so all foam collapses. Read ml liq. at rest; this reading −2 ml (added isopropanol) = total ml beer formed by collapse of 200 ml foam.

10.044 *Calculations*

Foam Value Units (FVU) = 200 $(B_2 − B_1)/B_2$, where 200 = arbitrary factor chosen to give FVU generally near 100, B_2 = total ml beer from collapse of 200 ml foam, B_1 = ml beer formed from foam collapsed in 90 sec. Report ml to nearest whole number.

Sulfur Dioxide (7)—Official Final Action
10.045 *Reagents*

(a) *Color reagent.*—Weigh 100 mg *p*-rosaniline .HCl into 250 ml vol. flask and dissolve in ca 200 ml H_2O. Add 40 ml HCl (1 + 1), mix, and dil. to vol. with H_2O. Let stand ca 15 min before use. Store in brown, g-s bottle in refrigerator.

(b) *Formaldehyde soln.*—Dil. 5 ml 40% HCHO soln to 1 L with H_2O and store in brown g-s bottle in refrigerator.

(c) *Mercury stabilizing soln.*—Dissolve 27.2 g $HgCl_2$ and 11.7 g NaCl in H_2O, and dil. to 1 L with H_2O. (*Caution: See* **46.079.**)

10.046 *Calibration*

Accurately weigh ca 250 mg $NaHSO_3$ into exactly 50 ml 0.1N I soln in g-s flask. Let stand at room temp. 5 min. Add 1 ml HCl, and titr. excess I with 0.1N $Na_2S_2O_3$, using 1% aq. starch soln as indicator (1 ml 0.1N I consumed = 3.203 mg SO_2 or 5.20 mg $NaHSO_3$). From results of $NaHSO_3$ assay, prep. soln contg 10 mg SO_2/ml (ca 8.6–9.0 g $NaHSO_3$/500 ml) (*Soln A*).

Transfer 100 ml Hg stabilizing soln to 500 ml g-s vol. flask. Add 1.00 ml *Soln A*, and dil. to vol. with H_2O (1 ml = 20 μg SO_2) (*Soln B*).

Using 10 ml graduated cylinder contg 1 drop *n-hexyl alcohol* as antifoam, transfer 10 ml portions of cold, undegassed beer (preferably of low SO_2 content) into series of eight 100 ml vol. flasks. To series add 0, 1.0, 2.0, 3.0, 4.0, 5.0, 6.0, and 8.0 ml *Soln B* (0–160 μg SO_2). Dil. to vol. with H_2O, and mix. Transfer 25 ml aliquots of each soln to sep. 50 ml vol. flasks. To each flask, add 5 ml color reagent. Mix, and add 5 ml HCHO soln. Mix, dil. to vol. with H_2O, mix, and hold in 25° H_2O bath 30 min. Read color in spectrophtr at 550 nm or in photometer with green filter. Plot A as ordinates against μg SO_2 added to beer as abscissas (color follows Beer's law over range). Calc. calibration factor F, converting readings to μg SO_2 in 25 ml aliquot used, or convert directly to ppm SO_2.

10.047 *Preparation of Sample*

Using pipets, add 2 ml Hg stabilizing soln and 5 ml 0.1N H_2SO_4 to 100 ml vol. flask. Measure 10 ml cold, undegassed beer into 10 ml cylinder contg 1 drop *n*-hexyl alcohol, and add to vol. flask. Swirl gently, and add 15 ml 0.1N NaOH. Swirl, and hold 15 sec. Add 10 ml 0.1N H_2SO_4, then H_2O to vol., and mix thoroly. Transfer 25 ml aliquot to 50 ml vol. flask.

10.048 *Color Development*

To soln in 50 ml vol. flask, add 5 ml color reagent, swirl, add 5 ml HCHO soln, swirl, and dil. to vol. with H_2O. Mix, and hold in 25° bath 30 min. Read color as in **10.046,** using cells of same size and same instrument settings.

Correct for blank as follows: Measure 10 ml cold, undegassed beer into 100 ml vol. flask. Add 0.5 ml 1% aq. starch soln, then 0.05N I soln, dropwise until permanent bluish tinge persists. Add 1 drop more, dil. to vol., and mix thoroly. When blue fades, develop color in 25 ml aliquot as above.

(Color readings for I blanks are usually low and uniform; when test is run upon series of similar beers, blank tests on all may be unnecessary.)

10.049 *Calculation*

Ppm $SO_2 = (A_s − A_b) \times F$, where A_s = A of sample (or photometric reading with green filter equiv. to A), A_b = A of I blank, and F = factor derived from **10.046** for converting A to μg SO_2 in aliquot, or directly to ppm SO_2.

10.050 Iodine Reaction for Unconverted Starch—Procedure

(a) *For light beer.*—Fill 15 mm diam test tube to within 1″ from rim with beer, **10.001.** Carefully add 0.02N I from dropper to form distinct layer on top of beer. Observe at once, by transmitted light, color developed at interface. Report blue as indicating presence of starch; purple, amylodextrin; and reddish tinge, erythrodextrin. Qualify results by using terms faint trace, trace, and plain trace according to whether the color developed is faint, distinct, or strong.

(b) *For dark beer, but applicable also to a light beer.*—To 5 ml beer in test tube add 25 ml alcohol, shake thoroly, and let stand. Decant, pouring off last trace of beer-alcohol mixt. Dissolve ppt (dextrin) in 5 ml H_2O and to this soln add 0.02N I soln dropwise. Interpret as in (a).

Copper
Direct, Nonashing Method (8)— Official Final Action
10.051 *Reagents*

(a) *Zinc dibenzyldithiocarbamate (ZDBT) soln.*— 0.5%. Dissolve 5 g ZDBT (available from Uniroyal Chemical under trade name "Arazate") in toluene and dil. to 1 L with toluene. Filter, if necessary, thru Whatman No. 42 paper, and store in brown bottle in cool, dark place. CCl_4 may be used instead of toluene.

(b) *Copper std solns.*—(1) *Stock soln.*—1 mg/ml. Dissolve 3.93 g $CuSO_4.5H_2O$ (free of whitish deposit of lower hydrates) and dil. to 1 L with H_2O. Or dissolve 1.000 g pure Cu wire or foil in 75 ml HNO_3 (1 + 4) by warming. Boil to expel fumes, cool, and dil. to 1 L with H_2O. (2) *Working soln.*—10 µg/ml. Prep. immediately before use by dilg 5 ml stock soln with Cu-free distd H_2O to 500 ml in vol. flask.

(c) *Copper-free distilled water.*—Shake out distd H_2O with ZDBT soln in separator.

10.052   *Apparatus*

(a) *Photometer.*—Any com. instrument with blue filter (430–460 nm) or spectrophtr set at 435 nm.

(b) *Copper-free centrifuge tubes.*—Clean and rinse 50 ml centrf. tubes; add 15 ml H_2O, 3 ml H_2SO_4 (1 + 3), and 5 ml ZDBT soln. Stopper with corks or glass stoppers and shake thoroly. Discard soln and let tube drain.

10.053   *Preparation of Standard Curve*

Into series of cleaned, corked, or g-s 50 ml centrf. tubes add 0.0, 1.0, 2.0, 3.0, 4.0, and 5.0 ml Cu working std soln, contg 0.0, 0.4, 0.8, 1.2, 1.6, and 2.0 ppm Cu, resp. Add 25 ml beer, degassed as in **10.054**, and 1 drop *n-hexyl alcohol;* mix, and proceed as in detn, **10.055**.

Color over this range follows Beer's law. Calc. factor, *f*, to convert *A* to ppm Cu after subtracting *A* of std contg 0.0 ppm Cu from those contg added Cu. If instrument response is not linear, use calibration curve.

10.054   *Preparation of Sample*

Cool bottle or can and shake thoroly immediately before opening. Let gas bubbles leave liq. before removing cap or puncturing can. Discard ca ⅓ of sample and degas by swirling. Remove sample directly from container.

10.055   *Determination*

To cleaned 50 ml centrf. tube add 25 ml cold sample, measured in graduated cylinder, 3 ml H_2SO_4 (1 + 3), and 1 ml 30% H_2O_2. If foam interferes with sample measurement, add 1 drop hexyl alcohol. Mix, and place tube in boiling H_2O bath 0.5 hr. If excessive foaming occurs, add 1 drop hexyl alcohol. Remove tube and cool to 25°. Add 5 or 10 ml, accurately measured, ZDBT soln, depending upon size of photometer cell, and stopper tube. Ext at 25° by shaking vigorously 60 times. Re-ext again 4 times, giving 60 snapping shakes each time to obtain fine emulsion, allowing partial sepn between extns. Digested sample must be shaken vigorously with the ZDBT soln; thoro and complete emulsification must be obtained during each series of extns or results may be low.

Centrf. tube 2–3 min and draw off clear, colored layer to photometer cell of same size used in calibration, and det. *A*. If droplets of aq. layer are carried into pipet, remove by flowing solv. from pipet down wall of clean, dry test tube. H_2O droplets will adhere to test tube and clear solv. can be poured off into cell.

Prep. reagent blank by extg in clean 50 ml centrf. tube 25 ml Cu-free H_2O at 25° and 3 ml H_2SO_4 (1 + 3) with 5 (or 10) ml ZDBT soln and det. A_1. To correct for *A* of color extd by solv., perform entire detn, omitting ZDBT soln, but shaking with toluene (or CCl_4) and det. A_2. Do not give tubes used for this solv.-extractable beer color blank preliminary cleaning with ZDBT soln, since carryover of ZDBT may give high readings.

Ppm Cu = $[A - (A_1 + A_2)] \times f$, where *f* is factor for converting *A* to ppm Cu.

Iron (9)—Official Final Action

10.056   *Apparatus*

Photometer.—Spectrophtr set at ca 505 nm or photometer with filter in blue-green region, 500–550 nm, or preferably, 505–520 nm.

10.057   *Reagents*

(a) *Color reagent:* (1) *2,2'-bipyridine.*—0.2%. Dissolve 1 g 2,2'-bipyridine in 20 ml HOAc (1 + 2) and dil. to 500 ml with H_2O; or—

(2) *o-Phenanthroline.*—0.3%. Dissolve 1.5 g *o*-phenanthroline in 500 ml H_2O at 70°.

(b) *Iron std soln.*—0.1 mg/ml. (1) *From iron wire.* —Dissolve 0.500 g reagent grade Fe wire, wiped free of oxide, in 5 ml HCl (1 + 4) and 1 ml HNO_3. Cover with watch glass, heat, and evap. to dryness; add H_2O and evap. to dryness again. Dissolve residue in 3–5 ml HCl, cool, and transfer quant. to 500 ml vol. flask. Add 2 drops satd $Br-H_2O$, dil. to vol. with H_2O, and mix. Transfer 50 ml of this soln to 500 ml vol. flask, add 2 drops $Br-H_2O$, dil. to vol. with H_2O, and mix.

(2) *From ferrous ammonium sulfate.*—Dissolve 3.512 g $Fe(NH_4)_2(SO_4)_2.6H_2O$ in H_2O, add 5 ml HCl, transfer quant. to 500 ml vol. flask, dil. to vol. with H_2O, and mix. Transfer 50 ml of this soln to 500 ml vol. flask, dil. to vol. with H_2O, and mix.

(c) *Ascorbic acid.*—USP, ground to fine powder.

10.058   *Preparation of Standard Curve*

Prep. series of *beer stds* contg 0.0, 0.25, 0.50, 1.00, 2.00, and 3.00 ppm Fe as follows: Pipet 0.0, 0.25, 0.50, 1.00, 2.00, and 3.00 ml Fe std soln to series of 100 ml vol. flasks, add, from pipet, enough H_2O to total 3.00 ml, and dil. to vol. with decarbonated beer, **10.059.** Depending upon size cell to be used, develop color in 25 or 50 ml aliquots of each of the beer stds as in **10.060(a)** or **(b).**

If *T* values are obtained, convert to $A = -\log T$, and plot *A* against ppm Fe. If straight line results, calc. factor, *m*, for converting *A* to ppm Fe, *y*, by use of equation $y = mA + b$ ($b = 0$ if line passes thru origin). If instrument response is such that curve is obtained, use this curve to calc. results.

10.059 *Preparation of Sample*

Adjust temp. of beer to 20–25°. Decarbonate by transferring sample to large erlenmeyer and shaking, first gently and then vigorously, until all gas is released. Do not filter unless necessary. If filtration is required, make sure filter paper is Fe-free by spotting sample of paper with drop of reagent prepd by dissolving 25 mg ascorbic acid in 2 ml color reagent, **10.057**(a).

If beer sample is suspected of high Fe content, degas by shaking only, and permit foam to subside before sampling.

10.060 *Determination*

Pipet 2 aliquots of degassed beer (25 or 50 ml as used in prepn of std curve) into 50 ml or 125 ml erlenmeyers; add 25 mg ascorbic acid to each aliquot, and add 2 ml color reagent, **10.057**(a), to one and 2 ml H_2O to other. (a) Stopper and heat both aliquots 15 min at 60°, or (b) let stand 30 min at room temp.

Cool, and read both solns in photometer against H_2O as ref., or read colored aliquot against beer blank as ref. Use same size cell and wavelength as used in prepn of std curve.

10.061 *Calculations*

If H_2O is used as ref. and factor is used, ppm $Fe = (A_{sample} - A_{blank}) \times$ factor. If values are taken from std curve, ppm Fe = ppm Fe in sample − ppm Fe in blank.

If beer blank is used as ref. and factor is used, ppm $Fe = A_{sample} \times$ factor. If values are taken from std curve, ppm Fe = ppm Fe directly.

10.062 Other Metals—*See* Chap. 25

10.063 Chlorides—Official Final Action

Place 50 ml sample in Pt dish, add 20 ml 5% Na_2CO_3 soln, and proceed as in **3.067**. Det. Cl as in **3.068** or **3.070**.

10.064 End Fermentation (Yeast Fermentable Extract) (Fermentable Sugars)—Official Final Action

Det. real ext, **10.023**, or apparent ext, **10.017**. Ferment 250 ml beer with 1 g active compressed brewers yeast 24–48 hr at 15–25°, or until fermentation is complete, providing fermentation flask with H_2O or Hg seal. Filter; det. real ext, **10.023**, or apparent ext, **10.017**. Fermentable sugars = difference in real ext before and after fermentation; or fermentable sugars = 0.82 × difference in apparent ext before and after fermentation.

10.065 Caramel—Official Final Action— *See* 11.051

Beer Bitterness (*10*)—Official First Action

(Certain preservatives, such as heptyl-*p*-hydroxybenzoate and sorbates and possibly some brewing adjuncts or coloring agents, may contribute to *A* at

wavelengths specified. Interference from UV-absorbing material is greater for Bitterness Units method than for Iso-Alpha Acids.)

Bitterness Units

10.066 *Reagents*

(a) *2,2,4-Trimethylpentane (isooctane).*—Spectral grade or equiv. (ASTM certified ref. fuel grade isooctane may be used after 1 distn or use practical grade isooctane, purified by passage thru silica gel column (12–28 mesh, Fisher Scientific Co. No. S-156, grade 408).) *A* at 275 nm in 1 cm cell should be equiv. to that of H_2O ($A \leq 0.005$).

(b) *Octyl alcohol.*—Reagent grade or redistd equiv. One drop added to 20 ml isooctane increases *A* at 275 nm ≤ 0.005 in 1 cm cell.

10.067 *Apparatus*

(a) *Mechanical shaker.*—Platform or wrist-action type with extending arm adjusted vertically so that tube is held horizontally.

(b) *Spectrophotometer.*—For use in UV range.

(c) *Centrifuge tubes.*—50 ml, g-s or screw-cap with Teflon lining.

10.068 *Determination*

Transfer 10.0 ml chilled (50°F) carbonated beer to 50 ml centrf. tube, using pipet which has minute amt octyl alcohol in tip. Add 1 ml 3*N* HCl and 20 ml isooctane. Tightly stopper centrf. tube and shake vigorously 15 min on mech. shaker. If required, centrf. long enough to sep. phases. Immediately transfer portion clear upper (isooctane) layer to cuvet. Set instrument to read 0 *A* at 275 nm for isooctane-octyl alcohol blank (20 ml isooctane + 1 drop octyl alcohol). Record *A* in 1 cm cell at 275 nm.

Calc. bitterness units (BU) = $A_{275} \times 50$. Report BU to nearest 0.5 unit.

Iso-Alpha Acids

10.069 *Reagents*

(a) *2,2,4-Trimethylpentane (isooctane).* — *See* **10.066**(a). *A* at 255 nm in 1 cm cell should be equiv. to that of freshly redistd H_2O from all-glass still.

(b) *Methanol.*—Reagent grade, with *A* ≤ 0.04 at 260 nm in 1 cm cell compared with freshly redistd H_2O from all-glass still.

(c) *Acid methanol.*—Mix 6.8 parts MeOH with 3.2 parts 4*N* HCl.

(d) *Alkaline methanol.*—Just before use, mix 1.0 ml 1.5*N* NaOH with 500 ml MeOH.

(e) *Octyl alcohol.*—*See* **10.066**(b).

10.070 *Apparatus*

See **10.067**.

10.071 *Determination*

Transfer 15.0 ml chilled carbonated beer to 50 ml centrf. tube, using pipet with minute amt octyl alcohol in tip. Add 2.0 ml 6*N* HCl and 15.0 ml isooctane.

Close tube tightly and shake vigorously on mech. shaker ≥30 min until completely extd. Place tube in centrf. set to run at highest permissible speed. Centrf. long enough to sep. phases. Break difficult emulsions by adding 1 drop detergent to centrf. tube. Verify that detergent does not contribute to A at 255 nm. (Union Carbide Chemicals Co. "Tergitol Anionic 7" is satisfactory.)

Transfer 10.0 ml clear upper layer to 50 ml g-s graduate contg 10.0 ml acid MeOH. Stopper and invert 100 times at rate causing contents to pass from end to end. Let phases sep.

Transfer 5.0 ml upper layer to 25 ml vol. flask and dil. to vol. with alk. MeOH. Read A in 1 cm cell at 255 nm in spectrophtr set to read 0 A for reagent blank consisting of 5 ml isooctane dild to 25 ml with alk. MeOH.

Calc. ppm iso-alpha acids of beer = 96.15 A_{255} + 0.4. Report to nearest 0.5 ppm.

Proteolytic Chillproofing Enzymes (11)—
Official Final Action
Casein Coagulation Method

10.072   *Reagent*

Substrate mixture.—Thoroly mix by grinding in large mortar and pestle 50 g com. skim milk powder (do not use special casein powder prepd for microbiological or other uses), 5.0 g L(+)-cysteine. HCl .H₂O, 4.4 g Na₂HPO₄, 2.5 g NaCl, and 1.8 g citric acid.H₂O. Store at 0–4° and let warm to room temp. before use.

10.073   *Test*

Place ca 100 ml degassed beer into 150 ml beaker and adjust pH to 6.4±0.1 with 1N NaOH. Transfer 50 ml aliquot to 25 × 200 mm test tube contg 250 ±30 mg substrate mixt. Suspend substrate mixt. with rubber-tipped glass stirring rod. Invert tube twice to mix uniformly, and place in 60° H₂O bath.

Progressive change in appearance of suspension, initially clouding, then formation of "pebbles," followed by coagulation and settling of casein indicates pos. test. Control beers, without chill-proofing enzymes, should remain unchanged. If semi-quant. data are desired, record time required to reach first stage of "pebbling."

MALT
10.074 Sampling—Official Final Action

For complete descriptions of trier, divider, sampler, and bushel weight tester, see "Grain Inspection Manual" GR Instruction 918-6 (latest edition available from Grain Div., C&MS, US Dept. of Agriculture, Washington, DC 20250).

(a) *Bulk malt in cars or bins.*—Using 60″ trier, take at least 6 probes from different parts of car, preferably 2 from center and 2 from each end.

(b) *Bulk malt during discharge thru spouts or openings.*—At different times during filling or un-loading of car, take, with trier or Pelican sampler, at least 6 samples, each representing complete cross section of grain stream from spout.

(c) *Bagged malt.*—Sample lengthwise thru center of open bags, ≥2% of bags selected from different parts of car or storage room. Use 36″ trier.

Indicate approx. proportion of inferior grain and take representative samples from each portion as outlined above. Immediately place each portion of sample in suitable large dry container and keep tightly closed.

10.075 Preparation of Sample— Official Final Action

Divide samples, either by quartering or by using sample divider, until ca 3 lb remains. Place reduced sample in air-tight container (preferably tin with screw or friction type cover); do not use cartons, bags, wooden boxes, glass Mason jars, or wrapping paper. Remove foreign particles, such as stone, wood, and twine. Do not remove foreign seeds or dust particles.

Bushel Weight (12)—Official Final Action
10.076 Method I

Place sample in filling hopper of Winchester tester, open slide underneath, and let malt fill measuring cylinder to overflowing. Without jarring, level off with straight-edge longer than diam. of measuring cylinder, making one forward stroke consisting of 3 distinct zigzag motions. Weigh and report to nearest ¼ lb.

10.077 Method II

Weigh 110 g sample to nearest 0.1 g and pour evenly into metal funnel provided with plunger discharge and placed on top of 250 ml cylinder graduated to meet NBS specifications. (Funnel must fit snugly into graduate and be large enough to hold the grain without danger of spilling when plunger is raised.) Then drop material into cylinder by pulling plunger up. Do not jar or tap cylinder during operation or before reading vol., and do not read uppermost grain level, as compensation must be made for ends of few kernels that protrude. If grain surface has slant, repeat test.

Calc. bushel wt of malt (lb) as = 8545/vol. in ml of 110 g.

Constant 8545 is derived from W, wt in lb of US (Winchester) bushel of 2150.42 cu. in. (35,239 ml). If V = vol. in ml of 110 g malt,

$$\frac{110}{453.6W} = \frac{V}{35,239}. \quad W = 8545/V.$$

10.078 Length of Acrospire—Procedure

For methods (a) and (b), quarter sample until ca 200 kernels remain in 2 opposite quarters, and count out 100 kernels, rejecting those that are broken or those in which growth is not ascertainable.

(a) *Cutting.*—Hold each kernel, furrow downward, on flat surface with pair of tweezers, cut thru kernel longitudinally with razor blade or other sharp instrument, and examine cut acrospire in both halves, comparing its length with that of kernel. Tally according to classifications below.

(b) *Peeling.*—Remove husk covering acrospire with sharp instrument and examine acrospire length in comparison with kernel length. Tally according to classifications below.

(c) *Boiling.*—Boil 10–15 g av. sample with 100–150 ml H_2O 20–30 min. After boiling, add cold H_2O to cool contents of beaker. Decant, and pour grain on glass plate. Select 100 kernels at random, inspect acrospire, and tally according to classifications below.

Classify kernels as follows and report % in each group:

0–¼: includes those kernels without apparent growth, or having acrospire development up to, but not including, ¼ length of grain.

¼–½: includes those kernels having acrospire development from ¼ up to, but not including, ½ length of grain.

½–¾: includes those kernels having acrospire development from ½ up to, but not including, ¾ length of grain.

¾–1: includes those kernels having acrospire development of ¾ but not greater than entire length of grain.

Overgrown: includes those kernels having acrospire development in excess of length of grain.

If it is apparent that overgrown acrospire has been broken off during processing, include kernel in overgrown classification regardless of length of remaining stub.

10.079 Mealiness—Procedure

Count out 100 kernels remaining from preceding test if method **10.078**(a) or (b) was used. Otherwise select 100 kernels as in **10.078** and cut kernels in longitudinal halves. Det. % mealy, half glassy, and glassy kernels. In case of uncertainty, pierce starch body with sharp point; if mealy, it will break away and crumble from point.

Classify kernels as follows:

Mealy kernels—includes those kernels in which ≤¼ of the endosperm body is glassy.

Half glassy—includes those kernels in which >¼ but <¾ of the endosperm body is glassy.

Glassy—includes those kernels in which ≥¾ of the entire endosperm body is glassy.

10.080 1,000 Kernel Weight—Procedure

Quarter sample until ca 500 kernels remain in 2 opposite quarters. Count out 500 kernels and weigh to nearest 0.1 g. Calc. results to 1,000 kernels on as-is and dry basis.

10.081 Assortment—Procedure

Weigh 100 g from quartered sample to nearest 0.1 g. Place in top compartment of grader (frame and screens available from S. Howes Co., Silver Creek, NY 14136) and shake 3 min. Weigh portions remaining on various screens and in catch pan to nearest 0.1 g, and report % on each of following screens: 7/64″, 6/64″, 5/64″, and thru 5/64″, in percentages totaling 100%. (When testing large berried malts (2 row, California, etc.), addn of 8/64″ screen is optional.)

10.082 Mold—Procedure

Det. presence or absence of mold by visual inspection and report as "none," "trace," etc.

10.083 Foreign Seeds and Broken Kernels—Procedure

Weigh 50 g sample. Pick out foreign seeds and broken kernels, classify, and report sep. in %.

Moisture—Official Final Action

10.084 *Apparatus*

(a) *Weighing dish.*—Use glass bottle or Al dish, with tight-fitting cover, ca 40 mm diam. for 5 g sample, or 55 mm for 10 g sample.

(b) *Oven.*—With automatic control holding temp. within ±0.5°, and large enough to hold all samples on 1 shelf in such manner that no sample is outside area indicated by test to give comparable results in duplicate samples. Stdze oven as follows: Place weighed duplicate samples in oven at 103–104° and dry 3 hr. Weigh, and redry 1 hr longer. If loss of moisture is >0.1%, raise temp. 1° and again test with new duplicate samples. Take, as std, lowest temp. <106° giving moisture content that, after 3 hr of drying, is within 0.1% of value attainable at same temp. within 4 hr. Keep ventilators of oven open during entire drying period, and do not open door during the 3 hr of drying.

10.085 *Preparation of Sample*

(a) *If extract determination is to be made.*—Grind sample as in **10.090**, and transfer in one continuous operation. When many samples are to be analyzed, grind first sample, remove beaker, and grind second sample while adjusting wt of first sample. Remove second sample, insert third sample, and repeat operation.

(b) *If extract determination is not to be made.*—Have sample of same fineness as finely ground malt used to det. ext. Weigh ca 5 g whole malt (or 10 g if 55 mm diam. weighing bottle is used) and grind thru clean dry mill directly into weighing bottle. Brush all malt from mill into weighing bottle and cover immediately.

10.086 *Determination*

Weigh sample to 1 mg and place in oven previously heated to std temp. Remove cover of weighing bottle and heat exactly 3 hr at std temp. Replace cover, transfer to desiccator, cool to room temp., and weigh to 1 mg. Report moisture to nearest 0.1%.

Extract—Official Final Action

10.087   *Reagent*

Iodine std solns.—(a) 0.01N. Dissolve 0.63 g I and 1.25 g KI in H_2O, and dil. to 500 ml. (b) 0.02N. Dissolve 1.27 g I and 2.50 g KI in H_2O, and dil. to 500 ml. Prep. fresh solns monthly and store in dark. For daily use, keep portion of soln in small brown dropper bottle.

10.088   *Apparatus*

(a) *Mills.*—Miag-Seck (available from Pfaudler Co., PO Box 1600, Rochester NY 14603). For fine grinding use cone-type, 300 rpm, and for coarse grinding, roller-type, 150 rpm.

(b) *Sieves.*—Half-ht, 8″ std sieve No. 30 (with pan and cover). For classification of laboratory and brewery grindings use addnl std sieves Nos. 10, 14, 18, 60, and 100.

(c) *Mash beakers and counter weights.*—Made of either pure Ni, stainless steel, or brass, not Cu, and of such dimensions as to assure tight connection between beakers and Miag-Seck mill while grinding. If counter wts are used for the mash beakers, check tare wts frequently.

(d) *Mashing apparatus.*—Use beakers, stirrers, and solder made of same metal. Provide each stirrer with blade that in operation has clearance of ca 2 mm from bottom and 5 mm from wall of mash beaker. Blade is ca 8 mm wide, and each side has 45° pitch, arranged as in a propeller, to force mash upward. Speed of mash stirrer must be 80–100 rpm, each stirrer of each beaker having same speed. Mech. stir H_2O in bath thoroly to assure uniformity of temp. and have level of H_2O above max. mash level.

(e) *Gypsum plate.*—Thoroly mix 100 ml H_2O with 135 g plaster of Paris. Pour mixt., while still free-flowing, into suitable flat molds (cigar boxes, etc.). Porcelain plate for color reactions, Coors No. 550, size 00, may be used.

(f) *Filter paper.*—Use S&S 32 cm fluted paper No. 560 (or No. 597, 32 cm, fluted by analyst) or Eaton-Dikeman Co., Mt. Holly Springs, PA 17065, 32 cm fluted paper No. 509 (or No. 609, 32 cm, fluted by analyst).

(g) *Funnels.*—Use short-stem glass funnels ca 20 cm diam. and do not let paper project above rim. Stem must extend 3–5 cm into receiving flask.

(h) *Flasks.*—Use dry 500 ml erlenmeyers marked at 100 ml level.

(i) *Pycnometers.*—Use any suitable pycnometer, but preferably Reischauer or Boot (vac.) type. Reischauer type is ca 15 cm high with neck ca 9 cm long and 2.5–3.5 mm id. Fine, well-defined mark is found 55–70 mm below upper rim of neck. When filled with H_2O at 20° its capacity must be 48–50 g.

Use ca 15 ml capacity glass funnels to fill pycnometers.

Boot type is cylindrical and holds ca 50 g H_2O at 20°. Vac. seal must be well rounded off and not pointed. Pycnometer opening is wide enough to permit easy filling and emptying, and stopper has fine capillary opening. Walls of bottle meet stopper in rising acute angle of ca 45° so that no depression or groove retaining moisture is formed at this point.

(j) *Emptying device for Reischauer pycnometer.*—Bend piece of metal capillary tubing (brass, stainless steel), <2 mm od, to ca 45° angle. End to be inserted into pycnometer must reach within 2–3 mm of bottom. Connect other end either to rubber aspirator bulb or to compressed air supply ≤5 lb/sq in.

(k) *Water bath.*—Automatically controlled. If automatic control is not available, use following app. Have H_2O level of bath (5–15 L) reach above neck marks of pycnometer, keep H_2O bath temp. at 20 ±0.05°, and read on accurate thermometer, calibrated to 0.1°. Maintain temp. of H_2O bath by very slow but continuous flow of ice-H_2O from container (2–4 L, contg ice and H_2O). Regulate flow of ice-H_2O by hand. Stir H_2O in bath mech. and continuously without splashing.

10.089   *Standardization*

(a) *Setting of mill.*—Use malt of following characteristics:

Variety: Malt made from 6-rowed midwestern variety of barley	
Moisture	4.2–4.8%
Ext in finely ground malt, dry basis.	74.0–77.0%
Color of laboratory wort, Lovibond ½″ cell, series 52	≤1.8
Diastatic power, dry basis	≥100
Ratio sol. protein to total protein	36–42
Mealiness: Glassy	≤5%
Mealy	≥90%
Acrospire development: 0–¼ grown.	≤5%
¾ to full grown	≥80%
Overgrown	≤5%

Assortment: From malt meeting above specifications, take that portion passing thru ⁷⁄₆₄″ screen and remaining on ⁶⁄₆₄″ screen for actual stdzg operation.

Fine grinding.—Weigh 50 g specified malt into mash beaker, grind, and collect in same beaker. Mill must not be in motion when sample is introduced. Transfer to No. 30 sieve placed on receiving pan and shake in horizontal plane on flat surface 3 min, pausing every 15 sec long enough to give screen and pan 2 sharp taps on surface over which it is sliding. Transfer and weigh particles remaining on and adhering to screen. Consider mill as having stdzd setting when wt of ground malt remaining on No. 30 sieve is between 4.5 and 5.5 g (9–11%). Stdze mill at least twice yearly. Suitable mech. shaking device, giving equiv. results, may be used to stdze mill.

Coarse grinding.—Proceed as for *fine grinding*. Consider mill as having stdzd setting when portion of ground malt remaining on No. 30 sieve is between 37 and 38 g (74–76%).

(b) *Reischauer type pycnometer*.—Clean interior and exterior of pycnometer with $Na_2Cr_2O_7$-H_2SO_4 soln, discharge carefully with air, and wash several times with H_2O, then alcohol, and finally ether. To remove last traces of ether vapor and to replace with laboratory air, connect dry metal capillary tubing to vac. and insert into pycnometer 1–2 min. Carefully wipe pycnometer, let stand few min, and det. wt to 0.2 mg.

Fill with freshly distd H_2O and place in H_2O bath held at 20±0.05°. Tap gently to force out air bubbles. After 25 min, remove liq. above mark with capillary pipet provided with small rubber bulb. To make final adjustment of meniscus, absorb last portion of liq. with thin strips of blotting paper; also remove any liq. adhering to inner surface of neck. Adjust H_2O level so that lower part of meniscus rests on mark. Make all adjustments of liq. level within pycnometer neck while holding by neck, without touching body of pycnometer with hands. Keep body of pycnometer submerged during entire period of meniscus adjustment.

Raise pycnometer to room temp. by insertion into H_2O bath kept at exactly that temp., and hold 10 min. Remove pycnometer, carefully dry exterior, and weigh to 0.2 mg. Subtract wt empty pycnometer. Difference between weighings represents H_2O capacity of pycnometer at 20°. Redet. tare wt and H_2O capacity at frequent intervals.

(c) *Boot type pycnometer*.—Clean pycnometer and det. its wt in same way as for Reischauer type. Cool H_2O in ice bath to temp. slightly <20°. Rinse pycnometer once with the cool H_2O, fill, stopper, and dry exterior. Remove stopper, insert thermometer adjusted to 20° in H_2O, and note temp., which should be 20±0.1°. If it is not, choose different "filling" temp., which may vary with analyst and season from 19.4° to 19.7° or more. Make subsequent detns, using predetd filling temp. Place cap over stopper and weigh.

Redet. wt, H_2O capacity, and filling temp. at least weekly.

10.090 *Determination*

Fine grinding.—Weigh ca 55 g sample (at room temp.) into tared mash beaker and grind thru mill set for stdzd fineness of grind. Collect finely ground malt in same mash beaker, carefully brushing malt particles remaining in mill into mash beaker. Mix, and without delay, place mash beaker with contents on balance accurate to within ±0.05 g under 750 g load and adjust wt malt to 50±0.05 g by removing excess into tared dish for moisture detn.

Coarse grinding.—Weigh 50.5 g sample (at room temp.) into tared mash beaker and grind thru mill set for stdzd coarseness of grind. Collect coarsely ground malt in same mash beaker, carefully brush-ing particles remaining in mill into mash beaker. Without delay, place mash beaker with contents on balance accurate to within ±0.05 g under 750 g load and adjust wt malt to 50±0.05 g by removing excess.

(a) *Mashing procedure*.—"Mash in" ground malt with 200 ml H_2O at 46° and mix well with glass rod to prevent formation of lumps. Carefully rinse glass rod and wall of beaker with small quantity of H_2O. Note odor of mash and report as aromatic, slightly aromatic, musty, green, stale, etc. Promptly place mash beakers in mashing app. contg H_2O previously heated to 46°, and set stirrers in motion. Place thermometer in each mash beaker. Keep temp. at 45° exactly 30 min from time beakers were placed in mashing app. Raise mash temp. 1°/min to 70°. Add 100 ml H_2O, previously heated to 70–71°, and hold mash 60 min at 70°. (Temp. deviations during mashing procedures should not exceed 0.5°.)

(b) *Conversion*.—Transfer drop of mash with thin glass rod (ca 3 mm diam.) onto absorbent gypsum plate, **10.088(e)**, or into one cavity of porcelain plate, and test with drop of 0.01N I soln on gypsum plate, or with drop of 0.02N I soln, **10.087(b)**, on porcelain plate. Make tests 5, 7, and 10 min after 70° is reached, and thereafter if necessary, at 5 min intervals. Conversion is complete when test drop and I soln produce only yellow stain on gypsum or porcelain plate. Report time of conversion in periods: <5 min, 5–7 min, etc. Time of conversion is not detd on coarsely ground malt.

(c) *Cooling and filtration*.—After 60 min, cool mash promptly (within 10–15 min) to prevailing room temp. Stop stirrers. Remove thermometers after adhering mash particles are rinsed into beaker with H_2O. Remove each beaker with its stirrer from mashing app. Rinse mash particles adhering to stirrer into beaker with H_2O. Dry outside of each beaker, taking care to remove moisture adhering to rim. Without delay, adjust wt of contents of mash beaker to 450.0 ±0.05 g by adding H_2O.

Stir mash thoroly with glass rod, once when removing beakers from balance pan and again immediately before pouring mash onto filter. (Stirrings must be ≥5 min but <15 min apart.) While stirring cooled mash, take care to prevent splashing or spilling. Mix drops adhering to beaker wall into mash by rotary stirring with glass rod.

Pour entire contents of beaker into funnel provided with specified filter paper. Cover funnel with ca 20 cm diam. watch glass during entire filtration. Return first 100 ml filtrate to filter. When no more liq. is present above filter cake, discontinue filtration and remove receiving flask contg wort for later observations and tests. In case of slow running worts, stop filtration after 2 hr. In case of coarse ground malt mash, collect exactly 200±2 ml wort. When filtration is complete, mix wort in receiving flask thoroly by rotary motion. Speed of filtration is normal if filtration is complete (as defined above) within 1 hr after returning the 100 ml filtrate to filter bed;

slow, if filtration takes longer. Observe degree of clarity and report as clear, slightly hazy, or hazy.

Remove ca 100 ml wort for detn of color. (Color is not detd on wort from coarsely ground malt.)

(d) *Specific gravity.*—Rinse empty pycnometer twice with ca 10 ml wort, and if Reischauer pycnometer is used, remove rinsings each time with emptying device. Fill with wort, place in H_2O bath, and proceed as in **10.089**(b). Weigh filled pycnometer within 3 hr of completed filtration. Difference between this wt and that of empty pycnometer represents wort capacity of pycnometer at 20°. Calc. sp gr of wort to fifth decimal place, rounding off to 0.00005 or 0.00010, by dividing wt wort by wt H_2O.

No calcn is made of sp gr *in vacuo.* If duplicate detns made by same analyst in different beakers differ by more than 2 units in fourth decimal place, repeat entire detn.

(e) *Extract.*—Det. ext yield of wort by ref. to sp gr values given in **47.009**, and calc. ext yield of malt by following formulas:

Ext as-is basis = $P(800 + M)/(100 - P)$, where P = g ext in 100 g wort (Plato, **47.009**); and M = % H_2O in the malt.

Ext dry basis = $(E \times 100)/(100 - M)$, where E = ext as-is basis; and M = % H_2O in malt.

Report ext as-is basis and dry basis to nearest 0.1%.

10.091   Extract in Caramel Malt— Official Final Action

Use mill for fine grinding as in **10.088**(a). Weigh ca 30.5 g caramel malt, grind, and adjust to 25 ±0.05 g, removing excess for moisture detn. Weigh ca 25.5 g malt of known moisture, ext, and color, and having diastatic power ≥100°; grind, and adjust to 25±0.05 g. Quant. transfer the 2 portions to mash beaker, mash, and det. sp gr as in **10.090**(d). Det. moisture as in **10.085**(b) and **10.086**.

Calc. by following formulas:

Total ext = $P \times (800 + M$ in 50 g malt
    $+ M$ in 50 g caramel malt)$/(100 - P)$,

where P = g ext in 100 g wort (Plato, **47.009**), and M = moisture (g).

Ext in caramel malt
    = (total ext − ext in 50 g malt) $\times$ 100/50.

10.092   Color in Caramel Malt— Official Final Action

Use mixed wort obtained for ext detn, dilg wort enough to make color reading ca 4.0 units. Det. color on dild wort as in **10.094** or **10.096**.

Calc. by following formula: Color of caramel malt = $2[C \times (D + 1)]$ − color of malt used for conversion, where C = color reading on dild wort, and D = parts of H_2O to dil. one part of wort.

Report diln used for making color reading. Report color to nearest whole number.

10.093   Color in Black Malt— Official Final Action

Use mill for fine grinding as in **10.088**(a). As precautionary measure grind small quantity of sample to be analyzed and clean out mill. For detn weigh 5.5 g, grind, and collect all particles by careful brushing of mill.

Weigh 5.00 g on analytical balance, transfer to 600 ml beaker, add 400 ml H_2O at room temp., and heat to boiling in ≥15 but <20 min. Boil gently exactly 5 min, cool to room temp., and without delay transfer to 500 ml vol. flask; dil. to vol. with H_2O, mix, and filter thru 32 cm fluted paper. Pipet 10 ml filtrate into 100 ml vol. flask, dil. to vol. with H_2O, and mix.

Det. color of dild wort as in **10.094** or **10.096**. Calc. color found for this filtrate to same concn of materials used for regular malt mash (12.5 g malt to 100 ml H_2O) by formula:

Color of black malt = $L \times 10 \times 12.5$, where L = color reading on dild filtrate. Report color to nearest whole number.

Color of Laboratory Wort (13)— Official Final Action

10.094   *Spectrophotometric Method*

Fill spectrophtr cuvet with filtrate from malt ext, **10.090**(c), and det. A of wort at 430 and 700 nm in spectrophtr, **10.002**.

Wort color = $10 \times (A_{430} - A_{700}) \times$ correction to ½″ cell size.

Report color to nearest 0.05 unit.

Example.—A of wort sample in 10 mm cuvet (inside) is 0.139 at 430 nm and 0.015 at 700 nm.

$10 \times (0.139 - 0.015) \times 12.7$ (mm)/10.0 (mm) = 1.57 wort color.

Photometric Method

10.095   *Calibration*

Calibrate photometer, **10.006**, against spectrophtr as in **10.007**. In calibrating filter photometer against spectrophtr in terms of color, size of photometer cell, transmission characteristics of photometer filters, etc., are inherent in calibration factor; once photometer readings are taken, difference need only be multiplied by instrument factor to give wort color.

10.096   *Determination*

Fill photometer cell with filtrate from malt ext, **10.090**(c), and take scale reading with 430 and then with 700 nm filter or with filters whose rated transmissions are close to these wavelengths.

Multiply difference between 430 and 700 nm readings times instrument calibration factor, **10.007**. Report color to nearest 0.05 unit.

10.097   Protein—Official Final Action

Weigh 1.4 g finely ground malt, **10.090**, and proceed as in **2.051**. %N $\times$ 6.25 = % protein.

10.098 Wort Nitrogen—Official Final Action

Using 25 ml laboratory wort, **10.090(c)**, det. N as in **10.036**. Calc. as wort N in terms of % malt (dry basis) as follows:

Wort N (% malt, dry basis) = (ml $0.1N$ H_2SO_4 − ml $0.1N$ NaOH) $\times$ 0.0056 $\times$ % malt ext (dry basis)/(° Plato of wort $\times$ sp gr of wort).

Report to second decimal.

Diastatic Power (14)—Official Final Action

10.099 *Preparation of Glassware*

Wash all glassware with $Na_2Cr_2O_7$-H_2SO_4 cleaning soln, rinse with tap H_2O at least 4 times, and finally rinse with H_2O at least twice. Thoroly dry digestion flasks. (*Caution:* $Na_2Cr_2O_7$-H_2SO_4 can cause severe burns. *See* **46.023** and **46.030**.)

10.100 *Reagents*

(a) *Acetate buffer soln.*—Dissolve 68 g NaOAc .$3H_2O$ in 500 ml $1N$ HOAc and dil. to 1 L with H_2O.

(b) *Fehling soln.*—Stdze as in **31.036**–**31.037**. Check soln from time to time by detg its oxidizing value against std soln of invert sugar, **31.035(c)**, as in **31.036**.

(c) *Alkaline ferricyanide soln.*—$0.05N$. Dissolve 16.5 g dry $K_3Fe(CN)_6$ and 22 g anhyd. Na_2CO_3 in H_2O, and dil. to 1 L with H_2O. Soln keeps its strength for long period if stored in dark glass bottle in dark.

(d) *Sodium thiosulfate std soln.*—$0.05N$. Prep. daily by dilg $0.1N$ soln, **45.038**–**45.039**. Check $Na_2S_2O_3$ against $K_3Fe(CN)_6$ soln as follows: To 10 ml $K_3Fe(CN)_6$ soln add 25 ml HOAc reagent, 1 ml 50% KI soln, and 2 ml starch indicator. Titr. with the $Na_2S_2O_3$. (Exactly 10 ml $Na_2S_2O_3$ soln should completely discharge blue starch-I color. Adjust if necessary.)

(e) *Acetic acid reagent.*—200 ml HOAc, 70 g KCl, and 20 g $ZnSO_4$.$7H_2O$/L.

(f) *Potassium iodide soln.*—50%. Dissolve 50 g KI in H_2O, add 1 drop NaOH soln (1 + 1), and dil. to 100 ml with H_2O. (Adding NaOH soln substantially delays deterioration of soln, with liberation of I, on standing; soln must be colorless.)

(g) *Starch soln.*—Have final concn of 2 g sol. starch (weighed on dry basis) in 100 ml soln. Use sol. starch, according to Lintner, special for diastatic power detn, with solubility at least 1:50 in hot H_2O, that contains no dextrins, contains <0.75% reducing substances calcd as maltose, and has moisture content of 10–12%. Freshly made 2% soln must have pH of 4.5–5.5 without adjustment with buffer. Subsequent batches of starch, when tested on a malt of ca 100° Diastatic Power (dry basis) having other characteristics as specified under detn of ext in malt, must show variation $\leq \pm 3°$ Diastatic Power from value obtained by using original starch in parallel detn. Test addnl batches of starch, when purchased, in parallel with starch in use. Permit no variation $> \pm 3°$ Diastatic Power. In no case may cumulative correction as referred to original starch, approved above, amt to >5° Diastatic Power. (Starch meeting these specifications is available as No. 09903 from Merck & Co.)

Macerate starch with just enough cold freshly distd H_2O to form smooth, thin paste ($\leq 5\%$ of final vol.). Pour, with constant stirring, into boiling freshly distd H_2O representing $\geq$ ca 75% of final vol. of starch soln, at such rate that boiling does not cease. Continue boiling 2 min after thin paste is completely added. Quickly add to beaker addnl 10% of final vol. of cold, freshly distd H_2O and quant. transfer mixt. to g-s vol. flask; mix by inverting flask, wash down neck of flask, and cool to 20° before adding buffer soln. Add 2 ml buffer soln for each 100 ml of final vol. of starch soln and dil. to vol. Mix again by inverting flask and keep tightly stoppered at 20° until used.

(h) *Soluble starch indicator.*—1% sol. starch in 30% NaCl soln. Prep. sol. starch suspension and pour slowly into boiling H_2O. Add NaCl and dil. to vol. (Soln should be transparent and colorless.)

10.101 *Determination*

Grind sep. ≤ 25.5 g malt as in **10.090**. Collect finely ground malt in mash beaker, carefully brushing in malt particles remaining in mill. Without delay, adjust wt contents to 25 ± 0.05 g. Transfer quant. to container (ca 1 L) in which infusion is to be made. Add 500 ml 0.5% NaCl soln at 20° and close container. Let infusion stand 2.5 hr at $20 \pm 0.2°$ and agitate by rotating at 20 min intervals. Take care that in agitation of malt suspension min. amt of grist is left adhering to inner surface of flask above level of the H_2O. (Do *not* invert flask to mix; gentle whirling of contents without splashing on sides of container is sufficient.) Filter infusion by transferring entire charge to 30–32 cm fluted filter (S&S No. 588 or equiv.) in 185 mm funnel. Return first 50 ml filtrate to filter. Collect filtrate for 3 hr after H_2O and ground malt were first mixed. Prevent evapn during filtration as far as possible by placing watch glass over funnel and some suitable cover around stem of funnel, resting on neck of receiver.

Immediately dil. 20 ml of this infusion to 100 ml with 0.5% NaCl soln at 20°, transfer 10 ml dild infusion to 250 ml vol. flask, and bring to 20°. Add 200 ml buffered starch soln from fast-flowing pipet, all at 20°. Mix soln by rotating flask during addn. Keep "starch infusion" mixt. at $20 \pm 0.1°$ exactly 30 min, timed on stop-watch from time addn of starch was begun. Add 20 ml $0.5N$ NaOH rapidly and mix well by whirling flask. Dil. to vol. at 20° and mix thoroly.

Det. reducing power by (a) Fehling soln modification, or (b) ferricyanide modification:

(a) *Fehling soln modification.*—Boil 10 ml Fehling soln and 10 ml H_2O in 200 ml erlenmeyer. (For heating soln, elec. plate is preferable to gas flame.) Add, from buret, ca ⅔ of quantity of above digested starch soln probably required and boil 15–20 sec, rotating constantly. Remove from heat. If still decidedly blue, add more soln, boil ca 10 sec, and again observe color. When blue is almost discharged, and after soln boils gently ca 2 min, add 3 drops *1% aq. methylene blue soln.* Continue boiling and add more soln until 0.1 ml, or even 1 drop, upon boiling, discharges blue. (Color becomes violet-lavender as end point nears.)

Repeat titrn, adding at once almost whole quantity of digested starch required, and proceed to end point as directed. Designate quantity of digested starch soln required to reach end point in this second titrn as *A.* Interrupt boiling as little as possible after indicator is added, so that flask remains filled with steam, preventing much access of air. (Upon cooling, blue usually returns.)

Prep. blank by processing exactly as in par. 2, except add the 0.5*N* NaOH to malt infusion before adding starch soln. To 10 ml Fehling soln and 10 ml H_2O add a vol. of this blank soln equal to final vol. of digested starch soln required in above detn. Boil and again det. end point as in detn. Designate quantity of digested starch soln used as *B.*

(b) *Ferricyanide modification.*—Pipet 5 ml dild digested starch soln into 125 ml erlenmeyer. Pipet exactly 10 ml $K_3Fe(CN)_6$ soln into soln, and immerse flask in vigorously boiling H_2O bath. Have surface of liq. in flask 3–4 cm below surface of boiling H_2O. Let flask remain in boiling H_2O bath *exactly* 20 min; then cool under running H_2O, and add 25 ml HOAc reagent with thoro mixing. Add 1 ml KI soln, followed by 2 ml sol. starch indicator, **10.100(h)**, and mix thoroly. Titr. with 0.05*N* $Na_2S_2O_3$ to complete disappearance of blue color (10 ml buret is recommended). Designate ml 0.05*N* $Na_2S_2O_3$ used as *A.*

Prep. blank by proceeding exactly as in par. 2, except add the 0.5*N* NaOH to malt infusion before adding starch soln. Det. reducing power of blank as in preceding par. Designate ml 0.05*N* $Na_2S_2O_3$ used for blank as *B.*

10.102   *Calculation of Diastatic Power*

(a) *Fehling soln modification.*—Degrees Diastatic Power as-is basis = $(5000/A) \times (B/A)$;

°Diastatic Power dry basis = (°Diastatic Power as-is basis $\times$ 100)/(100 − *M*), where *A* and *B* have same meaning as in **10.101(a)**, and *M* = % moisture.

In above formula, 5000/*A* is apparent diastatic power, which must be modified by fraction representing ratio of blank titrn to original titrn, which measures influence of starch in detn.

Report °Diastatic Power as-is and dry basis to nearest whole number.

(b) *Ferricyanide modification.*—°Diastatic Power, as-is = $(B − A) \times 23$, where *A* and *B* have same meaning as in **10.101(b)**. Calc. dry basis from this as in (a) and report to nearest whole number.

When conditions given in method are followed, net quantity of ferricyanide, after correcting for blank, $\times$ 23 = °Diastatic Power as-is basis.

Alpha-Amylase (15)—Official Final Action
10.103   *Reagents*

(a) *Special starch.*—Use Merck's sol. Lintner starch, special for diastatic power detn. *See* **10.100(g)**.

(b) *Beta-amylase.*—Use special β-amylase powder free from α-amylase, made by Wallerstein Co. This prepn has been stdzd to 2000° and should comply with following specifications: At addn level used, variation is ≤5% in dextrinization of std malt infusion when 1 and 3 day old substrates are compared. Further, substrate prepd by adding twice the level of β-amylase indicated must deviate by ≤5% from that prepd with recommended level after 24 hr standing. Store powder in tightly closed bottle in refrigerator. To avoid moisture condensation on cold enzyme prepn, let bottle warm to room temp. before opening.

(c) *Stock iodine soln.*—Dissolve 5.50 g I crystals (ACS) and 11.0 g KI in H_2O, and dil. to 250 ml with H_2O. Store in dark bottle and make fresh soln monthly.

(d) *Dilute iodine soln.*—Dissolve 20.0 g KI in H_2O, add 2.00 ml of the stock I soln, and dil. to 500 ml with H_2O. Series of 13 $\times$ 100 mm test tubes contg 5 ml dil. I soln must be made up beforehand and adjusted to 20° in readiness for testing. All-glass automatic pipet such as the Machlett type is recommended for rapidly dispensing this soln.

(e) *Buffer soln.*—Dissolve 120 ml HOAc and 164 g anhyd. NaOAc in H_2O, and dil. to 1 L.

(f) *Sodium chloride soln.*—0.5%. Dissolve 5 g reagent NaCl in 1 L H_2O. This soln need not be made up in vol. flask.

(g) *Buffered limit-dextrin (alpha-amylodextrin) substrate.*—Prep. suspension of 10.00 g (dry wt) Merck's sol. starch in cold H_2O and pour slowly into boiling H_2O. Boil with stirring 1–2 min, cool, and add 25 ml buffer soln and 250 mg β-amylase dissolved in small amt H_2O. Dil. to 500 ml with H_2O, sat. with toluene, and store at ca 20° for ≥18 hr but ≤72 hr before use.

10.104   *Apparatus*

(a) *Constant temperature bath.*—Set at 20±0.05°.

(b) *Reference color std.*—Use special Alpha-Amylase Color Disk (Cat. No. 620S-5) made by Hellige Inc., 877 Stewart Ave, Garden City, NY 11530.

(c) *Comparator.*—Use either std Hellige comparator (Cat. No. 607) or pocket comparator (Cat. No. 605) with prism attachment (Cat. No. 605-A). Illuminate comparator with 100 watt frosted lamp mounted in such manner that direct rays from lamp do not shine in operator's eyes. Place lamp 6″ from rear opal glass of comparator. Slight differences in color discrimination between different operators are minimized by use of prism attachment, by maintaining 6–10″ reading distance between eye and comparator, and by experience gained with continued practice.

(d) *Comparison tubes.*—Use precision bore square tubes with 13 mm viewing depth. Place tube filled with distd H_2O behind color disk.

The α-amylase color disk is correct only when used with specified 13 mm viewing depth. Precision bore square tubes are specified to obviate need for individual calibration of test tubes and to ensure use of std viewing depth. The 13 mm precision square tubes are supplied as std equipment with Hellige Comparator and are also used with Coleman Universal spectrophtr. They may be secured from either Hellige Inc., distributors of Coleman instrument, or Fischer & Porter Co.

10.105 *Determination*

(a) *Preparation of malt infusion.*—Ext 25 ± 0.05 g finely ground malt exactly as in **10.101**, par. 1, using 500 ml 0.5% NaCl soln. Dil. 20 ml malt infusion to 100 ml with 0.5% NaCl soln at 20°.

(b) *Dextrinization.*—Transfer 20.0 ml substrate soln at 20° to 50 ml erlenmeyer, add 5 ml 0.5% NaCl soln, and again adjust to 20°. Add 5 ml dild malt infusion at 20°, blowing it in and counting time from instant first of the dild malt infusion reaches starch substrate in flask. After 10 min reaction time, add 1 ml hydrolyzing mixt. to 5 ml dil. I soln at 20°, shake, pour into 13 mm square tube, and compare with α-amylase color disk in comparator. At appropriate intervals remove addnl 1 ml aliquots hydrolyzing mixt., add to dil. I soln, mix, and compare with color disk until α-amylase color is reached. Take care to keep tubes contg reaction mixt. plus I from changing temp. while comparing colors. If color comparisons are made immediately after addn of reaction mixt. to I, there will be essentially no temp. change and no change in color.

During initial stages of reaction, 1 ml sample need not be measured precisely before addn to dil. I soln. As end point approaches make addn accurately with 1 ml pipet. (Use fast flowing pipet such as 1 ml bacteriological pipet for withdrawing 1 ml aliquot.) Blow contents of pipet into I soln. Near end point, take readings every 0.5 min on the min or half min. In case two readings 0.5 min apart show that one is darker than α-amylase color disk and other is lighter, record end point at nearest 15 sec. Shake out 13 mm square tube used for color comparison between successive readings.

For accuracy and convenience, it is desirable that dextrinization times fall between 10 and 30 min. With malts of low α-amylase activity it may be necessary to use 10 ml dild infusion. In this case, do not add 5 ml NaCl soln. Final vol. of reaction mixt. should always be 30 ml.

10.106 *Calculation of Alpha-Amylase Activity*

From time interval in min necessary for dextrinization, T, and wt malt in g represented by infusion aliquot taken, W, calc. α-amylase units. An α-amylase unit is defined as quantity of α-amylase which will dextrinize sol. starch in presence of excess of β-amylase at rate of 1 g/hr at 20°.

$$20° \ D.U. \text{ (as-is basis)} = 24/(W \times T);$$
$$20° \ D.U. \text{ (dry basis)} = D.U. \text{ (as-is)}$$
$$\times 100/(100 - M);$$

where $M = \%$ moisture in sample and $24 =$ wt starch used (0.4 g) multiplied by 1 hr (60 min).

Example: $W = 0.05$ g; $T = 20$ min; $20° \ D.U.$ (as-is) $= 24/(0.05 \times 20) = 24$.

Report dextrinizing units to nearest 0.1 unit.

CEREAL ADJUNCTS

10.107 **Sampling—Official Final Action—** *See* **10.074**

10.108 **Preparation of Sample—Official Final Action—***See* **10.075**

10.109 **Physical Characteristics—Procedure**

(a) *Accidental foreign particles.*—Before proceeding with laboratory detns remove any accidental foreign particles from sample. Report presence and amt.

(b) *Color.*—Spread suitable portion of sample evenly and observe against white background. Report as white, cream, yellow, buff, gray, brown.

(c) *Odor.*—Det. after shaking sample in closed container. Report as clean and normal, moldy, musty, rancid, or other foreign odor.

(d) *Husks, germs, and foreign seeds.*—Classify and report in %.

(e) *Mold.*—Det. by visual inspection and report as none, trace, considerable.

(f) *Weevils, larvae, etc.*—Det. presence or absence by visual inspection. Report as none, very few, few, considerable; indicate if alive or dead.

Assortment of Corn Grits (16)— Official Final Action

10.110 *Apparatus*

(a) *Sieve shaker.*—Such as Ro-Tap testing sieve shaker (W. S. Tyler Co., 8200 Tyler Blvd, Mentor, OH 44060).

(b) *Nested set of sieves and pan.*—8″ sieve diam., Nos. 20, 30, 40, 60, 100, or other similar series.

10.111 *Determination*

Accurately weigh ca 50 ± 0.1 g of well-mixed, representative sample of grits, **10.107–10.108**. (To obtain representative sample <100 g, pass successively thru sample divider.) Transfer sample to top sieve of set of sieves with pan, assembled and fixed in shaker, and shake 5 min. Weigh, to 0.1 g, grits particles remaining on and adhering to each of sieves, or caught in pan.

Calc. wt of each sieve fraction and pan fraction as % of sample wt. Report % of each fraction to 1 decimal place.

Moisture—Official Final Action
Air Oven Method (103–104°)

10.112   *Apparatus*

See **10.084**.

10.113   *Determination*

Grind as in **10.090** and proceed as in **10.086**.

Oil or Petroleum Ether Extract— Official Final Action

10.114   *Reagent*

Petroleum ether.—AOCS. Initial boiling temp., 35–38°; dry-flask end point, 52–60°; ≥95% distg under 54°, and ≤60% distg under 40°; sp gr at 60°F, 0.630–0.660; appearance, colorless; evapn residue, ≤0.0011 g/100 ml; doctor test, sweet; copper-strip corrosion test, noncorrosive; only trace of unsatd compds permitted; residue in distg flask, neut. to Me orange; blotter strip odor test, odorless within 12 min; aromatic compds, no nitrobenzene odor; saponification value, <1.0 mg KOH/100 ml.

Make distn test according to ASTM method D216-54 and make blank detn by evapg 250 ml with ca 0.25 g stearin or other hard fat (previously brought to constant wt by heating) and drying as in actual detn. Blank must be ≤3 mg.

10.115   *Determination*

(*Caution: See* **46.011, 46.039,** and **46.073.**)

Accurately weigh 5–10 g sample ground as in **10.090**. Without previous drying, ext in Soxhlet or other suitable extractor with pet ether for ≤6 hr. Filter ext thru small, hardened paper into weighed vessel, washing paper finally with small portion of hot fresh solv. Distill or evap. solv. at temp. ≤100° and dry vessel contg residue in air oven 1 hr at 100–105°. Report as % oil to second decimal place.

Extract—Official Final Action

10.116   *Apparatus*

Same as in **10.088** except that mill may be of any suitable type.

10.117   *Standardization*

Setting of mill.—Use sample of rice or grits with moisture content ≤12%. Grind enough sample to obtain at least 51 g ground portion. Det. fineness of grinding as in **10.089**(a). Fine grinding of rice should show 40±2.5 g (= 80±5%) and grits 35±2.5 g (= 70±5%) of ground portion passing thru std sieve.

10.118   *Determination*

Grind enough sample so that at least 21 g is obtained. Grind ca 31 g malt made mainly from 6-rowed barley of Manchurian type, conversion time ≤7 min, Diastatic Power 100–120°. Det. ext of malt simultaneously with that of the cereal.

Mash in 20±0.05 g sample (with exception of flaked corn and flaked rice) and 5±0.05 g ground malt with 200 ml H_2O at 46°. Mix well with glass rod, place on wire gauze over flame, and bring to boil in ≥10 min but <15 min, stirring constantly. Boil grits and rice gently 30 min, and refined grits 10 min, avoiding burning, spattering, and excessive frothing. During boiling, stir mash and keep vol. constant by adding boiling H_2O every 15 min. After boiling, cool to 46° and add 25±0.05 g remaining ground malt. When ext is detd on flaked corn or flaked rice, do not boil, but mash in 20 g unground sample and 30 g ground malt with 200 ml H_2O at 46°. Mix well to prevent formation of lumps, rinse inner walls of beaker, promptly place mash beakers in mashing app. contg H_2O previously heated to 46°, and set stirrers in motion. Hold 30 min at 45° from time mash beakers were placed in app. Raise mash temp. 1°/min until 70° is reached. Add 100 ml H_2O, previously heated to 70–71°, and hold mash 60 min at 70°. (All temps refer to mash, not H_2O bath temp. Temp. deviation during mashing should be ≤0.5°.)

To test conversion, transfer drop mash to one cavity of porcelain plate and add drop 0.02N I soln, **10.087**(b); conversion is complete when test drop and I soln give yellow soln. Report time of conversion in periods: <15 min, 15–30, 30–45, 45–60, incomplete at 60 min. Cool, filter as in **10.090**(c), and det. sp gr and corresponding ext as in **10.090**(d) and (e).

10.119   *Calculation*

$$\text{Total ext} = P \times (800 + M \text{ in } 60 \text{ g malt} + M \text{ in } 40 \text{ g sample})/(100 - P)$$

where P = ext from Plato's table, **47.009**, and M = % moisture.

Ext in sample

$$= (\text{total ext} - \text{ext in } 60 \text{ g malt}) \times 100/40.$$

Enzyme Method for Corn Grits (17)— Official Final Action

10.120   *Reagents*

(a) *Enzyme mixture.*—Alpha-amylase and malt diastase, "Special for Analytical Purposes." (Wallerstein Co.) Mix in proportions 1 + 4.

(b) *Iodine soln.*—0.02N. See **10.087**(b).

10.121   *Apparatus*

(a) *Wiley or other mill.*—For fine grinding, equipped with 1 mm (openings) sieve (No. 18 or similar).

(b) *Other apparatus.*—Same as for **10.088**, except (a), (b), and (e).

10.122   *Determination*

Preparation of corn grits for mashing.—Grind enough grits to yield 36 g grist passing thru 1 mm sieve openings (collect 72 g if detn is to be made in duplicate). Prep. addnl 24 g if single detns of moisture, oil, protein, and ash are to be made.

Mashing procedure.—Weigh, into mash beaker, 35 ±0.05 g ground corn grits and 0.5±0.05 g enzyme mixt. Mix dry ingredients, add 200 ml H_2O at 46°, and mix well with glass rod. Mark liq. level on beaker wall. Place mash beaker on wire gauze over flame. With constant stirring, bring contents to boil within 15 min and boil gently 30 min, avoiding burning, spattering, and excessive frothing. During boiling, dil. contents to original vol. every 15 min with boiling H_2O.

Cool to 46° and add 2.5±0.05 g enzyme mixt. Mix well to disperse mixt. thoroly and to prevent formation of lumps. Wash down inside walls of beaker with rubber policeman and little H_2O.

Promptly place mash beaker in mashing app. contg H_2O previously heated to 46°, insert thermometer in beaker, and start stirrers. Starting at 45°, raise mash temp. 1°/min to 70°. Add 100 ml H_2O previously heated to 70–71°. Hold mash 30 min at 70°. Do not let temp. deviations during mashing exceed 0.5.° (All temps are *mash* temps, not H_2O bath temps.)

Conversion.—Using ca 3 mm diam. glass rod, transfer 1 drop mash to cavity of porcelain spot test plate and test with 1 drop 0.02N I. Judge color exactly 2 min after addn. Make spot test every 15 min after mash temp. has reached 70°. Conversion is complete when I produces only yellow color with mash. Report conversion time in periods of <15 min, 15–30, or incomplete in 30 min.

Cooling and filtration.—After 30 min at 70°, cool and filter mash as in **10.090**(c).

Determination of specific gravity.—See **10.090**(d). Obtain Plato value of ext corresponding to its sp gr from **47.009**.

Enzyme extract blank.—Det. ext value of enzyme reagent by carrying 3.0 g enzyme mixt., without ground corn grits, thru mashing operation as above. Omit conversion tests. Cool, filter, and det. Plato value of filtrate from its sp gr as above.

Make single ext detn for each lot of enzyme mixt.

10.123   *Calculations*

Calc. % ext in corn grits, (GE), as follows: GE, as-is, % =

$$\left[\frac{Pg(830 + 0.7M - 2D)}{100 - Pe} - EE\right] \times \frac{100}{70}$$

GE, dry basis, % = GE, as-is × 100/(100 − M),

where M = % moisture in grits sample, D = g enzyme reagent mixt. used, Pe = g ext in 100 g enzyme blank filtrate (°Plato), Pg = g ext in 100 g grits mash filtrate (°Plato), and EE = ext added with enzyme reagents mixt. = $Pe(900 − 2D)/(100 − Pe)$.

Report % ext in corn grits to nearest 0.1%.

10.124   Crude Fat or Ether Extract— Official Final Action

See **7.048**.

10.125   Protein—Official Final Action

See **2.051**. Multiply results by 6.25.

10.126   Ash—Official Final Action

See **14.006**.

10.127   Crude Fiber—Official Final Action

See **7.053–7.057**.

HOPS

10.128   Sampling—Official Final Action

(Oregon sampler, Bates divider, and excellent sampling procedure are described in "Hop Inspection Manual Covering the Determination of Leaves and Stems and Seeds in Hops," Instruction No. 918(GR)-1, July 1, 1951, available from Grain Division, C&MS, US Dept. of Agriculture, Washington, DC 20250.)

(**a**) *Unpressed hops.*—Draw equal portions from 5 or 10 different parts of heap, from surface as well as from different depths, until ca 200 g is obtained. Place sample in suitable container such as tin can having screw- or friction-type cover, moisture-proof plastic bags, or jars.

(**b**) *Baled hops.*—Use Oregon sampling device or sharp knife to cut 200 g samples from ≥10% of bales in shipment <100 bales and square root of number of bales if >100, avoiding sampling at press seam. Place each bale sample in sep. container. (If chemical tests are to be made, store in tin cans having friction or screw tops, not cartons, paper bags, wrapping paper, or wooden boxes.) Take sufficient equal quantity from each bale sample so that total of 100 g is combined in one composite sample. (Use of Bates divider gives most accurate results.)

10.129   Physical Examination (*18*)— Official Final Action

(**a**) *Leaves and stems.*—Pick out, with tweezers or forceps, stems and leaves from 20±0.01 g sample. Det. wt leaves and stems to 1 decimal place. Use remainder of sample for seed detn, if required.

(**b**) *Size and condition of cones.*—Report size according to following classification:

	Length (Inches)
Large	2¼–3
Medium	1¼–2
Small	¾–1

Report condition of cones as unbroken, partly broken, much broken.

(**c**) *Lupulin.*—Break 10 cones into longitudinal halves and examine lupulin grains thereby exposed in good light, preferably daylight, as to amt, color, and condition. Report amt as plentiful, fairly plentiful, scarce. Report color as lemon-yellow, orange-yellow, brownish. Report condition as sticky, fairly sticky, not sticky.

(**d**) *Seeds.*—Dry portion remaining from leaf and stem detn, or sep. 20 g sample, in oven 3–6 hr at >100° or 2 hr at 114–116° (long enough to eliminate stickiness). (If rapid drying is necessary, place sample in 2 foot square muslin cloth, immerse in bowl of MeOH or trichloroethylene 1 min, press out excess liq. by hand, using rubber gloves for protection, and spread cloth contg hops on screen to dry in air or over steam radiator. *Caution: See* **46.040.**)

Fold portions of the dried hops in dry square of muslin and rub between hands to crush petals completely; then empty finely pulverized material onto 4 × 20 wire mesh screen to sep. petal substance. Continue this process until portion left on screen consists mainly of seeds and rachillae; sep. these by rolling seeds off large sheet of sandpaper into tared dish, weigh, and report % by wt to 1 decimal place.

(e) *Color and luster.*—Det. color and luster on whole cones and refer findings to predominating character of sample. Report color as greenish-yellow, yellowish-green, pale green, olive-green, dark green. Describe presence of amts of differently colored cones as: small, medium, or large amt of _____ cones present, using appropriate color terminology, such as brownish, reddish, etc.

(f) *Aroma.*—Rub several cones between hands. Report odor as aromatic, mildly aromatic, abnormal. Use term flowery to describe exceptionally fine aroma. Use proper designations, such as musty, cheesy, etc., to describe abnormal odors.

10.130 Aphids—Official First Action

See **40.008–40.010.**

10.131 Preparation of Sample for Chemical Analysis—Official Final Action

Grind hop samples immediately before analysis. Let samples stored in refrigerator come to room temp. before grinding.

Grind 50–75 g sample in No. 2 or 72 Universal food chopper, using 12-tooth cutter (available from Union Manufacturing Co., New Britain, CT 06050). Discard first 5 or 10 g. Place polyethylene bag over discharge of chopper so that hops pass directly into bag. Pass hops evenly and slowly thru grinder, taking care to avoid choking orifices so as to prevent undue heating of hops. Thoroly mix ground portion into homogeneous mass and store in air-tight container in cool, dark place. (In some cases definite quantities of ground portions from several samples may be mixed together, and analyses run, in duplicate, on mixed portion.) For accurate results in analysis for resins, detn must be completed on same day as grinding, since resins are subject to oxidn.

10.132 Moisture—Official Final Action

Use one of following methods which are listed in order of accuracy:

(1) Me cyclohexane or *n*-heptane distn method with 10.00 g sample, **7.004–7.005.**

(2) Vac. drying 3 hr at 60° at 22–23″ Hg, **7.003.**

(3) Drying 1 hr at 103–104°, **10.084–10.086.**

For (2) and (3) use 2.5 g ground sample in 55 mm weighing bottle or Al dish, or 5 g ground sample in 70 mm dish. (Quantity of hops and dimensions of dish used are important for accurate results.) Report results in % to 1 decimal place, and state method used.

Alpha and Beta Acids (19)— Official Final Action

10.133   *Reagents*

(a) *Methanol.*—Reagent grade. A in 1 cm cell <0.060 at 275 nm against H_2O.

(b) *Alkaline methanol.*—Add 0.2 ml 6N NaOH to 100 ml MeOH, (a). Soln must be fresh.

(c) *Benzene.*—Reagent grade. A in 1 cm cell <0.110 against H_2O at 275 nm when 1 ml is dild to 100 ml with reagent (b). (*Caution: See* **46.018, 46.040,** and **46.045.**)

10.134   *Apparatus*

Spectrophotometer.—For UV use with 1 cm cells (Beckman Instruments DU or equiv.). Calibrate with soln contg 0.0400 g K_2CrO_4/L of 0.05N KOH. *See* Definitions of Terms and Explanatory Notes, p. xvii, (22).

10.135   *Determination*

Weigh 5±0.001 g ground hops into 250 ml g-s bottle or flat-bottom flask. With pipet, add 100 ml benzene, **10.133**(c). Grease stopper with Dow Corning high vac. silicone stopcock grease and stopper tightly. Weigh bottle or flask to nearest 0.1 g and record. Shake vigorously 30 min on mech. shaker and reweigh. If wt loss is >0.2–0.3 g, start new detn. Let flask stand until supernatant clears.

Dil. appropriate aliquot of benzene ext with alk. MeOH, **10.133**(b), so that A falls within most accurate range of instrument used. (For Beckman DU, A of 1.1–1.4 at 325 and 355 nm are preferred, with selector switch at 0.1 position, thus expanding scale so that readings are made in 0.1–0.4 region of calibrated scale. For hops contg ca 8% total *alpha* and *beta* acids, pipet 5 ml benzene ext into 50 ml vol. flask and dil. to vol. with alk. MeOH (*Diln A*); then dil. 4.00 ml *Diln A* to 50 ml with alk. MeOH (*Diln B*). For hops of high *alpha* and *beta* acid content, dil. 4.00 ml *Diln A* to 100 ml for *Diln B*.)

Det. A of *Diln B* at 275, 325, and 355 nm, first setting instrument to 0 A with blank prepd by dilg 5 ml benzene, (c), with alk. MeOH in same sequence used for samples.

10.136   *Calculations*

(a) % *alpha acids* = $d \times (-51.56A_{355} + 73.79A_{325} - 19.07A_{275})$, where d = diln factor, and A_{355}, A_{325}, and A_{275} = A of *Diln B* at resp. wavelengths. For diln sequence 5 to 50 ml, followed by second diln of 4 to 50 ml,

$$d = (50 \times 50 \times 100 \times 20)/$$
$$(1000 \times 4 \times 5 \times 1000) = 0.25$$

(b) *% beta acids* $= d \times (55.57A_{355} - 47.59A_{325} + 5.10A_{275})$, where d, and A_{355}, and A_{325}, and A_{275} have same values as in (a).

Report both *alpha* and *beta* acids to 1 decimal place.

BREWING SUGARS AND SIRUPS

10.137 Color and Clarity—Official Final Action

(a) *Clarity.*—Observe degree of clarity of unfiltered "10% soln," **10.138**(a). Report as clear, slightly hazy, or hazy.

(b) *Color.*—Free "10% soln," **10.138**(a), from suspended matter and, if possible, from haze by filtration thru dry paper. Det. color as in **10.004**, **10.094**, or **10.096**. Report as color of "10% soln" to nearest 0.1 unit.

10.138 Extract—Official Final Action

(a) *Preparation of "10% soln."*—Accurately weigh ca 50 g well mixed representative sample, dissolve in warm H_2O, transfer quant. to 500 ml vol. flask, and dil. to vol. at 20°. Mix thoroly.

(b) *Determination.*—With suitable pycnometer det. sp gr of soln at 20/20°, as in **10.089**(b) or (c). Obtain corresponding ext from **47.009**. Calc. % ext in original sample, E, from following formula:

$$E = P \times B \times 500/W,$$

where P = ext of dild sample; B = sp gr of dild sample; and W = actual wt (ca 50 g) of sample taken. Report to 1 decimal place.

(c) *Degrees Baumé.*—Obtain degrees Baumé (Modulus 145) equiv. to ext of original sample, (b), from **47.009**.

10.139 Nonextract (Apparent Water)—Official Final Action

Obtain by subtracting ext of original sample, **10.138**(b), from 100.

10.140 Fermentable Extract (20)—Official Final Action

(a) *Regular fermentation method.*—Ferment 250 ml "10% soln" of sample, **10.138**(a), with equiv. of 5 g washed, active brewers' compressed yeast 48 hr at 15–25° or until fermentation is complete. In case of refined sugars and sirups, such as corn sirup, add to soln, before fermenting, 0.8 g K_2HPO_4 crystals, 1 g $NH_4H_2PO_4$, and 0.5 g dried yeast ext, stdzd for bacteriological culture media purposes, as nutrients. If such nutrient material needs to be added, redet. ext of the "10% soln" after adding nutrient material, but before adding yeast. Use fermentation flasks equipped with either H_2O, Hg, or acid seals, and shake flasks several times a day during fermentation. When fermentation is complete, filter soln thru dry paper, refiltering first 20–30 ml filtrate. (Filtrate should be clear, but not necessarily brilliant.) Det.

real ext in filtrate as in **10.023**(a), after removal of alcohol.

Use following formulas for calcn:

Fermentable ext (ext basis) $= (p - n) \times 100/P$;

and

Fermentable ext (as-is basis) $= (p - n) \times E/P$;

where P = ext of "10% soln" before addn of any nutrients; p = ext of "10% soln" before fermentation; n = real ext of "10% soln" after fermentation; and E = ext of original sample, **10.138**(b).

If nutrients have not been used (as in case of malt sirups), $p = P$, and will have been detd in **10.138**(b), and no redetn before fermentation is required. Report to 1 decimal place.

(b) *Rapid fermentation method.*—Proceed as in (a), but instead of 250 ml "10% soln" of sample, **10.138**(a), use equiv. of 32 g fresh compressed brewers' yeast or liq. yeast that has been de-watered by suction on buchner (more precise results are obtained by washing yeast with "10% soln" of sample before final suction filtration). For refined sugars and sirups, use nutrients as in (a). Ferment mixt. at room temp. (20–23°) and stir continuously with 4 blade glass stirrer (ca 2″ diam.) at 100–120 rpm until fermentation is complete (4–5 hr). As evapn can be important variable, keep stirring and time at min. Filter, det. real ext, and calc. as in (a).

Yeast autolysis can affect results by contributing solids to fermented liq. Effect may be checked by detg pH of fermented liq., its alcohol content, and calcd original gravity, **10.024**. If pH is high and original gravity is appreciably higher than ext of "10% soln" originally detd, yeast autolysis has probably occurred and detn should be repeated with fresh yeast.

10.141 Protein—Official Final Action

(a) Transfer 25 ml "10% soln," **10.138**(a), to Kjeldahl digestion flask, and proceed as in **10.036**.

% protein (N $\times$ 6.25) in original as-is sample
$$= 100 \times (\text{ml } 0.1N\ H_2SO_4 - \text{ml } 0.1N\ NaOH)$$
$$\times 0.0014 \times 6.25 \times 500/(25 \times W)$$

where W = actual wt sample used in prepg "10% soln." Report to 2 decimal places.

(b) Det. N as in **31.019**, and calc. protein, using factor N $\times$ 6.25.

10.142 Diastatic Power—Official Final Action

(Malt sirups only)

Transfer 10 ml "10% soln," **10.138**(a), to 100 ml vol. flask and dil. to vol. at 20° with H_2O. Transfer 10 ml "1% soln" so prepd to 250 ml vol. flask, bring to 20°, add 200 ml buffered starch soln at 20°, **10.100**(g), and proceed as in **10.101**, last 4 sentences in second par., beginning "Mix soln . . ." and ending "mix thoroly." Follow Fehling soln modification, **10.101**(a).

Calc. on as-is basis according to formula:

°Diastatic Power (as-is basis)
$$= (5000 \times B \times 50)/(A \times A \times W)$$

where A = ml digested starch soln required to reach end point in detn; B = ml digested starch soln required to reach end point in blank; and W = wt sirup used to prep. "10% soln."

10.143 Iodine Reaction for Unconverted Starch—Official Final Action

Use "10% soln," **10.138**(a), and proceed as in **10.050**.

10.144 Acidity—Official Final Action

Transfer 100 ml "10% soln," **10.138**(a), to suitable beaker or flask and proceed as in **10.027**, second par., or **10.028**, beginning "titr. potentiometrically..." Calc. and report results as follows (W = actual wt sample, in g, used to prep. "10% soln"):

(a) In terms of ml $1N$ NaOH/100 g original sample, as-is basis:

Acidity = ml $0.1N$ NaOH consumed
$$\times 500/(10 \times W).$$

Report to 1 decimal place.

(b) In terms of "lactic acid" as % original sample, as-is basis:

Acidity = ml $0.1N$ NaOH consumed
$$\times 0.009 \times 500/W.$$

Report to 2 decimal places.

10.145 Hydrogen-Ion Concentration (pH)—Official Final Action

Using "10% soln," **10.138**(a), proceed as in **10.029**.

10.146 Ash—Official Final Action

Proceed as in **31.012** or **31.013**.

Total Reducing Sugars (21)—Official Final Action

10.147 Munson-Walker General Method

Transfer 50 ml "10% soln," **10.138**(a), to 250 ml vol. flask. Clarify, if necessary, with alumina cream or neut. Pb(OAc)$_2$ soln only (never basic Pb(OAc)$_2$), and dil. to vol. at 20° with H$_2$O. Mix thoroly and either centrf. or filter until clear. If Pb(OAc)$_2$ soln was used for clarification, remove excess Pb with dry Na$_2$C$_2$O$_4$. Filter, and det. reducing sugars on 10 ml aliquot as in **31.039–31.040, 31.053,** or **31.065.** Calc. results in terms of invert sugar for invert sirups and sugars; glucose for corn sugars and sirups; and maltose for malt sirups. If character of sample is in doubt, express reducing sugars as glucose.

% Reducing sugar, as-is = $25M/W$, where M is mg sugar from appropriate column of **47.019,** and W is g sample used to prep. "10% soln."

10.148 Lane-Eynon General Volumetric Method

Dil. 50 ml soln, clarified as in **10.147,** to 100 ml and proceed as in **31.036–31.037, 31.052,** or **31.064,** referring titer to **47.017** or **47.018.** Calc. results as in **10.147.**

10.149 Glucose—Official Final Action

To 5 ml aliquot of soln prepd as in **10.147,** add 15 ml H$_2$O and proceed as in **31.214** or **31.218.**

10.150 Other Determinations—See Chap. 31

WORT—OFFICIAL FINAL ACTION

10.151 Preparation of Sample

Store 1 gal. wort 12–15 hr at 4–7°; then filter all but last portion of this sample at 4–7° thru paper of types specified in **10.088**(f). If filtrate is not brilliant after first filtration, return to filter, but do not use filter-aid. (Some worts cannot be filtered brilliantly clear.) To prevent spoiling, keep sample in refrigerator, and if necessary, place in beer bottles and pasteurize. Mix sample well to insure uniformity before removing portion for analysis.

10.152 Specific Gravity

Proceed as in **10.016** or **10.090**(d). Report to 5 decimal places.

10.153 Original Extract or Original Gravity

From **47.009,** find ext corresponding to sp gr detd at 20/20°. Report as °Plato (g/100 g) to 2 decimal places.

10.154 Fermentable Extract

(a) *Regular method.*—Ferment 250 ml wort with equiv. of 5 g washed, active brewers' compressed yeast 48 hr at 15–25°, or until fermentation is complete. Use either H$_2$O, Hg, or acid seal to prevent evapn. Filter soln and det. real ext in filtrate as in **10.023**(a) after removal of alcohol.

Calc. % by wt of fermentable ext as in **10.140.** Report to 2 decimal places.

Calc. also real degree of fermentation as in **10.025.** Report to 1 decimal place.

(b) *Rapid method.*—(Dets fermentability of worts contg up to ca 14% ext in 4–5 hr within 0.3–0.1% of attenuation limit.)

To 200 ml wort in 400–600 ml glass beaker add 32 g fresh, compressed, washed brewers' lager yeast or liq. yeast that has been dewatered by suction on buchner (more precise results are obtained by washing yeast with wort to be pitched before final suction filtration). Keep mixt. at room temp. (20–23°) and stir continuously with glass stirrer until fermentation is complete (4–5 hr). Filter mixt. thru ordinary filter paper, refiltering first 20–30 ml filtrate. (Filtrate should be clear, but not necessarily brilliant. As evapn can be important variable, keep stirring and time at min. Four-blade glass stirrer (ca 2″ diam.) operating at 100–120 rpm is satisfactory. Abnormal effects due to autolysis are likely to be indicated by too high pH of final beer and high calcd original gravity compared to actual original gravity. See 10.140(b).) Det. real ext and calc. as in (a).

10.155 Iodine Reaction
See 10.050.

10.156 Total Acidity
See 10.027–10.028.

10.157 Hydrogen-Ion Concentration (pH)
See 10.029.

10.158 Color
Prep. sample as in 10.151. If prepd wort has developed haze or sediment that would interfere with detn, clarify by centrfg or filtering without use of filter-aid. Indicate such clarification in report. Det. depth of color of prepd sample as in 10.094 or 10.096.

10.159 Protein
Prep. sample as in 10.151. If prepd sample shows sediment, mix thoroly to ensure perfect distribution of sediment before removing portion for analysis. To det. protein in the brilliant wort (free from any haze or sediment), reclarify prepd sample by centrfg or filtering without use of filter-aid. Indicate such clarification in report.

Pipet 25 ml prepd sample, measured at 20°, into 800 ml Kjeldahl flask and proceed as in 10.036.

10.160 Total Reducing Sugars
Prep. sample as in 10.151. If prepd wort contains appreciable quantities of suspended matter, remove by centrfg or filtering. Transfer 50 ml sample to 250 ml vol. flask, dil. to vol. at 20°, and mix thoroly. In general, worts do not require clarification for detn of reducing sugars, but if clarification is necessary, proceed as in 10.147. Det. reducing sugars in 10 ml of this soln by Munson-Walker method as in 31.065. Or dil. 50 ml of this soln with H_2O to 100 ml and use Lane-Eynon method as in 31.064. Express results as % maltose.

YEAST
LIQUID AND PRESSED YEAST
Sampling (22)—Procedure
10.161 *Apparatus*
Dry, wide-mouth 1 L containers with suitable cover or dry Mason jars with covers are acceptable for collecting samples. Jar should hold ca twice vol. of original sample.

10.162 *Collecting Primary Sample*
(a) *Bottom fermenting yeast.*—(1) From small fermenters from which the yeast is collected in cans or tubs, collect at least five 100 ml portions of the yeast slurry at intervals as it is forced out thru bung hole into brink. (2) From large tanks from which the yeast is removed by pump, collect 5–10 100 ml portions of the yeast slurry from sampling cock at regular intervals on discharge side of yeast pump.

(b) *Top fermenting yeast.*—Push aside upper fluffy layer of yeast and take portion from under layer. Collect at least five 100 ml portions from various parts of tank. (For routine work, top fermenting yeast is usually sampled after it has been skimmed into yeast buggy. Mix thoroly before sampling.)

(c) *Any liquid yeast from small tanks or tubs.*—Mix contents of tub thoroly to uniform consistency, taking care to blend in heavier deposits on bottom of vessel and to remove gases. Take at least 500 ml sample from this mixt.

(d) *Pressed yeast.*—Remove portions from different parts of cake—from surface as well as from center—and collect ca 150 g in 1 L beaker. Weigh to nearest 0.1 g. Prep. slurry by adding H_2O at rate of ca 3 parts H_2O to 1 part pressed yeast. Again weigh to nearest 0.1 g. With stirring rod, break up yeast portions and stir until liq. suspension is completely uniform.

10.163 *Preservation of Samples*
To prevent changes in analytical results due to autolysis and fermentation, proceed with examination immediately after samples have been obtained. Keep sample at 2° or below.

10.164 *Preparation of Laboratory Sample*
Mix primary composite sample thoroly and transfer working quantity to sep. container. If lumps or particles of trub are present, pass thru sieve entire bulk sample of liq. yeast, which should amt to ≥500 ml if yeast requires screening, or slurry prepd from ca 150 g pressed yeast. Make sure all lumps and particles are broken up and forced thru sieve. Recover, by scraping, any liq. or solids adhering to sieve, and reincorporate them with sieved sample. Mix well by stirring.

Total Solids
(When reporting total solids, state whether alcohol method, 10.167, or 16 hr drying method, 10.170, was used.)

Alcohol Method—Official Final Action
10.165 *Apparatus*
(a) *Sieve.*—Approx. 100-mesh.

(b) *Moisture oven.*—See 10.084(b).

(c) *Weighing dish.*—Glass or Al, at least 65 mm id, with cover, and glass stirring rod of such length that it fits within covered dish.

10.166 *Reagents*
(a) *Alcohol.*—Pure alcohol or MeOH, or alcohol denatured with completely volatile liq., such as SDF Nos. 1, 2-B, 3-A, 12-A, 13-A, 23-A.

(b) *Sand.*—Use clean, sharp sand. Wash with H_2O and dry overnight at 105°. Cool in desiccator. Keep in closed container. Loss of wt of 5 g of this sand when dried 3 hr at 105° must be ≤0.005 g.

10.167   *Determination*

Place ca 5 g dry sand in weighing dish. Weigh dish together with sand, cover, and stirring rod. Transfer to weighing dish ca 10 g well-mixed liq. yeast or yeast slurry from pressed yeast, cover, and weigh to nearest mg. Remove cover and add 5 ml alcohol. Mix thoroly with stirring rod. Drop rod into weighing dish. Dry 3 hr (±2 min) at 105°. Cover, cool in desiccator, and weigh.

For liq. yeast calc. drying loss of aliquot used as % and report total solids to 1 decimal place. For pressed yeast calc. according to following formula: % total solids = $D \times S \times 100/(W \times P)$, where P = wt (g) pressed yeast used for prepg slurry; S = total wt (g) yeast slurry; W = wt (g) slurry aliquot before drying; and D = wt (g) slurry aliquot after drying.

16 Hour Drying Method (23)— Official First Action

10.168   *Apparatus*

(a) *Drying oven.*—Forced-draft or convection type, regulated at 100±2°.

(b) *Moisture dish.*—Diam. 50–65 mm, depth 20 mm, Al, with tight-fitting cover.

(c) *Glass rods.*—3 mm diam. and of such length to fit into covered moisture dish. Fire polish both ends.

10.169   *Standardization of Oven*

Adjust oven to 98–102° after operation at least 30 min with door closed. Then note and record temp. at 10 min intervals for 2 hr. If temp. at any time is <98° or >102°, replace thermostat.

Accurately weigh (to 0.1 mg) ca 5 g dried yeast into weighed moisture dish previously dried 1 hr at 100±2° and cooled in desiccator, **10.171**(b). Dry in oven 16 hr at 100±2°, cover, transfer to desiccator, and weigh soon after it reaches room temp. Redry 2 hr, cool, and weigh. If moisture has increased by 0.1%, oven is not operating properly and should be serviced.

10.170   *Determination*

Dry moisture dish and stirring rod in oven 1 hr at 100±2°. Cover, transfer to desiccator, and weigh to 1 mg soon after it reaches room temp. Remove cover, transfer to dish ca 10 g well mixed liq. yeast or yeast slurry from pressed yeast, cover, and reweigh. Spread evenly with stirring rod and place rod in dish. Transfer dish, with cover loose, to oven and dry 16 hr at 100±2°. Cover, transfer to desiccator, and weigh soon after attaining room temp. Calc. drying loss and report total solids as in **10.167**.

DRIED YEAST
Total Solids—Official Final Action
Vacuum Oven Method (24)

10.171   *Apparatus*

(a) *Metal dish.*—Diam. ca 55 mm, ht ca 15 mm, provided with inverted slip-in cover fitting tightly on inside. Or, diam. ca 65 mm, ht ca 20 mm, provided with slip-over cover fitting tightly on outside.

(b) *Air-tight desiccator.*—$CaCl_2$, reignited CaO, and Drierite are satisfactory drying agents.

(c) *Vacuum oven.*—Connected with pump or vac. system capable of maintaining pressure ≤50 mm Hg, and provided with thermometer passing into oven with bulb near samples. Connect H_2SO_4 gas-drying bottle to oven to admit dry air when releasing vac.

10.172   *Determination*

Accurately weigh ca 2 g well-mixed sample in covered dish, previously dried at 98–100°, cooled in desiccator, and weighed soon after attaining room temp. Loosen cover (do not remove) and heat 5 hr at 98–100° at pressure of ≤50 mm Hg. Admit dry air into oven to bring to atm. pressure. Immediately tighten cover on dish, transfer to desiccator, and weigh soon after it reaches room temp.

Air Oven Method (25)

10.173   *Determination*

Accurately weigh ca 2 g well-mixed sample in covered dish, **10.171**(a), previously dried at 100±1°, cooled in desiccator, and weighed soon after it reaches room temp. Loosen cover (do not remove) and heat 16 hr at 100±1°. Tighten cover, transfer to desiccator, and weigh soon after it reaches room temp.

10.174   Protein—Official Final Action

Proceed as in **2.051**, using 0.5 g sample. Digest 30 min after soln clears. % Protein = %N × 6.25.

BREWERS' GRAINS* (26)—
OFFICIAL FINAL ACTION

10.175   *Sampling*

(a) *Wet brewers' grains.*—Using scoop, collect numerous small samples at uniform intervals during emptying of tub, so that at end of operation composite sample of 25–30 lb is obtained in clean, dry bucket. From mash filters collect numerous small samples in similar manner at equal time intervals from grain conveyor. Mix thoroly and quarter grains carefully so as to obtain representative sample of 3–4 lb. Place reduced sample in suitable container with screw or friction type cover, add few drops of toluene as preservative, close tightly, and refrigerate.

---

* For examination of brewers' grains for feeding purposes *see* Chap. 7.

(**b**) *Dry brewers' grains.*—*See* **10.074**. Take great care in sampling dry brewers' grains for analysis, particularly for feed, as it is very difficult to obtain truly representative sample. Because brewers' grains are composed of large husks and small, heavy particles, there is usually difference in composition at different levels of container.

If brewers' grains are in sacks, sample $\geq 2\%$ of the sacks, using trier as long as ht of sacks. Quarter sample down to ca 0.5 lb for laboratory sample.

If brewers' grains are in car, unsacked, it is practically impossible to obtain representative sample because of segregation at bottom of fine heavy material, which is higher in protein than lighter material at top.

Store sample in refrigerator pending laboratory analysis. On each sample container show date of sampling; name of company owning grains at time of sampling; and brew, lot, car, or ref. number or letter for identification. Before making analysis, mix grains thoroly.

10.176 Preliminary Drying (Wet Brewers' Grains)

Accurately weigh (± 0.1 g) ca 1000 g quartered wet brewers' grains on weighed, shallow, galvanized Fe or Al tray so that layer is $\leq \frac{1}{4}''$ thick. After spreading, moisten grains with little toluene to inhibit fermentation during drying. Dry in oven at 55–60°, or overnight in air by means of fan and heater, until grains appear air-dry. Note accurately (± 0.1 g) wt dried grains and store in moisture-proof container. Thoroly mix dried sample and grind finely 100 g, as in **10.090**. Keep ground portion in moisture-proof container.

10.177 Moisture

(**a**) *On sample after preliminary drying (when available and soluble extracts are determined).*—Use 5–10 g accurately weighed and ground sample and proceed as in **10.086**. Calc. % moisture in dried grains (W). Calc. % moisture, M, in original wet grains by following formula: $M = [(W \times D) + 100(G - D)]/G$, where G = wt wet grains before preliminary drying, D = wet grains after preliminary drying, and W = % moisture in grains after preliminary drying.

(**b**) *On sample in wet condition (when only soluble extract is determined).*—Use ca 15 g sample, accurately weighed into 70 mm Al dish, and dry first at temp. $<60°$ until air-dry; then dry addnl 3 hr as in **10.086**.

(**c**) *On dry brewers' grains.*—Proceed as in (a) and calc. % moisture.

Available Extract

10.178 Wet Brewers' Grains

(**a**) *Apparatus.*—Mash beakers and counter wts, mashing app., filter paper, funnels, flasks, pycnometers, emptying device, and H_2O bath. *See* **10.088**.

(**b**) *Preparation of sample.*—*See* **10.176**. *Preparation of finely ground malt.*—*See* **10.090**.

(**c**) *Mashing procedure.*—*See* **10.118**. Proceed as for flaked corn and flaked rice.

(**d**) *Cooling and filtration.*—*See* **10.090**(c).

(**e**) *Specific gravity.*—*See* **10.090**(d). Det. corresponding Plato values from **47.009**.

(**f**) *Calculation.*—Use following formulas:

$$\text{Total ext} = P \times (800 + W \text{ in 60 g malt} + W \text{ in 40 g dried grains})/(100 - P),$$

where P = g ext in 100 g wort (Plato), and W = moisture (g).

% available ext in wet grains, dry basis

$$= \frac{(E \text{ in mixt.} - E \text{ in 60 g malt}) \times 10,000}{40(100 - M \text{ of dried grains})},$$

where E = ext, and M = % moisture.

% available ext in wet grains, as-is basis = (available E, dry basis) $\times (100 - M$ of wet grains)/100, where E = ext, and M = % moisture.

10.179 Dry Brewers' Grains

Preparation of sample.—Grind finely 100 g sample and proceed as in **10.178**. Calc. ext as in **10.119**.

Soluble Extract (Wet Brewers' Grains)

10.180 On Sample After Preliminary Drying

(**a**) *Mashing procedure.*—"Mash in" in mash beaker 25$\pm$0.05 g unground sample with 350 ml H_2O at 70°. Place mash beakers in mashing app., **10.088**(c) and (d), contg H_2O previously heated to 70–71°, and set stirrers in motion. Hold mash 60 min at mash temp. of 70$\pm$0.5°.

(**b**) *Cooling and filtering.*—*See* **10.090**(c). Make mash to 425 g.

(**c**) *Specific gravity.*—*See* **10.090**(d). Det. corresponding Plato values from **47.009**.

(**d**) *Calculation.*—Use following formulas:

% sol. ext in wet grain, dry basis

$$= P(M \text{ of dried grains} + 1600) \times 100/(100 - P)(100 - M \text{ of dried grains}).$$

% sol. ext in wet grains, as-is basis

$$= (E, \text{ dry basis})(100 - M \text{ of wet grains})/100$$

where P = g ext in 100 g wort (Plato, **47.009**), E = ext, and M = % moisture.

10.181 On Sample in Wet Condition

Mashing method.—Using 100$\pm$0.05 g well-mixed and quartered brewers' grains and 300 ml H_2O at 71°, proceed as in **10.180**. Make mash to 450 g.

Calculation.—Use following formulas:

% sol. ext, as-is basis = $P(M + 350)/(100 - P)$;

% sol. ext, dry basis = $E \times 100/(100 - M)$;

where P = g ext in 100 g wort (Plato, **47.009**), M = % moisture content, and E = sol. ext, as-is.

Report sol. ext on as-is and dry basis in %, to 1 decimal place.

10.182   Soluble Extract (Dry Brewers' Grains)

Proceed as in **10.180,** but use following formula:

% sol. ext, as-is basis = $P(1600 + M)/(100 - P)$;

% sol. ext, dry basis = $E \times 100/(100 - M)$;

where P = g ext in 100 g wort (Plato, **47.009**), E = sol. ext, as-is, and M = % H_2O in dry brewers' grains.

SELECTED REFERENCES

(1) Am. Soc. Brewing Chemists, Methods of Analysis, 6th Ed., 1958, The Society, 501 N. Walnut St, Madison, WI 53705: Beer 10-A I and II.

(2) ASBC: Beer 20, Beer 24(1964); JAOAC **49,** 502(1966).

(3) ASBC: Beer 4.

(4) ASBC: Beer 8.

(5) ASBC: Beer 13B.

(6) ASBC: Beer 22(1964).

(7) ASBC: Beer 21(1961).

(8) ASBC: Beer 19.

(9) ASBC: Beer 18.

(10) ASBC: Beer 23(1968).

(11) ASBC: Beer 26.

(12) ASBC: Malt 2.

(13) ASBC: Malt 5(1962).

(14) ASBC: Malt 6.

(15) ASBC: Malt 7.

(16) ASBC: Cereal Adjuncts 8(1963).

(17) ASBC: Cereal Adjuncts 5B(1963).

(18) ASBC: Hops 2.

(19) ASBC: Hops 5(1960).

(20) ASBC: Brewing Sugars and Syrups 7.

(21) ASBC: Brewing Sugars and Syrups 14.

(22) ASBC: Yeast 1.

(23) JAOAC **44,** 394(1961).

(24) JAOAC **39,** 738(1956).

(25) JAOAC **40,** 446(1957).

(26) ASBC: Brewers' Grains 1–6.

11. Beverages: Wines [★]

11.001 Physical Examination—Procedure

Note and record following: (a) Whether container is "bottle full"; (b) appearance, whether bright or turbid and presence of sediment; (c) condition when opened, whether still, gaseous, or carbonated; (d) color and depth of color; (e) odor, whether vinous, foreign, or acetous; and (f) taste, whether dry, sweet, vinous, foreign, or acetous.

Immediately det. sp gr and those ingredients that are subject to change, such as alcohol, sugars, and acids.

11.002 Specific Gravity—Official Final Action

Det. sp gr at 20/20° by pycnometer as in **9.011**, or by small, accurately graduated hydrometer.

Alcohol

11.003 *By Volume from Specific Gravity— Official Final Action*

Measure 100 ml sample into 300–500 ml distn flask, noting temp., and add 50 ml H_2O. Attach flask to vertical condenser by means of bent tube, distill almost 100 ml, and dil. to 100 ml at same temp. (Foaming, which sometimes occurs, especially with young wines, may be prevented by adding small amt of antifoam material.) For wines that contain abnormal amt of HOAc, neutze exactly with $1N$ NaOH soln (calcd from acidity, **11.035**) before proceeding with distn (unnecessary for wines of normal taste and odor). Proceed as in **9.011**, at room temp. if desired, and obtain corresponding % alcohol by vol. from **47.003**.

11.004 *By Volume from Refraction (Rapid Method)—Official Final Action*

Det. immersion refractometer reading of distillate obtained in **11.003** and find corresponding % alcohol from **47.004**.

11.005 *By Weight—Official Final Action*

From **47.005**, obtain % alcohol by wt in distillate corresponding to % alcohol by vol., multiply by sp gr of distillate, and divide by sp gr of sample.

By Dichromate Oxidation (1)— Official Final Action

11.006 *Principle*

Sample is steam distd into acidified $K_2Cr_2O_7$ soln of known vol. and concn. Oxidation of alcohol to

HOAc is completed by heating. Unreacted dichromate is detd by titrn with std $Fe(NH_4)_2(SO_4)_2$ soln, using o-phenanthroline as indicator.

11.007 *Apparatus*

Micro Kjeldahl apparatus.—With gas microburner. *See* Fig. 11:1. (Glassware available from Scott Laboratories, Inc., 860 S. 19th St, Richmond, CA 94804.)

11.008 *Reagents*

(a) *Potassium dichromate soln.*—Add 325 ml H_2SO_4 to ca 400 ml H_2O in 1 L vol. flask. Mix and cool to 80–90°. Add 33.768 g $K_2Cr_2O_7$ (primary std). Dissolve, and dil. to vol. with H_2O at 20°.

(b) *Ferrous ammonium sulfate soln.*—Dissolve 135.5 g $FeSO_4(NH_4)_2SO_4.6H_2O$ in ca 500 ml H_2O in 1 L vol. flask. Add 30 ml H_2SO_4. Dil. to vol. with H_2O at 20°.

(c) *1,10-Phenanthroline ferrous sulfate indicator.*—Dissolve 0.695 g $FeSO_4.7H_2O$ in ca 50 ml H_2O, add 1.485 g o-phenanthroline.H_2O, and dil. to 100 ml with H_2O. (Prepd soln available from G. Frederick Smith Chemical Co.)

11.009 *Determination*

See Fig. 11:1. To begin distn, boil H_2O in steam generator. Open steam trap discharge. Turn 3-way stopcock so that steam from trap vents thru side tube and distg bulb is closed. Place 25 ml $K_2Cr_2O_7$ soln in 50 ml erlenmeyer under condenser with tip below surface of soln. Close sample stopcock and place small amt H_2O in sample funnel. Distg bulb is empty and micro burner is not lighted.

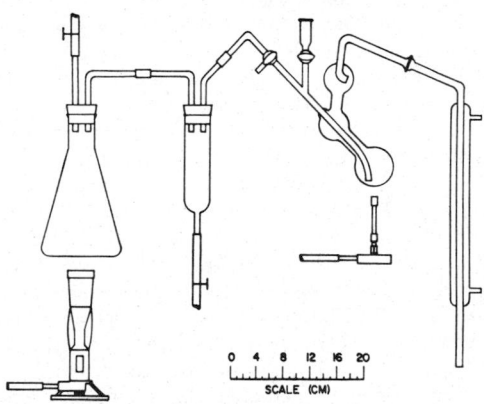

FIG. 11:1—Distillation apparatus for chemical determination of alcohol in wine.

Pipet 1 ml samples as follows: Fill 1 ml pipet (class A) slightly over mark, and wipe excess wine from exterior. Hold pipet vertical; with tip touching inside neck of sample bottle, drain to mark. Drain pipet completely into sample funnel. Open sample stopcock to drain sample into still; then reclose. Add small amt H_2O to funnel, drain into still, and rinse with H_2O until distg bulb is half filled. Place H_2O in funnel to ensure seal.

Close steam trap discharge with pinch clamp. Open 3-way stopcock, permitting steam to enter bulb while vent is closed. Light micro burner. Distill until receiving flask contains ca 40 ml, lower flask, and rinse outside of condenser outlet into flask with H_2O. Stopper flask and immerse to shoulder in $60 \pm 2°$ H_2O.

Admit cold H_2O into steam generator to flush contents of distg bulb into steam trap. Refill bulb with H_2O, flush again, open trap discharge, and vent 3-way stopcock. App. is now ready for next sample.

Remove flask from bath after 20–25 min. Rinse contents into 500 ml flask with H_2O. Titr. with $FeSO_4(NH_4)_2SO_4$ soln to almost clear green in front of daylight fluorescent light, add 3 drops indicator, and titr. to end point (change is from blue-green to brown).

Since $FeSO_4(NH_4)_2SO_4$ soln is slowly oxidized by air, perform blank detn daily by titrg 25 ml $K_2Cr_2O_7$. Discard $FeSO_4(NH_4)_2SO_4$ soln that has been standing in buret >30 min.

Calc. % alcohol by vol. = $25.00 - (25 \times$ sample titer/blank titer).

11.010 Glycerol in Dry Wines— Official Final Action

(At no time during evapns should surface of dish exposed to bath be greater in circumference than that covered by liq. in dish, arranged by floating dish in bath.)

(a) *By direct weighing.*—Evap. 100 ml sample to ca 10 ml in porcelain dish on H_2O bath held at 85–90°. Treat residue with ca 5 g fine sand and 4-5 ml *milk of lime* (contg 15 g CaO/100 ml) for each g ext present and evap. almost to dryness. Treat moist residue with 50 ml alcohol, 90% by vol., remove substance adhering to sides of dish with spatula, and rub whole mass to paste. Heat mixt. on H_2O bath to incipient boiling with constant stirring, and decant liq. thru filter into small flask. Wash residue repeatedly by decantation with 10 ml portions hot 90% alcohol until filtrate totals ca 150 ml. Evap. filtrate to sirupy consistency in porcelain dish, transfer residue to small, g-s graduated cylinder with 20 ml absolute alcohol, and add three 10 ml portions anhyd. ether, shaking thoroly after each addn. Let stand until clear, pour thru filter, and wash cylinder and filter with mixt. of absolute alcohol-anhyd. ether $(2 + 3)$, also pouring wash liquor thru filter. Evap. filtrate to sirupy consistency, dry 1 hr at 98–100°, weigh, ignite, and reweigh. Loss on ignition = wt glycerol.

(b) *By oxidation with dichromate.*—Evap. 100 ml

sample to ca 10 ml in porcelain dish on H_2O bath held at 85–90°. Treat residue with ca 5 g fine sand and 4–5 ml *milk of lime* (contg 15 g CaO/100 ml). Proceed as in **30.077**, beginning "evap. almost to dryness, with frequent stirring . . ." except dil. soln of glycerol after treatment with Ag_2CO_3 and $Pb(OAc)_2$ to 100 ml instead of 50 ml. Observe precautions concerning temp. at which all evapns are to be made.

11.011 Glycerol in Sweet Wines— Official Final Action

If ext is >5 g/100 ml, heat 100 ml to boiling in flask and treat with successive small portions of *milk of lime* until wine becomes first darker, then lighter in color. Cool, add 200 ml alcohol, let ppt settle, filter, and wash with alcohol. Treat combined filtrate and washings as in **11.010**.

11.012 Extract—Official Final Action

(a) *By specific gravity of dealcoholized wine.*—Calc. sp gr of dealcoholized wine, D, by following formula: $D = S + 1 - A$; S = sp gr of sample, **11.002**; and A = sp gr of alc. distillate, **11.003**.

From **47.008** ascertain % by wt of ext in dealcoholized wine corresponding to value of D. This figure $\times$ value of D = g ext/100 ml wine.

(b) *By evaporation.*—(*1*) *In dry wines, extract content less than 3 g/100 ml.*—In 75 ml flat-bottom Pt dish, ca 85 mm. diam., evap. 50 ml sample on H_2O bath to sirupy consistency. Heat residue 2–5 hr in drying oven at 100°, cool in desiccator, and weigh as soon as room temp. is reached.

(*2*) *In sweet wines.*—If ext content is 3–6 g/100 ml, treat 25 ml sample as in (*1*). If ext is >6 g/100 ml, accept result obtained as in (a), and attempt no gravimetric detn because of inaccurate results obtained by drying fructose at high temp.

11.013 Nonsugar Solids (Sugar-Free Extract)—Official Final Action

Subtract amt of reducing sugars before inversion, **11.014**, plus sucrose, if present, from ext, **11.012**.

11.014 Reducing Sugars— Official Final Action

(a) *Dry wines.*—Place 200 ml sample in porcelain dish, exactly neutze with $1N$ NaOH, calcg amt required from acidity, **11.035**, and evap. to ca 50 ml. Transfer to 200 ml vol. flask, add enough neut. $Pb(OAc)_2$ soln, **31.021**(d), to clarify, dil. to vol. with H_2O, shake, and filter thru folded paper. Remove Pb with dry K oxalate and det. reducing sugars as in **31.039**.

(b) *Sweet wines.*—Approximate sugar content by subtracting 2 from ext, **11.012**, and use such amt of sample that aliquot taken for Cu reduction contains $\leq$240 mg invert sugar. Proceed as in (a).

11.015 Sucrose—Official Final Action

(a) *By reducing sugars before and after inversion.*—Proceed as in **9.092(b)**.

(b) *By polarization.*—Polarize before and after inversion in 200 mm tube, as in **31.025** or **31.026**, portion of filtrate obtained in **11.014**. In calcg % sucrose do not fail to take into consideration relation of wt sample contained in 100 ml to normal wt for instrument.

11.016 Commercial Glucose—Procedure

Polarize portion of filtrate obtained in **11.014**, after inversion in 200 mm jacketed tube at 87°, as in **31.034**. In calcg % glucose do not fail to take into consideration relation of wt sample contained in 100 ml to normal wt for instrument.

11.017 Ash—Official Final Action

Proceed as in **31.012** or **31.013**, using residue from 50 ml sample. Char carefully (decrepitation), and ash at ≤550°.

11.018 Alkalinity of Ash—Official Final Action

Evap. 10 ml sample to dryness in Pt dish and ash at 550°. If solid content of sample is high, it may be necessary to moisten ext with ether and to burn off carefully over flame to prevent spattering. If any C remains, add few ml H_2O, dry, and again heat to 550°. To ash add 10 ml 0.1N H_2SO_4, bring acid in contact with all of the ash, and fill dish ca ¾ full of boiling H_2O. Cool, add 4 drops *Me purple* (available from Fisher Scientific Co.) or Me orange, and immediately titr. excess acid with 0.1N NaOH. Express alky as ml 0.1N H_2SO_4 required to neutze ash from 100 ml sample.

11.019 Copper—Official Final Action

See **9.030–9.036**.

Iron—Official First Action

11.020 *Atomic Absorption Method*

Pipet 20 ml 40° proof wine into 200 ml vol. flask, add 88 ml 95% alcohol from graduated cylinder, and mix well. Dil. almost to vol. with H_2O and mix well. Let soln reach room temp., dil. to 200 ml with H_2O, and mix well. Proceed as in **9.039**. Multiply results by 10 to obtain ppm Fe in original wine sample.

11.021 *TPTZ Colorimetric Method*

Prep. sample as in **11.020**, and proceed as in **9.043**.

Potassium (2)—Official Final Action

11.022 *Reagents and Apparatus*

(a) *Potassium std solns.*—Dry reagent grade KCl at 100° overnight and make 1.9067 g to 1 L with H_2O. Dil. 10 ml of this soln to 100 ml and further dil. 1, 2, 4, 6, 8, and 10 ml of dild soln to 100 ml to make std solns contg, resp., 1, 2, 4, 6, 8, and 10 ppm K in H_2O. Store std solns in clean, dry polyethylene bottles.

(b) *Flame spectrophotometer.*—Beckman Instruments DU with oxy-hydrogen flame and photomultiplier accessory, or equiv. instrument.

11.023 *Determination*

Dil. 10 ml sample 50–200 times with H_2O if necessary to fall within %T range of stds. Set instrument, fill sample cup, and burn. Read %T 3–5 times at 740 nm (T_b), 768 nm (T_{max}), and 790 nm (T_a). (T_{max} = T at max. emission, T_b = T before max., T_a = T after max.) Det. %T for 1–10 ppm K std solns immediately after sample under same conditions, and plot "unit rise" against ppm K to obtain "semipermanent" calibration curve:

For stds: T_{max}. − $[(T_a + T_b)/2]$ = "Unit Rise X"

For sample: T_{max}. − $[(T_a + T_b)/2]$ = "Unit Rise Y"

Jet correction: Check "semipermanent" calibration curve frequently with stds. Calc. % deviation, if any, and apply correction to sample, as:

Theoretical Unit Rise from Calibration Curve/ Unit Rise X = Corr. factor. Then, Unit Rise Y × corr. factor = corrected Unit Rise Y.

ppm K in sample = Diln factor × ppm equiv. to Unit Rise Y taken from calibration curve.

Sodium (2)—Official Final Action

11.024 *Reagents and Apparatus*

Prep. std solns as in **11.022(a)**, except use 2.5421 g reagent grade NaCl. Use flame spectrophtr, **11.022(b)**.

11.025 *Determination*

Proceed as in **11.023**, except dil. sample 50–100 times as necessary to fall within %T range of stds. For Na, (T_b) = 570, (T_{max}.) = 589, and (T_a) = 610. Calc. ppm Na in sample as in **11.023**.

11.026 Chlorides—Official Final Action

Method I

To 100 ml dry wine or 50 ml sweet wine add enough Na_2CO_3 to make distinctly alk. Evap. to dryness, ignite at dull redness, cool, ext residue with hot H_2O, acidify H_2O ext with HNO_3 (1 + 4), and det. Cl as in **3.068** or **3.070**.

Method II (3)

11.027 *Apparatus*

(a) *pH meter.*—With millivolt scale, Beckman Zeromatic, or equiv.

(b) *Electrodes.*—Beckman Instruments general purpose glass electrode No. 41263 as ref. electrode and Beckman No. 19151 Ag-AgCl pressed billet electrode with 30″ lead and pin connector or Beckman No. 39261 Ag billet electrode as indicating electrode. Other electrode combinations such as Beckman No. 39187 Ag billet combination electrode may be used.

(c) *Magnetic stirrer.*—With glass or plastic coated stirring bar.

(d) *Buret.*—10 ml with 0.05 ml subdivisions.

11.028   Reagents

(a) *Potassium chloride.*—Reagent grade contg ≤0.005% Br. Dry in desiccator several days before use.

(b) *Distilled water.*—Cl-free. Use wherever H_2O is specified.

(c) *Chloride std soln.*—1 mg Cl/ml. Weigh 2.1027 g KCl, transfer to 1 L vol. flask, and dil. to vol. with H_2O.

(d) *Silver nitrate std soln.*—1 ml = 1 mg Cl. Weigh 4.7914 g reagent grade $AgNO_3$, transfer to 1 L vol. flask, and dil. to vol. with H_2O.

11.029   Determination

Connect glass electrode to input terminal and indicating electrode to ref. terminal of pH meter set to read on ±700 millivolt (mv) scale. Warm up at least 30 min. Pipet 5.0 ml std Cl soln into 250 ml beaker. Adjust vol. to ca 100 ml with H_2O and add 1.0 ml HNO_3 by pipet. Insert electrodes so that billet is completely covered, add stirring bar, and titr. with std $AgNO_3$ soln, stirring moderately. Add in 1.00 ml increments until 4.0 ml have been added, then 0.20 ml increments until 2.0 ml more have been added, then 1.00 ml increments to total of 10.00 ml. Read buret to 0.01 ml and millivolt scale to 1 mv after addn of each increment. Record readings. Allow at least 30 sec for pH meter to stabilize before each reading. Plot observed mv against ml soln added and det. equivalence point (inflection) voltage from resulting curve. This value will vary with electrode system used.

Use of glass electrode as ref. electrode is reverse of usual function; hence curve obtained will be reverse of those produced by other electrode combinations. Rinse electrodes before each use.

Pipet 5.0 ml std Cl soln into 250 ml beaker, and add 95 ml H_2O and 1.0 ml HNO_3. Insert electrodes, stir, and titr. with std $AgNO_3$ soln to predetd equivalence voltage, adding titrant dropwise as end point is reached. Repeat until results are in close agreement. Conduct all titrations within 5° of temp. of equivalence point detn. Repeat this detn at least daily or before each group of samples.

Pipet 50 ml wine into 250 ml beaker, add 50 ml H_2O and 1.0 ml HNO_3, and titr. as above.

ppm Cl = $(V_w/V_s) \times C \times 2 \times 10$, where V_w = ml std $AgNO_3$ used by sample, V_s = ml std $AgNO_3$ used by std Cl soln, and $C = 5.0$ = mg Cl in 5 ml std Cl soln used.

Phosphorus (4)—Official Final Action
(*Caution: See* **46.018, 46.019, 46.026,** and **46.028.**)

11.030   Reagents

(a) *Molybdovanadate reagent.*—Prep. as in **2.019(a)** except use 200 ml 70% $HClO_4$.

(b) *Phosphate std soln.*—1 mg P_2O_5/ml. Dissolve 1.9175 g pure, dry (2 hr at 105°) KH_2PO_4 in 1 L H_2O. Prep. fresh weekly.

11.031   Preparation of Standard Curve

Prep. series of std solns contg 0.0, 0.1, 0.2, 0.3, and 0.4 mg P_2O_5/ml. Perform following operations within 5 min: Pipet 5 ml aliquots into 100 ml vol. flasks, and add 50 ml H_2O and 4 ml 70% $HClO_4$. Pipet 20 ml molybdovanadate reagent into each flask, dil. to vol. with H_2O, and shake thoroly. Let stand 15 min.

Det. A of blank and stds in set of matched cells against H_2O as ref. at 400 nm. Correct stds for A of blank and plot corrected A against concn in mg P_2O_5/100 ml soln.

11.032   Determination

(a) *Wet ash method.*—Pipet 5 ml sample into 100 ml Pyrex beaker and evap. to dryness on steam bath. Add 15 ml HNO_3 and few SiC boiling chips, cover with watch glass, and heat gently until residue dissolves. Boil gently 10–15 min to oxidize easily oxidizable org. matter, cool, add 4 ml 70% $HClO_4$, and boil gently until soln fumes copiously and is nearly colorless. (Remove watch glass when soln starts to fume. Do not evap. to dryness.) If soln is brown, add 2 ml HNO_3 and boil again. Cool slightly, add ca 25 ml H_2O, boil few min, and transfer to 100 ml vol. flask. Rinse beaker with H_2O, adding washings to flask to total vol. of 50–60 ml.

Within 5 min for series, add 20 ml molybdovanadate reagent to each flask, dil. to 100 ml, mix thoroly, and read A after 15 min at 400 nm. Carry blank and std thru entire detn. Subtract A of blank from that of sample.

(b) *Dry ash method.*—Pipet 5 ml sample into Pt dish and evap. to dryness on steam bath. Carefully char over low flame and ash in muffle furnace at ≤550°. Pipet in 4 ml 70% $HClO_4$, add ca 20 ml H_2O, and warm to dissolve ash. Transfer quant. to 100 ml vol. flask, cool to room temp., and proceed as in (a).

mg P_2O_5/100 ml = $A_{sample} \times 20/A_{1\ mg\ std}$.

**11.033   Sulfates—Official Final Action—
            See 30.080**

11.034   pH—Official Final Action

Let pH meter with glass and calomel electrodes warm up before use according to manufacturer's instructions. Check meter with freshly prepd, satd, aq. soln of K bitartrate, **45.007(b)**. Adjust meter to read 3.55 at 20°, 3.56 at 25°, or 3.55 at 30°.

Rinse electrodes free of bitartrate by dipping in H_2O and then in sample. Place electrodes in fresh sample, det. temp., and read pH to nearest 0.01 unit.

11.035 Total Acidity—Official Final Action

American Society of Enologists Method (5)

Remove CO_2, if present, by either of following methods: (1) Place ca 25 ml sample in small erlenmeyer and connect to H_2O aspirator. Agitate 1 min under vac. (2) Place ca 25 ml sample in small erlenmeyer, heat to incipient boiling and hold 30 sec, swirl, and cool.

Add 1 ml phthln indicator soln to 200 ml hot, boiled H_2O in 500 ml wide-mouth erlenmeyer. Neutze to distinct pink. Add 5.00 ml degassed sample and titr. with $0.1N$ (or $0.0667N$) stdzd NaOH to same end point, using well-illuminated white background.

Calc. g tartaric acid/100 ml wine = ml NaOH $\times$ normality $\times$ 0.075 $\times$ 100/5. If $0.0667N$ alkali is used, g tartaric acid/100 ml = ml NaOH/10.

Total Volatile Acidity (6)— Official Final Action

11.036 Apparatus

(a) *Cash electric still.*—See Fig. 11:2. Consists of outer chamber, inner chamber, trap, 2-way stopcock, elec. coil heater, and glass "T" inlet-outlet for H_2O. All parts are of Pyrex. Residue in inner chamber after distn has been completed is flushed out automatically by vac. action when current is shut off. Addn of H_2O thru funnel above stopcock gives automatic spray bath to inner chamber, and waste drains thru outlet in glass "T." Two-way stopcock permits introduction of sample, serves as escape vent for CO_2, and allows introduction of wash H_2O. (Available from Van Waters and Rogers, PO Box 3200, San Francisco, CA 94119, Cat. No. 26308 001.)

(b) *Steam distillation apparatus.*—See Fig. 9:3.

11.037 Preparation of Sample

Remove dissolved CO_2 from ca 50 ml sample by either: Placing under low vac. (H_2O aspirator) 2 min with continuous stirring; or bringing to incipient boiling under air condenser and cooling immediately.

11.038 Determination

(a) *Steam distillation apparatus.*—Add ca 600 ml boiled H_2O to outer chamber of still. Pipet 25 ml freshly prepd sample into inner chamber and stopper. Boil H_2O 3 min with sidearm open. Close and distill ca 300 ml into erlenmeyer. Add 0.5 ml phthln to distillate and titr. rapidly with $0.1N$ NaOH until pink persists 15 sec. Express results as g HOAc/100 ml = ml $0.1N$ NaOH $\times$ 0.006 $\times$ 4.

(b) *Cash electric still.*—Add H_2O and pipet sample as in (a). Rinse funnel with ca 5 ml H_2O. Distill ca 300 ml into erlenmeyer. Titr. and express results as in (a). (Disconnect heating coil immediately and empty still by opening drain tube and stopcock to inner tube. Rinse still with two 10–15 ml portions H_2O by adding thru funnel; evacuate each portion thru drain tube.)

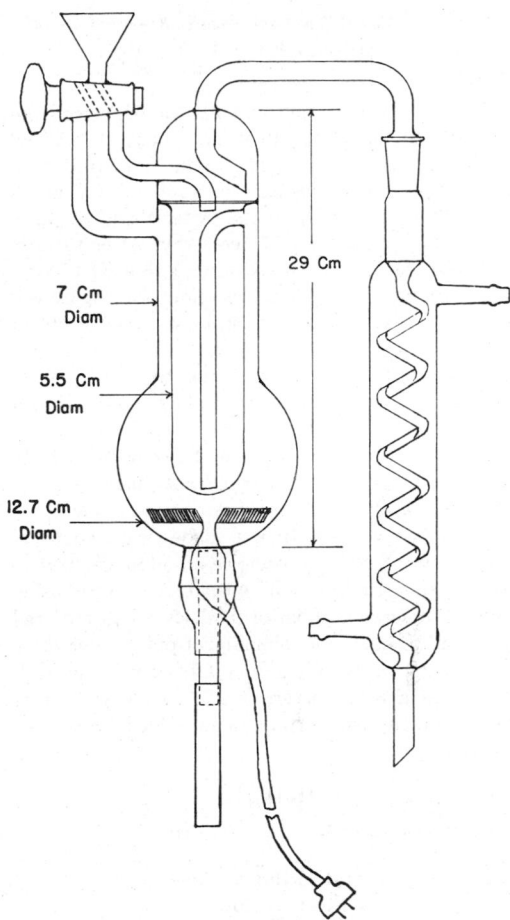

FIG. 11:2—Volatile acid still (Cash still)

11.039 Volatile Acidity—Exclusive of SO_2 (7)—Official First Action

Pipet 50 ml sample into 100 ml vol. flask. If white, add 2–3 drops phthln, and neutze to decided pink with clear satd $Ba(OH)_2$ soln; if red, add enough $Ba(OH)_2$ soln to bring mixt. to ca pH 8, using phthln as external indicator. Let mixt. stand 30 min and keep at phthln end point by adding more $Ba(OH)_2$ if necessary. Dil. to 100 ml, mix, and filter rapidly thru fluted, rapid paper (such as Whatman No. 2). Pipet 50 ml prepd sample and 1 ml H_2SO_4 (1 + 3) into inner chamber of still, **11.036(a)** or **(b)**, and stopper. Proceed as in **11.038.** Express results as g HOAc/100 ml as in **11.038(a).**

11.040 Fixed Acidity—Official Final Action

Calc. fixed acidity by multiplying total volatile acidity by 1.25 for tartaric, 1.12 for malic, or 1.17 for citric acid (hydrate), and subtracting product from total acidity.

Total Tartaric Acid (8)—
Official Final Action

11.041 Titration Method

Neutze 100 ml sample with 1N NaOH, calcg from acidity, **11.035**, ml 1N alkali necessary. If >10 ml alkali is added, evap. to ca 100 ml. Add, to neutzd soln, 0.075 g tartaric acid for each ml 1N alkali added. It is essential that the tartaric acid be pure; recrystallize from H_2O, if necessary. After tartaric acid dissolves, add 2 ml HOAc and 15 g KCl. After KCl dissolves, add 15 ml alcohol, stir vigorously until $KHC_4H_4O_6$ begins to ppt, and refrigerate at 15–18° at least 15 hr.

Decant onto gooch prepd with very thin film of asbestos, or onto filter paper in buchner. Wash ppt from beaker with filtrate (keep cold) and finally rinse beaker and filter 3 times with few ml mixt. of 15 g KCl, 20 ml alcohol, and 100 ml H_2O, using ≤20 ml wash soln in all. Transfer asbestos or paper and ppt to beaker in which pptn was made; wash gooch or buchner with hot H_2O, using ca 50 ml in all; heat to boiling, and titr. hot soln with 0.1N NaOH, using phthln. Increase number of ml 0.1N alkali required by 1.5 ml to allow for solubility of ppt. Under these conditions 1 ml 0.1N alkali = 0.015 g tartaric acid. To obtain g total tartaric acid/100 ml wine, subtract quantity of tartaric acid added from this result.

11.042 Bitartrate Method

See **22.061–22.063.**

11.043 Citric and Malic Acids—
Official First Action

For citric and malic acids occurring in normal wines in small amts only, use 100 ml sample and evap. to 45 ml. After saponification, **22.062**, proceed as in **22.066, 22.067, 22.078,** or **22.086.**

11.044 Lactic Acid (9)—Official Final Action

Transfer 25 ml sample to 250 ml vol. flask, add ca 25 ml H_2O and 100 ml alcohol, and shake vigorously. Dil. to vol. with alcohol and filter thru folded paper. Transfer 200 ml filtrate to 400 ml beaker and evap. to ca 25 ml. Add 50 ml H_2O and again evap. to 25 ml. Transfer material to continuous extractor with 25 ml H_2O and proceed as in **16.030–16.031.**

11.045 Tannin—Official Final Action—
See 9.083

11.046 Crude Protein—Official Final Action

Det. N in 50 ml sample as in **2.051** and multiply result by 6.25.

11.047 ★ Pentosans—Official ★
Final Action

(Applicable to dry wines only)
See **11.044**, 10th ed.

Aldehydes (10)—Official Final Action

11.048   Reagents

(a) *Potassium metabisulfite soln.*—Dissolve 15 g $K_2S_2O_5$ in H_2O, add 70 ml HCl, and dil. to 1 L with H_2O. Bisulfite titer of 10 ml soln should be ≥24 ml 0.1N I soln.

(b) *Phosphate-EDTA soln.*—Dissolve 200 g $Na_3PO_4.12H_2O$ (or 188 g $Na_2HPO_4.12H_2O$ + 21 g NaOH; or 72.6 g $NaH_2PO_4.H_2O$ + 42 g NaOH; or 71.7 g KH_2PO_4 + 42 g NaOH) and 4.5 g Na_2H_2-EDTA in H_2O and dil. to 1 L.

(c) *Sodium borate soln.*—Mix 100 g H_3BO_3 with 170 g NaOH and dil. to 1 L with H_2O.

11.049   Determination

Pipet 50 ml wine (contg ≤30 mg acetaldehyde) into 500 ml distg flask, add 50 ml *satd borax soln*, and distill ca 50 ml into 750 or 1 L erlenmeyer contg 300 ml H_2O and 10 ml each of metabisulfite and phosphate-EDTA solns. (pH should be 7.0–7.2. If necessary, adjust by adding HCl or NaOH solns to metabisulfite soln and start with fresh sample.) Add 10 ml HCl (1 + 3) (when analyzing series, make complete detn on first sample before adding acid to next) and ca 10 ml fresh *0.2% starch indicator*. Swirl to mix. Add enough ca 0.1N I soln to just destroy excess bisulfite and bring soln to light blue end point.

Add 10 ml Na borate soln and rapidly titr. liberated bisulfite with 0.05N I soln from 10 ml buret (or 0.02N I soln from 25 ml buret) to same light blue end point as above, swirling gently and continuously (avoid direct sunlight). (pH should be 8.8–9.5. If necessary, adjust by adding HCl or NaOH solns to Na borate soln and start with fresh sample.)

mg CH_3CHO/100 ml = ml I soln × normality I soln × 22.0 × 100/ml sample.

Caramel—Official Final Action
Mathers Test (11)

11.050   Reagents

(a) *Pectin soln.*—Dissolve 1 g pectin in 75 ml H_2O, add 25 ml alcohol to preserve, and shake well before using.

(b) *2,4-DNPH soln.*—Dissolve 1 g 2,4-dinitrophenylhydrazine in 7.5 ml H_2SO_4 and dil. to 75 ml with alcohol. (If kept in g-s bottle, soln will remain clear and stable several months.)

11.051   Preliminary Test

Place 10 ml filtered sample in Babcock cream bottle, **16.115(a)**, or other centrf. tube. Add 1 ml pectin soln and mix; add 3–5 drops HCl and mix; fill bottle with alcohol (ca 50 ml), mix, centrf., and decant. Dissolve ppt in 10 ml H_2O, and add HCl and alcohol as above; shake well, centrf., and decant. Repeat operation until alc. liq. is colorless. Finally, dissolve gelatinous residue in 10 ml hot H_2O. If soln is colorless, caramel is absent; if soln is clear brown, caramel may be present. Confirm as follows: Add 1 ml 2,4-DNPH soln, mix, and heat 30 min in boiling H_2O. Ppt forms if caramel is present.

11.052   ★ *Confirmatory Test* ★

See 11.047, 10th ed.

Carbon Dioxide—Official First Action
Manometric Method (12)

11.053   *Reagents*

(a) *Sodium bicarbonate std solns.*—Dry 150–200 g $NaHCO_3$ over H_2SO_4 24 hr. Weigh designated amts of dried $NaHCO_3$, transfer to 1 L vol. flasks with ca 700 ml recently boiled H_2O, and add 15 ml NaOH soln, (c). Add 200 ml absolute alcohol, mix, cool, and dil. to vol. with boiled H_2O. Use 4.2955 g for 225 mg CO_2/100 ml std; 4.7727 g for 250; and 5.2500 g for 275.

(b) *Hydrogen peroxide soln.*—10%. Dil. 20 ml 30% H_2O_2 with 40 ml recently boiled H_2O.

(c) *Sodium hydroxide soln.*—50%. Transfer 763 g reagent grade NaOH pellets to 1 L Pyrex graduated cylinder, add recently boiled H_2O, cool, and dil. to 1 L. Mix until soln is complete and set aside at least 5 days until Na_2CO_3 settles, leaving clear soln.

11.054   *Apparatus*

(a) *Carbon dioxide apparatus.*—See Fig. 11:3. Vol. of system is ca 350 ml. (Available from New York Laboratory Supply Co. and Scott Labs, Inc., 860 S 19th St, Richmond, CA 94804.) Test all glass joints with vac. tester.

(b) *Vacuum tester.*—High frequency self-contained generator operated from 115 v ac outlet. Consists of adjustable interrupter, vibrating spark gap, condenser, resonator coil, and gap tip.

(c) *Magnetic stirrer with Teflon stirring bar.*—Fisher Flexa-Mix or equiv. with stirring bars 1–1⅜″ long.

(d) *Vacuum pump.*—Welch Dist-O-Pump or equiv., with motor, single stage, vented exhaust; to be operated with vented exhaust valve open for pumping condensable vapors. Insert 3-way stopcock between pump and app. to allow air to enter system. Ordinary high vac. pump can be used if H_2SO_4 trap with 3-way stopcock is inserted between pump and app. Change acid frequently.

(e) *Silicone grease, high vacuum type.*—Stable to heat and contains no carbon-to-carbon linkages. Grease may be removed from glassware with Varsol or hot kerosene.

11.055   *Calibration of Vacuum System*
(Caution: See 46.015.)

Pipet 50 ml std $NaHCO_3$ soln and 3 ml 10% H_2O_2 soln into reaction flask, and carefully grease joints. Start magnetic stirrer and evacuate system ca 1 min. Close system to pump at 3-way stopcock, gently tap Hg columns, and read manometer to nearest 0.5 mm to obtain initial reading. Hg levels should remain

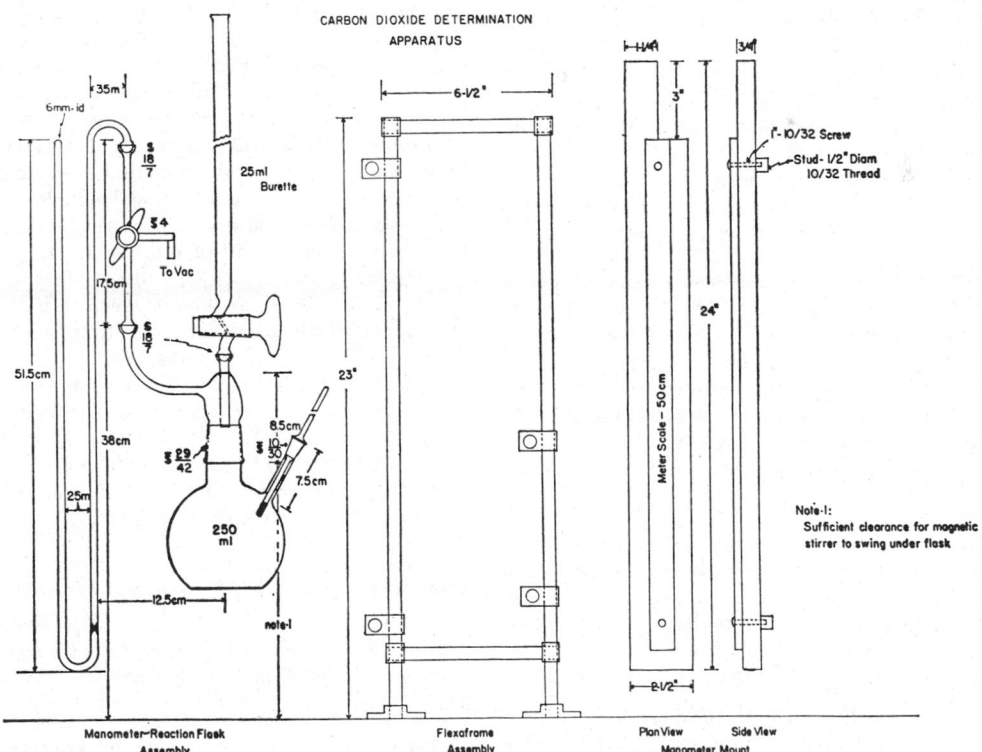

FIG. 11:3—Carbon dioxide apparatus; manometric method

constant; changes indicate leak, probably caused by insufficient grease at joints.

Add 10 ml H_3PO_4 and continue rapid stirring 5 min. Gently tap Hg columns and read total pressure in cm Hg to nearest 0.5 mm to obtain final reading. Record gas temp. in °C.

Open 3-way stopcock on app. to pump. Then slowly open 3-way stopcock between pump and app. to let air flow into system. Disconnect app. and thoroly wash inner portion of acid dispensing unit and reaction flask. Rinse with acetone and dry with suction.

Det. total pressure from each $NaHCO_3$ std soln in triplicate and calc. av. vol. of system as follows:

From final pressure reading in cm Hg, subtract initial reading and vapor pressure increase due to H_3PO_4 effect as given in table:

% Alcohol	Vapor Pressure, cm, Increase Due to H_3PO_4
0	0.67
5	0.68
10	0.69
15	0.75
20	0.77
25	0.77
50	1.00
75	1.53
100	2.80

Then $V = 76RTg/MP$, where V is system vol. in L; R is gas constant in L-atm./degree/mole, 0.08205; T is absolute temp., $273 +$ room temp. in °C; g is g CO_2 in 50 ml sample; M is molecular wt of CO_2 in g; and P is corrected pressure of CO_2 in cm Hg.

Calc. correction for Hg displaced in manometer tubing, $V_m = \pi r^2 L/2$, where L is difference in ht of Hg column in cm and r is radius of manometer tubing.

Calibrated vol. of system, $V_o = V - V_m$.

In calcg wt CO_2 in sample, Hg displaced in manometer tubing, V_m, is added to calibrated vol. of system, V_o. $(V = V_o + V_m)$

11.056   Preparation of Sample

Chill unopened bottle of wine in ice-salt bath to slightly $<32°F$ (30 min for $\frac{1}{10}$ gal. bottle and 1 hr for $\frac{1}{5}$). Open bottle and rapidly add 1.5 ml 50% NaOH soln for each 100 ml wine. Quickly close bottle with rubber stopper, remove from bath, and shake several min. Let contents come to room temp.

11.057   Determination

Pipet 50 ml sample and 3 ml 10% H_2O_2 into reaction flask, carefully grease joints, and proceed as in 11.055.

From total pressure in cm Hg, subtract vapor pressure of alcohol-H_2O and pressure due to H_3PO_4 effect. Calc. g CO_2/100 ml wine = $14.327PV/T$.

Volumetric Method (13)
11.058   Reagents

(a) Sodium hydroxide std soln.—0.25N. Prep. as in 45.033–45.035. Stdze as in 45.036 or 45.037, using phthln-thymolphthalein indicator, (e). Restdze daily against std HCl, (b), in presence of 5 ml $BaCl_2$ soln, (c), and indicator, (e).

(b) Hydrochloric acid std soln.—0.25N. Stdze against std NaOH, (a), using indicator (e).

(c) Barium chloride soln.—Dissolve 60–65 g $BaCl_2.2H_2O$ in 1 L H_2O and neutze to phthln.

(d) Acid phosphate soln. — Dissolve 20 g $NaH_2PO_4.H_2O$ in H_2O, add 3 ml H_3PO_4, and dil. to 100 ml.

(e) Phenolphthalein-thymolphthalein mixed indicator.—Dissolve 1 g phthln and 0.5 g thymolphthalein in 100 ml alcohol.

11.059   Apparatus

See Fig. 11:4. Connect 500 ml special distg flask (rubber stopper and ordinary distg flask may be used) thru ca 8 mm glass tubing to series of 3 Pyrex test tubes, 25×200 mm, each fitted at inlet with gas dispersion tube with 12 mm fritted end of coarse porosity and 8 mm stem (Fisher No. 11–138 or equiv.). Connect final exit tube to trapped vac. line or filter pump.

11.060   Determination

Connect app. and place test tube receivers in beaker of H_2O at $<27°$. Pipet 20 ml std 0.25N NaOH into first 2 receivers and 10 ml 0.25N NaOH and 10 ml $BaCl_2$ soln into third.

Pipet 50 ml alk. wine, 11.056, into distg flask and add 3 ml 10% H_2O_2, 11.053(b). Add boiling chips (not marble). Attach vac. line to last receiver and slowly increase vac. until bubbling practically stops; then open vac. line fully. (This keeps system under partial vac. so that stoppers will not be blown out on heating by sudden surge of steam or CO_2.) Add ca 35 ml acid phosphate soln to dropping funnel and carefully admit ca 30 ml into distg flask. Agitate flask gently to mix acid and sample.

Heat gently and when CO_2 evolution slows, heat vigorously. After few ml of liq. distills and top of first receiver is warm, all CO_2 will have been driven into receivers. Close vac. line between trap and receivers and slowly admit air thru dropping funnel until pressure equilibrium is reached.

Transfer contents and rinsings of first 2 receivers and dispersion tubes into titrn flask. (Also add contents of third if $BaCO_3$ has pptd.) Add 50 ml $BaCl_2$ soln and titr. with std HCl to phthln end point.

Wt CO_2 in g/100 ml = [(ml NaOH $\times$ normality) $-$ (ml HCl $\times$ normality)] $\times$ 0.022 $\times$ (100/50) $\times$ 1.015.

Enzymatic Method (14)—Official Final Action
11.061   Reagent

Carbonic anhydrase soln.—Prep. aq. soln contg ca 1 mg enzyme/ml. This soln is stable ca 2 weeks in refrigerator.

11.062   Determination

Cool sample to $\leq 0°$, so that it can be pipetted without loss of CO_2. With automatic 25 or 30 ml

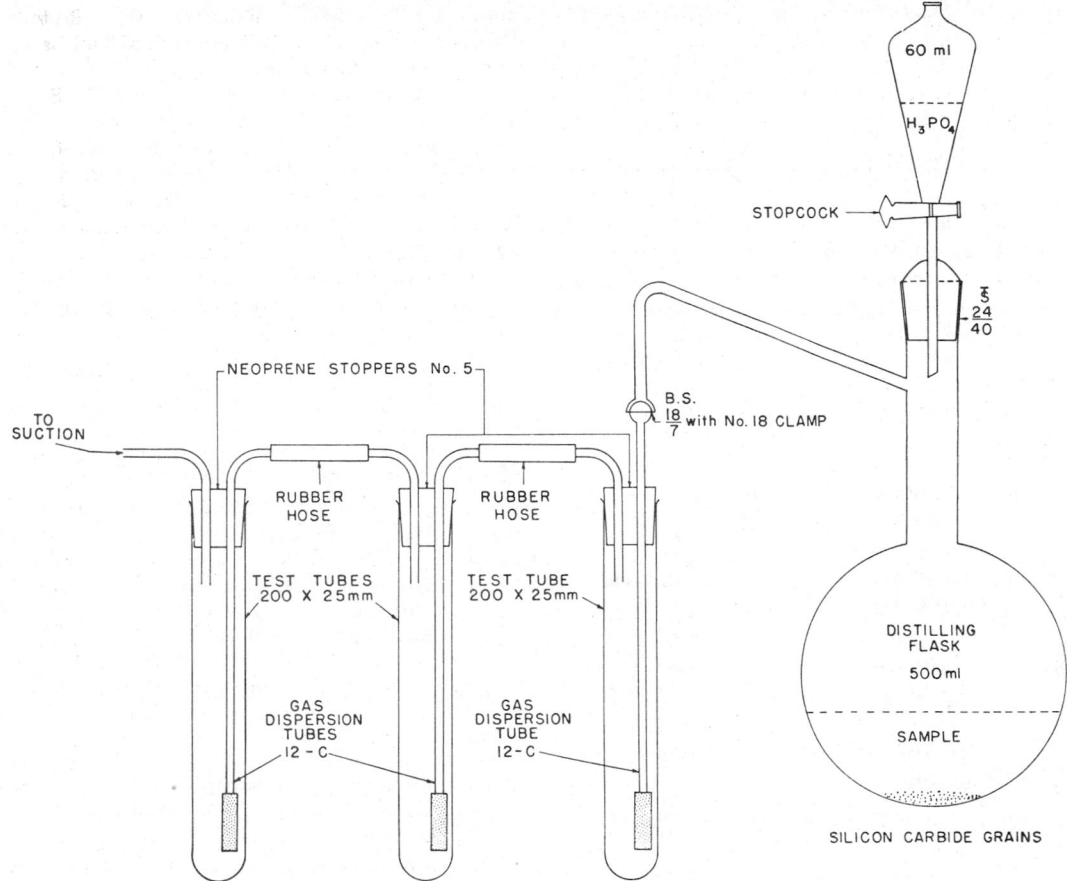

FIG. 11:4—Carbon dioxide apparatus; volumetric method.

pipet with Teflon stopcock, dispense aliquot of $0.1N$ NaOH into beaker. Rinse 20 ml pipet with sample to prevent warming sample with possible loss of CO_2. Pipet sample with tip submerged just below surface of NaOH in beaker. Add 3–4 drops enzyme, and place beaker under glass and calomel electrodes. (Beckman 41263 and 40463 are satisfactory.) Titr. to pH 8.45 with $0.1N$ H_2SO_4 from 5 ml buret graduated in 0.01 ml.

To correct for presence of acids other than H_2CO_3, place 50 ml wine in 500 ml heavy-wall flask at room temp. and agitate 1 min under vac. of ca 27″. Titr. 20 ml to pH 7.75 with $0.1N$ NaOH as above. Subtract ml used from that used in first titrn. Calc. as follows: (Net ml   NaOH $\times$ normality $-$ ml H_2SO_4 $\times$ normality) $\times$ 100 $\times$ 44/ml sample = mg CO_2/100 ml wine.

11.063   Sulfurous Acid (15)—
Official Final Action

Proceed as in **20.092**, using 100–300 ml sample. Report results as mg SO_2/L. (As SO_2 in wine is unstable, give sample no preparatory degassing treatment and expose to air for min. time prior to detn.)

11.064   Preservatives—Official Final Action—
See **Chap. 20**

SELECTED REFERENCES

(1) Wines and Vines **30**, 65(1949); JAOAC **52**, 85(1969).

(2) JAOAC **37**, 945(1954); **46**, 299(1963).

(3) JAOAC **49**, 498(1966).

(4) JAOAC **45**, 624(1962).

(5) Am. J. Enol. Viticult. **13**, 40(1962); JAOAC **46**, 32, 134(1963).

(6) JAOAC **47**, 722(1964).

(7) JAOAC **23**, 183(1940).

(8) USDA Bur. Chem. Bull. **162**, p. 72.

(9) JAOAC **20**, 605(1937).

(10) JAOAC **50**, 305(1967).

(11) JAOAC **31**, 178(1948).

(12) JAOAC **42**, 679(1959).

(13) JAOAC **43**, 652(1960).

(14) JAOAC **47**, 711(1964).

(15) JAOAC **23**, 189(1940); **25**, 70, 82, 296(1942); **27**, 85(1944).

12. Beverages: Nonalcoholic and Concentrates*

12.001 Preliminary Examination—Procedure

Note and record (a) appearance, whether bright or turbid, or any sediment; (b) color and depth of color; (c) odor, whether fruity, foreign, or artificial; (d) taste, whether tart or sweet, fruity, artificial, or foreign, and whether any synthetic substance can be identified by odor or taste.

12.002 Specific Gravity—Official Final Action—See 9.011

12.003 Alcohol—Official Final Action—See 9.013, 9.016, and 9.022

12.004 Total Solids—Official Final Action—See 31.007 or 31.008

Sucrose—Official Final Action

12.005 By Polarization

Det. by polarizing before and after inversion as in 31.025 or 31.026.

12.006 By Reducing Sugars Before and After Inversion—See 31.032

12.007 Reducing Sugars—Official Final Action

Use value obtained for reducing sugars before inversion, 12.006.

12.008 Commercial Glucose—Procedure—See 31.034

12.009 Ash—Official Final Action

Proceed as in 31.012 or 31.013, using sample contg ≤10 g solids.

12.010 Soluble and Insoluble Ash—Official Final Action

Proceed as in 31.015, using ash of 12.009.

12.011 Alkalinity of Soluble Ash—Official Final Action

Proceed as in 31.016, using sol. ash of 12.010.

12.012 Alkalinity of Insoluble Ash—Official Final Action

Proceed as in 31.017, using insol. ash of 12.010.

12.013 Analysis of the Ash—Official Final Action—See Chap. 22

12.014 Monochloroacetic Acid—Official Final Action—See 20.058(b), 20.059(b), and 20.062

12.015 Quaternary Ammonium Compounds—Official Final Action—See 20.079–20.080

12.016 Total Acidity—Official Final Action—See 9.099

12.017 Preparation of Sample for Determination of Dibasic Acids—Official First Action

(a) *Alcoholic products.*—See 9.100.

(b) *Nonalcoholic products.*—Use sample contg ≤30 g solids and ≤200 mg acid to be detd, as calcd from acidity. Evap. to 30 ml, if necessary, and treat as in 12.018–12.021.

12.018 Tartaric Acid—Official Final Action

Designate as x the ml of $1N$ alkali required to neutze sample, add 3 ml $1N$ H_2SO_4, heat to 50°, and continue as in 22.062, beginning "Transfer adjusted sample to 250 ml vol. flask ..."

12.019 Citric Acid—Official First Action

Transfer sample to 250 ml vol. flask, using enough H_2O to make total vol. of 70 ml, and continue as in 22.065, beginning "Add 2 ml $1N$ HNO_3 ..."

12.020 Total Malic Acid (Laevo and Inactive)—Official First Action

Proceed as in 12.018 to obtain filtrate and washings from KH tartrate; then evap. soln to ca 15 ml and continue as in 22.071, beginning "Transfer with small amt H_2O ..."

12.021 Laevo Malic Acid—Official First Action

Proceed as in 12.018 to obtain filtrate and washings from KH tartrate; proceed as in 22.079.

★ Methods so marked are surplus methods. *See* "Definitions of Terms and Explanatory Notes," item (29).

12.022 Volatile Acids—Official Final Action— See 11.039

12.023 Esters—Official Final Action

Proceed as in **9.105**, collecting ca 300 ml distillate.

Methyl Anthranilate—Official Final Action
Colorimetric Method (1)
(Applicable to samples contg <500 mg/L)

12.024 *Reagents*

(a) *Dilute hydrochloric acid.*—Dil. 83 ml HCl to 1 L with H_2O.

(b) *Sodium nitrite soln.*—Dissolve 2 g $NaNO_2$ in 100 ml H_2O.

(c) *Hydrazine sulfate soln.*—Dissolve ca 3 g $N_2H_4.H_2SO_4$ in 100 ml H_2O.

(d) *Sodium-α-naphthol-2-sulfonate soln.*—Dissolve 5 g of the sulfonate in 100 ml H_2O.

(e) *Sodium carbonate soln.*—Dissolve 25 g Na_2CO_3 in 75 ml H_2O.

(f) *Methyl anthranilate std soln.*—1 mg/ml. Dissolve 0.25 g Me anthranilate in 60 ml alcohol and dil. to 250 ml with H_2O.

12.025 *Apparatus*

(a) *Steam generator filled with H_2O.*—Oil can holding 1 gal. serves purpose.

(b) *Distillation flask.*—Kjeldahl flask, ca 750 ml, with shortened neck, ca 10″ over-all ht.

(c) *Spray tube.*—Glass tube with small perforated bulb at end, passing thru rubber stopper and reaching to bottom of distn flask.

(d) *Connecting bulb.*—Kjeldahl bulb with bent connecting tube.

(e) *Worm condenser.*—With H_2O jacket 10–12″ long, and outlet tube reaching bottom of 500 ml erlenmeyer receiving flask.

12.026 *Determination*

Place just enough H_2O in receiving flask to seal end of extended condenser tube. Place 10–100 ml sample in distn flask and add, if necessary, enough H_2O to make 100 ml. Insert stopper carrying spray tube and connecting bulb, and connect with condenser and receiving flask. Immerse distn flask in near bp H_2O bath to level of contents. When sample reaches temp. of nearly boiling bath, connect to steam generator with H_2O boiling and pass steam rapidly thru sample until ca 300 ml distillate collects.

Disconnect app. and wash out condenser with little H_2O. Add to distillate 25 ml dil. HCl and 2 ml $NaNO_2$ soln, mix well, and let stand exactly 2 min. Add 6 ml $N_2H_4.H_2SO_4$ soln and mix well 1 min, so that liq. comes in contact with all parts of flask that soln may have touched when it contained free HNO_2. Keep liq. in flask in rapid motion, quickly add 5 ml Na α-naphthol-2-sulfonate soln, and then immediately add 15 ml Na_2CO_3 soln. Dil. colored soln to 500 ml with H_2O, mix, and compare color of aliquot

with color of std, or set of stds, prepd as nearly as possible at same time. Calc. results as mg Me anthranilate/L.

Gravimetric Method (2)
(Applicable to samples contg ≥500 mg/L)

12.027 *Reagents and Apparatus*

(a) *α-Naphthol soln.*—Dissolve 0.2 g α-naphthol in 100 ml 30% alcohol.

(b) *Sodium bicarbonate soln.*—Dissolve 8.4 g $NaHCO_3$ in 100 ml H_2O.

(See **12.024** for other reagents and **12.025** for app.)

12.028 *Determination*

Place sample contg 50–125 mg Me anthranilate in distn flask and dil., if necessary, to 100 ml with H_2O. Steam distill as in **12.026**, collecting ca 400 ml distillate.

Wash out condenser with little H_2O and dil. distillate to 500 ml. Mix, and to 200 ml aliquot add 5 ml dil. HCl and 5 ml $NaNO_2$ soln. Mix well and let stand 1 min. Mix 25 ml α-naphthol soln and 6 ml $NaHCO_3$ soln, pour diazotized soln into mixt., and let stand 10 min. Fold 2 Whatman 1 or S&S 595 papers, 12.5 cm diam., and det. difference in their wts by placing one on each pan of balance and counterpoising with added wts. Place heavier inside lighter paper, fit into funnel, and moisten. Pour mixt. thru this filter and wash ppt 7 or 8 times, using total of ca 100 ml H_2O. Fill filter only to ca 1 cm from top. Place funnel carrying filter and washed ppt in oven, and dry ca 10 min at 100°. Sep. and dry filter papers ca 1 hr at same temp. Det. difference in wts, dry again, weigh again, and repeat until difference in wts remains constant. (Constant difference in wts − original difference in wts of 2 papers) × 0.4935 = wt anthranilic acid ester, as Me anthranilate. Report as g/L.

12.029 Benzaldehyde (3)— Official Final Action

Measure 500 ml beverage, 100 ml flavoring sirup, or 10–25 ml flavor into distg flask. Add 32 ml alcohol, and in case of sirup or flavor, ca 300 ml H_2O, and proceed as in **19.095**.

12.030 ★ Gamma Undecalactone ★ (4)—Official Final Action

See **8.030**, 10th ed.

12.031 Essential Oils—Official First Action— See 19.118

Caffeine (5)—Official First Action
12.032 *Apparatus*

(a) *Continuous extractor.*—Similar to Fig. 36:3C, with outer part of 43 mm od tubing, 45 cm long, with side tube 25 cm above bottom, fitted with drip tip ⚗ 24/40 joint; inner tube of 30 mm od tubing,

39–40 cm long; receiver is 250 ml erlenmeyer with ℥ 24/40 joint.

(b) *Filtering device.*—Glass buchner with 30 mm fine fritted disk and 45 mm high side wall, fitted with 2 interchangeable rubber stoppers, one to fit suction flask, other to fit 20 × 150 mm side arm test tube.

12.033   Reagents

(a) *Phosphomolybdic acid soln.*—Dissolve 10 g phosphomolybdic acid in ca 25 ml warm H_2O, cool to room temp., and dil. to 50 ml with H_2O. Let stand overnight and filter thru S&S 589 blue ribbon paper. Store in dark.

(b) *Caffeine std soln.*—1 mg/ml. Weigh 100 mg caffeine alkaloid, dissolve in H_2O, and dil. to 100 ml.

12.034   Extraction
(*Caution: See* **46.011, 46.040,** *and* **46.056.**)

Place few glass beads in receiver, assemble extractor, and add 210–220 ml $CHCl_3$ to inner tube. Measure 150 ml sample in graduated cylinder and make alk. with ca 2 ml 10N NaOH, using litmus paper as indicator. Place funnel in top of extractor and add sample to inner tube, letting $CHCl_3$ in outer tube overflow into receiver. Remove funnel and attach condenser. If tip of condenser is >2 cm above inner tube, place small funnel with 2–3 cm stem in top of inner tube to prevent splashing. Ext 2 hr, keeping steady stream of solv. flowing from condenser.

Remove hot plate and let receiver cool somewhat. Disconnect condenser and tilt extractor to permit as much $CHCl_3$ as possible to flow into receiver without letting any aq. phase rise into space between the 2 parts of extractor. Transfer entire contents of extractor to separator. Rinse extractor with H_2O and discard. Attach outer part of extractor to receiver and to condenser, and heat carefully until vol. $CHCl_3$ in receiver is 30–40 ml. Do not let soln bump or foam into extractor. Cool somewhat, drain $CHCl_3$ ext from separator into receiver, and distill $CHCl_3$ into extractor as before until 10–15 ml remains in receiver. Cool $CHCl_3$ in receiver and transfer to weighed 50 ml beaker, rinsing with several small portions $CHCl_3$. Evap. to dryness and weigh.

If residue wt is ≤5 mg, dissolve in 5 ml H_2O, filter thru very small circle of paper into 50 ml beaker, and wash beaker and paper with 5 ml H_2O; if wt is >5 mg, dissolve, using several successive 5 ml portions H_2O, and filter into vol. flask (25 ml for residue of ≤15 mg; 50 ml if >15 mg). Dil. to vol. with H_2O and mix.

12.035   Determination

Place soln or aliquot contg 2–5 mg residue in 50 ml beaker; add 1 ml HCl (1 + 1) and enough H_2O to make 11 ml. Cover with watch glass and warm on steam bath. Add 2 ml phosphomolybdic acid soln dropwise with stirring, re-cover, and continue heating 20 min. Filter hot soln thru buchner into suction

flask, and wash ppt and funnel with three 5 ml portions HCl (1 + 9), using policeman to scrub down walls of beaker. Aspirate dry. Wipe away any aq. soln at tip of buchner, change stopper to fit side arm test tube, and assemble. Dissolve ppt in three 5 ml portions acetone. Wash tip of buchner with few drops acetone, transfer to 25 ml vol. flask, and dil. to mark with acetone. Det. A at 440 nm against acetone, and det. mg caffeine from std curve. Calc. to g/100 ml.

12.036   Preparation of Standard Curve

Pipet 0, 1, 2, 3, 4, and 5 ml portions std caffeine soln into 50 ml beakers and proceed as in **12.035**, beginning "add 1 ml HCl (1 + 1) . . ." Plot A against mg caffeine.

Alternative Method (6)—Official First Action
12.037   Reagents

(a) *Reducing soln.*—Dissolve 5 g Na_2SO_3 and 5 g KCNS in H_2O and dil. to 100 ml.

(b) *Dilute phosphoric acid soln.*—Dil. 15 ml H_3PO_4 to 85 ml with H_2O.

(c) *Sodium hydroxide soln.*—Dissolve 25 g NaOH in 75 ml H_2O.

(d) *Caffeine std soln.*—1 mg/ml $CHCl_3$. Purify caffeine, if necessary, by recrystn and/or sublimation. Dissolve 100 mg in $CHCl_3$ and dil. to 100 ml with $CHCl_3$.

12.038   Preparation of Standard Curve

Prep. dild std solns contg 0.10, 0.25, 0.50, 1.00, 1.50, and 2.00 mg caffeine/100 ml $CHCl_3$. Det. wavelength of max. A of 1 mg/100 ml soln at ca 276.5 nm and det. A of all solns at this wavelength against $CHCl_3$ in 1 cm matched cells. Plot A against concn or calc. factor = 10/av. reading for 1 mg/100 ml std calcd from all readings.

12.039   Determination

Remove carbonation by pouring beverage from one beaker to another until effervescence ceases. Pipet 10 ml sample into 125 ml separator, add 5 ml *1.5% $KMnO_4$ soln*, and mix. After exactly 5 min, add 10 ml reducing soln and mix. Add 1 ml dil. H_3PO_4 soln, mix, add 1 ml NaOH soln, mix, and ext with 50 ml $CHCl_3$ 1 min. After sepn, drain lower layer thru 7 cm paper into 100 ml g-s vol. flask. Add 2–3 ml solv. to separator and drain thru paper to rinse separator stem. Wash paper with 2–3 ml $CHCl_3$. Re-ext soln with 40 ml $CHCl_3$ and wash stem and paper as before. Dil. to vol. with $CHCl_3$. Det. A of this soln at wavelength of max. A against $CHCl_3$. Det. amt caffeine from std curve or from factor and calc. mg/100 ml beverage.

Spectrophotometric Method (7)—
Official First Action
(Method is preferable to **12.037–12.039** when only few samples are to be analyzed. Use **12.032–12.036** for complex mixts requiring extensive cleanup.)

12.040 *Apparatus*

Chromatographic tubes.—Glass, ca 25 cm × 250 mm.

12.041 *Reagents*

(Use CHCl₃ and ether washed with ½ vol. H₂O thruout.)

Caffeine std solns.—(1) *Stock soln.*—See **12.037**(d). (2) *Working solns.*—Prep. dilns of stock soln contg 0.25, 0.50, and 0.75 mg caffeine/50 ml CHCl₃. Check factor, **12.045**, frequently to minimize instrument variations.

12.042 *Preparation of Sample*

Remove any gas by pouring sample back and forth in beakers. Pipet appropriate amt sample (5 or 10 ml) into 250 ml beaker. Evap. to near dryness on steam bath. Dissolve residue in 5 ml NH₄OH (1 + 2) and heat 2 min on steam bath. Remove from heat, add 6 g Celite 545, and mix carefully to homogeneous consistency before prepg column.

12.043 *Preparation of Columns*

(a) *Column I.*—Carefully mix 2 ml 4N H₂SO₄ with 2 g Celite 545, place in chromatgc tube over glass wool plug, and tamp to uniform mass with moderate pressure. Top with glass wool plug to minimize damage to column surface.

(b) *Column II.*—(1) *Layer A.*—Carefully mix 3 g Celite 545 with 2 ml 2N NaOH, transfer to tube over glass wool plug, and tamp to uniform mass. (2) *Layer B.*—Transfer prepd sample and Celite mixt. to column directly over layer *A* and tamp. Dry wash beaker with 1–2 g dry Celite and transfer to column. Tamp to uniform mass and top column with glass wool plug.

12.044 *Determination*

Mount column II over column I. Pass 150 ml ether thru column II and into column I using initial portion of ether to rinse sample beaker. Drain well and remove column II. Pass addnl 50 ml ether thru column I and drain well. Pass 50 ml CHCl₃ thru column I, using initial portion to wash tip of column II. Collect eluate in 50 ml vol. flask and adjust vol. to 50 ml. Read *A* of CHCl₃ soln at 276 nm against CHCl₃ ref. using Beckman DU, or equiv. spectrophtr, with 1 cm silica cells. If necessary, adjust concns to acceptable levels by dilg with CHCl₃.

12.045 *Calculations*

Factor F = mg caffeine in 50 ml std soln/A.
mg Caffeine in sample = F × A.
Express results as mg caffeine/100 ml beverage.

Methyl Salicylate (8)—
Official First Action

12.046 *Reagents*

All solvs must be chromatographically pure and meet following test: Conc. 500 ml solv. to 10 ml in evaporative concentrator and chromatograph on prepd column with instrument set at max. sensitivity to be used during analysis; 5 μl concd solv. must not show any trace of peaks beyond solv. front. (Distd-in-glass solvs generally conform to test stds.) Purify solvs not passing test as in (a) and (b).

(a) *Methanol.*—Anhyd. Reflux 1 L with 10 g KOH and 25 g Zn dust 3 hr. Distill, discarding first 100 ml. (*Caution: See* **46.011, 46.037,** *and* **46.066.**)

(b) *Chloroform.*—Redistill at bp. Add 1% MeOH if stored. (*Caution: See* **46.056.**)

(c) *Methyl salicylate std soln.*—79 mg/ml (10,000 ppm). Dil. 7.90 g Me salicylate to 100 ml with MeOH.

(d) *n-Decyl alcohol internal std.*—79 mg/ml (10,000 ppm). Dil. 7.90 g n-decyl alcohol to 100 ml with MeOH.

12.047 *Apparatus*

(a) *Steam distillation apparatus.*—500 ml r-b flask with long neck, $\bar{\$}$ 24/40 joint; adapter, $\bar{\$}$ 24/40 inner joint at bottom and at side at 75° angle and with $\bar{\$}$ 10/30 joint at top; gas inlet tube, 30 cm, $\bar{\$}$ 10/30 inner joint and perforated 8 mm bulb at dispersion tip; condenser, 200 mm $\bar{\$}$ 24/40 joint; and adapter, vac. takeoff type with extended lower tube, straight joint $\bar{\$}$ 24/40.

(b) *Concentrator.*—500 ml evaporative concentrator, Kuderna-Danish type, with 10 ml receiving flask.

(c) *Gas chromatograph.*—With flame ionization detector, with operating parameters as in **12.048**.

12.048 *Operating Parameters for GLC of Methyl Salicylate*

Parameter	Barber-Colman Model 5000	Warner-Chilcott Model 1600
Column (glass)	10' × 4 mm id, W-shaped	6' × 2 mm id, 6" diam. coil
Packing	15% Reoplex 400 on 60–80 mesh Gas Chrom P (w/w)	15% Reoplex 400 on 60–80 mesh Gas Chrom P (w/w)
Carrier gas and pressure	N, 40 lb/sq in. at 90 ml/min	N, 40 lb/sq in. at 75 ml/min
Column temp.	130° (isothermal) or 90–150° at 2°/min (programmed)	90° (isothermal) or 80–130° at 2°/min (programmed)
Detector temp.	220°	220°
Injection port temp.	180°	175°
Sample size	5 μl	3 μl
Analysis time	100 min (isothermal) or 30 min (programmed)	60 min (isothermal) or 20 min (programmed)

12.049   ***Determination of Relative Retention Time (RT) and Relative Response Factor (RF)***

Pipet 1 ml each of Me salicylate and *n*-decyl alcohol std soln into 10 ml vol. flask and dil. to vol. with MeOH. Inject 3–5 μl into gas chromatograph. Set sensitivity and attenuation controls to provide peak ht ≤80% of chart scale.

Calc. *RT* = time for Me salicylate peak to emerge/time for *n*-decyl alcohol peak to emerge. Use *RT* to identify Me salicylate peak in sample. Calc. peak area (*PA*) by triangulation.

Calc. *RF* = *PA* of Me salicylate/*PA* of *n*-decyl alcohol.

12.050   ***Determination***
(*Caution: See* **46.011** and **46.056**.)

Analyze samples on same day and under same conditions used for detn of *RT* and *RF*.

Place 200 ml sample in 500 ml r-b flask; add 10 ml MeOH and small amt Dow Corning antifoam A. Bring sample to incipient boil, connect steam generator, and collect 90 ml distillate at ca 2 ml/min in 100 ml Nessler tube or graduated cylinder contg 8 ml MeOH to cover delivery tube outlet. Flush condenser and delivery tubing twice with 5 ml MeOH. Quant. transfer distillate to 250 ml separator. Add 2

g NaCl and ext with 25, 25, and 10 ml CHCl$_3$ by carefully shaking 5 min for each extn. Filter CHCl$_3$ thru Whatman No. 30 paper contg 3–5 g Na$_2$SO$_4$ into 500 ml evaporative concentrator. Wash separator and paper with 10–15 ml CHCl$_3$ into concentrator. Add few SiC chips and evap. on steam bath to ca 7 ml. Cool, add 1 ml internal std, and dil. to 10.0 ml with CHCl$_3$. Use this mixt. for GLC analysis as in **12.049**.

Calc. mg/ml or ppm Me salicylate = (PA_{sample}/PA_{std}) × (concn internal std/RF) × (1/20), where concn internal std = 79 for mg/ml or 10,000 for ppm.

12.051   Alginates in Chocolate Beverage Products—Official Final Action— *See* 13.058

SELECTED REFERENCES

(*1*) J. Agr. Research **33**, 301(1926); JAOAC **11**, 46, 505(1928).
(*2*) Ind. Eng. Chem. **15**, 732(1923); JAOAC **11**, 47, 505(1928).
(*3*) JAOAC **19**, 408(1936).
(*4*) JAOAC **16**, 420(1933); **19**, 75(1936).
(*5*) JAOAC **39**, 714(1956); **40**, 433(1957).
(*6*) JAOAC **41**, 617(1958); **45**, 252(1962).
(*7*) JAOAC **50**, 195, 857(1967).
(*8*) JAOAC **52**, 481(1969).

13. Cacao Bean and Its Products[★]

13.001 Preparation of Sample—Procedure

(a) *Powdered products.*—Mix thoroly and preserve in tightly stoppered bottles.

(b) *Chocolate products.*—Chill sweet or bitter chocolate until hard, and grate or shave to fine granular condition. Mix thoroly and preserve in tightly stoppered bottle in cool place. Alternatively—

(c) Melt bitter, sweet, or milk chocolate by placing in suitable container and partly immersing container in bath at ca 50°. Stir frequently until sample melts and reaches temp. of 45–50°. Remove from bath, stir thoroly, and while still liq., remove portion for analysis, using glass or metal tube, 4–10 mm diam., provided with close-fitting plunger to expel sample from tube, or disposable plastic syringe.

13.002 Moisture (1)—Official First Action

Dry 2 g prepd sample, **13.001**, to constant wt in Pt dish in air oven at 100°. (Al dish may be used when ash is not detd on same sample.) Report loss in wt as H_2O.

13.003 Ash—Official Final Action

Proceed as in **31.012** or **31.013**, using enough sample to contain ca 1 g H_2O-, sugar-, and fat-free material.

13.004 Soluble and Insoluble Ash—Official Final Action

Proceed as in **31.015**, using ash from **13.003**.

13.005 Alkalinity of Soluble Ash—Official Final Action

Proceed as in **31.016**, using filtrate from **13.004**.

13.006 Alkalinity of Insoluble Ash—Official Final Action

Proceed as in **31.017**, using insol. ash obtained in **13.004**.

13.007 Ash Insoluble in Acid—Official Final Action

Proceed as in **30.005**, using total ash obtained in **13.003**, or H_2O-insol. residue obtained in **13.004**.

13.008 pH (2)—Official First Action

Office International du Cacao et du Chocolat-AOAC Method

(a) *For products other than cacao butter.*—Weigh 10 g sample into 150 ml beaker and slowly add, with

stirring, 90 ml boiling H_2O. Suspension must be free from lumps. Filter, cool filtrate to 20–25°, and immediately det. pH, using electrodes and potentiometer stdzd with buffers at pH 4.00, **45.007**(c), and 6.86, **45.007**(d). Report to nearest 0.1 pH unit.

(b) *For cacao butter.*—Melt sample and mech. stir 5 min with equal wt of H_2O at 50°. Sep. aq. layer, cool to 20–25°, filter, and det. pH as in (a).

13.009 Total Nitrogen—Official Final Action

AOAC-Office International du Cacao et du Chocolat Method

Proceed as in **2.051**, using 0.7–2.2 g sample. Small amt of paraffin or silicone antifoam may be added to reduce foaming. Digest 1–2 hr after soln is clear. Protein = N × 6.25 (includes N from purines and other N-contg compds). Report % N to nearest 0.01%; protein, 0.05%. Duplicate detns should agree within 0.30% protein.

SHELL (3)

In Cacao Nibs—Official Final Action

13.010   Trier for Sampling

Use double-tube, separate-compartment grain trier to collect samples of nibs from bins, trucks, and sacks. Tubes of trier are of No. 16 B&S gage (0.0508″) seamless metal. Outer tube is $1\frac{3}{8}″$ od, and outer and inner tubes fit each other closely. Width of openings in outer tube is $\frac{15}{16}″$, and in inner tube 1″. Length of such openings in both tubes is $3\frac{1}{2}″$, except that length of opening of compartment nearest point of trier may be 3–$3\frac{1}{2}″$. Each compartment coincides with and is of same length as its opening in inner tube. Openings of inner and outer tubes match when trier is open for sampling. Distance between adjacent compartments is $1\frac{1}{2}$–2″, and distance between point of trier and compartment end nearest point is $\leq 1\frac{1}{8}″$.

13.011   Collection of Sample

(a) *From bins or trucks.*—Collect ca 10 lb sample by probing with trier, **13.010**. Probe nibs to floor of bin or truck, spacing individual probings ca equidistant from each other thruout top area of nibs. If contents of bin are inaccessible, or depth is greater than length of trier from its point to 2″ above compartment end nearest handle, take sample from chute thru which bin is being filled or emptied as in (c).

(b) *From sacks.*—Collect ca 10 lb sample by probing with trier, **13.010**. Length of trier from its point to 2″ above compartment end nearest handle equals or exceeds depth to which sacks are filled. Probe with trier thru entire depth of nibs in sack. Probe number

★ Methods so marked are surplus methods. *See* "Definitions of Terms and Explanatory Notes," item (29).

of sacks equal to at least square root of total number of sacks in lot. If lot is <12 sacks, probe at least ⅔ of them; if ≥12, probe at least 8.

(c) *From chutes.*—Collect ca 10 lb sample by catching momentarily and at regular intervals, in suitable receptacle, cross section of stream of nibs from chute. Continue sampling thruout time lot of nibs being sampled is passing thru chute.

13.012   *Reduction of Sample*

Using Boerner sampler No. 34 (Seedburo Equipment Co., 618 W. Jackson Blvd, Chicago IL 60606, 1962–1963 catalog), reduce size of sample collected, **13.011**, to ca ½ lb. Weigh reduced sample to nearest 0.05 g.

13.013   *Division of Sample*

(a) *Hand division.*—Screen reduced sample, **13.012**, in successive portions of 75–100 g, on circular ca 8″ diam. No. 10 sieve. Collect material remaining on sieve and designate as *L*. Screen material that passed thru sieve on another circular No. 20 sieve 6 or 8″ diam. Collect portion remaining on sieve and designate as *S*. Collect material passing thru sieve and designate as *F*. Treat portions *L*, *S*, and *F*, resp., as in **13.014(a)**, **(b)**, and **(c)**.

(b) *Machine division.*—Use sample-size, grain-cleaning mill (No. 400 Office Clipper Tester and Cleaner, Seedburo Equipment Co., Chicago IL 60606, manufactured by A. T. Ferrell and Co., 1621 Wheeler St, Saginaw, MI 48602). Fit into lower slot of mill single screen with circular openings 0.083–0.093″ diam. Machine is provided with settling traps to catch all material blown out by fan. Inclined slide under screen is provided with removable slat in such position that, when it is removed, material passing thru screen is discharged from mill without going to fanning chamber. Remove this slat, start mill, and slowly pour reduced sample, **13.012**, over upper part of screen. Designate as *L'* material that does not pass thru screen and is not removed by fanning. Collect material that passes thru screen and screen again thru No. 20 sieve, **(a)**. Collect portion remaining on sieve and designate as *S*. Collect portion passing thru sieve and designate as *F*. Reserve *F* for treatment as in **13.014(c)**.

Replace slat in mill and, without removing *L'* or fannings, start mill and pour *S* slowly onto upper part of screen. Let material thus cleaned combine with *L'*, and designate combination as *L'S'*. Treat *L'S'* as in **13.014(a)**. Remove combined fannings from settling traps, and screen on No. 10 sieve, **(a)**. Collect portion remaining on sieve and designate as *LS*. Collect portion passing thru sieve and designate as *SS*. Treat *LS* as in **13.014(a)** and *SS* as in **13.014(b)**.

13.014   *Determination*

(a) Place *L* (from hand division), or *L'S'* (from machine division), on large sheet of sized paper.

Scatter 2–3 g *L* or 4–5 g *L'S'* over area of paper 3–4″ diam. Examine scattered portion and remove pieces of shell with spatula or tweezers. Examine entire portion of *L* or *L'S'* progressively in this manner. Sep. shell from *LS* (from machine division) in same manner. Reserve sepd shell for later combination with shell from other fractions.

(b) If *S* (from hand division) weighs >4.5 g and appears to contain large amt of shell, accurately weigh it to nearest 10 mg. Mix entire portion by pouring gradually several times from one glazed paper to another, each time forming conical pile; flatten and quarter last pile formed, and combine alternate quarters. If necessary, mix and again reduce by quartering to obtain 3–4.5 g, and accurately weigh fraction thus obtained to nearest 10 mg. If amt of shell in *S* appears to be small, use entire portion. Sep. shell from *S* or fraction thereof and from *SS* (from machine division) as follows:

Place blotting paper ca 19 × 24″ on firm supporting plane inclined at 21–24° from horizontal. Pour all material gradually and in successive portions from elevation of 2–3″ along upper end of blotter. Shake blotter slowly parallel to plane to cause nib material to roll down, and at intervals remove material collected at bottom. Toward end of operation shake blotter more rapidly to detach most of nib material. After removing shell adhering to blotter, repeat operation on last portions of material collected at bottom of blotter. Using reading glass, complete sepn of shell and nibs with spatula or tweezers by examining portions until all material is examined. Except in sepns from a fraction of *S*, reserve sepd shell for combination with that obtained from other sepns. In case of sepns from a fraction of *S*, weigh sepd shell to nearest mg and calc. total wt shell in *S*.

(c) (*Caution: See* **46.040**, **46.049**, and **46.055**.) Place *F* (obtained from either hand division or machine division) in 400 ml beaker ca half full of alcohol-CCl₄ mixt. $(1 + 2⅛)$. (Mixt. should have sp gr of 1.335–1.345 at temp. used as compared to H₂O at 20°.) Stir ca 1 min, slowly at the last, and let stand 3–4 min. Skim off floating nibs with tea strainer made with ca No. 40 wire cloth. Decant liq. and any suspended material from beaker without disturbing residue until 2–4 ml remains. Wipe inside of beaker above liq. with filter paper, moistened in the alcohol-CCl₄ mixt., to remove all nib material. Add ca 25 ml pet ether, swirl liq. in beaker few times, let residue of shell settle, and carefully decant liq. Let remaining liq. evap. and dry shell on steam bath. Reserve shell for combination with other fractions of shell.

(d) Combine all shell obtained from *L*, *S*, and *F* (from hand division), or *L'S'*, *LS*, *SS*, and *F* (from machine division) and weigh combined shell from reduced sample. If fraction of *S* was used, combine *L* and *F*, weigh, and add calcd wt shell in *S* to obtain wt shell from reduced sample. Report results as % by wt of shell in nibs.

In Cacao Products Other Than Cacao Nibs

(Following methods include detns the results of which can be used to est. amt of shell when compared with corresponding values obtained on authentic samples of cacao shell.)

13.015   Crude Fiber (4)—Official Final Action

(a) *In cacao products not containing dairy ingredients.*—Treat 7 g liquor (or amt of sweet chocolate or cocoa equiv. to 7 g liquor) in centrf. bottle with two 100 ml portions ether, centrfg and decanting after each addn. Dry residue in oven at ca 100° and then powder in bottle with flat-end rod. If necessary, grind material in mortar and ext third time with ether. Wash mixt. in bottle with three 100 ml portions H_2O at room temp., shaking well each time, until no cacao material adheres to bottle. Centrf. 10–15 min after each washing, and decant aq. layer. Wash residue in same fashion with two 100 ml portions alcohol and one 100 ml portion ether. Transfer residue to Pt dish, dry to constant wt, and grind in mortar. Weigh 2 g dried material and det. % crude fiber (D) as in **7.057**. Calc. % crude fiber on H_2O-, fat-, and sugar-free basis (E) by formula $E = 0.7D$.

(b) *In cacao products containing dairy ingredients.*—Treat 50 g milk chocolate with three 100 ml portions ether in centrf. bottle, centrfg and decanting after each addn. Dry residue in bottle and powder with flat-end glass rod. Shake with 100 ml *1% $Na_2C_2O_4$ soln*, and let stand 30 min. Centrf. and decant. Wash in bottle with three 100 ml portions H_2O at room temp., shaking well each time, until no cacao material adheres to bottle. Centrf. 10–15 min after each washing and decant. Wash residue in same fashion with two 100 ml portions alcohol and one 100 ml portion ether. Transfer residue to Pt dish, dry to constant wt at 100°, and grind in mortar. Weigh 2 g dried material and det. % crude fiber as in **7.057**. % Crude fiber found $\times$ 0.7 = % crude fiber on fat-, sugar-, H_2O-, and milk-free basis.

13.016   Pectic Acid (5)—Official Final Action

(Sweet chocolate, usually characterized by its color, may contain small quantities of milk solids. When in doubt, use method for milk chocolate, (c).)

(a) *In sweet chocolate containing no milk solids.*—(1) *Extraction of fat.*—Weigh, within ±0.15 g, quantity (14–60 g) of well-mixed grated sample contg 4.7–5.2 g dry, fat-free cacao, and place in one or two 250 ml centrf. bottles. (If sample is >50 g, distribute it ca equally between 2 bottles.) (Make detns in duplicate.) Add 120 ml pet ether (bp 30–65°), or ether, at ca 30°, to each bottle, shake thoroly, centrf., and decant. Repeat extn with another 100 ml solv.; then ext with 100 ml alcohol, decant, and discard exts.

(2) *Extraction of color, tannins, etc.*—To each bottle add (from graduate) 150 ml *acidified 82% alcohol* (10 ml HCl + 432 ml alcohol dild to 500 ml with H_2O) that has been warmed so that temp. of

liq. in centrf. bottle is 55°. Stopper, shake vigorously 2 min, centrf. 6–8 min, decant, and discard supernatant. Add 100 ml alcohol to residue in each bottle, shake, centrf. as before, decant, and discard exts.

(3) *Extraction of pectin.*—Measure 150 ml H_2O in graduate, add ca 75 ml to 1 bottle, stopper, shake vigorously to disperse residue thoroly, decant into other bottle contg remainder of sample, and again shake vigorously until residue is thoroly dispersed. Decant mixt. into 500 ml wide-mouth erlenmeyer, rinse mouth of bottle with ca 1 ml H_2O from wash bottle, and complete transfer of residue from bottles with ca 45 and 30 ml successive portions of H_2O remaining in graduate. Make mixt. in flask just alk. to litmus with NH_4OH (1 + 1) (ca 0.7 ml; note quantity used; *See Note*). Acidify with HOAc, add 0.5 ml excess, and then add 50 ml 2% $(NH_4)_2C_2O_4 \cdot H_2O$ soln, using soln to wash down sides of flask.

Pass glass stirrer, with 1–1¼″ diam. loop (perpendicular to shaft on end), loosely thru hole in rubber stopper or thru glass tube of slightly larger diam. held in rubber stopper placed in mouth of flask. Attach shaft of stirrer to motor, or air rotor, to stir contents of flask continuously, immerse flask below level of contents in H_2O bath held at 90–92°, and stir moderately 3 hr. If level of liq. in flask is appreciably reduced, add enough hot H_2O to bring back to original level.

Remove flask, cool to 45°, quant. transfer contents to 250 ml vol. flask, dil. to vol. with H_2O at 45°, and add 1.5 ml excess to correct for vol. of cacao solids. Mix contents well, pour into centrf. bottle, and centrf. at 1800 rpm ca 15 min. Decant supernatant ext, which may be turbid or opalescent, into 400 ml beaker. Rinse any residue in flask into centrf. bottle with alcohol and reserve this cacao residue for further treatment to est. fat-free cacao in the sample. Warm ext to 45°, pour into graduate, note vol., and return to beaker. Rinse graduate with two 5 ml portions H_2O, and add to beaker. Cool in bath to 15–17°, make alk. to phthln (internal indicator) with *15% NaOH soln*, and add 11 ml excess. (*See Note.*) Stir, and let stand in bath 20 min at 15–17°. Decant alk. liq. into two 250 ml centrf. bottles, distributing vol. ca equally. Let drain, and rinse twice with 5–8 ml cold H_2O, adding 1 rinsing to each bottle. Add to each bottle, with stirring, 10 ml HCl, and then add gradually, with continued stirring, 40 ml alcohol. Add to each bottle 0.8–1.0 g *mixt. of Filter-Cel and Celite 545* (1 + 1). Stir, rinse rod, stopper bottles, shake well, and centrf. 10–12 min. Decant and discard supernatants without disturbing sediment, and wash residues once by shaking contents of each bottle with 100 ml alcohol, centrfg, and decanting.

Add 75 ml H_2O to 1 bottle, stopper, and shake well. Make slightly alk. with few drops NH_4OH (1 + 1) and shake again. Decant liq. into second bottle, stopper, shake again, make alk. to litmus with NH_4OH (1 + 1), and add 0.5 ml excess. Stopper, and shake thoroly 1–1.5 min to dissolve pectic acid ppt. (Drops of liq. clinging to lip of bottle may be washed into second bottle with small squirt of H_2O from wash bottle; otherwise do not rinse at this point.) Filter, with suction, thru hardened paper (Whatman No. 41-H or 54, or equiv.) on 11 cm buchner. Let bottle drain well; then rinse bottle twice with 25 ml portions H_2O, each contg 1–2 drops NH_4OH (1 + 1), pour rinsings on filter, and wait for each rinse to drain thru filter before adding another.

Pour filtrate into 250 ml centrf. bottle, let flask drain, and rinse twice with 5 ml H_2O. (Use of bell jar permits filtration directly into centrf. bottle.) Add 5 ml HCl to contents of centrf. bottle, stir in 90–100 ml alcohol, rinse rod with alcohol (do not add filter-aid), stopper, shake, and centrf. 8 min at 1500–1800 rpm. Decant supernatant into beaker, retaining most of ppt in bottle, and filter liq. thru 15 cm Whatman No. 41-H paper (or equiv.) on fluted funnel. Pour ppt and liq. remaining in centrf. bottle onto filter paper and drain thoroly. (Do not rinse.)

Quant. transfer ppt in bottle and on filter to 250 ml beaker, using total of 75 ml 60–75° H_2O. Cool beaker and contents in bath at 15–17° and add, with stirring, 15% NaOH soln (also cooled) until mixt. is alk. to phthln (internal indicator). Add 3 ml excess and let stand in bath 15 min at 15–17°. During this time, heat on steam bath 2 wash bottles, contg, resp., *wash solns: A*, mixt. of 200 ml H_2O, 50 ml alcohol, and 20 ml HCl (1 + 2.5); *B*, 400 ml alcohol dild to 950 ml with H_2O.

Remove beaker from bath, acidify contents with 10 ml HCl (1 + 2.5) while stirring, and dil. to 100 ml with H_2O. (Est. vol. by comparison with 100 ml in similar beaker.) Add few glass beads, cover, bring contents to boil, and boil 5 min. Remove from heat; add 10 ml HCl, with stirring, and then 400 mg *prepd asbestos* (previously alkali- and acid-washed and ignited, and free of coarse particles). Stir 40 sec, and immediately filter thru Whatman No. 41-H paper (or equiv.) on 7–11 cm buchner with very gentle suction. (Suction should be so gentle that it can hardly be felt when thumb is placed on rubber tube before attaching tube to flask; sample should filter in small steady stream, and filtrate should be clear or only slightly opalescent, with no immediate sepn of ppt.) Wash beaker and filter with three ca 25 ml portions wash soln *A*, and then with four or five ca 25 ml portions wash soln *B* to remove acid. (Washings should be clear and pass thru filter readily. Ignore any appearance of ppt in flask at this stage.)

Place filter and ppt on fairly large, short-stem funnel, and wash pectic acid ppt and asbestos into Pt dish with hot H_2O. Det. blank on 400 mg asbestos by adding it to hot acid soln, filtering, and drying in same manner as sample. Heat dishes on steam bath until asbestos and ppt appear thoroly dry. Dry sample and blank in oven at 100° to constant wt (±0.2 mg; ca 1 hr), cool in desiccator, weigh, ignite, cool, and reweigh. Loss in wt of sample − loss in wt of blank = wt of pectic acid in aliquot taken.

This wt × 250/vol. ext taken
$$= \text{wt pectic acid in sample.}$$

To obtain dry, fat-free cacao in sample, add 100 ml alcohol to cacao residue reserved in centrf. bottle, stopper bottle, shake well, centrf., and decant. Again shake with 100 ml alcohol, rinse stopper, and wash down sides of bottle with alcohol from wash bottle; centrf. and decant. Repeat extn, using 100 ml ether, washing down sides, centrfg, and decanting. Let residual ether evap. Using brush and spatula, quant. transfer residue to tared Al dish with cover; dry dish and contents 1–2 hr in oven at 100°; cover dish, cool in desiccator, and weigh. Wt residue × 1.9 = wt dry, fat-free cacao in sample,

Wt pectic acid × 100/wt dry, fat-free cacao
$$= \% \text{ pectic acid.}$$

(b) *In chocolate liquor, breakfast cocoa, cocoa, and low-fat cocoa.*—Place ca 15 g cocoa or 25 g chocolate liquor, prepd as in **13.001**, in centrf. bottle. To remove most of fat, shake contents of bottle thoroly with 100 ml pet ether (bp 30–65°) or ether; centrf., decant, and repeat extn with another 100 ml pet ether or ether. Shake residue with third portion solv., and filter thru Whatman No. 41-H or 54 paper (or equiv.) on 11 cm buchner with gentle to moderate suction. (Apply vac. and wet filter with solv. before starting filtration.) Let residue suck dry, transfer to porcelain dish or casserole, grind gently with pestle to pulverize and mix, and transfer to Al dish with cover. Dry ca 45 min in oven at 100°, cover dish, and cool in desiccator. Weigh 5 g of the dry, fat-free residue into 250 ml centrf. bottle, and proceed as in **(a)**(*1*), last sentence, beginning "then ext with 100 ml alcohol . . ." and continue as in (*2*) and (*3*) thru next-to-last par. (directions for calcg wt pectic acid in sample).

(Wt pectic acid found/5) × 100
$$= \% \text{ pectic acid in dry, fat-free cacao.}$$

(No estn of dry, fat-free cacao is necessary, since weighed amt of dry, fat-free cacao is used for pectic acid detn.)

(c) *In products containing milk solids.*—(*1*) *Removal of fat.*—Weigh (±0.2 g) sample contg ca 5 g dry, fat-free liquor (60–110 g milk chocolate, etc.), and distribute ca equally between two 250 ml centrf. bottles. Add 120 ml pet ether or ether at 25–30°, shake thoroly, centrf., and decant. Add another 120 ml portion tepid solv. to each bottle, shake thoroly, centrf., and decant. In same manner ext contents of each bottle with 100–110 ml acetone.

(*2*) *Extraction of milk protein.*—Add enough acetone (ca 90 ml) to make total of ca 110 ml with acetone remaining in residue. (Est. on basis that ½ original sample of 75 g retains ca 20 ml acetone in residue of each bottle.) Stopper, and shake vigorously to disperse residue thoroly. Quickly add to each bottle 100 ml *triethanolamine soln* (90 ml triethanolamine dild to 500 ml with H_2O), stopper immediately, and shake well 2 min. Let stand ca 1 min for foam to rise; then centrf. 12–14 min at 1500–1800 rpm. Carefully decant and discard supernatant without disturbing residue, and ext residue with 100–120 ml mixt. of acetone and the triethanolamine soln (110 + 100), centrfg and decanting as before. Then add 100 ml 85% alcohol to each bottle, shake, centrf., decant, and discard ext.

To residue in each bottle add 15–20 ml acidified 82% alcohol, (a)(2), stir, and add enough HCl to make residue acid to litmus. Continue as for sweet chocolate, beginning with (a)(2).

Note: Quantity of NH_4OH used should be noted, excess avoided, and approx. concn of NH_3 detd. (Soln becomes much less concd on standing from loss of NH_3 around stopper.) This is necessary because in first hydrolysis (saponification) of pectin, part of NaOH soln added (after soln of sample has been made alk. to phthln) is used up in replacing with Na the NH_4 in NH_4 salts present. The 11 ml 15% NaOH soln added furnishes excess of 4–5 ml of this soln over quantity required to neutze acid and replace NH_4 with Na, provided $\leq$1.15 ml 7.5N NH_4OH (= 2.3 ml 15% NaOH soln) is added to neutze residual HCl. (Approx. 3.75 ml 15% NaOH soln is needed to replace with Na the NH_4 in $(NH_4)_2C_2O_4$ soln used in extn of pectin.) If >1.15 ml of the NH_4OH soln is needed to neutze HCl in (a)(3), correspondingly increase quantity of 15% NaOH soln used for saponification, but avoid excess of >5–6 ml.

Spiral Vessel Count (6)—Official First Action

13.017   *Apparatus*

(a) *Sieve.*—No. 230, 5″ diam., stainless steel.

(b) *Grinding equipment.*—(1) *Coarse grinding (cutting action).*—Labconco mill No. 900 (Laboratory Construction Co., 8811 Prospect Ave, Kansas City, MO 64132), or equiv. (2) *Fine grinding.*—5″ glass mortar and pestle or Torsion Balance Co. electric mortar grinders MG1 or MG2 (Torsion Balance Co., 35 Monhegan St, Clifton, NJ 07013). Adjust MG2 so that pestle and shaft are not under tension by loosening top knob and lock nut by 3 turns and adjust closing spring control to ½ tension.

(c) *Aluminum dish.*—Diam. ca 77 mm, ht ca 33 mm; with cover.

(d) *Brush.*—No. 10, nylon, rubber set, oval sash paint brush with bristles cut to 1.5–1.75″ (available from Sherwin-Williams Co., Prospect Ave, Cleveland, OH 44101, or distributors).

13.018   *Preparation of Sample*

(a) *Chocolate liquor, chocolate.*—Prep. as in 13.001(a).

(b) *Expeller cake.*—Crush with mortar and pestle and grind to pass No. 30 sieve in mill, (b)(1), ca ½ teaspoonful at time. Mix well and store in tightly stoppered jar.

(c) *Cocoa press cake.*—Prep. and store as in (b). (Many samples can be easily pulverized after drying 2–3 hr at 60–70°.)

(d) *Cocoa.*—Use as is. Store as in (b).

13.019   *Defatting and Grinding*
(*Caution: See* **46.054.**)

Set up in hood No. 230, 5″ sieve in 6″ glass funnel with tip dipping ca 1″ into 500 ml flat-bottom Pyrex centrf. bottle.

Place 15 g cocoa, coarsely ground (30–40 mesh) cocoa press cake, or expeller cake, or 25–30 g chocolate or chocolate liquor in 250 ml centrf. bottle. Add 100 ml ether, stopper, shake thoroly to dissolve fat, and pour onto sieve. Wash material on sieve well with ether. Wash lower rim and both sides of sieve and inside of funnel with ether. Let material on sieve stand until dry (ca 15 min).

Centrf. mixt. in 500 ml centrf. bottle 10 min at 2000 rpm. Decant and discard supernatant. Replace centrf. bottle under funnel.

Place sieve with dried cocoa material in receiver (sieve bottom pan). Brush material thru sieve with No. 10 sash paint brush. Transfer retains, using brush, to 5″ glass mortar and grind ca 45 sec with glass pestle, or grind 2 min in motor-driven mortar grinder. Transfer to sieve and rebrush. Repeat grindings and brushings until virtually all material passes thru sieve. Quant. transfer material, including small amt on sieve (<20 mg), thru funnel to the 500 ml centrf. bottle. Clean with brush, and clean brush against rim of sieve. Wash screen, receiver, mortar and pestle, and funnel (but not brush) with ether, letting washings run into centrf. bottle. Rub off coated material on funnel and other app. with policeman, rinsing with ether thru funnel to centrf. bottle. Stopper bottle and shake thoroly. Remove stopper and rinse with ether. Centrf. 10 min at 2000 rmp. Decant and discard supernatant. Add 100 ml ether and repeat extn. Add 100 ml ether, stopper, and shake. Immediately pour into fritted glass crucible (disk diam. 60 mm; medium porosity) under vac. Wash material from bottle into crucible with ether. Wash twice with ca 35 ml ether and continue vac. until dry (ca 20 min).

Quant. transfer material from crucible to glass mortar and grind gently until fine. (Spoon may be used in transfer but use rubber policeman to scrape disk.) Quant. transfer ground material to Al dish. With cover in place, rotate dish until contents are well mixed. Dry on steam bath 10–15 min to remove traces of ether, and then in oven 1 hr at 100°.

13.020   *Determination*

Make duplicate detns. Accurately weigh 0.350 g extd and dried material and transfer to 150 ml beaker. Gradually stir in 25 ml *4% NaOH soln* until smooth. Bring to initial boil, using asbestos mat over flame. Immediately reduce to weak flame and boil gently 2 min with frequent stirring. Cool somewhat and transfer to 25 × 100 mm Pyrex culture tube with small portions H_2O. Centrf. 3 min at full speed until clear in International Clinical Centrifuge, using No. 571 curved rubber cushion in No. 320 shield, or equiv. Decant carefully and discard supernatant. Add H_2O to tube until ca ¾ full, stopper, and shake until residue is well dispersed. Centrf. and decant as before.

Add H_2O to tube until ca half full, stopper, and shake until product is well dispersed. Transfer soln to 50 ml g-s graduate contg 25 ml glycerine. Wash remaining material from tube to graduate with small portions H_2O, stoppering and shaking tube to aid transfer. Stopper graduate, shake, dil. to 50 ml with H_2O, and shake. Transfer to 100 ml beaker. Stir well with vertical rotary motion. While stirring, withdraw small drop to Howard mold counting chamber, and make slide as in **40.085.** Fisher Scientific Co. Scoopula (Cat. No. 14–357) bent at right angles ca ¾″ from broad end is useful for stirring; metal prong strip of Acco paper fastener ca 6 mm wide bent ca 135°, ¼″ from end, is useful for withdrawing drop.

With microscope adjusted for mold counting (field of view 1.382 mm at 100×), count spiral vessels at 200×, at varying depths, number of positive fields in 25 fields of each of 8 slides of each of the 2 detns (total of 400 fields). Report as pos. field one that contains any portion of section of spiral vessels, but none smaller than well developed "S" or "Z" either sep. or attached to piece of shell. (*See* **13.022.**) Average results and report as % pos. fields present. This is spiral vessel count.

Det. % shell in chocolate component by comparison with std curve prepd from spiral vessel count values listed in **13.021** plotted against % shell in chocolate component. Use column for counts listed under "Up to 15% shell."

13.021   Standard Spiral Vessel Count Values

% Shell in Chocolate Component	Spiral Vessel Counts	
	Up to 15% Shell (0.350 g/50 ml)	Over 15% Shell (0.200 g/100 ml)
0	4.5	1.5
1	15	5.8
2	24.4	9.7
3	32.8	13.2
4	40	16.6
5	47	19.7
8	62.2	27.7
11	72.9	34.8
15	83.4	42.4
20	91.1	50.1
30	98.2	62.1
60		80.0
100		86.8

For 1–15% shell (spiral vessel counts of 15–83.4), following formula gives comparable values:

$S = (538P − 1777)/(7043 − 50P)$, where S = % shell in chocolate component and P = spiral vessel count.

For samples contg >15% shell (spiral vessel count >83.4) repeat detn thruout, but weigh 0.200 g

sample and dil. to 100 ml with H_2O in 100 ml g-s graduate contg 50 ml glycerine. Count at 200×. Use column for counts listed under "Over 15% shell" for prepg std curve.

13.022   Counting Instructions

Spiral vessels vary greatly in size. No distinction is made in counting because of size differentiation. In appearance spiral vessels have parallel walls of even intensity with clear centers. On occasional piece, walls may be frayed due to grinding. Walls of very small spiral vessels do not appear as sharp as those of the larger ones at 200×. Some spirals are closely knit together. Photomicrographs of spiral vessels and pos. sections of them are shown in Fig. 13:1.

In counting spiral vessels, most pos. fields counted will have easily recognized pos. spiral vessel figures such as long or short mass of spiral vessels, large broken sections of these, or sometimes tangled mass of spiral vessels. Some sine wave-like figures and some full "S"- or "Z"-like figures will be found. There will, however, be some smaller figures and some poorly formed "S"- or "Z"-like figures present in some fields. For these figures, the following applies:

"S"- or "Z"-like figures or mirror images of these should have ⅓ or more of top and bottom normal linear distance for such figure and not just stubs. One-third of center section is est. of this distance. If "2"-like figure is found, lower portion or "V" part of figure should be well extended and sufficient top curve should be present so that figure does not appear essentially like a "V." Figures may be stretched out. Spiral vessels in breaking sometimes break so that there will be joined sections of half circles or less. Count as pos. any such section consisting of 3 or more nearly ½ circles joined. Two spiral circles joined together are counted pos. Circles showing no spiraling are not counted. A "W" figure is pos.; a "V" or "C" is not. In viewing small section of spirals perpendicular to axis, 2nd and 3rd spiral, etc., may be just faintly seen, but the section should be counted as pos.

There is some fine cell wall structure present which when broken may fracture into "Z"-like characters similar in appearance to "Z" formed from small thin spiral vessels. Care should be exercised in discriminating between the two.

Stone Cell and Group Count Method (7)— Official First Action

13.023   Apparatus and Reagents

(a) *Slide and cover glass.*—75 × 38 mm slide with lines 0.5 mm apart, nearly across slide, parallel to 75 mm side, and ruled from top to bottom; 33 × 33 × 0.2 mm cover glass.

(b) *Scoop.*—Thin (ca 0.01–0.02 mm thick) stainless steel strip ca 4.8 mm wide with 90° bend extending outward 3 mm.

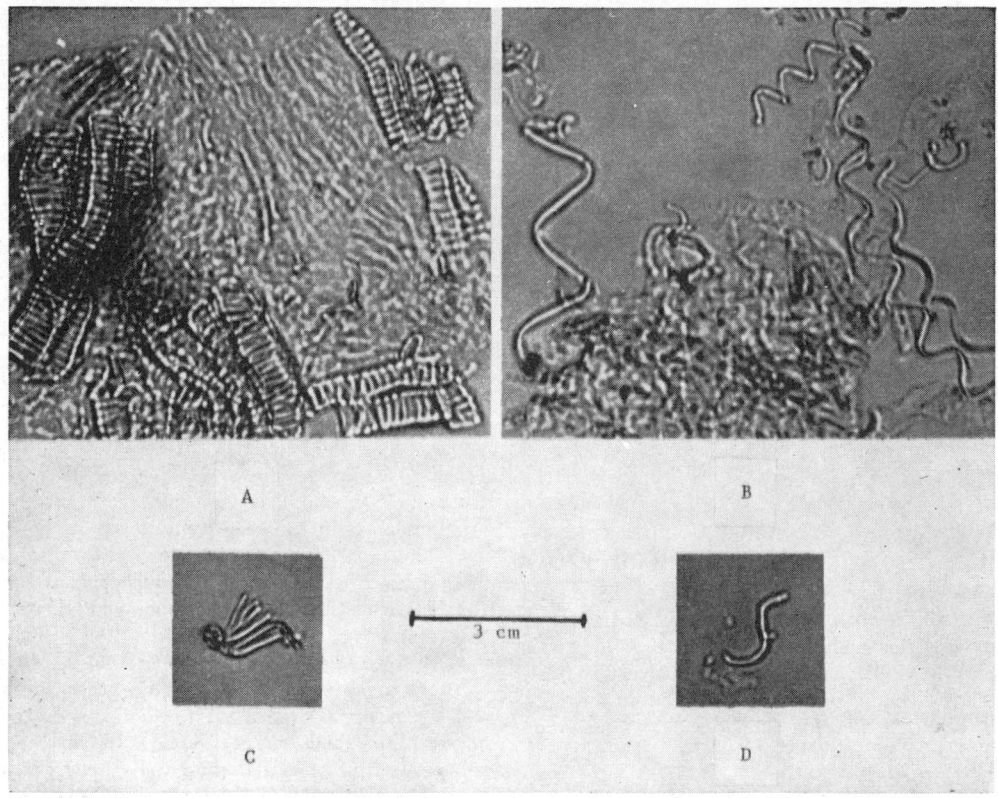

FIG. 13:1—Spiral vessel sections ca 340×. A, Mass of spiral vessels; note size differential and narrowing effects. B, Spiral vessels stretched out; note difference in size. C, Broken section; count pos. if three joined rods are present. D, Pos. ''S''-shaped section.

(c) *Magnetic stirrer.*—With stirring bar ca $\frac{5}{8}''$ long × $\frac{1}{4}''$ diam. Stirring bar $\frac{1}{2}'' \times \frac{5}{16}''$ with ridge in center will circle walls of 1 oz ointment jar (ca 36 mm diam × 40 mm high internal measurements) with distinct convex bottom, giving both vortex mixing and stirring.

(d) *Bellucci's reagent.*—$HOAc$-H_2O-HNO_3 (36 + 9 + 5).

13.024   *Defatting and Grinding*
See **13.019.**

13.025   *Determination*

Mix dried (1 hr at 100°) product by tumbling in covered dish. Make duplicate detns. Accurately weigh 0.500 g extd and dried material and transfer to 150 ml beaker. Gradually stir in 20 ml portion Bellucci's reagent until smooth; rinse walls of beaker and stirring rod with remainder. Stir gently. Fill short-neck, 100 ml, r-b flask with cold H_2O to neck and place on top of beaker; let rod rest in spout of beaker. Bring soln to initial boil, using asbestos mat over small flame. Immediately reduce to very weak flame and boil gently 10 min with frequent gentle swirling, keeping beaker and flask together. Cool ca 5 min.

Accurately weigh 25 × 100 mm Pyrex, rimless culture tube in 30 ml beaker (holder). Quant. transfer sample to culture tube with small portions H_2O, scrubbing beaker and rod with rubber policeman. Centrf. ≥ 3 min at full speed in International Clinical centrf., using IEC No. 571 curved rubber cushion in IEC No. 320 shield, or equiv. Decant carefully and discard supernatant (some flocculent material may be present). Add H_2O to tube to ca $\frac{3}{4}$ full, stopper, and shake until residue is well dispersed. Remove stopper, rinse, centrf., and decant as before.

Add aq. glycerine (3 + 2) to culture tube until tube and holder weigh 20±0.03 g more than original wt. Stopper, shake vigorously until well mixed, and transfer immediately to 1 oz ointment jar contg small magnetic bar. Stopper jar and let stand until bubbles disappear (ca 5–10 min).

Accurately weigh together ruled glass slide and cover glass. Stir liq. in jar 1 min on magnetic stirrer at max. speed at which small bubbles do not form. Stop. In rapid sequence, push jar (to put magnetic bar next to wall of jar) and, using scoop, immediately transfer drop liq. (ca 0.04±0.01 g) to center of tared slide, rulings up. Tap slide gently with scoop several times to remove as much liq. as possible. Place cover slip so that one edge rests just above and parallel to lower edge of slide. Lower cover slip carefully until it touches liq. and then let it drop. Liq. will ooze to edges. Do not press cover slip. Weigh prepd slide to 4 decimal places. Place rubber stopper in jar to prevent evapn.

Place slide on compd microscope with or without upper half of condenser and with transmitted day-light-type filtered and diffused light. Count 2 slides from each of 2 detns as in (a) or (b):

(a) *Stone cell count.*—For cocoa, cocoa press cake, chocolate liquor, and expeller cake. Scan slide at 100× and count stone cells at ≥200×. Count whole stone cells, both single and in groups, and all broken stone cells which are ≥0.5 cell. Do not count smaller fragments.

(b) *Stone cell group count.*—For other chocolate products. Proceed as in (a), counting only stone cell groups contg ≥2 stone cells.

13.026   *Description of Stone Cells*

Stone cells vary considerably in size, shape, and general appearance. Some are very distinct and others are relatively indistinct. Their size varies from ca 10 to 38 μm; the longest are very slender. Some very coarse stone cells up to ca 40 μm with thick, beaded-appearing outside wall ca 7 μm wide are occasionally found. Stone shapes are polygonal, generally irregular, and may contain curved areas. On well developed stone cells outside walls are 2–3.5 μm wide. On less distinct stone cells, outside walls are narrower and thinner; such cells are not fully developed or immature. Several near-parallel thin walls or lines, viewed microscopically, are easily visible in many stone cells. They are generally more distinct in those where outside wall is thin. *See* Fig. 13:2 for photomicrographs of stone cells. Stone cells usually are in group formation, consisting of ≥2 stone cells.

13.027   *Calculations*

For either method, average four S values from one of formulas below and report as % shell in chocolate component:

(a) *Stone cell count.*—$S_1 = 84C/(17200M - C)$

(b) *Stone cell group count.*—$S_2 = 84G/(1700M - G)$,

where W = g sample; L = g dild sample; D = g of drop counted; C = stone cell count of drop; M = mg dry fat-free sample in drop counted (= 1000 WD/L); S = % shell in chocolate component; G = stone cell groups in drop; and 9340 = number stone cells in 1 mg dry, fat-free, 250 mesh shell.

(*Example:* for 0.5 g sample dild to 20 g, S_1 = $84C/(430000D - C)$ and $S_2 = 84G/(42500D - G.)$

13.028   Ash Insoluble in Acid—Official
Final Action—*See* 13.007

CACAO PRODUCTS PROCESSED
WITH ALKALIES

13.029   Ash—Official Final Action—
See **13.003**

**13.030   Soluble and Insoluble Ash—Official
Final Action—*See* 13.004**

**13.031   Alkalinity of Soluble Ash—Official
Final Action—*See* 13.005**

**13.032   Alkalinity of Insoluble Ash—Official
Final Action—*See* 13.006**

13.033   CHOCOLATE LIQUOR (*8*)—
OFFICIAL FIRST ACTION
(*Caution: See* **46.011, 46.039,** and **46.054.**)

Ext 25–50 g sample (50 g if light color, indicating low liquor) as in **13.015,** except to use in first aq. extn 200 ml H_2O for products referred to in (a) and 200 ml *1% $Na_2C_2O_4$ soln* for products referred to in (b). Follow method thru aq., alcohol, and ether extns only.

With aid of small portions ether (45, 20, 15 ml, etc.) transfer residue resulting from ether, alcohol, and aq. extns to tared Al dish provided with tight-fit cover. Use small amt of acetone and policeman to transfer any material that sticks to bottle. Evap. liq. carefully on steam bath or hot plate, and dry residue in oven at 100°. Cover dish, cool in desiccator, and weigh.

To obtain wt dry, fat-free cacao mass, multiply wt residue by factor 1.43. To obtain wt chocolate liquor multiply wt dry, fat-free cacao mass by factor 2.2. (This factor is based on fat content of 54% in chocolate liquors.)

FAT
Quantitative Determination
(*Caution: See* **46.011, 46.039,** and **46.073.**)

13.034   *Method I (9)—Official Final Action*

(Not applicable to cacao products contg milk ingredients or to products prepd by cooking with sugar and water, and drying; cacao nibs must be finely ground.)

Prep. in Knorr extn tube, **17.020**(d), first par., 6 mm tightly packed mat of asbestos purified as for detn of crude fiber, **7.054**(c), and carefully freed from coarse pieces. (Allihn type filter tube with coarse fritted disk such as Ace Glass Inc. No. 7195 is also satisfactory.) Wash filter with alcohol, ether, and little pet ether. (*All* pet ether used in this detn must be redistd at <60°.) Weigh 2–3 g prepd sample, **13.001,** into tube and insert tube into rubber stopper in filtering bell jar connected to suction thru 2-way stopcock, taking care that no rubber particles adhere to tip of stem. Place weighed 200 ml erlen-meyer at such ht that tube stem passes thru neck into flask. (Lengthen stem of tube if necessary.) Fill

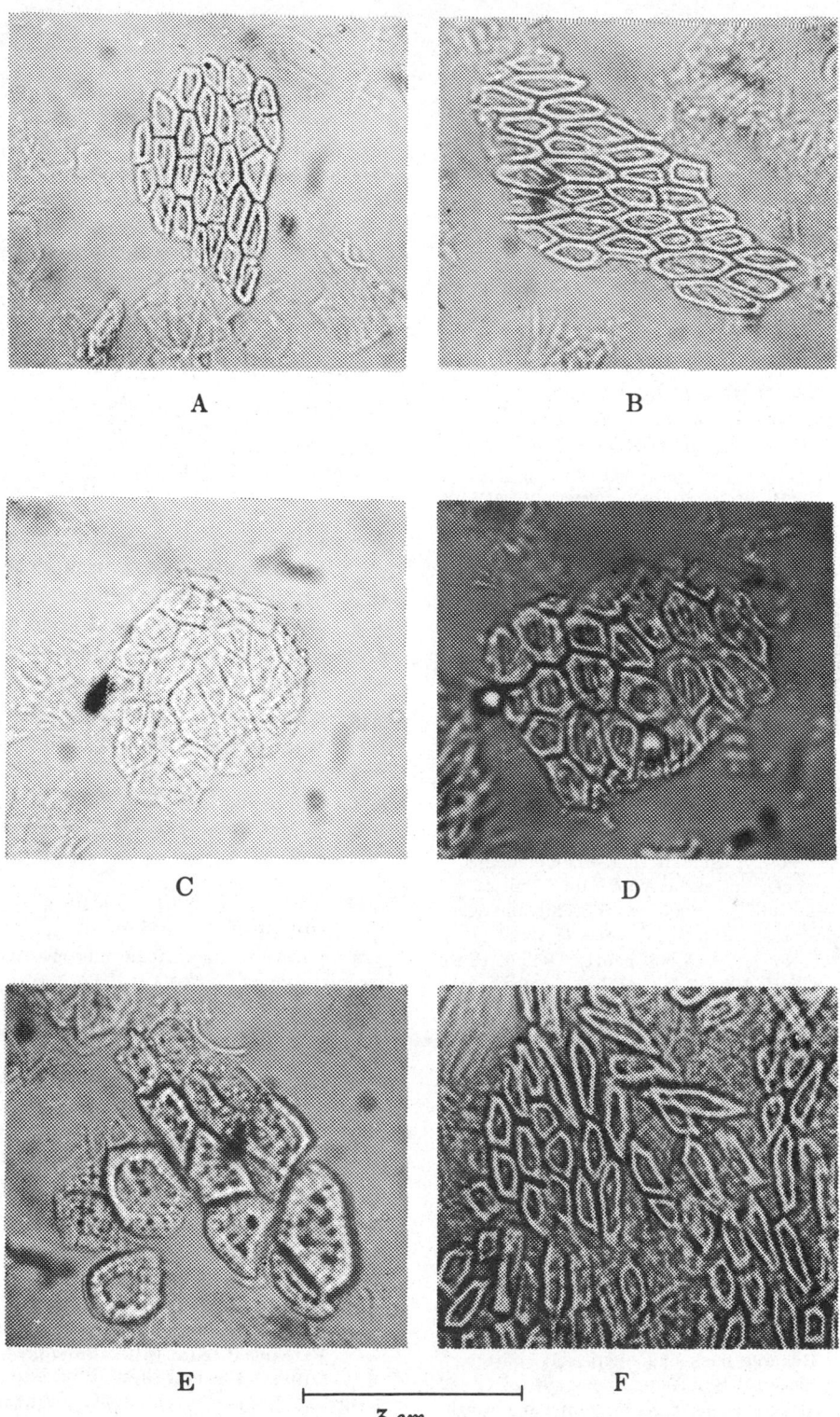

FIG. 13:2—Stone cells ca 330X: A and B, distinct stone cells; C, indistinct stone cells; D, stone cells showing distinct parallel lines in central area; E, very large stone cells infrequently found; F, long stone cells attached to a large piece of shell, showing separations between stone cells on shell

tube to ca $\frac{2}{3}$ capacity with redistd pet ether, and with flat-end rod stir sample thoroly, crushing all lumps. Let stand 1 min and drain by suction. Regulate suction so that collected solv. will not boil violently. Release vac. after each draining before adding more solv. Add solv. from wash bottle while turning tube between thumb and finger so that sides of tube are washed down by each addn. Repeat extns, with stirring, until fat is removed (usually 10 extns). Remove tube with stopper from bell jar, wash traces of fat from end of stem with pet ether, evap. solv., and dry to constant wt at 100°.

Method II (10)—Official First Action (Office International du Cacao et du Chocolat-AOAC Method)

(Applicable to cacao products with or without milk ingredients or to products prepd by cooking with sugar and H_2O and drying)

13.035   Apparatus and Reagents

(a) *Soxhlet apparatus.*—With ⴲ joints, siphon capacity ca 100 ml (33 × 80 mm thimble), 250 ml erlenmeyer, and regulated heating mantle.

(b) *Petroleum ether.*—Distd in glass, bp 30–60°.

13.036   Determination

If necessary, chill product until hard and grate or shave to fine, granular condition. Accurately weigh 3–4 g chocolate liquor, 4–5 g cocoas, 4–5 g sweet chocolate, or 9–10 g milk chocolate into 300–500 ml beaker. Add slowly, while stirring, 45 ml boiling H_2O to give homogeneous suspension. Add 55 ml ca $8N$ HCl (2 + 1) and few defatted SiC chips or other antibumping agent, and stir. Cover with watch glass, bring slowly to boil, and boil gently 15 min. Rinse watch glass with 100 ml H_2O. Filter digest thru 15 cm S&S No. 589 medium fluted paper, or equiv., rinsing beaker 3 times with H_2O. Continue washing until last portion of filtrate is Cl-free as detd by addn of $0.1N$ AgNO₃. Transfer wet paper and sample to defatted extn thimble and dry 6–18 hr in small beaker at 100°. Place glass wool plug over paper.

Add few defatted antibumping chips to 250 ml erlenmeyer and dry 1 hr at 100°. Cool to room temp. in desiccator and weigh. Place thimble contg dried sample in soxhlet, supporting it with spiral or glass beads. Rinse digestion beaker, drying beaker, and watch glass with three 50 ml portions pet ether, and add washings to thimble. Reflux digested sample 4 hr, adjusting heat so that extractor siphons at least 30 times. Remove flask and evap. solv. on steam bath. Dry flask at 100–101° to constant wt (1.5–2 hr). Cool in desiccator to room temp. and weigh. Constant wt is attained when successive 1 hr drying periods show addnl loss of <0.05% fat. % Fat = g fat × 100/g sample. Duplicate detns should agree within 0.1% fat.

13.037   Separation and Preparation of Fat for Determination of Constants— Procedure

(*Caution: See* 46.011, 46.039, and 46.054.)

(a) *Not applicable to cacao products containing milk ingredients or to products prepared by cooking with sugar and H_2O, and drying.*—Sep. fat from 10–40 g sample (depending upon fat content) by shaking material with two or three 100 ml portions ether. Centrf. and decant each portion. Combine portions in beaker and evap. most of ether on steam bath. Filter ether exts thru dry, folded paper and dry at 100°.

(b) *Applicable to cacao products containing milk ingredients or to products prepared by cooking with sugar and H_2O, and drying.*—Proceed as in 13.036, using 20 g sample in case of milk chocolate and combining fat obtained in duplicate detns for examination.

13.038   Iodine Absorption Number—Official Final Action—See 28.020 or 28.022

13.039   Melting Point—Official Final Action

Proceed as in 28.012. Keep fat at least 24 hr in cool place before making detn.

13.040   Index of Refraction—Official Final Action—See 28.007 or 28.009

13.041   Reichert-Meissl and Polenske Values (11)—Official Final Action—See 28.032

13.042   Milk Fat in Milk Chocolate— Official Final Action

Est. quantity of milk fat in milk chocolate from following formula: $C = (AX + BY)/5$; where A = g butter fat in 5 g mixed fat; $B = (5 - A)$ = g cacao fat in 5 g mixed fat; C = Reichert-Meissl number of extd fat; X = Reichert-Meissl number of authentic butter fat; and Y = Reichert-Meissl number of authentic cacao butter.

Then wt butterfat, A, in 5 g mixed fat $= 5(C - Y)/(X - Y)$, and

% butterfat = % total fat × $(C - Y)/(X - Y)$.

13.043   Saponification Number—Official Final Action—See 28.027

13.044   Detection of Coconut and Palm Kernel Oils in Cacao Butter and Fat Extracted from Milk Chocolate (12)— Official First Action

(a) *Examination of cacao butter.*—Saponify 5 g sample with 15 ml *alc. KOH soln* (25 g in 200 ml alcohol) and evap. alcohol on steam bath. Prep. blank on pure cacao butter at same time. Add 5 ml H_2O and again evap. to remove last trace of alcohol. Dissolve soap in 100 ml H_2O, cool to room temp., and add, while stirring, 100 ml satd NaCl soln. Let stand 15 min, stirring occasionally, and then sep. soap by filtration thru buchner. To 100 ml filtrate add, while stirring, 100 ml satd NaCl soln and let stand 15 min. (Only slight ppt should appear.) Filter, add 1 drop phthln to filtrate, neutze with HCl $(1 + 3)$, and add 0.5 ml excess. If sample consists of pure cacao butter, acidified soln will remain clear; if coconut or palm kernel oil is present, soln will become turbid or milky.

(b) *Examination of fat extracted from milk chocolate (13).*—Milk fat, if present in cacao butter subjected to this test, produces turbidity less intense than that produced by same % coconut or palm kernel oil. For example, cacao butter contg 10, 15, or 20% milk fat produces, resp., no opalescence, faint opalescence, or more pronounced opalescence. For this reason, when fat to be examined has been extd from cacao product that contains lactose or casein, multiply % lactose in cacao product by 0.8, or % casein by 1.1, to obtain % milk fat in product, and from this result calc. % milk fat in total fat. If this corresponds to ≤15%, blank of cacao butter contg 15% milk fat may be used; otherwise make up mixt. of cacao butter and milk fat in proportions indicated by calcns.

Test fat extd from sample under examination as in (a), but use prepd mixt. of cacao butter and milk fat intead of pure cacao butter for blank. If fat being tested contains coconut oil or palm kernel oil, last filtrate, when acidified, will be more turbid or milky than blank.

Silver Number for Detection of Coconut and Palm Kernel Oils (14)—Official Final Action

13.045 *Reagents*

(a) *Potassium hydroxide soln.*—Dissolve 750 g KOH in H_2O and dil. to 1 L with H_2O.

(b) *Magnesium sulfate soln.*—Dissolve 150 g $MgSO_4.7H_2O$ in H_2O and dil. to 1 L with H_2O.

(c) *Sodium nitrate.*—Crystals as Cl-free as practicable (≤0.002%).

(d) *Ferric indicator.*—See **45.031**(a).

13.046 *Determination*

Weigh 10 g fat into 250 ml beaker and add 40 ml alcohol and 5 ml KOH soln. Saponify mixt. and evap. to dryness on steam bath. Take up soap in 150 ml H_2O, warming if necessary, and transfer to 250 ml vol. flask. Cool, and dil. to vol.

Pipet 200 ml soln into 500 ml erlenmeyer. Close flask with stopper holding thermometer and having small groove lengthwise in side. Place flask in H_2O bath held at ca 80°. When sample reaches ca 80°, loosen stopper, and pipet in 50 ml $MgSO_4$ soln. Shake flask with rotary motion. Replace stopper and thermometer and let flask remain in bath 8–10 min longer at 70–80°, shaking occasionally. Remove flask

and cool under tap, with shaking, to 20–25°. Remove stopper and thermometer, stopper tightly, and shake vigorously 4 min. Let flask stand in bath at 20–25° until aq. layer seps at bottom. Filter thru buchner, removing all liq. possible by pressing with glass spoon. Det. blank on cacao butter in same way.

Neutze 200 ml filtrate in 250 ml vol. flask with ca $0.5N$ H_2SO_4 until colorless to phthln. Add 20 g $NaNO_3$ crystals, and when dissolved, add 22.5 ml $0.2N$ $AgNO_3$. Dil. to vol. and shake 3 min. Let soln stand short time and filter thru folded paper. To 200 ml filtrate add 6 ml ferric indicator and 4 ml HNO_3 $(4 + 3)$. Titr. with $0.1N$ NH_4SCN to first color change (reddish brown).

Ag number (mg Ag used/g fat) = $(a - b) \times 2.107$, where $a = 1.6 \times$ ml $0.2N$ $AgNO_3$ added and $b =$ ml $0.1N$ NH_4SCN used in back-titrn.

Factor 2.107 = 10.787 × (mg Ag/ml $0.1N$ soln)/5.12 × (g fat in aliquot titrd).

Ag number of palm kernel and coconut oils and of stearins varies from ca 26 for stearins to 60 for whole coconut oil. Milk fat gives value of ca 11.6, and cacao butter, 0.6.

Critical Temperature of Dissolution of Fat in Acetic Acid (15)—Official Final Action

13.047 *Apparatus*

Insert thermometer reading to 0.1° into cork that fits $6 \times \frac{3}{4}''$ test tube and extend it far enough into tube so that bulb will be covered by 10 ml liq. Place test tube in larger tube $(4 \times 1\frac{1}{4}'')$ contg glycerol and hold firmly in place with cork having groove cut in side to equalize pressure when heat is applied.

13.048 *Determination*

To remove traces of moisture, filter portion of sample to be examined thru dry paper in 110° oven. Let filtered sample cool until barely warm, and weigh 5 g sample and 5 g 99.5% HOAc into test tube. Insert cork holding thermometer and place test tube in glycerol bath. Heat and shake app. frequently until clear soln of fat and HOAc is obtained. Cool, with constant shaking, without removing from bath. Note temp. at which first sign of turbidity appears. Make similar test with same HOAc on sample of pure cacao butter.

As free fatty acids lower turbidity temp., correction must be made for acid value of sample. If concn of the HOAc reagent is such that turbidity temp. of pure cacao butter is ca 90°, one unit of acid value causes reduction of 1.4° in critical temp. of dissolution. If turbidity temp. is ca 100°, one unit of acid value causes reduction of 1.2°. For intermediate temp., reduction is proportional.

Det. acid value (mg KOH required to neutze free fatty acids in 1 g sample) of both sample and pure cacao butter as in **28.030**, using 5 g fat. Multiply acid value by correction factor and add result to observed turbidity temp. Figure obtained is true critical temp. of dissolution. If this temp. is lower than that of pure cacao butter by >3° in case of fat from chocolate liquors or sweet chocolates, and by >6° in case of fat from milk chocolates, adulteration with coconut, palm kernel, corn, peanut, cottonseed oils, etc., or their stearins, is indicated.

13.049   Lecithin (16)—Official First Action
(Caution: See **46.011, 46.040,** and **46.056.**)

Weigh 5 g prepd sample, **13.001,** into 200 ml vol. flask, add ca 150 ml CHCl3-absolute alcohol (1 + 1), and shake occasionally during day. At end of day dil. to vol. with same solv., pour into 250 ml centrf. bottle, stopper, and let stand overnight. Next day centrf. stoppered bottle until clear (ca 15 min at 1800 rpm). Pipet 100 ml clear liq. into 500 ml Kjeldahl flask. Place Kjeldahl flask on steam bath, remove solv. with air current and det. P_2O_5 as in **22.038** and **22.039.** $P_2O_5 \times 11.19 =$ lecithin.

P_2O_5 may be detd by **3.064,** in which case conc. the 100 ml clear liq. in 250 ml beaker, wash into small crucible with solv., evap., and proceed as in **3.063.** After digestion on steam bath, crucible must be heated cautiously on gauze until dry, and heating continued until frothing ceases and most of fat has smoked off before ashing in furnace. Ashing may be done in beaker in which ext is evapd.

DAIRY INGREDIENT CONSTITUENTS
13.050   Milk Fat in Milk Chocolate—Official Final Action—See 28.032 and 13.042

13.051   Milk Protein (17)—Official Final Action
(Not applicable to chocolate products contg milk protein which has been subjected to high heat treatment)

Weigh 10.0 g finely divided milk chocolate into 250 ml or larger centrf. bottle and ext twice with ca 100 ml ether by shaking until uniform, centrfg, and decanting supernatant ether layer each time. Place in bottle 2-hole stopper carrying bent glass tube, and straight glass tube that extends into bottle ca ⅓ of way to bottom. Expel ether by applying suction to bent tube and drawing moderate air current thru bottle while it is in moderately warm (not hot) place. When ether is expelled, pipet 100 ml H_2O into bottle. Stopper bottle, and shake vigorously 4 min. Pipet in 100 ml *1% $Na_2C_2O_4$ soln.* Stopper bottle, and shake vigorously 3 min. Let bottle stand ca 10 min and again shake 1–2 min. Centrf. ca 15 min at high speed (ca 1800 rpm).

Remove bottle from centrf. and decant supernatant into beaker. Pipet 100 ml into dry 250 ml beaker and add 1 ml HOAc while stirring gently. Let sample stand few min so ppt can partly sep., and add with stirring 4 ml *10% tannic acid soln* (soln should be ≤1 week old). Let ppt settle few min; then filter on 7 cm buchner with moderate suction. Filtrate

should be clear. Use as filter S&S No. 589 white ribbon paper (or equiv.), overlaid with medium layer of paper pulp, prepd by shaking one 15 cm No. 1 Whatman paper, torn to bits, with H_2O. Using *wash soln* (add 1 ml HOAc and 2 ml 10% tannic acid soln to 100 ml 1% $Na_2C_2O_4$ soln), transfer all ppt to funnel with aid of policeman. Wash on filter 1 or 2 times. Loosen filter around edge with spatula. Carefully roll up and remove filter and ppt to Kjeldahl flask. Transfer to flask any particles of ppt clinging to funnel or spatula with small pieces of damp filter paper. Det. N as in **2.051.** $N \times 2 \times 6.38 =$ total casein and albumin in the 10 g taken for analysis. Casein and albumin $\times 1.07 =$ total milk protein.

13.052   Lactose (18)—Official Final Action
(In absence of other reducing sugars)

Det. reducing sugars before inversion as in **31.039** in aliquot (usually 20 ml) of the Pb-free filtrate obtained in **13.053.** Det. reduced Cu as Cu_2O by volumetric thiosulfate method, **31.042.** Correct for Cu_2O due to sucrose as follows: Obtain approx. % lactose from following formula, using data obtained in **13.053:**

$$\text{Approx. lactose} = [P(1.1 + X/100) - S]/0.79.$$

From calcd polarimetric sucrose/lactose ratio and total Cu_2O obtained as above, det. quantity of Cu_2O to be subtracted from total Cu_2O found, using graph, Fig. 13:3. Convert corrected Cu_2O to g lactose (*L*), using table, **47.019.** Then obtain % lactose from following relationship:

$$\% \text{ lactose} = L(110 + X)/0.26C,$$

where $X =$ value obtained in polarimetric sucrose detn and $C =$ vol. soln (ml) used in above lactose detn.

SACCHARINE INGREDIENTS OTHER THAN LACTOSE
13.053   Sucrose (18)—Official Final Action

Transfer 26 g prepd sample, **13.001,** to 250 ml centrf. bottle, add ca 100 ml pet ether, shake 5 min, and centrf. Decant clear solv. carefully and repeat treatment with pet ether. Place bottle contg defatted residue in warm place until pet ether is expelled. Add 100 ml H_2O and shake until most of chocolate is detached from sides and bottom of bottle. Loosen stopper and carefully immerse bottle 15 min in H_2O bath kept at 85–90°, shaking occasionally to remove all chocolate from sides of bottle. Remove from bath, cool, and add *basic $Pb(OAc)_2$ soln* (sp gr 1.25) to complete pptn (5 ml is usually enough). Add H_2O to make total of 110 ml added liq. Mix thoroly, centrf., and decant supernatant thru small filter. Ppt excess Pb with powd dry $K_2C_2O_4$ and filter. Dil. 10 or 20 ml filtrate with equal vol. H_2O, mix, and polarize in 200 mm tube at 20°. Obtain invert reading as in **31.026(b).** Multiply both readings by 2 to obtain direct and invert polariza-

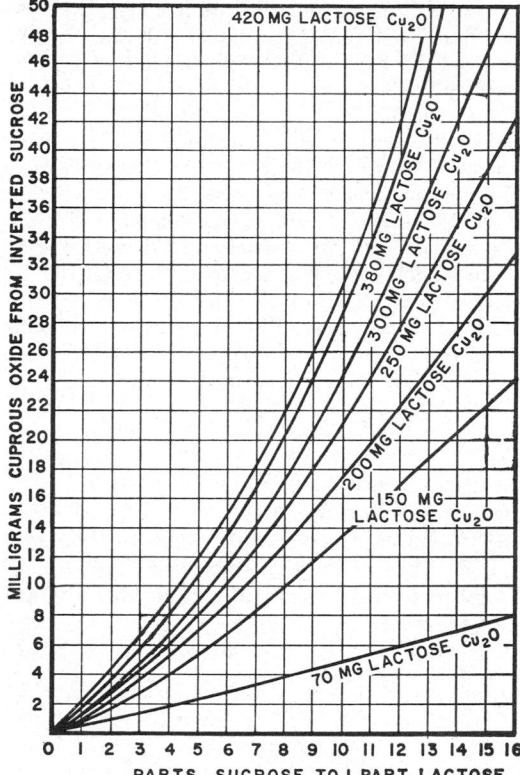

FIG. 13:3—Graph used in correcting cuprous oxide for effect of sucrose

tions "P" and "I." From data obtained, calc. % sucrose (S) from following formulas:

$$S = \frac{(P - I)(110 + X)}{143.0 - t/2},$$

where

$$X = \frac{0.2244(P - 21d)}{1 - 0.00204(P - 21d)},$$

where

$$d = \frac{P - I}{143.0 - t/2}.$$

13.054 Glucose (19)—Official First Action

Prep. clarified and deleaded sample soln as in **13.053** except use only 10 g. Proceed as in **31.214** or **31.218.**

STARCH—OFFICIAL FIRST ACTION

13.055 Direct Acid Hydrolysis Method

(*Caution: See* **46.039, 46.054,** and **46.070.**)

Weigh 4 g sample if unsweetened, or 10 g if sweetened, into small porcelain mortar; add 25 ml ether and grind. After coarser material settles, decant ether, together with fine suspended matter, on 11 cm paper of sufficiently fine texture to retain crude starch. Repeat treatment until no more coarse ma-

terial remains. After ether has evapd from filter, transfer fat-free residue to mortar by means of jet of cold H_2O and rub to smooth paste, filtering on paper previously used. Repeat this process until all sugar is removed. (In case of sweetened products filtrate should measure at least 500 ml.) Det. crude starch in extd residue as in **8.017.**

13.056 ★ Diastase Method ★

See **12.043,** 10th ed.

CHOCOLATE PRODUCTS

Alginates (20)—Official Final Action

13.057 Reagent

Ferric hydroxide-sulfuric acid reagent.—Dissolve 10 g $FeCl_3 \cdot 6H_2O$ in ca 100 ml H_2O in each of 2 centrf. bottles, and ppt $Fe(OH)_3$ by adding excess NH_4OH (by odor). Wash ppt with ca 5 successive portions H_2O, centrfg and decanting until little odor of NH_3 remains. Break up centrfd ppt each time before washing. Dry ppt on steam bath or in oven overnight, break up, and dry again. Mix with spatula or grind in mortar to obtain moderately fine powder. Keep in closed container.

Ferric hydroxide (moist) (K&K Laboratories, Inc.) may be used instead of pptg $Fe(OH)_3$ as above. Transfer this product to centrf. bottles, shake, centrf., decant, wash, and dry as above. Place 0.5 g dry powder in 50 ml g-s graduated cylinder, add 50 ml H_2SO_4, shake vigorously, and let settle until clear (usually 4–7 days). Some ferric sulfate appears to stick to sides, but reagent is ready for use after 7 days. Prep. fresh after 3 weeks. Check as follows before use:

Dissolve small amt (1–5 mg) of com. alginate in H_2O contg 5 drops 0.1N NaOH, add 4 vols alcohol to ppt alginate, centrf., decant, and dry on steam bath until no odor of alcohol remains, using air current to remove last traces of alcohol. Add 3 drops 0.1N NaOH, dissolve with aid of glass rod, and add 2 ml Fe-H_2SO_4 reagent. Soln turns purple slowly, usually within 1 hr, depending on amt of algin present, but may take longer. If soln appears to be turning brown, add addnl 2 ml reagent, mix with glass rod, and let stand.

13.058 Test

Weigh sample contg 10–20 mg aliginate into 250 ml centrf. bottle, add H_2O to total vol. of 40–50 ml, and dissolve by swirling. Adjust pH to 8–9 with satd Na_3PO_4 soln; usually 5 drops is enough. Add ca 0.5 g *pancreatin* and 3 drops HCHO, and shake vigorously 1 min. Let stand 2–16 hr.

Centrf. at 1200 rpm 2–3 min, decant into 250 ml centrf. bottle, and discard residue. Add 3–4 vols alcohol, shake, and let stand $\geq$1 hr, shaking several times. Centrf. as before and discard liq. Add 50 ml H_2O and 1 drop 10% NaOH to residue and shake vigorously until no more residue appears to dissolve.

Add 3 g decolorizing C (Nuchar) and shake vigorously 1 hr, preferably on shaking machine. Do not centrf. but pour directly into folded filter paper, collecting filtrate in 250 ml centrf. bottle. If filtrate is not clear, pour back thru paper several times. If filtration is slow, let filter overnight. Since C retains some alginate, for recovery of very small amts (ca 1 mg) re-ext C by shaking with another 50 ml portion H_2O and 5 drops $0.1N$ NaOH, and add this filtrate to first extn.

To filtrate add 4 vols alcohol, shake, and let stand ≥1 hr, or overnight if convenient. Centrf. and decant, saving residue. Residue contains alginates, gums, and gelatin. Dry residue on steam bath, using air current, if desired, until no odor of alcohol can be detected. Cool, add 3 drops $0.1N$ NaOH, and dissolve residue, using glass rod, as completely as possible. Add 2 ml $Fe-H_2SO_4$ reagent, mixing with glass rod. If soln turns purple very soon, enough reagent was added; if brown appears, add addnl 2 ml reagent. Let stand overnight, since color develops slowly. Deep purple is pos. test for alginates. If test is neg., repeat detn, using twice the size sample, increasing Nuchar to 4 g, and shaking 1.5 hr, for confirmation.

13.059 THEOBROMINE (21)—OFFICIAL FIRST ACTION

(*Caution: See* **46.011** and **46.040.**)

(Not applicable to materials contg >ca 12% sweetening ingredients)

Ext materials contg considerable fat, such as chocolate liquor or cacao nibs, with pet ether (bp <65°) to remove fat. (This preliminary extn is unnecessary with samples of cocoas or cacao shell.)

Place 10 g sample or prepd sample in small porcelain dish. Add 2–3 g freshly *calcined MgO* and mix well with flat-end glass rod. Add ca 14 (9–20) ml H_2O, few ml at time, and triturate carefully and thoroly until every particle is damp. (Material should be compressible to firm cake.) Place dish contg damp mixt. on steam bath 30 min, mixing at intervals to prevent any part from becoming dry, during which time material should granulate.

After 30 min remove dish and triturate mixt. well so that every particle is damp; then transfer to 250 ml flask. Add 150 ml *tetrachloroethane*, attach air condenser, and boil 30 min. Filter nearly boiling hot liq. into second ca 200 ml flask, preferably with ₮ joint. (Filtrate should be clear and almost colorless.)

Transfer residue and filter to first flask with 120 ml addnl solv. and again reflux 20–30 min. Meanwhile, distill most of liq. in second flask from first extn thru air condenser. Filter hot liq. (second extn) into second flask and repeat process of refluxing and distn twice more, using 120 ml portions tetrachloroethane. Receive filtrates from all extns in flask 2, intermittently distg off portions as above. Distill liq. after last extn until reduced to 3–5 ml.

Cool flask and residue, and add 65 ml ether with rotation; mix well, stopper, and let stand ≥1 hr (until supernatant is clear). Collect ppt on tared filter paper, using several 5–7 ml portions ether to transfer and wash. Dry filter and ppt at 100°, and weigh. Add 0.004 g to wt found to compensate for theobromine dissolved in the ether. Calc. % theobromine in original material.

SELECTED REFERENCES

(*1*) JAOAC **14**, 529(1931).

(*2*) Analytical Methods of the Office International du Cacao et du Chocolat, Niklausstrasse 4, Zurich, Switzerland, page 9-E/1963; JAOAC **53**, 474(1970).

(*3*) Federal Register, October 19, 1940, p. 4152; JAOAC **23**, 593(1940).

(*4*) JAOAC **13**, 482(1930); **14**, 526, 530(1931); **16**, 66(1933).

(*5*) JAOAC **35**, 650(1952).

(*6*) JAOAC **51**, 457, 725(1968).

(*7*) JAOAC **53**, 476(1970).

(*8*) JAOAC **14**, 526, 530(1931); **24**, 720(1941).

(*9*) JAOAC **8**, 705(1925); **9**, 469(1926).

(*10*) JAOAC **28**, 482(1945); **33**, 342(1950); **34**, 442 (1951); **53**, 490(1970); Analytical Methods of the OICC (Ref. *2*), page 8a-E/1963.

(*11*) JAOAC **13**, 43, 255(1930).

(*12*) JAOAC **11**, 45, 517(1928); **13**, 486(1930).

(*13*) JAOAC **11**, 517(1928); **13**, 45, 78, 486(1930).

(*14*) JAOAC **15**, 549(1932); **17**, 64, 375(1934).

(*15*) JAOAC **5**, 263(1921); **7**, 152(1923).

(*16*) JAOAC **32**, 167(1949); **35**, 656(1952); **36**, 263 (1953).

(*17*) JAOAC **22**, 603(1939); **24**, 715(1941); **25**, 716 (1942); Analyst **93**, 116(1968).

(*18*) JAOAC **16**, 564(1933); **17**, 377(1934).

(*19*) Ind. Eng. Chem., Anal. Ed. **10**, 669(1938); JAOAC **28**, 533(1945).

(*20*) JAOAC **40**, 47, 478(1957); **42**, 370(1959).

(*21*) Analyst **46**, 35(1921).

14. Cereal Foods[*]

WHEAT FLOUR (1)

14.001 Sampling—Official Final Action

Sample number of sacks equiv. to square root of number in lot, but ≥ 10, i.e., 10 from 100 or less, 15 from 225, 20 from 400 sacks, etc.

Select sacks to be sampled according to their exposure in ratio of 4 from most exposed, 3 from next less exposed, 2 from next, and 1 from least exposed portion of lot.

From each sack to be sampled, draw core from one corner of top diagonally to center of sack by means of cylindrical, pointed, polished metal trier, $\frac{1}{2}''$ diam., with slit at least $\frac{1}{8}$ of circumference. Draw second core from other top corner to $\frac{1}{2}$ distance to center of sack.

Deliver the 2 cores at once to clean, dry, air-tight container that has stood open for few min near lot of flour to be sampled, and seal immediately. Use sep. container for each sack sampled. Use one of following containers: (1) pt fruit jar provided with rubber gasket; (2) rubber or plastic pouch that can be tied or sealed to exclude moisture or air; (3) tin can or box with moisture- and air-tight friction top.

Before opening sample for analysis, alternately invert and roll each container 25 times, or more if necessary, to secure homogeneous mixt. Avoid extreme temps and humidities when opening containers for analysis. Keep sample tightly sealed at all other times.

Total Solids (Moisture, Indirect Method)

(Also applicable to flour mixes contg $NaHCO_3$ as ingredient)

Vacuum Oven Method (2)— Official Final Action

14.002 Apparatus

(a) *Metal dish.*—Diam. ca 55 mm, ht ca 15 mm, with inverted slip-in cover fitting tightly on inside.

(b) *Air-tight desiccator.*—Reignited CaO is satisfactory drying agent.

(c) *Vacuum oven.*—Connect with pump capable of maintaining partial vac. in oven with pressure equiv. to ≤ 25 mm of Hg and provided with thermometer passing into oven in such way that bulb is near samples. Connect H_2SO_4 gas-drying bottle with oven to admit dry air when releasing vac.

14.003 Determination

Accurately weigh ca 2 g well-mixed sample in covered dish previously dried at 98–100°, cooled in desiccator, and weighed soon after attaining room temp. Loosen cover (do not remove) and heat at 98–100° to constant wt (ca 5 hr) in partial vac. having pressure equiv. to ≤ 25 mm of Hg. Admit dry air into oven to bring to atm. pressure. Immediately tighten cover on dish, transfer to desiccator, and weigh soon after reaching room temp. Report flour residue as total solids and loss in wt as moisture (indirect method).

14.004 Air Oven Method (3)— Official Final Action

(Results closely approximate those obtained by **14.003**)

In cooled and weighed dish (provided with cover) previously heated to $130\pm 3°$, accurately weigh ca 2 g well-mixed sample. Uncover sample, and dry dish, cover, and contents 1 hr in oven provided with opening for ventilation and maintained at $130\pm 3°$. (1 hr drying period begins when oven temp. is actually 130°.) Cover dish while still in oven, transfer to desiccator, and weigh soon after reaching room temp. Report flour residue as total solids and loss in wt as moisture (indirect method).

14.005 Extract Soluble in Cold Water (4)—Official Final Action

Weigh 20 g flour into 500 ml erlenmeyer and add gradually 200 ml H_2O at ca 0°. Shake vigorously after ca 50 ml H_2O is added and continue shaking while adding remaining H_2O. Let mixt. stand 40 min at 0°, shaking occasionally. Filter rapidly, returning first runnings to filter until filtrate is clear. Pipet 20 ml clear filtrate into weighed dish, evap. to dryness on steam bath, and dry in vac. oven at ca 100° for 30 min periods to constant wt.

Ash (5)

14.006 Direct Method—Official Final Action

Weigh 3–5 g well-mixed sample into shallow, relatively broad ashing dish that has been ignited, cooled in desiccator, and weighed soon after reaching room temp. Ignite in muffle at ca 550° (dull red) until light gray ash results, or to constant wt. Cool in desiccator and weigh soon after reaching room temp. Reignited CaO is satisfactory drying agent for desiccator.

---

[*] Methods so marked are surplus methods. *See* "Definitions of Terms and Explanatory Notes," item (29).

Magnesium Acetate Method (6)— Official Final Action

14.007   Reagent

Magnesium acetate soln.—Dissolve 4.054 g $Mg(OAc)_2.4H_2O$ in 50 ml H_2O and dil. to 1 L with alcohol.

14.008   Determination

From buret add 5 ml of the reagent to 3–5 g flour, bread, etc., or 10 ml to 1 g bran, wheat germ, etc. Let mixt. stand 1–2 min, evap. excess alcohol, and place in muffle maintained at 700°, closing door after flaming ceases. When incineration is complete, place dish in desiccator until cool; then weigh. Det. blank on soln and deduct blank from wt crude ash. Evap. blank cautiously.

Original Ash of Flour in Phosphated and Self-Rising Flour (7)

(Caution: See 46.040 and 46.049.)

14.009   Gustafson Method—Official Final Action

To 20–25 g sample in metal centrf. tube (cup 2″ diam., 6″ deep), add enough CCl_4 to fill tube to within 1″ of top (ca 250 ml). Centrf. 5–7 min at 1600 rpm and let centrf. come to rest slowly. With large tablespoon, carefully skim off flour, which is in compact layer on surface of CCl_4, recovering as much flour as possible in 1 spoonful. (With care, ca 90% of original flour may be recovered.) Let wet flour dry overnight and proceed as in 14.006. (CCl_4 may be filtered, distd, and used again.)

14.010   Added Inorganic Material in Phosphated Flour (8)—Official Final Action

Transfer 20 g flour to dry 250 ml separator, add ca 200 ml CCl_4, shake well, and let stand until soln at bottom is nearly clear, usually ca 15 min. Draw off sediment with min. of soln, by turning stopcock quickly from side to side, into 100 ml CCl_4 in dry 125 ml separator. Again shake 250 ml separator and let stand, with occasional gentle swirling if necessary to dislodge sediment from sides, until lower portion of soln clears. Draw off sediment from 125 ml separator into prepd and weighed gooch, using suction. Draw off sediment from 250 ml separator into 125 ml separator as before, and let stand with occasional gentle swirling to dislodge sediment from sides of separator. After lower portion of liq. clears, draw off into gooch as before, taking care that no sediment remains on ledge in separator. Wash crucible and contents with 25 ml fresh CCl_4, continue aspirating 2 or 3 min, weigh at once, and report as % added phosphate. Ignite crucible at 700°, cool, and weigh as $Ca(PO_3)_2$. Wt $Ca(PO_3)_2 \times 1.27 \times 5 = \%$ $Ca(H_2PO_4)_2.H_2O$ in flour.

Iron (9)—Official Final Action

(Applicable to enriched, enriched self-rising, and phosphated flours)

14.011   Reagents

(a) *Orthophenanthroline soln.*—Dissolve 0.1 g *o*-phenanthroline in ca 80 ml H_2O at 80°, cool, and dil. to 100 ml.

(b) *Alpha,alpha-dipyridyl soln.*—Dissolve 0.1 g α,α-dipyridyl in H_2O and dil. to 100 ml.

(Reagents (a) and (b) kept in cool, dark place will remain stable several weeks.)

(c) *Iron std soln.*—0.01 mg Fe/ml. (*1*) Dissolve 0.1 g analytical grade Fe wire in 20 ml HCl and 50 ml H_2O, and dil. to 1 L. Dil. 100 ml of this soln to 1 L. Or—(*2*) Dissolve 3.512 g $Fe(NH_4)_2(SO_4)_2.6H_2O$ in H_2O, add 2 drops HCl, and dil. to 500 ml. Dil. 10 ml of this soln to 1 L.

(d) *Hydroxylamine hydrochloride soln.*—Dissolve 10 g $NH_2OH.HCl$ in H_2O and dil. to 100 ml.

(e) *Magnesium nitrate soln.*—Dissolve 50 g $Mg(NO_3)_2.6H_2O$ in H_2O and dil. to 100 ml.

(f) *Acetate buffer soln.*—Dissolve 8.3 g anhyd. NaOAc (previously dried at 100°) in H_2O, add 12 ml HOAc, and dil. to 100 ml. (It may be necessary to redistill the HOAc and purify the NaOAc by recrystn from H_2O, depending on amt of Fe present.)

(g) *2 Molar acetate buffer soln.*—Contg 272 g $NaOAc.3H_2O/L$.

(h) *Buffer soln, pH 3.5.*—Dil. 6.4 ml $2M$ acetate buffer soln, (g), and 93.6 ml $2M$ HOAc (120 g/L) to 1 L with H_2O.

14.012   Preparation of Standard Curve

Prep. 11 solns contg 0.0, 2.0, 5.0, 10.0, 15.0, 20.0, 25.0, 30.0, 35.0, 40.0, and 45.0 ml, resp., of the final dild stock soln, plus 2.0 ml HCl, in 100 ml. Using 10 ml of each of these solns proceed as in 14.013, beginning "add 1 ml $NH_2OH.HCl$ ...." Plot concn against scale reading.

14.013   Determination

(a) *By dry ashing.*—Ash 10.0 g flour in Pt, SiO_2, or porcelain dish (ca 60 mm diam., 35 ml capacity) as in 14.006. (Porcelain evapg dishes of ca 25 ml capacity are satisfactory. Do not use flat-bottom dishes of diam. >60 mm.) Cool, and weigh if % ash is desired. Continue ashing until practically C-free. To diminish ashing time, or for samples that do not burn practically C-free, use one of following ash aids:

Moisten ash with 0.5–1.0 ml $Mg(NO_3)_2$ soln or with redistd HNO_3. Dry and carefully ignite in muffle, avoiding spattering. (White ash with no C results in most cases.) Do not add these ash aids to self-rising flour (products contg NaCl) in Pt dish because of vigorous action on dish. Cool, add 5 ml HCl, letting acid rinse upper portion of dish, evap. to dryness on steam bath, dissolve residue by adding 2.0 ml HCl, accurately measured, heat 5 min on steam bath with watch glass on dish, rinse watch glass with H_2O, filter into 100 ml vol. flask, cool, and dil. to vol.

Pipet 10 ml aliquot into 25 ml vol. flask, and add 1 ml $NH_2OH \cdot HCl$ soln; in few min add 5 ml buffer soln, (f), and 1 ml o-phenanthroline or 2 ml dipyridyl soln, and dil. to vol. Read intensity of color in spectrophtr at ca 510 nm. From reading, det. Fe concn from equation of line representing std points or by ref. to std curve for known Fe concn. Det. blank on reagents and make correction. Calc. quantity of Fe in flour as mg/lb. Rinse all flasks, beakers, funnels, etc., with H_2O before use, and filter all reagents to remove suspended matter.

(b) *By wet digestion.*—(*Caution: See* **46.011, 46.019, 46.026,** and **46.030.**) Transfer 10.00 g flour to 800 ml Kjeldahl flask, previously rinsed with dil. acid, then with H_2O; add 20 ml H_2O and mix; pipet 5 ml H_2SO_4 into flask and mix; add 25 ml HNO_3 and mix well. After few min, heat flask very gently at brief intervals (to avoid foaming out of flask) until heavy evolution of NO_2 fumes ceases. Continue to heat gently until material begins to char; then add few ml HNO_3 cautiously at intervals until SO_3 fumes evolve and colorless or very pale yellow liq. is obtained (60–65 ml HNO_3 in all in ca 2 hr). Cool, add 50 ml H_2O and 1 Pyrex glass bead, and heat to SO_3 fumes; cool, add 25 ml H_2O, and filter thru 11 cm paper into 100 ml vol. flask; rinse out flask, cool, and dil. to vol.

Pipet 10 ml into 25 ml vol. flask, add 1 ml $NH_2OH \cdot HCl$ soln, rotate flask, and let stand few min. Add 9.5 ml $2M$ NaOAc soln, (g), and 1 ml o-phenanthroline soln, dil. to vol., and mix. Let stand at least 5 min and read in photometer or other instrument of equiv. precision.

With self-rising flour, the 9.5 ml $2M$ NaOAc soln, (g), may be reduced to 8.0 ml. To det. exact amt of buffer soln, (g), needed to adjust each digest to most desirable pH range, mix 10 ml aliquot of sample with measured amt of buffer soln, (g), dil. with H_2O to 25 ml, and det. pH either electrometrically or colorimetrically.

For colorimetric detn, add 5 drops bromophenol blue indicator, **6.018**(f), to soln and compare color with that of equal vol. of pH 3.5 buffer soln, (h), also treated with 5 drops indicator. Altho color develops from pH 2–9, avoid pH <3.0 and preferably work at pH 3.5–4.5. With cereal products, 9.5 ml buffer soln, (g), is satisfactory. With samples high in Fe, aliquot of 5 ml instead of 10 ml may be used with 4.8 ml buffer soln, (g). Conduct digestion so as to avoid contamination with Fe, and det. blank. After correction for blank, calc. as mg Fe/lb.

14.014 Calcium (*10*)—Official Final Action

(Applicable to enriched, enriched self-rising, and phosphated flours)

Ash 10 g flour or air-dried bread as in **14.006,** and proceed as in **14.013**(a) thru "rinse watch glass with H_2O . . .", then filter into 400 ml beaker; or transfer 50 ml soln from Fe detn to 400 ml beaker. Dil. to ca 150 ml.

Add 8–10 drops bromocresol green indicator, **45.009,** and enough *20% NaOAc soln* to change pH to 4.8–5.0 (blue). Cover with watch glass and heat to boiling. Ppt Ca slowly by adding *3% oxalic acid soln,* 1 drop every 3–5 sec, until pH is 4.4–4.6 (optimum for Ca oxalate pptn) as indicated by distinct green shade. (Avoid excess of oxalic acid indicated by yellow tints, showing undesirable displacement of pH.) Boil 1–2 min and let mixt. settle until clear or overnight. Filter supernatant thru quant. paper, gooch, or fritted glass filter (fine porosity), and wash beaker and ppt with ca 50 ml NH_4OH (1 + 50) in small portions, using wash bottle delivering very small stream. Break point of filter and wash filter or crucible with mixt. of 125 ml H_2O and 5 ml H_2SO_4 at 80–90°. Titr. at 70–90° with $0.05N$ $KMnO_4$ until slight pink is obtained, add filter paper, and continue titrn if necessary. Correct for blank and calc. Ca as mg/lb. 1 ml $0.05N$ $KMnO_4$ = 1 mg Ca.

Phosphorus (*11*)—Official Final Action

14.015 *Reagent*

(a) *Magnesium nitrate soln.*—Dissolve 8 g MgO in HNO_3 (1 + 1), avoiding excess acid; add little MgO in excess, boil, filter from excess MgO, Fe_2O_3, etc., and dil. to 100 ml.

(b) *Molybdate soln.*—See **2.029**(a).

14.016 *Determination*

(a) Transfer 1.00 g sample to ca 140 ml porcelain casserole, add 3 ml $Mg(NO_3)_2$ soln, and mix well, using small glass rod. Clean rod with small piece filter paper and place in casserole. Drive off most of moisture by drying in oven at 100° ca 2 hr, transfer to cold muffle, and ignite at 550° to white or gray ash (6–8 hr). Cool, cover with watch glass, take up with 10 ml HCl (1 + 4), and add 5 ml HCl. Rinse watch glass and evap. to dryness on steam bath. Add 5 ml HCl and 50 ml H_2O, heat 15 min on steam bath, filter into 100 ml vol. flask, cool, and dil. to vol. Pipet 50 ml into 300 ml erlenmeyer, neutze to litmus paper with NH_4OH, make just faintly acid with HNO_3, dil. to 75–100 ml, add ca 15 g NH_4NO_3, and proceed as in **2.031**(a), beginning "Add . . . enough acidified molybdate soln to insure complete pptn . . ." Or—

(b) Transfer 5.00 g sample to 35 ml porcelain evapg dish, mix well with 0.5 g Na_2CO_3, and ignite at 550° to gray ash. Cool, cover with watch glass, take up with 2 ml HCl (1 + 4), and add 5 ml HCl. Rinse watch glass, evap. to dryness, add 5 ml HCl and 10 ml H_2O, heat ca 10 min on steam bath, filter into 100 ml vol. flask, cool, and dil. to vol. Pipet 10 ml aliquot into 300 ml erlenmeyer and proceed as in (a), beginning "neutze to litmus paper with NH_4OH, . . ."

Report results as % P.

14.017 Total Carbon Dioxide in Self-Rising Flour (12)—Official Final Action

(Not applicable to flours contg added $CaCO_3$)

Use 17 g flour, 15–20 glass beads (4–6 mm diam.), and 45 ml H_2SO_4 (1 + 5). Proceed as in **8.002–8.004**, as far as calcn, except to agitate flask vigorously 3 min and let stand 10 min to attain equilibrium.

Calc. as follows: Subtract vol. acid used from total buret reading and correct for temp. and pressure. Divide corrected reading by 100 to obtain % CO_2 (by wt). Correct apparent % CO_2 to compensate for varying atm. conditions by immediately assaying synthetic sample of known composition and like ingredients by same method in same app. Divide wt CO_2 recovered from synthetic sample by wt CO_2 contained in $NaHCO_3$ used and record quotient. Apparent % total CO_2 in official sample ÷ this quotient = corrected % total CO_2 in sample.

14.018 Crude Fat or Ether Extract—Official Final Action

Proceed as in **7.048**; with fine flour, addn of equal wt clean, dry sand may be necessary.

14.019 Fat (Acid Hydrolysis Method) (13)—Official Final Action

(*Caution: See* **46.011(a)**, **46.054**, and **46.073**.)

Place 2 g sample in 50 ml beaker, add 2 ml alcohol, and stir to moisten all particles to prevent lumping on addn of acid. Add 10 ml HCl (25 + 11), mix well, set beaker in H_2O bath held at 70–80°, and stir at frequent intervals during 30–40 min. Add 10 ml alcohol and cool.

Transfer mixt. to Mojonnier fat-extn app. Rinse beaker into extn tube with 25 ml ether, added in 3 portions; stopper flask (with cork, Neoprene, or other synthetic rubber stopper not affected by solvs) and shake vigorously 1 min. Add 25 ml redistd pet ether (bp <60°) and again shake vigorously 1 min. Let stand until upper liq. is practically clear, or centrf. 20 min at ca 600 rpm.

Draw off as much as possible of ether-fat soln thru filter consisting of cotton pledget packed just firmly enough in funnel stem to let ether pass freely into weighed 125 ml beaker-flask contg porcelain chips or broken glass. Before weighing beaker-flask, dry it and similar flask as counterpoise in oven at 100°; then let stand in air to constant wt.

Re-ext liq. remaining in tube twice, each time with only 15 ml of each ether. Shake well on addn of each ether. Draw off clear ether solns thru filter into same flask as before and wash tip of spigot, funnel, and end of funnel stem with few ml of mixt. of the 2 ethers in equal vols free from suspended H_2O. Evap. ethers slowly on steam bath; then dry fat in oven at 100° to constant wt (ca 90 min). Remove flask and counterpoise from oven, let stand in air to constant wt (ca 30 min), and weigh. (Owing to size of flask and nature of material, there is less error by cooling in air than by cooling in desiccator.) Correct this wt by blank detn on reagents used. Report as % fat by acid hydrolysis.

14.020 Crude Fiber—Official Final Action—See 7.057

14.021 Fat Acidity (14)—Official Final Action—See 14.066

Hydrogen-Ion Concentration—Official Final Action

14.022 *Electrometric Method* (15)

Weigh 10.0 g sample into clean, dry erlenmeyer and add 100 ml recently boiled H_2O at 25°. Shake contents of flask until particles are evenly suspended and mixt. is free of lumps. Digest 30 min, shaking frequently. Let stand 10 min more, decant supernatant into the H-ion vessel, and immediately det. pH, using electrode and potentiometer stdzd by buffer solns of pH 4.01, **45.007**(c), and of pH 9.18, **45.007**(f), both at 25°.

Reducing and Non-Reducing Sugars (16)—Official Final Action

14.023 *Reagents*

(a) *Acetate buffer soln.*—Dil. 3 ml HOAc, 4.1 g anhyd. NaOAc, and 4.5 ml H_2SO_4 to 1 L with H_2O.

(b) *Sodium tungstate soln.*—12%. Dil. 12.0 g $Na_2WO_4.2H_2O$ to 100 ml with H_2O.

(c) *Alkaline ferricyanide soln.*—0.1N. 33.0 g pure dry $K_3Fe(CN)_6$ and 44.0 g Na_2CO_3/L.

(d) *Acetic acid-salts soln.*—Dil. 200 ml HOAc, 70 g KCl, and 40 g $ZnSO_4.7H_2O$ to 1 L with H_2O.

(e) *Soluble starch-potassium iodide soln.*—Add 2 g sol. starch to small amt cold H_2O and pour slowly into boiling H_2O with constant stirring. Cool thoroly (or resulting mixt. will be dark colored), add 50 g KI, and dil. to 100 ml with H_2O. Add 1 drop NaOH soln (1 + 1). Use 1 ml.

(f) *Thiosulfate std soln.*—0.1N. 24.82 g $Na_2S_2O_3$ .5H_2O and 3.8 g $Na_2B_4O_7.10H_2O$/L.

Make blank detn with each day's series of sugar detns to guard against changes in the $K_3Fe(CN)_6$ soln and correct for any reducing impurities in reagents as follows:

Combine 5 ml alcohol, 50.0 ml acid buffer soln, and 2 ml Na tungstate soln. To 5 ml of this mixt. (used in place of 5 ml flour ext) add 10.0 ml $K_3Fe(CN)_6$ soln and proceed as for reducing sugars. (10.0 ml $Na_2S_2O_3$ soln should discharge the blue starch-I color.) If titrn falls within 10±.05 ml do not discard reagents but correct in subsequent sugar calcns by using $Na_2S_2O_3$ equiv. of 10 ml $K_3Fe(CN)_6$ soln (*i.e.*, ml $Na_2S_2O_3$ soln required in above titrn) instead of 10.0 as basis for subtraction.

14.024 *Determination*

(a) *Preparation of extract.*—Place 5.675 g flour in 100 or 125 ml erlenmeyer. Tip flask so that all flour is at one side; then wet flour with 5 ml alcohol. Tip flask so that wet flour is at upper side and add 50.0 ml acetate buffer soln, keeping soln from coming in contact with flour until all is added to flask. Then shake flask to bring flour into suspension. Immediately add 2 ml Na tungstate soln and again mix thoroly. Filter at once (Whatman No. 4 or equiv.), discarding first 8–10 drops filtrate.

(b) *Reducing sugars.*—Pipet 5 ml flour ext into ca 75 ml test tube (Pyrex 1 × 8″). Add exactly 10 ml $K_3Fe(CN)_6$ soln to test tube, mix, and immerse test tube in vigorously boiling H_2O bath so that liq. in tube is 3–4 cm below surface of boiling H_2O.

After exactly 20 min in boiling H_2O bath, cool tube and contents under running H_2O, and pour at once into 100 or 125 ml erlenmeyer. Rinse test tube with 25 ml HOAc-salts soln, add to erlenmeyer, and mix thoroly. Then add 1 ml starch-KI soln. Titr. with $0.1N$ $Na_2S_2O_3$ soln until blue completely disappears (10 ml micro buret recommended). Subtract ml $0.1N$ $Na_2S_2O_3$ used in titrn from 10.00. In case of slight blank in $K_3Fe(CN)_6$-$Na_2S_2O_3$ titrn, correct by subtracting from $Na_2S_2O_3$ equiv. of $K_3Fe(CN)_6$ soln. This difference represents definite quantity of reducing sugar/10 g flour, calcd as maltose from table, **14.025**.

(c) *Nonreducing sugars.*—Pipet 5 ml flour ext into 8″ test tube and immerse in vigorously boiling H_2O bath. After boiling 15 min cool test tube and contents under running H_2O and add exactly 10 ml $K_3Fe(CN)_6$ soln. Proceed as in (b). $K_3Fe(CN)_6$ reduced after hydrolysis − $K_3Fe(CN)_6$ reduced by maltose in flour = nonreducing sugars calcd as sucrose and detd from table, **14.025**.

14.025   *0.1N Ferricyanide Maltose-Sucrose Conversion Table**

0.1N Ferricyanide Reduced	Maltose per 10 g Flour	Sucrose per 10 g Flour	0.1N Ferricyanide Reduced	Maltose per 10 g Flour	Sucrose per 10 g Flour
ml	mg	mg	ml	mg	mg
0.10	5	5	4.50	237	214
0.20	10	10	4.60	244	218
0.30	15	15	4.70	251	223
0.40	20	19	4.80	257	228
0.50	25	24	4.90	264	233
0.60	31	29	5.00	270	238
0.70	36	34	5.10	276	242
0.80	41	38	5.20	282	247
0.90	46	43	5.30	288	251
1.00	51	48	5.40	295	256
1.10	56	52	5.50	302	261
1.20	60	57	5.60	308	266
1.30	65	62	5.70	315	270
1.40	71	67	5.80	322	275
1.50	76	71	5.90	328	280
1.60	80	76	6.00	334	285
1.70	85	81	6.10	341	290
1.80	90	86	6.20	347	294
1.90	96	91	6.30	353	299
2.00	101	95	6.40	360	304
2.10	106	100	6.50	367	309
2.20	111	104	6.60	373	313
2.30	116	109	6.70	379	318
2.40	121	114	6.80	385	323
2.50	126	119	6.90	392	328
2.60	130	123	7.00	398	333
2.70	135	128	7.10	406	337
2.80	140	133	7.20	412	342
2.90	145	138	7.30	418	347
3.00	151	143	7.40	425	352
3.10	156	148	7.50	431	357
3.20	161	152	7.60	438	362
3.30	166	157	7.70	445	367
3.40	171	161	7.80	451	372
3.50	176	166	7.90	458	377
3.60	182	171	8.00	465	382
3.70	188	176	8.10	472	387
3.80	195	181	8.20	478	392
3.90	201	185	8.30	485	397
4.00	207	190	8.40	492	402
4.10	213	195	8.50	499	407
4.20	218	200	8.60	505	—
4.30	225	204	8.70	512	—
4.40	231	209	8.80	519	—

* These values are arbitrarily given for 10 g flour altho detn is made on only 0.5 g flour.

14.026 Total Protein—Official Final Action

Det N as in **2.051**, and multiply % N by 5.7 to obtain % protein. Use factor 5.7 to convert N to protein in wheat used either for manufacturing purposes or for human food.

14.027 Water-Soluble Protein-Nitrogen Precipitable by 40 Per Cent Alcohol (*17*)—Official Final Action

Weigh 20 g sample (20-mesh or finer) into 250 ml centrf. bottle. Pipet in 100 ml H_2O, shaking bottle to prevent lumping of sample. Add 100 ml more H_2O from pipet. Stopper bottle and shake 1 hr in shaking machine or by hand. (Preferably horizontal shaker with bottle lengthwise. If vertical wrist-type motion machine is used, shake by hand 5 min after the 1 hr shaking.) Temp. of H_2O should be $\leq 30°$. Centrf. at 1200 rpm ca 15 min and filter into 500 ml suction flask thru pad of fine asbestos on buchner (ca 2″ diam.), using suction. Det. N in 50 ml filtrate as in **2.051** with glass bead in each flask, distg NH_3 into 20 ml $0.1N$ acid. Digest 1 hr after clear. Correct for blank on reagents used in digestion.

Pipet 100 ml of above filtrate into 200 ml vol. flask, add 15 ml *NaCl soln* (28 g dild to 300 ml), fill nearly to mark with alcohol, mix well, cool to room temp., dil. to vol., mix, and let stand overnight. Pipet off supernatant and filter thru 18.5 cm fluted paper (S&S 588 or equiv.). Det. N in 100 ml filtrate as above, using glass bead to avoid bumping. Add H_2SO_4, mix, and carefully boil off alcohol before adding Na_2SO_4-HgO mixt. Rinse Na_2SO_4-HgO mixt. down neck of flask. Digest 1 hr after clear. (Watch for foaming before clearing and keep contents out of neck of flask.) Distill into 20 ml $0.1N$ acid as before. Correct for blank on reagents used in digestion. Subtract this number of ml acid used from number of ml acid used for H_2O-sol. N detn and convert to % H_2O-sol. N precipitable by 40% alcohol.

14.028 Lipids (*18*)—Official Final Action

(*Caution: See* **46.011, 46.054,** and **46.055.**)

Add 15 ml alcohol, 70% by vol., to 5 g sample (20-mesh or finer) in 250 ml centrf. bottle. Give bottle gentle rotary motion so as to moisten all particles, stopper firmly (to keep in place during heating), and set in H_2O bath kept at 75–80°. (Consider that temp. of bath may drop when bottles are introduced.) Heat 15 min, frequently mixing with same rotary motion. Immediately add 27 ml alcohol, stopper bottle, and *shake vigorously* 2 min. Cool, add 45 ml ether, and shake vigorously 5 min. (Sample should now be finely divided.) Centrf. at ca 1000 rpm few min and decant into 250 ml beaker contg some bits of broken porcelain or glass; rinse bottle neck with ether. Re-ext sample with three 20 ml portions ether, shaking ca 2 min each time, centrfg, and decanting into beaker contg first ext. Break up sample each time with glass stirring rod, rinsing with ether on removal.

Evap. combined ether-alcohol exts just to dryness on steam bath. Drive off any remaining moisture on sides of beaker by placing in oven 5 min at 100°. Dissolve dry ext in ca 15 ml $CHCl_3$ and filter soln into previously dried and weighed 100 ml Pt dish thru asbestos mat 3–4 mm thick, covered with ca 10 mm layer of sand in Knorr type extn tube (20 mm diam. $\times$ 11 cm long; stem 10 cm long). Wash sides of dish and tube with 10 ml and two 5 ml portions $CHCl_3$. Free with glass rod any solid ext adhering to dish to be sure all lipids dissolve. Finally wash tube and tip with 5 ml $CHCl_3$. Evap. $CHCl_3$ on steam bath and dry in oven at 100° to constant wt (ca 90 min). Weigh. Report ext as lipids.

14.029 Lipid Phosphorus (*18*)— Official Final Action

Wash sides of Pt dish with 10 ml $CHCl_3$ to dissolve lipids, **14.028**; likewise wash sides of dish with 10 ml *4% alc. KOH soln*. Cautiously evap. to dryness on steam bath and ash 1 hr at 500°. Cover dish with watch glass, add 15 ml HNO_3 (1 + 9) to make soln definitely acid, heat on steam bath ca 5 min, and filter into 300 ml erlenmeyer. Wash residue and filter with ca 25 ml hot H_2O. Make soln slightly alk. to litmus paper with NH_4OH from Mohr pipet and then slightly acid with HNO_3 (1 + 9). Keep vol. $<$ca 60 ml. Add 20 ml NH_4NO_3 soln, **22.035(b),** and heat in H_2O bath to 45–50°. Add 20 ml freshly prepd and filtered molybdate soln, **2.029(a)**, and proceed as in **22.036**, line 8, beginning "and let flasks remain in bath 30 min . . ." Det. blank and make correction.

14.030 Unsaponifiable Residue—Official Final Action—*See* **14.139**

Starch (*19*)—Official First Action

14.031   Reagent

Calcium chloride soln.—Dissolve 2 parts $CaCl_2$.$6H_2O$ in 1 part H_2O and adjust to density of 1.30 at 20° (soln contains ca 33% $CaCl_2$). Make faintly pink to phthln by adding $0.1N$ NaOH. (Anhyd. $CaCl_2$ may be used, but it is usually alk. and requires addn of acid to bring it to correct pH.)

14.032   Determination

Grind sample finely (100-mesh if possible) and weigh 2.0–2.5 g into 50 ml r-b centrf. tube with lip. Wash with ether to remove fat, then with 10 ml ca 65% by wt alcohol (d_{20} 0.88), and stir thoroly with glass rod. Centrf. (if no centrf. is available, wash samples on filter paper, using Pt cone and slight suction) and pour off soln. Repeat washing until 60 ml wash liq. has been used, stirring each time with same rod.

Stir residue with 10 ml H_2O and pour into 200–250 ml erlenmeyer. Complete transfer by washing with total of 60 ml $CaCl_2$ soln contg 2 ml 0.8% HOAc. Transfer rod to flask and bring mixt. to boiling quickly over wire gauze, stirring frequently. Boil briskly 15–17 min, taking precautions to prevent burning and foaming. Rub down particles on sides of flask with rod from time to time.

Cool soln quickly in running H_2O and pour into 100 ml vol. flask, rinsing thoroly with $CaCl_2$ soln from wash bottle with medium jet. In dilg to vol., add 1 drop alcohol, if necessary to destroy froth.

After thoroly mixing sample pour ca 10 ml soln onto fluted filter (Whatman No. 42 or 44), wetting paper completely. Let filter run dry and discard filtrate. Resume filtration, using dry receiver, and collect 40–50 ml. As filtering aids, use Celite with Pyrex glass filters and Hirsch-type funnel with asbestos and suction.

Polarize liq. in 10 cm tube, taking 2 sets of 10 readings each. (Av. of 2 sets should agree within 0.006°.)

$$\% \text{ starch} = \frac{100 \times R \times 100}{1 \times 200 \times W} = \frac{50 \times R}{W},$$

where R is observed angular rotation and W is wt sample; 200 is arbitrarily taken as specific rotation for all starches until better figure is detd for individual starches. If 200 mm tube and saccharimeter are used, 2 g sample weighed, and mixt. dild to 100 ml, °S $\times$ 4.3225 = % starch.

14.033 Vitamins in Enriched Flours— See Chap. 39

Chlorine in Fat of Flour

14.034 Qualitative Test (Chlorine-Bleached Flours)—Official Final Action

Ext 30 g flour with 50 ml pet ether and let solv. evap. (Small quantity of oil remains.) Heat piece of Cu wire in colorless gas flame until it is black and no longer colors flame green. Dip hot end of wire into oil and again bring into flame. If Cl or Br has been used as bleaching agent, green or blue coloration is produced.

Quantitative Method (20)— Official Final Action

14.035 Extraction of Fat
(*Caution: See* **46.011(a)** *and* **46.073.**)

Weigh 500 g flour into 2 L flask. Add 700 ml pet ether and shake at 5 min intervals 30 min. Filter thru buchner, pressing flour to obtain as much solv. as practicable. Transfer pet ether ext to large beaker and evap. on steam bath to ca 10 ml. Filter into container thru small funnel contg pledget of cotton packed firmly in stem. (Filtrate must be clear and free from flour.)

14.036 Determination

Heat ca 90 ml porcelain crucible contg 10 g *fusion mixt.* (138 g K_2CO_3, 106 g Na_2CO_3, and 75 g powd KNO_3) 30 min in 100° oven; dry in desiccator and weigh. Transfer filtered 10 ml pet ether ext to cruci-

ble, using pet ether for rinsing. Evap. pet ether on steam bath and dry fat in 100° oven 30 min. Cool, and det. wt fat by difference. Add 5 g more fusion mixt. to crucible and spread evenly. Ignite to white ash in muffle at 525° (ca 1 hr) and cool.

Add 25 ml hot H_2O to mixt. and transfer with small amt of hot H_2O to 200 ml tall beaker or beaker-flask. Add HNO_3 cautiously until soln is slightly acid to litmus paper. Add 25 ml more HNO_3. Add 5 ml $0.3N$ $AgNO_3$. Boil 5 min in hood and cool to room temp. Filter thru 9 cm Whatman No. 1 paper, or similar Cl-free paper. Use 1% HNO_3 soln for rinsing. Digest as in **3.072**, beginning "Place paper and contents in Kjeldahl flask . . ." After digestion use 175 ml H_2O. Det. blank on reagents. Report Cl as mg/g fat.

Nitrite Nitrogen (21)—Official Final Action

14.037 Reagents

(a) *Sulfanilic acid soln.*—Dissolve 0.5 g sulfanilic acid in 150 ml HOAc (1 + 4), warming slightly if necessary.

(b) *Alpha-naphthylamine hydrochloride soln.*—Dissolve, by heating, 0.2 g of the salt in 150 ml HOAc (1 + 4).

(c) *Nitrite std soln.*—Dissolve 0.1097 g dry $AgNO_2$ in ca 20 ml hot H_2O, add 0.10 g NaCl, shake until AgCl flocculates, and dil. to 1 L. Draw off 10 ml clear soln and dil. to 1 L; 1 ml = 0.0001 mg N. Prep. just before use.

Prep. $AgNO_2$ as follows: To cold soln of ca 2 g $NaNO_2$ or KNO_2 in 50 ml H_2O, add soln of $AgNO_3$ as long as ppt forms. Decant liq. and thoroly wash ppt with cold H_2O. Crystallize from boiling H_2O and dry crystals in dark at room temp. (preferably in vac.).

14.038 Determination

Select series of 100 ml vol. flasks of uniform dimensions and color (125 ml erlenmeyers can be used). Place 2 g untreated (nitrite-free) flour in each flask. To flasks add 0, 5, 10, 15, 20, 25, 30, and 35 ml std nitrite soln, resp., and dil. with H_2O to make 80 ml. Shake while adding std soln and H_2O to moisten and disperse flour before mixt. becomes too dil.

Add 2 g flour sample to similar flask, and add 80 ml H_2O. Place flasks in H_2O bath at 40° and digest at least 15 min. Add 2 ml sulfanilic acid soln from Mohr pipet to each flask in succession, mix well, and add 2 ml α-naphthylamine . HCl soln. Continue digestion at 40° for 20 min from time of addn to last flask. Shake samples occasionally during first 10 min and let flour settle during last 10 min.

Remove from bath without disturbing settled flour. Compare unknown with series of stds and est. closest match. Multiply ml std nitrite soln in flask by 0.05 to obtain ppm N (*e.g.*, unknown may be between 30 and 35 ml, ca 32 ml; or 32 $\times$ 0.05 = 1.6 ppm N).

14.039 Benzoyl Peroxide Bleach (Benzoic Acid) (22)—Official Final Action

(Caution: See 46.018, 46.026, and 46.030.)

Place 50 g flour in (preferably) 500 ml g-s erlenmeyer, and add 30–40 glass beads (ca 6 mm diam.), 0.1 g *powd Fe*, and 100 ml ether. Let stand few min, shake with rotary motion, and slowly (preferably dropwise) add 2.5 ml HCl from Mohr pipet. Let stand ca 30 min, rinse down sides with small amt of ether, and let stand overnight. Shake well with rotary motion, let flour settle few min, and decant thru 100 mm buchner, fitted with paper moistened with ether, into 500 ml suction flask. Add 50 ml ether, shake, and let settle few min. Decant as before, repeat twice more, and after last addn, transfer whole contents to filter.

Transfer ether thru large funnel into 250 ml separator, add 20 ml *5% NaHCO₃ soln*, mix without too much vigorous shaking, and drain clear lower layer into 125 ml erlenmeyer. Repeat with one more 20 ml portion and two 10 ml portions NaHCO₃ soln. To this soln add 0.3 g *Nuchar W*, shake, and filter (11 cm S&S 589 white ribbon, or equiv.) into 200 ml erlenmeyer. Wash flask and filter with 20–25 ml H_2O, using fine stream from wash bottle. Add 2.0 ml H_2SO_4 (1 + 1) dropwise to avoid foaming out of flask and swirl contents gently to reduce foaming. (Soln should be definitely acid to litmus paper.)

Transfer to 125 ml separator, rinse flask with 12 ml ether, and add to separator. Shake gently, frequently releasing pressure. (During first extn with ether, it is preferable to release pressure after each shake to avoid possible loss.) Repeat with 2 more 12 ml ether extns. Rinse flask each time with ether. After each extn drain aq. soln into same 200 ml erlenmeyer and transfer ether to ca 50 ml Pyrex test tube (25 mm diam. × 150 mm long). Add 2 ml 10% NaOH soln, hold top of tube firmly against palm of hand, and shake vigorously. Insert piece of *Cu wire* (1 mm diam. × 200 mm) into tube, and evap. ether very slowly on steam bath. Remove wire, place tubes in beaker of boiling H_2O, and evap. nearly to dryness. Slowly add up to 0.5 ml *30% H_2O_2*, followed by another 0.5 ml as soon as foam permits. (Min. frothing is desirable to permit better contact for nitration.) Break crust or film that forms before complete dryness by tapping tube against hands as evapn proceeds. Continue evapn to absolute dryness. (Introduction of gentle air current into tube hastens evapn.)

From Mohr pipet, add 4 ml mixt. of H_2SO_4 and *fuming HNO_3* (1 + 1), taking care that it washes down sides of tube, and heat 20 min in gently boiling H_2O bath. Place slender glass rod in test tube, and occasionally rotate or rub rod against sides of tube to ensure contact with nitrating mixt. Immediately cool under tap to below room temp. and add 6 ml H_2O while keeping tube cool. Then *slowly* add 5 ml NH₄OH from Mohr pipet with continuous shaking

under tap to keep soln cool. Add 10 ml addnl NH₄OH, keeping soln cool. Add 2 ml *6% NH_2OH .HCl soln*, stir, and place in 65° H_2O bath 5–6 min, stirring occasionally. (Temp. of bath should be few degrees above, since cold tubes cause some decrease.) Cool to room temp. under tap, filter immediately thru folded paper into similar tube, and observe color of filtrate. Red or definite pink indicates presence of benzoic acid.

Transfer this soln (within 30 min) to 2″ glass cell and read in photometer, using No. 51 filter, or other equally precise instrument set at 510 nm. Prep. std curve by placing in test tubes 0.0, 0.4, 0.8, 1.0, and 1.2 mg *benzoic acid in acetone soln* (0.5 mg/ml). Add 2 ml 10% NaOH soln, shake to mix well, and proceed as in par. 3, beginning "place tubes in beaker of boiling H_2O, . . ." Report as ppm benzoic acid.

Bromates and Iodates in White and Whole Wheat Flour—Official Final Action

14.040 *Qualitative Test for Bromates and Iodates*

Cover bottom of white pan (ca 150 sq in.) with reagent prepd by mixing equal vols HCl (1 + 7) and *1% KI soln*. Distribute ca 4 g flour evenly over liq. by sifting thru No. 60 sieve. Alternatively, sift flour over surface of dry pan and spray mixed reagent onto flour from glass atomizer until all particles are wetted. Black specks or purple spots not observed previous to addn of the reagent indicate presence of bromate or iodate.

14.041 *Qualitative Test for Iodates*

(a) *Applicable to 10 ppm or more.*—Distribute ca 1 g flour evenly over bottom of petri dish and completely cover with freshly prepd mixt. of 1 vol. *1% KSCN* to 4 vols HCl (1 + 32). Break up any lumps with stirring rod and observe with dish on white surface. Interpret results as in **14.040**.

(b) *Applicable to 1 ppm or more.*—Proceed as in **14.040** but use acid-KSCN reagent, (a).

Quantitative Method for Bromates (23)
(Applicable in absence of iodates)

14.042   *Reagents*

(a) *Zinc sulfate soln.*—Dissolve 20 g $ZnSO_4.7H_2O$ in 800 ml H_2O and dil. to 1 L.

(b) *Sodium hydroxide std soln.*—0.4N. Dissolve 17 g NaOH in 1 L H_2O. Titr. soln against std acid and adjust to 0.4±0.01N.

(c) *Sodium hydroxide std soln.*—0.5N. Dissolve 21 g NaOH in 1 L H_2O. Titr. soln against std acid and adjust to 0.5±0.01N.

(d) *Dilute sulfuric acid.*—Approx. 4N. Add 112 ml H_2SO_4 to 800 ml H_2O. Cool, and dil. to 1 L.

(e) *Potassium iodide soln.*—Dissolve 25 g KI in 30 ml H_2O and dil. to 50 ml. Store in amber bottle in cool place. Discard soln showing yellow (free I).

(f) *Ammonium molybdate soln.*—Dissolve 3 g $(NH_4)_6Mo_7O_{24}.4H_2O$ in 80 ml H_2O and dil. to 100 ml.

(g) *Potassium bromate std solns.*—(1) *Stock soln.*— 5 mg/ml. Dissolve 5.000 g $KBrO_3$ (dried 1 hr at 110°) in ca 800 ml H_2O and dil. to 1 L. (2) *Working soln.*— 0.25 mg/ml. Dil. 25 ml stock soln to 500 ml.

(h) *Potassium iodate std solns.*—(1) *Stock soln.*— 0.0898N. Dissolve 3.204 g KIO_3 (dried 1 hr at 110°) in ca 800 ml H_2O and dil. to 1 L. (2) *Working soln.*— 0.00359N. Dil. 10 ml stock soln to 250 ml. Prep. fresh daily.

(i) *Sodium thiosulfate std solns.*—(1) *Stock soln.*— Dissolve 22.5 g $Na_2S_2O_3.5H_2O$ and 0.06 g anhyd. Na_2CO_3 in 800 ml H_2O, and dil. to 1 L. Dil. 10 ml to 250 ml. Transfer 5 ml dild soln to 200 ml erlenmeyer. Add 100 ml H_2O, 10 ml dil. H_2SO_4, and 1 ml KI soln. Add 5 ml freshly prepd starch soln, **2.129**(c), and titr. with 0.00359N KIO_3 from 10 ml buret graduated in 0.05 ml. Adjust stock $Na_2S_2O_3$ soln so that 10 to 250 diln is 0.00359N. Store stock soln in amber bottle in cool place.

(2) *Sodium thiosulfate working soln.*—0.00359N. Dil. 10 ml stock soln to 250 ml. Prep. fresh daily and check titer at least monthly. 1 ml = 0.1 mg $KBrO_3$.

14.043 *Determination*

Quant. transfer 200 ml $ZnSO_4$ soln to 600 or 800 ml beaker and stir with speed-controlled, motor-driven glass stirrer. (Enough agitation to disperse flour is provided by vortex ca 1.5″ deep which does not extend to bottom of beaker.) Transfer 50±0.1 g sample to stirred soln in 2–5 g portions. Continue stirring ca 5 min, or until all dry flour on surface is uniformly dispersed in liq. While stirring, add 50 ml 0.4N NaOH from pipet. Decrease speed of stirrer and stir ca 5 min. Filter or centrf., clarifying supernatant by filtration, if necessary (24 cm Whatman No. 12 folded paper, or equiv., is satisfactory).

Transfer 50 ml of this sample soln to 200 ml erlenmeyer. If smaller aliquot is taken, dil. to ca 50 ml with H_2O. Add 10 ml 4N H_2SO_4, 1 ml KI soln, 1 drop NH_4 molybdate soln, and 50 ml H_2O. While stirring, add 5–10 ml 0.00359N $Na_2S_2O_3$ (an excess). Add 5 ml freshly prepd starch soln, **2.129**(c), and titr. excess $Na_2S_2O_3$ with 0.00359N KIO_3. (Use 10 ml buret graduated in 0.05 ml for std solns. End point is best observed straight down.) As end point approaches, add KIO_3 soln slowly, 1 or 2 drops at time, swirling and viewing flask after placing it on white surface after each addn. Take first reddish or purple tinge as end point; then add several more drops to confirm. Add addnl 1 ml $Na_2S_2O_3$ soln, and again titr. to addnl end point. Average the 2 differences between amts of $Na_2S_2O_3$ soln added and KIO_3 used in titrns; ppm $KBrO_3$ = 10 × (ml 0.00359N $Na_2S_2O_3$ − ml 0.00359N KIO_3). Correct results by recovery factor detd as below.

14.044 *Recovery Factor*

Dil. known vol. (x ml), >3 ml but <10 ml, of std $KBrO_3$ soln to 250 ml. Using 50 ml aliquot, proceed as in second par. of detn. "Added bromate" in ppm = 10 × (ml 0.00359N $Na_2S_2O_3$ − ml 0.00359N KIO_3).

Suspend 50 g portions nonbromated flour in 2 sep. 200 ml portions $ZnSO_4$ soln by stirring as above. To 1 (blank) suspension, add 10 ml H_2O; to other (recovery) suspension, add x ml std $KBrO_3$ soln and (10 − x) ml H_2O. Continue as above except to add 40 ml 0.5N NaOH from pipet with continuous stirring. Use 5 ml std $Na_2S_2O_3$ for "blank" and 10 ml for "recovery." Deduct blank value, if any, from value of $KBrO_3$ found in "recovery" detn and multiply result by 10 to obtain ppm "recovered bromate."

Recovery factor = added bromate/recovered bromate.

14.045 Pigments in Flour (24)—
Official Final Action

Place 10 g flour in 125 ml g-s flask and from pipet add 50 ml *H_2O-satd n-butyl alcohol*. Stopper flask tightly, shake well 1 min, and let stand 15 min protected from sunlight. Reshake well and filter thru 12.5 cm folded paper (Eaton-Dikeman Co., Mt. Holly Springs, PA 17065, No. 192, or equiv.), collecting filtrate in 50 ml erlenmeyer or suitable container. Fill 1 cm cell with flour ext and duplicate cell with corresponding solv. Read A at 435.8 nm with spectrophtr. From av. of 3 readings calc. pigment as carotene in ppm from std curve, or in absence of std carotene, from following formula:

$C = 5.0 \times A/bK = 30.1 \times A$, where C = pigment as carotene in ppm; b = cell thickness (cm); and $K = 0.16632$ (a (mg/L) for carotene at 435.8 nm in H_2O-satd *n*-butyl alcohol in 1 cm cell).

Caution: Use strictly clean cells and filter thru paper the H_2O-satd *n*-butyl alcohol used as blank.

Diastatic Activity of Flour (25)—
Official Final Action

14.046 *Reagent*

Acetate buffer soln.—pH 4.6–4.8. Dil. 3 ml HOAc and 4.1 g *anhyd.* NaOAc to 1 L with H_2O.

14.047 *Determination*
(Total maltose after diastasis 1 hr)

Place 5 g flour and teaspoonful ignited *quartz sand* in 100 or 125 ml erlenmeyer, and mix by rotating flask. Add 46 ml acetate buffer soln, and again mix by rotating flask until all flour is suspended. Bring flask and all ingredients *individually* to 30° before mixing. Digest 1 hr at 30°, preferably in thermostat-controlled H_2O bath, rotating flask every 15 min. After 1 hr add 2 ml H_2SO_4 (3.58±0.05N, ca 1 + 9), and mix thoroly. Add 2 ml *12% $Na_2WO_4.2H_2O$ soln*, mix, and let stand 1–2 min. Filter thru paper (Whatman No. 4 or equiv.), discarding first 8 or 10 drops. Proceed as in **14.024(b)**.

These operations may be used with all ordinary flours whose values for mg maltose produced by 10 g flour in 1 hr seldom, if ever, exceed 350. For material giving higher values, such as products from malted or sprouted grain, use smaller portions of ext, *i.e.*, 1, 2, or 3 ml instead of 5 ml. In such cases, however, add enough H_2O to make up difference, and use appropriate factor to convert results into mg maltose/10 g flour. If material in test tubes is colorless instead of yellow after treatment in boiling H_2O bath and does not turn blue upon addn of KI, there is too much maltose to reduce all $K_3Fe(CN)_6$, and detn must be repeated with smaller amt of ext.

14.048   *Blank Determination*

Blank detn to indicate quantity of reducing sugar originally present in the flour—value for which presumably should be deducted from total maltose value after 1 hr diastasis—has been generally regarded as essential step in estn of flour diastatic activity. This operation ordinarily is unnecessary when dealing with flour milled from *sound* wheat, because quantity of reducing sugars originally present as such is so small and so nearly constant that it may be disregarded for all practical purposes. Blank detn may therefore be omitted in routine testing. It need be used only when there is occasion to doubt soundness of the wheat, or where there is known to have been appreciable amt of frosted, sprouted, heat-damaged, or otherwise unsound kernels in wheat from which flour was milled.

If blank detn is desired, proceed as in **14.024(a)**.

Proteolytic Activity of Flour and Malted Wheat Flour (26)—Official Final Action

(Applicable to slightly active materials such as patent flour or to dild exts of active proteolytic prepns)

14.049   *Reagents*

(a) *Buffer stock soln.*—pH 4.7. Dil. 120 ml HOAc and 164 g anhyd. NaOAc to 1 L with H_2O. Dil. with 20 vols H_2O before using.

(b) *Bacto-hemoglobin substrate.*—Obtainable from Difco Laboratories.

(c) *Trichloroacetic acid (TCA) soln.*—Dissolve 180 g trichloroacetic acid in 320 ml H_2O. (*Caution: See* **46.082.**)

14.050   *Determination*

(a) *Preparation of enzyme solns.*—For slightly active materials such as flour, weigh as much as 10 g directly into digestion flasks. For active enzyme prepns, prep. ext or suspension in dild buffer, **14.049** (a), immediately before digestion. (Quantity of ext or dilns thereof used in digestion mixt. may vary up to 2 ml; appropriate activation technics may be applied to enzyme exts.)

(b) *Digestion procedure.*—Weigh 2.50 g (H_2O-free basis) Bacto-hemoglobin into each of two 125 ml erlenmeyers, add ca 5 g or 1 teaspoon fine pumice and flour sample, (a), to each flask, and agitate mixt. by rotation until flour and substrate are intimately mixed. Then add, to each flask, 50 ml dild acetate buffer soln, previously warmed to $40\pm0.1°$ in thermostat-controlled bath, and agitate mixt. to suspend uniformly. Place tightly stoppered flasks in 40° bath and agitate either continuously or at 1 hr intervals.

Add 10 ml portion TCA soln, (c), to one flask after 15 min digestion and to second flask after 5.25 hr digestion. Shake each flask, using 25 vigorous horizontal movements, and keep flasks in bath at 40° exactly 30 min. Centrf. suspension 5 min at 1800 rpm and filter. (Some materials such as flour may remain turbid after final filtration; clear by boiling centrfd digestion mixt. few sec before final filtration. Replace liq. lost thru evapn by adding H_2O.) Pipet duplicate 10 ml aliquots directly into Kjeldahl flasks and det. sol. N.

Follow essentially same operations in detg enzyme activity of an ext. In place of solid material, use total of 2 ml ext or ext plus dild buffer soln. After zero time and 5 hr digestion periods, add 10 ml aliquot of TCA soln, (c), to each flask. Mix contents thoroly, keep in H_2O bath exactly 30 min, and filter without centrfg. Analyze 10 ml aliquots for sol. N.

(c) *Determination of soluble nitrogen.*—Proceed as in **2.051**. Use definite vol. H_2O (350 ml) to dil. cooled digest and add in such way as to wash down all TCA that has condensed in neck of flask during digestion. Also add NaOH soln, **2.049(f)** (1.5 times usual quantity), so as to rinse neck of flask. After distn, back-titr. unneutzd std acid with stdzd ca $0.07N$ NaOH.

(d) *Expression of proteolytic activity.*—Proteolytic activity is measured by difference in back-titrn vols for 15 min or zero time digestions and corresponding long-time digestion, calcd as ml $0.0714N$ NaOH. Transform proteolytic activity detd for 10 ml aliquot to 3/2 power. Multiply this value by 6 (total final vol. of digest/10 ml aliquot) and by 1000/mg enzyme source. This value is activity expressed in hemoglobin units (HU)/g enzyme prepn (Arch. Biochem. **32**, 200(1951)).

(e) *Curve method.*—Use 3 to 5 levels of flour or dilns of active enzyme prepns, and digest and det. sol. N as in (b) and (c). Plot mg sample (for 60 ml final vols of digest) against ml $0.0714N$ NaOH titrn difference (= mg increase in sol. N) for the 10 ml aliquots. From smooth curve obtained, read mg sample equiv. to titrn difference of 5.00 ml. Raise 5.00 to 3/2 power (= 11.18). Multiply this value by 6 and by 1000/mg enzyme source to obtain activity as HU/g.

(f) *Std curve method.*—Use 5 dilns of active enzyme prepn to be used as std, and digest and det. sol. N as in (b) and (c). Plot curve and calc. HU/g as in (e) for this std sample. For each unknown sample, using single sample size, digest and det. sol. N as in

(b) and (c). From std curve det. mg std sample to give titrn difference found for unknown sample. Multiply proteolytic value HU/g for std by ratio obtained by dividing wt std sample by wt unknown sample. Result is activity of unknown as HU/g.

Notes: (1) Careful washing down of TCA from neck of digestion flasks is mandatory. If not neutzd, TCA steam distills.

(2) More reproducible results will be obtained if Kjeldahl detns are completed without delay between digestion and distn.

(3) If other than 10 ml aliquots are analyzed for sol. N, convert results to 10 ml aliquot basis before transforming to 3/2 power. If titrn difference, using 10 ml aliquot, is >10 ml $0.0714N$ NaOH, reanalyze, using smaller quantity of enzyme. For most precise results, titrn difference should be 4.0–6.0 ml $0.0714N$ NaOH.

(4) For each lot of hemoglobin, adjust pH of stock buffer, if necessary, so that pH of mixt. of 50 ml dild buffer, 2.5 g hemoglobin, and ca 5 g pumice will be 4.70 ± 0.05. This pH for buffer substrate mixt. is critical for accuracy of method.

(5) Accurate results are obtainable only when titrn difference for detn is close to 5.00 ml $0.0714N$ NaOH. For single point method, restricted range of titrn difference between 4.0 and 6.0 is recommended, but even within extremes of this range variations in sol. N for different wt enzyme samples will cause differences of several % in calcd HU/g values.

(6) Curve methods for detn of proteolytic activity have advantage of using exactly 5.00 ml titrn difference (5.00 mg increase in sol. N) as ideal ref. point. They permit working in range 3.0–8.0 ml titrn difference.

(7) Std curve method using std sample and unknowns each at 1 level is especially useful where routine assays on large no. of samples are required. Advantage of using std sample is that it affords automatic check on minor day-to-day variations in technic.

(8) It is convenient for routine analyses to use $0.0714N$ NaOH for back-titrn, since 1 ml titrn difference = 1 ml increase in sol. N.

Apparent Viscosity of Acidulated Flour-Water Suspension—Official Final Action

By MacMichael Viscosimeter (27)

14.051 *Adjustment of Machine*

(a) Use No. 30 MacMichael viscosimeter wire.

(b) Have diam. of disk plunger $2.375\pm0.01''$.

(c) Adjust clearance between bottom of disk and inner surface of bottom of bowl to $0.25\pm0.005''$. Carefully check clearance with depth gage reading in $0.001''$.

(d) Use viscosimeter bowl with ca 7 cm diam. (depth of bowl will vary according to age of machine).

(e) Adjust regulating device to permit speed of exactly 12 rpm and check carefully and frequently with stop-watch, because as motor warms up machine tends to increase its speed.

(f) Adjust machine and keep it level, and when bob is placed see that it is riding freely and not touching sides of guide.

(g) Adjust dial so that when it comes to rest pointer is on zero mark.

14.052 *Preparation of Lactic Acid*

To concd lactic acid add ca proportion of H_2O to give slightly $>1N$ soln. Reflux this soln 3 hr, cool, and adjust to $1N$ by addg H_2O. Or proceed as follows: Use enough concd lactic acid to prep. soln ca $0.85N$ when stdzd with $0.1N$ NaOH. Transfer soln to erlenmeyer fitted with air condenser to prevent undue evapn of H_2O, and heat 24 hr at 80° (soln will have increased in strength to ca $1.18N$). Adjust to exactly $1N$ with H_2O.

14.053 *Preparation of Flour-Water Suspension*

In clean, dry, 500 ml erlenmeyer, place 20 g flour (15% moisture basis) and add 100 ml H_2O at 30°. Close with rubber stopper and shake vigorously 1 min. Place flask in constant temp. cabinet or H_2O bath 1 hr at 30°, shaking ca 10 times every 15 min. Remove flask, add 3 or 4 drops *capryl alcohol*, shake 10 times to remove any foam that may be present, and pour suspension into bowl of viscosimeter.

14.054 *Determination*

After pouring suspension into viscosimeter bowl, make sure bowl is flush on its supports. Start machine, but before placing bob or disk in place, stir soln with bob 25 times to ensure uniform suspension. Place wire of bob in holder and take reading after damping swing of dial by placing a finger on indicator pointer and then gradually touching swinging dial. Make second reading after adding 1 ml $1N$ lactic acid, and likewise third and following readings after adding 2 ml increments $1N$ lactic acid. Do not stop motor between readings. After or during addn of lactic acid, stir suspension 25 times by up-and-down motion of bob. Suspend bob by the wire and take reading. Det. max. apparent viscosity of the acidulated flour-H_2O suspension by plotting apparent viscosity readings against vol. acid added. Usually total of 7 ml $1N$ lactic acid is enough for max. reading, but 2 ml increments should be added continuously until apparent viscosity no longer increases.

Soybean Flour in Uncooked Cereal Products (28)

14.055 **Qualitative Test—Official First Action**

Place ca 0.5 g sample in small test tube contg strip of red litmus paper partly immersed in 5 ml *2% urea soln*. Mix, stopper tube, and heat 3 hr at 40°. If soybean flour is present in more than traces, litmus paper turns blue. (Bromothymol blue may also be used as indicator; it likewise turns blue if soybean flour is present.)

14.056 Uric Acid in Flour—Official First Action
See 40.141–40.145.

WHEAT, RYE, OATS, CORN, BUCKWHEAT, RICE, AND BARLEY AND THEIR PRODUCTS EXCEPT CEREAL ADJUNCTS (29)—OFFICIAL FINAL ACTION

14.057 *Preparation of Sample*

Grind sample to pass No. 20 sieve, or sieve having circular openings $\frac{1}{25}''$ (1 mm) diam., and mix thoroly.

14.058 Moisture—*See* 14.003

14.059 Ash—*See* 14.006

14.060 Crude Fiber—*See* 7.057

14.061 Iron in Degerminated, Bolted, Whole Corn Meal—*See* 14.013

14.062 Crude Fat or Ether Extract— *See* 7.048

14.063 Protein—*See* 2.051

(Protein = N $\times$ 6.25, except for wheat in which protein = N $\times$ 5.7)

Fat Acidity
Method I (14)

14.064 *Reagents*

(a) *Benzene-alcohol-phenolphthalein soln.*—To 1 L C_6H_6 add 1 L alcohol and 0.4 g phthln to form 0.02% soln.

(b) *Alcohol-phenolphthalein soln.*—To 1 L alcohol add 0.4 g phthln (0.04% soln).

(c) *Potassium hydroxide std soln.*—0.0178N, CO_2-free. 1 ml = 1 mg KOH.

14.065 *Apparatus*

(a) *Grain mill.*—Suitable for grinding small samples.

(b) *Fat extraction device.*—Soxhlet or other suitable type. (Double paper thimbles or Alundum RA-360 thimbles are suitable for extn.)

14.066 *Determination*

(*Caution: See* 46.009, 46.011(a), and 46.073.)

Obtain representative sample of ca 50 g grain (corn, 200 g) by hand quartering or by use of mech. sampling device. Preferably grind sample so that $\geq 90\%$ will pass No. 40 sieve (somewhat coarser grind will not materially affect results). If sample is too moist to grind readily, dry at temp. of ca 100° just long enough to remove excess moisture.

Ext 10±0.01 g ground sample with pet ether ca 16 hr in extractor. Start extn as soon as possible after grinding and never let ground sample remain overnight. Completely evap. solv. from ext on steam bath. Dissolve residue in extn flask with 50 ml

benzene-alcohol-phthln soln. Titr. dissolved ext with std KOH soln to distinct pink, or in case of yellow soln to orange-pink. If emulsion forms during titrn, dispel by adding second 50 ml portion of benzene-alcohol-phthln soln. End point should match color of soln made by adding 2.5 ml *0.01% KMnO₄ soln* to 50 ml $K_2Cr_2O_7$ *soln* of proper strength to match color of original soln being titrd. (Add 0.5% $K_2Cr_2O_7$ soln dropwise to 50 ml H_2O until color matches. Then add 2.5 ml 0.01% $KMnO_4$ soln.)

Make blank titrn on 50 ml benzene-alcohol-phthln soln and subtract this value from titrn value of sample. If addnl 50 ml portion benzene-alcohol-phthln soln was added, double blank titrn. Report fat acidity as mg KOH required to neutze free fatty acids from 100 g grain (dry basis). Fat acidity = 10 $\times$ (titrn − blank).

14.067 *Method II. Rapid Method for Corn*
(Results may be obtained in <1 hr)

Prep. sample as in **14.066**. Weigh 20±0.01 g into 100 ml g-s flask or bottle. Add exactly 50 ml benzene, insert stopper, shake few sec to sat. air in flask with benzene vapor, momentarily loosen stopper to release pressure, and replace stopper. Shake flask 30 min in mech. shaker, or periodically by hand 45 min. Tilt flask and let meal settle at an angle at least 3 min. Carefully decant as much liq. as possible into 15 cm folded paper inserted in 8 cm glass funnel, and cover funnel with cover glass to reduce evapn. Collect exactly 25 ml filtrate in 25 ml vol. flask. Transfer this filtrate to 250 ml Florence flask. Refill vol. flask to 25 ml mark with alcohol-phthln soln and transfer to flask contg benzene ext.

Using color std prepd as in **14.066**, titr. ext with std KOH soln to distinct pink in case of white corn, and to orange-pink for yellow corn. If emulsion forms during titrn, dispel by adding 25 ml each of benzene and of alcohol-phthln soln. Det. blank titrn on mixt. of 25 ml benzene and 25 ml alcohol-phthln soln. If addnl benzene and alcohol were added, double blank titrn. Report fat acidity as mg KOH required to neutze free fatty acids from 100 g corn (dry basis). Fat acidity = 10 $\times$ (titrn − blank), calcd on dry basis.

14.068 Vitamins in Enriched Grains— *See* Chap. 39

Starch (30)—Official First Action
(Applicable to grains, stock feeds, and cereals)

14.069 *Reagents*

(a) *80% Isopropanol-salt soln.*—Dissolve 10 g NaCl in ca 150 ml H_2O, add 800 ml isopropanol (NF or reagent grade) on basis of 100% purity, and dil. to 1 L at ca 20°.

(b) *Acetate buffer, 4M.*—Dissolve 330 g anhyd. NaOAc in 1 L H_2O, add 240 ml (or 251 g) HOAc, cool, and dil. to 2 L.

(c) *Acetate buffer, 0.4M.*—pH 4.7–4.8. Dil. 4M acetate buffer to 0.4M. Check pH with pH meter.

(d) *Enzyme prepn.*—Rhozyme-S, high potency conc., low reducing sugar content (Rohm and Haas Co.). Prep. daily required vol. of 2% aq. soln.

Note: 25 mg enzyme prepn, Factor 4 (manufacturer's activity factor based on maltose hydrolysis), yields 99% calcd glucose from 200 mg ash-free dry matter of NF Reference Potato Starch at pH 4.7 after 6 hr at 50°. Use 100 mg enzyme to hydrolyze ≤400 mg total available carbohydrate. Thus at least twice necessary quantity is used. This quantity will completely hydrolyze sucrose, maltose, lactose, and cellobiose, if present.

(e) *2-Octanol (capryl alcohol).*—Ketone-free, bp 178–180° (Eastman Kodak Co.).

(f) *Zinc sulfate soln.*—10% $ZnSO_4.7H_2O$.

(g) *Ferricyanide (FeCy) reagent.*—0.04N. Dissolve 100 g anhyd. Na_2CO_3 and 26.40 g anhyd. $K_3Fe(CN)_6$ in H_2O and dil. to 2 L at 20°. Protect from strong light during prepn. Store in bottle completely covered with heavy Al foil or black paint. Soln is stable indefinitely at 25° when protected from light; however, prep. fresh soln every 6 months. 5 ml FeCy soln with 5 ml H_2O, 1 ml KI soln, and 5 ml $ZnSO_4$-HOAc soln should yield I equiv. to 20.0 ml 0.01N thiosulfate.

(h) *Potassium iodide soln.*—20 g/100 ml. Protect from strong light; keep cold when not in use. Prep. fresh after 1–2 months.

(i) *Zinc sulfate-acetic acid soln.*—60 ml HOAc and 60 g $ZnSO_4.7H_2O$/L.

(j) *Sodium thiosulfate std solns.*—(1) Approx. 0.1N. Prep. and stdze as in **45.038–45.039**. Normality decreases rapidly during first week, but thereafter remains virtually constant, decreasing ca 0.0001N/ month under usual laboratory conditions. (2) *Working soln.*—Prep. daily from (1) exactly 0.01N soln. Protect 0.01N soln from heat and strong light.

(k) *Starch soln.*—Suspend 10 g sol. starch in cold H_2O. Add to ca 500 ml boiling H_2O, dil. to ca 1 L with boiling H_2O, and boil several min. Keep in refrigerator. Prep. fresh soln after 1–2 months. Decant supernatant soln as needed in titrns.

(l) *Glucose std solns.*—(1) *Stock soln.*—10 mg/ml. To 500 vol. flask transfer 5.0025 g (assume 99.95% purity) NBS Dextrose Std Sample No. 41, dried in vac. at 25–40°, add 5 ml 0.1N HCl, and dil. to vol. at 20°. Store in refrigerator. (2) *Working solns.*—0.5–5.0 mg glucose/5 or 10 ml. Dil. 1–10 ml aliquots stock soln to 100 or 200 ml.

14.070   *Apparatus*

(a) *Weighing funnels.*—Glass, 15 × 45 mm (similar to No. 30287, Van Waters and Rogers, Inc., PO Box 3200, San Francisco, CA 94119, or No. 12803, New York Laboratory Supply Co.).

(b) *J-Rods.*—Glass rods, 3 mm diam. and 300 mm long, bent and shaped at one end to fit round bottom of 25 mm diam. test tube.

(c) *Test tubes.*—Pyrex, 32 × 200 mm, calibrated at 50 and 75 ml for starch detn. Pyrex, thin-wall, 29 × 200 mm, for reducing sugars detn.

(d) *Water baths.*—Electrically heated, thermostatically controlled to ±1°, fitted with elec. stirrer, 14 × 24″ od.

(e) *Cooling bath.*—With running H_2O at ca 20°, 14 × 24 × 5″.

(f) *Beckman spectrophotometer.*—Model DU, DB, or B with Corex 1 cm square cuvets, or equiv.

14.071   *Extraction*

(Carry blanks thru entire detn.)

Transfer 250–1000 mg sample, contg ≤400 mg starch and sol. sugars, to test tube. Use weighing funnel for <500 mg samples, letting tared funnel and sample slide to bottom of tube. Add ca 500 mg NaCl. Pipet in 35 ml isopropanol (on basis of 100% purity). Insert J-rod, mix thoroly, and let stand ca 10 min, mixing frequently to ext lipids. Add H_2O to 50 ml, plus 1.5 ml to allow for vol. of weighing funnel. Let stand 60 min in H_2O bath at ca 20°, mixing frequently to assure soln of sol. carbohydrates. Add ca 200 mg Celite and continue extn 30 min (total of 90 min) at ca 20°, mixing frequently.

Decant thru 15 cm diam. Whatman No. 54 paper; let liq. drain completely from paper. Transfer remaining solids in tube, using 80% isopropanol–NaCl soln cooled to 15–20°. Save tube and J-rod. Wash paper and contents with small vols cooled isopropanol–NaCl soln, letting contents drain after each washing. Use ca 150 ml cooled isopropanol–NaCl soln for transfer and washings. Keep funnel covered thruout. Discard filtrate and washings.

With cool H_2O, transfer residue from paper to original test tube. (Quant. removal requires care and previous practice.) Remove last traces of sample by rubbing entire surface of paper several times with rubber policeman, followed by washing with fine jets of cool H_2O. Finally, wash entire surface and funnel. Vol. in test tube should be ≤75 ml. (At this point analysis may be delayed 24–48 hr without significant loss of enzymatic digestibility of starch.) Store in refrigerator.

14.072   *Enzymatic Hydrolysis*

Add 1–2 drops octanol; heat 60 min in H_2O bath at ≥90°, mixing frequently with J-rod, especially during first 10 min. (Residues of some samples, especially those which contain much starch, may "explode" and foam over when heated >90°.) Cool and, *without delay, perform enzymatic hydrolysis.* (Storage in refrigerator overnight or longer may significantly decrease yield of reducing sugar.) Add 5 ml 0.4M acetate buffer and 5 ml enzyme soln. Incubate 6 hr at 50°, mixing frequently, especially during first 10 min.

14.073   *Clarification*

Quant. transfer contents to 250 ml vol. flask. Add 10 ml $ZnSO_4$ soln, 2–3 drops phthln, and 1–2 drops octanol. While rotating flask, rapidly add $0.5N$ NaOH until $Zn(OH)_2$ begins to ppt, and carefully add alkali until contents are faint pink. Add $0.5N$ HCl drop by drop until colorless, and dil. to vol. Let stand ca 10 min, mixing frequently, and filter.

Store filtrate in refrigerator; analyze within 24 hr.

14.074　　Ferricyanide Reduction and Determination of Starch

(a) *Titrimetric method.*—Transfer 2, 3, 4, or 5 ml sample and reagent blank, from **14.073**, to bottom of 29×200 mm test tubes, covered with small beakers or, preferably, with large glass bulbs; add H_2O to *exactly* 5 ml. Add *exactly* 5 ml FeCy reagent, and mix immediately by gently rotating tube. Incubate *exactly* 30 min in H_2O bath at $80 \pm 1°$; cool rapidly in running H_2O bath at $20–25°$. (Greatest accuracy is obtained with vol. of sample soln contg 3–3.5 mg glucose and resulting in ca 50% reduction of FeCy. Accuracy in measurement of 5 ml FeCy reagent is important since errors are increased in detn of residual FeCy.)

If 5 ml sample soln contains <1 mg glucose, use 10 ml sample and blank soln, add 5 ml FeCy reagent, mix immediately, and proceed as before.

Add 1 ml KI soln and 5 ml $ZnSO_4$-HOAc soln, mixing by gentle rotation after each addn. To prevent I loss, cover tubes immediately and keep covered until titrn. Let stand ≥ 20 min, mixing contents twice. Titr. with $0.01N$ $Na_2S_2O_3$ until almost colorless, adding first few ml around sides of tube to prevent loss of I vapors. Add ca 0.5 ml starch soln; wash sides of tubes and continue titrn drop by drop until color is pure white.

(b) *Spectrophotometric method.*—To enzymatic digest, in 250 ml vol. flask, add 10 ml $ZnSO_4$ soln and $0.5N$ NaOH to ca pH 7.5. (Phthln interferes in detn. Det. vol. $0.5N$ NaOH required by titrg blank contg 5 ml $0.4M$ acetate buffer and 10 ml $ZnSO_4$ soln, using pH meter or titrg until red to phenol red and colorless to phthln.) Dil. to vol., mix, filter, and check pH. Transfer 2, 3, 4, 5, or 10 ml to 29×100 mm test tube and conduct ferricyanide reduction as in (a).

Dil. FeCy reaction mixt. to 250 ml, and det. % T at 418 nm, using 1 cm square Corex cuvets.

(c) *Standardization.*—Stdze detn, using 5 ml std glucose soln contg 1–5 mg glucose or 10 ml std soln contg 1–5 mg glucose. Use 5 ml FeCy reagent in all stdzns. Calc. av. mg glucose/ml FeCy reagent reduced of 4 detns.

(d) *Calculations.*—Calc. % reducing sugar, RS, expressed as glucose. Assume 97.5% recovery of RS, due to incomplete mobilization of starch from sample tissues, recovery from paper, hydrolysis to RS, and loss during pptn and filtration.

% Starch = $0.923 \times$ % RS.

14.075　Antioxidants

(Applicable to corn and rice breakfast cereals)
See **20.009–20.012**.

SOYBEAN FLOUR (31)—OFFICIAL FINAL ACTION

14.076　Moisture

Proceed as in **14.004**, except use 5 g sample and dry 2 hr.

14.077　Ash—See 7.010

14.078　Nitrogen—See 2.051

14.079　Crude Fiber—See 7.057

Petroleum Ether Extract or Oil

14.080　　Reagent

Petroleum ether.—Initial boiling temp., 35–38°; dry-flask end point, 52–60°; at least 95% distg <54°, and $\leq 60\%$ distg <40°; sp gr at 60°F, 0.630–0.660; evapn residue $\leq 0.002\%$ by wt.

14.081　　Determination

Accurately weigh duplicate samples of 2 g full-fat or 5 g low-fat soy flour and wrap each portion in 150 mm filter paper (S&S No. 597 or equiv.); rewrap in second paper or papers so as to prevent escape of sample, leaving top of second paper open like thimble. Place piece of absorbent cotton in top of thimble to distribute the dropping ether. Place 25 ml pet ether in 125 ml tared flask, and ext sample 5 hr in Butt type or similar extractor. (Ether should drop on center of thimble at rate of ≥ 150 drops/min, and vol. solv. should be kept ca constant.) Evap. solv. until no trace remains, cool sample to room temp., and weigh. As last traces of ether are sometimes difficult to detect by odor, heat 1 hr, or longer, to constant wt.

BREAD

14.082　Preparation of Sample—Official Final Action

(When total solids of original loaf are not desired)

(a) *All types of bread not containing fruit (32).*—Cut loaf, or ½ loaf, of bread into slices 2–3 mm thick. Spread slices on paper and let dry in warm room until sufficiently crisp and brittle to grind well in mill. Grind entire sample to pass No. 20 sieve, mix well, and keep in air-tight container.

(b) *Raisin bread.*—Proceed as in (a), except comminute by passing twice thru food chopper instead of grinder.

14.083　Total Solids in Entire Loaf of Bread—Official Final Action

(a) *All types of bread not containing fruit (32).*—Accurately weigh loaf of bread immediately upon receipt (X), using scales sensitive to at least 0.2 g. If impossible to weigh accurately at this time, seal sample in air-tight container and accurately weigh as soon thereafter as is practicable (X). Preserve sample in such manner that no loss of bread solids can occur whereby loss would be calcd as moisture.

Cut bread into slices 2–3 mm thick (½ loaf may be

used). Spread slices on paper, let dry in warm room (15–20 hr), and when apparently dry, break into fragments. If bread is not entirely crisp and brittle, let it dry longer—until it is in equilibrium with moisture of air—so that no moisture changes may occur during grinding. Quant. transfer air-dried bread to scale pan and accurately weigh (Y). Grind sample to pass No. 20 sieve, mix well, and keep in air-tight container. Det. % total solids (Z) of ground sample as in **14.003** or **14.004**. Calc. total solids (TS) of bread from formula:

$$TS = (100 \times Y \times Z/100)/X, \text{ or } Y \times Z/X,$$

where X = wt loaf (or ½ loaf) at time of receipt; Y = wt air-dried sliced bread; and Z = % total solids in prepd ground sample.

(**b**) *Raisin bread and bread containing raisins and fruit.*—Proceed as in (**a**), except comminute by passing twice thru food chopper instead of grinder and dry air-dried sample in uncovered dish ca 16 hr at 70° under pressure ≤ 50 mm Hg.

14.084   Total Solids of Air-Dried Ground Sample (*32*)—Official Final Action

Use 2 g prepd sample. **14.082,** and proceed as in **14.003** or **14.004**.

14.085   Fat and Fat Number (*33*)— Official Final Action

(*Caution: See* **46.011, 46.054,** and **46.073.**)

Slice one loaf of bread, and let dry overnight, or until dry enough to grind. Grind bread to ca size of openings on No. 20 sieve, mix, and transfer 50 g to 600 ml beaker. Add 100 ml H_2O and mix. Add 100 ml HCl, mix, cover, and heat on steam bath 1 hr, stirring well 6 or 7 times. Cool in cold H_2O bath ($\leq 15°$) and stir. Add 10 g Filter-Cel, or similar absorbent, stir, and mix completely. Prep. 90 mm buchner as follows:

Place two 9 cm S&S No. 590 (or equiv.) filter papers in funnel and apply suction. Mix 10 g Filter-Cel with 50 ml H_2O and rapidly pour mixt. into funnel. (This should make smooth, even layer of Filter-Cel over paper, without cracks or openings.) Immediately filter sample. Rinse beaker several times with ice-cold H_2O. Just before filtration is complete, wash sides of buchner with ca 100 ml ice-cold H_2O (or until clear filtrate comes thru). Up to this point do not let pad suck dry. Continue with suction until Filter-Cel pad seems dry. Transfer this mass, without paper, from buchner to original beaker. Break up mass with rod, dry (overnight) on steam bath, and then heat in oven at 100° ca 30 min to remove all moisture (material must be dry or fat results will be low). Break up any lumps.

Prep. large Knorr extn tube of ca 200 ml capacity (glass tubing 5 cm diam., 12 cm high from shoulder to top of tube). Pack tube with asbestos tamped tightly to form pad ca 1 cm thick. Insert stem of tube into 2-hole rubber stopper in filtering bell jar connected to suction thru 2-way stopcock. Place 500 ml

erlenmeyer within bell jar so that stem of tube passes thru neck of flask. To cool beaker and contents, add 100 ml ether-pet ether (1 + 1) and macerate 3–4 min against sides of beaker with medium-size, stiff metal spatula. Decant into extn tube. Suck dry. Add 80 ml mixed ethers to beaker. Work as before 2 min. Transfer contents of beaker to extn tube, suck dry, and tamp with flat-end stirring rod until all ether is removed. To material in tube add 80 ml mixed ethers used just previously to rinse out beaker, mix thoroly with stirring rod few min, let stand 1 min, then suck dry, and tamp material as before. Make 2 addnl extns, turning suction on and off carefully to avoid loss of sample in erlenmeyer. Transfer to 1 L beaker. Evap. on steam bath, completely transfer fat with small amts of pet ether to weighed 150 ml beaker, carefully evap. pet ether on steam bath, dry at 100° to constant wt (ca 30 min), cool, and weigh. Calc. % total fat on H_2O-free basis.

Weigh duplicate samples of $1 \pm .03$ g fat into 300 ml Florence flasks and add 4 ml glycerol-soda soln, **28.031**(b). Heat flask carefully over asbestos gauze until bubbles start to appear; then hold flask ca 1″ over the heated gauze until cloudiness or turbidity disappears and mixt. is perfectly clear. After mixt. first becomes clear, 30–60 sec addnl gentle heating insures complete saponification. Cool; add few pieces of previously ignited pumice stone, 138 ml CO_2-free H_2O, and 3 ml H_2SO_4 (1 + 4); and proceed as in **28.032,** using same app. Use 0.02N NaOH for titrn. Multiply ml 0.02N NaOH used by 1.1 and divide by wt fat used. Perform blank detn and make correction. Report number of ml 0.02N NaOH/g fat as "fat number."

Acetic and Propionic Acids (*34*)— Official Final Action

14.086   *Preparation of Sample*

(**a**) *Air-dried bread.*—Prep. sample as in **14.082– 14.083.**

(**b**) *Fresh bread.*—For analysis of fresh product, which may be difficult to air-dry without spoilage or loss of volatile acids, pass sample thru meat grinder equipped with ⅛″ hole plate, and divide finely by rubbing thru No. 8 sieve. Proceed with analysis promptly (24–48 hr) or preserve with $CHCl_3$ as follows:

To prepd bread in Mason jar filled to ¾ capacity, add washed $CHCl_3$ absorbed in ca 1 g cotton (ca 5 ml $CHCl_3$/pint container). Close jar tightly (selfsealing lids are recommended) and roll to mix contents thoroly. Store samples at ca 25° or refrigerate where higher temps occur.

14.087   *Reagents*

See **18.027.**

14.088   *Apparatus*

(**a**) *Distillation apparatus.*—Use steam distn app. **18.026**(a), or gas-fired steam generator.

(b) *Chromatographic tubes.*—Approx. 15 × 250 mm or ca 15 × 450 mm, constricted at lower end to ca 4 mm id.

(c) *Test tubes.*—Approx. 16 × 150 mm, g-s.

(d) *Eyedropper pipet.*—Approx. 180 mm long.

14.089   *Distillation*

Transfer 10 g air-dried bread or 15 g prepd fresh bread to 150 ml distg flask. Add 50 ml H_2O and 10 ml ca $1N$ H_2SO_4. Mix thoroly and add 10 ml *20% phosphotungstic acid soln.* Mix by swirling and add 40 g $MgSO_4.7H_2O$. Swirl again to partially dissolve salt. Mixt. should now be acid to *congo red paper;* if not, acidify with H_2SO_4 (1 + 1). Connect to condenser and steam generator, heat contents of distg flask to boiling, and distill 200 ml in 35–40 min. (Connect steam source just before heating bread solids suspension to prevent clogging of steam tube and to agitate bread solids.) Keep vol. in distg flask at ca 60–80 ml by means of small burner.

Transfer distillate to 400–600 ml beaker, add ca 10 ml *ca 0.01N formic acid,* make alk. to phthln with ca $1N$ NaOH, and evap. to ca 5 ml. Transfer to 25–30 ml g-s test tube, rinsing beaker with 3 portions H_2O. If insol. material adheres, add few drops of ca $1N$ H_2SO_4 with 1 rinse. Make alk. to phthln and evap. just to dryness by inserting tube in steam bath or in boiling H_2O. (Air current hastens evapn.) Det. acetic and propionic acids in evapd distillate by the sepn technic, **18.033**(d), after prepg, testing, and stdzg column as in **14.090**.

14.090   *Chromatographic Separation*

(a) *Preparation of partition column.*—See **18.032**. (Where amt of propionic acid approaches 20 mg in column and definite band is observed below propionic acid band, use long chromatgc tube (450 mm) and ca 10 g silicic acid. Then take twice amts of H_2O, indicator, and NH_4OH as used for 5 g silicic acid.)

(b) *Test of silicic acid for suitability and standardization of column.*—Prep. stock solns of formic, acetic, and propionic acids (reagent grade) by dilg 5 ml acid to 250 ml and stdze acetic and propionic acids by titrg 1.0 ml aliquots with $0.01N$ NaOH, using cresol red indicator, to pink persisting ca 45 sec.

Prep. following dil. stock solns from stock solns and boiled H_2O: Formic acid, 10 ml to 50 ml; acetic acid, 20 ml to 50 ml.

Prep. following trial mixts of formic acid and known amts of acetic and propionic acids:

Acids and Water	Mixture A; Stock Solns	Mixture B; Stock Solns	Mixture C
	ml	ml	
Formic	10	10	1 ml dil. stock soln
Acetic	10	10	1 ml dil. stock soln
Propionic	10	30	1 ml stock soln
Water	20	None	None
Total vol.	50	50	3 ml
Test aliquot	1	1	3 ml

(Above mixts cover range of acetic and propionic acids usually present when 15 g fresh bread preserved with propionate is used as initial sample.)

Pipet indicated test aliquots from mixts A and B and entire mixt. C into bottom of g-s test tubes (16 × 150 mm), neutze with ca $1N$ NaOH, using phthln, and add 1 drop excess.

Proceed with evapn, sepn, and titrn as in **18.033**(c) and (d). Calc. results for acetic and propionic acids to mg/100 g sample. Following factors are based on 15 g fresh bread or 10 g air-dried bread:

Fresh bread (mg/100 g):

Acetic acid   = 4.00 × ml $0.01N$ $Ba(OH)_2$
Propionic acid = 4.93 × ml $0.01N$ $Ba(OH)_2$

Air-dried bread (mg/100 g):

Acetic acid   = 6.00 × ml $0.01N$ $Ba(OH)_2$
Propionic acid = 7.40 × ml $0.01N$ $Ba(OH)_2$

(c) *Identification of acids.*—See also **18.034** and **14.093**. With trial mixts A, B, and C and with most breads to which propionate has been added, only 3 definite bands appear on column and they elute in this order: propionic, acetic, and formic acids. Method provides for addn of enough formic acid to supply definite following band to ensure that acetic acid is completely eluted. Amt of mobile solv. required to move each acid from top of column to point of emergence is function of concn of that acid. For amt of acetic acid normally present in bread, differences in threshold vol. are not critical. To identify propionic acid by threshold vol., however, it is necessary to check threshold vol. for the concn indicated by titrn. Sepn of mixts A, B, and C supply enough data for amt normally found. Threshold vols may be predicted for intervening concns by plotting concn against detd threshold vols.

Due to differences in propionic threshold vol., make change in mobile solv. from 1% butanol-$CHCl_3$ to 10% butanol-$CHCl_3$ at a constant vol. of 1% butanol-$CHCl_3$ rather than at propionic acid threshold, preferably when greater part of propionic acid has been eluted. Then acetic acid threshold vol. will not be affected by changes in propionic acid threshold vol.

Acids as sepd in butanol-$CHCl_3$ solns may be further identified by formation of mercurous acetate or mercurous propionate crystals (JAOAC **28**, 644 (1945)) or by paper chromatgy, **14.093**.

Identification of Volatile Acids by Paper Chromatography (35)—Official Final Action

(Also applicable to confirming identity of acids sepd by **18.030–18.034** and as qual. test for propionates in bread)

14.091   *Apparatus*

Chromatographic tank and accessories.—See **29.007**.

14.092   *Reagents*

(a) *Mobile solvent.*—Mix acetone, *tert*-butanol, *n*-butanol, and NH_4OH (2 + 1 + 1 + 1). Prep. fresh daily.

(b) *Chromogenic reagent.*—Add 200 mg each Me red and bromothymol blue to mixt. of 100 ml formalin and 400 ml alcohol. Adjust to pH 5.2 with 0.1N NaOH.

(c) *Acids std solns.*—Pipet 1 ml each acetic, propionic, butyric, and valeric acids into sep. 100 ml vol. flasks and dil. to vol. with H_2O to prep. stock solns. Pipet 1 ml each of these stock solns into sep. 25 ml beakers; pipet 1 ml each of the 4 stock solns into single 25 ml beaker to prep. known mixt. Neutze acids and mixt. with 0.1N NaOH, using cresol red indicator, **16.179(f)**, avoiding excess alkali. Evap. to ca 0.5 ml, or evap. just to dryness and take up in 0.5 ml H_2O.

14.093   *Technic*

Steam distill 20 g well-mixed sample as in **14.089**, collecting 200 ml distillate. Immediately neutze distillate, using cresol red, **16.179(f)**, and 0.1N NaOH. Evap. to 0.5 ml, or evap. just to dryness and then take up in 0.5 ml H_2O. (To save time, place distillate in large porcelain evapg dish, and evap. to 5–10 ml; transfer to 25 ml beaker and evap. to 0.5 ml.)

With hard pencil, rule starting line 1″ from bottom edge of 8 × 8″ Whatman No. 1 unwashed chromatgc paper. Spot seven 1 μl spots with 1 μl pipet on paper, 1″ apart, leaving 1″ margin, to permit 1 spot for each acid, 1 for mixt., and 2 for unknowns. Spot in following order: acetic, propionic, unknown, mixt. of 4, unknown, butyric, valeric. Let dry. Clip paper to glass rod and suspend in tank with 50 ml mobile solv. in trough. (Since mobile solv. is heavy liq., use 3 clips to fasten paper to glass rod to prevent sagging and to give more uniform solv. front. Do not sat. tank with mobile solv. before inserting paper.) Seal glass cover with cellophane or other suitable tape and let develop until solv. is ca 1″ from top of paper. Remove paper from tank, let air-dry, and spray on front side with chromogenic reagent. (Spraying should be uniform and rather heavy but not to extent that chromogenic reagent runs or drips.) Faint yellow spots indicate presence of acids; heavier blue spots are due to Na ion. To intensify acid spots, place paper in atm. of NH_3 fumes momentarily (e.g., by placing ca 50 ml NH_4OH in 2 L beaker, rolling paper, and exposing to fumes by placing each end in beaker momentarily); entire paper immediately turns green. Remove paper from NH_3 fumes. Acids gradually appear as red spots, and presence of specific acids in sample may be detd by comparing their R_f values with those of mixt. and individual acids.

Since color of acids is not stable, mark spots with pencil as soon as they are completely developed.

14.094 ★ **Citric Acid (36)—** ★
Official First Action

See **13.088**, 10th ed. (*Caution: See* **46.059**.)

14.095 Ash (37)—Official Final Action

Use 3–5 g prepd sample, **14.082**, and proceed as in **14.006** or **14.008**.

14.096 Chlorides in Ash—Official Final Action—*See* **14.129**

Iron—Official Final Action

14.097   *Preparation of Sample*

Slice bread, let air-dry until in equilibrium with air, and crush to ca 20-mesh size on wooden surface with wooden rolling pin. (Grinding may be done in mill if tests show no increase in Fe due to grinding of particular material under examination. In general, grinding in mills increases Fe content.)

Proceed as in **14.013**.

14.098 Calcium—Official Final Action—
See **14.014**

**Vitamins in Enriched Bread—
Official Final Action**

14.099   *Preparation of Sample*

Det. fresh wt of entire sample taken for drying, usually 6 loaves of 1 lb size or alternate slices from 6 loaves of 1.5 lb size. Slice unsliced bread into slices ca 1 oz each. Spread slices on coarse screens, elevated to provide good air circulation, and let air-dry until crisp enough for efficient grinding. (If riboflavin is also to be detd, drying should be done in absence of light.) Weigh air-dried bread and grind entire amt to pass No. 20 sieve. Mix well, and store in air-tight glass jars at ca 10°. Det. air-dry wt:fresh wt ratio for subsequent use in calcn of results to fresh basis.

Proceed as in **39.035–39.038, 39.039–39.042**, and **39.044–39.046**.

14.100 Protein—Official Final Action

Det. N as in **2.051**, using 2 g prepd air-dried ground sample, **14.082**. Multiply % N by factor 5.7 to obtain % protein.

**14.101 Fat (Acid Hydrolysis Method)—
Official Final Action**

See **14.019**.

**14.102 Sterols (As Cholesterol)—
Official Final Action**

Weigh 5 g air-dried, ground sample and proceed as in **14.141**.

14.103 Crude Fiber—Official Final Action
(For bread and other baked products
not contg fruit)

Proceed as in **7.057**.

14.104 Sugars—Official Final Action

See **7.058** and **7.059**.

Lactose (38)—Official First Action

14.105   *Apparatus*

(a) *Rack.*—Metal rack so constructed as to prevent agitation of tubes while in boiling H_2O bath.

(b) *Titration stirrer.*—For stirring soln during titrn; rod made from glass tubing, sealed and flared at lower end to form button-like foot, is convenient. Make side arm consisting of several layers adhesive tape attached near enough to top of tube to prevent breaking bottom of titrn tube.

14.106 *Reagents*

(a) *Yeast suspension.*—Wash 25 g fresh com. bakers' yeast with five 100 ml portions of H_2O or until last washings are clear. Centrf. and decant after each wash. Suspend in 100 ml H_2O and store 24 hr at 0–4° before use. Discard after 1 week.

(b) *Yeast nutrient soln.*—Dissolve 1.7 g Bacto peptone (Difco Laboratories), 0.50 g K_2HPO_4, and 0.33 g $MgSO_4.7H_2O$ in H_2O, and dil. to 100 ml with H_2O.

(c) *Protein precipitant.*—Dissolve 50 g Na tungstate and 6 g Na_2HPO_4 in 200 ml H_2O. Slowly add 220 ml $2N$ HCl, mix, and dil. to 500 ml with H_2O.

(d) *Somogyi reagent.*—Dissolve 12 g Rochelle salt, 20 g Na_2CO_3, and 25 g $NaHCO_3$ in ca 500 ml H_2O and pour into soln, with stirring, 6.5 g $CuSO_4.5H_2O$ dissolved in ca 100 ml H_2O; add soln of 10 g KI, 0.80 g KIO_3, and 18 g $K_2C_2O_4.H_2O$, and dil. to 1 L. (Only KIO_3 need be weighed accurately.) Let stand few days; then filter off any small amt of ppt.

(e) *Sodium thiosulfate soln.*—$0.005N$. Prep. daily by dilg $0.1N$ soln, **45.038–45.039.**

14.107 *Determination*

Weigh 10 g air-dried bread, add 5 g Filter-Cel, and mix well. Transfer mixt. to extn thimble (ca 30 × 77 mm), cover with cotton pad, place in Soxhlet extractor, add 150 ml alcohol-H_2O mixt. (126 ml alcohol + 61 ml H_2O), and ext overnight on hot plate set at medium heat. Transfer ext to 250 ml beaker (previously marked at 40 ml), evap. on steam bath with aid of weak air blast to ca 40 ml, and transfer to 100 ml vol. flask, rinsing well. Cool, dil. to vol., and mix well. Pipet 10 ml aliquot into 50 ml erlenmeyer; add 6 ml yeast suspension and 5 ml yeast nutrient soln. Prep. blank test, using 10 ml H_2O in place of bread ext. Stopper flask with 1-hole rubber stopper fitted with piece of 6 mm (not smaller) glass tubing ca 10 cm long. Shake at moderate rate 2.5 hr in constant temp. H_2O bath at 30°.

Transfer to 50 ml centrf. tube and centrf. ca 10 min at ca 1000 rpm. Decant supernatant into 50 ml vol. flask. Rinse erlenmeyer with 10 ml H_2O, decanting onto residue in centrf. tube. Mix residue and H_2O with glass rod. Centrf., and combine washing with previous supernatant in 50 ml vol. flask. Repeat washing, using 10 ml H_2O. Add, with shaking, 2.5 ml protein precipitant. Dil. to vol., mix well, and filter, discarding first few ml filtrate. (This is convenient stopping point; stopper flask for continuation next day.)

Pipet 5.0 ml clear filtrate into Pyrex test tube (22 × 175 mm) and neutze to phenol red end point with $0.5N$ NaOH. Add 5.0 ml Somogyi reagent, mix by rotary motion, and add 2 drops benzene. Cap tube with glass bulb and place in metal rack. Immerse rack contg tubes in vigorously boiling H_2O bath exactly 15 min. Cool, avoiding agitation, to ca 35° in H_2O bath. Add 2.5 ml $2N$ H_2SO_4, shake with rotary motion, let stand ca 1 or 2 min, and titr. excess I with $0.005N$ $Na_2S_2O_3$, adding 6 drops 1% starch indicator near end of titrn. (Titrns should be finished in 30 min.) From difference between titrn value of blank (H_2O, yeast suspension, and yeast nutrient) and that of sample, det. quantity of lactose present from std curve. This value in mg lactose represents amt in 100 mg air-dry bread or % lactose.

Prep. std curve, using 0–4.5 mg pure *lactose hydrate* (0, 0.2, 0.5, 1.0, 2.0, 3.0, 4.0, and 4.5 mg from portions of soln contg 1.0 mg/ml) in enough H_2O to make 5 ml. Add 5.0 ml Somogyi reagent, mix by rotary motion, and add 2 drops benzene. Proceed as above from "Cap tube . . ." Plot difference between titrn value for 0 mg lactose and that for each lactose soln against corresponding lactose concn in mg.

14.108   Hydrogen-Ion Concentration—Official Final Action—See 14.022

BAKED PRODUCTS

Mineral Oil (*39*)—Official First Action

(*Caution: See* **46.004, 46.011, 46.056,** and **46.073.**)

14.109 *Reagents and Apparatus*

(a) *Chromatographic tube.*—250 ml dispensing burets or tube 30 × 450 mm, with stopcock at lower constricted end.

(b) *Alumina.*—Adsorption, Brockmann I, basic, or equiv., 80–200 mesh, suitable for chromatgy, pH 9–11 in aq. slurry (Fisher Scientific Co. No. A-540, A-941, or equiv.).

14.110 *Preparation of Sample and Oil Separation*

Air- or oven-dry weighed sample at 50° on nonabsorbent surface until sufficiently crisp and brittle to crush and grind (do not char). Grind, mix thoroly, weigh, and store in air-tight container. Det. dry wt:fresh wt ratio for use in calcg results to fresh basis and detg sample wt to be used, calcd to fresh basis.

Weigh dried sample equiv. to 225 g, fresh basis, into large mortar. Add, with stirring, 50 ml HCl (1 + 1) until thoroly mixed and uniformly wet. Let stand ca 1 hr. Break up lumps with pestle or spatula, transfer to 800 ml beaker, add 450 ml $CHCl_3$, and heat on steam bath until $CHCl_3$ boils, stirring constantly. Transfer to large size high-speed blender, blend, and decant $CHCl_3$ thru buchner fitted with rapid paper, using suction. Repeat blending, decanting, and filtering with 2 addnl 300 ml portions $CHCl_3$. Dry combined $CHCl_3$ exts by passing thru 3″ Na_2SO_4 in 3 cm diam. column. If filter or Na_2SO_4

column becomes clogged, loosen surface enough to permit free flow. Wash Na_2SO_4 with ca 50 ml $CHCl_3$. Evap. combined $CHCl_3$ to small vol. on steam bath under dry air stream. Transfer quant. to weighed beaker, evap. remainder of solv., dry oil overnight in convection oven at 100°, and weigh.

14.111 *Preparation of Alumina Column*

Pack pledget of glass wool into constricted end of glass tube. Add, thru powder funnel, 175 g alumina, tapping tube to ensure uniform packing. Cover surface with disk cut from rapid paper of slightly smaller diam. than inside of tube. Pre-wash column with 200 ml pet ether. Just before last of pet ether settles into alumina, stop flow.

14.112 *Determination*

Accurately weigh 5 g warmed, well-mixed, extd oil into small beaker. Mix well with 5–10 ml pet ether. Pour carefully onto alumina column, open stopcock, and collect eluate at rate <5 ml/min. Close stopcock when ether-oil mixt. has settled to just above surface of alumina. Rinse sample beaker with two 5 ml portions pet ether, rinsing sides of column with each rinse. Open stopcock and let ether settle almost to surface of alumina. Fill column with pet ether. Continue adding pet ether to column until total of 400 ml collects. Evap. pet ether to small vol. on steam bath, using gentle stream of dry air to aid solv. removal. Stirring rod placed in flask will help prevent superheating and possible boiling over. Transfer quant. to small weighed beaker. Evap. to dryness on warm surface, using gentle stream of dry air. Dry in convection oven 1 hr at 100°. Calc. % by wt of this unsaponifiable oil to fresh basis of product.

Transfer ca 2 drops residue oil to face of NaCl or Irtran plate. Cover with another plate and prep. IR spectrum. Prep. similar curve, using USP mineral oil. If vol. of residue oil is too small to transfer to plate directly, transfer with aid of CS_2. Evap. solv. completely before covering plate with second plate. Peaks occur at 3.4, 6.82, and 7.25 μm.

Obtain refractive index on another drop or two of residue oil and compare with refractive index of USP mineral oil read at same temp.

BAKED PRODUCTS OTHER THAN BREAD (NOT CONTAINING FRUIT) (40)

14.113 Solids—Official Final Action—
See **14.083**

14.114 Ash—Official Final Action—
See **14.006**

14.115 Protein—Official Final Action—
See **14.100**

14.116 Fat—Official Final Action—*See* **14.019**

14.117 Sterols (As Cholesterol)— Official First Action

Weigh 5 g air-dried, ground sample and proceed as in **14.141**.

14.118 Crude Fiber—Official Final Action—
See **7.057**

14.119 Sugars—Official First Action—
See **7.058 and 7.059**

14.120 Hydrogen-Ion Concentration—Official Final Action—*See* **14.022**

14.121 Acetic and Propionic Acids in Cake (34)—Official Final Action

Proceed as in **14.089**, using 15 g sample prepd as for fresh bread or fresh bread preserved with $CHCl_3$.

FIG BARS AND RAISIN-FILLED CRACKERS (41)—OFFICIAL FINAL ACTION

14.122 Moisture

Place 25–30 g prepd sand and short stirring rod in dish ca 55 mm diam. and 40 mm deep, fitted with cover. Dry thoroly, cover dish, cool in desiccator, and weigh immediately. Remove cover, place 3–5 g prepd sample, **14.082**(b), in dish, and weigh accurately. Remove dish contg sand, stirring rod, and weighed sample from balance. Add 5–10 ml H_2O and mix with the sand. Heat carefully on H_2O bath, stirring at 2–3 min intervals, until excess H_2O is removed and contents of dish are consistency of heavy paste. Place uncovered dish in vac. oven and dry ca 16 hr at 70° under pressure ≤50 mm Hg. After drying, cover dish, transfer to desiccator, cool to room temp., and weigh immediately.

Notes: Quartz sand that passes No. 40 sieve but is retained on No. 60 sieve, has been digested with HCl, washed free of acid, and ignited, is recommended. Al dishes with fit-over covers are most convenient. Dish can be set in cover during heating on H_2O bath and during oven-drying period. After drying, cover can be easily and quickly refitted on dish as it is transferred to desiccator.

14.123 Fat
(*Caution: See* **46.011, 46.054,** and **46.073.**)

Accurately weigh ca 2 g well-mixed sample, prepd by grinding twice thru food chopper, and transfer to Mojonnier tube. Add 2 ml alcohol, warm to 60–70°, and shake gently until sample is thoroly disintegrated and mixed with alcohol. Add 10 ml HCl (25 + 11). Place tube in H_2O bath held at 70–80° and shake frequently until sample is thoroly digested (40–80 min).

If weighed sample cannot be transferred to tube directly, digest in 50 ml beaker. Transfer digested mixt. to tube as completely as possible by draining from lip of beaker down small stirring rod. Rinse beaker thoroly with 10 ml alcohol, transfer to tube, mix thoroly, and cool. Rinse beaker with portions of first 25 ml ether added for first extn. Repeat rinsing with portions of pet ether (bp <60°) as it is added for first extn. Rinse thoroly so that all fat is transferred to extn tube. (After digestion, all particles should be completely disintegrated, except hard seeds (in fig fillers) and strong fibers. Very small amt of fat may be retained by such particles after digestion, but in analysis of biscuits and crackers this loss will be within experimental error.)

When digesting in extn tube, add 10 ml alcohol to digested charge and cool. (Level of liq. should be in neck of Mojonnier tube just below pour-off level.) Add 25 ml ether, stopper flask with cork, Neoprene, or other synthetic rubber stopper not affected by solvs, and shake thoroly ca 1 min. Carefully release pressure so that none of solv. contg fat is lost. Wash adhering solv. and fat from stopper into extn tube with few ml pet ether. (Wash bottle producing fine jet is convenient.) Let mixt. stand few min; then add 25 ml pet ether (bp <60°), stopper tube tightly, and again shake thoroly ca 1 min. Carefully release pressure, remove stopper, and again wash adhering solv. and fat into tube with few ml of pet ether. Let mixt. stand until ether layer is clear (10–20 min), or centrf. 20 min at ca 600 rpm.

Pour off as much as possible of clear ether-fat soln thru small, fast filter by tilting tube gradually. (Plug of ether-extd cotton packed just firmly enough in stem of funnel to let ether pass freely makes excellent filter for these extns.) Catch ether-fat solns from extns in clean 250 ml beaker or flask. Re-ext digested sample remaining in tube 3 times more as for first extn. (Vol. of ether may be reduced to 15 or 20 ml for last 3 extns.) Wash mouth of tube each time after draining ether-fat soln, and filter this ether thru funnel into receptacle.

Evap. combined ethers from extns by fanning or suction. After ethers are practically off, heat ca 10 min on hot H_2O or steam bath to drive off most of alcohol and H_2O carried over with ethers. Transfer beaker to 100° oven, dry 1 hr, remove, and let cool. Redissolve dried fat in 15–20 ml mixt. of equal parts of ether and pet ether, and filter thru small fat-free paper into beaker or flask previously dried at 100°, cooled in desiccator, and weighed.

Wash all traces of fat from first receptacle, filter paper, and funnel into the tared beaker or flask with jet of pet ether from wash bottle. Evap. ethers from tared receptacle by fanning or suction and dry purified fat to constant wt in 100° oven (1–1.5 hr). Cool in desiccator and weigh as soon as room temp. is attained. Make blank detns on reagents.

Notes: Good quality rubber stoppers thoroly cleaned with alcohol are satisfactory for stoppering extn tubes. Remove stoppers from tubes after each shaking period and do not allow to remain in contact with solvs longer than necessary. Solv. may have some action on rubber. Very fine grain cork stoppers washed with alcohol and ether are also satisfactory

for stoppering extn tubes, provided leakage of solvs can be prevented during shaking.

If trouble is experienced in releasing pressure after shaking extn tube contg ethers, cool tube slightly by holding it under stream of cold H_2O before removing stopper.

Al beakers are very satisfactory for weighing purified fat; they are light in wt and cool to room temp. rapidly.

MACARONI, EGG NOODLES, AND SIMILAR PRODUCTS— OFFICIAL FINAL ACTION

14.124   Collection and Preparation of Sample (42)

Select from lot to be analyzed enough strips or pieces to assure representative sample, break these into small fragments with hands or in mill, and mix well. Grind 300–500 g in mill until all material passes thru No. 20 sieve. Keep ground sample in sealed container to prevent moisture changes.

Total Solids and Moisture

14.125   *Vacuum Oven Method (43)*

Use 2 g prepd sample, **14.124,** and proceed as in **14.003.**

14.126   *Air Oven Method*

Use 2 g prepd sample, **14.124,** and proceed as in **14.004.**

14.127   Ash

Use 3–5 g prepd sample, **14.124,** and proceed as in **14.006.**

14.128   Original Ash in Macaroni Products Containing Added Salt But Not Containing Added Eggs (44)

Proceed as in **14.006.** Dissolve ash in 25 ml HNO_3 (1 + 3), transfer to 150 ml beaker, dil. to 75 ml with H_2O, and boil 15 min, maintaining original vol. (necessary to convert all phosphate to ortho form). Det. P_2O_5 as in **2.031.** $P_2O_5 \times 2$ = NaCl-free ash.

14.129   Chlorides in Ash as Sodium Chloride (45)

Dissolve ash obtained in **14.127** in HNO_3 (1 + 9), filter, wash paper with hot H_2O, and det. Cl in combined filtrate and washings as in **3.068** or **3.070.** Calc. Cl to its equiv. of NaCl. (This NaCl value deducted from total ash gives only approx. NaCl-free ash.)

14.130   Iron—*See* 14.013

14.131   Vitamins in Enriched Macaroni and Noodle Products—*See* Chap. 39

14.132   Fat (Acid Hydrolysis Method) (46)

Place 2 g sample in Mojonnier extn tube, add 2 ml alcohol to prevent lumping on addn of acid, and shake to moisten all particles. Add 10 ml HCl

(25 + 11), mix well, set tube in H_2O bath held at 70–80°, and shake at frequent intervals during 30–40 min. Fill to within 1–2 ml of mark with alcohol and cool. Add 25 ml ether and shake mixt. well. Then add 25 ml pet ether (bp <60°) and mix well. Let stand until upper liq. is practically clear and proceed as in **14.019,** beginning "Draw off as much as possible . . ."

14.133   Crude Fiber—See 7.057

14.134   Protein (47)

Det. N as in **2.051,** using 1 g prepd sample, **14.124.** % protein = % N × 5.7.

14.135   Water-Soluble Protein-Nitrogen Precipitable by 40 Per Cent Alcohol—See 14.027

14.136   Hydrogen-Ion Concentration— See 14.022

14.137   Lipid and Lipid Phosphorus

Proceed as in **14.028** and **14.029.**

Unsaponifiable Residue (48)
14.138   *Reagents and Apparatus*

See **17.016** and **17.017.** (The concd KOH soln is not needed.)

14.139   *Determination*

Weigh 10 g sample, ground to pass No. 20 sieve, into 500 ml erlenmeyer and add, with shaking, 30 ml HCl (1 + 1). Heat on steam bath 30 min, shaking flask occasionally to break up any lumps. While cooling inclined flask under tap, carefully add, with shaking, 30 g KOH pellets at such rate that liq. may boil, but not so violently as to cause loss by spurting. Place flask on steam bath while still hot, cover with small watch glass, and heat 3 hr, swirling mixt. occasionally to carry down any material adhering to sides. Cool until just warm, add 30 ml alcohol and 50 ml H_2O, and mix well. Add 100 ml ether, vigorously swirl mixt. 1 min, and transfer to separator, washing flask with 50 ml and 25 ml portions ether. Wash flask with 50 ml KOH soln, pour washings into separator in slow stream while gently swirling liq., and continue gentle swirling 10–15 sec. Proceed as in **17.018,** beginning "Let liq. sep. (ca 10 min) . . ." but omitting first acid wash. If emulsion forms and does not break to give sharp interface in 10 min, pour 5 ml alcohol into separator and let stand until sharp interface appears.

Sterols (as Cholesterol)
14.140 ★ *Bromination Method (48)* ★

Det. sterols in unsaponifiable matter as in **17.021.** However, to unsaponifiable matter from egg-free products or from any product contg <0.23% unsaponifiable matter (as-is basis), add 10 mg cholesterol before applying cholesterol method and correct result accordingly. (For the added cholesterol use highest quality obtainable (mp ≥147°) and test its purity by carrying 20 mg thru detn.)

14.141   Digitonin Method (49)
(*Caution: See* **46.011(a)** and **46.054.**)

Weigh 5 g sample, ground to pass No. 20 or finer sieve, into 300 ml erlenmeyer and add, with shaking, 15 ml HCl (1 + 1) in such manner as to keep particles on sides at min. Heat on steam bath 30 min, shaking flask frequently to break up any lumps and ensure complete hydrolysis. While cooling inclined flask under tap, carefully add, with swirling, 15 g KOH pellets at such rate that liq. may boil, but not so violently as to cause loss by spurting. Cool, add 20 ml alcohol, rinsing down sides of flask, and heat on steam bath 45 min with air condenser, shaking frequently.

Add 25 ml H_2O, rinsing down sides of flask, mix well, and cool. Add 50 ml ether, vigorously swirl mixt. 1 min, and transfer to 500 ml separator. Wash flask with 25 and 10 ml portions ether and with 50 ml 1% KOH soln, pouring washings into separator in slow stream while gently swirling liq., and continue gentle swirling 10–15 sec. Let liq. sep. and slowly drain. soap soln into 250 ml separator, but do not drain any small amt of emulsion or of insol. matter at interface. Rinse down sides of 500 ml separator with 5 ml 1% KOH soln and drain this into smaller separator. Add 25 ml ether to smaller separator and shake vigorously ca 1 min. After liqs sep., discard lower layer. Add ether layer to soln in larger separator, rinsing 250 ml separator with 10 ml ether. Wash ether soln as before with 3 addnl 50 ml portions 1% KOH, still keeping any insol. matter or emulsion in separator. Wash ether soln twice by swirling with 50 ml H_2O. Finally drain as much of aq. layer as possible without loss of ether soln. Add porcelain chip to 300 ml erlenmeyer, transfer ether to flask, rinse separator with three 5 ml portions ether, and rinse stem of separator with ether. Add rinsings to flask and evap. ether on steam bath.

Dissolve residue in 5 ml acetone; filter, with suction if necessary, thru Knorr type extn tube contg medium porosity fritted glass disk (Ace Glass, Inc., No. 8571, porosity D, or equiv.), covered with few g washed and ignited sand, into 100 ml centrf. tube or test tube under bell jar. Wash flask and tube 3 times with 4 ml portions acetone, and rinse tube and stem with few ml acetone (total vol. ca 20 ml). Add 5 ml freshly prepd *digitonin soln in 80% alcohol* contg 40 mg digitonin. (Hasten soln of digitonin by warming to ca 40–50° under hot H_2O tap.) (Products contg >6% egg yolk solids or equiv. (moisture-free basis) require addnl digitonin soln or use of aliquot portion for pptn.) Rotate to mix. Place porcelain chip in the tube, suspend tube in steam bath with small amt of steam to avoid boiling or spattering, evap. nearly to dryness, add 50 ml hot H_2O (near boiling), and stir well with glass rod to disperse ppt and dissolve excess digitonin. Place tube in boiling H_2O bath and hold several min with frequent stirring. Cool to ca 60°, add 25 ml acetone, mix well by stirring, and cool to room temp. in beaker of cold H_2O.

When ppt has nearly all settled (ca 15 min), remove glass rod, rinsing off any adhering ppt with acetone. Decant into previously dried and weighed gooch (preferably 10 ml capacity) contg asbestos pad covered with ca 1 g washed and ignited sand. Using wash bottle, wash tube several times with few ml portions acetone to transfer all ppt. (*Caution:* avoid transfer of any particles of chips.) Finally rinse crucible with acetone to dissolve any fat-like material, rinse with 5 ml ether, dry 30 min at 100°, and weigh. Check wt after second 30 min of drying. Wt residue $\times$ 0.243 = wt sterol. Report as % sterol on moisture-free basis.

Fluorometric Method (50)— Official First Action
(*Caution:* See **46.008, 46.018, 46.022,** and **46.056.**)

14.142   *Apparatus*

(a) *Soxhlet extractor.*—Medium-size, with 250 ml flask and 33 × 94 mm thimble.

(b) *Spectrophotofluorometer.* — Aminco-Bowman, with Xe energy source and slit arrangement No. 3 (American Instrument Co.), or equiv. Filter instrument is not adequate. Instrument parameters: Xe lamp; meter multiplier, ca 0.003; sensitivity, ca 30; excitation wavelength, 546 nm; emission wavelength, 577 nm. Cells must be scrupulously clean on all 4 sides. Rinse exterior of cells with alcohol and dry with lint-free absorbent tissue before placing in instrument.

14.143   *Reagents*

(a) *Cholesterol std soln.*—Prep. soln contg 6.0 mg cholesterol/100 ml $CHCl_3$. Pipet duplicate 2 ml aliquots into 25 ml erlenmeyers and evap. to dryness on steam bath under gentle stream of air. Proceed as in **14.144,** beginning "Into each flask ..."

(b) *Chloroform-acetic anhydride soln.*—5 + 1, freshly prepd for each series of detns. Use Ac_2O from fresh or recently opened bottle.

14.144   *Determination*

Ext ca 5 g noodles, ground to pass No. 40 or finer sieve, in Soxhlet 4 hr with ca 120 ml vigorously boiling $CHCl_3$ and boiling chip. Wash ext into 100 ml vol. flask with $CHCl_3$, cool, dil. to vol., and mix.

Pipet duplicate 2 ml aliquots into 25 ml erlenmeyers and evap. to dryness on steam bath under gentle stream of air. Into each flask, pipet 10 ml $CHCl_3$-Ac_2O; swirl to mix; let stand 15 min; then add exactly 0.4 ml H_2SO_4. Stopper, mix, and let stand 40 min. (Solns should contain no turbidity due to H_2O.) Read within 1 hr from end of fluorescence development step.

Adjust fluorometer to ca 60% T with cholesterol std soln. Transfer ca 4 ml sample soln to clean 10 × 10 mm cell and read. Use 5 ml $CHCl_3$-Ac_2O and 0.2 ml H_2SO_4 as blank.

14.145   *Calculation*

% Cholesterol in sample = 100 ml $\times C \times (F_u/F_s) \times 100/W$, where C is concn of ref. std in mg/ml (0.060); F_u and F_s are, resp., av. fluorescence at 577 nm of sample duplicates and std duplicates, each corrected for blank; and W is wt sample in mg.

14.146   Extraction, Separation, and Identification of Coloring Matter* (51)

Place ca 500 g coarsely ground sample (depending on amt of color present) in 1 L erlenmeyer, add ca 700 ml 80% alcohol, and shake at intervals for 24 hr, or until no more color is extd. Place in refrigerator overnight to permit dissolved protein to ppt. Filter, and evap. filtrate to 100 ml. Add ca ¼ vol. *25%* $NaCl$ soln and slight excess of NH_4OH to filtrate; cool, and transfer to separator. Ext with equal vol. pet ether, bp <60°; sep. lower layer and repeat extns with addnl portions solv. until no more color is extd. Reserve lower layer, if colored, for further treatment; if colorless, discard.

Combine pet ether exts and wash with several small portions NH_4OH (1 + 50) to remove any material mech. adhering to solv. This ether soln contains fats; it also may contain oil-sol. synthetic dyes, which can be identified as in (a). If colored, immediately acidify alk. aq. soln, freed from fat and oil-sol. synthetic dyes, with HOAc and ext in 25 ml portions with two 50 ml portions ether. Solv., if colored, may contain turmeric, annatto, and trace of saffron, which may be identified as in (b).

If original aq. soln, freed from ether-sol. colors, is still colored and H_2O-sol. dyes are suspected, proceed as follows: Ext aq. soln with 50 ml portions *isoamyl alcohol* to remove balance of saffron, as well as common orange dyes and Martius yellow; to sep., proceed as in (c). Drain lower aq. layer, which, if colored, may contain naphthol yellow S, tartrazine, and sunset yellow. Ext these dyes with isoamyl alcohol after acidifying soln with HCl to ca 1N. Remove tartrazine from solv. with 0.25N HCl. Sunset yellow is also removed at this stage with slightly lower acid concn, and naphthol yellow S from nearly neut. soln. Proceed as in Chap. **34.**

(a) Ext original pet ether ext with two or three 10 ml portions of mixt. consisting of HCl and HOAc (1 + 5).

In presence of yellow OB or yellow AB, pink or red soln is obtained. Test small portion of this acid ext with few drops *40%* $SnCl_2$ *soln,* which in presence of these dyes causes either decoloration or decided fading. Dil. balance of acid ext with H_2O, make slightly

---

* See **34.021(b)** for corresponding color numbers.

alk., and ext color with pet ether. Wash solv. with two 5 ml portions H_2O to remove excess alkali. Proceed as in Chap. **34**. Remaining coloring matters in pet ether ext may be due to natural coloring matter of wheat or coloring matter of egg. Coloring principle of egg yolk, lutein, when heated with *alc.* $FeCl_3$, produces green soln. This test, however, is not specific for lutein; carotene and xanthophyll give similar reactions.

(b) Wash ether ext with 5 ml portions H_2O to remove excess acid. To remove annatto and traces of saffron, wash successively with 20 ml portions *5% $NaHCO_3$ soln.* Divide alk. soln into 2 portions. Heat one portion to 60° on steam bath, dye the color on unmordanted cotton, and compare spot tests with a std. Acidify remaining portion of the alk. annatto soln with HOAc and re-ext with ether. Divide ether ext into 2 small casseroles and evap. to dryness. Dissolve contents of one casserole in 10 ml NH_4OH (1 + 9) and impregnate on strip of cotton or filter paper. Orange-yellow to orange-red stain is obtained, depending on amt of dye present. Dry filter paper or cotton, add drop *40% $SnCl_2$ soln*, and again dry. In presence of annatto, purple stain is produced. Spot contents of other casserole with H_2SO_4 and HNO_3, which yield blue and greenish-blue colors, resp.

Transfer 2 portions (ca 10 ml each) of original ether ext, from which annatto has been removed, into test tubes and treat with equal vol. 10% NaOH soln and equal vol. HCl (1 + 1), resp. In presence of turmeric (curcuma), alk. soln is reddish brown; acid soln is red.

Turmeric can be further confirmed by its behavior with H_3BO_3. Test as follows: Shake portion of original ether ext with equal vol. 70% alcohol; add $\frac{1}{10}$ vol. HCl, mix, and divide soln equally into 2 test tubes. To one tube add few crystals H_3BO_3 and shake. Use other tube as control. In presence of turmeric, red soln is produced after short time.

(c) To sep. and identify saffron and the orange synthetic dyes, dil. isoamyl alcohol ext with 2 vols pet ether and ext the mixed dyes with several 10 ml portions H_2O. To small portion of this aq. ext. add $\frac{1}{10}$ vol. HOAc and few mg dry *Na hyposulfite* to reduce all the azo dyes. This treatment will not affect saffron, which can then be re-extd with isoamyl alcohol. After washing solv. repeatedly with small portions of H_2O (to remove decomposition products), evap. to dryness, and confirm presence of saffron by spot tests. Examine remainder of color soln as in Chap. **34**.

14.147 Rapid Method for Tartrazine (52)

Place 800 ml cold H_2O and 5 ml NH_4OH in 1 L erlenmeyer and add 200 g unground sample. Stopper flask and shake at intervals; 3–4 hr is usually enough time to disintegrate material. Use glass rod to dislodge material caking on bottom. Centrf. and decant clear supernatant into 1 L flask. Add soln of 50 g

$MgSO_4$.$7H_2O$ dissolved in 100 ml H_2O, 10 ml *12% silicotungstic acid soln*, and 10 ml HCl; shake well, and let stand 1 hr. (This treatment will ppt almost all protein.)

Centrf., decant clear soln into container, and examine as in Chap. **34**.

Carotenoids (53)
(Applicable only to detn of carotenoids added for coloring purposes)

14.148 *Reagents*

(a) *Alcoholic potassium hydroxide soln.*—Dissolve 10 g KOH in 100 ml alcohol by warming on steam bath.

(b) *Methanol.*—92%. 8 ml H_2O + 92 ml absolute MeOH.

(c) *Adsorption mixture.*—Mix equal portions by vol. of activated magnesia (Micron brand No. 2641, 2642, or Sea Sorb 43 (Fisher Scientific Co.) and diat. earth (Hyflo Super-Cel, Johns-Manville Products Corp.)

14.149 Preparation of Standard Curve

Dissolve 100 mg *natural mixt. of α- and β-carotene* in 5–6 ml CS_2, add 35–40 ml absolute alcohol, cool in refrigerator ca 1 hr to ensure max. crystn, and filter on *hard* paper. Dissolve carotene crystals in 5–6 ml CS_2, add 40 ml pet ether, refrigerate as before, filter on *hard* paper, and dry crystals in vac. desiccator 1 hr.

Accurately weigh 20 mg purified crystals and wash with 20 ml absolute ether into 1 L g-s vol. flask. Continue to wash with pet ether, and dil. to vol. by adding pet ether as soon as carotene dissolves completely. Designate as stock soln.

Prep. 8 concns by adding following quantities of stock soln to 250 ml vol. flasks: 1.25, 2.50, 3.75, 5.00, 6.25, 7.5, 8.75, and 10.00 ml. Dil. to vol. with pet ether. These dilns represent concns of 0.10, 0.20, 0.30, 0.40, 0.50, 0.60, 0.70, and 0.80 mg/L. Read solns at 436 nm in spectrophtr or in photometer. Obtain line of best fit for data by method of least squares. In applying this method, let x represent scale reading and y concn in mg/L; M_x is mean value of x and M_y is mean value of y. Substitute in following expressions for values of a and b to give equation $y = a + bx$

$$b = \frac{\Sigma xy - nM_xM_y}{\Sigma(x)^2 - n(M_x)^2} \quad \text{and} \quad a = M_y - bM_x.$$

Stdze on same day stock soln is prepd.

14.150 Preparation of Sample

Grind macaroni and noodles to as near flour fineness as possible in ordinary coffee-type mill. (Products contg egg give no difficulty, but plain macaroni products require several grindings.) Take care not to set mill too tight, as enough heat may be generated to damage pigments.

14.151   *Determination of Total*
Carotenoids and Carotene

Weigh 20 g flour, semolina, or macaroni, or 10 g
egg noodles, or 2 g egg yolk into 125 ml erlenmeyer.
Add 50 ml alc. KOH soln and boil on steam bath 30
min under reflux condenser. Occasionally rotate
flask but be as careful as possible to keep sample from
collecting on sides of flask. Remove flask and cool to
room temp. Filter thru buchner-type medium fritted
glass filter into 250 ml suction flask, using suction,
transferring most of material with few ml alcohol
from wash bottle. Turn off suction, rinse flask with
25 ml ether, pour rinsing onto glass filter, and stir
material with rod to let ether come in contact with
all portions. Filter, and repeat this operation twice.

Transfer filtrate to 250 ml g-s separator and rinse
with ca 25 ml ether, disregarding soapy material in
flask. Add 175 ml H_2O, carefully invert, and rotate
several times. When layers sep., remove lower aq.-
alcohol layer and ext this layer again with 25 ml
ether. Discard lower layer and add the ether to original ether soln. Wash ether by pouring 50 ml H_2O
thru it. After layers sep., withdraw aq. layer and discard. Add 50 ml pet ether to ether soln, and wash
with five 50 ml portions H_2O, carefully inverting and
rotating separator. Discard all aq. layers (slight
emulsions usually clear in few min but may be discarded, especially if there is no significant yellow
tinge).

Transfer ether-pet ether mixt. to 250 ml distn
flask, rinsing separator with pet ether; place flask in
beaker of H_2O at 45–50°. Stopper flask, connect side
arm with vac., and conc. to ca 5 ml to remove ether.
Filter thru Allihn type adsorption tube with coarse
fritted glass plate contg ca $\frac{1}{8}''$ layer anhyd. powd
Na_2SO_4, or thru 5.5–7.0 cm paper half filled with the
Na_2SO_4 (use small, long-stem funnel reaching thru
neck of flask) into 25 ml vol. flask. Dil. to vol. with
pet ether used to rinse distn flask and which has been
passed portionwise thru the filter contg Na_2SO_4, and
mix by inverting few times. Transfer to 1 cm absorption cell and read A at 436 nm in spectrophtr, making at least 3 readings. From av. reading calc. total
carotenoid pigment in ppm from std curve. If pure
carotene is not available for stdzn, multiply A by
64.2 for yolk, 13.05 for noodles, or 6.52 for semolina
and macaroni.

14.152   *Separation of Carotene from*
Xanthophylls

(a) *Carotene by phase separation.*—Quant. transfer
all soln from cell and vol. flask to 125 ml separator,
rinse with pet ether, and dil. to ca 100 ml. Add 15 ml
92% MeOH, shake moderately ca 2 min by hand or
10 min on mech. shaker, and let separator stand in
upright position ca 1 min until layers sep. Decant
lower layer contg xanthophyll and repeat extns 5
more times or until aq. MeOH layer is nearly colorless for semolina. (Eight extns are generally enough

for noodles but higher than normal egg content may
require 10 extns.) Examine final MeOH layer recovered in test tube over white background to be sure
soln is nearly colorless.

Wash pet ether with 25 ml H_2O, inverting separator several times; discard aq. layer and repeat
twice more. Filter pet ether thru Allihn type adsorption tube contg $\frac{1}{4}''$ layer of anhyd. powd Na_2SO_4,
or thru 9 cm paper half filled with the Na_2SO_4, into
250 ml distn flask, washing color from filter with pet
ether. Conc. to 5 ml by vac. as in **14.151** and transfer
to 10 ml vol. flask; dil. to vol., mix by inverting and read A in
spectrophtr as in **14.151**. Calc. carotene in ppm from
std curve. If pure carotene is not available for stdzn,
multiply A by 5.22 for noodles, or by 2.61 for
semolina.

(b) *Carotene by chromatographic separation.*—
Prep. column in adsorption tube ca 18 mm od $\times$ 240
mm with ca 5 cm tip inserted thru rubber stopper.
Loosely plug with small pad of cotton, place in 250
ml suction flask, and turn on suction. Add adsorption
mixt., **14.148**(c), thru funnel in small amts from
spatula to ht of ca 11 cm; pack column by pressing
down (*only once after all this mixt. has been added*)
with cork stopper, just fitting the tube, on end of rod.
Place 1–2 cm anhyd. powd Na_2SO_4 on top.

Quant. transfer all soln from cell and vol. flask to
250 ml distn flask, and conc. as in **14.151** to ca 5 ml,
continuously applying suction to flask. Transfer to
prepd column and rinse with four ca 5 ml portions
pet ether to remove all color. Finally rinse down
sides of tube with few ml pet ether. After few drops
have come thru column, change to another 250 ml
suction flask. When nearly all pet ether is down to
Na_2SO_4 layer, add 50 ml pet ether-acetone mixt.
(9 + 1) to wash thru carotene. When all this solv.
has passed thru Na_2SO_4, turn off suction. (Keep top
of column covered with solv. during entire operation.) Transfer carotene soln (which should be only
few ml) to 10 ml vol. flask, using very small portions
of pet ether, dil. to vol. with pet ether, and mix by
inverting. Read as in (a) and calc. in ppm. (These
solns should be read on same day as extn.)

SELECTED REFERENCES

(1) JAOAC **8**, 424, 664(1925); **9**, 39, 89, 423(1926).
(2) JAOAC **8**, 665(1925); **9**, 39, 89(1926); **34**, 278
(1951).
(3) JAOAC **8**, 665(1925); **9**, 40(1926).
(4) JAOAC **21**, 406(1938); **22**, 76, 548(1939).
(5) JAOAC **7**, 132(1923).
(6) JAOAC **19**, 85(1936); **20**, 69(1937); **22**, 522
(1939).
(7) JAOAC **19**, 82(1936); "Cereal Laboratory
Methods, A.A.C.C.," 1962.
(8) JAOAC **31**, 259(1948); **32**, 258(1949).
(9) JAOAC **27**, 86, 396(1944); **28**, 77(1945).
(10) JAOAC **27**, 403(1944); **28**, 77(1945).

(11) JAOAC **31**, 269(1948).

(12) JAOAC **15**, 588(1932); **20**, 365(1937); **21**, 398 (1938); **23**, 502(1940); **25**, 71(1942).

(13) JAOAC **6**, 508(1922); **9**, 41, 429(1926).

(14) JAOAC **22**, 526(1939); **23**, 493(1940); **24**, 587 (1941); **50**, 198(1967).

(15) JAOAC **26**, 109(1943); **27**, 87(1944); **28**, 66 (1945).

(16) JAOAC **22**, 535(1939); Cereal Chem. **14**, 603 (1937).

(17) JAOAC **7**, 84(1923); **12**, 40(1929); **14**, 500 (1931); **35**, 701(1952).

(18) JAOAC **7**, 91(1923); **9**, 40, 89(1926); **35**, 693 (1952); **36**, 760(1953).

(19) Z. Untersuch. Lebensm. **40**, 1(1920); Can. J. Res. **11**, 751(1934); JAOAC **24**, 113(1941); **27**, 87(1944).

(20) JAOAC **22**, 539(1939); **23**, 498(1940).

(21) JAOAC **34**, 275(1951).

(22) JAOAC **18**, 493(1935); **19**, 86(1936); **33**, 166 (1950); **34**, 269(1951); Analyst **78**, 467(1953).

(23) JAOAC **39**, 664(1956).

(24) JAOAC **33**, 165(1950).

(25) JAOAC, **15**, 572(1932); **16**, 497(1933); **17**, 397 (1934); **18**, 76(1935); **19**, 86(1936); Cereal Chem. **9**, 378(1932); Amer. Inst. Baking Bull. **8** (1932).

(26) JAOAC **30**, 659(1947); **32**, 261(1949); **43**, 560 (1960); **44**, 141(1961); **49**, 219(1966).

(27) JAOAC **18**, 76(1935); **20**, 69, 380(1937); **22**, 76(1939); Cereal Chem. **11**, 121, 299(1934); Nebraska Agr. Expt. Sta. Bull. **8** (1916).

(28) JAOAC **17**, 329(1934).

(29) JAOAC **23**, 513, 520, 526(1940); **25**, 645(1942).

(30) JAOAC **50**, 198, 944, 958(1967).

(31) JAOAC **32**, 267(1949); **33**, 169(1950); **37**, 76(1954).

(32) JAOAC **9**, 42(1926); **15**, 72(1932); **17**, 65(1934).

(33) JAOAC **18**, 574(1935); **19**, 86(1936); **32**, 260 (1949).

(34) JAOAC **33**, 677(1950); **34**, 284(1951); **36**, 76, 769(1953).

(35) JAOAC **48**, 622(1965).

(36) JAOAC **16**, 427(1933); **19**, 86(1936).

(37) JAOAC **9**, 42(1936).

(38) JAOAC **35**, 56, 697(1952).

(39) JAOAC **49**, 218, 820(1966).

(40) JAOAC **16**, 518(1933); **17**, 404(1934); **23**, 537 (1940); **35**, 687(1952).

(41) JAOAC **26**, 305(1943); **28**, 497(1945).

(42) JAOAC **9**, 43, 396(1926).

(43) JAOAC **9**, 397(1926).

(44) JAOAC **25**, 618(1942).

(45) JAOAC **23**, 480(1940).

(46) JAOAC **6**, 508(1923); **11**, 38(1928).

(47) JAOAC **9**, 43(1926).

(48) JAOAC **24**, 75, 143(1941); **25**, 83, 639(1942).

(49) JAOAC **37**, 92, 408(1954); **50**, 851(1967); **51**, 590(1968); **52**, 319(1969).

(50) JAOAC **51**, 1220(1968).

(51) JAOAC **6**, 12(1922); **8**, 109(1924); **15**, 367 (1932); **19**, 83(1936); USDA Bull. **448**.

(52) JAOAC **27**, 231(1944).

(53) JAOAC **21**, 339(1938); **34**, 68(1951).

15. Coffee and Tea*

GREEN COFFEE

15.001 Macroscopic Examination—Procedure

Macroscopic examination usually shows presence of excessive quantities of blank and blighted coffee beans, coffee hulls, stones, and other foreign matter. Sep. these by hand picking and det. quantity by wt.

15.002 Coloring Matters—Procedure

Vigorously shake 100 g or more of sample with cold H_2O or 70% alcohol. Strain thru coarse sieve and let settle. Identify sol. colors in soln and insol. pigments in sediments as in Chap. **34.**

15.003 Caffeine (1)—Official First Action

Grind sample to pass No. 40 sieve. Use coffee grinder or large high-speed blender, and keep sample cold with solid CO_2 during grinding to avoid pastiness. Proceed as in **15.021** or **15.022.**

Chlorogenic Acid (2)—Official First Action

15.004   *Reagents*

(a) *Basic lead acetate soln.*—Sp gr 1.25. Soln **31.173**(a) may be used, or prep. soln from dry powder or Horne's Dry Lead.

(b) *Chlorogenic acid.*—Prep. from green coffee as in JAOAC **40,** 350(1957). Available from K&K Laboratories, Cat. No. 2172. Mp after drying in vac. over efficient desiccant is 207–209°; *a* is ≥52.0.

15.005   *Preparation of Sample Solution*

Weigh 0.7 g ground sample, **15.003,** into 50 ml centrf. tube. Add 25 ml pet ether, mix thoroly, centrf., and decant supernatant. Repeat twice. Dry residue in gentle stream of air until odor can no longer be detected. Transfer to 750 ml erlenmeyer with small amt of H_2O. Add 400 ml boiling H_2O, reheat quickly to boiling, and continue to boil gently exactly 15 min; then cool quickly to room temp. under tap. During boiling, frequently swirl flask to keep coffee submerged in soln. Transfer to 500 ml vol. flask and dil. to vol. Filter thru retentive paper, discarding first 25–50 ml filtrate. If filtrate is more than faintly cloudy, refilter thru fine porosity fritted glass filter, using suction. Do not use filter aids.

15.006   *Determination*

Transfer 10 ml filtrate to 100 ml vol. flask and dil. to vol. with H_2O. Det. *A* at 324 nm against H_2O.

★ Methods so marked are surplus method. *See* "Definitions of Terms and Explanatory Notes," item (29).

Transfer 100 ml sample soln to 200 ml Pyrex vol. flask or Kohlrausch flask. Add 2 ml *satd KOAc* soln and 10 ml basic $Pb(OAc)_2$ soln with swirling. Place flask in boiling H_2O bath 5 min, swirling occasionally. Remove, cool under tap, and place in ice-H_2O bath. Stir mech. 1 hr, using glass rod with paddle-shaped blade at lower end reaching bottom of flask, with flask immersed in bath. Remove, wash down stirrer, warm to room temp., and dil. to vol. with H_2O. Filter thru fluted paper, discarding first 25–50 ml filtrate. Immediately det. *A* of soln at 324 nm. Clean cells carefully after each use of Pb-treated solns because $PbCO_3$ slowly accumulates on optical surfaces.

From std curve det. (1) apparent concn of chlorogenic acid in soln taken for *A* measurement without Pb treatment (C_0); (2) apparent concn in filtrate after Pb treatment (C_1). From latter value subtract 0.00045 mg/ml to correct for solubility of Pb chlorogenate.

Calc. corrected concn = $C_0 - [(C_1 - 0.00045)/5]$.

15.007   *Preparation of Standard Curve*

Weigh 40.0 mg dried chlorogenic acid, transfer to 500 ml vol. flask, dissolve, and dil. to vol. with H_2O. Prep. series of stds by transferring 5, 10, 15, and 20 ml aliquots to 100 ml vol. flasks and dilg to vol. Det. *A* at 324 nm of each soln against H_2O. Plot concn of chlorogenic acid in mg/ml against *A*.

ROASTED COFFEE

15.008 Macroscopic Examination—Procedure

Pick out and microscopically identify artificial coffee beans, apparent from their regular form, and roasted legumes and lumps of chicory in whole roasted coffee. For ground coffee, sprinkle some of sample on cold H_2O and stir lightly. Fragments of pure coffee float, if not overroasted, while fragments of chicory, legumes, cereals, etc., sink immediately, chicory coloring the H_2O decidedly brown. In all cases use microscopic examination to identify particles that sink.

15.009 Preparation of Sample—
Official First Action

Grind sample to pass thru No. 30 sieve and store in tightly stoppered bottle.

Loss on Drying (3)—Official Final Action

15.010   *Apparatus*

(a) *Aluminum dish.*—Diam. ca 70 mm, ht ca 30 mm; with close fitting cover.

(b) *Desiccator.—See* **14.002**(b).

(c) *Vacuum oven.—See* **14.002**(c).

15.011 *Determination*

Sample directly without grinding. Accurately weigh ca 5 g well-mixed sample in dish previously dried at 98–100°, cooled in desiccator, and weighed with cover soon after attaining room temp. Place in oven, lean cover against dish, and heat to constant wt (ca 5.5 hr) at 98–100° at pressure ≤25 mm Hg. During heating admit slow current of air (ca 2 bubbles/sec thru H_2SO_4) into oven. Carefully admit dry air into oven to bring to atm. pressure. Cover dish, transfer to desiccator, and weigh soon after room temp. is attained. Report % loss in wt.

15.012 Soluble Solids—Official Final Action

Place 4 g prepd sample, **15.009**, in 200 ml vol. flask. Add H_2O to mark, let infuse 8 hr, with occasional shaking, and let stand 16 hr longer without shaking. Filter, and evap. 50 ml filtrate to dryness in flat-bottom dish. Dry at 100°, cool, and weigh.

15.013 Ash—Official Final Action

Proceed as in **31.012** or **31.013**, using sample prepd as in **15.009**.

15.014 Soluble and Insoluble Ash— Official Final Action

Proceed as in **31.015**, using the ash obtained in **15.013**.

15.015 Alkalinity of Soluble Ash— Official Final Action

Proceed as in **31.016**, using the filtrate obtained in **15.014**.

15.016 Ash Insoluble in Acid— Official Final Action

Proceed as in **30.005**, using the ash obtained in **15.013** or H_2O-insol. ash obtained in **15.014**.

15.017 Soluble Phosphorus in Ash— Official Final Action

Proceed as in **2.031** or **8.027**, using soln obtained in **15.014**.

15.018 Insoluble Phosphorus in Ash— Official Final Action

Boil insol. ash, **15.014**, with 25 ml HCl (1 + 2), filter, wash thoroly with hot H_2O, and det. P_2O_5 in combined filtrate and washings as in **2.031** or **8.027**.

15.019 Chlorides—Official Final Action— See 3.067 and 3.068

Caffeine

15.020 ★ *Power-Chesnut Method (4)—* ★ *Official Final Action*

(Not applicable to coffee exts. *Caution: See* **46.011** and **46.056**.)

See **14.019**, 10th ed.

15.021 *Bailey-Andrew Method— Official Final Action*

Proceed as in **15.048**, using 10 g regular coffee or 5 g regular sol. coffee.

15.022 *Micro Bailey-Andrew Method (5)— Official Final Action*

Weigh 2 g regular coffee or 1 g regular instant coffee, add 5 g powd MgO, and transfer to weighed 500 ml erlenmeyer. Add ca 150–200 ml H_2O, heat to boiling, and boil 45 min, shaking occasionally. Add H_2O, when necessary, to prevent frothing (final wt of H_2O must be 100 g). Cool to room temp. Make mixt. to tare wt + 105 g + sample wt.

Filter directly into 50 ml graduate until exactly 50 ml soln (equiv. to ½ sample wt) is obtained. Transfer soln to 125 ml separator. Wash graduate with 2 ml H_2O and add washing to separator. Add 4 ml H_2SO_4 (1 + 9). Ext with five 10 ml portions $CHCl_3$, shaking vigorously 1 min for each extn. Let emulsion break; then drain $CHCl_3$ into 125 ml separator. Add 5 ml 1% KOH soln. Shake vigorously 1 min, let emulsion break, and drain $CHCl_3$ thru cotton plug into 100 ml Kjeldahl flask. Ext KOH soln with 5 ml $CHCl_3$ and add to Kjeldahl flask. To digestion flasks add 1.9±0.1 g K_2SO_4, 40±10 mg HgO, and 2.0±0.1 ml H_2SO_4. Add boiling chips and rinse down neck of flask with 3 ml $CHCl_3$. Place flask on digestion rack and proceed as in **42.016**. 1 ml 0.02N acid = 0.971 mg caffeine.

Chromatographic-Spectrophotometric Method (1)—Official Final Action

(Applicable to decaffeinated coffee)

15.023 *Preparation of Sample*

Place 1.0 g ground decaffeinated coffee, **15.003** or **15.009**, or 0.5 g decaffeinated sol. coffee in 100 ml beaker. Add 5 ml NH_4OH (1 + 2) and heat 2 min on steam bath. Add 6 g Celite 545 and mix thoroly.

15.024 *Preparation of Column*

(a) *Acid column.*—Place fine glass wool plug in base of 25 × 250 mm tube. Add 2 ml 4N H_2SO_4 to 2.0 g Celite 545 and mix well by kneading with spatula blade. Transfer to tube, using powder funnel, and tamp, using gentle pressure, to uniform mass. Place small glass wool wad above surface. Insert tip into 50 ml vol. flask.

(b) *Basic column.—Layer A.*—Mix 3 g Celite 545 and 2 ml 2N NaOH, and place in 25 × 250 mm tube over glass wool plug as in (a). *Layer B.*—Transfer sample plus Celite mixt. to tube directly over layer

A. Dry-wash beaker with ca 1 g dry Celite, transfer to tube, and tamp to uniform mass.

(Both acid Celite and basic Celite mixts may be prepd in large batches and used as needed. In this case, use 4.2 g acid mixt. and 5 g basic mixt./column.)

15.025   *Determination*

Mount basic column above acid column. Pass 150 ml H_2O-satd ether sequentially thru basic column to acid column and discard ether. Then pass 50 ml ether thru acid column and discard ether. Place 50 ml vol. flask under acid column. Pass 50 ml H_2O-satd $CHCl_3$ thru acid column, washing tip of basic column with first portion. Dil. contents of vol. flask to 50 ml with H_2O-satd $CHCl_3$, mix, and read *A* at 276 nm against $CHCl_3$ blank.

Prep. caffeine stds contg 0.25, 0.5, and 0.75 mg/50 ml in H_2O-satd $CHCl_3$. Establish *a* for stds for spectrophtr used, and check occasionally. Calc. caffeine in samples from *a* of stds.

15.026   Chlorogenic Acid (2)— Official First Action

(a) *Roasted coffee.*—Weigh 1 g ground sample, **15.009**, transfer to 750 ml erlenmeyer, and proceed as in **15.005**, beginning "Add 400 ml boiling H_2O, ... "

(b) *Instant coffee.*—Weigh 0.35 g sample, transfer to 500 ml vol. flask, dil. to vol., and proceed as in **15.006**.

15.027   Crude Fiber—Official Final Action

Proceed as in **7.057**, using sample prepd as in **15.009**.

15.028   Starch—Official Final Action

Ext 5 g prepd sample, **15.009**, on hardened filter with five 10 ml portions ether, and wash with small portions alcohol until total of 200 ml has passed thru. Transfer residue from paper to beaker with 50 ml H_2O and proceed as in **31.110**, beginning with third par.

15.029   Sugars (6)—Official Final Action

Weigh 10 g prepd sample, **15.009**, into 250 ml vol. flask, add 1 g powd NH_4NaHPO_4, and proceed as in **7.058** and **7.059**. Det. Cu in Cu_2O ppt either volumetrically, **31.042**, or electrolytically, **31.045**.

15.030   Petroleum Ether Extract— Official Final Action

(*Caution: See* **46.011**, **46.039**, and **46.073**.)

Dry 2 g prepd sample, **15.009**, at 100°, ext with pet ether (bp 30–60°) 16 hr, evap. solv., dry residue at 100°, cool, and weigh.

15.031   Total Acidity—Official Final Action

Treat 10 g prepd sample, **15.003** or **15.009**, in erlenmeyer with 75 ml 80% alcohol, stopper, and let stand 16 hr, shaking occasionally. Filter, transfer aliquot of filtrate (25 ml for green coffee, 10 ml for roasted coffee) to beaker, dil. to ca 100 ml with H_2O, and titr. with 0.1*N* alkali, using phthln. Express result as ml 0.1*N* alkali required to neutze acidity of 100 g sample.

15.032   Coating and Glazing Substances— Procedure

(*Caution: See* **46.011**, **46.039**, and **46.073**.)

(a) *Sugar and dextrin.*—To 100 g whole coffee in beaker, add exactly 300 ml H_2O, stir, and let stand 5 min, stirring frequently. Filter thru dry paper and carefully add dry $Pb(OAc)_2$ to filtrate until pptn is complete, avoiding excess reagent. Filter thru dry filter and remove Pb from filtrate by adding slight excess of dry, powd $K_2C_2O_4$. Filter thru dry filter and det. reducing sugars as invert sugar in 50 ml of the filtrate as in **31.039**.

Invert 75 ml aliquot filtrate as in **31.026(b)**. Cool, nearly neutze with NaOH soln (1 + 1), dil. to 100 ml, and det. reducing sugars as invert sugar in resulting soln as in **31.039**.

Measure 100 ml aliquot filtrate into 200 ml vol. flask, add 10 ml HCl (sp gr 1.125), and hydrolyze as in **8.017**. Cool, neutze with NaOH soln (1 + 1), dil. to vol., filter thru dry filter, and det. reducing sugars as invert sugar in 50 ml filtrate as in **31.039**.

Calc. reducing sugars in each instance to % by wt original coffee. Calc. sucrose from reducing sugars before and after inversion as in **31.032**, and calc. dextrin as follows: Subtract reducing sugars after inversion from reducing sugars after hydrolysis and multiply difference by factor 0.86.

In some instances presence of sucrose in H_2O ext may be verified by polarization. Presence of dextrin in H_2O ext may be verified by polarization as in **31.034**, and by erythrodextrin test, (b).

(b) *Erythrodextrin test for commercial glucose.*— To aq. ext, (a), prior to clarification with $Pb(OAc)_2$, add few ml I soln (1 g I, 3 g KI, 50 ml H_2O). In presence of com. glucose, soln turns red or violet, depth and character of color depending upon quality and nature of glucose used. If amt of glucose is very small, ppt dextrin that may be present by adding several vols alcohol. Let ppt settle (do not filter), decant liq., dissolve residue of dextrins in hot H_2O, cool, and apply I test. Neg. result does not prove absence of com. glucose, because some glucose, especially of high conversion, does not give reaction with I.

(c) *Egg albumen and gelatin.*—Add 500 ml H_2O to 100 g whole coffee and let stand 5 min, stirring frequently. Filter and treat sep. portions of filtrate with (*1*) *5% soln of tannic acid,* and (*2*) *Millon reagent,* **7.100(g)**. Boil third portion of filtrate. In presence of egg albumen more or less heavy ppt will form in each case.

As confirmatory test, treat aliquot of filtrate with excess tannic acid soln, add little NaCl if necessary to secure flocculation of ppt, filter, and without washing, insert paper and contents into Kjeldahl flask and det. N. By this method coffee not coated with albumen or gelatin yields <10 mg N/100 g sample.

(d) *Fats and waxes.*—Treat 100–200 g coffee beans 10 min with low-boiling pet ether, pour off pet ether, and repeat process. Filter combined ext, evap., and det. refractive index and saponification number of the residue as in **28.007** and **28.027.**

15.033 Chicory Infusion—Procedure

Cover 100–150 g whole coffee with H_2O, let soak 2–3 min, stirring frequently, and drain aq. washings thru coarse sieve. Wash coffee on sieve with ca 100 ml H_2O and centrf. combined washings. Decant clear liq. from sediment, drain sediment almost dry on filter paper, mount in chloral hydrate soln, **30.026**(b), and examine under microscope for chicory.

TEA

15.034 Preparation of Sample— Official Final Action

Grind sample to pass thru No. 30 sieve.

15.035 Moisture—Official Final Action— See 7.003

15.036 Water Extract (7)—Official Final Action

To 2 g ground sample in 500 ml vol. flask, add 200 ml hot H_2O and boil over low flame 1 hr, rotating occasionally. Close flask with rubber stopper thru which passes tube 30″ long for condenser. Boil very slowly so that no steam escapes from top of air condenser. Cool, dil. to vol., mix thoroly, and filter thru dry paper. Transfer 50 ml aliquot to weighed dish and evap. to dryness on steam bath. Place in oven, heat 1 hr at 100°, cool, and weigh.

15.037 Ash—Official Final Action— See 31.012 or 31.013

15.038 Soluble and Insoluble Ash— Official Final Action

Proceed as in **31.015**, using the ash obtained in **15.037.**

15.039 Alkalinity of Soluble Ash— Official Final Action

Proceed as in **31.016**, using the filtrate obtained in **15.038.**

15.040 Alkalinity of Insoluble Ash— Official Final Action

Proceed as in **31.017**, using insol. ash obtained in **15.038.**

15.041 Ash Insoluble in Acid— Official Final Action

Proceed as in **30.005**, using total ash obtained in **15.037**, or insol. residue obtain in **15.038.**

15.042 Soluble Phosphorus in Ash— Official Final Action

Proceed as in **2.031** or **8.027**, using soln of sol. ash obtained in **15.039.**

15.043 Insoluble Phosphorus in Ash— Official Final Action

Proceed as in **2.031** or **8.027**, using soln obtained in **15.040.**

15.044 Petroleum Ether Extract—Official Final Action—*See* 15.030

15.045 Protein—Official Final Action

Det. N as in **2.051.** Protein = (% total N − % N present as caffeine) × 6.25.

15.046 Crude Fiber—Official Final Action— *See* 7.057

Caffeine

15.047 ★ *Power-Chesnut Method (8)* ★ *Official Final Action—See* 15.020

15.048 *Modified Bailey-Andrew Method (9)— Official Final Action*

Weigh 5 g prepd sample, **15.034,** into weighed 1 L erlenmeyer. Add ca 500 ml H_2O, swirl, and heat to boiling. Add 10 g *heavy MgO.* Boil gently over low flame 2 hr with occasional shaking. Add H_2O to prevent frothing and to wash down sides of flask. Cool, and make to wt with H_2O (tare wt + 510 g + wt sample). Filter, collect 200 ml clear filtrate (equiv. to 0.4 sample wt), add 20 ml H_2SO_4 (1 + 9), and transfer to 500 ml separator. Shake 6 times with $CHCl_3$, using 25, 20, 15, 10, 10, and 10 ml portions. Treat combined exts with 5 ml 1% KOH soln; when liqs sep. completely, drain $CHCl_3$ layer into Kjeldahl flask. Wash alk. soln in separator with two 10 ml portions $CHCl_3$ and combine washings with remaining bulk of ext. Evap. or distill off the $CHCl_3$ to <25 ml, and proceed as in **2.051.** 1 ml $0.1N$ H_2SO_4 = 4.85 mg anhyd. caffeine.

Ultraviolet Spectrophotometric and Gas-Liquid Chromatographic Methods for "Instant Tea" (10)— Official Final Action
(First action for leaf tea)

15.049 Reagents

(a) *Caffeine std solns.*—(1) *Soln No. 1.*—500 μg/ml. Accurately weigh ca 100 mg caffeine, USP; dissolve and dil. to 200 ml with $CHCl_3$ in vol. flask. (2) *Soln No. 2.*—10 μg/ml. Pipet 20 ml *Soln No. 1* into 100 ml vol. flask and dil. to vol. with $CHCl_3$; dil. 10.0 ml of this soln to 100 ml with $CHCl_3$.

(b) *Pentobarbital internal std soln.*—2 mg/ml. Accurately weigh ca 200 g pentobarbital; dissolve and dil. to 100 ml with alcohol in vol. flask.

(c) *GLC working std soln.*—250 μg caffeine and 1 mg pentobarbital/ml. Pipet equal vols caffeine std *Soln No. 1* and pentobarbital internal std into g-s flask and mix thoroly. Prep. fresh daily.

15.050   *Apparatus*

(a) *Gas chromatograph.* — Barber-Colman Co. Model 10 or equiv. equipped with thermionic KCl detector. Use KCl disk prepd as follows: Place ca 0.9 g KCl, triple recrystd from H_2O, in die designed for IR spectrographic analysis (Beckman No. 195786 Model D-01, or equiv.). Insert ram, turning it in 1 direction as it is inserted. Place die in press, connect die to vac., and evacuate 1 min at ca 1 mm Hg. Continue vac., apply enough force to move needle to ca 2,000 lb, and hold 2 min. Then increase ram pressure to 20,000 lb and maintain 3 min under continued vac. Release vac. and pressure and disconnect die. Remove die from press and sep. body and base by gently pulling and twisting. Place body of die over press-out ring on hydraulic press and press out disk with gentle pressure. By hand, using gentle pressure, drill hole thru center of disk 3–4 mm in diam., or large enough to fit over tip of burner. Place disk horizontally and center vertically over top of burner *in contact* with flame. Alternatively, taper hole to smaller size and center disk on top of burner. Tapering may be done by drilling 2 concentric holes in disk as follows: Drill 1 hole, smaller in diam. than burner jet, completely thru disk; drill second hole, slightly larger than outside diam. of burner, half way thru center of disk so that when in position, half of disk is above jet. If necessary, use tripod or other support to hold disk in contact with flame.

Operating conditions for gas chromatograph.— Operate according to instructions of manufacturer. For Barber-Colman Co. Model 10, set column temp. at 190°, detector at 220°, and injector at 220°. Use N as carrier gas. Inject 5 μl GLC working std soln and record chromatogram. Adjust attenuation and sensitivity (ca 10×), if necessary, to bring peaks to ca half-scale deflection. Adjust flow rate of N so that caffeine is eluted in ca 7 min.

(b) *Gas chromatographic column.*—Glass, 6′ × 4 mm id packed with 10% DC-200 oil on 80–100 mesh Gas Chrom Q (Applied Science Laboratories, Inc., precoated, or equiv.). Condition column >24 hr at 250–260° (with N flow of 100±20 ml/min).

(c) *Syringe.*—10 μl (Hamilton Co. No. 701N, or equiv.).

(d) *Recording spectrophotometer.*—350–250 nm range with matched 1 cm cells.

(e) *Chromatographic tubes.*—(1) *For acid column.* —Glass, 25 × 50 mm. (2) *For basic column.*— 25 × 250 mm.

15.051   *Preparation of Sample*

(a) *Leaf tea.*—Grind sample in high-speed blender or other suitable device to pass No. 30 or 40 sieve. Accurately weigh ca 1 g tea into 100 ml beaker, add ca 40 ml NH_4OH (1 + 2), and heat 5 min on steam bath. Transfer quant. to 100 ml vol. flask, cool, and dil. to vol. with NH_4OH (1 + 2). Transfer 5.0 ml aliquot to 6 g Celite 545 (acid-washed) in 100 ml beaker and proceed as in **15.023**.

(b) *Instant tea.*—Place 0.5 g sample in 100 ml beaker and continue as in **15.023**.

15.052   *Preparation of Columns and Sample Solution*

Prep columns as in **15.024**(a) and (b). Isolate caffeine as in **15.025**, dil. to 50 ml, and proceed as in **15.053**.

15.053   *Spectrophotometric Determination*

Transfer 10.0 ml aliquot leaf tea sample soln to 50 ml vol. flask and dil. to vol. with $CHCl_3$. Transfer 10.0 ml aliquot instant tea sample soln to 100 ml vol. flask, dil. to vol. with $CHCl_3$, and further dil. 20.0 ml aliquot to 100 ml with $CHCl_3$. Det. *A* at 276 nm on recording spectrophotometer, using $CHCl_3$ as ref. Compare with *A* of std caffeine *Soln No. 2* (10 μg/ml). Calc.

$$\% \text{ caffeine} = (A/A') \times (C'/C) \times 100$$

where *A* and *A'* refer to sample and std, resp., and *C* and *C'* refer to sample and std concns, resp.

15.054   *Gas Chromatographic Determination*

Complete detn within 1 day. Pipet equals vols internal std pentobarbital soln and concd sample soln into g-s flask and mix (assay soln). Inject 5 μl working std soln and record chromatogram. Inject 5 μl assay soln and record chromatogram. Measure ht of each peak. Let P_s = ht of std peak of GLC working std soln; P_u = ht of sample peak of assay soln; I_s = ht of internal std peak of std; I_u = ht of internal std peak of assay soln; C_s = mg caffeine/ml in GLC working std soln; C_u = mg sample/ml.

$$\% \text{ Caffeine in sample} = (P_u \times I_s \times C_s \times 100)/(P_s \times I_u \times C_u).$$

Tannin (11)—Official Final Action
15.055   *Reagents*

(a) *Potassium permanganate soln.*—Prep. soln contg 1.33 g/L and obtain its equiv. of 0.1N oxalic acid.

(b) *Indigo carmine soln.*—Prep. soln contg 6 g indigo carmine (free from indigo blue) and 50 ml H_2SO_4/L.

(c) *Gelatin soln.*—Soak 25 g gelatin 1 hr in satd NaCl soln, heat until gelatin dissolves, cool, and dil. with satd NaCl soln to 1 L.

(d) *Acid sodium chloride soln.*—Acidify 975 ml satd NaCl soln with 25 ml H_2SO_4.

15.056 *Determination*

Boil 5 g sample 30 min with 400 ml H_2O, cool, transfer to 500 ml vol. flask, and dil. to vol. To 10 ml infusion (filtered, if not clear) add 25 ml indigo carmine soln and ca 750 ml H_2O. Add $KMnO_4$ soln from buret, little at time while stirring, until soln becomes light green; then dropwise until color changes to bright yellow or to faint pink at rim. Designate ml $KMnO_4$ used as x.

Mix 100 ml clear infusion of tea with 50 ml gelatin soln, 100 ml acid NaCl soln, and 10 g *powd kaolin*, and shake several min in stoppered flask. Let mixt. settle and decant thru filter. Mix 25 ml filtrate with 25 ml indigo carmine soln and ca 750 ml H_2O, and titr. with $KMnO_4$ as before. ml $KMnO_4$ used subtracted from that obtained above, x, gives quantity $KMnO_4$ required to oxidize tannin. 1 ml $0.1N$ oxalic acid $= 0.0042$ g tannin (gallotannic acid).

SELECTED REFERENCES

(*1*) JAOAC **48**, 705(1965).

(*2*) JAOAC **40**, 350(1957).

(*3*) JAOAC **51**, 577(1968).

(*4*) J. Am. Chem. Soc. **41**, 1298(1919); JAOAC **5**, 267(1921); **13**, 265(1930); **14**, 533(1931); **16**, 567(1933); **17**, 380(1934); **27**, 168(1944); **29**, 37(1946); **30**, 416(1947).

(*5*) JAOAC **40**, 346(1957); **43**, 620(1960); **49**, 218 (1966).

(*6*) JAOAC **3**, 498(1920).

(*7*) JAOAC **7**, 154(1923).

(*8*) J. Am. Chem. Soc. **41**, 1298(1919); JAOAC **5**, 288(1921); **6**, 107(1922).

(*9*) JAOAC **5**, 291(1921); **6**, 107(1922); **43**, 620 (1960).

(*10*) JAOAC **52**, 653, 1133(1969).

(*11*) USDA Div. Chem. Bull. **13** (VII), 890(1892).

16. Dairy Products *

SAMPLING (1)—OFFICIAL FINAL ACTION

(Prepd by a joint committee of International Dairy Federation, International Organization for Standardization, and AOAC, 1965, for the Joint FAO/WHO *Code of Principles Concerning Milk and Milk Products and Associated Standards.* Methods are intended to obtain from unit (e.g., bulk container, small retail container, individual cheese, etc.) portion (subsample) which is as representative as possible of that unit.)

General Instructions
16.001   *Instructions of Administrative Character*

(This section is usually prescribed by specific regulatory agency. It is included for completeness.)

Sampling should be performed by authorized or sworn independent agent, properly trained in appropriate technic. Agent should be free from any infectious disease. If possible, representatives of parties concerned should be given opportunity to be present when sampling is performed.

Samples should be accompanied by report, signed by sworn or authorized sampling agent and countersigned by any witnesses present. Report should give particulars of place, date, and time of sampling; name and designation of agent and of any witnesses; precise method of sampling which is followed if this deviates from prescribed std method; nature and number of units constituting consignment together with their batch code markings, where available; number of samples duly identified as to batches from which they are drawn; and place to which the samples will be sent.

When appropriate, report should also include any relevant conditions or circumstances, for example, condition of packages and their surroundings, temp. and humidity of atm., method of sterilization of sampling equipment, whether preservative has been added to samples, and any other special information relating to material being sampled.

Each sample should be sealed and labeled to give nature of product, identification number, and any code markings of batch from which sample has been taken, date of sampling, and name and signature of sampling agent. When necessary, addnl information may be required, for example, wt of sample and unit from which it was taken.

All samples should be taken at least in duplicate, one set being held if necessary in cold storage and put at disposal of second party as soon as possible. Precise method of sampling and wt or vol. of product to be taken as sample vary with nature of product and purpose for which sampling is required and are defined for each particular case.

When previously agreed between parties, take addnl sets of samples and retain for independent arbitration, if necessary. Send samples to testing laboratory immediately after sampling.

16.002   *Technical Instructions*

(*See* sampling equipment specifications laid down for each product to be sampled.)

(a) *Sampling for chemical purposes.*—Clean and dry all equipment.

(b) *Sampling for bacteriological purposes.*—Clean and treat equipment by one of following methods: (*1*) Expose to hot air 2 hr at 170° (may be stored if kept under sterile conditions). (*2*) Autoclave 15–20 min at 120° (may be stored if kept under sterile conditions). (*3*) Expose to steam 1 hr at 100° (use equipment same day). (*4*) Immerse in H_2O 1 min at 100° (use equipment immediately). (*5*) Immerse in 70% alcohol and flame to burn off alcohol immediately before use. (*6*) Expose to hydrocarbon (propane, butane) torch flame so that all working surfaces contact flame immediately before use.

Choice of treatment depends on nature, shape, and size of equipment and on conditions of sampling. Sterilize wherever possible by method (*1*) or (*2*).

Methods (*3*), (*4*), (*5*), and (*6*) are regarded as secondary methods only.

(c) *Sampling for organoleptic purposes.*—Use equipment as in (a) or (b), or as specified for specific product. Equipment should not impart any flavor or odor to product.

16.003   *Sample Containers*

(a) *For liquids.*—Use clean and dry containers of suitable waterproof, greaseproof material (glass, stainless metal, suitable plastic material) of quality suitable for sterilization by **16.002**(b), if necessary, and of suitable shape and capacity for material to be sampled (as defined in each particular case).

Securely close containers either with suitable rubber or plastic stopper or by screw cap of metal or plastic having, if necessary, liq.-tight plastic liner which is insol., nonabsorbent, and greaseproof, and

---

★ Methods so marked are surplus methods. *See* "Definitions of Terms and Explanatory Notes," item (29).

which will not influence odor, flavor, or composition of milk products.

If rubber stoppers are used, cover with non-absorbent, flavorless material (such as suitable plastic) before pressing into sample container. Suitable plastic bags may also be used.

(b) *For solids or semisolids.*—Use clean and dry wide-mouth, cylindrical receptacles of suitable waterproof, greaseproof material (glass, stainless metal, suitable plastic material) of quality suitable for sterilization by 16.002(b), if necessary, and of capacity suited to size of sample to be taken (as defined in each particular case). Make air-tight as in (a). Suitable plastic bags may also be used.

(c) *Small retail containers.*—Contents of intact and unopened containers constitute samples.

16.004 *Preservation of Samples*

To samples of liq. products or cheese intended for chemical analysis, suitable preservative may be added. Such preservative should not interfere with subsequent analysis. Indicate nature and quantity of addn on label and in any reports.

Do not add preservatives to samples of semisolid, solid (except cheese), or dried products intended for chemical analysis. Rapidly cool and store samples in refrigerator at 0–5°. Dried milks may be kept at room temp.

Do not add preservatives to samples intended for bacteriological or organoleptic examination. Hold at 0–5°, except for condensed (conserved) milk products when sample comprises unopened hermetically sealed containers in which products are sold. Keep liq. products and butter cold. Start bacteriological examination of liq. products as soon as possible and never >24 hr after sampling.

16.005 *Transport of Samples*

Transport samples to laboratory as quickly as possible after sampling. Take precautions to prevent, during transit, exposure to direct sunlight, or to temp. <0° or >10° in case of perishable products. For samples intended for bacteriological examination, use insulated transport container capable of maintaining temp. at 0–5°, except for samples of condensed (conserved) milk products in unopened containers, or in case of very short journeys.

Maintain samples of cheese under such conditions as to avoid sepn of fat or moisture. Maintain soft cheese at 0–5°.

**Sampling of Milk and Liquid Milk
Products (Except Evaporated and
Sweetened Condensed Milk)**

16.006 *Sampling Equipment*

(a) *Plungers or agitators, necessary for mixing liquids in bulk.*—Use equipment, 16.008(a), of sufficient area to produce adequate agitation of product and sufficiently light in wt for operator to be able to

move it rapidly thru liq. Mix contents of large vessels by mech. stirring.

(b) *Dipper of suitable size, for collecting sample.*—When sample is required for bacteriological examination, sterilize sampling equipment as in 16.002(b).

16.007 *Sampling Technic*

Thoroly mix all liqs by pouring from one vessel to another, by plunging, or by mech. stirring. With large containers, continue agitation until liq. is thoroly mixed. In case of cream, plunge sufficient number of times to ensure thoro mixing. Move submerged plunger from place to place with special care to avoid foaming, whipping, and churning. Take sample with dipper immediately after mixing. If obtaining perfect homogeneity presents difficulties, take sample from different positions of container totaling ≥200 ml.

(For addnl instructions, see 16.019 for milk and 16.102 for cream.)

**Sampling of Condensed Milk and
Evaporated Milk**

16.008 *Bulk Containers
(Barrels, Drums, Etc.)*

(a) *Sampling equipment.*—Broad-bladed metal stirrer fitted with wide perforated disk at bottom and long enough to reach bottom of container.

(b) *Sampling technic.*—Use stirrer to mix contents very carefully and to scrape adhering material from sides and bottom of container. Remove 2–3 L well-mixed contents to smaller receptacle, repeat stirring, and take sample ≥200 ml.

(c) *Sample containers.*—Use wide-mouth sample jars with air-tight lids.

16.009 *Small Retail Containers*

Sample unit is one intact, unopened container that, whenever possible, bears manufacturer's code markings. Do not open container until just before analysis.

(For prepn of sample, see 16.125 for evapd milk and 16.138 for sweetened condensed milk.)

**Sampling of Dried Milk and
Dried Milk Products**

(Perform sampling for bacteriological examination first, independent of other sampling, from same bulk container, whenever possible.)

16.010 *Sampling for Chemical Analysis
and Organoleptic Examination*

(a) *Sampling equipment.*—Use suitable clean, dry borer tube or trier of stainless steel, Al, or Al alloy.

(b) *Sampling technic.*—Pass tube steadily thru powder at even rate of penetration. When tube reaches bottom of container withdraw contents and discharge immediately into sample container. Do not touch powder with fingers. Take one or more bores to make up 300–500 g samples.

(c) *Sample containers.*—Place samples in clean, dry containers, air-tight and, if required for examination, opaque. Use sample container large enough to allow mixing by shaking.

(d) Submit unopened original container of gas-packed dried milk if gas analysis is required.

16.011   *Sampling for Bacteriological Examination*

Take samples for bacteriological examination, whenever possible, from same package as for chemical and organoleptic examination. Take sample for bacteriological examination first.

(a) *Sampling equipment.*—Sterilize suitable stainless steel or Al spoon or trier as in **16.002**(b)(*1*), (*2*), (*5*), or (*6*).

(b) *Sampling technic.*—Using sterile metal implement (for example, broad-bladed knife or spoon), remove surface layer of powder from sampling area. With another sterile spoon or trier, take sample of 50–200 g, if possible, from point near center of container. Place sample as quickly as possible into sample container, and close immediately, using aseptic precautions. In case of dispute concerning bacteriological conditions of top layer of powder in packing, take special sample from this top layer.

(c) *Sample containers.*—Place samples in clean, dry, sterile containers, preferably brown if transparent, capable of air-tight closure.

(For addnl instructions, *see* **16.147**.)

Sampling of Butter

16.012   *Sampling Equipment*

Use butter triers long enough to pass diagonally to base of container. Use stainless steel spatulas or knives for removing portions of sample from trier. Clean and dry triers, spatulas, and knives before use, and if sampling for bacteriological purposes is required, sterilize as in **16.002**(b)(*4*), (*5*), or (*6*).

16.013   *Sampling Technic*

(a) *Butter in bulk.*—Take two or more cores of butter so that min. wt of total sample is ≥200 g. For butter in barrels, take 1 core by inserting trier diagonally thru butter from edge of barrel. Take others by inserting trier from arbitrary points of surface, vertically downward to bottom. For butter in cubes, take cores by inserting trier from top corners diagonally thru center to bottom. In both cases, make one complete turn and withdraw full core. Hold point of trier over mouth of sample container and immediately transfer core from trier in ca 75 mm pieces with spatula or knife. Leave plug ca 25 mm or more to place in hole from which core was removed. Do not include moisture adhering to outside of trier.

Clean and dry trier before each drawing. Soften butter, frozen so hard as to resist trier, by storing 24 hr at ca 10°.

(b) *Butter in pats or rolls of small size.*—Divide

units weighing ≥250 g in 4, and take 2 opposite quarters. In sizes weighing <250 g take whole unit.

(For addnl instructions, *see* **16.160**.)

16.014   *Sample Containers*

Use wide-mouth jars conforming to **16.003**(b). Fill jar ≥½ full and hermetically seal. Immediately after closure, wrap jars in paper or store in dark, if examination so requires. Do not let butter come into contact with paper or any H_2O or fat absorbing or trapping surface.

Sampling of Cheese

16.015   *Sampling Equipment*

(a) *Cheese triers of shape and size suited to cheese to be sampled.*

(b) *Stainless steel knife with pointed blade.*

(c) *Sealing compounds.*—(*1*) Mix by heating paraffin, beeswax, and white petrolatum (1 + 1 + 2); or (*2*) mix by heating white petrolatum and paraffin (1 + 1).

16.016   *Sampling Technic*

Draw enough subsamples to give total sample of ≥50 g. Use one of following technics, depending on shape, wt, type, and maturity of cheese (when choice is necessary between (a) and (b), method (a) is preferable but (b) is acceptable, especially with hard cheese of large size).

(a) *Sampling by cutting.*—Using knife with pointed blade, make 2 cuts radiating from center of cheese, if cheese has circular base, or parallel to sides if base is rectangular. Size of piece thus obtained should be such that, after removal of inedible surface layer, remaining edible portion weighs ≥50 g.

(b) *Sampling by means of trier.*—According to shape, wt, and type of cheese, use one of the following sampling technics: (*1*) Insert trier obliquely towards center of cheese once or several times into one of flat surfaces at point ≥10 cm from edge. (*2*) Insert trier perpendicularly into one face and pass thru center of cheese to reach opposite face. (*3*) Insert trier horizontally into vertical face of cheese, midway between 2 plane faces, toward center of cheese. (*4*) In case of cheese transported in barrels, boxes or other bulk containers, or cheese which is formed into large compact blocks, perform sampling by passing trier obliquely thru contents of container from top to base. (*5*) For large cheeses, use outer 2 cm or more of plug contg rind for closing hole made in cheese. Remainder of plug constitutes sample. Close plug holes with great care and, if possible, seal over with sealing compd, **16.015**(c).

(c) *Sampling by taking entire cheese.*—Normally use for small cheese and for wrapped portions of cheese packaged in small containers. Take enough packages to have ≥50 g.

Weigh, at time of sampling, cheese sold by piece

for which min. wt dry matter in unit is specified by national legislation, and state wt on label.

(d) *Sampling of cheese in brine.*—Take fragments of ≥200 g each and enough brine to cover cheese in sample container. Prior to analysis, place sample on filter paper 1–2 hr.

(For addnl instructions, *see* **16.190.**)

16.017 *Sample Containers*

Use sample containers with air-tight closures. Immediately after sampling, place samples (plugs, sectors, entire small cheese, fragments of brine cheese) in container of suitable size and shape. Sample may be cut into pieces for insertion into container but do not compress or grind.

16.018 *Treatment of Samples*

In prepn of sample, whatever method of sampling is used, carefully remove only inedible surface layer of cheese, if any, such as moldy and horny portions, unless prescribed otherwise. Do not remove outer rind or crust from soft cheese sold by piece, and for which min. wt of dry matter in unit is specified by national legislation.

(For addnl instructions, *see* **16.191.**)

MILK

16.019 *Collection of Sample—Procedure*
(*See* also **16.001–16.007.**)

Sample size necessary varies with analyses required. For usual analysis collect 250–500 ml (½–1 pt) sample; for fat detn only, collect 50–60 ml (ca 2 fl oz).

For bottled milk collect one or more containers as prepd for sale. Thoroly mix bulk milk by pouring from one clean vessel into another 3 or 4 times or stir at least 30 sec with utensil reaching to bottom of container. If cream has formed, detach all of it from sides of vessel and stir until liq. is evenly emulsified or use hand homogenizer.

Place in nonabsorbent, air-tight containers and keep cold, but above freezing temp., until examined. When transporting samples, completely fill containers, stopper tightly, and identify. Tablets contg $HgCl_2$, $K_2Cr_2O_7$, or other suitable preservative, at least 0.5 g active ingredient per tablet for each 8 fl oz milk, but total wt of such tablet ≤1 g, or 36% soln of HCHO, 0.1 ml (2 drops) per fl oz, may be used unless presence of preservative is objectionable in physical or chemical tests to be made in addn to detn of fat. If phosphatase test is to be made, only $CHCl_3$ can be used as preservative, and stoppers must be of phenol-free material such as red rubber.

16.020 *Preparation of Sample—Procedure*

Bring sample to ca 20°, mix until homogeneous by pouring into clean receptacle and back repeatedly, and promptly weigh or measure test portion. If lumps of cream do not disperse, warm sample in

H_2O bath to ca 38° and keep mixing until homogeneous, using policeman, if necessary, to reincorporate any cream adhering to container or stopper. Where practical and fat remains dispersed, cool warmed samples to ca 20° before transferring test portion.

When Babcock method, **16.054,** is used, adjust both fresh and composite samples to ca 38°, mix until homogeneous as above, and immediately pipet portions into test bottles.

16.021 Specific Gravity—Procedure

Det sp gr at 15.6/15.6° with pycnometer or std hydrometer.

16.022 Acidity (2)—Official Final Action

Measure or weigh suitable quantity (ca 20 ml or 20 g) sample into suitable dish and dil. with twice its vol. CO_2-free H_2O. Add 2 ml phthln, and titr. with $0.1N$ NaOH to first persistent pink. If measured vol. sample was used, det. its wt from sp gr of sample. Report acidity as % lactic acid by wt. (1 ml $0.1N$ NaOH = 0.0090 g lactic acid.) If Babcock milk pipet, **16.053(b)**, is used, ml $0.1N$ NaOH required ÷ 20 = % acid as lactic acid.

Results may also be expressed as ml $0.1N$ NaOH/ 100 g sample.

Citric Acid (3)—Official Final Action
16.023 *Preparation of Sample*

To 50 g milk in 150 ml beaker, add ca 100 mg *tartaric acid* and 6 ml $1N$ H_2SO_4 and heat on steam bath 15 min. Immediately add 3 ml *20% phosphotungstic acid soln*, mix well, and return to steam bath for 5 min. Transfer to 250 ml vol. flask with alcohol, cool, dil. to vol. with alcohol, mix, and filter thru folded paper. Pipet 200 ml clear filtrate into centrf. bottle.

16.024 *Reagents*

Use reagents specified in **22.064.**

16.025 *Determination*

To soln in centrf. bottle add 10 ml $Pb(OAc)_2$ soln, shake vigorously ca 2 min, and centrf. at ca 1000 rpm 15 min. Carefully decant supernatant from pptd Pb salts and test with little $Pb(OAc)_2$ soln. If ppt forms, return to centrf. bottle, add more Pb soln, shake, and again centrf. If sediment lifts, centrf. again, increasing speed and time, and decant. Invert bottle and drain thoroly several min. To Pb salts in centrf. bottle add ca 150 ml H_2O, shake thoroly, and sat. with H_2S. (*Caution: See* **46.059.**) Transfer to 250 ml vol. flask, dil. with H_2O to vol., mix, and filter thru folded paper. Proceed as in **22.067.**

Lactic Acid (4)—Official Final Action
16.026 *Preparation of Solution*

(a) *Liquid, whole, and skim milks.*—Weigh 50 g into 100 ml vol. flask.

(b) *Dried, whole, and skim milks.*—Weigh 5 g into 100 ml beaker, and using heavy stirring rod, make into smooth paste with H_2O. Transfer contents of beaker to 100 ml vol. flask with ca 50 ml H_2O.

(c) *Cream and ice cream.*—Weigh 20 g into 100 ml vol. flask and add ca 50 ml H_2O.

(d) *Sweetened condensed milk.*—Weigh 25 g into 100 ml beaker and transfer to 100 ml vol. flask with ca 50 ml H_2O.

(e) *Evaporated milk.*—Weigh 25 g into 100 ml vol. flask and add ca 50 ml H_2O.

To mixts add 6 ml $1N$ H_2SO_4 and mix, avoiding vigorous agitation. Add 5 ml *20% phosphotungstic acid soln* (1 ml for cream and 2 ml for ice cream) and dil. to vol. with H_2O. Mix, and filter thru folded paper.

(f) *Butter.*—Weigh 20 g into centrf. bottle, add 25 ml H_2O, and warm on steam bath. Neutze contents of bottle with $1N$ NaOH, using phthln. Cool, add 50 ml ether, and mix well, avoiding violent agitation. Add 50 ml pet ether, mix well, and centrf. Draw off ether layer as completely as possible by siphon with lower end bent upward. Repeat extn, using 25 ml of each ether. Place bottle on steam bath to remove most of remaining ethers. Transfer residue in bottle to 100 ml vol. flask, add 3 ml $1N$ H_2SO_4, and mix. Cool mixt. and ppt proteins with *20% phosphotungstic acid soln*, adding reagent dropwise until pptn stops. Dil. to vol., mix by shaking, and filter thru folded paper.

16.027   *Reagents*

(a) *Barium lactate std soln.*—(*Caution: See* **46.011, 46.039,** and **46.054.**) Dissolve in ca 10 ml H_2O quantity of a pure lactate, such as Li, Zn, or Ca lactate, contg equiv. of ca 300 mg free lactic acid. Transfer material to extractor, Fig. 16:1, add 0.5 ml H_2SO_4 (1 + 1), and adjust vol. to 50 ml. Ext with ether 3 hr. Add ca 20 ml H_2O to extn flask, evap. ether on steam bath, and carefully titr. with $0.1N$ $Ba(OH)_2$, using phthln. Transfer neutzd material to 200 ml vol. flask, dil. to vol., and mix. Pipet into 500 ml vol. flask quantity of this Ba lactate soln contg equiv. of exactly 250 mg free lactic acid, dil. to vol., mix, and designate as *lactate std soln.* (2 ml equiv. to 1 mg lactic acid. To plot std curve use freshly prepd soln.) Transfer 20 ml lactate std soln to 100 ml vol. flask, dil. to vol., and designate as *dil. std lactate soln* (10 ml equiv. to 1 mg lactic acid).

(b) *Carbon.*—To 10 g high-grade C (Nuchar C-190-N, Suchar, or Darco G60) in 600 ml beaker, add ca 200 ml H_2O and 30 ml $1N$ HCl, and keep on steam bath 20 min, agitating continuously with air passed thru cotton. Filter on buchner and suck as dry as possible, tamping with flat-end rod. Transfer cake to beaker, add ca 200 ml H_2O, mix thoroly, and refilter. Repeat washing and filtering twice, and dry at 100°.

(c) *Ferric chloride soln.*—Dissolve 2 g $FeCl_3 \cdot 6H_2O$ in H_2O, add 5 ml $1N$ HCl, and dil. to 200 ml.

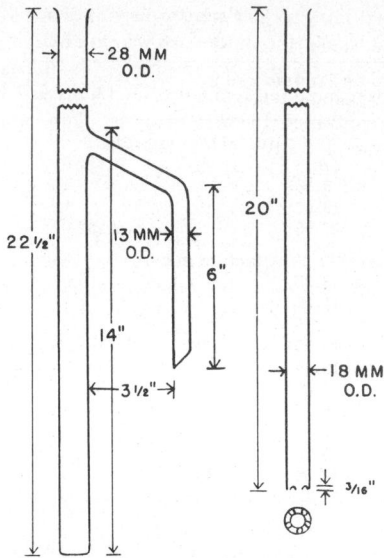

FIG. 16:1—Liquid extractor

16.028   *Preparation of Standard Curve*

Transfer from buret to vol. flasks, graduated at 50 and 55 ml, quantities of std solns in left-hand column of **16.029**. Right-hand column gives mg of lactic acid in 40 ml filtrate from each sample after C treatment described below, and that will therefore be read in spectrophtr. Blank using 40 ml H_2O in place of lactate soln must be included in each series.

To each flask, including blank, add 6.6 ml $0.1N$ HCl and H_2O until vol. is ca 40 ml. Now add 200 ± 1 mg prepd C, shake, and keep on steam bath 10 min, mixing frequently. Cool, dil. to 55 ml mark with H_2O at room temp., and promptly filter thru quant. paper, pouring back until clear.

Transfer 40 ml of each clear filtrate to 50 ml vol. flask, painted black or wrapped in black paper. As 40 ml filtrate used contains only 4.8 ml acid added during C treatment, add 1.2 ml $0.1N$ HCl. (Total of 6 ml $0.1N$ HCl is required in flask.) Pipet 5 ml $FeCl_3$ soln into one flask at time, dil. to vol., and mix. Pour soln into 1 cm quartz cell and det. wavelength of max. A on recording spectrophtr between 350 and 600 nm, using baseline correction at 600 nm. If recording spectrophtr is not available, manually scan region around 365 nm to det. wavelength of max. A. Read all std solns at this wavelength against blank set at zero A. (On exposure to direct light, color fades, but protected as provided it is stable for number of hr.) From readings obtained, prep. std curve, plotting mg lactic acid as abscissa and scale readings as ordinates. (Large-scale graph paper is recommended to permit more accurate interpolations.)

Recheck wavelength of max. A and std curve occasionally and whenever new batch of C or $FeCl_3$ is used. If different, adjust spectrophtr or prep. new std curve at new wavelength of max. A.

16.029 *Preparation of Dilutions for Standard Curve*

Soln to be Transferred to 50–55 ml Vol. Flask	Lactic Acid in 40 ml Aliquot
dil. lactate std soln	
ml	mg
6.90	0.5
13.80	1.0
27.60	2.0
lactate std soln	
8.25	3.0
11.00	4.0
13.75	5.0
16.50	6.0
19.25	7.0
22.00	8.0
24.75	9.0
27.50	10.0
30.25	11.0
33.00	12.0

16.030 *Extraction*

(*Caution: See* **46.011, 46.039,** *and* **46.054.**)

Place 50 ml filtrate from prepd sample and 0.5 ml H_2SO_4 (1 + 1) in inner tube of extractor and connect to longest bulb-type condenser available, having outlet $\geq \frac{1}{2}''$ id to minimize ether regurgitation. Run H_2O thru condenser at max. condensation efficiency. Connect extn flask contg 200 ml ether, and lower flask slowly onto preheated heating mantle or hot plate to prevent superheating the ether. Protect extractor from heat of hot plate by upright sheet of asbestos and ext all the lactic acid.

When ether in extn flask is kept at rapid boiling and condenser H_2O is cold enough to let condensed ether return to extn flask in steady stream, extn for 3 hr delivers all the lactic acid. When this rate of extn cannot be maintained because of high temp. of H_2O passing thru condenser, continue extn until equiv. of 7500 ml ether has passed thru soln. Time required, T, established for each set of new conditions, is calcd from 2 factors: x, quantity of ether necessary to fill extractor to overflowing at side-arm, which is constant for each app.; and y, time in min required for quantity x to pass from extn flask and fill extractor.

To det. x, place 50 ml H_2O and 0.5 ml H_2SO_4 (1 + 1) in extractor. With extractor held upright, carefully pour ether from graduate into inner tube until it just starts passing out of side-arm. Det. y in ordinary course of starting each detn. With stopwatch, record interval from time ether first drops from condenser and falls into inner tube to time first drops return to extn flask from overflow into side-arm. Time, T, necessary for 7500 ml to pass thru app. $= 7500\,y/x$. Calcd T holds only if rate of boiling and condensing is constant thruout extn period.

16.031 *Determination*

To flask contg ether ext add 20 ml H_2O and expel ether on steam bath. Do not let flask remain on steam bath after ether is expelled. Neutze with *satd* $Ba(OH)_2$ *soln*, using phthln. Wash into 110 ml vol. flask with alcohol until vol. is ca 90 ml. Heat almost to boiling on steam bath, cool, dil. to vol. with alcohol, and filter thru quant. paper. To expel alcohol, evap. 100 ml filtrate to ca 10 ml, add ca 50 ml H_2O, and again evap. to ca 10 ml (or evap. the 100 ml filtrate to dryness on steam bath).

Add, from buret, 6.6 ml 0.1N HCl and transfer contents of beaker with H_2O to 50–55 ml vol. flask until vol. is ca 40 ml. Prep. blank contg 6.6 ml 0.1N HCl dild to ca 40 ml with H_2O. Add 200 mg prepd C, mix immediately, and keep on steam bath 10 min, mixing frequently. Cool, dil. to 55 ml mark with H_2O at room temp., and filter thru quant. paper, pouring back until clear.

Transfer 10 ml filtrate to 50 ml black vol. flask. (Total of 6 ml 0.1N HCl must be in flask; 10 ml filtrate contains 1.2 ml 0.1N HCl from C treatment; therefore, add 4.8 ml addnl acid.) Add 5 ml $FeCl_3$ soln from buret or pipet, dil. to vol., and mix. (After color develops, dilg to reduce color intensity is not permissible.) Fill 1 cm quartz cell with soln and read in spectrophtr at wavelength of max. A against blank set at zero A.

Det. quantity of lactic acid present in the 10 ml aliquot from std curve. If quantity of lactic acid in 10 ml portion is <2 mg, repeat detn on 40 ml portion of remaining filtrate. The 40 ml aliquot contains 4.8 ml 0.1N HCl; therefore, add 1.2 ml acid. Report lactic acid in mg/100 g.

$$\text{mg lactic acid in ether ext} = Z =$$
$$\text{mg read} \times (55/10 (\text{or } 40)) \times (110/100).$$

$$\text{mg lactic acid/100 g} = Z \times$$
$$(\text{ml sample diln/ml aliquot for extn})$$
$$\times (100/\text{g sample}).$$

Total Solids

16.032 *Method I—Official Final Action*

Weigh 2.5–3 g prepd sample, **16.020,** into weighed flat-bottom dish ≥ 5 cm diam.; use ca 5 g and Pt dish if ash is to be detd on same portion. Heat on steam bath 10–15 min, exposing max. surface of dish bottom to live steam; then heat 3 hr in air oven at 98–100°. Cool in desiccator, weigh quickly, and report % residue as total solids.

16.033 *Method II—(Approximate)— Procedure*

Det. sp gr of milk with Quévenne lactometer (reading top of meniscus), observe temp., and correct reading L to 60°F by **47.026.** Calc. total solids either from formula 0.25 L + 1.2 F, in which F = % fat in milk, or from **47.025.**

16.034 Ash (5)—Official Final Action

Into suitable Pt dish weigh ca 5 g prepd sample, **16.020,** and evap. to dryness on steam bath. Ignite in muffle at temp. ≤550° until ash is C-free. Cool in desiccator, weigh, and calc. % ash.

16.035 Total Nitrogen—Official Final Action

Transfer 5 g sample to Kjeldahl digestion flask and proceed as in **2.051**. % N × 6.38 = % "protein."

Dye Binding Method (6)—Official Final Action

16.036   Reagents

(a) *Reagent dye soln.*—Dissolve 1.300 g (corrected for assay) twice recrystd Acid Orange 12 in 1 L 0.05M phosphate buffer, (c). Make assay correction by calcg dye concn, c, in soln from A, using equation $c = A/(5.90 \times b)$, where b is mm path length of cuvet. Check soln further against either milk of known protein content or previous valid dye soln.

(b) *Reference dye soln.*—Dissolve 0.600 g twice recrystd (from alcohol) Acid Orange 12 and 1 ml propionic acid in ca 900 ml H_2O. Dil. to 1 L with H_2O. Correct for assay as in (a) above.

(Recrystd dye and solns available from Udy Analyzer Co., Boulder, CO 80302.)

(c) *0.05 M phosphate buffer.*—pH 1.8–1.9. Dissolve 3.4 g KH_2PO_4, 3.4 ml H_3PO_4 (1 (85%) + 1), 60 ml HOAc, 1 ml propionic acid, and 2 g oxalic acid in ca 800 ml H_2O. Dil. to 1 L with H_2O.

16.037   Apparatus

(a) *Spectrophotometer.*—Photoelec. colorimeter or spectrophtr set at 480 nm. Use buffer dilns of reagent dye soln representing 0.350, 0.600, 0.750, and 0.850 g/L to calibrate spectrophtr. Plot A against concn to use as calibration chart.

(b) *Short path cuvet.*—Cuvet with path length ca 0.3 mm; flow-thru type is convenient. Measure A_s at 370 nm of 0.0400 g/L K_2CrO_4 in 0.05N KOH. Calc. path length in mm, b, from $b = A_s/0.09914$. Arrange cuvet drain tube, and supply tube if any, according to manufacturer's instructions to ensure proper flow and liq. levels.

Suitable colorimeter with short-path, flow-thru cuvet, and calibration curve are available from Udy Analyzer Co.

(c) *Automatic pipet.*—Adjust to deliver 40.44 g reagent dye soln at 20° (equiv. to 39.887 g H_2O; 40 ml). Adjust so that 10 successive deliveries are all within 40.44±0.02 g by wt.

(d) *Syringe.*—Stdze sampling syringe to deliver 2.24 ml at 20° (equiv. to 2.2337 g H_2O).

(e) *Polyethylene plastic bag.*—6 oz capacity. Whirl-Pak (available from W. H. Curtin Co., Box 1546, Houston, TX 77023), or equiv.

16.038   Preparation of Samples

(a) *Fluid milk, ice cream mix.*—Use as received.

(b) *Buttermilk, half-and-half, chocolate drink.*—Warm to 35–38° and agitate thoroly.

(c) *Nonfat dry milk (NFDM).*—Use as powder or reconstitute as follows: Weigh plastic bag to nearest 0.5 mg. Add 1 level tablespoon NFDM (ca 7.5 g) and reweigh. Add ca 75 ml (ca 60°) H_2O. Seal bag and shake vigorously 3 min. Let cool to room temp. Do not use H_2O bath. Reweigh. Refrigerate overnight. Reconstitute new portion of NFDM sample for each replicate.

16.039   Determination

Zero spectrophtr. Adjust gain so that ref. dye soln, (b), reads 42%T at 480 nm. Place 2.24 ml milk, buttermilk, or half-and-half, 2.5–2.8 ml chocolate drink or reconstituted NFDM, from syringe, or 2.0–2.3 g ice cream mix or 0.22–0.24 g NFDM powder in 2 oz squeeze-type polyethylene dispenser bottle with fitted spun glass paper inside cap. Det. sample wt to 0.5 mg. Add 40.44 g reagent dye soln, (a), to bottle by automatic pipet. Shake vigorously 30 sec, except shake bottle contg NFDM powder 3 min. Reset ref. dye soln reading at 42%T, if necessary. Drop filtrate from dispenser bottle into cuvet funnel and draw into cuvet. When reading is constant, record to nearest 0.1%, avoiding parallax. Check spectrophtr gain. If reading is not 42% with ref. dye soln, adjust instrument, and re-read sample.

All solns must be 25±1° when placed in cuvet. Measure temp. before reading; soln warms while in instrument.

16.040   Calculations

Using calibration chart prepd for instrument, det. dye concn (mg/ml) in sample filtrate from observed reading. Vol. = (1/1.012) × (g sample + 40.44); mg dye not bound = vol. × dye concn; mg bound dye = 52 mg dye available − mg dye not bound. Protein in mg = mg bound dye/0.312. % Protein = mg protein/(g sample × 10).

% Protein in NFDM = % protein in reconstituted NFDM × g reconstituted NFDM prepd/g NFDM sample used.

Casein—Official Final Action

(Make detn while milk is fresh or nearly so. If delayed >24 hr, add HCHO to milk (1:2500) and keep mixt. cool.)

16.041 Method I

Place 10 g sample in beaker with 90 ml H_2O at 40–42° and immediately add 1.5 ml HOAc (1 + 9). Stir and let stand 3–5 min. Decant on acid-washed filter, wash by decanting 2 or 3 times with cold H_2O, and transfer ppt to filter. Wash once or twice on filter. (Filtrate should be clear, or nearly so.) If first portions of filtrate are not clear, refilter, and complete washing ppt. Retain filtrate for detn of albumin, **16.044**. Det. N in washed ppt and paper as in **2.051**, and multiply result by 6.38 to obtain equiv. of casein.

To preserved sample of milk, add HOAc (1 + 9) dropwise with stirring, and continue addn until liq. above ppt becomes clear, or very nearly so.

Method II (7)

16.042 *Reagent*

Pipet 250 ml 1N HOAc into 1 L vol. flask. Add 125 ml CO_2-free 1N NaOH, dil. to vol. with CO_2-free H_2O, and mix thoroly.

16.043 *Determination*

Pipet 20 ml sample into 100 ml vol. flask. Add 50 ml reagent, mix, dil. to vol. with H_2O, and shake well. Set flask in 50–60° H_2O (*not* >60°) for 15 min. Cool to room temp., add 0.5 g Celite analytical filter-aid, shake thoroly, and filter clear thru suitable folded paper, avoiding evapn during filtration. Det. N, x, in 50 ml clear filtrate, and det. total N, y, in 10 ml of the milk. $(y - x) \times 6.38$ = casein in 10 ml milk. Report g casein/100 ml milk, or divide g/100 ml by density of milk and report as % by wt.

16.044 Albumin—Official Final Action

Exactly neutze filtrate obtained in **16.041** with 10% NaOH soln, add 0.3 ml HOAc (1 + 9), and heat on steam bath until albumin is completely pptd. Collect ppt on acid-washed filter, wash with cold H_2O, and det. N as in **2.051**. N $\times$ 6.38 = albumin.

Protein-Reducing Substances (8)—Official First Action

(Complete analyses same day they are begun. Do not permit tests to stand too long after cooling or after filtration. Oxidizing or reducing fumes (H_2S, Cl, HNO_3, etc.) must be absent from laboratory during detn.)

16.045 *Reagents*

(a) *Phthalate buffer soln.*—pH 5.6. Dissolve 2.0 g NaOH in H_2O and dil. to 250 ml. Dissolve 10.2 g KH phthalate in H_2O and dil. to 250 ml. Mix 159 ml NaOH soln with 200 ml phthalate soln and dil. to 800 ml in graduate. Adjust to pH 5.6 by addn of NaOH or phthalate soln.

(b) *Potassium ferricyanide soln.*—1%. Dissolve 10 g $K_3Fe(CN)_6$ in H_2O and dil. to 1 L. Discard if soln appears green or contains blue ppt. Prep. new std curve with each new batch of reagent.

(c) *Ferric chloride soln.*—0.1%. Dissolve 0.1 g or 0.1 ml liquefied portion of $FeCl_3.6H_2O$ in 100 ml H_2O. Prep. fresh daily.

16.046 *Apparatus*

(a) *Centrifuge tubes.*—50 ml graduated, Pyrex, conical red line, Corning No. 8100.

(b) *Spectrophotometer.* — Beckman Instruments Model B or equiv. with matched set of 10 mm Corex cells.

16.047 *Preparation of Standard Curve*

Weigh 0.1147 g $K_4Fe(CN)_6.3H_2O$ just before use and dil. to 1 L with H_2O. Dil. 50 ml to 100 ml in vol. flask (1 ml = 0.05 mg $K_4Fe(CN)_6$). Pipet 0, 0.5, 1.0, 1.5, 2.0, 2.5, 3.0, 3.5, and 4 ml of the dil. soln into series of clean, dry test tubes. Pipet in H_2O to give total vol. of 5.0 ml. To each tube add 5 ml of "blank soln" prepd as follows: Dil. 3 ml *satd urea soln* to 15 ml with H_2O; add 5 ml phthalate buffer soln, 5 ml $K_3Fe(CN)_6$ soln, (b), and 5 ml *10% trichloroacetic acid* soln. Mix with stirring rod.

At convenient intervals add 1 ml of the $FeCl_3$ soln to each tube, mix, and after exactly 10 min read in spectrophtr set to read 100%T at 610 nm with control soln (0.0 ml $K_4Fe(CN)_6$ soln). Plot %T against mg $K_4Fe(CN)_6$ on semilog paper.

16.048 *Determination*

Store samples preferably at ca 3°. Frozen or preserved samples are unsuitable for test.

Mix sample thoroly by pouring into container and back until homogeneous. Pipet 15 ml sample into 50 ml graduated centrf. tube contg 15 ml H_2O. Add 3 ml 5% HOAc soln, stir thoroly, and centrf. 5 min at 1000–1500 rpm. Decant supernatant. (Small amt of floating curd may be disregarded; if sample contains excessive cream, curd will float and supernatant cannot be decanted. Discard test and remix sample thoroly.) Wash ppt twice with 15 ml portions H_2O, mixing ppt each time with rod, centrfg 5 min, and decanting.

To ppt and to clean centrf. tube as blank add 3 ml satd urea soln and then dil. to 15 ml with H_2O. Stir thoroly, add 5 ml phthalate buffer soln and 5 ml 1% $K_3Fe(CN)_6$ soln, and stir. Place in 70° H_2O bath exactly 20 min and cool in ice-H_2O.

When cool, add 5 ml 10% trichloroacetic acid soln, stir, and filter thru 11 cm Whatman No. 40 paper, or equiv. Use first few ml filtrate to wash sides and bottom of receiver, and discard. Filter remainder of soln and let drain completely; then refilter if cloudy.

Add 5 ml H_2O to clean, dry test tube and then add 5 ml clear filtrate. Add 1 ml 0.1% $FeCl_3$ soln to develop color. Stir and let stand exactly 10 min. Read in spectrophtr set to read 100%T at 610 nm against blank. With series of samples, add $FeCl_3$ soln at convenient intervals to permit readings 10 min after addn. From std curve det. amt of reducing substances as mg $K_4Fe(CN)_6$ and calc. to 100 ml milk basis by multiplying by 40 (100/2.5 ml equiv. aliquot).

Lactose—Official Final Action

Polarimetric Method (9)

16.049 *Reagents*

(a) *Acid-mercuric nitrate soln.*—Dissolve Hg in twice its wt HNO_3 and dil. with 5 vols H_2O. Or—

(b) *Mercuric iodide soln.*—Dissolve 33.2 g KI and 13.5 g $HgCl_2$ in 200 ml HOAc and 640 ml H_2O.

16.050 *Determination*

Weigh 65.8 g (2 normal wt) milk into each of 2 vol. flasks, 100 and 200 ml, resp. Add to each flask 20 ml acid-Hg(NO_3)$_2$ soln or 30 ml HgI_2 soln. To 100 ml flask add *5% phosphotungstic acid* soln to mark, and to the 200 ml flask add 15 ml 5% phosphotungstic acid soln and dil. to mark with H_2O. Shake both flasks frequently during 15 min, filter thru dry filter, and polarize. (It is preferable to read soln from 200 ml flask in 400 mm tube to reduce error of reading; soln from 100 ml flask may be read in 200 mm tube.) Calc. % lactose in sample as follows: (1) Subtract reading of soln from 200 ml flask (using 400 mm tube) from reading of soln from 100 ml flask (using 200 mm tube); (2) multiply difference by 2; (3) subtract result from reading of soln from 100 ml flask; (4) divide result by 2.

16.051 Gravimetric Method

Dil. 25 g sample with 400 ml H_2O in 500 ml vol. flask. Add 10 ml $CuSO_4$ soln, **31.035(a)**, and ca 7.5 ml KOH soln of such concn that 1 vol. is just enough to ppt completely the Cu as hydroxide from 1 vol. of the $CuSO_4$ soln. (Instead, 8.8 ml 0.5N NaOH may be used. After addn of alkali soln, mixt. must still be acid and contain Cu in soln.) Dil. to vol., mix, filter thru dry filter, and det. lactose in aliquot of filtrate as in **31.039**. From **47.019** obtain wt lactose equiv. to wt Cu_2O.

Fat

16.052 Roese-Gottlieb Method (10)—Official Final Action

(Details of this method comply with method which has been agreed upon by International Dairy Federation, International Organization for Standardization, and AOAC for publication by each organization and which is published as international std in *FAO/WHO Code of Principles Concerning Milk and Milk Products and Associated Standards*.)

(*Caution: See* **46.011, 46.039, 46.054,** and **46.073.**)

Prep. as in **16.020** and weigh, to nearest mg, ca 10 g sample into fat-extn flask or tube. Add 1.25 ml NH_4OH (2 ml if sample is sour) and mix thoroly. Add 10 ml alcohol and mix well. Add 25 ml ether (all ether must be peroxide-free), stopper with cork or stopper (synthetic rubber) unaffected by usual fat solvs, and shake very vigorously 1 min. Cool if necessary; add 25 ml pet ether (boiling range 30–60°) and repeat vigorous shaking. Centrf. flask at ca 600 rpm or let it stand until upper liq. is practically clear. Decant ether soln into suitable flask or metal dish. Wash lip and stopper of extn flask or tube with mixt. of equal parts of the 2 solvs and add washings to weighing flask or dish. Repeat extn of liq. remaining in flask or tube twice, using 15 ml of each solv. each time and adding H_2O if necessary, but omitting rinsing with mixed solvs after final extn. (Third extn is not necessary with skim milk.)

Evap. solvs completely on hot plate or steam bath at temp. that does not cause spattering or bumping (boiling chips may be added). Dry fat to constant wt in oven at 102±2° or vac. oven at 70–75° under pressure <50 mm Hg. Weigh cooled flask or dish, without wiping immediately before weighing. Remove fat completely from container with 15–25 ml warm pet ether, dry, and weigh as before. Loss in wt = wt

fat. Correct wt fat by blank detn on reagents used. If blank is >0.5 mg, purify or replace reagents. Difference between duplicate detns obtained simultaneously by same analyst should be ≤0.03 g fat/100 g product.

Babcock Method (11)—Official Final Action
16.053 Apparatus

(a) *Standard Babcock milk-test bottle.*—8%, 18 g, 6″ milk-test bottle, total ht 150–165 mm (5.9–6.5″). Bottom of bottle is flat, and axis of neck is vertical when bottle stands on level surface. Charge of milk for bottle in 18 g.

(*1*) *Bulb.*—Capacity of bulb to junction with neck must be ≥45 ml. Shape of bulb may be either cylindrical or conical. If cylindrical, od must be between 34 and 36 mm; if conical, od of base must be between 31 and 33 mm, and max. diam. between 35 and 37 mm.

(*2*) *Neck.*—Cylindrical and of uniform diam. from ≥5 mm below lowest graduation mark to ≥5 mm above highest mark. Top of neck is flared to diam. of ≥10 mm. Graduated portion of neck has length ≥63.5 mm and is graduated in whole %, 0.5%, and 0.1%, resp., from 0.0 to 8.0%. Tenths % graduations are ≥3 mm long; 0.5% graduations are ≥4 mm long and project 1 mm to left; and whole % graduations extend at least half-way around neck to right and project at least 2 mm to left of tenths % graduations. Each whole % graduation is numbered, with number placed to left of scale. Capacity of neck for each whole % on scale is 0.20 ml. Max. error of total graduation or any part thereof must not exceed vol. of smallest unit of graduation.

Each bottle must be constructed so as to withstand stress to which it will be subjected in centrf.

(*3*) *Testing.*—Hg and cork, alcohol and buret, and alcohol and brass plunger methods may be used for rapid testing of bottles, but accuracy of any questionable bottle must be detd by calibration with Hg (13.5471 g clean, dry Hg at 20° to be equal to 5% on scale of 18 g bottle and 10% on scale of 9 g bottle, **16.115(a)**), bottle having been previously filled to zero with Hg.

(b) *Pipet.*—Std milk pipet conforms to following specifications:

	mm
Total length	≤330
Od of suction tube	6–8
Length of suction tube	130
Od of delivery tube	4.5–5.0
(Must fit into bottle (**a**))	
Length of delivery tube	100–120
Distance of graduation mark above bulb	15–45

Nozzle parallel with axis of pipet, but slightly constricted so as to discharge in 5–8 sec when filled with H_2O.

Graduation, to contain 17.6 ml H_2O at 20° when bottom of meniscus coincides with mark on suction tube.

Max. error in graduation, ≤0.05 ml. Pipet is to be marked "Holds 17.6 ml."

Test pipet by measuring from buret vol. H_2O (at 20°) which it holds up to graduation mark.

(c) *Acid measure.*—Device used to measure H_2SO_4, whether graduated cylinder or pipet attached to Swedish acid bottle, must be graduated to deliver 17.5 ml.

(d) *Centrifuge or "tester."*—Std centrf., however driven, must be constructed thruout and so mounted as to be capable, when filled to capacity, of rotating at necessary speed with min. vibration and without liability of causing injury or accident. It must be heated, elect. or otherwise, to temp. of $\geq 55°$ during centrfg. It must be provided with speed indicator, permanently attached, if possible. Proper rate of rotation may be detd by ref. to table below. By "diam. of wheel" is meant distance between inside bottoms of opposite cups measured thru center of rotation of centrf. wheel while cups are horizontally extended.

Diam. of wheel, inches	rpm
14	909
16	848
18	800
20	759
22	724
24	693

(e) *Dividers or calipers.*—For measuring fat column.

(f) *Water bath for test bottles.*—Provided with thermometer and device to maintain temp. of 55–60°.

16.054   *Determination*

With pipet, (b), transfer 18 g prepd sample, **16.020,** to milk-test bottle. Blow out milk in pipet tip ca 10 sec after free outflow ceases. Add portionwise ca 17.5 ml H_2SO_4 (sp gr 1.82–1.83 at 20°) tempered at 15–20°, washing all traces of milk into bulb. Shake until all traces of curd disappear; place bottle in heated centrf., counterbalance, and after proper speed is reached, centrf. 5 min. Add soft H_2O at 60°, or above, until bulb of bottle is filled. Centrf. 2 min. Add hot H_2O until liq. column approaches top graduation of scale. Centrf. 1 min longer at 55–60°. Transfer bottle to warm H_2O bath kept at 55–60°, immerse it to level of top of fat column, and leave until column is in equilibrium and lower fat surface assumes final form (≥ 3 min). Remove bottle from bath, wipe it, and with aid of dividers or calipers measure fat column, in terms of % by wt, from lower surface to highest point of upper meniscus.

Fat column, at time of measurement, should be translucent, golden-yellow or amber, and free from visible suspended particles. Reject all tests in which fat column is milky or shows presence of curd or of charred matter, or in which reading is indistinct or uncertain; repeat test, adjusting quantity of H_2SO_4 added.

★ *Rapid Detergent Method for Raw Milk* ★
(12)—Official Final Action

(Applicable only as rapid screening test for fresh raw milk ≤ 24 hr old)

16.055   *Reagents*

(a) *Solid detergent reagent.*—Grind together 3 parts (by wt) urea, 3 parts Na_2CO_3, 2 parts EDTA, and 1 part anhyd. Na_2HPO_4 until finely divided and lump-free. Add 4 parts polyoxyethylene esters of mixed fatty and resin acids (16 EtO/mole) (available under designation "PFR-16" from Atlas Chemical Industries, Inc., or from Technical Industries, 2711 S.W. Second Ave, Fort Lauderdale, FL 33315) and mix thoroly by mixing and rubbing thru No. 8 sieve until mass is lump-free and has soft, moldable consistency. Store in dry place at room temp. ≥ 10 days to react and set up. Break up dry, hard cake, reduce to free-flowing powder, pass thru No. 20 sieve, and mix thoroly. (If cake cannot be powdered, let it age longer.) (Prepd reagent is available as "TeSa Reagent Concentrate®" from Technical Industries.)

(b) *Fat test reagent.*—Dissolve 156 g solid reagent, (a), in distd or good quality (drinking) tap H_2O and dil. to 1 L. Mix thoroly and let stand ≥ 6 hr before use. Prep. fresh every 2 weeks.

(c) *Milk test reagent.*—Mix 1 vol. MeOH with 5 vols fat test reagent, (b), and mix thoroly. Prep. fresh every 2 days.

16.056   *Apparatus*

(a) *Milk test bottles with side neck.*—8%, 18 g, total ht 160–175 mm. Bottom of bottle is flat, and axis of neck is vertical when bottle stands on level surface. Charge of milk for bottle is 18 g. (Available as "TeSa Milk Test Bottles®" from Technical Industries, **16.055(a).**)

(1) *Bulb.*—Capacity of bulb to junction with center neck must be ≥ 48 ml. Shape of bulb is cylindrical with max. od ≤ 37 mm. Min. taper of bulb to junction with center neck at any point must be $\leq 50°$ to axis of center neck.

(2) *Center neck.*—Cylindrical and of uniform diam. from ≥ 5 mm below lowest graduation mark to 5 mm above highest mark. Top of neck is flared to diam. ≥ 10 mm and highest graduation mark must be 17–20 mm below open, flared top. Graduated portion of neck has length ≥ 65 mm and is graduated and marked as in **16.053(a)(2),** with same max. error.

(3) *Secondary side arm tube.*—Tube, 7–8 mm od, is sealed into tapered portion of bulb at ca right angle to taper so that closest portion of seal to junction of bulb and center neck is ≥ 5 mm. Portion of tube within bulb is bent and extends downward parallel to axis of center neck, and terminates in open end 2–6 mm from inside bottom of bulb. Portion of tube outside bulb is bent and extends upward parallel to axis of center neck at distance 2–5 mm from neck and terminates in open end flared to diam. ≥ 10 mm at

2–5 mm above highest graduation of center neck. Tube is placed opposite center neck so that it does not obstruct reading of scale. Each bottle is constructed to withstand stresses required in normal use.

(*4*) *Testing.*—See **16.053**(a)(*3*).

(**b**) *Pipet.*—See **16.053**(b).

(**c**) *Reagent measure.*—Any device graduated to deliver 15 ml.

(**d**) *Water baths.*—(*1*) *Reaction bath.*—Provided with thermometer and heater for maintaining H_2O at bp (97–100°). If altitude is such that bp is <97°, add glycerol or ethylene glycol to raise bp to ≤100°. (*2*) *Tempering bath.*—See **16.053**(f).

16.057   Determination

With pipet, **16.053**(b), transfer 18 g prepd sample, **16.020,** to milk test bottle, **16.056**(a), thru side tube. Blow out milk in pipet tip ca 10 sec after free outflow ceases. Add 15 ml milk test reagent, **16.055**(c), thru side tube, washing all traces of milk into bulb, and immediately swirl to obtain uniform mixt. Place bottle in boiling H_2O bath 10–12 min. Remove bottle and slowly add hot H_2O thru side arm until full. Let stand at room temp. 5–6 min. Place bottle in tempering bath to level of top graduation 3 min. Add H_2O at 55–60° thru side arm to raise fat level to, or just below, 0 graduation. Read lower meniscus and report difference between upper and lower menisci in % by wt of fat. (Upper meniscus may also be adjusted to exact 0 mark by inserting small rod into side tube, or fat column may be measured with calipers. Read meniscus as in usual volumetric measurements— not as in Babcock tests.)

If small amt of foam or undigested material obscures lower meniscus, add few drops 40% MeOH thru fat column, retemper, and read as above.

If large amt of undigested material obscures lower meniscus, repeat test, using 17–18 ml milk test reagent, and leaving in boiling H_2O bath 15–20 min, shaking 3 or 4 times during first 10 min.

Automated Light Scattering Method (13)—Official First Action
(Applicable to raw, unhomogenized milk)

16.058   Principle

Milk is homogenized to produce uniform-size fat globules, treated with EDTA soln to dil. sample and eliminate turbidity caused by casein micelle, and passed thru photocell to measure light scattering of soln which is proportional to amt of fat in milk. Amt of light passing thru photocell is registered on galvanometer calibrated to read % fat directly.

16.059   Apparatus and Reagents

(**a**) *Milko-tester.*—Consists of heating bath, 4-stage homogenizer, mixing chamber, syringe for delivering EDTA soln, and photometer. Manufactured by Foss Electric, Hillerod, Denmark, and available from Foss American, Inc., Route 82, Fishkill, NY 12524.

(**b**) *Sodium (tetra) ethylenediamine tetraacetate (EDTA) soln.*—Dissolve 45.0 g Na_4EDTA, 10.0 ml polysorbate 20 (Tween 20®), and 7.6 g NaOH in 10 L H_2O, using container connected to tester with plastic hose.

16.060   Operation of Tester

Following operations are performed automatically: Transfer ca 33 ml milk into tester from sample bottle thru coil immersed in 60° H_2O bath and then into homogenizer. Most of sample purges instrument of previous sample. Mix 1 ml aliquot of homogenized sample with predetd amt of EDTA soln. Let flow into photometer where light at 600 nm passes thru mixt. and is automatically measured with galvanometer. Galvanometer scale is graduated from 0.0–9.3 and results can be read directly in % fat when tester is calibrated by testing samples of milk by ref. method as in **16.061**.

16.061   Calibration of Milko-tester

Test in triplicate 20 representative milks, ranging from 3 to 6% fat by **16.052** or **16.054** and Milko-tester. Calc. av. for each sample by each method to nearest 0.01%. Calc. std deviation of difference, S_D, as follows:

$$S_D = \sqrt{[\Sigma(D^2) - ((\Sigma D)^2/N)]/(N - 1)}$$

where D = av. of results by **16.052** or **16.054** on sample minus the av. of Milko-tester results on same sample, e.g., $[(B_1 + B_2 + B_3)/3] - [(M_1 + M_2 + M_3)/3)] = D$; where B = reading by **16.052** or **16.054** and M = reading by Milko-tester; and N = number of samples tested. If specification of 20 samples is exceeded, include all samples tested in calcns except for those for which an error in 1 or more detns can be proven.

Milko-tester is properly calibrated when S_D so calcd is ≤0.10 for individual cow sample or ≤0.06 for herd or composite samples. Should S_D exceed these values, adjust vol. EDTA soln and/or elect. input to galvanometer of Milko-tester in accordance with manufacturer's instructions for calibration and operation.

During any calendar day of use, make performance check consisting of comparison of results obtained on 1 milk bulk sample, using both Milko-tester and **16.052** or **16.054**. If difference is >0.04% fat, repeat detn on 3 addnl samples. If av. differences of 3 addnl samples is >0.04% fat, re-calibrate Milko-tester.

16.062   Collection and Preparation
                                              of Samples

See **16.019–16.020.**

16.063   Determination

Bring sample(s) in loosely stoppered bottle to 35–40° in H_2O bath. Mix by pouring gently from original container into another container. Repeat 4 times. Do *not* mix all samples at once and then let them stand before testing. *Immediately* after mixing sample, obtain readings as in **16.060**.

Added Water

16.064 *Acetic Serum Method (14)—Official Final Action*

(a) *Zeiss immersion refractometer reading.*—To 100 ml sample, measured at 20° into beaker, add 2 ml 25% HOAc (sp gr 1.035). Cover beaker with watch glass, keep in H_2O bath 20 min at 70°, then in ice-H_2O 10 min, and sep. curd from serum by rapid filtration thru small filter. Transfer portion of clear serum to refractometer beaker, place in constant temp. bath, and take refractometer reading when temp. of serum is exactly 20°, as detd by thermometer graduated in 0.1°. (Scale readings are identical on Bausch and Lomb refractometers except those with serial Nos. 4000–10,000, for which readings of 38.6 and 39.6 correspond, resp., to 39 and 40 on Zeiss instrument. (Zeiss scale = B & L scale × 1.0092.))

(b) *Ash.*—Transfer 25 ml serum to weighed flat-bottom Pt dish and evap. to dryness on H_2O bath. Heat over low flame (to avoid spattering) until contents are thoroly charred, place dish in muffle, preferably temp. controlled, and ignite to white ash at ≤500°. Cool and weigh. Express result as g/100 ml.

16.065 *Copper Serum Method (15)—Official Final Action*

To 1 vol. $CuSO_4$ soln (72.5 g $CuSO_4.5H_2O$/L, adjusted if necessary to read 36 at 20° on scale of Zeiss immersion refractometer, or to sp gr of 1.0443 at 20/4°), add 4 vols milk. Shake well and filter. Det. refractometer reading of clear serum at 20°. (Scale readings are identical on Bausch and Lomb immersion refractometers except those with serial Nos. 4000–10,000 for which reading of 35.6 corresponds to 36 on Zeiss instrument.)

Cryoscopic Method (16)—Official Final Action

16.066 *Apparatus*

(a) *Cryoscope.*—See Fig. 16:2. 1 L cylindrical Dewar flask, 28 cm internal depth, encased in metal, is tightly closed by large cork ca 3 cm thick. Thru center of cork is tightly fitted, medium thin wall glass or metal tube, 250 mm long × 33 mm od. At one side of cork is inserted narrow metal inlet tube, lower end of which is formed into perforated loop near bottom of flask. At opposite side is T-shaped metal tube 6 mm id, for escape of vapors, and also for addn of volatile fluid into app. At back portion of cork is fitted control thermometer, bulb of which extends nearly to bottom of flask.

Freezing test tube is of thin glass, ca 240 mm long × 29 mm od, and fits closely into larger tube sealed into cork. In rubber stopper of freezing tube is fitted

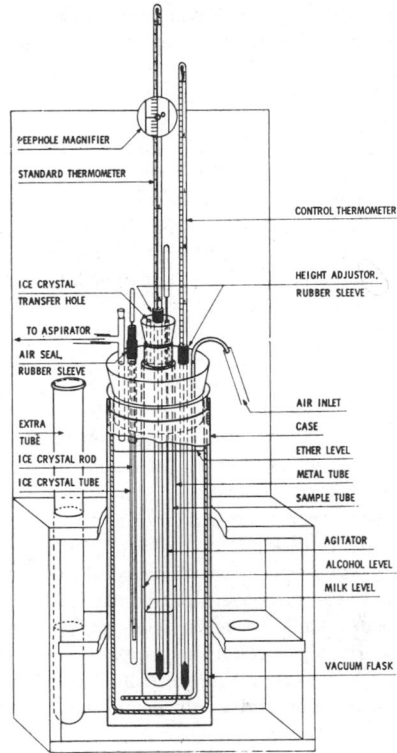

FIG. 16:2—Hortvet cryoscope

the std thermometer so that bottom of thermometer is 15 mm above bottom of sample tube. Length of thermometer permits insertion of bulb nearly to bottom of tube and at same time allows complete exposure of scale above stopper. At right side of thermometer stirring device made of noncorrodible low conductivity metal is fitted into stopper thru short section of thin-wall metal tubing; lower end extends nearly to bottom of test tube and is provided with horizontal loop encircling thermometer. At left of thermometer is freezing-starter attachment inserted thru opening in stopper formed by short section of metal tubing. This device consists of noncorrodible metal rod, at lower end of which is opening 10 mm long to carry small fragment of ice.

At one side of cryoscope is installed air-drying arrangement which consists of Folin absorption bulb inserted thru tightly fitting stopper and extending nearly to bottom of large test tube. Short section of glass tubing is inserted thru second opening in stopper and is connected to vaporizing tube which enters cryoscope. H_2SO_4 is poured into drying tube to level slightly above small inner bulb.

At opposite side of app. is arranged a drain tube to conduct vapors away from operator. Pressure or suction pump forces dry air into app. at suitable rate and conducts mixed vapors out thru base of drain tube into sink.

Adjustable lens is mounted in convenient position in front of thermometer to magnify the scale. *See* Fig. 16:2.

(b) *Standard thermometer.*—Solid-stem instrument 58 cm total length, with scale portion measuring ca 30 cm. Total scale range is 3°, from +1° to −2°, and each degree division is subdivided into tenths and hundredths. Length of 1° division is ca 10 cm, thus making smallest subdivisions of such magnitudes as to enable easy observation and readings estd to 0.001°. Stdze thermometer as in **16.067**. Check fp of freshly distd H_2O at beginning of each day. If fp deviates >0.002° from that obtained on H_2O when thermometer was stdzd, check to det. if Hg column is sepd. (Rejoin column as in (**d**).) If Hg column is not sepd, restdze thermometer.

(c) *Control thermometer.*—Solid-stem instrument ca 58 cm long with scale range of +20° to −30°. Test in bath of melting crushed ice to det. whether 0-mark on scale is correct. Scale graduations should be accurate to within 0.10°.

(d) *Care of Hortvet thermometers.*—Store thermometers vertically in refrigerator. Do not wash in warm H_2O. Examine before use to det. that Hg column is not sepd. If sepd, rejoin by tapping thermometer gently. If necessary warm thermometer slightly but avoid excessive warming which may alter the zero.

16.067   *Standardization of Thermometer*

Make 3 fp detns as in **16.068** on each of following:

(a) *Recently boiled distilled water.*

(b) *Sucrose soln.*—Dissolve 7 g pure sucrose in H_2O and dil. to 100 ml at 20°.

(c) *Sucrose soln.*—Dissolve 10 g pure sucrose in H_2O and dil. to 100 ml at 20°.

(Pure sucrose may be obtained from National Bureau of Standards, Washington, DC 20234.)

Express results as degrees freezing-point depression below av. of observed fps obtained on sample of pure H_2O (±W), which may be above (+) or below (−) 0-mark on scale. Obtain each fp depression of sucrose solns by algebraically subtracting av. of fp readings of pure H_2O (±W) from each observed fp.

Omit adventitious results, *i.e.*, results that are in marked disagreement with other results obtained by carefully following instructions.

Tabulate results in following form:

Apply av. of fp depressions obtained on std sucrose solns for correcting thermometer readings obtained on sample of milk as illustrated in tables accompanying Fig. 16:3.

(d) *Salt secondary std solns.*—Prep. solns by adding 0.6892 and 1.0206 g NaCl to 100 *grams* of H_2O, resp. These solns give fps equiv. to 7 and 10% sucrose solns, resp.

16.068   *Determination*

(If titratable acidity, **16.022**, is >0.18%, results may underest. actual amt of added H_2O in sample.)

Insert funnel-tube into vertical portion of T-tube at one side of app. and pour in 400 ml ether previously cooled to ≤10°. Close vertical tube with small cork and connect pressure pump to inlet tube of air-drying attachment. Adjust pump to pass air thru app. at moderate rate, judged by agitation of H_2SO_4 in drying tube. Continuous vaporization of ether causes lowering of temp. in flask from room temp. to 0° in 5–10 min. Continue temp. lowering until control thermometer registers near −3°. At this stage, by lowering gage tube into ether bath, then closing top with forefinger and raising to suitable ht, est. can be made of amt of ether necessary to pour in to restore 400 ml vol. After adjusting vol. ether to 400 ml, successive addns of 10–15 ml for each sample are usually sufficient.

Pour into freezing test tube enough H_2O (30–35 ml), boiled and cooled to ≤10°, to submerge thermometer bulb. Insert thermometer together with stirrer and lower test tube into larger tube. Small amt of alcohol, enough to fill lower space between 2 test tubes, serves to complete conduction medium between freezing bath and liq. to be tested. Keep stirrer in steady up-and-down motion of ca 1 stroke every 1 or 2 sec, or even at slower rate, provided cooling proceeds satisfactorily.

Keep air passing thru app. until temp. of cooling bath reaches −2.5° (top of Hg thread in thermometer usually recedes to position near fp of H_2O). Keep temp. of cooling bath at −2.5° and continue manipulating stirrer until super-cooling of sample of 1.0–1.2° is observed. As a rule, at this time liq. begins to freeze, indicated by rapid rise of the Hg. Manipulate stirrer slowly and carefully 3 or 4 times as Hg column approaches its highest point, *i.e.*, ca 0.07°

Freezing-Point Observations	Pure Water	7 Grams Sucrose Solution		10 Grams Sucrose Solution	
		Observed Freezing Point (−S)	Freezing-Point Depression S − W (Algebraic)	Observed Freezing Point (−S)	Freezing-Point Depression S − W (Algebraic)
1st					
2nd					
3rd					
Averages	±W	xxxxxxx		xxxxxxx	

Laboratory Thermometer No. 2.

Water	7 Grams Sucrose to 100 ml	10 Grams Sucrose to 100 ml
Av. +0.056°	−0.425°	−0.621°

Interval = 0.196
0.196 equiv. 0.199
Correction factor = 1.015

Laboratory Thermometer No. 24.

Water	7 Grams Sucrose to 100 ml	10 Grams Sucrose to 100 ml
Av. 0.000°	−0.420°	−0.625°

Interval = 0.205
0.205 equiv. 0.199
Correction factor = 0.971

Example:
Laboratory Thermometer No. 24.
Fp Depression Sample Milk = 0.548
(0.548 − .420) 0.971 = 0.124
True fp = 0.422 + 0.124
(= 0.546° below zero C)

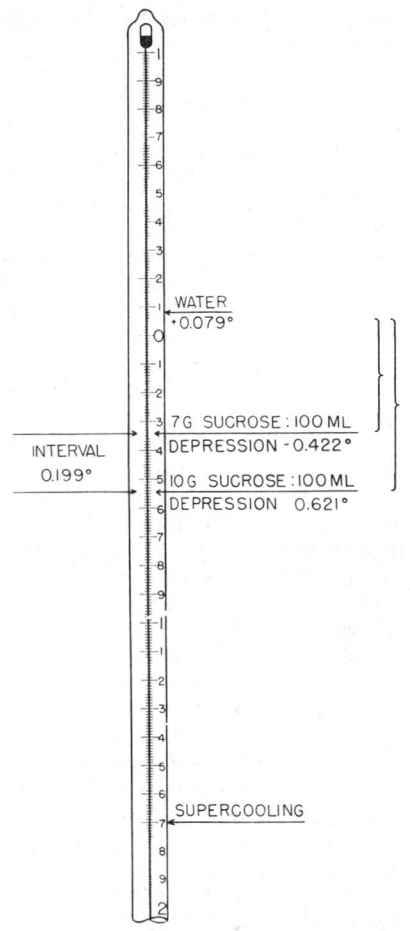

FIG. 16:3—National Bureau of Standards tested thermometer

below expected fp. With suitable light-wt mallet tap top of thermometer cautiously and continuously until top of Hg column remains stationary ≥1 min. Avoiding parallax, observe exact reading on scale and est. to 0.001°. When observation is satisfactorily completed, make duplicate detn; then remove thermometer and stirrer, and empty H_2O from freezing tube.

Rinse tube with ca 25 ml milk sample, cooled to ≤10°; measure 30–35 ml milk into tube or enough to submerge thermometer bulb, and insert tube into app. Keep temp. of cooling bath at 2.5° below probable fp of sample. Make detn on the milk as performed in detg fp of H_2O. As a rule, however, it is necessary to start freezing action in milk by inserting freezing-starter (kept in contact with ice for several min, and in open end of which is wedged fragment of ice) at time when Hg column has receded to 1.0–1.2° below probable fp. Rapid rise of the Hg results almost immediately.

Remove starter and manipulate stirrer slowly and

carefully 2 or 3 times when Hg approaches its highest point. Complete adjustment of Hg column in same manner as in preceding detn; then, avoiding parallax, observe exact reading on thermometer scale and est. to 0.001°. Make duplicate detn on new aliquot of milk. *Algebraic difference* between averages of readings obtained on the H_2O and readings obtained on milk sample represents *fp depression* of the milk. To det. true *fp* (T') of milk, subtract from fp depression, fp depression of 7% sucrose soln as detd by laboratory thermometer. Multiply difference by correction factor for thermometer. Add to product 0.422 (fp depression of 7% sucrose soln by NBS thermometer). See example in Fig. 16:3.

For interpretation, *see* 16.073.

Thermistor Instrument Method (17)—Official Final Action

16.069 *Apparatus*

Cryoscope.—Consists of cooling bath, sample agitator, seeding rod, thermistor probe (elec. resistance thermometer), and Wheatstone bridge and galvanometer, or taut band meter measuring circuit. Bath may be cooled by mech. or elec. means or by insulated ice-salt mixt. Sample may be immersed in cooling bath or bath may be "brought up" to sample mech. Observed fp value is read from measuring dial, calibrated in millidegrees C (0.001°C; more correctly, degrees Hortvet or "H"), when galvanometer or meter is nulled by rotation of dial.

Fill cooling bath at room temp. to proper level each time instrument is used. Proper coolant level is detd by observing coolant issuing from bath overflow or by visually checking coolant level, depending on the make and model of cryoscope. Cooling bath temp. should be −7 or −8±0.5°, depending on make of cryoscope, and temp. is measured by placing thermometer in empty sample well.

Locate thermistor probe, both horizontally and vertically, at midpoint of sample. Check location visually, using 2.5 ml H_2O in sample tube.

Amplitude of stirring wire should be great enough to assure uniform temp. in sample thruout detn and may be checked visually, using 2.5 ml H_2O in sample tube to which small amt of dust, powder, or dye has been added.

(App. available as Advanced Cryoscope from Advanced Instruments, Inc., 45 Kenneth St, Newton Highlands, MA 02161; as Fiske Cryoscope from Fiske Associates, Inc., Quaker Hwy, Uxbridge, MA 01569; and as Precision Cryoscope from Precision Systems, 44 Rumford Ave, Waltham, MA 02154.)

16.070 Preparation of Standards

(Use distd H_2O recently boiled and cooled to 20° for prepn of stds.)

Prep. following sucrose primary stds or salt secondary stds. Det. fp values as in (b).

(a) −0.422° Standard.—(1) Weigh 7.0000 g NBS std sucrose sample No. 17 into 100 ml vol. flask and dil. to vol. with H_2O; or (2) weigh 100 g H_2O into 100 ml vol. flask and add 0.6892 g reagent grade NaCl (dried to constant wt just before weighing).

(b) −0.621° Standard.—(1) Weigh 10.0000 g NBS sucrose into 100 ml vol. flask and dil. to vol. with H_2O; or (2) weigh 100 g H_2O into 100 ml vol. flask and add 1.0206 g reagent grade NaCl.

(Secondary salt stds with fp values equiv. to 7 and 10% sucrose primary stds may be purchased from all cryoscope manufacturers.)

Microorganisms attack sucrose after limited storage at refrigerator temps, changing fp value of primary stds. Salt (sucrose equiv.) secondary stds, stored in polyethylene bottles with screw caps, have long shelf life at room temp.; use these each time fp value detns are made. If it is suspected that salt secondary stds are in error, check them against *freshly* prepd sucrose primary stds. It is responsibility of the analyst to be certain that fp values of salt secondary stds are same as fp values of *freshly* prepd sucrose primary stds.

16.071 Calibration of Cryoscope

Using calibration controls and fp values of stds, calibrate cryoscope to obtain correct "span" (0.621° − 0.422° = 0.199°) and reference values (−0.621° and −0.422°). Follow directions in manufacturer's operating manual. Calibration controls and procedures vary with make and model of cryoscope but with all instruments 2 calibration controls (A and B or I and II) are adjusted, individually or in combination, so that 7 and 10% sucrose primary stds and/or sucrose equiv. salt secondary stds yield fp values of −0.422° and −0.621°, resp., with 0.199° span.

16.072 Determination

(If titratable acidity, 16.022, is >0.18%, results may underest. actual amt of added H_2O in sample.)

Apply following technic in exactly same manner for both stds and sample to obtain valid sample fp value.

Check cooling bath level, cooling bath temp., stirring efficiency, and probe position in sample tube as in 16.069.

Check ref. fp values and "span," using salt secondary stds or sucrose primary stds. If "span" is other than 0.199°, recalibrate cyroscope as in 16.071. If "span" is correct but reference fp values differ from known values of stds, it is not necessary to recalibrate cryoscope; simple arithmetic correction will give correct observed fp value of sample.

Using clean, dry syringe or pipet, measure 2–3 ml sample and transfer to clean, dry sample tube supplied by manufacturer. Set measuring dial to expected fp value. Place sample tube in cooling bath sample well or in operating head and lower operating head to position sample in cryoscope cooling bath.

Cool sample if not already being cooled above. Proper cooling is indicated by rapid and uniform (steady) movement of light spot or needle from right to left over scale of galvanometer or meter.

If cryoscope raises cooling bath to sample level, begin slow cooling at −1.5 to −2.0°, depending on extent of supercooling desired. If cryoscope immerses sample in cooling bath, do *not* isolate sample in air above cooling bath.

Seed sample at −2.0 or −3.0°, depending on make of cryoscope. Galvanometer spot or meter needle will jump to right as temp. of supercooled sample rises toward fp. Extent of supercooling (seeding point) must be same for sucrose primary stds or salt secondary stds as for milk samples.

Adjust galvanometer spot or meter needle to zero if necessary. Switch galvanometer or meter to high sensitivity position. With temp. dial, keep galvanometer or meter nulled (reading zero). Galvanometer spot or meter needle will cease to move to right, remain steady at zero, and finally begin to move to left. Read fp value from measuring dial to nearest millidegree, while spot or needle is steady just before movement to left begins. Do *not* read fp value from measuring dial at some predetd time after seeding sample; always wait for movement of galvanometer spot or meter needle to left before recording fp value. Spot or needle will become steady and begin to move to left sooner with stds than with milk samples. Check zero point of galvanometer or meter.

16.073 *Interpretation*

Official First Action.—If fp is $-0.525°$ or below, milk *may* be presumed to be H_2O-free *or may* be confirmed as H_2O-free by tests specified below. If fp is above $-0.525°$, milk *will* be designated "presumptive added H_2O" and *will* be confirmed as "added H_2O" or "H_2O-free" by tests specified below. Evaluate extreme daily fluctuations in fp of herd, pooled herd, or processed milk for presence of added H_2O.

To confirm herd milk as "added H_2O" or "H_2O-free," det. fp of authentic sample of herd milk obtained ≤ 48 hr after sample to be "confirmed." Authentic sample is sample of milk from 1 complete, supervised herd milking (either AM or PM but beginning not <11 or >13 hr after beginning of previous milking) obtained from bulk tank after entire herd has been milked thru approved, properly sanitized, and thoroly drained milking system into empty bulk tank but before rinsing or washing of system has begun. Compare fp of authentic sample and sample to be confirmed. If fps differ by $\leq 0.010°$, sample is confirmed as H_2O-free.

To confirm pooled herd milk as "added H_2O" or "H_2O-free," det. fp of authentic samples of all herd milks composing pooled herd milk, calc. weighted av. fp for the authentic samples of herd milk, and compare values as above.

To confirm processed milk as "added H_2O" or "H_2O-free," det. fp of samples of all pooled herd milk received by processing plant, calc. weighted av. fp for milk received, and compare with fp value to be confirmed. If fps differ by $\leq 0.010°$, processed sample is confirmed as H_2O-free during processing. If 1 or more samples of pooled herd milk are "presumptive added H_2O," proceed as above for pooled herd milk. Fp for pasteurized-homogenized milk should be same as that of pooled herd milk unless processing includes vac. pasteurization, which raises fp approx. $0.005°$.

Gelatin (18)

16.074 *Qualitative Test—Official Final Action*

(*Caution: See* **46.029** and **46.079.**)

To 10 ml sample add 10 ml *acid-Hg(NO₃)₂ soln* (Hg dissolved in twice its wt HNO_3 and this soln dild to 25 times its vol. with H_2O). Shake mixt., add 20 ml H_2O, shake again, let stand 5 min, and filter. If much gelatin is present, filtrate will be opalescent and cannot be obtained quite clear. To portion of filtrate in test tube add equal vol. *satd aq. picric acid*

soln. Yellow ppt is produced in presence of any considerable amt of gelatin; smaller amts are indicated by cloudiness.

Note: In applying this test to sour, fermented, cultured, or very old samples of milk, cream, or buttermilk; to sterilized cream or evaporated milk; or to cottage cheese, use care to recognize ppts produced by picric acid when added to the $Hg(NO_3)_2$ filtrates from these materials in absence of gelatin. Such samples, with or without rennet and entirely free from gelatin, give, on standing, distinct ppts when treated as above. In every case, however, these ppts differ in character from those produced by picric acid with gelatin.

Gelatin-picric acid ppt is finely divided, more apt to remain in suspension, settles only slowly, and adheres tenaciously to sides and bottom of container, from which it is rinsed with difficulty. Ppts produced by picric acid in absence of gelatin are flocculent, sep. readily (leaving serum practically clear), do not adhere to walls of container, and are easily removed by rinsing with H_2O. When gelatin is present in sample, gelatin-picric acid ppt will remain in suspension long after flocculent ppt has settled, but on standing overnight the characteristic sticky deposit will be found adhering tenaciously to bottom and sides of test vessel. If gelatin is present in relatively high concn (1%), gelatin-picric acid ppt will be voluminous and will settle rather quickly.

16.075 Preservatives—Official Final Action

Proceed as in Chap. **20.** To test for benzoic acid or salicylic acid, acidify 100 ml milk with 5 ml HCl $(1 + 3)$, shake until curdled, filter, and treat clear filtrate as in **20.020** and **20.085** or **20.086.**

To test for HCHO proceed as in **20.052–20.054.**

Hypochlorites and Chloramines (19)— Procedure

(Unreliable in presence of >2.5 ppm Cu)

16.076 *Reagents*

(**a**) *Potassium iodide soln.*—Dissolve 7 g KI in 100 ml H_2O. Prep. fresh.

(**b**) *Dilute hydrochloric acid.*—To 100 ml HCl add 200 ml H_2O.

(**c**) *Starch soln.*—Boil 1 g starch in 100 ml H_2O. Cool before using.

16.077 *Tests*

(**a**) To 5 ml milk in test tube add 1.5 ml KI soln, mix thoroly by shaking, and note color of milk.

(**b**) If unaltered, add 4 ml dil. HCl, mix thoroly with flat-end stirring rod, and note color of curd.

(**c**) Next place tubes in large H_2O bath, previously heated to $85°$, and let stand 10 min (during this interval curd rises to surface); then cool rapidly by placing in cold H_2O. Note color of curd and liq.

(**d**) Then add 0.5–1 ml starch soln to liq. below curd and note color.

16.078   *Reactions with the various tests*

Concentration of Available Cl	1:1,000	1:2,000	1:5,000	1:10,000	1:25,000	1:50,000
Test **a**	Yellowish brown	Deep yellow	Pale yellow, fades	—	—	—
Test **b**	Yellowish brown	Deep yellow	Light yellow	—	—	—
Test **c**	Yellowish brown	Deep yellow	Yellow	Yellow	Pale yellow	Yellowish
Test **d**	Blue purple	Blue purple	Blue purple	Dark red-purple	Red purple	Pale red-purple

16.079   Coloring Matters (20)—Official Final Action

Warm ca 150 ml milk in casserole over flame, add ca 5 ml HOAc (1 + 3), and continue to heat slowly nearly to bp while stirring. Gather curd, when possible, into one mass with stirring rod and pour off whey. If curd breaks up into small flecks, sep. from whey by straining thru sieve or colander. Press curd free from adhering liq., transfer to small flask, macerate with ca 50 ml ether, keeping flask tightly corked and shaking at intervals, and let stand several hr, preferably overnight. Decant ether ext into evapg dish, remove ether by evapn, and test fatty residue for annatto as in **34.020(b)**.

Curd of uncolored milk and milk colored with annatto is perfectly white after complete extn with ether. If extd fat-free curd is distinctly orange or yellowish, synthetic dye is indicated. In many cases if lump of fat-free curd in test tube is treated with little HCl, color changes to pink, indicating presence of dye similar to aniline yellow or butter yellow or perhaps one of the acid azo yellows or oranges. In such cases, sep. and identify coloring matter present in curd as in Chap. **34**.

In some cases presence of synthetic dyes can be detected by directly treating ca 100 ml milk with equal vol. HCl in porcelain casserole, giving dish slight rotary motion. In presence of some dyes sepd curd becomes pink.

16.080   Sediment Test—Official Final Action—See 40.013–40.016

Residual Phosphatase

All glassware, stoppers, and sampling tools must be scrupulously clean, and it is desirable to soak them in hot running H_2O after cleaning. Phenolic plastic closures on reagent bottles may cause phenolic contamination and their use should be avoided.

**16.081   ★   *Method I (21)—Official*   ★
*Final Action***

Colorimetric method using Folin-Ciocalteu phenol reagent. *See* **15.049–15.055**, 10th ed.

Method II (22)—Official Final Action

16.082   *Reagents*

(a) *Buffers:*

(1) *Barium borate-hydroxide buffer.*—pH 10.6 ±0.15 at 25°. Dissolve 25.0 g $Ba(OH)_2 \cdot 8H_2O$ (fresh, not deteriorated) in H_2O and dil. to 500 ml. Sep. dissolve 11.0 g H_3BO_3 and dil. to 500 ml. Warm each soln to 50°, mix solns, stir, cool to ca 20°, filter, and keep filtrate in tightly stoppered container. (For use with milk, dil. 500 ml of this buffer with 500 ml H_2O.)

(2) *Color development buffer.*—pH 9.8±0.15 at 25°. Dissolve 6.0 g Na metaborate ($NaBO_2$) and 20 g NaCl in H_2O, and dil. to 1 L with H_2O.

(3) *Color dilution buffer.*—Dil. 100 ml color development buffer, (*2*), to 1 L with H_2O.

(4) *Borax std buffer for checking pH meter.*—0.00996M, pH 9.180 at 25°, **45.007(f)**.

(b) *Buffer substrates:*

(1) *For evaluating pasteurization.*—Dissolve 0.10 g phenol-free cryst. disodium phenyl phosphate in 100 ml dild (1 + 1) Ba borate-hydroxide buffer, (a)(*1*). (Cryst. $Na_2C_6H_5PO_4$ should be stored in freezing compartment of refrigerator or in desiccator.) If $Na_2C_6H_5PO_4$ is not phenol-free, purify it as follows: Dissolve 0.5 g in 4.5 ml H_2O, add 0.5 ml buffer (a)(*1*) and 2 drops BQC reagent, (d), and let stand 30 min. Ext color with 2.5 ml butyl alcohol, (f), and let stand until alcohol seps. Remove alcohol with dropper and discard. Dil. 1.0 ml aq. soln to 100 ml with dil. Ba borate-hydroxide buffer, (a)(*1*), for prepn of buffer substrate. Heat soln to 85° for 2 min, stopper immediately, and store in refrigerator. Soln is stable 1 year if portions are withdrawn with min. exposure to atm. Develop color, and re-ext before use, if necessary.

(2) *For quantitative results with raw milk.*—Prep. as in (*1*), except to use 0.20 g $Na_2C_6H_5PO_4$ or 2.0 ml purified soln.

(c) *Zinc-copper protein precipitant.*—Dissolve 3.0 g $ZnSO_4 \cdot 7H_2O$ and 0.6 g $CuSO_4 \cdot 5H_2O$ in H_2O and dil. to 100 ml with H_2O.

(d) *BQC   (2,6-dibromoquinonechloroimide)   soln (Gibbs reagent).*—Dissolve 40 mg BQC powder in 10 ml absolute alcohol or MeOH and transfer to dark-color dropper bottle. (Reagent remains stable ≥1 month if kept in ice tray of refrigerator; do not use after it begins to turn brown. Store powd BQC in freezing compartment of refrigerator or in desiccator. (*Note:* Explosions of BQC reagent stored in bottles on reagent shelf have been reported.) Check new lots of BQC before use by prepg std curve with phenol and comparing curve obtained with that from lot of BQC known to be suitable. Repeat test at least semi-annually.)

(e) *Copper sulfate soln for stds.*—0.05%. Dissolve 0.05 g $CuSO_4.5H_2O$ in H_2O and dil. to 100 ml.

(f) *Butyl alcohol.*—Use *n*-butyl alcohol, bp 116–118°. To adjust pH, mix 1 L with 50 ml color development buffer, (a)(*2*). Store in g-s container.

(g) *Phenol std solns:*

(*1*) *Stock soln.*—Accurately weigh 1.000 g pure phenol, transfer to 1 L vol. flask, dil. to vol. with H_2O, and mix (1 ml = 1 mg phenol). (Soln is stable several months in refrigerator.)

(*2*) *Working stds.*—Dil. 10.0 ml stock soln to 1 L with H_2O and mix (1 ml = 10 µg, 0.00001 g, or 10 units of phenol). Use this std soln to prep. more dil. std solns: *e.g.*, dil. 5, 10, 30, and 50 ml to 100 ml with H_2O to prep. std solns contg 0.5, 1.0, 3.0, and 5.0 µg or units of phenol/ml, resp. Keep these std solns in refrigerator ≤1 week.

In similar manner prep. from stock soln std solns contg 20, 30, and 40 units/ml.

Measure appropriate quantities of working std solns into series of tubes (preferably graduated at 5.0 and 10.0 ml) to provide suitable range of stds as needed, contg 0 (control or blank), 0.5, 1.0, 3.0, 5.0, 10.0, 20.0, 30.0, and 40.0 units. To increase brightness of blue solns and improve stability of std, add 1.0 ml $CuSO_4$ soln, (e), to each tube. Then add 5.0 ml color diln buffer, (a)(*3*), and dil. to vol. of 10.0 ml with H_2O. Add 4 drops (0.08 ml) BQC soln, (d), mix, and let blue develop 30 min at room temp. If butyl alcohol extn method is used, ext stds as in **16.084,** *Step 10(b).*

Read color intensities in photometer with 610 nm filter, subtract value of blank from value of each phenol std, and prep. std curve (should be straight line).

If stds are to be used for visual comparison, store in refrigerator. Prep. new set weekly.

16.083 *Sampling*

Mix product well, pour several ml into small tube, stopper, and keep in refrigerator. If preservative is necessary, add 1–3% $CHCl_3$, and label "*Poison, preservative added.*"

16.084 *Determination*

Chemical principles involved in detection and measurement of milk phosphatase activity are same for all dairy products, but different dairy products require modifications of methods because of their different physical properties, compositions, and especially buffering capacities.

For milk and other fluid products, proceed as follows:

Step 1.—Pipet 1.0 ml portions of sample into 2 or 3 tubes (one tube is needed for control or blank; it is preferable to have 2 more tubes for duplicate detns). (For goat's milk, use 3 ml portions.)

Step 2.—Heat *blank* ca 1 min in covered beaker of boiling H_2O (temp. of entire tube must be 85–90°) and cool to room temp. From this point on, treat blank and test identically.

Step 3.—Add 10.0 ml Ba buffer substrate, (b)(*1*) or (*2*), stopper tube, and mix (pH 10.0±0.15).

(This substrate is satisfactory for fresh milk, sweet buttermilk, or cheese whey. For old or slightly sour milk use substrate prepd from undild buffer, (a)(*1*); for chocolate drinks prep. substrate from buffer dild with ¼ vol. H_2O; for very acid (pH <4.5) buttermilk prep. substrate from the 26-11 buffer, **16.216(a)(*2*)**; and for goat's milk prep. substrate from the 27-11 buffer, **16.216(a)(*2*)**.

For precise quant. results on unknown samples, adjust pH to 10.0–10.05.

Step 4.—Immediately after adding substrate, incubate in H_2O bath 1 hr at 37–38°, mixing or shaking contents occasionally.

Step 5.—Heat in beaker of boiling H_2O nearly 1 min. (Temp. of contents of tubes should reach 85–90°, as detd by thermometer in another tube of same size and shape contg same vol. liq.) Cool to room temp. in vessel of cold H_2O.

Step 6.—Pipet in 1.0 ml Zn-Cu protein precipitant, (c), for fresh milk, sweet buttermilk, or cheese whey. (For old or slightly sour milk or acid buttermilk substitute 1.0 ml 6.0 g/100 ml $ZnSO_4.7H_2O$ soln; for chocolate drinks use 1.0 ml of soln contg 4.5 g $ZnSO_4.7H_2O$ and 0.1 g $CuSO_4.5H_2O$/100 ml; and for goat's milk use 1.0 ml of soln 7.5 g $ZnSO_4.7H_2O$ and 0.1 g $CuSO_4.5H_2O$/100 ml.) Mix thoroly (pH of mixt. should be 9.0–9.1).

Step 7.—Filter (5 cm funnel, 9 cm Whatman No. 42 or No. 2 paper, or equiv.) and collect 5.0 ml filtrate in tube, preferably graduated at 5.0 and 10.0 ml.

Step 8.—Add 5.0 ml color development buffer, (a)(*2*), (pH of mixt. should be 9.3–9.4).

Step 9.—Add 4 drops BQC soln, (d), mix, and let color develop 30 min at room temp. (For merely detecting underpasteurization, add only 2 drops of the BQC soln).

Step 10.—Det. intensity of blue color by one of following methods:

(a) *With photometer.*—Read color intensities of blank and test solns (using filter with max. *T* ca 610 nm), subtract reading of blank from that of test, and convert result to phenol equivs by ref. to std curve, (g)(*2*). [Ordinarily butyl alcohol extn is unnecessary when photometer is used; if butyl alcohol extn is made as in (b), centrf. sample 5 min to break emulsion and remove H_2O suspended in alcohol layer. (Babcock centrf. can be adapted for this purpose by making special tube holders as follows: Slice section ¼" thick from rubber stopper of suitable diam. to fit into bottom of centrf. cup. Glue together 2 cork stoppers of appropriate diam., bore thru center a hole of proper size to hold tube snugly, and insert double cork section into cup.) After centrfg, remove nearly all butyl alcohol by pipet with rubber bulb on top end. Filter into photometer cell and read with filter with max. T ca 650 nm.

(b) *With visual stds.*—With samples yielding >5 units, compare colors in tubes with those of aq. phenol stds, (g)(2). For quant. results in borderline instances (*e.g.*, tests yielding 0.5–5 units of color), ext with butyl alcohol, (f). Add 5.0 ml of the alcohol and invert tube slowly several times; centrf. as in (a) if necessary to increase clearness of alcohol layer, and compare blue with colors of phenol stds, (g)(2), similarly treated.

Step 11.—In tests observed to be strongly pos. during color development (*e.g.*, ≥20 units), in which 4 drops of BQC soln may be insufficient to combine with all the phenol, pipet appropriate proportion of contents into another tube, dil. to 10.0 ml with color diln buffer, (a)(3), and add 2 drops addnl BQC soln. With each test, dil. and treat blank similarly. If test on dild sample is still very strongly pos., dil. again in same manner until final color is within range of visual stds or photometer std curve. Allow 30 min for color development after last addn of BQC soln before making final reading. To correct reading for diln, multiply by 2 for 5 + 5 diln, by 10 for 1 + 9 diln, and by 50 for 1 + 9 diln followed by 2 + 8 diln, etc.

Step 12.—When using 1.0 ml sample and adding 11.0 ml reagents (total liq. 12.0 ml, 5.0 ml filtrate used), multiply value of reading by 1.2 to convert to phenol equivs/0.5 ml sample. (If desired, results may be converted to phenol equivs/1 ml by multiplying by 2.4.) Phenol equivs >2/0.5 ml indicate underpasteurization in cow's milk, chocolate drinks, buttermilk, and cheese whey; phenol equivs >1/1.5 ml indicate underpasteurization in goat's milk.

Notes: To test concd milk products, reconstitute product with H_2O to original concn of milk solids and test in manner specified for original product. *See also Notes in* **16.218.**

Method III (23)—Official First Action
16.085   *Principle*

Milk is incubated with disodium phenyl phosphate in carbonate buffer at pH 9.5–9.7 for 1 hr in seamless, cellulose bag of critical pore diam. Free phenol is liberated by residual alk. phosphatase of milk and passes thru cellulose membrane, that retains proteins, into $CuSO_4$ soln for color reaction with CQC. Color produced reflects concn of alk. phosphatase. This is related to prior heat treatment given milk, as enzyme is largely destroyed at min. pasteurization times and temps.

16.086   *Reagents*

(a) *Carbonate buffer substrate.*—Dissolve 11.5 g Na_2CO_3 and 10.2 g $NaHCO_3$ in 1 L vol. flask and dil. to ca 950 ml with H_2O. Dissolve 1.1 g disodium phenyl phosphate in 10 ml of this soln in separator. Add 4 drops CQC reagent, (c), swirl, and let stand 30

min. Ext color with two 5 ml portions butanol, letting layers sep. Quant. add colorless aq. layer to remainder of buffer in vol. flask and dil. to 1 L with H_2O. Heat soln to 85° for 2 min, stopper immediately, and store in refrigerator. Soln is stable 1 year if soln is withdrawn with min. exposure to atm. Develop color and re-ext before use, if necessary.

(b) *Copper sulfate soln.*—Dissolve 100 mg $CuSO_4.5H_2O$ in H_2O and dil. to 1 L.

(c) *2,6-Dichloroquinonechloroimide (CQC).*—Dissolve 50 mg CQC (Aldrich Chemical Co., 2371 N 30th St, Milwaukee, WI 53210, No. D7410) in 10 ml absolute alcohol or MeOH, and store in dark brown dropper bottle in freezing compartment. (Observe storage precautions as for BQC, **16.082**(d).)

(d) *Dialyzing, seamless, cellulose tubing.*—Available as "Dialysis Tubing, formerly Visking," from Union Carbide Corp., Food Products Div., 6733 W. 65 St, Chicago, IL 60638. Order No. 27 DC; 0.001″ wall thickness, pore openings 4.8 nm, width flat 1.31″, diam. round 21 mm, 1000 ft random lengths. Cut enough 8″ lengths of tubing and immerse in H_2O ≥30 sec. Remove, and wrinkle one end with fingers. Twist and tie this end tightly into leakproof knot, and cut off excess cellulose beyond knot with scissors. Immerse bag in H_2O until ready to use. During use, take precautions against phenol or enzyme contamination from contact with fingers or phenol-contg substances, e.g., plastics.

(e) *Carbonate buffer soln.*—Dissolve 11.5 g Na_2CO_3, 10.2 g $NaHCO_3$, and 0.1 g $CuSO_4.5H_2O$ in H_2O, and dil. to 1 L.

(f) *Dilute phenol soln.*—4 μg/ml. Dil. 2 ml phenol stock soln, **16.082**(g)(1), to 500 ml with carbonate buffer soln, (e).

16.087   *Preparation of Standard Curve*

Prep., in 16 × 150 mm test tubes, 10 ml portions of mixts as follows:

Carbonate Buffer Soln, ml	Dil. Phenol Soln, ml	Phenol Concn μg/10 ml
0	10	40
5	5	20
6	4	16
7	3	12
8	2	8
9	1	4
9.5	0.5	2
9.75	0.25	1
10.0	0	0

Add 2 drops CQC to each std with swirling. Incubate 5 min at 37°. Read at 650 nm within 30 min after development. Plot A against μg phenol/10 ml.

16.088   *Determination*

Remove cellulose bag, prepd as in (d), from H_2O. Open top end by wrinkling wet cellulose with fingers, and pipet in 10.0 ml warm (40°) carbonate buffer substrate, (a), and 5.0 ml milk. Press air out of bag and knot top end tightly. Mix by inverting several times, kneading closed bag with fingers.

Rinse cellulose bags with H_2O, drain for moment, and slide bags, bottom end first, into 25 × 150 mm test tubes contg 10.0 ml $CuSO_4$ soln so that knot just touches bottom of tube. Top of knotted end must be kept free from contact with soln. (If, during filling, milk inadvertently gets on outside of bag and is not rinsed adequately, turbidity appears in $CuSO_4$ soln and detn must be repeated.)

Temper test tube contg filled dialysis bag in H_2O bath 5 min at 37° and incubate 1 hr at 37°.

Remove bag from test tube and discard. Add 2 drops CQC soln to clear soln in test tube, and swirl. Develop color at 37° exactly 5 min, transfer colored solns to spectrophtr cells, and read at 650 nm within 30 min.

Perform reagent blank detn on buffer substrate. Add 2 drops CQC to 10 ml buffer substrate and incubate 5 min at room temp. If substrate turns blue, reagents must be repurified.

Perform control detn with each batch. Heat milk 2 min in clean test tube in boiling H_2O bath. Cool, and test as for sample. Control should show no blue.

Qualitative (Screening) Method (24)—Official
First Action

(Applicable to skim and whole milk and light cream)

16.089   *Reagents*

(a) *Phenolphthalein monophosphate soln* (*substrate concentrate*).—pH 10.15 at 25°. Dissolve 3.9 g dicyclohexylamine salt of phthln monophosphate and 73.2 g 2-amino-2-methyl-1-propanol in 21.9 ml HCl. Soln is stable indefinitely under refrigeration. (Available as Phosphastrate® Alkaline from General Diagnostics Div., Warner-Chilcott Laboratories, Morris Plains, NJ 07950.)

(b) *Phenolphthalein-tartrazine soln* (*std concentrate*).—0.01 and 0.04% by wt, resp.; pH 10.15 at 25°. Dissolve 10 mg phthln, 40 mg tartrazine, and 73.2 g 2-amino-2-methyl-1-propanol in 21.9 ml HCl. Soln is stable indefinitely under refrigeration.

(c) *Color developer.*—2.5N NaOH.

16.090   *Determination*

Pipet 1 ml milk into each of two 15 × 100 mm test tubes and warm to 37°. To 1 tube add 1 drop (0.04 ml) substrate conc. (pH of incubation mixt. 10.0) and to other add 1 drop std conc. Mix and incubate 30 min at 37°. Add 1 drop 2.5N NaOH to each tube, mix, and compare visually. If sample soln (in tube contg substrate conc.) is less pink than std soln, milk has been pasteurized to extent equiv. to <0.1% raw milk.

Reactivated and Residual Phosphatase, Differential Test (25)—Official
First Action

16.091   *Reagent*

Magnesium chloride soln.—0.1196 g Mg/ml. Dissolve 100 g $MgCl_2.6H_2O$ in 25 ml H_2O, warming slightly. Transfer to 100 ml vol. flask, rinsing with H_2O. Cool, and dil. to 100 ml.

16.092   *Controls*

Place 50 ml of each sample to be tested in boiling H_2O bath and hold 1 min after temp. of sample reaches 95°. Cool, and use portion of each for diln as required and for boiled control.

16.093   *Determination*

Place 10 ml aliquot of sample in screw cap (phenolfree) test tube. To second 10 ml aliquot in identical tube add $MgCl_2$ soln as follows:

Fat Content of Sample (%)	MgCl₂ Soln/10 ml Aliquot (ml)
3–7	0.40
8–12	0.35
13–18	0.30
19–25	0.25
26–31	0.20
32–40	0.15

Incubate both aliquots 1 hr at 34°. Remove samples from bath and dil. 1 ml sample contg Mg with 5 ml of corresponding boiled control. Test undild sample contg no Mg and 1 + 5 diln contg Mg for phosphatase activity by **16.084, 16.088,** or **16.122.**

16.094   *Interpretation*

If 1 + 5 diln contg Mg has equal or greater phosphatase activity than undild sample contg no Mg, sample is regarded as neg. for residual phosphatase and indicates phosphatase originally measured is of reactivated origin. If dild sample contains less activity than undild sample, it is considered pos. for residual phosphatase provided that initial conventional phosphatase test was pos. False pos. test for residual phosphatase may be obtained if reactivatable sample stood at elevated temp. (70–75°F) for ≥2 hr.

Penicillin (26)—Official Final Action
Qualitative Field Disk Assay
(Sensitive to ca 0.05 unit/ml)

16.095   *Culture Media*

(a) *Agar medium A.*—For carrying test organism and for performing assay. *See* **38.164(a).**

(b) *Agar medium AM.*—For prepg test suspension. Prep. as in (a), adding 0.30 g $MnSO_4.H_2O/L$.

16.096   *Reagents*

(a) *Stock penicillin soln.*—Accurately weigh, in atm. of 50% relative humidity or less, ca 10 mg USP Na Penicillin G Ref. Std. Dissolve in enough pH 6 buffer (8.0 g anhyd. KH₂PO₄ and 2.0 g anhyd. K₂HPO₄/L) to give concn of exactly 100 units/ml. Store in dark at ca 5° ≤2 days.

(b) *Control disks* —Dil. stock penicillin soln with antibiotic-free whole, homogenized milk to final concns of 0.05 and 0.1 unit/ml. Use S&S No. 740E ¼″ disks or prep. ¼″ round, white disks from S&S No. 470W or 470 paper, of equiv. absorption performance qualities and purity. Dip disks into std penicillin contg milks and shake off excess. Dry on rust-proof wire screening under fan. Stored in refrigerator in tightly stoppered vial with desiccant, disks are usable 1 month.

16.097   *Stock Culture of Test Organism*

Maintain *Bacillus subtilis* on agar medium A, transferring to fresh slant monthly. Inoculate fresh slant of agar medium A with test organism and incubate 16–24 hr at 37°. Wash culture from slant with 2–3 ml *sterile 0.9% NaCl soln* with aid of sterile glass beads onto surface of Roux bottle contg 300 ml agar medium AM. Incubate 5 days at 37°. Wash resulting growth from surface with aid of the beads and 50 ml sterile 0.9% NaCl soln into sterile centrf. tube, centrf., and decant supernatant. Reconstitute sediment with ca 70 ml sterile 0.9% NaCl soln and heat-shock spore suspension by heating 30 min at 70°. Store in g-s flask in refrigerator. Suspension is stable several months.

With each new suspension, det. amt to be used as follows: Prep. plates as directed below with varying amts of inoculum, *i.e.*, 0.2, 0.5, 1.0, and 2.0 ml/100 ml medium. Refrigerate 3–5 days. Place on plates control disks of 0.05 and 0.1 unit/ml and incubate as in test. Use as concn of inoculum that concn showing best response, considering both sensitivity and discernibility of zones of inhibition.

16.098   *Preparation of Plates*

Melt agar medium A, cool to 55–60°, and add 0.2–2.0 ml spore suspension, **16.097,** to each 100 ml agar medium A. Mix well.

Add 10 ml inoculated agar to each 20 × 100 mm glass or plastic petri dish. Distribute agar evenly, cover with porcelain covers glazed only on outside, and let harden on level surface. Store in refrigerator ≥3 but ≤5 days. Remove each dish from refrigerator as needed and use within 15 min.

16.099   *Assay*

With forceps place 0.05 and 0.1 unit/ml control disks on each plate.

Thoroly shake each milk sample to disperse fat evenly. Using forceps, dip blank disk completely into sample, withdraw, and shake off excess milk by vigorously waving in air several times. Place disk on surface of agar and touch gently with tip of forceps to assure proper contact. *Do not touch so heavily that milk is squeezed out of disk.* Place disks so that they are at least 20 mm apart, measured center to center,

to avoid overlapping of zones. Flame tips of forceps to avoid carryover from contaminated samples. Place control and sample disks on plate within few min of one another.

Incubate plates 2.5–3 hr at 37°, and examine for zones of inhibition. Hold plates at various angles to light (either elec. bulb or daylight) to det. optimum conditions for observation. Zones around control disks indicate sensitivity of test.

To det. if zone of inhibition is due to penicillin, add 0.05 ml (ca 1 drop) *penicillinase conc.* (BBL or Difco penicillinase have been found satisfactory) to 5 ml aliquot milk sample and shake well. Prep. 3 disks from this treated sample and from untreated sample. Place all disks on same plate, incubate as before, and observe. Zone around untreated sample disks but no zone around treated sample disks in pos. test for penicillin. Zone of inhibition around both treated and untreated sample disks indicates antibacterial activity other than penicillin.

16.100   *Quantitative Overnight Method*

Use method for penicillin in feed, **38.214–38.217,** prepg std solns for std curve with antibiotic-free, whole, homogenized milk instead of pH 6 buffer. Cylinders must be used for application of samples and stds for detection of as little as 0.01 unit penicillin/ml. Disk method of application, **16.099,** instead of cylinders may be used for concns >0.025 unit/ml. Milk sample is assay soln unless concn >0.2 unit/ml is anticipated, in which case dil. sample with antibiotic-free milk to estd concn of 0.05 unit/ml.

16.101   Vitamin D in Milk—*See* 39.149–39.162

CREAM

16.102   Collection of Sample—Procedure
(*See* also **16.001–16.007.**)

Proceed as in **16.019.** Promptly analyze sample, preferably within 3 days after collection.

16.103   Preparation of Sample—Procedure

Immediately before withdrawing test portions, mix sample by shaking, pouring, or stirring (or use hand homogenizer) until it pours readily and uniform emulsion forms. If sample is very thick, warm to 30–35° and mix. In case lumps of butter have sepd, heat sample to ca 38° by placing in warm H₂O bath. (Temp. appreciably >38° may cause fat to "oil off," especially in case of thin cream.) Thoroly mix portions for analysis and weigh immediately. (In com. testing for fat by Babcock method, it may be advisable to warm all samples to ca 38° in H₂O bath previous to mixing.)

16.104   Preparation of Sample of Pressurized Cream—Official Final Action

Place containers in freezer overnight to freeze contents. Release as much gas as possible from frozen contents thru nozzle, holding container upright. Refreeze if necessary. Open container, using can opener on nonreturnable type or wrench on heavier, returnable type. Empty contents into weighed 1 L jar of high-speed blender, and weigh to 0.1 g. Let thaw (complete thawing is not necessary). Beat to smooth, creamy liq., keeping blender covered. Beat intermittently to prevent overheating sample and blender. (Process may require 15 min. "Butter" stage is intermediate, and beating must be continued until this stage is passed.) When sufficiently mixed, weigh blender jar and contents again. Calc. % loss in wt and apply this correction to subsequent detns. Weigh samples for fat, solids, sucrose, or other analyses, beating few sec between withdrawals of samples.

16.105 Lactic Acid—Official Final Action—See 16.026–16.031

16.106 Water-Insoluble Fatty Acids (27)—Official Final Action

Weigh 50 g prepd sample, **16.103**, into 250 ml centrf. bottle, add 20 ml alcohol, shake, and add 50 ml ether. Proceed as in **16.177**, par. 2, except use 10 ml Na$_2$WO$_4$ soln. (When Na$_2$WO$_4$-treated mixt. is shaken with ether, emulsions may form and not break completely on centrfg. These emulsions may be broken by adding 10–20 ml alcohol, mixing gently, and again centrfg.)

16.107 Rapid Method—Official First Action—See 16.185

16.108 Volatile Acids (28)—Official Final Action

Weigh 100 g sample into 250 ml vol. flask, add 100 ml H$_2$O and 2 ml H$_2$SO$_4$ (1 + 1), and mix, avoiding violent shaking. Add 15 ml *10% Na$_2$WO$_4$.2H$_2$O soln*, dil. to vol., mix, and filter thru rapid paper. Transfer 150 ml filtrate to distn flask and proceed with distn, chromatgc sepn, and detn as in **18.030–18.034** or **18.035–18.038**. Calc. to mg acids/100 g fat.

See **14.091–14.093** for identification of volatile acids.

16.109 Total Solids—Official Final Action

Proceed as in **16.032**, using 2–3 g sample.

16.110 Added Water (29)—Official Final Action

Proceed as in **16.068**.

16.111 Ash—Official Final Action—See 16.034

16.112 Total Nitrogen—Official Final Action—See 16.035

Lactose

16.113 Gravimetric Method—Official Final Action—See 16.051

Fat

16.114 Roese-Gottlieb Method—Official Final Action

Using 5 g sample and dilg with H$_2$O to ca 10.5 ml, proceed as in **16.052**, beginning "Add 1.25 ml NH$_4$OH ..."

Babcock Method—Official Final Action

16.115 Apparatus

(a) *Test bottles.*—Std Babcock cream-test bottles are as follows:

(1) *50%, 9 g, short-neck, 6" cream-test bottle.*—Total ht 150–165 mm (5.9–6.5"). Bottom of bottle must be flat, and axis of neck must be vertical when bottle stands on level surface. Charge of cream for bottle is 9 g.

Bulb.—Capacity of bulb to junction with neck is ≥45 ml. Shape of bulb may be either cylindrical or conical. If cylindrical, od must be 34–36 mm; if conical, od of base must be 31–33 mm, and max. diam., 35–37 mm.

Neck.—Cylindrical and of uniform diam. from ≥5 mm below lowest graduation mark to ≥5 mm above highest. Top of neck is flared to diam. of ≥15 mm. Graduated portion of neck has length ≥63.5 mm. Total % graduation is 50. Graduations shall represent 5, 1, and ½%, resp., from 0.0 to 50%. 5% graduations must extend at least half-way around neck to right; ½% graduations must be ≥3 mm long; and 1% graduations must be intermediate in length between 5% and ½% graduations and project 2 mm to left of ½% graduations. Each 5% graduation must be numbered (thus: 0, 5, 10, ... 45, 50), number being placed to left of scale. Capacity of neck for each whole % on scale must be 0.1 ml. Max. error in total graduation or any part thereof must not exceed vol. of smallest unit of graduation.

(2) *50%, 9 g, long-neck, 9" cream-test bottle.*—Same specifications apply to this bottle as to 50%, 9 g, 6" cream-test bottle, except that total ht of this bottle is 210–229 mm (8.25–9.0") and graduated portion of neck has length of ≥120 mm.

(3) *50%, 18 g, long-neck, 9" cream-test bottle.*—Same specifications apply to this bottle as to 50%, 9 g, 9" cream-test bottle, except that charge of cream for this bottle is 18 g.

Each bottle must bear on top of neck above graduations, in plain legible characters, mark denoting wt charge to be used, *viz.*, "9 g" or "18 g," as case may be.

Each bottle must be constructed so as to withstand stress to which it will be subjected in centrf.

(4) *Testing.*—Proceed as in **16.053**(a)(3).

(b) *Water bath for cream samples.*—Provided with thermometer and device to maintain temp. of 38°.

(c) *Cream weighing scales.*—With sensibility reciprocal of 30 mg, *i.e.*, addn of 30 mg to either pan of scale, when loaded to capacity, causes deflection of ≥ 1 subdivision of graduation. Set scales level upon support and protect from drafts.

(d) *Weights.*—9 g and 18 g, resp., and plainly marked "9 g" or "18 g," as case may be. Must be made of material capable of resisting corrosion or other injury, and preferably of low squat shape, with rounded edges. Verify them at frequent intervals by comparison with stdzd wts.

(e) *Acid measure.*—See **16.053**(c).

(f) *Centrifuge or "tester."*—See **16.053**(d).

(g) *Dividers or calipers.*—See **16.053**(e).

(h) *Water bath for test bottles.*—See **16.053**(f).

16.116   *Determination*

Weigh 9 g prepd sample, **16.103,** directly into 9 g cream-test bottle, or 18 g into 18 g bottle, and proceed by one of following methods.

(a) *Method 1.*—After weighing cream into test bottle, add 8–12 ml H_2SO_4 (sp gr 1.82–1.83 at 20°) to 9 g bottle; or 14–17 ml to 18 g bottle; or add acid until mixt. of cream and acid, after shaking, is chocolate-brown. Shake until all lumps completely disappear and add 5–10 ml soft H_2O at 60° or above. Transfer bottle to centrf., counterbalance it, and after proper speed is reached, centrf. 5 min. Add soft hot H_2O until liq. column approaches top graduation of scale; then centrf. 1 min longer at 55–60°. Adjust temp. as in **16.054,** and with aid of dividers or calipers measure fat column, in terms of % by wt, from lower surface to bottom of upper meniscus.

(b) *Method 2.*—For 9 g bottle only.—After weighing cream into test bottle, add 9 ml soft H_2O and mix thoroly; add ca 17.5 ml of the H_2SO_4 and shake until all lumps completely disappear. Transfer bottle to centrf., counterbalance it, and after proper speed is reached, centrf. 5 min. Fill bottle to neck with hot H_2O and centrf. 2 min. Add hot H_2O until liq. column approaches top graduation of scale, and centrf. 1 min longer at 55–60°. Adjust temp. and measure fat column as in (a).

Whichever method is followed, fat column, at time of reading, should be translucent, golden yellow to amber, and free from visible suspended particles. Reject all tests in which fat column is milky or shows presence of curd or of charred matter, or in which reading is indistinct or uncertain; repeat test, adjusting amt of H_2SO_4 added.

If glymol or pure white mineral oil (sp gr ≤ 0.85 at 20°) is used, introduce only few drops into bottle just before reading is made, letting it flow down inside of neck. For purpose of measurement, surface sepg glymol and fat is regarded as representing upper limit of column. Oil-sol. artificial color may be added to the white mineral oil.

16.117   Gelatin—Official Final Action—*See* 16.074

Observe note

16.118   Preservatives—Official Final Action— *See* **16.075** and Chap. 20

16.119   Coloring Matters—Official Final Action—*See* **16.079** and Chap. 34

Residual Phosphatase—Official Final Action

16.120   ★   *Method I—See* **16.081**   ★

Method II (22)

16.121   *Reagents and Sampling*

See **16.082** and **16.083.**

16.122   *Determination*

Proceed as in **16.084,** except for following:

In *Step 1*, use 1.0 g instead of 1 ml sample if desired.

In *Step 3*, treat fresh cream in same manner as fresh milk; for old or slightly sour cream use 8 ml of the Ba borate-hydroxide buffer, **16.082**(a)(*1*), and 2 ml H_2O.

In *Step 6*, treat fresh cream in same manner as fresh milk; for old or slightly sour cream substitute 1.0 ml 4.5 g/100 ml soln $ZnSO_4 \cdot 7H_2O$ for the Zn-Cu precipitant.

Phenol equivs $>2/0.5$ ml or 0.5 g indicate underpasteurization.

16.123   Reactivated and Residual Phosphatase —Official First Action—*See* 16.091–16.094

EVAPORATED MILK (UNSWEETENED)

16.124   Sampling—Official Final Action—*See* 16.001–16.005 and 16.008–16.009

16.125   Preparation of Sample (*30*)— Procedure

(FAO/WHO method. *See Introduction*, **16.052.**)

(a) Temper unopened can in H_2O bath at ca 60°. Remove and vigorously shake can every 15 min. After 2 hr, remove can and let cool to room temp. Remove entire lid and thoroly mix by stirring contents in can with spoon or spatula. (If fat seps, sample is not properly prepd.)

(b) Dil. 40 g prepd mixt. (a) with 60 g H_2O and mix thoroly.

16.126   Lactic Acid—Official Final Action— *See* 16.026–16.031

16.127   Total Solids (*5*)—Official Final Action

Proceed as in **16.032,** using 4–5 g dild sample, **16.125**(b). Correct result for diln.

16.128 Ash (5)—Official Final Action

Ignite residue from total solids detn, **16.127**, at temp. ≤550° until ash is C-free. Correct result for diln.

16.129 Fat (30)—Official Final Action

(FAO/WHO method. *See Introduction*, **16.052**.)

Weigh, to nearest mg, 4–5 g undild sample, **16.125(a)**, into fat-extn flask or tube; dil. with ca 7 ml H_2O to ca 10.5 ml and shake with slight warming (40–50°) until sample is completely dispersed. Proceed as in **16.052**, beginning "Add 1.25 ml NH_4OH ..." Some evapd milks may require centrfg as long as 20 min at 600 rpm for complete sepn of emulsion. Difference between duplicate detns obtained simultaneously by same analyst should be ≤0.05 g fat/100 g product.

16.130 Total Nitrogen—Official Final Action

Weigh 5 g undild sample, **16.125(a)**, transfer to Kjeldahl flask, and proceed as in **2.051**. % N × 6.38 = % "protein."

16.131 Casein—Official Final Action

Weigh 10 g dild sample, **16.125(b)**, into beaker, and proceed as in **16.041** or **16.043**. Correct result for diln.

16.132 Albumin—Official Final Action

Proceed as in **16.044**, using filtrate from casein detn, **16.131**. Correct result for diln.

16.133 Lactose—Official Final Action

Proceed as in **16.050** or **16.051**, using dild sample, **16.125(b)**, and correct result for diln.

16.134 Gelatin—Official Final Action—*See* 16.074

16.135 Preservatives—Official Final Action—*See* 16.075 and Chap. 20

16.136 Coloring Matters—Official Final Action—*See* 16.079 and Chap. 34

SWEETENED CONDENSED MILK

16.137 Sampling—Official First Action—*See* 16.001–16.005 and 16.008–16.009

16.138 Preparation of Sample—Procedure

(a) Temper unopened can in H_2O bath at 30–35° until warm. Open, scrape out all milk adhering to interior of can, transfer to dish large enough to permit stirring thoroly, and mix until whole mass is homogeneous.

(b) Weigh 100 g thoroly mixed sample into 500 ml vol. flask, dil. to vol. with H_2O, and mix thoroly. If sample will not emulsify uniformly, weigh out sep. portion of (a) for each detn.

16.139 Lactic Acid—Official Final Action—*See* 16.026–16.031

16.140 Total Solids—Official Final Action

Transfer 10 ml prepd soln, **16.138(b)**, to weighed flat-bottom dish, ≥5 cm diam., contg 15–20 g dry sand or asbestos fiber. Heat on steam bath 30 min and then in vac. oven at 100° to constant wt. Cool in desiccator and weigh quickly to avoid absorption of H_2O. Correct result for diln.

16.141 Ash—Official Final Action

Evap. 10 ml prepd soln, **16.138(b)**, to dryness on H_2O bath and ignite residue as in **31.012** or **31.013**. Correct result for diln.

16.142 Fat (30)—Official Final Action

(FAO/WHO method. *See Introduction*, **16.052**.)

Accurately weigh 4–5 g prepd sample, **16.138(a)**, into fat-extn flask or tube; dil. with H_2O to ca 10.5 ml, and proceed as in **16.129**.

16.143 Protein—Official Final Action

Det. N as in **2.051**, using 10 ml prepd soln, **16.138(b)**, and correct result for diln. % N × 6.38 = % total "protein."

16.144 Lactose—Official Final Action

Dil. 100 ml prepd soln, **16.138(b)**, in 250 ml vol. flask to ca 200 ml; add 6 ml $CuSO_4$ soln, **31.035(a)**, and alkali soln of concn and in proportion as in **16.051**. Dil. to vol. and mix thoroly. Filter thru dry filter and det. lactose as in **31.039**. Correct result for diln.

Sucrose—Official Final Action

16.145 *Reagent*

(*Caution: See* **46.079** and **46.084**.)

Mercuric nitrate soln.—To 220 g yellow HgO, add 300–400 ml H_2O and enough (but with min. excess) HNO_3 to form clear soln (ca 140 ml), being careful to use least possible excess of acid. Dil. to 800–900 ml and slowly add 10% NaOH soln with constant shaking until slight permanent ppt forms. Dil. to 1 L and filter. As soln tends to become acid with age owing to deposition of basic Hg salts, add dil. alkali occasionally until slight permanent ppt forms and refilter.

16.146 *Determination*

Place 50 ml prepd soln, **16.138(b)**, in 100 ml vol. flask; add 25 ml H_2O, mix, add 5 ml $Hg(NO_3)_2$ soln, and shake thoroly. Without delay and with constant shaking, neutze to litmus paper with 0.5N NaOH, but avoid alk. reaction (12–13 ml). Dil. to 100 ml with H_2O, mix thoroly, and filter thru dry paper. Polarize filtrate in 200 mm tube; then invert at room temp. as in **31.026(c)** and polarize inverted soln. Correct both readings for vol. occupied by protein, **16.143**, and fat, **16.142**; 1 g protein occupies 0.8 ml and 1 g fat, 1.075 ml. Calc. % sucrose by following formula, using corrected direct and invert readings obtained above:

$$S = \frac{100(a - b)}{142.35 - \frac{t}{2}} \times \frac{26}{W},$$

where S = % sucrose in sample; a = corrected direct polarization; b = corrected invert polarization; t = temp. of soln polarized; and W = wt sample taken (10 g).

DRIED MILK, NONFAT DRY MILK, AND MALTED MILK

16.147 Sampling Dried Milk (31)—Procedure
(See also 16.001–16.005 and 16.010–16.011.)

Avoid sampling on rainy day or when humidity is high, so as to reduce moisture absorption from air to min.

On surface of milk at top of barrel locate point on each end of a diam. and on radius perpendicular to this diam., 1–2″ in from edge of barrel. Midway on each side of triangle between these points locate one point. At 6 points so located, using tubular trier long enough to extend full length of barrel, draw core parallel to vertical axis of barrel. Transfer cores to clean, dry, air-tight container and seal immediately.

Before opening sample for analysis, make homogeneous either by shaking or by alternately rolling and inverting container. Avoid excessive temp. and humidity when opening sample container.

16.148 Preparation of Sample—Procedure

Avoid absorption of moisture during prepn of sample. Mix sample by transferring to dry, air-tight container with capacity ca twice vol. of sample. Carefully mix by shaking and inverting repeatedly. When sampling, operate as rapidly as possible. If lumps are present, sift sample thru No. 20 sieve, rubbing material thru sieve and tapping vigorously, if necessary.

16.149 Moisture (32)—Official Final Action

Weigh 1–1.5 g sample into round, flat-bottom metal dish ($\geq$5 cm diam. and provided with tight-fitting slip-in cover). Loosen cover and place dish on metal shelf (dish resting directly on shelf) in vac. oven at 100°. Dry to constant wt (ca 5 hr) under pressure $\leq$100 mm (4″) of Hg. During drying admit slow current of air into oven (ca 2 bubbles/sec), dried by passing thru H_2SO_4. Stop vac. pump and carefully admit dried air into oven. Press cover tightly into dish, remove from oven, cool, and weigh. Calc. % loss in wt as moisture.

Protein—Official Final Action
16.150 Kjeldahl Method

Weigh 1 g sample into Kjeldahl digestion flask and det. N as in 2.051. % N × 6.38 = % "protein."

16.151 Dye Binding Method
See 16.036–16.040.

16.152 Casein in Malted Milk and Chocolate Malted Milk (33)—Official Final Action

Place 10 g sample in 250 ml (or larger) centrf. bottle and ext with two 100 ml portions pet ether by shaking until uniform, centrfg, and decanting supernatant. To dry residue add exactly 200 ml 3% $Na_2C_2O_4$ soln. Shake occasionally over 4 hr period. Centrf. 15 min at high speed (1800 rpm if Size 1 type SB centrf. is used). Pipet 50 ml supernatant (100 ml for chocolate malted milk product) into 250 ml beaker. Add 50 ml paper pulp suspension (1 filter paper) and 2 ml HOAc dropwise with constant stirring. Set beaker in 45–50° H_2O 15 min. Cool to room temp. and filter with moderate suction thru 7 cm buchner, previously fitted with No. 589 S&S white ribbon paper or equiv. and overlaid with layer of paper pulp. Wash ppt 2 or 3 times with cold H_2O. (Filtrate should be clear, or nearly so. If first portions of filtrate are not clear, repeat filtration and finish washing ppt.) Det. N in washed ppt and filter paper as in 2.051, and multiply by 6.38 to obtain equiv. casein. Correct result for blank on reagents and paper pulp.

16.153 Ash—Official Final Action

Ignite 1 g sample at $\leq$550° until C-free. If suitable dish was used for moisture detn, 16.149, ash may be detd on same portion. Cool in desiccator and weigh.

16.154 Alkalinity of Ash in Dry Skim Milk (34)—Official Final Action

Ash 2 g dry skim milk 1 hr at $\leq$550°. Add few ml H_2O to ash, break up with flat-end stirring rod, evap. to dryness over steam bath, again ash 1 hr, and weigh. Again add few ml H_2O to ash, break up, and transfer to beaker with 50–75 ml H_2O. Add 50 ml 0.1N HCl, heat to boiling, and boil gently 5 min. Cool, add 30 ml 40% $CaCl_2$ soln (neutzd with 0.1N HCl and filtered) and ca 10 drops phthln, and titr. excess acid with 0.1N NaOH. Acid used (ml) × 50 = alky of ash.

16.155 Fat in Malted Milk (35)—Official Final Action

Quickly weigh ca 1 g well-mixed sample into small, lipped beaker. Add 1 ml H_2O and rub to smooth paste. Add 10 ml more of H_2O, warm on steam bath, and transfer to fat-extn flask or tube with 10 ml alcohol. Mix thoroly, cool, and proceed as in 16.052, beginning "Add 25 ml ether ..." rinsing beaker with this ether.

Fat in Dried Milk (36)—Official Final Action
(FAO/WHO method. See Introduction, 16.052.)

16.156   Preparation of Solution
Proceed as in one of following methods:

(a) Quickly weigh to nearest mg ca 1 g well-mixed sample into small beaker. Add 1 ml H_2O and rub to smooth paste. Add 9 ml addnl H_2O and 1–1.25 ml NH_4OH, and warm on steam bath. Transfer to fat-extn flask or tube. Cool, and proceed as in **16.157**, rinsing beaker successively with the alcohol and ethers used in first extn.

(b) Quickly weigh to nearest mg ca 1 g well-mixed sample and transfer to fat-extn flask or tube. Add 10 ml H_2O and shake until homogeneous, warming if necessary. Add 1–1.25 ml NH_4OH and heat in H_2O bath 15 min at 60–70°, shaking occasionally. Cool, and proceed as in **16.157**.

16.157 *Determination*

Add 10 ml alcohol to sample and mix. Ext with ether and pet ether as in **16.052**. For second extn add 4 ml alcohol, and again ext as in **16.052**. With whole milk and cream powders make third extn, using 15 ml of each solv. after adding, if necessary, enough H_2O to bring aq. layer in tube to original vol.

Difference between duplicate detns obtained simultaneously by same analyst should be ≤ 0.2 g fat/100 g product.

16.158 Citric Acid in Dried Milk (3)—Official Final Action

Weigh 6 g well-mixed sample, mix well with 44 ml H_2O, and proceed as in **16.023**, beginning "add ca 100 mg *tartaric acid . . .*"

16.159 Lactic Acid (4)—Official Final Action—*See* 16.026–16.031

BUTTER

(Methods are also applicable to renovated or process butter and margarine)

16.160 Sampling (37)—Procedure

(*See* 16.001–16.005 and 16.012–16.014.)

(a) *Tub or cube butter.*—Sample lots as follows:

(1) *Tubs (or cubes) marked with churn numbers.*—Sample 1 tub of each churn of 1–9 tubs, 2 of each churn of 10–14 tubs, and 3 of each churn of >14 tubs. In no case sample <2 tubs in lot.

(2) *Tubs (or cubes) not marked with churn numbers.*—Sample number of tubs equiv. to square root of number in lot, with min. of 3 and max. of 25. If square root is not whole number, sample 1 extra tub.

(b) *Print butter.*—Withdraw 1 print from each of number of cases equiv. to square root of number of cases in lot, with min. of 5 and max. of 25. When square root is not whole number, sample 1 extra case. Select cases to include each churn or batch mark when so marked. With <5 cases, sample all, taking 5 prints as min. Remove wrapper and transfer each print to sep. sample container.

These directions provide min. sampling, to be increased if object of examination demands.

Preparation of Sample (38)

16.161 *Shaking Method—Official Final Action*

Soften entire sample in sample container, **16.014**, by warming in H_2O bath kept at as low temp. as practicable, $\leq 39°$. Avoid overheating, which causes visible sepn of curd. Shake frequently during softening process to reincorporate any sepd fat, and observe fluidity of sample. Optimum consistency is attained when emulsion is still intact but fluid enough to reveal sample level almost immediately. Remove from bath and frequently shake vigorously or place sample container in mech. shaking machine that simulates hand shaking, with arm 9″ long, set to oscillate at 425 ± 25 times/min thru arc of 1.75″. Continue shaking until sample cools to thick, creamy consistency and sample level can no longer readily be seen. Promptly weigh portion for analysis.

16.162 Moisture—Official Final Action

Weigh 1.5–2.5 g prepd sample, **16.161**, into flat-bottom dish ≥ 5 cm diam. and dry to constant wt in oven kept at temp. of boiling H_2O. Clean, dry sand or asbestos may be used if fat is not to be detd in residue by **16.163**.

Fat (38)—Official Final Action

16.163 *Indirect Method*

Take up dry butter obtained in moisture detn in which no absorbent was used, **16.162**, by macerating with 15 ml absolute ether or pet ether; transfer to weighed gooch with aid of wash bottle filled with the solv.; and wash free from fat with 100 ml solv. (Pass last 25 ml solv. thru crucible without suction.) Dry crucible and contents at 100° to constant wt. Repeat washing with 25 ml solv. and dry to constant wt. Repeat operation until there is no loss in wt due to washing. % fat = 100 − (% moisture + % residue).

16.164 *Direct Method*

From dry butter obtained in detn of moisture either with or without use of absorbent, ext fat with anhyd., alcohol-free ether or pet ether (bp <65°), receiving soln in weighed flask. Evap. solv. and dry ext to constant wt at 100°.

16.165 Casein, Ash, and Salt—Official Final Action

Cover crucible contg residue from fat detn by indirect method, **16.163**; heat, gently at first, and gradually raise temp. to $\leq 500°$. Remove cover and continue heating until residue is white. Loss in wt represents casein; residue in crucible represents mineral matter. Dissolve residue in H_2O slightly acidified with HNO_3 and det. Cl, either gravimetrically as in **3.068**, or volumetrically as in **3.070**, and calc. % NaCl.

16.166   Salt (39)—Official Final Action

(FAO/WHO method. *See Introduction*, **16.052.**)

Weigh accurately (±10 mg) ca 5 g sample into 250 ml erlenmeyer and add 100 ml boiling H_2O. Let stand, swirling occasionally, 5–10 min while cooling to 50–55°. Add 2 ml K_2CrO_4 indicator, **33.009**(a), and titr. with 0.1N $AgNO_3$, stdzd as in **45.030**, until orange-brown color persists 30 sec.

ml 0.1N $AgNO_3$ × 0.585/g sample = % NaCl.

16.167   Examination of Fat—Official Final Action

Melt butter and keep 2–3 hr in dry place at ca 60°, or until H_2O and curd sep. completely. Filter clear supernatant fat thru dry paper in hot H_2O funnel or in oven at ca 60°. If filtered liq. fat is not perfectly clear, refilter. Det. physical and chemical constants as in Chap **28**, particularly mole per cent butyric acid, **28.033–28.038**, cholesterol and phytosterol in mixtures of animal and vegetable fats, **28.067–28.069, 28.071–28.080,** and sol. and insol. volatile acids (Reichert-Meissl and Polenske values), **28.031–28.032.**

Acid Value of Fat (40)—Official First Action

(Prepd by joint committee of International Dairy Federation, International Organization for Standardization, and AOAC for publication by each organization and published as an international standard in *FAO/WHO Code of Principles Concerning Milk and Milk Products and Associated Standards.*)

16.168   *Definition and Principle*

Acid value of fat from butter = mg KOH required to neutze 1 g fat. Fat is sepd by melting butter, dissolved in alcohol-ether mixt., and titrd with std alkali.

16.169   *Reagents*

(a) *Alcoholic potassium hydroxide std soln.*—0.1N. Use absolute alcohol or alcohol denatured with MeOH.

(b) *Alcohol-ether mixture.*—Equal vols alcohol (or alcohol denatured with MeOH) and ether neut. to phthln.

(c) *Phenolphthalein soln.*—1% in alcohol or alcohol denatured with MeOH.

16.170   *Determination*

Weigh, to nearest mg, 5–10 g well mixed sample, **16.167,** into 250–300 ml erlenmeyer. Add 50–100 ml alcohol-ether mixt. and 0.1 ml phthln soln. Titr. with 0.1N alc. KOH until permanent faint pink appears and persists for ≥10 sec.

Acid value = ml alc. KOH soln × normality alc. KOH soln × 56.1/g sample. Difference between duplicate detns should be ≤0.1 mg KOH/g fat.

16.171   Refractive Index of Fat (40)—Official Final Action

(*See Introduction*, **16.168.**)

Prep. sample as in **16.167** and proceed as in **28.006,** adjusting circulating H_2O to 40±0.1°. Correct observed refractive index by adding 0.000045 for each unit of acid value if latter is ≥2 as detd in **16.170,** rounding off to fourth decimal.

Difference between duplicate detns should be ≤0.0002.

Critical Temperature of Dissolution (41)—Official Final Action

16.172   *Reagent*

Alcohol isoamyl alcohol reagent.—Mix 2 vols 95% (by vol.) alcohol (checked by sp gr) with 1 vol. redistd isoamyl alcohol (bp 128–132°), both measured with pipet or vol. flask. Keep well-stoppered.

16.173   *Apparatus*

(a) *Test tubes.*—Pyrex, 18 × 150 mm, marked at 2 and 4 ml, measured by adding H_2O from buret.

(b) *Micro burner.*

(c) *Pipet.*—Glass tube, ca 2–3 ml capacity, drawn to fast-flowing tip.

(d) *Thermometer.*—Range 0–100°, graduated in degrees.

16.174   *Determination*

Prep. oil from butter or margarine as in **16.167.** Oil must be clear. Fill test tube to 2 ml mark with oil, using pipet. Immediately add alcohol reagent to 4 ml mark (or add 2 ml with pipet). Using thermometer as stirring rod, mix the two layers and heat in flame of micro burner. Keep stirring and heating until mixt. becomes clear and homogeneous. *Do not boil.* Remove from heat and keep stirring until definite turbidity appears in *mixture proper.* Record temp. at first discernible turbidity. (Opalescence will immediately follow thruout entire mixt. with further drop in temp.)

16.175   Coloring Matters—Official Final Action

Pour ca 2 g filtered fat, dissolved in ether, into each of 2 test tubes. To one tube add 1–2 ml HCl (1 + 1) and to other ca same vol. 10% NaOH soln. Shake tubes well and let stand. In presence of some azo dyes, acid soln turns pink to wine-red, while alk. soln in other tube shows no color. If, on other hand, annatto or other vegetable color is present, alk. soln is yellow, while no color is apparent in acid soln. (Red changing to yellow, especially on warming, in alk. soln may be due to presence of gallate antioxidants.)

General test.—Proceed as in Chap. **34** for detection of oil-sol. synthetic dyes and annatto.

16.176   Lactic Acid—Official Final Action— See 16.026–16.031

Water-Insoluble Fatty Acids (WIA)

16.177 Gravimetric Method (27)—Official Final Action

(Caution: See 46.011, 46.039, and 46.054.)

Weigh 50 g prepd sample, 16.161, into 250 ml centrf. bottle, and add 10 ml H_2O; if necessary, remelt in warm H_2O (not steam) bath and add 50 ml ether. Shake until fat dissolves.

Add $1N$ NaOH in ca 0.2 ml increments to mixt. in centrf. bottle until neutzd to decided pink, using 10 drops phthln, and shaking between addns of alkali. Then add 0.5 ml excess and shake again ≥2 min. During this and all subsequent shakings, carefully release pressure several times to avoid blowing out stopper and losing some of contents. (It is difficult to shake >1 bottle at a time because of greasy stoppers and pressure that develops.)

Remove stopper and add 50 ml pet ether, shake few times, and centrf. 5 min at ca 1200 rpm (longer if sepn is not sharp). Set bottle on horizontal surface and siphon off ether-fat layer. (If ether layer, after centrfg, is reddish, add 10 ml H_2O, shake, and again centrf. as before. If reddish tinge still persists in ether layer, add 25 ml ether, shake, and again centrf.) Wash aq. layer remaining in centrf. bottle by adding 25 ml ether; mix thoroly by shaking several sec, add 25 ml pet ether, and again mix by shaking. Centrf., siphon off ether layer as before, and repeat washing as above. If after any washing, basic red of phthln fades, add addnl phthln and alkali to give decided red (not pink).

Add 1 ml H_2SO_4 (1 + 1) to residue in centrf. bottle and shake vigorously few sec. Then add 5 ml 10% $Na_2WO_4.2H_2O$ soln and again shake vigorously few sec. (Mixt. should be distinctly acid to Congo red paper; if it is not, add more H_2SO_4.) Now add 75 ml ether, shake violently ≥2 min, and centrf. Siphon off ether layer into 500 ml separator. Wash siphon inside and out with 75 ml ether so that washings drain into centrf. bottle. Shake bottle violently ≥2 min, centrf., and siphon off ether layer into the separator. (Disregard slight opalescence of ether layer.)

Add 100 ml alcohol (1 + 1) to combined exts in separator and neutze in same manner as before with $1N$ NaOH to decided pink. Add 0.5 ml excess and shake violently 2 min more. Immediately add 25 ml H_2O, mix by single inversion of separator, and let stand until aq. layer is clear. (Sepn usually occurs in few min; slow sepn may sometimes be hastened by playing fine stream of H_2O on ether surface. If vol. of emulsion at interface is only ca 10 ml it may be included in subsequent extn.) Drain aq. layer into 600 ml beaker. Add 50 ml 1 + 1 alcohol and ca 10 drops phthln to separator and neutze with $1N$ alkali, shaking vigorously ca 2 min. Add 50 ml H_2O, mix by single inversion of separator, and let stand until aq. layer is clear. Drain aq. layer into the beaker. Then add 10 ml H_2O to separator, mix by single inversion, let sep. until aq. layer is clear, and drain into beaker.

Place beaker contg combined exts and washings on steam bath (or carefully heat on hot plate) to expel any ether. Evap. to ca 25 ml (small fan is useful if foaming is serious). (Soln should remain decided red thru all these operations and up to point where soaps are acidified.) Transfer to 250 ml beaker with ca 25 ml H_2O. (As alternative, material may be evapd to dryness on steam bath and residue dissolved in ca 50 ml H_2O.)

Dissolve 5 g anhyd. Na_2SO_4 in warm soln (vol. must be ≥50 ml when Na_2SO_4 and H_2SO_4 are added), heating if necessary. Cool to ≤20°, stirring frequently to keep soaps from forming hard crust on surface. Make acid by adding H_2SO_4 (1 + 1) dropwise, using Congo red paper as indicator. Stir vigorously to effect thoro liberation of fatty acids, mashing all pink soap curds. Add ca 500 mg filter-aid and mix. Filter with suction on suitable filter crucible. Rinse beaker with three ca 15 ml portions H_2O at ≤20° and transfer rinsings to crucible. Maintain suction several min after visible dripping ceases to dry ppt. (Heavy ppts can be sucked drier if cracks are plastered up with some of ppt. Filtrate should be clear.)

Substitute tared beaker or flask (weighed with similar vessel as counterpoise), contg few glass beads or grains of sand, for receiving flask of filtering app. Ext acids with four ca 15 ml portions ether, breaking up ppt with stirring rod between extns and thoroly mixing with the ether. Let ether drip thru filter before applying suction. (Filter pad must not be disturbed.) Evap. ether ext, which should be no more than faintly opalescent, on steam bath, and dry acids in 100° oven 1 hr. Cool and weigh. Report results as mg H_2O-insol. acids (WIA)/100 g butterfat.

Dissolve weighed acids in 10 ml neut. benzene and titr. with $0.1N$ Na ethylate (prepd similarly to $0.05N$ Na ethylate, 17.032(b)), using 10 drops phthln as indicator, until end point holds at least 1 min. (Neut. alcohol instead of benzene and $0.1N$ NaOH instead of Na ethylate may be used.) Compute mean molecular wt of fatty acids by dividing mg acids found by ml $0.1N$ alkali used for titrn and multiplying by 10. (Mean molecular wt should be ≤290. When quantity of acids is <150 mg/100 g butterfat, mean molecular wt is without significance.)

Notes: To siphon off ether use tube similar to delivery tube of ordinary wash bottle but with intake end bent up into U shape in opposite direction to outlet end, with opening ¼–½″ higher than bottom of U, cut off horizontally. (Avoid excessive constriction when bending.) Set delivery tube loosely enough in stopper that it can be raised or lowered. In operating, adjust opening of U bend to ca ⅛″ above surface of aq. layer and blow ether layer off by gently blowing thru mouthpiece tube inserted in adjacent hole in stopper.

Following setup is convenient for filtration of fatty acids: Bell jar and gooch with removable bottom charged with thin layer of asbestos overlaid with small amt of filter-aid (flux calcined diatomite "Speedex," Dicalite Div., Grefco, Inc., 3435 W.

Lomita Blvd, Torrance, CA 90505, added as suspension in H_2O). Use long fiber, amphibole variety, acid and alkali-washed asbestos for gooch, washed twice by decantation. (Coarse fritted glass crucibles overlaid with small amt of filter-aid are also satisfactory.)

Water-Insoluble Fatty Acids (WIA) and Butyric Acid

Chromatographic Method—Official First Action

16.178   Apparatus

Chromatographic tube.—Approx. 2 × 40–50 cm. Tube described in **28.033** is also satisfactory.

16.179   Reagents

(a) *n-Hexane-butanol soln.*—n-Hexane contg 1% n-butanol. *See* **28.034**(d).

(b) *Silicic acid.*—Mallinckrodt's powder especially prepd for chromatgy. Dry 2 hr at 130° and keep in tightly stoppered bottles.

(c) *Ammoniacal glycol soln.*—Dissolve 500 mg bromocresol green in 500 ml ethylene glycol by warming on steam bath. Cool, add NH_4OH dropwise until soln is dark blue (1–3 drops), and then add 1 drop excess. This soln should turn olive-green when mixed with the silicic acid.

(d) *Alcoholic KOH std soln.*—0.05N. Dissolve 4 g KOH pellets in 100 ml isopropanol by warming and swirling on steam bath. Decant supernatant from small amt of aq. KOH soln clinging to flask. Dil. to 1 L with 400 ml isopropanol and 500 ml alcohol. Stdze with NBS benzoic acid, using 2 drops thymol blue as indicator.

(e) *Thymol blue soln.*—Dissolve 300 mg thymol blue in 10 ml 0.05N alc. KOH and add 90 ml isopropanol. Soln should be blue; if not, add enough 0.05N alc. KOH to make soln dark blue.

(f) *Cresol red indicator.*—Dissolve 50 mg o-cresolsulfonphthalein in 20 ml alcohol. Add 1.3 ml 0.1N NaOH and dil. to 50 ml with H_2O.

16.180   Preparation of Sample

(*Caution: See* **46.011**, **46.039**, **46.054**, and **46.073**.)

Weigh 100 g prepd sample, **16.161**, into 250 ml beaker. Melt on steam bath and transfer to 500 ml separator. Rinse beaker with 20 ml H_2O and then with 100 ml ether, and add rinsings to separator. Shake until fat dissolves.

Add 1N NaOH in ca 0.2 ml increments to mixt. in separator until neutzd to decided pink, using 10 drops phthln as indicator and shaking between addns of alkali. Then add 0.5 ml excess and shake again ≥2 min. Add 100 ml pet ether, shake few times, and let layers sep. (5–10 min). Drain aq. layer and any emulsion into 250 ml centrf. bottle. Shake fat layer with 10 ml H_2O and add aq. layer to centrf. bottle after sepn. Wash soln in centrf. bottle by adding 50 ml ether, mixing thoroly by shaking; add 50 ml pet ether and again mix by shaking.

Centrf. 5 min at ca 1200 rpm and siphon off ether-fat layer. If sepns have not been sharp and if much fat is still present, repeat washing with 50 ml ether and 50 ml pet ether. Continue as in **16.177**, beginning, 4th par., "Add 1 ml H_2SO_4 (1 + 1) . . .", except use 10 ml 10% $Na_2WO_4.2H_2O$ instead of 5 ml and two 100 ml portions ether instead of 75 ml. When material has evapd to 25 ml on hot plate or steam bath, transfer to 100 ml beaker and evap. to dryness on steam bath or, with extreme care, on hot plate.

16.181   Preparation of Chromatographic Column

To 20.0 g silicic acid in mortar add 14 ml ammoniacal glycol soln. Mix thoroly with pestle until homogeneous. Add few ml hexane-butanol soln and mix to form smooth paste; then add enough solv. to form slurry. Add slurry with spoon thru funnel to chromatgc tube contg small, loosely-packed cotton plug in constricted end, and ca 30 ml hexane-butanol soln. Force excess solv. thru column, using pressure of 5–10 psi, **18.026**(c). Remove pressure when all of solv. has passed into gel but before column "cracks." Keep small amt of solv. on top of column until ready for use. Do not use cracked column.

16.182   Separation of Fatty Acids

To dry residue of Na salts in 100 ml beaker, **16.180**, add 0.50 ml H_2O and mix well. Add 0 50 ml H_2SO_4 (1 + 1) and mix well, being careful to break up and neutze all lumps. (Sharp needle or stirring rod is sometimes needed to scrape material from bottom of beaker.) Add 2.0 g silicic acid and stir to uniform powder.

Add enough solv. to top of column to make 5 ml. Dry sides of tube by stream of air from glass tube and rubber bulb. Transfer powder to liq. in tube. Mix powder and solv. on top of column with long stirring rod. Do not disturb surface of original gel. Force excess solv. into column with pressure. Rinse stirring rod, funnel, beaker, and sides of tube with two 10 ml portions solv., forcing excess solv. into column after each addn.

Fill tube with solv. and force solv. thru column dropwise (2–3 ml/min) with as much pressure as necessary. If column cracks or solv. flows thru column too rapidly, prep. new column, reducing amt of ammoniacal glycol soln added to silicic acid (use ca 1 ml less). If solv. flows too slowly even with pressure, use more ammoniacal glycol soln.

Collect first 125 ml eluate and titr. with std 0.05N alc. KOH, using 10 drops thymol blue soln as indicator. 1 ml 0.05N KOH = 13.5 mg WIA. Discard next 40–60 ml or until yellow band of butyric acid starts to elute. Collect next 75 ml eluate and titr. with 0.01N NaOH, using 25 ml CO_2-free, neutzd H_2O and 2–3 drops cresol red indicator. 1 ml 0.01N NaOH = 0.88 mg butyric acid. Calc. WIA and butyric acid to mg/100 g fat.

Rapid Method (42)—Official First Action

(Does not recover salts of WIA produced by neutzn)

16.183 *Reagent*

Sodium ethylate.—See **17.032(b)**. (MeOH or 95% alcohol may be substituted for absolute alcohol, and K may be substituted for Na.) (*Caution: See* **46.034** and **46.038**.)

16.184 *Preparation of Sample*

(a) *Cream.*—Weigh 20 g into 125 ml g-s erlenmeyer, ⸸ No. 22. Add 25 ml ice-cold H_2O, cool to 10°, and shake until butterfat seps in granular form. Discard if the granular fat conglomerates into one lump.

(b) *Butter.*—Weigh 10 g into 125 ml g-s erlenmeyer, ⸸ No. 22, warm to melt butter, and cool until butter is of thick, creamy consistency. Add 50 ml ice-cold H_2O, shake, cool to 10°, and shake ca 5 sec.

16.185 *Determination*

Insert filter sieve, Fig. 16:4 (available from Clark Dairy Supply Co., Inc., PO Box 157, Greenwood, IN 46142) into ⸸ erlenmeyer and pour off serum layer. Add 50 ml ice-cold H_2O, insert glass stopper, and shake ca 5 sec. Pour off liq. thru inserted filter sieve. Wash 3 addnl times. Dissolve washed butter in 25 ml ether, pour into small separator, wash erlenmeyer with few ml ether, and add to separator. Let settle few min and drain off aq. curd layer. Drain ether-fat soln into 125 ml erlenmeyer, wash separator with few ml ether, add to erlenmeyer, and titr. with $0.05N$ Na ethylate, using phthln. Calc. WIA in mg/100 g fat. 1 ml $0.05N$ Na ethylate = 13.5 mg WIA.

16.186 Volatile Acids—Official Final Action

Weigh 50 g sample into each of 2 centrf. bottles and proceed as in **16.177**, beginning "Add $1N$ NaOH ..." and continuing thru second washing with mixed ethers to remove fat. Then remove residual ethers from bottles by evapn on steam bath, transfer contents of both to single 200 ml vol. flask with H_2O, and add 1 ml H_2SO_4 $(1+1)$ and 10 ml *10% $Na_2WO_4 . 2H_2O$ soln*. Dil. to vol., mix, and filter. Transfer 150 ml filtrate to distn flask and proceed with distn, chromatgc sepn, and detn as in **18.030**–**18.034** or **18.035**–**18.038**. Calc. to mg acids/100 g fat.

See **14.091**–**14.093** for identification of volatile acids.

16.187 Preservatives—Official Final Action— *See* 16.075 and Chap. 20

16.188 ★ Microscopic Examination— ★ Procedure

See **15.153**, 10th ed.

16.189 Residual Phosphatase (22)—Official Final Action

See **16.084**. Take sample from beneath surface with clean knife or spatula and proceed as follows:

Step 1.—Weigh 1.0 g sample (preferably in duplicate) on piece of waxed paper ca 1″ square and insert paper with sample into tube. Similarly, weigh another sample and place in tube as control or blank.

Step 2.—Heat *blank* ca 1 min to 85–90° in beaker of boiling H_2O (covered so entire tube is heated to 85–90°), and cool to room temp. From this point treat blank and test alike.

Step 3.—Add 10.0 ml buffer substrate prepd as in **16.082(b)**, except dissolve $Na_2C_6H_5PO_4$ in 100 ml undild Ba borate-hydroxide buffer made from 18 g $Ba(OH)_2 . 8H_2O$ and 8 g H_3BO_3/L. Stopper tube and mix.

Step 4.—Immediately after adding substrate, incubate 1 hr in H_2O bath at 37–38°, mixing or shaking contents occasionally.

Step 5.—Heat in beaker of boiling H_2O nearly 1 min, heating to 85–90° (use thermometer in another tube of same size and shape contg same vol. of liq.), and cool to room temp. in vessel of cold H_2O.

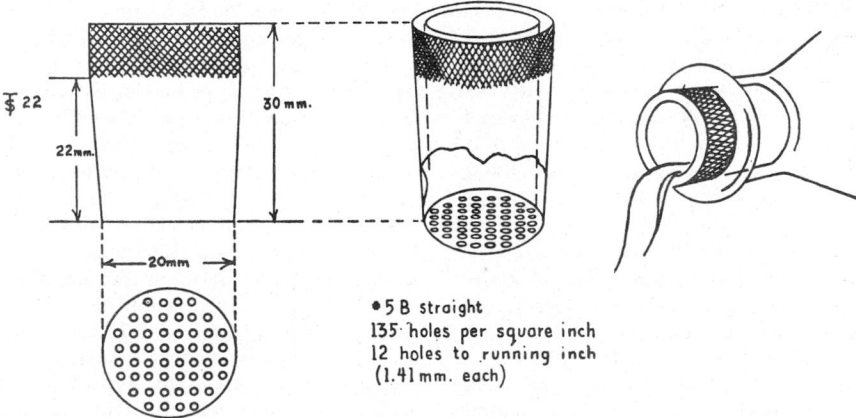

⸸ 22   30 mm.

22mm.

20mm

●5 B straight
135 holes per square inch
12 holes to running inch
(1.41 mm. each)

FIG. 16:4—Filter sieve

Step 6.—Pipet in 1 ml 6.0 g/100 ml soln of $ZnSO_4.7H_2O$, and mix thoroly (pH of mixt. should be 9.0–9.1).

Step 7.—Filter (5 cm funnel, 9 cm Whatman No. 42 or No. 2 paper recommended), and collect 5.0 ml filtrate in tube, preferably graduated at 5.0 and 10.0 ml.

Steps 8–11.—Proceed as in **16.084.**

Step 12.—When using 1.0 g butter and adding 11.0 ml liq., multiply value of reading by 1.1 to convert result to phenol equivs/0.5 g butter. (Values >2 equivs/0.5 g indicate underpasteurization.)

See **16.091–16.094** for differential test for reactivated and residual phosphatase.

CHEESE

16.190 Collection of Sample—Procedure

(*See* also **16.001–16.005** and **16.015–16.018.**)

When cheese can be cut, take narrow, wedge-shape segment reaching from outer edge to center. When not permissible to cut cheese, take sample with cheese trier. If only one plug can be obtained, take it perpendicular to surface of cheese at point $\frac{1}{3}$ distance from edge to center and extending either entirely or half way thru. When >1 plug can be taken, draw 3 plugs, 1 from center, 1 near outer edge, and 1 midway between other two Use ca $\frac{3}{4}''$ of rind portion of core to reseal hole.

Sample bulk containers of cottage and similar cheeses by stirring can thoroly for ≥ 5 min with dairy stirrer (ca $5\frac{1}{2}''$ perforated concave metal disk attached to ca $27''$ metal rod as handle) so that all portions of container are reached. Remove portions from top surface with small spoon to fill pt jar and cover.

16.191 Preparation of Sample—Procedure

Cut wedge sample into strips and pass 3 times thru food chopper. Grind plugs in food chopper (preferable method), or cut or shred very finely and mix thoroly.

With cottage and similar cheeses, place 300–600 g sample at <15° in qt cup of high-speed blender and blend for min. time (2–5 min) required to obtain homogeneous mixt. Final temp. should be $\leq 25°$. This may require stopping blender frequently after channeling and spooning cheese back into blades until blending action starts. (Use of variable transformer in line to permit slow speed at first minimizes channeling when speed is increased later.)

Moisture

16.192 Method I (43)—Official Final Action

Weigh 2–3 g prepd sample, **16.191,** into weighed round, flat-bottom metal dish, ≥ 5 cm diam. and provided with tight fit, slip-in cover. In case of soft cheese and process cheese of high moisture content, weigh 1–2 g and partially dry on steam bath. Place loosely covered dish on metal shelf (dish resting directly on shelf) in vac. oven, kept at 100°. Dry to constant wt (ca 4 hr) under pressure ≤ 100 mm (4″) of Hg. During drying admit into oven slow current of air (ca 2 bubbles/sec) dried by passing thru H_2SO_4. Stop vac. pump and carefully admit air into oven. Press cover tightly into dish, remove dish from oven, cool, and weigh. Express loss in wt as moisture.

16.193 Method II (Rapid Screening Method) (44)—Official First Action

Weigh 2–3 g prepd sample into moisture dish with tight-fitting cover. Partially dry on steam bath with lid removed and then insert in forced-draft oven that has come to equilibrium at $130\pm1°$. Dry 1.25 hr (with cover entirely off), cover tightly, remove from oven, cool, and weigh.

Method III (Distillation Method) (45)—Official First Action

(Applicable to blue and other cheeses contg significant amts of substances other than H_2O volatile at 100°)

16.194   Apparatus

(a) *Receiver.*—Bidwell & Sterling, or modified Bidwell & Sterling, with 5 ml volumetric tube 146–156 mm long, graduated in 0.05 or 0.1 ml divisions, with $\mathbar{S}$ or $\mathbar{S}$ joints, upper 24/40, lower 24/40 or 40/50 (Scientific Glass Apparatus Co., Cat. No. D8580 or JD7780, or equiv.).

(b) *Condenser.*—Cold-finger type, supported by smooth, uniform shoulder in uniformly and symmetrically flared glass tube connected to receiver by $\mathbar{S}$ joint. Diam. of shoulder is 20–35 mm, and length below shoulder 75–100 mm. Powder funnel with $\mathbar{S}$ or $\mathbar{S}$ joint is suitable support. Flare exceeds diam. of condenser shoulder, and makes close, uniform, but never tight, fit with condenser at entire ring of contact with shoulder. Maintain ring of solv. between shoulder and support during heating-up period, while allowing expanding air in system to bubble past. Portion of condenser below shoulder should hang free, and cooling H_2O entrance and exit tubes should be clear of condenser support. Lower tip should be well above the surface of solv. in receiver.

(c) *Boiling flask.*—250 ml, r-b, short neck, $\mathbar{S}$ or $\mathbar{S}$ 40/50 joint with, if necessary, reducing adapter, $\mathbar{S}$ 24/40–40/50, for receivers with lower joint $\mathbar{S}$ 24/40.

(d) *Heating mantle connected to voltage controller.*

16.195   Distillation Solvent

Mix *n*-amyl alcohol and xylene, $1 + 2$, and distill at temp. plateau, ca 129–134°. Add ≤ 5 ml H_2O to convenient vol. of distd solv. mixt., distill off H_2O as in stdzn of app., cool, and store solv. mixt. in g-s container. If in stdzn of app., using solv. mixt. without distg or equilibrating, no significant difference is found from value obtained with distg, these steps may be omitted. (Baker's Analyzed Reagent or equiv. *n*-amyl alcohol and xylene have been found satisfactory as received.)

16.196 *Standardization of Apparatus*

Support app. adequately to maintain tight connections. Lubricate lower joints with USP White Petrolatum. Sep. insulate side arm of receiver and exposed portion of flask with fiber-glass, non-absorbent cotton, or other suitable material. Thoroly clean and dry interior of app., rinse with anhyd. MeOH and then with distn solv., and fill volumetric tube of receiver with solv. Likewise rinse interior portion of condenser, wipe with clean, dry wiping tissue, and immediately insert it in app. Dry externally exposed portion of condenser with tissue wipes and shield as needed to prevent accumulation of condensed atm. H_2O.

Add to clean, dry boiling flask enough SiC fragments, or similar sharp, non-porous boiling aids of mixed size, 6–25 mesh, mostly 10–20, to cover bottom to diam. $\geq 1\frac{1}{2}''$. Add ca 10 ml distn solv., and redry by distn, if necessary, at low heat. Cover flask loosely and cool; then cover flask tightly to exclude H_2O and weigh to 0.001 g. Add ca 4.5 g H_2O, quickly re-cover flask, and reweigh to obtain wt H_2O to ±0.001 g.

Immediately add ca 60 ml distn solv. to flask and connect to receiver. Heat slowly until refluxing starts; adjust heat to distill 20–30 min at ca 0.2–0.3 ml H_2O/min; then increase rate of refluxing gradually to rate attained by full voltage. When no more H_2O droplets fall from tip of condenser, lift condenser and rinse walls of receiver and that portion of condenser inside system with distn solv. from plastic squeeze-type bottle with fine tip. Continue distn few min and repeat rinsing. Repeat this operation at intervals of 1–2 min until no more H_2O droplets are seen to fall into volumetric tube. Remove condenser and support it in dry, clean flask, e.g., 125 ml 𝔗 24/40 erlenmeyer. Remove boiling flask, first tilting receiver slightly to return some of solv. to flask, and place on supporting ring to cool.

Immerse volumetric tube in H_2O at convenient temp. (25° or room temp.) and when equilibrium is reached, read and est. vol. distd H_2O to nearest 0.01 ml. Magnifier is helpful; avoid parallax.

Calc. distn factor at temp. selected = g H_2O added/ml H_2O distd.

Repeat stdzn until consecutively detd factors agree within ±0.002 of av. of 2. Use av. of the 2 detns as distn factor.

16.197 *Determination*

Prep. app. and distn solv. as in **16.196**. Place in covered, dry, weighed boiling flask, contg boiling aids and ca 10 ml distn solv., portion of well mixed sample contg ca 4.5 g H_2O, e.g., 9–11 g soft cheeses (camembert, etc.), 11–13 g cheddar, blue, etc. (35–40% H_2O), and 13–15 g hard, dry cheeses. Immediately re-cover tightly and re-weigh to ±0.005 g.

Add ca 60 ml distn solv. and connect to app. (or, after addn of solv., samples may be held in tightly closed flasks until ready to distill). Start heating slowly and distill H_2O in same manner as in **16.196**, but refluxing slowly at low heat for ca 40–50 min, then increasing heat gradually to full voltage for few min, using same criteria for completion of distn. Cheese will spread in thin layer over bottom of flask and will become tan to brownish yellow, depending on variety, but not dark brown or scorched in appearance. Complete distn in 1–1¼ hr. Read vol. distd H_2O under exactly same conditions as in **16.196**. Calc. % H_2O in sample = (distn factor × vol. H_2O distd × 100)/g sample.

Remove dried cheese from flask by digesting with dil. alkali soln on steam bath until dispersed, then washing with hot H_2O, returning washed boiling aids. Used solv. may be distd for re-use.

16.198 Ash (*46*)—Official Final Action

Weigh 3–5 g prepd sample, **16.191**, into Pt dish, place on steam bath, and dry ca 1 hr. (If cheese is high in fat, place small amt of absorbent cotton in dish.) Ignite cautiously to avoid spattering and remove burner while fat is burning. When flame ceases, complete ignition in muffle at temp. $\leq 550°$.

16.199 Total Chlorides (*46*)—Official Final Action

Weigh ca 3 g prepd sample, **16.191**, into 200 ml erlenmeyer. Add 25 ml 0.1*N* $AgNO_3$, which is more than enough to combine with all the Cl. Add 10 ml halogen-free HNO_3 and 50 ml H_2O, and boil. As soln boils, add ca 15 ml 5% $KMnO_4$ soln in 5 ml portions. (Soln becomes yellowish and clear.) Cool, filter into 200 ml vol. flask, washing paper thoroly with H_2O at ca 20°, and dil. to vol. Titr. excess $AgNO_3$ in 100 ml clear soln with 0.1*N* KSCN, using 2 ml *satd soln of Fe alum* as indicator. Det. blank on reagents used in same manner, except to add sugar to destroy excess $KMnO_4$. Calc. Cl found to NaCl.

16.200 Nitrogen—Official Final Action

Det. N in weighed portion (ca 2 g) prepd sample, **16.191**, as in **2.051**. % N × 6.38 = % "protein."

16.201 Acidity—Official Final Action

To 10 g prepd sample, **16.191**, add H_2O at 40° to vol. of 105 ml, shake vigorously, and filter. Titr. 25 ml portion filtrate, representing 2.5 g sample, with std NaOH, preferably 0.1*N*, using phthln. Express result as lactic acid. 1 ml 0.1*N* NaOH = 0.0090 g lactic acid. Results may also be expressed as ml 0.1*N* NaOH/100 g.

16.202 Coloring Matters—Official First Action
(*Caution: See* **46.011**, **46.039**, and **46.054**.)

Ext 25–50 g prepd sample, **16.191**, with ether, remove ether by evapn, and proceed as in Chap. **34**.

16.203   Fat (47)—Official Final Action

(FAO/WHO method. *See Introduction,* **16.052.**)

Weigh, to nearest mg, ca 1 g prepd sample, **16.191,** into small tall-form beaker; add 9 ml H_2O and, if desired, 1 ml NH_4OH. Mix until smooth; then warm mixt. at low heat until casein is well softened. If NH_4OH was used, neutze with HCl, using litmus as indicator. Add 10 ml HCl and few glass beads or other inert material previously digested with HCl to prevent bumping, cover with watch glass, and boil gently 5 min, or place beaker in boiling H_2O bath 20 min. Cool soln; transfer to fat-extn flask or tube; rinse beaker successively with 10 ml alcohol, 25 ml ether, and 25 ml pet ether (boiling range 30–60°); transfer rinsings to flask; and mix thoroly after adding each reagent. Proceed as in **16.052,** begining "Centrf. flask ..." Difference between duplicate detns obtained simultaneously by same analyst should be ≤0.2 g fat/100 g product.

16.204   Examination of Fat—Official Final Action

(a) *Alkaline extraction.*—In large, wide-mouth flask, treat ca 300 g sample, cut to ca pea-size, with 700 ml 5% KOH soln at 20°, shaking vigorously to dissolve casein. (In 5–10 min, casein dissolves, and fat rises to surface in lumps.) Collect lumps of fat into as large mass as possible by shaking gently. Pour cold H_2O into flask until fat is driven up into neck, and remove by suitable means. Wash fat thus obtained with just enough H_2O to remove residual alkali. Fat is not perceptibly attacked by alkali in this treatment, is practically all sepd in short time, and is then easily prepd for chemical analysis by filtering and drying as in **16.167.** Examine fat as in Chap. **28.**

(b) *Acid extraction.*—Pass cheese thru grinding machine, transfer to large flask, and cover with warm H_2O, using 1 ml/g cheese. Shake thoroly and add H_2SO_4 slowly and in small amts, shaking after each addn of acid. (Vol. H_2SO_4 should equal vol. H_2O used.) Remove fat, which seps after standing few min, in separator; wash free from sulfate, filter, and dry as in **16.167.** Examine fat as in Chap. **28.**

Tartaric Acid (48)

16.205   Qualitative Test—Procedure

To 5 g ground cheese, **16.191,** add 40 ml H_2O at ca 50° and shake until cheese is thoroly broken up. Add 3 ml 1% H_2SO_4 and shake vigorously. Add 2 ml *20% phosphotungstic acid soln* and again shake vigorously. Let stand 5 min and filter. To 25 ml filtrate add enough satd $Ba(OH)_2$ soln to make alk. and 25 ml alcohol, shake vigorously, and let settle. Filter thru buchner, using light suction, and wash residue on filter several times with H_2O. Transfer portion of paste to small evapg dish and dry on steam bath. Add few ml H_2SO_4 and few crystals of *resorcin,* and

heat slowly. If tartaric acid is present, soln turns rose-red; color is slowly discharged on diln with H_2O.

Quantitative Method (48)—Official Final Action

16.206   Reagents

(a) *Potassium chloride wash soln.*—Dissolve 15 g KCl in 100 ml H_2O and add 20 ml alcohol.

(b) *Tartaric acid soln.*—Dissolve 1.5 g pure tartaric acid in previously boiled and cooled H_2O and dil. to 100 ml at 20°. Titr. with 0.1N NaOH to det. tartaric acid in 10 ml soln.

(c) *Hydrochloric acid soln.*—2%. Dil. 47 ml HCl to 1 L with H_2O.

16.207   Determination

Weigh 25 g prepd sample, **16.191,** into 500 ml wide-mouth bottle and add, 25 ml at time, 100 ml H_2O at 50–60°, shaking vigorously after each addn. Continue shaking until cheese is thoroly broken up. Add 25 ml *2% $Na_2C_2O_4$ soln* and shake vigorously 1 min. Add 100 ml 2% HCl, 25 ml at time, shaking vigorously after each addn. Add 50 g powd KCl and shake 5 min. To avoid churning, keep mixt. warm (ca 50°) during shaking. Transfer mixt., with aid of H_2O, to 300 ml vol. flask, cool to 20°, and dil. to vol. with H_2O. Mix thoroly; let stand 10 min, with occasional shaking; and filter thru dry folded paper, discarding first few ml filtrate. Disregard any opalescence and transfer 200 ml filtrate to 250 ml vol. flask. Neutze with 1N NaOH, using phthln, and add 5.2 ml in excess. Dil. to vol. with H_2O, mix thoroly, let stand few min, and filter thru dry folded paper, discarding first few ml filtrate.

To 100 ml filtrate in 250 ml beaker add, with constant stirring, 10 ml of the tartaric acid soln, 2 ml HOAc, and 23 ml alcohol. Cool in ice bath, stir vigorously until cream of tartar begins to crystallize, and let stand in refrigerator overnight. Prep. Caldwell crucible with pad of asbestos ca 10 mm thick. Decant most of liq. thru this filter, wash ppt into crucible with KCl wash soln, and wash beaker and ppt 3 times, using total quantity of 20–30 ml wash soln. Place asbestos and ppt in beaker in which pptn was made and wash crucible with ca 50 ml hot H_2O. Heat soln to boiling and titr. while hot with 0.1N NaOH, using phthln. Calc. % tartaric acid in cheese by formula:

$$X = 14.26[0.015(B + 1.5) - A], \quad \text{where} \quad A = g$$

tartaric acid in 10 ml of the tartaric acid reagent; and B = ml 0.1N NaOH required for titrn.

In factor 14.26, concn caused by insol. solids of cheese of av. composition is taken into consideration.

Citric Acid (49)

16.208   Qualitative Test—Procedure

To 10 g prepd sample, **16.191,** add 20 ml H_2O at ca 50° and shake vigorously until cheese is thoroly broken up. Add 20 ml H_2SO_4 (1 + 1) and 2 ml *20%*

phosphotungstic acid soln, and shake vigorously. Let stand 5 min and filter. To 20 ml filtrate add 10 ml Br-H₂O (*Caution: See* **46.047**) and 5 ml KBr soln (15 g in 40 ml H₂O), and proceed with oxidn as in **16.209**. Add enough FeSO₄ soln (**16.209**, par. 3) to dissolve pptd MnO₂. If citric acid is present, heavy white ppt forms which settles rapidly.

16.209 Quantitative Method—Official Final Action

Prep. suspension as in **16.207** thru addn of Na₂C₂O₄ soln. Shake vigorously 1 min and add 100 ml 1% H₂SO₄, 25 ml at time, shaking vigorously after each addn. Add 3 ml *20% phosphotungstic acid soln* and shake; then add 25 g powd anhyd. Na₂SO₄, and shake 5 min. To avoid churning, keep mixt. warm (ca 50°) during shaking. Transfer mixt. with aid of warm H₂O to 300 ml vol. flask, cool to 20°, and dil. to vol. with H₂O. Mix thoroly, shake occasionally during 10 min, and filter thru dry folded paper, discarding first few ml filtrate.

Heat 200 ml filtrate to boiling and while still hot add 20 ml H₂SO₄ (1 + 1) and 2 ml phosphotungstic acid soln. Mix and let stand 15 min. With aid of H₂O transfer mixt. to 250 ml vol. flask, cool to 20°, dil. to vol. with H₂O, and filter thru dry folded paper.

Transfer 100 ml clear filtrate to 500 ml erlenmeyer (ca 0.3 g washed and dried asbestos may be added). Add 10 ml freshly prepd satd Br-H₂O (*Caution: See* **46.047**) and 5 ml KBr soln (15 g KBr in 40 ml H₂O), mix thoroly, and heat to 48–50°. Hold at this temp. 5 min, add 25 ml 5% KMnO₄ soln, shake, and let stand ca 5 min. Cool flask and contents to ca 8°, add 40 ml cold *FeSO₄ soln* (20 g FeSO₄.7H₂O in 100 ml H₂O and 1 ml H₂SO₄), shake continuously 5 min, and let mixt. stand overnight in refrigerator.

Decant supernatant thru gooch, measure vol. filtrate (*v*), and wash ppt from erlenmeyer into crucible with this filtrate. Wash ppt with three 20 ml portions ice-cold H₂SO₄ (1 + 100), sucking dry after each addn, and finally wash with three 20 ml portions ice-cold H₂O. Dry ppt to constant wt over H₂SO₄ in vac. desiccator, protecting ppt from strong light or, to save time, dry in current of air passed thru H₂SO₄, and weigh.

Remove pentabromacetone by extg first with three 20 ml portions alcohol and then with three 20 ml portions ether. Dry and weigh crucible. To wt pentabromacetone add 0.004 g/100 ml filtrate (*v*) to compensate for solubility of pentabromacetone and multiply result by 6.06 to obtain % anhyd. citric acid in cheese. (In this factor, concn caused by insol. solids in 25 g cheese is taken into consideration. It is assumed that solids of cheese are almost insol. under conditions maintained and that av. process cheese contains ca 60% solids. No allowance is made for variation in salt or moisture content or for variation in specific vol. of solids, as such variations do not appreciably affect results.)

16.210 Lactose in Process Cheese (50)—Official Final Action

Prep. suspension as in **16.207** thru addn of Na₂C₂O₄ soln. Shake vigorously 1 min; add 25 g powd Na₂SO₄ and shake 2 min; add 10 ml H₂SO₄ (1 + 1) and shake; then add 25 ml *20% phosphotungstic acid soln* and shake vigorously. Transfer contents of bottle to 500 ml vol. flask, cool at once to 20°, and dil. to vol. with H₂O. Mix thoroly, let stand 10 min, and filter thru dry folded paper. Transfer 150 ml filtrate to each of two 250 ml vol. flasks, add 10% NaOH soln to one flask until mixt. is alk. to litmus, and then add 5 g solid KCl and mix thoroly. Cool to 20° and dil. to vol. with H₂O. Mix well, let stand 10 min, and filter thru dry folded paper.

Det. lactose in 50 ml aliquot as in **31.039**. Treat the 150 ml in second flask as in **31.026(c)**, using 10 ml HCl, etc. Add 10% NaOH soln until alk. to litmus, and add 5 g solid KCl. Mix thoroly, cool to 20°, and dil. to vol. with H₂O. Let stand 10 min. Filter if necessary thru dry paper. Det. lactose in 50 ml aliquot as before. Agreement between amts of Cu₂O reduced before and after inversion establishes absence of sucrose.

Since insol. material of cheese and phosphotungstic acid ppt occupy some space in flask as originally prepd, it is necessary to correct for this vol. From av. composition of cheese, vol. of ppt was calcd to be 14 ml. To obtain true quantity of lactose present, multiply all results by factor 0.97.

Gums in Soft Curd Cheese (51)—Official Final Action

(Not applicable to detection of alginates)

16.211 Reagents

(a) *Benedict soln* (*qualitative*).—Dissolve 17.3 g Na citrate and 10 g anhyd. Na₂CO₃ in ca 80 ml hot H₂O; dissolve 1.73 g CuSO₄.5H₂O in 10 ml H₂O. Filter alk. citrate soln, add CuSO₄ soln slowly with constant stirring, and dil. with H₂O to 100 ml.

(b) *Trichloroacetic acid* (*TCA*) *soln*.—(1) 50%. (2) 10%. Prep. just before use from nonhydrolyzed reagent. (*Caution: See* **46.082**.)

16.212 Preparation of Sample

Weigh 100 g cheese into 250 ml centrf. bottle. Add hot H₂O to total vol. of 170 ml, heat in hot H₂O bath 30 min, and cool to room temp. Add 50 ml pet ether, shake, and centrf. Remove pet ether layer by decantation or by use of blow-off siphon, **16.177**, *Notes*. Repeat extn with pet ether at least twice. (Small amt of fat remaining is harmless.)

Warm bottle in hot H₂O bath to remove residual pet ether from cheese. Centrf., if necessary, to break any foam. Make vol. to ca 190 ml with H₂O and add 3.5 ml NH₄OH, few drops at time, while stirring. Keep in hot H₂O bath and stir until all curd dissolves. If curd fails to dissolve completely, add few more drops NH₄OH, stir, and macerate to dissolve. Add HOAc, few drops at time, with shaking, until pH is ca 4.75 (nitrazine test paper or pH meter). Use care in approaching pH point because isoelec. point for casein is ca pH 4.73. (If acid is added very slowly with constant shaking and centrf. bottle is kept hot, marked sepn of casein and liq. will be noted at this point.) Stopper bottle, shake thoroly, and let stand overnight in the hot H₂O bath as H₂O cools. Check pH and centrf. at 1200 rpm 10 min. Decant supernatant into 250 ml beaker with 40 ml graduation mark. Do not wash ppt.

16.213   *Separation of Gum*

Evap. decanted liq. on steam bath to 40 ml mark of beaker. Remove beaker from bath and cool to room temp. Disregard ppt formed during concn and add 10 ml 50% TCA soln (note directions under **16.211(b)**). Replace on steam bath ≥15 min to coagulate protein. Remove beaker from steam bath, cool, transfer to 250 ml centrf. bottle with 5 ml 10% TCA soln, and centrf. at 1200 rpm 10 min. Decant supernatant into another 250 ml centrf. bottle and add alcohol with stirring until bottle is full. (Vol. before addn of alcohol should be ≤50 ml and ca 4 vols alcohol should be added.) Let mixt. stand 1 hr to coagulate gums. Centrf. at 1800 rpm, decant, and discard liq.

Add ca 50 ml 70% alcohol to residue in bottle, stopper, and shake to break up material thoroly. Wash down stopper and sides of bottle with little 70% alcohol, centrf. at 1800 rpm, decant, and drain. Add 40 ml hot H₂O to bottle and shake well to dissolve gum and disperse insol. material. Add 10 ml 50% TCA to bottle and heat on steam bath 15 min to coagulate any protein left after first treatment.

Remove bottle, cool, and centrf. at 1200 rpm 10 min. Decant supernatant into another 250 ml Pyrex centrf. bottle, and fill bottle with alcohol while stirring contents. Add 0.5 ml 5% $KAl(SO_4)_2$ soln. Shake, and let stand ≥1 hr. Centrf. at 1800 rpm and decant. Add 50 ml 70% alcohol, shake to disperse material, and centrf. at 1800 rpm. Decant supernatant and drain. Add 40 ml hot H₂O and shake well to dissolve gum. Transfer to 50 ml conical heavy-duty centrf. tube, keeping vol. to 40 ml. Centrf. at 1200 rpm 10 min to remove any undissolved material, and decant supernatant back into 250 ml centrf. bottle. Reppt in bottle by filling with alcohol plus 1 drop HOAc. To ensure pptn of gum tragacanth and karaya, add 0.5 ml 5% $KAl(SO_4)_2$ soln.

Let stand ≥1 hr to coagulate ppt, centrf., and decant liq. If ppt is small and will not remain on bottom of 250 ml centrf. bottle, centrf. the alcohol and pptd gum, portion at time, at 1500 rpm 15 min in 50 ml conical heavy-duty centrf. tube, until all contents of 250 ml bottle are transferred to 50 ml tube. After decanting supernatant from last portion centrfd, add 40 ml 70% alcohol to tube (or bottle if

tube is not used), and shake until ppt is dispersed; centrf., decant, and drain.

16.214   *Detection of Gum*

Add 10 ml hot H₂O to residue in tube or bottle, shake, and transfer to 50 ml beaker. Rinse tube or bottle with 10 ml hot H₂O and add rinse to beaker. Warm on elec. hot plate to dissolve gum and evap. to 10 ml. Add 2 ml HCl, cover beaker with watch glass, and boil gently 5 min. Cool, transfer to 10 ml graduated cylinder, adjust to 10 ml with H₂O, and mix. Place 1 ml aliquot in 30 ml beaker and neutze with 10% NaOH soln, using litmus paper as indicator. Remove litmus paper, add 5 ml Benedict soln, boil vigorously 2 min, and let cool spontaneously. Voluminous ppt appearing on cooling, which may be yellow, orange, or red, caused by reducing sugars formed by hydrolysis of the gums, indicates presence of gums.

Gelatin in Cottage Cheese

**16.215   Qualitative Test—Official
              Final Action**

Thoroly mix 5 g sample with 10 ml H₂O at 50–60° and add 5 ml Hg(NO₃)₂ soln, **16.074**. Shake, let stand 5 min, and filter thru medium-fast retentive paper. To filtrate add 5 ml addnl Hg(NO₃)₂ soln and test as in **16.074**, using filtrate so obtained. *See also Note* in **16.074**.

Residual Phosphatase (22)—Official
Final Action

16.216   *Reagents*

(a) *Buffers:*

(1) *25-11 Barium borate-hydroxide buffer.*—See **16.082(a)(1)**.

(2) *26-11, 27-11, 28-11, and 29-11 Barium borate-hydroxide buffers.*—Prep. as in **16.082(a)(1)**, except use 26.0, 27.0, 28.0, or 29.0 g Ba(OH)₂.8H₂O, resp., instead of 25.0 g.

(b) *Buffer substrates:*

Dissolve 0.10 g phenol-free cryst. $Na_2C_6H_5PO_4$ in 100 ml appropriate buffer, (a), specified in **16.219**. *See* **16.082(b)(1)** for prepn of phenol-free substrate.

(c) *Protein precipitants:*

(1) *6.0–0.1 Precipitant.*—Dissolve 6.0 g ZnSO₄ .7H₂O and 0.1 g CuSO₄.5H₂O in H₂O and dil. to 100 ml.

(2) *6.0 Precipitant.*—Dissolve 6.0 g ZnSO₄.7H₂O in H₂O and dil. to 100 ml.

For other reagents, *see* **16.082**.

16.217   *Sampling*

(a) *Hard cheese.*—Take sample from interior with *clean* Roquefort trier, place in small tube, stopper, and keep in refrigerator.

(b) *Soft and semisoft ripened cheese.*—Harden cheese by chilling in freezing compartment of refrigerator. Take special precautions to avoid contaminating sample with phosphatase that may be present on surface. Sample by either of following methods:

(1) Cut portion from end of loaf or side of cheese, extending in $\geq 2''$ if possible, to point somewhat beyond center in case of small cheese. Cut slit $\frac{1}{4}-\frac{1}{2}''$ deep at least half way around portion and midway between top and bottom. Break portion into 2 parts, pulling apart so that break occurs on line with slit and taking care not to contaminate freshly exposed broken surface. Remove sample from freshly exposed surface at or near center of cheese.

(2) Remove surface of area to be sampled (e.g., end and adjacent sides), with clean knife or spatula, to depth of $\frac{1}{4}''$. Clean instrument and hands with hot H_2O and phenol-free soap, and wipe dry. Remove freshly exposed surface to same or greater depth, and repeat cleaning. Take sample from center of freshly exposed area, preferably at or near center of cheese if cheese is small.

(c) *Process cheese and cheese spreads.*—Take sample from beneath surface with clean knife or spatula.

If preservative is necessary, put 1–3 ml $CHCl_3$ in container, cover with plug of cotton, insert sample, and stopper tightly. Label *"Poison, preservative added."*

16.218 *Determination*

(*See* **16.084.**) Different kinds of cheese and cheeses of different ages have different buffering capacities and therefore require different concns of reagents. Modifications of the Ba buffer needed to produce optimal pH conditions during incubation (9.85–10.20) and of precipitant to yield uniformly clear filtrates and minimize interference during development of color under optimal pH conditions (9.3–9.4) are specified in **16.219.**

Proceed as follows:

Step 1.—Weigh, on clean balance pan or watch glass, 0.50 g sample (preferably in duplicate) and place in culture tube 16 or 18 × 150 mm. Similarly weigh another sample and place in tube as control or blank. If cheese is sticky, weigh sample on piece of wax paper ca 1 × 1″ and insert paper with sample into tube. Macerate blank and test samples with glass rod ca 8 × 180 mm.

Step 2.—Add to *blank* 1.0 ml appropriate Ba buffer, **16.219** (without substrate), macerate with rod, leave rod in tube, and heat ca 1 min to 85–90° in beaker of boiling H_2O (covered, to insure that entire tube will be heated to 85–90°); cool to room temp., and again macerate with rod.

Step 3.—To each *test sample* add 1.0 ml appropriate Ba buffer substrate, **16.216(b),** and macerate.

From this point, treat blank and test alike.

Add 9.0 ml more Ba buffer substrate (total 10.0 ml), and mix. (Rod may be left in tube during incubation. If it is removed at this point, wrap piece of ca 1 × 1″ filter paper tightly around it and wipe it clean

by rotating while withdrawing from tube. Insert paper with adhering fat in tube.) Stopper tube.

For precise quant. results on unknown samples, adjust pH to 10.0–10.05 by dropwise addn of $1N$ or $0.5N$ Na_2CO_3 or HCl.

Step 4.—Immediately incubate in H_2O bath 1 hr at 37–38°, mixing or shaking contents occasionally.

Step 5.—Heat in beaker of boiling H_2O nearly 1 min (temp. of contents of tube ca 85° as detd by thermometer in another tube of same size and shape contg same vol. liq.), and cool to room temp. in vessel of cold H_2O.

Step 6.—Pipet in 1.0 ml appropriate protein precipitant, **16.219,** and mix thoroly (pH of mixt., 9.0–9.1).

Steps 7–11.—Proceed as in **16.084.**

Step 12.—When using 0.5 g solid sample and adding total of 11.0 ml liq., multiply value of reading by 1.1 to convert to units of color or phenol equivs/0.25 g cheese. (If desired, multiply by 4.4 to convert result to phenol equivs/g.) Evaluate result by comparing with criteria of pasteurization in **16.219.**

Notes: With some cheese samples of unknown history, slight deviations from optimal pH range may occur, but such deviations do not materially affect results. For example, pH values as low as 9.6 or as high as 10.35 during incubation have been found to result in av. decrease of $\leq 20\%$ in quantity of phenol liberated. Use of 25–11 buffer substrate with samples for which 27–11 buffer substrate is specified yields pH values ≥ 9.8.

Trace of cloudiness in filtrate, following use of prescribed precipitant, indicates concn of $Ba(OH)_2$ in buffer was insufficient (i.e., buffer substrate was insufficiently alk.). For example, the 25–11 buffer, for use with unripened cheese, may yield cloudy filtrate if used with ripened cheese. Increasing concn of $ZnSO_4$ in precipitant also eliminates turbidity of filtrate.

In testing cheese of unknown history or age, information as to % solids, especially nonfat solids, is useful as indication of correct buffer to use; cheese with relatively high % of nonfat solids generally requires use of relatively concd buffer to adjust pH of mixt. correctly. Av. buffer within cheese group (generally 26–11) is usually satisfactory for cheese of uncertain age.

Cottage cheese curd is heated in presence of considerable acid during manufacture, and therefore its phosphatase values are comparatively low. To increase sensitivity of test on cottage cheese, apply following modifications: Use 1.0 g sample, 27–11 buffer substrate, 2 hr incubation, 6.0–0.1 precipitant, and pasteurization criterion of 2 units/0.5 g.

To test for presence of microbial phosphatase, e.g., in surface ripened cheeses and their processed products, (a) indicated by blue tinge in blank of *Step 2*, repeat detn, adding 1 ml of the Ba buffer (without substrate) to blank and heating 5 min in boiling H_2O in covered beaker. If blank so treated is neg., blue tinge in original blank was due to microbial phosphatase. (b) In suspected instances in absence of blue tinge in blank of *Step 2*, heat sample itself 5 min at 70° to completely destroy milk phosphatase and then perform test. If pos., microbial phosphatase is present.

See also Notes under **16.084.**

16.219   *Phosphatase Test Modifications for Different Kinds of Cheese and Cheese of Differerent Ages*

Kind of Cheese	Age or Extent of Curing; Other Details	Buffer for Opt. pH[a] (9.85–10.20)	Precipitant	Criterion, Experimental, Phenol Equivalent[b]
				µg/0.25 g
Cheddar, granular, stirred curd, hard cheese	<1 wk	25–11	6.0–0.1[c]	3
	1–6 wk	25–11	6.0[d]	3
	1.5–4 mo.	26–11	6.0[d]	3
	>4 mo.	27–11	6.0[d]	3
Washed curd, soaked curd, colby	<1 wk	25–11	6.0–0.1[c]	3
	1–8 wk	25–11	6.0[d]	3
	>2 mo.	26–11	6.0[d]	3
Swiss, gruyère	<1 wk	25–11	6.0–0.1[c]	3
	1–4 wk	25–11	6.0[d]	3
	1–3 mo.	26–11	6.0[d]	3
	>3 mo.	27–11	6.0[d]	3
Brick, muenster	<1 wk	25–11	6.0–0.1[c]	3
	1–4 wk	25–11	6.0[d]	3
	1–2 mo.	25–11	6.0[d]	3
	>2 mo.	26–11	6.0[d]	3
Edam, gouda	<1 wk	25–11	6.0–0.1[c]	3
	1–8 wk	25–11	6.0[d]	3
	2–4 mo.	26–11	6.0[d]	3
	>4 mo.	27–11	6.0[d]	3
Blue mold, blue, gorgonzola	<1 wk	25–11	6.0–0.1[c]	3
	1–4 wk	26–11	6.0[d]	3
	1–4.5 mo.	27–11	6.0[d]	3
	>4.5 mo.	28–11	6.0[d]	3
Camembert, limburger	<1 wk	25–11	6.0–0.1[c]	4
	1–4 wk	25–11	6.0[d]	4
	1–2 mo.	26–11	6.0[d]	4
	>2 mo.	27–11	6.0[d]	4
Monterey	<1 wk	25–11	6.0–0.1[c]	3
	1–8 wk	25–11	6.0[d]	3
	>2 mo.	26–11	6.0[d]	3
High moisture Jack	<1 wk	25–11	6.0–0.1[c]	3
	1–10 wk	25–11	6.0[d]	3
	>2.5 mo.	26–11	6.0[d]	3
Provolone, pasta filata	<1 wk	25–11	6.0–0.1[c]	3
	1–4 wk	25–11	6.0[d]	3
	1–3 mo.	26–11	6.0[d]	3
	>3 mo.	27–11	6.0[d]	3
Parmesan, reggiano, monte, modena, romano, asiago old	<1 wk	25–11	6.0–0.1[c]	3
	1–8 wk	26–11	6.0[d]	3
	2–6 mo.	27–11	6.0[d]	3
	6–12 mo.	28–11	6.0[d]	3
	>1 yr	29–11	6.0[d]	3
Asiago, fresh	Same as Cheddar			
Asiago, medium	<1 wk	25–11	6.0–0.1[c]	3
	1–4 wk	25–11	6.0[d]	3
	1–3 mo.	26–11	6.0[d]	3
	>3 mo.	27–11	6.0[d]	3
Cottage[e], cook cheese, koch kaese	Dry	25–11	6.0–0.1[c]	1
	Moist	25–11 (8 + 2)[f]	4.5–0.1[c]	1
Cream cheese		25–11 (7 + 3)	4.5–0.1[c]	3

[a] $Ba(OH)_2 \cdot 8H_2O$ and H_3BO_3, resp., g/L.
[b] Higher values indicate underpasteurization.
[c] $ZnSO_4 \cdot 7H_2O$ and $CuSO_4 \cdot 5H_2O$, resp., g/100 ml.
[d] $ZnSO_4 \cdot 7H_2O$ g/100 ml.
[e] See also alternative more sensitive modification in Notes, **16.218**.
[f] 8 parts 25–11 buffer + 2 parts of H_2O.

(Continued)

16.219   *Phosphatase Test Modifications for Different Kinds of Cheese and Cheese of Different Ages—Continued*

Kind of Cheese	Age or Extent of Curing; Other Details	Buffer for Opt. pH[a] (9.85–10.20)	Precipitant	Criterion, Experimental, Phenol Equivalent[b]
				μg/0.25 g
Semisoft cheese	<1 wk	25–11	6.0–0.1[c]	3
	1–4 wk	25–11	6.0[d]	3
	>1 mo.	26–11	6.0[d]	3
Soft ripened cheese	<1 wk	25–11	6.0–0.1[c]	4
	1–4 wk	25–11	6.0[d]	4
	>1 mo.	26–11	6.0[d]	4
Nokkelost, kuminost, sage cheese	<1 wk	25–11	6.0–0.1[c]	3
	1–6 wk	25–11	6.0[d]	3
	1.5–4 mo.	26–11	6.0[d]	3
	>4 mo.	27–11	6.0[d]	3
Past. proc.; ditto, pimiento; ditto, with fruits, meats, etc.	Soft, mild	25–11	6.0[d]	3
	Med. firm	26–11	6.0[d]	3
	Firm, sharp (incl. swiss, gruyère)	27–11	6.0[d]	3
Past. proc. cheese foods; ditto, with fruits, meats, etc.	Same as past. proc.			
Past. proc. cheese spreads; ditto, with fruits, meats, etc.	Soft, high moisture, incl. cream spreads	25–11	6.0[d]	3
	Less soft, incl. blue	26–11	6.0[d]	3
Cold pack, club; cold pack cheese foods; ditto, with fruits, meats, etc.	Mild-med. flavored, soft	26–11	6.0[d]	3
	Sharp, firm	27–11	6.0[d]	3

ICE CREAM AND FROZEN DESSERTS
Weight per Unit Volume of Packaged Ice Cream—Official Final Action
★ *Method I (52)* ★

16.220   *Apparatus*

(a) *Overflow can.*—Fig. 16:5. No. 10, or 1 gal. can with overflow spout of ⅛–3⁄16″ id metal tubing soldered to opening in side of can ca 1″ from bottom and bent upward and extending parallel to sides. Tube should be bent over at upper end to form spout ca 1½″ below top of can. Upper edge of opening of spout should be above and lower edge below highest point of interior surface of top bend, *B*. Iron bar, slightly longer than diam. of can, equipped with "bridge" of tinned metal, may be used to submerge sample in kerosene of known density at 20/4° and cooled to 5–10° (refrigerator temp.) before use. "Bridge" should extend ½″ below level of *B*.

(b) *Balance.*—Capacity 1 kg, sensitive to 1 g.

(c) *Cylinders or beakers.*—500 to 1000 ml, graduated.

16.221   *Determination*

Obtain packaged samples (pts preferred) from freezing compartment or cold room and immediately place in insulated container with solid CO_2 for transportation to laboratory. Surround package with slabs or pieces of solid CO_2 until frozen solid.

Place overflow can on level table so that overflow

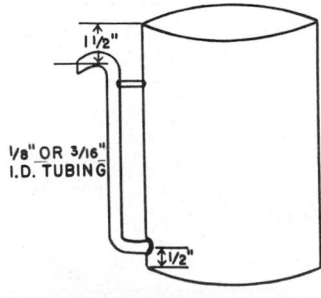

FIG. 16:5—Overflow can

discharges into sink. Fill can with cooled kerosene until it overflows thru spout. When overflow ceases, placed weighed 500 ml graduated cylinder (or beaker) under spout.

Remove frozen brick from solid CO_2, quickly remove from carton, and weigh to accuracy of 1–2 g. Designate this wt *W*. Slowly immerse brick in the kerosene, finally submerging it completely by holding it under surface with small spatula, or "bridge," **16.220**(a), until overflow ceases. Weigh displaced kerosene to accuracy of 1–2 g, and subtract tare wt cylinder or beaker to det. net wt kerosene displaced. Divide net wt kerosene by its sp gr and designate resultant vol. *V*.

$$\text{Wt/unit vol. (as lb/gal.)} = W \times 8.345/V.$$

If products are so packed that they are difficult to remove from carton, det. gross wt carton and contents, then open ends or sides of carton enough to avoid formation of entrapped air bubbles, and submerge entire carton and contents in the kerosene as directed. After overflow ceases and displaced kerosene has been weighed, remove contents from carton, dry empty carton, and weigh. Transfer kerosene to 100 ml or 200 ml graduated cylinder, filling to halfway mark, and record vol. Roll up dried carton so that it will slip into cylinder, avoiding entrapment of air. Push carton into cylinder until it is completely immersed in the kerosene. Increase in vol. is vol. occupied by carton. Correct for wt and vol. of carton in formula given above and calc. unit wt in lb/gal.

Graduated cylinder may be used instead of beaker to catch overflow. Vol. reading may be used as check against calcd vol. of the kerosene. Vol. as calcd from wt is more nearly accurate.

Method II (53)

16.222 Apparatus and Materials

(a) *Container.*—See Fig. 16:6. Plastic desiccator, ca 1 to 1½ qt capacity (Ace Glass Co., Cat. No. 1810, or equiv.) modified to include ca ¼″ hole in cover center for air escape and leak-free side arm tube. Clean with detergent before use and grease rims lightly.

(b) *Clamps.*—To secure desiccator lid (Hoge No. 25 binder clips (available from stationery stores), or equiv.); see Fig. 16:6.

(c) *Balance.*—Approx. 10 lb capacity and 0.01 oz sensitivity.

(d) *Ice chest.*—Approx. 4–5 gal. capacity, packed with solid CO_2.

(e) *Immersion fluid.*—Approx. 0.001% polysorbate 80 (Tween 80) soln in H_2O. Prep. ca 4 L for each detn and cool to $4\pm4°$.

16.223 Determination

Pack and store samples overnight in solid CO_2. Unwrap hard frozen sample. If sample is 0.5 gal. or

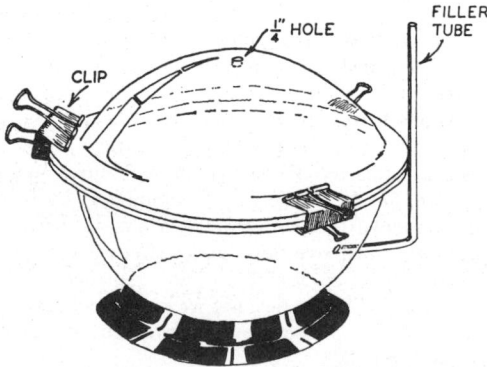

FIG. 16:6—Modified plastic desiccator

larger unit, break by scoring with chisel or other sharp instrument and driving knife or wedge into block along scored line. Quickly det. wt in air (W_a, oz) of piece selected for wt/vol. detn and return to ice chest.

Place container on level surface and secure lid in place with 4 clamps. Completely fill container thru inlet tube with chilled immersion fluid dispensed from separator with rubber tubing attached. Wipe outer surface dry and det. wt (W_p, oz).

Place container in sink or on drainboard and remove lid. Place previously weighed sample piece in container and secure lid with 4 clamps. Fill container completely with immersion fluid, letting all air bubbles escape thru air hole in lid. Wipe outer surface and det. wt (W_i, oz).

Wt per unit vol. (lb/gal.) $= (W_a \times 8.338)/[W_a + (W_p - W_i)]$, where $8.338 =$ density of H_2O at 0–8° (lb/gal.) and wts W_a, W_p, and W_i are in oz.

16.224 Preparation of Sample (54)—Procedure

Cut frozen blocks of product into ca ½ pt pieces. Select 2 or 3 pieces at random, place in cup of high-speed blender, and close tightly. Let soften at room temp. and mix 2 min for plain products and up to 7 min for those contg nuts or hard candy chips. Immediately pour mixt. into wide-mouth jar and cap tightly. If allowed to stand, shake vigorously before removing samples.

16.225 Total Solids (55)—Official Final Action

Into round, flat-bottom dish ≥ 5 cm diam., quickly weigh 1–2 g sample. (Sample may be weighed by means of short, bent, 2 ml measuring pipet.) Heat on steam bath 30 min and then in air oven 3.5 hr at 100°. Cool in desiccator and weigh quickly to avoid absorption of moisture.

Nitrogen—Official Final Action
16.226 Kjeldahl Method

Proceed as in 2.051, using 4–5 g sample. % N $\times$ 6.38 = % "protein."

16.227 Dye Binding Method
See 16.036–16.040.

Fat
16.228 Roese-Gottlieb Method (56)—Official Final Action

Accurately weigh 4–5 g thoroly mixed sample directly into fat-extn flask or tube, using free-flowing pipet; dil. with H_2O to ca 10 ml, working charge into lower chamber and mixing by shaking. Add 2 ml NH_4OH, mix thoroly, and heat in H_2O bath 20 min at 60° with occasional shaking. Cool, and proceed as in 16.052, beginning "Add 10 ml alcohol and mix well."

16.229 Separation of Fat from Ice Cream— Official Final Action

(*Caution:* See **46.011, 46.039,** and **46.054.**)

Melt sample and screen out any large pieces of fruit, nuts, etc. on No. 20 sieve. Place 300 ml melted sample in 1 L separator, add 100 ml H_2O and 50 ml NH_4OH, and shake well. Add 200 ml alcohol and shake 1 min. Add 200 ml ether and shake 1 min. Add 200 ml pet ether and shake 1 min. Let stand until emulsion breaks, and drain and discard lower layer. Add 25 g anhyd. Na_2SO_4, shake, and decant thru rapid folded paper. Evap. ether and alcohol, and dry fat at 55° overnight. Examine fat as in Chap **28.**

16.230 Lactic Acid—Official Final Action— See 16.026–16.031

Gums

Infrared Method (57)—Official First Action

(Guar flour gum and locust bean gum cannot be distinguished by this method. Karaya gum cannot be identified when isolated by this method.)

16.231 Reagents

(a) *Dioxane.*—Tech. grade is satisfactory. (*Caution:* Vapors are obnoxious and harmful.)

(b) *Trichloroacetic acid (TCA) soln.*—50%. See **16.211(b).**

(c) *Organo-silicone compound.*—To prep. nonwettable surface. Desicote® (Beckman Instruments) has been found satisfactory.

16.232 Apparatus

(a) *Infrared spectrophotometer.*—Recording, for operation in 2–15 μm region.

(b) *Water-repellent plate.*—Wash 3–4″ glass square thoroly with detergent, rinse, and dry with towel. Dip glass rod in organo-silicone compd and streak adhering liq. across plate. Repeat streaking several times. Rub plate with lens paper to distribute evenly; then rub with clean lens paper to remove excess. Plate is now ready for use. Wash plate with cold H_2O and dry with towel after each use. Plate can be reused as long as it remains nonwettable.

16.233 Preparation of Sample

Weigh 50 g sample of frozen dessert into 250 ml centrf. bottle and heat to 60° in H_2O bath. Add 150 ml dioxane, shake vigorously 2 min, and centrf. 10 min at 1800 rpm. Decant and discard supernatant. Add 30 ml ether, and shake vigorously to break mass at bottom, using rod if necessary. Decant ether and repeat ether wash once. Heat in H_2O bath to remove residual ether. Add 30 ml 80° H_2O and shake vigorously 2 min to dissolve or disperse residue.

16.234 Separation of Gum

Add 20 ml 50% TCA soln and heat to 60° in H_2O bath. Shake 1 min and centrf. 10 min at 1200 rpm. Decant soln thru fast folded paper into second centrf. bottle, and discard residue.

Fill centrf. bottle with alcohol, add 1 ml satd NaCl soln, mix, and let stand until coagulation occurs. If ppt does not form, gums are absent. (Let opalescent solns stand overnight to facilitate pptn. Centrf., and discard if no ppt is present.) Centrf. 10 min at 1800 rpm and immediately decant and discard supernatant.

Purify pptd gum by adding 30 ml 80° H_2O and shake vigorously to dissolve or disperse ppt. Fill centrf. bottle with alcohol, add 1 ml satd NaCl soln and 1 drop HCl (1 + 1), mix, let ppt coagulate, centrf. 10 min at 1800 rpm, decant, and discard supernatant. Repeat purification step twice.

16.235 Detection of Gum

(a) *Chemical test for small amounts.*—Scrape small amt of pptd gum from centrf. bottle with spatula and transfer to 50 ml beaker with ca 10 ml hot H_2O. Add 2 ml HCl and boil 5 min. Neutze to multirange indicator paper, using 30% NaOH soln first and completing with 10% NaOH soln. Remove paper and continue as in **16.214,** beginning "... add 5 ml Benedict soln ..."

(b) *Chemical test for entire precipitate.*—If IR spectrum is not desired, spectrum indicates presence of 2 or more gums, or pptd gum will not form film (as with karaya), proceed as in **16.214,** beginning "Add 10 ml hot H_2O ..."

(c) *Infrared method.*—(May not be applicable to mixts of gums.) Dissolve or disperse residue in 35 ml H_2O. Prep. film as in **16.236,** obtain IR spectrum against air, and compare with spectra of ref. gums.

16.236 Preparation of Gum Films

Place H_2O repellent glass plate over 2″ opening on steam bath. Pour enough of aq. gum soln on plate to form circle ca 2″ diam. (Vol. required to produce film of sufficient area to cover light path of app. and of thickness to produce characteristic spectrum varies depending upon nature of gum, and its concn.) Heat plate until film is dry and remove film with forceps. If film sticks to plate, remove with razor blade or tissue lifter. Transfer film to beaker and dry 15–30 min at 100°. (Excessive heating may char some gums.) Place piece of film between 2 salt plates and obtain IR spectrum against air.

16.237 Preparation of Reference Gum Films

Disperse 0.2 g gum in 30 ml 80° H_2O and add 20 ml 50% TCA soln. Continue as in **16.234,** beginning "Shake 1 min and centrf. 10 min at 1200 rpm."

16.238 Alginates in Chocolate Frozen Desserts —Official Final Action—See 13.057–13.058

16.239 Gelatin—Official Final Action

Using 10 g sample, proceed as in **16.074.**

16.240   Coloring Matters—Official Final Action

Curdle 150–200 g melted sample by adding equal vol. H_2O and 10–20 ml HOAc. Heat mixt. to 70–80°, with stirring, and let cool. Continue as in **16.079** and **16.175**, and in Chap. **34** for detection of oil-sol. synthetic dyes and annatto.

16.241   Residual Phosphatase (22)—Official Final Action

Melt portion of sample and let it remain melted 1 hr or longer before testing. Then proceed as in **16.084** except as follows:

In *Step 3*, proceed as for milk in case of sherbets; for ice cream, substitute buffer substrate made by dissolving $Na_2C_6H_5PO_4$ in mixt. of 4 parts Ba buffer, **16.082**(a)(*1*). and 1 part H_2O.

In *Step 6*, proceed as for milk in case of sherbets; for ice cream, ppt with 1.0 ml soln contg 4.5 g $ZnSO_4$.$7H_2O$ and 0.1 g $CuSO_4$.$5H_2O$/100 ml.

Controls are essential since phenols may be present from flavors or plastic containers.

SELECTED REFERENCES

(*1*) JAOAC **49**, 58(1966); **50**, 200, 531(1967); **51**, 461(1968).

(*2*) JAOAC **30**, 130(1947); **34**, 239(1951).

(*3*) JAOAC **15**, 643(1932); **16**, 427(1933).

(*4*) JAOAC **20**, 130(1937); **25**, 253(1942); **26**, 199 (1943); J. Dairy Sci. **27**, 743(1944); **46**, 135 (1963).

(*5*) JAOAC **23**, 453(1940); **28**, 212(1945); **34**, 239 (1951).

(*6*) JAOAC **50**, 542, 557(1967); **51**, 811(1968); **52**, 138(1969).

(*7*) JAOAC **10**, 259(1927); **13**, 254(1930); **14**, 246 (1931); **16**, 489(1933); **17**, 357(1934); **19**, 383 (1936).

(*8*) J. Milk Food Technol. **16**, 241(1953); JAOAC **38**, 310(1955); **39**, 345(1956); **43**, 407(1960).

(*9*) Analyst **21**, 182(1896); JAOAC **25**, 603(1942); **27**, 232(1944).

(*10*) Z. Nahr. Genussm. **9**, 531(1905); JAOAC **34**, 237(1951); **52**, 235(1969).

(*11*) JAOAC **8**, 4(1924); **8**, 471(1925).

(*12*) JAOAC **43**, 746(1960).

(*13*) JAOAC **52**, 131(1969).

(*14*) J. Am. Chem. Soc. **26**, 1195(1904); JAOAC **31**, 124(1948); **32**, 309(1949); **34**, 248(1951).

(*15*) JAOAC **31**, 124(1948); **32**, 309(1949); **34**, 248 (1951).

(*16*) J. Ind. Eng. Chem. **13**, 198(1921); JAOAC **5**, 172, 470, 484(1922); **6**, 424, 429(1923); **43**, 411 (1960).

(*17*) JAOAC **44**, 438(1961); **51**, 460, 816(1968); **53**, 539(1970).

(*18*) JAOAC **19**, 386, 476(1936).

(*19*) USDA Bull. **1114** (1922); JAOAC **28**, 417 (1945); **30**, 655(1947).

(*20*) J. Am. Chem. Soc. **22**, 207(1900).

(*21*) J. Dairy Res. **6**, 191(1935); J. Milk Technol. **1**, 18(1938); JAOAC **21**, 82(1938).

(*22*) J. Dairy Sci. **29**, 737(1946); **30**, 909(1947); JAOAC **31**, 306(1948).

(*23*) JAOAC **48**, 811(1965).

(*24*) JAOAC **51**, 802(1968).

(*25*) JAOAC **44**, 444(1961).

(*26*) JAOAC **45**, 301, 307(1962).

(*27*) JAOAC **30**, 575(1947); **31**, 739(1948); **32**, 731 (1949).

(*28*) JAOAC **31**, 750(1948).

(*29*) JAOAC **10**, 281(1927).

(*30*) JAOAC **28**, 210(1945); **52**, 239(1969).

(*31*) JAOAC **18**, 402(1935).

(*32*) JAOAC **10**, 308(1927); **11**, 289(1928).

(*33*) JAOAC **24**, 546(1941)

(*34*) JAOAC **24**, 744(1941); **25**, 253, 610(1942); **28**, 205(1945).

(*35*) JAOAC **5**, 508(1922); **6**, 435(1923); **23**, 465 (1940).

(*36*) JAOAC **15**, 524(1932); **52**, 240, 394(1969).

(*37*) JAOAC **18**, 396(1935).

(*38*) JAOAC **21**, 361(1938); **35**, 194(1952).

(*39*) JAOAC **49**, 518(1966).

(*40*) JAOAC **52**, 235, 394(1969).

(*41*) JAOAC **33**, 495(1950).

(*42*) JAOAC **36**, 1077(1953).

(*43*) JAOAC **9**, 44(1926); **18**, 57(1935).

(*44*) JAOAC **31**, 300(1948); **32**, 303(1949).

(*45*) JAOAC **52**, 117(1969).

(*46*) JAOAC **18**, 401(1935); **20**, 340(1937).

(*47*) JAOAC **16**, 584(1933); **31**, 300(1948); **32**, 303 (1949); **52**, 240, 394(1969).

(*48*) JAOAC **11**, 287(1928).

(*49*) JAOAC **3**, 402(1920); **10**, 264(1927); **11**, 288 (1928); **15**, 520(1932).

(*50*) JAOAC **13**, 243(1930); **16**, 485(1933).

(*51*) JAOAC **20**, 527(1937); **23**, 597(1940); **28**, 245 (1945); **34**, 361(1951).

(*52*) JAOAC **28**, 601(1945).

(*53*) JAOAC **51**, 807(1968).

(*54*) JAOAC **52**, 236(1969).

(*55*) JAOAC **24**, 575(1941).

(*56*) JAOAC **35**, 212(1952).

(*57*) JAOAC **43**, 624(1960).

17. Eggs and Egg Products

17.001 Collection and Preparation of Sample (1)—Procedure

No simple rules can be made for collection of sample representative of av. of any particular lot of egg material, as conditions may differ widely. Experienced judgment must be used in each instance. For large lots, preferably draw several samples for sep. analyses rather than attempt to get one composite representative sample. Sampling for microbiological examination, if required, should be performed first; see **41.009–41.018** and **41.026–41.040**.

(a) *Liquid eggs.*—Obtain representative container or containers. Mix contents of container thoroly and draw ca 300 g. (Long-handle dipper or ladle serves well.) Keep sample in hermetically sealed jar in freezer or with solid CO_2. Report odor and appearance.

(b) *Frozen eggs.*—Obtain representative container or containers. Examine contents as to odor and appearance. (Condition of contents can be detd best by drilling to center of container with auger and noting odor as auger is withdrawn. If impossible to secure individual containers, samples may consist of composite of borings from contents of each container.) Take borings midway between center and circumference of top of can from at least 3 widely sepd parts and extend them as near to bottom of can as possible. Collect ca 300 g and keep sample in hermetically sealed jar in freezer or with solid CO_2, if possible. Before analyzing, warm sample in bath held at <50°, and mix well.

(c) *Dried eggs.*—Obtain representative container or containers. For small packages, take entire parcel or parcels for sample. For boxes and barrels, remove top layer to depth of ca 6″ with scoop or other convenient instrument. Draw small amts of sample totaling 300–500 g from accessible parts of container and place in hermetically sealed jar. Report odor and appearance. Prep. sample for analysis by mixing 3 times thru domestic flour sifter to thoroly break up lumps. (Grind flake albumen samples to pass entirely thru No. 60 sieve. Mix well.) Keep in hermetically sealed jar in cool place.

Yolk Color (2)—Official First Action

17.002 Preparation of Standard Carotene Solution

Prep. solns contg 0.5, 1.0, 2.0, 3.0, 4.0, and 5.0 μg β-carotene/ml by weighing 0.25, 0.50, 1.0, 1.5, 2.0, and 2.5 g std 0.05% β-carotene in oil soln into series of 250 ml vol. flasks, and dilg to vol. with acetone.

Solns are stable at least 1 week in dark under refrigeration. Equiv. amts of std β-carotene soln of different strength may be used.

17.003 Preparation of Standard Curve

Det. % T or A of dild std solns as soon as possible with spectrophtr at 450 nm or with instrument with suitable filter system such as Klett photometer with No. 44 filter, Evelyn photoelec. colorimeter with 440 filter, or with Cenco-Sanford-Sheard Photelometer, Industrial Type B-2 with 410 filter. Plot μg β-carotene against % T, omitting values >90% or <10%, on semilog paper or against A on plain coordinate paper.

17.004 Determination

Weigh sample contg ca 1.0 g egg yolk solids (1 g dried yolk, 2.5 g liq. yolk, 5.0 g liq. whole egg, or equiv.) into 150 ml beaker. Add ca 1–2 ml acetone and stir to smooth paste. Add ca 50 ml acetone, mix, and filter. Add ca 2.5 ml H_2O before the acetone to products contg sugar or salt. Wash material onto Whatman No. 4 filter paper or equiv. with successive small portions of acetone, catching filtrate in g-s 100 ml vol. flask. Dil. to vol. with acetone. Det. A or % T as soon as possible. Report yolk color equiv. to μg β-carotene/g sample.

Total Solids
Vacuum Method (3)—Official Final Action

17.005 Apparatus

Vacuum oven.—Connected with pump to maintain partial vac. in oven with pressure equiv. to ≤25 mm Hg and provided with thermometer passing into oven with bulb near samples. Connect H_2SO_4 gas-drying bottle to oven for admitting dry air to release vac.

17.006 Determination

(a) *Liquid eggs.*—Accurately weigh by difference, using weighing buret, ca 5 g sample, **17.001**(a) or (b), in covered dish previously dried at 98–100°, cooled in desiccator, and weighed soon after coming to room temp. Remove cover and evap. most of H_2O by heating on steam bath. Replace cover loosely and complete drying in vac. oven as in (b).

(b) *Dried eggs.*—Weigh ca 2 g sample, **17.001**(c), in covered dish previously dried at 98–100°, cooled in desiccator, and weighed soon after coming to room temp. Loosen cover (do not remove) and heat at 98–100° to constant wt (ca 5 hr) in vac. oven. Admit dry air into oven to bring to atm. pressure. Immediately tighten cover of dish, transfer to desiccator contg fresh efficient desiccant, and weigh soon after room temp. is reached. Report as % total solids.

Nitrogen (4)—Official Final Action

17.007 *Preparation of Sample*

(a) *Liquid eggs.*—Weigh 2–3 g well-mixed sample, 17.001(a) or (b), by difference into 500 ml Kjeldahl flask.

(b) *Dried eggs.*—Transfer ca 1 g prepd sample, 17.001(c), accurately weighed, to 500 ml Kjeldahl flask.

17.008 *Determination*

Det N as in **2.051**. Distill NH₃ into 30–50 ml 0.1N std acid.

Water-Soluble Nitrogen and Crude Albumin Nitrogen in Liquid Eggs (5)—Official Final Action

17.009 *Preparation of Solution*

Accurately weigh, by difference, into 250 ml vol. flask contg 150 ml H₂O, ca 10 g well-mixed sample 17.001(a) or (b), and mix gently. Add 5 ml 0.01N HOAc for each g egg substance, dil. to vol. with H₂O, shake gently, and filter thru 18.5 cm folded paper, covering filter with watch glass during filtration. If filtrate is cloudy, let filtration continue until drops of filtrate are clear, change receiver, return cloudy filtrate to filter, and proceed as in **17.010**.

17.010 *Determination*

(a) *Water-soluble nitrogen.*—Transfer 50 ml clear filtrate to 500 ml Kjeldahl flask, and det. N as in **2.051**. Calc. N and report as % H₂O-sol. N.

(b) *Crude albumin nitrogen.*—Transfer 100 ml clear filtrate to 200 ml vol. flask, add 15 ml NaCl soln (28 g NaCl dild to 300 ml), fill nearly to vol. with alcohol, and mix. Cool to room temp., dil. to vol. with alcohol, mix, and let stand overnight. Filter, transfer 100 ml filtrate to 500 ml Kjeldahl flask, and det. N as in **2.051**. Calc. % N, subtract it from % H₂O-sol. N, and report difference as % crude albumin N.

Fat by Acid Hydrolysis (6)—Official Final Action

17.011 *Preparation of Solution*

(a) *Liquid eggs.* — From well-mixed sample, 17.001(a) or (b), accurately weigh, by difference, into Mojonnier fat-extn tube ca 2 g yolks, or 3 g whole eggs or 5 g whites. Slowly, with vigorous shaking, add 10 ml HCl, set tube in H₂O bath heated to 70°, bring to boiling, and continue heating at boiling 30 min, shaking tube carefully at 5 min intervals. Remove tube from bath, add H₂O to nearly fill lower bulb of tube, and cool to room temp.

(b) *Dried eggs.*—Transfer 1 g well-mixed sample to fat-extn tube, slowly add 10 ml HCl (4 + 1), washing down any egg particles adhering to sides of tube, and proceed as in (a).

17.012 *Determination*

To extn tube contg treated sample, 17.011, add 25 ml ether and mix. Add 25 ml redistd pet ether (bp <60°), mix, and let stand until solv. layer is clear. Proceed as in **14.019**, beginning "Draw off as much as possible ..." but omitting filtration.

Lipids and Lipid Phosphorus (P₂O₅) (7)—Official Final Action

17.013 *Reagents*

(a) *Mixed solvent.*—Equal vols CHCl₃ and absolute alcohol.

(b) *Alcoholic sodium hydroxide soln.*—Prep. CO₃-free soln by dissolving 100 g NaOH in 100 ml H₂O. Let stand until clear, or filter thru hardened paper previously soaked in alcohol. (5 ml NaOH soln contains ca 4 g NaOH.) Dissolve 50 ml of this soln in 900 ml alcohol and dil. with alcohol to 1 L.

17.014 *Preparation of Solution*

(a) *Liquid eggs.*—Accurately weigh, by difference, ca 4 g well-mixed sample, 17.001(a) or (b), into 100 ml vol. flask, and add 25 ml mixed solv. very slowly (dropwise) from pipet, shaking constantly until proteins coagulate and are then thoroly broken up. Add 60–65 ml addnl solv. and let stand 1 hr, shaking at 5 min intervals. Dil. to vol. with solv., mix, and let mixt. stand until clear.

(b) *Dried eggs.*—Transfer 2 g well-mixed sample, 17.001(c), to 100 ml vol. flask, add 85–90 ml mixed solv., and let stand 1 hr, mixing at 5 min intervals. Proceed as in (a).

17.015 *Determination*

(a) *Lipids.*—Transfer 50 ml aliquot to 150 ml beaker and evap. ext to dryness on steam bath. (Elec. fan or gentle blast of dry air may be used to hasten evapn.) Place beaker in oven 5–10 min at 100° to remove any remaining H₂O. Dissolve dry ext in 5–10 ml CHCl₃, and filter into weighed 100 ml Pyrex beaker thru pledget of cotton packed into stem of funnel, transferring all sol. ext from bottom and sides of beaker with CHCl₃. Finally wash funnel and stem tip. (Filtrate should be clear.) Evap. CHCl₃ on steam bath and dry beaker and contents in oven at 100° to constant wt (ca 90 min). Let beaker stand in air to constant wt (ca 30 min), weigh, and report % lipids.

(b) *Lipid phosphorus (P₂O₅).*—Dissolve dried lipids in 2–3 ml CHCl₃, add 10–20 ml alc. NaOH soln, evap. to dryness on steam bath, using care to avoid spattering, and place beaker in oven 30 min at 100° to remove any remaining H₂O. Transfer beaker while hot to muffle heated to 500° (faint red), and keep at this temp. 1 hr. Cool, add few drops

H_2O, and break up charge with flat-end glass rod. Cover beaker with watch glass, slowly add 5 ml HNO_3 (1 + 3), mix, wash watch glass, and filter, collecting filtrate in 300 or 500 ml erlenmeyer. Thoroly wash charred material and filter paper with H_2O.

Det. P in filtrate as in **2.031**, using 20–50 ml molybdate soln. Report % lipid P_2O_5 in eggs.

Cholesterol (8)—Official Final Action
Separation of Unsaponifiable Matter

17.016 *Reagents*

(a) *Concentrated potassium hydroxide soln.*—Dissolve 60 g KOH in 40 ml H_2O.

(b) *Dilute potassium hydroxide soln.*—Dissolve 10 g KOH in 1 L H_2O.

(c) *Ether.*—USP or ACS, peroxide-free. Test immediately before use.

(d) *Dried ether.*—Immediately before use shake peroxide-free ether with anhyd. $CaCl_2$ equal to 10% of the vol. of the ether, and filter.

(e) *Anhydrous sodium sulfate.*—Powder to pass No. 60 sieve.

17.017 *Apparatus*

(a) *Separators.*—One 250 ml and one 500 ml. *Wash separators free of grease.* Should be ether-tight with stopcocks lubricated only with H_2O.

(b) *Filtration bell jar.*—Large enough to hold 300 ml erlenmeyer and provided with air-leak valve to control vac.

(c) *Fritted glass filter.*—Fine porosity.

17.018 *Determination*

(*Caution: See* **46.011, 46.039,** and **46.054.**)

Accurately weigh into 125 ml erlenmeyer ca 2.5 g whole egg, 1.5 g yolk, 1 g dried whole egg, or 0.7 g dried yolk, and add 10 ml concd KOH soln. Cover with small watch glass and heat 3 hr on steam bath, swirling occasionally to disintegrate any large lumps. Cool until just warm, add 30 ml alcohol, and swirl until all insol. matter is *finely* dispersed. Add 50 ml ether, mix thoroly by swirling, and transfer to 500 ml separator. Wash flask with 2 addnl 50 ml portions ether and thoroly mix ether soln by swirling. Wash saponification flask with 100 ml dil. KOH soln, pour soln slowly into separator, while gently swirling liq., and continue gentle swirling 10–15 sec. Let liq. sep. (ca 10 min) and slowly drain soap soln into 250 ml separator, but do not draw off any small quantity of emulsion or insol. matter at interface. Rinse down sides of 500 ml separator with 10 ml dil. KOH soln and drain this into smaller separator. Add 50 ml ether to smaller separator and shake vigorously. After liq. seps, discard lower layer. Add ether layer to soln in large separator, rinsing 250 ml separator with 10 ml ether. Wash ether soln as before with 100 ml dil. KOH soln, keeping any insol. matter or emulsion in separator. Add 20 ml HCl (1 + 4) to ether,

swirl, add 100 ml H_2O, and swirl again. Discard acid washings.

Wash ether soln as before with 2 addnl 100 ml portions of dil. KOH soln. Test portion of last washings for soap by acidifying with HCl (1 + 4) (acidified washings should be clear or only faintly turbid). If necessary, repeat washing with dil. KOH soln until acidified washings are clear. Wash ether soln by successively swirling with 50 ml H_2O, 50 ml H_2O contg 0.5 ml 0.1N HCl, and 2 addnl 50 ml portions H_2O. Finally, drain as much H_2O as possible without loss of ether soln. Filter ether soln into dry 300 ml erlenmeyer thru 15 g layer Na_2SO_4 on fritted glass filter, using no suction for first few ml and then gentle suction for remainder. Rinse separator and filter successively with 10, 5, 5, and 5 ml ether. Rinse filter stem with ether, add porcelain chip to flask, and evap. ether on steam bath.

Dissolve residue in 20 ml dried ether, transfer ether soln thru small short-stem funnel to 50 ml erlenmeyer contg porcelain chip, and rinse with 10, 5, and 5 ml dried ether. Approx. unsaponifiable matter can be detd by collecting ether solns in flask previously dried and weighed as follows: Dry the flask contg the chip, and similar flask used as counterpoise, 1 hr at 100–105°; remove from oven and place near balance 30 min; weigh flask, using counterpoise. Evap. ether on steam bath. Wipe flask with clean towel, dry, and weigh with counterpoise as before. From wt unsaponifiable matter, deduct blank obtained from reagents used, detd by same procedure.

Determination of Cholesterol

17.019 *Reagents*

(a) *Ice.*—For 4 detns have available ca 3 gal. crushed ice.

(b) *Bromine soln.*—(*Caution: See* **46.047.**) Weigh, to 0.1 g, narrow-mouth, g-s 25 ml flask contg 5 ml CCl_4. Add 0.6 ml Br from graduated 1.0 ml pipet, weigh again, and dil. with CCl_4 to calcd final concn of 0.22±0.02 g Br/ml. Use reagent within 48 hr after prepn.

(c) *Acetic acid soln.*—Pipet 200 ml HOAc into 250 ml g-s vol. flask; dil. to vol. with H_2O, mix cautiously, dil. to vol., and mix again.

(d) *Asbestos.*—Prep. asbestos as in **31.038.**

(e) *Sand.*—Pass clean sand thru No. 60 sieve and treat with warm HCl until exts are practically colorless. Wash, dry, and ignite.

(f) *Sodium hypochlorite soln.*—Dissolve 88 g NaOH (*Caution: See* **46.037** and **46.047**) in 200 ml H_2O in wide-mouth 3 L flask. Add ca 1.5 L crushed ice and pass in Cl until 71 g is absorbed; dil. to 2 L and store in dark bottles in refrigerator. (Soln should be alk. to phthln.) Before use, check concn of available Cl as follows: Pipet 5 ml into flask contg soln of 2 g KI in 100 ml H_2O, add 5 ml 6N HCl, and titr. with 0.1N $Na_2S_2O_3$. Soln should be equiv. in available Cl to 0.95–1.05N NaOCl. Reagent or com.

NaOCl soln, 5%, checked for concn as above, is also satisfactory.

(g) *Sodium formate soln.*—Prep. aq. soln contg 0.5 g $NaCHO_2$/ml.

(h) *Hydrochloric acid.*—Approx. $6N$; mix 520 ml HCl ($\geq 35\%$ HCl by wt) with H_2O and dil. to 1 L.

(i) *Methyl red indicator.*—Dissolve 0.5 g Me red in 50 ml alcohol, dil. to 100 ml with H_2O, and filter. Since soln must be free from insol. matter, refilter immediately before use if necessary.

(j) *Potassium iodide soln.*—20%. (Soln must be colorless when acidified with HCl.)

(k) *Starch soln.*—1% soln of sol. starch.

(l) *Sodium thiosulfate soln.*—$0.02N$. Prep. daily by dilg $0.1N$ soln, 45.038–45.039.

(m) *Potassium hydroxide soln.*—Dissolve 10 g KOH in 10 ml H_2O.

(n) *Ammonium molybdate soln.*—Dissolve 5 g $(NH_4)_6Mo_7O_{24}.4H_2O$ in 100 ml H_2O.

17.020   *Apparatus*

(a) *Ice bath.*—Container holding ca 4 L, 10–15 cm deep, filled with crushed ice.

(b) *Mohr pipets.*—One graduated to 0.01 ml; one graduated to 0.1 ml.

(c) *Filtration bell jar.*—Size to hold 300 ml erlenmeyer, connected to vac. by 2-way stopcock.

(d) *Device for filtering at 0°.*—Filter tube of Knorr extn tube style, ca 20 mm id, with body ca 11 cm long and stem 6–8 mm od, ca 10 cm long, provided with removable, close fitting perforated Ni, monel metal, glass, or porcelain disk at bottom of larger tube. (Allihn fritted glass filter, coarse porosity, Ace Glass, Inc. No. 8571 with 10 cm stem is suitable.)

Remove stem at apex from 60° Bunsen funnel, 11 cm diam. Enlarge opening at apex to ca 1 cm diam. by grinding or grating off glass. Cut ca 1 cm from end of 1-hole rubber stopper of size that fits snugly in opening of funnel. Pass stem of filter tube thru stopper in funnel apex and then thru stopper in bell jar.

Prep. mat of the asbestos 6–8 mm thick in filter tube and cover with ca 12 mm layer of the sand.

17.021   *Determination*

Pack Br soln and 25 ml graduated cylinder in ice. Pack ice around filter tubes, taking care none gets into filters. Cool HOAc soln to ca $-5°$ in ice-NaCl mixt.

Wash down sides of 50 ml erlenmeyers contg unsaponifiable matter, while rotating them, with 2.0 ml absolute ether delivered from Mohr pipet; stopper with cork, swirl until porcelain chips no longer stick to flasks, and pack flasks in ice bath up to necks at least 10 min. To one of flasks add, from Mohr pipet, 0.20 ml cold Br soln, mix by swirling, stopper, and replace in ice bath. Start this operation at 3 min intervals with other flasks (4 detns can be made at one time if bell jars are available).

After 10 min, rapidly add 15 ml HOAc soln from cold 25 ml cylinder, swirl 3 min while holding in ice-H_2O, and replace in ice bath 10 min. With suction on, pour all mixt. down stirring rod into filter tube, leaving rod in filter. Wash down sides of flask with 5 ml cold HOAc soln and replace in ice bath. When liq. in filter just recedes below surface of sand, add HOAc from flask. Repeat washing similarly with 5 ml HOAc soln and suck filter free of excess liq. Wash flask and filter with cold H_2O, filling filter tube ca 3 times. Drain flask thoroly and apply suction to filter until drops of H_2O cease to fall from stem. Remove ice pack from around filter tube and discard filtrate and washings.

Place 300 ml erlenmeyer under filter so that stem projects well into neck of flask. Wash filter tube and filter with 10 ml alcohol; 10, 5, and 5 ml portions ether; and finally with 10 ml alcohol, gently stirring sand with each portion of solv. and letting mixt. stand ca 1 min before applying suction. Wash stem of filter with few ml ether, add 1 ml KOH soln, mix, and wash down sides of flask with 5 ml ether. Evap. ether and alcohol completely on steam bath, finally using stream of clean air to remove last of alcohol vapors.

Add 40 ml hot H_2O to residual alk. liq., mix, and neutze alkali with $6N$ HCl, using *1 drop* Me red. (This neutzn need be only approx.) Add 10 g NaCl, 3 g $NaH_2PO_4.H_2O$, and 20 ml NaOCl soln. Bring soln just to vigorous boiling, remove from heat, and immediately add, with care, 5 ml $NaCHO_2$ soln. Cool, and dil. to ca 150 ml with H_2O. Add 5 ml KI soln, 1 or 2 drops of NH_4 molybdate soln, and 25 ml $6N$ HCl. Titr. rapidly at once with $Na_2S_2O_3$ soln, using starch soln as indicator. Correct titer for blank detn on reagents, starting at point where KOH soln is added to alcohol-ether soln.

$$\text{mg Cholesterol} = 0.55 + 0.688 \times \text{ml } 0.02N \text{ } Na_2S_2O_3$$

Total Phosphorus (P_2O_5) *(9)*—Official Final Action

17.022   *Preparation of Solution*

(a) *Liquid eggs.* — From well-mixed sample, 17.001(a) or (b), accurately weigh, by difference, into 250 ml Pyrex beaker, ca 2 g yolks, 4 g whole eggs, or 10 g whites. Add 20 ml 10% Na_2CO_3 soln and evap. to dryness on hot plate or in oven overnight at 100–105°. Transfer beaker while hot to muffle at 500° (faint red), and keep at this temp. 1 hr. Cool, add few drops H_2O, break up charge with flat-end glass rod, cover beaker with watch glass, slowly add 10 ml HNO_3 (1 + 3) while stirring, mix, wash watch glass, and filter, collecting filtrate in 300 or 500 ml erlenmeyer. Thoroly wash charred material and filter with H_2O.

(b) *Dried eggs.*—Transfer 1 g well-mixed sample, 17.001(c), to 150 ml Pyrex beaker, add 20 ml 10% Na_2CO_3 soln, and proceed as in (a).

17.023   *Determination*

Det. P_2O_5 in prepd filtrate as in **2.031**, using 40–50 ml molybdate soln. Report as total P_2O_5.

Chlorine (10)—Official Final Action

17.024   *Method I*

(a) *Liquid eggs (in absence of added salt).*—From well-mixed sample, **17.001(a)** or **(b)**, accurately weigh, by difference, into 150 ml Pyrex beaker, ca 4 g yolks, 7 g whole eggs, or 10 g whites; add 20 ml 10% Na_2CO_3 soln, mix, and evap. to dryness on hot plate or overnight in oven at 100°. Transfer beaker while hot to muffle at 500° (faint red), and keep at that temp. 1 hr. Cool, add few drops H_2O, and break up charge with glass rod. Add 50 ml H_2O, cover beaker with watch glass, slowly add 20 ml HNO_3 (1 + 3), and wash watch glass. Mix, filter, and wash charred material and filter paper thoroly with H_2O. Proceed by one of following alternatives:

(1) To combined filtrate and washings add known vol. 0.1N $AgNO_3$ in slight excess and proceed as in **3.070**.

(2) Collect filtrate and washings in 250 ml vol. flask, keeping total vol. filtrate to ≤180 ml. Add known vol. 0.1N $AgNO_3$ in slight excess and dil. to vol. Filter, and using aliquot of filtrate, proceed as in **3.070**, beginning "add 5 ml ferric indicator ..."

(b) *Liquid eggs (in presence of added salt).*—From well-mixed sample, **17.001(a)** or **(b)**, accurately weigh 1–2 g, by difference, into 150 ml Pyrex beaker, and proceed as in (a).

(c) *Dried eggs.* — From well-mixed sample, **17.001(c)**, transfer 2 g whole eggs or yolks or 1 g whites to 150 ml Pyrex beaker, and proceed as in (a).

17.025   *Method II (11)*

From well-mixed sample, **17.001(a)**, **(b)**, or **(c)**, accurately weigh, by difference, ca 4 g yolks, 7 g whole eggs, or 10 g whites; or transfer 2 g dried whole eggs or yolks or 1 g dried whites to 300 ml erlenmeyer. Add known vol. 0.1N $AgNO_3$ in slight excess and 20 ml HNO_3, and place mixt. on steam bath 15–30 min. Add 15 ml 5% $KMnO_4$ soln and let stand 60–90 min longer on steam bath. Cool to ≤25°; add 75 ml H_2O and 1 ml *nitrobenzene* (or 1 ml for each 50 mg NaCl present); stopper flask, and shake vigorously to coagulate ppt. Add 5 ml satd ferric alum indicator and titr. with 0.1N thiocyanate soln to end point that persists after soln stands 15 min. (Make titrn at ≤25°; soln is yellow-green before end point and yellow-orange at end point.) At first permanent color change, note buret reading and time; stopper flask, shake vigorously, and let stand 15 min. If soln fades, add thiocyanate soln in half-drop portions until end point color reappears. From ml $AgNO_3$ used, calc. NaCl after deducting blank detd on reagents, using ca 0.25 g sucrose instead of egg.

Glucose and Sucrose (12)—Official Final Action

17.026   *Preparation of Solution*

(a) *Liquid eggs.*—Accurately weigh, by difference, ca 25 g well-mixed sample, **17.001(a)** or **(b)**, into 250 ml vol. flask contg 1 g $CaCO_3$ and 50 ml 5% NaCl soln. Add 130 ml alcohol with continuous mixing. Let stand few min for gas bubbles to rise to surface, cool to room temp., dil. to vol. with H_2O, mix, and filter (18.5 cm folded paper). Transfer 150 ml filtrate to 250 ml beaker and evap. to 20–30 ml to remove alcohol. Cool, and wash with H_2O into 100 ml vol. flask, holding vol. to 80–90 ml. Add dry powd *phosphotungstic acid* in small amts in slight excess to ppt any protein, mix, let stand few min for gas bubbles to rise to surface, dil. to vol. with H_2O, mix, and filter. To filtrate add, in very small portions, enough dry powd KCl to ppt any excess phosphotungstic acid, filter if necessary, and test filtrate for complete pptn.

To correct for error due to vol. occupied by ppt in samples contg added sucrose, repeat detn, weighing same amt of sample into 500 ml vol. flask contg 1 g $CaCO_3$ and 100 ml 5% NaCl soln. Add 260 ml alcohol with continuous mixing. Let stand few min for gas bubbles to rise to surface, cool to room temp., dil. to vol. with H_2O, mix, and filter thru 18.5 cm folded paper. Transfer 300 ml filtrate to 400 ml beaker, evap. to 20–30 ml, and proceed as above. To obtain amt of sucrose, subtract % sucrose obtained in 250 ml diln detn from twice the % obtained in 500 ml diln detn.

(b) *Dried eggs.* — From well-mixed sample, **17.001(c)**, transfer 2.5 g whites or 10 g yolks or whole eggs to 250 ml vol. flask contg 1 g $CaCO_3$ and 50 ml 5% NaCl soln, and let stand 1 hr, mixing at 5 min intervals. Add 130 ml alcohol with continuous mixing, and proceed as in (a), beginning with third sentence.

17.027   *Determination*

(a) *Reducing sugars direct.*—Transfer 25 ml prepd filtrate to 400 ml beaker, and proceed as in **31.039**. Report as % glucose.

(b) *Reducing sugars invert.*—Transfer 50 ml prepd filtrate to 100 ml vol. flask, and invert sucrose as in **31.026(b)** or **(c)**. Neutze with NaOH soln, cool to room temp., and dil. to vol. with H_2O. Transfer 50 ml (or less) to 400 ml beaker, and proceed as in **31.039**. Deduct % invert sugar obtained before inversion from that obtained after inversion, multiply difference by 0.95, and report as % sucrose.

Glycerol (13)

Qualitative Test—Procedure

17.028   *Reagent*

Fuchsin-bisulfite soln.—Dissolve 0.2 g basic fuchsin in 120 ml hot H_2O and cool; add soln of 2 g anhyd.

Na_2SO_3 in 20 ml H_2O, and then 2 ml HCl. Dil. soln with H_2O to 200 ml and let stand 1 hr.

17.029   *Detection*

Add 20 ml alcohol to ca 5 g sample in erlenmeyer or beaker-flask, shake vigorously, and filter thru 12.5 cm fluted paper. Evap. filtrate rapidly until no odor of alcohol is perceptible, cool, and add 3–4 drops H_2O and then 10–15 ml anhyd. ether. Carefully mix solns, let sep., and pour off as much of ether layer as possible, disregarding cloudiness in this layer. Shake well with two 10 ml portions anhyd. ether, pouring off ether carefully in each case. (Vol. aq. soln should be $\geq$0.4–0.5 ml.) Evap. remaining liq. on steam bath to 0.1–0.2 ml. Cool, and add 15 ml mixt. of equal vols absolute alcohol and $CHCl_3$. Cool, shake, and let stand 5 min.

Shake, and filter thru fluted paper into 6 × 1″ Pyrex test tube. Evap. filtrate rapidly (small flame and current of air is convenient) until no odor of $CHCl_3$ or alcohol is perceptible. Add several g powd $KHSO_4$ and insert stopper with glass tube leading into 2 ml H_2O in test tube immersed in ice-H_2O. Heat with small flame until frothing ceases and contents of tube are liq. Remove receiver, immediately add 4–5 drops of fuchsin-bisulfite reagent, and warm to room temp. In presence of glycerol, strong pink (due to acrolein) develops within 1 min and becomes deep violet within 5 min.

Quantitative Method (14)—Official Final Action

17.030   *Reagents*

(a) *Sodium tungstate soln.*—Dissolve 10 g Na_2WO_4 .$2H_2O$ and dil. to 100 ml.

(b) *Potassium periodate soln.*—0.02M. Dissolve 4.6 g KIO_4 in ca 500 ml hot H_2O, dil. to ca 900 ml with H_2O, cool to room temp., and dil. to 1 L. Test for alky by adding 0.02N H_2SO_4 to 25 ml of the soln contg bromocresol purple, (c). Do not use if >1 drop acid is required to give yellow acid color.

(c) *Bromocresol purple indicator.*—Dissolve 0.1 g bromocresol purple in 100 ml alcohol and filter if necessary.

(d) *Calcium oxide, powdered.*—Reagent grade.

17.031   *Determination*

(a) *Eggs with no added sugars.*—Accurately weigh, by difference, ca 2 g well-mixed sample, 17.001(a) or (b), into 100 ml vol. flask contg 50–75 ml H_2O. Mix and add 2.0 ml Na_2WO_4 soln. Add 2.0 ml 1N H_2SO_4 slowly with continuous mixing. Dil. to vol. with H_2O, mix well, and filter (18.5 cm folded paper). Transfer aliquot of filtrate contg $\leq$40 mg glycerol to 300 ml erlenmeyer, and dil. with H_2O to 20 ml if necessary. Add 2 ml 10% NaOH soln, heat to boiling, and boil 30 sec. Cool slightly, add 3 drops bromocresol purple, neutze with 1N H_2SO_4 (use buret), and add 1–2 drops excess. Boil 1 min, cool to room

temp., and neutze carefully with 0.02N NaOH, titrg to light purple shade.

Quant. transfer neut. soln to 100 ml vol. flask, restricting total vol. to <50 ml. (As aid, mark side of flask to indicate vol. of ca 45 ml.) If necessary, add more 0.02N NaOH to maintain light but definite purple. Continue as in 35.082(b), beginning "add 50 ml KIO_4 soln." and using 35.083(a) for detn.

Excess periodate must be present after oxidn. If periodate test is neg., repeat detn, using smaller aliquots.

(b) *Eggs containing added sugars.*—Prep. sample soln as in (a), using ca 2 g sample.

Transfer aliquot of filtrate contg $\leq$40 mg glycerol to 400 ml beaker. Adjust vol. to 20 ml by evapn on steam bath or by addn of H_2O. Add 0.5 g powd CaO, mix, and let stand 30 min at room temp. with occasional mixing. Add 25 ml alcohol, mix, and filter with suction, using buchner and 7 cm S&S 597 paper, or equiv. Rinse beaker, funnel, and paper with several portions alcohol. Transfer as much residue as possible to paper but do not attempt to remove film of lime salts adhering to beaker. Quant. transfer filtrate to original 400 ml beaker, rinsing flask with several portions H_2O. Evap. filtrate on steam bath to ca 10 ml. Filter thru 9 cm S&S 597 paper, or equiv., collecting filtrate in 300 ml erlenmeyer. Rinse beaker, funnel, and paper with small amts of H_2O, restricting total filtrate vol. to $\leq$25 ml. Add 1 ml 10% NaOH soln to filtrate and complete detn as in (a), beginning "heat to boiling, and boil 30 sec."

Acidity of Ether Extract (15)—Official Final Action

(Not applicable to egg white)

17.032   *Reagents*

(*Caution: See* 46.038.)

(a) *Benzene.*—Use best quality available. If not neut., titr. 50 ml with 0.05N Na ethylate, (b), and correct subsequent results accordingly.

(b) *Sodium ethylate std soln.*—0.05N. Dissolve piece of metallic Na (*Caution: See* 46.034), ca 1 ml in vol., in 800 ml absolute alcohol. Titr. 10 ml 0.1N HCl with this soln and add calcd vol. absolute alcohol to make soln 0.05N. Stdze against 0.1N HCl on day soln is used.

17.033   *Determination*

(*Caution: See* 46.011, 46.039, *and* 46.054.)

(a) *Dried eggs.*—Weigh 2 g dried eggs into small lipped erlenmeyer, add 30 ml ether, and mix well. After ether layer clears, decant thru small filter paper into weighed flask. Repeat extn with three 20 ml portions ether. Evap. ether on steam bath and dry ext 15 min at 100°. Cool, weigh, dissolve in 30 ml benzene, add 3–4 drops phthln, and titr. with NaOEt soln. (End point is reached when yellow changes to orange.) Report as ml 0.05N NaOEt required/g ether ext.

(b) *Liquid eggs.*—Weigh ca 8 g liq. eggs into 9 cm lipped evapg dish, and dry at 55° under pressure ≤125 mm Hg until eggs are thoroly dry (ca 5 hr). Grind dried eggs in evapg dish with small pestle, and proceed as in (a), beginning "add 30 ml ether, and mix well."

Lactic and Succinic Acids (16)—Official First Action

17.034 *Reagents*

(a) *Boron trifluoride-1-propanol soln.*—10%. Prep. as follows: In fume hood, assemble following or equiv. gas train. Connect two 500 ml all-glass gas washing bottles (Corning Glass Works No. 1760), with longer arms adjacent, in tandem to BF₃ cylinder (Matheson Co., E. Rutherford, NJ 07073) with short lengths of Teflon tubing. Transfer 250 ml PrOH to end bottle, weigh, and cool in ice bath. Connect bottle in ice bath to gas train and bubble BF₃ slowly into PrOH until 22 g is taken up. (BF₃ must be passing thru glass tube before tube is placed in and until after it is removed from PrOH.) If >22 g BF₃ is added, dil. with PrOH until total ml PrOH is 11.4 × g BF₃. Store reagent in g-s bottle in refrigerator.

Com. reagent, 14% w/v (Applied Science Laboratories, Inc.), may be used undild or dild 1 vol. + 0.6 vol. PrOH. (*Note:* Remove BF₃ vapors with effective fume removal device. Avoid contact with skin, eyes, and respiratory tract. *See* **46.010.**)

(b) *Calcium lactate std solns.*—Prep. fresh daily. Dissolve 0.856 g NF Ca lactate.5H₂O in H₂O and dil. to 100 ml (*Soln A:* 5.0 mg lactic acid equiv./ml). Dil. 25, 20, 15, and 5 ml *Soln A* to 50 ml with H₂O to prep. solns contg 2.5 (*B*), 2.0 (*C*), 1.5 (*D*), and 0.5 (*E*) mg lactic acid equiv./ml, resp.

(c) *Succinic acid std solns.*—Prep. fresh daily. Dissolve 1.000 g succinic acid (Fisher Certified, or equiv.) in H₂O and dil. to 100 ml (*Soln A:* 10.0 mg/ml). Dil. 25, 25, and 15 ml Soln *A* to 50, 100, and 100 ml with H₂O to prep. solns contg 5.0 (*B*), 2.5 (*C*), and 1.5 (*D*) mg/ml, resp.

(d) *Acetophenone (AP) solns.*—(*1*) *Std soln.*—Dissolve 0.800 g acetophenone (Matheson Coleman & Bell CQ 2221 AX 164) in PrOH and dil. to 100 ml in vol. flask. Store at room temp. (*2*) *Diluting soln.*—Prep. fresh daily. Pipet 20.0 ml PrOH, 10.0 ml AP std soln *1*, and 20.0 ml CHCl₃ into 125 ml separator. (Use anhyd. ether instead of CHCl₃ if gas chromatograph has components other than glass or stainless steel.) Add 40 ml satd (NH₄)₂SO₄. Stopper, shake separator ca 1 min, and let layers sep. Drain bottom aq. layer and discard. Transfer upper layer to g-s flask and add 5 g anhyd. Na₂SO₄.

(e) *Ether.*—Anhyd., contg ≤0.05% alcohol.

17.035 *Apparatus*
(*Caution: See* **46.039** and **46.046.**)

(a) *Gas chromatograph.*—Barber-Colman Co. Model 5000, or equiv., with flame ionization detec-tor. Operating conditions: 10′ × 4 mm id glass column packed with 10% stabilized diethyleneglycol succinate (DEGS) on 100–120 mesh Gas Chrom Z. Temps: column 130°, injection zone 200°, detector 200°; He 80 ml/min; H 37 ml/min; air 400 ml/min; electrometer sensitivity 9 × 10⁻¹⁰ amp full scale; 5 mv recorder; chart speed 20″/hr.

(b) *GLC column.*—Dissolve 1.2 g stabilized DEGS (Analabs, Inc., 80 Republic Drive, North Haven, CT 06473) in 100 ml acetone in 250 ml beaker. Add 10.8 g 100–120 mesh Gas Chrom Z to DEGS-acetone soln. Evap. acetone on steam bath, occasionally stirring with glass rod, and complete evapn in 50–60° vac. oven for 1 hr. Rinse GLC column with acetone and dry with vac. line. Fill column with 5% soln of dimethyldichlorosilane in toluene and let stand ca 5 min. Rinse column with MeOH until washings are neut. to litmus (ca 300 ml) and dry with vac. line. Pack column with coated support and condition 48 hr at 200° with N flow of ca 30 ml/min. Do *not* pack inlet portion of column that may be exposed to flash heater. (Any column giving equiv. sepn of propyl esters may be used.)

(c) *Filtering funnel.*—Glass, short stem, ca 35 mm diam. (Kimble Products No. 28950, or equiv.).

17.036 *Calibration*
(*Caution: See Note,* **17.034(a)**, *and* **46.018.**)

See **17.037** for std solns to be used for calibration. For each combination, pipet indicated vols Ca lactate and succinic acid std solns into 250 ml 〒 24/40 r-b flask and evap. to dryness on steam bath or, more rapidly, in rotary evaporator at 100°. Remove only enough BF₃-PrOH for one day's use to 25 ml g-s erlenmeyer. Pipet 2.0 ml BF₃-PrOH into 250 ml r-b flask, insert short-stem filtering funnel, (c), into neck, and reflux 10 min on steam bath.

Remove from steam bath and let cool to room temp. Add 4 ml satd (NH₄)₂SO₄, pipet 1.0 ml AP std soln and 2.0 ml CHCl₃ into flask, and swirl to mix. (Use anhyd. ether instead of CHCl₃ if gas chromatograph has components other than glass or stainless steel.) Pour contents of flask into 30 ml separator. Stopper, shake 1 min, and let layers sep. Drain bottom aq. layer and discard. Transfer upper layer to screw-capped glass vial, add ca 3 g anhyd. Na₂SO₄, cover with Al foil, seal with cap, and shake briefly. Store in refrigerator if soln is to be used after day of prepn.

Adjust sensitivity and attenuation of gas chromatograph to fit range of stds without addnl diln. (With gas chromatograph so adjusted, ht of internal std (AP) peak is ca ⅓ full scale.) Use same attenuation and sensitivity settings for calibration stds and sample solns.

When withdrawing soln for GLC, insert syringe needle thru Al foil. Make duplicate injections of 3 μl clear soln into gas chromatograph. For each run, measure peak hts and calc. peak ht ratio, *r*, for each acid. Make calibration charts by plotting values of r against W. For each acid, r = ht of acid ester peak/ht of internal std (AP) peak and W = total mg acid esterified with PrOH.

When solv. peak tails into region of propyl lactate peak, extend tail of solv. peak as if no other peak were present. Use this extension as baseline for measuring ht of propyl lactate peak.

17.037   Standard Solutions for Calibration of Gas Chromatograph

Combination	Calcium Lactate (b)[a]			Succinic Acid (c)[a]		
	mg[b]	ml	Std Soln	mg	ml	Std Soln
1	1	2	E	3	2	D
2	3	2	D	5	2	C
3	4	2	C	7.5	3	C
4	5	2	B	10	2	B
5	6	4	D	15	3	B
6	8	4	C	20	2	A
7	10	2	A	25	5	B
8	12.5	5	B	30	3	A
9	15	3	A	40	4	A

[a] Letters refer to solutions under *Reagents*.
[b] Lactic acid equivalent.

17.038   Determination

(Caution: See 46.011, 46.039, and 46.054.)

Use reagent grade anhyd. ether contg $\leq 0.05\%$ alcohol. Otherwise, results may be low due to formation of Et lactate, di-Et succinate, and Et Pr succinate with retention times, relative to AP, of ca 0.27, 1.02, and 1.38, resp.

Prep. sample soln and ext lactic and succinic acids with anhyd. ether in continuous extractor as in 17.042(a), 17.044, and 17.045. In 17.044, note that sample is made to 1 kg (by wt) before filtering; 24 cm fluted S&S No. 588 filter paper is satisfactory for filtration. Cover funnel and receiver with Al foil during filtration to prevent evapn. Evap. aliquot filtrate (usually 500 ml) gently to ca 100 ml on hot plate and then to ca 25 ml on steam bath. In 17.045, make calibration mark on extractor at 40 ml. Use 250 ml ℥ 24/40 r-b extn flask. Add few SiC chips. Ext as long as necessary for complete extn, making sure that all ether from condenser returns to inner tube of extractor. (Det. time necessary for complete extn as follows: Ext mixt. of 0.342 g Ca lactate.5H₂O (equiv. to 0.200 g lactic acid), 0.5 ml 18N H₂SO₄, 15 g (NH₄)₂SO₄, and 40 ml H₂O for time required for min. 98% recovery (ca 3–5 hr). Add 20 ml H₂O to flask and expel ether on steam bath. Do *not* let flask remain on steam bath after ether is expelled. Det. recovery by titrn with std alkali (1 ml 0.1N NaOH = 9.008 mg lactic acid).)

Do *not* add 5 ml H₂O to ether ext as specified in **17.045**. Remove ether with rotary evaporator at room temp. Alternatively, insert short-stem filtering

funnel, (c), into neck of flask contg ether ext and evap. on steam bath. Use only enough heat to evap. ether to ca 1 ml. Do *not* evap. to dryness. Pipet 2.0 ml BF₃-PrOH into flask and continue as in **17.036**.

Measure peak hts and calc. r for each acid. Det. W from calibration chart. Make duplicate GLC analyses and calc. av. wt of acid, W.

If acid concns give responses greater than full scale, pipet 1.0 ml sample soln and 1.0 ml or more AP dilg soln into screw-capped glass vial, add ca 0.2 g anhyd. Na₂SO₄, cover with Al foil, seal with cap, and shake briefly. Record vols of sample and dilg solns used. Make duplicate injections of 3 μl dild soln into gas chromatograph. Store in refrigerator if soln is to be used after day of prepn.

If further dilns are required, pipet addnl AP dilg soln into dild sample soln and mix. Alternatively, pipet greater vol. of AP dilg soln into 1.0 ml undild sample soln, mix, and make duplicate injections of 3 μl into gas chromatograph.

For each acid, use max. peak ht (min. diln factor) consistent with range and response limitations of recording device used. (For example, if only lactic acid is concd enough to require diln, calc. lactic acid from chromatogram of dild soln and succinic acid from chromatogram of undild soln.) Multiply result by diln factor (F): F = vol. after diln/vol. before diln.

Lactic Acid (17)—Official Final Action

(If succinic acid is also to be detd, proceed as in **17.042–17.047**.)

17.039   Preparation of Solution

(a) *Liquid or frozen eggs.*—Transfer 40 g sample to weighed 300 ml erlenmeyer, add ca 75 ml H₂O, and shake thoroly. Add 15 ml 1N H₂SO₄ and 25 ml *20% phosphotungstic acid soln*, dil. to 200 g with H₂O, shake ca 1 min, and filter thru folded paper.

(b) *Dried eggs.*—Mix 10 g sample and 100 ml H₂O into uniform paste with stirring rod and add, with constant stirring, 10 ml 1N H₂SO₄, followed by 15 ml *20% phosphotungstic acid soln*. Transfer mixt. with H₂O to weighed 300 ml erlenmeyer, dil. to 200 g with H₂O, shake ca 1 min, and filter thru folded paper.

Weigh 100 g filtrate obtained as in (a) or (b) into 250 ml beaker and evap. to ca 25 ml. Transfer material to liq. extractor with 25 ml H₂O and proceed as in **16.030–16.031**. Report lactic acid in terms of mg/100 g, making no correction for insol. solids in portion taken for analysis.

Volatile Fatty Acids (18)—Official Final Action

17.040   Preparation of Solution

(a) *Liquid or frozen eggs.*—Weigh 80 g sample, **17.001(a)** or (b), into weighed 500 ml erlenmeyer, add ca 150 ml H₂O, and shake vigorously.

(b) *Dried eggs.*—Weigh 25 g sample, **17.001(c)**,

into 250 ml beaker, and with heavy stirring rod make into smooth paste with H_2O. Transfer mixt. to weighed 500 ml erlenmeyer, using ca 200 ml H_2O.

Add 25 ml $1N$ H_2SO_4 to mixt. obtained as in (a) or (b) and shake ca 1 min. Add *20% phosphotungstic acid soln* (40 ml usually enough to give clear filtrate), dil. to 350 g with H_2O, and shake 1 min. Filter thru 24 cm folded paper.

17.041   *Determination*

Pipet 150 ml filtrate, **17.040** (equiv. to 150 g; sp gr is ca 1.00), into distn flask of app. (Fig. 18:1) and proceed as in **18.030–18.034** or **18.035–18.038**.

Fraction of each acid recovered in first 200 ml distillate is: Formic 0.405, acetic 0.57, propionic 0.81, and butyric 0.92; fraction of formic acid recovered in second 200 ml distillate is 0.24. To calc. mg of each acid in wt of sample used for distn, divide mg detd in distillate by fraction recovered. For liq. or frozen eggs, multiply by 2.92 and for dried eggs by 9.34 to obtain mg acid/100 g sample.

Succinic Acid (*19*)—Official Final Action

17.042   *Apparatus*

(a) *Continuous extractor.*—See Fig. 16:1.

(b) *Chromatographic tube.*—Approx. 17 mm od × 250 mm, plugged at constricted end with either cotton or glass wool.

17.043   *Reagents*

(a) *Solvent.*—*Tert*-butanol-$CHCl_3$ (1 + 4). Store over granular anhyd. Na_2SO_4.

(b) *Glycerol indicator soln.*—Dissolve 75 mg mono NH_4 salt of 3-(4-anilino-1-naphthylazo)-2,7-naph-thalenedisulfonic acid (Alphamine Red R, Eastman Kodak Co. No. 6410) in 50 ml glycerol, warming on steam bath.

(c) *Phenol red indicator.*—Rub 100 mg phenol-sulfonphthalein in mortar with 5.7 ml $0.05N$ NaOH until dissolved; then dil. to 100 ml with H_2O.

17.044   *Preparation of Solution*

(a) *Liquid or frozen eggs.*—Weigh 200 g sample into 1 L erlenmeyer, add 500 ml H_2O, and mix well, avoiding violent shaking; add 75 ml $1N$ H_2SO_4 and mix well. Add 125 ml *20% phosphotungstic acid soln*, dil. to 1 kg with H_2O, and shake 1 min. Divide between two 24 cm rapid folded filter papers. Transfer 250 ml filtrate to 400 ml beaker, evap. to ca 50 ml, add another 250 ml to same beaker, and evap. to 10 ml. If material starts to bump when vol. becomes low, use steam bath.

If <200 g sample is available, take 100 g sample and half quantities of reagents, and dil. to 500 g with H_2O. Filter ppt on buchner with suction, collecting as much filtrate as possible. Use total weighed filtrate for evapn.

(b) *Dried eggs.*—Weigh 50 g sample into 400 ml beaker, and with heavy stirring rod make into smooth paste with H_2O. Transfer to 1 L erlenmeyer and add enough H_2O to make total wt of 700 g. Add 50 ml $1N$ H_2SO_4 and mix well. Add 75 ml *20% phosphotungstic acid soln* and proceed as in (a), beginning "dil. to 1 kg with H_2O ..."

17.045   *Extraction*
(*Caution: See* **46.011, 46.039,** and **46.054.**)

Place 15 g $(NH_4)_2SO_4$ in dry extractor. Transfer evapd material, **17.044**(a) or (b), to inner tube of extractor by washing thru small funnel with enough H_2O to make total vol. of 40 ml, add 0.5 ml H_2SO_4 (1 + 1), and mix by raising and lowering inner tube. Rinse beaker with 50 ml ether and pour rinsings into inner tube of extractor. Connect efficient condenser to extractor and proceed with extn as in **16.030,** placing 150 ml ether in extn flask and extg 3 hr or as long as necessary for complete extn.

(To det. time necessary for complete extn, transfer ca 20 mg *succinic acid*, accurately weighed, to extractor contg 20 g $(NH_4)_2SO_4$, add enough H_2O to give total vol. of 40 ml, and proceed with extn as above. After 3 hr add 10 ml H_2O to extn flask, evap. ether on steam bath, and titr. If recovery is <95%, ext another 20 mg succinic acid for longer period and titr. Continue until 95% recovery is obtained, and use this period of extn for detn.)

To flask contg ether ext add 5 ml H_2O and evap. ether on steam bath. Using graduated 5 ml pipet, neutze contents of flask with satd $Ba(OH)_2$ soln, using phthln. Adjust vol. to 20 ml with H_2O, add 90 ml alcohol, heat almost to boiling on steam bath, and cool. Add ca 0.5 g filter-aid and filter with suction thru suitable filter, such as Caldwell crucible charged with thin layer of asbestos overlaid with small amt of filter-aid added from suspension in H_2O. Rinse flask with 3 portions of alcohol (9 + 2), transferring each rinsing to crucible and sucking dry before adding another portion. Reserve filtrate for detn of lactic acid, **16.031,** beginning line 7, "To expel alcohol, evap ...", using entire filtrate and modifying calcns.

Transfer contents of crucible to 100 ml beaker with 15–20 ml H_2O, acidify to *Congo red paper* with 1–2 drops H_2SO_4 (1 + 1), warm on steam bath, and refilter with suction, rinsing beaker with three 10 ml portions H_2O, transferring each rinsing to crucible, and sucking dry before adding another. Evap. filtrate to ca 5 ml, neutze with $1N$ NaOH, transfer with H_2O to 50 ml beaker, and evap. to dryness on steam bath.

17.046   *Preparation of Partition Column*

Place 5 g H_2SiO_3, **18.027**(g), in glazed porcelain evapg dish and add 0.5 ml freshly prepd glycerol indicator soln. (More soln may be necessary if it has stood several weeks.) Then add max. amt of glycerol (1 + 1) that gel will hold without becoming sticky (usually 1–3 ml) and 1 drop (ca 0.05 ml) ca $1N$ NH_4OH. Grind into uniform powder with pestle, make into slurry with ca 30 ml of solv., and transfer to chromatgc tube, which is clamped vertically. Apply 5–10 lb air pressure to top of tube until solv. just disappears into top of gel; release pressure, add 1 ml CHCl₃ contg ca 5 mg HOAc, and again apply pressure until solv. just disappears into gel. Release pressure, add 5 ml solv., and once more apply pressure just long enough for solv. to disappear into gel. (Pressure should never be left on with no liq. above gel; gel would then dry and crack, becoming useless.)

17.047   *Determination*

To dry residue of Na succinate, 17.045, add 2 ml solv. and 3 drops H₂SO₄ (1 + 1), and stir with glass rod until all particles are moistened (material should be acid to Congo red paper). Add anhyd. Na₂SO₄ in 0.5 g portions until material is dry (not gummy), stir, and decant onto prepd partition column, pouring it slowly down side of tube in order to keep surface of gel level. Apply pressure until solv. just disappears into gel. Again wash beaker with 1 ml solv., pour onto column, and with stirring rod transfer residue in beaker to column. Wash beaker with another 1 ml solv., transfer to column, wash inside of tube with 1 ml solv., and apply pressure until solv. just disappears into gel. Fill tube with solv. and apply pressure. Let HOAc band pass out of tube. When front of succinic acid band reaches constricted portion of tube, start collecting eluate in 50 ml graduated cylinder. Continue collecting until band has passed entirely from column or until lower edge of any following band reaches 2–5 mm above narrowest portion of constriction of tube and until enough eluate collects to ensure removal of succinic acid from column. (Light placed adjacent to column, but not so close as to heat it, increases visibility of bands.)

(To ensure complete removal of succinic acid from column when there is no following band, det. total amt of eluate to be collected by prepg soln of known amt of Na succinate, transferring free acid to column, eluting, etc., as above, and titrg 25 ml and successive 10 ml fractions of eluate until last fraction requires <0.2 ml 0.01N alkali to neutze. Total amt of eluate required is amt to collect in detn.)

Add 10 ml H₂O to flask and titr. with 0.01N Ba(OH)₂, using phenol red indicator. As end point approaches, stopper flask and shake vigorously to ext acid completely from solv. phase. Correct titrn for blank detn on equal vol. of eluate from blank column. 1 ml 0.01N Ba(OH)₂ = 0.59 mg succinic acid. If crystallographic identification of Ba succinate (JAOAC **32**, 787(1949)) is not desired, 0.01N NaOH may be used for titrn.

Water-Insoluble Fatty Acids (20)— Official First Action
17.048   *Preparation of Solution*

(a) *Liquid or frozen eggs.*—Weigh 10 g prepd sample, 17.001(a) or (b), into 250 ml centrf. bottle, add 25 ml H₂O, and mix. Add 20 ml alcohol, shake vigorously, and add 50 ml ether.

(b) *Dried eggs.* — Weigh 2 g prepd sample, 17.001(c), into 100 ml beaker and stir to uniform paste with small amt H₂O, using heavy stirring rod. Transfer material to 250 ml centrf. bottle with H₂O, using total of 25 ml for entire operation, and shake vigorously. Rinse beaker with 25 ml alcohol, transfer rinsings to centrf. bottle, shake vigorously, and add 50 ml ether.

17.049   *Determination*
Proceed as in 16.177.

Pyoverdine (21)—Official Final Action
(Protect from daylight and other sources of UV light. Incandescent light and pink fluorescent light may be used. Avoid dissolved metals and contact with rubber.)

17.050   *Reagents*
(a) *Alcohol.*—95% USP, redistd from glass.

(b) *Chloride buffer soln.*—pH 1. Dry ca 50 g KCl at 120° overnight. Weigh 37.28 g into 500 ml vol. flask, dissolve in H₂O, and dil. to vol. Add 50 ml of this 1N KCl to 97 ml stdzd 1N HCl in 200 ml vol. flask, and dil. to vol. with H₂O.

(c) *Potassium acid phthalate soln.*—0.1M. Dry ca 20 g at 120° overnight. Weigh 10.21 g into 500 ml vol. flask, dissolve in H₂O, and dil. to vol. with H₂O.

(d) *Riboflavin std soln.*—0.50 μg/ml, pH 4. Pipet 5 ml riboflavin intermediate soln, 39.040(a)(2), into 100 ml vol. flask, add 50 ml 0.1M K acid phthalate, and dil. to vol. with H₂O. Prep. weekly and store in refrigerator.

17.051   *Determination*
Weigh 50±0.1 g foam-free sample, thawed and warmed to 25° on day of analysis, into dry 250 ml centrf. bottle. Add 154 ml alcohol at ca 25°, using pipets, with continuous stirring. Insert polyethylene stopper and shake ca 50 strokes by hand. Centrf. ca 15 min at ca 1200 rpm. Pipet 100 ml supernatant into 250 ml separator, add ca 125 ml CHCl₃, and shake ca 100 strokes by hand. Freeze by immersing separator to base of stopper 10 min in alcohol-solid CO₂ bath; remove from bath.

As soon as ice crystals in CHCl₃ layer thaw, but while outside of separator is still frosty, drain and discard CHCl₃. Wash sides of separator with 10 ml CHCl₃, added from pipet without disturbing aq. layer. Let stand 10 min, and drain and discard CHCl₃. Pass stream of air into emulsion in separator thru small glass tube until soln clears. Remove tube and rinse with small vol. H₂O. Pipet 10 ml pH 1 buffer into 50 ml vol. flask, quant. add contents of separator, and dil. to vol. with H₂O.

Measure fluorescence of test and std solns in photofluorometer, using Corning 5874 as primary filter, and Corning 3486 as secondary filter. Swirl std soln before each reading. Calc. concn of pyoverdine expressed as μg riboflavin/100 g egg = $2 \times C \times R/S$, where 2 is derived from concn sample in final ext, C = concn riboflavin std in μg/100 ml, R = reading of sample, and S = reading of std riboflavin soln.

17.052 Quaternary Ammonium Compounds
—*See* **20.079(d)**

SELECTED REFERENCES

(1) JAOAC 8, 599(1925).
(2) JAOAC 41, 274(1958).
(3) JAOAC 8, 600(1925); 9, 354(1926); 14, 395 (1931).
(4) JAOAC 8, 601(1925).
(5) JAOAC 15, 344(1932).
(6) JAOAC 8, 601(1925); 16, 298(1933).
(7) JAOAC 7, 91(1923); 8, 602(1925); 16, 298 (1933).
(8) JAOAC 24, 119(1941); 25, 365(1942).
(9) JAOAC 14, 416(1931); 16, 298(1933).
(10) JAOAC 16, 298(1933); 22, 302(1939).
(11) Ind. Eng. Chem., Anal. Ed. 7, 38(1935); JAOAC 26, 352(1943).
(12) JAOAC 14, 397(1931); 16, 305(1933); 22, 302 (1939).
(13) JAOAC 15, 331(1932); 16, 293(1933).
(14) JAOAC 31, 498(1948); 32, 506(1949).
(15) JAOAC 10, 411(1927); 15, 341(1932); 20, 155 (1937); 21, 179(1938); 31, 498(1948); 33, 696 (1950).
(16) JAOAC 52, 41, 471(1969); 53, 28(1970).
(17) JAOAC 27, 204(1944); 31, 134(1948).
(18) JAOAC 21, 684(1938); 27, 204(1944); 28, 644 (1945); 33, 848(1950).
(19) JAOAC 31, 134(1948); 32, 787(1949).
(20) JAOAC 30, 575(1947); 31, 731(1948).
(21) JAOAC 42, 289(1959); 44, 493(1961).

18. Fish and Other Marine Products

18.001 Net Contents of Frozen Seafoods (1)—Procedure

Set scale, 32.032, on firm support and level. Adjust zero load indicator or rest point and check sensitivity.

(a) *Glazed seafoods.*—Remove package from low temp. storage, open immediately, and place contents under gentle spray of cold H_2O. Agitate carefully so product is not broken. Spray until all ice glaze that can be seen or felt is removed. Transfer product to circular No. 8 sieve, 8″ diam. for ≤2 lb and 12″ for >2 lb. Without shifting product, incline sieve to facilitate drainage and drain exactly 2 min (stop watch). Immediately transfer product to tared pan (*B*) and weigh (*A*). Wt product = $A - B$.

(b) *Unglazed seafoods.*—See 32.033.

18.002 Preliminary Treatment and Preparation of Sample (2)—Procedure

To prevent loss of H_2O during prepn and subsequent handling, use as large samples as practicable. Keep ground material in container with air-tight cover. Begin all detns as soon as practicable. If any delay occurs, chill sample to inhibit decomposition. Prep. samples for analysis as follows:

(a) *Fresh fish.*—Clean, scale, and eviscerate large fish in usual way. In case of small fish (≤6″), use 5–10 whole fish, including heads if desired. In case of large fish, cut from each of at least 3 fish, 3 transverse slices, 1″ thick: one slice from just back of pectoral fins, one slice halfway between first slice and vent, and one slice just back of vent. Skin and bones may be sepd if desired. For fat detns, include skin since many fish store large quantities of fat directly beneath skin.

Pass sample rapidly thru meat chopper 3 times. Remove unground material from chopper after each grinding and mix thoroly with ground material. Meat chopper should have holes as small as practicable (1/16–1/8″ diam.) and should not leak around handle end. As alternative for soft fish, high-speed blender may be used. Blend several min, stopping blender frequently to scrape down sides of cup.

(b) *Canned fish, shellfish, and other canned marine products.*—Place entire contents of can (meat and liq.) in blender and blend until homogeneous or grind 3 times thru meat chopper. For large cans, drain meat in large buchner or sieve and collect all liq. Det. wt of meat and vol. of liq. Recombine portion of each in proportionate quantities. Blend re- combined portions in blender (or grind) until homogeneous.

(c) *Canned marine products packed in oil.*—Drain 2 min on No. 8 sieve. Prep. solid portion as in (b). Oil and brine may be analyzed sep., if desired, or reincorporated with solids.

(d) *Fish packed in salt or brine.*—Drain brine and rinse off adhering salt crystals with satd NaCl soln. Drain again 2 min and proceed as in (a).

(e) *Dried smoked or dried salt fish.*—Cut large samples into small pieces, mix, and quarter down to ca 1/4 lb. Cut, shred, grind, or otherwise comminute the 1/4 lb sample as finely as possible so that reasonably representative samples may be weighed for analysis after thoro mixing. (Duplicate or triplicate detns may be necessary to establish uniformity of sample.)

(f) *Shellfish other than oysters, clams, and scallops.* —If sample is received in shell, wash as in (g) and sep. edible portions in usual way. Prep. edible portion for analysis as in (b).

(g) *Shell oysters, shell clams, and scallops.*—Wash shells in potable H_2O to remove all loose silt and dirt, and drain well. Shuck enough oysters or clams into clean dry container to yield at least 1 pt drained meats. Transfer shellfish meats to skimmer, 18.004, pick out pieces of shell, drain 2 min on skimmer, and proceed as in (h) or (i).

(h) *Shucked clams or scallops.*—Prep. as in (b).

(i) *Shucked oysters (3).*—Blend meats, including liq., 1–2 min in high-speed blender.

18.003 Volume Determination (2)—Official Final Action

(Shucked oysters, clams, or scallops)

Fluff entire contents of com. container, or container in which sample is received (≤1 gal.), by pouring into std measuring vessel thru distance of ≥1′, then pouring back into container from same ht, and again pouring into measuring vessel. Use metal funnel (stainless steel preferable) 8–10″ diam. at top, with stem 3″ diam. and ca 3″ long, to facilitate pouring from one vessel to another. Measures are straight-side, cylindrical, made of metal (stainless steel preferable), holding exactly 1 gal. or 1 qt, resp., and having smooth rims. Plane of rim must be level when measure is standing on level surface. Diam. of top of gal. measure is 4.25–5.25″, and that of qt measure is 3.25–3.5″. Calibrate with std glass measures, and for estg vols less than level full, use graduated mechanic's depth gage to measure distance from rim to surface of contents. Tabulate depth gage readings against vols or % shortages as desired for each measuring vessel. Measure head space with depth gage and det. vol. For ≤1 pt containers, calibrated glass cylinders may be used.

Drained Liquid (4)—Official Final Action
(Shucked oysters)

18.004 *Apparatus*

Skimmer or strainer.—Flat-bottom metal pan or tray with ca 2″ sides, with area of ≥300 sq in. for each gal. of oysters to be poured on tray, and with perforations 0.25″ diam. and 1.25″ apart in square pattern, or perforations of equiv. area and distribution. Support skimmer over slightly larger solid tray so that liq. drains into solid tray.

18.005 *Determination*

Weigh tared container with shellfish meats, transfer contents to skimmer, and quickly distribute meats evenly over draining surface with min. of handling. Drain 2 min, return meats to container, and reweigh. Calc. loss of wt as % drained liq. Make detns at 7 ± 1° (45 ± 2°F). If further analysis is desired, proceed as in **18.002**(i).

Drained Weight (5)—Official First Action
(Applicable to frozen shrimp and Alaska king crabmeat)

18.006 *Apparatus*

(a) *Container.*—Wire mesh basket large enough to contain contents of 1 package and with openings small enough to retain all pieces. Expanded metal test-tube basket or equiv., fully lined with std 16 mesh per linear in. insect screen is satisfactory.

(b) *Balance.*—Sensitive to 0.01 oz or 0.25 g.

(c) *Sieves.*—U.S. No. 8, 8″ and 12″ diam.

18.007 *Determination*

Place contents of individual package in wire mesh basket and immerse in 4 gal. (or larger) container of fresh H_2O at 80±5°F so that top of basket extends above H_2O level. Introduce H_2O of same temp. at bottom of container at flow rate of 1–3 gal./min. As soon as product thaws, as detd by loss of rigidity, transfer all material to 12″ (for package >1 lb) or 8″ (for package ≤1 lb) No. 8 sieve, distributing evenly. Without shifting material on sieve, incline sieve to ca 30° from horizontal to facilitate drainage. Two min from time placed on sieve, transfer product to previously weighed pan, and weigh. Wt so found minus wt of pan is drained wt of product.

Alaska King Crab Marketing and Control Board Method
(Applicable to Alaska king crabmeat)

18.008 *Apparatus*

(a) *Balance.*—Sensitive to 0.01 lb or 1 g.

(b) *Thermometer.*—Accurate in 30–80°F range.

(c) *Plastic bowls.*—Marked at 48 oz, 64 oz, or 1 gal. level for 6 oz, 8 oz, or 1 lb packages, resp.

18.009 *Determination*

Weigh bare block free of all wrappings and record wt. Place block in bowl contg amt fresh potable water at 80°F equal to 8× declared wt. Leave block in H_2O until all ice is melted. Turn block over several times during thawing. Point at which thawing is complete can be detd by probing block apart.

Pour entire thawed sample onto tared 8″ No. 8 sieve. Incline screen to aid drainage, drain exactly 2 min, and weigh. Subtract tare wt of sieve for thawed drained wt of sample.

% Drained wt
= (thawed drained wt × 100)/declared net wt.

Total Solids

18.010 *For All Marine Products Except Raw Oysters (6)—Official Final Action*

Cut into short lengths ca 2 g asbestos fibers of type used in prepg gooches. Place cut fibers and glass stirring rod ca 8 cm long with flat end into flat-bottom metal weighing dish, ca 9 cm diam., with cover. Dry dish, asbestos, and rod in oven 1 hr at 100°, cool, and weigh. Quickly weigh into dish, to nearest mg, 9.5–10.5 g prepd sample. Add 20 ml H_2O and mix sample thoroly with asbestos. Support end of rod on edge of dish and evap. just to dryness on steam bath, stirring once while still moist. Drop rod into dish and heat 4 hr in oven at 100°, or in preheated forced-draft oven set for full draft, 1 hr at 100°. Cover dish, cool in desiccator, and weigh promptly.

18.011 *For Raw Oysters Only (7)—Official Final Action*

Quickly weigh, to nearest mg, 9.5–10.5 g prepd sample into weighed, flat-bottom metal dish ca 9 cm diam. and 2 cm high with cover. Spread sample evenly over bottom of dish. Then:

(a) Evap. just to dryness on steam bath and dry 3 hr in oven at 100°; or—

(b) Insert directly into preheated forced-draft oven set at full draft and dry 1.5 hr at 100°.

Cover, cool in desiccator, and weigh promptly.

18.012 Ash (8)—Official Final Action

Dry sample representing ca 2 g dry material and proceed as in **31.012** or **31.013**, using temp. ≤550°. If material contains large amt of fat, make preliminary ashing at low enough temp. to allow smoking off of fat without burning.

18.013 Total Nitrogen (8)—Official Final Action—See 2.051

Salt (Chlorine as Sodium Chloride)
(9)—Official Final Action

18.014   *Reagents*

(a) *Silver nitrate std soln.*—0.1N. Prep. as in
45.028 and stdze against 0.1N NaCl contg 5.844 g
of pure dry NaCl/L.

(b) *Ammonium thiocyanate std soln.*—0.1N. Prep.
as in **45.031(b)** and stdze against 0.1N AgNO$_3$.

(c) *Ferric indicator.*—Satd soln of FeNH$_4$(SO$_4$)$_2$
.12H$_2$O.

18.015   *Determination*

(a) *Shellfish meats.*—Weigh 10 g meats, liq., or
mixed meats and liq., into 250 ml erlenmeyer or
beaker.

(b) *Other fish products.*—Use suitable size sample,
depending on NaCl content.

Add known vol. 0.1N AgNO$_3$ soln, more than
enough to ppt all Cl as AgCl, and then add 20 ml
HNO$_3$. Boil gently on hot plate or sand bath until
all solids except AgCl dissolve (usually 15 min).
Cool, add 50 ml H$_2$O and 5 ml indicator, and titr.
with 0.1N NH$_4$CNS soln until soln becomes permanent light brown. Subtract ml 0.1N NH$_4$CNS used
from ml 0.1N AgNO$_3$ added and calc. difference to
NaCl. With 10 g sample each ml 0.1N AgNO$_3$ =
0.058% NaCl.

Sodium and Potassium (*10*)—Official
First Action

18.016   *Apparatus*

(a) *Instruments.*—Beckman Instruments Model
DU spectrophtr with flame attachment or Perkin-
Elmer Corp. Model 303 atomic absorption spec-
trophtr, or equivs. (*Caution: See* **46.006** and **46.007.**)

(b) *Glassware.*—Borosilicate glassware and intact
Vycor, Pt, or Si crucible precleaned with dil. HNO$_3$
and rinsed in distd H$_2$O immediately before use.

18.017   *Reagents*

(a) *Distilled water.*—H$_2$O, free from Na and K;
either double-distd or deionized. Use for prepg stds
and dilns.

(b) *Sodium std solns.*—(*1*) *Stock soln.*—1 mg
Na/ml. Dry reagent grade NaCl 2 hr at 110°; cool
in desiccator. Weigh 2.5422 g into 1 L vol. flask and
dil. to vol. with H$_2$O. (*2*) *Working solns for flame
emission.*—0.01, 0.03, and 0.05 mg Na/ml. Pipet 1,
3, and 5 ml Na stock soln into sep. 100 ml vol. flasks;
add 7 ml K stock soln and 2 ml HNO$_3$ to each flask;
dil to vol. with H$_2$O. (*3*) *Working solns for flame
absorption.*—0.0003, 0.001, 0.003, and 0.005 mg
Na/ml. Pipet 1 ml Na stock soln into 100 ml vol.
flask and dil. to vol. with H$_2$O. Pipet 0.3, 1.0, 3.0,
and 5.0 ml dild stock soln into sep. 100 ml vol. flasks
and dil. to vol. with H$_2$O.

(c) *Potassium std solns.*—(*1*) *Stock soln.*—1 mg
K/ml. Dry and cool reagent grade KCl as in (b).
Weigh 1.9068 g into 1 L vol. flask and dil. to vol.

with H$_2$O. (*2*) *Working soln for flame emission.*—0.04,
0.07, and 0.10 mg K/ml. Pipet 4, 7, and 10 ml stock
soln into sep. 100 ml vol. flasks; add 3 ml Na stock
soln to each flask; dil. to vol. with H$_2$O. (*3*) *Working
std solns for flame absorption.*—0.001, 0.005, 0.007,
and 0.010 mg K/ml. Pipet 1 ml K stock soln into
100 ml vol. flask and dil. to vol. with H$_2$O. Pipet 1,
5, 7, and 10 ml dild stock soln into sep. 100 ml vol.
flasks and dil. to vol. with H$_2$O.

18.018   *Wet-Ashing*
(*Caution: See* **46.011**, **46.019**, and **46.026.**)

Prep. sample as in **18.002.**

Weigh 1 g sample into 50 ml Pyrex beaker. Dry
2.5 hr at 110°, cool, and weigh if % solids is to be
detd.

(a) *Samples with unknown or known high oil content.*—Add ca 10 ml pet ether to each sample, and
warm on steam bath or low temp. hot plate until
oil is extd. Decant and repeat until sample is defatted. Proceed as in (b).

(b) *Samples with low oil content.*—Add 5 ml HNO$_3$
(if total Cl content is desired, add enough 0.1N
AgNO$_3$ to ppt chlorides (3.0 ml)) to each beaker.
Digest on steam bath or low temp. hot plate until
sample dissolves; take to dryness. Add 5 ml HNO$_3$
and take to dryness. Repeat. Add 2 ml HNO$_3$ and
warm to dissolve. Proceed as in (c) or (d).

(c) *For flame emission.*—Transfer digest to 25 ml
vol. flask with hot H$_2$O, wash down sides of beaker
3 times with hot H$_2$O, and add washings to flask.
Cool, and dil. to vol. with H$_2$O. If particles are too
finely dispersed to settle, centrf. aliquot at 2000 rpm
to clear soln.

(d) *For flame absorption.*—Transfer digest to 100
ml vol. flask and proceed as above. Dil. for direct
readout as follows: Place 1 ml aliquot in 25 ml vol.
flask and dil. to vol. with H$_2$O for Na; place 2 ml
aliquot in 10 ml vol. flask and dil. to vol. with H$_2$O
for K.

Prep. blank soln by dilg 2 ml HNO$_3$ to 100 ml
with H$_2$O.

18.019   *Dry-Ashing*

Prep. sample as in **18.002.**

Weigh 4 g sample into crucible, and char on elec.
hot plate or over low flame. Place in cold muffle oven
and bring to 525°. Ash 2 hr to white ash. Cool, and
weigh if total ash is desired.

Add 15 ml dil. HNO$_3$ (1 + 4) to crucible, breaking
up ash with stirring rod if necessary. Filter thru
Whatman No. 42 paper (or equiv. acid-washed
paper) into 100 ml vol. flask. Wash residue and
paper 3 times with H$_2$O. Dil. to vol. Proceed as in
(a) or (b).

(a) *For flame emission.*—Read directly.

(b) *For flame absorption.*—Dil. for direct readout
as follows: Place 1 ml aliquot in 100 ml vol. flask and

dil. to vol. with H_2O for Na; place 1 ml aliquot in 25 ml vol. flask and dil. to vol. with H_2O for K.

Prep. blank soln by dilg 2 ml HNO_3 to 100 ml with H_2O.

18.020   *Determination*

Follow established procedure for type of instrument available. Dil. samples if necessary to bring T readings within range of working stds. Read blank, stds, and samples at 589 nm for Na and 767 nm for K until results are reproducible; record $\% T$ or $\%$ absorption for each.

18.021   *Calculations*

For flame emission photometers not equipped with direct readout:

mg Na or K/100 g $= 100 \times F \times$

$$\left(\left[\frac{(E_x - E_1)}{(E_2 - E_1)} \times (C_2 - C_1) \right] + C_1 \right) /\text{g sample},$$

where E_x = (% T of unknown) − (% T of blank); E_1 = (% T of std of lower concn than sample) − (% T of blank); E_2 = (% T of std of higher concn than sample) − (% T of blank); C_1 = mg Na or K/ml in std of lower concn than sample; C_2 = mg Na or K/ml in std of higher concn than sample; F = diln factor.

For flame absorption photometers: Convert % absorption to absorbance (A). Plot std curve of A against concn. Read unknown concns.

mg Na or K/100 g

$$= (\text{Concn unknown} \times F)/(\text{g sample} \times 10)$$

Crude Fat
By Acid Hydrolysis (11)—Official Final Action

18.022   *Preparation of Sample*

Prep. sample according to type of pack as in **18.002** and keep ground material in sealed jar. If jar has been chilled, let sample come to room temp. and shake jar so that any sepd liq. is absorbed by fish. Open jar and stir contents with spatula, thoroly scraping sides and lid so as to incorporate any sepd liq. or fat.

18.023   *Determination*

Weigh into 50 ml beaker 8 g well-mixed sample and add 2 ml HCl. Using stirring rod with extra large flat end, break up coagulated lumps until mixt. is homogeneous. Add addnl 6 ml HCl, mix, cover with watch glass, and heat on steam bath 90 min, stirring occasionally with rod. Cool soln and transfer to Mojonnier fat-extn flask. Rinse beaker and rod with 7 ml alcohol, add to extn flask, and mix. Rinse beaker and rod with 25 ml ether, added in 3 portions; add rinsings to extn flask, stopper with cork or stopper of synthetic rubber unaffected by usual fat solvents, and shake vigorously 1 min. Add 25 ml pet ether (bp <60°) to extn flask and repeat vigorous

shaking. Centrf. Mojonnier flask 20 min at ca 600 rpm and proceed as in **14.019**, beginning "Draw off as much as possible of ether-fat soln . . ."

Drying to constant wt takes ca 40 min for fish. Long heating periods may increase wt of fat. If centrf. is not available, extn can generally be made by letting Mojonnier flask stand until upper liq. is practically clear, then swirling flask and again letting stand until clear. If troublesome emulsion forms, pour off from Mojonnier flask as much of ether-fat soln as possible after letting flask stand, add 1–2 ml alcohol to Mojonnier flask, swirl, and again let mixt. sep.

Rapid Modified Babcock Method (12)—Official First Action

(Applicable to raw, canned, and frozen fish)

18.024   *Determination*

(*Caution: See* **46.022**, and **46.028**(a) and (d).)

Weigh 9.0 g ground and mixed sample into Paley-type Babcock cheese bottle (Kimble Products No. 508, 20% size), stopper, and add ca 30 ml reagent prepd by mixing equal vols HOAc and 70–72% $HClO_4$. Place in H_2O bath (2 L stainless steel beaker is satisfactory) maintained at 92±2°, swirling occasionally until no lumps remain (usually ca 20 min). Remove from bath, add reagent until fat is well up in calibrated neck of bottle, centrf. 2 min at ca 600 rpm, and read % fat with dividers, using bottom of top meniscus. If fat falls below calibration, add more reagent, centrf. 1 min, and read again.

With very fat fish, it may be necessary to use <9 g sample. In this case, correct reading by multiplying % fat by factor 9/g sample.

18.025   Fat in Fish Meal—Official First Action—*See* **7.052**

Volatile Fatty Acids
Column Chromatographic Method (13)—Official Final Action

18.026   *Apparatus*

(a) *Steam distillation assembly.*—Fig. **18:1**. Assembly consists of boiler flask (3 L) giving steam at constant rate so as to produce constant rate of distn, distn flask, condenser, and 200 ml vol. flasks as receivers. Std distn flask with side arm (ca 9 mm od) attached near center of neck, and with steam inlet tube (ca 10 mm od), is satisfactory. Heating coil of steam generator is made by winding 5′ 28 gage Chromel wire (or equiv.) around hollow pipe ca 0.25″ diam. and heating red hot to detemper wire. Leads into boiler flask are brass, Cu, or other nonferrous metal ca 3/32″ diam. Insulate and shield elec. leads and contacts to avoid possible shorting and elec. shocks.

Any similar distn assembly may be used if it is of

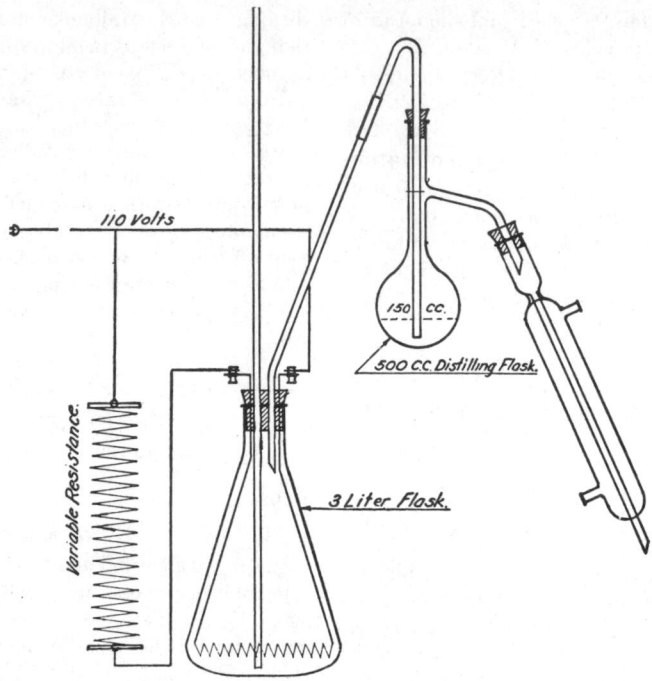

FIG. 18:1—Steam distillation assembly

capacity to handle vols specified in method and gives $57 \pm 2\%$ recovery of acetic acid on distn.

(**b**) *Chromatographic tube.*—Approx. 15 × 250 mm.

(**c**) *Source of air pressure or compressed N gas equipped with pressure regulator.*—If such source is not available, following system serves purpose: Fit 1 L side arm flask with 2-hole rubber stopper. Pass glass manometer tube 70 cm long thru one hole in stopper so that it reaches bottom of flask, and thru other hole pass glass tube ca 8 cm long, whose upper end is connected to top of chromatgc tube by rubber tubing. Connect rubber hand-aspirator bulb to side arm of flask. Fill flask with Hg to depth of 1.5 cm. (Ht of Hg column in manometer tube indicates pressure in system; 25 cm is equiv. to ca 5 lb.) To maintain reservoir pressure when chromatgc tube is disconnected, fit stopcock into line leading from flask to chromatgc tube; and to prevent valve in hand aspirator from leaking, insert second stopcock between side arm and bulb.

(**d**) *Rubber bulb.*—5 ml. (Type used on dropping bottles.)

(**e**) *Micro funnel.*—Buchner-type, 2 ml capacity with coarse fritted disk; Corning No. 36060.

18.027   *Reagents*

(**a**) *Butanol in chloroform.*—1 %. Remove alcohol from NF CHCl$_3$ by washing 3 times with ½ vol. H$_2$O. Add 10 ml *n*-butanol to 1 L washed CHCl$_3$ in separator, shake vigorously, add 25 ml H$_2$O, and shake again. Let lower layer stand until clear, and

drain. Discard aq. layer. Store in contact with granular anhyd. Na$_2$SO$_4$.

(**b**) *Butanol in chloroform.*—10%. To 900 ml NF CHCl$_3$ (*not* previously washed) in separator add 100 ml *n*-butanol, shake vigorously, add 25 ml H$_2$O, and shake again. Let CHCl$_3$ stand until clear, and drain. Discard aq. layer. Store in contact with **granular** anhyd. Na$_2$SO$_4$.

(**c**) *Alphamine Red R indicator.*—Dissolve 50 mg mono-NH$_4$ salt 3-(4-anilino-1-naphthylazo)-2,7-naphthalene disulfonic acid (Eastman Kodak Co. No. 6410) in 25 ml H$_2$O. (Red soln produced by 1 drop indicator in 20 ml H$_2$O must be changed to violet by 1 drop 0.01N HCl.) Prep. fresh weekly.

(**d**) *Cresol red indicator.*—Dissolve 50 mg *o*-cresolsulfonphthalein in 20 ml alcohol, add 1.3 ml 0.1N NaOH, and dil. to 50 ml with H$_2$O. Use 2 drops for each 25 ml aq. soln.

(**e**) *Barium hydroxide std soln.*—0.01N. (Store in polyethylene or paraffin-lined bottle and protect from CO$_2$ of atm. with soda-lime or Ascarite; dispense from 10 ml buret.) (0.01N NaOH may be used instead of Ba(OH)$_2$ except in titrn of Soln *B*, **18.030**. NaOH soln must be used in titrn of Soln *A*, **18.030**, since Na salts are required for chromatgy.)

(**f**) *Sodium acetate-sodium chloride soln.*—Dissolve 12 g NaCl and 25 g NaOAc.3H$_2$O in H$_2$O and dil. to 500 ml.

(**g**) *Silicic acid.*—Reagent grade "100-mesh" powder, suitable for chromatgy (Mallinckrodt Chemical Works No. 2847 or equiv.).

18.028   *Standardization of Distillation Apparatus*

Place app., **18.026(a)**, in laboratory so that it is free from drafts and sudden changes in temp. Make mark on boiler flask at 1.5 L level, fill to this mark with H_2O, heat to boiling, and boil several min before starting distn. Transfer 150 ml H_2O to distn flask, add 1 drop H_2SO_4 (1 + 1), connect condenser, insert steam inlet tube into distn flask, and bring contents of flask to incipient boiling with burner. Connect steam inlet tube with steam supply from boiler and steam distill. Regulate rate of evolution of steam and ht of small flame of burner under distn flask so that vol. of liq. in distn flask is kept constant at 150 ml and distillate collects at rate of 200 ml/hr. (Period of collection may vary 5 min for 200 ml distillate. The 150 ml vol. in distn flask should remain constant within ±10 ml. Boiling may be stopped to permit test of constancy of 150 ml vol. by momentarily interrupting steam supply. Few trials will show conditions necessary to maintain constant vol. in distn flask and constant rate of distn.) Det. blank on 2 successive 200 ml portions of distillate by titrg with 0.01N alkali (phthln) in CO_2-free atm.

Transfer 50 ml ca 0.1N HOAc (concn must be accurately known) to distn flask; add 1 drop H_2SO_4 (1 + 1) (avoid contact with neck of flask) and 100 ml H_2O. Collect 200 ml distillate and titr. with 0.1N alkali. Correct for titrn blanks and compute % acid distd. Distn technic and app. are satisfactory when recovery is 57±2%. App. so adjusted gives recoveries (±2%) of formic, propionic, and butyric acids of 40.5, 81, and 92%, resp. (JAOAC **21**, 684, 688(1938)), on 200 ml distillate.

18.029   *Preparation of Solution*

Weigh 50 g comminuted material, **18.002**, into tared 500 ml wide-mouth erlenmeyer, add ca 150 ml H_2O, stopper flask, and shake vigorously ca 1 min to effect thoro suspension of material. Add 25 ml 1N H_2SO_4, mix, ppt proteins with *20% phosphotungstic acid soln* (40 ml is usually enough), make to 300 g with H_2O, shake vigorously ca 1 min, and filter thru 24 cm rapid folded paper.

18.030   *Distillation and Computation of Volatile Acid Number*

Pipet 150 ml prepd soln into distn flask of app. and make acid to *Congo red paper* with H_2SO_4 (1 + 1). Steam distill as in **18.028**. Collect 200 ml distillate, titr. with 0.01N NaOH to phthln end point, and designate as *A*. Collect second 200 ml portion distillate, titr. with 0.01N Ba(OH)$_2$ soln to phthln end point, and designate as *B*. To calc. volatile acid number multiply titrn obtained on distillate *A*, corrected for blank, by 4.

18.031   *Determination of Formic Acid (14)*
*(Caution: See **46.079**.)*

Add 2 drops satd Ba(OH)$_2$ soln to distillate *B*, **18.030**, and evap. to dryness on steam bath. Add ca 5 ml H_2O to residue and 1 ml more of 1N HCl than necessary to liberate volatile acids. Filter thru small paper into 125 ml erlenmeyer with ⑤ joint, and wash paper with H_2O in such manner that total filtrate equals 30–40 ml. Add 10 ml NaOAc-NaCl soln and 10 ml *5% HgCl$_2$ soln*. Connect flask with ⑤ air condenser and place on steam bath 2.5 hr.

With suction thru glass siphon attached to funnel by rubber stopper, transfer ppt of Hg$_2$Cl$_2$ to previously weighed microfunnel, **18.026(e)**, provided with mat of asbestos ca 2 mm thick. Rinse flask with H_2O followed by alcohol. Dry 30 min at 100°, cool, and weigh. Weigh funnel with another funnel, prepd with asbestos and treated similarly to one contg ppt, as counterpoise.

Wt Hg$_2$Cl$_2$ (mg) × 0.0975 = mg formic acid in distillate. To calc. total formic acid originally present in aliquot of sample in distn flask before distn, divide mg formic acid found by 0.24 (fraction formic acid distd in second 200 ml distillate) and multiply by 4 to obtain formic acid in 100 g sample being analyzed. (*Note:* Factor 4 applies only to products prepd as in **18.029**. If other sample wts and aliquots are used as for eggs, **17.040**, appropriate factor must be used.)

Chromatographic Separation of C$_2$ to C$_4$ Saturated Fatty Acids (15)

18.032   *Preparation of Partition Column*

To 5 g silicic acid in glazed porcelain evapg dish add 1 ml Alphamine Red R indicator soln and just enough 1N NH$_4$OH to give alk. color of the indicator (1 drop is usually enough). Add max. amt of H_2O that the silicic acid will hold without becoming sticky or agglomerating in the butanol-CHCl$_3$ soln. (This amt must be detd for each batch of silicic acid and usually varies from 50 to 75% of wt of silicic acid.) Mix thoroly with pestle until homogeneous. Add ca 25 ml 1% butanol in CHCl$_3$, and mix to form slurry that pours readily. Pour this slurry into chromatgc tube contg small cotton plug in neck of constricted end. To avoid air pockets, tilt tube slightly while pouring. If air bubbles form while pouring, eliminate by stirring suspension in tube with long glass rod.

Clamp tube vertically in ring stand. In top insert 1-hole rubber stopper fitted with glass tube bent to 90° angle and held in place by Bunsen clamp against pressure to be exerted. Connect bent glass tube to pressure source, **18.026(c)**. Adjust pressure to 5–10 lb/sq in. so that excess solv. is forced thru column dropwise.

During removal of excess solv. gel packs down. As column packs down, particles of gel adhere to wall of tube, but eventually gel leaves wall of tube relatively clean. This is point of optimum density of column, and column is ready for use. Apply pressure until solv. reaches surface of column. If solv. passes below surface, causing drying or "cracking" of column, or if air pockets are present, extrude packing from tube, reslurry with solv., and repack column.

18.033   Test of Silicic Acid for Suitability and Standardization of Column

(a) *Preparation of std acid solns.*—Pipet 1 ml of each of following acids into sep. 1 L vol. flasks: Acetic, propionic, butyric, and valeric. Dil. to vol. with H$_2$O, and mix. Pipet 10 ml of each soln into sep. 125 ml erlenmeyers and titr. with 0.01N NaOH, using cresol red indicator, to pink persisting ca 45 sec.

ml 0.01N NaOH × normality × F = mg acid/ml std acid soln, where F = 6.01 for HOAc; 7.41, propionic; 8.81, butyric; and 10.2, valeric acid.

(b) *Preparation of std acid mixture.*—Pipet 50 ml of each std acid soln into same 250 ml vol. flask and dil. to vol. with H$_2$O. Concn of each acid in std acid mixt. = 1/5 concn in std acid soln.

(c) *Preparation of known samples.*—Pipet 5 and 25 ml aliquots of std acid mixt. into sep. 50 ml beakers. Just neutze with 0.1N NaOH, using phthln, and add 10 drops excess. Evap. to dryness on steam bath. If desired, chromatograph acids individually by using 5 ml aliquots of each std acid soln and 5 ml aliquots of 5-fold dilns of each std acid soln. Combinations approximating compositions in samples may also be prepd.

(d) *Column separation.*—(Good sepn and yields depend upon transfer of sample to column with amt of solv. specified.) To dry residue of Na salts add 2 ml 1% butanol in CHCl$_3$ soln and while stirring with glass rod add H$_2$SO$_4$ (1 + 1) dropwise until all Na salts are converted to free acids (acid to Congo red paper). Add 1 g anhyd. Na$_2$SO$_4$.

Acids elute in following order: Valeric, butyric, propionic, and acetic. Place 50 ml graduate under column as receiver. Decant supernatant onto column, pouring it slowly down side of tube without disturbing level surface of column. Apply pressure until solv. reaches surface of gel. Wash beaker with 1 ml solv., pour onto column, and with stirring rod transfer residue in beaker to column. Apply pressure until solv. just disappears into Na$_2$SO$_4$ layer. Wash beaker with another 1 ml solv., transfer to column, wash inside of tube with 1 ml solv., and apply pressure until solv. just disappears into Na$_2$SO$_4$ layer. Fill tube with solv. and apply pressure. Each time front (lower edge) of a band reaches point 2–5 mm above narrowest portion of constriction of tube, record vol. collected and change receiver. For each acid, total cumulative vol. is threshold vol. used for identifying bands in succeeding runs. After propionic acid (third band) has been eluted, fill tube with 10% butanol in CHCl$_3$ and use this solv. to elute HOAc. (Propionic acid is eluted after ca 50 ml 1% butanol

in CHCl$_3$ has passed thru column. Observe vol. actually used. In succeeding runs, change to 10% butanol in CHCl$_3$ at that vol. whether or not propionic acid is present.)

Transfer eluates to sep. 125 ml erlenmeyers, rinsing each graduated cylinder with three 5 ml portions H$_2$O. Add 1 drop cresol red indicator soln and titr. with 0.01N alkali. As end point approaches, stopper flask and shake vigorously to completely ext acids from solv. phase. Correct titrn of each eluted band for blank as follows: Collect 25 ml butanol-CHCl$_3$ mixt. from column before any acids are transferred, add 15 ml boiled and cooled H$_2$O, and titr. as above with 0.01N alkali.

If bands are not clearly differentiated or recoveries are <90%, reject the silicic acid. (Addnl stdzn with respect to threshold vol. may be desirable for identification in some instances, **18.034**.)

18.034   Identification and Determination

Add 1 drop 1N NaOH to neutzd distillate A obtained in **18.030** and evap. to small vol. Transfer to 50 ml beaker, evap. to dryness on steam bath, and proceed exactly as in **18.033**(d).

Identify acids by comparing their threshold vols with those for ca same amts and ratios of known acids found in stdzn procedure. Threshold vol. of given amt of each fatty acid is characteristic and quite reproducible under similar conditions. However, if conditions change, such as by use of different batch of silicic acid or different amt of same batch, or different amt of H$_2$O, threshold vol. for each acid must be redetd. (If present, isobutyric acid is measured as *n*-butyric acid.) For further identification as characteristic salts see JAOAC **28**, 644(1945). Acids may also be identified by paper chromatgy, **14.093**.

mg Acid/100 g sample = ml 0.01N NaOH (corrected for blank) × normality × F, where F includes equiv. wts of acids, corrected for distn recoveries, and dilns. F = 421 for HOAc; 366, propionic; and 383, butyric acid.

(*Note:* Factors given apply only to products prepd as in **18.029**. If other sample wts and aliquots are used as for eggs, **17.040**, appropriate factors must be used.)

Gas Chromatographic Method (16)— Official Final Action

18.035   Reagents

(a) *Acetone.*—Redistd.

(b) *Dichloroacetic acid (DCA) soln.*—0.5N. Redistill DCA, weigh 0.645 g into 10 ml vol. flask, and dil. to vol. with acetone. Prep. daily. (*Caution: See* **46.082**.)

(c) *Methyl enanthate.*—Transfer 250 ml anhyd. MeOH to 500 ml flask, weigh, and cool in ice bath in hood. With flask in bath, bubble BF$_3$ slowly thru glass tube into MeOH until 31.3 g BF$_3$ is taken up.

(BF₃ must be passing thru glass tube before tube is placed in and until after it is removed from MeOH.) If >31.3 g BF₃ is added, dil. with MeOH until total ml MeOH = 8 × wt BF₃ in g. Remove BF₃ vapors with effective fume removal device. Avoid contact with skin, eyes, and respiratory tract. (*Caution: See* **46.010.**)

Weigh 7 g enanthic acid (heptanoic acid) (bp 223°) into erlenmeyer and add 70 ml 12.5% (w/v) BF₃-MeOH soln. Boil 3 min on steam bath. Cool, and transfer to 750 ml separator contg 210 ml H₂O and 140 ml pet ether. Shake 3 min. Remove lower layer. Add 10 ml 5% Na₂CO₃ soln to separator and shake. Remove lower layer. Add 20 ml H₂O to separator, shake, and drain H₂O; repeat once. Filter pet ether ext thru funnel with glass wool plug covered with Na₂SO₄ into erlenmeyer. Evap. solv. to 40 ml on steam bath; complete solv. removal in N stream. Distill residual Me enanthate, collecting fraction boiling at 172–172.5°. Store in tightly stoppered glass vial in refrigerator.

(**d**) *Methyl enanthate (ME) internal std soln.*—Dil. ca 0.35 g Me enanthate, weighed to nearest mg, to 100 ml with acetone.

(**e**) *Dilute methyl enanthate (dil. ME) internal std soln.*—Dil. 1 ml ME internal std soln to 10 ml with acetone.

(**f**) *Std acid solns.*—Formic, acetic, propionic, and butyric acids, 0.05N. Check purity of stock solns of acids initially by gas chromatgy. Prep. acid dilns for calibration by pipeting calcd vol. of each acid into sep. 200 ml vol. flasks (0.39 ml formic, 0.57 ml acetic, 0.75 ml propionic, and 0.92 ml butyric acid). Dil. to vol. with acetone. Pipet 20 ml acid diln into erlenmeyer, add 20 ml H₂O and 2 drops phthln, and det. acid content by titrg with 0.05N NaOH.

mg Acid/ml std soln = ml 0.05N NaOH × normality × F, where F = 2.30 for formic; 3.00, acetic; 3.70, propionic; and 4.40, butyric acid.

18.036 *Apparatus*

(Gas chromatgc equipment, column packings, and operating conditions other than those described below may be used if they provide at least equiv. peak sepn.)

(**a**) *Gas chromatograph.*—Use gas chromatograph equipped with Ar ionization detector and all-glass injection and column system.

Parameters for modified Research Specialties gas chromatograph:

Column temp. 100°, detector temp. 170°, injection zone temp. 200°, Ar flow rate 50 ml/min, high voltage 1400 v, attenuation ×5, and 6′ glass column.

Optimum conditions for gas chromatgc sepn are obtained when peaks for solv., Me enanthate std, and formic acid are completely resolved. Std and acid peaks are sharp, altho formic and acetic acid peaks are not completely resolved. Conditions vary to some degree from instrument to instrument and should be experimentally reestablished.

(**b**) *Preparation of column packing.*—Weigh 1.3 g ethylene glycol adipate (Applied Science Laboratories, Inc.), into 150 ml beaker and dissolve by stirring in 70 ml acetone. Weigh 0.26 g 85% H₃PO₄ into second beaker and dissolve in 30 ml acetone. Combine both solns. Weigh 12.5 g Anakrom ABS (Analabs, 80 Republic Drive, North Haven, CT 06473) into 500 ml r-b flask, add combined acetone solns, and evap. in rotating evaporator at reduced pressure in H₂O bath at 35° (enough to pack one 6′ column).

Pack column evenly. Condition in column oven >12 hr at 150° by passing Ar or N thru column at ca 20 ml/min. Direct effluent thru 1/16″ stainless steel tubing into small test tube shielded from heat of oven. Column is ready for use when bleeding of column substrate into test tube over 2 hr period has practically stopped.

18.037 *Calibration*

Pipet, into same 5 ml vol. flask, vol. each std acid soln and vol. ME internal std, as follows:

Individual Acid Concn in Sample, mg	C₁–C₄ Acid Std Soln (0.05N), ml	Vol. of Internal Std Added	
		ml	Concn
<1	0.25–0.5	1.0	dil. ME std
1.0–2.5	0.5–1.0	0.5	ME std
2.0–5.0	1.0–2.0	1.0	ME std

Dil. to vol. with acetone and mix. Repeat, using varying vols of acids to provide range of concn for each acid. Inject 3 μl aliquots into gas chromatograph. Measure peak hts on chromatograms and calc. R value for each acid:

$R_A = h_A c_{ME}/c_A h_{ME}$, where c_{ME} and c_A = mg Me enanthate and acid, resp., in total vol. acetone soln, and h_{ME} and h_A = respective peak hts corresponding to the 3 μl injected.

When solv. peak tailing extends into region of ME and acid peaks, draw tail of solv. peak as it would normally appear if no other peaks were present. Use this curved extension as baseline for measuring hts of all peaks above it. Measure hts of remaining peaks to normal baseline.

18.038 *Determination*

Quant. neutze steam distillate of volatile acids obtained by **18.030** with 0.01N NaOH and phthln as indicator. Add 1 ml 0.1N NaOH excess. If color is discharged, repeat addn. Conc. to ca 45 ml on steam bath in air stream (if color is discharged, add 0.5 ml more 0.1N NaOH), transfer to 50 ml beaker, and evap. to dryness in air stream. Loosen salts with micro spatula and transfer carefully thru funnel (1.5 cm diam.) into tube-type, g-s vol. flask (see following table, last column, for vol.).

0.01N NaOH for Neutzn of Steam Distillate (Before Addn of Excess), ml	Volatile Acid Content as Acetic Acid, mg	Vol. of Internal Std Added,		Total Vol. After Diln. ml
		ml	Concn	
1.0–1.5	0.6–0.9	1.0	dil. ME std	2.0
1.5–3.0	0.9–1.8	0.5	ME std	5.0
3.0–6.0	1.8–3.6	1.0[a]	ME std	5.0
6.0–8.0	3.6–4.8	1.0	ME std	5.0
9.0–12.0	5.4–7.2	2.0	ME std	10.0

[a] For fish samples, add 1 ml ME internal std; for egg samples, add only 0.5 ml (because volatile acids are more evenly distributed between formic and acetic acid).

Add to beaker, rinsing walls, vol. 0.5N DCA equiv. to total NaOH added to distillate. (Add slight excess DCA and carefully observe liberation of volatile acids. Red due to phthln disappears before volatile acids are completely liberated. Add DCA until irregular, coarse particles of salts of volatile acids are completely replaced by fine flocculent Na dichloroacetate. Liberation of volatile acids can be accelerated by stirring with thin (2–3 mm) glass rod.) Transfer thru funnel into vol. flask. Repeat rinsing with 0.5 ml or more acetone, and add to vol. flask. Swirl flask to disperse salts and to liberate volatile acids. Pipet vol. of dil. ME std or ME std (as specified for acid content of sample in table above) to vol. flask and mix. Centrf. 3 min at low speed in g-s tube to sep. pptd Na dichloroacetate. Inject 3 μl clear soln in gas chromatograph. Measure peak hts as in **18.037** and calc. acid concns (mg in total vol. acetone soln) with R values established in calibration. $c_A = h_A \cdot c_{ME}/R_A \cdot h_{ME}$.

Neither total vol. acetone soln nor injection vol. is critical, as these values do not appear in equations for calcg R values or concns of acids. Therefore use of internal std provides wide latitude in operating conditions. If hts of acid peaks on chromatogram differ considerably, first calc. concns represented by smaller peaks by ref. to ME peak. Add known increments of internal std soln and develop addnl chromatograms for calcg higher concns of acids. If necessary, and particularly for off-scale peaks, also dil. test soln with acetone or operate electrometer or recorder at lower sensitivity settings.

Store acetone solns of acids and Me enanthate in refrigerator if they are to be chromatographed after day of prepn. If they are used after ca 5 days, det. new R values on std solns in acetone stored in refrigerator for same period of time.

To calc. mg of each acid in wt of sample used for distn, divide by fraction recovered in distn. Typical recoveries for first 200 ml distillate are: Formic acid 0.405, acetic acid 0.57, propionic acid 0.81, and butyric acid 0.92 (see **18.028**, last par.).

Histamine-Like Substances

Biological Method (17)—Official Final Action

18.039   Apparatus

(a) *Kymograph.*—With horizontal muscle lever arm having friction or gravity writing point.

(b) *Muscle bath.*—At least 50 ml capacity, in 37° constant temp. bath. *See* Fig. 18:2. May be conveniently filled and emptied thru 3-way stopcock; 1 tube connected to reservoir of Ringer-Locke soln thru bulb or coil immersed in bath; other tube connected to vac. thru suction flask as waste receiver. Bubble air, filtered thru cotton, slowly and continuously around intestine from fine capillary tube.

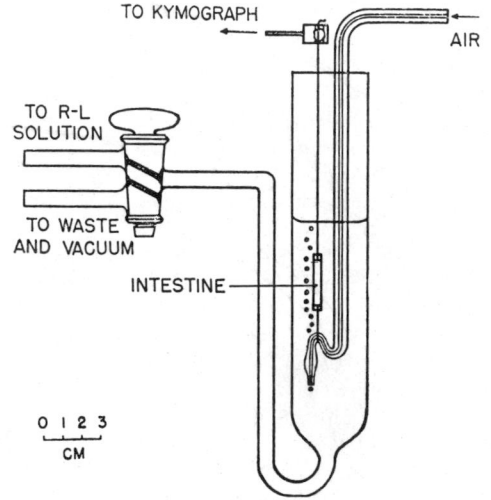

FIG. 18:2—Muscle bath

18.040   Reagents

(a) *Sodium chloride stock soln.*—180 g/L.

(b) *Potassium chloride stock soln.*—42 g/500 ml.

(c) *Sodium bicarbonate stock soln.*—15 g/500 ml.

(d) *Atropine sulfate stock soln.*—1.0 g/500 ml.

(e) *Calcium chloride stock soln.*—24 g anhyd. salt/500 ml.

(f) *Ringer-Locke soln.*—NaCl, 0.9%; KCl, 0.042%; CaCl₂, 0.024%; NaHCO₃, 0.015%; glucose, 0.1%; and atropine sulfate, 0.001%. Add 100 ml (a) and 10 ml (b), (c), and (d) to 2 L vol. flask. Add H₂O to vol. of ca 1800 ml and then 10 ml (e) while swirling. Add 2 g anhyd. glucose before use. Dil. to vol. with H₂O. Keep soln contg glucose in refrigerator when not in use, discarding when it becomes moldy.

(g) *Histamine diphosphate std solns.*—0.1 mg histamine diphosphate/ml in boiled H₂O. If stored in refrigerator when not in use, it will keep ≥3 months. Prep. dild stds of 0.01 mg/ml and 0.005 mg/ml as required. If bath smaller than 50 ml is used, prep. dilns of (g) with (f) to avoid diln of bath when stds are added.

(h) *Guinea pig intestine.*—Use guinea pigs weighing 300–400 g. Starve pig 24 hr, kill by blow on head, and remove intestine, severing at point proximal to ileocecal junction, retaining ca 12 cm of terminal ileum. Wash this section with soln (f) and use ca first 2 cm for first series of assays. Place remainder of intestine on cotton in petri dish, just covering with soln (f). Prop lid to admit air and store in refrigerator at ca 40–45°F. (Below 40°F intestine loses its activity.) Use addnl portions of intestine as required as long as material shows enough response to histamine stimulus (usually 8 days). These addnl portions of intestine are not as sensitive as ileum but give uniform response with barely noticeable pendulum movements after storage.

18.041   *Preparation of Sample*

See **18.002.** Freeze ground sample for storage, if desired.

18.042   *Assay*

Weigh 10 g prepd sample into small mortar. Add enough H_2O to make smooth paste while grinding with pestle. Transfer paste with little addnl H_2O to 100 ml Kohlrausch flask and add 1 ml HCl (1 + 1). Add H_2O to total vol. of ca 70 ml, mix well, and heat flask in boiling H_2O bath ca 20 min. Remove from bath, cool, dil. to vol. with H_2O, mix, and filter on Whatman No. 12 folded paper (or equiv.). (Ext filters slowly but only ca 5 ml need be collected for analysis.) Filtrate may be stored in refrigerator 10 days without diminished activity. Neutze 1 ml filtrate with 2 ml 1% $NaHCO_3$ soln. Dil. to 10 ml with Ringer-Locke soln (without glucose).

Attach intestine to muscle lever and let stand at least 0.5 hr in 50 ml Ringer-Locke soln, (f), in constant temp. bath at 37°. With fresh ileum, contractions and relaxations may be nonrhythmic for ca 2–3 hr with extreme and not always uniform responses to histamine stimuli. Detns may be performed during this period, but it is necessary to add small and increasing amts of dild stds to stabilize intestine response, and to check responses several times until readings are reproducible.

Add known amt of dil. std soln, (g), to bath, record response, and remove writing lever from contact with drum. Drain inner bath, add fresh 37° soln (f) to wash chamber and intestine, remove, and refill with fresh soln. Let intestine rest 3 min. Est. amt and diln of neutzd fish ext that will give approx. equal response, and add to bath. Repeat recording of response, washing muscle chamber, and resting 3 min. During this interval, measure step hts with mm scale and calc. quantity std necessary to match assay step ht. Alternately add ext and std as above until exact match is obtained.

Chemical Method (18)—Official Final Action

(Use H_2O redistd from glass for prepn of reagents and for detns. Do not clean glassware with soap; use fresh chromic acid cleaning soln, rinsing well with tap H_2O, then 3 times with distd H_2O, and 3 times with redistd H_2O. Alcohol may be used to soak or rinse glassware.)

18.043   *Reagents*

(a) *Benzene-n-butanol mixture.*—(3 + 2) v/v.

(b) *Cotton acid succinate.*—Dissolve 5 g anhyd. NaOAc, fused just before use, and 40 g succinic anhydride in 300 ml HOAc in 500 ml erlenmeyer. Immerse 10 g absorbent cotton, cut into strips, in soln; attach drying tube contg drying agent, and heat 48 hr at 100°. (Flask may be immersed to neck in active steam bath.) Filter; wash well with H_2O, HCl (1 + 9), H_2O, and finally with alcohol. Dry in vac. oven at 100°.

(c) *Diazonium reagent.*—Dissolve 0.1 g *p*-nitroaniline, recrystd from hot H_2O, and dil. to 100 ml with 0.1N HCl. Store in refrigerator. Dissolve 4 g $NaNO_2$ in H_2O and dil. to 100 ml. Store in refrigerator. Just before use place 10 ml *p*-nitroaniline soln in ice bath 5 min, add 1 ml $NaNO_2$ soln, mix, and let stand in bath at least 5 min before use.

(d) *Coupling buffer.*—Dissolve 7.15 g Na metaborate ($NaBO_2$) and 5.7 g Na_2CO_3 in H_2O, and dil. to 100 ml. Store in polyethylene bottle.

(e) *Barbital buffer.*—Dissolve 10 g Na barbital in 1 L H_2O and adjust to pH 7.7 with HOAc (1 + 15) (ca 25–30 ml), using pH meter. Store in refrigerator to prevent mold growth. Dissolve any ppt by warming before use. (50–250 ml bottle of the buffer may be kept at room temp. and replenished from main supply when mold growth is apparent.)

(f) *Histamine std solns.*—Dry histamine.2HCl (USP Reference Standard or material checked against Standard as in **18.045**) 2 hr over H_2SO_4. Dissolve 0.1656 g dried histamine.2HCl in H_2O and dil. to 100 ml (1 ml = 1 mg histamine). Dil. 10 ml of this stock soln to 100 ml with H_2O (1 ml = 100 μg histamine). Dil. 5 ml of this dil. std soln and 5 ml MeOH to 100 ml with H_2O (1 ml = 5 μg histamine). Store in cold. Prep. fresh stds weekly.

(g) *4-Methyl-2-pentanone (methyl isobutyl ketone).*—Com. purified grade (Eastman Kodak Co. No. 416 has been found satisfactory). To recover used ketone, wash once with satd $NaHCO_3$ soln and 3 times with H_2O, distill, retaining fraction boiling at 115–118°, and check A at 475 nm.

(h) *Benzaldehyde.*—Cl-free.

(i) *Dilute sulfuric acid.*—0.40±0.02N, accurately stdzd.

18.044   *Preparation of CAS Column*

Prep. column by firmly placing small plug of cotton acid succinate (CAS) (ca 50 mg) in column prepd by cutting off or blowing out bottom of 15 ml centrf. tube. Wash plug with three 15 ml portions H_2O and two 3 ml portions alcohol. Let solvs drip thru CAS, syringing out column by blowing out last portion of each solv., using 10 ml syringe with needle inserted thru rubber stopper. CAS plugs may be reused for months by washing shortly after use with

H₂O and alcohol as above, and protecting from dust with inverted beaker.

18.045   *Determination*

Transfer 10 g prepd sample, **18.041**, to semi-micro container of high-speed blender, add ca 50 ml MeOH, and blend ca 2 min. Transfer to 100 ml g-s vol. flask, rinsing lid and blender jar with MeOH and adding rinsings to flask. Heat in H₂O bath to 60° and let stand at this temp. 15 min. Cool to 25°, dil. to vol. with MeOH, and filter thru folded paper. Alcohol filtrate may be stored in refrigerator several weeks. (Light powdery ppt sepg on storage may be ignored.)

Dil. 5 ml filtrate to 100 ml with H₂O (disregard turbidity). Pipet 5 ml aliquot into 16 × 150 mm g-s test tube, and add 1 drop benzaldehyde (Cl-free) and 0.2 ml 20% NaOH. (pH after adding alkali should be ca 12.4–12.5.) Shake vigorously ca 25 times. Let stand 2 min and add 5 ml benzene-butanol mixt. Shake vigorously ca 25 times and let stand 5 min to sep. If emulsion forms, centrf.

Transfer upper layer with fine-tip tube equipped with rubber bulb to previously prepd CAS column, avoiding transfer of any aq. phase. Re-ext aq. soln with 5 ml benzene-butanol mixt. as before, shaking, letting stand 5 min, and transferring upper layer to column. Rinse lip and sides of column with fine stream of alcohol from wash bottle, syringing out CAS. Wash column with 3 ml alcohol; syringe out; wash with two 3 ml portions H₂O, and syringe out. Discard solvs and washings.

Elute histamine from CAS into 25 ml g-s erlenmeyer by washing down sides of tube with 2.0 ml 0.40±0.02N H₂SO₄ (vol. and concn of acid are critical) followed by 3 ml H₂O. Syringe out after dripping ceases.

Cool eluate in ice bath, weighting flask with lead ring or clamp to prevent tipping, and let stand 5–10 min. Add 0.5 ml cooled diazonium reagent and let stand 5 min in ice bath. Add 0.50 ml coupling buffer (vol. is critical; Ostwald pipet is convenient) with continuous shaking or swirling to avoid localized alky (pH after addn of coupling buffer, 5–6). Let stand 5 min in ice bath. Sat. soln with ca 0.25 g powd Na₂B₄O₇.10H₂O added in one portion. Shake soln immediately and continuously ca 30 sec to ensure rapid and complete satn (final pH ca 8.6). Let stand in ice bath 15 min.

Pipet in 5.0 ml methyl isobutyl ketone and shake vigorously 25 times. Immediately transfer both layers to 16 × 150 mm test tube (do not rinse) and let stand 10 min at room temp. to sep. and to warm up. Transfer upper layer with fine-tip dropper to second 16 × 150 mm g-s test tube contg 5.0 ml barbital buffer. Avoid transferring aq. and solid phases (if present) (transfer need not be quant.). Shake vigorously ca 25 times (pH of barbital buffer after washing, ca 8.3–8.4). Let stand 10 min to sep.

Transfer upper layer with fine-tip dropper to 1 cm cell and det. A at 475 nm against methyl isobutyl ketone. Repeat detn on samples yielding A values

>25 μg std by dilg 1 ml MeOH filtrate to 100 ml with H₂O. Alternatively, aq. diln may be dild 1 + 4 (or more) with H₂O.

Conduct std and blank thru detn as follows: Pipet 5 ml 5 μg/ml histamine std soln into 16 × 150 mm g-s test tube and pipet 5 ml 5% MeOH into similar tube for blank. Proceed as in detn, beginning, par. 2, line 3, "... add 1 drop benzaldehyde ..."

Subtract blank A from A of std (A') and of sample (A) and calc. histamine in sample aliquot as follows:

$$\mu g \text{ histamine} = A(\text{corr.}) \times 25/A'(\text{corr.})$$

Indole in Shrimp, Oysters, and Crabmeat
(19)—Official First Action

18.046   *Apparatus and Reagents*

(a) *Color reagent.*—Dissolve 0.4 g *p*-dimethyl-aminobenzaldehyde in 5 ml HOAc and mix with 92 ml H₃PO₄ and 3 ml HCl. As purity of *p*-dimethyl-aminobenzaldehyde exerts strong influence on intensity of reagent blank, purify yellow com. reagent as follows:

Dissolve 100 g in 600 ml HCl (1 + 6). Add 300 ml H₂O and ppt aldehyde by slowly adding 10% NaOH soln with vigorous stirring. As soon as pptd aldehyde appears white, stop addn of NaOH soln, filter, and discard ppt. Continue neutzn until practically all aldehyde is pptd, but do not carry to completion, because last 4–5 g may be colored. Filter, and wash ppt with H₂O until washings are no longer acid. Dry aldehyde, which should be practically white, in desiccator.

(b) *Acetic acid, purified.*—If this reagent turns pink with color reagent, purify as follows: Add, in order specified, to ⨎ 1 L r-b flask: 500 ml HOAc, 25 g KMnO₄, and 20 ml H₂SO₄. Distill in all-glass still *not* >400 ml.

(c) *Dilute hydrochloric acid.*—Dil. 5 ml HCl to 100 ml with H₂O.

(d) *Indole std soln.*—Accurately weigh 20 mg indole into 200 ml vol. flask and dil. to vol. with alcohol. Keep refrigerated and discard after 2 weeks.

(e) *Distillation apparatus.*—Use sep. steam generator for each unit. Steam generator may be made from 1 L erlenmeyer and connected to all-glass steam distn app. with min. use of rubber tubing. Distn flask (capacity ≥500 ml) is connected to straight bore condenser thru spray trap. 500 ml erlenmeyer is effective receiver. Foil-covered rubber stoppers may be used in absence of all-glass app. (Unprotected natural or synthetic rubber connections and stoppers cause variable distn blanks.)

Ensure absence of Cl in the H₂O which may partly or entirely inhibit development of indole color.

18.047   *Preparation of Sample*

Crabmeat, oysters, and shrimp.—For oyster meats weigh 50 g; for drained crabmeat or peeled raw or cooked shrimp, weigh 25 or 50 g (depending upon amt of indole expected). Transfer weighed portion to high-speed blender, add 80 ml H₂O (if oysters or crabmeat) or 80 ml alcohol (if shrimp), and mix several min until homogeneous. Quant. transfer mixt. to distn flask, and rinse mixing chamber with min. amt of same solv. used for prepg mixt.

18.048 Determination

Connect flask for steam distn and gently apply steam until distn is well started, using care not to pass in steam so vigorously as to cause excessive foaming. Apply enough heat to distn flask to maintain vol. of 80–90 ml. Collect 350 ml distillate in ca 45 min. (If alcohol was used in prepn of sample, collect 450 ml.) Wash condenser with small amt of alcohol and drain into receiving flask contg distillate.

Transfer distillate to 500 ml separator and add 5 ml dil. HCl and 5 ml satd Na_2SO_4 soln. Ext successively with 25, 20, and 15 ml portions $CHCl_3$, shaking vigorously ≥ 1 min each time. Combine the 25 and 20 ml exts in 500 ml separator and wash with 400 ml H_2O, 5 ml satd Na_2SO_4 soln, and 5 ml dil. HCl. Save wash H_2O. Filter combined exts thru cotton plug into dry 125 ml separator. Wash 15 ml portion, using same wash H_2O, and combine with other portions in same 125 ml separator.

Add 10 ml color reagent to combined exts, shake vigorously exactly 2 min, and let acid layer sep. as completely as possible. Transfer 9.0 ml acid layer to 50 ml vol. flask, dil. to vol. with HOAc, mix well, transfer soln to suitable photometer cell, and measure color photometrically at 560 nm. Color soln may be dild with HOAc contg 9.0 ml color reagent/50 ml of soln, provided blanks are detd at same dilns.

Prep. std curve as above by steam distg series of freshly prepd dilns of std indole soln. Det. distn blank similarly, omitting addn of indole.

Paralytic Shellfish Poison

Biological Method (20)—Official Final Action

(*Caution:* Use rubber gloves when handling materials which may contain paralytic shellfish poison.)

18.049 Materials

(a) *Paralytic shellfish poison std soln.*—100 μg/ml. Available from Division of Criteria and Standards, Environmental Control Admin., 12720 Twinbrook Pkwy, Rockville, MD 20852, as acidified 20% alc. soln. Std is stable indefinitely in cool place.

(b) *Paralytic shellfish poison working std soln.*—1 μg/ml. Dil. 1 ml std soln to 100 ml with H_2O. Soln is stable several weeks at 3–4°.

(c) *Mice.*—Healthy mice, 19–21 g, from stock colony used for routine assays. If <19 g or >21 g, apply correction factor to obtain true death time (see Table, **18.056**). Do not use mice weighing >23 g and do not reuse mice.

18.050 Standardization of Bioassay

Dil. 10 ml aliquots of 1 μg/ml std soln with 10, 15, 20, 25, and 30 ml H_2O, resp., until intraperitoneal injection of 1 ml doses into few test mice causes

median death time of 5–7 min. pH of dilns should be 2–4 and must not be >4.5. Test addnl dilns in 1 ml increments of H_2O, e.g., if 10 ml dild with 25 ml H_2O kills mice in 5–7 min, test solns dild 10 + 24 and 10 + 26.

Inject group of 10 mice with each of 2 or preferably 3 dilns that fall within median death time of 5–7 min. Give 1 ml dose to each mouse by intraperitoneal injection and det. death time as time elapsed from completion of injection to last gasping breath of mouse.

Repeat assay 1 or 2 days later, using dilns prepd above which differed by 1 ml increments of H_2O. Then repeat entire test, starting with testing of dilns prepd from newly prepd working std soln.

Calc. median death time for each group of 10 mice used on each diln. If all groups of 10 mice injected with any 1 diln gave median death time <5 or >7 min, disregard results from this diln in subsequent calcns. On other hand, if any groups of 10 mice injected with 1 diln gave median death time falling between 5 and 7 min, include all groups of 10 mice used on that diln, even though some of median death times may be <5 or >7 min. From median death time for each group of 10 mice in each of selected dilns, det. number of mouse units/ml from Sommer's Table. Divide calcd μg poison/1 ml by mouse units/1 ml to obtain conversion factor (CF value) expressing μg poison equiv. to 1 mouse unit. Calc. av. of individual CF values, and use this av. value as ref. point to check routine assays. Individual CF values may vary significantly within laboratory if technics and mice are not rigidly controlled. This situation will require continued use of working std or secondary std, depending on vol. of assay work performed.

18.051 Use of Standard with Routine Assays of Shellfish

Check CF value periodically as follows: If shellfish products are assayed less than once a week, det. CF value on each day assays are performed by injecting 5 mice with appropriate diln of working std. If assays are made on several days during week, only 1 check need be made each week on diln of std such that median death time falls within 5–7 min. CF value thus detd should check with av. CF value within ±20%. If it does not check within this range, complete group of 10 mice by adding 5 mice to the 5 mice already injected, and inject second group of 10 mice with same diln of std. Average CF value detd for second group with that of first group. Take resulting value as new CF value. Variation of >20% represents significant change in response of mice to poison, or in technic of assay. Changes of this type require change in CF value.

Repeated checks of CF value ordinarily produce consistent results within ±20%. If wider variations are found frequently, possibility of uncontrolled or unrecognized variables in method should be investigated before proceeding with routine assays.

18.052   *Preparation of Sample*

(a) *Clams, oysters, and mussels.*—Thoroly clean outside of shellfish with fresh H_2O. Open by cutting adductor muscles. Rinse inside with fresh H_2O to remove sand or other foreign material. Remove meat from shell by sepg adductor muscles and tissue connecting at hinge. Do not use heat or anesthetics before opening shell, and do not cut or damage body of mollusk at this stage. Collect ca 100–150 g meats in glazed dish. As soon as possible, transfer meats to No. 10 sieve without layering, and let drain 5 min. Pick out pieces of shell and discard drainings. Grind in household-type grinder with ⅛–¼″ holes or in blender until homogeneous.

(b) *Scallops.*—Sep. edible portion (adductor muscle) and apply test to this portion alone. Drain and grind as in (a).

(c) *Canned shellfish.*—Prep. by blending as in 18.002(b).

18.053   *Extraction*

Weigh 100 g well-mixed material into tared beaker. Add 100 ml 0.1N HCl, stir thoroly, and check pH. (pH should be <4.0, preferably ca 3.0. If necessary, adjust pH as indicated below.) Heat mixt., boil gently 5 min, and let cool to room temp. Adjust cooled mixt. to pH 2.0–4.0 (never >4.5) as detd by *BDH Universal Indicator, phenol blue, Congo red paper,* or pH meter. To lower pH add 5N HCl dropwise with stirring; to raise pH add 0.1N NaOH dropwise with constant stirring to prevent local alkalinization and consequent destruction of poison. Transfer mixt. to graduated cylinder and dil. to 200 ml.

Return mixt. to beaker, stir to homogeneity, and let settle until portion of supernatant is translucent and can be decanted free of solid particles large enough to block 26-gage hypodermic needle. If necessary, centrf. mixt. or supernatant 5 min at 3000 rpm or filter thru paper. Only enough liq. to perform bioassay is necessary.

18.054   *Mouse Test*

Intraperitoneally inoculate each test mouse with 1 ml acid ext. Note time of inoculation and observe mice carefully for time of death as indicated by last gasping breath. Record death time from stopwatch or clock with sweep second hand. One mouse may be used for initial detn, but 2 or 3 are preferred. If death time or median death time of several mice is <5 min, make diln to obtain death times of 5–7 min. If death time of 1 or 2 mice injected with undild sample is >7 min, total of ≥3 mice must be inoculated to establish toxicity of sample. If large dilns are necessary, adjust pH of diln by dropwise addn of dil. HCl (0.1 or 0.01N) to pH 2.0–4.0 (never >4.5). Inoculate 3 mice with diln that gives death times of 5–7 min.

18.055   *Calculation of Toxicity*

Det. median death times of mice, including survivors, and from Sommer's table det. corresponding number of mouse units. If test animals weigh <19 g

or >21 g, make correction for each mouse by multiplying mouse units corresponding to death time for that mouse by wt correction factor for that mouse from Sommer's Table; then det. median mouse unit for group. (Consider death time of survivors as >60 min or equiv. to <0.875 mouse unit in calcg median.) Convert mouse units to μg poison/ml by multiplying by CF value.

μg Poison/100 g meat = (μg/ml) × diln factor × 200.

Consider any value >80 μg/100 g as hazardous and unsafe for human consumption.

18.056   *Sommer's Table*

Death time: mouse unit relations for paralytic shellfish poison (acid)

Death Time[a]	Mouse Units	Death Time[a]	Mouse Units
1:00	100	5:00	1.92
10	66.2	05	1.89
15	38.3	10	1.86
20	26.4	15	1.83
25	20.7	20	1.80
30	16.5	30	1.74
35	13.9	40	1.69
40	11.9	45	1.67
45	10.4	50	1.64
50	9.33		
55	8.42	6:00	1.60
		15	1.54
2:00	7.67	30	1.48
05	7.04	45	1.43
10	6.52		
15	6.06	7:00	1.39
20	5.66	15	1.35
25	5.32	30	1.31
30	5.00	45	1.28
35	4.73		
40	4.48	8:00	1.25
45	4.26	15	1.22
50	4.06	30	1.20
55	3.88	45	1.18
3:00	3.70	9:00	1.16
05	3.57	30	1.13
10	3.43	10:00	1.11
15	3.31	30	1.09
20	3.19		
25	3.08	11:00	1.075
30	2.98	30	1.06
35	2.88		
40	2.79	12:00	1.05
45	2.71		
50	2.63	13	1.03
55	2.56	14	1.015
		15	1.000
4:00	2.50	16	0.99
05	2.44	17	0.98
10	2.38	18	0.972
15	2.32	19	0.965
20	2.26	20	0.96
25	2.21	21	0.954
30	2.16	22	0.948
35	2.12	23	0.942
40	2.08	24	0.937
45	2.04	25	0.934
50	2.00	30	0.917
55	1.96	40	0.898
		60	0.875

[a] Minutes:Seconds.

Correction table for weight of mice	
Wt of Mice, g	Mouse Units
10	0.50
10.5	0.53
11	0.56
11.5	0.59
12	0.62
12.5	0.65
13	0.675
13.5	0.70
14	0.73
14.5	0.76
15	0.785
15.5	0.81
16	0.84
16.5	0.86
17	0.88
17.5	0.905
18	0.93
18.5	0.95
19	0.97
19.5	0.985
20	1.000
20.5	1.015
21	1.03
21.5	1.04
22	1.05
22.5	1.06
23	1.07

Identification of Fish Species by Electrophoresis

Starch Gel-Zone Method (21)—Official Final Action

(*Caution:* Cover for electrophoresis chamber should have switch to disconnect current to electrodes when chamber is open. Shield contacts and electrodes against body contact.)

18.057 *Apparatus*

(¼″ Lucite or Plexiglas is suitable plastic for trays, cabinet, and containers; Fig. 18:3.)

(a) *Trays.*—Plastic; 20 × 250 mm, 6 mm deep, to hold starch gel.

(b) *Cabinet.*—Plastic; 3 × 8 × 14″ with flat cover. Make slots in rear for inserting electrodes.

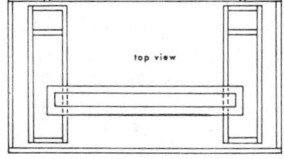
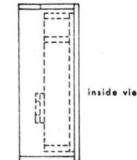

FIG. 18:3—Electrophoresis cabinet
(Scale: 1″ = 10″)

(c) *Buffer and electrode containers.*—Plastic; 2 × 2 × 7″ with electrode compartment 2 × 2 × 1″ at one end.

(d) *Electrodes.*—18 gage Ag wire. Make tight coil at one end and insert in electrode compartment; place other end thru glass tube and attach to power supply.

(e) *Filter paper strips.*—Whatman No. 3; 6 × 19 mm for samples; 18 × 75 mm for connecting gel to buffer and buffer to electrode compartment.

(f) *Power supply.*—To supply constant 15 ma at 190–210 volts, *e.g.*, Heathkit or Constat.

18.058 *Reagents*

(a) *Borate buffer.*—pH 8.65. Dissolve 18.5 g H_3BO_3 and 4.8 g NaOH in H_2O and dil. to 1 L. Adjust with 10% NaOH soln, if necessary. Dil. 1 + 9 for prepg starch gel.

(b) *Sodium chloride soln.*—Prep. satd soln and dil. 1 + 2 for use in electrode compartment.

(c) *Hydrolyzed potato starch.*—Hydrolyze 300 g potato starch 1 hr at 40° in 600 ml acetone contg 6 ml HCl. Stop reaction by addn of 150 ml 1*M* NaOAc.3H_2O (136 g/L) and filter with suction. Wash pptd starch with 2–3 L H_2O. Resuspend starch in 1.5 L H_2O and stir 1 hr. Refilter and wash with 2 L H_2O, and dry overnight at 50°. Grind to fine powder and test for correct gel consistency by prepg test lots contg 12, 13, 14% etc. starch in pH 8.65 buffer, heat to just below boiling, and pour into starch gel trays to cool and harden. Prep. night before use and store in refrigerator. Using known protein ext, det. starch concn giving best pattern sepn in detn. Use this concn for all detns with this batch of starch. (Prepd starch available from Connaught Medical Research Laboratories, University of Toronto, Toronto, Canada, and Fisher Scientific Co.)

(d) *5-5-1 solvent.*—Mix 5 parts H_2O, 5 parts MeOH, and 1 part HOAc.

(e) *Amido black 10B.*—1.0%. Dissolve 2 g dye in 200 ml 5-5-1 solv.

18.059 *Determination*

Weigh 20–30 g minced sample into blender cup. Add 40–60 ml H_2O and blend at high speed 2 min. Pour mixt. into 50 ml centrf. tubes and centrf. at 1800 rpm until sepn is complete (10–15 min). Filter supernatant thru folded Whatman No. 1 paper or on buchner with suction to obtain protein ext.

Dip small filter paper strips into protein ext and insert into starch strips by cutting starch crosswise at midpoint of length of strip. Place loaded trays into cabinet (Fig. 18:3). Place one end of large paper strip satd with pH 8.65 buffer on each end of starch tray and dip other end into tray of pH 8.65 buffer. Connect buffer compartment to electrode compartment contg dild NaCl soln with similar strip satd with the NaCl soln. Immerse Ag electrodes in both electrode compartments. Pass constant 15 ma current (190–210 volts) thru system 5 hr.

Remove trays and immerse starch strips 5 min in dye soln. Return excess dye to stock soln (may be used 6–9 times). Wash dyed strips with several portions 5-5-1 solv. to remove dye from unstained portions of starch, leaving protein fractions permanently stained as blue bands.

Compare pattern with patterns of authentic materials and stds run simultaneously.

Acrylamide Disk Method (22)—Official First Action

18.060   **Apparatus**

(a) *Disk electrophoresis.*—Canalco Model 6, 12, or 1200 (Canalco, 5635 Fisher Ln, Rockville, MD 20852) or assemble app. shown in Fig. 18:4, consisting of regulated power source (60 ma, 500 volts, DC); 2 plastic reservoirs, ca 5″ diam.; C or Pt electrodes; tube grommets (std elec. grommets); glass tubes, 65 × 5 mm id. "Top view" represents base of upper reservoir showing holes lined with rubber grommets. Gel tubes protrude from base of upper reservoir and dip into lower reservoir buffer. (*See Caution* above **18.057.**)

Polyacrylamide gel column is composed of 3 layers: upper, large-pore (stacking) gel contg sample ions in which electrophoretic concn of ions is initiated; middle, large-pore gel (spacer gel) in which electrophoretic concn of sample ions is completed; and lower, small-pore gel in which electrophoretic sepn occurs.

Thoroly clean and rinse app. after each detn. Wash sample tubes and soak in $K_2Cr_2O_7$-H_2SO_4 cleaning soln followed by thoro rinsing with H_2O. When app. is not in use remove buffer, **18.061**(b)(*7*), from upper and lower reservoirs and store in sep. containers in

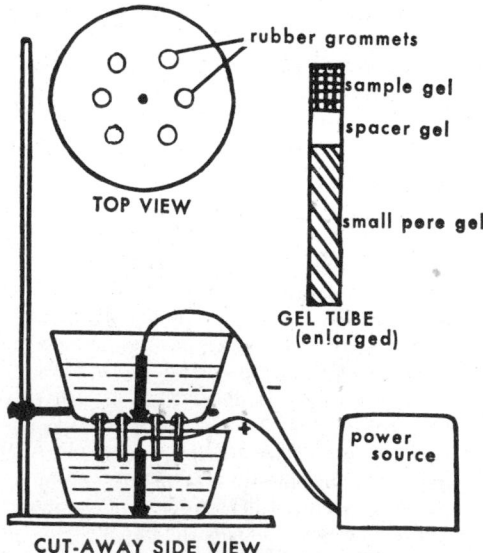

TOP VIEW

GEL TUBE (enlarged)

power source

CUT-AWAY SIDE VIEW

FIG. 18:4—Disk electrophoresis apparatus

refrigerator. Upper buffer is usually good for ca 6 detns. Discard buffer when pH drops to <8.2.

(b) *Photopolymerizing light.*—15 watt fluorescent light, 15″ long.

18.061   **Reagents**

(a) *Relatively stable.*—Acrylamide monomer, N,N′-methylenebisacrylamide (Bis), 2-amino-2-hydroxymethyl-1,3-propanediol (Tris), N,N,N′,N′-tetramethylethylethylenediamine (Temed), ammonium persulfate, riboflavin, glycine (NH_3-free), aniline black.

(b) *Relatively unstable (solns).*—Stable ca 6 months; refrigerate solns *1–6*. (*1*) 48 ml 1*N* HCl, 36.3 g Tris, 0.23 ml Temed, H_2O to 100 ml (pH 8.8–9.0). (*2*) 25.6 ml 1*M* H_3PO_4, 5.7 g Tris, 0.46 ml Temed, H_2O to 100 ml (pH 6.6–6.9). (*3*) 30.0 g acrylamide, 0.8 g Bis, H_2O to 100 ml. (*4*) 10.0 g acrylamide, 2.5 g Bis, H_2O to 100 ml. (*5*) 4.0 mg riboflavin, H_2O to 100 ml. (*6*) *Catalyst.*—0.14 g $(NH_4)_2S_2O_8$, H_2O to 100 ml (mix fresh weekly). (*7*) *Buffer.*—3.0 g Tris, 14.4 g glycine, H_2O to 1 L (pH 8.8–9.0). (*8*) *Specimen stain.* —1.0 g aniline black, 7.5% HOAc (v/v) to 200 ml. (*9*) *Tracking dye.*—0.005% aq. bromophenol blue.

(Solid reagents and solns are available from Canalco.)

(c) *Working solns.*—Prep. fresh for each detn. (*1*) *Lower gel (sepg gel).*—Mix solns (b)(*1*), (*3*), and H_2O (1 + 2 + 1), pH 8.8–9.0. To form gel, mix with catalyst soln, (*6*) (1 + 1). (*2*) *Upper gel (stacking gel).*—Mix solns (b)(*2*), (*4*), and (*5*) (1 + 2 + 1), pH 6.6–6.8. To form gel, expose to fluorescent light.

18.062   **Preparation of Column**

(a) *Lower and spacer gels.*—Cap base of glass tube and set tube in rack. Prep. sepg gel with catalyst soln, (c)(*1*), in 20 ml syringe and add mixt. to tube to ca 0.5″ from top. Tap tube occasionally during filling to avoid trapping air bubbles under gel surface. Place few drops tracking dye in ca 20 ml H_2O and with eye dropper cautiously layer 0.25″ dye soln on top of sepg gel without disturbing gel surface by touching dropper to tube edge (dye soln aids in differentiating H_2O and gel layers). Discard tubes in which distinct, sharp boundary line is not visible. Let gel polymerize 30 min. (Polymerization time is based on reaction at 24°. Let refrigerated reagents stand at room temp. ca 20 min before using.) Gently shake off H_2O layer and add ca 0.1 ml stacking gel soln, (c)(*2*), to top of column (functionally this is "spacer gel layer"). Cautiously layer ⅛″ H_2O atop gel. Set photopolymerizing light 3–5″ in front of gel column rack to polymerize spacer gel in 10–15 min. Polymerization is complete when spacer gel changes from light green to translucent white. Shake off top H_2O layer.

(b) *Sample gel.*—Prep. sample ext as in first par., **18.059,** and mix ext, H_2O, and solns, (b)(*2*), (*4*), and (*5*) (1 + 3 + 1 + 2 + 1) (sample stacking mixt.). If inadequate (no bands or only very faint band

appears in detn), prep. new sample stacking mixt.
$(2 + 2 + 1 + 2 + 1)$.

Add 0.1 ml sample stacking mixt. to tube prepd in
(a) and polymerize, using fluorescent light as in (a).
Remove base cap from tube by pressing at bottom
and peeling off edge to break vac. Avoid displacement of gel column from tube wall. Do not touch gel
or sharp glass edge of column.

18.063 Determination

Pour ca 500 ml buffer soln, (b)(7) (contg enough
tracking dye soln to produce definite blue tinge), into
lower bath or enough to cover lower electrode $\geq \frac{1}{4}''$.
Insert sample end of column (top) into rubber holes
in under side of upper bath until tops of glass tubes
are flush with tops of rubber holes. Plug unused holes
with stoppers to avoid top buffer leakage. Place
upper bath over lower bath.

Slowly pour ca 250 ml buffer soln (contg tracking
dye) into middle of upper bath. Fill slowly to avoid
cross contamination of samples. Take extra caution
to liberate all air entrapped between sample gel and
buffer to permit elec. current to flow by gently introducing buffer soln into top of each sample tube, using
syringe to drive out air. Set polarity of electrodes
so that sample ions migrate to lower bath (pos.
electrode). Turn on current and adjust power unit to
give 5 ma/sample tube (5 ma × no. sample columns = total ma adjustment of power supply). Turn
off current when "front" band is within 5 mm of
bottom of sample column (ca 30–40 min).

Transfer gel column ("sample end" or "top" first)
to test tube, $\frac{2}{3}$ full with specimen stain dild with
H_2O (1 + 1), *immediately* after electrophoresis to
stain and fix. Protein fractions in gel diffuse if not
properly fixed or stained. Remove gel column from
tube under H_2O in pan as follows: Fill 10 or 20 ml
syringe with cold H_2O and insert gel-removing
needle at sample end of column between glass and
gel so that needle tip reaches sepg gel. Keeping
needle flat against glass surface to avoid scratching
gel, rotate needle completely around circumference
of gel. Remove needle and insert it from other end to
depth of ca 1 cm, holding it against inner surface of
glass column and at same time forcing stream of H_2O
thru needle. If these steps are carefully performed,
entire intact gel will come free and can be slipped out
of tube. If necessary, little air pressure from rubber
bulb will assist in ejecting column.

While gel is being stained (above), prep. 75 × 7
mm id glass destain tube as follows: Place fire polished end of tube in large diam. base cap. Add about
$\frac{3}{8}''$ sepg gel with catalyst to bottom of column and
let polymerize. When staining is complete, ca 15
min, decant stain by placing lip of test tube against
inside lip of beaker to retain gel in tube. Rinse twice
with 7.5% HOAc (v/v) to remove excess stain.
Transfer gel bottom "front" first into destain tube in
which bottom plug of gel has been cast and cap
removed.

Place destaining tubes in rubber holes in under
side of upper bath. Plug any vacant holes. Pour ca
500 ml 7.5% HOAc in lower bath and ca 250 ml into
upper bath. As previously, use syringe contg 7.5%
HOAc to insure no air bubbles exist between gel and
HOAc bath. Turn on current, adjusting to 5 ma/
column (5 × no. columns = total ma). Gels will be
destained in ca 45–60 min. When gel part contg no
protein is clear of stain, or has pale blue color, remove specimens, and place in small test tube contg
7.5% HOAc for viewing and storage. Visually compare finished tubes with patterns prepd from authentic samples and stds run simultaneously.

Cellulose Acetate Strip Method
(23)—Official First Action

18.064 Principle

Fish protein is applied to cellulose acetate supporting medium and travels when fixed voltage is
applied for definite length of time. Finished strips
are stained, washed, and dried to fix patterns.

18.065 Apparatus and Reagents

(a) *Electrophoresis cabinet.*—Divided into 4 compartments with adjustable constant voltage power
supply with 300 v min. output voltage (Gelman
Instrument Co., 600 S. Wagner Rd, Ann Arbor, MI
48106) and equipped with voltammeter which permits reading and adjusting voltage to produce desired current (Beckman Instrument Duostat power
supply, or equiv.). (*See Caution* above **18.057.**)

(b) *Gelman applicator.*

(c) *Cellulose acetate strips.*—6¾ × 1″ (Gelman
Instrument Co.).

(d) *Capillary tubes.*—1.6–1.8 × 100 mm.

(e) *Filter paper.*—Whatman No. 1 sheets cut to
convenient size.

(f) *Veronal buffer.*—pH 8.6, ionic strength 0.04;
Na diethylbarbiturate 8.64 g, diethylbarbituric
acid 1.2 g, and H_2O to 1 L.

(g) *Stain.*—Dissolve 20 mg Ponceau S stain in
100 ml 5% trichloroacetic acid.

(h) *Wash.*—5% HOAc.

18.066 Preparation of Samples

(a) *Fresh.*—Grind ca 3 g fish flesh in mortar with
3 ml H_2O and squeeze through several thicknesses
of cheesecloth. If centrf. is available, pieces of fish
may be placed in centrf. tubes and fluid may be expressed by centrfg; no added H_2O is required.

(b) *Frozen.*—Thaw sample and use drip that
forms undild.

(c) *Freeze-dried.*—Reconstitute samples with
H_2O and treat in same manner as fresh samples.

(d) *Breaded raw sticks and portions.*—Remove
breading by soaking for few sec in H_2O and scraping
breading off with spatula. Treat in same manner as
fresh or frozen samples.

(e) *Precooked sticks and portions.*—Trim breading and all surface meat until internal center section remains. Treat as fresh sample.

18.067   *Determination*

Soak cellulose polyacetate strips 30 min in buffer (soaking is required to bring strips back to original gel structure). Use new buffer supply each time. Since 6 strips can be run simultaneously, each with different sample, identify each strip with pencil notation before soaking.

Add chilled (34°F) buffer to each chamber of cabinet and level to point slightly below compartment dividers. Remove 1 strip from buffer and gently blot between sheets of filter paper to remove excess buffer.

Take up sample of tissue fluid into capillary tube and transfer to applicator. Draw capillary tube along applicator to within ¼″ of both ends. Then press applicator firmly against strip about 2″ from one end. Place strip contg sample across cabinet dividers so that sample is on cathode side and both ends are immersed in buffer in the 2 outer chambers. Secure acetate strips at each end with magnets or glass wedges to prevent slippage. Keep taut. Repeat sample application with each strip, working quickly to prevent strips from drying out.

Put cabinet cover in place, connect electrodes, and set power supply to give constant voltage. Adjust voltage (between 200 and 300 v) to produce initial current of 1.5 ma/strip. Maintain this voltage 30 min. Shut off power supply, remove strips from cabinet, and place in Ponceau S stain 5 min. Immerse strips in series of 3 rinsing solns of 5% HOAc to remove excess dye. Rinse strips until only protein bands are left stained and remainder of strip is free from dye. Finally, blot strips and dry between several sheets of filter paper. Compare protein patterns of samples with those of authentic flesh samples.

SELECTED REFERENCES

(1) JAOAC **46**, 31(1963).

(2) JAOAC **20**, 70(1937); **21**, 85(1938); **35**, 218 (1952); **36**, 608(1953); **38**, 194(1955).

(3) JAOAC **35**, 218(1952); **36**, 608(1953); **38**, 194 (1955).

(4) CFR Title **21**, **36.10**(c)(2)(*i*); JAOAC **36**, 947 (1953); **38**, 194(1955).

(5) JAOAC **50**, 205, 275(1967); **52**, 692(1969); **53**, 9(1970).

(6) JAOAC **35**, 216(1952); **37**, 602(1954).

(7) JAOAC **20**, 71(1937); **35**, 218(1952); **36**, 608 (1953); **37**, 607(1954); **44**, 141, 276(1961); **46**, 744(1963).

(8) JAOAC **21**, 85(1938); **23**, 589(1940).

(9) JAOAC **20**, 410(1937); **23**, 589(1940).

(10) JAOAC **52**, 55(1969).

(11) JAOAC **31**, 334(1948).

(12) JAOAC **40**, 343(1957); **42**, 261(1959); **45**, 259 (1962); **46**, 746(1963); **47**, 181(1964).

(13) JAOAC **21**, 684(1938); **25**, 176(1942); **28**, 644 (1945); **33**, 848(1950).

(14) Biochem. Z. **51**, 253(1913); JAOAC **21**, 684, 688(1938).

(15) JAOAC **28**, 644(1945); **33**, 848(1950); **48**, 628 (1965).

(16) JAOAC **46**, 486(1963); **48**, 628(1965).

(17) JAOAC **37**, 568(1954); **39**, 91(1956).

(18) JAOAC **40**, 52, 892(1957).

(19) JAOAC **31**, 96, 507(1948).

(20) JAOAC **42**, 263(1959).

(21) JAOAC **45**, 206, 275(1962); **48**, 123(1965).

(22) JAOAC **50**, 205, 282(1967).

(23) JAOAC **52**, 703(1969); **53**, 7(1970).

19. Flavors[★]

VANILLA EXTRACT AND ITS SUBSTITUTES

19.001 Specific Gravity—Official Final Action

Det. sp gr at 20/20° with pycnometer as in **9.011**.

19.002 Alcohol—Official Final Action

Proceed as in **9.013** or **9.022**, but measure sample at 15.56° in pycnometer, Fig. 9:1, calibrated at that temp.

19.003 Glycerol—Official Final Action

Proceed as in **11.010** or **11.011**, selecting method according to quantity of sugar present. Use quantity of sample contg 0.1–0.4 g glycerol.

Propylene Glycol (*1*)—Official Final Action

19.004 *Apparatus*

All-glass distn app. with ⑀ 24/40 joints: 250 ml erlenmeyer, 20 ml Barrett H₂O trap with ⑀ stopcock, and West condenser with drip tip.

19.005 *Reagents*

(a) *Heptane.*—Eastman Kodak Co. practical grade, bp 96–100°, or equiv.

(b) *Potassium arsenite std soln.*—0.02N. (*Caution:* See **46.078** and **46.084**.) Dissolve 4.9460 g reagent As₂O₃, pulverized and dried to constant wt at 100°, in 75 ml 1N KOH. Add 40 g KHCO₃, dissolved in ca 200 ml H₂O, and dil. with H₂O to 1 L at 25°. Dil. 200 ml of this soln to 1 L with H₂O.

(c) *Potassium periodate std soln.*—0.02M. Dissolve 4.6 g KIO₄ in ca 500 ml hot H₂O. Dil. to ca 900 ml with H₂O, cool to room temp., and dil. to 1 L. Stdze frequently since this soln decomposes on standing.

(d) *Bromocresol purple indicator soln.*—Dissolve 0.1 g indicator in 100 ml alcohol and filter if necessary.

(e) *Propylene glycol.*—Reagent grade or com. product which meets following test: Dil. 0.5 ml to 25 ml with H₂O, add 25 ml 0.02M KIO₄ soln, and let stand 10 min. Titr. with 0.02N NaOH, using 3 drops bromocresol purple. Vol. NaOH soln consumed minus end point correction obtained by titrg 50 ml H₂O should be ≤0.1 ml.

19.006 *Isolation of Propylene Glycol*

Place sample contg ca 1 g propylene glycol in 250 ml ⑀ erlenmeyer; add enough H₂O, if necessary, to make total vol. 10 ml. Add 60 ml heptane, few glass beads, and/or SiC grains. Connect flask to receiver attached to condenser. Fill receiver with heptane, heat flask with variable heat hot plate, and reflux at such rate that rapid stream of distillate flows from tip. Reflux ca 8 hr and cool.

Open stopcock of receiver and transfer aq. layer to 250 ml (or other convenient size) vol. flask. Wash condenser, receiver, and solv. layer by pouring six 10 ml portions H₂O down condenser, collecting each portion in receiver, and draining it into vol. flask. Finally wash with enough H₂O (ca 25 ml) to completely fill receiver, causing solv. layer to return to distn flask. Dil. to vol. and mix well.

19.007 *Determination*

(a) *Glycerol absent.*—Place aliquot of aq. soln contg ≤45 mg propylene glycol in g-s flask, add 35 ml 0.02M KIO₄ soln, dil. to ca 100 ml with H₂O, and let stand 1 hr. Add ca 1.0 g NaHCO₃, 0.5 g KI, and 2.5 ml starch indicator, **2.129**(c). Titr. with 0.02N KAsO₂ soln to disappearance of blue. Stdze 25 ml 0.02M KIO₄ soln by same titrn, using H₂O for sample, and calc. amt of KIO₄ reduced by sample. 1 ml 0.02N KAsO₂ = 0.76 mg propylene glycol.

(b) *Glycerol present.*—Proceed as in (a). If I is not liberated on addn of NaHCO₃ and KI, insufficient KIO₄ was present. Repeat detn, using smaller aliquot or increasing vol. of KIO₄ soln.

To det. glycerol in the aq. soln, place same vol. aliquot used above in g-s flask, add 1 drop bromocresol purple, and add 0.02N NaOH until soln is light purple. Add same vol. KIO₄ soln used above, dil. to ca 100 ml, and let stand 1 hr. Add 10 drops propylene glycol (ca 0.5 ml), mix well, wash down sides of flask with H₂O, and let stand 10 min. Add 3 drops indicator and titr. with 0.02N NaOH to light purple end point. Titr. rapidly but do not shake flask violently in order to avoid excessive absorption of interfering CO₂ from air. Det. blank for this detn as above, using H₂O in place of sample and omitting 1 hr standing. Subtract blank from titrn obtained for sample aliquot. 1 ml 0.02N KAsO₂ = 0.46 mg glycerol; 1 ml 0.02N NaOH = 1.84 mg glycerol.

mg Propylene glycol in aliquot = [ml 0.02N KAsO₂ − (4 × ml 0.02N NaOH)] × 0.76

★ Methods so marked are surplus methods. *See* "Definitions of Terms and Explanatory Notes," item (29).

Vanillin

19.008   *Ultraviolet Screening Method (2)—*
Official Final Action

(Caution: See 46.016.)

(In absence of coumarin and Et vanillin)

Pipet 5 ml sample (for imitations and concentrates, use 2 ml) into 100 ml vol. flask, dil. to vol. with H_2O, and mix well. Pipet 2 ml of this soln into second 100 ml vol. flask, add 2 ml 0.1N NaOH, and dil. to vol. with H_2O. Pour ca 20 ml of this soln into small beaker and place under UV lamp in dark room. If coumarin is present to extent of 0.01% in original ext, brilliant green fluorescence will develop in 5 min.

If no coumarin is observed, read A of remaining alk. soln at 270, 348, and 380 nm. Obtain background $A = 0.29 \times A_{270} + 0.71 \times A_{380}$. Subtract this value from A_{348} and divide by A of 1 ppm vanillin (ca 0.150), detd from std soln of 3 ppm vanillin contg 2 ml 0.1N NaOH in 100 ml, and multiply by diln (1000) to give ppm vanillin in original sample. Make all readings within 2 hr of final diln.

If background A is too high (>0.15), clarify with isopropanol as follows:

Pipet 5 ml sample into 50 ml vol. flask and dil. to vol. with isopropanol. Transfer to centrf. bottle and centrf. ca 10 min at high speed. Without disturbing sepd solids, carefully pipet 1 ml liq. into 100 ml vol. flask, add 2 ml 0.1N NaOH, dil. to vol. with H_2O, and proceed as above.

Prep. std vanillin soln by dissolving 0.1000 g vanillin in 3 ml alcohol in 100 ml vol. flask, and dil. to vol. with H_2O (1 ml = 1 mg). Pipet 3 ml into 1 L vol. flask, add 2 ml 0.1N NaOH, and dil. to vol. with H_2O. Det. A at 270, 348, and 380 nm against H_2O contg 2 ml 0.1N NaOH dild to 100 ml with H_2O. Calc. corrected A as $A_{348} - (0.29A_{270} + 0.71A_{380})$, where A_{348}, A_{270}, and A_{380} are observed A at these wavelengths. Divide this value by 3 to obtain corrected A of 1 ppm vanillin.

Ultraviolet Spectrophotometric Method (3)—
Official Final Action

19.009   *Preparation of Standard Curve*

Dissolve 0.100 g vanillin in 5 ml alcohol and dil. to 100 ml with H_2O. Transfer 15, 10, and 5 ml, resp., to 250 ml vol. flasks, dil. to vol. with H_2O, and mix (*Solns A*). Pipet 10 ml of each *Soln A* into 100 ml vol. flask, dil. to vol. with H_2O, and mix. Pipet another set of 10 ml *Solns A* into 100 ml vol. flasks, add ca 80 ml H_2O and 2 ml 0.1N NaOH, mix, dil. to vol. with H_2O, and mix again. Obtain A of alk. solns at 348 nm, using neut. solns as ref. blanks. Plot std curve.

19.010   *Determination*

If sample contains >0.3 g vanillin/100 ml, dil. with 35% alcohol to below this level. Pipet 10 ml sample (or dild sample) into 100 ml vol. flask, dil. to vol. with H_2O, and mix. Pipet 2 ml dild soln into

each of two 100 ml vol. flasks. Dil. one with H_2O and mix. To other flask add 80 ml H_2O and 2 ml 0.1N NaOH, mix, dil. to vol. with H_2O, and mix again. Det. A of alk. soln at 348 nm, using neut. soln as ref. blank. Obtain vanillin content from std curve.

Vanillin and Ethyl Vanillin (4)—
Official Final Action

19.011   *Reagents and Apparatus*

(**a**) *Mobile solvent.*—Cyclohexane (practical)-EtOAc-MeOH, 100 + 30 + 20.

(**b**) *Immobile solvent.*—10% dimethylformamide in ether.

(**c**) *Sodium carbonate soln.*—Dissolve 4 g Na_2CO_3 in H_2O and dil. to 1 L.

(**d**) *Chromatographic paper.*—Whatman No. 3 MM, 8 × 8″.

(**e**) *Chromatographic tank.*—Mitchell tank and equipment, 29.007(a).

(**f**) *Spotting pipet.*—10 μl.

(**g**) *Long wave ultraviolet light.*—(*Caution: See* **46.016.**)

19.012   *Preparation of Standard Curve*

Prep. solns of vanillin and Et vanillin in 35% alcohol, contg 0.10, 0.15, 0.20, 0.30, and 0.40 g/100 ml. Draw parallel lines on chromatgc paper 1″ and 1½″ above bottom edge, using hard pencil. Apply one 10 μl spot of each soln on the 1″ line, keeping spots 1″ apart and starting 2″ from left side of paper. Use sep. papers for vanillin and Et vanillin curves. Use same micropipet for all spottings, rinsing thoroly before each application. Let spots air-dry, without heat. Handle paper carefully near edges to avoid high blanks.

Meanwhile place 100 ml H_2O in bottom of chromatgc tank contg one trough. Fill trough with mobile solv., cover tank, and seal. Let stand 15 min. Dip paper into immobile solv. from top down to 1½″ line, leaving bottom 1½″ of paper free from immobile solv. Do not permit solv. to reach spots. (Dipping can readily be done by use of shallow pan contg solv.) Air-dry paper few min, remove seal from tank, and place paper in tank with bottom edge dipping into mobile solv. Reseal tank and develop 2 hr, even tho solv. front reaches top before end of this period. Remove paper and air-dry. Do not expose developed paper to air >1 hr. If delay is necessary, place paper in jar and store in refrigerator.

Expose paper to NH_3 fumes for few min by placing paper in wide-mouth half-gal. jar contg small beaker with NH_3 on bottom, and capping jar. Examine paper under long wave UV light and outline dark blue areas with soft pencil. Et vanillin will show higher R_f value than vanillin. Remove marked areas with scissors and cut each into smaller pieces before placing them in 50 ml erlenmeyers. Cut out 2 blanks from side of paper, each approx. equal in area to developed spots. Use side area for these blanks, away from spotted areas and their developed rise.

Pipet 10 ml Na_2CO_3 soln into each flask, swirl, and let stand 10–15 min, with frequent swirling. Centrf. or filter thru rapid paper, discarding first portion of filtrate. Det. A at 348 nm, using Na_2CO_3 soln as ref. Also obtain av. A of the 2 blanks and correct std A before plotting std curve.

19.013   *Determination*

If sample contains >0.4 g vanillin/100 ml, dil. below this level with 35% alcohol. Make one 10 μl spotting on the 1″ line with same micropipet used to prep. std curves. Proceed as above and det. vanillin and Et vanillin by comparison with appropriate std curves.

Coumarin—Official Final Action

19.014   ★   *Photometric Method (5)*   ★

See **19.009–19.011**, 10th ed. (*Caution: See* **46.068.**)

Vanillin, Ethyl Vanillin, and Coumarin (6)— Official Final Action

Chromatographic Separation Method
19.015   *Apparatus*

(a) *Spectrophotometer.*—Capable of detg A at 270 and 325 nm. Adjust to high sensitivity to utilize slit width <10 nm.

(b) *Silica cells.*—1 cm. Match cells at 270 and 325 nm, using isooctane-$CHCl_3$ solv., **19.016**(c). (This solv. dets differences that other media do not.) Cells must be free of other solvs before adding isooctane-$CHCl_3$ solv., std, and sample solns. Drain each cell well between readings by inverting on towel. Fill cells for reading so that meniscus is >3 mm above light path.

(c) *Chromatographic tube.*—Melt glass tube 11–12.5 mm id ca 18″ from one end, draw out short distance, cool, and break at constriction. Partially close constricted end in flame, and dry.

19.016   *Reagents*

(Same batch of isooctane must be used to prep. solv. mixt. and all dilns for set of detns.)

(a) *Silicic acid.*—Reagent grade "100-mesh" powder, suitable for chromatgy (Mallinckrodt Chemical Works No. 2847, or equiv.). Det. SiO_2 content as follows: Accurately weigh ca 1 g silicic acid into weighed Pt crucible. Ignite in muffle 15 min at 615°, cool in desiccator, and reweigh. Calc. % SiO_2 (z) in silicic acid. Calc. quantity of silicic acid (x) required for 5.8 g column from equation: $x = 3.384 \times 100/z$. Quantity of H_2O (y) required for column is $5.80 - x$.

(b) *Isooctane.*—Practical grade 2,2,4-trimethylpentane, 99.5+ %, bp 98–100°.

(c) *Isooctane-chloroform solvent mixture.*—Add 40 ml $CHCl_3$ to 1 L isooctane and mix. Store in air-tight bottle. (Do not use rubber stopper.) Soln contains ca 3.85% $CHCl_3$.

(d) *Coumarin std soln.*—1 mg/ml. Accurately weigh 100 mg coumarin into 100 ml vol. flask, dissolve in 50 ml $CHCl_3$, and dil. to vol. with isooctane.

(e) *Ethyl vanillin std soln.*—Prep. as in (d), using Et vanillin.

(f) *Vanillin std soln.*—Prep. as in (d), using vanillin.

19.017   *Determination of Absorptivities*

Pipet 1 ml vanillin std soln into 100 ml vol. flask, add 3.4 ml $CHCl_3$, dil. to vol. with isooctane, and mix. Det. A at 270 and 325 nm against solv., (c), as ref. in the 1 cm silica cells. Calc. a (g/L; 1 cm) for vanillin at 270 and at 325 nm from equation: $a = 100A$.

Det. a for Et vanillin and vanillin similarly.

19.018   *Preparation of Chromatographic Column*

Pack small cotton wad in bottom of *dry* chromatgc tube. To x g silicic acid in mortar add from buret y ml H_2O, mix thoroly and quickly to uniform powdery consistency with pestle, and immediately add 25 ml solv., (c). Mix and rapidly pour slurry thru funnel into tube. Rinse mortar and funnel with small vol. solv. Remove any air bubbles formed by stirring with long thin glass rod. Pack column with ca 2 lb/sq in. air pressure until bottom of meniscus of free solv. just touches top surface of silicic acid but outer part of meniscus is still clearly visible. *Immediately release pressure.* (*Important:* If column channels or cracks, discard. During packing and thereafter, keep column vertical. Tipping ruins column for further use altho it may appear normal.) Carefully add 15 ml solv. down side of tube with aid of glass rod so column is not disturbed. Drive solv. thru column. Washed column is now ready for calibration.

19.019   *Calibration of Column*

Pipet and combine 1 ml of each std soln, (d), (e), and (f), in 25 ml vol. flask. Dil. to vol. with isooctane and mix. Pipet 2 ml soln down one side of chromatgc tube onto top of column. Drive soln into column with ca 2 lb air pressure and collect eluate in 10 ml graduated cylinder. Release pressure when bottom of meniscus touches top of column and outer part of meniscus is still clearly visible. Pipet 1 ml solv., (c), down same side of tube onto column and drive into column. Repeat with 2 addnl 1 ml portions solv. Fill tube to within 1″ of top with solv. Drive solv. thru column at rate of 5 ml/2–2.5 min, collecting 5 ml eluate fractions, alternating two 10 ml graduated cylinders during collection. Pour fractions into sep. test tubes in rack, numbering fractions consecutively. Drain cylinder before reusing by inverting on towel. Collect 10 fractions and det. A at 270 and 325 nm against solv., (c), as ref. in 1 cm silica cells. Drain cells by inverting on towel before refilling; rinsing is not necessary. Permit column to elute by gravity while reading first 10 fractions, changing cylinders for each 5 ml portion.

Coumarin elutes first, Et vanillin second, and vanillin third. In ideal column coumarin begins to elute in fraction 6–7, reaches max. in 8–9, and fades considerably in 10. Earlier elution does not sep. compds entirely; later elution takes more fractions and time but does give good recoveries. Somewhat slower elution does not matter. Et vanillin elutes in ca fraction 11–18, and vanillin in ca 19–30.

If column is satisfactory, collect 25 addnl fractions (35 in all) or until vanillin is completely eluted. Det. A of each fraction at 270 and 325 nm as above.

If coumarin begins to elute at fraction 5 or earlier, discard, prep. another column with less H_2O in the silicic acid, and recalibrate. If coumarin does not elute by fraction 9–10, prep. new column with more H_2O in the silicic acid.

Use calibrated column for identification, **19.022**.

19.020   *Preparation of Sample Solution*

If concn of none of the compds is >0.4 g/100 ml, pipet 25 ml sample into 250 ml centrf. bottle. If concn of any compd is >0.4 g/100 ml, dil. 25 ml sample with H_2O to vol. specified in table, **19.021**, and use 25 ml aliquot. Add 75 ml H_2O, 20 ml H_2SO_4 (1 + 4), and 50 ml $CHCl_3$. Stopper with rubber stopper and shake well 3 min. Centrf. 5 min at 1500 rpm. If emulsion persists, break with thin glass rod and recentrf. Pour contents slowly thru large-bore, short-stem funnel into 250 ml separator. Break emulsion with glass rod and drain $CHCl_3$ into 100 ml vol. flask. Pour aq. phase thru same funnel back into bottle.

Rinse separator with 15 ml $CHCl_3$, add to bottle thru funnel, and repeat extn by mixing phases thoroly with rocking motion. Do not shake vigorously as in first extn. Centrf., sep., and drain $CHCl_3$ into 100 ml vol. flask. Repeat extn with 15 ml portions $CHCl_3$ until flask is filled to mark. Pipet 2 ml

19.021   *Dilutions and Dilution Factors for Flavorings*

Concn of Most Abundant Constituent, g/100 ml	Dil. to: (ml)	Diln Factor (F)
<0.4	none	12.5
0.4–0.8	50	25.0
0.8–1.6	100	50.0
1.6–3.2	200	100
>3.2	200	200

aliquot into 25 ml vol. flask, dil. to vol. with isooctane, and mix.

19.022   *Identification*

Pipet 2 ml sample soln (use 1 ml if concn of most abundant compd is >3.2 g/100 ml) onto prepd column, letting it flow down one side of tube without disturbing column. Drive soln into column with ca 2 lb air pressure and collect eluate in 10 ml graduated cylinder. Pipet 1 ml solv., (c), down same side of tube and drive into column. Repeat with 2 addnl 1 ml portions of solv. Fill tube with solv. and elute compds by same technic and conditions as for calibration. Collect 3 more fractions than indicated necessary by calibration. Det A of all fractions at 270 and 325 nm as in calibration.

Positions of absorbing fractions compared to those obtained during column calibration reveal compds present in sample. Coumarin is also identified by absorbing at 325 nm slightly >⅓ its A at 270 nm. Vanillin and Et vanillin absorb very little at 325 nm. If desired, confirm by obtaining UV spectrum of one high absorbing fraction of each compd. Compare with spectra prepd on same instrument. Spectra of compds exhibit approx. max. and min. given in Table 19:1. Approx. ratio of A at given wavelength to that at highest max. for respective compd is given in parentheses after that wavelength. Ratio of 1.00 indicates highest max.

19.023   *Determination*

Add A at 270 nm of all fractions contg coumarin and calc. coumarin concn in original sample from equation:

$$c = F \times \Sigma A/a,$$

where ΣA is sum of A at 270 nm of fractions contg coumarin, a is absorptivity of coumarin at 270 nm, c is concn coumarin in g/100 ml original sample, and F is diln factor, given in **19.021**.

Calc. concns of Et vanillin and vanillin similarly.

If neg. A are obtained on fractions not contg the compds, correct A of fractions contg compds by adding to each A the av. of the neg. readings.

Lead Number (Wichmann) (7)— Official Final Action

19.024   *Principle*

Org. acids from vanilla are pptd with neut. $Pb(OAc)_2$ under std conditions, insol. Pb salts are removed, and excess Pb is detd by chelometric titrn with Na_2EDTA. From this titrn and blank titrn, Wichmann lead number is calcd. Applicable to single-fold exts.

Table 19:1—Spectrophotometric characteristics of coumarin, ethyl vanillin, and vanillin

Compound	Maxima, nm			Minima, nm		
Coumarin	271 (1.00)	282 (0.82)	313 (0.46)	243 (0.30)	278.5 (0.81)	291.5 (0.31)
Et vanillin	270 (1.00)	297 (0.59)	—	242.5 (0.24)	286 (0.46)	—
Vanillin	269.5 (1.00)	296 (0.60)	—	242.5 (0.24)	286 (0.48)	—

19.025   *Reagents*

(a) *Disodium ethylenediamine tetraacetate* (Na_2EDTA) *std soln.*—0.025N. Dissolve 9.3061 g $Na_2EDTA.2H_2O$ in 1 L boiled, cooled CO_2-free H_2O.

(b) *Buffer soln.*—Mix 2 vols 0.1N NaOAc with 1 vol. 0.1N HOAc.

(c) *Xylenol orange soln.*—Dissolve 0.1 g xylenol orange in 100 ml 35% alcohol.

(d) *Lead acetate soln.*—Dissolve 8 g neut. $Pb(OAc)_2$ in 100 ml boiled H_2O, let stand 24 hr, and use clear supernatant.

(e) *Phenolphthalein soln.*—Dissolve 0.1 g phthln in 100 ml alcohol.

19.026   *Preparation of Sample Solution*

Place 175 ml boiled H_2O in 1 L r-b distn flask. From pipet add 25 ml clear $Pb(OAc)_2$ soln and 50 ml single-fold ext. Swirl to mix thoroly and ppt Pb salt. Support distg flask on asbestos or transite board, placing flask over 10 cm diam. hole cut in board to permit distn without overheating upper portion of flask. Fit flask with distn head and condenser, apply moderate heat, and distill 200 ml into vol. flask, reserving distillate for detn of alcohol. When vol. in distn flask is reduced to ca 50 ml, level of liq. should be ca even with board. Quant. transfer residue to 100 ml vol. flask with small vols CO_2-free H_2O, using bent glass rod with rubber tip to loosen residue. Cool, and dil. to vol. with CO_2-free H_2O. Mix thoroly and filter thru dry paper. Filtrate (*Soln A*) contains excess Pb after forming Pb salt complex.

Prep. blank, using 5 drops HOAc in place of sample and distill 150 ml. Cool, dil. to 100 ml with boiled H_2O, and filter.

19.027   *Determination of Lead*

(a) *As sulfate.*—Pipet 10 ml *Soln A* into 250 ml beaker and add 25 ml H_2O, 2 ml H_2SO_4 (1 + 1), and 100 ml alcohol; stir and let settle overnight. Filter on gooch, wash with alcohol, ignite at 525–550°, cool in desiccator, and weigh. (Wt $PbSO_4$ obtained from blank − wt obtained from sample) × 13.66 = Pb number.

(b) *As chromate.*—Pipet 10 ml *Soln A* into 400 ml beaker and add 2 ml HOAc, 25 ml H_2O, and 25 ml ca 0.1N $K_2Cr_2O_7$. Immediately heat beaker and contents with moderate flame until ppt changes from yellow to orange. Filter on gooch, and wash thoroly with hot H_2O, then with few ml each of alcohol and ether. Dry at 100°, cool in desiccator, and weigh. (Wt $PbCrO_4$ obtained from blank − wt obtained from sample) × 12.82 = Pb number.

(c) *By chelometric titration.*—Pipet 10 ml *Soln A* into 125 ml erlenmeyer. Add 1 drop phthln and make just alk. with 1.0N NaOH, forming $Pb(OH)_2$ ppt. Add 10 ml buffer soln and 1 ml xylenol orange indicator. Titr. with 0.025N Na_2EDTA soln to end point, indicated by abrupt change from reddish pink to yellow or orange. Ten ml micro buret is convenient for titrn, and fluorescent lamp should be arranged so indirect light illuminates flask.

Perform titrn on blank soln in same manner.

Lead number = 20 × (ml Na_2EDTA blank − ml Na_2EDTA sample) × 0.025 × (207.2/1000) = (ml Na_2EDTA blank − ml Na_2EDTA sample) × 0.1036.

19.028   Total Solids (*8*)—Official Final Action

Proceed as in **31.007** or **31.008,** using 10 ml sample.

19.029   Ash—Official Final Action

Evap. 10 ml ext and proceed as in **31.012** or **31.013.**

19.030   Sucrose (*9*)—Official Final Action— *See* **31.025, 31.026,** or **31.032**

Vanilla Resins

19.031   *Quantitative Method (10)— Official Final Action*

Pipet 50 ml sample into 150 or 250 ml beaker and dil. to total vol. of 100 ml with H_2O. Boil rapidly on hot plate or over flame to vol. of ca 50 ml. Cool, and add NH_4OH (1 + 3) dropwise until slightly alk. Add 3 drops excess and stir vigorously 2 min to ensure soln of resins. Add HCl (1 + 1) dropwise, with stirring, until acid to indicator paper and then 2 ml excess. Stir, and let stand at room temp. ≥1 hr but ≤24 hr. Add 0.5 g filter aid (Celite, Hyflo Super-Cel) and filter with suction thru long stem, medium porosity fritted glass buchner funnel (30 ml capacity) contg pad prepd by pouring aq. suspension of 1 g filter aid thru funnel and washing with H_2O. If filtration slows, scratch surface of pad gently to break resin film. Quant. transfer resins to funnel with aid of policeman, using six 20 ml portions 0.05N HCl to wash beaker and funnel. Let each portion of wash soln drain before adding next portion. Dry material as much as possible by suction, transfer funnel to dry suction flask, and dissolve resins from filter with boiling alcohol added in small portions, using some of alcohol to rinse beaker. Suck each portion thru funnel before adding next portion. Mix filter aid in funnel with the hot alcohol, using small glass rod. Repeat extns until alcohol soln is colorless. Rinse tip of funnel stem with hot alcohol and quant. transfer soln to weighed beaker or Pt dish. Evap. to dryness on steam bath and dry 1 hr at 100°. Cool in desiccator and weigh. Report results to 2 decimal places only. Reserve resins for qual. tests.

19.032   *Paper Chromatographic Qualitative Test (11)—Official First Action*

Sep. and dissolve resins in warm alcohol as in **19.031,** collecting alc. ext in 50 ml vol. flask. Cool, and dil. to vol. with alcohol. Evap. 40 ml aliquot to dryness on steam bath and dry to constant wt at 100° to obtain mg resins/ml alc. ext. (Alternatively, use *value* obtained from **19.031.** Do not use dried resins obtained from **19.031** for this detn.) Evap. 5 ml aliquot of alc. ext nearly to dryness on steam bath and complete drying with aid of gentle heat such as warm air current from hair dryer. Dissolve residue in calcd vol. of $0.1N$ NaOH in 50% alcohol to give soln of 5 mg resins/ml.

Spot 6 μl alk. soln (using two 3 μl spottings with intervening drying) on $8 \times 8''$ paper as in **19.038**(a). Develop as in **19.039**, using solv. systems **19.036**(a) or (b). On same paper spot alk. soln of alc. ext of resins from authentic vanilla ext, **19.037**, at same concn, 5 mg/ml. Compare developed patterns under longwave UV light.

19.033   Methanol—Official Final Action

Proceed as in **9.074** or **9.075**, using distillate from alcohol detn, **19.002**.

19.034   Color Insoluble in Amyl Alcohol (12)— Official First Action

Evap. 25 ml sample just to dryness on steam bath. Dissolve residue in H_2O and alcohol, and dil. to vol. of 50 ml, using total vol. of 26.3 ml alcohol. Place 25 ml of this soln in separator and add 25 ml freshly shaken Marsh reagent, **9.077**, shaking lightly so as not to form emulsion. Let layers sep. completely, drain aq. lower layer (which contains any caramel present) into 25 ml cylinder, and dil. to vol. with alcohol (50% by vol.). Compare this soln in colorimeter with 25 ml untreated sample. From this reading, calc. % color insol. in amyl alcohol.

Foreign Plant Material
Paper Chromatographic Method (13)— Official Final Action

19.035   *Apparatus*

(a) *Chromatographic chamber for small papers.—* See **29.007**(a).

(b) *Chromatographic chamber for large papers.—* Use box suitable for this size paper chromatgy. A satisfactory box is approx. $29.5 \times 21.5 \times 23.75''$ covered with Formica or other material resistant to org. solvs, acid, alkali, etc. Lid of box is hinged and plastic gasket is used to obtain tight seal to prevent escape of vapors. Front of box contains window $11 \times 17''$ to observe progress of solv. front. Semicircular glass troughs ca $26.5 \times 2''$ are supported by stainless steel clamps on metal strips ca $2''$ wide placed $2.5''$ from top and extending from front to back along sides. Clamps also support glass rods on both sides of trough and parallel to it.

(c) *Chromatographic papers.—*Whatman No. 1, $8 \times 8''$; Whatman No. 1, $22 \times 18''$; Whatman No. 3 MM, $8 \times 8''$.

(d) *Ultraviolet light.—*Long wavelength. Two 15 watt Black Light tubes, $18''$ long, preferably enclosed in glass filters (such as No. 5873 tubular glass filters, George W. Gates & Co., PO Box 216, Franklin Sq., LI, NY 11010). (*Caution: See* **46.016**.)

19.036   *Solvent Systems*

(a) Dissolve 20 g KOH and 50 g KBr in H_2O, add 200 ml alcohol, and dil. to 1 L with H_2O.

(b) Dissolve 20 g $KHCO_3$ and 50 g KBr in H_2O, add 200 ml alcohol, and dil. to 1 L with H_2O.

(c) Shake 20 parts isobutanol, 0.8 part HOAc, and 15 parts H_2O in separator, let sep., and drain and discard lower layer. Use upper layer.

(d) Mix 8 parts isopropanol, 5 parts NH_4OH, and 15 parts H_2O.

(e) Mix 30 parts HOAc, 3 parts HCl, and 10 parts H_2O.

(f) Dissolve 20 g $KHCO_3$ in H_2O, add 200 ml alcohol, and dil. to 1 L with H_2O.

(g) Mix 75 parts isopropanol with 25 parts H_2O.

19.037   *Preparation of Authentic Vanilla Extract*

Prep. single-fold authentic vanilla ext with and without added sugar by either NF or Flavoring Extract Manufacturers Association (FEMA) method. Prep. concs by evapg single-fold ext under vac. in rotating evaporator and dilg with 50% alcohol to appropriate vol.

(a) *NF method.—*Cut 100 g vanilla beans in small pieces, add 200 ml H_2O, and macerate 12 hr in covered container, preferably in warm place. Add 200 ml alcohol, mix well, and macerate ca 3 days. Transfer mixt. to percolator contg 200 g coarse granular sucrose (omit sucrose for prepn without sucrose) and drain. Pack solids firmly and percolate slowly with alcohol $(1 + 1)$ to obtain total vol. of 1 L.

(b) *FEMA method* (Proc. 40th Flavoring Extract Manufacturers Association Convention 1949, pp. 49–67 (as revised)).—(Boil all rubber stoppers in 5% NaOH soln and use Tygon tubing for connections.) Prep. laboratory continuous percolator as follows:

Fit 2-hole rubber stopper into neck of custommade Pyrex gas washing bottle made from No. 2962 cylinder, $4.5''$ od $\times 12''$ long, plain neck opening ca $3''$ diam., with coarse porosity fritted glass disk sealed in as close to bottom as possible but above side arm, 9 mm od, extending out from side wall between disk and base (available from Corning Glass Works or H. S. Martin Co., 1916 Greenleaf St, Evanston, IL 60204). Thru one hole place 0–220°F thermometer with bulb at ca center of bottle; thru other hole insert short piece of glass tubing so that end is $1''$ above level of chopped vanilla beans. Attach piece of 100 mesh stainless steel wire cloth tied with cord to end of tubing in bottle as strainer and attach other end to Fischer & Porter Co. Flowrator Meter, Model 10A 1017A (tube $\frac{1}{4}''$ to meter liq., sp gr 0.96, 700 ml/min max., direct reading scale, stainless steel float). Attach upper end of flowmeter with right-angle bend tube to side arm of T-tube with upper end connected with Tygon tubing to glass tube in 1-gal. jar fitted with 2-hole rubber stopper. Other hole of stopper holds glass tube fitted with Bunsen valve (rubber tube, closed at one end, with short longitudinal slit) as safety valve. Place gal. jar above rest of equipment (serves as overflow reservoir when percolator runs overnight).

Attach lower end of T-tube thru Y-tube and 1-hole rubber stoppers to 2 Pyrex buchners (connected in parallel) with coarse porosity fritted disks (80 mm diam., Corning No. 36060-C). Place circles of Whatman 41H paper on disks, and cover with ⅛″ clean sand. Place stems of funnels thru rubber stoppers inserted in filter tubes (Corning No. 9480, 32 × 160 mm). Tubes are connected in parallel with Tygon tubing to Y-tube connected to menstruum reservoir (Corning No. 1220, 2 L aspirator bottle) with 45° bend glass tube thru 2-hole rubber stopper. Thru second hole, fit stem of thermoregulator (No. 17502-0, Ni plated, Fenwal, Inc., Ashland, MA 01701) which controls 200 watt mantle fitted to reservoir. Connect mantle to thermoregulator thru relay. Connect outlet of bottle to inlet of stainless steel pump with nipple connections (Model B 1, 1/20 h.p., Eastern Industries, 100 Skiff St, Hamden, CT 06514, or Model 07FGEP-M, Tuthill Metering Pump, 1/15 h.p., ⅜″ RT fittings, Tuthill Pump Co., 12500 S. Crawford Ave, Chicago, IL 60658). Control flow rate by pinch clamp on tubing from discharge side of pump to bean reservoir, to give flow rate of 575 ml/min. Set thermoregulator so thermometer reads 120°F.

Cut vanilla beans to ⅛″ pieces with razor blade, or preferably shred in Model D Fitzpatrick Comminuter, or equiv., using No. 4 screen (Wm. J. Fitzpatrick, 832 Industrial Drive, Elmhurst, IL 60127). Charge extractor with 10 oz, dry wt, cut beans (calcd from moisture detn) and place several 3″, 90° bends of glass rod on surface to keep beans submerged. Charge reservoir with dild alcohol (1136 g alcohol plus 1090 g H_2O). Percolate at least 16 hr and remove 25 ml sample for alcohol detn, 19.002. Calc. g H_2O to add to give 47.5% alcohol (= 2790 − 132414/% alcohol), add this quantity to reservoir, and continue percolation at least addnl 24 hr.

Drain ext from both reservoirs and remove 25 ml sample for alcohol detn. Det. vol. remaining ext, and calc. vol. H_2O needed to adjust to 35% alcohol. If desired, add sugar equiv. to 10%, det. final vol., and dil. to 35% alcohol with H_2O.

19.038 Preparation of Papers

(a) *For 8 × 8″ papers, single dimension development.*—Use Whatman No. 1 for ext with little or no sugar, and No. 3MM for ext with considerable sugar. Apply no more than 7 samples, including authentics, to single paper. Spot samples equal distance apart. For single strength exts apply four 3 μl spots at same point, drying between applications with hair dryer, IR lamp, or other source of mild heat. Do not apply next spot until previous one is

dry. For concd exts, dil. to 4-fold concn with 50% alcohol and apply one 3 μl spot.

For products contg large amts of sugar, ext 1 ml with 1 ml $CHCl_3$, centrf., and spot $CHCl_3$ ext as above. Compare with authentic ext treated similarly. (JAOAC **44**, 552(1961).)

(b) *For 22 × 18″ papers, single dimension development.*—For single strength exts, apply four 10 μl spots at same point with intervening drying as in (a). For concd exts, dil. to 4-fold concn with 50% alcohol and apply one 10 μl spot.

(c) *For 8 × 8″ papers, two dimension development.*—Use Whatman No. 3MM paper. Apply four 3 μl spots of single strength vanilla ext sample at lower right side of 8 × 8″ paper and eight 3 μl spots at lower left side, locating each spot ca 1″ from outer edges of paper. Apply each set of spots at same point, drying between applications with warm air dryer or other source of mild heat. Do not apply next spot until previous one is dry.

19.039 Development

(a) *Single dimension.*—Use ascending technic with small papers and descending technic with large papers. Use solvs (a), (b), (c), (d), or (e), listed in approx. order of usefulness. Develop small papers 2–3 hr and large papers 12–16 hr until solv. approaches end of paper. Remove papers from tank and let air-dry. Examine under transmitted UV light and compare fluorescent pattern of spots from samples with those from authentic material.

It is sometimes useful to return dry paper to original solv. and repeat development. Second development may cause greater sepn of some fluorescent constituents.

(b) *Two dimension.*—Transfer papers, prepd as in **19.038**(c), to tank, and develop first dimension with solv. (f) and ascending technic. Remove paper when solv. front reaches upper edge, and air-dry. Turn paper 90° so that 24 μl spot is at bottom; then develop second dimension in solv. (g). Remove paper before front reaches developed 12 μl spot, and air-dry. Examine paper under long UV light, and compare chromatogram with one made from authentic vanilla ext. Foreign plant material is indicated by spots not found in authentic ext.

Flavoring Additives
Thin Layer Chromatographic Method (14)—
Official Final Action

19.040 Apparatus

(a) *Applicator.*—For depositing thin layer on glass plates. (Brinkmann Instrument, Inc.; Kensington Scientific Co., Oakland, CA 94608.)

(b) *Glass plates.*—8 × 8″ or 2 × 8″; of uniform thickness.

(c) *Plastic board.*—22 × 113 cm, with retaining edges 1.8 cm wide along short and long sides.

(d) *Developing jars or tanks.*—Use equipment,

29.007(a), for 8 × 8″ glass plates and glass cylinders for small plates. Cylinders can be covered with plastic caps.

19.041   *Reagents*

(a) *Solvents.* — Hexane (99%)-EtOAc (4 + 1); benzene-MeOH (97 + 3).

(b) *Chromogenic agents.*—(1) 90 ml 0.1N KMnO₄ and 10 ml 0.1N NaOH. (2) Sat. 1N HCl with N₂H₄.H₂SO₄. (3) 5% KOH in MeOH. (4) 10% phosphomolybdic acid in alcohol.

(c) *Silica Gel G.*—Fine grade silica gel with added plaster of Paris. Check ability to make satisfactory sepns by testing activated plates with known mixts of additives.

19.042   *Test*

Place glass plates on plastic board held on laboratory bench so that long edge faces worker and short retaining ledge is on right. Mix 30 g Silica Gel G in beaker with 60 ml H₂O, stirring thoroly ca 1 min. Slurry must be uniform and free from air bubbles. Pour into applicator, which is on glass plate at left side of board. Make film 0.250 mm thick by slowly moving applicator across row of plates. Total time from addn of H₂O to silica gel until end of spreading operation must be ca 4 min. Air-dry plates 10–20 min and then dry 2 hr at 110° to activate layers. Cool, wipe backs and edges of plates free from excess silica gel, and store plates in storage cabinet. Protect from laboratory fumes.

Scratch line across a plate 17 cm from bottom edge and apply 10 μl spot of single-fold sample 2 cm from bottom edge. Spots should be ca 0.5 cm in diam. (It may be necessary to apply small portion at time, drying between applications.) Different samples can be spotted 2 cm apart. Apply ref. stds similarly. Place plate in jar or tank so that bottom edge dips 1 cm into solv. and lean top of plate against side of jar or tank, so that plate has slight angle. Cover tank or jar and let development proceed to 17 cm scratch line. Remove from solv. and air-dry.

All additives, if present in sufficient quantity, can be detected by KMnO₄ spray. Tan spots appear on pink background, which soon turns brown. Second spraying helps bring out spots. Small amts of coumarin may not show up for several min, so that it is necessary to examine plate ca 10 min after spraying.

Yellow spots are shown by *p*-hydroxybenzaldehyde, vanillin, Et vanillin, veratraldehyde, and piperonal when plates are sprayed with N₂H₄.H₂SO₄ soln. Let air-dry and examine under reflected UV light (long wave). *p*-Hydroxybenzaldehyde usually shows up as lemon-yellow spot, vanillin and Et vanillin appear orange to brown, veratraldehyde is bright orange, and piperonal is bluish-yellow. Shades depend on amts of additive present and amt of spray, and may vary somewhat.

To detect coumarin, spray with alc. KOH, and let air-dry. Examine under reflected UV light; coumarin appears as bright blue-white spot.

Vanitrope can be detected by spraying with phosphomolybdic acid soln. Blue spot develops after plate is dried at 100° few min.

Approx. R_f values, with vanillin = 1, are: Hexane-EtOAc solv.: Et vanillin, 1.6; veratraldehyde, 1.7; coumarin, 2.3; piperonal, 3.0; and vanitrope, 4.0. Benzene-MeOH solv.: *p*-hydroxybenzaldehyde, 0.4; Et vanillin, 1.4; coumarin, 1.7; veratraldehyde, 1.9; piperonal, 2.4; and vanitrope, 2.4.

p-Hydroxybenzaldehyde is difficult to detect with hexane-EtOAc solv. since vanillin spot is near origin. With this solv., Et vanillin and veratraldehyde cannot usually be sepd. *p*-Hydroxybenzaldehyde can be detected with benzene-MeOH solv., and Et vanillin and veratraldehyde show good sepn, but piperonal and vanitrope appear at same R_f value. These can be distinguished by phosphomolybdic acid and N₂H₄.H₂SO₄ tests on sep. plates.

Paper Chromatographic Sorting Method (15)

19.043   *Apparatus*

(a) *Chromatographic tank.*—For ascending chromatgy with 12 × 12″ sheets; cylindrical glass jar with ground top and glass plate cover, or rectangular jar with tight lid. Use smallest jar that will hold paper. (Neoprene gasket may be used to ensure tight fit.)

(b) *Chromatographic paper.*—Whatman No. 1, 12 × 12″.

19.044   *Reagents*

(*Caution: See* **46.040** *and* **46.042**.)

(a) *Developing soln.*—Ether + HCOOH + H₂O (20 + 4 + 3). If necessary, add HCOOH in small amts until soln is clear.

(b) *Chromogenic agents.*—(1) *Aniline-furfural.*—Dissolve 0.3 ml aniline and 0.3 ml furfural in 100 ml acetone. Use as dip. Hang paper in air until spots are fully developed (red spots on pink background). For spray use, replace acetone with MeOH. (2) *Aniline-xylose.*—Dissolve 1 g xylose in 3 ml H₂O, add 57 ml MeOH, and mix. Add 1.0 ml aniline and 40 ml acetone, and mix. (Dip or spray.) Hang paper in air 5 min to let excess solv. evap.; then place in oven 10 min at 105° (stable brown spots on tan background). (3) *pH indicators:* (a) Dissolve 0.02 g bromocresol purple in 10 ml alcohol and dil. to 100 ml with acetone. Add NH₄OH dropwise until soln is red by transmitted light. Use as dip, and air-dry. Repeat until best contrast is obtained. If used as spray, replace acetone with alcohol. (b) Dissolve 0.02 g bromocresol green in 10 ml alcohol and dil. to 100 ml with acetone. Add 1N NaOH until soln is blue-green by transmitted light. Use as dip. For spray use, replace acetone with alcohol.

19.045 *Determination*

(Caution: See **46.059.***)*

Place 10 ml single strength vanilla ext, or equiv. of concd ext dild to 10 ml with 35% alcohol, in 50 ml centrf. tube and add 25 ml alcohol. Mix, add 2.5 ml Pb(OAc)$_2$ soln (8 g/100 ml), mix thoroly, and centrf. Decant clear supernatant. Wash residue twice with 10 ml portions 80% alcohol, mixing well each time and discarding clear wash. Disperse ppt in 10 ml H$_2$O (no lumps) and pass in H$_2$S 5 min. Filter thru small rapid paper into beaker and wash ppt twice with small portions H$_2$O satd with H$_2$S. Mix ppt well with each wash to break up all large clumps. (Filtrate should be clear.) Evap. nearly to dryness on steam bath, using air jet if desired. Complete drying carefully and remove from heat as soon as dry. Cool, and take up with exactly 1 ml H$_2$O, warming gently if necessary.

Spot 12 μl soln on 12 $\times$ 12″ paper, 1″ from bottom and 1.5″ from side edge, by applying four 3 μl portions at same place and drying between applications with warm air. Spot different samples 1.5″ apart. Hang paper in rectangular jar with lower end dipping 1 cm into solv. If cylindrical jars are used, roll paper and connect edges slightly apart (use stainless steel clips or cotton thread to connect). If small jars arc not available, equilibrate by adding large excess of solv. to larger jars and let stand overnight before inserting paper. (Line larger jars with blotting paper with lower edge immersed in solv.) Cover jars with weighted covers or seal with tape. Develop, preferably at 20–23°, until front is 1″ from top (ca 6 hr); spottings can be made in afternoon and development started early next day).

Air-dry overnight. To ensure complete removal of HCOOH, steam paper, without wetting, by rolling and inserting into 6″ stove-pipe section with bottom over rapid source of steam (paper must not touch sides). Steam 15 min, remove, and air-dry. Treat with one of chromogenic agents, **(b)**, by dipping or spraying ((**b**)(*1*) preferred for initial tests). Mark spots with pencil, indicating weak and strong spots, and compare pattern with authentic vanilla org. acid sample treated simultaneously. Note position, size, and intensity of acid spots. Vanilla ext org. acid chromatogram will show four strong spots and several weak ones.

Gas-Liquid Chromatographic Method (16)— Official Final Action

19.046 *Apparatus*

(**a**) *Vials.*—5 ml, with screw caps provided with Teflon liners. (Other plastic or metal liners are not satisfactory.)

(**b**) *Gas chromatograph.*—Varian Aerograph Model 1520, dual column, and thermal conductivity detectors, at 225° and 200 ma. Operating conditions: 6′ $\times$ ¼″ stainless steel column packed with 3.8% SE-30 on 60–80 mesh Diatoport S (silanized) (Varian Associates, 611 Hansen Way, Palo Alto, CA 94303), programmed at 6°/min, from 75 to 210°; injector temp. 225°; He gas flow 40 ml/min; sample injection 5 μl; attenuation, to give 50% chart width response to internal std.

Other equipment may be used with following conditions: thermal conductivity detector temp. 225–275°; injection port temp. 200–300°; programming rate 6–10°/min; He flow 40–60 ml/min; sample injection 5–25 μl. (Flame ionization detectors may also be used, with proper adjustment of sample size and sensitivity.)

19.047 *Reagents*

(*Note:* Tri-Sil reagent and pyridine may be harmful. *Caution:* Protect skin and eyes when using. Use effective fume removal device.)

(**a**) *Neutral lead acetate soln.*—Dissolve 8 g Pb(OAc)$_2$.3H$_2$O in H$_2$O and dil. to 100 ml with H$_2$O.

(**b**) *Internal std soln.*—Dissolve 0.100 g glutaric acid in 80% alcohol and dil. to 100 ml with 80% alcohol. Store in tightly closed bottle.

(**c**) *Tri-Sil reagent.*—Pyridine soln of trimethylchlorosilane (TMS) and hexamethyldisilazane (10 + 1 + 2) (Pierce Chemical Co., PO Box 117, Rockford, IL 61105). Use to prep. TMS derivatives.

19.048 *Determination*

Transfer 2.0 ml single-strength vanilla ext to 15 ml screw-capped centrf. tube, and add ca 0.2 g Celite 545 and exactly 1.0 ml internal std soln. Mix and add 0.7 ml Pb(OAc)$_2$ soln; mix again and add 5.0 ml alcohol. Cap tube, mix, and centrf. at moderate speed until ppt is well packed and supernatant is clear. Discard supernatant, add 5.0 ml 80% alcohol to ppt, mix, and centrf. again. Discard clear supernatant and repeat washings twice more, using 5.0 ml alcohol for first wash and 5.0 ml ether for second. Each time mix thoroly, cap, centrf., and discard clear supernatant. Drain ether for few min; then place tube in 50–55° H$_2$O bath. Stir residue with stainless steel wire until most of ether is removed and solid material in tube appears dry and powdery. Brush any powder adhering to wire into tube and place open tube in 100° oven 1 hr. Remove tube from oven, cool somewhat, add 3 pieces of *Drierite*, and cap tightly. Inject 1.5 ml Tri-Sil reagent into cool tube from 2 ml syringe, recap, and mix thoroly, making sure that all residue in tube is wet with pyridine soln. Place tube in 37° oven 1 hr, with occasional mixing. Centrf. and decant clear supernatant into dry 5 ml vial contg several pieces of Drierite. Cap tightly with Teflon-lined screw cap.

Inject sample into gas chromatograph and program as in **19.046**(**b**). Compare sample curve with curves of authentic vanilla exts obtained under same conditions. Authentic vanilla exts show many peaks, with eight major ones. Internal std appears between peaks 1 and 2. Peak 7 is always highest peak in pure vanilla samples. Sum of 8 peak hts, calcd on basis of internal std peak ht = 1.00, provides useful information on quantity of vanilla acids present. Ratio peak 2:peak 7 also provides significant information. Note also presence or absence of foreign peaks. If some peaks are too high for measurement, repeat detn with greater attenuation.

(*Note:* TMS derivatives tend to break down with heat, and continued use may impair column efficiency. Also, artifacts occur sometimes, particularly on first run of day. Columns usually can be reconditioned by overnight heating at 250° with slow stream of He. Disconnect column from detector when performing such reconditioning. Special regenerating liqs (e.g., Silyl-8, Pierce Chemical Co.) are also available for injection into columns used for TMS work. Heating thermal conductivity detectors at higher temps, without current, helps keep them free from decomposition products.)

LEMON, ORANGE, AND LIME EXTRACTS AND FLAVORS

19.049   Specific Gravity—Official Final Action

Det. sp gr at 20/20° with pycnometer as in **9.011**.

19.050   Alcohol (*17*)—Official Final Action

(Applicable to exts consisting only of oil, alcohol, and water)

Det. sp gr at 15.56/15.56° or at 20/20° as in **9.011** and oil content as in **19.060, 19.061,** or **19.116,** and apply following formula: Let S represent sp gr of sample; O, sp gr of oil; and p, % oil found. Then $100 - p = \%$ H_2O-alcohol soln, sp gr of which, represented by P, is calcd as follows:

$$S = [Op + P(100 - p)]/100;$$

therefore

$$P = (100S - Op)/(100 - p).$$

Det. E, alcohol equiv. of P, from **47.003.** It gives % alcohol in alcohol-H_2O soln. To find % alcohol in ext, apply following formula:

$$\% \text{ by vol. of alcohol in ext} = E(1 - p/100).$$

Value of O for lemon oil may be taken as 0.86 and for orange oil as 0.85.

19.051   ★   Methanol—Official   ★ Final Action

See **19.047,** 10th ed.

Isopropanol—Official Final Action

Applicable to Lemon Extract in Absence of Acetone (18)

19.052   *Preparation of Sample*

Place sample contg ≤8 g total alcohols (approximation of alc. content may be made from sp gr detn and ref. to **47.003**), into separator contg in stem cotton pledget wet with H_2O. Add 25 ml 10% NaCl soln and 25 ml pet ether. Shake well and when layers sep. drain lower layer into flask. Repeat extn with 3 addnl 25 ml portions NaCl soln or until alcohol is completely extd. Add H_2O to combined aq. exts until vol. is ca 150 ml. Connect flask to vertical condenser and distill into 100 ml vol. flask, removing flask when distillate is 2–3 ml below mark. Dil. to vol. and mix.

19.053   *Qualitative Test for Acetone*

To 2 ml distillate add 0.5 ml *5% alc. o-nitrobenzaldehyde soln* and 1 ml 10% NaOH soln. Mix; then shake with small quantity of $CHCl_3$. If $CHCl_3$ turns blue, acetone is present.

19.054   *Determination*

Pipet 10 ml distillate into 500 ml erlenmeyer contg 50 ml ca $2N$ $K_2Cr_2O_7$ and add 100 ml H_2SO_4 (1 + 3). Stopper flask, swirl, and let stand 30 min. Add 100 ml 30% $FeSO_4 \cdot 7H_2O$ soln. Connect flask to vertical condenser thru foam trap. Slowly distill ca 100 ml into 500 ml vol. flask contg 200–300 ml cold H_2O. Dil. to vol., mix, and pipet 25 ml into g-s flask contg 25 ml $1N$ NaOH; add 50 ml stdzd $0.1N$ I with swirling. Let stand 15 min. Add 26 ml $1N$ HCl and at once titr. residual I with stdzd $0.1N$ $Na_2S_2O_3$, adding starch soln when I color is nearly discharged. Each ml $0.1N$ I consumed in reaction = 1.001 mg isopropanol.

Applicable to Lemon and Orange Flavors in Presence of Acetone (19)

19.055   *Apparatus*

Glassware.—Use foil wrapped stoppers or preferably all-glass still. Provide condenser with adapter which reaches several inches into vol. flask.

19.056   *Preparation of Sample*

Proceed as in **19.052**, placing 100 ml vol. flask in ice-H_2O bath.

19.057   *Determination of Acetone*

Pipet aliquot preferably contg 0.1–0.3 g acetone into 100 ml vol. flask and dil to vol. with H_2O. Det. A at 265 nm with H_2O as ref. soln in Beckman Instruments Model DU spectrophtr or equiv. instrument. Correct for A of H_2O in same cell as used for sample, if necessary. Det. quantity of acetone in the 100 ml vol. flask by ref. to std curve prepd from redistd acetone.

In absence of purified acetone, g acetone/100 ml may be estd from equation: $C = A/3.08$, where C = g acetone/100 ml, A = corrected A in 1 cm cell, and 3.08 = assumed A of 1 g/100 ml soln of acetone in 1 cm cell. Calc. to g acetone/100 ml sample.

19.058   *Determination of Isopropanol*

Proceed as in **19.054**, distg ca 100 ml into 250 ml vol. flask contg ca 100 ml cold H_2O and held in ice-H_2O bath. Dil. to vol. with H_2O and det. corrected

A as in **19.057**. Det. quantity of acetone in 250 ml vol. flask by ref. to std curve prepd as in **19.057**.

In absence of purified acetone, g acetone/250 ml may be estd from equation: $C' = 2.5A/3.08$, where $C' = $ g acetone/250 ml, 2.5 = diln factor, *A* and 3.08 are defined in **19.057**. Calc. to g acetone/100 ml sample. Deduct quantity of free acetone as detd in **19.057**, and multiply by 1.035 to obtain g isopropanol /100 ml sample.

19.059 Glycerol—Official Final Action

Proceed as in **11.010** or **11.011**, selecting method according to quantity of sugar present. Use sample contg 0.1–0.4 g glycerol.

Oils of Lemon and Orange in Extracts

19.060 *By Polarization (20)—*
Official Final Action

Without dilg, polarize sample at 20° in 200 mm tube. Divide reading in °S, **31.020(a)**, by 3.2 for lemon ext and by 5.2 for orange ext. In absence of other optically active substances, result will be % oil by vol. If sucrose is present, det. as in **19.072** and correct reading accordingly. To obtain % oil by wt from % by vol., multiply vol. % by 0.86 for lemon exts, and by 0.85 for orange exts, and divide results by sp gr of original ext.

19.061 *By Precipitation (21)—*
Official Final Action

Pipet 20 ml sample into Babcock milk bottle, **16.053(a)**. Add 1 ml HCl (1 + 1), then 25–28 ml H_2O previously warmed to 60°. Mix, and let stand in H_2O 5 min at 60°. Centrf. 5 min, fill bottle with warm H_2O to bring oil into graduated neck of flask, again centrf. 2 min, and place flask in H_2O at 60° few min. Note % oil by vol. If >2% oil is present, add 0.4% to % oil noted to correct for solubility of oil. If <2% but >1% is present, add 0.3% for this correction. To obtain % oil by wt from % by vol., multiply vol. % by 0.86 for lemon exts, and by 0.85 for orange exts, and divide result by sp gr of original ext.

19.062 *By Precipitation in Presence of Mineral Oil—Official First Action*

Proceed as in **19.116**.

Oils of Lemon, Orange, or Lime in Oil Base Flavors

By Steam Distillation (22)—Official Final Action

19.063   *Apparatus*

(a) *Steam generator filled with H_2O.*—Oil can holding 1 gal. will serve purpose.

(b) *Distillation flask.*—750 ml Kjeldahl flask with short neck; total ht ca 10″.

(c) *Spray tube.*—Glass tube connected to steam generator; with small perforated bulb at end of tube

passing thru rubber stopper and reaching bottom of distn flask.

(d) *Bent glass tube.*—Approx. 8 mm diam. Connects distn flask to upright condenser. Shape of this tube allows vapor condensing in tube to return to distn flask.

(e) *Liebig condenser.*—With 20″ H_2O jacket.

(f) *Wilson receiving flask.*—(Fig. 19:1.) Babcock test bottle shape with graduated neck but of 250 ml capacity and with vertical glass outlet tube sealed on near bottom. Upper end of outlet tube is turned down. Neck may consist of portion of buret graduated from 0 to 25 ml with flared top. Outlet tube is ca 3 mm diam.; end is at such ht that when flask is filled with H_2O, meniscus in neck will be between 0 and 1 ml marks.

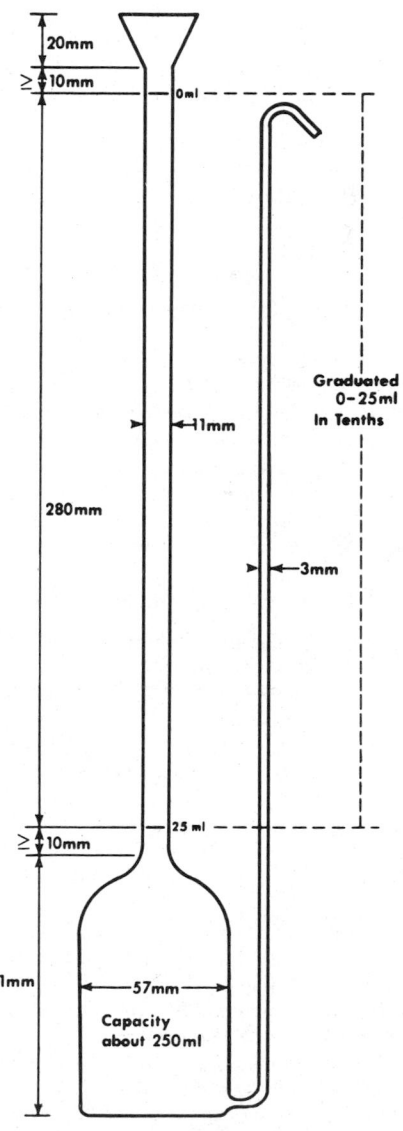

FIG. 19:1—Wilson flask

19.064   *Determination*

Measure 100 ml sample in graduated cylinder and transfer to distn flask. Immerse flask in H_2O bath and connect to condenser with the bent glass tube. Fill receiving flask with H_2O and so place under condenser that end of condenser is ca 0.5″ above level of H_2O in receiving flask. Place 200 ml graduated cylinder under end of outlet tube to catch displaced liq. Heat H_2O bath to boiling and pass steam thru sample until 200 ml liq. collects in graduated cylinder.

Disconnect app., let receiving flask stand 15 min, or until sepn of oil is complete, and read vol. of oil in flask. Calc. % (by vol.) of essential oil in sample by dividing reading by 0.90 for lemon oil in corn and cottonseed oils, 0.95 for orange oil in corn and cottonseed oils, and 0.78 for distd or expressed lime oil in corn and cottonseed oils. Where menstruum is mineral oil, subtract 0.3 ml from reading before dividing by factors 0.90, 0.95, and 0.78 for lemon oil, orange oil, and lime oil, resp.

19.065   *By Polarization (23)—*
 Official First Action

Polarize sample at 20° in 200 mm tube, making 5 readings. From av. of readings in °S, **31.020(a)**, subtract: for corn oil $+0.6°$, for cottonseed oil $-0.3°$, for peanut oil $+0.2°$, and for mineral oil $+5.5°$, as correction for rotatory effect of menstruum. To obtain % by vol. of essential oil in mixt., divide corrected polariscopic reading so obtained by factor 3.4 for lemon oil in corn oil, 3.7 for lemon oil in cottonseed oil, 3.6 for lemon oil in peanut oil, 3.5 for lemon oil in mineral oil, 5.4 for orange oil in corn oil, 5.7 for orange oil in cottonseed oil, 5.6 for orange oil in mineral oil, 2.0 for lime oil in corn oil, 2.3 for lime oil in cottonseed oil, and 2.2 for lime oil in mineral oil.

Total Aldehydes (24)—Official Final Action
19.066   *Reagents*

(a) *Aldehyde-free alcohol.*—Let alcohol, contg 5 g m-phenylenediamine hydrochloride/L, stand at least 24 hr with frequent shaking. (Nothing is gained by previous treatment with KOH.) Reflux at least 8 hr, longer if necessary; let stand overnight, and distill, rejecting first 10 and last 5 ml distillate. Store in dark, cool place in well-filled bottles. (25 ml of this alcohol, on standing 20 min at 14–16° with 20 ml of the fuchsin-bisulfite soln, should develop only faint pink tinge. If stronger color develops, repeat treatment with m-phenylenediamine hydrochloride as above.) (Avoid skin and eye contact and breathing m-phenylenediamine dust.)

(b) *Fuchsin-bisulfite soln.*—Dissolve 0.5 g fuchsin in 250 ml H_2O, add aq. soln contg 16 g SO_2, let stand until colorless or nearly so, and dil. to 1 L with H_2O. Let stand 12 hr before use and keep in refrigerator. (This soln may deteriorate and should be reasonably fresh when used.)

(c) *Citral std soln.*—1 mg/ml. Weigh 0.5 g citral into 50 ml vol. flask, dil. to vol. with aldehyde-free alcohol at room temp., stopper flask, and mix by shaking. Dil. 10 ml of this soln with aldehyde-free alcohol to 100 ml in vol. flask, stopper, and mix.

19.067   *Determination*

Weigh ca 25 g sample in stoppered weighing flask, transfer to 50 ml vol. flask, and dil. to vol. at room temp. with aldehyde-free alcohol. Measure, at room temp., 2 ml (or other suitable quantity) of this soln into comparison tube. Add 25 ml aldehyde-free alcohol (previously cooled to 14–16°), then 20 ml fuchsin-bisulfite soln (also cooled), and dil. to 50 ml mark with aldehyde-free alcohol. Mix thoroly, stopper, and keep 15 min at 14–16°.

Prep. std for comparison at same time and in same manner, using 2 ml std citral soln, and compare colors developed. Calc. quantity of citral present and repeat detn, using quantity sufficient to give sample ca strength of the std. From this result calc. quantity of citral in sample. If comparisons are made in Nessler tubes, stds contg 1, 1.5, 2, 2.5, 3, 3.5, and 4 mg citral may be prepd and trial comparison made against these, final comparison being made with stds lying between 1.5 and 2.5 mg with 0.25 mg increments.

It is absolutely essential to keep reagents and comparison tubes at required temp., 14–16°. If comparisons are made in a bath (possible only when bath is of glass), use stds within 25 min after adding fuchsin-bisulfite soln. Treat samples and stds identically.

Citral (25)—Official Final Action
(Lemon and orange exts)
19.068   *Reagent*

Metaphenylenediamine hydrochloride-oxalic acid soln.—Remove interfering colored impurities in m-phenylenediamine hydrochloride by digesting 3–5 g ca 5 min with ca 25 ml alcohol, decanting, and repeating 3 times. Dry crystals short time on steam bath. Dissolve 1 g in ca 45 ml 85% alcohol, dissolve 1 g crystd oxalic acid in 45 ml 85% alcohol, and pour 2 solns into 100 ml vol. flask. Add 2 or 3 g fuller's earth, dil. to vol. with 85% alcohol, mix, and filter thru double folded paper. (Avoid skin and eye contact and breathing m-phenylenediamine dust.)

19.069   *Determination*

Weigh 25 g sample into 50 ml vol. flask, dil. to vol. with alcohol (95% by vol. for exts made with the oils; 50–95% by vol. for terpeneless exts), and mix. Pipet 2 ml or other suitable quantity of this soln into colorimeter tube, add 10 ml reagent, dil. to suitable vol., and compare resulting color with colors of set of stds contg known quantities of citral std soln, **19.066(c)**.

19.070 Total Solids—Official Final Action

Proceed as in 9.023, using 10 ml sample measured at 20°.

19.071 Ash—Official Final Action

Ignite residue from 10 ml sample as in 31.012 or 31.013.

19.072 Sucrose—Official Final Action

Neutze normal wt of sample, evap. to dryness, wash several times with ether, dissolve in H_2O, and proceed as in 31.025, 31.026, or 31.032.

LEMON AND ORANGE OILS

19.073 Specific Gravity—Official Final Action

Det. sp gr at 20/20° with pycnometer as in 9.011.

19.074 Refractive Index—Official Final Action

Use any std instrument, making reading at 20°. See 28.009.

19.075 Optical Rotation—Official Final Action

Det. rotation at 20° with any std instrument, 50 mm tube, and Na light. State results in angular degrees on 100 mm basis. If instruments having sugar scale are used, reading for orange oils is above range of scale, but readings may be obtained by use of std levorotatory quartz plates, or by 25 mm tube. (True rotation cannot be obtained by dilg oil with alcohol and correcting rotation in proportion to diln.)

19.076 Spectrophotometric Absorbance Characteristics (26)—Official Final Action

Accurately weigh 1 g (to nearest mg) sample in g-s weighing bottle. Dissolve in alcohol and transfer quant. to 100 ml vol. flask. Dil. to vol., mix well, and pipet 25 ml aliquot into another 100 ml vol. flask, dil. to vol. with alcohol, and mix well.

Det. A of the prepd soln in UV region from 260 to 375 nm with recording or manual spectrophtr against alcohol in matched cell. Obtain readings at 5 nm intervals if manually operated instrument is used. Readings at closer intervals (ca 3 nm) are preferred between 305–320 nm. Above 325 nm readings can be made at intervals of 10 nm.

If instrument does not read directly in A, calc. from % T from tables or from equation: $A = 2 - \log T$. Plot A against wavelength and draw smooth curve thru points.

Correct for background A as follows: Draw straight (base) line AB tangent to curve at point of min. A near 285 nm (285–295 nm) and at inflection point where curve levels off at ca 365 nm (365–370 nm). Drop vertical line CD from absorption peak (ca 315 nm) to base line AB. Obtain length of vertical line CD in A units and record as corrected A.

19.077 Physical Constants of 10 Per Cent Distillate (27)—Official Final Action

Place 50 ml sample in 3 bulb, 120 ml Ladenburg flask having main bulb 6 cm diam. and condensing bulbs 3.5, 3, and 2.5 cm. Distance from bottom of flask to opening of side arm should be 20 cm. Distill oil at rate of 2 ml/min until 5 ml distills. Det. refractive index and optical rotation of this distillate as in 19.074 and 19.075.

Residue after Steam Distillation (28)—Official Final Action

19.078 *Apparatus*

Use steam distn assembly, Fig. 18:1, except use 250 ml distg flask.

19.079 *Determination*

(Caution: See 46.011, 46.039, 46.040, 46.054, and 46.056.)

Add 50 ml H_2O and 15 ml sample to 250 ml distn flask. Weigh 15 ml oil delivered by same pipet to obtain wt sample. Place steam inlet tube in flask, heat contents of flask just to boiling, and connect inlet tube to steam. Adjust flame so that H_2O level remains approx. constant. Steam distill at constant rate of ca 200 ml/hr until 100 ml H_2O collects. Discontinue distn and let flask partially cool; then decant contents into 125–250 ml separator, and drain.

Rinse flask twice with 15 and 8 ml portions alcohol, warming if necessary to dissolve any residue. Pour alcohol rinsings into tared 150 ml beaker. Ext cooled liq. in separator with 25 and 20 ml portions $CHCl_3$. (Add 1–2 drops HCl (1 + 2) to separator if there is any tendency for liqs to emulsify.) Add exts to tared beaker contg alcohol washings. Ext once with 25 ml ether and add this ext to others. Evap. exts carefully without spattering on cover of steam bath until ether and $CHCl_3$ are removed. Then evap. residual liq. on open steam bath. Let beaker remain on bath 15 min after odor of alcohol disappears. Remove, wipe outside of beaker with clean dry cloth, let cool, and weigh. Reheat, cool, and weigh until loss is <2 mg/5 min heating period. Calc. % residue by steam distn.

Total Aldehydes—Official Final Action

19.080 *Hiltner Method* (25)

Accurately weigh ca 2 g lemon oil or 8 g orange oil into 100 ml vol. flask, dil. to vol. with alcohol, and proceed as in 19.069, using 2 ml dild soln for comparison.

Kleber Method (29)

(For orange oil)

19.081 *Reagent*

Phenylhydrazine soln.—Prep. 10% soln in absolute alcohol. Sufficiently pure phenylhydrazine can be obtained by distg com. product *in vacuo*, rejecting first portions coming over that contain NH₃. (*Caution:* See **46.015**.)

19.082   *Determination*

Accurately weigh ca 15 g sample into small, g-s flask, and add 10 ml phenylhydrazine soln. Let stand 30 min at room temp. and titr. with $0.5N$ HCl, using Me or Et orange indicator. Similarly titr. 10 ml phenylhydrazine soln. Difference in ml $0.5N$ acid used in these 2 titrns $\times$ 0.076 = wt citral in sample. If end point is difficult to detect, titr. until soln is distinctly acid, transfer to separator, and drain alc. portion. Wash oil with H_2O, adding washings to alc. soln, back-titr. with $0.5N$ alkali, and make necessary corrections.

Kirsten Modification of the Kleber Method (30)
(For lemon oil)
19.083   *Reagents*

(a) *p-Toluenesulfonic acid.*—$0.5N$. Dissolve 95 g p-toluenesulfonic acid ($CH_3C_6H_4SO_3H \cdot H_2O$) in absolute alcohol and dil. to 1 L with absolute alcohol. Mix thoroly and filter. Stdze against $0.5N$ NaOH, using Me red.

(b) *Methyl yellow indicator.*—Dissolve 0.1 g p-dimethylaminoazobenzene in 100 ml absolute alcohol.

19.084   *Determination*

Accurately weigh ca 15 g sample into 125 ml g-s flask and pipet in 10 ml phenylhydrazine soln, **19.081**. Let stand 30 min at room temp. and add 25 ml benzene. Titr. with $0.5N$ p-toluenesulfonic acid, using 0.2 ml Me yellow. Similarly titr. 10 ml phenylhydrazine soln. Difference in ml $0.5N$ acid used in 2 titrns $\times$ 0.076 = g citral in sample.

Hydroxylamine Method (28)
(For lemon oil)
19.085   *Reagents*

(a) *Bromophenol blue indicator.*—Dissolve 0.1 g bromophenol blue in 5 ml $0.05N$ NaOH and dil. to 100 ml with 60% alcohol.

(b) *Ethyl orange indicator.*—Dissolve 0.05 g Et orange in 60% alcohol and dil. to 50 ml.

(c) *Potassium hydroxide std soln.*—$0.5N$. Dissolve 28.06 g KOH in 60% alcohol and dil. to 1 L with same solv. Stdze against std HCl.

(d) *Hydroxylamine soln.*—Dissolve 7.0 g NH_2OH $\cdot$HCl in 175 ml 60% alcohol. Add either: (*1*) 0.3 ml bromophenol blue indicator and enough $0.5N$ KOH to give permanent blue soln, or (*2*) 0.3 ml Et orange and enough $0.5N$ KOH to give permanent yellow soln. In either case dil. resulting soln to 200 ml with 60% alcohol.

19.086   *Determination*

Weigh to nearest 10 mg ca 10 g sample into g-s 50 ml graduate and add 7 ml hydroxylamine soln

and 0.1 ml indicator. Shake and neutze liberated acid with $0.5N$ KOH to permanent full alk. color of indicator used. Continue shaking and neutzg until permanent alk. color remains in lower layer after shaking mixt. vigorously 2 min and letting sep. (Reaction is complete in ca 15 min.) 1 ml $0.5N$ KOH = 0.0761 g citral.

This titrn approximates citral in the oil. Repeat detn as above, using as color std for end point titrd liq. of first detn, and as vol. $NH_2OH \cdot HCl$ soln 1–2 ml more than vol. $0.5N$ KOH used in first detn.

Esters (30)—Official Final Action
(For lemon oil)
19.087   *Apparatus*

Expeller.—Prep. rubber stopper with glass inlet and outlet tubes similar to wash bottle. Adjust outlet tube to just reach bottom of centrf. bottle and place soda-lime tube between inlet tube and source of air.

19.088   *Reagents*

(a) *Aldehyde-free isoamyl alcohol.*—Reflux ca 1 L reagent grade isoamyl alcohol over 35–40 g KOH 60–70 min. Distill in all-glass app., reject first 25 ml distillate, and collect next 850 ml. Store at ca 5°.

(b) *Sodium chloride soln.*—Dissolve 160 g NaCl in 500 ml H_2O.

(c) *Carbon dioxide-free water.*—Use freshly boiled and cooled H_2O thruout detn.

19.089   *Determination*

Weigh 5 ml oil in beaker or bottle and transfer to 125 ml separator, using exactly 25 ml alcohol to complete transfer. Add 1 ml *50% $NH_2OH \cdot HCl$ soln* and few drops phthln, and mix. Add, from buret or graduated pipet, enough 4% KOH in 80% alcohol to make soln just pink and add drop or so excess. Add 1 drop 20% $NH_2OH \cdot HCl$ soln and shake; pink should be discharged. Add 25 ml isoamyl alcohol and shake. Add 50 ml NaCl soln, shake vigorously, let layers sep. (line of division should be sharp), drain, and discard lower layer. Repeat extn with four 30 ml portions NaCl soln and once with 6 ml H_2O, draining and discarding exts each time. Drain remaining isoamyl alcohol-oil layer into 500 ml erlenmeyer. Wash separator once with 25 ml Et alcohol and combine with soln in flask. Add phthln, make liq. just pink with ca $0.2N$ stdzd KOH, and then add from pipet exactly 20 ml std KOH in excess.

Reflux soln 45 min on hot plate; then cool with flask loosely stoppered. Add ca 150 ml H_2O and rotate ca 30 sec, but avoid violent shaking. Transfer liq. into 500 ml separator thru short-stem funnel, rinse flask with 20 ml H_2O, and add to separator. Stopper funnel and let layers sep. Drain lower layer into original flask. Add ca 60 ml H_2O to separator, invert, and rotate to mix; then let layers sep. until most of aq. layer seps. (Small layer of emulsion may remain between layers.)

Drain aq. layer into flask, retaining any emulsion in separator. Keep flask and separator stoppered between addns to avoid contact with air. Add ca 100 ml H_2O to separator, shake vigorously, and drain entire contents into 250 ml centrf. bottle. Stopper, and centrf. until 2 well-sepd layers are obtained. Blow off lower layer in centrf. bottle, using expeller, into flask contg aq. fractions previously sepd, add ca 0.2 ml phthln, and titr., using std 0.2N HCl. As end point approaches, repeat addn of indicator and titr. to disappearance of pink. (Liq. becomes white or grayish.)

Conduct blank detn similarly, using same amts of all reagents. Subtract titrn of sample from that of blank to obtain equiv. of 0.2N alkali consumed. 1 ml 0.2N alkali = 39.2 mg esters as linalyl acetate.

Pinene (31)—Official Final Action

19.090   Qualitative Test

(*Caution:* Ethyl nitrite may be harmful. Avoid contact with skin and breathing vapor.)

Mix 10% distillate, **19.077**, with 5 ml HOAc, cool mixt. thoroly in freezing bath, and add 10 ml *Et nitrite*. Add 2 ml HCl (2 + 1) slowly with constant stirring. Keep mixt. in freezing bath 15 min. Collect crystals formed on filter, using suction, and wash with alcohol. Return combined filtrate and washings to freezing bath 15 min. Collect addnl crystals formed on original filter. Wash combined crops of crystals thoroly with alcohol. Dry at room temp. and dissolve in min. quantity of $CHCl_3$. Add MeOH to $CHCl_3$ soln, little at time, until nitrosochlorides crystallize out. Mount sepd and dried crystals in olive oil and examine under microscope. Pinene nitrosochloride crystals have irregular pyramidal ends; limonene nitrosochloride crystallizes in needles.

ALMOND EXTRACT
Alcohol—Official First Action

19.091   Method I (32)

Fill 50 ml pycnometer with sample at 15.56°, and empty into separator contg ca 10 g NaCl. Wash out pycnometer several times with satd NaCl, using total of ca 100 ml. Ext twice with 50 ml portions pet ether (bp 40–60°). Collect pet ether ext in second separator and wash with two 25 ml portions satd NaCl soln. Combine original NaCl soln with washings, add little *powd pumice*, and distill into 100 ml pycnometer (Fig. 9:1). When almost 100 ml collects, dil. to vol. with H_2O at convenient temp. and det. alcohol from sp gr as in **9.013**, using table, **47.003**.

19.092   Method II (33)

Det. sp gr of ext at 15.56/15.56° or at 20/20° as in **9.011** and benzaldehyde content as in **19.093**. Apply formula given in **19.050**, using benzaldehyde content as % oil found.

Benzaldehyde

19.093   Gravimetric Method (34)—
Official First Action

Measure 10 ml sample into each of two 300 ml erlenmeyers and add 10 ml *phenylhydrazine soln* (3 ml HOAc, 40 ml H_2O, 2 ml phenylhydrazine) to one flask and 15 ml to other. Let mixts stand overnight in dark place.

Add 200 ml H_2O and filter thru weighed gooch provided with thin layer of asbestos. Wash ppt first with cold H_2O and finally with 10 ml 10% alcohol. Dry 3 hr at 70° at pressure ≤100 mm Hg or to constant wt over H_2SO_4. Wt ppt × 5.408 = wt benzaldehyde in 100 ml sample. If the 2 detns do not agree, repeat operation, using larger quantity phenylhydrazine soln.

Alternative Gravimetric Method (35)—
Official Final Action

19.094   Reagent

2,4-Dinitrophenylhydrazine soln.—Add 50 ml alcohol to 3.0 g 2,4-dinitrophenylhydrazine. Slowly add 10.0 ml H_2SO_4 while stirring. After reagent dissolves, add addnl 40 ml alcohol and filter thru Whatman No. 12 paper.

19.095   Determination

Measure sample contg ca 10–50 mg benzaldehyde (ca 5 ml flavors, 100–200 ml cordials) into distn flask. Add enough alcohol to ensure ≥10% by vol. in distillate and dil. to ca 150 ml for flavors and 250 ml for cordials with H_2O. Distill ca 100 ml flavors and 200 ml cordials and collect in vol. flask in ice bath. Transfer distillate to 600 ml beaker (also in ice bath) with 100 ml chilled alcohol. Add 25 ml H_2SO_4, mix thoroly, and immediately add 25 ml 2,4-dinitrophenylhydrazine soln, while stirring. Heat on steam bath or hot plate 30 min at ca 75°, stirring occasionally (avoid boiling).

Remove from heat, let ppt settle, and filter by decanting most of supernatant thru weighed gooch prepd with thin asbestos mat before transferring bulk of ppt. Wash ppt with ca 25 ml H_2O at room temp. or below.

Dry at 100° to constant wt (ca 2 hr). Wt ppt × 0.3707 = wt benzaldehyde.

Ultraviolet Spectrophotometric Method (35)—
Official Final Action

19.096   Reagents and Apparatus

(a) *Spectrophotometer.*—Quartz spectrophtr, Beckman Instruments Model DU, or equiv., with UV sensitive phototube and H lamp.

(b) *Benzaldehyde.*—Redistd; sp gr 1.041–1.046.

(c) *Alcohol.*—Reagent grade alcohol or MeOH.

(d) *Benzaldehyde std soln.*—Weigh 1 g benzaldehyde into 100 ml vol. flask and dil. with alcohol. Transfer 1 ml of this soln to 100 ml vol. flask, using 10% alcohol. Dil. 1, 2, 4, 6, 8, 10 ml aliquots to 100 ml with 10% alcohol (1, 2, 4, 6, 8, 10 ppm benzaldehyde).

19.097   *Determination*

Pipet sample (usually ca 5 ml flavor or 25 ml cordial) into distn flask. Add enough alcohol to ensure min. of 10% alcohol in distillate. Add ca 110 ml H_2O to flavor or 200 ml H_2O to cordial and distill, collecting 100 ml or 200 ml, resp. If necessary, dil. aliquot of distillate with 10% alcohol to produce A of ca 0.5 at 249 nm, using 10% alcohol blank.

Det. A of std benzaldehyde solns at 249 nm against blank of 10% alcohol, and plot std curve.

Det. benzaldehyde concn from A of sample at 249 nm and std curve, or calc. av. A of 1 ppm benzaldehyde (A'). Concn of benzaldehyde in ppm = $(A/A') \times F$, where F is diln factor. (For most accurate work conduct 5 ppm std with each detn.)

For flavors giving higher A than std at 222 nm, subtract av. of A for min. at 222 and 350 nm from A for max. at 249 nm to calc. A.

19.098   Benzoic Acid (*36*)—Official First Action

Measure 10 ml sample into 100 ml flask and add 10 ml 10% NaOH soln and 20 ml 3% H_2O_2 soln; cover with watch glass and place in 100° oven. Oxidation of aldehyde to benzoic acid begins almost immediately; continue heating 5–10 min after all benzaldehyde odor disappears (20–30 min).

Remove flask from oven; transfer contents to separator, rinsing off watch glass; add 10 ml H_2SO_4 (1 + 5); and cool contents of funnel to room temp. under tap. Ext benzoic acid with 25, 25, 20, and 20 ml portions ether, and wash combined exts with 2 portions of 5–10 ml H_2O, or until all H_2SO_4 is removed. Filter into weighed dish, evap. at room temp., dry overnight in desiccator, and weigh the benzoic acid. Multiply result by 10.

Multiply g/100 ml benzaldehyde obtained in 19.093, 19.095, or 19.097 by 1.151 to obtain equiv. of benzoic acid and subtract this product from g/100 ml total benzoic acid obtained above. Difference = g benzoic acid/100 ml ext.

Hydrocyanic Acid
19.099   *Qualitative Test—Procedure*

To several ml sample add several drops freshly prepd 3% $FeSO_4.7H_2O$ soln and single drop 1% $FeCl_3.6H_2O$ soln. Mix thoroly and add 10% NaOH soln, dropwise, until no further ppt forms and then H_2SO_4 (1 + 9) to dissolve ppt. In presence of even small quantities of HCN, Prussian blue coloration or suspension develops.

19.100   *Quantitative Method—*
         Official Final Action
                 (In absence of chlorides)
Measure 25 ml sample into small flask and add 5 ml *freshly pptd* $Mg(OH)_2$, Cl-free. Titr. with 0.1N

$AgNO_3$, using K_2CrO_4 as indicator. 1 ml 0.1N $AgNO_3$ = 0.0027 g HCN.

Nitrobenzene
19.101   ★   *Qualitative Test—Procedure*   ★
See 19.094, 10th ed.

CASSIA, CINNAMON, AND CLOVE EXTRACTS
Alcohol—Official Final Action
19.102   *Method I*
See 19.091.

19.103   *Method II (33)*

Det. sp gr of ext at 15.56/15.56° or 20/20° as in 9.011, and oil as in 19.105, and apply formula given in 19.050. Use following values for sp gr of the oil: cassia, 1.05; cinnamon, 1.03; and clove, 1.055.

19.104   Isopropanol—Official Final Action
Proceed as in 19.052–19.054.

19.105   Oil (*37*)—Official First Action

Pipet 10 ml sample into Babcock milk test bottle. Remove nearly all alcohol by blowing air into bottle thru small glass tube 30 min, or longer if necessary. From 10 ml buret add 1 ml *solv.* (equal parts USP mineral oil and H_2O-free kerosene), shake well, and fill with satd $MgSO_4$ soln. Centrf. 10 min and read vol. of oil from extreme bottom to extreme top of column. To obtain % oil subtract 5 divisions and multiply remainder by 2.

GINGER EXTRACT
19.106   Alcohol—Official First Action—
         See 9.013

19.107   Solids (*38*)—Official First Action

Evap. 10 ml sample nearly to dryness on steam bath, dry 2 hr in oven at temp. of boiling H_2O, and weigh.

19.108   Ginger (Qualitative Test) (*39*)—
         Official First Action
(*Caution: See* 46.011, 46.039, and 46.054.)

Dil. 10 ml sample to 30 ml, evap. to 20 ml, decant into separator, and ext with equal vol. ether. Let ether evap. spontaneously in porcelain dish, and to residue add 5 ml 75% H_2SO_4 (by wt) and ca 5 mg *vanillin*. Let stand 15 min and add equal vol. H_2O. In presence of ginger ext, soln turns azure blue.

19.109   ★   Capsicum (Qualitative Test)   ★
         (*40*)—Official First Action
(*Caution: See* 46.011, 46.039, and 46.054.)
See 19.102, 10th ed.

PEPPERMINT, SPEARMINT, AND WINTERGREEN EXTRACTS
Alcohol—Official First Action

19.110   Method I

See 19.091.

19.111   Method II (31)

Det. sp gr at 15.56/15.56° or at 20/20° as in **9.011,** and oil content as in **19.105,** and apply formula in **19.050.** Use following values for sp gr of oil: peppermint, 0.90; spearmint, 0.93; and wintergreen, 1.18.

19.112   Isopropanol—Official Final Action
See **19.052–19.054**

19.113   Oil—Official First Action—See 19.116

ANISE AND NUTMEG EXTRACTS
Oil (41)—Official First Action

19.114   Method I

To 10 ml sample in Babcock milk test bottle add 1 ml HCl (1 + 1), then enough half-satd NaCl soln, previously heated to 60°, to fill flask nearly to neck. Stopper and let stand in H_2O at 60° ca 15 min, rotate occasionally, and centrf. 10 min at ca 800 rpm. Fill bottle to neck with satd NaCl soln and again centrf. 10 min. If sepn is not satisfactory or liq. is not clear, cool to ca 10° and centrf. addnl 10 min. Reading × 2 = % oil by vol.

19.115   Method II

See **19.116.**

OTHER EXTRACTS AND TOILET PREPARATIONS

19.116   Essential Oil (42)—Official First Action

(Applicable to exts of allspice, anise, caraway, lemon, nutmeg, orange, peppermint, pimiento, rosemary, thyme, wintergreen, and methyl salicylate)

Pipet 10 ml sample (5 ml when oil content is >5% by vol.) into Babcock milk test bottle, add 0.50 ml *solv.* (equal parts USP mineral oil and H_2O-free kerosene) and 1 ml HCl (1 + 1), and fill to shoulder with satd NaCl soln. Shake bottle 3 min; then add the NaCl soln to bring column of oil within graduations on neck. Centrf. 10 min at high speed and read vol. of oil from extreme bottom to extreme top of column. (Read from extreme bottom to bottom of meniscus at top of column for allspice, peppermint, and pimiento exts.) To obtain % oil, subtract 2.5 divisions and multiply remainder by 2. (Multiply by 4 if 5 ml sample is used.)

Essential Oil in Emulsion (43)—
Official First Action

19.117   Apparatus

Use modified oil separator trap, Fig. 19:2, connected to 500 ml r-b flask thru ⌡ 24/40 joint, and equipped with tight fitting finger condenser having

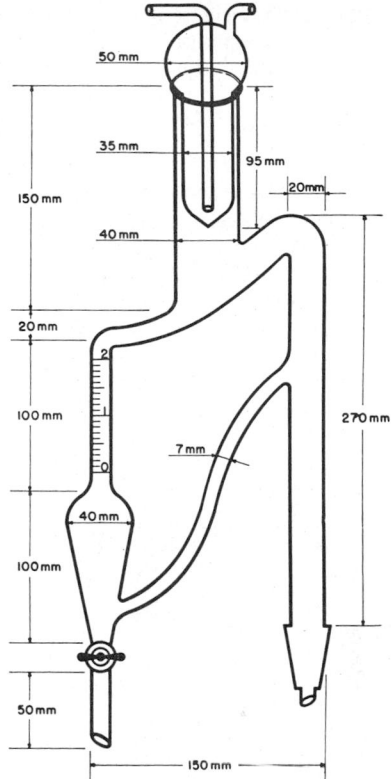

FIG. 19:2—Oil separator trap

projection at bottom to facilitate return of oil to trap.

19.118   Determination

Weigh 5–10 ml sample contg ≤2 ml essential oil in tared g-s graduated cylinder. Transfer to the 500 ml flask contg ca 200 ml H_2O, rinsing cylinder by shaking with several 5 ml portions H_2O. Add rinsings to flask.

Fill oil trap with H_2O to overflowing, connect to flask and condenser, and carefully boil 1 hr. Remove heat and let stand several min. Remove enough H_2O from trap to bring oil layer within graduations, let stand 5 min to complete drainage, and measure amt of oil from bottom of lower meniscus to highest point of upper meniscus.

Citral—Official Final Action
Barbituric Acid Condensation Method (44)

19.119   Reagent

Barbituric acid soln.—Transfer 1.0 g reagent grade barbituric acid to dry 100 ml vol. flask. Add 20 ml H_2O from pipet, rinsing down neck of flask. Stopper lightly and dissolve by warming gently on hot plate or immersing in beaker of hot H_2O. Dil. gradually to vol., with shaking, with alcohol (or, preferably, anhyd. alcohol). Temper soln in H_2O bath at 25° (soln will contract slightly). Dil. back to vol. and mix thoroly. If some barbituric acid ppts on prolonged standing, redissolve by warming soln gently; then adjust to 25°.

19.120   *Determination*

Weigh suitable amt of oil into vol. flask of appropriate size, dil. to vol. with reagent, and place in H_2O bath at 25°. After 40 min, withdraw aliquots into vol. flasks half-filled with alcohol, shake gently to quench reaction, dil. to vol. with alcohol, and det. *A* of soln at 336 nm. Use similarly dild aliquot of reagent as cell blank. From *A* of sample, subtract corresponding *A* of untreated oil when similarly dild.

Use following table as guide for sample wts and dilns. Except as noted, weigh indicated amts of oil into vol. flask for reaction; then dil. 2 ml to 50 ml with alcohol for *A* measurements:

Oil	Sample Wt (mg)	Reaction Vol. (ml)
Bergamot	70–80	10
Citronella	50–90	10
Grapefruit	100–150	10
Lemon	50–150	25
Lemongrass[a]	20–30	25
Lime		
expressed	30–60	25
distilled	100–600	5
Mandarin	100–250	10
Neroli	75–100	5
Orange		
sweet	150–400	10
bitter	150–400	10
Petitgrain	150–250	5
Tangerine	200–350	10

[a] Dil. 1 ml to 200 ml for *A* measurements.

19.121   *Calculations*

Convert *A* values to *a* at 336 nm of 1 g/L soln in 1 cm cell, and substitute in equation:

% citral = 0.6153 × [*a* of sample after reaction
                    − *a* of unreacted, similarly dild sample]

β-Ionone (45)—Official Final Action

19.122   *Method I*

(Applicable to pure solns contg ≤100 mg in 5 ml alcohol)

Place 5 ml alc. sample contg 10–100 mg β-ionone in 125 erlenmeyer. Add 95–100 mg solid *m-nitrobenzhydrazide* and dissolve by warming soln on steam bath, taking precautions to prevent loss of alcohol thru evapn. Add 5 ml H_2O, and if soln becomes cloudy, warm until clear. Remove soln from steam bath, add 0.2 ml HOAc, stopper flask lightly, and place on wooden surface to prevent too rapid cooling.

If ca 20 mg or more of β-ionone is present, crystals begin to form within 30 min after soln reaches room temp. Let stand in room at least 2 hr (overnight does no harm) and add 5 ml H_2O dropwise, mixing soln

continuously during addn by rotating flask. Stopper, let stand in room at least 1 hr, and refrigerate overnight (≤48 hr). Filter thru fine fritted glass crucible, wash with 30 ml dil. alcohol (3 + 7), using wet policeman to remove ppt adhering to flask, and dry at 100°. Wt ppt × 0.541 = wt β-ionone. Identify crystals microscopically, 19.125.

Method II (46)
(Applicable to raspberry concs)

19.123   *Apparatus*

(a) *Steam generator filled with water.*—Oil can holding 1 gal. is convenient.

(b) *Distillation flask.*—R-b boiling flask with ⊤ 24/40 joint, capacity ca twice vol. of sample to be used.

(c) *Still head.*—Adapter, 75° angle, with male connections ⊤ 24/40 at bottom and side, and female connection 14/35 at top, with side arm lengthened and bent to fit vertical condenser.

(d) *Spray tube.*—Adapter, for use with Woulff bottles equipped with ⊤ joints; aeration tube with ⊤ 14/35, holes in bulb ca 2 mm diam., length of tubing such that when app. is set up, bulb is situated ≤20 mm above bottom of distg flask.

(e) *Condenser.*—Coil type with female connection ⊤ 24/40 at top with 250–300 mm jacket and outlet tube lengthened to ca 200 mm to reach bottom of 500 ml erlenmeyer receiving flask.

19.124   *Determination*
(*Caution:* See 46.011, 46.039, and 46.054.)

Place 250–1000 ml sample contg ≤100 mg β-ionone in distg flask and connect with app. Add enough H_2O to receiving flask to just cover outlet of condenser. Heat sample nearly to boiling on asbestos mat with flame or by immersing it in boiling H_2O bath. As soon as sample reaches temp. of bath or just begins to boil, connect with steam generator and pass rapid current of steam thru sample until ca 500 ml distillate collects.

Add enough H_2O to distillate to reduce alcohol content to ca 10% or less and transfer to large separator. Add 150–200 ml ether, depending upon vol. of soln, so that ca 100 ml is obtained upon sepn. Shake thoroly ca 2 min. Let mixt. settle till clear and drain aq. layer till ca 25 ml remains in separator. Centrf. liq. and again let settle.

When clear, drain remainder of aq. layer; then drain ether soln into 125 ml erlenmeyer contg 95–100 mg *m-nitrobenzhydrazide*. After separator drains ca 1 min, close stopcock, pour 10–15 ml ether into separator to wash down sides, let soln settle 1 min, and add to main ether soln. Add 0.2 ml HOAc and dissolve solid reagent by stirring and breaking up lumps with glass rod, warming if necessary to complete soln. Let mixt. stand ca 1 hr and evap. on steam bath to ca 10 ml, passing current of air into flask to hasten evapn and keep down temp.

In meantime make second extn of distillate, using 100 ml ether. Add sepd ether soln to flask contg residue from first ether ext, follow with ether washings of separator, let stand at least 15 min, and evap to 10 ml as before. Similarly make third extn, using 100 ml ether, add to flask, and evap. as before until 1–3 ml watery liq. and perhaps some oily residue remain.

While flask is still warm, add 5 ml alcohol from pipet, washing down sides of flask, and dissolve residue completely by warming on steam bath, protecting liq. against loss by evapn. Add 5 ml H_2O and warm if necessary to obtain clear soln. Add 0.2 ml HOAc, close with cork stopper, and place flask on wooden surface to prevent too rapid cooling.

After 2 hr, add 5 ml H_2O dropwise, mixing liq. by continuously rotating flask, stopper, and keep at room temp. at least 1 hr (overnight does no harm); then refrigerate overnight (≤ 48 hr).

Filter on fine fritted glass crucible and wash with ca 30 ml dil. alcohol (3 + 7). Dry in vac. oven at 70° and weigh. Wt ppt $\times$ 0.541 = wt β-ionone. Identify crystals microscopically, **19.125**.

If pptd material consists of oily matter mixed with cryst. matter, place fritted glass crucible in gooch holder attached to suction flask. Support test tube with wire within suction flask so as to catch any liq. that passes thru crucible. Add ca 5 ml pet ether, cover crucible, and let stand ca 5 min. Apply suction just long enough to carry thru any solv. that remains in crucible. Transfer pet ether soln to small beaker and let evap. spontaneously. Repeat several times until no more sol. matter is obtained by extn. Examine remaining contents of crucible and several residues microscopically for crystals of β-ionone-m-nitrobenzhydrazide.

19.125 Optical-Crystallographic Properties of β-Ionone-m-Nitrobenzhydrazide (47)—Procedure

This substance in mass is yellowish, but when examined in ordinary light under microscope it is essentially colorless and crystallizes in thin, rod-like plates, many having lath-like or frayed ends, some having 6-side outline. In parallel polarized light (crossed nicols), extinction is parallel and sign of elongation neg. Refractive indices are the min. value, $n_\alpha = 1.548$, invariably shown on elongated fragments when their long dimension is parallel to vibration plane of lower nicol (lengthwise), and max. value, $n_\gamma = 1.648$, usually shown on elongated fragments when their long dimension is at right angles to vibration plane of lower nicol (crosswise).

SELECTED REFERENCES

(1) JAOAC **30**, 651(1947); **33**, 103(1950); **38**, 87, 726(1955).

(2) JAOAC **47**, 555(1964); **49**, 220(1966).

(3) JAOAC **48**, 509(1965); **49**, 566(1966); **50**, 859 (1967).

(4) JAOAC **47**, 1161(1964); **49**, 566(1966); **50**, 207 (1967).

(5) JAOAC **34**, 73, 335(1951); **35**, 77, 268(1952); **36**, 78, 695(1953).

(6) JAOAC **38**, 730(1955); **39**, 715(1956).

(7) J. Ind. Eng. Chem. **13**, 414(1921); JAOAC **8**, 689, 691(1925); **9**, 456(1926); **51**, 822(1968).

(8) J. Am. Chem. Soc. **24**, 1132(1902).

(9) J. Am. Chem. Soc. **24**, 1133(1902).

(10) JAOAC **9**, 446, 456(1926).

(11) JAOAC **43**, 600(1960).

(12) USDA Bur. Chem. Bull. **152**, p. 149.

(13) JAOAC **42**, 638(1959); **43**, 596(1960); **46**, 626 (1963).

(14) JAOAC **47**, 551(1964); **48**, 507(1965).

(15) JAOAC **46**, 626(1963).

(16) JAOAC **51**, 1224(1968).

(17) J. Ind. Eng. Chem. **1**, 84(1909); JAOAC **4**, 472 (1921); **5**, 308(1922); **8**, 695(1925); **33**, 302 (1950).

(18) JAOAC **25**, 693(1942); **41**, 42, 616(1958).

(19) JAOAC **35**, 78, 272(1952); **41**, 42, 616(1958).

(20) JAOAC **4**, 472(1921); **8**, 692(1925).

(21) J. Ind. Eng. Chem. **1**, 84(1909); JAOAC **8**, 692 (1925).

(22) JAOAC **9**, 450(1926); **11**, 45, 503(1928).

(23) JAOAC **9**, 453(1926); **10**, 495(1927).

(24) J. Am. Chem. Soc. **28**, 1472(1906).

(25) J. Ind. Eng. Chem. **10**, 608(1918); JAOAC **12**, 83, 405(1929); **13**, 475(1930).

(26) JAOAC **36**, 112(1953).

(27) Schimmel and Co., Semi-Annual Rpt., Oct. 1898, p. 41.

(28) JAOAC **36**, 119(1953); **39**, 93(1956).

(29) USDA Bur. Chem. Bull. **137**, p. 72; JAOAC **4**, 474(1921); **14**, 68, 519(1931).

(30) JAOAC **38**, 738(1955); **39**, 93(1956).

(31) USDA Bur. Chem. Circ. **46**, p. 9.

(32) JAOAC **33**, 307(1950).

(33) JAOAC **33**, 302(1950).

(34) JAOAC **19**, 408(1936); **24**, 665(1941).

(35) JAOAC **49**, 504(1966); **50**, 319(1967).

(36) J. Ind. Eng. Chem. **1**, 84(1909).

(37) JAOAC **15**, 539(1932); **19**, 407(1936).

(38) USDA Bur. Chem. Bull. **137**, p. 76.

(39) USDA Bur. Chem. Bull. **152**, p. 137.

(40) USDA Bur. Chem. Bull. **152**, p. 145.

(41) J. Ind. Eng. Chem. **1**, 84(1909); JAOAC **2**, 212 (1917).

(42) JAOAC **15**, 539(1932); **16**, 65, 541(1933); **17**, 364(1934); **19**, 407(1936).

(43) JAOAC **25**, 692(1942); **31**, 200(1948); **35**, 78, 261(1952).

(44) JAOAC **45**, 475(1962).

(45) JAOAC **22**, 383(1939); **23**, 572(1940).

(46) JAOAC **22**, 386(1939); **24**, 663(1941).

(47) JAOAC **22**, 390(1939).

20. Food Additives: Direct

ACIDULANTS

Fumaric Acid (1)—Official Final Action

20.001 Apparatus

Polarograph.—Davis Differential Cathode-Ray Polarotrace, Sargent Polarograph No. 15 or No. 16, Leeds and Northrup Electro Chemograph Type E, or equiv.

20.002 Reagents

(a) *Fumaric acid std solns.*—(1) *Stock soln.*—500 μg/ml. Transfer 50 mg fumaric acid to 100 ml vol. flask. Dissolve and dil. to vol. with MeOH. (2) *Working std soln.*—25 μg/ml. Pipet 5 ml stock soln into 100 ml vol. flask, add 15 ml MeOH, and dil. to vol. with electrolyte soln.

(b) *Electrolyte soln.*—Dissolve 7.70 g $(CH_3)_4NBr$ and 0.210 g LiCl in H_2O and dil. to 500 ml. (LiCl is very hygroscopic; weigh rapidly with min. exposure to air.)

(c) *Nitrogen gas.*—Purified H_2O-pumped N in cylinder.

20.003 Preparation of Sample Solutions

(a) *Sample soln A.*—(1) *Aqueous samples (fruit juice drinks, etc.).*—If insol. matter is present, shake with Celite and filter. Transfer 25.00 g clear soln to 100 ml vol. flask, using MeOH, and dil. to vol. with MeOH. (2) *Powders.*—Shake weighed sample with measured vol. MeOH. Filter, or use clear supernatant.

(b) *Sample test soln B.*—Use in preliminary detn. Transfer $\leq$5 ml *sample soln A* to 25 ml vol. flask (if <5 ml is taken, add MeOH to make 5 ml) and dil. to vol. with electrolyte soln.

(c) *Sample test soln C.*—Use in final detn. After preliminary detn is performed on *sample test soln B*, adjust wt of sample to give final concn of *sample test soln C* of 25 μg fumaric acid/ml, prepg soln as in (b).

20.004 Preparation of Standard Curve

Transfer 1, 3, and 5 ml fumaric acid stock soln to sep. 25 ml vol. flasks. To flasks contg 1 and 3 ml stock soln, add 4 and 2 ml MeOH, resp. Dil. all flasks to vol. with electrolyte soln. Polarograph solns as in **20.005.** Plot numerical values of solns against μg fumaric acid/ml.

20.005 Determination

Prep. polarograph cell and pass N thru *sample test soln B* 3 min at ca 3–5 bubbles/sec. Polarograph, using starting potential of -0.8 v. Peak potential of fumaric acid under these conditions is ca -1.15 v

with Hg pool electrode. Wave ht $\times$ instrument scale factor gives "numerical value," which shows relative concn of fumaric acid in polarographed soln. From numerical value of *sample test soln B* and std curve, calc. approx. % fumaric acid in sample.

Make second detn, using calcd wt sample for *sample test soln C* contg 25 μg fumaric acid/ml and working std soln contg exactly 25 μg fumaric acid/ml. Polarographic values of sample and std should be very close. From second detn calc.:

(a) mg fumaric acid/ml in *sample test soln C* = (mg fumaric acid/ml in working std soln (= 0.025)) $\times$ (numerical value of *sample test soln C*)/(numerical value of working std soln).

(b) % fumaric acid in sample = (mg fumaric acid/ml in *sample test soln C*) $\times$ (ml *sample test soln C* (= 25)) $\times$ 100/(mg sample in aliquot *sample soln A* used in prepg *sample test soln C*).

ANTIOXIDANTS

Qualitative Tests (2)—Official Final Action
(*Caution: See* **46.011, 46.039,** and **46.073.**)

20.006 Reagents

(a) *Barium hydroxide.*—1% $Ba(OH)_2 \cdot H_2O$ in boiled distd H_2O. Keep in tightly stoppered bottle.

(b) *Ehrlich reagent.*—Diazobenzene sulfonic acid. Prep. 0.5% soln $NaNO_2$ in H_2O and 0.5% soln sulfanilic acid in HCl (1 + 19). Prep. $NaNO_2$ soln fresh every 3 weeks. Keep solns refrigerated. Mix $NaNO_2$ and sulfanilic acid solns (1 + 100) daily.

(c) *Dianisidine soln.*—(*Caution:* Dianisidine may be harmful. *See* **46.084.**) Dissolve 250 mg dianisidine (3,3'-dimethoxybenzidine) in 50 ml anhyd. MeOH. Add 100 mg activated charcoal, shake 5 min, and filter. Mix 40 ml clear filtrate with 60 ml 1N HCl. Prep. daily and protect from light.

(d) *Activated Florisil adsorbent.*—60–100 mesh. Activated by manufacturer at 260° or 650° (available from Floridin Co.).

Test Florisil for BHT retention as follows: Add 0.2 mg BHT in 25 ml pet ether to prepd column, **20.007,** elute with 150 ml pet ether, and apply BHT test after evapg ether just to dryness as in **20.008**(d). If BHT is not eluted, activate remaining Florisil by heating 2 hr at 650°, cool, add 6.5% H_2O by wt, and homogenize by shaking 1 hr in closed container.

20.007 Preparation of Florisil Column for Cleanup of BHT Extract

Insert small glass wool plug into chromatgc tube 25 cm long $\times$ 20 mm diam. with Teflon stopcock, and add ca 12 g Florisil with gentle tapping. Wash with two 15 ml portions pet ether, adding second portion when liq. level drops to just above top of Florisil. When level of second portion is ca 1 cm above Florisil, close stopcock. Do not let column become dry.

20.008   *Tests*

(a) *Propyl gallate (PG).*—Weigh ca 30 g fat (melted by gentle warming) or oil, dissolve in ca 60 ml pet ether, and transfer to 250 ml separator. Add 15 ml H_2O and shake gently 1 min. Let sep. and drain aq. phase into 125 ml separator, leaving any emulsion in org. phase. Repeat extn of pet ether with 2 addnl 15 ml portions H_2O and reserve pet ether soln for further extn with acetonitrile, (b). Add 15 ml ether to combined aq. exts and shake 1 min. Discard aq. phase and evap. ether just to dryness in small beaker. Add 4 ml 50% alcohol to residue, swirl, and add 1 ml NH_4OH. If soln turns rose, PG is present. (Color is unstable and fades after few min.)

(b) *Nordihydroguaiaretic acid (NDGA).*—Ext pet ether soln from (a) by shaking 2 min with 20 ml acetonitrile. Let layers sep. and drain acetonitrile into 1 L separator. Repeat extn with 2 addnl 30 ml portions acetonitrile and discard pet ether. Dil. combined acetonitrile exts with 400 ml H_2O, add 2–3 g NaCl, and shake 2 min with 20 ml pet ether. Let layers sep., and drain dild acetonitrile into second 1 L separator. Ext dil. acetonitrile with 2 addnl 20 ml portions pet ether and reserve dild acetonitrile soln for further extn. Combine pet ether exts in 100 ml beaker and set aside for BHA and BHT tests.

Add 50 ml ether-pet ether (1 + 1) to dild acetonitrile and shake 2 min. (*Caution:* Vent separator.) Let layers sep., discard acetonitrile, and evap. ether just to dryness in small beaker. Add 4 ml 50% alcohol, swirl, and then add 1 ml 1% $Ba(OH)_2$ soln and mix. If NDGA is present, soln turns blue and fades rapidly.

(c) *Butylated hydroxyanisole (BHA).*—Take ⅓ of combined pet ether soln reserved for BHA-BHT tests and evap. just to dryness in small beaker, using gentle heat, under air current. Add 2.5 ml alcohol to dissolve residue and dil. with 2.5 ml H_2O. Swirl, add 1 ml Ehrlich reagent, immediately add 1 ml 1N NaOH, and swirl again. If soln turns red-purple, BHA is present.

(d) *Butylated hydroxytoluene (BHT).*—Pass remaining ⅔ combined pet ether soln thru Florisil column and elute with 150 ml pet ether. Collect eluate in 200 ml beaker and evap. just to dryness. Add 2.5 ml alcohol, swirl, and dil. with 2.5 ml H_2O. Add 2 ml dianisidine soln and mix. Add 0.8 ml 0.3% $NaNO_2$ soln. Mix, and let stand 5 min; then transfer to small separator. Add 0.5 ml $CHCl_3$, shake vigorously 30 sec, and let sep. If $CHCl_3$ turns pink to red, BHT is present. Confirm BHT by comparing spectrophtric curve of colored $CHCl_3$ ext with control prepd from

ref. std BHT as follows: Dissolve ca 15 mg BHT in 5 ml aq. alcohol (1 + 1), add 2 ml dianisidine soln, and proceed as above.

Butylated Hydroxyanisole (BHA) and Butylated Hydroxytoluene (BHT)
(3)—Official Final Action
(*Caution: See* **46.011, 46.039, 46.040, 46.048,** and **46.049.**)

20.009   *Principle*

BHA and BHT are extd from ready-to-eat breakfast cereals with CS_2 and detd by GLC, using flame ionization detection.

20.010   *Apparatus*

(a) *Gas chromatograph.* — Barber-Colman Co. Model 5000, or equiv., with H flame ionization detector and strip chart recorder. *Operating conditions:* temps—column 160°, detector 210°, flash heater 200°; N flow rate, to elute BHT in 3–4 min from QF-1 column and elute BHA in 3–4 min from Apiezon column; H flow rate, ca 40 ml/min for Apiezon and ca 25 ml/min for QF-1; air flow rate, ca 340 ml/min; electrometer sensitivity, 500× $(5 \times 10^{-10}$ amp full scale deflection) with 1 mv recorder. Adjust H and air flow rates if necessary. Alternatively, adjust electrometer sensitivity so 0.1 μg BHA gives ca 50% deflection. Repeat injections until constant peak hts are obtained on successive injections of identical vol. of std mixt.

Order of appearance from Apiezon column (4'): BHA, BHT, di-BHA. Order of appearance from QF-1 column (6'): BHT, BHA, di-BHA.

Use of 2 GLC columns serves to identify BHA and BHT. Use Apiezon L/Gas Chrom Q, 4' column to resolve 2- and 3-isomers of BHA. Adjust GLC parameters to obtain good sepn of BHA isomers, such as adjusting column temp. to 150° and electrometer sensitivity to 1000×. Adjust amt BHA std injected to give 50% deflection.

(b) *GLC columns.*—Glass, 4' × 4 mm and 6' × 4 mm, packed with Apiezon L and QF-1 silicone oil (Fluoro silicone fluid, FS 1265), resp., on 80–100 mesh Gas Chrom Q (Applied Science Laboratories). Prep. columns and column material by carefully washing insides of 4' and 6' columns and small amt fine glass wool with dichlorodimethylsilane soln, rinsing with MeOH, and drying. (*Caution:* Dichlorodimethylsilane is toxic. Avoid contact with skin and eyes. Use effective fume removal device.)

Slowly sprinkle ca 50 g Gas Chrom Q into 800 ml beaker almost filled with CCl_4. Remove fine particles that remain on surface with vac. line and trap. Decant solv. and dry GLC support.

Transfer 20.0 g dried Gas Chrom Q to 500 ml r-b flask. Add 100 ml $CHCl_3$ or CH_2Cl_2 and mix gently. Dissolve 1.0 g Apiezon L or 2.0 g QF-1 in 50 ml $CHCl_3$ or CH_2Cl_2, add to flask, and mix gently. Evap. to dryness, using rotary vac. evaporator and H_2O bath (35° for CH_2Cl_2 and 70° for $CHCl_3$).

Carefully plug exit of column with small plug of fine glass wool and thru-hole septum. Apply vac. to exit port and slowly add coated support (Apiezon L/Gas Chrom Q for 4' column; QF-1/Gas Chrom Q for 6' column) thru injection port, tapping very gently to aid compaction. Pack to within 1 cm of area heated by flash heater. Plug with fine glass wool and condition ca 3 days at 200° with slow stream of N (ca 10 ml/min) or until steady baseline is obtained.

(c) *Chromatographic tube.*—25 × 200 mm glass tube with small drip tip (4 mm id, 6 mm od × 50 mm long), with or without medium porosity fritted disk, with close-fitting tamping rod.

(d) *Fine glass wool.*—Wash with CS_2 and dry.

20.011   Reagents

(a) *Carbon disulfide.*—Reagent grade; nearly colorless. If distinctly yellow, distill before use.

(b) *BHA, BHT, and di-BHA std mixture.*—0.02 $\mu g/\mu l$ each of BHA, BHT, and di-BHA in CS_2. Dissolve 1.00 mg each of BHA and BHT in small amt CS_2, add 10.0 ml internal std soln, and dil. to 50 ml with CS_2 or prep. by diln of more concd solns with CS_2. Prep. fresh and store in low-actinic glassware.

(c) *Internal std soln.*—0.1 μg di-BHA/μl CS_2. Prep. fresh and store in low-actinic glassware.

(d) *Dichlorodimethylsilane soln.*—Dil. 5 ml to 100 ml with toluene.

20.012   Determination

(Protect all solns from light; complete assay in 1 day. Use either GLC column for analysis.)

Grind sample to pass No. 20 sieve and mix well. (When necessary, ground sample may be stored frozen under N for few days.) Place, if necessary, small plug of fine glass wool at bottom of chromatgc tube, add 20.0 g sample to column, using tamping rod to pack it firmly without solv., and top column with another small glass wool plug, tamped down. Mark 100 ml beaker at 50 ml level and place under column to collect eluate. Add three 5 ml portions of CS_2 to column, letting each portion sink into column before adding next. Elute CS_2 at ca 5 ml/min; use N, if necessary, to maintain flow rate.

Add several 10 ml portions of CS_2, letting each portion sink into column until 50 ml eluate collects. Rinse tip of column with small amt CS_2. Accurately add di-BHA to eluate to obtain concn after evapn of 0.02 μg di-BHA/μl final soln. Evap. eluate under gentle stream of N in hood at room temp. to small vol. (<5.0 ml). Accurately dil. evapd sample to appropriate vol. (e.g., 5.0 ml) for GLC analysis. Inject 3.0–9.0 μl sample, using 10 μl syringe, into gas chromatograph. Before and after each series of sample chromatograms, inject 3.0–9.0 μl std mixt. and average std values for calcns. Measure each peak ht in mm. (Ht of BHA, BHT, and di-BHA peaks should be in range of 30–95% full scale deflection.)

Calc. ppm antioxidant present, correcting for internal std, as follows:

ppm BHA or BHT = $(H_x/H_s) \times (C_s/C_x) \times (H_{si}/H_{xi}) \times (C_{xi}/C_{si})$, where H_x and H_s = ht (mm) of sample and std peaks, resp.; H_{xi} and H_{si} = ht (mm) of internal std peaks in sample and std, resp.; C_x and C_s = concn of sample (g/μl) and std ($\mu g/\mu l$), resp.; and C_{xi} and C_{si} = concn ($\mu g/\mu l$) of internal std in sample and std solns, resp.

Propyl Gallate (4)—Official First Action

(Caution: See 46.011, 46.039, and 46.073.)

20.013   Reagents

(a) *Petroleum ether reagent.*—Mix 1 vol. 30–60° pet ether (14.080 or equiv.) with 3 vols 60–100° pet ether (Skellysolve B and H have been found satisfactory) and shake mixt. 5 min with $\frac{1}{10}$ its vol. H_2SO_4. Discard acid layer, wash several times with H_2O, then once with 1% NaOH soln, and then again with H_2O until washings are substantially neut. Discard all washings and distill pet ether in all-glass app.

(b) *Ammonium acetate solns.*—1.25%, 1.67%, and 10% aq. solns. Soln contg 1.67% NH_4OAc in 5% alcohol may also be required.

(c) *Ferrous tartrate reagent.*—Dissolve 0.100 g $FeSO_4 \cdot 7H_2O$ and 0.500 g Rochelle salt ($NaKC_4H_4O_6 \cdot 4H_2O$) in H_2O and dil. to 100 ml. Reagent must be used within 3 hr of prepn.

(d) *Propyl gallate std soln.*—50 $\mu g/ml$. Dissolve 50 mg propyl gallate in H_2O and dil. to 1 L with H_2O.

20.014   Preparation of Standard Curve

Place at least 7 aliquots of std soln, **20.013**(d), covering range from 50 to 1000 μg, in 50 ml g-s erlenmeyers. Add exactly 2.5 ml 10% NH_4OAc to each flask, dil. to exactly 24 ml with H_2O, and pipet 1 ml ferrous tartrate reagent into each flask. Let solns stand ≥3 min. Measure A at 540 nm relative to soln contg 20 ml 1.25% NH_4OAc soln, 4 ml H_2O, and 1 ml ferrous tartrate soln. Plot μg propyl gallate against A.

20.015   Determination

Dissolve 40 g fat or oil in the pet ether reagent and dil. to 250 ml with this reagent. (Gentle warming may be necessary to obtain complete soln.) Pipet 100 ml fat soln into 250 ml separator. Ext fat soln with 20 ml aq. 1.67% NH_4OAc soln by continuously inverting separator 2.5 min. After phases sep. completely, drain aq. layer into 100 ml vol. flask, being careful not to let any oil droplets fall into flask. (Some shortenings show strong tendency to emulsify during aq. extn. To prevent emulsification, add 2 ml *n*-octanol to fat soln aliquot before beginning extn and use 1.67% NH_4OAc soln in 5% alcohol for extn in place of aq. soln. This procedure need be used only when usual method fails.)

Repeat extn twice with 20 ml portions 1.67% NH_4OAc soln, combining aq. layers in vol. flask.

Finally, ext fat soln with 15 ml H_2O 30 sec and combine aq. layer with previous washings. Let layers sep. completely after each washing. Add exactly 2.5 ml 10% NH_4OAc soln to combined exts in vol. flask and dil. to vol. with H_2O. This soln now contains 1.25% NH_4OAc. Filter thru dry rapid paper to remove any turbidity. (Colors must be developed on same day ext is prepd. If combined exts stand more than several hr, yellow color may develop and solns must be discarded.)

Pipet aliquot of ext, $\leq$20 ml, into 50 ml g-s erlenmeyer. Dil. to 20 ml with 1.25% NH_4OAc soln. Add exactly 4 ml H_2O and pipet 1 ml ferrous tartrate reagent into flask. Mix well, and measure A at 540 nm relative to soln contg 20 ml 1.25% NH_4OAc soln, 4 ml H_2O, and 1 ml ferrous tartrate reagent. Calc. amt of propyl gallate from std curve.

CHEMICAL PRESERVATIVES

BENZOIC ACID

(*Caution: See* 46.011, 46.039, 46.040, 46.054, and 46.056.)

Qualitative Tests—Official Final Action

20.016 *Preliminary Test*

Ext benzoic acid as in 20.085 or 20.087. If appreciable benzoic acid is present, it will crystallize from ether in shining leaflets having characteristic odor on warming. Dissolve cryst. deposit in hot H_2O, divide into 2 portions, and test as in 20.017 or 20.018. Deposit may also be purified as in 20.085(c) and mp detd.

20.017 *Ferric Chloride Test*

Make soln, 20.016, alk. with few drops of NH_4OH, expel excess NH_3 by evapn, dissolve residue in few ml hot H_2O, filter if necessary, and add few drops *aq. 0.5% $FeCl_3$ soln*. Salmon-color ppt of ferric benzoate indicates presence of benzoic acid.

20.018 *Modified Mohler Test (5)*

(Presence of phthln interferes)

To aq. soln, 20.016, add 1 or 2 drops ca 10% NaOH soln and evap. to dryness. To residue add 5–10 drops H_2SO_4 and small crystal KNO_3. Heat 10 min in glycerol bath at 120–130° (must be $\leq$130°). Cool, add 1 ml H_2O, and make distinctly ammoniacal. Boil soln to decompose any NH_4NO_2 that may form. Cool, and add drop of fresh, *colorless $(NH_4)_2S$ soln*, but do not let layers mix. Red-brown ring indicates benzoic acid. On mixing, color diffuses thruout liq., and on heating finally changes to greenish-yellow. This change differentiates benzoic acid from salicylic or cinnamic acids. Salicylic and cinnamic acids form colored compds that are not destroyed by heating.

Quantitative Methods—Official Final Action

(Presence of vanillin interferes (6))

Titrimetric Method

20.019 *Preparation of Sample*

(a) *General method.*—Mix sample thoroly, grinding if solid or semi-solid. Transfer 150 ml or 150 g to 500 ml vol. flask, add enough pulverized NaCl to sat. H_2O in sample, make alk. to litmus paper with 10% NaOH soln or with milk of lime (1 part powd recently slaked $Ca(OH)_2$ suspended in 3 parts H_2O), and dil. to vol. with satd NaCl soln. Shake thoroly, let stand $\geq$2 hr, shaking frequently, and filter. If sample contains large amts of fat, portions of which may contaminate filtrate, add few ml 10% NaOH soln to filtrate and ext with ether before proceeding as in 20.020. If alcohol is present, proceed as in (d). If sample contains large amts of matter precipitable by NaCl soln, proceed as in (e).

(b) *Catsup.*—Add 15 g pulverized NaCl to 150 g sample, and transfer mixt. to 500 ml vol. flask, rinsing with ca 150 ml satd NaCl soln. Make slightly alk. to litmus paper with 10% NaOH soln and dil. to vol. with satd NaCl soln. Let stand $\geq$2 hr, shaking frequently. Squeeze thru heavy muslin bag, and filter.

(c) *Jellies, jams, preserves, and marmalades.*—Digest 150 g sample in ca 300 ml satd NaCl soln. Add 15 g pulverized NaCl. Make alk. to litmus paper with milk of lime. Transfer to 500 ml vol. flask and dil. to vol. with satd NaCl soln. Let stand $\geq$2 hr, shaking frequently; centrf. if necessary, and filter.

(d) *Cider containing alcohol, and similar products.*—Make 250 ml sample alk. to litmus paper with 10% NaOH soln and evap. on steam bath to ca 100 ml. Transfer to 250 ml vol. flask, add 30 g pulverized NaCl, and shake until dissolved. Dil. to original vol. of 250 ml with satd NaCl soln; let stand $\geq$2 hr, shaking frequently, and filter.

(e) *Salted or dried fish.*—Wash 50 g ground sample into 500 ml vol. flask with H_2O. Make slightly alk. to litmus paper with 10% NaOH soln and dil. to vol. with H_2O. Let stand $\geq$2 hr, shaking frequently, and filter. Pipet as large a measured portion of filtrate as possible ($\geq$300 ml) into second 500 ml vol. flask, and add 30 g pulverized NaCl for each 100 ml soln. Shake until NaCl dissolves and dil. to vol. with satd NaCl soln. Mix thoroly, and filter off pptd protein and other extraneous matter.

20.020 *Determination*

Pipet 100–200 ml filtrate, 20.019, into separator. Neutze to litmus paper with HCl (1 + 3) and add 5 ml excess. With salted fish, protein usually ppts on acidifying, but ppt does not interfere with extn. Ext carefully with $CHCl_3$, using successive portions of 70, 50, 40, and 30 ml. To avoid formation of emulsion, shake cautiously each time, using rotary motion. $CHCl_3$ layer usually seps readily after standing few min. If emulsion forms, break it by stirring

CHCl$_3$ layer with glass rod, by drawing off into second separator and giving 1 or 2 sharp shakes from one end of separator to other, or by centrfg few min. As this is progressive extn, carefully draw off as much clear CHCl$_3$ soln as possible after each extn, but do not draw off any of emulsion with CHCl$_3$ layer. If this precaution is taken, CHCl$_3$ ext need not be washed.

Transfer combined CHCl$_3$ exts to porcelain evapg dish, rinse container several times with few ml CHCl$_3$, and evap. to dryness at room temp. in current of dry air.

Ext may also be transferred from separator to 300 ml erlenmeyer and separator rinsed with three 5–10 ml portions CHCl$_3$. Distill very slowly at low temp. to ca ¼ original vol. Transfer residue to porcelain evapg dish, rinsing flask with three 5–10 ml portions CHCl$_3$, and evap. to dryness at room temp. in current of dry air.

Dry residue overnight (or until no odor of HOAc can be detected if product is catsup) in desiccator contg H$_2$SO$_4$. Dissolve residue of benzoic acid in 30–50 ml alcohol neut. to phthln; add ca ¼ this vol. of H$_2$O and 1 or 2 drops phthln; and titr. with 0.05N NaOH. 1 ml 0.05N NaOH = 0.0072 g anhyd. Na benzoate.

Spectrophotometric Method (7)

(Applicable to catsup, other tomato products, jams, jellies, beverages contg small amts of alcohol, soft drinks, and fruit juices. Not applicable to solids.)

20.021   *Preparation of Standard Curve*

Prep. soln of benzoic acid in ether contg 50 mg/L. Det. A of this soln in well stoppered cuvet in Beckman DU or recording spectrophtr between 265 and 280 nm in 1 nm intervals. Plot A against wavelength and record wavelength of min. at ca 267.5 nm as point B, other min. at ca 276.5 nm as point D, and highest max. at ca 272 nm as point C.

Prep. solns of benzoic acid in ether contg 20, 40, 60, 80, 100, and 120 mg/L. Det. A of these solns in well stoppered cuvet in spectrophtr at points B, C, and D. For each concn, average A at B and D and subtract this value from A at C. Plot difference against concn.

20.022   *Preparation of Sample*

Mix sample thoroly. Transfer 10 g or 10 ml to separator and dil. to 200 ml with satd NaCl soln. Make soln definitely acid to litmus with HCl and mix well.

20.023   *Determination*

Ext prepd soln with 70, 50, 40, and 30 ml portions ether, shaking well to ensure complete extn. (Break emulsions by standing, stirring, or centrfg.) Drain and discard aq. phase. Wash combined ether exts with 50, 40, and 30 ml portions HCl (1 + 1000) and

discard HCl washings. (If ext requires no purification, proceed to next par.) Ext ether soln with 50, 40, 30, and 20 ml portions 0.1 % NH$_4$OH and discard ether. Neutze combined NH$_4$OH exts with HCl and add 1 ml excess. Ext acidified soln with 70, 50, 40, and 30 ml ether.

Dil. combined ether exts to 200 ml with ether and det. A in well stoppered cuvet in spectrophtr at wavelengths B, C, and D, dilg with ether if necessary to obtain optimum concn of 20–120 mg/L. Average A at B and D and subtract this value from A at C. Det. concn benzoic acid from std curve, correcting for dilns. Benzoic acid $\times$ 1.18 = Na benzoate.

Conduct detn similarly on benzoate-free sample of product and det. A in region 265–280 nm at 1 nm intervals. If curve is straight line in this region, method is applicable to this product.

Thin Layer Chromatographic Method (8)— Official First Action

20.024   *Apparatus and Reagents*

(a) *Steam distillation apparatus.*—See Fig. 20:1 for arrangement. (1) Connecting tube only, with flask joint ⊤ 34/54 and condenser joint ⊤ 24/40 (JD 1710); (2) Kjeldahl flask, 800 ml capacity with outer joint ⊤ 34/54 (JF 6030); (3) condenser, 30 cm with outer joint ⊤ 24/40 at top and drip tip at delivery end (JC 6400); (4) steam generator, see **18.026** (a) and Fig. 18:1; (5) Powerstats (9-521); and (6) Glas-Col heating mantle, 500 ml (11-472-10V4). (Items 1–3 cite Scientific Glass Apparatus Co. Nos; items 5 and 6 cite Fisher Scientific Co. Nos.)

(b) *Ultraviolet recording spectrophotometer and accessories.*—Recording between 250 and 350 nm; with 5 cm micro cells and cell adapter (Pyrocell Mfg. Co., 91 Carver Ave, Westwood, NJ 07675, Nos. 5009, 5009A).

(c) *Thin layer chromatographic equipment and absorbents.*—See **29.006**; kieselguhr G and silica gel GF 254 (Brinkmann Instruments, Inc.).

20.025   *Preparation of Plates*

In 250 ml erlenmeyer, mix 10 g each of kieselguhr G and silica gel GF 254. Add 45 ml H$_2$O and shake 30 sec. Set applicator at 0.25 mm and apply mixt.; coat 5 glass plates. Air-dry 10 min and dry in forced-draft oven 1 hr at 100°.

20.026   *Preparation of Sample*

(a) *Liquids.*—Accurately weigh ca 50–60 g sample directly into 800 ml Kjeldahl flask. Continue as in (c), beginning "Add 200 g MgSO$_4$.7H$_2$O ..."

(b) *Solids.*—Accurately weigh ca 40 g sample into high-speed blender. Add 100 ml H$_2$O (or more if necessary) and blend until homogeneous. Quant. transfer to 800 ml Kjeldahl flask with small portions H$_2$O. Continue as in (c), beginning "Add 200 g MgSO$_4$.7H$_2$O ..."

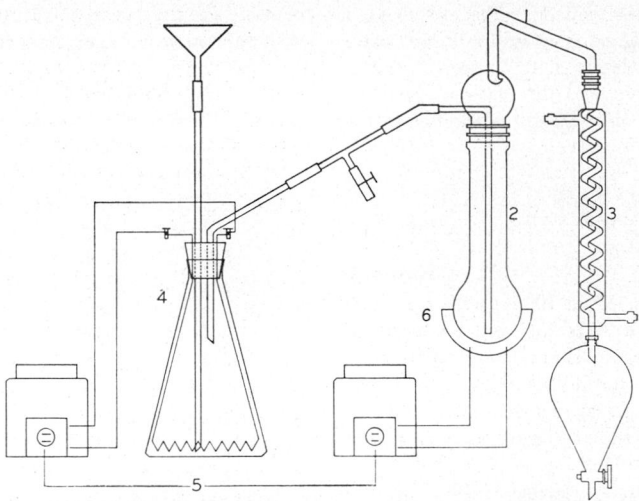

FIG. 20:1—Steam distillation apparatus

(c) *Semisolids and solid-liquid mixtures.*—Blend entire unit sample in high-speed blender to homogeneous mixt. Quant. transfer ca 50–60 g blended sample (accurately weighed) to 800 ml Kjeldahl flask with small portions H_2O, if necessary. Add 200 g $MgSO_4 \cdot 7H_2O$ and 25 ml H_3PO_4. Wash down neck of flask with H_2O until total vol. is 350–375 ml. Steam distill sample directly into 1 L separator contg 50 ml NaOH soln (4 g/100 ml); collect 725–750 ml distillate in $\geq$90 min by adjusting Powerstats. (Distn rate is very critical; typical drop time is 50 drops/20 sec.) Rinse condenser with ca 20 ml H_2O. Acidify distillate to litmus with ca 20 ml HCl. Ext with one 100 ml and four 50 ml portions CHCl$_3$-ether (2 + 1). Shake each ext vigorously $\geq$1 min and collect exts in 600 ml beaker. Evap. combined CHCl$_3$-ether exts carefully on steam bath, using gentle air current, to ca 25 ml, washing down sides of beaker occasionally with CHCl$_3$-ether. (Do not let exts go to dryness.) Transfer to 50 ml vol. flask, wash beaker with small portions CHCl$_3$-ether, and transfer washings to vol. flask. Dil. to vol. with CHCl$_3$-ether for TLC analysis.

20.027   *Determination*

Spot 100 μl sample soln, using 50 μl Hamilton syringe twice, under gentle air draft on prepd plate. Also, spot 100 μl std benzoic acid soln (50 mg/50 ml alcohol). Spot sample(s) and std ca 1″ from bottom edge of plate and 1.5″ apart, beginning 1″ in from side edge. Place plate in chromatgc chamber contg 250–300 ml mobile solv., *n*-hexane-HOAc (96 + 4), and develop chromatogram for 10 cm. Remove and air-dry 5 min. Observe under UV shortwave radiation (2540Å). Sample and std benzoic acid appear as dark blue-purple spots on light fluorescent background. With pencil, circle spots 0.5″ from outer edge of each spot. (This gives exact location of each acid when plate is removed from radiation.) Scrape encircled

area with steel spatula onto piece of Glassine paper and carefully transfer to 10 ml vol. flask. From unused portion of plate, scrape off area ca equal to that used for sample into 10 ml vol. flask to serve as blank. To each, add 7 ml alcohol, stopper, and shake 30 sec. Dil. to vol. with alcohol, transfer to centrf. tube, and centrf. until clear (ca 5 min) at high speed. Decant clear supernatant soln into 5 cm micro cell and scan on recording spectrophtr from 310 to 250 nm against blank. Compare sample and std.

% Benzoic acid = [(A_{sample}/A_{std}) × (g std/50 ml)/(g sample/50 ml)] × 100

% Na benzoate = % benzoic acid × 1.180

20.028   *Qualitative Tests*

Evap. 2 ml portions CHCl$_3$-ether ext to dryness. On this residue, perform test for benzoic acid, **14.039**, par. 4, beginning "From Mohr pipet, add ..." and ending "benzoic acid." Use 50 ml Pyrex test tube (25 × 150 mm).

Run IR spectrum. Evap. 5 ml CHCl$_3$-ether exts to dryness and make KBr disk with residue.

BORIC ACID AND BORATES

20.029   Qualitative Test (9)—Official Final Action

(a) *Preliminary test.*—Acidify sample with HCl (7 ml acid to each 100 ml sample). Heat solid or pasty samples with enough H_2O to make sufficiently fluid before acidifying. Immerse strip of turmeric paper, **20.030**(a), in acidified liq., and let paper dry spontaneously. If $Na_2B_4O_7$ or H_3BO_3 is present, paper turns characteristic red, changed by NH_4OH to dark blue-green, but restored by acid.

(b) *Confirmatory test.*—Make ca 25 g sample decidedly alk. with lime-H_2O or milk of lime and evap. to dryness on steam bath. Ignite dry residue at low red heat until org. matter is thoroly charred. Cool, digest with ca 15 ml H_2O, and add HCl dropwise until soln is distinctly acid. Immerse piece of turmeric paper in soln and dry without heat. In presence of $Na_2B_4O_7$ or H_3BO_3 color change will be same as in (a).

Semiquantitative Method (10)—Official Final Action
(Applicable to meat)

20.030 *Reagents*

(a) *Turmeric paper.*—Add 100 ml 80% alcohol to 1.5–2.0 g turmeric powder in 250 ml g-s erlenmeyer. Shake 5 min and filter. Dip sheets of Whatman No. 2 filter paper into the clear filtrate in flat-bottom dish (petri dish). Hang paper to dry. After 1 hr cut into $2\frac{1}{4} \times \frac{3}{8}''$ strips and store in tightly stoppered container protected from light.

(b) *Boric acid std soln.*—10 mg H_3BO_3/ml. Dissolve 1.000 g H_3BO_3 in H_2O and dil. to 100 ml.

20.031 *Preparation of Reference Standards*

Transfer 0.00, 0.10, 0.20, 0.50, 0.75, 1.00, 2.50, and 5.00 ml std H_3BO_3 soln to 15 ml test tubes. Dil. to 10 ml with H_2O and add 0.7 ml HCl. Keep tubes tightly stoppered to prevent evapn. These stds represent 0.00, 0.02, 0.04, 0.10, 0.15, 0.20, 0.50, and 1.00% H_3BO_3 in meat (based on 25 g sample extd with 50 ml H_2O and 10 ml aliquot used for test). Std solns may be stored in Pyrex test tubes >6 months. On long storage, borate is leached from Pyrex.

20.032 *Determination*

Disperse 25 g ground meat in 50 ml H_2O in 125 ml erlenmeyer, using flat-end stirring rod. Cover with watch glass or small funnel. Bring to boil on hot plate (or over medium flame) with agitation. Do not overheat. Cool in ice bath or in beaker of H_2O in refrigerator until fat solidifies (ca 0.5 hr). Filter thru pledget of glass wool. Transfer 10 ml filtrate to 15 ml test tube, add 0.7 ml HCl, stopper, and mix.

Mark identification on end of piece of turmeric paper and dip unmarked end into unknown soln to $\frac{1}{2}$ the length of paper. Quickly remove moistened paper and place on sheet of white filter paper. Flat-tipped forceps are useful in handling paper.

Place freshly prepd std strips of test paper (made by dipping turmeric papers in similar manner into series of std solns) alongside sample turmeric strips.

After ≥1 hr (but <2 hr) at room temp., strips are dry enough for comparison. Good natural light is preferred. Place std strips ca 0.5" apart on white filter paper background and bring "unknown" sample strips between adjacent stds for close color matching. If color falls between 2 stds, est. value. Disregard streaks of color that may develop at edge of test strip.

If color intensity is beyond range of stds, repeat test with appropriate diln of meat filtrate (i.e., 5 ml filtrate, 5 ml H_2O, 0.7 ml HCl and multiply final reading by 2). Use freshly prepd set of std papers with each series of samples tested.

Quantitative Methods

20.033 Titrimetric Method—Official Final Action

Make 10–100 g sample (depending upon material and quantity of H_3BO_3 present) distinctly alk. with 10% NaOH soln and evap. to dryness in Pt dish. Ignite residue until org. matter is thoroly charred, avoiding intense red heat; cool, digest with ca 20 ml hot H_2O, and add HCl dropwise until reaction is distinctly acid. Filter into 100 ml vol. flask and wash with little hot H_2O. (Vol. filtrate should be <50–60 ml.) Return filter contg any unoxidized C to Pt dish, make alk. by wetting thoroly with lime-H_2O, dry on steam bath, and ignite to white ash.

Dissolve ash in few ml HCl (1 + 3) and add to liq. in 100 ml vol. flask, rinsing dish with few ml H_2O. To combined solns add 0.5 g $CaCl_2$ and few drops phthln, then 10% NaOH soln until permanent light pink is produced. Finally dil. to vol. with lime-H_2O, mix, and filter thru dry filter. To 50 ml filtrate add $1N$ H_2SO_4 until pink disappears; then add Me orange, **6.004**(g), and continue addn of acid until yellow changes to pink. Boil ca 1 min to expel CO_2. Cool, and carefully add $0.2N$ NaOH until liq. becomes yellow, avoiding excess alkali. (All H_3BO_3 is now in free state with no uncombined H_2SO_4 present.) Add 1–2 g neut. mannitol and few drops phthln, read buret, and again titr. soln with the std NaOH until pink. Add little more mannitol, and if pink disappears, continue addn of the std alkali until pink reappears. Repeat alternate addn of mannitol and std alkali until permanent end point is reached. Vol. glycerol (neut. to phthln) equal to vol. soln to be titrd may be substituted for mannitol. 1 ml $0.2N$ NaOH = 0.0124 g H_3BO_3.

Spectrophotometric Method (11)—Official First Action

(Applicable to caviar. Rinse all glassware with H_2O before use. Carry reagent and caviar blanks thru detn with stds and samples. For caviar blank use caviar shown to be B-free by **20.041**.)

20.034 *Principle*

B reacts with curcumin in nonaq. acid soln to form stable color complex. Intensity of color is measured spectrophtric at 555 nm.

20.035 *Apparatus*

(a) *Spectrophotometer.*—Beckman DK-2A ratio recording spectrophtr (or DU spectrophtr) with silica 1 cm cells with g-s stoppers.

(b) *Platinum dishes.*—3 cm deep × 7 cm diam.

20.036 *Reagents*

(a) *Curcumin soln.*—0.125%. Dissolve 125 mg curcumin (available from Eastman Kodak Co.) in 100 ml HOAc. Prep. fresh daily.

(b) *Sodium hydroxide.*—10%. Keep in plastic bottle.

(c) *Sulfuric acid-acetic acid.*—(1 + 1). Use new bottles of acids.

(d) *Anhydrous alcohol (used thruout method).*— MeOH may be substituted. Let stand 24 hr over CaO, decant, and distill twice from KOH.

(e) *Boron std solns.*—(1) *Soln A.*—100 µg B/ml. Accurately weigh 57±3 mg H_3BO_3, ACS crystal, into 100 ml vol. flask. Add 50 ml H_2O and place on shaking machine 20 min. Dil. to vol. and mix. (Prep. on day method is run.) (2) *Soln B.*—1 µg B/ml. Pipet 1 ml *Soln A* into 100 ml vol. flask, dil. to vol. with H_2O, and mix.

20.037   *Preparation of Sample Solutions*

Weigh 270±25 mg caviar into 250 ml 2-neck, r-b flask; place sample in exact center of bottom of flask. Connect flask to straight tube H_2O condenser to facilitate rinsing, and place condenser in center hole of flask and glass stopper in side hole. (Do *not* use lubricating grease.) Add 1 ml H_2SO_4, close flask with glass stopper, apply small flame from bunsen burner to circumference of acid soln, and heat until surface of liq. begins to move. Remove flame. Promote gentle evolution of bubbles with intermittent flame. Do not cause acid to spatter or to evolve copious fumes. Continue heating 5 min, or until solids are dissolved; soln will be black and smooth. Cool flask in ice-H_2O. If fumes are present, let settle. With syringe, quickly add 1 ml 30% H_2O_2 thru stoppered opening, close flask immediately, and gently heat soln with intermittent flame to initiate boiling. Heat ca 5 min, or until fumes start to evolve. (Soln should be generally clear with some minute particles.) Cool flask to room temp. in ice-H_2O. Rinse condenser directly into reaction flask with H_2O. Disconnect flask, quant. transfer soln, using glass funnel, with H_2O into 100 ml vol. flask, dil. to vol., and mix. (Solns should be pale yellow or colorless.)

20.038   *Determination*

Pipet following into individual Pt dishes: 1 ml H_2O for reagent blank; 1, 2, 3, 4, and 5 ml std *Soln B;* 1 ml caviar sample soln; 1 ml caviar blank soln (B-free). Add 1 ml 10% NaOH to each dish and swirl to mix thoroly. Place dishes on vigorous steam bath (expose directly to steam) and dry until chalk white (ca 2.5–3 hr). Transfer dishes to 100±5° oven and continue to dry residue 0.5 hr. (*Caution:* Higher temps will cause spattering.) Remove dishes and cool. Add 3 ml curcumin soln. Use individual spatula for each dish and stir residue with stainless steel or plastic spatula to dissolve. (All std residues will dissolve in 2–3 min, but sample soln does not dissolve completely and must be stirred 5 min. Very gentle heat may be applied to promote soln.) Cool dishes to room temp. and add 3 ml HOAc-H_2SO_4 soln. Stir with same spatula to mix completely until no visible

yellow color remains in dish or on spatula; continue to stir and rotate dish for 2 min after yellow color disappears. Let soln stand 15 min. Transfer solns with ca 50 ml anhyd. alcohol (eye dropper works well) to 100 ml vol. flasks, using glass funnels. Thoroly rinse dishes into flasks with anhyd. alcohol and dil. to vol. within 5 ml of mark. Treat each soln sep. as follows: Dil. to vol. and mix. Filter thru dry paper and discard first 3 ml. Collect filtrate directly in spectrophtr cells and read A against anhyd. alcohol at 700 and 555 nm.

Calc. ΔA of std solns ($A_{555} - A_{700}$). Subtract reagent blank ΔA from std readings. Likewise, calc. ΔA caviar solns. Subtract caviar blank ΔA from sample ΔA. Plot std curve on graph paper: µg B/100 ml as abscissa against ΔA as ordinate. Det. µg B/100 ml for caviar from graph.

g B = [µg B/100 ml (from graph)]/10^4

% Boric acid = (g B $\times$ 5.7142 $\times$ 100)/g sample.

Qualitative Thin Layer Test for Boron in Caviar (Screening Technique)

20.039   *Reagents*

(a) *TLC plates.*—3 $\times$ 1″ microscopic slides coated with 250 µm silica gel G (Merck).

(b) *Developing solvent.*—Anhyd. alcohol-benzene (1 + 10).

(c) *Spray reagents.*—(1) NH_4OH; (2) HOAc-H_2SO_4 (1 + 1). (*Caution:* caustic spray; *see* 46.017.)

20.040   *Preparation of Silica Gel Slides*

Clean slides with soap and rinse thoroly until they drain cleanly (without beading). Place slides on template, as shown in Fig. 20:2.

To make slides adhere to template, place 1 drop H_2O under each slide as it is set in place.

Weigh 30 g silica gel into 250 ml g-s erlenmeyer. Add 60 ml H_2O and agitate gently 45 sec. Pour quickly into Desaga-Brinkmann spreader set to give 250 µm thickness. Pull applicator evenly over slides. Air-dry slides 30 min. Place slides in oven 30 min at 100°.

20.041   *Determination*

(*Caution: See* 46.017.)

Put 10 ml developing solv. into 250 ml lipless beaker or suitable jar. Place filter paper wick (1 $\times$ 3″) in solv., cover beaker with watch glass, and let equilibrate 5 min.

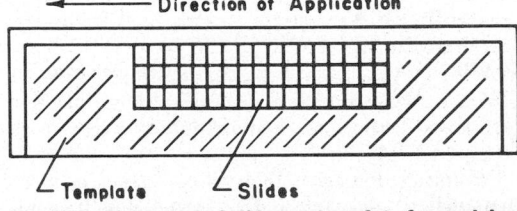

FIG. 20:2—Placement of slides on template for applying silica gel coating

Place 100±20 mg caviar in mortar. Grind and ext with 20 ml H_2O. Transfer washings to g-s centrf. tube and centrf. 5 min. Decant supernatant into 100 ml vol. flask. Add 10 ml H_2O to residue in tube, stopper, and shake vigorously 1 min. Centrf. and decant supernatant into same vol. flask. Repeat with 10 ml H_2O, dil. to vol., and mix. Place 2 ml each of sample soln, std soln, and H_2O for blank in sep. Pt dishes. Add ca 6 drops 10% NaOH to each dish and swirl to mix thoroly. Evap. to chalk white dryness on vigorous steam bath (expose directly to steam). (Hot plate may be used; avoid spattering.) Dissolve residue in ca 1.5 ml 0.125% curcumin soln, applying gentle heat if necessary to dissolve residue. Add ca 1.5 ml $HOAc-H_2SO_4$ soln (1 + 1), mix thoroly with stainless steel or plastic spatula, and let stand 15 min. Transfer solns to graduated beakers with absolute alcohol, dil. to 50 ml, and stir. Spot 40 μl blank, std soln, 20.036(e)(2), and sample soln on same slide. Place slide in beaker, cover, and let chromatogram develop 10 min. Remove slide, airdry, and note red-purple spot at origin and excess curcumin dye above. Spray with spray reagent (1) and note blue color change in spot at origin. Respray with spray reagent (2) and note change to red-purple.

DEHYDROACETIC ACID

20.042   Qualitative Test (12)—Official
First Action

(*Caution:* See 46.011, 46.039, and 46.054.)

(a) *Salicylaldehyde reagent.*—Dissolve 10 ml salicylaldehyde in alcohol and dil. to 50 ml.

(b) *Test.*—Transfer dehydroacetic acid soln remaining in 500 ml vol. flask after quant. detn, 20.043, to 1 L separator. Add 100–125 ml ether and shake vigorously. Let sep., drain aq. layer, and discard. Drain ether into 125 ml erlenmeyer, taking care not to include any emulsion or H_2O. Evap. ether ext to dryness on steam bath and dissolve residue in 1 ml ca 0.5N NaOH. Pour alk. soln into test tube (do not rinse flask); add 0.5 ml of alc. salicylaldehyde soln and 1 ml NaOH (1 + 1). Mix, and place in boiling H_2O bath 5 min. Remove tube from bath, add 2 ml H_2O, and observe color. Include reagent blank and control contg 0.2 or 0.3 mg dehydroacetic acid for comparison. With ≤10 ppm dehydroacetic acid in cheese, red or orange soln is obtained. Intensity of color is approx. proportional to quantity of dehydroacetic acid present.

Quantitative Method (12)—Official
First Action

20.043   *Determination*

Weigh 50–60 g cheese to nearest 0.1 g, place in high-speed blender, and comminute (covered) with 80 ml $CHCl_3$ 3 min, scraping down walls and cover once during operation. Place filter paper on 2–3″ diam. fritted glass buchner (if fritted glass funnel is not available, use ordinary buchner), transfer mixt.

to funnel with spatula, and filter with suction. Return cake and paper to blender, add 80 ml $CHCl_3$, blend 1 min, and refilter into same flask. Use fresh paper for each filtration. Repeat extn and filtration for third time with 80 ml portion $CHCl_3$. Wash sides of filter and cake once with 25 ml $CHCl_3$. Greater portion of $CHCl_3$ may be removed if cheese cake is compressed.

Transfer combined $CHCl_3$ filtrates to 500 ml separator. Rinse filter flask with 2 small portions $CHCl_3$ and add to separator. Ext $CHCl_3$ soln with ca 33 ml ca 0.5N NaOH. Transfer $CHCl_3$ layer to 600 ml beaker and aq. layer to 300 ml erlenmeyer. Return $CHCl_3$ to separator and repeat above alk. extn twice. Emulsion may be formed during extn, but most of it will break on standing. Transfer emulsified layer to alk. soln only in final extn. Acidify alk. ext with 70 ml ca 1N HCl, and rapidly aerate for such time as required to remove dissolved $CHCl_3$ (5–10 min). To check complete removal of $CHCl_3$, smell top of flask while aerating. Be sure to remove all $CHCl_3$ by aeration, or low values will be obtained. Filter soln thru medium or fine porosity fritted glass funnel fitted with filter paper and dil. to vol. with H_2O in 500 ml vol. flask. If soln is turbid, clarify by refiltering thru fine filter or asbestos pad.

Prep. reagent blank by extg 250 ml $CHCl_3$ with alkali, adding acid to ext, aerating, and dilg to vol. with H_2O. Place portion of reagent blank in one cell and portion of sample soln in another. Det. A at 307 nm with Beckman DU spectrophtr or equiv. Dil. sample soln if necessary to obtain readings in range of std curve. (Ordinary range of diln for A readings is from no diln to diln of 1 + 5.)

20.044   *Preparation of Standard Curve*

To prep. std curve use fresh dehydroacetic acid soln, as low readings are obtained from older solns. Weigh exactly 100 mg *dehydroacetic acid* (Eastman or equiv.) and transfer to 100 ml vol. flask. Dissolve in ca 50 ml H_2O + 4 ml ca 0.5N NaOH. Dil. to vol. with H_2O and mix. Pipet 1.0, 3.0, and 5.0 ml (1.0, 3.0, and 5.0 mg dehydroacetic acid) aliquots of this stock soln into sep. 500 ml vol. flasks. To each add equiv. of ca 100 ml ca 0.5N NaOH and 70 ml ca 1N HCl, dil. to vol., and mix. Det. A at 307 nm, using reagent blank prepd as above. Plot A against mg dehydroacetic acid/500 ml prepd soln. Calc. dehydroacetic acid to ppm:

$$ppm = (mg/500\ ml) \times 1000/wt\ sample.$$

SOLUBLE FLUORIDES

Qualitative Tests

20.045   *Hydrofluoric Acid Test (13)—Official*
Final Action

(a) *Not applicable in presence of silicates.*—After thoroly mixing sample transfer to beaker 150 ml, or equiv. quantity of aq. ext in case of solid foods, and boil, adding 5 ml *10% K_2SO_4 soln* and 10 ml *10% $Ba(OAc)_2$ soln*. Collect ppt in compact mass (centrf. may be used advantageously) and wash upon small filter. Transfer to Pt crucible and ignite.

Dip carefully cleaned glass plate, while hot, in mixt. of equal parts of *carnauba wax* and *paraffin*, and let cool. Make distinctive mark thru wax with sharp instrument, taking care not to scratch surface of glass.

Add few drops H_2SO_4 to residue in crucible and cover crucible with waxed plate, having mark over center of crucible and making sure edge of crucible is in close contact with plate. Keep top surface of plate cool, and heat crucible 1 hr at as high temp. as practicable without melting wax (elec. stove gives most satisfactory form of heat). If fluorides are present, distinct etching is apparent on exposed glass.

(b) *Applicable in presence of silicates.*—Mix small amt of pptd SiO_2 with pptd BaF_2, (a), and proceed as in **20.049** or **20.050**. (This method is valuable for foods which contain considerable amt of SiO_2 in the ash. Under these circumstances H_2SO_4 liberates SiF_4, which would escape detection in (a).)

Quenching of Aluminum 8-Hydroxyquinolate Fluorescence—Official First Action

20.046 **Reagents**

(a) *Aluminum soln.*—Dissolve 2.22 g $AlNH_4$-$(SO_4)_2 . 12H_2O$ in H_2O, add 3 drops HCl, and dil. to 250 ml with H_2O.

(b) *Oxine reagent.*—Dissolve enough 8-hydroxyquinoline in *2N* HOAc to make 5% soln. 1 ml of this soln is equiv. to ca 5 ml Al soln.

(c) *Ammonium acetate soln.*—Dissolve 77 g NH_4OAc in H_2O and dil. to 500 ml with H_2O.

(d) *Aluminum 8-hydroxyquinolate.*—Warm 250 ml Al soln to 50–60° and add excess of oxine reagent. Slowly add NH_4OAc soln until permanent ppt forms. Then add 20–25 ml more to ensure complete pptn. Let ppt settle and filter thru fritted glass crucible. Wash ppt well with at least seven or eight 30 ml portions cold H_2O and dry at 120–140°. Store in desiccator.

(e) *Chloroform soln of aluminum 8-hydroxyquinolate.*—Dissolve Al oxine in $CHCl_3$ to prep. 0.5 mg/ml soln. Prep. daily.

(f) *Sulfuric acid.*—Concd. If blank detn reveals presence of F, purify as in **25.032**(c), dilg and boiling 3 times.

20.047 **Test**

Proceed as in **20.045**(a), adding 3 ml HOAc to soln in addn to K_2SO_4 and $Ba(OAc)_2$ solns. Transfer ignited residue to small porcelain crucible (≤ 5 ml).

Wet piece of filter paper with $CHCl_3$ soln of Al oxine in spot larger in diam. than top of crucible and let air-dry. Add H_2SO_4 to cover ash, crimp paper over crucible edge, and put wt (e.g., beaker) on paper. Heat crucible covered with paper 5 min at 50–60°. Observe paper under UV light. In presence of F, fluorescence of the Al oxine is quenched in area of spot over crucible. Limit of identification is ca 0.05 mg F. Conduct blank detn on H_2SO_4.

INSOLUBLE FLUORIDES
(Fluoborates, fluosilicates, etc.)

20.048 **Preparation of Sample—Official Final Action**

Make ca 200 g sample alk. with lime-H_2O, evap. to dryness, and ash. Ext crude ash with H_2O contg enough HOAc to decompose carbonates; filter, ignite insol. portion, ext with HOAc $(1 + 2)$, and again filter. Insol. portion now contains $CaSiO_3$ and CaF_2, while filtrate contains all H_3BO_3 present.

20.049 **Qualitative Test I (14)—Official Final Action**

Ash filter contg insol. portion from **20.048**, mix with little pptd SiO_2, transfer to short test tube attached to small U-tube contg few drops H_2O, and add 1–2 ml H_2SO_4. Keep test tube in beaker of H_2O on steam bath 30–40 min. If any F is present, SiF_4 generated is decomposed by H_2O in U-tube and forms gelatinous deposit on walls of tube.

Test filtrate for H_3BO_3 as in **20.029**. If both HF and H_3BO_3 are present, it is probable that they are combined as BF_3. If, however, SiF_4 is detected and H_3BO_3 is not, repeat test without adding SiO_2, in which case formation of SiO_2 skeleton is conclusive evidence of presence of fluosilicate. In ash contg appreciable quantity of SiO_2, H_2SO_4 liberates SiF_4 rather than HF. Therefore presence of fluosilicate, not fluoride, is indicated.

20.050 **Qualitative Test II—Official Final Action**

Ash filter contg insol. portion from **20.048** in Pt crucible, mix with little pptd SiO_2, and add 1 ml H_2SO_4. Cover crucible with watch glass from underside of which drop of H_2O is suspended, and heat 1 hr at 70–80°, keeping watch glass well cooled. The H_2O decomposes SiF_4 formed, leaving gelatinous deposit of SiO_2 and etching ring at periphery of drop of H_2O. Test filtrate for H_3BO_3 as in **20.029**.

20.051 **Quantitative Method—Official Final Action—See 25.029–25.035**

FORMALDEHYDE
(*See also* **31.184–31.189**.)

20.052 **Preparation of Sample—Official First Action**

If sample is solid or semisolid, macerate 100 g with 100 ml H_2O in mortar. Transfer to 800 ml Kjeldahl flask, acidify with H_3PO_4, add 1 ml excess, connect with condenser thru trap, and slowly distill 50 ml. For milk, dil. 100 ml with 100 ml H_2O, and acidify and distill as for solids. With other liq. foods, acidify 200 ml and distill as for solids.

Qualitative Tests—Official First Action

20.053 *Chromotropic Acid Test (15)*

(a) *Reagent.*—Prep. satd soln of 1,8-dihydroxy-naphthalene-3,6-disulfonic acid (ca 500 mg/100 ml) in ca 72% H_2SO_4 (pour 150 ml H_2SO_4 into 100 ml H_2O and cool). Soln is light straw-colored.

(b) *Test.*—Place 5 ml reagent in test tube and add, with mixing, 1 ml distillate, **20.052.** Place in boiling H_2O bath 15 min, and observe during heating period. Presence of HCHO is indicated by appearance of light to deep purple (depth of color depending on amt of HCHO present).

20.054 *Hehner-Fulton Test (16)*

(*Caution: See* **46.030** and **46.047.**)

(a) *Reagent.—Oxidizing soln.*—To cold H_2SO_4 add, in small portions, equal vol. satd $Br-H_2O$, cooling thruout operation.

(b) *Test.*—To 6 ml cold H_2SO_4 add slowly and with cooling 5 ml distillate, **20.052.** Place 5 ml mixt. in test tube, and add slowly and with cooling 1 ml aldehyde-free milk, then 0.5 ml oxidizing soln. Mix. Purplish-pink indicates HCHO.

20.055 FORMIC ACID—OFFICIAL FINAL ACTION—See 18.026–18.031; 18.035–18.038

HYDROGEN PEROXIDE

20.056 Qualitative Test (17)—Official Final Action

(Applicable to milk)

(a) *Reagent.*—Dissolve 1 g V_2O_5 in 100 ml H_2SO_4 (6 + 94).

(b) *Test.*—Add 10–20 drops reagent to ca 10 ml sample and mix. Pink or red indicates H_2O_2.

MONOCHLOROACETIC ACID (18)— OFFICIAL FINAL ACTION

Qualitative Tests

20.057 *Optical-Crystallographic Properties of Barium Salt*

(Applicable to com. preservatives)

Dil. 4–5 ml sample to 100 ml, add 6 ml H_2SO_4 (1 + 1), and ext with equal vol. ether in separator. If emulsions form, ext in continuous extractor 1 hr. Transfer ether ext to separator, add few drops phthln and 5 ml $0.1N$ $Ba(OH)_2$, and shake 30 sec. If aq. layer takes on pink typical of phthln, filter thru paper into small beaker. Add ca $0.05N$ HOAc until colorless and evap. to 1–2 ml on steam bath. Let remaining liq. evap. spontaneously in air and finally in desiccator. If 5 ml $0.1N$ $Ba(OH)_2$ does not give pink aq. layer, add 5 ml more before sepg. Repeat extn with $Ba(OH)_2$ soln several times or until pink soln is obtained, evapg each Ba soln in sep. beaker. Examine crystals under polarizing microscope.

Barium monochloroacetate monohydrate crystallizes from H_2O in plates, many of which are hexagonal in habit and frequently form in overlapping layers. Even in material that has been finely powd for microscopic examination, pointed terminations of the plates, often in pairs, can be observed. In parallel polarized light (crossed nicols) extinction is parallel and sign of elongation is neg. on more elongated plates. Plates invariably extinguish sharply with crossed nicols and therefore interference figures are not observed in convergent polarized light (crossed nicols). Since plates persistently lie in one orientation, significant refractive indices are detd by statistical method, lowest and highest indices resp. being measured on plates showing max. double refraction. These two indices are therefore arbitrarily designated as n_α (min. value) and n_γ (max. value). Two significant refractive indices are: $n_\alpha = 1.582$ and $n_\gamma = 1.611$, both ±0.002, frequently shown on the platey fragments.

20.058 *Indigo Test*

(*Caution: See* **46.011, 46.039,** and **46.054.**)

(a) *Commercial preservatives.*—Dil. 2 ml sample to 100 ml, add 3 ml H_2SO_4, and shake with 100 ml ether. Add 3 ml *anthranilic acid reagent* (1 g + 0.3 g NaOH/50 ml) to ether ext, evap. at low temp., filter off any insol. matter, and proceed as in (c), beginning "Test with litmus paper."

(b) *Carbonated beverages, orange juice, and wine.*—Acidify 100 ml sample with 3 ml H_2SO_4 and ext, using either continuous extractor or separator. Add 3 ml anthranilic acid reagent, (a), to ether ext and evap. at low temp. If any insol. matter seps, filter thru small wet paper. To clear liq. in 50 ml beaker add 30 mg Na_2CO_3 and proceed as in (c), beginning "Test with litmus paper."

(c) *Barium monochloroacetate.*—Dissolve 0.17 g Ba salt, **20.057,** in 5 ml H_2O in 10 ml graduate, add 1.05 ml $1.0N$ H_2SO_4, dil. to 10 ml, and mix. Let stand until ppt settles, or filter. Pipet 3 ml clear liq. into small beaker; add 2 ml *anthranilic acid reagent*, (a), and 30 mg Na_2CO_3 (weighed). Test with litmus paper. If acid, add addnl 30 mg Na_2CO_3. Pour mixt. into test tube and heat in H_2O bath 30 min. Place tube in oven at 125±5° until only moist residue remains. Remove tube from oven, and drop 2 drops NaOH soln (1 + 1) directly upon residue. (If residue is entirely dry, add 1–2 drops H_2O and let stand until absorbed before adding NaOH soln.)

Return to oven until completely dry (≥1 hr); then remove from oven and heat test tube at 310–320° until contents become orange. (This requires 15 sec to 2 min, but must be carefully watched and tube removed from heat as soon as reaction is complete.) Cool slightly; add 5–7 ml H_2O from wash bottle, splashing H_2O to incorporate air into it. Warm over flame and blow air thru soln 1–2 min, using pipet or glass tube. Heat to boiling over flame and again blow air thru soln. (As oxidn progresses, soln turns red if monochloroacetic acid is present, then green or blue or combination of two, and finally solid particles of indigo sep. out. These tend to rise to surface at first.) Let mixt. stand ca 10 min; then acidify slightly with HCl (1 + 1). Let stand 30 min more, filter, and wash pptd indigo with H_2O to remove acid. Let paper dry in air and preserve as exhibit.

Note: For fusion at 310–320° use brass block having one well to contain test tube and second well to contain thermometer. Block is wrapped with coil of nichrome wire and heat is controlled by variable voltage transformer. Muffle furnaces, microburners, Wood's metal, solder baths, etc., may be used for fusion with equal success.

20.059 Pyridine Test

(*Caution: See* **46.011, 46.039,** and **46.054.**)

(a) *Commercial preservatives.*—Ext 2 ml sample as in **20.058**(a). Transfer ether ext to separator and add small piece of universal indicator paper and enough satd $NaHCO_3$ soln (ca 5 ml) to make aq. layer alk. (pH 7–8) after vigorous shaking. Add enough H_2O to make total vol. of aq. layer ca 10 ml, and shake again. Drain aq. layer into small separator, wash ether with two 5 ml portions H_2O, and add washings to original aq. layer. Wash combined aq. exts once with 5–10 ml ether and discard ether; then add ca 1 ml H_2SO_4 (1 + 1) in excess of quantity required to neutze alk. soln (ca 1.5 ml), and ext acidified soln with two 25 ml portions ether. Wash combined ether exts once with 1 or 2 ml H_2O and let ether soln stand few min after draining most of H_2O and swirling to get as complete sepn of H_2O from ether as possible. Pour ether thru folded paper into 200 ml flask, and wash separator and paper with two 10 ml portions ether.

To ether filtrate add 0.5 ml pyridine and small glass beads, mix, and evap. ether on steam bath to 2–3 ml. Transfer immediately with eye dropper to 15 ml centrf. tube, and wash flask successively with 2, 1, and 1 ml portions ether. Evap. liq. in tube to ca 0.3 ml, add enough pyridine to increase vol. to ca 0.5 ml, and place in constant temp. bath at 60±2°.

If crystals appear, test is pos. If they do not appear, remove tube from bath and evap. excess pyridine under reduced pressure. (Placing tube in beaker of hot H_2O hastens evapn.) When all liq. has been removed, add 0.5 ml pyridine, mix well, centrf., and decant supernatant. Add ca 5 ml ether to residue, shake well, centrf., and decant. To residue add 1–3 ml absolute alcohol, varying amt of alcohol with amt of ppt, place tube in holder, and heat in hot H_2O or steam bath until ppt dissolves, being careful to swirl tube gently to avoid superheating and to boil alcohol so slowly that no loss occurs. Cool in ice bath, add ca 10 ml ether, mix well, and let stand in ice bath ca 5 min. Centrf., pour off supernatant, and wash ppt

once with ca 5 ml ether. If tube now contains crystals of pyridine betaine, test is pos.

(b) *Carbonated beverages, orange juice, and wine.*— Acidify 100 ml sample with 3 ml H_2SO_4 and ext with ether, using either continuous extractor or separator. Continue as in (a), beginning "Transfer ether ext ..."

Quantitative Method

(Applicable to carbonated beverages, fruit juices, and wine)

20.060 Apparatus

Continuous extractor similar to Fig. 36:3B.—Outer part is made from 43 mm tubing, 45 cm long, with side tube, 25 cm above bottom, fitted with drip tip, ℥ 24/40 joint. Inner tube is made from 12 mm tubing 40 cm long. Receiver is 250 ml conical flask with ℥ neck to fit side tube.

20.061 Reagents

(a) *Silver nitrate soln.*— 1 ml = ca 5 mg $CH_2ClCOOH$. Dissolve 9 g $AgNO_3$ in H_2O and dil. to 1 L.

(b) *Ammonium thiocyanate std soln.*—1 ml = ca 5 mg $CH_2ClCOOH$. Dissolve 4.03 g NH_4CNS in H_2O and dil. to 1 L. Stdze against pure NaCl soln, 3.093 g/L, which contains 1.876 g Cl (equiv. to 5 g monochloroacetic acid)/L.

(c) *Ferric indicator.*—Satd soln of $FeNH_4(SO_4)_2$. $12H_2O$.

20.062 Determination

(*Caution: See* **46.011, 46.039,** and **46.054.**)

In outer part of continuous extractor place quantity of sample (≤150 ml) contg 50–100 mg $CH_2ClCOOH$. (With com. preservatives, make preliminary diln to permit convenient measurement of proper size aliquot.) Dil. if necessary to 150 ml, add 3–5 ml H_2SO_4, mix, and ext with ether 2–3 hr. (Extn time for particular app. should be established by detg time required to ext at least 95% of known amt of $CH_2ClCOOH$.)

Tilt extractor so as to drain as much ether as possible into flask. Disconnect flask, add 25 ml 1N NaOH in excess of that required to make aq. layer alk. to litmus paper after shaking, shake, and evap. ether on steam bath to ca 25 ml, hastening process by passing air current into mouth of flask. Digest on steam bath 2 hr or boil under reflux condenser 30 min.

Add 50 ml H_2O, 15 ml HNO_3, and known vol. of the $AgNO_3$ soln in excess. Shake 0.5–1 min, add the ferric indicator, and titr. excess Ag with the NH_4CNS soln. In titrn, carefully add NH_4CNS soln until pink formed fades slowly on mixing; shake soln ca 30 sec and filter thru folded paper into second flask. When first flask is empty, wash down walls with ca 50 ml H_2O and add this to filter after all soln has passed thru. When wash H_2O has passed thru, complete titrn. Similarly titr. quantity of $AgNO_3$ soln equal to that added to sample. Difference between 2 titrns is measure of $CH_2ClCOOH$.

Instead of using the continuous extractor, $CH_2ClCOOH$ may be extd equally efficiently (except with orange juice) as follows: To 100 ml sample add 3 ml H_2SO_4 and shake in separator with three 100 ml portions ether. Combine ether exts and wash by shaking with two 30 ml portions $1N$ NaOH. Combine the two NaOH solns and digest as above.

NITRITES (19)—OFFICIAL FIRST ACTION
(Applicable to dry cure mix or curing pickle)

20.063   *Apparatus*
Bend piece of glass tubing 250 mm long, 6 mm od, to form right angle ca 60–70 mm from one end. Connect short end with rubber tube to outlet of pressure regulator on CO_2 tank.

20.064   *Preparation of Sample*
(a) *Dry cure mix.*—Weigh 50.0 g sample and dissolve in 1 L H_2O. Transfer 25 ml aliquot to 250 ml erlenmeyer.

(b) *Pickle soln.*—Filter thru dry paper. Weigh 50.0 g filtrate into 250 ml erlenmeyer.

20.065   *Determination*
To soln in flask, add 20 ml colorless 15% KI soln and ca 2 ml starch soln, 32.037(g). Insert long end of gas inlet tube and adjust flow of CO_2 to ca 5 bubbles/sec.

After ca 5 min, raise CO_2 delivery tube to just above surface of liq., add 20 ml H_2SO_4 $(1 + 7)$ from buret, and mix thoroly. Titr. with std $0.0725N$ $Na_2S_2O_3$, with CO_2 flowing, to first complete disappearance of starch-I color. 1 ml $0.0725N$ $Na_2S_2O_3$ = 0.0050 g $NaNO_2$.

20.066   PROPIONATES (MOLD INHIBITORS)
—*See* 14.086–14.093

QUATERNARY AMMONIUM COMPOUNDS (QAC)
Qualitative Tests

20.067   *Bromophenol Blue Method (20)—Official First Action*
(Applicable to milk. Note precautions of **20.075–20.080**. *Caution: See* **46.011, 46.039,** and **46.046.**)

Pipet 25 ml milk into 250 ml vol. flask contg 10 mg bromophenol blue, **20.076**(d), and agitate until solid reagent dissolves. Gradually add 50 ml acetone with shaking; then add, dropwise, enough HCl $(1 + 1)$ to produce bright yellow in mixt. (ca 1 ml); then add 0.2–0.3 ml excess. Gradually, with continuous mixing, dil. to vol. with acetone. Mix, let stand 30 min, and filter thru folded filter.

Measure 200 ml filtrate in graduated cylinder and pour into 500 ml separator; fill cylinder to 200 ml with H_2O and add to separator. Wash aq. acetone mixt. by shaking with three 50 ml portions pet ether. When sepd, pour each portion of pet ether thru filter paper and reserve paper for filtration of ethylene chloride ext later. Evap. aq. acetone soln on steam bath under air current until vol. is reduced to ≤ 100 ml and acetone odor is gone. Cool, transfer to 250 ml separator with H_2O (reserve beaker), and add 5 ml HCl $(1 + 1)$.

Pipet 50 ml *ethylene chloride* (1,2-dichloroethane) into separator and shake 1–2 min. Drain lower layer into beaker used for evapn in such manner as to wash down sides and return this liq. to separator, washing beaker with little H_2O. Again shake 2–3 min, let stand until clear, and drain lower layer thru paper reserved above into 125 ml separator contg 10 ml 1% Na_2CO_3 soln. Stopper, invert separator, and shake carefully 2–3 min, using rotary motion. Reverse funnel to normal position and let stand to sep. Top layer will be usual purple of alk. soln of strong bromophenol blue; blue lower layer is pos. test for QAC. To better observe color, drain lower layer into g-s flask contg 1–2 g anhyd. granular (not powd) Na_2SO_4 which will absorb on contact any drops of purple soln that may unavoidably enter flask. Decant ethylene chloride layer into another vessel, if necessary, to avoid any color reflected from colored salt in flask. Ethylene chloride layer must not be filtered, since most papers contain enough residual acid to change the bromophenol blue-QAC complex from blue to practically invisible yellow.

20.068   *Optical-Crystallographic Properties of the Reineckates (21)—Procedure*
Use reineckate salt obtained in **20.074** or proceed as follows: Add excess of NH_4 reineckate to aq. soln of QAC and stir. In most cases, if >20 mg QAC is present, ppt forms at once. With smaller quantities, let soln stand at room temp. ≥ 30 min and then stir 1–2 min. Let mixt. stand several hr, filter thru fine porosity fritted glass crucible, and wash several times with H_2O. Dry ppt with suction, dissolve thru filter with acetone, and evap. off acetone. Dissolve dry residue by warming with min. amt alcohol. If considerable amt of ppt is used, crystals deposit on cooling. Filter thru fritted glass crucible and dry by suction. With <30 mg ppt, dissolve in 10 ml alcohol and let solv. evap. on warm, but not hot, surface with aid of gentle current of air.

Det. optical-crystallographic properties of the crystals as in **36.543** and compare with those listed in **20.069** or with those detd on crystals obtained from known QAC compds.

20.069 Optical-crystallographic properties of reineckates of quaternary ammonium compounds

Compound	Quant. Factor (Anhyd.)	Refractive Indices[a] α	β	γ	Optic Sign	Extinction[b]	Elongation	Habit
Cetyldimethylbenzylammonium Reineckate (Zettyn®)	0.5834	1.572	1.651	1.660	—	i, s		Rhomboid plates
Alkyldimethylbenzylammonium Reineckate	0.5579	1.576	1.651		—	s		Rhomboid plates
Lauryldimethylbenzylammonium Reineckate (DC-12)	0.5457	1.576	1.669^i	1.678	—	p, s	—	Rhomboid plates
Di-isobutylphenoxyethoxyethyldimethylbenzylammonium Reineckate (Hyamine 1622®, Phemerol®)	0.6130	1.577	1.671	1.678	—	p, i	+	Rods, plates, fibrous
Cetylpyridinium Reineckate (Ceepryn®)	0.5458	Unsatisfactory for optical study				p		Fibrous
Lauryldimethyldichlorobenzylammonium Reineckate (Dichloran)	0.5220	1.582	1.593^i	1.677	—	p	—	Rods and plates
Di-isobutylcresoxyethyldimethylbenzylammonium Reineckate (Hyamine 10-X®)	0.6028	1.582	1.638	1.670	—	p	+	Plates
Dodecyldimethylacetamidobenzylammonium Reineckate (Dobenzyl chloride)	0.5911	1.582	1.599	1.664		p	+	Plates and rods
Cetyldimethylethylammonium Reineckate (Ethyl Cetab)	0.6135	1.587	1.609^i	1.626		p	++	Plates and rods
Cetyltrimethylammonium Reineckate (Cetab)	0.6045	1.591	1.609^i	1.616		p	++	Rods
Triethylbenzylammonium Reineckate	0.4460	1.593	1.687	1.697 (ca)	—	s		Rhomboid plates
Laurylpyridinium Reineckate	0.5112	1.609	1.636^i	1.651		p	+	Plates

[a] Refractive indices ±0.003, at 24–26°; i = intermediate index.
[b] Extinction: p = parallel; i = inclined; =s symmetrical.

Quantitative Methods
Ferricyanide Method (20)—Official
Final Action
(Applicable to com. preservatives)

20.070   *Reagents*

(a) *Acetate buffer soln.*—Dissolve 130 g NaOAc .3H$_2$O in H$_2$O, add 42 ml HOAc, and dil. to 500 ml.

(b) *Ferricyanide soln.*—Dissolve 6.6 g K$_3$Fe(CN)$_6$ in H$_2$O and dil. to 1 L.

(c) *Zinc sulfate soln.*—Dissolve 20 g ZnSO$_4$.7H$_2$O in 180 ml H$_2$O.

(d) *Thiosulfate std soln.*—0.02N. Prep. daily by dilg 0.1N soln, **45.038–45.039.** 1 ml 0.02N soln = 0.02142 g alkyldimethylbenzylammonium chloride, molecular wt 357.

20.071   *Determination*
(*Caution: See* **46.018** *and* **46.050.**)

Det. approx. QAC concn as follows: Pipet 1 ml buffer soln, 2 ml K$_3$Fe(CN)$_6$ soln, and 20 ml H$_2$O into each of 4 small erlenmeyers. To these flasks add 0.5, 1.0, 2.0, and 4.0 ml, resp., of sample, mix, and filter. Add 2 ml addnl sample to each filtrate, mix, and compare results with table, **20.072.**

Into 100 ml Kohlrausch flask pipet aliquot of sample contg ca 0.5 g QAC, as indicated by **20.072,** dil. if necessary to 50 ml, add 5 ml buffer soln, and mix. Add 30 ml K$_3$Fe(CN)$_6$ soln from pipet while swirling flask. Dil. to 100 ml mark with H$_2$O and mix. After 30 min, filter, discarding first 10–15 ml filtrate. Pipet 50 ml filtrate into 500 ml erlenmeyer, and add 100 ml H$_2$O and 1–2 g KI. Rotate flask until salt dissolves, add 10 ml HCl (1 + 1), mix, and let stand 2 min. Add 10 ml ZnSO$_4$ soln, mix, and titr. with 0.02N Na$_2$S$_2$O$_3$ soln, adding starch indicator, **6.004(f),** when color fades to tinge of yellow. Make blank detn including all of above operations but substituting H$_2$O for sample. Calc. QAC content from difference in 2 titrns.

If sample contains ca 0.5 g QAC/100 ml, instead of proceeding as above pipet 100 ml sample into 200 ml vol. flask, add 10 ml buffer soln and 30 ml K$_3$Fe(CN)$_6$ soln, dil. to vol. with H$_2$O, mix, let stand 30 min, filter, and titr. 100 or 150 ml aliquot filtrate as above.

20.072   *Approximation of Content of Alkyldimethylbenzylammonium Chloride (mol. wt 357)*

Quaternary Ammonium Chloride, %	Sample Added A 0.5 ml	B 1.0 ml	C 2.0 ml	D 4.0 ml
≥8.4	No ppt	No ppt	No ppt	No ppt
5	Ppt	No ppt	No ppt	No ppt
2.5	Ppt	Ppt	No ppt	No ppt
1.25	Ppt	Ppt	Ppt	No ppt
≤1	Ppt	Ppt	Ppt	Ppt

Reineckate Method (22)—Official Final Action
(Applicable to preservatives, tinctures, and isotonic solns)

20.073   Reagent

Reineckate reagent.—Place 0.75 g NH₄ reineckate (NH₄[Cr(NH₃)₂(SCN)₄].H₂O; mol. wt = 354.47) in 125 ml erlenmeyer, add 50 ml H₂O, stopper, shake ca 2 min, and filter.

20.074   Determination

Place 100 ml sample contg 10–100 mg QAC in 250 ml beaker; add, with stirring, 5 ml portions reineckate reagent until liq. is bright pink. Let stand 30 min and add more reagent unless supernatant is deep pink. Stir again 1–2 min. After several hr filter thru fine porosity fritted glass crucible, and wash beaker and filter with at least three 15 ml portions H₂O. (It is unnecessary to transfer all ppt to crucible.) Wash down sides of crucible with H₂O and dry by suction. If ppt forms cake in filter, mix with the wash H₂O with stirring rod used before.

Dissolve reineckate salt in acetone as follows: Set up suction app. to fit glass crucible, using as receiver side-arm test tube for application of suction. With 5 ml pipet, wash down sides of beaker used for pptn and add this liq. to crucible. Rinse beaker second time and add to liq. in crucible. Stir to dissolve and draw liq. thru with suction. Wash out beaker third time and wash down sides of crucible several times with small portions of acetone. When liq. passing thru is colorless, disconnect, and wash into test tube with acetone any pink material which may have dried on bottom or outside of crucible or on inside of funnel. Discard small amt of greenish solid in crucible due to impurities and decomposition products of reagent.

Transfer acetone soln to tared beaker (50 ml beaker for ≤20 mg QAC and 100 ml beaker for >20 mg) and evap. on warm (but not hot) surface. If few drops of moisture remain, pass gentle air current into beaker until it appears dry. Dissolve residue by warming in 10 ml alcohol (or more, if needed); let solv. evap. spontaneously, dry in desiccator, and weigh. Wt QAC = factor (20.069) × wt ppt. Ppt may be used for detn of optical-crystallographic properties, 20.069.

(To remove greenish solid from crucible, add 10–12 ml HCl (1 + 1) and stir to dissolve. Draw liq. thru by suction and wash several times with H₂O. Reverse crucible and wash by filling bottom cavity with solv. Use 2 fillings each of H₂O, alcohol, H₂O, acetone, and H₂O in order given.)

Bromophenol Blue Method* (20)

(*Precaution:* Have all glassware scrupulously clean, and especially avoid soap, since reaction occurs between soap and QAC. If soap is used in

---

* Official final action for bottled beverages contg fruit juices, beer, and table sirup; official first action for eggs.

---

cleansing, rinse all glassware with H₂O, and as extra precaution rinse all pipets with alcohol and dry by suction.)

20.075   Apparatus

Steam distillation apparatus.—See Fig. 18:1, **18.026**(a), for generator. Use 500 ml or 1 L distn flask, fitted with spray tube, **12.025**(c), reaching to within 1 or 2 cm of bottom of flask (all connections ﬅ joints), and with stopper for steam inlet (to be used during early part of distn). Suitable app. is described in **19.123**.

20.076   Reagents

(a) *Sodium carbonate soln.*—Dissolve 5 g Na₂CO₃ in 500 ml H₂O.

(b) *Sodium sulfate.* — Anhyd. granular (not powd). (Mallinckrodt A.R. granular grade is satisfactory.)

(c) *D.C. 12.*—Lauryldimethylbenzylammonium chloride, or other solid QAC.

(d) *Bromophenol blue soln.*—Dissolve 40 mg tetrabromophenolsulfonphthalein in warm H₂O, cool, and dil. to 100 ml.

Bromophenol blue should pass following test for purity: Place 20 mg bromophenol blue in 125 ml separator; add 50 ml ethylene chloride and 5 ml 1% Na₂CO₃ soln, and shake until dissolved. Let stand until mixt. seps into 2 layers. Lower layer should be colorless; upper layer purple. Add 10 ml soln contg 0.1 mg D.C. 12 or other QAC, shake again, and let sep. Lower layer should be clear blue. Drain lower layer and examine in spectrophtr. Absorption peak should be at ca 608 nm. Compare absorption curve with that of sample purified as in **20.077**. If test gives yellow or green soln or if absorption curve is essentially different from that of purified sample, purify as in **20.077**.

20.077   Purification of Bromophenol Blue

Place 2 g bromophenol blue in 400 ml beaker and dissolve in 25 ml 1% Na₂CO₃ soln. Transfer to 1 L separator, using ca 300 ml H₂O. Add 500 ml ethylene chloride and shake. Add 1 ml soln contg 10 mg D.C. 12 or other QAC and shake until thoroly extd. If lower layer is yellow, repeat addn of D.C. 12 soln in 1 ml portions with shaking until upon sepn of the 2 layers, lower one has greenish tint. Drain lower layer and discard. Add 200 ml ethylene chloride and 1 ml D.C. 12 soln to separator and shake. This time lower layer should be clear blue. If layer is green, drain and repeat addn of ethylene chloride and D.C. 12 until blue soln is obtained. Wash aq. layer with 100 ml portions ethylene chloride until lower layer is colorless or only faint blue. Acidify aq. layer with HCl and ext yellow ppt with ethylene chloride until aq. soln is only faint yellow. Distill off most of ethylene chloride and permit remainder to evap. spontaneously in beaker. Grind residual powder. Test portion for purity as in **20.076**(d) and if suitable, use as reagent.

20.078   *Preparation of Standard Curve*

Stdze 1% soln QAC to be detd as in **20.071**. (If this compd is not available, use any solid QAC of known composition such as D.C. 12, lauryldimethyl-benzylammonium chloride. If necessary, prep. std soln from com. soln stdzd by ferricyanide method, **20.071**.) By performing method below, det. max. and min. concns of this compd that produce, in 50 ml ethylene chloride, A at 610 nm suited to color-measuring instrument used. Prep. set of 3 or more stds contg, in 50 ml, quantities of QAC covering range between these max. and min. concns, and plot curve as directed below. (If Beckman spectrophtr is used, 0.0, 0.1, 0.2, and 0.25 mg/50 ml are suitable stds.)

Pipet 50 ml of each std into separator; add 3 ml bromophenol blue soln, 1 ml HCl (1 + 1), and 50 ml ethylene chloride; and shake 2–3 min. When clear, drain lower layer into another separator contg 10 ml Na_2CO_3 soln, and shake 2–3 min. Let stand until clear, drain lower layer into g-s flask contg 1–2 g Na_2SO_4, and after 30 min read in instrument. (Use same or similar cell for all stds, and light filter centering at 610 nm.) Plot scale readings, if these are in terms of A or proportional to it, against concns used; if instrument reads in terms of T, convert readings to A before plotting.

20.079   *Preparation of Sample*

(a) *Bottled beverages containing fruit juices.*—Mix thoroly, and measure 50 ml sample into graduated cylinder. Filter on 7 cm buchner and dil. filtrate to 100 ml with H_2O (Soln A). Place filter paper in 400 ml beaker and ext with small portions of alcohol until no more color is extd and paper remains white. Transfer alc. ext to 500 ml distg flask; add 10 mg bromophenol blue, 2 ml HCl (1 + 1), and 100 ml H_2O. Steam distill and collect vol. distillate $\geq$100 ml greater than vol. alcohol in ext. Cool residue in distg flask, transfer to separator, wash with 40, 30, and 30 ml portions pet ether, and proceed as in **20.080**.

Also take suitable aliquot of Soln A (first try 5 ml), transfer to separator, add 3 ml bromophenol blue soln and 1 ml HCl (1 + 1), and proceed as in **20.080**.

(b) *Beer.*—Place 100 ml decarbonated beer, **10.001**, in steam distn flask and add 10 mg bromophenol blue and 2 ml HCl (1 + 1). Steam distill and collect ca 200 ml distillate. Cool residue, transfer to separator, wash with 100 and 50 ml portions pet ether, and proceed as in **20.080**.

(c) *Table sirup.*—Transfer 20 g sample to 100 ml vol. flask, dil. to vol. with H_2O, and mix thoroly. Pipet aliquot of soln into separator, add 5 ml bromophenol blue soln and 1 ml HCl (1 + 1), and proceed as in **20.080**.

(d) *Eggs.*—Weigh 12.5±0.25 g well-mixed sample in tared 50 ml beaker. Add 10 ml H_2O, mix well with rod, pour carefully into 250 ml vol. flask, and wash beaker with 5–10 ml more H_2O, adding washings to flask. While swirling flask, gradually add acetone, little at time, mixing constantly, until flask is filled to mark; stopper and invert several times. Let stand 10–15 min and filter thru folded paper (Whatman No. 12, 18.5 cm) into 250 ml graduated cylinder until 200 ml filtrate is obtained. Pour filtrate into 1 L separator, wash down sides of cylinder with 25 ml acetone, and add to separator; fill cylinder to 250 ml with H_2O and add to separator. Add 25 ml HCl (1 + 1) to separator and mix. Ext liq. in separator with pet ether, using 300, 250, 150, and 100 ml, and shaking gently to prevent formation of emulsions. Transfer extd aq. layer to 600–800 ml beaker, add 2–3 glass beads, and evap. to 50–75 ml on steam bath.

After evapn, add 10 mg bromophenol blue and wash down sides of beaker with little H_2O. When soln is cool, pipet 50 ml ethylene chloride into beaker, letting solv. flow down sides of beaker. Pour contents of beaker into 250 ml separator, washing out beaker with little H_2O. Shake ca 1 min. Return liq. to beaker, letting it flow down sides of beaker. Again return liq. to separator and shake ca 2 min. Proceed as in **20.080**, beginning "Let stand until clear ..."

20.080   *Determination*

Pipet 50 ml ethylene chloride into separator, **20.079**(a), (b), or (c), and shake 3–4 min. Let stand until clear, drain lower layer into second separator contg 10 ml 1% Na_2CO_3 soln, and shake 3–4 min. Let sep. and observe lower layer. If blue, quaternary. base is present. Judge from depth of color whether or not it is suitable for reading in photometer. If color is suitable for reading without diln, dry by draining lower layer into g-s flask contg 1–2 g of the Na_2SO_4, let stand 30 min, transfer to suitable cell, and read color in instrument at 610 nm. Det. quantity QAC present from std curve, **20.078**, and calc. to mg/100 ml.

If color is too deep for direct reading, acidify contents of second separator with 1 or 2 ml HCl (1 + 1), shake until contents become yellow, and return to first separator. Pipet second 50 ml portion ethylene chloride into first separator, shake 3–4 min, let stand until lower layer is clear, and drain lower layer into flask. (If sample is known to contain >1 mg QAC/100 ml, entire 100 ml ethylene chloride may be added at one time.)

Det. proper aliquot as follows: Pipet 5 ml into 125 ml separator, dil. with 25 ml ethylene chloride, add 10 ml 1% Na_2CO_3 soln, and carefully shake 2 min. Let sep. and observe lower layer. If depth of color is suitable for reading, dil. to 50 ml by adding 20 ml ethylene chloride from pipet, shake 1 min, let settle, drain lower layer, dry as above, and read. If color is not deep enough, add addnl soln in 5 ml increments until suitable color is obtained, add solv. if necessary to total vol. of 50 ml, shake, drain, dry, and read in instrument.

When proper aliquot has been detd, check as follows: Pipet aliquot of ethylene chloride soln into 50 ml vol. flask, fill to vol. with ethylene chloride, and pour into 125 ml separator. Pipet 10 ml 1% Na_2CO_3 soln into vol. flask, swirl, pour into separator, and wash out vol. flask with 2–3 ml H_2O from wash bottle. Shake, settle, drain, dry, and read, adding ca 5 mg dry bromophenol blue to separator if aliquot used was ≤10 ml.

For bottled beverages contg fruit juices, add amt of QAC found in residue to amt found in Soln *A* to obtain total amt in sample.

Eosin Yellowish Method (23)—Official First Action

(Applicable to aq. solns and milk)

20.081   Apparatus

(a) *Centrifuge.*—Clinical high speed type fitted for 50 ml tubes. International No. 2 centrf. with head No. 241 at speed of 2500 rpm is also satisfactory.

(b) *Centrifuge tubes.*—Heavy wall, 40 ml centrf. tubes, Pyrex, No. 8400 or equiv.

(c) *Test tubes.*—Pyrex, g-s, 15 × 150 mm.

20.082   Reagents

(a) *Acetylene tetrachloride.*—(*Caution:* Toxic reagent. *See* **46.040**.) Should give distinct pink lower layer after sepn, when 5 ml is shaken 1 min with 2 ml buffer soln (c), 0.5 ml eosin yellowish soln (d), and 5 ml aq. soln contg 1 ppm Cetab, Dobenzyl chloride, Et Cetab, Hyamine 10-X, or laurylpyridinium chloride, or 2 ppm lauryldimethylbenzylammonium chloride. If reagent does not meet this test, distill under reduced pressure, rejecting first 10% of distillate and collecting ca 80% of vol. placed in distn flask.

(b) *Aerosol OT std solns.*—(*1*) *Stock soln.*—Prep. soln of dioctyl Na sulfosuccinate to contain 100 mg/100 ml. Det. strength as follows: Pipet 2 ml soln contg, in 100 ml, 100 mg QAC to be detd, into g-s test tube contg 2 ml acetylene tetrachloride, 2 ml buffer soln, and 0.5 ml eosin yellowish soln. Carefully add Aerosol OT soln from buret in small amts, violently shaking mixt. ≥30 sec after each addn until, after sepn into 2 layers, only light pink is noticeable when test tube is placed against white background. Continue addns in 0.01 or 0.02 ml portions until lower layer is no longer pink. (*2*) *Working soln.*—Dil. to 100 ml such quantity stock soln as will produce soln 1 ml of which is equiv. to 0.1 mg QAC to be detd. Stdze against std soln (1 ml = 0.1 mg) of QAC to be detd.

(c) *Citrate buffer soln.*—pH 4.5. Dissolve 25 g citric acid in 75 ml H_2O and add enough 50% NaOH soln (ca 13 ml) to bring pH to 4.5.

(d) *Eosin yellowish soln.*—Dissolve 25 mg D&C Red No. 22 in H_2O and dil. to 50 ml.

(e) *Lactic acid soln.*—50%. Add 41 g H_2O to 59 g lactic acid, 85% reagent grade, and mix.

(f) *Sodium hydroxide soln.*—4M. Dissolve 32 g NaOH in H_2O and dil. to 200 ml.

20.083   Determination

(a) *Milk.*—Pipet 15 ml acetylene tetrachloride (*Caution: See* **46.018**) into centrf. tube, add 6 ml lactic acid soln and 15 ml milk to be tested, stopper, and shake ca 3 min. Add 6 ml NaOH soln and mix carefully until curd seps thruout mixt.; then shake ≥30 sec. Centrf. at high speed (ca 3200 rpm) 7 min. Decant serum and discard; puncture layer of curd at 2 points and drain acetylene chloride ext into small beaker. Avoiding any drops of aq. soln, transfer 5 ml ext with pipet into g-s test tube contg 2 ml buffer soln and 0.5 ml eosin yellowish soln; stopper and shake ca 2 min. Let stand to sep. and observe color of lower layer. If color is faint, place against white background. If layer is pink, QAC is present. If deep pink or red, titr. with std Aerosol OT soln; after each addn of std soln, shake mixt. violently 0.5–1 min, let sep., and observe lower layer. Continue addns until no pink is observed in lower layer when placed against white background or compared with blank detn. Titrn found represents quantity QAC in 5 ml sample. Calc. to ppm.

(b) *Water solns.*—Pipet 5 ml sample into g-s test tube contg 2 ml acetylene tetrachloride, 2 ml buffer soln, and 0.5 ml eosin yellowish soln, and proceed as in (a), beginning "... stopper and shake ca 2 min."

SALICYLIC ACID

20.084 Preparation of Sample—Official Final Action

(a) *Nonalcoholic liquids.*—Many liqs may be extd directly as in **20.085** or **20.087** without further treatment. If troublesome emulsions form during extn, pipet 100 ml into 250 ml vol. flask and add ca 5 g NaCl, shaking until dissolved. Dil. to vol. with alcohol, shake vigorously, let stand 10 min, shaking occasionally, filter, and treat aliquot of filtrate as in (b).

(b) *Alcoholic liquids.*—Make 200 ml of sample alk. to litmus paper with ca 10% NaOH soln and evap. on steam bath to ca ⅓ its original vol. Dil. to original vol. with H_2O and filter if necessary.

(c) *Solid or semisolid substances.*—Grind sample and mix thoroly. Transfer convenient quantity (50–200 g according to consistency of sample) to 500 ml vol. flask, add enough H_2O to make ca 400 ml, and shake until mixt. becomes uniform. Add 2–5 g $CaCl_2$ and shake until dissolved. Make distinctly alk. to litmus paper with ca 10% NaOH soln, dil. to vol. with H_2O, shake thoroly, let stand ≥2 hr, shaking frequently, and filter.

Qualitative Tests—Official Final Action

20.085 Ferric Chloride Test

(*Caution: See* **46.011, 46.039,** and **46.054.**)

Place 50 ml sample or equiv. quantity of aq. ext, prepd as in **20.084,** in separator; add $\frac{1}{10}$ its vol. HCl (1 + 3) and ext with 50 ml ether. If mixt. emulsifies, add 10–15 ml pet ether (bp <60°) and shake. If this treatment fails to break emulsion, centrf., or let stand until considerable portion of aq. layer seps; drain latter, shake vigorously, and again let sep. Wash ether layer with two 5 ml portions H_2O, evap. greater portion of ether in porcelain dish on steam bath, let remainder evap. spontaneously, and add 1 drop 0.5% neut. $FeCl_3$ soln. Violet color indicates salicylic acid.

If coloring matter or other interfering substance is present in residue after evapn of ether, purify salicylic acid by one of following methods:

(a) Dissolve original residue from ether ext, obtained as above, in ca 25 ml ether; transfer soln to separator and shake with equal vol. H_2O made distinctly alk. with several drops 10% NH_4OH. Let sep., filter aq. layer thru wet filter into porcelain dish, evap. almost to dryness, and test residue with $FeCl_3$ as above.

(b) Dry original residue from ether ext, obtained as above, in desiccator over H_2SO_4 and ext with several 10 ml portions CS_2 (*Caution: See* **46.040** and **46.048**) or pet ether (bp <60°), rubbing contents of dish with glass rod and filtering successive portions of solv. thru dry paper into second porcelain dish. Evap. greater portion of solv. on steam bath, let remainder evap. spontaneously, and test residue with $FeCl_3$ as above.

(c) With few ml of ether, transfer original residue from ether ext obtained as above to small porcelain crucible, and let solv. evap. spontaneously. Cut hole in asbestos board large enough to admit ca $\frac{2}{3}$ of crucible, cover crucible with small r-b flask filled with cold H_2O, and heat over small flame until any salicylic acid present sublimes and condenses upon bottom of flask. Test sublimate with $FeCl_3$ as above.

20.086 Jorissen Test (24)

Dissolve residue from ether ext, **20.085,** or, if impurities are present, purified material obtained as in **20.085**(a), (b), or (c), in little hot H_2O. Cool 10 ml soln in test tube and add 4 or 5 drops 10% KNO_2 soln, 4 or 5 drops HOAc (ca 50%), and 1 drop 1% $CuSO_4$ soln. Mix thoroly, boil liq. 0.5 min, and let stand 2 min. In presence of salicylic acid Bordeaux-red color develops.

Quantitative Method—Official Final Action

20.087   Extraction

(*Caution: See* **46.011, 46.039,** and **46.054.**)

Transfer to separator 100 ml sample, or quantity of soln prepd as in **20.084** that represents ≥20 g original material. If alk., neutze to litmus with HCl

(1 + 3) and add excess of HCl equiv. to 2 ml acid for each 100 ml soln. Ext 4 times with ether, using for each extn vol. ether equiv. to $\frac{1}{2}$ vol. aq. layer. If emulsion forms on shaking, this may usually be broken by adding little ($\frac{1}{5}$ vol. ether layer) pet ether (bp <60°) and shaking again, or by centrfg. If small amt of emulsion still persists, let remain with aq. layer, where frequently it is broken during next extn. If emulsion remains after fourth extn, sep. it from clear ether and clear aq. layer and ext sep. with 2 or 3 small portions ether.

Combine ether exts, wash with vol. H_2O equal to $\frac{1}{10}$ total vol. ether exts, let sep., and discard aq. layer. Wash in this way until aq. layer after sepn yields yellow soln upon addn of Me orange soln and 2 drops 0.1N NaOH. Slowly distill greater part of ether, transfer remainder to porcelain dish, and let evap. spontaneously. If no interfering substances are present, proceed as in **20.088;** if interfering substances are present, purify residue by one of following methods:

(a) Thoroly dry residue *in vacuo* over H_2SO_4. Ext 10 times with 10–15 ml portions CS_2 (*Caution: See* **46.040** and **46.048**) or pet ether (bp <60°), rubbing contents of dish with glass rod, and filter successive portions of solv. thru dry filter into porcelain dish. Test extd residue with drop *2% Fe alum soln,* and if it gives reaction for salicylic acid, dissolve in H_2O; acidify soln with HCl (1 + 3), ext with ether, evap., ext dry residue thus obtained with CS_2 or pet ether, and add to ext first obtained. Distill greater portion of the CS_2 or pet ether and let remainder evap. spontaneously. Proceed as in **20.088.**

(b) Dissolve residue in 40–50 ml ether. Transfer ether soln to separator and ext with three 15 ml portions 1% NH_4OH. (If fat is known to be present in original ether ext, ext latter directly with 4 portions 1% NH_4OH instead of 3.) Combine alk. aq. exts, acidify, again ext with ether, and wash combined ether exts as directed previously. Slowly distill greater portion of ether, let remainder evap. spontaneously, and proceed as in **20.088.**

20.088   Determination

Dissolve residue, **20.087,** in small amt of hot H_2O, and after cooling dil. to definite vol. (usually 50 or 100 ml). If soln is not clear, filter thru dry paper. Dil. aliquots of the soln and treat with 0.5% $FeCl_3$ soln or 2% Fe alum soln until max. color is developed. Generally few drops will suffice.

(The Fe alum soln should be boiled until ppt appears, allowed to settle, and filtered. Acidity of soln is slightly increased in this manner, but soln remains clear for considerable time, and turbidity caused by its diln with H_2O is much less and does not appear so soon as when unboiled soln is used. This turbidity interferes with exact matching of color.)

Compare colors developed with color obtained when std *salicylic acid soln* (contg 1 mg salicylic acid in 50 ml) is similarly treated, using Nessler tubes or colorimeter. In either case, and especially with $FeCl_3$, avoid excess reagent, although excess of 0.5 ml 2% Fe alum soln may be added to 50 ml comparison soln of salicylic acid without negating results.

SULFUROUS ACID

20.089 Qualitative Test (*25*)—Official Final Action

Add small amt of S-free Zn and several ml HCl to ca 25 g sample (with addn of H_2O, if necessary) in 200 ml erlenmeyer. H_2S generated in presence of sulfites may be detected with $Pb(OAc)_2$ paper. Traces of metallic sulfides occasionally present in vegetables give same reaction as sulfites under conditions of above test. Verify positive results obtained by this method by Monier-Williams method, **20.092**.

It is always advisable to make quant. detn of sulfites because of possibility of pos. test caused by traces of sulfides. Trace should not be considered sufficient indication of presence of SO_2 either as bleaching agent or as preservative.

Total Sulfurous Acid

Modified Monier-Williams Method (26)—Official Final Action

(Applicable in presence of other volatile S compds; not applicable to dried onions, leeks, and cabbage.)

20.090 ***Reagents***

(**a**) *Hydrogen peroxide soln.*—3%. Check 30% ACS reagent to ensure compliance with sulfate specification. Det H_2O_2 content by $KMnO_4$ titrn, dil. to ca 6% H_2O_2, neutze to Me red, (**b**), and dil. to calcd vol. to give 3.0%.

(**b**) *Methyl red indicator.*—0.25% in alcohol. Adjust to transition color.

20.091 ***Apparatus***

See Fig. 20:3. Connect 3 neck (₮ 24/40) 1 L distg flask at an outer neck to 30 cm Allihn condenser (Ful-Jak, Scientific Glass Apparatus Co. No. JC-5450, or equiv.) in reflux position. Place inner joint adapter with right angle hose connection in condenser and connect thru piece of $\frac{1}{4} \times 6''$ silicone tubing (Scientific Glass Apparatus No. R-8425) preboiled in HCl (1 + 20) and rinsed with H_2O, to set of 2 U-tubes of 20 mm tubing, ball joint 35/20, 55±5 mm center to center and 150±5 mm long, connected with cross-over tube, ball joint 35/20, 55±5 mm center to center and 115±5 mm long. To each U-tube add 2 ca 25 mm lengths of solid glass tube, 10 ml 3 mm glass beads at exit side, and 10 ml 3% H_2O_2 contg drop Me red.

Attach either curved gas inlet tube for outer neck or straight tube for center neck of distg flask with tip reaching nearly to bottom.

Alternatively substitute app. shown in Fig. 20:4 for U-tubes. Connect right angle hose connection to 30–50 ml bulb (*D*) and fritted cylindrical gas dispersion tube (*A*) (Scientific Glass Apparatus No. G-5420, or equiv.). Suspend fritted end near bottom of Kuderna-Danish Evaporative Concentrator (*B*, *C*) (Kontes Glass Co. No. K-570000, part *B*, vol. 500 ml, ₮ 24/25 lower joint; part *C*, ca 15 ml, ₮ 24/25 joint) contg 10–12 ml 3% H_2O_2 and drop Me red. Diam. of *C* should provide min. gas scrubber path of 10 cm with 10 ml H_2O_2.

Grind 4.5 g *pyrogallol* with 5 ml H_2O in small mortar and transfer slurry to 250 ml ₮ 24/40 gas washing bottle. Repeat grinding and transfer with two 5 ml portions H_2O. Pass H_2O-pumped N from tank thru 2 stage regulator into gas washing bottle to flush out air and add to bottle, thru long stem

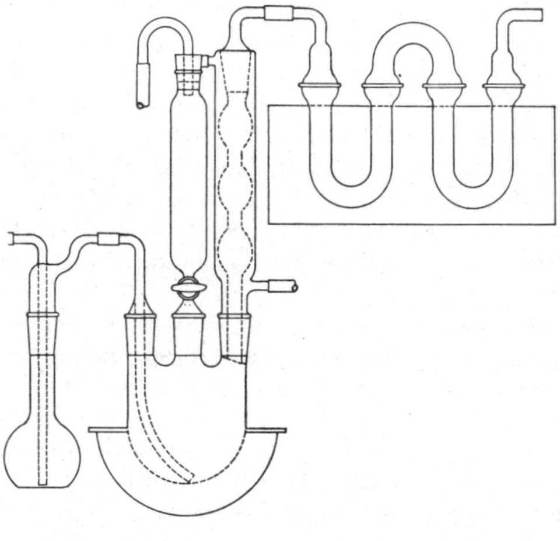

FIG. 20:3—Apparatus for modified Monier-Williams method for sulfur dioxide

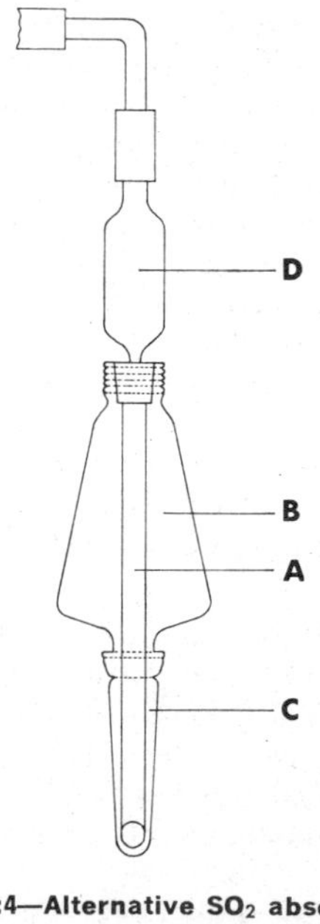

FIG. 20:4—Alternative SO_2 absorber

funnel, cooled soln of 65 g KOH in ca 85 ml H_2O. (Prep. complete soln fresh daily.) Turn off N, and attach $\frac{1}{4} \times 6''$ silicone tubing, preboiled in HCl $(1 + 20)$ and rinsed with H_2O, to exit end and to gas inlet tube of distg flask. Clamp off both ends of washing bottle.

Attach 125 ml separator thru ⌷ 24/40 joint to third neck of distg flask. Attach piece of rubber tubing to short U-tube inserted thru rubber stopper in neck of separator. Blow into rubber tubing, and close separator stopcock. Let stand for few min to check for leaks shown by liqs leveling in U-tubes.

Place distg flask in heating mantle controlled by variable transformer.

20.092 *Determination*

Place sample, contg min. of 45 mg SO_2, in distg flask, using H_2O for transferring, if necessary. Dil. to ca 400 ml with H_2O. Add 90 ml HCl $(1 + 2)$ to separator and force HCl into flask with gentle pressure. Start N flow at slow steady stream of bubbles. Heat flask to cause refluxing in 20–25 min (ca 80 volts on 7 amp transformer). When steady refluxing is reached, apply line voltage and reflux 1.75 hr. Turn off H_2O in condenser and continue heating until inlet joint of first U-tube shows condensation and slight warming. Remove separator, and turn off heat. When joint at top of condenser cools, remove connecting assembly and rinse into second U-tube. Attach cross-over tube to exit joint of first U-tube, rotate until open ends touch, add drop Me red, and titr. with 0.1N NaOH just to clear yellow, mixing with gentle rocking. 1 ml 0.1N NaOH = 3.203 mg SO_2. Titr. second U-tube similarly. If alternative app. is used, disconnect, and rinse bulb *D* and tube *A* with few ml of H_2O into Kuderna-Danish app. *B*, *C*. Add 2 drops Me red and titr. with 0.1N NaOH.

Gravimetric detn may be made after titrn by rinsing tubes into 400 ml beaker. Add 4 drops 1N HCl and excess of filtered 10% $BaCl_2$ soln, and let stand overnight. Wash ppt by decantation 3 times with hot H_2O thru weighed gooch. Wash with 20 ml alcohol and 20 ml ether, and dry at 105–110°.

mg $BaSO_4 \times 274.46/g$ sample = ppm SO_2.

Det. blank on reagents, both by titrn and gravimetrically, and correct results accordingly.

Colorimetric Method (27)—Official
Final Action

(Applicable to dried fruit)

20.093 *Reagents*

(a) *Formaldehyde soln.*—0.015%. Prep. from 40% HCHO by dilg in 2 steps: 10 to 1000, and 75 to 2000.

(b) *Acid-bleached p-rosaniline hydrochloride.*— Place 100 mg *p*-rosaniline . HCl (Allied Chemical Corp.) and 200 ml H_2O in 1 L vol. flask. Add 160 ml HCl $(1 + 1)$ and dil. to vol. Let stand 12 hr before use.

(c) *Sodium tetrachloromercurate.*—Place 23.4 g

NaCl and 54.3 g $HgCl_2$ in 2 L vol. flask. Dissolve in ca 1900 ml H_2O and dil. to vol. (*Caution: See* **46.079.**)

(d) *Sulfur dioxide std soln.*—Dissolve ca 170 mg $NaHSO_3$ in H_2O and dil. to 1 L. Stdze with 0.01N I soln before use (ca 100 μg SO_2/ml).

20.094 *Preparation of Standard Curve*

Add 5 ml mercurate reagent to series of 100 ml vol. flasks; then add 0, 1.0, 2.0, 3.0, etc., ml of std SO_2 soln. Dil. to vol. and mix. Transfer 5.0 ml portions to 200 mm test tubes contg 5 ml rosaniline reagent. Add 10 ml 0.015% HCHO soln, mix, and hold 30 min at 22°. Read *A* at 550 nm against 0 std and plot to obtain std curve.

20.095 *Determination*

Weigh 10 ± 0.02 g ground dried fruit and transfer to blender with 290 ml H_2O. Cover and blend 2 min. Withdraw 10 g aliquot from bottom of blender with 10 ml calibrated free-running pipet, and transfer to 100 ml vol. flask contg 4 ml 0.5N NaOH. (Use 2 ml for apples and 1 ml for golden raisins.) Swirl and mix ca 13–30 sec. Add 4 ml 0.5N H_2SO_4 (2 ml for apples and 1 ml for golden raisins) and 20 ml mercurate reagent, and dil. to vol. For blank, omit 10 ml fruit ext.

Transfer 2 ml sample soln to 200 mm test tube contg 5 ml rosaniline reagent. Add 10 ml 0.015% HCHO soln, mix, and hold 30 min at 22°. Read *A* at 550 nm against blank. Refer to std curve and convert results to ppm SO_2.

(If same colorimeter tube or cell is used for successive samples, clean between use with HCl $(1 + 1)$ and H_2O.)

Sulfites in Meats (28)—Official Final Action

Qualitative Test

20.096 *Reagent*

Malachite green soln.—Dissolve 200 mg malachite green, certified by Biological Stain Commission, in H_2O and dil. to 1 L. Soln is stable for several weeks if dispensed from polyethylene dropper bottle assembly with neoprene bulb. Discard when visible deterioration occurs. (Tablets for prepn of 15 ml quantities of reagent are available from LaMotte Chemical Products Co., Chestertown, MD 21620.)

20.097 *Test*

Transfer ca 3.5 g ($\frac{1}{2}$ teaspoonful) ground meat to $4 \times 4''$ square of waxed white freezer paper or other impervious white surface. Add 0.5 ml reagent and mix vigorously 2 min with hardwood tongue blade or spatula, turning mass frequently. Observe color after few min.

Dye is decolorized in presence of sulfites. Normal meat becomes blue-green. Verify pos. results by Monier-Williams method, **20.092.**

20.098 Free Sulfurous Acid (29)—Official Final Action

Treat 50 ml sample in 200 ml flask with ca 5 ml H_2SO_4 (1 + 3), add ca 0.5 g Na_2CO_3 to expel air, and titr. H_2SO_3 with 0.02N I, using few ml starch indicator, **6.004**(f). Add I soln as rapidly as possible and continue addn until soln stays blue several min. 1 ml 0.02N I = 0.64 mg SO_2.

THIOUREA (30)
Qualitative Tests—Procedure
(Applicable to orange juice)

20.099 *Pentacyanoammonioferroate Test*

(a) *Reagent.*—(*Caution: See* **46.050.**) Dissolve 10 g $Na_2Fe(CN)_5NO.2H_2O$ in 40 ml NH_4OH and let stand at ca 0° until all nitrosoferricyanide decomposes (shown when few drops mixt. no longer give red soln when added to soln of creatinine in 1N NaOH; decomposition is complete after 24 hr). Filter, and add absolute alcohol to filtrate until there is no further pptn of pentacyanoammonioferroate. Filter, wash with absolute alcohol until NH_3-free, dry *in vacuo* over H_2SO_4, and store in desiccator over $CaCl_2$ in dark. Reagent is 1 % soln of this salt in H_2O, exposed to light and air 1 day and then stored in brown glass bottle in dark. It gains in potency for several weeks, and can be kept ca 6 months.

(b) *Test.*—Ext orange juice with ca ⅔ vol. ether, centrf., and sep. lower layer. Stir in some Filter-Cel and filter with suction. Keep vac. on short time and agitate soln to remove most of ether. To ca 5 ml filtered soln add 5 drops reagent and note color. If blue color does not develop, add I soln, ca 0.1N, dropwise, shaking after each drop. Blue-green soln indicates presence of $CS(NH_2)_2$. (Usually ca 5 drops I soln are necessary to develop max. color; excess I tends to reduce color.)

20.100 *Grote Reagent Test*

To 5–10 ml orange juice, ether-extd and filtered as in **20.099**(b), add 0.02N I dropwise until I color does not immediately disappear. Add few ml dil. Grote reagent, **20.102**(b). Blue-green or blue color developing rather gradually indicates presence of $CS(NH_2)_2$.

Quantitative Methods
Rapid Oxidation Method for Orange Juice—Official Final Action

20.101   *Apparatus*

Siphon.—Insert 2 bent glass tubes in 2-hole cork or stopper, one terminating just below stopper (blow tube) and other (siphon tube) long enough to reach bottom of centrf. bottle when cork with tubes is inserted in mouth of bottle. Attach another glass tube to outside end of siphon tube with flexible rubber tube so that end of outside tube is below end of inside tube. This assembly is used to siphon lower layer from centrf. bottle, and rate of flow is controlled by squeezing rubber connection. Prep. cap

for inner siphon tube by boring hole of same diam. as tube part way thru small cork.

20.102   *Reagents*

(a) *Modified Grote reagent.*—Dissolve 0.5 g $Na_2Fe(CN)_5NO.2H_2O$ in 10 ml H_2O in 50 ml erlenmeyer. Weigh 0.5 g $NH_2OH.HCl$ and 1 g $NaHCO_3$. Uniformly mix the 2 solids in small beaker or porcelain dish by gentle grinding with small pestle or flat-end glass rod, crushing any lumps in sample. Brush off rod or pestle and quant. transfer mixed solid to nitroprusside soln with aid of short-stem funnel and brush. Do not agitate flask but let it stand until CO_2 evolution nearly stops. Then swirl to dissolve any remaining $NaHCO_3$. When evolution of CO_2 practically ceases, add 0.10 ml Br (11 small drops). Second evolution of gas occurs. When agitation no longer produces effervescence, dil. to 25 ml with H_2O and filter. Test reagent as follows: Dil. 2 ml as in (b); add 1 ml dild reagent to 10 ml soln composed of 5 ml thiourea stock soln, (c), (dild 10×), 5 ml H_2O, and 1 drop HOAc. Strong blue color should develop in 5 min. If it does not, prep. new reagent and repeat test. Store at room temp. 5–10 hr to age soln. (Soln should be mahogany brown. If it has greenish cast, it is not as effective and soon loses its value.) This stock soln keeps several weeks when stored in refrigerator.

(b) *Dilute Grote reagent.*—Dil. 1 vol. reagent (a) with 4 vols H_2O. Use 1 ml dild reagent for each detn. Dild reagent keeps 1 day.

(c) *Thiourea stock soln.*—Dissolve 100 mg $CS(NH_2)_2$ in H_2O and dil. to 200 ml.

(d) *Citric acid-potassium citrate soln.*—Dissolve 0.84 g $K_3C_6H_5O_7.H_2O$ and 1 g citric acid in H_2O, and dil. to 100 ml.

(e) *Sulfuric acid.*—1.00±0.02N.

20.103   *Preparation of Sample*

Juice oranges in ordinary reamer, strain out seeds and pulp, and mix well. Measure 125 ml into 250 ml centrf. bottle, add 70 ml ether, and shake well 1–2 min. Centrf. ca 10 min at 1800 rpm. Cap short end of siphon (inside bottle), insert into bottle, and lower thru top layer into lower aq. layer. Push off cork cap with glass rod. Lower tube to bottom of bottle, push cork (which carries siphon) into mouth of bottle, and blow in short tube to start flow of liq. Carefully siphon into beaker as much of lower layer as possible, controlling rate of flow by squeezing on rubber connection. Stop flow when material from center emulsion layer begins to enter tube.

Add teaspoonful of Filter-Cel to siphoned liq. in beaker, stir well, and filter on buchner (7–11 cm) with suction, using Whatman No. 54 or 41-H paper. Measure filtrate with graduate, pour into separator, and add ca ½ its vol. ether. Shake well, let sep., drain lower layer into beaker, add pinch of Filter-Cel, stir well, and filter thru Whatman No. 12 folded filter. Place filtrate in clean, dry suction flask, warm on steam bath to 36°, and apply suction to remove ether.

Pipet 25 ml filtrate (clear or nearly so) into clean 50 ml vol. flask. In 2 similar flasks place 25 ml aliquots citric acid-K citrate soln. To one flask add 2 ml thiourea stock soln; use other as a blank. To each of the 3 flasks add 5 ml $1N$ H_2SO_4. Slowly add $0.1N$ I, **45.019**, with rotation, to each flask until I color does not disappear; then add 1 ml excess. Let flasks (samples, std, and blank) stand 10 min at room temp. Now add soln of $NaHSO_3$ (2.5 g/L) to contents of flasks until I color disappears; add 3 or 4 drops excess. Add 4 ml 25% NaOAc soln gradually and slowly to each flask, with swirling, dil. to vol. with H_2O, and mix. Filter if cloudy. Designate oxidized dild sample as Soln X.

20.104   *Determination*

Prep. 2 stds by placing 5 and 10 ml portions of soln from the std flask in test tubes. Dil. first tube to 10 ml by adding 5 ml liq. from blank soln (no thiourea). Place 10 ml portions blank soln and sample Soln X in 2 other test tubes. Pipet 1 ml dild Grote reagent (*Caution: See* **46.018** and **46.050**) into each tube with shaking or stirring. Let tubes stand 1 hr at ca 25°, or 10–15 min in bath at 45–50°, to develop blue color. Read developed color of solns from each tube (sample, blank, and stds) in spectrophtr at 610 nm. From readings of blank and stds construct curve (linear), plotting A readings against ppm of $CS(NH_2)_2$. Oxidized std in flask represents 20 ppm (1 mg/50 ml); 10 ml aliquot therefore represents 20 ppm, and 5 ml 10 ppm.

Slight correction on sample color reading obtained is necessary because of natural color present in Soln X before addn of the Grote reagent. Obtain readings on blank soln and sample Soln X contained in vol. flask, without added reagent, using same photometer cell. Subtract difference between these readings (X − blank) from sample reading with the Grote reagent. Obtain from graph ppm $CS(NH_2)_2$ corresponding to corrected reading. This value $\times$ 2 = $CS(NH_2)_2$ concn in original orange juice.

Method for Frozen Peaches—Official First Action
20.105   *Preparation of Sample*
(*Caution: See* **46.011**, **46.039**, and **46.046**.)

Weigh 200–400 g frozen sample on rough balance (0.1–0.2 g sensitivity) into tared 800 ml beaker. Cut contents of 1 lb package into quarter or eighth portions, select alternate portions for detn, and keep remainder as reserve sample. (Several packages can be composited in this manner if desired.)

Immediately add to sample, quantity of $NaHSO_3$ soln (2.5 g/L) equal to ½ wt sample (*See Note*). Mix and pour into high-speed blender (or other mixing machine), drain well, and blend 20–30 sec. Return dild comminuted sample to beaker.

Weigh 150±0.2 g blended sample, transfer to 250 ml vol. flask, and dil. to ca 200 ml with H_2O. Add ca 4 drops *hexyl alcohol* and attach to flask 2-hole stopper (No. 0), carrying small bent glass tube and another straight tube, extending ca 3″ into flask, end of which is drawn to small bore (near capillary). Remove most of air by applying gentle suction to bent tube and shaking flask with rotation. (Bore of small tube should be large enough so that reduction of pressure is not too great.) If froth rises in neck, release vac. for moment. Continue with suction and rotation until most of air is removed, add 20 ml addnl $NaHSO_3$ soln, and dil. to vol. with H_2O. Mix well and pour ca 165 ml into 250 ml centrf. bottle. Add 50 ml ether to contents of bottle, rotate few times, stopper, and shake; open once to release pressure; then shake vigorously 1–1.5 min. (If preferred, divide liq. in vol. flask between 2 centrf. bottles and ext each with ca 30 ml ether, etc.)

Centrf. at ca 1800 rpm ca 10 min. Carefully pour off little of top ether layer into beaker; then inclining bottle, push sludge cake toward bottom of bottle with glass rod and pour liq. contents on cotton filter in funnel. To prep. filter, place small cotton pledget in apex of 85–100 mm funnel, and insert piece of absorbent cotton of half thickness (split sheet), ca 3½″ diam.

Pipet 100 ml lower aq. filtrate into 200 ml vol. flask, squeezing cotton on side of funnel with rod if necessary to obtain enough filtrate. Add gradually to contents of flask (from separator), with constant shaking, enough acetone to bring contents to 200 ml mark. As surface of liq. enters neck of flask, stopper, and mix by inverting few times before dilg to mark. Mix, cool to room temp. (in bath if desired), dil. to mark again, and mix well. (Acetone causes some rise in temp.) Let ppt sep. and pour contents of flask into 250 ml centrf. bottle. Add 1 spoonful of Filter-Cel, stopper, and shake well. Centrf. ca 8 min at ca 1800 rpm. Decant off supernatant and filter if turbid. Measure 125 ml clear liq. into 250 ml beaker, add several glass beads, and boil off acetone on steam bath. Then boil down to ca 35 ml on hot plate, remove, and cool to room temp. Add dropwise 15% NaOH soln until alk. and ca 2 drops excess. Add HOAc (1 + 5) with stirring until just acid and add 2 drops excess.

Quant. transfer liq. to 50 ml vol. flask, dil. to vol. with H_2O, and mix. Pour contents of flask into small beaker or flask (100–125 ml), add 1 spoonful Filter-Cel, and mix well by stirring or stoppering and shaking. Filter liq. on 12.5 cm folded paper (E. & D. No. 195 is suitable). Pour thru filter again if not clear. Filtrate or final sample soln is designated *FS*.

20.106   *Determination*

Pipet 10 ml of Soln *FS* into 6″ test tube. For quantities of $CS(NH_2)_2$ up to 50 ppm, prep. stds contg 0, 1, 2, and 4 ml portions of 1 + 9 diln $CS(NH_2)_2$ stock soln, **20.102(c)** (5 mg $CS(NH_2)_2$/100 ml). Add *0.6%*

Na citrate soln to tubes to make stds to 10 ml; then add 1 drop HOAc (1 + 5) to each tube (samples and stds). Place stirring rod in each tube and stir up and down to mix, leaving rod in tube. Place tubes in bath or room held at 20–25°.

Add to each tube, with stirring, 1 ml dil. Grote reagent, **20.102**(b) (recently dild). Let tubes stand 60 min at 20–25° and det. A of each soln in spectrophtr at ca 610 nm. Designate reading of sample as X. Construct linear curve from std readings, plotting ppm $CS(NH_2)_2$ (1 ml std soln = 10 ppm $CS(NH_2)_2$ in sample) against A readings. Extrapolate std curve up to 50 ppm.

To correct reading X for natural color present in soln before reagent is added, make readings of Soln *FS* with no added reagent in same cell and also that of H_2O. *FS* reading − H_2O reading = d; $X - d = R$ (corrected reading). From reading R obtain ppm $CS(NH_2)_2$ in Soln *FS*, using curve. Multiply $CS(NH_2)_2$ thus found by factor 1.065 to correct for vol. increase due to solubility of ether and obtain true $CS(NH_2)_2$ content of original sample. Repeat detn (color development) on smaller aliquot (1–5 ml) for quantities >50 ppm.

Note: Sample of 200 g is enough to be representative and should be used where portion is to be reserved. Keep unused portion of sample frozen. It is necessary to add the $NaHSO_3$ soln to frozen sample immediately before blending to prevent losses of $CS(NH_2)_2$ due to attack by enzyme systems present. Blender whips air thruout the material, and if enzymes are not inactivated, large losses of $CS(NH_2)_2$ may occur. Enzymes can also be inactivated by plunging frozen sample into boiling H_2O and boiling 3 or 4 min. Action of enzymes is slow in frozen condition if material is unbroken cakes or chunks.

Method for Orange Peel—Official
Final Action

20.107   *Reagents*

(a) *Thiourea std soln.*—0.5 mg/ml. *See* **20.102**(c).

(b) *Diluted modified Grote reagent.*—Dil. modified Grote reagent, **20.102**(a), with 2 vols H_2O just before use.

(c) *Extraction solvent.*—Mix EtOAc with acetone (2 + 1).

(d) *Dilute phosphoric acid.*—0.9±0.1N, stdzd to phthln end point.

20.108   *Preparation of Sample*
(*Caution: See* **46.004, 46.039,** and **46.054.**)

Bisect 6–8 fruit and ream firmly to remove all possible juice without removing peel. Pass peel thru food chopper or grinder and mix thoroly in bottle.

Weigh 75 g sample into high-speed blender cup. Add 250 ml ether and blend 2 min in hood with draft operating. Filter on 11 cm buchner with moderate suction and rinse blender and filter with ether, pressing down cake with bottom of 100–150 ml beaker. Remove ether from suction flask, discard ether, and continue suction on cake to remove ether.

Remove buchner from flask and transfer cake to 750 ml (5½″ diam.) casserole. Strip off paper, and transfer any remaining peel on paper or in funnel to casserole with spatula. Add 100 g anhyd. Na_2SO_4 and mix well with spatula and spoon. Transfer mixt. to blender, dry-wash casserole with little more Na_2SO_4, and add to blender. Add ca 275 ml extn solv., blend at low speed, and gradually increase to full speed, using variable transformer. Blend at full speed 3 min, and filter into 11 cm buchner, using Whatman 41-H paper with moderate suction, transferring most of residue with policeman and few small spurts of extn solv. from wash bottle. Distribute residue over filter, press down cake with bottom of 100–150 ml beaker, and suck dry. Remove cake and return to blender, stripping off paper. Add 150 ml extn solv., and blend ca 2 min. Filter on buchner, rinse blender and filter with ca 50 ml extn solv., and suck dry. Combine extn solv. filtrates, add 1.2 ml 0.9N H_3PO_4, dil. to convenient vol. in vol. flask or graduate, and mix.

Accurately measure 2 aliquots of solv. ext, each equiv. to 10 g sample, into 150 ml beakers, and evap. on steam bath sep. to ca 12 ml. Cool, add small amt Celite, and stir. Filter each soln into sep. side arm test tube thru fritted filter tube or crucible overlaid with fine, firm asbestos mat or thru small buchner and S&S 589 Blue Ribbon paper, using moderate suction. Rinse beaker and filter with 3 ml EtOAc.

Quant. transfer filtrates to small separators with aid of eyedropper pipet and bulb, rinsing with ca 1 ml EtOAc. Ext with two 5 ml portions H_2O, shaking well and letting sep. each time. Combine aq. exts of each detn in small beaker and boil ca 20 sec to remove most of org. solv. Cool, dil. each to 10 ml with H_2O in vol. flask, and mix well.

20.109   *Determination*

Pipet 5 ml aliquots of final aq. solns from each detn into 1″ test tubes. Add 0.5 ml dild modified Grote reagent, **20.107**(b), mix, and det. A after 75 min against blank as in **20.110**. Det. mg thiourea from std curve.

To correct for loss of thiourea, if any, during evapn of org. solv., place same vol. extn solv. as contained equiv. of 10 g sample in 150 ml beaker, add 0.6 ml thiourea std soln (0.3 mg) and 0.12 ml 0.9N H_3PO_4, and evap. to ca 12 ml on steam bath. Proceed as in **20.108**, beginning "Cool, add small amt Celite, and stir."

Correct thiourea found in sample aliquot, if necessary, for loss on evapn. Calc. to original sample basis.

20.110   *Preparation of Standard Curve*

Prep. blank soln contg 1.20 ml 0.9N H_3PO_4 dild to 100 ml with H_2O. Pipet 6 ml thiourea std soln into 100 ml vol. flask, add 1.20 ml 0.9N H_3PO_4, and dil. to vol. with H_2O. Place 1.0, 2.5, and 5.0 ml aliquots of this std soln in 1″ test tubes and add 4.0, 2.5, and 0 ml blank soln. Place 5.0 ml blank soln in similar tube. To all solns add 0.5 ml dild modified Grote reagent, mix, and let stand 1 hr. Read A of stds against blank at 610 nm. Plot mg thiourea against A. Check std curve occasionally and prep. new curve with each new lot of modified Grote reagent.

EMULSIFYING AGENTS

Sodium Lauryl Sulfate (31)—Official Final Action

20.111 *Reagents*

(*Caution: See* **46.022, 46.028**(a) and (d), and **46.079**.)

(a) *Crystal violet indicator.*—See **3.127**(d).

(b) *Methyl yellow indicator.*—Dissolve 40 mg *p*-dimethylaminoazobenzene in 100 ml MeOH.

(c) *Standard acetous perchloric acid.*—0.1N. Mix 8.5 ml 72% HClO₄ with 500 ml HOAc and add 30 ml Ac₂O. Cool, and dil. to 1 L with HOAc. Let stand 24 hr before using. Stdze as follows: Accurately weigh 400–500 mg KH phthalate, previously dried 2 hr at 105°, into 250 ml erlenmeyer and dissolve in 80 ml HOAc. Add 3 drops crystal violet indicator and titr. with acetous HClO₄ to blue-green end point, which is stable 60 sec. Perform blank titrn on 80 ml HOAc and 3 drops indicator soln, and correct vol. of titrant.

$$N = mg\ KHC_8H_4O_4/(204.23 \times ml\ HClO_4)$$

(d) *Mercuric acetate soln.*—6%. Dissolve 6.0 g Hg(OAc)₂ crystals in 100 ml HOAc, heating gently, if necessary, to dissolve. (*Caution: See* **46.079**.)

(e) *Azure A soln.*—Dissolve 40 mg in H₂O, add 10 ml 0.1N H₂SO₄, and dil. to 100 ml. Dye is available from Allied Chemical Corp.

(f) *Benzethonium chloride.*—Approx. 99% pure (available from Rohm and Haas Co.). Det. purity as follows: Accurately weigh ca 1 g benzethonium chloride, previously dried 2 hr under vac. at 80°, into 250 ml erlenmeyer. Dissolve in 80 ml HOAc and add 10 ml 6% Hg(OAc)₂ in HOAc. Add 3 drops crystal violet indicator and titr. with 0.1N HClO₄ to same blue-green end point used in stdzn of HClO₄. Perform blank detn on 80 ml HOAc and 10 ml Hg(OAc)₂, and correct vol. of titrant.

% Purity = (corrected titrant vol. $\times N \times$ 44.81)/g benzethonium chloride

(g) *Benzethonium chloride std soln.*—0.005N. Accurately weigh ca 2.25 g dried benzethonium chloride and dil. to 1 L with H₂O.

$$N = (g\ benzethonium\ chloride \times \%\ purity)/448.1$$

(h) *Sodium lauryl sulfate (SLS).*—Approx. 95% pure. Det. purity as follows: Accurately weigh ca 500 mg SLS, transfer to 250 ml vol. flask with H₂O, and dil. to vol. Pipet 25 ml into 250 ml g-s erlenmeyer. Add 50 ml CHCl₃, 10 ml 1N H₂SO₄, and 1 ml Me yellow indicator. Titr. with 0.005N benzethonium

chloride as follows: Add 20 ml titrant, shake vigorously, and let layers sep. Add titrant in 1 ml increments, shaking vigorously after each addn until pink in CHCl₃ layer begins to change to orange. (Emulsion will begin to break rapidly at this time.) Add titrant in 2 drop increments until CHCl₃ layer changes to definite yellow. Make detn in duplicate. 1 ml 0.005N benzethonium chloride = 1.442 mg SLS.

(i) *Sodium lauryl sulfate (SLS) std soln.*—5 μg/ml. Transfer SLS equiv. to 100 mg pure SLS to 1 L vol. flask with H₂O and dil. to vol. Transfer 5.0 ml to 100 ml vol. flask, dil. to vol. with H₂O, and mix.

20.112 *Preparation of Standard Curve*

Pipet 0, 1, 3, 5, 10, and 15 ml aliquots std SLS soln into 125 ml separators. Dil. each to ca 25 ml with H₂O. Add 10 ml 0.1N H₂SO₄ and 1.0 ml Azure A. Ext with two 20 ml portions H₂O-satd CHCl₃. Drain each CHCl₃ ext thru pledget of glass wool into 50 ml vol. flask. Dil. to vol., read A at 637 nm against H₂O-satd CHCl₃, and prep. std curve.

20.113 *Determination*

(Rinse all glassware several times with H₂O to eliminate all traces of detergent.)

(a) *Liquid and frozen egg white.*—Let frozen egg white thaw at room temp. Accurately weigh ca 20 g liq. egg white into beaker and transfer to 500 ml g-s erlenmeyer with 400 ml H₂O. Swirl gently ca 1 min and let stand 1 hr with occasional swirling. Add 400 ml alcohol and mix by gentle shaking. Heat mixt. on steam bath 15 min and shake at 3 min intervals to promote complete pptn. Let cool 45 min and filter thru Whatman No. 30 paper, using 11 cm buchner. Wash ppt in flask and on filter with three 50 ml portions alcohol. Transfer filtrate to 1 L vol. flask and dil. to vol. with alcohol. Pipet 2 aliquots, each contg 50 μg SLS, into sep. 100 ml beakers and evap. to dryness on steam bath with current of air. Take up residues with H₂O and transfer each to 125 ml separator with several small portions H₂O to make total of ca 25 ml. To one add 1.0 ml 0.005N benzethonium chloride to serve as blank. Continue with each as in **20.112**, beginning "Add 10 ml 0.1N H₂SO₄ ..." Read A of sample and blank against H₂O-satd CHCl₃. Subtract blank A from sample A. Det. SLS from std curve.

(b) *Powdered egg white.*—Accurately weigh ca 2.5 g powd egg white into 300 ml g-s erlenmeyer and add 40 ml H₂O. Let stand 2 hr with occasional swirling. If egg white is not completely suspended after 1 hr, break up lumps with stirring rod and swirl at 5 min intervals until all egg white is suspended. After 2 hr, add 20 ml alcohol and gently shake 1 min. Heat mixt. on steam bath 0.5 hr, remove, and let cool 0.5 hr. Continue as in (a), beginning "filter thru Whatman No. 30 ..."

(c) *Flake dried egg white.*—Grind flakes in mortar to pass No. 20 sieve. Proceed as in (b).

ENZYMES

Proteolytic Activity of Papain (*32*)—
Official First Action

20.114   *Reagents*

(a) *Casein soln.*—Make 6% soln of Hammarsten casein (obtainable from Nutritional Biochemicals Corp.) by rubbing 60 g with little H_2O in mortar and gradually adding 60 ml 1N NaOH and H_2O until vol. totals 1 L. Heat viscous soln 30 min in boiling H_2O bath, cool, and filter thru glass wool if necessary.

(b) *Citrate buffer soln.*—Prep. 0.2M monosodium citrate soln by partial neutzn of citric acid with NaOH.

(c) *Titrating soln.*—Stdzd 0.1N alc. KOH.

(d) *Indicator.*—1% alc. thymolphthalein soln.

20.115   *Preparation of Sample*

(a) *Unactivated.*—If enzyme prepn is solid, grind to smooth paste in small mortar with little freshly boiled, cold H_2O. Suspend in cold boiled H_2O in proportion of 10 mg original prepn/ml H_2O. After 5–10 min centrf. suspension and discard sediment.

(b) *Activated.*—Proceed as in (a), but use half-satd H_2S-H_2O (*Caution: See* **46.059**) instead of boiled H_2O. After centrfg, incubate enzyme soln 1 hr at 40° to complete activation.

20.116   *Determination*

Place 10 ml casein soln and small charge of 4 mm diam. glass beads in each of several 125 ml g-s bottles, and bring bottles and contents to 40°. Add desired vol. of prepd enzyme soln, but do not use >4 ml. If this quantity is insufficient (*see* **20.117**), prep. more concd soln of enzyme. Immediately add exactly 3 ml buffer soln (pH of system should be 5.0±0.1). Vigorously shake bottle few sec and place in constant temp. H_2O bath at 40°.

Incubate mixt. 20 min at 40°, counting time from addn of buffer. Add 1 ml indicator and begin titrg with alc. KOH soln. As soon as deep blue appears, shake bottle until color is discharged or ppt is completely dissolved. (It is usually best to add alkali in ca 0.5 ml portions.) When all pptd casein dissolves, transfer soln to 400–500 ml flask and rinse bottle 2 or 3 times with alcohol, using total of 25 ml. Add enough KOH soln to restore blue; then add 175 ml boiling alcohol. Carefully add more KOH soln until pale but distinct blue persists in soln.

Make control titrn exactly as described, but do it immediately after addn of buffer, without any incubation time. Difference between titrn of undigested sample and that of digested sample is measure of proteolytic activity of enzyme.

20.117   *Calculation of Proteinase Unit*

For smaller amts of enzyme, extent of hydrolysis detd by above titrn is straight line function of amts of papain used. For accurate work, det. this straight line by making several titrns with different amts of enzyme. If amts of papain used are too large, straight-line relationship no longer holds; if they are too small, detn is inaccurate. Amts of enzymes giving titrn differences of 0.6–1.2 ml 0.1N KOH are recommended.

Unit of papain may be considered to be amt of enzyme that produces, under conditions outlined, titrn difference of 1 ml 0.1N KOH, detd either graphically or arithmetically. Value of original prepn is then expressed in units/mg, or as mg papain prepn necessary to make one unit.

MISCELLANEOUS

Acetone Peroxides (*33*)—Official Final Action
20.118   *In Baking Premixes*

Accurately weigh ca 8 g sample into flat-bottom centrf. bottle, pipet in 100 ml H_2O, and stir 10 min after making sure no lumps remain. Centrf. at ca 1500 rpm ca 10 min. Pipet 25 ml supernatant into erlenmeyer, add 25 ml H_2SO_4 (1 + 4), and let stand ≥3 min, swirling occasionally. Titr. to light pink that lasts >20 sec with std 0.1N $KMnO_4$ soln, **45.026–45.027.**

Total peroxides in g H_2O_2 equiv./100 g premix = ml $KMnO_4$ × normality × 0.0170 × 100/0.25 × g sample.

20.119   *In Milling Premixes*

Accurately weigh ca 200 mg sample into **erlen**meyer, add 50 ml H_2SO_4 (1 + 9), let stand >3 min, stirring occasionally, and titr. with std **0.1N** $KMnO_4$, **45.026–45.027,** to light pink that persists >20 sec.

Total peroxides in g H_2O_2 equiv./100 g premix = ml $KMnO_4$ × normality × 0.0170 × 100/g sample.

Qualitative Test

(Acetone peroxides are extremely explosive. Do not ext more org. peroxides from adsorbents than necessary for test. *Caution: See* **46.070(b)**.)

20.120   *Apparatus*

(a) *Recording infrared spectrophotometer.*—Suitable for work from 2 to 16 μm.

(b) *Rock salt plate.*—Or other support stable to acetone and acetone peroxides and transparent in 2–16 μm region.

20.121   *Test*

Weigh sample contg ca 10 mg H_2O_2 equiv. of acetone peroxides into g-s flask. Add ca 1 g anhyd. Na_2SO_4 and 10 ml acetone for every g adsorbate. Shake 3 min, filter (Whatman No. 12 paper has been found satisfactory) or centrf. (for baking premix), and carefully evap. clear soln to ca 1 ml under vac. at room temp.

Under warm light and gentle current of dry warm air, add concd acetone ext dropwise to rock salt plate. When film of viscous liq. is visible on plate, check it in IR light path and, without recording, check T of peak at ca 12.1 μm. If necessary, add addnl portions of ext to give 20–25% T. Set spectrophtr at acetone peak at ca 9.2 μm. Let radiation pass thru sample on plate until raised pen reaches max. T (acetone has evapd). Then record spectrum of film on salt plate from 2 to 16 μm.

Compare curve to one obtained from ref. acetone peroxides treated in same manner.

NONNUTRITIVE SWEETENERS

Identification (34)—Official First Action
(Applicable to nonalcoholic beverages)

20.122 *Apparatus*

(a) *Thin layer apparatus.*—See **19.040**.

(b) *Ultraviolet light.*—Capable of providing short-wave (254 nm) radiation (Spectroline, Black Light Eastern Corp., 29 New York Ave, Westbury, NY 11590, or equiv.).

20.123 *Reagents*

Prep. solns fresh on day of use.

(a) *Developing solvent.* — *n*-Butanol-alcohol-NH₄OH-H₂O (40 + 4 + 1 + 9, by vol.).

(b) *Chromogenic agents.*—(*1*) Br in CCl₄, 5% by vol. (*Caution: See* **46.047** *and* **46.049**); (*2*) 0.25% fluorescein in dimethylformamide-alcohol (1 + 1); and (*3*) 2% N-1-naphthylethylenediamine.2HCl in alcohol.

(c) *Std mixture.*—50 mg Ca cyclamate, 10 mg Na saccharin, 4 mg dulcin, and 4 mg P-4000 in 10 ml dil. alcohol (1 + 1). (5 μl = 25 μg cyclamate, 5 μg saccharin, 2 μg dulcin, and 2 μg P-4000.) Warm soln to dissolve dulcin, if necessary. Avoid contact with P-4000.

(d) *Silica gel.*—Adsorbosil-1 (Applied Science Laboratories, Inc.) or silica gel H (Merck, distributed by Brinkmann Instruments, Inc.).

20.124 *Preparation of Sample*
(*Caution: See* **46.011**, **46.040**, *and* **46.057**.)

Decarbonate beverage by repeated shaking and pouring. To 50 ml sample in 125 ml separator, cautiously add 10 ml H₂SO₄ (1 + 1). Cool, ext with two 50 ml portions pet ether (shake *gently* but thoroly), and discard pet ether. To aq. layer, cautiously add 5 ml 50% NaOH soln (w/w), cool, and ext with two 50 ml portions EtOAc. (Use 60 ml for cola samples to prevent emulsions.) Filter EtOAc exts thru EtOAc-washed cotton into beaker or flask with pouring lip. Evap. to 5–10 ml on steam bath, using air current, and transfer to graduated tube. (Do *not* let soln evap. to dryness before transfer. Sweeteners may be difficult to redissolve.) Evap. soln in graduated tube to dryness on steam bath with air current. Dil. to 2.5

ml with NH₄OH-H₂O-alcohol (5 + 5 + 10) and mix thoroly. (Insol. residue in tube will not interfere with detn.)

20.125 *Preparation of Plates and Tank*

Slurry 35 g Adsorbosil with 50 ml H₂O or 30 g silica gel H with 75–80 ml H₂O, and apply as 0.25 mm layer to five 8 × 8″ plates. Dry plates >1 hr at room temp. Do *not* dry in oven. Do *not* store in desiccator cabinet. Score layer 5 mm from each side edge and remove 5 mm band of absorbent from bottom edge of layer. Use plates within 36 hr after prepn.

Line developing tank with adsorbent paper. Pour 25 ml developing solv. into tank, wetting paper. Place V-shaped trough in tank and add 25 ml developing solv. to trough. (Alternatively, put developing solv. in tank to ca 1 cm.) Place lid on tank, seal, and let stand ca ½ hr to sat. tank atm.

20.126 *Determination*
(*Caution: See* **46.016** *and* **46.017**.)

Mark TLC plate at side edges only, 1″ from bottom to designate spotting line. Mark dotted line 10 cm above spotting line. Spot total of 5 μl each of std and sample (*Level 1*). Dil. sample to 5 ml with NH₄OH-H₂O-alcohol (5 + 5 + 10) and spot 5 μl (*Level 2*). Place spots at least 2 cm apart and 2 cm from edges. Spot 1 μl at a time and use warm-air blower to dry spot between applications to confine spot diam. Use same technic to spot sample and std. (Total vol. spotted should be ≤5 μl. Use mixed std rather than superimposed single stds.)

Place plate in tank and develop to 10 cm line (ca 1 hr). Dry plate in hood until layer is no longer translucent (ca 10 min). View under shortwave (254 nm) UV. Outline fluorescent saccharin spot at R_f ca 0.5. (Spot may be crescent-shaped if large amt of cyclamate is present.) In hood, spray chromogenic agents (*1*) and (*2*), lightly to moderately, in immediate succession, on plate until cyclamate std appears as pink spot at R_f ca 0.3–0.4. P-4000 is brown-pink spot at R_f ca 0.85. Spray chromogenic agent (*3*) on plate until background pink fades to light yellow; contrast of cyclamate and P-4000 improves and at R_f ca 0.7 dulcin appears. Dulcin spot may be brownish-pink or blue, depending on condition of spray reagents and concn of sweetener. Plate may be resprayed with chromogenic agent (*3*) to restore contrast if pink background reappears.

CYCLOHEXYLSULFAMATE (CYCLAMATE) SALTS
Qualitative Test—Official First Action
20.127 *Sodium Nitrite Test*

Add 2 g BaCl₂ to 100 ml sample or aq. ext, prepd as in **20.084**(c). Let stand 5 min and filter. Acidify with 10 ml HCl and add 0.2 g NaNO₂. White ppt of BaSO₄ indicates presence of cyclohexylsulfamate.

20.128 Quantitative Method (35)—Official Final Action

(Applicable to aq. solns and clear carbonated beverages; if caramel is present, confirm cyclamates by 20.122–20.126.)

To 100 ml soln contg 10–300 mg Na or Ca cyclohexylsulfamate add 10 ml HCl and 10 ml 10% $BaCl_2$ soln. Stir and let stand 30 min. If ppt forms, filter and wash with H_2O. To filtrate or clear soln, add 10 ml 10% $NaNO_2$ soln, stir, cover with watch glass, and heat on steam bath ≥ 2 hr. Stir up ppt 3 times at 0.5 hr intervals. Remove from steam bath and leave in warm place overnight. Collect ppt on tared gooch, wash, and dry on asbestos mat over flame ≥ 10 min. Ignite, cool in desiccator, and weigh. Wt $BaSO_4 \times 0.8621 = $ Na cyclohexylsulfamate; $\times 0.9266 = $ Ca cyclohexylsulfamate.$2H_2O$.

Sodium Cyclamate and Calcium Cyclamate (36)—Official First Action

(Applicable to canned fruits)

20.129   Principle

Cyclamate is hydrolyzed by acid under pressure to cyclohexylamine, which is extd in $CHCl_3$ and allowed to react with ethanolic p-quinone to form colored product, 2-(cyclohexylamino)-1,4-benzoquinone.

20.130   Apparatus

(a) *Autoclave.*—American Sterilizer, Model 57CR, or equiv., operated at 15 psi (125°).

(b) *Homogenizer.*—"Willems" Polytron Model 45TE (Will Scientific, PO Box 1950, Rochester, NY 14603, No. 16131), or equiv., operated at ca 18,500 rpm.

20.131   Reagents

(a) *Cyclamate.*—Dry Na or Ca cyclamate (Abbott Laboratories, North Chicago, IL 60064) 4 hr at 100° just before weighing. (Solns of cyclamates do not pipet well.)

(b) *Color development soln.*—0.30% p-quinone in absolute alcohol. Prep. fresh just before use.

20.132   Determination

(Hydrolyze, develop color, and cool sample and std simultaneously.)

Shake can vigorously before opening. Blend entire contents of one or more cans in high-speed blender, transfer to beaker, and homogenize 2–3 min. Accurately weigh portion of homogenized fruit (≤ 15 g), contg 15–30 mg Na cyclamate or anhyd. Ca cyclamate, into 100 ml beaker. Into another 100 ml beaker, accurately weigh Na cyclamate std (previously dried 4 hr at 100°) ca equiv. to amt in sample taken. Dil. both sample and std to ca 40 ml with H_2O, add 13 ml 6N HCl, and dil. to ca 60 ml with H_2O. Place each beaker inside 400 ml beaker, cover larger beaker with watch glass, and autoclave 7 hr or overnight at 15 psi (125°).

Transfer cooled sample to 250 ml centrf. bottle with aid of H_2O, and rinse watch glass and both beakers with several portions H_2O. Centrf. at ca 1800 rpm and filter supernatant thru glass wool into 250 ml vol. flask. Repeat extn 2 times, swirling with 40 ml H_2O and decanting liq. thru the glass wool each time. Dil. both sample and std solns to vol. with H_2O and treat similarly. Pipet 25 ml aliquot into 125 ml separator, adjust to pH 12 with 10N NaOH (ca 12 drops), using narrow range pH paper, and add 4 drops excess. Pipet 25 ml $CHCl_3$ into each separator and shake vigorously 1 min.

Drain $CHCl_3$ layer thru tight glass wool pledget in stem of separator into small flask. Pipet 20 ml $CHCl_3$ ext into 50 ml vol. flask and add 10.0 ml freshly prepd 0.30% p-quinone soln in absolute alcohol. Similarly, prep. blank by adding 10 ml of the p-quinone soln to 20 ml $CHCl_3$. Place solns in 60° H_2O bath 2 hr, away from direct light. Cool, dil. to vol. with $CHCl_3$, and det. A at 493 nm against blank.

% Na cyclamate $= (A_u \times W_s)/(A_s \times W_u \times 10)$

where A_u and A_s refer to sample and std, resp., $W_s = $ wt std in mg, and $W_u = $ wt sample in g. To convert to anhyd. Ca cyclamate, multiply by 0.995.

DULCIN

20.133 Preparation of Sample—Official First Action

(*Caution: See* 46.011 *and* 46.054.)

Ext 100 ml sample (made alk. with 10% NaOH soln, if necessary), or alk. aq. ext, prepd as in 20.084(c), with two or three 50 ml portions ether. Divide ether ext equally between 2 porcelain dishes, let ether evap. at room temp., and dry residues in oven at 110°.

Qualitative Tests

20.134 Denigès-Tourrou Test (37)—Official First Action

Moisten dry residue, 20.133, with HNO_3 and add 1 drop H_2O. Presence of dulcin is indicated by formation of orange or brick-red ppt.

20.135 Modified LaParola-Mariani Test (38)—Official Final Action

Expose dry residue, 20.133, to HCl gas for 5 min and add 1 drop *anisaldehyde.* Presence of dulcin is indicated by orange-red to blood-red color. Presence of 25 mg/L or kg original sample can usually be detected by this test.

20.136 Quantitative Method (39)—Official First Action

(Applicable to nonalcoholic beverages)
(*Caution: See* 46.011, 46.039, *and* 46.054.)

Pipet 50 ml sample into separator. If 5-nitro-2-propoxyaniline (P-4000) is present, ext with four 50 ml portions pet ether, shaking 2 min each time, and discard pet ether. Make aq. phase alk. to litmus with 10% NaOH soln and ext with four 100 ml portions ether, shaking 2 min each time. Combine exts, wash with 10 ml H_2O, and discard H_2O. Evap. ether in 400 ml beaker and dry residue 30 min at 110°.

Dissolve residue in ca 50 ml redistd EtOAc, transfer to 100 ml vol. flask, dil. to vol. with 4 or 5 washings of the EtOAc, and mix. Read A in spectrophtr at 294 nm against redistd EtOAc. Det. quantity of dulcin in final soln from previously prepd std curve and calc. to mg/L.

5-NITRO-2-PROPOXYANILINE (P-4000)

Qualitative Tests

20.137 Organoleptic Test (40)—Official First Action

(*Caution: See* **46.011, 46.039,** and **46.073.**)

Make alk. (pH 7.5–8.0) with 10% NaOH 200 ml liq. food or aq. ext of 200 g solid food or semisolid product, **20.145**(c), and ext with three 25 ml portions pet ether. Wash combined exts once with 5 ml H_2O, transfer pet ether to small beaker or empty dish, let evap. spontaneously, and taste residue. Presence of 5 mg P-4000/L or kg original material may be detected by intensely sweet taste; or 12.5 mg/L or kg original material may be detected by its strong anesthetic effect.

20.138 Diamine Test (41)—Official Final Action

(*Caution: See* **46.011, 46.039, 46.047,** and **46.073.**)

Pipet 50 ml sample or aq. ext, **20.145**(c), into separator, make alk. with 10% NaOH, and ext ca 1 min with 50 ml pet ether. Repeat extn with two 50 ml portions pet ether. Combine exts, wash with 10 ml H_2O, and discard H_2O. Transfer ext to small beaker and add 4 ml HCl (1 + 1). Evap. pet ether on steam bath. Add small piece mossy Sn and keep 5 min longer on steam bath. Decant soln into test tube; add, dropwise, satd $Br-H_2O$. · Rose-red to deep burgundy-red soln is formed if P-4000 is present; this color is destroyed by excess Br.

Quantitative Method (41)—Official Final Action

(Applicable to nonalcoholic beverages)

20.139 Reagent

1-Naphthol soln.—Dissolve 50 mg 1-naphthol in 500 ml 1% Na_2CO_3 soln. Prep. fresh daily and store in brown glass bottle.

20.140 Preparation of Standard Curve

Dissolve 100 mg 5-nitro-2-propoxyaniline in ca 150 ml 60% alcohol. Transfer to 250 ml vol. flask, dil. to vol. with 60% alcohol, and mix. Transfer 1.00, 2.00, 3.00, and 4.00 ml aliquots to 250 ml vol. flasks, dil. to vol. with H_2O, and mix. Using 25 ml aliquots from each flask, proceed as in **20.141**, beginning "Ext with three 25 ml portions pet ether,..." Plot A against concn (0 to 0.16 mg/25 ml) final soln.

20.141 Determination

(*Caution: See* **46.011, 46.039,** and **46.073.**)

Pipet 20 ml sample into 250 ml vol. flask, dil. to vol. with H_2O, and mix. Transfer 25 ml aliquot to small separator, and add 10% NaOH soln, dropwise, until just alk. Ext with three 25 ml portions pet ether, shaking 1–2 min each time. Combine exts, wash with 5 ml H_2O, and discard wash H_2O. Transfer ext to small beaker, and add ca 10 ml H_2O and 0.5 ml 0.1N HCl. Evap. pet ether on steam bath. Remove when few ml pet ether remain; let remaining pet ether evap. spontaneously. Cool soln to ca 20°, add 1.0 ml 0.125% $NaNO_2$ soln, and stir. After 1 min, add 5.0 ml 1-naphthol soln, mix, and dil. to 25 ml. Det. A at 515 nm within 1 hr against blank carried thru detn. (mg P-4000/25 ml, from std curve) × 500 = mg/L.

SACCHARIN

Qualitative Tests—Official Final Action

20.142 Organoleptic Test

(*Caution: See* **46.011, 46.039,** and **46.054.**)

Acidify with HCl 50 ml nonalc. liq. food or aq. ext of 50 g solid or semisolid product, **20.145**(c), and ext with three 25 ml portions ether. Wash combined ether exts once with 5 ml H_2O, transfer to small beaker or evapg dish, let ether evap. spontaneously, and taste residue. (Presence of 20 mg saccharin/L or kg of original sample can usually be detected by its sweet taste.) Confirm by heating with NaOH and detecting salicylic acid formed thereby as in **20.143.**

20.143 By Conversion to Salicylic Acid

(*Caution: See* **46.011, 46.039,** and **46.054.**)

Acidify with HCl 50 ml nonalc. liq. food, or equiv. quantity of aq. ext, **20.145,** and ext with 3 portions ether as in **20.142.** Dissolve residue remaining after evapn of ether in little hot H_2O and test small portion of soln for salicylic acid as in **20.085** or **20.086.**

Dil. remainder of soln to ca 10 ml and add 2 ml H_2SO_4 (1 + 3). Heat to boiling and add slight excess of 5% $KMnO_4$ soln dropwise; partly cool soln, dissolve ca 1 g NaOH in it, and filter mixt. into Ag dish (Ag crucible lids are suitable). Evap. to dryness and heat 20 min at 210–215°. Dissolve residue in H_2O, acidify with HCl, and test ether ext for salicylic acid as in **20.085** or **20.086.** By this method all so-called "false saccharin" (J. Am. Chem. Soc. **26,** 1627(1904)) and any salicylic acid naturally present (also added salicylic acid when not present in too large amt) are destroyed, whereas 5 mg saccharin/L is detected with certainty.

20.144 Phenol-Sulfuric Acid Test (42)

(Applicable to nonalc. beverages, semisolid prepns, and baked goods; *Caution: See* **46.011, 46.039, 46.054,** and **46.073.**)

Prep. ether ext of sample as follows:

(a) *Nonalcoholic beverages.*—Add 3 ml HCl to 25 ml sample in separator. If vanillin is present, remove by extg with several portions of pet ether. Discard pet ether. Ext with 50, 25, and 25 ml ether-pet ether (1 + 1). Wash combined ether exts once with 5 ml H_2O, remove major portion of solv., transfer to 30 ml beaker, and evap. at room temp.

(b) *Semisolid preparations.*—Transfer 25 g sample to 100 ml vol. flask with small amt of hot H_2O and add enough boiling H_2O to make ca 75 ml. Let mixt. stand 1 hr, shaking occasionally. Then add 3 ml HOAc, mix thoroly, add slight excess (5 ml) of 20% neut. $Pb(OAc)_2$ soln, dil. to vol. with cold H_2O, mix, let stand 20 min, and filter. Transfer 60 ml or more of filtrate to separator and proceed as in (a).

(c) *Baked goods.*—Grind 25 g sample, mix thoroly with 50 g washed and ignited sea sand, and ext with pet ether in Soxhlet app. until ca fat-free (1–2 hr). Transfer extd mass to 300 ml erlenmeyer, add 100 ml alcohol, and reflux on boiling H_2O bath 30 min, shaking frequently. Filter thru buchner contg 7 cm Whatman No. 2 paper wet with alcohol. Transfer alc. filtrate to 100 ml beaker, evap. to ½ vol., add 50 ml H_2O and enough 10% Na_2CO_3 soln to make alk., and evap. to 50 ml. Transfer aq. soln. to separator and proceed as in (a).

To residue remaining after evapn of solv. add 5 ml *phenol-H_2SO_4 reagent* (pure colorless cryst. phenol dissolved in equal wt H_2SO_4) and heat 2 hr at 135–140°. Cool, dissolve in small amt hot H_2O, and pour into ca 250 ml H_2O. Add small amt of Filter-Cel, let stand 3 hr or overnight, and filter. Make alk. with 10% NaOH soln and dil. to 500 ml. Magenta or reddish-purple color develops if saccharin is present. Yellow, buff, or pale salmon shade is not significant.

Quantitative Methods
General Method I—Official Final Action

20.145 Preparation of Sample

(a) *Fruit juices and sirups.*—Transfer 100–200 g sample to 250 ml vol. flask with little H_2O and dil. to ca 200 ml with H_2O. Add 5 ml HOAc and mix. Add slight excess of 20% neut. $Pb(OAc)_2$ soln, mix thoroly, dil. to vol. with H_2O, again mix thoroly, and filter.

(b) *Alcoholic liquids.*—Heat 100–200 ml liq. on steam bath to remove alcohol (usually done by evapg to ½ original vol.). With heavy sirups, dil. liq. with equal vol. H_2O before beginning evapn. After removal of alcohol, transfer liq. to 250 ml vol. flask and proceed as in (a).

(c) *Solid or semisolid preparations.*—Transfer 50–75 g sample to 250 ml vol. flask with little hot H_2O and add enough boiling H_2O to make ca 200 ml. Let stand 2 hr, shaking occasionally. Add 5 ml HOAc, mix thoroly, add slight excess 20% neut. $Pb(OAc)_2$ soln, dil. to vol. with cold H_2O, mix, let stand 20 min, and filter.

20.146 Determination
(Caution: See 46.011, 46.039, and 46.054.)

Transfer 150 ml filtrate, 20.145, to separator, add 15 ml HCl, and ext with three 80 ml portions ether,

shaking separator 2 min each time. Wash combined ether exts once with 5 ml H_2O, remove ether by distn, and transfer residue to Pt crucible with little ether; or, if substances difficultly sol. in ether are present, use alternately small portions of H_2O and ether. Evap. ether on steam bath, add to residue 2–3 ml 10% Na_2CO_3 soln (or enough to make mixt. strongly alk.), rotate so that all saccharin is brought in contact with soln, and evap. to dryness on steam bath.

To dry residue add 4 g mixt. of equal parts of anhyd. Na_2CO_3 and K_2CO_3. Heat gently at first and then to complete fusion 30 min. (Fusion may be conducted by closely fitting crucible into hole cut into piece of heavy asbestos board so that ⅓ of crucible projects above asbestos, and heating lower portion of crucible by large Bunsen, Meker, or similar burner.) Cool, dissolve melt in H_2O, add ca 5 ml Br-H_2O, acidify with HCl, filter, wash paper with little H_2O, dil. filtrate and washings to ca 200 ml, heat to boiling, and slowly add excess of $BaCl_2$ soln (ca 10%). Let mixt. stand overnight, collect $BaSO_4$ on filter or on gooch, wash until Cl-free, dry, ignite, cool, and weigh. Correct results thus obtained for any S present in fusion mixt. as found by blank detn. Saccharin = corrected wt $BaSO_4$ × 0.7848.

Instead of mixed Na and K carbonates, 3–4 g Na_2O_2 may be used for fusion. In this case Ni crucible must be used, and time of fusion may be reduced to 5 min. Sepn of little $PbCl_2$ during extns does not interfere with accuracy of method.

20.147 General Method II (By Sublimation) (43)—Official First Action
(Caution: See 46.011, 46.039, 46.040, 46.049, and 46.054.)

Acidify 200 ml sample with 15 ml HCl and ext with three 50 ml portions CCl_4. Discard CCl_4, and ext aq. layer with three 80 ml portions ether. Let ether ext evap. to small vol. and transfer to sublimator with small amt of ether or alcohol. Evap. to dryness at room temp. or on H_2O bath, depending on whether ether or alcohol was used to transfer residue. Sublime residue 1 hr at 1–2 mm pressure and 140–160°. (Raise temp. so slowly that ca ½ hr is required to reach 140°). Wash saccharin from condenser bulb of sublimator with warm alcohol into weighed beaker, and repeat sublimation until no further residue appears on condensing bulb. Evap. alcohol on H_2O bath, heat residue 2 hr at 100°, cool, and reweigh beaker.

20.148 Special Method for Nonalcoholic Beverages (44)—Official Final Action
(Caution: See 46.011, 46.039, and 46.054.)

Add 2 ml HCl to 50 ml sample in separator. Ext with two 50 ml portions ether. Filter ether exts thru cotton, and wash combined filtrates with ca 5 ml H_2O contg 1 drop HCl.

Sep. ether layer and evap. to dryness on H_2O bath. Add 5 ml NH_3-free H_2O and 6 ml HCl to residue, and evap. soln to ca 1 ml on hot plate, stirring constantly. Again add 5 ml NH_3-free H_2O and 6 ml HCl, and evap. to ca 1 ml. Dil. to 50 ml with NH_3-free H_2O and dil. 2 ml of this soln to 25 ml with NH_3-free H_2O. Add 1 ml Nessler reagent, **33.007(b)**, and compare with NH_4Cl stds in usual manner; 0.2921 g $NH_4Cl = 1$ g saccharin, insol. form $(C_7H_5NO_3S)$, and 1.317 g Na salt $(C_7H_4NNaO_3S$ $.2H_2O)$. For convenience prep. NH_4Cl std equiv. to 200 ppm insol. form of saccharin.

NUTRIENTS

Monosodium Glutamate (45)—Official First Action

20.149   Apparatus and Reagents

(a) *Chromatographic column.*—50 × 2 cm id tube, 30 ml bed vol., with Dowex 50W-X8 (H^+ form), 100–200 mesh.

(b) *Activated carbon.*—Darco G-60.

20.150   Sample Preparation

For products in dry form, reduce ca 40 g to powder in mortar and weigh 10 g sample into 250 ml beaker. For undild, concd soups or canned green beans, homogenize entire undild content of can in blender and weigh 20 g sample into 250 ml beaker. For consommé-type (clear, condensed) soup, weigh 20 g into 250 ml beaker.

Dil. sample to ca 70 ml with H_2O at room temp., and mix until all H_2O-sol. substances are in soln (ca 15 min). Add 6 g C and mix thoroly. (For products contg starch, also add 60 ml acetone to ppt starch and to aid sample soln.) Let stand 30 min. Filter with vac. thru 60 ml coarse fritted-glass funnel contg asbestos pad. Wash flask and residue with six 25 ml portions H_2O or, if acetone was added, with six 25 ml portions acetone-H_2O (1 + 1). Collect filtrate and washings in 400 ml beaker, add 2 drops HCl (1 + 2.5), and evap. on steam bath to ca 40 ml. (HCl prevents conversion of glutamic acid to pyrrolidone carboxylic acid.) Quant. transfer to 50 ml vol. flask, dil. to vol. with H_2O, and mix. Use 25 ml aliquot for each detn.

20.151   Determination

Transfer 25 ml aliquot to prepd column and adjust flow to ca 0.5 ml/min. After all soln enters resin, wash column wall with ca 10 ml H_2O; let wash pass into resin. Add 120 ml 0.8N HCl and maintain flow rate (0.8N HCl will elute any serine, threonine, and aspartic acid). After all 0.8N HCl passes into resin, add 170 ml 1N HCl and adjust flow to between 25–30 drops/min to elute glutamic acid; collect eluate in 400 ml beaker. (Any glycine present will elute after 200 ml 1N HCl.) Nearly neutze eluate with 50% NaOH and potentiometrically adjust to pH 7 with 0.1N NaOH.

Neutze 25 ml 37% HCHO to pH 7 with 0.1N NaOH and add to prepd neut. sample. Mix 10 min

on magnetic stirrer and titr. potentiometrically to pH 8.9 with 0.1N NaOH.

Det. blank by titrg to pH 8.9 mixt. of 25 ml neutzd HCHO and 170 ml 1N HCl neutzd to pH 7.

$$\% \text{ glutamic acid} = [(S - B) \times N \times 0.147 \times 100]/w$$

where S = ml NaOH used to titr. sample, B = ml NaOH used to titr. blank, N = normality of NaOH, and w = g sample.

$$\% \text{ MSG} = \% \text{ glutamic acid} \times 1.15$$

Before using resin column again, remove any remaining amino acids by passing 150 ml 4N HCl thru column. Wash column with H_2O until $AgNO_3$ soln gives neg. test for Cl.

SOLVENTS

Ethylene Dichloride and Trichloroethylene (46)—Official First Action

(Applicable to spice oleoresins)

20.152   Apparatus

All glassware must be $CHCl_3$-free; rinse with alcohol if necessary. Rinse pipets with alcohol after each use.

(a) *Column.*—Porapak Q (50–80 mesh), available from Waters Associates, 61 Fountain St, Framingham, MA 01701. Pack 6′ × 6 mm od Al tubing column plugged at one end with glass wool, using slight vac. and light tapping to settle polymer beads. Add plug of glass wool to open end of column. Condition column 2 hr at 230°, passing N thru at 20 ml/min.

(b) *Gas chromatograph.*—Micro-Tek GC2503R or MT 220 gas chromatograph (Tracor Inc., 6500 Tracor Ln, Austin, TX 78721) or equiv., equipped with column, (a), Dohrmann Model C-200 or C-200-A microcoulometric detector (Dohrmann Instrument Co.) connected to 1 mv (full-scale) strip chart recorder, combustion furnace, and Dohrmann T-200 titrn cell sensitive to halogens. Prep. Vycor tube in injection port with Pt gauze wrapped around loose plug of glass wool. Do not plug tube too tightly.

Operating parameters are as follows:

Coulometer, Mode II (low gain) and ca 200 ohms range, or range that provides ca half-scale deflection for 40 μl injection of $C_2H_4Cl_2$ std; removable inlet temp. 200°; column temp. 160°; furnace temp. ca 825°; N flow 100 ml/min (measure with soap bubble flow meter); sweep 10–20 ml/min; O ca 25 ml/min.

20.153   Reagents

Densities $C_2H_4Cl_2$ and C_2HCl_3 for converting from vol. to wt are 1.25 and 1.46, resp. Use absolute alcohol for all dilns.

(a) *Internal std.*—(1) *Stock soln.*—Pipet 2.0 ml 1,2-dichloropropane into 200 ml vol. flask half filled with alcohol, immersing tip of pipet below surface of alcohol and then releasing contents. Wash pipet exterior with alcohol before withdrawing it from flask. Dil. to vol. and mix. (2) *Working std soln.*—Pipet 1.0

ml stock soln into 200 ml vol. flask half filled with alcohol, immersing pipet tip, as above, before release of contents. Wash pipet exterior into flask, dil. to vol., and mix. Soln contains 0.05 μl or 57.95 μg 1,2-dichloropropane/ml alcohol.

(b) *Reference stds.*—Prep. sep. $C_2H_4Cl_2$ and C_2HCl_3 stds as follows:

Pipet 2.0 ml chlorinated solv. into 200 ml vol. flask half filled with alcohol, immersing tip of pipet below surface of alcohol and then releasing contents. Wash pipet exterior with alcohol before withdrawing it from flask. Dil. to vol. and mix. Pipet 2.0 ml soln into 200 ml vol. flask as above, dil. to vol., and mix. Pipet 2.0 ml into 100 ml vol. flask as before, add 8.0 ml working internal std soln, and dil. to vol. Concn of stds:

Ethylene dichloride std = 2.50 ng $C_2H_4Cl_2/\mu$l and 4.64 ng 1,2-dichloropropane/μl.

Trichloroethylene std = 2.92 ng C_2HCl_3/μl and 4.64 ng 1,2-dichloropropane/μl.

20.154   *Determination*

Weigh 2.5 g well mixed oleoresin into 25 ml vol. flask, add 2.0 ml working internal std soln, and dil. to vol. with absolute alcohol. Shake vigorously ca 5 min.

Chromatograph duplicate portions, ca 30 μl, in microcoulometric gas chromatograph set at prescribed conditions. Chromatograph duplicate portions of appropriate stds required to identify and quantitate. Vent ca 2 min after each injection and clean Vycor tube and contents after every 4 sample injections. (Det. venting time experimentally to release all alcohol.)

Approx. relative retention ratios relative to $C_2H_4Cl_2 = 1$: C_2HCl_3, 1.6; 1,2-dichloropropane, 2.0.

Use relative retention ratios to identify chlorinated solv. residues found in samples. Inject 30 μl absolute alcohol as solv. blank.

20.155   *Calculations*

Det. area of each peak and calc. amt of chlorinated solv. residue as follows:

ppm chlorinated solv. residue
$$= [(D_v \times I_s)/(I_v \times D_s)] \times C_s \times (V_v/W_v)$$

where D_v = area of sample peak; D_s = area of std peak; I_v = area of internal std peak from sample soln; I_s = area of internal std from ref. std soln; C_s = concn, μg/ml, of std chromatgd; V_v = vol., ml, to which sample is dild; W_v = g sample weighed.

SELECTED REFERENCES

(*1*) JAOAC **49**, 701(1966); **51**, 533(1968).

(*2*) JAOAC **48**, 489(1965).

(*3*) JAOAC **50**, 880(1967); **51**, 490, 943(1968); **52**, 40(1970).

(*4*) JAOAC **35**, 186(1952).

(*5*) Z. Nahr. Genussm. **19**, 137(1910); Chem. Abstr **4**, 1523(1910).

(*6*) JAOAC **46**, 767(1963); **47**, 68(1964).

(*7*) JAOAC **42**, 486(1959); **43**, 587(1960).

(*8*) JAOAC **50**, 985(1967); **51**, 491(1968).

(*9*) USDA Div. Chem. Bull. **51**, p. 113.

(*10*) JAOAC **42**, 487(1959).

(*11*) JAOAC **51**, 987(1968); **52**, 485(1969).

(*12*) JAOAC **36**, 744(1953).

(*13*) Chem. News **91**, 39(1905); Ann. Rept. Mass. State Bd. Health 1905, p. 498.

(*14*) Mon. Sci. (4th Ser.) **9**, Part 1, 324(1895).

(*15*) Z. Anal. Chem. **110**, 22(1937).

(*16*) Ind. Eng. Chem., Anal. Ed. **3**, 199(1931).

(*17*) JAOAC **40**, 789(1957).

(*18*) JAOAC **25**, 145(1942); **27**, 195, 339, 446(1944); **28**, 302(1945); **29**, 100(1946); **31**, 484(1948); **32**, 489(1949).

(*19*) JAOAC **47**, 395(1964).

(*20*) J. Am. Med. Assoc. **120**, 289(1942); Ind. Eng. Chem., Anal. Ed. **15**, 492(1943); **16**, 739(1944); JAOAC **29**, 310, 311(1946); **31**, 480(1948).

(*21*) JAOAC **35**, 459(1952).

(*22*) JAOAC **35**, 455(1952).

(*23*) JAOAC **37**, 374(1954).

(*24*) J. Ind. Eng. Chem. **2**, 24(1910); **3**, 492(1911); JAOAC **14**, 76(1931); **16**, 77(1933).

(*25*) USDA Div. Chem. Bull. **13**(8), p. 1032.

(*26*) Monier-Williams, Repts on Public Health and Med. Subject No. 43 (London, Ministry of Health, 1927); JAOAC **12**, 120(1929); **16**, 77(1933); **17**, 70(1934); **18**, 82(1935); **45**, 905(1962); **49**, 235, 834(1966).

(*27*) JAOAC **44**, 641(1961); **46**, 618(1963); **48**, 796(1965).

(*28*) JAOAC **44**, 485(1961).

(*29*) J. prakt. Chem. **46**, 428(1892); Repts on Public Health and Med. Subject No. 43 (London, Ministry of Health, p. 12).

(*30*) JAOAC **31**, 476(1948); **44**, 476(1961).

(*31*) JAOAC **51**, 540(1968).

(*32*) JAOAC **18**, 140(1935); **19**, 373(1936); **21**, 97(1938).

(*33*) JAOAC **47**, 363(1964).

(*34*) JAOAC **52**, 487(1969).

(*35*) JAOAC **38**, 559(1955); **43**, 583(1960).

(*36*) JAOAC **51**, 1274(1968).

(*37*) Compt. Rend. **173**, 1184(1921).

(*38*) Ann. Chim. Applicata **36**, 134(1946).

(*39*) JAOAC **40**, 785(1957).

(*40*) JAOAC **35**, 321(1952).

(*41*) JAOAC **39**, 652(1956).

(*42*) Z. Nahr. Genussm. **31**, 67(1915); JAOAC **24**, 326(1941).

(*43*) JAOAC **30**, 492(1947).

(*44*) Z. Nahr. Genussm. **18**, 577(1909); JAOAC **17**, 193(1934); **18**, 56(1935); **21**, 186(1938).

(*45*) JAOAC **52**, 744, 1131(1969).

(*46*) JAOAC **52**, 389, 477(1969).

21. Food Additives: Indirect

Benzo(a)pyrene (1)—Official Final Action

21.001 *Principle*

Benzo(a)pyrene is extd from comminuted food sample after saponification with alc. KOH. It is purified by solv. partition and column chromatgy, sepd by TLC, detd by UV spectrophotometry, and confirmed by spectrophotofluorometry.

21.002 *General Instructions*

Because of sensitivity of method, possibility of errors from contamination is great. All glassware must be thoroly cleaned to remove all org. matter such as oil, grease, detergent residues, etc. Do not use grease on stopcocks or joints. Rinse all glassware with purified solvs immediately before use. Because benzo-(a)pyrene is somewhat susceptible to photooxidn, perform detn as far as possible under subdued light and store std solns in low actinic flasks. Use care in prepg stds and handling exts, as benzo(a)pyrene is potent carcinogen.

21.003 *Apparatus*

(a) *Separators.*—125, 500, 1000, and 2000 ml; with Teflon stopcocks.

(b) *Evaporation flasks.*—125 and 250 ml, all-glass flasks (Kontes Glass Co., Cat. No. K-617250, or equiv.) with ⊤ 24/40 wash bottle stopper (Cat. No. K-331751, or equiv.) having inlet and outlet tubes to permit passage of N across surface of liq. to be evapd. Inlet tube of stopper used to convey N is cut off 2 cm below joint, and outlet tube connected to vac. is bent downward at 45° angle to prevent backflow of condensate into flask.

(c) *Boiling flask.*—R-b, 1 L with ⊤ 24/40 joint, and pouring lip.

(d) *Condenser.*—Friedrich type, with ⊤ 24/40 joint.

(e) *Chromatographic tube.*—38 mm id × 230 mm long, with coarse porosity fritted filter.

(f) *Pressure filter.*—30 ml, fine porosity, with ⊤ 24/40 outer joint (Kontes Cat. No. K-953100, or equiv.) and adapter with ⊤ 24/40 inner joint (Kontes Cat. No. K-183000, or equiv.) for connection to N tank.

(g) *Nitrogen cylinder.*—H$_2$O-pumped, or equiv., purity N in cylinder with regulator and valve to control flow at 5 psig.

(h) *Heating mantle.*—Elec., hemispherical, for 1 L r-b flask. (Use with variable transformer heat control.)

(i) *Ultraviolet equipment.*—(1) Lamps: longwave,

3660 Å; shortwave, 2537 Å. (2) Chromato-Vue cabinet (available from Ultraviolet Products, Inc.).

(j) *Recording spectrophotometer and accessories.*—Cary 11 or 15 (Cary Instruments, 2724 S. Peck Rd, Monrovia, CA 91016), or equiv., with following fused quartz cells (available from Optical Cell Co., 4204 37th St, Brentwood, MD 20722): (1) Rectangular, optical path 10±0.005 mm; 1.5 ml capacity (Cat. No. 5-503 QS, or equiv.). (2) Cylindrical, optical path 50±0.05 mm; 15.0 ml capacity (Cat. No. 2-228 Q, or equiv.).

(k) *Spectrophotofluorometer and accessories.*—(1) *Aminco-Bowman:* With 1P28 photomultiplier tube and slit arrangement No. 2 (narrowest slit width, ⅟₃₂″) (available from American Instrument Co.), or equiv. (*Caution: See* 46.008.) (2) *Cells:* Fused rectangular quartz cells, optical path 10±0.005 mm; 3.0 ml capacity (Optical Cell Co., Cat. No. 5-501 QS, or equiv.).

(l) *Thin layer chromatography apparatus.*—(Available from Brinkmann Instruments, Inc.) (1) *Glass plates*, 100 × 200 mm (No. 25-10-110-3, or equiv.); (2) *applicator*, std adjustable, model S-II (No. 25-09-05); (3) *mounting board*, Plexiglas, std size for plate up to 200 mm wide (No. 04-10-00, or equiv.); (4) *drying rack* (No. 25-09-15, or equiv.); (5) *developing tank*, std, rectangular, 22 cm deep × 8.5 cm wide × 20.5 cm long (No. 04-10-08, or equiv.); (6) *desiccating storage cabinet*, stainless steel, 30 cm wide × 25 cm thick (No. 04-10-24, or equiv.).

21.004 *Reagents*

(Caution: See 46.011, 46.039, 46.040, 46.045, 46.062, *and* 46.066.)

Distill all reagents, where specified, with use of air-cooled 300 cm reflux condenser between distg flask and H$_2$O-cooled condenser. Use 2 L lots, discarding first 200 ml distillate and collecting next 1600 ml for use.

Purify isooctane, benzene, and MeOH to meet following test:

To specified quantity of solv. in 250 ml evapn flask, add 1 ml purified hexadecane and place on steam bath. Insert tube assembly; connect inlet tube to N and outlet tube to solv. trap and vac. line. Discontinue evapn when ≤1 ml residue remains. (To residue from benzene add 10 ml purified isooctane, re-evap., and repeat once to ensure complete removal of benzene.) Dissolve the 1 ml hexadecane residue in isooctane and dil. to 25 ml. Det. *A* in 5 cm path length cells compared to isooctane as ref.; *A* of soln of solv. residue (except for MeOH) must be ≤0.01/cm path length between 280 and 400 nm. For MeOH, *A* must be ≤0.03/cm path length between 250 and 275 nm; 0.015 between 275 and 300 nm; 0.010 between 300 and 350 nm; and 0.00 between 350 and 400 nm.

(a) *Isooctane.*—2,2,4-Trimethylpentane. Purify by distn or by passing thru column of activated silica gel (Grade 12, (l)(2)) ca 90 cm long × 5–8 cm id. Use 180 ml for test.

(b) *Benzene.*—ACS. Purify by distn. Use 150 ml for test.

(c) *Hexadecane.*—99% olefin-free. Purify by percolation thru column of activated silica gel, (l)(2). Dil. 1 ml hexadecane to 25 ml with isooctane and det. *A* between 250 and 400 nm in 5 cm cell against isooctane as ref.; *A* must be 0.00/cm path length in this range.

(d) *Methanol.*—ACS. Purify as follows: Reflux 2 L with 10 g KOH and 25 g Zn dust 3 hr. Distill thru air-cooled reflux condenser connected to H$_2$O-cooled condenser. Provide collection flask with drying tube to protect distd solv. from moisture. Use 50.0 ml for test.

(e) *Alcohol.*—USP. Redistill before use.

(f) *Toluene.*—ACS. Redistill before use.

(g) *Dimethyl sulfoxide (DMSO).*—Spectral grade (Crown Zellerbach Corp., Chemical Products Div., Camas, WA 98607, or equiv.). Completely sat. sample with N and record spectrum against H$_2$O ref. in 1 cm cells. *A* curve must have no irregularities within following wavelengths:

Wavelength (nm)	Absorbance (Max.)
261.5	1.00
270.0	0.20
275.0	0.09
280.0	0.06
300.0	0.015

Reagent grade DMSO may be purified as in JAOAC **48**, 304(1965).

(h) *Phosphoric acid.*—ACS.

(i) *Acetylated linters powder.*—21% acetylated (Schleicher and Schuell Co., Cat. No. 124/21 ac, or equiv.).

(j) *Florisil.*—60–100 mesh (available from Fisher Scientific Co., Cat. No. F-100, or equiv.). Place 300 g Florisil in 1 L g-s erlenmeyer. Add 500 ml redistd MeOH, stopper, and shake 1 min, removing stopper periodically to release pressure. Transfer slurry to 600 ml coarse porosity fritted buchner and let drain by gravity. Wash flask with three 35 ml portions redistd MeOH and pass thru buchner. Wash adsorbent in funnel with addnl 100 ml redistd MeOH and let drain. Apply vac. to remove most of MeOH. Transfer treated Florisil to tray lined with Al foil (free of rolling oil). Dry in vac. (26–28″) at 50° overnight. Store adsorbent in amber bottle.

Test prepd adsorbent before use as follows: Pour 10 g treated Florisil into clean 30 ml coarse porosity fritted glass funnel (30 mm diam.). Place 15 g anhyd. Na$_2$SO$_4$ on adsorbent and wash with 50 ml purified isooctane. Prep. 0.2 μg/ml soln of benzo(a)pyrene in isooctane. Pipet 10 ml soln onto anhyd. Na$_2$SO$_4$, let filter into 125 ml evapn flask, and wash adsorbent with four 20 ml portions isooctane, letting column drain completely between washes. Remove and retain first evapn flask and replace with second 125 ml evapn flask. Elute benzo(a)pyrene from column, using four 25 ml portions redistd benzene, letting column drain completely between washes. Add 1 ml hexadecane to each eluate in the 2 evapn flasks. Evap. under stream of N on steam bath to residue of 1 ml hexadecane. Add 5 ml isooctane to residue from benzene eluate in second evapn flask and re-evap. Repeat once to ensure complete removal of benzene. Dil. residues to 15 ml with isooctane and record *A* with recording spectrophtr from 350 to 400 nm, using 5 cm path length cells, against isooctane. No benzo(a)pyrene should be present in first (isooctane) eluate, and 95–100% of added benzo(a)pyrene should be found in benzene eluate as calcd from *A* at 383 nm max. Concn of 1 μg/ml benzo(a)pyrene in isooctane gives *A* of 0.12/cm path length at 383 nm max.

(k) *Sodium sulfate.*—Anhyd., ACS, granular form.

(l) *Silica gel.*—Activated (available from Fisher Scientific Co.). (1) *Desiccant.*—Grade 42, 6–16 mesh (Cat. No. S-160). (2) *Adsorbent.*—Grade 12, 28–200 mesh (Cat. No. S-157).

(m) *Benzo(a)pyrene.*—(*Caution:* Benzo(a)pyrene may be harmful.) Check purity by TLC on cellulose acetate adsorbent prior to use. No fluorescent impurities should be observed after chromtgy of 2–3 μg benzo(a)pyrene std. Std soln of benzo(a)pyrene at 1–2 μg/ml in isooctane exhibits following max.: 226, 254, 265, 272, 284, 296, 330, 345, 362, 377, 379, and 383 nm. Benzo(a)pyrene in isooctane (1 μg/ml) gives *A* of 0.12/cm path length at 383 nm max. If benzo(a)pyrene does not meet these criteria, purify by recrystn from benzene.

(n) *Benzo(a)pyrene std solns.*—(*Caution:* See **46.018.**) (1) *Stock soln.*—100 μg/ml. Dissolve 0.0100 g benzo(a)pyrene in MeOH and dil. to 100 ml with MeOH. (2) *Intermediate std soln.*—10 μg/ml. Dil. 10 ml stock soln to 100 ml with MeOH. (3) *Working std solns.*—0.5 and 1.0 μg/ml. Dil. 5 and 10 ml aliquots of 10 μg/ml std soln to 100 ml with MeOH. (*Note:* Std solns are stable indefinitely when protected from light.)

21.005   *Extraction*

Grind sample in meat grinder. Place 100 g in 1 L boiling flask and add 400 ml alcohol, 15 g KOH (10 g for cheese), and boiling chips. Insert Friedrich condenser and reflux 1.5 hr at rapid rate. (*Caution:* To prevent foaming, gradually increase heat to rapid reflux rate only after refluxing at relatively slow rate ca 5–10 min.)

21.006 Purification

(*Caution:* See **46.011, 46.039, 46.040, 46.045,** and **46.062.**)

Remove condenser and transfer material while warm into 2 L separator contg 250 ml H_2O. Wash boiling flask with two 100 ml portions alcohol and transfer washes to separator. Wash flask with 150 ml isooctane and pour into separator. Shake separator 3 min. Let layers sep. and drain lower layer into second separator. Let solids in first separator settle addnl min and carefully drain them completely into second separator. Repeat extn with 100 ml isooctane. Let sep., drain aq. layer and residual solids as before into third separator, and again ext with 100 ml isooctane. Drain aq. layer, let solids settle, and carefully remove. Discard aq. layer and solids. Wash each isooctane ext 4 times with 250 ml warm (ca 50°) H_2O by gently swirling. (Avoid vigorous shaking; it may cause emulsions.) Discard aq. layer after each wash.

Pour 60 g treated and tested Florisil into chromatgc tube, with gentle tapping to settle contents. Place 50 g anhyd. Na_2SO_4 on top of adsorbent, tapping to level surface. Prewet column with ca 75 ml isooctane, let drain by gravity, and discard eluate. Filter isooctane ext in first separator thru column. Let column drain by gravity. Wash first separator with ext contained in second separator and filter thru column by gravity. Wash second and first separators successively with ext in third separator, filter thru column, and again let drain. Wash third, second, and first separators in that order with 100 ml isooctane and pass thru column as before. Discard all isooctane eluates. Elute benzo(a)pyrene by passing 175 ml benzene thru column into 250 ml evapn flask. Let column drain completely. Add 2 ml hexadecane to benzene eluate. Fit tube assembly into evapn flask and evap. solv. under N on steam bath as for purified benzene under **21.004,** but evap. only to 2 ml residual hexadecane (loose Al foil jacket around flask speeds evapn). It is essential to add 10 ml isooctane, re-evap., and repeat once to ensure complete removal of benzene.

Quant. transfer 2 ml hexadecane conc. to 500 ml separator, using total of 198 ml isooctane. Wash soln twice with 100 ml portions H_3PO_4, shaking 1 min each time. After each wash, let layers sep. (ca 10 min) and discard lower (acid) layer. After draining acid in final wash, swirl separator and let stand few min. Carefully drain any residual acid which settles out. Add 50 ml DMSO (pre-equilibrated with isooctane) and shake 2 min. Set up three 125 ml separators contg 25 ml isooctane (pre-equilibrated with DMSO). After sepn of phases in 500 ml separator, drain lower (DMSO) layer into first 125 ml separator, and wash in tandem with isooctane in the three 125 ml separators, shaking each wash 1 min. Repeat extn with 2 addnl 50 ml portions DMSO, washing each ext in tandem thru same 3 portions isooctane.

Collect successive DMSO exts (150 ml total) in 1 L separator contg 300 ml H_2O and 50 ml isooctane. Let mixt. cool few min after last ext has been added, as some heat of diln is generated. Shake vigorously 2 min and let sep. Drain lower aq. phase into second 1 L separator, and repeat extn with 50 ml isooctane. Drain and discard aq. phase. Wash each 50 ml ext twice with 75 ml portions H_2O, shaking each wash ca 15 sec. Let sep. and discard aq. layer after each wash. Filter isooctane ext in first separator thru anhyd. Na_2SO_4 (ca 35 g in 30 ml coarse, fritted glass funnel or in 65 ml filter with glass wool plug, and previously washed with isooctane) into 250 ml evapn flask. Rinse first separator with ext from second separator, and pass thru filter. Wash second and first separators successively in tandem with two 25 ml portions isooctane and pass individual portions thru filter. Evap. combined filtrate on steam bath under N as before to ca 10 ml. Transfer soln quant. with benzene to 50 ml g-s erlenmeyer and conc. on steam bath under N to ≤ 0.5 ml. (*Caution:* Do not evap. to dryness, since prolonged heating of polycyclic hydrocarbons in dry state will cause losses.) Reserve concd soln for TLC.

21.007 Thin Layer Chromatography

Place 50 g cellulose acetate and 275 ml alcohol in g-s erlenmeyer. (Ten plates can be prepd with this amt of slurry.) Shake mixt. vigorously by hand 4 min. With thin layer applicator, apply adsorbent to plates (10×20 cm) to thickness of 1000 μm. Let plates air-dry 4 hr and store in desiccator over silica gel desiccant until needed.

Pour 50 ml mobile solv. (alcohol-toluene-H_2O ($17 + 4 + 4$, v/v/v)) in development tank and equilibrate ≥ 1 hr. In partially darkened room apply entire benzene ext conc. to plate with micropipet (50 μl syringe, available from Hamilton Co., or equiv., may also be used) in small spot at starting line 2 cm from bottom of plate. Wash down sides of flask with four 0.2 ml portions benzene from graduated pipet and transfer solv. from each wash to plate as before. Spot ca 0.5 μg benzo(a)pyrene std in isooctane next to unknown to aid identification. After solv. evaps, place plate in tank and let chromatogram develop in dark until solv. front reaches top of plate (ca 1.5 hr at 25°).

When development is complete, remove plate from chamber and observe under both longwave and shortwave UV light in ChromatoVue cabinet. (This operation may be carried out while plate is still wet.) Outline fluorescent spot of benzo(a)pyrene which moves up plate ca 6 cm from starting line (R_f 0.30–0.33).

21.008 Ultraviolet Spectrophotometry

Remove plate from cabinet, scrape off adsorbent around spot with spatula, and discard. Transfer outlined spot of adsorbent to 125 ml beaker and elute benzo(a)pyrene from adsorbent by extg with 5–10 ml portions hot MeOH until fluorescence under UV light can no longer be seen in last portion of solv. Swirl flask repeatedly during extn and successively filter individual exts thru 50 ml pressure filter under N pressure into 50 ml flask. (Three or 4 extns are usually enough to remove compd from adsorbent.) After extn, add 1.0 ml hexadecane to combined ext and evap. MeOH on steam bath under stream of N. Remove any residual MeOH in flask by adding two 5 ml portions isooctane and re-evapg under N.

(Prior to recording UV spectrum of each sample soln det. baseline in 250–400 nm range, using isooctane in ref. and sample cells. Baseline should be relatively flat thruout range, especially in 350–400 nm region.)

Carefully transfer the 1.0 ml hexadecane soln of benzo(a)pyrene into 1 cm path length cell (total capacity 1.5 ml) and record UV spectrum in 250–400 nm range, using isooctane in ref. cell. Compare any maxima observed with those in spectra obtained for std solns of benzo(a)pyrene (observable maxima will be 255, 267, 285, 297, 363, 382, and 386 nm).

Transfer 1 ml hexadecane to each of two 50 ml erlenmeyers and add 1 ml 0.5 μg/ml std to one flask and 1 ml 1.0 μg/ml std to other. Place flasks on steam bath and evap. MeOH under N. Remove any residual MeOH by adding two 5 ml portions isooctane and re-evapg under N. Record spectra. A of 1 μg/ml of benzo(a)pyrene in hexadecane is 0.12/cm path length at 386 nm (major max. in 350–400 nm region).

Calc. quantity benzo(a)pyrene in sample ext in hexadecane at 386 nm by using baseline technic in conjunction with spectra of std solns recorded under same instrumental conditions.

21.009   *Spectrophotofluorometry*

Carefully transfer benzo(a)pyrene soln from spectrophtr cell into fluorometer cell and record excitation spectrum at emission max. (415 nm uncorrected). Record emission spectrum at excitation max. (390 nm uncorrected). Compare fluoresence spectra obtained with those of 0.5 and 1.0 μg/ml std solns of benzo(a)pyrene and calc. quantity present.

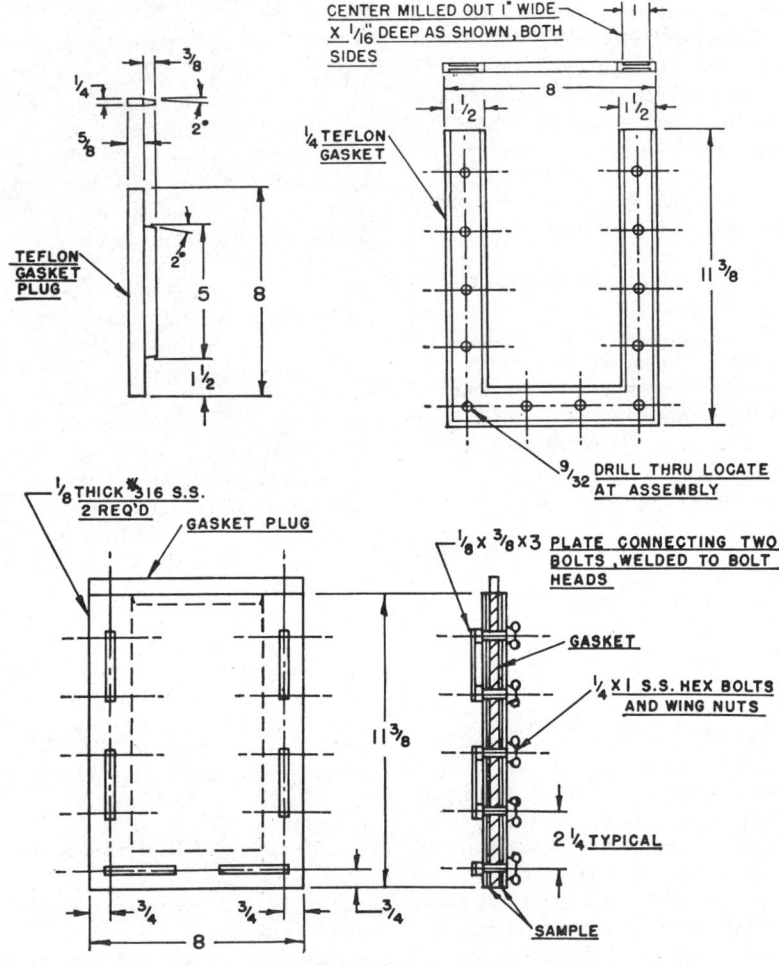

FIG. 21:1—Test cell

Exposing Flexible Barrier Materials for Extraction
ASTM-AOAC Method (2)—Official Final Action

21.010 *Principles*

Method provides std liq. extn method for flexible barrier materials, singly, coated, or combined, including extns thru flexible barrier materials of surface coating ingredients, by food-simulating solvs. Specimens of flexible barrier materials are exposed to extg liqs in test cell and amt of nonvolatile extractives remaining after exposure is measured.

21.011 *Apparatus*

(a) *Test cell.*—See Fig. 21:1. Consists of two $8 \times 11\frac{3}{4} \times \frac{1}{8}''$ No. 316 stainless steel plates, degreased; one $\frac{1}{4} \times 1\frac{1}{2}''$ U-shaped virgin TFE-fluorocarbon (Teflon) gasket, grooved on both sides as shown; twelve $\frac{1}{4} \times 1''$ stainless steel bolts with wing nuts; one $\frac{1}{4} \times 1 \times 8''$ TFE-fluorocarbon gasket plug tapered to provide tight fit. (Available from Scientific Products, Inc., No. 6200.) To prep. app. for use, wash plates and gaskets in aq. detergent soln. Rinse with H_2O and dry at 100°. Wash with *n*-heptane and redistd acetone. Immerse new gaskets in *n*-heptane overnight. Rinse gaskets with fresh *n*-heptane and dry at 100°.

(b) *Oven rack.*—See Fig. 21:2. To hold extn test cells.

(c) *Hot air oven.*—With safety provisions for flammable solvs. Vac. oven or autoclave is suitable.

21.012 *Reagents*

Use solvs (usually H_2O, dil. alcohol, and *n*-heptane) specified in regulations (Code of Federal Regulations, Title 21, Sec. 121.2514(d)(2); 121.2526(d)). Solv. for blanks and detn should be from same container.

21.013 *Preparation of Cells*

Select samples of flexible barrier material and protect from exposure to liqs or contamination by migration from contact with other materials, and from wrinkling or abrasion. Samples shall equal or exceed dimensions of cell where possible, and shall in all cases have 1 dimension at least width (8″) of cell.

Place 1 stainless steel plate of cell on flat surface with bolts protruding up thru holes in plate. Place prepunched specimen (side to contact liq. up) on plate with 1 edge aligned with bottom of plate, 2 edges aligned with sides of plate, and bolts passing thru prepunched holes. Place gasket on specimen with outer edges of gasket aligned with cell bottom and sides. If desired, place second prepunched specimen (side to contact liq. down) on top of gasket. If only 1 sheet is used for test, place inert barrier sheet such as Teflon or electrolytically cleaned tinfoil in place of second sheet. Place second stainless steel plate on top of assembly. Place wing nuts on bolts and tighten.

Preheat assembly (including TFE-fluorocarbon gasket plug) to test temp. and retighten nuts so that assembly is liq.-tight.

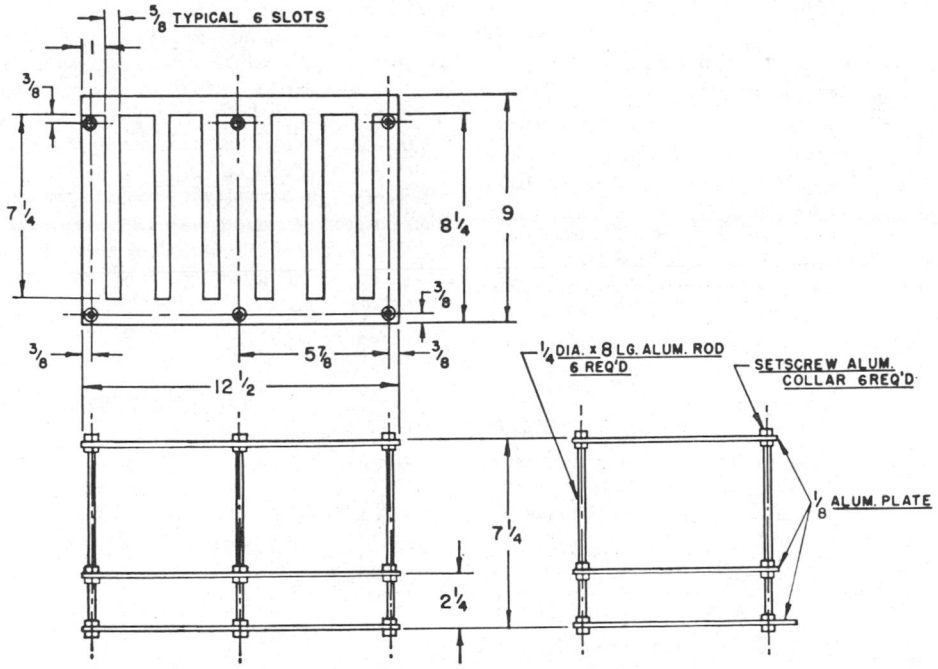

FIG. 21:2—Oven rack

21.014 — *Determination*

Place measured vol., A, of extg liq., preheated to test temp., into assembly. Use vol. of liq. such that top of liq. is 0.5″ below top of specimen. In no case should vol. of extg liq. be >200 ml. Insert gasket plug in top of cell. Expose cell in rack in oven to conditions of time and temp. specified by regulations. If vac. oven is used, operate it at atm. pressure. Align cells in rack in oven parallel with air flow.

After exposure, remove cell from rack, remove gasket plug, and immediately pour out extg liq. into graduate. (If solids flake from specimen and it is desired to det. only sol. materials, filter thru fritted glass filter from cell into graduate.) If vol. of extg liq. is <90% of original vol., investigate cause.

Det. total nonvolatile extractives by evapg total vol. extg liq. to apparent dryness in weighed Pt evapg dish on steam bath. Dry in oven 30 min at 100°. Cool 30 min in desiccator and weigh.

Perform ≥2 blank detns with 200 ml extg liq. each and glassware that will be used in detn. Preclean glassware with chromic acid soln followed by H_2O rinse. Place equal vol. extg liq. into each of blank-receiving containers. If filter is used on extg liq. from exposed samples, include contact of solv. of blank with filter. Wt blank must be <2.0 mg/200 ml and <30% of wt extractives.

21.015 — *Calculation*

With 2 sheets in cell, ratio of exposure area to vol. extg liq. used to fill cell is 2 ml/sq in. Calc. mg extractives/sq in. exposed sample = (mg extractives − mg blank)/sq in. exposed sample.

Extractives from Rubber Articles (3)—
Official First Action

21.016 — *Apparatus*

(a) *Extraction flasks.*—500 ml wide-mouth erlenmeyer, neck id ca 35 mm (500 ml Pyrex g-s ⊤ 40/50 flasks are satisfactory).

(b) *Reflux condenser.*—Block Sn coil (Cenco Instruments Corp. No. 28022, or equiv.).

(c) *Measuring tools.*—Micrometer and precision ruler.

(d) *Punch.*—1-, 2-, or 3-hole conventional paper punch with punch of ≥⅜″ diam.

21.017 — *Preparation of Sample*

Punch out disks of ca ⅜″ diam. from test material. Wash disks by hand in dil. soap soln at ca 40°; rinse with 40° H_2O and then distd H_2O and blot dry with paper towel.

21.018 — *Measurement of Surface Area*

Measure thickness of 20 disks with micrometer (±0.001″) and calc. av. thickness. Measure diam. to nearest ⅟₃₂″ and verify measurements for ≥10 disks. If deviations of ±⅟₃₂″ are noted, then det. av. diams for ≥20 disks. Calc. total surface area for disks tested as follows:

Total surface area $= N[2 \times (22/7) \times (d^2/4) + (22/7) \times d \times t]$, where N = no. of disks, d = av. diam. in in., and t = av. thickness in in.

21.019 — *Determination*

(*Caution: See* **46.011, 46.039,** and **46.061.**)

Place counted number of disks into extn flask; add few SiC chips and measured vol. of solv. (*n*-hexane or H_2O). (Total surface area of disks should be 10–20 sq in. and vol. of solv., in ml, is 20 times number of sq in. surface area.) Mark level of solv. and add fresh solv. if losses occur during extn. Attach thoroly cleaned and acetone-rinsed condenser to flask and reflux 7 hr on hot plate. Adjust temp. of hot plate to give boiling rate that keeps disks in motion without excessive foaming. If disks tend to stick together, agitate them 5–6 times during extn. Rinse condenser with small amt solv. and remove flask from hot plate. Decant ext into beaker and rinse flask and disks with three small portions hot solv. Discard disks.

Weigh 125 ml fat flask, or 100 ml beaker, contg few SiC chips, after heating 1 hr at 100° and cooling 1 hr in desiccator. Transfer ext and rinses, in 50–80 ml portions, to tared flask or beaker. For blank, transfer vol. solv. equal to ext plus rinses to similar weighed beaker or flask. Evap. each portion to ca 20 ml before adding more ext. Swirl flask or beaker frequently while heating until soln begins to boil. Hexane ext can be evapd to dryness entirely on steam bath with stream of filtered air; H_2O ext can be concd to ca 10 ml on hot plate before heating to dryness on steam bath.

Wipe outside of flask with damp paper towel and place flask on its side in oven. Dry hexane ext at 70° and H_2O ext at 105° 1 hr. Cool in desiccator 1 hr and weigh on analytical balance. Subtract wt of solv. blank from wt of residue. Divide corrected wt of residue in mg by total surface area of test disks and report as mg/sq in.

SELECTED REFERENCES
(*1*) JAOAC **49,** 611(1966); **51,** 449, 544(1968).
(*2*) JAOAC **45,** 70(1962); **47,** 386(1964); **51,** 449 (1968); ASTM F34-63T, 1963 Sup. to Book of ASTM Stds, Part 6, pp. 105–109.
(*3*) JAOAC **50,** 840(1967); **53,** 43(1970).

22. Fruits and Fruit Products[*]

22.001 Sampling (1)—Procedure

(a) *Boxed dried fruit.*—Remove cover, bottom, or one side of box, as convenient. Remove block comprising ⅛ of contents of box taken from one corner as follows: With sharp knife make vertical cut midway between *ends* of box to center of top surface, extending cut half way to bottom. Make another vertical cut midway between *sides* of box, extending half way to bottom, and continue it until it meets first cut. Remove all fruit included in angle formed by the 2 cuts. Working rapidly, break up lumps, mix thoroly, and take enough sample to fill qt Mason jar, replacing remainder in box. Seal jar and send to laboratory. Sample enough boxes from different parts of pile to constitute at least square root of lot.

(b) *Frozen pack fruit in barrels* (JAOAC 30, 274(1947)).—Use stainless steel or corrosion-resistant tube ca 1¼″ diam. and 36″ long, one end serrated and set to run freely, other end with removable cap and arrangement for use of elec. motor in drilling. To aid in removal of core samples use wooden ram smaller in diam. but longer than tube.

Remove bottom of barrel and take 3 cores evenly spaced around its circumference near chime parallel to and thru full length of barrel. Take fourth core at approx. center of barrel.

(c) *Frozen pack fruit in small containers (30–50 lb)* (JAOAC 30, 274(1947)).—Use modified corrosion-resistant auger 1–1½″ diam. and 19″ long that can be operated by elec. motor. (Auger should have no lead screw or cutters and angle of face should not be flat but 170–175°.) Collect borings in corrosion-resistant sampling can ca 6″ diam. and 4″ high, open at one end, with outlet at other end ca 1″ long and of diam. slightly larger than that of auger. Place sampling can on surface of frozen fruit and operate auger thru small opening at bottom. Take 3 vertical cores evenly spaced around circumference and ca ½″ from edge of container and take 1 core at or near center. Remove both sampling can and auger simultaneously to prevent borings from falling thru delivery outlet.

22.002 Net Contents of Frozen Fruits—Procedure

See **32.032–32.033.**

22.003 Preparation of Sample—Procedure

Transfer samples received in open packages (*i.e.,* not sterile) without delay to g-s containers and keep in cool place. To avoid effects of fermentation make prompt detns of alcohol, total and volatile acids, solids, and sugars, particularly in case of fruit juices and fresh fruits. (Portions for detn of sucrose and reducing sugars may be weighed and kept several days without fermenting if the slight excess of neut. $Pb(OAc)_2$ soln required in detn is added. *Note:* $Pb(OAc)_2$ is toxic. Label samples to show its addn.) Prep. various products for analysis as follows:

(a) *Juices.*—Mix thoroly by shaking to ensure uniform sample, and filter thru absorbent cotton or rapid paper. Prep. fresh juices by pressing well-pulped fruit and filtering. Express juice of citrus fruits by one of common devices used for squeezing oranges or lemons, and filter.

(b) *Jellies and sirups.*—Mix thoroly to ensure uniform sample. Prep. soln by weighing 300 g thoroly mixed sample into 2 L flask and dissolve in H_2O, heating on steam bath if necessary. Apply as little heat as possible to minimize inversion of sucrose. Cool, dil. to vol., mix thoroly by shaking, and use aliquots for the various detns. If insol. material is present, mix thoroly and filter before taking aliquots.

(c) *Fresh fruits, dried fruits, preserves, jams, and marmalades.*—Pulp by passing thru food chopper, or by use of blender (without knives, such as Fisher Scientific Co. No. 14-333V4), Hobart mixer, or other suitable mech. mixing app., or by grinding in large mortar, and mixing thoroly, completing operation as quickly as possible to avoid loss of moisture. With dried fruits, pass sample thru food chopper 3 times, mixing thoroly after each grinding. Set burrs or blades of food chopper as closely as possible without crushing seeds. Grind entire contents of No. 10 or smaller container. Mix contents of larger containers thoroly by stirring and remove portion for grinding. With stone fruits, remove pits and det. their proportion in weighed sample.

Prep. soln by weighing into 1.5–2 L beaker 300 g fresh fruit, or equiv. of dried fruit, preserves, jams, and marmalades, well pulped and mixed in blender or other suitable type of mech. grinder; add ca 800 ml H_2O; and boil 1 hr, replacing at intervals H_2O lost by evapn. Transfer to 2 L vol. flask, cool, dil. to vol., and filter. With unsweetened fruit, ashing is facilitated by addn of sugar before boiling; therefore weigh 150 g fruit, add 150 g sugar and 800 ml H_2O, and proceed as above.

(d) *Canned fruits.*—See **32.001–32.002.** Carefully invert by hand all fruits having cups or cavities if they fall on sieve with cups or cavities up. Cups or cavities in soft products may be drained by tilting sieve, but no other handling of these products while

---

[*] Methods so marked are surplus methods. *See* "Definitions of Terms and Explanatory Notes," item (29).

draining is permissible. Examination of sirup in which fruits are preserved is often enough. Sep. liquor by draining, **32.002,** and treat as in (**a**).

Fill of Container of Frozen Fruits (2)— Official First Action

22.004   *Apparatus*

(**a**) *Overflow can.*—With device for lowering frozen fruit into liq. and for removing it, Fig. 22:1. Can is ca 8″ diam. and ca 9″ high with overflow spout of 3/16″ id (1/4″ od) Cu tubing. Solder tubing to opening on side of can ca 1/2″ from bottom and bend upward parallel to side of can to ca 2″ below top where it is bent away and downward to form inverted U. Form spout by cutting tubing on outer side of U where it makes ca 45° angle with can, making cut parallel to bottom of can. Opening of spout is ca 1/8″ below lower surface of U-bend. Bend end of spout up or down until overflow, caused by adding excess of liq. to can, will end abruptly. (Proper adjustment of tube and addn of enough liq. will secure this effect.) Lowering device consists of 1/2″ metal frame 5 3/4″ square contg 1/2″ mesh screening attached on one side to perpendicular handle 12″ long bent outward at top.

(**b**) *Plastic bags.*—Pliable at 0°F; capable of holding vac.; ca 8 × 10″ when flat. (Cryovac bags, Type L, W. R. Grace & Co., Duncan, SC 29334, or equiv.)

(**c**) *Freezer or cold room.*—At or near 0°F.

(**d**) *Refined light mineral oil such as odorless kerosene.*

22.005   *Determination*

Transfer frozen sample from container and inner wrapper, if any, to plastic bag. Remove excess air from bag by inserting glass tube attached to vac. line. Twist bag top to close, hold twist with pinch clamp, and trim off loose end. Pretest bags to be certain they will not leak.

Place overflow can in freezing compartment and fill can, in which lifting device is inserted, with light mineral oil at temp. of freezing compartment (ca 0°F). Add enough excess mineral oil (ca 300 ml) to produce siphon effect in overflow, collecting overflow in beaker. Place empty, calibrated graduated cylinder under overflow tube and immerse frozen fruit sample completely in the mineral oil, using lifting device. Record vol. of overflow in cylinder to nearest ml. Correct this vol. for displacement of empty plastic bag and pinch clamp (ca 7 ml) to obtain net displacement of frozen fruit. Redet. displacement of sample to check reproducibility of operation.

For packages with square corners, calc. H_2O capacity of outer container by multiplying inside length, width, and ht in cm. For packages with curved edges or irregular shape, det. H_2O capacity as follows: Place empty container in beaker or pan contg enough H_2O to reach to within 1 cm of top of container when it is resting on bottom of beaker or pan. Note that no air is trapped by bottom of container. Add H_2O from calibrated 500 ml buret to fill container to capacity, or to measured headspace if indented top has been removed. Read H_2O capacity directly from buret.

Det. % fill of container by dividing net displacement of frozen fruit by H_2O capacity of outer container and multiply by 100.

22.006 Drained Weight of Frozen Fruits (3)— Official First Action

After obtaining gross wts, immerse packages in H_2O agitated and maintained at 20±1°. (If packages are not H_2O-tight, place in suitable plastic bag, remove excess air by use of vac., and tie off.) Avoid agitation of packages during thawing by using clamps or weights if necessary. When center of packages reach bath temp. as detd by preliminary experi-

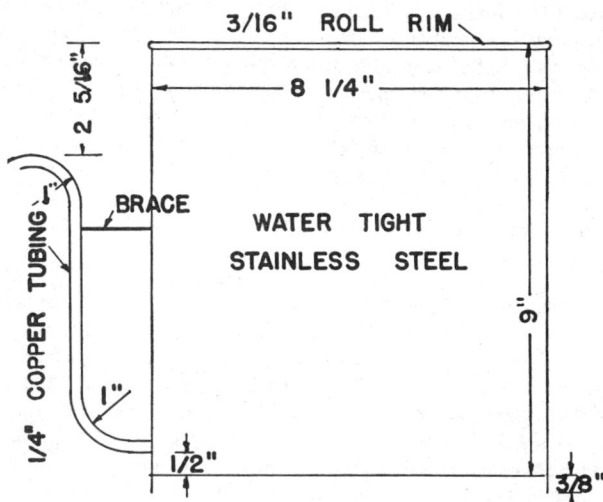

FIG. 22:1—Apparatus for determining volume of frozen fruits by displacement

ments (ca 2–3 hr for 10.5–16 oz containers), remove from bath, blot off adhering H_2O, and open with min. agitation.

Tare No. 8 sieve with light-wt drip pan. Use 8″ diam. sieve if container holds ≤3 lb, 12″ if more. With screen tilted and supported for drainage, distribute contents of package evenly over screen in one sweeping motion. After 2 min from time drainage begins, transfer sieve with fruit to drip pan and weigh. Obtain net wt of packages by subtracting wt empty containers from their gross wts.

22.007 Approximate Fruit Content of Fruit-Sugar Mixtures (4)—Procedure

Let sample thaw and come to room temp. in original container. Mix sample thoroly in high-speed blender. Filter portion of sample thru strong lens paper or other suitable medium. Det. refractometer reading, 31.011, correct to 20°, and report as % sol. solids (sucrose). Calc. % fruit, X, from equation: $X = (100 - M)\ 100/(100 - F)$, where M is sol. solids (as sucrose) of fruit-sugar mixt. and F is sol. solids of fruit ingredient in mixt. if known; otherwise use av. sol. solids of authentic fruits (JAOAC 21, 502(1938); 47, 1068(1964); 48, 523(1965); 51, 1203 (1968)).

Apparent Viscosity (Consistency) (5)— Official Final Action

(Applicable to fruit nectars and fruit juice products)

22.008 *Apparatus*

Capillary viscometer.—See Fig. 22:2. *A*, Lucite tube chamber; *B*, inner tube, ground 120° included angle; *C*, Lucite plug, 60° included angle; *D*, Tygon packing gland, turned 60° included angle (both ends); *E*, brass outer tube, ground 60° for packing gland nut; *F*, brass tube, chrome plated; *G*, inner tube, precision Pyrex glass, id 3±0.01 mm; *H*, Tygon sleeve. Scribe calibration line around outside of reservoir at level reached by H_2O in 13 sec under conditions specified in **22.009**. (Available from California Laboratory Equipment Co., 1165–67th St, Oakland, CA 94608.)

22.009 *Calibration*

Add H_2O to tube at 24±2° and establish steady flow. Stop flow by placing finger over end of capillary tube. Fill tube completely full to overflow point and level off with spatula or by sighting across top of tube. Remove finger from tube and immediately begin timing. Time required for top of meniscus to reach calibration line must be 13.0±0.2 sec.

22.010 *Determination*

Clean and dry app. and maintain at 24±0.5° during detn. Adjust sample to 24±0.5° and mix thoroly without incorporating air bubbles. Add sample to tube and let flow until steady flow is obtained. Place finger over end of capillary tube to stop flow. Fill tube almost full and check for air bubbles; if air bubbles occur, remove by gently stirring with stir-

ring rod or thermometer (check temp. at this point). Fill to overflow point and level off as in **22.009**. Remove finger from tube and immediately begin timing. Record time to nearest 0.1 sec for top of meniscus to reach calibration line.

Obtain at least two readings on each sample, mixing sample before each detn. Rinse viscometer with H_2O between each reading of viscous samples (>30 sec flow time). (Do not let product dry in app. or let app. become greasy or develop air leak at packing seal of capillary tube.) Remove H_2O in capillary tube by letting sample flow thru before making detn. Check calibration at frequent intervals.

22.011 Alcohol—Official Final Action

Det. alcohol in 50 g original material as in **11.003**.

22.012 Moisture in Dried Fruits (6)—Official Final Action

Spread 5–10 g prepd sample, **22.003**(c), as evenly as possible over bottom of metal dish ca 8.5 cm diam.

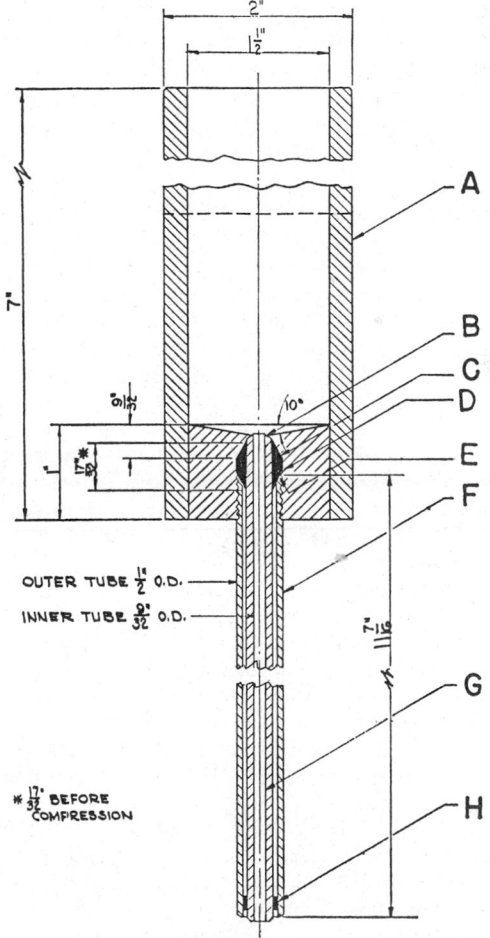

OUTER TUBE ½″ O.D.

INNER TUBE ⁹⁄₃₂″ O.D.

* ¹⁷⁄₃₂″ BEFORE COMPRESSION

FIG. 22:2—Capillary viscometer

provided with tight-fit cover, weigh, and dry 6 hr at 70° under pressure $\leq$100 mm Hg. (Metal dish must be in direct contact with metal shelf of oven.) During drying admit to oven slow current of air (ca 2 bubbles/sec) dried by passing thru H_2SO_4. Replace cover, cool dish in desiccator, and weigh. Disregard any temporary drop in oven temp. during early part of drying period owing to rapid evapn of H_2O.

With raisins, and other fruit rich in sugar, use ca 5 g sample and dry and weigh in dish with ca 2 g finely divided asbestos. Moisten with hot H_2O, mix sample and asbestos thoroly, evap. barely to dryness on steam bath, and complete drying as above.

Total Solids—Official Final Action

22.013   *Insoluble Matter Present*

Fresh and canned fruits, jams, marmalades, and preserves.—Accurately weigh, into large flat-bottom dish, 20 g pulped fresh fruit, or quantity of fruit products that will give $\leq$3–4 g dry material. If necessary to secure thin layer of material, add few ml H_2O and mix thoroly. Dry at 70° under pressure $\leq$100 mm Hg until consecutive weighings made at 2 hr intervals vary $\leq$3 mg.

22.014   *Insoluble Matter Absent*

Fruit juices, jellies, and sirups.—Proceed as in **31.007, 31.008, 31.009, 31.010,** or **31.011,** using sample prepd as in **22.003**(a) or (b).

Water-Insoluble Solids (7)—Official First Action

22.015   *Method I*

For use with buchner, prep. filtering medium consisting of either circular disk of absorbent cotton ca 80 mm diam., weighing ca 1.5 g, or coarse, qual. filter paper (7–15 cm diam., Whatman No. 4 or 41-H or equiv.). For use with 60° funnel, prep. absorbent cotton circle ca 12.5 cm diam. weighing ca 2 g, or 12.5 cm filter paper. Wash filtering medium with hot H_2O, and dry overnight at 100–110° in open, flat-bottom Al dish of suitable size provided with tight-fit cover. Cool closed dish and contents 1 hr in desiccator and weigh to nearest mg.

Weigh 25 or 50 g well-mixed sample, **22.003**(c), to nearest 10 mg, transfer to 400 ml beaker, dil. to ca 200 ml mark with hot H_2O, mix, and boil gently 15–20 min, occasionally replacing H_2O lost by evapn. Filter by gravity thru the prepd cotton or paper, and keep H_2O-insol. solids from forming closely adhering mat on surface of filtering medium by frequent addns of portions of sample. Wash with ca 800 ml hot H_2O, loosening H_2O-insol. solids from filter with each addn. Remove excess H_2O from cotton by gently squeezing it on 60° funnel, or by application of suction on buchner. Transfer to original weighing dish, and wipe off any remaining portions of H_2O-insol. solids on filter or funnel with previously weighed portion of prepd filtering medium. Dry

overnight at 100–110°, cool 1 hr in desiccator, and weigh.

Method II (Rapid Method)

22.016   *Apparatus*

(a) *Weighing dishes.*—Al or tinned Fe, $5\frac{1}{4}''$ diam. $\times \frac{3}{4}''$ high, with tight-fit cover (16 mm film holders obtainable from camera stores; Al dishes weigh ca 40 g, tinned Fe ca 85–90 g).

(b) *Rapid drying device.*—Moisture Teller, model 276, manufactured by Harry W. Dietert Co., 9330 Roselawn Ave, Detroit, MI 48204, or forced-draft drying oven set at 100°.

22.017   *Determination*

Fit 15 cm filter paper (Whatman No. 4 or 41-H, or equiv.) into 12.5 cm buchner, add half of 7 cm paper (used to wipe any insol. solids from buchner after filtering and washing sample), wash with boiling H_2O, apply suction, and dry, using Moisture Teller and pan or forced-draft oven. Transfer to weighing dish, cool, and weigh, using tare consisting of weighing dish and paper. (Approx. time of drying, 5 min at 102±3°.)

Weigh 25 or 50 g well-mixed sample (high-speed blender) to nearest 10 mg, transfer with hot H_2O to 400 ml beaker, adjust to ca 200 ml with hot H_2O, stir, and boil gently few min. Place prepd filter in buchner; attach to suction flask, but do not attach flask to suction line. Pour 50–100 ml boiling H_2O on filter, and when steady flow of H_2O passes thru filter, transfer sample to filter, portionwise if necessary. Wash insol. solids with boiling H_2O and collect 850–900 ml filtrate. During washings, keep solids from forming tight mat on surface by portionwise addns of boiling H_2O. When washing is finished, apply suction and aspirate thoroly. Transfer paper and H_2O-insol. solids to Moisture Teller pan, using extra piece of weighed filter paper to complete transfer, and dry at 102±3° ca 15 min, depending on quantity of H_2O-insol. solids. After drying, transfer sample to weighing dish, cool in desiccator, and weigh. (Wt H_2O-insol. solids/wt sample) × 100 = % H_2O-insol. solids.

22.018   Seeds in Berry Fruits (8)—Official First Action

Prep. sample by mixing with blender, **22.003**(c). Transfer 50±0.01 g with ca 500 ml hot H_2O to blender and mix 1–2 min. Transfer mixt. to No. 20 screen and use addnl hot H_2O to transfer and wash bare seeds (hot H_2O from tap is suitable). Transfer seeds on screen to Al dish, previously weighed, with tight-fit cover (readily accomplished by transferring to 7 cm Whatman No. 4 paper previously dried and weighed with the dish, in 12.5 cm buchner). Dry at 100° in forced-draft oven 30 min and weigh. To det. av. wt of one seed, count out and weigh sep. several 100-unit lots. Report av. wt of one seed in mg and number of seeds/100 g sample. After detn of H_2O-insol. solids of sample, calc. and report % of total due to bare seeds and % due to nonseed H_2O-insol. solids.

22.019 Soluble Solids (By Refractometer) in Fresh and Canned Fruits, Jams, Marmalades, and Preserves (9)— Official First Action

(Insol. matter present)

Proceed as in **31.011**. % sol. solids = % solids detd by refractometer $\times (100 - b)/100$, where b = % H_2O-insol. solids.

Note: U.S. Federal std for jams and preserves makes no correction for H_2O-insol. solids.

22.020 Ash (10)—Official Final Action

Proceed as in **31.012** or **31.013**, ashing at $\leq 525°$, using 25 g juices, fresh fruits, or canned fruits, and 10 g jellies, sirups, preserves, jams, marmalades, or dried fruits.

If ash of H_2O-sol. portion only is desired, evap. on steam bath to dryness 100 ml prepd soln, **22.003**(b) or (c). Proceed as in **31.012** or **31.013**.

22.021 Alkalinity of Ash—Official Final Action

Introduce measured excess of $0.1N$ HCl into Pt dish contg ash obtained in **22.020**, warm on steam bath, cool, add few drops Me orange, and titr. excess acid with $0.1N$ NaOH. Report as alky, number of ml $0.1N$ acid required to neutze ash from 100 g sample, and as alky number, number of ml $1N$ acid required to neutze 1 g ash. Reserve soln for detn of S in ash.

Potassium (11)—Official Final Action

22.022 *Ashing of Sample*

(a) *Slow ashing.*—Ash 15–30 g sample (representing ca 15 g fruit) as in **22.020**.

★(b) *Rapid ashing.* ★—See **20.019**(b), 10th ed.

Chloroplatinate Methods

22.023 *Reagent*

Chloroplatinic acid soln.—Dissolve 4.4 g H_2PtCl_6 (contains 2.1 g Pt) in H_2O and dil. to 100 ml. 1 ml of of this soln ppts ca 10 mg K_2O. Use ca 20% excess.

22.024 *Preparation of Ash Solution*

Wet down ash, **22.022**, with 5–10 ml H_2O, cover dish with watch glass, and acidify with slight excess of HCl $(1 + 4)$ (2–3 ml).

22.025 *Determination*

(a) *Gravimetric chloroplatinate method.*—Rinse watch glass into dish and evap. ash soln to dryness on steam bath. Add 5 drops HCl $(1 + 1)$ to residue. Add 5–10 ml hot H_2O and rub sides and bottom of

container with policeman. Transfer ash soln to 250 ml beaker with 50–75 ml hot H_2O, add few glass beads, and heat to boiling. Make distinctly alk. with NH_4OH and add enough satd $(NH_4)_2C_2O_4$ soln for complete pptn (usually ≤ 1 ml), cover beaker, and heat until ppt becomes granular enough to filter readily (incipient boiling 30 min usually suffices). Filter thru 5 or 7 cm fine texture paper into large Pt dish and wash thoroly with hot H_2O (5–6 fillings of filter usually suffice).

Evap. soln nearly to dryness on steam bath and add 1 ml H_2SO_4 $(1 + 1)$. So rotate dish that H_2SO_4 comes in contact with all residue, adding little H_2O if necessary. Return dish to steam bath and evap. all H_2O possible at that temp. Heat dish, preferably on hot plate, at ca 150° until bubbling caused by decomposition of oxalates ceases, and gradually increase temp. until H_2SO_4 evaps. (When properly controlled, this treatment takes 45–90 min.) Cautiously heat sample over burner, being careful to avoid loss due to sputtering during decomposition of NH_4 compds. Finally heat dish to redness to remove traces of NH_4 compds and complete ignition. Cool, and add 5 drops HCl $(1 + 1)$ to residue.

Transfer ash soln to 100–200 ml r-b porcelain dish using ca 50 ml hot H_2O. Add small excess H_2PtCl_6 soln. Place mixt. on steam bath and rotate dish from time to time to prevent ppt from baking on side of dish, and evap. to paste. (It is advisable to start evapn with several steam bath rings removed, and as concn progresses to replace rings so that heat is applied only to surface of dish covered by liq.) Avoid exposure to NH_3 fumes at all times.

Add ca 50 ml 90% alcohol to dish and transfer to gooch with asbestos mat, or 30 ml gooch with medium porosity fritted disk. Wash 8 or 10 times with 20 ml portions 90% alcohol; then 5 or 6 times with 10 ml portions NH_4Cl soln, **2.076**(a). Again wash well 6 or 8 times with 20 ml portions 90% alcohol.

Dry ca 30 min in 100° oven, cool, and weigh. Wash the K_2PtCl_6 thru gooch with hot H_2O, using slight suction; then wash gooch with alcohol, dry, cool, and weigh. Difference in wt $\times$ 0.1938 = K_2O. Report results as mg/100 g original sample.

(b) *Short gravimetric chloroplatinate method.*—Proceed as in (a), pars. 3–5, using ash soln, **22.024**, from ash, **22.022**(a).

★(c) *Short volumetric chloroplatinate method.* ★—See **20.022**(c), 10th ed.

★(d) *Long volumetric chloroplatinate method.* ★—See **20.022**(d), 10th ed.

★ *Gravimetric Cobaltinitrite Method* ★

22.026 *Reagents*

(a) *Trisodium cobaltinitrite soln.*—Prep. aq. soln contg 2.0 g Na cobaltinitrite in each 10 ml and test to ensure that it gives recovery of 98–102% with 20 mg quantities K_2O. Filter before use and prep. fresh soln before each set of detns.

(b) *Nitric acid solns.*—Approx. $1N$, $0.1N$, and $0.01N$.

(c) *Nitric acid-dipotassium sodium cobaltinitrite wash soln.*—Sat. portions of the $0.01N$ HNO_3 with few mg $K_2NaCo(NO_2)_6 \cdot H_2O$ by shaking (ca 1 hr). Filter thru Pyrex fine fritted glass crucible or equiv.

22.027   *Determination*

Add enough $1N$ HNO_3 to ash, **22.022**(a), in Pt dish to yield excess of ca 2 ml acid in 20 ml soln used in pptn (ca 3 ml). Wash into 25 ml vol. flask, dil. to vol., and mix. Let stand ≥ 1 hr and filter, if necessary, thru small paper. Withdraw 10 or 20 ml aliquot (3–35 mg K_2O), adjust to 20 ml with $0.1N$ HNO_3 if necessary, and cool to ca 20°.

Add from pipet, while stirring, 10 ml Na cobaltinitrite soln cooled to 20°. In range 3–18 mg K_2O (most preserves) add reagent dropwise with stirring; in range 18–35 mg (most fruits) add reagent in steady stream from fairly rapid delivery pipet (20–22 sec). Let stand 2 hr at ca 20°. Protect from laboratory fumes. Filter thru tared fine fritted glass crucible (Pyrex, 30 ml capacity, is convenient), using cobaltinitrite wash soln to make transfer.

Wash ppt 9 times with ≥ 4 ml portions of wash soln, once with 2 ml $0.01N$ HNO_3, and 5 times with 2 ml portions alcohol, releasing vac. each time before adding washing fluid. Aspirate until apparently dry. Dry 1 hr at 100°, cool in desiccator, and weigh. Formula of ppt is $K_2NaCo(NO_2)_6 \cdot H_2O$, and mg ppt $\times$ 0.2074 $\times$ 100/g sample in aliquot = mg K_2O/100 g sample.

Notes: Pyrex F or Jena 1G4 porosity crucibles or equiv. are acceptable and can be used number of times before cleaning with hot 5% H_2SO_4. Final wash with $0.01N$ HNO_3 should be restricted to 2 ml. $K_2NaCo(NO_2)_6$ ppt obtained in K detns is suitable for satg wash soln. Perform control detn on pure dry KCl from time to time. Stock soln of 2 mg K_2O/ml is convenient. Adjust to 20 ml, using 2 ml $1N$ HNO_3 for acidification.

22.028 *Rapid Flame Photometric Method (12)—Official Final Action*

(*Caution: See* **46.007**.)

Prep. sample soln as in **22.003**. Dil., if necessary, to reduce K concn to range covered by flame photometer (preferably 40–80 ppm). Aspirate sample soln (dild or undild) directly into flame.

Prep. stds as in **11.022**(a) except cover range 10–100 ppm K in 10 ppm steps. Det. %T for stds or use procedure specified in instruction manual supplied with flame photometer used, making check detns as necessary. If internal std instrument is used, add appropriate amt of LiCl to both std and sample solns.

From %T of sample and std curve, det. ppm K. Report as mg K_2O/100 g sample. K $\times$ 1.2046 = K_2O.

Sodium (13)—Official Final Action
(*Caution: See* **46.007**.)

22.029   *Reagents and Apparatus*

(a) *Sodium std solns.*—Dry reagent grade NaCl at 100° overnight and dil. 2.5422 g to 1 L with H_2O. (Soln contains 1000 ppm Na.) Dil. 10 ml to 100 ml, and further dil. 1, 2, 4, 6, 8, and 10 ml dild soln to 100 ml to make std solns contg, resp., 1, 2, 4, 6, 8, and 10 ppm Na. Store in clean, dry polyethylene bottles.

(b) *Flame spectrophotometer.*—See **11.022**(b).

22.030   *Determination*

Prep. sample soln as in **22.003**. Dil., if necessary, to reduce Na concn to range covered by flame photometer (preferably 4–10 ppm Na). Aspirate sample soln (dild or undild) directly into flame.

Det. %T for stds and plot curve of %T against ppm Na. Det. %T for sample and use std curve to det. ppm Na in sample or use procedure specified in instruction manual supplied with flame photometer used, making check detns as necessary. If internal std instrument is used, add appropriate amt of LiCl to both std and sample solns.

Report as mg Na_2O/100 g sample. Na $\times$ 1.3480 = Na_2O.

22.031 ★ **Manganese (14)—Official** ★
First Action

(*Caution: See* **46.047** and **46.081**.)
See **20.026–20.027**, 10th ed.

★ **Calcium (15)—Official First Action** ★

22.032 *Double Precipitation Method*
See **20.028**, 10th ed.

22.033 *Single Precipitation Method*
See **20.029**, 10th ed.

22.034 ★ **Magnesium (16)—Official** ★
First Action

See **20.030**, 10th ed.

Phosphorus
Volumetric Method (17)—Official Final Action
(Not applicable to acid fruit products stored for appreciable time in tin cans)

22.035   *Reagents*

(a) *Molybdate soln.*—(1) Thoroly mix 50 g MoO_3 (99.5–100%) and 140 ml H_2O and dissolve by addn of 72 ml NH_4OH with stirring; (2) dissolve 50 g powd tartaric acid in 140 ml H_2O; (3) mix 295 ml colorless HNO_3 with 400 ml H_2O. When solns are cool, pour soln (1) into soln (2) with stirring, and then pour combined solns into soln (3). Keep in warm place (ca 40°) overnight, filter thru asbestos, and store in bottle with loosely stoppered, plastic screw cap. When free from phosphates, soln is practically colorless.

(b) *Ammonium nitrate soln.*—Dissolve 500 g NH_4NO_3 in H_2O and dil. to 1 L.

(c) *Carbon dioxide-free water.*—Recently boiled and cooled H_2O.

(d) *Sodium hydroxide and hydrochloric acid std solns.*—$0.1N$. Prep. as in **45.033–45.037** and **45.012–45.014.**

22.036   *Determination*

Dissolve ash, **22.020**, in 10–15 ml H_2O and 3 or 4 ml HCl and evap. to dryness on steam bath. Take up in 10 ml hot HCl (1 + 9) and transfer to 300 ml erlenmeyer, keeping vol. to ca 50–60 ml. (If P_2O_5 is likely to be >10 mg, take aliquot.) Add 20 ml NH_4NO_3 soln and heat in H_2O bath to 45–50°. Add 20 ml freshly filtered molybdate soln (this quantity will ppt up to 20 mg P_2O_5) and let flasks remain in bath 30 min at 45–50°, swirling contents at ca 5 min intervals. To prevent tipping, weight flask with lead rings or by other means.

For filtration, use filter-tube (so-called carbon filter), ca 28 mm id, fitted with removable, perforated porcelain dish from Caldwell crucible. (Caldwell crucible or gooch may also be used.) Prep. quick filtering pad $2/_{16}$–$3/_{16}''$ thick, using short-fiber asbestos. For convenience in washing and in transferring filter tubes, provide suction flask with rubber stopper having hole somewhat larger than stem of filter tube.

With full suction, filter ppt and wash flask and then filter tube with ca 6 portions cold H_2O, using 150–200 ml total. Test for complete washing by passing 25 ml CO_2-free H_2O thru flask and filter tube into clean suction flask. Immediately disconnect suction and add 1 drop each of $0.1N$ NaOH and phthln, which should yield strong pink color.

Loosen pad and porcelain disk with wire or narrow rod inserted in stem end, and transfer to flask. Place filter tube in neck of flask, dissolve any ppt on walls with measured vol. std alkali, and rinse down filter tube with ca 25 ml CO_2-free H_2O. (Enough std alkali must have been added to dissolve ppt.) Stopper flask, swirl, and let stand, mixing from time to time, until yellow ppt completely dissolves. Dil. to ca 75 ml with CO_2-free H_2O, add 10 drops phthln, and titr. with std acid to complete disappearance of pink, matching end point with another flask contg H_2O and asbestos only. If alkali adheres to fragments of asbestos, making end point uncertain, add slight excess of std acid and complete titrn with std alkali. 1 ml $0.1N$ NaOH = 0.3086 mg P_2O_5. Subtract alkali consumed in blank detn.

★ *Colorimetric Method (18)* ★
22.037   *Reagents*

(a) *Molybdenum blue soln.*—Place 9.78 g MoO_3 (99.5–100%) in 500 ml Kjeldahl flask, add ca 150 ml H_2SO_4 ($36±0.5N$), and heat with gentle mixing until dissolved. Cool to 150°. Weigh, on small watch glass, 0.440 g very finely powd Mo metal (99.5–100%) and transfer to Kjeldahl flask by sliding watch glass down neck of flask. Keep at 140–150° and mix vigorously until Mo is dissolved (some larger particles may remain). Cool, transfer to 250 ml vol. flask, rinse Kjeldahl with H_2SO_4, and transfer rinsings to vol. flask. Dil. to vol. with H_2SO_4 and mix well. Dil. 10 ml of this reagent with H_2O and titr. with $0.1N$ $KMnO_4$ to pink that persists 1 min (reagent should be $0.110±0.001N$; if <$0.109N$ add calcd quantity of Mo and dissolve by reheating in Kjeldahl flask to 150°). Preserve deep green soln in g-s bottles, carefully avoiding *all* contamination.

(b) *Dilute molybdenum blue soln.*—With pipet previously wet inside with H_2O, pipet 10 ml (a) into ca 60 ml H_2O in 100 ml vol. flask. Rinse pipet into flask, mix, cool, dil. to vol. with H_2O, and mix. Use within 8–10 hr of prepn.

(c) *Sodium hydroxide soln.*—$3.60±0.05N$. Should contain $≤0.0005\%$ PO_4. Dissolve NaOH in H_2O, using As-free Pyrex or porcelain vessel, cool, and titr. with std acid. Preserve in paraffin-lined container. Avoid leaving this reagent in glass equipment for any extended period.

(d) *Normal sodium hydroxide.*—From (c) prep. ca $1N$ NaOH. Preserve in As-free Pyrex or paraffin-lined container fitted with 1-hole stopper bearing Pyrex medicine dropper.

(e) *Sodium alizarin sulfonate soln.*—Dissolve 0.20 g Na alizarin monosulfonate in 100 ml H_2O and filter. Preserve in indicator bottle.

(f) *Phosphate std soln.*—0.05 mg P_2O_5/ml. Dissolve 0.1917 g pure dry KH_2PO_4 in ca 200 ml H_2O and add 10 ml ca $1N$ H_2SO_4 and 6 drops $0.1N$ $KMnO_4$. Dil. to exactly 2 L. This soln keeps indefinitely in well-stoppered Pyrex bottle.

(g) *Glass beads.*—Boil supply of small glass beads (2 or 3 mm diam.) in aqua regia, wash clean with H_2O, and dry.

22.038   *Preparation of Sample*
(Caution: See **46.019, 46.026, 46.028,**
and **46.030.***)*

Transfer portion of sample contg 0.5–2.5 mg P_2O_5 to 500 ml Kjeldahl flask. (For detn of P_2O_5 on H_2O-sol. portion of fruits or fruit juices, 25 or 30 ml (equiv. to 3.75 or 4.5 g fruit) of sample soln prepd as in **22.003**(a) or (c) is convenient aliquot. For jams and jellies 50 ml prepd soln, **22.003**(b) or (c), may be taken. If sample has low fruit content, take larger aliquot.)

Add 5 ml H_2SO_4 from pipet or buret; then add 10 ml HNO_3 and 5 or 6 glass beads. Place flask on digestion rack over free flame. Protect flask from flame by intervening asbestos mat with hole of such size that surface of H_2SO_4 is above mat. Boil over moderate flame until darkening begins (avoid excessive charring). Add few ml HNO_3 and again boil until slight darkening begins or until SO_3 fumes are evolved from clear colorless or amber soln. (In case of jams or jellies, 3 or 4 addns (ca 5 ml each) of HNO_3 may be necessary.) Add 0.5 ml 60% $HClO_4$ to hot flask and continue fuming few min. (To avoid violent explosions of $HClO_4$ in presence of org. matter do not add >0.5 ml at one time and then only after practically all org. matter has been removed with HNO_3; *do not fail to take all precautions advised in use of $HClO_4$.*) When digest is colorless or very slightly greenish-yellow, cool somewhat, cautiously add 50 ml H_2O, and boil to fumes to remove traces of HNO_3. Cool, add ca 25 ml H_2O, transfer to 100 ml vol. flask, mix, cool, dil. to vol., and mix thoroly.

22.039   *Determination*

Transfer 20 ml aliquot of sample digest and 0, 2, 4, 6, 8, 10, and 12 ml std phosphate soln to 100 ml vol. flasks (Kohlrausch sugar flasks are convenient) marked at 70 ml. To stds add 30 ml ca $1N$ H_2SO_4. To samples add 20 or 25 ml H_2O, and to all flasks add 3 drops Na alizarin sulfonate soln and then exactly 10 ml $3.6N$ NaOH soln. Adjust acidity to just yellow with $1N$ H_2SO_4 and $1N$ NaOH until single drop of acid just changes color of soln to yellow. Dil. to 70 ml and mix by swirling. Place flasks in boiling H_2O bath and bring to that temp. With pipet add exactly 10 ml dil. Mo blue reagent, directing stream into soln (do not let it run down side of flask), mix by swirling, and continue to heat in boiling H_2O bath exactly 20 min. Cool rapidly in cold H_2O, dil. to vol., and mix.

Keep stds and unknowns at same temp. by immersing flasks in boiling H_2O bath in which H_2O comes above level of soln in flask. (Simple H_2O bath may be prepd by placing ½″ mesh wire screen in bottom of 12 or 14″ pan and filling with H_2O to such depth that liq. in flasks is below level of H_2O. Place pan on stand and heat with large Meker burner with flame so adjusted that it spreads over bottom of pan and keeps entire contents at gentle rolling boil. Place flasks only around edge of pan and weight with Pb rings or otherwise support to prevent tipping. Keep bath at rolling boil thruout heating period and add *boiling* H_2O to bath as needed to keep level of H_2O above level of liq. in flasks. Keep thermometer in bath and do not permit variation of >2° between center and edge of pan.

Det. A at 650 nm with suitable photometer or spectrophtr.

This method covers range up to 0.6 mg P_2O_5 in final 100 ml soln. Plot mg P_2O_5 against A. (Graph paper 20 × 36″ with 10 lines/in. is convenient.) From graph convert A to mg P_2O_5/100 ml final soln. Or calc. equation of line as in JAOAC **22**, 121(1939) and use this equation for conversion.

Notes: Instrument need be calibrated only once for each batch of reagents provided adjustment is not altered and temp. of boiling H_2O bath remains same. It is advisable, however, to develop 1 or 2 stds with each batch of unknowns to detect possible change of conditions.

Stdzn under these conditions automatically corrects for blank on reagents, except HNO_3 and $HClO_4$. These reagents have not been found to contain significant amts of As or P. It is well, however, to det. digestion blank on these reagents from time to time.

In analysis of heterogeneous samples, such as lots of fresh fruit, for total P_2O_5, it may be necessary to digest larger portion than specified to minimize sampling and weighing error. In that case it is convenient to take double size sample and double quantity of H_2SO_4 (10 ml), dil. digest to 200 ml, and finally transfer 20 ml aliquot to 100 ml vol. flask for color development. Quantity of sample digested may be varied to suit nature of sample if final aliquot taken for color development contains ≤1 ml H_2SO_4 and ≤0.6 mg P_2O_5.

Fe, nitrate, and As interfere in color development. Nitrates are not present in solns prepd as described, and neither Fe nor As is ordinarily present in fruit or fruit products in sufficient quantity to interfere. If presence of excessive As or Fe is suspected, their interference may be prevented by method of Zinzadze (Ind. Eng. Chem., Anal. Ed. **7**, 227(1935)). Proceed as above to point, "Adjust acidity to just yellow . . ." after which add 10 ml exactly $1N$ H_2SO_4 and then 10 ml of 8% Na_2SO_3 soln, and dil. to 70 ml. Heat in boiling H_2O bath 1 hr. Then again refer to previous directions and continue with "add exactly 10 ml dil. Mo blue reagent . . ." Stds and blank must then be treated identically.

Spectrophotometric Molybdovanadate Method (19)—Official First Action

(Do not clean glassware with P-contg detergents.)

22.040   *Apparatus and Reagents*

(a) *Spectrophotometer.* — Beckman Instruments Model B or DU, or equiv., with matched 1 cm cells.

(b) *Molybdovanadate reagent.*—Dissolve 60 g NH_4 molybdate.$4H_2O$ in 900 ml hot H_2O, cool, and dil. to 1 L. Dissolve 1.5 g NH_4 metavanadate in 690 ml hot H_2O, add 300 ml HNO_3, cool, and dil. to 1 L. Gradually add molybdate soln to vanadate soln with stirring. Store at room temp. in polyethylene or g-s Pyrex bottle. (Reagent is stable indefinitely in polyethylene, but in Pyrex, ppt gradually forms after several months. Discard reagent if ppt forms.)

(c) *Phosphate std solns.*—(1) *Stock soln.*—0.5 mg P_2O_5/ml. Dissolve 0.2397 g pure (if assay <100% KH_2PO_4, 0.2397 g × 100/% KH_2PO_4 = correct wt) and dried (2 hr at 105°) primary std KH_2PO_4 in H_2O and dil. to 250 ml. (2) *Working solns.*—Dil. 0, 5, 10, 15, 20, 25, 30, and 35 ml stock soln to 500 ml to obtain 0.00, 0.05, 0.10, 0.15, 0.20, 0.25, 0.30, and 0.35 mg P_2O_5/10 ml, resp.

22.041   *Preparation of Standard Curve*
(*Caution: See* **46.018** *and* **46.026**.)

Pipet 10 ml of each working soln into 25 ml erlenmeyers and stopper immediately to prevent evapn. As rapidly as possible for entire series, pipet 5.0 ml molybdovanadate reagent into each, stopper, and mix. Let stand 10 min for color development and read A of each soln within 1 hr.

Fill 4 matched cells with 0.00 mg standard. Set spectrophtr at 400 nm and adjust to 0 A with 1 cell.

Read each cell A against this cell. Use cell with lowest A with 0.00 mg std in future measurements. If A of 0.00 mg std in other cells are >0.001 against this std in ref. cell, subtract these A from subsequent readings. Det. A of each std with instrument adjusted to 0 A for 0.00 mg std. After every 3 detns, refill cell contg 0.00 mg std to avoid error due to evapn and temp. changes. Plot A against mg P_2O_5/ 10 ml (vol. working std soln).

(*Note:* Use Pyrex dropper to fill and empty cells. Do *not* remove cells from holder. Use dropper tube with greater capacity than cell to prevent liq. from entering bulb. Bulb should be just large enough that cell can be filled or emptied in one operation. Rinse cell with succeeding std or sample soln. Use different dropper to fill and empty ref. cell.)

22.042 *Preparation of Sample*

Proceed as in **22.020**. (Add 1 teaspoon sucrose to samples low in sugar to speed ashing.) Dissolve ash in 10 ml HCl (1 + 3) and evap. to dryness on steam bath. Dissolve residue in 10 ml HCl (1 + 9) on steam bath and transfer to 100 ml vol. flask. Cool, dil. to vol., and mix. Filter thru dry paper if any insol. matter is present. If ash has >3.5 mg P_2O_5, dil. to >100 ml or make secondary dilns so 10 ml aliquot contains <0.35 mg P_2O_5. (*See* Watt, B. K., and Merrill, A. L., *Composition of Foods*, USDA Handbook No. 8, p. 6–67, Superintendent of Documents, U.S. Government Printing Office, Washington, DC 20402, rev. Dec. 1963 for data on P content of fruit products and other foods.) If ash wt is not desired, use smaller sample aliquot to reduce drying and ashing time.

22.043 *Determination*

Into sep. 25 ml erlenmeyers pipet 10 ml aliquots std solns contg 0.00 and 0.20 mg P_2O_5/10 ml. Develop color as for std curve. Adjust instrument to 0 A for 0.00 mg std and det. A of 0.20 mg std. (A of this std should be within ±1% of A of std curve; if not, prep. new std curve.) Develop color and det. A of sample ash solns concurrently with and in same manner as for std solns. Calc. as follows:

(a) *From std curve.*—mg P_2O_5/100 g sample = 100 × (mg P_2O_5/10 ml from std curve)/g sample in 10 ml ash soln.

(b) *From formula.*—mg P_2O_5/100 g sample = A × S × 100/W, where A refers to sample soln at 400 nm, S = slope of std curve = $(\Sigma r)/n$; Σr = sum of ratios of mg P_2O_5/10 ml to A of each std, and n = number of std solns used in calcns; and W = g sample in 10 ml ash soln.

Gravimetric Quinoline Molybdate Method (19)—Official First Action

22.044 *Reagent*

See **2.023**(c).

22.045 *Preparation of Sample*

Prep. as in **22.042**, but transfer HCl (1 + 9) soln of residue to 500 ml erlenmeyer. Filter into 500 ml erlenmeyer if any insol. matter is present. If sample ash has >25 mg P_2O_5 (*see* Watt and Merrill, **22.042**), dil. to 100 ml or other definite vol. and pipet aliquot contg <25 mg P_2O_5 into 500 ml erlenmeyer. Dil. soln to ca 100 ml with H_2O.

22.046 *Determination*

Proceed as in **2.025**(b), except boil 3 min. Report results as mg P_2O_5/100 g.

22.047 Sulfur in Ash (*20*)—Official Final Action

(For products contg a basic ash)

Add 5 ml HCl (1 + 2.5) to soln after detn of alky of ash, **22.021**, and evap. to dryness. Heat 1 hr at 110° to dehydrate any SiO_2. Take up in 5 ml of the HCl and filter, washing paper well with hot H_2O. Heat filtrate to boiling and add 5 ml 10% $BaCl_2$ $.2H_2O$ soln dropwise from buret or pipet. Evap. to 100 ml and let stand overnight.

Filter on weighed gooch or Munroe crucible or on 7 cm ashless paper, wash with hot H_2O until filtrate is Cl-free, dry, ignite over Bunsen burner, and weigh as $BaSO_4$. As quantity of ppt is small, exercise great care and make detn in duplicate. Report result as mg S/100 g.

22.048 Total Sulfur (*21*)—Official First Action

(For sulfured products and for samples contg little ash or acidic ash)

In largest available casserole that fits in elec. muffle furnace, place 1–3 g MgO (1 g for fruit juices, 3 g for heavily sugared products and for dried fruits) or equiv. quantity $Mg(NO_3)_2.6H_2O$ (6.4 or 19.2 g), 1 g powd sucrose, and 50 ml HNO_3. Add 5–10 g prepd sample, **22.003**. Place same quantities of reagents in another casserole for blank. Evap. on steam bath to paste. Place casserole in cold elec. muffle and gradually heat (≤525°) until all NO_2 fumes are driven off. (All org. matter will have been destroyed.)

Cool, dissolve, and neutze with HCl (1 + 2.5), adding excess of ca 5 ml. Filter, heat to boiling, and add 5 ml 10% $BaCl_2.2H_2O$ soln dropwise. Evap. to 100 ml, let stand overnight, filter, wash, ignite, and weigh the $BaSO_4$. Correct result for $BaSO_4$ obtained in blank and report as mg S/100 g. (Detn should be made in room free from S fumes.)

22.049 Total Chlorine (*22*)—Official First Action—See 3.067–3.070

22.050 Alcohol Precipitate (*23*)—Official First Action

To 100 ml prepd soln, **22.003**(b) or (c), in beaker, add 4–8 g sucrose (1 or 2 lumps cube sugar) if sugar is not already present, and evap. to 20–25 ml. If

H_2O-insol. matter seps during evapn add more sugar. Cool to room temp. and add, slowly and with constant stirring, 200 ml alcohol. Let stand ≥ 1 hr, filter on 15 cm qual. paper, and wash ppt with alcohol. Do not permit alcohol ppt to dry before transferring from paper.

Wash ppt back into original beaker with hot H_2O, rinsing paper thoroly. Evap. soln to ca 20 ml and add 5 ml HCl (1 + 2.5). If H_2O-insol. matter seps, stir well and, if necessary, warm slightly to dissolve. Again ppt with 200 ml alcohol, let stand 1 hr, and filter thru paper. Wash ppt and paper thoroly with alcohol to remove all HCl. Rinse ppt from paper into Pt dish with hot H_2O, evap. to dryness on steam bath, dry to constant wt in oven at 100°, and weigh; ignite and reweigh. Loss in wt is alcohol ppt.

As ppt in many samples is colorless and almost invisible, take care that none is lost in dissolving and transferring operations. If amt of alcohol ppt, indicated by its vol. on first pptn, is not excessive, second filtration may be made thru gooch contg thin asbestos mat. If alcohol ppt is very pure and amt is small it may not be visible at first; in this case add small amt of electrolyte, like NaCl, to flocculate alcohol ppt and render it visible.

22.051   Pectic Acid (24)—Official First Action

Transfer 200 ml aliquot prepd soln, **22.003**(b) or (c), to beaker, add 8–12 g sucrose (2 or 3 lumps cube sugar) if soln does not already contain sugar, and evap. to ca 25 ml. If org. acids are to be detd in filtrate from pectin, cool, add 3 ml $1N$ H_2SO_4, and immediately add 200 ml alcohol with constant stirring. Let ppt settle, filter on 15 cm qual. paper, and wash with alcohol. If org. acids are not to be detd, omit addn of H_2SO_4.

Transfer ppt to original beaker with hot H_2O, evap. to ca 40 ml, and cool to $\leq 25°$. If H_2O-insol. matter seps during evapn, stir vigorously, and if necessary add few drops HCl (1 + 2.5), and warm; then cool again. Dil. 2–5 ml 10% NaOH soln, depending on vol. ppt, to 50 ml, and add to soln of alcohol ppt. Let stand 15 min, add 40 ml H_2O and 10 ml HCl (1 + 2.5), and boil 5 min. Filter and wash ppt of pectic acid with hot H_2O. (This filtration should be rapid and filtrate clear. If filtrate is cloudy or of colloidal nature, reject detn. Colloidal filtrates are due to insufficient alkali or to saponification at too high temp., or both. In such cases, repeat detn, using more alkali and keeping temp. low.)

Wash ppt of pectic acid back into beaker, adjust to vol. of 40 ml, cool to <25°, and repeat saponification with dil. NaOH soln, pptn with dil. HCl, and boiling as above. Again filter and wash ppt of pectic acid with hot H_2O, but only to point where test of filtrate shows negligible amt of acid. (≤ 500 ml total filtrate should be necessary.) Wash pectic acid into Pt dish; dry on steam bath and finally in oven at 100° to constant wt. Weigh, ignite, and reweigh. Loss in wt = pectic acid.

22.052   Protein—Official Final Action

Proceed as in **2.051,** using 5 g jelly or other fruit product contg large amt of sugar, or 10 g juice or fresh fruit, and larger amt of H_2SO_4 if necessary for complete digestion. % N $\times$ 6.25 = % protein.

Betaine (25)—Official First Action
(Applicable to orange juice)

22.053   Reagents

(a) *Ammonia soln.*—2%. Dil. 140 ml NH_4OH to 2 L with H_2O.

(b) *Ammonium reineckate soln.*—2.5%. Shake 2.5 g in 75 ml H_2O 30 min. Filter thru paper and dil. to 100.0 ml. Adjust pH to 1.0 with HCl and filter thru fine porosity glass crucible. Prep. fresh before betaine pptn. Do *not* use reagent contg ppt.

(c) *Acetone soln.*—70%. Dil. 70 ml to 100 ml with H_2O.

(d) *Aqueous ether.*—Add 1 ml H_2O to 140 ml ether.

(e) *Ion exchange resins.*—(1) *Amberlite IR-120 C.P. medium porosity (20–50 mesh, wet).*—Prep. 250 g in H form by treating with 2 bed vols $2N$ HCl (ca 500 ml). Soak 2 hr. Drain resin and wash with H_2O until neut. and Cl-free. (2) *Amberlite IRA-400 (20–50 mesh, wet).*—Prep. 250 g in OH form by treating with 2 bed vols $2N$ NaOH (ca 500 ml). Drain and wash NaOH-free with H_2O. Mix with IRC-50 C.P. immediately for column II prepn. (3) *Amberlite IRC-50 C.P.*—Prep. 125 g in H form by treating with 2 bed vols $2N$ HCl. Drain and wash Cl-free with H_2O.

(f) *Betaine std soln.*—1 mg anhyd. betaine/ml. Weigh 0.2623 g betaine . HCl in 200 ml vol. flask and dil. to vol. with H_2O.

22.054   Preparation of Columns

(a) *Column I.*—Use 18 mm id chromatgc tube with medium or coarse porosity fritted glass and with stopcock. Add aq. slurry Amberlite IR-120 C.P. (H) to 12.5 cm bed depth (wet resin). To regenerate resin, pour thru 100–200 ml $1N$ HCl and wash Cl-free with H_2O.

(b) *Column II.*—Intimately mix 2 vols Amberlite IRA-400 (OH) with 1 vol IRC-50 (H) and transfer to column as above to 7.5 cm bed depth. Resins have different densities and excess H_2O causes undesirable sepn. Bed must be intimate mixt. Resin mixt. cannot be regenerated. Use for 2 detns only.

22.055   Preparation of Sample

Prep. juice as in **22.003**(a).

22.056   Determination

Add accurately measured amt prepd juice (10–20 ml) contg 5–7 mg betaine to small beaker. Dil. to ca 30 ml with H_2O and adjust to pH 3.0 with $0.1N$ HCl, using pH meter. Transfer to column I. Collect eluate at ca 3 ml/min. When liq. reaches top of resin, wash column with 200 ml H_2O or until carbohydrate-free. Discard eluate and wash soln. Elute betaine by washing column with $\geq$150 ml 2% NH_4OH, ensuring eluate is alk. Follow with 100 ml H_2O. Reduce eluate to ca 25 ml by boiling. Cool, adjust to pH 7.0 with 0.1N HCl, and transfer to Column II. (Reduce vol. in erlenmeyer and then transfer to small beaker for pH adjustment.)

Collect eluate at 1 ml/min. When liq. reaches top of resin bed, wash with 50 ml H_2O. Conc. combined eluates and washings to 15–20 ml, cool, and adjust to pH 1.0 with 1N HCl. Cool to 0±3° and gradually add, with stirring, 20 ml 2.5% NH_4 reineckate, adjusted to pH 1.0 and cooled to 0±3°. Let stand 3 hr at 0±3°. Filter while cold thru medium porosity 60 ml fritted glass crucible with vac. Transfer ppt with small amts cold filtrate. Wash ppt with three 5 ml portions aq. ether. Dissolve ppt in 10 ml 70% acetone and transfer to 25 ml vol. flask. Dil. to vol. with 70% acetone. Det. A at 525 nm on spectrophtr, using 1 cm cell against 70% acetone as ref. (Make readings within 4 hr.) Det. amt betaine from std curve.

22.057 *Preparation of Standard Curve*

Transfer 2.5, 5.0, 7.5, 10.0, 12.5, and 15.0 ml betaine std soln to beakers, using 10 ml buret. Add H_2O to ca 20 ml and proceed as in **22.056**, beginning, "... adjust to pH 1.0 with 1N HCl."

Plot of mg anhyd. betaine/ml against A should be straight line.

Titratable Acidity (26)—Official Final Action
22.058 *Indicator Method*

(a) *Colorless or slightly colored solns.*—Dil. to ca 250 ml, with neutzd or recently boiled H_2O, 10 g prepd juice, **22.003**(a), or 25 ml prepd soln, **22.003**(b) or (c). Titr. with 0.1N alkali, using 0.3 ml phthln for each 100 ml soln being titrd. Report as ml 0.1N alkali/100 g or 100 ml original material.

(b) *Highly colored solns.*—Dil. sample of known wt with neutzd H_2O and titr. to just before end point with 0.1N alkali, using 0.3 ml phthln for each 100 ml soln being titrd. Transfer measured quantity (2 or 3 ml) of soln into ca 20 ml neut. H_2O in small beaker. (In this extra diln, color of fruit juice becomes so pale that phthln color is easily seen.) If test shows that end point is not reached, pour extra dild portion back into original soln, add more alkali, and continue titrn to end point. By comparing dilns in small beakers, differences produced by few drops 0.1N alkali can be easily observed.

Glass Electrode Method—Official First Action
22.059 *Determination*

Before use, check app. with std buffer solns, **45.007–45.008**. Rinse glass electrode in H_2O several times until reading is ca pH 6. Immerse electrodes in sample contained in beaker. (Sample should titr. 10–50 ml 0.1N NaOH and be contained in initial vol.

of 100–200 ml.) Stir moderately. Add alkali quite rapidly until near pH 6. Then add alkali slowly to pH 7. After pH 7 is reached, finish titrn by adding 0.1N alkali 4 drops at time, and record total vol. and pH reading after each addn. (Add whole drops, so that fraction of drop does not remain on buret tip.) Continue titrn at least 4 drops beyond pH 8.1, and interpolate data for titrn corresponding to pH 8.1. pH values used for interpolation should lie in range 8.10±0.2.

Notes: (1) Always keep glass electrode covered with H_2O when not in use.
(2) If strongly acid cleaning solns are used, electrode requires several hr to come to equilibrium on standing in H_2O.
(3) If electrode and stirrer are wiped lightly with piece of filter paper before insertion into std buffer, same soln may be used for several checks on instrument.

22.060 Volatile Acidity—Official Final Action

Dissolve 10 g sample, dil. to 25 ml, and steam distill as in **11.038**. 1 ml 0.1N alkali = 0.0060 g HOAc.

Total Tartaric Acid (27)
Bitartrate Method—Official Final Action
22.061 *Apparatus*

Device for filtering at 0°.—Use app. similar to that described in **17.020**(d).

22.062 *Removal of Pectin*

Take sample prepd as in **22.003** with titratable acidity ca 3 ml 1N acid and solids content $\leq$20 g. Designate as x, ml 1N alkali required to neutze sample. Adjust vol. sample to ca 35 ml by evapn or by addn of H_2O, add 3 ml 1N H_2SO_4, and heat to 50°. Transfer adjusted sample to 250 ml vol. flask, rinse with 10 ml hot H_2O, and finally with alcohol; cool, dil. to vol. with alcohol, shake, and let stand overnight if necessary, until pptd pectin seps, leaving clear liq. Transfer to centrf. bottle, add 0.2 g filter-aid, shake vigorously, centrf., and decant thru retentive paper (cover funnel with watch glass). Pipet 200 ml filtrate into centrf. bottle.

If sample contains alcohol, esters of org. acids may be present, and saponification is necessary. Adjust vol. to 35 ml, add x + 3 ml 1N KOH, heat to ca 60°, and let stand overnight. Add x + 6 ml 1N H_2SO_4, transfer to 250 ml vol. flask, and proceed as above.

22.063 *Determination*
(Caution: See **46.059**.)

To soln in centrf. bottle add vol. $Pb(OAc)_2$ soln, **22.064**(c), equal to x + 3 ml, or in case saponification was made, x + 6 ml, and 0.2 g filter-aid; shake vigorously 2 min and centrf. Test supernatant with few drops of the $Pb(OAc)_2$ soln and if ppt forms, add addnl $Pb(OAc)_2$ soln, shake, and again centrf. Decant and let drain thoroly by inverting bottle several min. To material in centrf. bottle add 50 ml 80% alcohol, shake vigorously to disperse ppt, add 150 ml more 80% alcohol, shake, centrf., decant, and drain.

To Pb salts in centrf. bottle add ca 150 ml H_2O, shake thoroly, and pass in H_2S to satn. Unsatn is indicated by presence of partial vac. obtained by stoppering bottle, shaking, and observing partial vac. when carefully removing stopper. Transfer to 250 ml vol. flask, dil. to vol. with H_2O, and filter thru folded paper. Transfer 100 ml clear filtrate to 250 ml I flask, tared with 2 or 3 glass beads. (Harvard trip balance sensitive to 0.1 g is convenient.) Evap. on gauze over flame to ca 30 ml, remove from flame, add second 100 ml aliquot, and evap. to 19 ± 0.5 g. Neutze with 30% KOH soln, 1 drop at time, using phthln, and add *one* drop alkali in excess. Add 2 ml HOAc and 0.2 g filter-aid (Celite 545 is satisfactory), and slowly, with agitation, add 80 ml 95% alcohol. Cool in cracked ice-salt mixt., shake vigorously 2 min, place in refrigerator, and hold overnight at 0°.

Cover filtering disk, **22.061**, with thin layer of asbestos and place over it thin layer of filter-aid. Place cracked ice in outer funnel, wash filter mat with ice-cold alcohol, and let stand few min to cool filter thoroly. Swirl flask to suspend filter-aid and ppt, and filter at 0°, sucking mat dry. (Use filtrates and washings for *l*-malic acid detn.) Wash stopper with ca 15 ml ice-cold 80% alcohol, letting wash liq. run into pptn flask. Stopper and shake to wash flask well. Stirring rod bent at 45° angle 1″ from end helps in washing inside of filter tube. Conduct wash liq. completely around inside of filter tube and suck dry. Wash flask and filter tube with two 15 ml portions ice-cold 80% alcohol. While filtering, keep flask cold with cracked ice. Remove ice from outer funnel and transfer ppt and pad to pptn flask with boiling CO_2-free H_2O. Heat almost to boiling and titr. with 0.1N alkali, using phthln. 1 ml 0.1N alkali = 0.015 g tartaric acid. Tartaric acid/0.64 = tartaric acid in sample taken.

Citric Acid

Pentabromacetone Method (28)—
Official Final Action

22.064   Reagents

(a) *Potassium permanganate soln.*—Dissolve 5 g $KMnO_4$ in H_2O and dil. to 100 ml.

(b) *Ferrous sulfate soln.*—Dissolve 200 g $FeSO_4$ $.7H_2O$ in H_2O, dil. to 500 ml with H_2O, and add 5 ml H_2SO_4.

(c) *Lead acetate soln.*—Dissolve 75 g $Pb(OAc)_2$ $.3H_2O$ in H_2O, add 1 ml HOAc, and dil. to 250 ml.

22.065   Removal of Pectin

Accurately measure or weigh desired amt of prepd sample, **22.003**, with titratable acidity ca 3 ml 1N acid and solids content ≤ 20 g, into 250 ml vol. flask and add H_2O to make total vol. 70 ml. Add 2 ml 1N

HNO_3 to liberate acids and heat to 50°. Dil. nearly to neck of flask with alcohol and cool to room temp. Dil. to vol. with alcohol, mix, filter on funnel lined with cotton, and collect ≥ 220 ml filtrate. (Toward end, filtration is slow; by gathering ends of the cotton and squeezing enclosed residue, desired amt of filtrate may be obtained.)

22.066   Isolation of Polybasic Acids
(Caution: See 46.059.)

Det. titer, t, of 10 ml alc. filtrate in terms of ml 0.1N NaOH, using phthln.

Pipet 200 ml alc. soln into 400 ml beaker, add $(2t + 2)$ ml 1N NaOH, and place on steam bath 30 min. Cool mixt. to room temp., add 5 ml 1N HOAc, and rinse with alcohol into 250 ml centrf. bottle. Add 0.6t g finely powd $Pb(OAc)_2$. (Quantity 0.6t, derived from 0.03$t(200/10)$, expresses g $Pb(OAc)_2$ required to form Pb salts of acids in 200 ml soln. Quantity indicated is greater than necessary by factor of 1.5 and is generally enough.) Shake vigorously 5 min, add 0.2 g Filter-Cel, fill bottle with alcohol, and mix thoroly. Centrf. and add few drops $Pb(OAc)_2$ soln to supernatant. If ppt forms within 1 min, add more $Pb(OAc)_2$ and repeat centrfg. Decant and discard supernatant. Completely disperse Pb salts by adding portions of 80% alcohol and shaking.

Fill bottle with 80% alcohol, mix thoroly, and centrf. Discard liq. and repeat washing with 80% alcohol. Disperse Pb salts in 50 ml H_2O, dil. to 150 ml, and sat. with H_2S. Shake 1 min and rinse into 250 ml vol. flask. Dil. to mark and filter thru large fluted paper, *pouring back until bright*.

22.067   Determination

Evap. 200 ml isolated acid soln, **22.066**, to ca 20 ml, rinse into 250–300 ml tared, g-s erlenmeyer, and adjust with H_2O to net wt of ca 40 g. Add 2 g KBr and 5 ml H_2SO_4, and, if necessary, heat to ca 50° and let stand 5 min. Add 20 ml $KMnO_4$ soln from pipet or buret slowly (1–2 ml portions), swirling flask few sec after each addn. Let stand undisturbed 5 min and cool to 15°. Slowly add $FeSO_4$ soln with constant agitation until mixt. starts to clear. Shake 1 min, continue addn of $FeSO_4$ soln until MnO_2 is dissolved, and add few ml excess. Add 20 g anhyd. Na_2SO_4, with swirling to assure soln (if Na_2SO_4 remains substantially undissolved, repeat detn). Cool to 15° and shake vigorously 5 min.

Immediately, while still cold, collect pentabromacetone ppt on asbestos in gooch and wash residual ppt from flask with portion of filtrate. Wash crucible with 50 ml cold H_2O and leave under suction few min. Dry crucible overnight in H_2SO_4 desiccator and weigh, or place crucible in drying train and aerate until loss in wt does not exceed few tenths mg, making first weighing after 20 min.

Remove pentabromacetone from crucible with alcohol followed by ether, filling crucible 3 times with each solv. Dry crucible 10 min at 100°, cool in desiccator, and weigh. Difference in 2 wts = wt pentabromacetone. Calc. g anhyd. citric acid from formula: $X = 0.424P$, where X = g citric acid in aliquot; P = g pentabromacetone; and 0.424 = theoretical factor for converting pentabromacetone to anhyd. citric acid. Anhyd. citric acid in sample taken for analysis = $X/0.64$.

For drying pentabromacetone by aspiration, use app. shown in Fig. 22:3, where A is gooch, 28 mm diam., loosely packed with cotton; B is gooch, 35 mm diam., for pentabromacetone; and C is 500 ml suction flask. Dry air by passing thru H_2SO_4 and soda-lime, and finally filter thru cotton. Cool air entering drying train by passing thru spiral condenser cooled with H_2O.

Let crucible, B, contg pentabromacetone, remain under suction ca 1 min to remove surface moisture before placing in app. If air does not pass thru freely, place crucible in desiccator short time. Maintain slow uniform flow of air by just "cracking" suction.

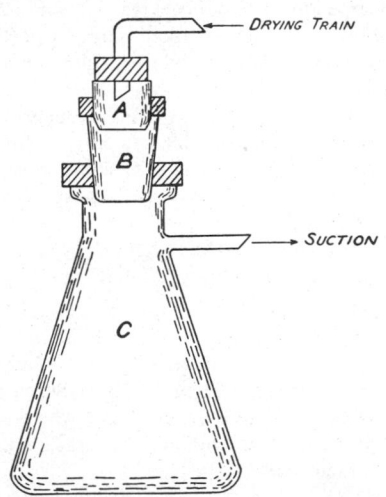

FIG. 22:3—Apparatus for drying pentabromacetone by aspiration

Total Malic Acid (Laevo- and Inactive)
(29)—Official First Action
(Either isocitric acid or tartaric acid or both may be present.)

22.068 *Reagents*

(a) *Solvent.*—Either 30% *tert*-amyl alcohol, or 30% *n*-butyl alcohol in $CHCl_3$. (Eastman Kodak Co. Practical *tert*-amyl alcohol and NF $CHCl_3$ without further treatment have been found satisfactory.)

(b) *Silicic acid suitable for chromatography.*—See **19.016**(a).

22.069 *Apparatus*

(a) *Chromatographic tubes.*—Approx. 13 mm id and 400 mm long; may have perforated disk or coarse fritted disk at beginning of constriction. Glass piston to fit tube.

(b) *Source of pressure.*—See **18.026**(c).

22.070 *Standardization of Silicic Acid Column*

Mix in mortar, to uniform powder, 6 g silicic acid and amt of $0.5N$ H_2SO_4 that will allow solv., (a), to elute at rate of 1–1.5 ml/min with pressure of <1 atm. Amt of $0.5N$ H_2SO_4 required may vary with different batches of silicic acid; however, silicic acid and $0.5N$ H_2SO_4 must be measured accurately and column for detn made up exactly as in stdzn. (3 ml $0.5N$ H_2SO_4 has been found satisfactory for 1 batch of silicic acid.) Slurry with enough $CHCl_3$ to fill tube. Place small amt of cotton at bottom of tube and pour slurry into tube so that no air bubbles are occluded. Cut disk of filter paper with cork borer to fit tightly inside tube and pack silicic acid with piston until no more $CHCl_3$ is forced out. Column packing in this manner permits sample to be stirred with solv. without disturbing column and gives sharper sepn of acids. Remove piston, pour remaining $CHCl_3$ out of tube, and place 10 ml cylinder under tube.

Dissolve ca 10 mg malic acid in 1 ml $5N$ H_2SO_4 in small beaker. Stir with 2 g silicic acid, or enough to make free-flowing powder that does not adhere to beaker. Transfer thru funnel to column, rinse beaker with ca 5 ml solv., and pour thru funnel into tube. With long thin rod stir powder and solv. in tube until all air bubbles are removed. Remove rod and stand it in sample beaker.

With pressure, pack sample until solv. just disappears into gel. Rinse long rod, beaker, and funnel with ca 2 ml solv. and sink into gel. Repeat washing with another 2 ml solv. Place plug of cotton in top of tube, wet it with solv., and with rod push it down to top of sample. Fill tube with solv. and apply pressure so that eluate is forced out at rate of 1–1.5 ml/min. Titr. eluate in 10 ml portions, rinsing cylinder with 10 ml CO_2-free H_2O and using thymol blue indicator, **34.097**(g). If mixt. being titrd is swirled gently so that no emulsion is formed, end point is sharp and easily seen. When excess acid is present, indicator goes into lower layer and as neutrality is reached, indicator turns yellow and enters aq. phase. Swirl and add alkali until lower layer is colorless and aq. layer is blue. Note vol. of solv. required to bring malic acid to bottom of gel (threshold vol.) and vol. required to elute all malic acid.

In same manner, det. threshold vol. for citric acid. Vol. solv. necessary to bring citric acid to bottom of column should be at least 20 ml more than that required to elute all malic acid. During elution, column will become semitransparent at top and progressively downward, but when malic acid is all eluted, 1 cm or more of column should be unchanged in appearance. When semitransparency reaches bottom of column, H_2SO_4 may be carried into eluate. (It has been found that first 70 ml eluate contains no malic acid and that next 70 ml contains all the malic acid and no citric acid. However, vol. required should be detd for app. and particular batch of silicic acid used.)

22.071   *Determination*

Proceed as in tartaric acid method, **22.063,** thru par. 2, sentence 3. (The 30% KOH and device for filtering at 0° are not used.) Conc. 200 ml filtrate (do *not* neutze) to ca 15 ml. Transfer with small amt of H_2O to tared beaker with bottom ca 3 cm diam. and evap. on steam bath to 1 ± 0.5 g. Jet of air over surface of liq. may be used to hasten evapn but no portion of bottom of beaker should be allowed to dry, as darkening of soln may occur with loss of malic acid.

Cool, add 0.25 ml H_2SO_4 $(1 + 1)$ and 2 g silicic acid or slightly more if necessary to make free flowing powder, and transfer to column prepd as above. Discard vol. eluate equal to detd threshold vol. of malic acid and collect in 150 ml beaker the eluate that will contain all the malic acid and no citric. Evap. solv. on steam bath. (Jet of air over liq. hastens evapn and reduces danger of loss by bumping.) Dissolve residue in ca 10 ml CO_2-free H_2O and titr. with 0.02N NaOH, using phthln. Correct titrn for blank on eluate passed thru column as above. 1 ml 0.02N NaOH = 1.34 mg malic acid; mg malic acid/0.64 = total malic acid in sample.

Acidify soln contg neutzd malic acid with drop 1N HOAc, evap. to ca 15 ml, transfer to 25 ml vol. flask, and proceed as in **22.079,** beginning ". . . and dil. to vol. with H_2O." Total malic acid in sample minus laevo-malic acid = inactive malic acid.

Citric and Isocitric Acids
Chromatographic Method (30)—
Official First Action
22.072   *Reagents*

(a) *tert-Amyl alcohol in chloroform, 30%.*—Wash NF $CHCl_3$ 3 times with ca 0.5 vol. H_2O to remove alcohol. Dil. 300 ml *tert*-amyl or *n*-butyl alcohol to 1 L with washed $CHCl_3$ and shake well with ca 50 ml H_2O. Let liqs sep. and discard H_2O. To *tert*-amyl alcohol-$CHCl_3$ layer add excess anhyd. powd Na_2SO_4. Shake well and filter thru dry paper.

(b) *tert-Amyl alcohol in chloroform, 40%.*—Prep. as in (a), using 400 ml *tert*-amyl or *n*-butyl alcohol.

(c) *Silicic acid suitable for chromatography.*—See **19.016**(a).

(d) *Lead acetate soln.*—Dissolve 75 g $Pb(OAc)_2$ .3H_2O in H_2O, add 1 ml HOAc, and dil. to 250 ml.

(e) *Metaphosphoric acid.*—20%. Store in refrigerator.

(f) *Sodium sulfide soln.*—Dissolve 4 g $Na_2S.9H_2O$ in H_2O and dil. to 100 ml. Store in refrigerator.

(g) *Sodium thiosulfate std soln.*—0.01N (2.482 g/L). Stdze against 0.01N KIO_3 (0.3567 g/L) as follows: To 5 ml KIO_3 soln, add 1 ml 2M H_3PO_4 and

1 ml 10% KI, and titr. with $Na_2S_2O_3$ soln, using starch indicator at end point.

(h) *Filter paper.*—Cl-free, 9 cm. Wash well with hot H_2O and dry.

(i) *Sodium hydroxide std soln.*—0.01N. Protect from CO_2.

(j) *Potassium chloride soln.*—0.9319 g dried KCl/L of 0.085M H_3PO_4.

(k) *Silver iodate.*—Protect from light.

22.073   *Apparatus*

(a) *Chromatographic tube.*—Approx. 13 mm id and 400 mm long, with 250 ml reservoir at top; piston to fit tube for packing silicic acid. Plug bottom of tube with cotton. For convenience in packing, reservoir may be connected to column thru male ╤ joint.

(b) *Centrifuge tube.*—Approx. 3 × 11 cm; 60 ml capacity.

(c) *Device for titrating in CO_2-free atmosphere.*—125 ml pear-shaped separator with rubber stopper having 5 holes for following: (*1*) tube, with drawn-out tip extending to stopcock for CO_2-free air; (*2*) std acid buret tip; (*3*) std alkali buret tip; (*4*) funnel for transferring eluate; and (*5*) tube for exhaust vapors.

(d) *CO_2-free air.*—Pass air (conveniently obtained from pressure app., **18.026**(c)) twice thru 20% NaOH soln and then thru H_2O contg phthln and enough 0.1N NaOH to produce pink soln.

22.074   *Standardization of Silicic Acid Column*

Thoroly mix, in mortar, 6 g silicic acid and amt of 0.5N H_2SO_4 detd as follows: Ignite ca 1 g silicic acid, accurately weighed, in small crucible at red heat ca 15 min (gas burner is satisfactory). Cool in efficient desiccator and weigh. Calc. ml 0.5N H_2SO_4 required, V, in formula: $V = W(1.9X - 1)$; where $W =$ g silicic acid used for column and $X =$ ratio anhyd. to hydrous silicic acid.

Add $CHCl_3$, little at time, and mix, making uniform slurry that pours readily. With $CHCl_3$ wash bottle, transfer *all* of slurry to chromatgc tube, pouring it down thin rod, and stirring until all air bubbles are removed. Cut circle of coarse filter paper (Whatman No. 4 or equiv.) with cork borer to fit snugly in tube. Sat. with $CHCl_3$ and push down with piston until silicic acid is packed in firm column. Remove piston, letting paper remain at top of column. Just before transferring sample to column, pour off excess $CHCl_3$ and place empty graduate under tube.

Prep. 5 ml aq. soln of citric and isocitric acids, contg total acidity of ca 12 ml 0.01N (ca 4 mg each acid). (If laevo and inactive malic acids and tartaric acid are also included, total acidity should be ca 30 ml 0.01N—ca 4 mg each acid.) Transfer soln to centrf. tube, **22.073**(b), and add 1N NaOH until alk. to phthln plus 2 drops excess. Heat in boiling H_2O 15 min, cool to ca 20°, and add 5.5 vols alcohol, 0.5 ml 1N HOAc, and 0.5 ml $Pb(OAc)_2$ soln. Mix at intervals or continuously 5 min, centrf., and decant clear supernatant. Test liq. with drop of $Pb(OAc)_2$ soln, and if ppt forms in 1 min, add it to ppt in centrf. tube. Stir or mix ppt with ca 20 ml acetone, centrf., and decant and discard acetone. Lay tube on side until acetone evaps or remove it with very gentle current of air at room temp. When ppt is dry, add 0.5 ml $2N$ H_2SO_4 and mix with rod to smooth slurry. Add 1 g silicic acid and mix until powder does not adhere to sides of tube, adding little more silicic acid if necessary.

Transfer thru funnel to prepd column, rinse centrf. tube with ca 5 ml 30% $tert$-amyl alcohol in $CHCl_3$, (a), and pour thru funnel. With long thin rod stir powder and solv. until all air bubbles are removed. Apply pressure, 18.026(c), to column until solv. just sinks into gel. Wipe centrf. tube, funnel, and rod with cotton, and place cotton in chromatgc tube; rinse centrf. tube, funnel, and rod with 2 ml solv., pour into cotton, and push cotton to top of gel. Let solv. sink into gel. Add ca 200 ml solv. to reservoir and apply pressure until solv. elutes at rate of 1–1.5 ml/min.

Promptly transfer eluate in 10 ml portions (see Note) to titrg app., 22.073(c). Rinse graduate with 10 ml freshly washed neut. $CHCl_3$ and then with 10 ml CO_2-free H_2O. Add thymol blue indicator, 34.097(g), and 0.01N NaOH until, after thoro mixing by forcing CO_2-free air thru app., lower layer is colorless and upper aq. layer is blue. Back-titr. with std acid and alkali until 1 drop of alkali produces characteristic blue of indicator.

From titrn values, det. threshold vol. and vol. required to elute each acid for particular app. and reagents used. Acids elute in following order: Unremoved HOAc is eluted in second and third 10 ml; both inactive and laevo-malic acids appear in 100–160 ml fractions. When malic acid is all removed (ca 170 ml), pour off remaining solv., add 40% $tert$-amyl alcohol in $CHCl_3$, and continue elution. Both citric and isocitric acids appear in 180–300 ml fractions. Continue elution until tartaric acid is eluted (ca 330–440 ml). Immediately titr. eluate contg citric and isocitric acids.

22.075   *Determination*

Take amt of sample prepd as in 22.003 with titratable acidity ca 30 ml 0.01N and with solids content $\leq$2 g. Transfer to centrf. tube, 22.073(b), adjust vol. to 5 ml by evapn or addn of H_2O, and proceed as in stdzn, beginning "... add 1N NaOH until alk...." and continue to "Back-titr. with std acid and alkali ..."

(a) *Total citric and isocitric acids.*—After malic acid is eluted, change to 40% $tert$-amyl alcohol in $CHCl_3$, elute, and promptly titr. 10 ml aliquots as in 22.074. 1 ml 0.01N NaOH = 0.64 mg anhyd. citric and isocitric acids. Correct titrn for blank. After each titrn collect lower layer and aq. layer in sep. containers After citric and isocitric acids are eluted,

wash combined lower layers with small amt of H_2O and alkali, sep., and add aq. portion to titrd combined citric and isocitric acid solns. Save this soln for detn of normal citric acid.

Note: If eluted acid is allowed to stay in contact with eluate, some esters may be formed, causing low results. After titrn, aq. solns may be held until convenient to det. normal citric acid.

(b) *Isocitric acid.*—Subtract normal citric acid from total citric acid to obtain isocitric acid.

(c) *Determination of reagent blank.*—Prep. silicic acid column as 22.074, add to it 1 g silicic acid and 0.5 ml $2N$ H_2SO_4, elute, and titr. as in 22.074.

(d) *Normal citric acid.*—Adjust soln contg citric and isocitric acids to convenient vol. (50 ml or less) and take aliquot contg $\leq$4 mg citric acid as estd from titrn of fraction. Add 2 ml H_2SO_4 to aliquot, cool, and hold below 22°. Add 1 ml 20% metaphosphoric acid, dil. to ca 35 ml, add 2 ml 12% KBr and 5 ml 4% $KMnO_4$, mix, and hold 10 min, without stirring, below 22°. Cool to ca 10° and add cold 3% H_2O_2 dropwise, while stirring, until soln is colorless.

Transfer to 125 ml separator and rinse container with ca 25 ml pet ether, adding rinsings to separator. Shake well, sep., and discard aq. portion. Wash pet ether 4 times with ca 3 ml portions H_2O, draining and discarding aq. layer each time. Halides must be completely removed from pet ether and tip of funnel. Add 3 ml Na_2S soln to pet ether, shake well, and drain aq. layer into 25 ml vol. flask. Ext with another 3 ml Na_2S soln and wash with 2 ml portions H_2O until all color is removed, draining both exts and washings into flask. Discard pet ether. Add 2.0 ml $2M$ H_3PO_4 to contents of flask, mix, and then add very small quartz or porcelain chip to facilitate smooth boiling and boil 5–6 min. Cool, and add *exactly* 5.00 ml KCl soln, (j). Dil. to vol. and transfer soln, without rinsing, to 50 ml erlenmeyer contg 0.25 g dry $AgIO_3$, (k). Shake vigorously 5 min and filter immediately thru dry Cl-free paper.

To 5 ml filtrate add 1 ml 10% KI soln and 2 drops $0.085M$ H_3PO_4, and titr. at once with 0.01N $Na_2S_2O_3$, using starch indicator. Correct titrn for blank detn on 5 ml H_2O and 6 ml Na_2S soln in 25 ml vol. flask, beginning as above, "Add 2.0 ml $2M$ H_3PO_4 ..." Blank titrn includes value for KCl as well as any halide in reagent. ml 0.01N $Na_2S_2O_3$ $\times$ 0.064 = mg anhyd. normal citric acid in filtrate aliquot.

Laevo-Malic Acid
Method I (31)—Official First Action

(As method is empirical, all directions must be rigidly followed, particularly with respect to dilns. Substitution of vol. flasks of capacities different from those specified is not permissible.)

22.076   *Reagents*

(a) *Lead acetate soln.*—Dissolve 40 g $Pb(OAc)_2$.$3H_2O$ in H_2O, add 0.5 ml HOAc, and dil. to 100 ml.

(b) *Tribasic lead acetate std soln.*—Prep. soln from tribasic Pb(OAc)₂, **(c).** To 5 g of the salt in 500 ml erlenmeyer add 200 ml H₂O and shake vigorously. Neutze 3 ml 1N H₂SO₄, dild with 200 ml H₂O, with the soln, using Me red as indicator. Note vol. Pb soln required. In detn use 2 ml in excess of this quantity. (Soln should be freshly prepd.)

(c) *Tribasic lead acetate.*—Dissolve 82 g Pb(OAc)₂ .3H₂O in 170 ml H₂O. Prep. 100 ml dil. NH₄OH soln contg 5.8 g NH₃ as detd by titrn (Me red). Heat solns to 60°, mix thoroly, and let stand overnight. Shake vigorously to break up ppt, and filter on buchner. Wash once with H₂O and suck dry, then twice with alcohol, and finally with ether. Let dry in air.

22.077   *Preparation of Sample*

Proceed as in **22.062**, omitting addn of the 3 ml 1N H₂SO₄ to adjusted sample. In case of saponification add $x + 3$ ml 1N H₂SO₄ to saponified material instead of $x + 6$ ml.

22.078   *Determination*
(*Caution: See* **46.018, 46.059, 46.083,** and **46.084.**)

(a) *Isolation of laevo-malic acid.*—To material in centrf. bottle add ca 75 mg *tartaric acid* and amt of Pb(OAc)₂ soln, **(a)**, equal to x ($x + 3$ ml in case saponification was made), shake vigorously 2 min, and centrf. Carefully decant supernatant from pptd Pb salts and test with small amt of Pb(OAc)₂ soln. If ppt forms, return to centrf. bottle, add more Pb(OAc)₂ soln, shake, and again centrf. If sediment lifts, repeat centrfg, increasing speed and time. Let ppt drain thoroly by inverting bottle several min.

Add ca 200 ml 80% alcohol, shake vigorously, and again centrf., decant, and drain. To Pb salts add ca 150 ml H₂O, shake vigorously, and pass in rapid stream of *H₂S to saturation*. Stopper bottle and shake ca 1 min. Transfer mixt. to 250 ml vol. flask with H₂O, dil. to vol., shake, and filter thru folded paper.

Pipet 220 ml filtrate into 600 ml beaker and evap. on gauze to ca 50 ml. Cool, neutze with 1N KOH (phthln), and add 5 drops excess. Add 2 ml HOAc and transfer with alcohol to 250 ml vol. flask. Add alcohol to vol., shake, and pour into 500 ml erlenmeyer. Add small handful of glass beads and cool to 15°. Stopper flask, shake vigorously 10 min, and place in refrigerator 30 min. Again shake 10 min, and filter thru folded paper.

Pipet 220 ml clear filtrate into centrf. bottle, add Pb(OAc)₂ soln equal to x ($x + 3$ ml in case of saponification), shake vigorously ca 2 min, centrf., decant, and drain. Add 200 ml 80% alcohol, shake, centrf., decant, and drain.

Transfer Pb salts to 500 ml erlenmeyer with ca 175 ml H₂O. Add 3 ml 1N H₂SO₄, heat to boiling, and add 1 ml HOAc (5 + 95) and amt of std tribasic Pb(OAc)₂ soln previously detd, **22.076(b)**. Boil mixt.

5 min, cool to room temp., transfer to 250 ml vol. flask with H₂O, dil. to vol., shake, and pour into 500 ml erlenmeyer. Add small handful of glass beads, cool to 15°, shake vigorously 5 min, and place in refrigerator 30 min. Again shake 5 min and filter thru folded paper. Sat. *clear* filtrate with H₂S, shake vigorously, and filter.

(b) *Polarization.*—Evap. 225 ml clear filtrate over gauze to ca 10 ml, neutze with 1N KOH (phthln), make slightly acid with HOAc (5 + 95), and evap. to ca 5 ml. Transfer to 25–27.5 ml Giles flask with H₂O, dil. to 27.5 ml mark, shake, and pour into small g-s erlenmeyer. If Giles flask is not available, use 25 ml measuring cylinder, dil. to vol., and add 2.5 ml H₂O from buret. Add small handful of glass beads and 4 g powd *uranyl acetate*, shake vigorously 10 min, and filter. (As U-malic complex is light sensitive, wrap flask in towel while shaking and protect from light as much as possible during filtration and polarization.) Polarize in 200 mm tube at 20°, using white light. After filling tube, release tension on glass disks by slightly loosening caps, and let stand at 20° at least 30 min before making readings.

°S **(31.020(a))** × 30.1 = mg laevo-malic acid contained in portion taken for analysis. If control for adjusting to std temp. 20° is lacking, det. temp. of polariscope and at this temp. prep. soln of U-complex as above. Make readings after letting tube remain in trough of instrument 30 min.

22.079 *Method II (32)—Official First Action*
(Not applicable in presence of isocitric acid— blackberry)
(*Caution: See* **46.083** and **46.084.**)

Conc. filtrate from tartaric acid detn, **22.063**, to ca 5 ml on steam bath. (Jet of air over surface of liq. speeds evapn and reduces danger of loss by bumping.) Cool, add NaOH (1 + 1) drop at time until alk. to phthln, and then add just enough 1N HOAc to discharge phthln color. Transfer to 25 ml vol. flask and dil. to vol. with H₂O.

Pour soln into fine porosity fritted filter tube contg mat of C several mm thick. (Merck's activated charcoal for decolorizing and Nuchar W have been found satisfactory.) Force liq. slowly thru disk, 1–2 ml/min, into 50 ml flask, using pressure. If soln is not colorless, pass thru another fresh C mat. Mix soln and polarize in 200 mm tube at room temp., using white light. Return soln in polariscope tube to remainder in flask. Add 2.5 g finely powd *uranyl acetate, protect from light,* and shake in machine 0.5 hr.

Filter on retentive paper in *dark*, mix, and polarize as before. Do not let treated soln be exposed to light; this causes the U-complex to become insol., and if it is filtered off, loss of malic acid occurs. Algebraic difference between readings in °S **(31.020(a))** × 15.3 gives mg laevo-malic acid in sample taken for tartaric acid detn.

Method III (33)—Official First Action
(*Caution: See* **46.083** and **46.084.**)

22.080 **Apparatus and Reagents**

(a) *Polarimeter.*—Accurate to 0.01°, with Na lamp.

(b) *Carbon.*—Activated, acid-washed (Darco G-60, or equiv.).

(c) *l-Malic acid.*—Calbiochem A Grade, or equiv. Must meet following purity test: Dissolve 0.5 g *l*-malic acid in ca 50 ml H_2O, adjust pH to 5.5 with $1N$ NaOH, and dil. to 100 ml with H_2O. To ca 35 ml, add 1.5 g uranyl acetate.$2H_2O$ and let stand in dark 30 min. Filter, and read optical rotation in 200 mm tube. Optical rotation of $\alpha = -4.88°$ to $-4.84°$ should be obtained.

(d) *l-Malic acid std solns.*—(*1*) *Stock soln.*—10 mg/ml. Place 1.0 g *l*-malic acid and 4.0 g citric acid in 150 ml beaker, add ca 50 ml H_2O, and adjust to pH 5.5 with 50% NaOH soln, using pH meter and stirring with magnetic stirrer. Quant. transfer to 100 ml vol. flask and dil. to vol. with H_2O. (*2*) *Working solns.*—1, 2, and 3 mg/ml. Pipet 10, 20, and 30 ml stock soln to sep. 100 ml vol. flasks and dil. to vol. with H_2O.

22.081 **Preparation of Standard Curve**

Det. optical rotation (α_l) on each std soln in 200 mm polarimeter tube. To ca 35 ml of each std soln in 50 ml erlenmeyer, add 1.5 g uranyl acetate.$2H_2O$. Keep in dark 30 min and swirl occasionally. Filter and det. optical rotation (α_u) of clear uranyl-malate complex in 200 mm polarimeter tube. Plot mg *l*-malic acid/100 ml against difference in rotation ($\alpha = \alpha_u - \alpha_l$).

22.082 **Preparation of Sample**

(a) *Fruit juices.*—Weigh 62.5 g into 250 ml vol. flask. Add 0.1 g KOAc and 100 ml absolute alcohol and mix. Dil. to vol. with absolute alcohol, mix, and let stand 1 hr. Filter thru rapid paper.

(b) *Preserves and high sugar content products containing pieces of fruit.*—Comminute, and weigh 62.5 g into 250 ml beaker. Add 0.1 g KOAc, 30 ml H_2O, and 100 ml absolute alcohol, mix, and quant. transfer to 250 ml vol. flask, using absolute alcohol. Dil. to vol. with absolute alcohol, mix, and let stand 1 hr. Filter thru rapid paper.

(c) *Fruit.*—Comminute, and weigh 62.5 g into 250 ml beaker. Proceed as in (b) except omit addn of 30 ml H_2O.

(d) *Grape juice.*—Weigh 125 g into 500 ml vol. flask, add 1.0 ml satd KOAc soln and 200 ml absolute alcohol, and mix. Dil. to vol. with absolute alcohol, mix, and let stand overnight. Filter thru Whatman No. 40 paper, or equiv.

(e) *Grape preserves and other high-sugar content grape products.*—Comminute and weigh 125 g into 500 ml beaker. Add 1.0 ml satd KOAc soln, 50 ml H_2O, and 200 ml absolute alcohol. Mix and quant.

transfer to 500 ml vol. flask with absolute alcohol. Dil. to vol. with absolute alcohol, mix, and let stand overnight. Filter thru Whatman No. 40 paper, or equiv.

(f) *Grapes.*—Comminute and weigh 125 g into 500 ml beaker. Proceed as in (e) except omit addn of 50 ml H_2O.

22.083 **Determination**

Transfer 200 ml aliquot filtrate to 8 oz widemouth bottle, $2\frac{1}{4}''$ od $\times$ 5″ high. Add magnetic stirring bar and 30 ml absolute alcohol. Potentiometrically titr. 10 ml remaining filtrate to pH 8.4, using $0.1N$ NaOH. Calc. ml NaOH necessary to neutze the 200 ml aliquot. Add to bottle 0.6 ml satd $Pb(OAc)_2$ soln for each ml $1N$ NaOH calcd to neutze 200 ml aliquot. Stir 10 min with magnetic stirrer and centrf 6 min at 1500 rpm. Test supernatant for complete pptn with few drops satd $Pb(OAc)_2$ soln. Decant and wash ppt by stirring 5 min with 200 ml alcohol. (Use 85% alcohol with grapes and grape products.) Centrf. 5 min, decant, add 25 ml H_2O to ppt, and mix well to slurry. Use pH meter and adjust pH to 1.5 with H_2SO_4 (1 + 9). Remove $PbSO_4$ by vac. filtering on coarse porosity 60 ml fritted glass crucible contg asbestos pad. Wash ppt with 10 ml portions H_2O and combine washings with filtrate in 150 ml graduated beaker. Total vol. should be <90 ml. Adjust pH to 5.5 with 50% NaOH, using pH meter. Quant. transfer to 100 ml vol. flask and dil. to vol. with H_2O. Add ca 6 g C and mix thoroly. Let stand 30 min and filter thru fine paper. Filtrate must be colorless. Det. optical rotation (α_l) on this filtrate, using 200 mm tube. To ca 35 ml filtrate in 50 ml erlenmeyer add 1.5 g uranyl acetate.$2H_2O$ and keep in dark 30 min with occasional swirling. Filter and det. optical rotation (α_u) of clear soln of uranylmalate complex. Calc. mg *l*-malic acid/100 g sample by one of following:

(a) $(\alpha_x \times C \times 100)/(\alpha_s \times W)$, where α_x = difference in rotation of sample = $\alpha_{ux} - \alpha_{lx}$; α_s = difference in rotation of std = $\alpha_{us} - \alpha_{ls}$; C = mg *l*-malic acid in 100 ml std soln; and W = g sample in 100 ml final soln.

(b) $\alpha_x \times 2 \times$ (sum of mg *l*-malic acid in std curve solns)/(sum of number degrees in std curve solns).

(c) (mg *l*-malic acid/100 ml from std curve) $\times$ 2.

Inactive Malic Acid (34)—Official First Action

(As method is empirical, all directions must be rigidly followed, particularly with respect to dilns. Substitution of vol. flasks of capacities different from those specified is not permissible.)

22.084 **Reagents**

Use reagents described in **22.076** and in addn—

(a) *Potassium permanganate std soln.*—Dissolve 14.5214 g purest $KMnO_4$ in H_2O and dil. to 1 L. Stdze as follows: Pipet 50 ml oxalic acid soln, (b), into 600 ml beaker and add 70 ml H_2O and 10 ml H_2SO_4 (1 + 1). Heat to 80°, immediately add

KMnO₄ soln to faint pink, again heat to 80°, and finish titrn. 50 ml KMnO₄ soln should be equiv. to 50 ml oxalic acid soln.

(b) *Oxalic acid std soln.*—Dissolve 28.7556 g purest $H_2C_2O_4.2H_2O$ in H_2O and dil. to 1 L. (1 ml = 5 mg malic acid (laevo or inactive)).

22.085 *Preparation of Sample*

Subject 2 portions of sample to isolation, **22.086 (a)**; use one portion for detn of laevo-malic acid (polarization), **22.086(b)**, and other for total malic acid, laevo + inactive (oxidn), **22.086(c)**. Choose amt of sample with titratable acidity ≤150 mg acid calcd as malic acid. Designate as x ml $1N$ alkali required to neutze amt of sample chosen. In no case should solids content be >20 g (200 ml sample soln of jam or jelly).

Adjust sample soln to ca 35 ml by evapn or addn of H_2O, pour into 250 ml vol. flask, rinse with 10 ml hot H_2O and then with alcohol, and dil. to vol. with alcohol. Shake, let stand until pectin seps, leaving clear liq. (overnight if necessary), and filter thru folded paper, draining thoroly and covering funnel with watch glass. Pipet 225 ml filtrate into centrf. bottle.

22.086 *Determination*
(*Caution: See* **46.018** and **46.059**.)

(a) *Isolation of total malic acid.*—To soln in centrf. bottle add ca 25 mg *citric acid* and amt of Pb(OAc)₂ soln, **22.076(a)**, equal to x ($x + 3$ ml if saponification was made), shake vigorously 2 min, and centrf. Carefully decant supernatant from pptd Pb salts and test with small amt of Pb(OAc)₂ soln. If ppt forms, return to centrf. bottle, add more Pb(OAc)₂, shake, and again centrf. If sediment lifts, repeat centrfg, increasing speed and time. Let ppt drain thoroly by inverting bottle several min.

Add 200 ml 80% alcohol, shake vigorously, and again centrf., decant, and drain. To Pb salts add ca 150 ml H_2O, shake vigorously, and pass in rapid stream of *H_2S to saturation.* Stopper bottle and shake ca 1 min. Transfer mixt. to 250 ml vol. flask with H_2O, dil. to vol., shake, and filter thru folded paper.

Pipet 225 ml filtrate into 600 ml beaker, and evap. to ca 100 ml to expel H_2S. Transfer to 250 ml vol. flask with H_2O. (Vol. in flask should be ca 200 ml.) Add 5 ml HOAc (1 + 9) and same amt of Pb(OAc)₂ soln previously used. Shake vigorously, dil. to vol. with H_2O, and filter.

Pass rapid stream of H_2S into *clear* filtrate *to saturation,* stopper flask, shake vigorously, and filter. Pipet 225 ml filtrate into 600 ml beaker, add ca 75 mg *tartaric acid,* and evap. on gauze to ca 50 ml. Cool, neutze with $1N$ *potassium hydroxide* (phthln), and add 5 drops excess. Add 2 ml HOAc and transfer mixt. to 250 ml vol. flask with alcohol. Dil. to vol. with alcohol, shake, and pour into 500 ml erlenmeyer. Add small handful of glass beads and cool to 15°. Stopper flask, shake vigorously 10 min, and

place in refrigerator 30 min. Again shake 10 min and filter thru folded paper.

Adjust *clear* filtrate to 20° and pipet 225 ml into centrf. bottle. Add Pb(OAc)₂ soln equal to x ($x + 3$ ml if saponification was made), shake vigorously ca 2 min, centrf., decant, and drain. Add 200 ml 80% alcohol, shake, centrf., decant, and drain.

Transfer Pb salts to 500 ml erlenmeyer with ca 175 ml H_2O. Add 3 ml $1N$ H_2SO_4 and heat to boiling; add 1 ml HOAc (5 + 95) and amt std tribasic Pb(OAc)₂ soln previously detd in **22.076(b)**. Boil mixt. 5 min, cool to room temp., transfer to 250 ml vol. flask with H_2O, dil. to vol., shake, and pour into 500 ml erlenmeyer. Add small handful of glass beads, cool to ca 15°, shake vigorously 5 min, and place in refrigerator 30 min. Again shake 5 min and filter thru folded paper. Sat. *clear* filtrate with H_2S, shake vigorously, and filter. Use one of the two portions for polarization and other for oxidn.

(b) *Polarization.*—Evap. 225 ml clear soln over gauze to ca 10 ml and proceed as in **22.078(b)**. °S $(31.020(a)) \times 10.2$ = mg laevo-malic acid contained in aliquot (l in formula (d)).

(c) *Oxidation.*—Evap. 225 ml clear soln at ca 10 ml to expel last traces of alcohol, dil. to ca 120 ml with H_2O, and add 10 ml 30% NaOH soln and 25 ml KMnO₄ soln. Heat to ca 80° and keep in boiling H_2O bath 30 min. Add 25 ml oxalic acid soln and 10 ml H_2SO_4 (1 + 1), stirring vigorously. Adjust to 80°, and titr. to faint pink with KMnO₄ soln. Again heat to 80° and finish titrn. ml KMnO₄ soln used $\times$ 5 = total oxidizable material (as malic acid) present in aliquot (t in formula (d)).

(d) *Calculation.*—Calc. mg inactive malic acid, X, in portion taken for analysis by following formula: $X = 4(t - 5 - l)$, where t = mg oxidizable as malic acid; l = mg laevo-malic acid; 5 = correction factor for mg nonmalic material as malic acid; and 4 = factor for reverting inactive malic acid in aliquot back to amt of inactive acid in sample taken for analysis.

22.087 Lactic Acid (*35*)—Official Final Action

Pipet 200 ml prepd soln, **22.003(c)**, into 400 ml beaker and evap. to 50 ml. Cool and transfer contents of beaker to 250 ml vol. flask with alcohol. Dil. to vol. with alcohol, shake, and filter thru folded paper. Pipet 200 ml filtrate into 400 ml beaker and evap. to ca 25 ml. Add 50 ml H_2O and again evap. to 25 ml. Transfer material to continuous extractor, Fig. 16:1, with 25 ml H_2O and proceed as in **16.030–16.031**.

Foreign Organic Acids (*36*)—Official First Action
(*Caution: See* **46.059**.)

22.088 *Apparatus*
See **19.043**.

22.089 *Reagents*

(a) *Sodium acetate soln.*—Dissolve 15 g anhyd. NaOAc in H_2O and dil. to 100 ml.

(b) *Lead acetate soln.*—Dissolve 8 g $Pb(OAc)_2$.$3H_2O$ in H_2O and dil. to 100 ml.

(c) *Std acid soln.*—Dissolve 1.5 g DL-malic acid, 0.85 g anhyd. citric acid, and 0.25 g tartaric acid in H_2O, and dil. to 100 ml.

(d) *Aniline-furfural chromogenic agent.*—See **19.044**(b)(1).

22.090 Determination

Place 10 ml single-strength juice in 50 ml capped centrf. tube, add 1 ml $1N$ HNO_3 and 25 ml alcohol, and mix. Centrf. and filter supernatant thru small cotton plug into second 50 ml capped centrf. tube. Discard material in first tube. Add 1 ml NaOAc soln and 2.5 ml $Pb(OAc)_2$ soln to second tube and mix. Centrf. and discard supernatant. Wash ppt with 25 ml portions 80% alcohol, 95% alcohol, and ether, successively mixing, centrfg, and discarding supernatant each time. Let ether evap. spontaneously ca 10 min, add 2.0 ml H_2O, and break up any lumps with narrow end of glass tube. Pass H_2S thru this tube 5 min and then pass air thru same tube 5 min to remove excess H_2S. Centrf. and decant clear supernatant into small vial. In some cases it may be necessary to transfer material to 15 ml conical centrf. tube and centrf. until clear supernatant is obtained.

Spot 20 μl liq. on $12 \times 12''$ Whatman No. 1 chromatgc paper, using two 10 μl spottings and drying each spotting with warm air jet. Also spot 20 μl std acid soln in same way. Develop paper as in **19.045**, beginning "... roll paper and connect edges slightly apart ..." except use ether-HCOOH-H_2O developing solv. (20 + 5 + 3).

After development, let paper air-dry overnight. Treat portion of air-dried paper with aniline-furfural chromogenic agent by dipping and note color of background. If not pink, steam and dry paper as in **19.045**, last par., to insure complete removal of HCOOH.

If pink, it is not necessary to treat paper with steam. If background is dark, redistill furfural and prep. new chromogenic agent. Dip paper in chromogenic agent and let spots form by air drying. Note position and intensity of spots and compare with std acid soln. Top std spot (malic acid) has intensity value of I (intense); center spot (citric acid) has intensity value of D (dense); lowest spot (tartaric acid) has intensity value of F (faint). Classify acid spots obtained from juices as VI (very intense), I, D, F, or VF (very faint). Compare with chromatograms made simultaneously from pure fruit juices.

Sucrose—Official Final Action
22.091 By Polarization

Det. by polarizing before and after inversion. *See* **31.025**, **31.026**, or **31.031**.

22.092 By Reducing Sugars Before and After Inversion

Transfer sample representing (if possible) ca 2.5 g total sugars to 200 ml vol. flask; dil. to ca 100 ml and add excess of satd neut. $Pb(OAc)_2$ soln, **31.021**(d) (ca 2 ml is usually enough). Mix, dil. to vol., and filter, discarding first few ml filtrate. Add dry K or Na oxalate to ppt excess Pb used in clarification, mix, and filter, discarding first few ml filtrate. Take 25 ml filtrate or aliquot contg (if possible) 50–200 mg reducing sugars and proceed as in **31.039–31.040**.

For inversion at room temp. transfer 50 ml aliquot clarified and deleaded soln to 100 ml vol. flask, add 10 ml HCl (1 + 1), and let stand at room temp. (20° or above) 24 hr; exactly neutze with concd NaOH soln, using phthln, and dil. to 100 ml. Take aliquot and det. total sugars as invert as in **31.039–31.040**. Calc. sucrose as in **31.032**.

22.093 Reducing Sugars—Official Final Action

Proceed as in **22.092**, par. 1. Express results as invert sugar.

22.094 Commercial Glucose—Procedure— See 31.034

Starch
22.095 Qualitative Test—Official Final Action

Dil. portion of sample with H_2O, heat nearly to boiling, add several ml H_2SO_4 (1 + 9), and then 10% $KMnO_4$ soln until all color is destroyed. Cool, and test with I soln, **30.026**(d). (Presence of starch is not necessarily indication of its addn as adulterant. It is usually present in small amt in apples and occasionally in other fruits, and unless it is found in the fruit product in considerable amt its presence may be due to these natural sources.)

Essential Oil (37)—Official First Action
22.096 Apparatus

Use app. of **19.117**, substituting 2 L flask with ₮ 24/40 joint.

22.097 Determination

Place 1 L sample in boiling flask and add few glass beads to facilitate boiling. Fill oil separatory trap with H_2O, connect with boiling flask and condenser, and boil 1 hr. Remove heat and let stand several min. Drain enough H_2O to bring oily layer within graduated portion of trap, let stand ≥ 5 min to complete drainage, and measure amt of oil from bottom of lower meniscus to highest point of upper meniscus.

Recoverable Oil (38)—Official Final Action
22.098 Principle

Oil recoverable by distn from orange, tangerine, and grapefruit juices is $\geq 98\%$ d-limonene, which, after co-distn with isopropanol, is detd after acidification by titrn with std KBr-$KBrO_3$ soln. Reaction involves release of Br *in situ* and subsequent formation of limonene tetrabromide. Oil from lemon juice contains up to 5% α-pinene and 4% citral. Since α-pinene consumes Br at same rate, and citral at ½ rate, as d-limonene, method is only slightly less accurate with lemon juice.

22.099   *Reagents*

(a) *Potassium bromide-bromate std solns.*—(1) *Stock soln.*—0.099N. Prep. and stdze as in **45.021–45.022.** (2) *Titrating soln.*—0.0247N. Dil. stock soln 1 + 3. 1 ml 0.0247N KBr-KBrO₃ = 0.0010 ml (equiv. to 0.00084 g) d-limonene. Solns are stable 6 months.

(b) *Methyl orange indicator.*—0.1% in H₂O. Use 1 drop per titrn, or add 5 ml to 1 L HCl (1 + 2).

22.100   *Apparatus*

(a) *Electric heater.*—With recessed refractory top, 500–750 watts.

(b) *Still, all-glass.*—500 ml distn flask with ℥ 24/40 neck; 200 mm Graham condenser with 28/15 receiving socket and drip tip; connecting bulb and adapter. *See* Fig. 22:4.

(c) *Buret.*—10 ml, 0.05 ml subdivisions; suitable for rapid and dropwise titrn.

22.101   *Determination*

Preheat elec. heater. Pipet 25 ml well-mixed sample into distn flask contg SiC chips or glass beads, and add 25 ml isopropanol. Distill into 150 ml beaker. Continue distn until solv. ceases to reflux, and remove flask, leaving heater on for next detn. Place short magnetic bar in beaker, and add 10 ml

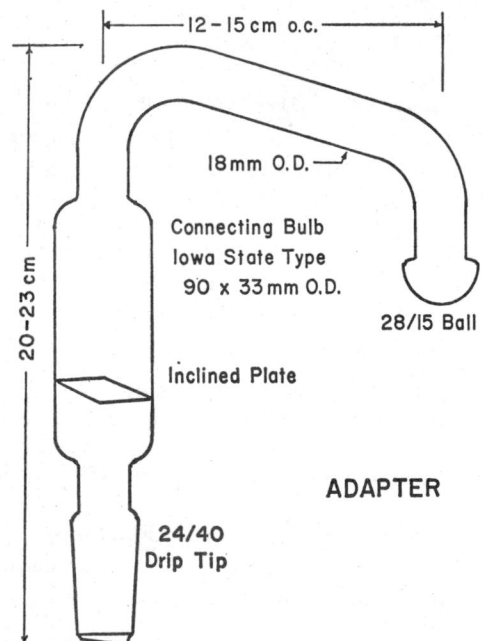

FIG. 22:4—Connecting tube adapter for direct distillation

HCl (1 + 2) and indicator. Titr. with std KBr-KBrO₃ while stirring. Major portion of titrant may be added rapidly, but end point (disappearance of color) must be approached at ca 1 drop/sec.

Det. reagent blank by titrg 3 sep. mixts of 25 ml isopropanol, 10 ml HCl (1 + 2), and indicator without refilling buret. Total ml titrant/3 = av. blank. % recoverable oil by vol. = (ml KBr-KBrO₃ soln used in titrn − ml av. blank) × 0.001 × 100/25.

Anthocyanins (39)—Official Final Action
(Applicable to grape and dark colored fruit juices. *Caution: See* **46.017.**)

22.102   *Apparatus*

(a) *Chromatographic tank or cylinder.*—To hold cylinder made from 12 × 12″ Whatman No. 1 chromatgc paper. (18 × 6″ glass cylindrical tank, with ground top and glass cover, is convenient.)

(b) *Spectrophotometer.* — Beckman Instruments Model DU, Bausch & Lomb Spectronic 20, or equiv.

22.103   *Reagents*

(a) *Lead acetate soln.*—*See* **22.089**(b).

(b) *Developing solvent.*—n-Butanol-HOAc-H₂O, 6 + 1 + 2.

(c) *Modified Forestal solvent.*—Dissolve 0.5 g oxalic acid in 60 ml H₂O, add 30 ml HCl and 150 ml HOAc, and mix.

(d) *Chromogenic spray.*—2% phosphomolybdic acid in H₂O.

(e) *Eluting solvent.*—Dissolve 0.2 g oxalic acid in 100 ml alcohol, add 0.2 ml HCl, and mix.

22.104   *Extraction of Anthocyanins*

Add 10 ml Pb(OAc)₂ soln to 10 ml single strength juice in 50 ml screw-capped centrf. tube and mix. Add 0.5 ml NH₄OH and mix. Centrf. until ppt is well packed and discard clear supernatant.(If supernatant is not clear, add more Pb(OAc)₂ soln and recentrf.) Wash ppt twice with 25 ml portions 80% alcohol, mixing well each time before centrfg; discard washings. After second wash, invert tube 5 min to drain liq. Add 10 ml n-butanol and 1 ml HCl, shake vigorously until all colored ppt has been transformed into PbCl₂, and centrf. Decant clear liq. into 125 ml separator. Wash ppt with 5 ml n-butanol, mix well, and centrf. to obtain clear upper liq. Add washings to first ext in separator. Add 100 ml pet ether to separator, shake well, and swirl to bring down colored aq. soln. (If no aq. liq. seps, add 0.5 ml H₂O, shake, and swirl.) Let liqs sep. completely and drain lower aq. layer (usually ca 2 ml) into 15 ml conical graduated centrf. tube. Add 0.2–0.5 ml portions H₂O to separator, shaking each time and draining lower layers, until total of 2.5 ml is collected. (Occasionally, 2.5 ml or more will be collected in first sepn of liqs; make no addnl H₂O extns in this case.) Mix soln and use 0.5 ml for chromatgc test for anthocyanin. Retain anthocyanin soln in refrigerator until used.

22.105   *Preparation of Anthocyanidins*

Add equal vol. 2*N* HCl to liq. in centrf. tube contg small boiling chip. Fit tube with air condenser made from glass tubing and cork. Place tube in boiling H_2O bath and heat 30 min. Remove from bath and cool in H_2O. Add 1 ml isoamyl alcohol, shake vigorously, and centrf. With glass tube drawn out to capillary tip at one end and small bulb, transfer clear, upper layer to small bottle. (Do not remove any turbid aq. liq. in tube.) Keep anthocyanidin soln in refrigerator until used.

22.106   *Chromatography*

Use 12 × 12″ Whatman No. 1 papers for tests (a) and (b). Papers require overnight development; prep. in late afternoon to permit 16 hr development.

(a) *Qualitative anthocyanin ascending paper chromatography.*—(Definitive for fruit juices other than grape juice; not definitive for grape juice where pattern is extremely complicated, but may be useful as guide.) Prep. streaks of soln, **22.104**, 1″ above bottom of paper and ca 1″ apart. Make streaks 1.25″ long and ⅛–¼″ wide, using capillary mp tube 1 mm id, open at both ends, and drawn out to ca ½ diam. at one end. Concord grape juice requires 5–7 applications to obtain satisfactory intensity; other juices usually require more; some may require fewer. Make 2 sep. streakings from same soln, using different intensities, one of which may yield better chromatgc pattern. Dry between each application with cold air blast only. After streakings are completed, dry streaks, and make cylinder of paper by sewing ends with cotton, leaving ca 0.5″ space between ends. (Do not use metal clips to make cylinder.) Place developing solv., (b), to ca 0.5″ depth in tank and place cylinder in tank. Let develop overnight at room temp., remove paper, and air dry.

Simultaneously test authentic fruit juice anthocyanins and compare patterns. Note differences in daylight and under longwave UV light. Spray with phosphomolybdic acid soln and observe changes in pattern. Foreign natural coloring material is indicated by significant differences from authentic pattern.

(b) *Quantitative anthocyanidin ascending paper chromatography.*—(Definitive for grape juice but optional for other fruit juices.) Pipet 0.10 ml anthocyanidin soln, **22.105**, into small flask, add 10.0 ml eluting solv., and mix. Read *A* at 545 nm in 1 cm cell. Calc. vol. anthocyanidin soln to give *A* of 0.400 under these conditions; use this vol. for transfer to chromatgc paper.

Place calcd vol. anthocyanidin soln in small test tube. Using capillary tube, make successive applications on paper, each about 1.25″ long and ³⁄₁₆″ wide. Keep different sample streaks ca 1″ apart. Dry each application with cold air blast before applying next streak. Prep. streaked paper as in (a).

Develop overnight (16 hr) at room temp., using Forestal solv. Air-dry and examine under longwave UV light. (3 distinct orange to red spots should be present. For juices other than grape, compare pattern with authentic pattern. If no differences in intensities of the 3 spots are noted, it is not necessary to make quant. measurements of the anthocyanidin colors.) Alternatively, measure intensity of colors in spots with densitometer, using green filter. (Expose paper to HCl fumes few min before using densitometer.)

Elute colors and measure in spectrophtr as follows: Outline top spot and bottom 2 spots with soft pencil under longwave UV light. Cut out top spot, and cut it into several small pieces before transferring to screw-capped test tube or small g-s erlenmeyer. Cut out each of 2 lower spots, starting ca ¼″ above origin line for lowest spot. Combine these 2 spots for grape juice, but keep sep. for other juices. Cut strips into several smaller pieces and place in test tube(s) or flask(s). Pipet 10 ml eluting solv., (e), into each tube or flask, and agitate 1 hr. (Rotating device can be used with test tubes and agitator with flasks. In absence of agitating device, let eluting soln remain in contact with paper 3 hr in dark, with occasional swirling.) Centrf. alc. exts in 15 ml conical centrf. tube and decant clear, upper liq. for color measurements. Cover cuvets while reading to avoid loss. Read *A* at 445, 545, and 645 nm. Correct 545 nm (max.) readings for background error by subtracting ½ algebraic sum of 445 and 645 nm readings.

Designate the 3 spots as S1 (lowest), S2 (central), and S3 (top) spots. Calc. % color in each spot of total color (S1 + S2 + S3), using corresponding corrected *A*. Significant differences from authentic % indicate presence of foreign coloring.

Concord anthocyanidins show deeply colored S1 and S2 spots while S3 spot is faint. Significant increase in S3 color % indicates addn of other grape juice to Concord. Use qual. anthocyanin chromatograms to confirm presence of non-Concord grape juice.

Malvidin Glucosides (*40*)—Official First Action

22.107   *Principle*

Anthocyanin components are sepd by paper chromatgy, pigments are converted to oxychlorides with HCl vapor, and chromatogram is scanned for presence of malvidin mono- or diglucosides, which are present in minimal concns in Concord grape juice.

22.108   *Reagent*

Citric acid soln.—0.1*M* (MacIlvaine's buffer soln B). Dissolve 45 g citric acid.H_2O and dil. to 2 L with H_2O. Titr. 10 ml with 0.1*N* NaOH, **45.035–45.036**, using phthln. Adjust with H_2O or citric acid to require 30.00 ml 0.1*N* NaOH in repeat titrn.

22.109   *Apparatus*

(a) *Densitometer.*—Beckman Instruments Analytrol Model RB, 550 nm interference filter, or equiv.

(b) *Spectrophotometer.* — Beckman Instruments Model B, or equiv.

(c) *Melting point capillary tubes.*—1.5–2.0 × 100 mm. Heat and draw out to form application tubes, 1 mm id, open at both ends, and drawn out to ca ½ diam. at one end. Diam. should be such that streak 3 mm wide is deposited.

22.110   *Preparation of Sample*

Mix 5 ml grape juice sample with 5 ml MeOH. Filter thru glass wool.

Det. streaking vol. so amt of pigment in each streak is comparable. Mix sep. 1 ml Concord grape juice std and 1 ml of each sample filtrate with 25 ml citric acid buffer. Det. A at 525 nm with spectrophtr.

Calc. vol. of filtrate to be streaked:

Vol. = (A Concord grape juice std × 0.6 ml)/A sample.

0.6 ml Concord grape juice std with $A = 0.54$ gives optimum sepn and color intensity of bands.

Acidify filtrates with 4 drops HCl/5 ml filtrate. Transfer samples to small capped vials to prevent evapn of MeOH.

22.111   *Chromatography*

Draw line 1.5″ from bottom of paper, 46 × 57 cm, Whatman grade 3MM or equiv., along length of paper to locate five 3″ streaks. Apply filtrates 8–12 times with application tubes to form 3″ streaks, 3 mm wide. Let dry between applications. Apply one streak of Concord grape juice std and others of samples. Dry thoroly and acidify by exposing both sides of paper to HCl vapor.

Form streaked paper lengthwise into cylinder and staple both ends, making sure edges of paper do not touch. Fasten 2–3 addnl staples by hand thru holes made with needle.

Add 250 ml H_2O to cylindrical chromatgy jar, Pyrex or equiv., 10⅛″ diam., 18″ high. Carefully lower paper cylinder into jar (cylinder should not touch sides of jar), cover jar with plastic bag, 12 × 6 × 24″, Kordite Turkey Bag or equiv., and seal bag with masking tape. Remove bag when H_2O has risen to top of cylinder. Fold filter paper (46 × 57 cm Whatman grade 3MM or equiv.) lengthwise, cut semi-circle at folded edge with diam. ca that of cylindrical chromatogram, open, and place as collar around paper cylinder, resting on top edge of jar. Place cardboard over exposed top edge of cylinder which is just above top of jar and continue developing 10 hr. Pigments should be resolved into well-defined bands. Air-dry at room temp. Expose both sides of chromatogram to HCl vapor to convert pigments to red oxychlorides.

22.112   *Determination*

Cut 1½″ strip from center of each streak, mark origin and point 10″ from origin, and use second mark to position strip in densitometer with 550 nm filter. Obtain densitometer traces and compare std with samples.

Pigments sep. by classes. Sequence of classes from origin is: acylated monoglycosides, monoglycosides, acylated diglycosides, diglycosides, sugars, and more H_2O-sol. compds. Within classes from origin are: delphinidin, petunidin, cyanidin, peonidin, and malvidin. Malvidin compds, very intense purple or violet, travel at front edge of each class.

Concord grape juice contains min. concns of malvidin mono- and diglucosides while California red grape concs and Italian grape juice color (Enocianina) contain relatively high concns of malvidin mono- or diglucoside. Comparison of malvidin peak of Concord control with malvidin peak of sample will indicate presence of malvidin-contg products (JAOAC **50**, 299(1967); *J. Agr. Food Chem.* **11**, 263(1963)).

LEMON JUICE *(41)*— OFFICIAL FIRST ACTION

22.113   Preparation of Sample

Mix ca 5–6 g Celite analytical filter aid with 175 ml lemon juice (ca 80–100 milliequiv. acid/100 ml juice). Filter with suction (if not completely clear, refilter thru fresh Celite pad) and store in g-s flask.

22.114   Total Amino Acids

Pipet 25 ml prepd sample into 150 ml beaker. (If sample is suspected of contg SO_2, boil exactly 1 min and cool.) Add NaOH (1 + 1) dropwise to pH 6–7. Titr. potentiometrically with 0.1N NaOH to pH 8.4. Add 10 ml neutzd 37% HCHO (titrd potentiometrically with 0.1N NaOH to pH 8.4 ≤1 hr before use) and titr. resulting acidity back to pH 8.4 with 0.1N NaOH. Total amino acids (milliequiv./100 ml juice) = 0.4 × ml 0.1N NaOH for second titrn.

22.115   Total Polyphenolics

(a) *Calibration of spectrophotometer.*—Accurately weigh two 1.4–1.5 g portions KNO_3. Transfer to 250 ml vol. flasks, dissolve in H_2O, and dil. to vol. Zero instrument at 302 nm and measure A of each soln, in 1 cm cell. Calc. std A for each soln, $A' = a$ × molarity KNO_3 = (6.99 × g KNO_3)/(101.11 × 0.25) = 0.2765 × g KNO_3. Divide av. A' by av. measured A at 302 nm to obtain correction factor.

(b) *Determination.*—Pipet 0.5 ml prepd sample into 10 ml vol. flask, and dil. to vol. with alcohol. Transfer to centrf. tube, cover with Al foil to prevent evapn, and centrf. Measure UV spectrum of supernatant with recording spectrophtr from 300–400 nm or with manual spectrophtr at 2 nm intervals from 325–335 nm. Multiply A of 325–335 nm peak by correction factor, (a), and report as A of total polyphenolics.

l-Malic Acid (42)

22.116   Standard Rotation for l-Malic Acid

Accurately weigh ca 15, 25, 35 mg l-malic acid (Calbiochem) into 25 ml vol. flasks. Add ca 0.4 g citric acid to each flask. Dissolve in 5 ml H_2O, add 1 drop phthln, and neutze with NaOH (1 + 1). Add HOAc until phthln color disappears and 2 drops excess. Dil. to vol. with H_2O. Measure initial optical rotation (α_1) of each std soln. (Exercise great care in measuring optical rotation, since small uncertainty in measurement will cause large error in final result.) Sat. 10 ml of each std soln with 1.3 g uranyl acetate .$2H_2O$. Keep in dark 30 min with occasional shaking. (Exposure of uranyl complex to strong light causes it to become insol.; therefore conduct operations in semidarkness.) Filter off excess uranyl acetate and measure optical rotation (α_u) within 5 min after filtering. Calc. std rotation (R_{std}) for each soln as follows:

$$C_{malic} = (\text{mg malic acid}/67.04) \times 4$$
$$= \text{milliequiv. malic acid}/100 \text{ ml}$$
$$\Delta\alpha = \alpha_1 - \alpha_u$$
$$R_{std} = C_{malic}/\Delta\alpha$$

Use av. std rotation for subsequent calcns.

22.117   Determination

In graduated cylinder mix 15 ml sample, 22.113, with 45 ml alcohol and let stand 10 min. Centrf. pectin ppt. Evap. alc. juice to thick sirup (ca 1–2 ml) in rotary vac. evaporator ($\leq 50°$). Add 13–14 ml H_2O to sirup and mix thoroly. Pipet 2 ml pectin-free sample into 100 ml beaker, and add 25 ml H_2O. Titr. potentiometrically to pH 8.4 with stdzd 0.1N NaOH. Acidity (milliequiv./100 ml pectin-free sample) = 5 × (ml alkali).

Pipet 10 ml pectin-free sample into 25 ml vol. flask, add 1 drop phthln, and proceed as in detn of std rotation. l-Malic acid concn in dild, neutzd sample, $[MA]_D = R_{std} \times (\alpha_1 - \alpha_u)$. Calc. citric acid:malic acid ratio by dividing 0.4 times acidity of pectin-free sample by $[MA]_D$.

SELECTED REFERENCES

(1) JAOAC 17, 66(1934).

(2) JAOAC 36, 860(1953); 38, 609(1955).

(3) JAOAC 36, 270(1953); 37, 309(1954); 38, 611 (1955).

(4) JAOAC 36, 270(1953); 37, 309(1954); 38, 611 (1955); 47, 902(1964).

(5) JAOAC 42, 411(1959); 50, 288(1967).

(6) JAOAC 17, 215(1934); 18, 80(1935).

(7) JAOAC 6, 34(1922); 21, 504(1938); 30, 260 (1947); 32, 177(1949); 33, 349(1950).

(8) JAOAC 32, 179(1949); 33, 349(1950).

(9) JAOAC 15, 384(1932).

(10) JAOAC 23, 314(1940).

(11) JAOAC 12, 366(1929); 24, 391, 455(1941); 25, 91, 232, 429, 433(1942); 26, 324(1943); 27, 89 (1944); Ind. Eng. Chem., Anal. Ed. 9, 136 (1937).

(12) JAOAC 48, 521(1965).

(13) JAOAC 49, 221, 617(1966).

(14) JAOAC 14, 466(1931).

(15) JAOAC 12, 366(1929); 14, 466(1931).

(16) JAOAC 14, 473(1931).

(17) JAOAC 25, 441(1942); 27, 88(1944).

(18) Ind. Eng. Chem., Anal. Ed. 7, 116, 227(1935); JAOAC 22, 131, 167(1939); 23, 321(1940); 24, 393(1941); 25, 443(1942).

(19) JAOAC 52, 865(1969); 53, 575(1970).

(20) JAOAC 8, 125(1924).

(21) JAOAC 8, 126(1924).

(22) JAOAC 11, 216(1928); 26, 437(1943).

(23) JAOAC 8, 127(1924); 21, 505(1938).

(24) JAOAC 8, 129(1924); 21, 502(1938); 35, 872 (1952).

(25) J. Sci. Food Agr. 17, 316(1966); JAOAC 53, 568(1970).

(26) JAOAC 25, 412(1942); 28, 507(1945).

(27) Bull. soc. chim. 7, 567(1910); 11, 886(1912); JAOAC 8, 638(1925); 13, 103(1930); 36, 266 (1953).

(28) JAOAC 26, 444(1943); 34, 445(1951).

(29) JAOAC 37, 305(1954).

(30) Anal. Chem. 23, 467(1951); JAOAC 40, 333 (1957).

(31) JAOAC 15, 648(1932); 17, 214(1934); 18, 198 (1935).

(32) JAOAC 36, 268(1953).

(33) JAOAC 51, 934(1968); 52, 1153(1969).

(34) JAOAC 16, 281(1933).

(35) JAOAC 20, 605(1937); 26, 199(1943).

(36) JAOAC 52, 646(1969).

(37) JAOAC 27, 201(1944).

(38) JAOAC 49, 628(1966); 51, 928(1968).

(39) JAOAC 50, 293(1967); 51, 464, 937(1968); 52, 649(1969).

(40) JAOAC 51, 931(1968).

(41) JAOAC 46, 353, 359(1963); 48, 530(1965); 51, 464(1968).

(42) JAOAC 46, 353(1963); 48, 530(1965); 49, 221, 621(1966).

23. Gelatin, Dessert Preparations, and Mixes

GELATIN

23.001   Preparation of Sample—Procedure

Mix ground gelatin thoroly. Break sheet gelatin into small pieces by hand. Further comminution is unnecessary in either case.

23.002   Moisture—Official Final Action

Proceed as in **14.003**, using 2 g sample prepd as in **23.001**.

23.003   Ash—Official Final Action—*See* 31.012 or 31.013

23.004   Total Phosphorus— Official Final Action

(*Caution: See* **46.011** and **46.026**.)

Treat ash, **23.003**, with 2–3 ml HNO$_3$ and evap. to dryness on steam bath. Repeat HNO$_3$ treatment and evapn, take up residue in hot H$_2$O contg few drops HNO$_3$, and proceed as in **8.027**.

23.005   Nitrogen—Official Final Action

Proceed as in **2.051**, using 1 g sample. To convert to ash-free, anhyd. gelatin multiply by factor 5.55 (USDA Circ. **183**, August 1931).

23.006   Jelly Strength (*1*)— Official Final Action

(*Note:* Check shot hopper on Bloom Gelometer to assure it is grounded electrically.)

Pipet 105 ml H$_2$O at 10–15° into std Bloom bottle, add 7.5 g sample, and stir. Let stand 1 hr and then bring to 62° in 15 min by placing in H$_2$O bath regulated at 65° (sample may be swirled several times to aid soln). Finally mix by inversion, let stand 15 min, and place in H$_2$O bath at 10±0.1°. Chill 17 hr. Det. jelly strength in Bloom Gelometer (Ind. Eng. Chem., Anal. Ed. **2**, 348(1930)), adjusted for 4 mm depression and to deliver 200±5 g shot/5 sec, using 0.5″ plunger, Fig. 23:1.

GELATIN DESSERT POWDERS

23.007   Preparation of Sample—Procedure

Sift sample thru No. 30 sieve onto large sheet of paper, rubbing material thru sieve and tapping vigorously, if necessary. Sift sample 2 more times, mixing thoroly each time. To avoid absorption of moisture, operate as rapidly as possible, and store sample in air-tight container.

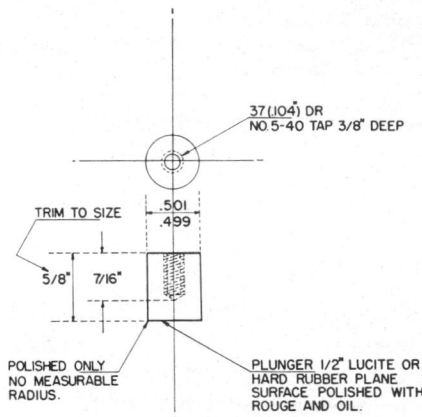

FIG. 23:1—0.5 Inch Bloom Gelometer plunger

23.008   Moisture—Official Final Action

Proceed as in **31.005**, using 2 g sample prepd as in **23.007**.

23.009   Ash—Official Final Action— *See* 31.012 or 31.013

23.010   Nitrogen—Official Final Action— *See* 23.005

23.011   Total Acidity—Official Final Action

Dissolve 20 g sample in 2 L recently boiled H$_2$O. Titr. 100 ml with 0.1N NaOH, using 0.3 ml phthln. Report as % by wt citric acid.

23.012   Jelly Strength—Official Final Action

(*Note:* Check shot hopper on Bloom Gelometer to assure it is grounded electrically.)

To 20 g sample in std Bloom bottle, add from pipet, with stirring, 100 ml H$_2$O at 10–15°. Let stand 15 min and then bring to 62° in 15 min in H$_2$O bath regulated at 65° (sample may be swirled several times to aid soln). Mix by inversion, let stand 15 min, place in H$_2$O bath controlled at 10±0.1°, and let stand 17 hr. Det. jelly strength in Bloom Gelometer (Ind. Eng. Chem., Anal. Ed. **2**, 348(1930)), adjusted for 4 mm depression and to deliver 200±5 g shot/5 sec, using 1.0″ plunger, Fig. 23:2, and light wt shot receiver (paper or plastic).

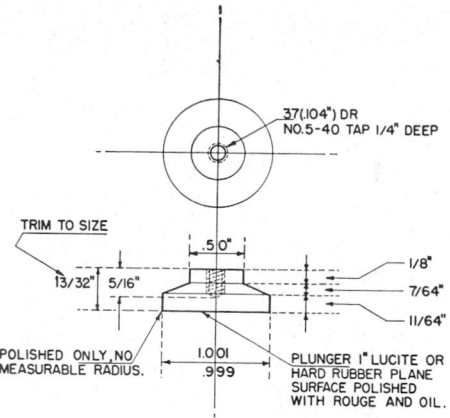

37(.104") DR
NO.5-40 TAP 1/4" DEEP

TRIM TO SIZE

.5|0"

13/32" 5/16"

1/8"
7/64"
11/64"

POLISHED ONLY, NO
MEASURABLE RADIUS.

1.0|01
.9|99

PLUNGER 1" LUCITE OR
HARD RUBBER PLANE
SURFACE POLISHED
WITH ROUGE AND OIL.

FIG. 23:2—1.0 Inch Bloom Gelometer plunger

Sucrose (2)—Official Final Action

23.013 *Reagents*

(a) *Tannin soln.*—Dissolve 5 g tannin in 100 ml cold H_2O.

(b) *Lead acetate soln.*—Dissolve 100 g $Pb(OAc)_2.3H_2O$ in 200 ml H_2O. (This makes 30° Bé. soln.)

23.014 *Determination*

Place 13 g sample in 300 or 400 ml beaker, add 2 g $CaCO_3$ and 2 g Filter-Cel, and mix well with glass rod. Add 175 ml boiling H_2O, creaming mixt. with little of the H_2O at first. Stir thoroly and let stand few min to ensure soln. Cool under cold H_2O to 30°, slowly add 25 ml tannin soln with stirring, and let stand 5 min. (This quantity tanning soln is enough for most powders; if 30 ml is required, use 170 ml H_2O instead of 175 ml.) Slowly add 10 ml $Pb(OAc)_2$ soln with stirring, and filter on 18.5 cm Whatman No. 2 paper. (Total quantity of liq. used in each case is 210 ml, which yields 200 ml after evapn and concn. If pptn has been conducted properly, soln will filter readily and filtrate will be clear.) Read optical rotation of this soln in 200 mm tube at 20°.

If sample contains reducing sugar, delead with $K_2C_2O_4$, add Filter-Cel, and filter. Invert by placing 50 ml filtrate in 100 ml vol. flask with 5 ml HCl and letting stand overnight. After inversion, neutze with concd NaOH soln, using phthln. Discharge color of indicator with $0.1N$ HCl. Cool to 20°, dil. to vol., and read optical rotation in 200 mm tube. Use fol-lowing Clerget formula modified for % sucrose in gelatin dessert powders:

$$S = \frac{100(4P - 8I)}{142.66 + 0.0676(m - 13) - t/2},$$

where S = % sucrose; P = direct reading; I = invert reading; t = temp. at which readings are made (20°); and m = g total solids from original sample/ 100 ml invert soln (3.25 g). Simplified:

$$S = 100(4P - 8I)/132.$$

23.015 Glucose—Official Final Action

Det. polarization due to glucose (D) by subtracting % sucrose (S) as found in **23.014** from direct reading of polariscope in circular degrees (P) multiplied by 4: $D = 4P - S$.

Calc. % glucose (D') from following formula:

$$D' = D \times 66.5/52.5 = 1.267D,$$

where D = polarization due to glucose; 66.5 = specific rotation of sucrose; and 52.5 = specific rotation of glucose.

STARCH DESSERT POWDERS

23.016 Preparation of Sample—Procedure— See 23.007

23.017 Moisture—Official Final Action

Proceed as in **31.005** or **31.006**, using 2 g prepd sample, **23.007.**

23.018 Ash—Official Final Action— See 31.012 or 31.013

23.019 Nitrogen—Official Final Action

Proceed as in **2.051**, using 1 g sample. To convert to protein multiply by factor 6.25.

23.020 Sucrose and Glucose—Official Final Action—See 23.014 and 23.015

23.021 Starch—Official Final Action

(a) *By direct acid hydrolysis.*—See **8.017.**

(b) *Polarimetric method.*—See **14.032.**

SELECTED REFERENCES

(1) JAOAC 31, 511(1948).

(2) Annual Report Dept. Farms and Markets, New York, 1926, Legislative Document No. 15, p. 78 (1927).

24. Meat and Meat Products

MEAT

24.001 Preparation of Sample—Procedure

To prevent H_2O loss during prepn and subsequent handling do not use small samples. Keep ground material in glass or similar containers with air- and H_2O-tight covers. Prep. samples for analysis in following manner:

(a) *Fresh meats, dried meats, cured meats, smoked meats, etc.*—Sep. as completely as possible from any bone; pass rapidly 3 times thru food chopper with plate openings $\leq \frac{1}{8}''$, mixing thoroly after each grinding; and begin all detns promptly. If any delay occurs, chill sample to inhibit decomposition.

(b) *Canned meats.*—Pass entire contents of can thru food chopper, as in (a).

(c) *Sausages.*—Remove from casings and pass thru food chopper, as in (a).

Dry portions of samples of (a), (b), and (c) not needed for immediate analysis, either *in vacuo* $<60°$ or by evapg on steam bath 2 or 3 times with alcohol. Ext fat from dried product with pet ether (bp $<60°$) and let pet ether evap. spontaneously, finally expelling last traces by heating short time on steam bath. Do not heat sample or sepd fat longer than necessary because of tendency to decompose. Reserve fat in cool place for examination as in Chap. **28,** and complete examination before it becomes rancid.

Moisture

24.002 *Drying in Vacuo at 95–100°—Official Final Action*

Proceed as in **7.003.** (Not suitable for high fat products such as pork sausage.)

24.003 *Air Drying (1)—Official First Action*

(a) Dry, with lids removed, sample representing ca 2 g dry material 16–18 hr at 100–102° in air oven (mech. convection preferred). Use covered Al dish ≥ 50 mm diam. and ≤ 40 mm deep. Cool in desiccator and weigh. Report loss in wt as moisture.

(b) Dry, with lids removed, sample representing ca 2 g dry material to constant wt (2–4 hr depending on product) in mech. convection oven at ca 125°. Use covered Al dish ≥ 50 mm diam. and ≤ 40 mm deep. Avoid excessive drying. Cover, cool in desiccator, and weigh. Report loss in wt as moisture.

(*Note:* Dried sample is not satisfactory for subsequent fat detn.)

24.004 Added Water in Sausage (2)— Procedure

Per cent H_2O added $= (W - 4P)/(1 - 0.01W + 0.04P)$; where $W = \%$ H_2O, and P (% protein) $= 6.25 \times \%N$, **24.010** (corrected if necessary for protein in added substances such as nonfat dry milk, cereal, soybean flour).

24.005 Crude Fat or Ether Extract— Official Final Action

(a) Weigh 3–4 g sample by difference into thimble contg small amt of sand or asbestos. Mix with glass rod, place thimble and rod in 50 ml beaker, and dry in oven 6 hr at 100–102° or 1.5 hr at 125°. Proceed as in **7.048.** Pet ether, **10.114,** may be used instead of anhyd. ether, if desired.

(b) Weigh 3–4 g sample by difference into small disposable Al dish, add sand or asbestos, and mix, spreading mixt. on bottom of dish with glass or Al paddle. Dry with paddle as in (a). Roll edges of dish and insert with paddle into thimble. Proceed as in **7.048.** Pet ether, **10.114,** may be used in place of anhyd. ether, if desired.

24.006 Ash—Official Final Action— *See 31.012 or 31.013*

24.007 Salt—Official First Action

Moisten 2.5–3 g sample in 300 ml flask with excess $0.5N$ $AgNO_3$ soln, **45.028** (5 ml or more, depending on NaCl content of sample). Add 15 ml HNO_3 and boil until meat dissolves (10 min usually enough). Add concd aq. $KMnO_4$ soln in small portions, boiling after each addn until $KMnO_4$ color disappears and soln becomes colorless or nearly so. Add 25 ml H_2O and boil 5 min. Cool, dil. to ca 150 ml, add 25 ml ether, and shake. Det. Cl as in **18.015.**

24.008 Total Phosphorus Method I—Official Final Action

Destroy org. matter as in **2.017**(c) or (d), and proceed as in **2.031** or **8.027.**

24.009 *Method II (3)—Official First Action*

Weigh, to nearest mg, 2.5±0.1 g sample (prepd as in **24.001**) into ashing dish (Pt, Vycor, or other suitable material) and dry 30 min at 125° in forced-draft oven. Ash in furnace at 550° to whiteness or near whiteness. Cool, add 25 ml HNO_3 (1 + 4), and heat on steam bath ca 30 min. Filter quant. into 400 ml beaker, using H_2O in transfer. Adjust vol. to ca 100 ml and proceed as in **2.025(b)**.

24.010 Nitrogen (4)—Official Final Action

Proceed as in **2.051**, using ca 2 g fresh sample and 40 ml H_2SO_4 for digestion.

Nitrates and Nitrites
Xylenol Method (5)—Official First Action
24.011   Apparatus

Use simple distn app., including distn bulb. Type of glass condenser utilizing thin, rapidly moving H_2O film as cooling medium (West type) is recommended. Quickly remove any nitroxylenol solidifying in condenser by stopping H_2O flow and letting condenser become warm.

24.012   Reagents

(a) *m-Xylenol.* — 1-Hydroxy-2,4-dimethylbenzene. Eastman Kodak Co. No. 1150, or equiv.

(b) *Silver ammonium hydroxide soln.*—Dissolve 5 g nitrate-free Ag_2SO_4 in 60 ml NH_4OH. Heat to boiling, conc. to ca 30 ml, cool, and dil. to 100 ml with H_2O.

(c) *Bromocresol green indicator.*—Dissolve 0.1 g bromocresol green in 1.5 ml 0.1N NaOH, and dil. to 100 ml with H_2O.

(d) *Nitrate std soln.*—Dissolve 0.1805 g recrystd KNO_3 in H_2O and dil. to 1 L, or dil. 17.85 ml 0.1N HNO_3 to 1 L; 10 ml contains 0.25 mg nitrate N.

24.013   Determination

Mix 5–10 g finely comminuted and thoroly mixed sample with 80 ml warm H_2O. Break up all lumps and heat on steam bath 1 hr, stirring occasionally. Transfer to 100 ml vol. flask, cool, dil. to vol., and mix. Filter, or let settle, and pipet 40 ml filtrate, or supernatant, into 50 ml vol. flask. (No correction for vol. occupied by meat is necessary.) Add 3 drops bromocresol green indicator. Add H_2SO_4 (1 + 10) dropwise until color changes to yellow. Oxidize nitrites to nitrates by adding 0.2N $KMnO_4$ soln dropwise with shaking until faint pink remains ca 1 min. Add 1 ml H_2SO_4 (1 + 10) and 1 ml *phosphotungstic acid soln* (20 g/100 ml). Dil. to vol., mix, and filter.

Measure into 500 ml flask (erlenmeyer is satisfactory) aliquot (≤20 ml) contg 0.025–0.25 mg nitrate N. (If >20 ml is required, make slightly alk. and conc. by evapn.) Add enough Ag-NH_4OH soln to ppt all chlorides and most of excess phosphotungstic acid. (Slight excess of Ag reagent is not harmful; 1 or 2 ml is usually enough.) Without decanting or filtering, add vol. H_2SO_4 (3 + 1) ca 3 times vol. liq. in flask. Stopper flask, mix, cool to ca 35°, add 0.05 ml (1–2 drops) of the *m*-xylenol, stopper, shake, and hold 30 min at 30–40°.

(Yellow to brownish yellow color, indicative of nitrates, appears. Bright red ppt, due to incomplete removal of phosphotungstic acid, may also appear. Slight excess of phosphotungstic acid causes no interference but large excess may do so.)

After nitration is complete, add 150 ml H_2O, taking care to wash off stopper, and distill 40–50 ml into receiver contg 5 ml NaOH (10 g/L). Transfer distillate to 100 ml vol. flask, dil. to vol. with H_2O, and det. nitrate N by comparing reading of color of suitable aliquot with std curve.

Prep. color std from 10 ml nitrate std soln, using 0.05 ml *m*-xylenol and 30 ml H_2SO_4 (3 + 1), and dilg distillate to 500 ml.

Nitrites (6)—Official First Action
(Applicable to cured meats)
24.014   Reagents
(*Caution: See* **46.084.**)

(a) *Modified Griess reagent.*—Dissolve 0.5 g sulfanilic acid in 150 ml 15% (v/v.) HOAc. Boil 0.1 g α-naphthylamine or 0.125 g of the hydrochloride in 20 ml H_2O until dissolved and pour while hot into 150 ml 15% HOAc. Mix the 2 solns, filter if necessary, and store in brown glass bottle.

(b) *Nitrite std soln.*—0.1 μg N/ml. Dissolve 1.1 g $AgNO_2$, **14.037(c)**, in nitrite-free H_2O, ppt Ag with NaCl soln, dil. to 1 L, mix, and let settle. Dil. 100 ml to 1 L, and then 10 ml of this soln to 1 L, using nitrite-free H_2O in each case.

24.015   Determination
(*Caution: See* **46.079.**)

Weigh 5 g finely comminuted and thoroly mixed sample into 50 ml beaker. Add ca 40 ml nitrite-free H_2O heated to 80°. Mix thoroly with glass rod, taking care to break up all lumps, and transfer to 500 ml vol. flask. Thoroly wash beaker and rod with successive portions of the hot H_2O, adding all washings to flask. Add enough hot H_2O to bring vol. to ca 300 ml, transfer flask to steam bath, and let stand 2 hr, shaking occasionally. Add 5 ml *satd* $HgCl_2$ *soln* and mix. Cool to room temp., dil. to vol. with nitrite-free H_2O, and mix again. Filter, dil. suitable aliquot to vol. in 50 ml. vol. flask, add 2 ml reagent, mix, and let color develop 1 hr. Transfer suitable portion of soln to photometer cell and det. A at 520 nm, setting instrument to zero A with blank of 50 ml H_2O plus 2 ml reagent.

Det. nitrite present by comparison with std curve prepd as follows: Dil. suitable vols std nitrite soln to vol. in 50 ml vol. flasks, add 2 ml reagent, and proceed as above. Std curve is straight line to 5 μg N in final soln.

Creatine—Official Final Action
24.016   Preparation of Solution

Exhaust 7–25 g sample (depending upon H_2O content) as follows: Weigh into 150 ml beaker, add 5–10 ml cold (15°) NH_3-free H_2O, and stir to homogeneous paste. Add 50 ml cold H_2O, stir at 3 min intervals during 15 min, let stand 2–3 min, and decant liq. thru quant. filter, collecting filtrate in 500 ml vol. flask. Drain beaker, pressing out liq. from meat residue with glass rod. Add 50 ml cold H_2O to residue in beaker, stir 5 min, let stand 2–3 min, and decant as before. If much meat is transferred to filter, return it to beaker with glass rod. Repeat extns, using two 50 ml portions and four 25 ml portions cold H_2O. After last extn transfer entire insol. portion to filter and wash with three 10 ml portions H_2O, letting material drain thoroly after each addn. Dil. to vol. and mix thoroly.

Measure 150 ml ext into 250 ml beaker and evap. to 40 ml on steam bath, stirring occasionally. Neutze to phthln, using indicator outside the soln. Add 1 ml $0.1N$ HOAc and boil gently 5 min. (Coagulum should sep. at once, leaving clear liq.) Filter thru quant. paper, wash beaker thoroly 4 times with hot H_2O, wash coagulum on filter 3 times, and discard coagulum.

24.017   *Determination*
(*Caution:* See **46.029** and **46.068**.)

Evap. filtrate and washings, **24.016**, to 5–10 ml, transfer with min. quantity hot H_2O to 50 ml vol. flask, keeping vol. < 30 ml, add 10 ml $2N$ HCl, and mix. Hydrolyze 20 min in autoclave at 117–120°, let flask cool somewhat, and chill under running H_2O. Partially neutze excess acid by adding 7.5 ml 10% NaOH soln (CO_3-free), dil. to vol., and mix.

Make preliminary reading after carrying thru reaction on 20 ml with Duboscq colorimeter to det. vol. needed to obtain reading of ca 8 mm. Transfer such vol. to 500 ml vol. flask and add 10 ml 10% NaOH soln and 30 ml satd (*1.2%*) *picric acid soln*. Mix, rotate 30 sec, and let stand exactly 4.5 min. Dil. to vol. at once with H_2O, shake thoroly, and compare, preferably in Duboscq colorimeter, with std soln prepd by treating with NaOH and picric acid, and dilg to 500 ml as above, 50 ml of soln contg 1.603 g *creatinine Zn chloride* in 1 L $0.1N$ HCl (1 ml = 0.001 g creatinine; g creatinine $\times$ 1.16 = g creatine).

Amino Nitrogen
Van Slyke Method (7)—Official First Action
24.018   *Apparatus*

Use app. shown in Figs. 24:1 and 24:2, former illustrating manner in which entire app. is arranged and latter showing details of deaminizing bulb and connections. Hempel gas pipet is filled with soln contg 50 g $KMnO_4$ and 25 g KOH/L.

24.019   *Determination*

Fill, with H_2O, buret (*F*), capillary tube leading to Hempel pipet, and other capillary as far as *c*. Introduce into *A* enough HOAc to fill $\frac{1}{5}$ of *D*, etching tube *A* with mark to measure this quantity. Let acid run into *D*, and turn cock *c* to let air escape from *D*.

Pour $NaNO_2$ soln (300 g/L) into *A* until *D* is filled and enough excess is present to rise little above cock into *A*. *A* is also marked for measuring off this quantity. Close gas exit from *D* at *c*, and with *a* open, shake *D* few sec until liq. is forced down to 20 ml mark in *D*. Close *a*, open *c*, and shake app. rapidly with motor 2 min. (These operations expel all air from *D*.) Turn *c* and *f* so that *D* and *F* are connected.

Measure in *B* 10 ml or less, as case may be, of sample soln contg ≤ 20 mg amino N (1–2 g sample in case of meat exts) and let it run into *D*. Connect *D* with motor as in Fig. 24:1 and shake 5 min.

If sample soln is viscous and threatens to foam over, rinse out *B*, and thru it introduce little *capryl alcohol* into *D*, or if it is known beforehand that sample will cause excessive foaming, introduce little capryl alcohol into *D* thru *B*, rinsing *B* with alcohol and ether or drying with roll of filter paper before adding sample soln.

During shaking, N mixed with NO is evolved, gases being collected in *F*. Force all gas in *D* into *F*,

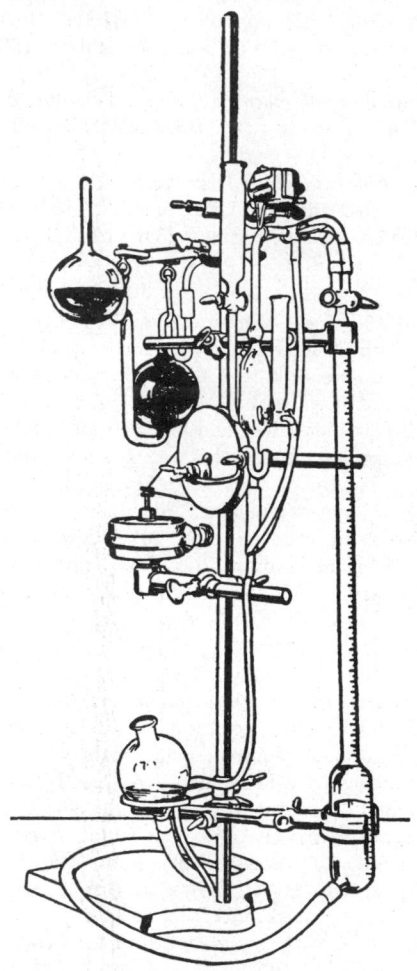

FIG. 24:1—Van Slyke apparatus for determining amino nitrogen

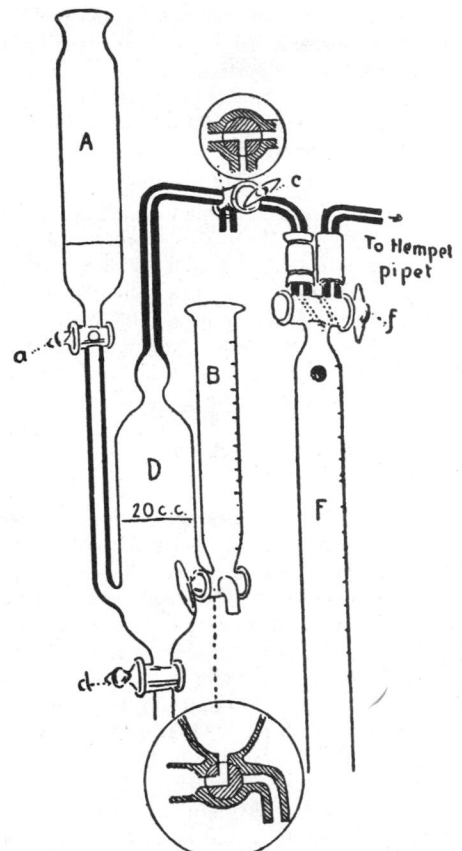

FIG. 24:2—Details of deaminizing blub and connection

by opening *a* and filling *D* with liq. from *A*. Connect *F* with Hempel pipet and force gas into latter by means of leveling bulb, letting cock *a* remain open during this and succeeding operation to permit displacement of liq. in *D* by NO formed in interval. Connect driving rod with pipet by lifting hook from shoulder of *D* and placing other hook on opposite side of driving rod, over horizontal lower tube of pipet. Shaking pipet rather slowly for few min completes absorption of NO except with almost completely exhausted $KMnO_4$ solns. Return gas to buret and adjust level with leveling bulb; note vol. N, temp., and barometric pressure, and calc. vol. N under std conditions of temp. and pressure. Obtain corresponding wt N, divide by 2, and from quotient calc. apparent % amino N in sample. Correct result for blank test performed as above, using 10 ml H_2O instead of sample soln. Quantity of gas obtained in blank is usually 0.3–0.4 ml, and nitrite solns giving much larger correction should be rejected.

With beef exts and similar prepns, 5 min is enough to allow for completion of reaction in *D*. In general, same time serves for decomposition of α-amino acids, but with NH_3, methylamine, and most amines other than α-amines allow 1–1.5 hr. For detns on such sub-stances mix sample soln with reagents, as described previously, let mixt. stand in app. till end of required time, and conclude reaction by shaking app. with motor 2–3 min. Continue detn as directed previously.

24.020   Sorensen Method (8)—
Official First Action

To 20 ml filtrate, **24.016**, second par., neutzd to phthln with $Ba(OH)_2$ or NaOH, or to 20 ml of equiv. ext of meat (sometimes larger vol. may be necessary) add 10 ml freshly prepd *phthln-formol mixt.* (50 ml 40% HCHO soln contg 1 ml 0.5% phthln soln in 50% alcohol, exactly neutzd with 0.2*N* $Ba(OH)_2$ or NaOH). Titr. mixt. with 0.2*N* $Ba(OH)_2$ until distinct red appears, add small but known excess 0.2*N* $Ba(OH)_2$, and back-titr. to neutrality with 0.2*N* HCl.

Conduct blank titrn with same reagents, using 20 ml H_2O in place of soln to be tested. From amt 0.2*N* $Ba(OH)_2$ required to neutze mixt., corrected for amt used in blank titrn, calc. amt amino N present (including NH_3 if this has not been removed). 1 ml 0.2*N* $Ba(OH)_2$ soln = 2.8 mg amino N.

24.021   Starchy Flour—Qualitative Tests—
Procedure

(In chopped meat, sausage, deviled meat, etc.)

(a) Treat 5–6 g sample with boiling H_2O 2–3 min, cool mixt., and test supernatant with I soln, **30.026(d)**. (In interpreting test note that small quantity of starch may be present from use of spices. If strong reaction is given, cereal products are present. This qual. test may be replaced by microscopic examination, which discloses not only presence of added starch but also variety used.)

(b) *Not applicable in presence of cellulosic material other than that from starchy flour and spice.*—To 10 g sample in 100 ml graduated oil tube (ASTM conical form with stem graduated from 0 to 3 ml in 0.1 ml) add 50 ml 8% alc. KOH soln and digest on steam bath 1 hr, stirring occasionally. Dil. to 100 ml with alcohol and mix. Let stand 1 hr, gently rotating once or twice during this period to loosen particles on sides of tube. After 1 hr read vol. of sediment in tube. Vol. >1 ml, if sample contains spices, or >0.5 ml if only spice oils are present, indicates presence of added starchy flour. Vol. <3 ml indicates that <3% flour is present, and vol. >3.5 ml indicates presence of >3.5% flour. (If sample contains dried skim milk or dried corn sirup, before proceeding with test remove lactose or maltose by shaking 10 g in 100 ml centrf. tube with two 50 ml portions warm H_2O and centrfg and decanting after each shaking.)

24.022   Soybean Flour—Qualitative Test
(9)—Procedure

Mix 10 g finely divided sample in 250 ml beaker with 75 ml 8% alc. KOH soln, and heat on steam bath until all meat is dissolved (30–45 min). Transfer liq. and residue to 100 ml graduated sedimentation tube, dil. to 100 ml with alcohol, and let settle. Decant as completely as possible, and cover residue with ca 50 ml warm H_2O. Stopper tube and shake vigorously; let stand few min until foam subsides; then transfer to 50 ml centrf. tube, and centrf. Pour off and discard supernatant, and add 10 ml HCl to centrf. tube. Stopper and shake, or mix contents thoroly with glass rod. Add ca 15 ml 25% alcohol, mix, and centrf. Decant supernatant and examine residue under microscope for characteristic "hourglass" or I-shaped cells (sometimes called "bearer cells"), preferably with polarized light.

24.023 Preservatives—Official Final Action— See Chap. 20

Qualitative Test for Agar—Official Final Action
24.024   Reagents

(a) *Trichloroacetic acid soln.*—25 g acid in 50 ml H_2O. (*Caution: See* **46.082**.)

(b) *Iodine soln.*—Approx. 0.033N.

(c) *Benedict qualitative soln.*—See **16.211**(a).

24.025   Preparation of Sample

(a) *Boned chicken or meat.*—Refrigerate overnight to jell broth. With thin-blade spatula, sep. as much jell as possible, and warm on steam bath until completely liquefied.

(b) *Consommé or broth.*—No prepn necessary.

24.026   Detection of Gum

Transfer up to 40 ml liquefied jell from meat, or 40 ml consommé, to 100 ml beaker. Add 5 ml trichloroacetic acid soln, stir, and let stand 15–30 min. Transfer to 50 ml conical centrf. tube and centrf. 15–20 min at ca 1200 rpm. Decant clear supernatant into 250 ml (8 oz) centrf. bottle or nursing bottle, add 4–5 vols alcohol, and let stand until ppt coagulates, or overnight. (No ppt indicates absence of gums.) Centrf. at 1200 rpm 15–30 min until ppt packs to bottom of centrf. bottle. Carefully decant alcohol, taking care not to disturb packed gum ppt. Remove few remaining drops of alcohol by spontaneous drying or by gentle air current. Add 1 drop 0.033N I soln. Evanescent violet or black color indicates presence of agar. (Neg. test does not necessarily mean agar is absent.)

Add 3 ml hot H_2O and warm on steam bath until gum ppt dissolves. Chill gum soln in ice and H_2O mixt. Thickening, or stiff jell, indicates agar. Warm cooled mixt. on steam bath, transfer to 50 ml beaker, rinse centrf. bottle with 3–4 ml H_2O, and add rinsings to jell soln. Add 1 ml HCl and boil 30 sec. Transfer 1 ml hydrolyzed gum soln to test tube, neutze with 10% NaOH soln, using litmus paper as indicator (ca 2 ml required), remove litmus paper, add 5 ml Benedict soln, and boil cautiously over free flame

30–60 sec. Green, yellow, or brick-colored ppt after spontaneous cooling indicates agar (or other hydrolyzable gum).

24.027 Nonfat Dry Milk (Qualitative Test) (*10*)—Procedure
(In absence of maltose)

To 10 g comminuted sample in small beaker add 20 ml hot (70–90°) H_2O. Mix thoroly and filter. Transfer 4 ml filtrate to test tube, add 3–4 drops *5% methylamine hydrochloride soln*, and boil 30 sec. Remove from flame, add 3–5 drops 20% NaOH soln, and shake 10 sec. Soln turns yellow immediately, then slowly changes to carmine if lactose is present, indicating presence of nonfat dry milk.

Lactose (*11*)—Official First Action
24.028   Reagents

(a) *Acclimated yeast suspension (for use in presence or absence of maltose).*—Macerate 2 cakes (0.6 oz each) bakers' yeast and wash with 3 ca 50 ml portions H_2O, centrfg between washings. Prep. medium contg 1.0 g anhyd. $MgSO_4$, 2.0 g NH_4Cl, 1.0 g anhyd. K_2HPO_4, 0.5 g KCl, 0.02 g $FeSO_4.7H_2O$, 0.7 g peptone, and 20.0 g tech. maltose. Dissolve each ingredient in small amt H_2O and add, in order given, to flask contg ca 500 ml H_2O. Dil. to 1 L. Warm, filter, bring filtrate to rolling boil, and let cool to room temp. Add washed yeast to 1 L medium and incubate ca 24 hr at 30°, stirring frequently first few hr. Sep. yeast by decanting and centrfg, wash twice with H_2O, add to 1 L fresh medium, and incubate addnl 24 hr with agitation first few hr. Sep. yeast from medium, wash thoroly at least 4 times with H_2O, dil. to 100 ml, and refrigerate. Yeast remains active 2–3 weeks. (Yeast may remain active longer if frozen.)

(b) *Washed yeast suspension (for use in absence of maltose).*—Mix 2 cakes bakers' yeast to smooth suspension with ca 150 ml H_2O. Centrf. 5 min and discard aq. layer. Repeat mixing with H_2O and centrfg 4 more times, or until supernatant after centrfg is practically clear. Again suspend yeast in H_2O and dil. with H_2O to 100 ml. Store in refrigerator at ca 4° and shake well before using. Discard after 2 weeks.

(c) *Benedict soln.*—Dissolve 16 g $CuSO_4.5H_2O$ in 125–150 ml H_2O. Dissolve 150 g Na citrate ($Na_3C_6H_5O_7.2H_2O$), 130 g anhyd. Na_2CO_3, and 10 g $NaHCO_3$ in ca 650 ml hot H_2O. Combine the 2 solns, cool, dil. to 1 L, and filter.

(d) *Lactose std soln.*—1.5 mg anhyd. lactose/ml. Dissolve 1.5789 g lactose.H_2O in H_2O and dil. to 1 L.

(e) *Iodine std soln.*—Mix 5.08 g I with 10.2 g KI, dissolve in small quantity of H_2O, filter, and dil. to 1 L.

(f) *Sodium thiosulfate std soln.*—Dissolve 9.92 g $Na_2S_2O_3.5H_2O$ in H_2O and dil. to 1 L.

(g) *Dilute acetic acid.*—Dil. 240 ml HOAc to 1 L with H_2O.

(h) *Dilute phosphoric acid.*—Dil. 240 ml H_3PO_4 to 1 L with H_2O.

(i) *Citric acid-phosphate buffer.*—pH 4.8. Mix solns in proportions of 10.14 ml $0.1M$ citric acid (19.21 g/L) and 9.86 ml $0.2M$ Na_2HPO_4 (28.4 g anhyd./L), and adjust to pH 4.8, using pH meter. Store in refrigerator and discard if soln becomes turbid.

(j) *Starch soln.*—Rub 2.5 g sol. starch and ca 10 mg HgI_2 in little H_2O. Dissolve in ca 500 ml boiling H_2O.

24.029   Determination (in Presence of Maltose)

Place 10 g sample in 100 ml vol. sugar flask, add small amt of H_2O, and break up sample by agitation. Add ca 50 ml H_2O and warm on steam bath ca 30 min. Cool to room temp., add 2 ml HCl, and dil. to vol., using bottom of fat layer as meniscus. Add 5.0 ml *20% phosphotungstic acid soln*, mix well, let stand few min., and filter thru moist paper. Pipet 40 ml filtrate into 50 ml vol. flask and neutze just to acid side of chlorophenol red or other indicator which shows pH change at ca 4.8. Add 5 ml pH 4.8 buffer soln, dil. to vol., and mix.

Transfer ca 40 ml of this soln to centrf. tube to which 5 ml yeast suspension, (a), has been added and from which H_2O has been sepd. Mix yeast and sample well and incubate 3 hr at 30°, stirring frequently. Centrf. and det. reducing sugars:

Pipet 10 ml clear soln into 300 ml erlenmeyer, add 20 ml Benedict soln, (c), bring to boil in 3–5 min, and boil slowly exactly 3 min. Remove from heat, cool, and add 100 ml H_2O and 10 ml dil. HOAc, (g), slowly while swirling. Add ca 30% excess std I, (e) (15 ml for ca 1.5% lactose), and agitate to dissolve CuO. Let flask stand at least 5 min, add 20 ml dil. H_3PO_4, (h), and titr. excess I with std $Na_2S_2O_3$ soln, (f), using starch indicator.

Det. lactose:I ratio by using 10 ml std lactose soln and carrying thru detn as above, beginning "... add 20 ml Benedict soln, ..." Det. I:$Na_2S_2O_3$ ratio by using 10 ml H_2O and carrying thru detn as above.

% lactose = $100 KV/W$, where K = g lactose/ml I soln, V = vol. I soln consumed, and W = g sample in aliquot, considering vol. original sample soln as 100 ml rather than 105 ml, to correct for vol. occupied by meat.

24.030   Determination (in Absence of Maltose)

Prep. soln as in **24.029**, first par. Place 5 ml washed yeast suspension, (a) or (b), in lipless centrf. tube, centrf., and drain and discard supernatant. Add 40 ml prepd soln to yeast residue in centrf. tube, stopper, and shake vigorously to dislodge and suspend yeast. Let stand with occasional shaking 1 hr. Centrf. and det. lactose in clear soln as in **24.029**, third par.

Starch (12)—Official Final Action

(Not applicable to liver products)

24.031   Reagents

(a) *Zinc acetate soln.*—Dissolve 12 g $Zn(OAc)_2$.$2H_2O$ in H_2O and dil. to 100 ml.

(b) *Potassium ferrocyanide soln.*—Dissolve 6 g $K_4Fe(CN)_6$.$3H_2O$ in H_2O and dil. to 100 ml.

(c) *Copper sulfate soln.*—Dissolve 40.0 g $CuSO_4$.$5H_2O$ in H_2O and dil. to 1 L.

(d) *Alkaline tartrate soln.*—Dissolve 200 g Rochelle salt and 150 g NaOH in hot H_2O, filter, and dil. to 1 L.

(e) *Glucose std soln.*—Dissolve 0.40 g pure glucose in H_2O and dil. to 200 ml.

(f) *Starch indicator soln.*—Mix 1 g powd sol. starch with 20 ml cold H_2O. Pour mixt. into 500 ml boiling H_2O and boil 10 min. Cool, and add few drops $CHCl_3$.

(g) *Phosphotungstic acid soln.*—Dissolve 20 g phosphotungstic acid in H_2O, dil. to 100 ml, and filter.

24.032   Extraction and Hydrolysis

Weigh 10 g finely ground and thoroly mixed sample into 250 ml heat-resistant centrf. bottle. If fat content is so high as to interfere with subsequent filtering, add 25 ml pet ether, mix thoroly with glass rod, decant, and repeat with 2 addnl 25 ml portions pet ether. Add 100 ml H_2O, 5 ml freshly prepd $Zn(OAc)_2$ soln, and 5 ml freshly prepd $K_4Fe(CN)_6$ soln. Stopper tightly and let stand 15 min, shaking vigorously several times during this period. Centrf. 15 min at 1500 rpm. Decant supernatant into 12.5 cm Whatman No. 3 filter paper in conical funnel, using light suction. To residue in centrf. bottle add 25 ml freshly prepd soln contg 1 ml $Zn(OAc)_2$ plus 1 ml $K_4Fe(CN)_6$ solns/200 ml soln. Let stand 10 min, shaking several times during this period; then centrf. 10 min at 1500 rpm and decant thru same paper. Repeat last extn with addnl 25 ml $Zn(OAc)_2$-$K_4Fe(CN)_6$ washing soln. Rinse stopper with H_2O.

Transfer funnel contg filter paper to centrf. bottle. From graduated cylinder contg 90 ml hot $1.5N$ HCl (ca 70°) pour 40 ml into paper to melt adhering fat and to free starch. Poke hole in tip of paper and let acid run into centrf. bottle. Wash paper with remainder of acid soln. Suspend bottle in open boiling H_2O bath so that level of H_2O in bath is at approx. level of soln within bottle. Do not reflux. Hydrolyze exactly 1.5 hr, keeping H_2O level of bath at original position, stirring contents of bottle occasionally. Do not transfer paper to centrf. bottle, as it will hydrolyze and give high values.

Cool immediately. (If necessary, sample may stand overnight at this point.) Make just alk. to litmus with 20% NaOH (ca 27 ml) and then add 10 ml HCl (1 + 2). Transfer to 200 ml phosphoric acid flask or 200 ml erlenmeyer marked at 200 ml. Rinse centrf. bottle with 15 ml phosphotungstic acid soln, followed by several 10 ml portions H_2O. Dil. to vol. with fat layer, if any, just above mark. Stopper, shake, let stand ca 30 min, and filter soln thru Whatman No. 1 paper.

24.033   *Determination of Reducing Sugars*

Pipet 20 ml filtrate into heat-resistant 200 ml erlenmeyer. Pipet in 20 ml $CuSO_4$ soln and 20 ml alk. Rochelle salt soln. Bring to boil within 2 min, swirling occasionally, and continue boiling 1 min. Cool immediately under running H_2O, transfer to 200 ml vol. flask, dil. to vol. with H_2O, stopper and shake.

Pipet 50 ml soln into 200 ml erlenmeyer. Add 25 ml 10% KI and 5 ml H_2SO_4 $(1 + 3)$. Titr. with ca $0.025N$ $Na_2S_2O_3$ soln, adding 2 ml starch indicator and ca 2.0 g solid KSCN when yellow has almost disappeared. (1 drop $Na_2S_2O_3$ soln should change color from blue to white or faint lilac shade.) Det. blank, using 20 ml H_2O instead of filtrate, starting at first par. Conduct detn on 20 ml std glucose soln similarly. % Starch $= 4 \times 0.9 \times (B - S)/(B - D)$, where B = blank titrn in ml; S = sample titrn in ml; D = std glucose titrn in ml; 0.9 = factor to convert glucose to starch.

MEAT EXTRACTS AND SIMILAR PRODUCTS

24.034   Preparation of Sample—Procedure

Remove liq. and semiliq. meat exts and similar prepns from container and mix thoroly. (Slight heating expedites mixing of pasty exts.) Carefully remove from bottom of container sediment that forms in many liq. prepns and include in sample. If sample is in form of cubes, grind 10–12 cubes in mortar.

24.035   Moisture—Official Final Action

Proceed as in **7.003**, using ca 2 g powd prepns, ca 3 g pasty prepns, and 5–10 g liq. exts, according to solid content. Dry powd prepns directly without admixture. Dissolve pasty prepns in H_2O and dry with enough ignited sand, asbestos, or pumice stone to absorb soln. When glycerol is present, proceed as in **7.007**.

24.036   Ash—Official Final Action

Proceed as in **31.012** or **31.013**. Add enough H_2O to pasty prepns to effect soln and evap. to dryness so as to distribute solids evenly over bottom of dish.

24.037   Total Phosphorus— Official Final Action

Destroy org. matter as in **2.017**(c) or (d), and proceed as in **2.031** or **8.027**.

24.038   Chlorides—Official Final Action

Dissolve ca 1 g prepd sample, **24.034,** in 20 ml 5% Na_2CO_3 soln and proceed as in **3.067–3.068.**

24.039   Total Nitrogen—Official Final Action—See 2.051

24.040   Creatine—Official Final Action

Dissolve ca 7 g sample in cool (20°) NH_3-free H_2O in 150 ml beaker, transfer soln to 250 ml vol. flask, dil. to vol., and mix thoroly. Transfer 20 ml aliquot to 50 ml vol. flask and proceed as in **24.017.** Subtract from total creatinine value equiv. of preformed creatinine, **24.041,** and multiply difference by 1.16 to convert to creatine. Express result as % creatine.

24.041   Creatinine—Official Final Action

(*Caution: See* **46.029** and **46.068.**)

Measure ca 5 ml soln used in **24.040** into 500 ml vol. flask, add 10 ml 10% NaOH soln and 30 ml *satd (1.2%) picric acid soln*, mix, and rotate 30 sec. Let stand exactly 4.5 min and dil. to vol. at once with H_2O. Shake thoroly and read color in colorimeter after standing. If reading is <7 or >9.5 mm, repeat, calcg quantity of soln necessary to obtain reading of ca 8 mm. Express result as % creatinine, making calcns as in **24.017.**

24.042   Preservatives—Official Final Action— *See* Chap. 20

24.043   Sulfur Dioxide (Distillation Method)— *See* 20.092

24.044   Pesticide Residues—*See* Chap. 29

SELECTED REFERENCES

(*1*) JAOAC **33**, 749(1950); **36**, 279(1953).
(*2*) JAOAC **11**, 112(1928); **12**, 407(1929); **33**, 749(1950).
(*3*) JAOAC **52**, 634(1969).
(*4*) JAOAC **11**, 408(1928).
(*5*) JAOAC **18**, 459(1935); **22**, 596(1939).
(*6*) JAOAC **8**, 277, 696(1925).
(*7*) J. Biol. Chem. **9**, 185(1911); **12**, 275(1912); **16**, 121(1913); **23**, 407(1915).
(*8*) Biochem. Z. **7**, 45(1907).
(*9*) Winton, "Microscopy of Vegetable Foods," 2nd ed., p. 248; "British Yearbook of Pharmacy," 1913, pp. 467–468.
(*10*) Analyst **67**, 130(1942).
(*11*) J. Biol. Chem. **75**, 33(1927); **79**, 649(1928); J. Dairy Research **7**, 41(1936); Conn. Agr. Expt. Sta. Bull. **401**, 869(1937); **415**, 695(1938); **426**, 14(1939); JAOAC **23**, 811(1940); **40**, 770(1957).
(*12*) JAOAC **41**, 288(1958).

25. Metals and Other Elements as Residues in Foods ★

ANTIMONY

American Conference of Governmental Industrial Hygienists-AOAC Method (1)— Official First Action

25.001 *Principles*

Pentavalent Sb in aq. HCl soln reacts with Rhodamine B to form colored complex extractable with org. solvs. Intensity of extd color is measured spectrophtric at 565 nm.

25.002 *Reagents*

(H₂O for aq. reagents should be double distd; final distn from glass.)

(a) *Hydrochloric acid soln.*—6N. Dil. concd acid with H₂O (1 + 1).

(b) *Dilute phosphoric acid.*—3N. Dil. 70 ml H₃PO₄ (85%) to 1 L with H₂O.

(c) *Rhodamine B soln.*—0.02% in H₂O.

(d) *Antimony std solns.*—(1) *Stock soln.*—100 μg Sb/ml. Dissolve 0.1000 g pure Sb in 25 ml H₂SO₄ with heat; cool, and cautiously dil. to 1 L with H₂O. (2) *Working soln.*—1 μg/ml. Dil. 2.0 ml stock soln to 200 ml with H₂O.

(Cool reagents (a), (b), (c), ca 100 ml benzene, and eight 125 ml separators with Teflon stopcocks in refrigerator before use; maintain temp. of 5–10° during extn and color development. Work in subdued light.)

25.003 *Preparation of Sample*

Digest sample as in **25.008**. Oxidizing conditions must be maintained.

25.004 *Determination*

(*Caution: See* **46.019, 46.028,** and **46.030.**)

Transfer digest or aliquot to 125 ml g-s erlenmeyer, add enough H₂SO₄ to make total of 5 ml H₂SO₄ and evap. to fumes of SO₃. Cool flask, add 10 drops 70% HClO₄, and again evap. to white fumes. Cool digest in ice-bath ≥30 min; then *slowly* add 5 ml precooled 6N HCl by pipet. Let stand in ice-bath 15 min; then add 8 ml precooled 3N H₃PO₄. (Until color is extd into benzene, perform subsequent operations as quickly as possible. Color is stable in benzene several hr.) Immediately add 5 ml precooled Rhodamine B soln, stopper, and shake vigorously. Transfer to precooled 125 ml separator. Pipet 10 ml precooled benzene into separator, shake vigorously 1 min, and discard aq. layer. Transfer benzene layer

(red if Sb is present) into test tube and let H₂O settle. Rinse 1 cm cell with ext, fill cell, and read at 565 nm against benzene blank taken thru entire detn. Refer readings to std curve.

25.005 *Preparation of Standard Curve*

Pipet 0, 2, 4, 6, 8, and 10 ml Sb working std soln into 125 ml g-s erlenmeyers, add 5 ml H₂SO₄ to each, and proceed as in detn. Plot *A* against μg Sb.

ARSENIC

★ Gutzeit Method (2)— ★ Official Final Action

25.006 *Reagents*

(*Caution: See* **46.078, 46.079,** and **46.084.**)

(a) *Stannous chloride soln.*—Dissolve 40 g As-free SnCl₂.2H₂O in HCl and dil. to 100 ml with HCl.

(b) *Zinc.*—Use 20- or 30-mesh, As-free granulated Zn (needs no preliminary treatment), or As-free stick Zn either cut into 1 cm lengths, or melted and cast into pellets in porcelain mold drilled (for example) 9 mm diam. and 12.5 mm deep. Activate the pieces of Zn with HCl (1 + 3), contg 2 ml SnCl₂ soln/100 ml, letting action continue 15 min. Discard distinctly inactive or overactive pieces and pour off liq. Wash Zn free from acid with clear tap H₂O, and rinse with hot H₂O. Select uniformly etched non-pitted Zn and store in suitable receptacle. To maintain supply of uniform Zn, withdraw Zn from original receptacle until stock is exhausted and store used Zn in second receptacle after discarding nonuniform or deeply pitted pieces. Draw Zn from second receptacle after washing it with running H₂O. Repeat procedure until pieces are too small for further use.

(c) *Potassium iodide soln.*—Dissolve 15 g KI in H₂O and dil. to 100 ml.

(d) *Sand.*—Clean 30-mesh (thru No. 30 but not No. 40) white sea sand by washing successively with hot 10% NaOH soln, hot HNO₃, and hot H₂O. Dry the clean sand.

(e) *Mercuric bromide paper.*—Use com. As papers cut from paper of uniform wt and texture into strips exactly 2.5 mm wide and ca 12 cm long. (Uniformity in width and texture of paper is of great importance. Irregular texture produces irregular impregnation with consequent inaccurate results.) To sensitize, soak strips in 3–6% (optimum 5%) filtered soln of HgBr₂ in alcohol, 1 hr or longer according to amt, character, and activity of Zn used. (Attenuated, unsatisfactory stains, caused by over-rapid evolution of

---

★ Methods so marked are surplus methods. *See* "Definitions of Terms and Explanatory Notes," item (29).

AsH₃, can be shortened and intensified by increasing concn of HgBr₂ and vice versa.) If strips are in sheets, cut off 2 sides before soaking and leave strips attached at ends. After sensitization, remove strips and dry individual ones on glass rods; dry groups by waving them in air. Place strips when nearly dry between clean sheets of paper and subject to pressure long enough to take out bends or curls. Store in dry, dark place. (Aging of impregnated strips usually results in markedly fainter and longer stains. Desirable types of stain result from use of impregnated strips ≤2 days old.) When ready for use, cut individual strips off squarely 0.5″ from one end and insert this end into narrow tube of app. Handle sheets by paper attached to either end and cut in half just before use. Strips must be clean and free of any contamination.

(f) *Arsenic std solns.*—(1) *Stock soln.*—1 mg As₂O₃/ml. Dissolve 1.000 g As₂O₃ in 25 ml 20% NaOH soln. Sat. soln with CO₂ and dil. to 1 L with recently boiled H₂O. (2) *Intermediate soln.*—0.04 mg As₂O₃/ml. Dil. 40 ml stock soln to 1 L. (3) *Working soln.*—0.002 mg As₂O₃/ml. Dil. 50 ml intermediate soln to 1 L and use to prep. std stains. Soln contg 0.001 mg As₂O₃ may also be prepd if desired. Prep. fresh dil. solns frequently.

25.007   *Apparatus*

(a) *Generators and absorption tubes.*—See Fig. 25:1. Use 2 oz wide-mouth bottles of uniform capacity and design as generators, and fit each by means of perforated stopper with glass tube 1 cm diam. and 6–7 cm long, with addnl constricted end to facilitate connection. Place small wad of glass wool in constricted bottom end of tube and add 3.5–4 g sand, taking care to have same amt in each tube. Moisten sand with 10% Pb(OAc)₂ soln and remove excess by light suction. Clean sand when necessary by treatment (do not remove sand from tube) with HNO₃ followed by H₂O rinse and suction. Treat with Pb(OAc)₂ soln. If sand has dried thru disuse, clean and remoisten it as directed. Connect tube by means of rubber stopper with narrow glass tube 2.6–2.7 mm id and 10–12 cm long, and introduce clean end of strip of HgBr₂ paper. (3 mm bore allows strip to curl, which results in uneven stain and poor end point.) Clean and dry tube before inserting HgBr₂ paper. (Ordinary pipe cleaner may be used.)

(b) *Water bath.*—Use constant temp. H₂O bath. If no H₂O bath is available, use flat-bottom container of suitable depth and capacity. (Deep H₂O bath is suggested to ensure uniform conditions during evolution and absorption of the AsH₃.)

25.008   *Preparation of Sample*
(*Caution: See* **46.019, 46.026,** and **46.030.**)

(For details of convenient churn-type washer that will remove arsenical spray residues from firm fruits or vegetables with an aq. NH₄NO₃-HNO₃ soln, *see* Fahey, Cassil, and Rusk (JAOAC **26,** 150(1943). Digest aliquot of "strip" soln and proceed as in (a).)

(a) *For fresh fruits (apples, pears, or similar products).*—Weigh and peel representative sample (1–5 lb). At blossom and stem ends cut out all flesh thought to be contaminated with As compds and include with peelings, if desired. Place peelings in 1 or more 800 ml Pyrex Kjeldahl flasks. (As-free Pyrex glassware and "wet ashing" app. of Duriron are available.) Add 25–50 ml HNO₃; then cautiously add 20 ml H₂SO₄. Place each flask on asbestos mat with 2″ hole. Warm slightly and discontinue heating if foaming becomes excessive.

When reaction has quieted, heat flask cautiously and rotate occasionally to prevent caking of sample upon glass exposed to flame. Maintain oxidizing conditions in flask at all times during digestion by cautiously adding small amts of HNO₃ whenever mixt. turns brown or darkens. Continue digestion until org. matter is destroyed and SO₃ fumes are copiously evolved. (Final soln should be colorless, or at most light straw color.) Cool slightly, and add 75 ml H₂O and 25 ml satd NH₄ oxalate soln to assist in expelling oxides of N from soln. Evap. again to point where fumes of SO₃ appear in neck of flask. Cool, and dil. with H₂O to 500 or 1000 ml in vol. flask.

(b) *For dried fruit products.*—Prep. sample by alternately grinding and mixing 4–5 times in food chopper. Place 35–70 g portions in 800 ml Kjeldahl

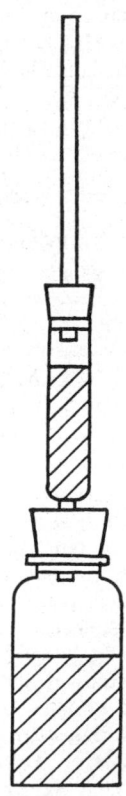

FIG. 25:1—Generator used with Gutzeit method for determining arsenic

flasks, and add 10–25 ml H_2O, 25–50 ml HNO_3, and 20 ml H_2SO_4. Continue digestion as in (a). Dil. digested soln to 250 ml.

(c) *For small fruits, vegetables, etc.*—Use 70–140 g sample and digest as in (a) or (b).

(d) *For materials other than* (a), (b), *or* (c).— Digest 5–50 g, according to moisture content and quantity of As expected, as in (a) or (b). Dil. to definite vol. dictated by circumstances.

(e) *For products containing stable organic As compounds, products liable to yield incompletely oxidized organic derivatives that inhibit arsine evolution, or products that are difficult to digest.*—Shrimp, tobacco, oils, and some other products require special treatment to complete oxidn of org. As to inorg. As_2O_5, or to destroy org. interferences previous to As detn. For details consult following refs:

(1) C. R. Gross, Ind. Eng. Chem., Anal. Ed. **5**, 58(1933).

(2) Carey, Blodgett, and Satterlee, Ibid. **6**, 327 (1934).

(3) Remington, Coulson, and von Kolnitz, Ibid., 280.

(4) C. C. Cassil, JAOAC **20**, 171(1937).

(5) Hoffman and Gordon, Ibid. **47**, 629(1964).

Dil. As solns obtained by these special methods of prepn to definite vol.

(f) *For ultra-micro quantities of As, very labile forms of As, and vacuum-accelerated Gutzeit reduction system for mercuric bromide spot filtration.*—Consult Satterlee and Blodgett, Ind. Eng. Chem., Anal. Ed. **16**, 400(1944).

25.009 Isolation of Arsenic

Before making detns, isolate As, when interfering substances are present in digests (*e.g.*, pyridine from tobacco), or when samples contain excessive amts of salts, or H_2SO_4 from digestions. Consult (1) of **25.008**(e) for method of isolating As after digestion, or isolate As by $AsCl_3$ distn (JAOAC **16**, 75, 325 (1933); **17**, 202(1934) or **36.296**, par. 2). Gelatin may be hydrolyzed with HCl and As isolated as in (1) of **25.008**(e).

25.010 Determination

Det. acid (HCl or H_2SO_4 according to previous treatment), by titrn if necessary, in definite vol. of sample soln. Place aliquots contg 0.01–0.03 mg As_2O_3 (0.020–0.025 mg is optimum), and $\leq$30 ml, in Gutzeit generators. If As in aliquot taken is found to be outside limits specified, repeat with proper aliquot. If aliquot contains only HCl, add enough HCl to make total vol. of 5 ml HCl; if it contains H_2SO_4, add enough 25% As-free NaOH soln (keep in As-free Pyrex) to exactly neutze it and add 5 ml HCl, or add enough HCl to the H_2SO_4 in aliquot to make total vol. of 5 ml mixed acids. Cool when necessary and add 5 ml KI reagent and 4 drops $SnCl_2$ soln, **25.006**(a).

Prep. stds corresponding to 0.010, 0.020, and 0.030 mg As_2O_3 from As working std soln, **25.006**(f). Since stds *must* contain same kind and amts of acid as samples, add 5 ml HCl, or H_2SO_4 and HCl (total 5 ml), according to prior treatment of unknown. If H_2SO_4 has been neutzd, add equiv. amt of As-free Na_2SO_4 to stds. Mix, and let stand 30 min at $\geq$25° or 5 min at 90°. Dil. with H_2O to 40 ml.

Prep. generator as in **25.007** and carefully center strip of $HgBr_2$ paper in narrow tube. If sheets of strips are used, prep. sample and std strips from same strip-group. According to activity of Zn, add to each std and sample 10–15 g activated stick Zn or 2–5 g granulated Zn; add same amt to each generator. Equalize as far as possible surface area of Zn exposed in std and sample.

Immerse app. to within 1″ of top of narrow tube in H_2O bath kept at temp. of 20–25°, and let evolution proceed 1.5 hr. Remove strip, and average length of stains on both sides in mm. Plot graph of std strips on cross-section paper, using length in mm as ordinate and mg As_2O_3 as abscissa. Locate length of unknown strip on std graph and read off on abscissa quantity of As present. Report only to third decimal as grains As_2O_3/lb. Take smaller or larger aliquots when stain is longer or shorter than highest or lowest std, resp. (Grains/lb) × 143 = ppm; ppm × 0.007 = grain/lb.

Perform blanks frequently. Blanks should not show >0.001 mg As_2O_3.

Colorimetric Methods—Official Final Action

25.011 Apparatus

See Fig. 25:2. Seal and bend capillary tubing (7 mm od, 2 mm id) to Pyrex $\mathbf{\overline{S}}$ 19/38 female ground joint. Taper other end to afford easier fit into connecting tubing and later into neck of 25 ml vol. flask. To transfer trap contents, attach bulb aspirator to male $\mathbf{\overline{S}}$ 19/38 joint and place in top of trap. Use generators and absorption tubes as in **25.007**. (App. available from Canadian Laboratory Supplies, Ltd., 8655 Delmeade Rd, Montreal, Quebec, Canada.)

Clean traps between detns without removing beads by flushing with H_2O, followed by HNO_3, soaking for 30 min or until HNO_3 becomes colorless. Remove all traces of acid with H_2O, rinse with acetone, and dry with air current applied by suction to tip of trap.

25.012 Reagents

(a) *Bromine water.*—Half satd. Dil. 75 ml satd Br-H_2O with equal vol. H_2O.

(b) *Sodium hypobromite soln.*—Place 50 ml 0.5N NaOH in 200 ml vol. flask, and dil. to vol. with half-satd Br-H_2O, (a).

(c) *Ammonium molybdate sulfuric acid soln.*—Dissolve 5.000 g $(NH_4)_6Mo_7O_{24}.4H_2O$ in H_2O and add slowly 42.8 ml H_2SO_4. Dil. to 100 ml with H_2O.

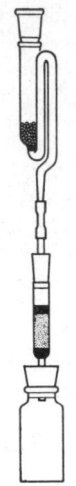

FIG. 25:2—Arsenic apparatus

(d) *Arsenious oxide std solns.—(1) Stock soln.—*1 mg/ml. Dissolve 1.000 g As_2O_3 in 25 ml 20% NaOH soln and dil. to 1 L. *(2) Intermediate soln.—*10 μg/ml. Dil. 10 ml stock soln to 1 L. *(3) Working soln.—*1 μg/ml. Dil. 100 ml intermediate soln to 1 L.

(e) *Hydrazine sulfate soln.—*1.5% $N_2H_4.H_2SO_4$ in H_2O.

(f) *Potassium iodide soln.—*15%. Keep in dark. Discard when soln turns yellow.

(g) *Stannous chloride soln.—See* **25.006**(a).

(h) *Dilute hydrochloric acid soln.—*Dil. 144 ml HCl to 200 ml with H_2O.

(i) *Lead acetate soln.—*10% $Pb(OAc)_2.3H_2O$ in H_2O.

(j) *Zinc metal.—*30-mesh.

(k) *Sea sand.—*To clean sand ("30-mesh") before use and between detns, mount piece of 3 mm id glass tubing thru rubber stopper in suction flask. Fit piece of rubber or Tygon tubing over top to take bottom of sulfide absorption tube easily and to maintain it upright. Add, in turn, with suction, aqua regia, H_2O, HNO_3, and H_2O to remove all traces of acid (≥5 washings). Wet sand with $Pb(OAc)_2$ soln and remove excess with suction.

(l) *Silver diethyldithiocarbamate.—*Chill 200 ml 0.1M $AgNO_3$ soln (3.4 g/200 ml) and 200 ml 0.1M Na diethyldithiocarbamate soln (4.5 g/200 ml) to 10° or lower. Add carbamate soln to $AgNO_3$ soln slowly with stirring. Filter thru buchner, wash with chilled H_2O, and dry under reduced pressure at room temp. Dissolve salt in pyridine (reagent grade) with stirring, chill, and add cold H_2O slowly until completely pptd. Filter thru buchner, and wash with H_2O to remove all pyridine. Dry pale yellow crystals under reduced pressure (mp 185–187°; recovery, 85–90%). Store in amber bottle in refrigerator. (Second recrystn may be necessary to obtain correct mp.)

(m) *Silver diethyldithiocarbamate soln.—*Dissolve 0.5000 g salt, (l), in pyridine in 100 ml vol. flask, and

dil. to vol. with pyridine. Mix, and store in amber bottle.

25.013   *Preparation of Sample*

Proceed as in **25.008**, except use 40 instead of 20 ml H_2SO_4. Conduct one or more blanks along with samples.

Molybdenum Blue Method (3)
25.014   *Determination*

Transfer 20 ml aliquots of sample and blank digest solns to generator bottles. Add, swirling after each addn, 10 ml H_2O, 5 ml dil. HCl, (h), 5 ml KI soln, (f), and 4 drops $SnCl_2$ soln, (g). Let stand ≥15 min.

Place 4 g sea sand over small glass wool wad in sulfide absorption tube and cap with glass wool. Place 3 mm diam. solid glass beads in trap over small glass wool wad until ¼ full and add 3.0 ml NaOBr, (b). Assemble app. except for generator bottle. Add 4 g Zn, (j), to generator bottle, attach immediately, and let react 30 min.

Disconnect trap and transfer contents to 25 ml vol. flask with aspirator assembly. Rinse trap with six 2 ml portions H_2O and aspirate into flask. Add, with swirling, 0.5 ml NH_4 molybdate-H_2SO_4 soln, (c), and 1.0 ml $N_2H_4.H_2SO_4$ soln, (e). Dil. to vol., mix, and let stand 75 min. Mix, and read in spectrophtr or colorimeter at 845 nm against blank prepd similarly. Alternatively, heat vol. flask and contents 10 min at 50° and cool in tap H_2O to room temp. before reading. Det. As_2O_3 in aliquot from std curve.

25.015   *Preparation of Standard Curve*

Place 0.0, 1.0, 2.0, 3.0, 5.0, 6.0 ml std soln contg 10μg As_2O_3/ml in 25 ml vol. flasks. Add 3.0 ml NaOBr soln, (b), and H_2O to 15 ml. Add, with swirling, 0.5 ml NH_4 molybdate-H_2SO_4 soln, (c), and 1.0 ml $N_2H_4.H_2SO_4$ soln, (e). Dil. to vol., mix, and let stand 75 min or heat 10 min at 50° as for samples. Mix, and read at 845 nm. Plot A against μg As_2O_3.

Silver Diethyldithiocarbamate Method (4)
25.016   *Determination*

Transfer aliquot sample digest (usually 2–5 ml) and same vol. blank to generator bottles. Add H_2O to 35 ml; then add, with swirling, 5 ml HCl, 2 ml KI soln, (f), and 8 drops $SnCl_2$ soln, (g), and let stand ≥15 min. Evolve AsH_3 as in **25.014**, except add 4.0 ml Ag diethyldithiocarbamate soln, (m), to trap.

Disconnect trap and mix trapping soln by gently drawing back and forth 5 times with aspirator assembly. Transfer soln directly to spectrophtr cell (g-s preferred) and read at 522 nm. Det. As_2O_3 in aliquot from std curve.

25.017   *Preparation of Standard Curve*

Place 0.0, 1.0, 3.0, 6.0, 10.0, 15.0 ml std soln contg 1.00 μg As_2O_3/ml in generator bottles. Add H_2O to

35 ml and proceed as in **25.016.** Read at 522 nm and plot A against μg As_2O_3.

CADMIUM (5)—OFFICIAL FIRST ACTION
25.018 *Principles*

Sample is digested with H_2SO_4 and HNO_3. All reactive metals are extd from soln (after adjustment to pH ca 9) with dithizone-$CHCl_3$. Cu, Hg, and most of any Ni or Co present are removed by stripping $CHCl_3$ soln with dil. HCl. Aq. layer, adjusted to 5% NaOH, is extd with dithizone-CCl_4. At this alky Zn, Pb, and Bi do not ext, whereas Cd dithizonate is relatively stable. Last 2 steps (stripping in dil. HCl and development of Cd dithizonate in 5% NaOH) are repeated. Cd is finally estd photometrically as dithizonate. Zn constitutes chief interference.

25.019 *Reagents*

(a) *Citrate.*—Diammonium salt or citric acid.

(b) *Chloroform.*—Distill from hot H_2O bath, collecting distillate in absolute alcohol in proportion of 10 ml alcohol to 1 L distillate. Intermittently shake receiver during distn.

(c) *Diphenylthiocarbazone (dithizone), twice purified.*—Purify as in **25.043(e)**, but make only 3 dil. NH_4OH extns of $CHCl_3$ soln. Carry thru, including H_2O-washing steps, and then repeat purification with 3 NH_4OH extns, pptn with dil. acid, etc. Instead of heating ext to dryness, evap. spontaneously, and complete drying under vac. in bell jar overnight.

(d) *Carbon tetrachloride.*—(*Caution: See* **46.011(b)** and **46.049.**) Reflux vigorously on steam bath 1 hr with ½₀ vol. 20% KOH in MeOH. Cool, add H_2O, drain off CCl_4 layer, and wash at least 3 times with copious vols of H_2O until alkali-free. Dry over $CaCl_2$, filter, and distill on hot H_2O bath. (Unless reagent is so purified, erratic Cd results may be obtained with some lots of CCl_4.)

(e) *Dithizone in carbon tetrachloride.*—20 mg/L CCl_4, (d). Prep. daily, as dil. solns of dithizone are unstable. (When many detns are to be made, dithizone reagent may be prepd by diln from 300 mg/L soln. Store concd reagent under $0.1M$ SO_2 soln in refrigerator.)

(f) *Dithizone in chloroform.*—1000 mg/L $CHCl_3$, (b), prepd as needed.

(g) *Sodium hydroxide soln.*—28%. Dissolve 28 g NaOH pellets in H_2O and dil. to 100 ml.

(h) *Absorbent cotton.*—Metal-free. If traces of metal are present, remove by digesting cotton several hr with warm $0.2N$ HCl, filtering on buchner, and finally washing with copious vols of redistd H_2O until acid-free.

(i) *Cadmium std solns.*—(*1*) *Stock soln.*—1 mg/ml. Dissolve 1 g pure Cd in 20–25 ml HNO_3 (1 + 9), evap. to dryness, add 5 ml HCl (1 + 1), evap. to dryness, and then add several ml H_2O and again evap. to dryness. Dil. to 1 L. (*2*) *Intermediate soln.*—100 μg/ml. Dil. 10 ml stock soln to 100 ml. (*3*) *Work-ing soln.*—2 μg/ml. Transfer 20 ml intermediate soln to 1 L vol. flask, add 15 ml HCl, and dil. to vol. to give final acidity of ca $0.2N$.

25.020 *Preparation of Standard Curve*

Prep. in duplicate 6 stds contg 0, 5, 10, 15, 20, and 25 μg Cd as follows: Add appropriate vols std soln to Squibb-type separators (125 ml size is convenient), adjust to 40 ml with $0.2N$ HCl, add 10 ml NaOH soln (soln is then 5% with respect to NaOH) and 25 ml dithizone soln, (e), shake vigorously exactly 1 min, let stand exactly 3 min, and filter org. layer thru pledget of absorbent cotton, discarding first 5 ml. Fill absorption cell (1 cm length is convenient) and det. A at 510 nm. Plot std curve or calc. ref. equation by method of least squares, **25.048(b)**.

25.021 *Preparation of Sample*

Use sample equiv. to 5–10 g of product, calcd to dry basis. (Sample size is of concern only when comparatively large proportions of Mg and P are present.) Digest with 10 ml H_2SO_4 (1 + 1) and HNO_3 as needed. If sample tends to char rather than to oxidize evenly, add 5 or 10 ml addnl H_2SO_4. Continue digestion, adding HNO_3 as required, until digestion is complete and SO_3 is evolved. Cool, add 15 ml satd NH_4 oxalate soln, and again heat to fumes.

Fat in biological materials, such as liver and kidney, may cause bumping and frothing during digestion. If comparatively large samples of such materials are available, make partial digestion with warm HNO_3 until only fat remains undissolved. Cool, filter free of solid fat, wash residue with H_2O, make combined filtrate to suitable vol., and digest appropriate aliquots as above.

25.022 *Determination*

Dil. digest, **25.021**, with 25 ml H_2O, filter free from excessive insol. matter (sulfates or silica) if present, and transfer to separator marked at 125 ml, using addnl 10 ml portions H_2O for rinsing and completing transfer. Add 1–2 g citrate reagent, (a), and 1 ml thymol blue indicator, **39.024(c)**, and adjust to ca pH 8.8 by adding NH_4OH slowly, while cooling intermittently, until soln changes from yellowish green to greenish blue. Dil. to 125 ml mark with H_2O. Ext vigorously with 5 ml portions dithizone soln, (f), until $CHCl_3$ layer remains green. Then ext with 3 ml $CHCl_3$.

Transfer all $CHCl_3$ exts to second separator previously wetted with 2–3 ml $CHCl_3$. Add to combined dithizone exts 40 ml $0.2N$ HCl, shake vigorously ≥ 1 min, and after layers sep., carefully drain $CHCl_3$ phase contg any Cu, Ni, Co, or Hg that may be present, and discard. Remove remaining droplets of dithizone by extg with 1–2 ml CCl_4, (d), carefully conducting draining operation so that no acid enters bore or stem of separator, as its presence there would in part decompose Cd dithizonate subsequently formed and extd in next step.

Adjust aq. phase to 5% alky by adding 10 ml NaOH soln, (g). Ext Cd with 25 ml dithizone soln, (e), shaking vigorously ≥1 min, and transfer to third separator previously wetted with 2–3 ml same dithizone soln. Repeat extn with addnl 10 ml portions dithizone soln until CCl₄ layer becomes colorless. Quantities of Cd usually found in foods or biological materials (ca 100 μg) are completely removed by third extn.

To verify assumption that pale pink persisting after third extn is due to Zn, transfer questionable ext to fourth separator contg 5% NaOH soln, add several ml dithizone soln, (e), and shake vigorously. If CCl₄ layer becomes colorless, original pink was due to Zn and no further extns are necessary. If, however, pink persists, indicating presence of Cd, add ext to contents of third separator, and continue extn.

Convert Cd and Zn dithizonates in third separator to chlorides by adding 40 ml 0.2N HCl and shaking vigorously ≥1 min. Carefully drain CCl₄ layer, which may contain traces of Co and Ni not removed in second step, and discard. Remove droplets of dithizone from aq. phase by rinsing with 1–2 ml CCl₄ and drain off as completely as possible but do not permit any acid to pass bore of separator. Again adjust alky to 5% by adding 10 ml NaOH soln, (g). Wipe separator stems dry with cotton, (h). Det. Cd present by adding exactly 25 ml dithizone soln, (e), shaking vigorously exactly 1 min, permitting layers to sep. exactly 3 min, and continuing as in **25.020**, beginning "filter org. layer ..." Calc. Cd in μg by substituting A in linear equation or from std curve.

Note: If photometric measurement indicates >25 μg Cd, make first approximation by dilg dithizonate soln with CCl₄ and evaluating A. For best results repeat analysis with wts or aliquots of samples contg ≤25 μg Cd; 30 μg is upper limit of solubility of Cd dithizonate in 25 ml CCl₄. Therefore quantities >30 μg are incompletely extd.

COPPER

International Union of Pure and Applied Chemistry Carbamate Method (6)— Official Final Action

25.023   *Principles*

Sample is digested with HNO₃ and H₂SO₄. Cu is isolated and detd colorimetrically at pH 8.5 as diethyldithiocarbamate in presence of chelating agent, EDTA. Bi and Te also give colored carbamates at pH 8.5 but are decomposed to colorless compds with 1N NaOH. Cu complex is stable. Range of color development is 0–50 μg. Blank is ca 1 μg Cu.

25.024   *Precautions*

Clean glassware with hot HNO₃. Use white petrolatum to lubricate stopcocks of separators, and do not use brass chains. Purify H₂O and HNO₃ by distn in Pyrex.

25.025   *Reagents*

(a) *Sodium diethyldithiocarbamate (carbamate soln).*—Dissolve 1 g of the salt in H₂O, dil. to 100 ml, and filter. Store in refrigerator and prep. weekly.

(b) *Citrate–EDTA soln.*—Dissolve 20 g dibasic NH₄ citrate and 5 g Na₂EDTA (Eastman Kodak Co.) in H₂O and dil. to 100 ml. Remove traces of Cu by adding 0.1 ml carbamate soln and extg with 10 ml CCl₄. Repeat extn until CCl₄ ext is colorless.

(c) *Copper std solns.*—(1) *Stock soln.*—1 mg/ml. Place 0.2000 g Cu wire or foil into 125 ml erlenmeyer. Add 15 ml HNO₃ (1 + 4), cover flask with watch glass, and let Cu dissolve, warming to complete soln. Boil to expel fumes, cool, and dil. to 200 ml. (2) *Intermediate soln.*—100 μg/ml. Dil. 20 ml stock soln to 200 ml. (3) *Working soln.*—2 μg/ml. Prep. daily by dilg 5 ml intermediate std to 250 ml with 2.0N H₂SO₄.

(d) *Ammonium hydroxide.*—6N. Purify as in (b).

25.026   *Preparation of Sample*
(Caution: See 46.026 and 46.030.)

Weigh sample contg ≤20 g solids, depending upon expected Cu content. If sample contains <75% H₂O, add H₂O to obtain this diln. Add initial vol. HNO₃ to equal ca 2 times dry sample wt and 5 ml H₂SO₄, or as many ml H₂SO₄ as g dry sample, but ≥5 ml. Digest as in **25.008.**

When sample contains large amt of fat, make partial digestion with HNO₃ until only fat is undissolved. Cool, filter free of solid fat, wash residue with H₂O, add H₂SO₄ to filtrate, and complete digestion as above. After digestion, cool, add 25 ml H₂O, and remove nitrosylsulfuric acid by heating to fumes. Repeat addn of 25 ml H₂O and fuming. If after cooling and dilg, insol. matter is present, filter thru acid-washed paper, rinse paper wth H₂O, and dil. to 100 ml.

Det. reagent blank.

25.027   *Isolation and Determination of Copper*

Pipet 25 ml sample soln into 100 or 250 ml short-stem separator and add 10 ml citrate-EDTA reagent. Add 2 drops thymol blue indicator, **34.097**(g), and 6N NH₄OH dropwise until soln turns green or blue-green. Cool, and add 1 ml carbamate soln and 15 ml CCl₄. Shake vigorously 2 min. Let layers sep. and drain CCl₄ through cotton pledget into g-s tube or flask. Det A or T in suitable instrument at ca 400 nm.

If >50 μg Cu is present in 25 ml aliquot, use smaller aliquot and dil. to 25 ml with 2.0N H₂SO₄. Highest accuracy is obtained at ca 25 μg Cu level (A ca 0.3 in 1 cm cell).

To test for Bi and Te, return CCl₄ soln to separator, add 10 ml 5% KCN soln, and shake 1 min. If CCl₄ layer becomes colorless, Bi and Te are absent.

If test is pos., develop color in another 25 ml aliquot as above (without KCN). Drain CCl₄ layer into second separator, add 10 ml 1*N* NaOH, and shake 1 min. Let layers sep. and drain CCl₄ into third separator. Again wash CCl₄ ext with 10 ml 1*N* NaOH. Det. *A* or *T* of CCl₄ layer and convert to μg Cu.

25.028 Preparation of Standards and Calibration Curves

Transfer 0, 1, 2.5, 5, 10, 15, 20, and 25 ml of std Cu soln (2 μg/ml) to separators and add 2.0*N* H_2SO_4 to make total vol. of 25 ml.

Add 10 ml citrate-EDTA reagent and proceed as in **25.027**, beginning "Add 2 drops thymol blue indicator ..."

Plot *A* against μg Cu on ordinary graph paper. If readings are in % *T*, use semilog paper, and plot *T* on log scale. Since there is usually some deviation from linearity, read sample values from smoothed curve.

FLUORINE (7)—OFFICIAL FINAL ACTION

25.029 Principles

Method involves ashing of sample with $Ca(OH)_2$ as F fixative, isolation of F by Willard-Winter distn (Ind. Eng. Chem., Anal. Ed. **5**, 7(1933)) from $HClO_4$, and estn in distillate by $Th(NO_3)_4$ backtitrn method (JAOAC **27**, 246(1944)). Technic and reagent concns are designed to handle $\leq$10.0 mg F conveniently. Modifications of this general procedure, applicable to specific products, are described.

25.030 Precautions and Interferences

Control magnitude of detn blank by careful choice and purification of reagents (*see* **25.032**). With care, blank will be low (1–3 μg F), but with low-F foods it may represent considerable part of total F detd. Hence it must be stable. Large part of it will be "distn blank" apparently resulting from F leached from glassware of still during distn. This blank can be minimized by preliminary treatment of stills, **25.034**, and an av. distn blank detd if stills of same material and design are routinely used; otherwise, each still must bear its special blank. New, unused stills will usually be found to exhibit high blank, which will diminish to constant low figure after several detns. They should not be used until several consecutive blank detns yield constant, low amt of F.

Check ashing utensils by blank detns with fixative soln to det. if they contribute appreciable F. Even Pt vessels may become contaminated (owing presumably to slight Ca content) if they have been used recently for HF volatilization of SiO_2. In addn, such blank detns are useful for testing reagents and app. used in method and also evaporators, hoods, muffles, and laboratory atm. for presence of F fumes and dust. If HF bottles are permitted in same laboratory, seal immediately after use; avoid contamination from roach powders.

Ordinary tap H_2O may be source of F contamina-tion, since 1 ml H_2O contg 2 ppm F will contribute 2 μg F if allowed to remain or to dry in still. Therefore routinely rinse all glassware (stills, flasks, burets, etc.) with H_2O, preferably redistd from alk. $KMnO_4$. Filter papers may contribute μg quantities of F, and glass filters are preferred if filtration is required in micro detns.

Interferences are gelatinous SiO_2, Al, and B compds, which repress evolution of F as H_2SiF_6 in distn; materials such as nitrates, nitrites, peroxides, Cl, SO_2, and H_2S, which act upon indicator in titrn or otherwise interfere; halides (Cl), which distill to give excessive acidity in distillate; and phosphates and sulfates, which react with Th in titrn to give high results. Method is so designed that most of these interferences are automatically eliminated, but analyst should be on guard against their possible occurrence under unusual circumstances.

General Method

25.031 Apparatus

(a) *Fluorine still.*—Claisen 100–125 ml distg flask is most practical for general work. It must be of Pyrex glass with auxiliary neck sealed off immediately above side arm to prevent pocketing and refluxing of distillate. Still should be as small and simply designed as practicable; ordinary distg flasks can be used for some work and they are slightly more efficient than Claisen type, except that danger of spraying over of distg acid is greater.

Equip still with dropping funnel and 0–150° thermometer, latter extending to within ¼″ of bottom of flask, so that bulb is immersed in boiling acid mixt. Acid-alkali washed beads, preferably Pyrex, should be on hand. Clean rubber stoppers by boiling in 10% NaOH soln. All-glass app. with $\mathbf{T}$ accessories is convenient, especially in routine work, and eliminates need for rubber stoppers.

While not entirely necessary for heating still, use of Wood metal (50Bi, 25Pb, 12.5Sn, 12.5Cd) bath, adequately shielded, will prevent undue decomposition of $HClO_4$ and aid materially in securing low blank and low-acid distillate; hence its use is strongly urged. If metal bath is used, do not immerse flask so deeply that bath level is above that of liq. in flask; if bath is not used, transite or asbestos shielding boards are essential, and flask should be heated thru small hole in such shield by low "clean" flame. (Bath and shielding boards prevent over-heating of upper still walls.)

At analyst's option, distg H_2O may be added as steam instead of thru dropping funnel; elec. boiler, Fig. 18:1, is convenient steam generator. If steam is used, inlet tube should dip below surface of liq. in still. One advantage in adding distg H_2O thru funnel is that last portions of rinse H_2O used in transferring an ash can be used in distn. If funnel plug is thinly notched with sharp file on either side of bore, dropping rate can be more easily controlled, and end of funnel stem need not extend into liq. in still. Still is used in conjunction with clean straight-tube condenser no longer than necessary for adequate cooling. (Vertical arrangement of condenser will conserve bench space.)

(b) *Nessler tubes.*—Tall form, 100 and 50 ml, g-s-type preferred. Matched in sets of at least 6. (100 ml size is used most frequently in general method.)

(c) *Additional apparatus.*—(See **25.030.**) Carefully cleaned and tested Pt, or well-glazed porcelain, dishes of $\geq$100 ml size; 150 ml vol. flasks, or if these are not available, 200 ml size; and 10 ml burets (conveniently automatic) to deliver various solns required in distn and titrn. Overhead radiant heater will be found invaluable for drying and preliminary charring of samples, especially those of high-sugar type.

25.032   *Reagents*

(*Caution:* See **46.011, 46.025, 46.028,** and **46.030.**)

(a) *Lime suspension.*—Carefully slake ca 56 g (1 mole) low-F CaO (ca 2 ppm F) with ca 250 ml H_2O, and *slowly* add 250 ml 60% $HClO_4$ with stirring. Add few glass beads and boil down to copious fumes of acid; cool, add 200 ml H_2O, and boil down again. Repeat diln and boiling down once more; cool, dil. considerably, and filter thru fritted glass filter, if pptd SiO_2 appears. Pour clear soln, with stirring, into 1 L NaOH soln (10 g/100 ml), let ppt settle, and siphon off supernatant. Remove Na salts from ppt by washing 5 times in large centrf. bottles, shaking mass thoroly each time. Finally, shake ppt into suspension and dil. to 2 L. Store in paraffined bottles. (100 ml of this supension should give no appreciable F blank when evapd, distd, and carried thru titrn described below.) Always shake suspension well before use.

(b) *Perchloric acid soln.*—60%. Dil. $HClO_4$ with 3–4 vols H_2O and boil down to original vol. Do not fume strongly. Repeat, and store in Pyrex. (Prepd acid should be Cl-free by test.)

(c) *Sulfuric acid soln.*—Carefully mix equal vols H_2SO_4 and H_2O, boil down to fumes, cool, dil. *carefully*, boil down once more, and dil. to 1 + 1 vol.

(d) *Silver perchlorate soln.*—50 g/100 ml.

(e) *p-Nitrophenol indicator.*—0.5% alc. soln.

(f) *Potassium hydroxide soln.*—Exactly 0.05N.

(g) *Potassium chloride soln.*—0.05N. 3.728 g/L.

(h) *Hydroxylamine hydrochloride soln.*—1.0%.

(i) *Hydrochloric acid soln.*—Exactly 0.05N.

(j) *Alizarin indicator.*—0.01% aq. soln of sodium alizarin sulfonate (Alizarin Red S).

(k) *Potassium fluosilicate std solns.*—(*1*) *Stock soln.*—0.5 mg F/ml. Dissolve and dil. 0.9662 g (corrected for purity as indicated below) K_2SiF_6 to 1 L (much more will not dissolve). Soln keeps indefinitely in paraffined bottle. (*2*) *Working soln.*—10 μg F/ml. Prep soln used in titrn, **25.035,** by dilg 20 ml stock soln to 1 L. Soln is stable several weeks in ordinary volumetric ware.

If pure K_2SiF_6 is not obtainable, prep. as follows: Add, thru dropping funnel, satd soln of NaF, or suspension of crude K_2SiF_6, into 500 ml Claisen distg app. contg 60 ml H_2SO_4 (1 + 1), some glass beads, and 10–20 g powd SiO_2 (or glass) kept at boiling temp. of 120–125°. Distill into 25% soln of KCl, held at simmering temp. on hot plate so that vol. of distillate does not become excessive. If necessary, add more H_2O to mixt. from dropping funnel in side-neck of still. Regulate rate of addn of fluoride to still and temp. of condensing H_2O so that side arm and condenser do not become clogged with evolved H_2SiF_6, which tends to lodge as gelatinous mass. K_2SiF_6 is formed in receiver and altho entirely cryst. it assumes appearance of gelatinous mass.

When substantial amt collects, pour contents of receiver into large centrfg bottle and wash repeatedly by centrfg (shaking up ppt thoroly each time), until washings are Cl-free by test. Collect on buchner and either air-dry or bring to constant wt *in vacuo* at 50–70°.

Det. purity by Travers titrn, **6.021,** at boiling temp. with 0.2N NaOH (1 ml = 0.01101 g K_2SiF_6); also by conversion to K_2SO_4 by treating 0.3–0.4 g in deep Pt dish with little H_2O, then H_2SO_4 plus little HF, fuming off excess acid *carefully* (if overheated, mixt. has tendency to spatter), and heating to constant wt of K_2SO_4 at 650°. With glass app. entirely pure product is not usually obtained, as some contamination with SiO_2 results from leaching effect of vapors on condenser. Pure product can be obtained by use of Pt still. Prep. stock soln, correcting wt of 0.9662 by purity factor of the K_2SiF_6 (figure for purity obtained from av. of 2 above methods of assay).

(l) *Thorium nitrate soln.*—0.25 g $Th(NO_3)_4$.$12H_2O$ or 0.20 g $Th(NO_3)_4$.$4H_2O$/L. Check titer against std (10 μg/ml) F soln as follows: Measure 10, 20, 30, etc., up to 80 μg F into 100 ml Nessler tubes, and add 4.00 ml 0.05N HCl (2.00 ml if 50 ml Nessler tubes are used, and carrying range to only 50 μg F) (JAOAC **24,** 350(1941)). Dil. mixt. to ca 80 (or 40) ml mark and add 1.00 ml 1.0% NH_2OH.HCl soln. Mix; then add exactly 2.00 ml alizarin indicator (or 1.00 ml for smaller tube) and measure in Th soln from buret, mixing frequently until, when sighting down tube toward white reflecting surface, incipient pink or salmon pink color is observed. Add little H_2O occasionally so that soln is nearly to mark as end point is approached. Finally, make exactly to mark and mix thoroly before checking final end point. Do not shake tube violently (5–6 gentle inversions are enough).

Make effort to secure end point shade intermediate between yellowish-green of acid indicator and reddish-purple of fully developed Th lake. Complete series and plot ml Th soln against ml std fluoride to obtain rough equivalence curve for 2 solns. Depending upon amt of F known to be present, add Th soln in 1–2 ml portions at first, with final addns of 0.25 ml.

25.033   *Preparation of Sample*

(*Caution: See* **46.011** and **46.028**.)

Methods of sample prepn are designed to furnish representative sample in workable quantity of material and to obtain sample in condition for final distn. Mineralization by ashing is usually involved. Some mineral food products can be dissolved in and distd from $HClO_4$, **25.034**, provided no interferences appear in final distillate.

In general, 20 g or more of dry material, 50–100 ml liq. samples, and 50–100 g undried food products or plant material can be taken for analysis, depending upon expected F content and interferences, such as excessive Cl, which use of large samples may introduce. For reasonable precision in analysis of low F foods, sample should be sufficient to yield titer of ≥ 0.5 ml for aliquot taken in final titrn. However, it may not always be possible to handle this amt of material. If adequate grinding and mixing equipment is available, it is often feasible to prep. large quantities of material (vegetables, mixed foods) and to take aliquot portions for analysis (Ind. Eng. Chem., Anal. Ed. **13**, 93(1941)).

Dry plant materials, feeds, bone meal, etc., can be ground to convenient size in Wiley mill and thoroly mixed before sample is taken. Following special methods for certain products are indicated:

(a) *Direct ashing.*—Applicable to fibrous (not highly fatty) food materials, liq. samples, and in general to all foods that can be thoroly wet with aq. fixative soln. This method will apply to majority of food products.

Weigh suitable portion of prepd sample into clean Pt dish and add 25 ml $Ca(OH)_2$ suspension. (Porcelain casseroles or dishes are second choice because they may contribute small amts of F and Al_2O_3 to sample). Mix in $Ca(OH)_2$ suspension with glass rod, adding addnl H_2O if necessary; rinse and remove rod. Dry *thoroly* on steam bath or in hot air oven; then slowly char sample by heating over low flame or elec. plate with thermostat. Overhead radiant heater is convenient for both drying and charring sample. Control excessive swelling of high sugar foods by playing small flame over surface of sample from time to time, and char these products *slowly* so that excessive acidity is not generated. When sample is charred past danger of catching fire, ash in muffle at 600°. (For very small samples and min. blanks it may be advisable to cover ashing vessel with inverted Pyrex petri dish while ashing.)

For plants high in silica, fusion with NaOH may be necessary (Anal. Chem. **25**, 450, 1061(1953)).

When clean ash is obtained, cool dish and wet ash with ca 10 ml H_2O. (Small amt of unburned C does not interfere but if much is apparent, dry down and repeat ashing.) Cover dish with watch glass and cautiously introduce under cover just enough $HClO_4$ soln to dissolve ash. Rinse down cover with little H_2O and transfer soln to freshly prepd F still, **25.034**, thru long-stem funnel. Rinse dish with re-mainder of distg acid, using ca 20 ml in all, and adding and transferring in several small portions. *Do not prolong transferring operation.* Finally rinse funnel and stirring rod into dish, assemble still, and complete rinsing of dish with several small portions H_2O, pouring these into dropping funnel of still. If distg H_2O is added as steam, **25.031**(a), rinse dish with little addnl H_2O and add directly to acid mixt. in still, but avoid excessive initial vol. Add ca 6 Pyrex beads and enough $AgClO_4$ soln, **25.032**(d), to ppt all Cl. (Reasonable excess of $AgClO_4$ does no harm; enough solid Ag_2SO_4 may also be used.) Proceed as in **25.034**.

(b) *Preliminary distillation.*—(Necessary with certain products high in phosphate, such as Ca phosphate and bone meal, in order to eliminate distd H_3PO_4 that may be present in appreciable amts in first distillates. Also advisable with certain excessively fatty materials that may not be thoroly wet with $Ca(OH)_2$ fixative, thus causing F loss in direct ashing method.)

(1) *For inorganic phosphatic materials, such as Ca phosphate.*—Weigh sample, usually 10 g, into still; add few glass beads, enough $AgClO_4$ to ppt possible Cl, and ca 20 ml $HClO_4$ soln. (If inorg. phosphatic material does not contain excessive Ca (enough to cause heavy ppt of $CaSO_4$ in still), use similar amt of $1 + 1$ H_2SO_4. Distill at 135–140°, collecting ca 200 ml distillate. (For this preliminary distn, extreme care in securing low-acid distillate is not essential.) Evap. distillate to dryness in Pt dish after addn of excess $Ca(OH)_2$ suspension, assuring alk. conditions by testing with drop of phthln. (If H_2SO_4 is used in this preliminary distn, add to distillate few drops of *F-free 30% H_2O_2* to oxidize possible sulfites.) Heat dried residue at 600° few min to destroy indicator residues and possible Cl-contg compds. Transfer contents of dish to freshly prepd still, **25.034**, with 20 ml distg $HClO_4$ soln as in (a), and proceed with final distn as in **25.034**.

Take 20 ml samples of sirupy H_3PO_4 and collect ≥ 300 ml first distillate at 135°, letting H_3PO_4 function as its own distg acid. (More distillate is necessary because H_3PO_4 is less effective as F distg acid.) Neutze with $Ca(OH)_2$ suspension, evap. to dryness, transfer to prepd still as above, and proceed as in **25.034**.

(2) *For organic phosphatic materials, such as bone meal, feed supplements, etc.*—As preliminary ashing treatment to destroy most org. matter, moisten sample with enough $Ca(OH)_2$ suspension, dry, char, and heat 2–3 hr at 600°. Transfer ashed material to still, which contains several beads and enough $AgClO_4$ to ppt Cl, with 20 ml distg acid ($HClO_4$ or H_2SO_4, depending on Ca content of sample) as in (a), and continue as in (b)(1), "Distill at 135–140° ..."

Certain organic phosphatic materials (small samples of bone, 2–5 g, such as entire bones of small test animals) *in which amt of organic matter is not excessive*, may be distd directly as in (b)(1) without preliminary ashing. If sample contains appreciable Ca (bone samples), use $HClO_4$ with reasonable precaution; if org. phosphatic material does not contain excessive Ca, use $1 + 1$ H_2SO_4. In either case add more $Ca(OH)_2$ to first distillates and ash for longer periods to completely destroy distd org. matter (fatty acids). Transfer contents of dish to freshly prepd still, **25.034**, with 20 ml $HClO_4$ soln as in (a) and proceed with final distn, **25.034**.

Baking powders (Ca phosphate and combination types): Place 10 g sample in deep, covered Pt dish or casserole and slake cautiously with ca 20 ml $Ca(OH)_2$ suspension. After action subsides, rinse cover, dry contents of dish *thoroly*, and ash 2–3 hr at 600°. Cool dish and, because of excess of carbonate in ash, treat it with several small portions of warm H_2O, breaking up with flat-end stirring rod, and transfer leachings to still. Transfer remaining contents of dish with 20 ml $HClO_4$ soln, avoiding excessive effervescence when acid is added to carbonate soln in still. Add several glass beads and enough $AgClO_4$ soln, and proceed as in (b)(*1*), "Distill at 135–140° ..." With *combination* or *Na Al sulfate* baking powders, collect ≥ 400 ml preliminary distillate, (b)(*4*).

Use of special still trap makes possible analysis of highly phosphatic *inorg. or thoroly ashed* materials, and phosphoric acids, with single distn. Special trap, or scrubber, consists of 12–15 g small, hollow glass beads supported in side-neck of the 125 ml Claisen flask by several indentations punched in side wall, and capped by glass disk or inverted bottom of 15 mm test tube. After construction of glass-bead scrubber, side-neck is sealed off immediately above outlet tube. (Beads in scrubber must be wet with little H_3PO_4 (by tipping flask) before distn to furnish liq. acid phase.) Take 20 ml sirupy H_3PO_4, by itself, and 10 g samples Ca phosphate with 20 ml $HClO_4$ soln, for distn, and collect ≥ 400 ml distillate at 135°. With single distn observe precautions outlined in **25.031**(a), and also in **25.034**, regarding neutzn of final distillates. (Distillates should show practically no acidity.) Presence of only *traces* of distd H_3PO_4 will vitiate titrn; as little as 20 μg P_2O_5 will definitely interfere. Accordingly, if single distn procedure is to be applied with confidence, it is necessary to test distillates obtained from phosphatic materials, by means of the special still, for presence of this interference.

For convenient test utilizing Schricker reagent (JAOAC **22**, 167(1939)), add 5 ml of $1 + 9$ diln of this reagent to 45 ml distillate in 50 ml cylinder or Nessler tube, mix, and immerse in steam bath 5–10 min. Compare against blank by sighting down tube. Blue or blue-green color indicates phosphate, and as little as 5 μg (as P_2O_5) is readily detected. If distillate shows traces, make sure that such amts are below interference level of 15 μg in titrn aliquot before titrg addnl portions of distillate. (Test with Schricker reagent is also useful in usual double distn where phosphate interference is possible. Use of special trap will save time where highly phosphatic

materials are handled routinely, but it is not justified in ordinary work because of poor efficiency owing to excessive refluxing in distn.)

(*3*) *For excessively fatty and oily food materials* (*oil-packed foods, certain meats, etc., also entire undried and unground organs of test animals*).—If there is danger of F loss thru incomplete wetting with $Ca(OH)_2$ fixative soln, handle as follows: Weigh appropriate quantity of sample, usually 10–25 g, into still, and add Ag (preferably 0.1–0.2 g solid Ag_2SO_4), several glass beads, and 20–25 ml H_2SO_4 $(1 + 1)$. Distill at 130–135° and collect 200–250 ml distillate in beaker or open vessel. If foaming is excessive, increase quantity of distg acid, and where necessary use larger (250–300 ml) still. If larger still or more acid is used, collect proportionately more first distillate. (Oil or fat of many of these products will tend to prevent foaming; and in some instances use of ca pea-size piece of pure paraffin is addnl aid.)

Oxidize distillate in cold by cautious addn of 2–3 ml *F-free 30% H_2O_2* to remove sulfites, let stand few min, and evap. portionwise in Pt dish contg excess (10–15 ml) $Ca(OH)_2$ suspension. Ash residue at 600° until clean. Proceed as in (b)(*1*), beginning "Transfer contents of dish to freshly prepd still ..."

Handle pure oils by similar procedure: Use 10 g sample with 25 ml H_2SO_4 $(1 + 1)$ and carry temp. at first to ca 170° to saponify; then carefully bring temp. down to 140° with distg H_2O and collect 250 ml or more of distillate. (It will probably be necessary to use higher reading thermometer for this procedure.) Oxidize distillate with 30% H_2O_2 and evap. to dryness after adding excess $Ca(OH)_2$ suspension. Ash at 600° and after brief preliminary ash period remove dish, add little H_2O plus addnl 1–2 ml of the H_2O_2 to remove sulfides, dry, and complete ashing. Proceed as in (b)(*1*), beginning "Transfer contents of dish to freshly prepd still ..."

(*4*) *For aluminum and boron compounds*.—Al and B repress evolution of F. Isolate F by preliminary distn at elevated temp. For this purpose, weigh sample, usually 5–10 g, into still, add 25 ml H_2SO_4 $(1 + 1)$, and conduct first distn at 160–165° (special thermometer), collecting 300 ml distillate. Oxidize distillate with 30% H_2O_2 as above, evap. in Pt dish with excess $Ca(OH)_2$ suspension, ash briefly at 600°, and proceed as in (b)(*1*), beginning, "Transfer contents of dish to freshly prepd still ..."

25.034   *Final Distillation*
(*Caution: See* **46.011** *and* **46.028**.)

Always make final distn from $HClO_4$, and take precautions to secure low acid distillate, **25.031**(a). Since interferences, such as org. matter, phosphate, sulfate, etc., must be absent from distillate, make distn with careful temp. control in presence of enough Ag salt to repress HCl evolution (**25.030**). It is well to check distillates for presence of possible phosphate as in **25.033**(b)(*2*), and where advisable, as in (b)(*4*), to test for sulfate with little dil. $BaCl_2$

soln. HClO$_4$ used in final distn is usually used in transferring ash to still, **25.033**(a). Few acid-alkali washed beads are used to control bumping. (Use of powd SiO$_2$ does not appear necessary for micro-detn.)

To promote better recoveries, and to minimize and render constant distn blank discussed in **25.030** and **25.035**, prep. still by special cleaning process before this transfer by treating it with *hot* 10% NaOH soln after each detn, flushing out with tap H$_2$O, and then rinsing with distd H$_2$O. Occasionally (at least once daily, and especially after it has stood idle for any length of time), give still addnl treatment by boiling down 15–20 ml H$_2$SO$_4$ (1 + 1) until still is filled with fumes. Cool, pour off acid, treat with the 10% NaOH soln, and *thoroly* rinse out. (Cleaning should be especially meticulous after high-F or high-SiO$_2$ samples have been distd, and in such cases condenser should also be cleaned.)

At this stage prepd sample has been transferred to specially treated still, as directed above, for final isolation of F. Begin distn, and when temp. reaches 137°, keep at this point (±2°) by adding H$_2$O from dropping funnel, **25.031**(a). Heat still at such rate that all distns require ca same time. (This promotes uniformity in blank correction.) Catch distillate in 150 or 200 ml vol. flask. After few ml distillate collects, add 1–2 drops *p*-nitrophenol indicator, (e), and keep distillate alk. to this indicator (faintest perceptible yellow) by occasionally adding 1–2 drops 0.05N KOH from 10 ml buret during distn while swirling receiver. So regulate this addn of alkali that distillate is neutzd (within 1 drop of alkali) as it approaches mark. Carefully note vol. alkali used. Dil. distillate to vol. and mix thoroly. Do not let F distillate stand more than few min before neutzg.

If sample contains such large amts of Cl that bumping in still cannot be controlled, dissolve ash of another sample, and acidify *slightly* with HClO$_4$. Dil. considerably and ppt Cl in dish with AgClO$_4$ soln, avoiding large excess. Filter thru glass filter, wash ppt *thoroly* with hot H$_2$O, and evap. filtrate and washings to dryness after adding excess (to alky) of Ca(OH)$_2$ suspension. Transfer residue to still with HClO$_4$ soln and repeat distn as above.

25.035 *Titration*

(*Caution: See* **46.011** and **46.028**.)

Place aliquot of final distillate in Nessler tube and mark "S" (sample). (Optimum F content for titrn is 60–70 μg for 100 ml Nessler tubes and 30–40 μg for 50 ml size, and it is well to make exploratory titrn on small aliquot to check approx. F content of distillate. Larger tubes are necessary for precise results on low-F foods.)

Add 0.05N HCl, 4.00 ml for 100 ml tubes and 2.00 ml for 50 ml size, and 1.00 ml NH$_2$OH.HCl soln. (For routine work *with 100 ml tubes*, dissolve 1.0 g NH$_2$OH.HCl in 500 ml 0.04N HCl and dil. to 500

ml. Then proper amt of both reagents can be added to tubes in single operation with 5 ml pipet.) Dil. to ca 90 (or 40) ml, mix well, then add proper amt alizarin indicator (2.00 or 1.00 ml), and mix again. Always add and mix in NH$_2$OH.HCl before adding indicator.

Prep. blank tube "B" by adding proper amt HCl and NH$_2$OH.HCl, and amt 0.05N KCl soln representing same proportion of total vol. of 0.05N KOH used to neutze distillate as aliquot vol. taken for sample tube represents of total distillate vol. (Thus, if 1.50 ml 0.05N KOH was used to neutze distillate of 150 ml and aliquot taken for tube "S" was 75 ml, add 0.75 ml 0.05N KCl to tube "B.") Dil. and mix, allowing slightly more headspace than in sample tube. Then add proper vol. alizarin indicator and mix.

Measure Th soln into tube "S," mixing between addns, until end point of about proper shade is reached. Dil. to mark, mix, and check this end point shade. Note from curve, **25.032**(l), approx. vol. std F soln corresponding to this vol. Th soln, and add ca 0.5 ml *less* than this amt of std F soln to "B." Mix; then add exactly same vol. Th soln. as was added to "S," duplicating approx. increments in which it was added and number of mixings. Dil. nearly to mark and compare colors of "S" and "B." (If vol. std F soln added to "B" was properly chosen, this tube should be only slightly pinker in shade than sample tube.)

Bleach "B" tube to exact match with tube "S" by adding more std F soln to "B" in increments of 1–2 drops, mixing gently between addns. Dil. to mark for final comparison and observe usual precautions of letting bubbles subside and of transposing tubes when final comparisons are made. (At match-point, F content of tube "S" equals amt added to tube "B.") Check this end point by adding 1–2 drops excess std F soln to tube "B." Distinct over-bleach should develop.

Repeat titrn on aliquots of different size to obtain total amt of F distd. If time is available, repeat entire detn with different wt sample.

For precise work, evaluation of reagent and of distn blank is necessary, **25.030**. Det. distn blank by making several distns with prescribed amts HClO$_4$ and AgClO$_4$ solns from freshly cleaned still, titrg distillate as above with as large aliquot as practicable. Av. of values found should be ≤3 μg F. If quantities found by individual blank detns are too small to be detd accurately, make 5 or more sep. distns and evap. distillates, 150 ml each time, successively in same Pt dish for final distn and average blank figure. Distn and total detn blanks can usually be *combined* by carrying run (with same amts of reagents and similar evapn and ashing treatment) thru entire detn. Reagents and manipulations should increase distn blank but little.

Calc. total quantity F distd from quantity found in aliquot titrd, subtract proper blank, and refer net figure to wt sample taken. If double distn procedure was used, make appropriate blank correction.

Rapid Method Restricted to Fluoride Residues on Apples and Pears

25.036   Principles

Acid filtrate from strip soln of apples and pears prepd with HCl rinse and acidification, **25.054**, is used. Aliquot of filtrate is oxidized colorless with $KMnO_4$, soln is then reduced with NH_2OH, and sub-aliquot is back-titrd in Nessler tubes; $Zr(NO_3)_4$ is used in titrn, with purpurin (1,2,4-trihydroxyanthraquinone) as indicator (Ind. Eng. Chem., Anal. Ed. **6**, 118(1934)). Principle of back-titrn, as applied here, is similar to that used in general method where $Th(NO_3)_4$ and alizarin occupy similar roles. Provision is made for removal of interfering anions, and high acidity used in titrn minimizes interference of metals that would otherwise lake with indicator.

25.037   Apparatus

Nessler tubes.—50 ml g-s, tall-form, matched for ht and color (*see* **25.040**).

25.038   Reagents

(a) *Mixed nitrate soln.*—Dissolve 3.0 g $Ba(NO_3)_2$ and 2.0 g $Th(NO_3)_4 \cdot 4H_2O$ in H_2O, and dil. to 100 ml.

(b) *Potassium permanganate soln.*—Satd; ca 6%.

(c) *Hydroxylamine hydrochloride soln.*—5%.

(d) *Ferrous chloride soln.*—Dissolve ca 1.0 g Fe powder or wire in 50 ml HCl (1 + 1), dil., and filter into 500 ml vol. flask. Add few ml 5% $NH_2OH \cdot HCl$ soln and dil. to vol. Dil. still further before use, if desired.

(e) *Purpurin indicator.*—0.01% w/v in alcohol. Dissolve 25 mg pure 1,2,4-trihydroxyanthraquinone in alcohol, heating if necessary, and dil. to 250 ml with same solv. *Prep. fresh weekly.*

(f) *Zirconium nitrate soln.*—Dissolve 1.50 g $Zr(NO_3)_4 \cdot 5H_2O$ in H_2O, acidify with 20 ml HCl, and dil. to 1 L. Filter if not clear.

(g) *Fluoride std soln.*—54.5 µg F/ml. Dissolve 0.1464 g pure NaF in H_2O and dil. to 1 L.

25.039   Determination

Place 20 ml well-mixed acid strip filtrate, **25.054**, in 50 ml vol. flask. Add 2.0 ml mixed nitrate soln, then 4.0 ml $KMnO_4$ soln. Rinse down neck of flask with little H_2O and place on active steam bath 5 min. Remove flask, and while still hot, add 5% $NH_2OH \cdot HCl$ soln from buret, slowly and with swirling, until MnO_2 is dissolved and soln is colorless. Add ca 0.5 ml of this reagent in excess. (Appreciable phosphate is revealed as flocculent $Th_3(PO_4)_4$, and sulfate as ppt with Ba. Sometimes $KMnO_4$ is occluded in sulfate and/or phosphate ppt, and pink color tends to persist but does not interfere.) Cool, dil. to vol., and filter. (Filtrate must be clear. If there is perceptible

turbidity, return filtrate thru filter several times if necessary, until filtrate is *brilliant*.) Pipet 25 ml clear filtrate into Nessler tube and mark "S."

For blank or comparison tube use 25 ml "blank" soln, contg reagents used in method, prepd as follows:

Dil. 50 ml 10% Na oleate soln, **25.043**(k), 50 ml 30 g/100 ml NaOH soln, and 15 ml HCl to 1 L. Acidify portions with $\frac{1}{10}$ vol. HCl as if soln were an actual "strip," and filter, refiltering until filtrate is perfectly clear. (Chilling soln and shaking vigorously will "churn" pptd oleic acid and aid in obtaining clear filtrate.) Carry 20 ml portions of acidified filtrate thru method exactly as above. (In order more closely to duplicate conditions of actual detn, use 50 ml vol. flasks and 20 ml aliquots in preference to using larger aliquots with correspondingly larger amts of reagents. After being dild to vol. and filtered, blank solns may be combined to form supply of "blank"; 10 portions worked up as above yield ca 500 ml "blank," or enough for ca 20 detns.)

Add 25 ml of this "blank" to second Nessler tube, "B," and to both tubes "S" and "B" add 15.0 ml HCl measured as carefully as possible from graduate. (Always add acid to soln instead of vice versa.) Mix, and match tubes for color. "S" tube will usually be found to have slight greenish tint in comparison with "B" tube, due presumably to traces of Fe. Balance both tubes to same shade by adding $FeCl_2$ soln dropwise to appropriate tube and mixing. *This operation must be done carefully.* When tints are indistinguishable, add exactly 1.00 ml purpurin indicator to each tube. Mix; then add 1.50 ml Zr soln to each tube from 10 ml buret, and mix. Do not shake tubes violently when mixing in reagents; 4 or 5 gentle inversions are enough. Observe color difference, if any, between tubes when looking down their length toward white reflecting surface. If there is no appreciable difference *after 5 min*, F content of sample is negligible. If color of tube "S" is yellower, presence of F is indicated. In this case, add addnl amts of $Zr(NO_3)_4$ soln to tube "S" until its color matches about that of tube "B" (to nearest 0.5 ml Zr soln). Dil. "S" to mark and mix.

Now add to "B" exactly same total vol. Zr soln as was added to tube "S," mix, and let tube stand 2 min for lake to develop fully. Back-titr. std F soln into "B" from 10 ml buret until tubes match, mixing frequently, and dilg nearly to vol. as end point approaches. Add NaF soln in increments of ca 0.1 ml at this stage, and observe usual precautions of transposing tubes and letting bubbles subside when making comparisons. Dil. to mark for final comparison. Check end point by adding 0.1–0.2 ml std F soln in excess. Distinct overbleach should develop.

For sample wt of 1 kg and aliquots prescribed above, each ml std F soln consumed in back-titrn is equiv. to F content on fruit sample, *removable by solv. treatment*, of 3.0 ppm. Correct result obtained in titrn by sample wt ratio. (Thus, titer of 3.27 ml std F soln, with 1.40 kg sample (ca 10 fruit), represents F content of 7.0 ppm. Vol. restrictions of 50 ml Nessler tube will allow estn of spray residue content up to ca 11 ppm F.) If calibration mark is exceeded in back-titrn, use 10 ml aliquot of acid filtrate in tube "S," and dil. to 25 ml with "blank" soln, correcting titer of std F soln by appropriate factor.

25.040   *Notes on Rapid Method*

G-s Nessler tubes are almost essential with concd acid prescribed in this detn and are likewise desirable in general method for F with Th and alizarin, **25.035.** Analysts familiar with Th-alizarin back-titrn method should have no difficulty with Zr-purpurin titrn. With latter, however, color changes are not so apparent and titrn is less sensitive. However, with careful work, results accurate to at least 0.5 ppm may be expected.

Indicator color at prescribed acidity is yellow, and fully laked indicator is orange-red. This contrasts with Th titrn where corresponding range is from yellowish-green to reddish-purple. Hence in rapid method choice of end point involves discrimination between varying shades of orange. Addn of 1.50 ml Zr soln to tube "B" at start is merely to provide intermediate shade of orange to guide analyst in amt of Zr to be added to tube "S." Analysts may prefer to work with redder or yellower end point shade. In any event, make number of titrns by adding varying amts of std F soln as unknowns to Nessler tubes and carrying thru back-titrn as above, for purpose of learning color changes involved. Pure aq. solns instead of "blank" may be used, with acidities of 20 ml HCl/50 ml.

Accuracy of results with rapid method presupposes complete removal of spray residue F by solv. process and good accuracy (not necessarily precision) in titrn. These conditions may not always hold; unless carefully done, solv. method may not be entirely effective, and results on strip solns contg known amts of F have tended to be slightly low. Hence accuracy >95% is not to be expected with this method.

LEAD (8)—OFFICIAL FINAL ACTION
25.041   *Principles*

General method calls for ashing, **25.044,** sepn of Pb, either as dithizone complex, **25.046,** or as sulfide, **25.047,** followed by colorimetric dithizone detn, **25.048,** in comparator tubes, or with spectrophtr. Subject of interference is treated sep., **25.049–25.051,** and analyst should familiarize himself with details of these sections before applying method. Special methods of sample prepn are presented in **25.052– 25.053.**

25.042   *Precautions*

Analyst should decide whether nature of detn requires unusual care in purification of reagents, or whether blank detn will suffice. Smaller the quantity of Pb to be detd, greater the care required in reduction of blank (*see also* **25.048**).

To test suitability of reagents place 10–15 g solid reagents dissolved in redistd H_2O or 15–20 ml concd acids previously neutzd with redistd NH_4OH in separator and add enough Pb-free citric acid to prevent pptn by NH_4OH of Fe, Al, alk. earth phosphates, or other substances. Make soln ammoniacal and add 2–3 ml 10% KCN soln. Shake soln with ca 5 ml dithizone soln, **25.043(e)** (5–10 mg/L). If lower layer is green, transfer it to another separator and ext excess dithizone with NH_4OH (1 + 99) to which has been added drop of KCN soln. If $CHCl_3$ layer is colorless, consider test neg. for general analytical purposes.

When special purification becomes necessary, redistill H_2O (distd H_2O stored in Sn-lined tanks usually contains Pb and Sn), HNO_3, HCl, HBr, Br, and $CHCl_3$ in all-glass stills (preferably Pyrex). Prep. NH_4OH by distg ordinary reagent into ice-cold redistd H_2O. If stills are new, steam them out with hot HCl or HNO_3 vapors to remove "surface" Pb. (Subsequent distillates may not be totally Pb-free.)

Purify citric acid, NaOAc or NH_4OAc, $Al(NO_3)_3$, $Ca(NO_3)_2$, and Na_2SO_4 by pptg Pb from their aq. solns with H_2S (*Caution: See* **46.059**), using 5–10 mg $CuSO_4$ as coprecipitant (citric acid and $Al(NO_3)_3$ solns require adjustment with NH_4OH to pH 3.0– 3.5, bromophenol blue indicator). Filter (fritted glass filter is most convenient), boil filtrates 20 min to expel excess H_2S, and refilter if necessary to obtain brilliantly clear solns. Purify other reagents by recrystn.

Store redistd acids or purified solns of reagents in resistant glass containers of min. Pb content (Pyrex is suitable), carefully cleaned of surface Pb with hot HNO_3. Paraffin-lined bottles may be used for alk. reagents.

Carefully clean new glass and chemical ware with hot 10% NaOH soln followed by hot HNO_3, and use only for Pb detns.

In prepn of samples for analysis, avoid Pb contamination. If mixing or grinding is necessary, use porcelain mortar if possible. Avoid use of metal food grinders unless previous experiment has shown that no contamination of sample with Pb or Sn results. If product to be analyzed cannot be thoroly mixed in its own container, or if composite sample of number of containers is desired, empty into large glass jar or porcelain dish and mix thoroly with wooden spoon or porcelain spatula. If liq. portion of sample cannot be incorporated into ground solid material to obtain homogeneous mixt., analyze sep. If food is packed in tins having soldered seams (sardines and meats), open tins from bottom to avoid contaminating sample with bits of solder. Avoid sifting in prepn of samples to prevent metallic contamination or segregation of Pb.

General Method
Sn and Bi Absent

(Applicable to such materials as carbohydrates, cereals and cereal products, cacao and dairy products, feeds, meats, fish, plant material, fruit and fruit products, fresh vegetables, etc., and in general to all org. materials (except fats) in which no Sn and Bi are encountered. For products contg Sn (canned foods) or Bi proceed as in **25.049–25.051**.)

25.043   **Reagents**

*(Caution: See **46.047**.)*

(a) *Lead std solns.*—(*1*) *Stock soln.*—2 mg Pb (3.197 mg Pb(NO₃)₂)/ml in 1% HNO₃. Prep. from Pb(NO₃)₂ purified as follows: Dissolve 20–50 g in min. of hot H₂O and cool with stirring. Filter crystals with suction on small buchner, redissolve, and recrystallize. Dry crystals at 100–110° to constant wt. Cool in desiccator and store in tightly stoppered bottle. (Product has no H₂O of crystn and is not appreciably hygroscopic.) (*2*) *Working solns.*—Prep. as needed by dilg stock soln with 1% HNO₃.

(b) *Nitric acid.*—1%. Dil. 10 ml fresh, colorless HNO₃ (sp gr 1.40) to 1 L with redistd H₂O. If acid has been redistd, boil off nitrous fumes before dilg.

(c) *"Ash-aid" soln.*—Dissolve 40 g Al(NO₃)₃ .9H₂O and 20 g Ca(NO₃)₂.4H₂O in 100 ml H₂O.

(d) *Citric acid soln.*—Concd Pb-free soln. 1 ml = 0.5 g citric acid (reagent partially neutzd with NH₄OH during purification, **25.042**, fourth par.).

(e) *Diphenylthiocarbazone (dithizone).*—Dissolve ca 1 g com. reagent in 50–75 ml CHCl₃ and filter if insol. material remains. Shake out in separator with four 100 ml portions metal-free (redistd) NH₄OH (1 + 99). (Dithizone passes into aq. phase to give orange soln.) Filter aq. exts into large separator thru cotton pledget inserted in stem of funnel. Acidify slightly with dil. HCl and ext pptd dithizone with two or three 20 ml portions CHCl₃. Combine exts in separator and wash 2 or 3 times with H₂O. Draw off into beaker and evap. CHCl₃ with gentle heat on steam bath, avoiding spattering as soln goes to dryness. Remove last traces of moisture by heating 1 hr at ≤50° *in vacuo*. Store dry reagent in dark in tightly stoppered bottle. Prep. reagent solns for extn to contain 100, 50, and 10 mg/L in freshly redistd CHCl₃ (JAOAC **21**, 695(1938); **26**, 26(1943)) and store in dark at 5–10°. (Stock soln of dithizone in CHCl₃ contg 1 mg/ml will keep long time and is convenient for use in making dilns.) Soln of 30 mg/L CHCl₃ stored in dispensing app. is required for use in rapid method, **25.055**.

(f) *Ammonia-cyanide mixture.*—To 100 ml 10% recrystd, PO₄-free KCN (JAOAC **20**, 191(1937)) in 500 ml vol. flask add enough redistd NH₄OH to introduce 19.1 g NH₃, and dil. to vol. with redistd H₂O. (Concn of redistd NH₄OH can be detd by sp gr or titrn.)

(g) *Pure metallic tin.*—Purest obtainable, such as NBS Sample No. 42 (99.9999 + % Sn). Granulate Sn as finely as possible by melting and pouring very slowly into H₂O. Det. Pb content as follows: Dis-

solve 1–2 g sample in HBr or HCl and volatilize Sn by evapg soln to dryness and treating with several 5 ml portions of the HBr-Br mixt., (h), evapg to dryness on steam bath after each treatment. Take up with 2–3 ml HNO₃, evap. to dryness to expel Br, and take up with ca 50 ml hot H₂O. Filter, and proceed as in **25.046** and **25.048**.

(h) *Hydrobromic acid-bromine mixture.*—To 250 ml 40% redistd HBr add 35 ml redistd liq. Br.

(i) *Sodium polysulfide soln.*—Dissolve 480 g Na₂S.9H₂O and 40 g NaOH in H₂O, add 16 g powd S, shake until S dissolves, filter, and dil. to 1 L.

(j) *Hydrochloric-citric acid soln.*—Add quantity reagent (d) equiv. to 50 g citric acid to 50 ml HCl and dil. to 250 ml.

(k) *Sodium oleate soln.*—10%. To 45 ml 30% NaOH soln and 400 ml H₂O in 1.5 L beaker, add slowly, while heating and stirring, 90 g (by difference from separator) oleic acid. Heat mixt. on steam bath until soap is entirely dissolved. (Small flocculent ppt of impurities may remain.) Cool, dil. to 1 L, mix, and filter.

(l) *Ammonia-cyanide-citrate soln.*—Dissolve 10 g PO₄-free KCN and 10 g citric acid in 250 ml NH₄OH (sp gr 0.90) and dil. to 1 L. Reagent is conveniently preserved in dispensing app. that causes min. volatilization of NH₃.

(m) *Washed filter paper.*—Soak 9 cm quant. papers overnight in 1% HNO₃. Wash with large vols H₂O on buchner to remove acid and any traces of Pb.

25.044   *Preparation of Sample (Ashing)*

*(Caution: See **46.025** and **46.028**.)*

Quantity of material taken for sample depends upon amt available and expected Pb content. In general, weigh representative sample of 5–200 g, depending upon amt sample available and expected Pb content, into suitable porcelain dish or casserole. Dry wet samples on steam bath or in oven. Add 2–5 ml "ash-aid" soln, (c), to products difficult to ash (meats), or to furnish ash bulk to low ash products (candies, and jellies low in fruit content); mix well, and dry.

Char gelatin, carbohydrate foods such as jam, and other products that tend to swell excessively by carefully heating over burner. (Swelling can be controlled by playing small flame from glass jet over surface of material in dish, but metallic burner must not be used for this purpose because of possible metallic contamination.) Do not let material ignite. Milk, candies, etc., may be charred without ignition by adding sample little at time to casserole heated over burner or hot plate. (Overhead radiant heater is often very convenient.) When samples are dry or charred, place in temp.-controlled muffle and raise temp. *slowly* to 500° without ignition.

If sample contains fat, "smoke" it away by heating long enough at ca 350°. Cover floor of muffle with piece of asbestos board or SiO₂ plate so that sample receives most of its heat by radiation from sides and roof and not by conduction from hotter floor of muffle.

If muffle has automatic control, ash overnight at ≤500°. If sample is not completely ashed next morning or if day-time ashings at 500° are not proceeding satisfactorily, remove casserole, cool, and moisten char with 2–5 ml ash-aid. Dry contents of casserole past danger of spattering (no free liq.) and replace in muffle. If ashing is not complete or proceeding rapidly after 30 min, remove casserole, cool, and cautiously add 2–3 ml HNO_3. Dry, place in muffle, and continue ashing until practically C-free. Avoid excessive use of ash-aid, and particularly HNO_3, if sample still contains much intermixed C, because local overheating or deflagration may result, especially if much K is present in ash.

When clean ash is obtained, cool, cover casserole with watch glass, and add cautiously 15–20 ml HCl. Rinse down watch glass with H_2O and heat on steam bath. If *clear* soln is not obtained, evap. again to dryness and repeat addn of HCl. If insol. matter persists, evap. HCl and dehydrate SiO_2 by heating to fumes with 5–10 ml 60% $HClO_4$ (double distd preferred). If $HClO_4$ is used, considerable H_2O (200 ml) may be necessary to completely dissolve $KClO_4$ later as when KCN is used in dithizone extn of Pb, **25.046**.

Dil. with H_2O and filter soln when necessary with suction thru fine fritted glass filter. Catch filtrate in 500 ml g-s erlenmeyer under bell jar. Leach insol. material on filter successively with few ml hot HCl, hot HCl-citric acid soln, and hot 40% NH_4OAc soln.

In certain instances take following special precautions:

(*1*) If amt of insol. material (SiO_2) remaining on filter is abnormal, flush it into Pt dish with H_2O, evap., and treat residue with one or two 5 ml portions HF. Evap. to dryness, take up residue with H_2O and few drops of HCl or $HClO_4$, and add to bulk of ash filtrate.

(*2*) When ashing is of long duration, no ash-aid has been used, or natural ash is low with little ash bulk, Pb may be baked on dish. To remove this Pb, add few pellets (2–3 g) of NaOH and dissolve in few ml hot H_2O. Tilt dish so that sirupy soln completely wets that portion of interior originally occupied by sample; then heat short time on steam bath, but do not bring to dryness. (Overheating with concd NaOH may result in extg few μg Pb from casserole. Porcelain retains Pb to less extent than does SiO_2 but may contain very small amts of Pb.) Take up residue with H_2O and add directly to filtrate. Finally rinse dish with few ml hot HCl followed by hot H_2O.

25.045 *Isolation of Lead: Principles*

Method **25.046**, while rapid and convenient, is limited to those materials that, with aid of citric acid, yield clear ammoniacal soln required for quant. extn of Pb with dithizone. Pb is readily oc-cluded by many alk. ppts (Mg and Ca phosphates, Al and Fe hydroxides and silicates). Many food materials may be handled in this way because the naturally occurring amts of these substances are not excessive. However, some materials contain more of these substances than can be kept in soln under alk. conditions with any reasonable quantity of citric acid (JAOAC **26**, 26(1943)). In these cases proceed as in **25.047**. Difficulty of ammoniacal pptn may sometimes be overcome by limiting sample size in cases where sampling is no problem.

25.046 *Dithizone Extraction*

(Applicable to most carbohydrates and cereal foods, fruit and fruit products, milk, fresh vegetables, plant materials, etc.)

Transfer ash soln to 300 ml short-stem separator and add citric acid reagent, (**d**), equiv. to 10 g citric acid. Make slightly alk. to litmus with NH_4OH, keeping soln cool, and let stand 1–2 min. If ppt forms, redissolve with HCl and isolate Pb as in **25.047**. If no ppt forms, add 5 ml 10% KCN soln (more may be necessary if large amts of Zn, Cu, Cd, etc., are present) and check pH of soln by adding drop of *thymol blue soln* and observing color of drop (pH should be ≥8.5, blue-green to blue with thymol blue).

If ash was highly colored with Fe, keep pH of soln comparatively low, because pH of ≥10 in presence of Fe may cause oxidn of dithizone. Immediately ext with 20 ml portions dithizone reagent, using more dil. solns unless exceptionally large amts of Pb are present. Shake 20–30 sec, let layers sep., and note color of $CHCl_3$ phase. (Pb dithizone complex is red, but color may be masked by excess green dithizone, giving intermediate hues of purple and crimson. Color of $CHCl_3$ ext gives first indication of amt of Pb present, and progress of extn can be followed by noting color of successive exts.)

Drain exts directly into smaller separator contg 25 ml 1% HNO_3, (**b**). When extn is complete, shake combined exts in smaller separator and drain green dithizone layer into another separator contg addnl 25 ml portion 1% HNO_3. Shake, let layers sep., and discard $CHCl_3$ fraction. Filter acid exts contg Pb in succession thru small pledget of wet cotton inserted in stem of small funnel, into 50 ml flask or g-s cylinder, using second acid ext to wash out separator in which first acid extn was made. (This procedure removes $CHCl_3$ globules.) Make up any slight deficiency in vol. with the 1% HNO_3 and mix. Proceed as in **25.048**.

25.047 *Sulfide Separation*

(Applicable to all products and usually necessary in case of cacao products, tea, sardines, and all food products contg high proportion of alk. earth phosphates, especially those of Mg, which promote formation of ppts in ammoniacal citrate solns. *Caution: See* **46.059**.)

Cool acid soln of ash, add citric acid soln, (**d**), equiv. to 10 g citric acid, and adjust to pH 3.0–3.4

(bromophenol blue) with NH_4OH. If enough Fe is present to color soln strongly, make final adjustment with help of spot plate. (Phosphates pptd by local action of NH_4OH may usually be redissolved by shaking and cooling.) If amt of Pb is small, add 5–10 mg pure $CuSO_4.5H_2O$ to soln to act as coprecipitant. Ppt sulfides by passing in H_2S until soln is satd (3–5 min). (*Caution: See* 46.059.) Immediately filter with suction into flask in bell jar (fine fritted glass filter is preferred).

Dissolve sulfides, without previous washing, with 5 ml hot HNO_3, drawing soln thru into original flask; wash with hot H_2O, stopper, shake, and boil to remove H_2S. Transfer to 200 ml separator, add citric acid soln equiv. to 5 g citric acid, make ammoniacal, ext, and det. Pb as in 25.046 and 25.048(a) or (b).

25.048   *Colorimetric Dithizone*
Determination (9)
(Pb 0.001–0.200 mg)

Limiting factor in detn of minute quantites of Pb by colorimetric dithizone method is size of reagent blank. Importance of careful blank detns must be especially stressed when quantities of Pb of order of 1–5 μg are being detd. With special care in purification of reagents and by use of carefully cleaned Pyrex ware, including separators, it is possible to reduce reagent blank to 1 μg or less. Owing to Pb-bearing dust, vapors, etc., it is necessary to expose blank detn in muffle or on steam bath for same length of time as sample is exposed, and to use exactly same quantities of reagents (even H_2O) for blank and actual detns.

Pb is extd from aq. soln, under std conditions of vol. and pH, with definite vol. of $CHCl_3$ soln of dithizone of std concn. Optimum pH of operation is 9.5–10.0. Dithizone strengths are so chosen that excess dithizone is always present in reaction mixt. Pb is brought into $CHCl_3$ phase in form of red complex, and uncombined green dithizone partitions between aq. and $CHCl_3$ phases and modifies color of ext according to relative quantities of Pb and dithizone. Thus, series of colors from red to green may be arranged with intermediate crimsons, purples, and blues. Vols and strengths of $CHCl_3$ solns depend upon Pb range it is desired to cover and are so chosen as to give same general color progression from red to green for each range. Limiting range increases accuracy at expense of flexibility. Colors produced with std quantities of Pb furnish basis for quant. estn by comparison. Vols and concns of std dithizone for various ranges are as follows when 1 cm cell is used:

Pb Ranges μg (0.001 mg)	Concn mg/L	Volume ml
0–10	8	5
0–50	10	25
0–200	20	40

See Snyder, Anal. Chem. **19**, 684(1947), for modification operated at pH 11.5.

(a) *Simple color matching.*—Prep. 10 stds covering in equal steps the desired concn range, as follows: Use std Pb soln, (a), in 1% HNO_3, 1 ml of which equals some simple fraction or multiple of 1 μg Pb. Measure quantities representing various steps of range into series of separators and add 1% HNO_3 so that total vol. is always 50 ml. (Add acid first so that Pb soln is not lost around stopcock of separator.) Add 10 ml NH_3-cyanide mixt., (f), and mix. Resultant pH will be ca 9.7. Immediately add appropriate vol. std dithizone soln, which depends on range to be covered (*see* table), and shake 1 min. Drain lower layers into series of tubes or vials and arrange in order. For lower ranges, i.e., up to 20 μg Pb, matching is best done by viewing longitudinally in small flat-bottom vials ca 3″ long. For higher ranges, 20–50 μg and above, depth of column must be reduced, and matching is conveniently done by viewing transversely in Nessler tubes of matched diam., because even pure dithizone solns appear red by transmitted light if concn or depth of column is increased beyond certain point. If stds are kept covered when not in use they should last $\geq$1 day.

For detn, place aliquot part, or entire amt, of the 50 ml 1% HNO_3 in which Pb has been isolated, 25.046 or 25.047, in separator, and if aliquot is taken, dil. to 50 ml with 1% HNO_3. Add 10 ml NH_3-cyanide mixt., (f), and mix. Immediately develop color by shaking 1 min with proper amt std dithizone soln. Drain lower layer into tube or vial similar to those used with stds and compare. If range is exceeded, repeat with smaller aliquot or re-ext with excess dithizone before draining from separator, isolate once more in 50 ml 1% HNO_3 reagent, and compare with stds covering higher range. Interpolation between steps of various ranges should be easily made.

If aliquot of the 50 ml 1% HNO_3 in which Pb has been isolated is taken, subtract only corresponding quantity of total reagent blank from quantity of Pb found.

(b) *Photometric methods.*—Absorption spectra of the 2 components in dithizone ext (Pb dithizone complex and free dithizone) show marked difference in their ability to absorb light of wavelength 510 nm, red Pb complex absorbing strongly and green dithizone transmitting freely. Thus, when absorption of light of this wavelength by individuals of std color series, measured thru suitable cell length, is detd photometrically, linear relationship is observed between quantities of Pb and A. In making measurements, spectrophtr set at this wavelength or photometer equipped with blue-green filter centered at about this point can be used.

Stdze dithizone solns as follows: Using appropriate vols and concns of solns specified for various ranges (*see* above) in separators, prep. std colors as in visual color-matching procedure, satg std Pb and 1% HNO_3 solns with clear $CHCl_3$ before use, and thereby eliminating differences in vol. of ext between stds and unknowns. (It is unnecessary to prep. full

10 steps of the range, and number of stds may be limited to 5 or 6.) Develop colors by shaking separators 1 min, let stand few min, and filter exts thru specially prepd papers, (m). (Fitting 9 cm paper directly into mouth of 50 ml Pyrex beaker eliminates need of funnel in filtering operation.) Fill cell with filtered exts and det. *A* for various steps of range.

Plot against quantity of Pb to obtain std curve for particular lot of dithizone. Preferably calc. slope of line connecting std points and intercept of line on *A* axis, making calcn by least squares method as follows: Take equation of line connecting std points as $Y = a + bX$, and let $X = \mu g$ Pb and $Y = A$; *a* then represents intercept on *A* axis and *b* represents tangent or slope of line. Calc. *a* and *b* from following formulae, where *n* = number of observations, including that for 0 Pb, and Σ represents "sum":

$$b = \frac{\Sigma XY - \dfrac{\Sigma X \Sigma Y}{n}}{\Sigma X^2 - \dfrac{\Sigma X \Sigma X}{n}}, \quad \text{and} \quad a = \frac{\Sigma Y}{n} - b\frac{\Sigma X}{n}.$$

Then det. Pb content of unknown falling within the range by detg *A*, using std dithizone and same cell with which std readings were made, and calc. Pb from equation $X = (Y/b) - (a/b)$, using values of *a* and *b* detd previously. If protected from evapn and direct sunlight, std factors of dithizone solns should not change appreciably for at least one month (JAOAC **21**, 695(1938); **26**, 26(1943)).

For actual detn proceed as in (a), except to filter ext thru prepd papers before photometric measurement. Det. *A*, using stdzd dithizone with same cell used in making std curve, and read quantity of Pb from this std curve or calc. from factor of dithizone soln. If range is exceeded, repeat with smaller aliquot, or re-ext and repeat with dithizone stdzd to cover higher range. If aliquot of the 50 ml 1% HNO3 in which Pb has been isolated is taken, subtract only corresponding quantity of total reagent blank from quantity of Pb found.

25.049 Interferences

Interferences in colorimetric dithizone method are limited by use of KCN to stannous Sn, Bi, and Tl. Rarity of Tl makes its interference unlikely in ordinary work, and no method of removal is given (JAOAC **26**, 26(1943)). Dithizone itself is destroyed by strong oxidizing agents, such as free halogens and large amts of ferric Fe, under conditions of dithizone extn of Pb.

25.050 _Removal of Tin_
(*Caution: See* **46.028, 46.047,** and **46.059.**)

Sn becomes problem in analysis of canned foods; in quantities >150 ppm it will usually appear in ash soln as milky suspension of SnO2. It must be dissolved to facilitate filtration and to release occluded Pb. Quantities of Sn of this order may cause trouble by pptg under conditions of dithizone extn of Pb, **25.046.**

Two procedures for elimination of larger quantities of Sn are given: (a) Volatilization as SnBr4 from acid soln of ash, and (b) leaching mixed sulfides with warm Na polysulfide soln, when sulfide method of isolation, **25.047,** has been applied. These methods may not eliminate Sn completely. Stannic Sn is not extd with dithizone, and as small quantities of residual Sn will be in stannic form after application of either (a) or (b), final isolation of Pb by dithizone extn will eliminate Sn completely.

In general, quantities <100 mg should not interfere in colorimetric dithizone methods of Pb detn provided Sn is in stannic form and preliminary isolation with dithizone is made; hence, this method of isolation should be applied wherever possible.

(a) _Volatilization as SnBr4 from acid soln of ash._—After almost C-free ash is obtained, **25.044,** add 15–20 ml 40% redistd HBr. If nitrates were used as ash aids, cover casserole with watch glass and heat on steam bath until Br evolution diminishes; then rinse off watch glass with H2O and bring to boil to complete expulsion of Br. (This process destroys undecomposed nitrates.) Add more HBr if necessary to dissolve ash, and examine solns for clearness. If there is insol. residue of SnO2, add 50–100 mg pure Sn, (g), to simmering HBr soln of ash and let it dissolve. (Metallic Sn is best agent to bring ignited SnO2 into soln. To be effective, ash soln must be in reduced state. Fe2O3 sometimes becomes "noble" during ashing and dissolves with difficulty, but treatment with metallic Sn also brings it into soln. Treatment with Sn is necessary only with contents of badly corroded cans.)

When soln of ash is free from milkiness due to SnO2, add 20 ml 60% HClO4 (double distd preferred), oxidize mixt. with few ml HBr-Br mixt., (h), and then add addnl 15 ml of the reagent portionwise, while soln is evapd to incipient fumes of HClO4 (ca 150°) on hot plate. Repeat with addnl 10 ml portion HBr-Br mixt. if >100 mg Sn was used to dissolve ash. (Hot HClO4 helps keep ash salts in soln and with Br holds Sn as volatile SnBr4.) When HBr and Br are completely volatilized, cool, and take up with hot H2O (200 ml may be necessary if much KClO4 is present). Filter off any small amts of dehydrated SiO2, ext residue twice with 5 ml hot HCl-citric acid reagent, (j), and hot H2O, treat dish if necessary with NaOH as in **25.044(2),** and isolate Pb by dithizone extn as in **25.046,** or by sulfide sepn, **25.047,** finally detg Pb as in **25.048(a)** or (b).

(b) _With sodium polysulfide._—(Recommended for routine work on canned foods.)

Isolate Pb by sulfide pptn, **25.047,** filter, and wash flask and filter with 3–6 portions of ca 5 ml each of warm Na polysulfide soln, (i). (Sn, As, and Sb sulfides are dissolved; CuS may be partially dissolved and repptd in filtrate.) Wash flask and residual sulfides several times with 3% Na2SO4 soln adjusted to pH 3.0–3.4 and satd with H_2S, and proceed as in **25.047**, beginning "Dissolve sulfides, without previous washing, . . ." When ash contains much Sn, as when metallic Sn has been added to dissolve insol. metallic oxides, sulfide ppt will be so bulky as to be difficult to handle, and it will be necessary to use volatilization method (a) before sulfiding. For colorimetric dithizone detn of Pb, ext HNO_3 soln of dissolved sulfides and proceed as in **25.047** and **25.048** (a) or (b).

25.051   Detection and Removal of Bismuth

(*Caution:* See **46.026**, **46.047**, **46.050**, and **46.078**.)

(a) *By dithizone at pH 2.0 after preliminary dithizone extraction at pH 8–11* (*10*).—(This method completely removes small amts of Bi.)

Ext metals from $CHCl_3$ dithizone ext with 50 ml 1% HNO_3 as in **25.046**. Adjust acid ext to pH 2.0 (metacresol purple indicator) with 5% NH_4OH soln and shake vigorously ca 1 min with 10 ml $CHCl_3$ soln of dithizone (200–250 mg/L). Let layers sep., and if $CHCl_3$ ext is orange red to red (Bi), drain off and ext with addnl 10 ml dithizone soln. If shades of green or purple are visible, indicating excess dithizone, drain $CHCl_3$ ext and ext aq. phase once more with 5 ml dithizone soln (shaking should be prolonged (3–5 min) to ensure complete extn of Bi). Continue extns until dithizone ext remains pure green. Adjust aq. soln to pH 8.5 with NH_4OH, add KCN, and ext with dithizone as in **25.046**. Det. Pb colorimetrically as in **25.048**(a) or (b).

(Method of Bambach and Burkey (Ind. Eng. Chem., Anal. Ed. **14**, 904(1942)) seps small amts of Bi from Pb by shaking out $CHCl_3$ soln of their mixed dithizonates with aq. soln buffered at pH 3.4; Bi remains as dithizonate in $CHCl_3$ phase, while Pb enters aq. phase and can be sepd Bi-free. Only *slight* excess of free dithizone should be present in $CHCl_3$ mixt. of dithizonates, otherwise Pb does not strip out completely. System of photometric detection and evaluation of Bi interference has also been outlined (JAOAC **26**, 26(1943)).

(b) *From acid soln of sulfides.*—(Intended for small quantities of Bi, particularly when sulfide sepns may be necessary.) Dissolve mixed sulfides, **25.047**, with hot HNO_3 and sep. Bi and Pb as in (a).

Special conditions.—(Intended for products contg large quantities of Bi.) Dissolve inorg. Bi compds directly in HBr-Br, (h). Prep. org. Bi compds or Bi prepns mixed with org. matter contg little ash, as in **25.044**, and dissolve residue in HBr-Br. If sample contains org. matter with appreciable ash material other than Bi compds, proceed as in **25.044** or **25.053**, apply sulfide sepn, **25.047**, and dissolve mixed sulfides in HNO_3. Evap. HNO_3 soln of sulfides to dryness in porcelain dish and treat with small portions HBr-Br mixt. Evap. contents of dish contg Bi dissolved in HBr-Br, after any of above methods of prepn, on steam bath to volatilize Sn

and to convert other metals to bromides. Evap. to dryness, place in muffle with temp. control, and raise temp. gradually to 300°. ($AsBr_3$ and $SbBr_3$ volatilize first at 100° or above; $BiBr_3$ volatilizes as dense orange fumes at 300°.) After 5 min, or when fumes cease, remove dish, cool and treat again with small portions HBr-Br. Again evap. to dryness and heat addnl 5 min at 300–325° ($PbBr_2$ does not volatilize appreciably at <350°). Remove dish, cool, and dissolve residue in hot HNO_3. Proceed with removal of last traces of Bi at pH 2.0 and det. Pb as in (a).

Special Methods of Sample Preparation

25.052   Solution in Acids

(Applicable to chemicals sol. in H_2O or acid, e.g., phosphates, sulfates, etc., and org. products of type of tartrates and citrates; *Caution:* See **46.059**.)

Dissolve 5–100 g sample, according to its nature and amt of Pb expected, in HCl in 400 ml beaker. With Ca phosphates use 10–50 g. Dissolve in smallest practicable vol. of soln by warming and adding alternately small amts of hot H_2O and HCl. Filter soln with suction (fritted glass preferred) into beaker or flask under bell jar and leach any residue with 10–25 ml hot HCl-citric acid, (j), followed by 10–25 ml hot 40% NH_4OAc soln. Rinse beaker and filter with hot H_2O and cool soln.

Proceed as in **25.046**. If interfering ppt forms, again acidify and isolate Pb by sulfide pptn, **25.047**. If it is difficult to obtain clear soln with Ca phosphates at pH 3.0–3.4 (sulfide ppt may be contaminated with excessive phosphates), redissolve ppt, add more citric acid soln, (d), readjust pH, and reppt sulfides; or make one sulfide pptn, dissolve sulfides in hot HNO_3, boil off H_2S, and ext Pb with dithizone, **25.046**. Sometimes difficulty due to ppt formation in **25.046** can be avoided by using smaller sample for extn and colorimetric detn. If Sn or Bi is suspected, remove by methods described in **25.050** and **25.051**. Finally det. isolated Pb colorimetrically, **25.048**.

25.053   Complete Digestion

(Applicable to most food or biological products; with difficulty to fats and oils, oily products, etc. *Caution:* See **46.011** and **46.078**.)

Digest representative sample in Kjeldahl flask as in **25.008**. Distill As, if desired, as $AsCl_3$, **25.009**. If As is not to be distd, add 100 ml H_2O and enough HCl to flask to dissolve any $CaSO_4$ in residue. Filter on fritted glass filter, pulverizing any insol. residue (anhyd. SiO_2 or $BaSO_4$) with flat-end stirring rod. Dissolve any $PbSO_4$ in flask and leach residue on filter with 10–20 ml hot HCl-citric acid soln, (j), followed by 10–20 ml hot 40% NH_4OAc soln. Finally rinse both flask and filter with hot H_2O. Isolate Pb by dithizone, **25.046**, or sulfide pptn, **25.047**, methods. (In general, sulfide method is preferable, especially when $BaSO_4$ or excessive $CaSO_4$ is present, as insol. sulfates readily occlude Pb.) If Bi and Sn are present, remove them as in **25.050** or **25.051**. After isolation, det. Pb by colorimetric method, **25.048**.

Rapid Method Restricted to Apples and Pears

(Efficiency of 95% expected)

(For rapid detn of Pb spray residue on apples and pears; ppm × 0.007 = grains/lb; (grains/lb) × 143 = ppm)

25.054 *Preparation of Sample*

Weigh ≥10 units and pull or cut out stems with narrow-blade knife, cutting no more of flesh than necessary. Trim off sepals (dried residue of blossom) and discard sepals and stems. To 25 ml 30% NaOH soln in 600 ml beaker, add 175 ml H₂O and 25 ml Na oleate soln, (**k**), and bring to gentle boil. Have ready in wash bottle 250 ml hot HNO₃ (2 + 98) or hot HCl (3 + 97). (Reasonably accurate figure for As₂O₃ can be obtained by using the HCl rinse and applying Gutzeit As detn, **25.010**, to portion of filtrate, after acidifying part of the 500 ml alk. strip soln with 1/10 vol. HCl instead of HNO₃ (*see* later in this section). Rapid method for F, **25.039**, likewise specifies HCl rinse and acidification.)

Impale each fruit in turn upon pointed glass rod; immerse in the alk. soln, with occasional rotation, until skin begins to check; then remove to large funnel inserted in 500 ml vol. flask and rinse with stream of the hot acid, being careful to flush out stem and calyx ends thoroly. When all fruit has been thus treated, cool alk. soln and add it thru funnel to acid soln in flask. Rinse beaker and funnel with any remaining acid and with H₂O, using entire 250 ml rinse acid. Cool, and dil. to vol.

In dry 200 ml erlenmeyer place exactly 10 ml HNO₃ (10 ml HCl for As or F). Thoroly mix contents of vol. flask and immediately add 100 ml to acid in erlenmeyer while swirling vigorously. Filter on rapid paper. If first portion of filtrate is cloudy, refilter until clear. Det. Pb as in **25.055** or **25.056**.

(*See* Fahey, Cassil, and Rusk (JAOAC **26**, 150 (1943)) for details of churn-type washer for removing Pb spray residues from apples and pears.)

25.055 *Determination with Nessler Tubes*

(At least 15 tall form tubes matched for uniformity in color *and diam.* are necessary. *Caution: See* **46.050**.)

(**a**) *Stds.*—To each of two 1 L vol. flasks add 47.5 ml 30% NaOH soln. If HNO₃ was used in rinsing and acidification, **25.054**, add 100 ml HNO₃ to each flask. If HCl (3 + 97) was used in rinsing, add 91 ml HNO₃ and 13.6 ml HCl to each flask. Do not mix in the acids unless solns are cold and dil. To one flask add stock reagent, (**a**), equiv. to 25.45 mg Pb. Mark this flask "std" and other "blank." Dil. both solns

to vol. at room temp. and mix. These 2 solns contain reagents as they occur in acidified and filtered sample soln. The "std" is equiv. in Pb content to acidified soln from sample of 1400 g carrying Pb load (removable by "stripping" operation) of 10 ppm. By combination of the 2 solns in suitable proportions, equiv. of any Pb load from 0 to 10 ppm may be obtained.

Std tubes made up in intervals corresponding to 1.0 ppm may be interpolated to 0.5 ppm. Following table gives quantities of "std" and "blank" to be added to Nessler tubes for each interval; measure into tube by burets:

Pb ppm	"Standard" ml	"Blank" ml
0.0	0.0	10.0
1.0	1.0	9.0
2.0	2.0	8.0
3.0	3.0	7.0
4.0	4.0	6.0
5.0	5.0	5.0
6.0	6.0	4.0
7.0	7.0	3.0
8.0	8.0	2.0
9.0	9.0	1.0
10.0	10.0	0.0

Working with 1 tube at time, add to each tube 10 ml NH₃-cyanide-citrate soln, (**l**), followed by 30 ml std dithizone soln, 30 mg/L, (**e**). Shake vigorously 1 min and let sep. The pH of aq. phase should be ca 9.4 regardless of whether HCl or HNO₃ is used in rinsing. Stopper each std tube securely with new cork stopper. It is unnecessary to make up entire series of stds if only portion of range, for example 5.0–10.0 ppm, is of quant. interest.

(**b**) *Comparison.*—Transfer 10 ml portions of clear filtrate from **25.054** to each of 3 Nessler tubes. First add 10 ml NH₃-cyanide-citrate soln, (**l**), to each tube; to one tube add 30 ml std dithizone soln, 30 mg/L, **25.043**(**e**), and to other 2 tubes 30 ml clear CHCl₃. Shake vigorously 1 min and let sep. With tube of clear CHCl₃ backing sample tube (contg the dithizone) and 1 sample tube contg CHCl₃ backing each of 2 std tubes, compare color in lower layer of sample with that of stds, looking thru tubes at right angles to their lengths toward strong diffused light. (Comparator box similar to boxes used in colorimetric pH measurements but of larger size is convenient. When working with apple strip solns, slight turbidity is produced in sample tube, which slightly changes color observed. To compensate for this effect, same turbidity is introduced in field of view of std tubes made up exactly as sample, except that CHCl₃ is substituted for the dithizone soln.)

If color produced by sample is redder than 10 ppm std, repeat with smaller aliquot of filtrate, dilg to 10 ml with "blank" soln. If, for example, 5 ml aliquot is taken, indicated reading must be doubled. After match is obtained, calc. result to basis of 10 ml aliquot and 1400 g sample.

25.056 *Determination with Photometer*

(This method is suitable for photometric measurement of "mixed color," **25.048**(b). Changes in **25.055** are introduced here to prevent formation of colors too dense for measurements. Use 5 ml instead of 10 ml aliquots of acidified wash soln, **25.054**. *Caution: See* **46.050**.)

(a) *Stds.*—Measure following proportions of "std" and "blank" solns, **25.055**(a), into separators:

Pb ppm	"Standard" ml	"Blank" ml
0.0	0.0	10.0
2.0	1.0	9.0
4.0	2.0	8.0
6.0	3.0	7.0
8.0	4.0	6.0
10.0	5.0	5.0

Add 10 ml NH_3-cyanide-citrate soln, (l), and working with 1 separator at time, immediately develop color by shaking 1 min with 50 ml pure dithizone soln of 10 mg/L strength. Let stand few min to cool, filter $CHCl_3$ layers thru specially washed papers, (m), and fill cell of appropriate length (1 cm is convenient). Det. *A* and plot against ppm Pb to obtain std curve.

(b) *Comparison.*—Place appropriate size aliquot of acidified strip soln in separator and dil. to 10 ml with "blank" soln. Add 10 ml NH_3 reagent, (l), and ext with 50 ml 10 mg/L std dithizone soln. Let stand few min to cool, filter, and read as above. Det. quantity of Pb from std curve prepd as in (a) and calc. to basis of 5 ml aliquot and 1400 g sample.

25.057 MANGANESE—OFFICIAL FINAL ACTION—*See* 3.014 or 22.031

MERCURY (*11*)—OFFICIAL FINAL ACTION

25.058 *Principles*

Sample is digested with HNO_3 and H_2SO_4 under reflux in special app., Hg is isolated by dithizone extn, Cu is removed, and Hg is estd by photometric measurement of Hg dithizonate.

25.059 *Precautions*

Critical step is digestion of sample, which must be almost complete, otherwise residual org. matter may combine with Hg and prevent or hinder extn with dithizone. Oxidizing material in digest must also be destroyed or dithizone reagent is decomposed and Hg is not quant. extd. Because of volatility of Hg compds, careful heating of digest during sample prepn is required. Acidity of final sample soln (after partial neutzn with NH_4OH) before extn should be ca $1N$ and not $>1.2N$. Do not use silicone grease in stopcocks.

25.060 *Apparatus*

Special digestion apparatus.—See Fig. 25:3. App. is made from Pyrex with $\overline{\text{S}}$ joints thruout. Unit *A* is modified Soxhlet extractor, 5 cm od, 200 ml capacity

to overflow, without inner siphon tube but equipped with stopcock on tube leading to digestion flask, *D*. With stopcock open, app. is in reflux position; when closed, unit serves as trap for condensed H_2O and acids. Top of *A* is attached to Friedrichs condenser, 35 cm long. Bottom of *A* is attached thru center neck

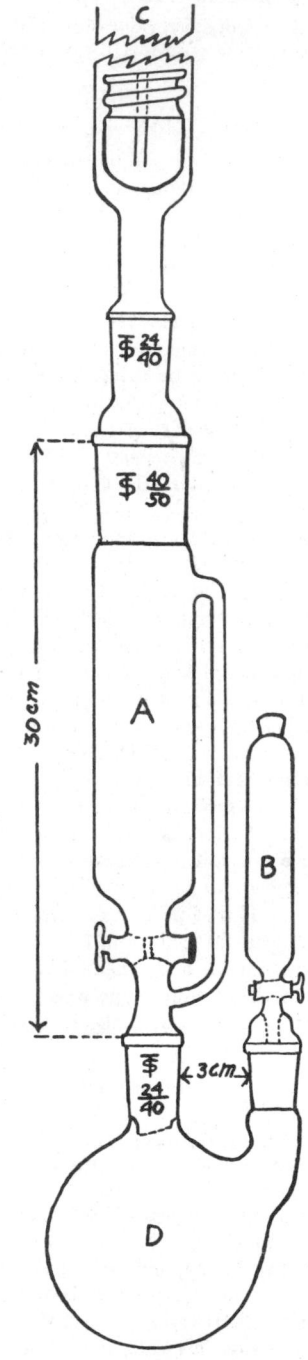

FIG. 25:3—Special digestion apparatus for mercury residues

of 2 neck ⊤ 24/40 r-b 500 ml flask, *D*. Necks are 3 cm apart to provide clearance. Second neck is used for attaching 75 ml dropping funnel, *B*.

Note: As Hg compds tend to adsorb on glassware, app. and particularly separators should be rinsed with dil. HNO_3 and then with H_2O.

25.061 *Reagents*

(a) *Mercury std solns.*—(*1*) *Stock soln.*—1 mg/ml. Prep. from dry, recrystd $HgCl_2$ (67.7 mg/50 ml). (*2*) *Working soln.*—2 µg/ml is convenient. Prep. from stock soln and store in Pyrex bottles. Add HCl in proportion of 8 ml/L to all stds before dilg to final vol.

(b) *Chloroform.*—See **25.019**(b).

(c) *Dithizone soln.*—See **25.043**(e). Reagent as now distributed needs no purification for this method. Prep. stock soln in redistd $CHCl_3$ (100 mg/L is convenient) and store in refrigerator. Prep. dilns as needed.

(d) *Sodium thiosulfate soln.*—1.5%. Prep. daily.

(e) *Sodium hypochlorite soln.*—Preferably 5% available Cl reagent. As distributed, reagent varies in available Cl content. Det. strength by **6.175**. Store in refrigerator when not in use and det. titer monthly. (Certain prepns of hypochlorite intended for household use contain traces of Hg. If these prepns are used, det. blank. Reagent with >0.1 µg Hg/ml should not be used.)

(f) *Dilute acetic acid.*—30% by vol.

(g) *Hydroxylamine hydrochloride soln.*—20% w/v. Ext with dil. dithizone until $CHCl_3$ layer remains green, remove excess dithizone with $CHCl_3$, and filter.

25.062 *Preparation of Sample*
(Conduct acid digestion in hood.)

In all detns use wt sample equiv. to ≤10 g dry wt.

(a) *Fresh fruits or vegetables and beverages.*—Place weighed sample in digestion flask with 6 glass beads, connect assembly, and add, thru dropping funnel, 20 ml HNO_3. Pass rapid stream of H_2O thru condenser, adjust stopcock of Soxhlet unit to reflux position, and apply small flame to flask. Use asbestos board with 1–2″ diam. hole between flask and flame. (Original reaction must not proceed violently or evolved NO_2 will carry vapors of digest mech. thru condenser and cause loss of Hg.) After initial reaction is complete, apply heat so that digest just refluxes. If mixt. darkens, add HNO_3 dropwise thru funnel as needed. Continue refluxing 0.5 hr, or until digest does not change consistency, and cool.

Slowly add 20 ml cold HNO_3-H_2SO_4 mixt. (1 + 1). (Use 10 ml acid mixt. for 5 g or less (dry wt) of sample.) Heat with small flame, subsequently adding HNO_3 dropwise as needed to dispel darkening of digest. Continue heating until fibrous material (fruit skin, cellulose, etc.) is apparently digested. Turn stopcock of Soxhlet unit to trap H_2O and acids, and continue heating. Let digest become dark

brown (not black) before adding further increments of HNO_3. (Fats and waxes cannot be totally digested by the hot acids under reflux. No attempt should therefore be made to effect complete digestion in this step.) When all except fat and wax is in soln, let digest cool, and cautiously drain H_2O and acids into main digest. Cool, and pour two 25 ml portions H_2O thru condenser and intermediate unit. Remove reaction flask, chill under cold H_2O or by surrounding with ice to solidify fats and waxes, and filter off insol. matter on small pledget of glass wool. Rinse reaction flask and filter pad successively with two 10 ml portions H_2O. Remove Soxhlet unit, and wash it and flask with hot H_2O to remove insol. material. Pour hot H_2O thru condenser to remove volatile fats and oils. Discard all washings.

Connect flask contg filtered sample soln to assembled app., heat, and collect H_2O and acids in trap. Complete digestion, using small addns of HNO_3 as needed. In final stage of digestion, adjust flame until digest reaches incipient boiling (soln simmers) and acid vapors do not rise beyond lower half of condenser. Continue heating 15 min after last addn of HNO_3. Digest should now be colorless or pale yellow. Let digest cool, drain trapped liqs carefully into reaction flask, and add two 50 ml portions H_2O thru condenser. Reflux soln until all NO_2 is expelled from app. Add 5 ml *40% w/v urea soln* and reflux 15 min. (Digest should be colorless or pale yellow.)

(b) *Dried fruit, cereal, seeds, and grains.*—Dil. sample with 50 ml H_2O before adding HNO_3, and proceed with sample prepn as in (a).

(c) *Meats, fish, and biological material.*—Because of high fat and protein content of these materials, conduct initial digestion carefully to avoid foaming of digest into condenser. Add 20 ml HNO_3 to sample, swirl flask, and let stand 0.5 hr in digestion assembly before heating. Add 25 ml H_2O and heat cautiously with small rotating flame until initial vigorous reaction is over and foaming ceases. Proceed as in (a).

25.063 *Isolation of Mercury*

Titr. 1 ml prepd sample soln, **25.062**, with std alkali. Add calcd amt of concd NH_4OH to reduce acidity to 1.0*N*; swirl flask during addn of the NH_4OH to avoid local excess. (Soln should never be ammoniacal to avoid formation of Hg complexes.)

Transfer sample soln to 500 ml separator. Add 10 ml 4 mg/L dithizone and shake vigorously 1 min. (If characteristic green of dithizone is visible in $CHCl_3$ layer, indicating excess of dithizone, amt of Hg is within 0–5 µg.) Let layers sep., and drain $CHCl_3$ layer quickly to second separator contg 25 ml 0.1*N* HCl and 5 ml $NH_2OH.HCl$ soln. (Small amt of oxidizing material may still be present. On long contact with dithizone soln, oxidizing substances may destroy dithizone reagent and prevent extn of Hg.)

Repeat extn of sample soln with two 5 ml portions dithizone soln, transferring $CHCl_3$ layer successively to second separator. If first extn indicates >5 μg Hg, add stronger concns of dithizone, as indicated by table, **25.065,** until, after 1 min vigorous shaking, $CHCl_3$ layer contains dithizone in marked excess. Drain $CHCl_3$ layer into second separator contg $0.1N$ HCl and again ext sample soln with two 10 ml portions 4 mg/L dithizone soln, draining each successive ext into second separator.

Shake contents of second separator vigorously 1 min, and drain $CHCl_3$ layer into third separator contg 50 ml $0.1N$ HCl. (Shaking dithizone ext with dil. acid in second separator removes entrained org. matter. With biological materials or those of high protein content, aq. layer is usually light yellow because of nitrated org. compds. Small amts are carried into third separator where they are destroyed by Cl.) Ext soln in second separator with 1–2 ml $CHCl_3$ and transfer org. layer to third separator.

To contents of third separator add 2 ml $Na_2S_2O_3$ soln, shake vigorously 1 min, let layers sep., drain off $CHCl_3$ as completely as possible, and discard. (Cu if present is removed as dithizonate.) Ext again with 1–2 ml $CHCl_3$, drain carefully, and discard. Add 3.5 ml NaOCl reagent (or enough soln of different titer to furnish 175 mg available Cl) to decompose Hg thiosulfate complex and to oxidize excess thiosulfate, and shake vigorously 1 min. Add 5 ml NH_2OH .HCl reagent from pipet, taking care to wet both stopper and neck of separator. Shake vigorously 1 min. Hold mouth of separator in front of air vent and blow out any remaining gaseous Cl. Stopper separator and shake vigorously 1 min. (It is imperative that all hypochlorite be reduced. Trace amts remaining would oxidize dithizone, subsequently added, to yellow oxidized form which would be measured in photometer as Hg.) Ext soln with 2–3 ml $CHCl_3$, drain off org. layer carefully, and discard. Final aq. soln should now be colorless.

25.064   *Determination*

To contents of third separator add 3 ml 30% HOAc and appropriate vol. and concn of dithizone soln as indicated by table, **25.065,** and proceed with colorimetric detn of Hg as in **25.065,** converting A, measured at 490 nm, to μg Hg from working curve.

25.065   *Preparation of Standard Curve*

Following table is useful in prepg std curve and for establishing approx. Hg range in sample soln when 1 cm cells are used:

Hg Range μg (0.001 mg)	Dithizone Concn, mg/L	Volume Dithizone, ml
0–10	6	5
0–50	10	25
0–100	10	40

Prep. working curve of required range, starting with blank and extending to final std of range, with 4 intermediate increments. Add appropriate amts of Hg to 50 ml $0.1N$ HCl in separator. Add 5 ml

$NH_2OH.HCl$ reagent and 5 ml $CHCl_3$, and shake vigorously 1 min. Let layers sep., drain off $CHCl_3$, and discard, being careful to remove as completely as possible all droplets of $CHCl_3$. Add 3 ml 30% HOAc and appropriate vol. dithizone soln, shake vigorously 1 min, and let layers sep. (HOAc aids in stabilizing mercuric dithizonate.) Insert cotton pledget into stem of separator and collect dithizone ext (discarding first ml) in test tube for transfer to appropriate cell. Make photometer readings at 490 nm. (Since both dil. dithizone and mercuric dithizonate are somewhat unstable, read immediately.) Plot A against μg Hg.

SELENIUM *(12)*—OFFICIAL FINAL ACTION

25.066   *Principles*

Sample is digested with HNO_3 and H_2SO_4 in presence of HgO fixative. Se is sepd by distn as volatile bromide. Bromide is reduced to elementary Se with SO_2, isolated, and estd as H_2SeO_3 by titrn with std $Na_2S_2O_3$ and I.

25.067   *Reagents*

(**a**) *Sulfuric-nitric acid soln.*—To 50 ml H_2SO_4 add 100 ml HNO_3. Cool mixt. before using.

(**b**) *Mercuric oxide fixative.*—Dissolve HgO in HNO_3 in proportion of 5 g/100 ml acid.

(**c**) *Concentrated hydrobromic acid-bromine soln.*— Mix 10 ml liq. Br with 990 ml HBr. (Reagent grade HBr is available com. in 2 concns: constant boiling mixt. of 48% (8.1N) and 40% concn (7N). Either may be used, as detn allows for varying quantity of reagent taken according to HBr concn.)

(**d**) *Dilute hydrobromic acid-bromine soln.*—To 5 ml HBr add 10 ml satd Br-H_2O and dil. to 100 ml with H_2O.

(**e**) *Sulfur dioxide.*—Gas supplied in com. cylinders is Se-free.

(**f**) *Hydroxylamine hydrochloride soln.*—10%, w/v.

(**g**) *Phenol soln.*—5%, w/v.

(**h**) *Sodium thiosulfate std soln.*—1 ml $0.001N$ $Na_2S_2O_3$ is theoretically equiv. to 19.8 μg Se. (For estn of Se in quantities >50–75 μg, proportionately higher concns of $Na_2S_2O_3$ are required.) Prep. from accurately stdzd $0.1N$ reagent with recently boiled H_2O. Before adjusting to final vol., add 5 ml isoamyl alcohol/L and shake vigorously.

(**i**) *Iodine std soln.*—Prep. from $0.1N$ reagent. Before final diln add KI in proportion of 20 g/L. Dil. to same normality as $Na_2S_2O_3$ soln.

(**j**) *Selenium std solns.*—(*1*) *Stock soln.*—1 mg/ml. Dissolve 250 mg Se in concd HBr-Br soln (1 ml liq. Br + 25 ml concd HBr, both of which have been distd). After soln is complete, *almost* neutze excess Br with SO_2, while shaking vigorously. Complete neutzn by adding phenol soln dropwise in slight excess. Dil. to 250 ml with H_2O. (SO_2 must not be present in excess because it would reduce H_2SeO_3 to Se.) If too much SO_2 has been used, add Br-H_2O

until selenite soln is slightly but definitely yellow and then complete neutzn with phenol soln.

(If Se reagent is not pure, purify as follows: Dissolve ca 1 g Se in excess concd HBr-Br soln, ppt with SO_2, warm on steam bath 30 min, cool, filter, first wash free of acids with H_2O and then wash with small portions alcohol, dry 1 hr at 100°, and prep. 1 mg/ml std as directed previously. This precaution is necessary since Se soln serves as ultimate std in detn.)

(*2*) *Working soln.*—Make appropriate dilns of std stock soln by adding H_2O, and do not let acidity, detd by titrn, fall to $<0.05N$, because neut. or very slightly acid solns of dil. H_2SeO_3 tend to oxidize and lose titer. Diln of 20 μg Se/ml is convenient for micro detns, since it is almost chemically equiv. to accurately prepd $0.001N$ $Na_2S_2O_3$ (1 ml = 19.8 μg Se.)

(**k**) *Starch indicator.*—Dil. 1 g sol. starch to 200 ml.

25.068   *Apparatus*

All-glass distn app. consisting of 250 ml r-b flask, still head, thermometer registering to 135°, and condenser with dipping end.

25.069   *Determination*

(*Caution: See* **46.019, 46.026, 46.028, 46.030, 46.047,** and **46.081.**)

Place 5–10 g (dry wt) sample in 600–800 ml Pyrex beaker and add 10 ml HgO fixative followed by 150 ml H_2SO_4-HNO_3 soln. Mix thoroly at once and place on steam bath 30 min, stirring intermittently. If product is high in Se, use 1 g representative material. To dry leafy products which oxidize violently, add 25 ml H_2O before adding fixative. Heat over burner (not full flame) until digestion mass lightens and then turns brown. Remove flame, cool, and after adding 10 ml HNO_3, again heat until first brown appears. Repeat this operation at least twice; then heat until liq. turns distinct brown (not black) or until SO_3 fumes appear. (It is imperative to expel excess HNO_3 and to oxidize org. matter enough so that Br reagent subsequently added is not reduced, but prolonged fuming to SO_3 is to be avoided.) As such products as molasses and honey, principally sugars, react vigorously with HNO_3, remove such samples from steam bath until reaction subsides and then proceed in usual manner.

Cool digest and transfer with two 25 ml portions H_2O to distg flask. (If digestion is performed in 250 ml distg flask, it is still necessary to add 50 ml H_2O so that HBr will distill later as liq. and not as vapor.) Rinse beaker carefully with 25 ml concd HBr-Br soln and add to cooled digest and washings. (If constant-boiling grade of HBr has not been used, equiv. vol. of less concd reagent must be added, e.g., 30 ml 40% concn, and distillate must have acidity of ca $2.5N$.) After swirling flask, distill until temp. of distn reaches 130°, into 125 ml erlenmeyer, marked at 50,

75, and 100 ml, contg 5 ml HBr and surrounded by cold H_2O. During distn lift tip of condenser out of liq. in flask after all Br and ca 15 ml acid have distd. (Free Br should distill in beginning, indicating excess of reagent. If this is not the case, stop distn, cool, and add addnl 10 ml HBr-Br soln. This contingency arises only with insufficient digestion of sample.) Rinse condenser tip carefully with two ≤ 2 ml portions H_2O. Between analyses rinse condenser tube free of fatty and waxy material with hot H_2O but *do not* add rinsings to distillate. For next 3 steps it is assumed that distillate contains no fats, waxes, or other insol. matter.

(*1*) If vol. distillate and rinsings is <75 ml, pass in SO_2 in excess (ca 30 sec after complete decolorization of Br), add 1 ml $NH_2OH.HCl$ soln, and place mixt. on active steam bath 30 min. Cap flasks with watch glasses during various heat treatments.

(*2*) If vol. distillate is 75–100 ml, reduce with SO_2 and $NH_2OH.HCl$ soln as in (*1*), add several glass beads, bring just to incipient boiling, and complete reduction at once with 30-min steam-bath treatment.

(*3*) If vol. distillate is >100 ml, transfer to 200 ml erlenmeyer and complete transfer with 4 successive 2 ml H_2O rinsings delivered from pipet. Add 10 ml HBr, reduce with SO_2 and $NH_2OH.HCl$, add several glass beads, bring to incipient boiling, and place flask at once on steam bath and heat 30 min. (When vol. soln is >100 ml, recovery of Se may be slightly low.)

If distillate contains fats, waxes, or other insol. material, filter off with suction on asbestos and rinse receiver flask carefully with four 2 ml portions H_2O from pipet. Use successive washings in turn to rinse asbestos filter. Transfer combined filtrates to 125 ml erlenmeyer (200 ml flask if vol. filtrate is >100 ml), and complete transfer with four 2 ml portions H_2O, delivered from pipet. According to final vol. soln, proceed with addn of reagents and heat treatment exactly as above. (Se is reduced rapidly from acid soln $\geq 2.5N$; steps (*2*) and (*3*) are necessary because acidity is $<2.5N$ in these instances.)

For assay of products of high Se content (>1.0 mg in sample analyzed) use 50 ml HBr-Br soln (or equiv. vol. of less concd grade) for initial distn. To such samples add 75 ml H_2O during rinsing instead of usual 50 ml. After usual distn, disconnect app., rinse condenser tube with 5 ml H_2O, and add rinsing directly to distillate. Heat residue in distn flask to incipient fumes of SO_3, cool, add 5 ml $HClO_4$, and heat to fuming. Repeat $HClO_4$ oxidn. (This treatment is necessary for substances like vetches and seedlings, which contain particularly refractory Se compds.) Cool digest, add two 25 ml portions H_2O and then 25 ml HBr-Br soln, and distill to 130° in usual manner. Combine all distillates, and if fatty, waxy, or other insol. matter is present, filter and wash as previously directed. In either case, adjust to 250 ml in vol. flask with H_2O, pipet 75 ml into 125 ml erlenmeyer, reduce Se with excess SO_2 and

$NH_2OH . HCl$, and complete reduction by heating on steam bath 30 min.

Place flasks in cold H_2O (ca 20°) for 30 min and then, with suction, collect Se on asbestos pad contained in filtration vessel, Fig. 25:4A. Rinse pptn flask and pad with 5 successive 1 ml portions H_2O from pipet, and then hold mouth of flask before air vent to remove last traces of SO_2.

Insert filtration vessel into titrg tube and dissolve Se with 1 ml dil. HBr-Br soln, first adding reagent from pipet to flask and then transferring carefully to pad. When Se has dissolved, apply gentle suction and repeat operation with addnl 1 ml dil. HBr-Br soln. Finally rinse flask and pad with 3 successive 1 ml portions H_2O, collecting filtrate before each addn; 2 ml dil. HBr-Br soln is enough for 500 μg Se. When more is present, use proportionately more reagent and rinse H_2O.

Agitate filtrate with pipet stirrer and dispel excess Br with 3 drops phenol soln. Using stirrer as pipet, rinse walls of vessel several times with the soln to neutze every trace of Br. Immerse titrg tube up to ⅔ its length in hot H_2O 5 min, stirring intermittently. (Heating is required to complete reaction between Br and phenol.) Then place vessel in cold H_2O ≥5 min (Norris-Fay titrn (Am. Chem. J. **18**, 705(1896)) works best when soln is <25°).

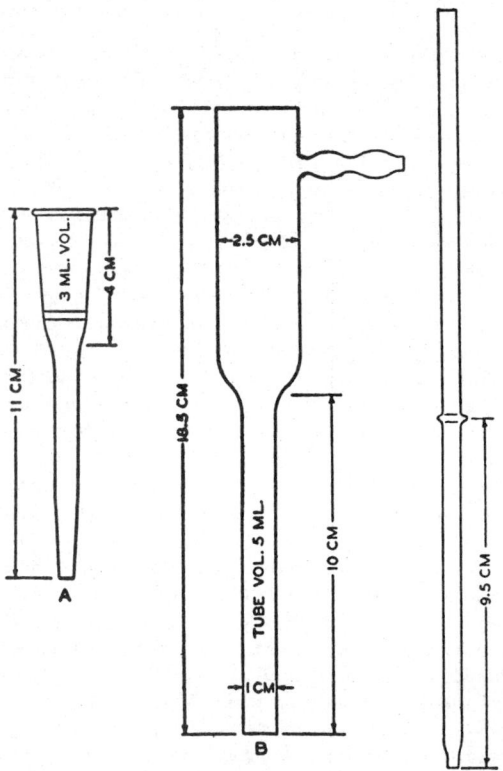

FIG. 25:4—Filtration and titration tubes and pipet for selenium determination

Using original ppt of Se as guide, add ≥50% excess of appropriate concn of std $Na_2S_2O_3$ soln and 3 drops starch indicator, (**k**). After stirring, add std I until permanent blue appears. If <1 ml I soln is required, add enough $Na_2S_2O_3$ so that ≥1 ml I is required. Titr. to colorless end point with $Na_2S_2O_3$ soln, adding reagent in 0.01 ml portions as end point is approached.

25.070   *Standardization*
(Cross titration)

To 2 ml HBr (5 + 95) contained in titrg tube add 3 ml H_2O and 3 ml std I. (HBr must be previously distd.) Titr. with std $Na_2S_2O_3$ soln and toward end add 3 drops starch indicator, (**k**). Complete titrn as in **25.069**, and obtain $Na_2S_2O_3$ equiv. of I.

Add 2 ml of the dil. HBr to appropriate vol. std Se soln, and after adding 50% excess $Na_2S_2O_3$ soln continue titrn exactly as above. Obtain Se equiv. of $Na_2S_2O_3$ soln. (As dil. solns of both $Na_2S_2O_3$ and I always slowly deteriorate, they must be stdzd frequently.)

25.071   *Sample Calculation*

Net $Na_2S_2O_3$ sample titer in ml × Se equiv. = quantity of Se in sample.

TIN—OFFICIAL FIRST ACTION
25.072   *Preparation of Sample*
Digest 50–100 g sample as in **25.008**.

Gravimetric Method (13)
25.073   *Reagents*

(a) *Wash soln.*—Mix 100 ml satd NH_4OAc soln with 50 ml HOAc and 850 ml H_2O.

(b) *Ammonium polysulfide soln.*—(Caution: See **46.059**.) Pass H_2S gas into 200 ml NH_4OH in bottle immersed in running H_2O or in ice-H_2O until gas is no longer absorbed; add 200 ml NH_4OH and dil. with H_2O to 1 L. Digest this soln with 25 g flowers of S several hr and filter.

25.074   *Determination*
(Caution: See **46.059**.)

Add 200 ml H_2O to digested sample and transfer to 600 ml beaker. Rinse Kjeldahl flask with 3 portions boiling H_2O, making total ca 400 ml. Cool, and add NH_4OH until just alk.; then add 5 ml HCl or 5 ml H_2SO_4 (1 + 3) for each 100 ml soln. Place beaker, covered, on hot plate; heat to ca 95° and pass in slow stream of H_2S 1 hr. Digest 1 hr at 95° and let stand 30 min longer.

Filter, and wash ppt of SnS alternately with 3 portions each of wash soln and hot H_2O. Transfer filter and ppt to 50 ml beaker, add 10–20 ml $(NH_4)_2S_x$ soln, heat to boiling, and filter. Treat contents of beaker with 2 addnl portions hot $(NH_4)_2S_x$ soln and wash filter with hot H_2O. Acidify combined filtrate and washings with HOAc (1 + 9), digest on hot plate 1 hr, let stand overnight, and filter thru double 11 cm paper. Wash alternately with 2 portions each of wash soln and hot H_2O and dry thoroly in weighed porcelain crucible. Ignite over Bunsen flame, very gently at first to burn off paper and to convert sulfide to oxide; then partly cover crucible and heat strongly over large Bunsen or Meker burner. (SnS must be roasted gently to SnO_2, which then may be heated to high temp. without loss by volatilization.) Weigh as SnO_2 and calc. to metallic Sn, using factor 0.7877.

Volumetric Method (14)

25.075   *Reagents*

(a) *Air-free wash soln.*—Dissolve 20 g $NaHCO_3$ in 2 L boiled H_2O and add 40 ml HCl. Prep. fresh.

(b) *Iodine std soln.*—$0.01N$. Stdze soln frequently against (c), adding asbestos mat and proceeding as in **25.076**, omitting pptn with H_2S and boiling with HCl and $KClO_3$. Quantity of Sn in soln used for stdzn should equal ca that contained in sample under examination.

(c) *Tin std soln.*—1 mg/ml. Dissolve 1 g Sn in ca 500 ml HCl and dil. to 1 L with H_2O.

(d) *Sheet aluminum.*—About 30 gage, Sn-free.

25.076   *Determination*

(*Caution: See* **46.047.**)

Proceed as in **25.074** thru "Digest 1 hr at 95° and let stand 30 min longer."

Filter thru asbestos in Caldwell crucible, using suction. Wash ppt of SnS few times with H_2O and transfer detachable bottom and asbestos pad to 300 ml erlenmeyer. Remove all traces of ppt from inside of crucible, using jet of hot H_2O and policeman, and using min. amt of H_2O for washing.

Add 100 ml HCl and 0.5 g $KClO_3$ to flask. Boil ca 15 min, making ca 4 more addns of smaller quantities of $KClO_3$ as Cl is boiled out of soln. Wash particles of $KClO_3$ down from neck of flask with H_2O and finally boil to remove Cl. Add ca 1 g sheet Al to dispel last traces of Cl.

Fit 2-hole rubber stopper to flask. Thru 1 hole pass bulbed glass tube that reaches nearly to surface of liq. Attach this tube to large CO_2 generator thru scrubber contg H_2O. The CO_2 passes out of flask thru short, bulbed tube inserted in second hole of stopper and ending slightly below it. With rubber tube connect this second glass tube to another glass tube, ca 10″ long, immersed in cylinder of H_2O to depth of ca 8″. (This connection acts as seal to restrain any strong flow of gas when not desired and to permit pressure in flask.)

Raise delivery tube nearly out of H_2O seal, allowing rapid flow of CO_2 for few min to dispel air from system. Then lower delivery tube into H_2O seal, slightly raise stopper, and quickly drop into flask 1–2 g sheet Al, folded into narrow bent strip to prevent breaking flask. After Al dissolves completely, raise tube in H_2O seal, letting CO_2 pass thru rapidly; place flask on hot plate and boil few min. Remove flask from heat and cool with tap or ice-H_2O, continuing flow of CO_2. Lower delivery tube into cylinder, disconnect flask, and, with glass plug, close rubber tube thru which CO_2 enters flask. Wash glass tubes, rubber stopper, and sides of flask with air-free wash soln, (a), add starch indicator, **25.067**(k), and titr. immediately with $0.01N$ I.

If desired, make titrn by slightly raising rubber stopper after cooling and adding excess $0.01N$ I. Then disconnect flask; wash tubes, rubber stopper, and sides of flask with air-free wash soln; and titr. excess I with $0.01N$ $Na_2S_2O_3$.

ZINC—OFFICIAL FIRST ACTION
Colorimetric Method (15)

25.077   *Principles*

Method involves wet oxidn of sample; elimination of Pb, Cu, Cd, Bi, Sb, Sn, Hg, and Ag as sulfides with added Cu as scavenger agent; simultaneous elimination of Co and Ni by extg metal complexes of α-nitroso-β-naphthol and dimethylglyoxime, resp., with $CHCl_3$; extn of Zn dithizonate with CCl_4; transfer of Zn to dil. HCl; and final extn of Zn dithizonate for color measurement.

25.078   *Reagents*

(All H_2O must be redistd from glass. Pyrex glassware should be used exclusively and must be scrupulously cleaned with hot HNO_3. Purify HNO_3 (usually unnecessary) and NH_4OH by distn in Pyrex if appreciably contaminated. Test H_2SO_4 if Zn contamination is suspected.)

(a) *Copper sulfate soln.*—2 mg Cu/ml. Dissolve 8 g $CuSO_4.5H_2O$ in H_2O and dil. to 1 L.

(b) *Ammonium citrate soln.*—Dissolve 225 g $(NH_4)_2HC_6H_5O_7$ in H_2O, make alk. to phenol red with NH_4OH (pH 7.4, first distinct color change), and add 75 ml in excess. Dil. to 2 L. Ext this soln immediately before use as follows: Add slight excess of dithizone and ext with CCl_4 until solv. layer is clear bright green. Remove excess dithizone by repeated extn with $CHCl_3$, and finally ext once more with CCl_4. (It is essential that excess dithizone be entirely removed, otherwise Zn will be lost during elimination of Co and Ni.)

(c) *Dimethylglyoxime soln.*—Dissolve 2 g reagent in 10 ml NH_4OH and 200–300 ml H_2O, filter, and dil. to 1 L.

(d) *α-Nitroso-β-naphthol soln.*—Dissolve 0.25 g in $CHCl_3$ and dil. to 500 ml.

(e) *Chloroform.*—Redistd.

(f) *Diphenylthiocarbazone (dithizone) soln.*—Dissolve 0.050 g dithizone in 2 ml NH_4OH and 100 ml H_2O, and ext repeatedly with CCl_4 until solv. layer is clear bright green. Discard solv. layer and filter aq. portion thru washed ashless paper. (This soln is best prepd as needed since it is only moderately stable, even when kept in dark and under refrigeration.)

(g) *Carbon tetrachloride.*—Redistd.

(h) *Dilute hydrochloric acid.*—0.04N. Dil. required amt of HCl with H_2O (redistd acid may be used altho usually unnecessary).

(i) *Zinc std solns.*—(*1*) *Stock soln.*—500 μg/ml. Dissolve 0.500 g pure granulated Zn in slight excess of dil. HCl and dil. to 1 L. (*2*) *Working soln.*—5 μg/ml. Dil. 10 ml stock soln to 1 L with 0.04N HCl.

25.079 — Preparation of Sample

(*Caution: See* **46.019, 46.026, 46.028,** and **46.030.**)

Weigh, into suitable size erlenmeyer, representative sample $\leq$25 g, estd to contain 25–100 μg Zn. If sample is liq., evap. to small vol. Add HNO_3 and heat cautiously until first vigorous reaction subsides somewhat; then add 2–5 ml H_2SO_4. Continue heating, adding more HNO_3 in small portions as needed to prevent charring, until fumes of SO_3 evolve and soln remains clear and almost colorless. Add 0.5 ml $HClO_4$ and continue heating until it is almost completely removed. Cool, and dil. to ca 40 ml. (Wet digestion and subsequent sulfide sepn may also be advantageously carried out in small Kjeldahl flask.)

25.080 — Separation of Sulfide Group

(*Caution: See* **46.047** and **46.059.**)

To H_2SO_4 soln add 2 drops Me red and 1 ml $CuSO_4$ soln, and neutze with NH_4OH. Add enough HCl to make soln ca 0.15N with respect to this acid (ca 0.5 ml excess in 50 ml soln is satisfactory); pH of soln as measured with glass electrode is 1.9–2.1. Pass stream of H_2S into soln until pptn is complete. Filter thru fine paper (Whatman No. 42 or equiv., previously fitted to funnel and washed with HCl (1 + 6), then with redistd H_2O). Receive filtrate in 250 ml beaker, and wash flask and filter with 3 or 4 small portions H_2O. Gently boil filtrate until odor of H_2S can no longer be detected; then add 5 ml satd Br-H_2O and continue boiling until Br-free. Cool, neutze to phenol red with NH_4OH, and make slightly acid with HCl (excess of 0.2 ml 1 + 1 HCl). Dil. resultant soln to definite vol. For optimum conditions of measurement, soln should contain 0.2–1.0 μg Zn/ml.

25.081 — Elimination of Nickel and Cobalt

Transfer 20 ml aliquot of prepd soln to 125 ml separator; add 5 ml NH_4 citrate soln, 2 ml dimethylglyoxime soln, and 10 ml α-nitroso-β-naphthol soln; and shake 2 min. Discard solv. layer and ext with 10 ml $CHCl_3$ to remove residual α-nitroso-β-naphthol. Discard solv. layer.

25.082 — Isolation and Estimation of Zinc

To aq. phase following removal of Ni and Co, which at this point has pH of 8.0–8.2, add 2.0 ml dithizone soln and 10 ml CCl_4, and shake 2 min. Let phases sep. and remove aq. layer as completely as possible, withdrawing liq. with pipet attached to vac. line. Wash down sides of separator with ca 25 ml

H_2O and without shaking again draw off aq. layer. Add 25 ml 0.04N HCl and shake 1 min to transfer Zn to acid-aq. layer. Drain and discard solv., being careful to dislodge and remove drop that usually floats on surface. To acid soln add 5.0 ml NH_4 citrate soln and 10.0 ml CCl_4 (pH of soln at this point is 8.8–9.0).

Det. quantity of dithizone to be added as follows: To separator contg 4.0 ml working Zn std (20 μg), dild to 25 ml with 0.04N HCl, 5.0 ml citrate buffer, and 10.0 ml CCl_4, add dithizone reagent in 0.1 ml increments, shaking briefly after each addn until faint yellow in aq. phase indicates bare excess of reagent. Multiply vol. dithizone soln required by 1.5 and add this vol. (to nearest 0.05 ml) to all samples. Shake 2 min. Pipet exactly 5.0 ml solv. layer into clean, dry test tube, dil. with 10.0 ml CCl_4, mix, and det. T (or A) at 540 nm.

25.083 — Preparation of Standard Curves

Prep. series of separators contg 0, 5, 10, 15, and 20 μg Zn dild to 25 ml with 0.04N HCl; add 5.0 ml citrate buffer, and proceed as with final extn of Zn, **25.082.**

Plot T on logarithmic scale (or A on linear scale) against concn and draw smooth curve thru points. (Intercept of this curve may vary slightly from day to day, depending on actual concn of dithizone used in final extn, but slope should remain essentially same.)

Atomic Absorption Method (16)

25.084 — Principle

Representative sample is dry- or wet-ashed. Residue is taken up in acid and dild to optimum working range. A of this soln as detd by atomic absorption spectrophotometry is converted to Zn concn thru calibration curve.

25.085 — Apparatus

Atomic absorption spectrophotometer.—Spectrophtr capable of operating as follows: wavelength, 2138Å; flame, air-C_2H_2 (oxidizing); range, 0–5 μg/ml. (*Caution: See* **46.006.**)

25.086 — Reagents

(Use Pyrex glassware exclusively; clean thoroly before use with hot HNO_3. If glass beads are used to prevent bumping, clean first with strong alkali followed by hot HNO_3. Since Pt used in laboratory may contain significant traces of metals, clean Pt dishes by $KHSO_4$ fusion followed by 10% HCl leach.)

(a) *Zinc std solns.*—(*1*) *Stock soln.*—500 μg/ml. Dissolve 0.500 g pure Zn metal in 5–10 ml HCl. Evap. almost to dryness and dil. to 1 L with H_2O. Soln is stable indefinitely. (*2*) *Working soln.*—Dil. aliquots of stock soln with H_2SO_4 (1 + 49) or 0.1N HCl (depending on method of ashing) to obtain min. of 5 solns within range of instrument. Prep. stds in

0–10 μg/ml range daily. (Do *not* use <2 ml pipets or <25 ml vol. flasks.)

(b) *Acids.*—Reagent grade HNO_3, HCl, and H_2SO_4. Test acids for freedom from Zn by atomic absorption measurement of appropriately dild sample. If contaminated, purify HNO_3 and HCl by distn. Further test purity of reagents and efficiency of cleaning by conducting blank detns by appropriate ashing method.

25.087 *Preparation of Sample Solution*

Prep. representative sample by mixing, blending, or grinding.

(a) *Wet-ashing.*—Accurately weigh, into 300 or 500 ml Kjeldahl flask, representative sample ≤10 g, estd to contain 25–100 μg Zn. (If sample is liq., evap. to small vol.) Add ca 5 ml HNO_3 and cautiously heat until first vigorous reaction subsides. Add 2.0 ml H_2SO_4 and continue heating, maintaining oxidizing conditions by adding HNO_3 in *small* increments (large amts may introduce Zn) until soln is colorless. Continue heating until dense fumes of H_2SO_4 are evolved and all HNO_3 has been removed. Cool, dil. with ca 20 ml H_2O, filter thru fast paper (pre-washed) into 100 ml vol. flask, and dil. to vol. with H_2O. Dil. further, if necessary, with H_2SO_4 (1 + 49) to attain working range of spectrophtr.

(b) *Dry-ashing.*—Accurately weigh, into clean Pt dish, representative sample estd to contain 25–100 μg Zn. Char under IR lamp and ash at temp. ≤525° until C-free. (Raise temp. of muffle slowly to 525° to avoid ignition.) Dissolve ash under watch glass in min. vol. HCl (1 + 1). Add ca 20 ml H_2O and evap. to near dryness on steam bath. Add 20 ml $0.1N$ HCl and continue heating ca 5 min. Filter thru fast paper into 100 ml vol. flask. Wash dish and filter with several 5–10 ml portions of $0.1N$ HCl, cool, and dil. to vol. with $0.1N$ HCl. Dil. further, if necessary, with $0.1N$ HCl to attain working range of instrument.

25.088 *Determination*

Set instrument to previously established optimum conditions or according to manufacturer's instructions. Det. *A* of ashed soln or diln, and min. of 5 stds within optimum working range, taking at least two readings (before and after sample readings). Flush burner with H_2O and check 0 point between readings. Det. Zn content from std curve obtained by plotting *A* against μg Zn/ml:

ppm Zn = [(μg Zn/ml from curve) × (diln factor, ml)]/g sample.

SELECTED REFERENCES

(1) Manual of Analytical Methods ACGIH, May 1963; JAOAC **47**, 191, 630(1964).
(2) USDA Bur. Chem. Circ. **102** (1912); JAOAC **7**, 48(1923); **16**, 398(1933); **18**, 189, 506(1935); **19**, 95(1936).
(3) Ind. Eng. Chem., Anal. Ed. **14**, 442(1942); JAOAC **46**, 246(1963).
(4) Chem. Listy **46**, 341(1952); Anal. Chem. **31**, 1589(1959); JAOAC **46**, 246(1963).
(5) JAOAC **28**, 257(1945); **32**, 349(1949); Anal. Chem. **21**, 300(1949).
(6) JAOAC **43**, 695(1960).
(7) JAOAC **27**, 90, 246(1944); **28**, 277(1945); **33**, 587(1950).
(8) JAOAC **17**, 108(1934); **18**, 315(1935); **19**, 130 (1936).
(9) JAOAC **19**, 130(1936); Ind. Eng. Chem., Anal. Ed. **11**, 400(1939).
(10) Ind. Eng. Chem., Anal. Ed. **7**, 285(1935).
(11) JAOAC **35**, 537(1952).
(12) JAOAC **22**, 346(1939); **26**, 346(1943).
(13) JAOAC **1**, 257(1915).
(14) Original communications, VIII Intern. Cong. Appl. Chem. **18**, 35(1912).
(15) JAOAC **27**, 325(1944); **28**, 271(1945).
(16) JAOAC **51**, 1042(1968); **52**, 404(1969).

26. Natural Poisons

MYCOTOXINS

AFLATOXINS

Aflatoxins are extremely potent carcinogens to many animals. Neither effects of aflatoxins on man nor possible routes of entry are presently known, but these materials should be handled as very toxic substances. Perform manipulations under hood whenever possible, and take particular precautions, such as use of glove box, when toxins are in dry form because of electrostatic nature and resulting tendency to disperse in working areas. Swab accidental spills of toxin with 5% NaOCl bleach. See JAOAC **48**, 681(1965) for more detail on decontamination.

(*Caution: See* **46.005, 46.011, 46.018, 46.039, 46.040, 46.046, 46.055, 46.056, 46.061, 46.066,** and **46.073.**)

26.001 *General Apparatus*

(a) *Apparatus for sample size reduction.*—Hobart Vertical Cutter/Mixer (VCM); Wiley mill, Std Model No. 3; hammer mill, e.g., Fitzpatrick, Micropulverizer; disk mill, e.g., Straub, Bauer; Waring Blendor; food cutter, e.g., Hobart Model 84181-D; meat chopper; Polytron; or equivs. Effective device for prepg subsample is Dickens-Satterwhite mill (available from Federal-State Inspection Service, PO Box 840, Macon, GA 31202).

(b) *Centrifuge.*—International Size 2, or equiv.

(c) *Centrifuge bottles.*—250 ml.

(d) *Chromatographic tube.*—45 × 500 or 600 mm, fitted with stopcock.

(e) *Chromatographic tubes.*—22 × 300 mm with Teflon stopcock, reservoir type (250 ml) (for 50 g samples); and 45 × 600 mm (for 1 kg samples).

(f) *Funnel.*—150 mm with fluted S&S No. 588, or equiv., paper to fit; or buchner, 32 cm diam., with Whatman No. 1 paper, or equiv., to fit.

(g) *Heating block.*—Al or brass. Drilled to accommodate vials.

(h) *High-speed blender.*—Explosion-proof, with 1 qt jar. Drill $\frac{1}{8}''$ hole ca $\frac{1}{2}''$ from center of lid to permit escape of vapors.

(i) *Hollow polyethylene stoppers.*—13 mm top diam., 7 mm bottom diam.

(j) *Rotary evaporator.*—With continuous feed.

(k) *Thin layer chromatographic apparatus.*—Glass plates, 20 × 20 cm (ca 8 × 8″); Desaga/Brinkmann applicator; mounting board; spotting template; microsyringe, 10 μl; desiccating storage cabinet, Brinkmann Instruments, Inc. No. 255051; storage rack, Scientific Glass Apparatus Co. No. C-4116-3; Thomas-Mitchell tank, Arthur H. Thomas Co. No. 3106-F05; long wave 15 watt UV lamp (use with UV-absorbing eyeglasses) or Chromato-Vue cabinet

equipped with one or two 15 watt lamps (Ultraviolet Products, Inc.); or equivs.

(l) *Tube shaking machine.*—Vortex, or equiv.

(m) *Vials.*—4 dram, foil-lined screw-cap (Kimble Products No. 60910-L).

(n) *Wrist-action shaker.*—Burrell or equiv., or stirring motor $\frac{1}{30}$ hp, 1400–1600 rpm, equipped with stainless steel shaft and propeller blade.

26.002 *General Reagents*

(a) *Benzene-acetonitrile soln.*—98 + 2; prep. from ACS solvs stored in glass.

(b) *Boiling chips.*—SiC (Carborundum Co.). Float off fines and extraneous matter with H_2O, wash with acetone, and dry.

(c) *Diatomaceous earth.*—(*1*) Acid-washed Celite 545. (*2*) Hyflo Super-Cel.

(d) *Silica gel for thin layer chromatography.*—Any silica gel that meets following test may be used (test each shipment). (Machery-Nagel GHR, Applied Science Adsorbosils 1 or 5, Mallinckrodt SilicAR 4G or 7G have been found satisfactory.) Prep. TLC plates, spot, develop, and observe as in **26.020(a)** and (**b**).

Prep. aflatoxin-free ext of commodity being examined as in **26.018(a)** and chromatograph as in **26.019(a)**. Dissolve in 500 μl benzene-CH_3CN (98 + 2). Place 10 μl soln on origin spot. Add to this spot, from solns of stds, 10 ng each of aflatoxins B_1 and G_1 and 2 ng each of aflatoxins B_2 and G_2. Repeat application of test spots to give ≥3 test spots evenly spaced across plate. Develop plate and examine. Four aflatoxins must be sepd from each other in clearly defined spots and sepd from nonaflatoxin fluorescent materials in ext of commodity being examined.

On second plate, place number of origin spots contg amt of each aflatoxin which is barely visible under UV illumination employed, plus adjacent spots contg twice these amts to serve as guide. Develop and observe. Store in dark in clean air for ≥18 hr. Observe again. Disappearance of one or both spots after storage is evidence of excessive fading and silica gel fails test.

(e) *Sodium sulfate.*—Anhyd. ACS grade.

(f) *Solvents.*—ACS grade in glass: Acetonitrile, acetone, alcohol, benzene, $CHCl_3$, hexane, HOAc, MeOH, and pet ether. Ether (anhyd., ≤0.01% alcohol).

26.003 *Sampling and Preparation of Sample (1)—Procedure*

(a) *Preparation of lot sample.*—Aflatoxin contamination of particulate products, such as grains and nuts, is likely to occur in pockets of high concn which may not be randomly distributed. Perform sampling and sample prepn with this factor in mind. Because of possibility of pockets of contamination, include total laboratory sample in sample prepn. Aim at max. practical size reduction and thoroness of mixing to achieve effective distribution of contaminated portions. One contaminated peanut (ca 0.5 g) can contain enough aflatoxins to result in significant level when mixed with 10,000 peanuts (ca 5 kg or 10 lb). To obtain at least 1 piece of contaminated nut in each 50 g portion, the single bad nut must be reduced to 100 pieces, and these 100 pieces must be uniformly blended thru entire mass. Altho further size reduction may not be needed with flours, liqs, or pastes, thoro mixing is still needed before removal of analytical sample. Adsorption of aflatoxins on sediments in liq. commodities is possible.

Batch-type size reduction equipment, 26.001(a), like Hobart VCM, Waring Blendor, Polytron, and food cutter reduce particle size and mix in one operation. With other types of size reduction equipment and when product is received in finely ground state, mixing is needed. Free flowing dry materials can be mixed in double cone or twin shell blender such as Patterson Kelly 8 qt twin shell blender. Pastes and powders can be mixed in food cutter or with flat beater in planetary mixer, e.g., Hobart Model A-120.

Greatest homogeneity of nut meats is achieved by reducing to paste with disk mill, liquefying the paste with *n*-heptane and mixing, and further grinding slurry with Polytron. Practical homogeneity of hard, in-shell nuts is achieved by size reduction in hammer mill, followed by mixing in planetary mixer or by simultaneous size reduction and mixing in Hobart VCM. Nut meats can be handled in Hobart VCM in same manner as in-shell nuts, if mixed with equal wt of grinding aid such as coarse-ground oyster shells.

(b) *Drawing of analytical sample.*—Draw with same precautions as apply to lot sample. Wherever practical, divide by riffling or similar random dividing procedure until subdivision is close to desired sample wt. Where such subdivision is not practical, composite number of small randomly taken portions. With liqs, suspend any particulate matter before drawing analytical sample.

Preparation of Standards— Official First Action

26.004 *Apparatus*

(Rinse all containers which contact aflatoxin solns with dil. acid, H$_2$O, and acetone, and dry.)

See **26.001(k), (l),** and in addn:

(a) *Spectrophotometer.*—Capable of measurements from 200 to 400 nm, with 1 cm quartz-face cells.

Calibrate as follows: Det. *A* of the 3 solns of K$_2$Cr$_2$O$_7$ in H$_2$SO$_4$ (0.4, 0.2, and 0.1mM), **26.005(b),** at max. absorption near 350 nm, against 0.018N H$_2$SO$_4$ as solv. blank. Calc. molar absorptivity (ϵ) at

each concn: $\epsilon = (A \times 1000)/$concn in mM. If the 3 values vary by more than guaranteed accuracy of A scale, check either technic or instrument. Average the 3 ϵ values to obtain $\bar{\epsilon}$. Det. correction factor (*CF*) for particular instrument and cells by substituting in equation: $CF = 3160/\bar{\epsilon}$, where 3160 is value for ϵ of K$_2$Cr$_2$O$_7$ solns. If *CF* is <0.95 or >1.05, check either technic or instrument to det. and eliminate cause. (Use same set of cells in calibration and detn of purity.)

(b) *Analytical microbalance.*—With sensitivity of 0.001 mg.

26.005 *Reagents*

See **26.002(a), (d), (f),** and in addn:

(a) *Sulfuric acid.*—Approx. 0.018N; dissolve 1 ml H$_2$SO$_4$ in 2 L H$_2$O.

(b) *Potassium dichromate std solns.*—(*1*) *Approx. 0.4 millimolar (mM).*—Accurately weigh ca 125 mg K$_2$Cr$_2$O$_7$ (primary std) and dissolve in 1.0 L 0.018N H$_2$SO$_4$; calc. molarity to 3 significant figs (molecular wt K$_2$Cr$_2$O$_7$ = 294.2). (*2*) *Approx. 0.2mM.*—Dil. 25 ml 0.4mM K$_2$Cr$_2$O$_7$ to 50 ml with 0.018N H$_2$SO$_4$ in vol. flask. (*3*) *Approx. 0.1mM.*—Dil. 25 ml 0.2mM K$_2$Cr$_2$O$_7$ to 50 ml with 0.018N H$_2$SO$_4$ in vol. flask.

Primary Standards (2)

(Aflatoxin stds are available from: USDA, Agricultural Research Service, SRRL, Box 19687, New Orleans, LA 70019; Calbiochem; Rijks Institute voor de Volksgezondheid, Sterrebos, Utrecht, The Netherlands; Makor Chemicals Ltd., Box 6570, Jerusalem, Israel.)

26.006 *Criteria of Purity*

Aflatoxins to be used as primary stds must meet following criteria of purity: (*1*) chromatgc purity as detd by **26.012,** (*2*) molar absorptivities within confidence limits given in **26.007,** (*3*) absorption peak ratios within confidence limits given in **26.008.**

26.007 *Molar Absorptivities of Aflatoxins in Methanol and 95% Confidence Limits Expected from Single Determination of Molar Absorptivity*

Aflatoxin	λ, nm	Molar Absorptivity in MeOH	95% Confidence Limits (±)
B$_1$	223	22,100	1,600
	265	12,400	800
	360	21,800	1,100
B$_2$	222	18,600	1,000
	265	12,100	600
	362	24,000	500
G$_1$	216	27,400	2,500
	242	9,600	300
	265	9,600	1,200
	362	17,700	700
G$_2$	214	25,300	2,300
	244	10,500	300
	265	9,000	1,100
	362	19,300	800

26.008 *Ratios of Major Peaks of UV Absorption Spectra of Aflatoxins in Methanol and 95% Confidence Limits Expected from Single Spectra*

Major Peaks Compared, nm	Parameter	Aflatoxins			
		B₁	B₂	G₁	G₂
223/265	Ratio	1.77	1.54		
	95% Conf. limits	±0.04	±0.05		
214/265	Ratio			2.86	2.83
	95% Conf. limits			±0.15	±0.13
242/265	Ratio			1.00	1.20
	95% Conf. limits			±0.02	±0.07
362/265	Ratio	1.76	1.98	1.84	2.09
	95% Conf. limits	±0.04	±0.08	±0.06	±0.18

26.009 *Preparation of Solutions in Methanol and UV Measurements*

Weigh ca 1 mg aflatoxin std to nearest 0.001 mg and transfer quant. to 100 ml vol. flask. Dissolve in and dil. to vol. with MeOH. Calc. concn of soln in μg/ml. Measure A of soln at max. absorption, **26.007**. Calc. molar absorptivities:

$$\epsilon = (A \times MW \times 1000)/(\mu g \text{ aflatoxin}/ml),$$

where MW = molecular wt of aflatoxin (B₁, 312; B₂, 314; G₁, 328; G₂, 330).

Calc. ratios of A for each aflatoxin at wavelengths given in **26.008**.

In each case use wavelength of max. absorption close to listed wavelengths.

Standards for Thin Layer Chromatography (3)

26.010 *Preparation of Solutions*

(a) *For aflatoxin stds received as dry films or crystals.*—To container of dry aflatoxin, add vol. benzene-CH₃CN, **26.002**(a), calcd to give concn of 8–10 μg/ml. Use label statement of aflatoxin wt as guide. Vigorously agitate soln 1 min on Vortex shaker and transfer without rinsing to convenient size g-s flask. Do *not* transfer dry aflatoxin for weighing or other purposes unless facilities are available to prevent dissemination of aflatoxins to surroundings due to electrostatic charge on particles.

(b) *For aflatoxin stds received as solns.*—Transfer soln to convenient size g-s flask. Dil., if necessary, to adjust concn to 8–10 μg/ml.

26.011 *Determination of Aflatoxin Concentration*

Record UV spectrum of aflatoxin soln from 330 to 370 nm against benzene-CH₃CN, **26.002**(a), in ref. cell. Det. concn of aflatoxin soln by measuring A at wavelength of max. absorption close to 350 nm and using following equation: μg aflatoxin/ml = (A ×

$MW \times 1000 \times CF)/\epsilon$, where CF = correction factor obtained in **26.004**(a) and MW and ϵ are as follows:

Aflatoxin	MW	ε
B₁	312	19,800
B₂	314	20,900
G₁	328	17,100
G₂	330	18,200

Return aflatoxin soln to original g-s flask. (Normal exposure to UV light during A measurement results in no observable conversion to photoproducts.)

26.012 *Determination of Chromatographic Purity*

Follow TLC technic described in **26.020**(a) and (e). Spot successively, at 2 cm intervals, 5 μl resolution ref. std, **26.014**, 5 μl aflatoxin soln, **26.010**, 5 μl this aflatoxin soln + 5 μl resolution ref. std, and 5 μl resolution ref. std. After development, spot of individual aflatoxin std should reveal no other aflatoxins and at most only faint fluorescent spots near origin.

26.013 *Preparation and Storage of TLC Standards*

After concn and purity of each std soln are established, dil. portion of each to spotting concn (0.5–1.0 μg aflatoxin B₁ or G₁/ml, depending on analyst preference, and ⅕ this concn for B₂ or G₂). Prep. no more than 1 ml of each at a time in g-s vol. flask.

Before storage, after aliquots have been removed for diln or spotting, weigh flasks contg std solns to nearest mg and record wts for future ref. Wrap flasks tightly in Al foil and store at 0°. When soln is to be used after storage, reweigh flask and record any change. To avoid incorporation of H₂O by condensation, bring all stds to room temp. before use; do *not* remove Al foil from flask until contents have reached room temp.

Recheck concn stored std soln by UV detn and recheck purity each time portion is taken for diln to spotting concn. When vol. of original soln becomes less than can be employed in std photometer cell, use microcells (accurately positioned). Instrument must be recalibrated with each set of cells, since calibration includes cell pathlength. Any observed change in concn should correspond with observed loss in wt due to solv. evapn.

26.014 *Preparation of Resolution Reference Standard*

Prep. resolution ref. std by mixing aflatoxin solns, **26.010**, to give concn at final diln with benzene-CH₃CN (98 + 2) the same as those prepd individually in **26.013**.

Peanuts and Peanut Products—
Official First Action
Method I (4)

26.015 *Apparatus*

See **26.001**(a), (e), (f), (g), (i), (j), (k), (l), (m), (n), and in addn:

Extractors.—500 ml g-s erlenmeyers, or 12 qt stainless steel pail.

26.016 *Reagents*

See **26.002**(a), (b), (c)(*2*), (d), (e), (f), **26.010–26.014**, and in addn:

(a) *Silica gel for column chromatography.*—Merck (Darmstadt) 0.05–0.2 mm for 50 g samples, or 0.2–0.5 mm for 1 kg samples (Brinkmann Instruments, Inc., or equiv.). Activate by drying 1 hr at 105°. Add H_2O, 1 ml/100 g, seal, shake until thoroly mixed, and store ≤15 hr in air-tight container.

(b) *Benzene-alcohol-water developing solvent.* — Prep. enough for several analyses. Shake benzene-alcohol-H_2O (45 + 35 + 19) in separator and let stand overnight at ≤22°. Then store the 2 layers that sep. in sep. g-s containers. Warm gently before use if they appear cloudy.

26.017 *Preparation of Sample*

Peanut butter and peanut meal need no prepn for extn unless they contain large particles, in which case reduce by milling. Use hammer mill or rotary cutter for meals. Grind raw and roasted peanuts and peanut butter with pieces of peanuts to paste with disk (burr) type mill before extn. See **26.003**.

26.018 *Extraction*

(a) *Fifty gram sample.*—Weigh 50 g prepd sample into 500 ml g-s erlenmeyer. Add 25 ml H_2O, 25 g diat. earth, and 250 ml $CHCl_3$, and secure stopper with masking tape. Shake 30 min on wrist action shaker and filter thru fluted paper. If filtration is slow, transfer to buchner precoated with ca 5 mm layer diat. earth, **26.002**(c)(*2*), and use light vac. (Use vac. filtration only for slow filtering samples since evapn of $CHCl_3$ is rapid, resulting in concn of ext.) Collect first 50 ml portion $CHCl_3$ filtrate and proceed as in **26.019**(a).

(b) *One kilogram sample.*—Weigh 1 kg prepd sample into 12 qt stainless steel pail. Add 500 ml H_2O and mix with spatula until visually uniform. Add 5 L $CHCl_3$ and cover pail, leaving small opening for stirrer shaft. Position stirrer to achieve max. agitation without splashing. Stir 30 min; mix in 500 g diat. earth, **26.002**(c)(*2*). For preliminary analysis remove enough mixt. to give 50 ml $CHCl_3$ filtrate and filter as in (a). Filter remainder thru buchner. Wash solids on funnel with 2 L $CHCl_3$; conc. combined $CHCl_3$ filtrate and washing in rotary evaporator to ca 800 ml when sample contains fat and to ca 200 ml for low-fat meals. Add 1 L hexane-$CHCl_3$ (1 + 1) to concd ext. If ppt appears, filter thru layer of filter-aid in buchner, washing with 1 L hexane-$CHCl_3$ (1 + 1).

26.019 *Column Chromatography*

(a) *Fifty gram sample.*—Place ball of glass wool loosely in bottom of 22 × 300 mm chromatgc tube and add ca 5 g anhyd. Na_2SO_4 to give base for silica gel. Add $CHCl_3$ until tube is ca ½ full; then add 10 g silica gel (0.05–0.2 mm). Wash sides of tube with ca 20 ml $CHCl_3$ and stir to disperse silica gel. When rate of settling slows, drain some $CHCl_3$ to aid settling, leaving 2–3″ above silica gel. Slowly add 15 g anhyd. Na_2SO_4. Drain $CHCl_3$ to top of Na_2SO_4. Add 50 ml sample ext to column, elute at max. flow rate with 150 ml hexane followed by 150 ml anhyd. ether, and discard. Elute aflatoxins with 150 ml MeOH-$CHCl_3$ (3 + 97), collecting this fraction from time of addn until flow stops.

Add few boiling chips to eluate, evap. nearly to dryness on steam bath, and transfer residue quant. to vial with $CHCl_3$. Add 2–3 boiling chips and evap., preferably under gentle stream of N. Seal vial with hollow polyethylene stopper and cap. Save for TLC.

(b) *One kilogram sample.*—Prep. column as in (a), using 45 × 60 mm chromatgc tube, 20 g Na_2SO_4 on glass wool ball, 100 g silica gel (0.2–0.5 mm), and 150 g Na_2SO_4 on top of silica gel. Add sample ext to column and elute at 40–60 ml/min with 500 ml $CHCl_3$-hexane (1 + 1), 1.5 L anhyd. ether, and 1 L MeOH-$CHCl_3$ (3 + 97). Evap. MeOH-$CHCl_3$ eluate as in (a). Retain final conc. for quantitation, **26.020**(c), and/or preparatory sepn of aflatoxin B_1 for confirmation by **26.046–26.053**.

If cleaner ext is required for preparatory TLC, direct bioassay, or quant. assay of sample contg low levels of aflatoxin, conc. MeOH-$CHCl_3$ eluate to ca 50 ml. Transfer to 10 g silica gel (0.05–0.2 mm) column and proceed as for 50 g samples, omitting hexane elution.

26.020 *Thin Layer Chromatography*

(a) *Preparation of plates.*—Weigh 30 g silica gel, **26.002**(d), into 300 ml g-s erlenmeyer, add amt of H_2O recommended by manufacturer, shake vigorously ≤1 min, and pour into applicator. Adjust amt of H_2O to obtain best consistency of slurry for spreading, as required by batch-to-batch variation in silica gel. Immediately coat five 20 × 20 cm glass plates with 0.25 mm thickness of silica gel suspension, and let plates rest undisturbed until gelled (ca 10 min). Adjust thickness of spread, if necessary, to provide good resolution of aflatoxins and tightness of spots. Dry coated plates ≥2 hr at 80° and store in desiccating cabinet with active silica gel desiccant until just before use. To prep. plate for chromatgy, scribe line 16 cm from bottom edge as solv. stop; scribe lines ca 0.5 cm in from each side or remove 0.5 cm gel from each side to prevent edge effects.

(b) *Preliminary thin layer chromatography.*— (This step may be omitted when approx. aflatoxin content is known.) Uncap vial contg sample ext, add

500 μl benzene-CH₃CN (98 + 2), and reseal with polyethylene stopper. Shake vigorously to dissolve, preferably with Vortex shaking machine. Puncture polyethylene stopper to accommodate needle of 10 μl syringe. In subdued incandescent light and as rapidly as possible, spot 1, 2.5, and two 5 μl spots on imaginary line 4 cm from bottom edge of TLC plate. Keep vial for quant. analysis. On same plate, spot 2, 5, and 10 μl std aflatoxins, **26.013.** Spot 5 μl std used on top of one of the two 5 μl sample origin spots as internal std. Spot at least one 5 μl resolution ref. std, **26.014,** to show whether adequate resolution is attained.

Place 50 ml acetone-CHCl₃ (1 + 9) in trough of unlined developing tank. If tank is other than Thomas-Mitchell, use vol. to provide solv. depth of ca ¾″. Composition of acetone-CHCl₃ can be varied from (5 + 95) to (15 + 85) to compensate for variations in silica gel and developing conditions. Use only one plate per tank, placing trough near one side to permit max. exposure of coated surface to tank vol. Immediately insert plate into tank and seal tank.

Develop plate 40 min at 23–25° or until aflatoxins reach R_f 0.4–0.7. Adjust development time to compensate if different developing temp. is used. Remove from tank, evap. solv. at room temp., and illuminate plate from below by placing it flat, coated side up, on longwave UV lamp in darkened room, or view plate in Chromato-Vue cabinet, or illuminate from above. (If illumination requires looking directly at lamps, protect eyes with UV-absorbing filter, such as Eastman Kodak Co. 2A.) Observe pattern of 4 fluorescent spots of resolution ref. std. In order of decreasing R_f they are B₁, B₂, G₁, and G₂. Note small color difference (bluish fluorescence of "B" contrasted with slightly green "G" aflatoxins). Examine patterns from sample for fluorescent spots having R_f close to those of stds and similar appearances. From this preliminary plate est. suitable diln for quant. TLC analysis. In final calcns, take into account amt of ext used for preliminary TLC.

(c) *Quantitative thin layer chromatography.*—If preliminary plate shows that new concn of sample ext is required, evap. to dryness on steam bath and redissolve in calcd vol. benzene-CH₃CN (98 + 2).

Spot successively 3.5, 5.0, and two 6.5 μl portions of sample ext. All spots should be approx. same size and ≤0.5 cm diam. On same plate, spot 3.5, 5.0, and 6.5 μl aflatoxin stds, **26.013,** corresponding to aflatoxins observed on preliminary plate. Spot 5.0 μl of each std used on top of one of the two 6.5 μl sample origin spots as internal std. Spot at least one 5 μl resolution ref. std, **26.014,** to show whether adequate resolution is attained. Proceed as in (**b**).

(d) *Interpretation of the chromatogram.*—Four clearly identifiable spots should be visible in resolution ref. std.

Examine pattern from sample spot contg internal std for aflatoxin spots. R_f values of aflatoxins used as internal stds should be same as or only slightly differ-

ent from those of resp. std aflatoxin spots. (Since spots from sample ext are compared directly with std aflatoxins on same plate, magnitude of R_f is unimportant. These may vary from plate to plate.)

Compare sample patterns with that contg internal std. Fluorescent spots in sample thought to be aflatoxins must have R_f values identical to and color similar to aflatoxin std spots when unknown spot and internal std spot are superimposed. Spot from sample and internal std combined should be more intense than either sample or std alone.

Compare fluorescent intensities of B₁ spots of sample with those of std spots and det. which sample portion matches one of stds. To aid in detn move plate away from lamp to attenuate UV light so any particular pair of spots can be compared at extinction. Interpolate if intensity sample spot is between those of 2 of std spots. If spots of smallest portion of sample are too intense to match stds, dil. sample and rechromatograph. Compare B₂, G₁, and G₂ spots in same manner.

Calc. concn of aflatoxin B₁ in μg/kg from formula: $\mu g/kg = (S \times Y \times V)/(X \times W)$, where $S = \mu l$ aflatoxin B₁ std equal to unknown; $Y =$ concn of aflatoxin B₁ std, μg/ml; $V = \mu l$ of final diln of sample ext; $X = \mu l$ sample ext spotted giving fluorescent intensity equal to S (B₁ std); $W =$ g sample applied to column (10 g if 50 ml CHCl₃ ext is used). If final ext diln does not represent 10 g, calc. correct sample wt and substitute. The 50 ml aliquot of CHCl₃ ext of peanut butter or whole nuts removed for analysis in **26.018**(a) or (b) usually contains 5–6 ml fat which adds to vol. Thus, 45 ml aliquot of CHCl₃ has been removed and ext actually represents 9 g starting material, instead of 10 g as for low fat materials.

Calc. aflatoxins B₂, G₁, and G₂ similarly.

(e) *Thin layer chromatographic confirmation of aflatoxin G₁ and/or G₂.*—If G₁ plus G₂ is ≥20% of total aflatoxins, confirm amt and identity of G₁ and G₂ by chromatgy, using solv. system, **26.016**(b).

Respot sample and stds on silica gel plate as in (c). Put 50 ml lower phase in bottom of insulated, unlined developing tank, and 50 ml upper phase in trough. Use only 1 plate per tank, placing trough near one side to permit max. exposure of coated surface to tank vol. Without equilibrating, insert plate in trough and seal. Let solv. rise to stop line 12–14 cm above origin (30–50 min) and remove plate. In order of decreasing R_f values, resolution ref. std gives B₁, B₂, G₁, G₂ as before, but many extraneous fluorescent substances found in samples will have completely different R_f values relative to those of aflatoxins in the 2 solv. systems. G₁ and G₂ aflatoxins of sample should have same R_f as those of resp. stds. Make quant. estn for G₁ and G₂ as in (c) and (d).

Method II (5)

26.021   *Apparatus*

See **26.001**(b), (c), (d), (g), (h), (i), (k), (l), (m).

26.022 *Reagents*

See **26.002**(a), (b), (c)(*1*), (d), (f), **26.010–26.014**, and in addn:

Cotton.—Absorbent, purified. Place 50 g absorbent cotton in beaker and wash with 1 L CHCl₃. Remove residual CHCl₃ by evapn and store cotton in closed container. Alternatively, ext with CHCl₃ in continuous extractor.

26.023 *Extraction*

Quant. transfer 50 g peanut butter to blender, using 100 ml hexane and 250 ml MeOH-H₂O (55 + 45). For peanuts, use 100 g sample and double solv. vols. For defatted peanut meal, use 100 g sample, omit hexane, and blend with 500 ml of the aq. MeOH. Blend 3.5 min at full speed.

Immediately after blending and before any sepn occurs, take portion of slurry for centrfg. Discard remainder. Centrf. 30 min at 1800–2000 rpm. Disregard any turbidity in middle aq. MeOH layer. Proceed with partition chromatgy without delay.

26.024 *Partition Column Chromatography*

Transfer 50 ml from aq. MeOH layer into 600–1000 ml beaker, add 5 ml H₂O, and swirl. Add 55 g acid-washed diat. earth and mix thoroly with spoon or spatula until mixt. appears uniform when pressed against bottom or side of beaker. Put ca 1.5″ diam. cotton plug loosely in bottom of chromatgc tube. Transfer diat. earth-sample mixt. to tube in ca ⅓ portions, packing each addn firmly with tamping rod to make smooth column. Wash beaker with hexane and elute column at flow rate of 20–60 ml/min, using total vol. of 500 ml. When last of hexane is about to disappear into diat. earth, change receiver. Wash diat. earth-sample mixing beaker with two ca 100 ml portions CHCl₃-hexane (1 + 1) and add to column. Continue adding this solv. so that 600 ml is collected in receiver. This fraction contains aflatoxins. Do not let column run dry any time during elution. Total elution time should be <1 hr.

Add few SiC chips to eluate, evap. to near dryness on steam bath, and transfer residue quant. to vial with CHCl₃. Add 2–3 SiC boiling chips and evap. CHCl₃, preferably under gentle stream of N. Seal with hollow polyethylene stopper and cap. Save for TLC.

26.025 *Thin Layer Chromatography*

Proceed as in **26.020**, except that no correction is required for fat carried by extg solv.

Method III (6)

26.026 *Apparatus*

See **26.001**(b), (e), (h), (i), (k), (l), (m), and in addn:

Beakers.—Stainless steel, 600 ml.

26.027 *Reagents*

See **26.002**(a), (b), (d), (f), **26.010–26.014**.

26.028 *Preparation of Sample*

Weigh 100 g peanuts or meal or 50 g peanut butter into blender jar. Add 250 ml MeOH-H₂O (55 + 45) and 100 ml hexane to peanut butter, and 500 ml MeOH-H₂O (55 + 45), 200 ml hexane, and ca 4 g NaCl to peanuts or meal.

26.029 *Extraction*

Blend 1 min at high speed. Transfer immediately to 250 ml centrf. tube and centrf. 5 min at 2000 rpm. (If time is unimportant or centrifuge is not available, let mixt. stand undisturbed in blender jar, as sepn will occur within 30 min for peanut butter and raw or roasted peanuts.)

Pipet 25 ml aq. MeOH phase into 125 or 250 ml separator, add 25 ml CHCl₃, stopper, and shake 30–60 sec. Let layers sep. and drain bottom CHCl₃ layer into 600 ml stainless steel beaker (if available). Do *not* include any meal with ext. Place beaker on steam plate under stream of N and add small amt of H₂O under beaker to improve heat transfer. (100 ml glass beaker is satisfactory, but more time is required for evapn.) Evap. solv. to between 2 ml and just dryness or as soon as condensing vapor is no longer visible on beaker lip. Do *not* leave beaker on hot plate after solv. has evapd. (Alternatively, evapn may be performed using erlenmeyers and steam bath (moderate heat).) Transfer ext. with careful washing, to 4 dram vial and evap. to dryness in hot H₂O bath. Dissolve ext in 250 μl benzene-CH₃CN (98 + 2) for spotting on TLC plate.

26.030 *Thin Layer Chromatography and Calculations*

Proceed as in **26.020**, except that no correction is required for fat carried by extg solv.

Cottonseed Products (7)—Official Final Action

26.031 *Apparatus*

See **26.001**(k), (l), (m), (n), and in addn:

(a) *Chromatographic tubes.*—400 × 20 mm id, with coarse fritted disk (Corning Glass Works No. 38450 or Kimble Products No. 28570); tubes may be fitted with Teflon stopcock.

(b) *Densitometer.*—Model 530 (Photovolt Corp., 115 Broadway, New York, NY 10010) with long wave (320–390 nm) source; primary UV filter; 520-A multiplier-photometer; search unit with 28-B, or 21-C phototube; secondary combination filter (preferred), 1¾₆″ diam. circle, made from Tiffen Photar UV-2A (Haze), 0.092″ thick (Tiffen Optical Co., 71 Jane St, Roslyn Hts, L.I., NY 11577) plus Corning Glass Works No. 5013 (3 mm thick, polished glass). Photovolt 445 or 465 nm filters can be used at sacrifice of sensitivity; collimating slit 0.1 × 15 mm (preferred), or 0.1 × 6 mm; automatic stage drive (1″/min); Varicord 43 (4″/min chart drive) or 42-B (3″/min chart drive) recorder; Integraph Model 49 integrator (optional). See J. Am. Oil Chemists' Soc.

43, 665(1966) for TLC stage modification. Other suitable TLC densitometers can be substituted.

26.032   *Reagents*

See **26.002**(a), (b), (c)(*2*), (d), (f), **26.010–26.014,** and in addn:

(a) *For column chromatography.—(1) Silica gel.—* Mallinckrodt CC-7, 100–200 mesh, for column chromtgy. Dry ca 2 hr at 110°, add 3% H_2O by wt, mix well, and equilibrate overnight before use. (*2*) *Wash solvent.—*Mix 900 ml anhyd. ether and 300 ml hexane. (*3*) *Aflatoxin elution solvent.—*Mix 800 ml $CHCl_3$ and 200 ml acetone.

(b) *Extraction solvent.—*Mix 850 ml acetone, 150 ml H_2O, and 8 ml HOAc.

(c) *Lead acetate soln.—*Dissolve 200 g $Pb(OAc)_2$.$3H_2O$ in H_2O with warming, add 3 ml HOAc, and dil. to 1 L.

26.033   *Preparation of Sample*

Grind whole seed or kernels in Wiley mill, or equiv., to pass 2 mm screen. For seed contg lint, screen ground sample on ⁴⁄₆₄″ screen to remove coarse lint. Grind meals to pass 1 mm screen. Quarter or riffle ground sample to obtain 50–100 g analytical sample.

26.034   *Extraction*

Weigh 25 g sample into 500 ml ₹ erlenmeyer, cover with layer of solid 6 mm diam. glass beads, add 250 ml extn solv., and stopper with leakproof polyethylene or glass stopper. Shake vigorously 30 min on mech. shaker, filter thru folded 18.5 cm diam. Whatman No. 4 paper, or equiv., and collect ca 150 ml filtrate.

26.035   *Preliminary Purification*

Measure 125 ml filtrate into 250 ml beaker, marked at 125 ml, and add 20 ml $Pb(OAc)_2$ soln, 25 ml H_2O, and several clean SiC boiling chips. Boil on steam bath until vol. is reduced to 125 ml and cool to room temp. Transfer quant. to ₹ 250 ml graduated cylinder with H_2O, and dil. to 200 ml with H_2O. Add 4–5 g diat. earth, **26.002**(c)(*2*), stopper, and mix well. Filter thru folded 18.5 cm diam. Whatman No. 4 paper, or equiv., and collect ca 170 ml filtrate.

Measure 160 ml filtrate into 250 ml separator, add 50 ml $CHCl_3$, stopper, and shake vigorously ca 1 min. Drain lower ($CHCl_3$) phase thru ca 2″ anhyd. powd Na_2SO_4 column in Butt or other suitable tube and collect filtrate in clean 250 ml beaker. Repeat extn with second 50 ml $CHCl_3$. Wash Na_2SO_4 with ca 20 ml $CHCl_3$ and add wash to filtrate. Evap. combined $CHCl_3$ exts to near dryness on steam bath; do *not* overheat dry ext.

This ext is suitable for screening by TLC, **26.037.** Use column chromatgc purification, **26.036,** for cleaner exts with min. of extraneous fluorescent materials.

26.036   *Column Chromatography*

Place small glass wool pad over fritted disk of chromatgc tube, and cover with ca 2 cm Na_2SO_4. Slurry 15 g silica gel, **26.032**(a)(*1*), with ca 40 ml ether-hexane wash solv. in 100 ml beaker and pour into tube; wash beaker with ca 25 ml wash solv. to effect transfer. When gel settles, add ca 2 cm Na_2SO_4 to top of column.

Dissolve sample ext from **26.035** in ca 2–3 ml $CHCl_3$ and add to column when ether-hexane wash solv. level just reaches top of Na_2SO_4. (Small funnel with elongated stem reaching just above top of column aids in uniform sample transfer.) Wash sample beaker twice with ca 2–3 ml $CHCl_3$ and transfer washings to column.

Measure 150 ml ether-hexane wash solv. into original sample beaker and add to column when $CHCl_3$ soln of sample just reaches top of Na_2SO_4. Keep column ca 80% filled during wash. Discard wash eluate.

Measure 200 ml $CHCl_3$-acetone (4 + 1) into original sample beaker, add to column when wash solv. level just reaches top of Na_2SO_4, and collect eluate in clean 250 ml beaker. Keep column ca 80% filled during elution.

Evap. $CHCl_3$-acetone eluate to near dryness on steam bath. Using wash bottle with fine tip, dissolve ext in $CHCl_3$ and quant. transfer to 4 dram vial. Evap. to dryness on warm surface, preferably under N stream. Cap and reserve for TLC. If preliminary TLC is delayed, store dry ext in freezer (0°F) until needed.

26.037   *Preliminary TLC*

See **26.020**(a) (except weigh 50 g silica gel, coat plates with 0.50 mm thick layer, and dry coated plates at 110°), (b), and (d). Dry remaining sample ext preferably under N stream, and reserve for **26.038.**

26.038   *Quantitative TLC*

Dissolve dried sample ext from **26.037** in appropriate vol. of benzene-CH_3CN (98 + 2) for either visual or densitometric analysis, as in (a).

(a) *Sample dilution and aliquots for visual and densitometric analysis.—*

Approx. B_1 Content from Prelim. TLC, μg/kg	Visual Analysis		Densitometric Analysis	
	Diln of Ext ml	Aliquots on Plate, μl	Diln of Ext ml	Aliquots on Plate, μl
0–10	0.25	3–5–7	0.25	10–10
10–25	0.50	3–5–7	0.25	5–5
25–50	1.0	3–5–7	0.50	6–6
50–75	1.5	3–5–7	1.0	6–6
75–125	2.0	3–5–7	1.0	5–5
125–150	2.5	3–5–7	1.5	5–5
150–175	3.0	3–5–7	2.0	6–6
175–200	4.0	3–5–7	2.5	6–6

(b) *Visual analysis.*—Spot 3, 5, and 7 μl sample ext on plate, along with 2, 3, 4, and 5 μl aflatoxin std (0.5 μg B_1 and G_1 and 0.25 μg B_2 and G_2/ml), **26.013.** Spot and develop plates as in **26.020(b)**. Interpret chromatogram as in **26.020(d)**.

(c) *Densitometric analysis.*—Spot suggested sample aliquots, (a), on plate, along with duplicate aliquots of mixed aflatoxin std to provide 5 ng aflatoxin B_1 and G_1 and 1.3 ng B_2 and G_2/spot. Also adjust sep. sample aliquots to these values for B_2, G_1, and G_2 by dilg, and spot sep. Place spots 2 cm apart along imaginary line ca 4 cm from bottom of plate. Develop as in **26.020(b)**. *Do not* damage gel layer during spotting, as significant errors may be introduced. If plate is visually inspected before densitometry, use low wattage UV source and min. exposure time.

Assemble and warm up app. according to manufacturer's instructions; operate in dimly lit room or under suitable protective cover.

Place suitable protective channels or spacers on top and bottom edges of plate and place plate, gel layer down, over longwave UV source on TLC stage so that direction of scan is from above B_1 downward to origin. Center B_1 spot of one std aliquot over inlet UV aperture of stage, and rack stage to locate blank plate zone just above B_1 spot over inlet UV aperture. Lower and adjust search unit to ca 1 mm above glass surface of plate.

Set multiplier photometer at suitable sensitivity (position 3 for Model 520-A) and recorder for mv operation in linear response mode and at suitable sensitivity (25–50 mv for Model 43). Adjust zero adjustment knob of multiplier to photometric scale value of 0 and recorder pen to baseline setting of 5, using recorder zero set (Model 43) or dark light control (Model 42-B).

Rack stage manually to center B_1 spot of std over exit slit of search unit, as noted by max. recorder pen response. Adjust pen to ca 70–80 full scale, using stepless sensitivity control of range switch (Model 43) or full light control (Model 42-B). If 0.1 × 6 mm exit slit is used, slide plate laterally for max. pen response of B_1 spot. (This adjustment is usually not required for 0.1 × 15 mm exit slit.)

Relocate blank plate zone just above B_1 spot over exit slit. Recorder pen should return to baseline setting of 5. If necessary, readjust baseline setting. Activate recorder chart drive and, if automatic integrator is used, set for min. baseline count, ca 1 count/10 sec. Activate automatic stage drive and scan std from just above B_1 down thru G_2.

Repeat scan for second std aliquot and sample aliquots. Readjust baseline as necessary. Do not change sensitivity scale expansion of recorder during scans on given plate.

If automatic integration is used, draw perpendicular lines from beginning of B_1 peak; valleys between B_1 and B_2, B_2 and G_1, G_1 and G_2; and end of G_2 peak, down thru integrator trace. Count unit and decade pips under each peak as measure of

peak area. Average area counts for each aflatoxin peak in duplicate std and sample aliquots. (Area counts should agree within 4–5%.)

If triangulation is used as measure of area, draw baseline and tangents to curves for each aflatoxin peak. Use intersection of tangents to baseline, in mm, as peak ht (h), and distance between intersection of tangents and baseline, in mm, as peak width (w). Multiply $h \times w$ as measure of area.

Calc. concn of aflatoxin B_1 in μg/kg as follows:

$$\mu g/kg = (B \times Y \times S \times V)/(Z \times X \times W),$$

where B = av. area aflatoxin B_1 peaks in sample aliquots; Y = concn aflatoxin B_1 std, μg/ml; S = μl aflatoxin B_1 std spotted; V = final diln of sample ext, μl; Z = av. area aflatoxin B_1 peaks in std aliquots; X = μl sample ext spotted; W = g sample represented by final ext (10 g if 25 g sample used for analysis).

Repeat calcn for each of other aflatoxins observed.

Correct aflatoxin concn values from densitometric measurement for amt of sample ext removed for either *Preliminary TLC*, **26.037**, or *Visual TLC*, (b), if used before densitometric measurements, as follows:

$$\text{Corrected } \mu g/kg = \frac{\text{apparent } \mu g/kg}{1 - [(p/P) + (q/Q)]}$$

where p = total μl sample ext spotted in **26.037**; P = μl sample ext prepd in **26.037**; q = total μl sample ext spotted in (b) (if done prior to densitometric analysis); Q = μl sample ext prepd for (b) (if done prior to densitometric analysis).

26.039   *TLC Confirmation of Aflatoxin G_1 and/or G_2*

Aflatoxins G_1 and G_2 are rarely observed in cottonseed products, but some exts may contain bluish fluorescent non-aflatoxin spot at or near R_f of G_1 or G_2, depending on TLC conditions. If G_1 or G_2 is judged to be present, confirm by respotting two 5 μl aliquots of sample ext on new plate. Spot 5 μl aflatoxin std on top of one sample aliquot and develop plate in 150 ml $CHCl_3$-MeOH (95 + 5). Although aflatoxins are not well resolved in this solv., bluish fluorescent non-aflatoxin component will be resolved from aflatoxins G_1 and G_2 as indicated by comparison of sample aliquots with and without internal std.

Green Coffee (8)—Official First Action

26.040   *Apparatus*

See **26.001(b)**, (c), (e), (h), (i), (k), (m), and (n).

26.041   *Reagents*

See **26.002(a)**, (b), (d), (e), (f), **26.010–26.014**, and in addn:

(a) *Tetrahydrofuran (THF).* — (*Caution: See* **46.070.**) Purify by passing 250 ml THF thru 25 g Woelm neut. alumina to remove peroxides. Adjust proportionately for larger amts of THF.

(b) *Deactivated Florisil.*—60–100 mesh, preactivated at 1200° (Fisher Scientific Co. No. F-100), washed and deactivated as follows: Wash 1.5 kg Florisil in chromatgc tube with 5 L pet ether or *n*-hexane contg 1 % (v/v) HOAc and rinse with 2 L pet ether or *n*-hexane to remove excess HOAc. Dry Florisil overnight at 120–135° in explosion-proof oven (or dry Florisil on hot plate in fume hood to remove last traces of solv. and then dry overnight in oven). Remove from oven, place in desiccator, and cool to room temp. Use proportionate amts of solv. to prep. less Florisil. (Acid-washed Florisil can be stored indefinitely.) Place ca 100 g washed Florisil in air-tight, g-s reagent bottle ca ⅔ full, add 5 % (w/w) H_2O, and shake vigorously by hand ca 5 min and then on mech. shaker 1 hr; let Florisil-H_2O equilibrate overnight. Prep. deactivated Florisil only in 100 g amts and use within 1 week.

(c) *Neutral alumina.*—Woelm (Alupharm Chemicals, PO Box 755, New Orleans, LA 70130).

26.042   *Preparation of Sample*

Freeze green coffee beans with solid CO_2 or liq. N and grind to fine powder in high-speed blender.

26.043   *Extraction*

Weigh 25 g powd green coffee beans in 500 ml g-s erlenmeyer, add 12.5 ml H_2O and 125 ml $CHCl_3$, and shake 30 min on mech. shaker. Transfer to centrf. bottle and centrf. 10 min at 2000 rpm. Use 50 ml aliquot of $CHCl_3$ layer for Florisil column cleanup.

26.044   *Florisil Chromatography*

Place glass wool plug loosely in bottom of 22 × 300 mm chromatgc tube, add ca 5 g anhyd. Na_2SO_4 to form even base, and add $CHCl_3$ until tube is ca ⅔ full; then add 10 g washed and deactivated Florisil with stirring to prevent air entrapment. Let Florisil settle and slowly add 15 g anhyd. Na_2SO_4.

Drain column until upper surface of $CHCl_3$ *just* reaches top of Florisil; then add 50 ml sample ext to column. When last of ext is about to drain into Florisil, begin elution with 200 ml purified THF at ca 10 ml/min. When upper surface of last portion of THF is ca 1 cm above Florisil, change collecting flask to 750 ml erlenmeyer and elute aflatoxins with 500 ml acetone-MeOH (99 + 1) at ca 10 ml/min. Discard $CHCl_3$ and THF fractions. Evap. acetone-MeOH fraction to dryness or near dryness under N in steam bath.

Quant. transfer residue to 4 dram vial with $CHCl_3$. Evap. $CHCl_3$ to dryness on steam bath under N. Let vial come to room temp., add 250 μl benzene-acetonitrile (98 + 2), seal with hollow polyethylene stopper, and cap. Reserve for TLC.

26.045   *Thin Layer Chromatography*

Proceed as in **26.020**(a), (b), (c), and (d), except use benzene-alcohol-H_2O developing solv., **26.016**(b).

Identification of Aflatoxin B₁ by Derivative Formation

26.046   *Apparatus*

(a) *Chromatographic tubes.*—See **26.001**(e), 22 × 300 mm.

(b) *Thin layer plate scraper.*—(Fig. 26:1.) Adapt from sealing tube with fritted disk (Corning Glass Works No. 39580, 30 M, or equiv.).

(c) *Vials.*—½ dram, 1 dram, and 4 dram, foil-lined screw cap (Kimble Products No. 60910-1, or equiv.).

(d) *Micro bell jar with suction side arm.*—Arthur H. Thomas Co. No. 2161, or equiv.

(e) *Thin layer chromatographic apparatus.*—See **26.001**(k).

(f) *Pipets.*—Pasteur disposable.

(g) *Distilling apparatus.*—All-glass with one 250 ml r-b flask; two 100 ml r-b flasks; Claisen distilling head-condenser; and flask adapter with side arm for drying tube attachment. Joints ⨊ 24/40.

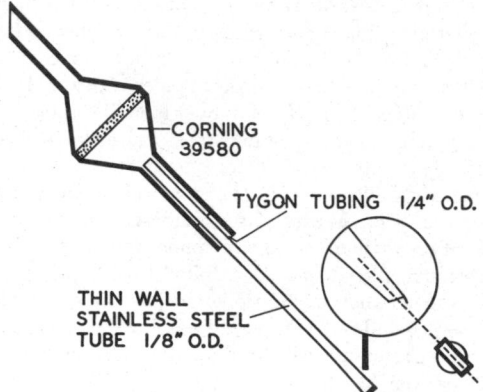

FIG. 26:1—Plate scraper for removing adsorbent from TLC plates

26.047   *Reagents*

See **26.002**(d), (f), **26.013**, **26.014**, and in addn:

(a) *Thionyl chloride.*—(*Note:* $SOCl_2$ is toxic. Use effective fume removal device, rubber gloves, and eye protection when using, distg, or evapg.) Eastman Kodak Co. No. 246 or purify as follows: Mix 20 ml quinoline (practical grade is satisfactory), slowly with stirring, into 60 ml $SOCl_2$ in 250 ml ⨊ flask flushed free of air with N. (*Caution:* Heat is generated on mixing.) Attach flask to all-glass, closed condenser and receiver system, protected from moisture with drying tube. Distill ca 45 ml $SOCl_2$. Add 30 ml *boiled linseed oil* to distillate and redistill. Collect fraction boiling between 76 and 78°. Store in tight, 4 oz, g-s amber bottle. Protect pure $SOCl_2$ from light and moisture.

To facilitate cleaning of distn flasks, remove residues immediately after use. Use dil. alkali to dissolve quinoline-$SOCl_2$; use warm nitrobenzene to dissolve linseed oil-$SOCl_2$.

Work with SOCl$_2$ in hooded area, sepd from that in which TLC is performed. Traces of SOCl$_2$ vapors picked up by silica gel can alter chromatgy.

(b) *Acetic anhydride, glacial acetic acid, formic acid, trifluoroacetic acid, hydrochloric acid.*—ACS grade.

(c) *Nitrogen.*—High purity.

26.048   *Extraction*

See 26.018(a) and (b). Sample ext should contain ≥ 2 μg aflatoxin B$_1$. If preparatory TLC is being used to obtain material for bioassay, 26.057–26.061, aflatoxin B$_1$ in ext should be ≥ 30 μg.

26.049   *Silica Gel Column Cleanup*

Proceed as in 26.019(a) and (b), if addnl cleanup is needed for preparatory TLC.

26.050   *Preparatory TLC*

Prep. plates and use TLC technic as in 25.020.

Dissolve residue from column cleanup in 250 μl CHCl$_3$. Transfer CHCl$_3$ soln to origin line of TLC plate, using 10 μl per spot at 5 mm spot intervals. About 1 cm beyond each spot at either end, place 5 μl spot of resolution ref. std which will also serve for locating line of aflatoxin B$_1$ spots.

Develop plate and examine. Expose plate to lowest intensity UV light required to see fluorescent spots. Keep time and intensity of irradiation by UV light at min. With needle, mark off area contg aflatoxin B$_1$. Collect silica gel from marked off area, using suction to pull coating loosened by plate scraper into filter portion of device. Elute aflatoxin from silica gel by swirling with six 5 ml portions MeOH-CHCl$_3$ (1 + 2). Use filter bell to pull MeOH-CHCl$_3$ thru fritted glass into 50 ml erlenmeyer by suction. Evap. solv. to dryness on steam bath under N stream. Dissolve residue in enough benzene-CH$_3$CN (98 + 2) to give estd aflatoxin B$_1$ concn of 1 μg/ml.

Det. purity and amt of aflatoxin B$_1$ in residue as in 26.020(c) and (d). If spots other than aflatoxin B$_1$ are present, repeat preparatory procedure until aflatoxin B$_1$ is chromatographically pure. Est. quantity of aflatoxin B$_1$ collected by comparison with spots of TLC std. Calc. aflatoxin B$_1$ from equation:

$$\mu g = (S \times Y \times V)/(X \times 1000)$$

where symbols are same as in 26.020(d).

Use residue soln for prepn of derivatives by 26.051 or 26.054.

Method I (9)—*Official Final Action*
26.051   *Preparation of Derivatives*

To each of three 1 dram vials transfer vol. of benzene-CH$_3$CN soln (98 + 2) calcd to contain 0.25 μg aflatoxin B$_1$. Remove solv. by evapn under N on steam bath. Prep. aflatoxin B$_1$ derivatives as follows, using disposable pipets:

Vial 1.—Add 3 drops *trifluoroacetic acid*, highest purity, shake, and hold 15 min at room temp. Evap. to dryness on steam bath under N stream. Pink color may appear in reaction soln when aflatoxin has been isolated from commodity ext.

Vial 2.—Add ca 0.2 ml HOAc and shake; add 1 drop SOCl$_2$, and shake again. Hold 5 min at room temp.; then evap. to dryness on steam bath under N stream. Anhyd. conditions must be maintained in reaction soln; therefore, apply stream of N before steam is turned on and maintain until steam is turned off and visible H$_2$O vapors are dissipated.

Vial 3.—Repeat as in *Vial 2*, substituting 90% *formic acid* for HOAc. (There is vigorous gas evolution upon addn of SOCl$_2$.)

Presence of H$_2$O is essential to proper completion of reactions in *Vials 1* and *3*. F$_3$CCOOH in *Vial 1* is hygroscopic; HCOOH used in *Vial 3* contains H$_2$O.

Remove reagents completely from each vial to ensure satisfactory derivative formation. Evapn under N stream is essential.

For controls, prep. 3 derivatives, as above, using 100 μl portions std aflatoxin B$_1$ soln, 26.013, in each vial.

26.052   *Thin Layer Chromatography*

Dissolve each derivative in the 6 vials in 30 μl benzene-CH$_3$CN (98 + 2). Using microsyringe, transfer 15 μl of each derivative soln to origin spots at ca 2 cm intervals on activated TLC plate. Place spots of each test and authentic derivative adjacent to each other. Finally add 1 spot (15 μl) of unmodified std aflatoxin B$_1$ and spot of resolution ref. std.

Develop plate as in 26.020(b).

Reactions should produce *dominant* characteristic *fluorescent* spots. Presence of other fluorescent spots in addn to those described does not invalidate test. Addnl spots can be caused by poorly cleaned aflatoxins, incomplete removal of reagents, incomplete mixing of sample with HCOOH or HOAc prior to addn of SOCl$_2$, or presence or absence of H$_2$O. Designated R_f values of dominant spots are subject to some fluctuation. Judge on basis of reaction products from std.

HOAc reaction produces 2 characteristic spots of approx. equal size and intensity migrating close to or slightly behind aflatoxin B$_1$-G$_2$ area. Appearance of spot at same R_f as dominant spot from other 2 reaction mixts is evidence that H$_2$O is present, possibly picked up by HOAc, which is hygroscopic. Some unreacted aflatoxin B$_1$ may also be present.

HCOOH and F$_3$CCOOH reactions both produce single characteristic spot at distance ca 10% of that traveled by unreacted aflatoxin. Since H$_2$O is essential ingredient of both reactions, incomplete formation of characteristic spot could mean that insufficient H$_2$O was present (*see* 26.051, par. 5). Less HCOOH than specified decreases H$_2$O from this source and can lead to reaction products similar to those obtained with HOAc system.

26.053   **Record**

Illuminate developed plate with long wave UV lamp used for viewing. Photograph plate, using 200 speed Polaroid black and white film. Operate camera with Kodak 3A lens filter or equiv., cutting off all light below 380 nm, and lens opening of f4.6 and shutter speed of 5 sec or other combination of lens opening and shutter speed which produces proper exposure. Cover developed area of plate with black mask, add legend strip to identify each spot, and superimpose legend on original picture by double exposure, using white light for second exposure.

Method II (10)—Official First Action
26.054   **Preparation of Derivatives**

Transfer ext contg 1 μg aflatoxin B_1 to 1 dram vial, remove $CHCl_3$ by evapn under N on steam bath, and dissolve residue in 1.0 ml benzene-CH_3CN (98 + 2). Transfer vol. benzene-CH_3CN soln calcd to contain 0.25 μg aflatoxin B_1 to 2 sep. $\frac{1}{2}$ dram vials. Add 100 μl H_2O and 1 drop HCl to vial 1 and 250 μl Ac_2O and 1 drop HCl to vial 2. Use disposable pipets for drop addn. Close vials with Teflon or Al foil-lined caps, shake both vials vigorously, and heat 10 min on steam bath with occasional agitation. Evap. to dryness on steam bath under N.

For controls, prep. 2 derivatives, as above, using 0.1 μg portions aflatoxin B_1 from std soln, **26.013.**

26.055   **Thin Layer Chromatography**

Dissolve each derivative in the 4 vials in 20 μl benzene-CH_3CN (98 + 2). Using 10 μl syringe, transfer 10 μl of each derivative soln to origin spots at ca 2 cm intervals on activated TLC plate in following sequence: vial 1 reaction product, vial 1 control, vial 2 reaction product, vial 2 control, 20 ng presumptive aflatoxin from original ext, 20 ng unmodified std aflatoxin B_1, and resolution ref. std. Develop plate as in **26.020(b).**

Reactions should produce *dominant* characteristic fluorescent spots. R_f values for these spots fluctuate; compare with derivatives prepd from std B_1.

Acid-catalyzed reaction with H_2O produces single, characteristic spot at R_f ca 10% of that of unreacted aflatoxin.

Acid-catalyzed reaction with Ac_2O produces 2 characteristic spots of ca equal size but of different intensity migrating close to or slightly behind aflatoxin B_1-G_2 area. The lower R_f spot is brighter of the two.

26.056   **Record**

See **26.053.**

Chicken Embryo Bioassay for Aflatoxin B_1 Toxicity (11)—Procedure
26.057   **Apparatus**

(Decontaminate all syringes, needles, vials, and other app. which have been in contact with afla-toxin B_1 by soaking in 5% NaOCl soln before disposal or cleaning.)

(a) *Egg candling light.*—60 watt candler (B-B Candling Light Co., 111 Sutter St, San Francisco, CA 94104, or equiv.).

(b) *Drill.*—Dremel Moto-Tool, Model No. 3 (27,000 rpm) with steel cutter No. 178 (Dremel Mfg. Co., 2420 18th St, Racine, WI 53403). Any drill with comparable speed may be used, but cutter *must* deflect removed shell outwards.

(c) *Forceps.*—Dissecting, medium fine point, curved, 4–5″ long (Model V34730, Aloe Scientific Co., 1831 Olive St, St. Louis, MO 63103, or equiv.).

(d) *Syringe.*—Microburet syringe, equipped to deliver 1–100 μl (Micro-Metric Instrument Co., PO Box 884, Cleveland, OH 44122, or equiv.).

(e) *Needles.*—B-D Yale, 1–1.5″ long, 22 to 27 gage (Becton-Dickinson Co., Rutherford, NJ 07070, or equiv.).

(f) *Sealing tape.*—Adhesive-cellophane tape, $\frac{1}{2}$″ wide. Scotch brand or equiv.

(g) *Incubator/hatcher.*—Forced-draft, controlled temp. and humidity, with automatic turning (Jamesway Model No. 252B, single-stage, 2500 egg capacity, James Mfg. Co., 104 W. Milwaukee Ave, Fort Atkinson, WI 53538, or equiv.).

26.058   **Reagents and Egg Supply**

(a) *Aflatoxin B_1 std soln.*—10 μg/ml absolute alcohol. *See* **26.004–26.013.** ϵ in absolute alcohol is same as in MeOH.

(b) *Hypochlorite soln.*—5% com. soln of NaOCl.

(c) *Egg supply.*—Eggs, fertile, from inbred Single-Comb White Leghorn flock (or other strain suitable for research or bioassay). Min. specifications are: (1) Nest clean (not dipped); (2) candled by supplier to eliminate misplaced and tremulous air cells, blood spots, hair-line cracks or other shell imperfections, and other abnormalities; (3) delivered in new cartons and filler flats; (4) Pullorum typhoid clean and *Mycoplasma gallisepticum* neg.; (5) av. wt $\leq$26 but $\geq$23 oz/dozen; (6) $\leq$48 hr laid; (7) stored at 60°F and 80% relative humidity prior to delivery; (8) fertility $\geq$85%; (9) feed of supplying flock must not contain any antibiotics, arsenicals, or nitrofurazones, but must be fully fortified to produce strong healthy chicks. Samples of feed must be supplied upon request for check analyses.

26.059   **General Technic**

Candle eggs and outline clearly with pencil location of air cell. Reject any eggs with imperfections such as those listed under **26.058**(c)(2).

Using random selection, divide eggs into groups of required number for each level of samples to be injected. Date and label each egg of all groups with identifying code. Use pencil with No. 3 hardness lead to avoid smearing of markings when handling.

In center of air cell of each egg, drill hole ca 5 mm diam. Remove visible *shell* membrane with forceps (see Fig. 26:2) so that no fragments remain to interfere with introduction of needle.

Using syringe, and needle bent to form 90° angle (see Fig. 26:2), dispense required amt of sample onto *egg membrane*, being careful *not to penetrate* membrane. Immediately seal hole with piece of cellophane-adhesive tape large enough to cover hole, but covering as little as possible of remaining air cell. Let eggs remain undisturbed in vertical position (air cell up) ca 1 hr to let material disperse.

Place eggs in incubator trays and load incubator set to maintain temp. and relative humidity (rh) recommended by manufacturer. Optima are 99.75°F and 60% rh. Fumigate incubator immediately after loading, using fumigant and technics recommended by manufacturer of incubator. If automatic turning is provided, set for turning every 2 hr; if no automatic turning is provided, turn by hand at least twice daily thru 17th day of incubation.

Candle eggs on fourth day, and daily thereafter. Remove clear eggs and dead embryos for opening and examination. Keep record of age at death and appearance of all embryos for all test solns and controls thruout incubation period. On 17th day, place eggs in hatching tray (no further turning necessary), replace in hatcher, set at recommended temp. and rh, and fumigate. Let eggs continue hatching and remove after all have hatched and dried (22nd or 23rd day).

Open and examine all unhatched eggs, examine chicks that hatch, and record observations.

26.060   Standard Aflatoxin B₁ Dose Response

Using aflatoxin B₁ std soln, det. dose response for egg supply under experimental conditions that will prevail in future assays:

Using ≥100 eggs/dose level, treat eggs as in **26.059**, at ≥5 dose levels ranging from no effect to 100% mortality. (Altho this may be done as single experiment, it is preferable to do it over period of time, e.g., 25 eggs/level repeated 4 times, or any combination until total of ≥100 eggs/level has been reached.)

Construct dose-response curve (μg–log % mortality), using method of Litchfield and Wilcoxon, *J. Pharm. Exptl. Therap.* **96**, 99–113(1949). Per cent mortality for each treatment is total of nonviable embryos and unhatched chicks divided by total eggs treated. (Precise LD_{50} and slope may vary depending upon sensitivity of embryos and environmental factors, but no-effect level to 100% mortality may be expected to fall between 0.01 and 0.20 μg/egg; *see* JAOAC **47**, 1003(1964).)

26.061   *Assay*

(a) *Complete protocol.*—For initial assay of system or when new std, new supply of solv., or eggs from new flock are employed. Include ≥30 noninjected controls in all assays to check fertility and hatchability of eggs used, and to monitor incubation conditions.

Prep. ext as in **26.048–26.050**. Dissolve material to

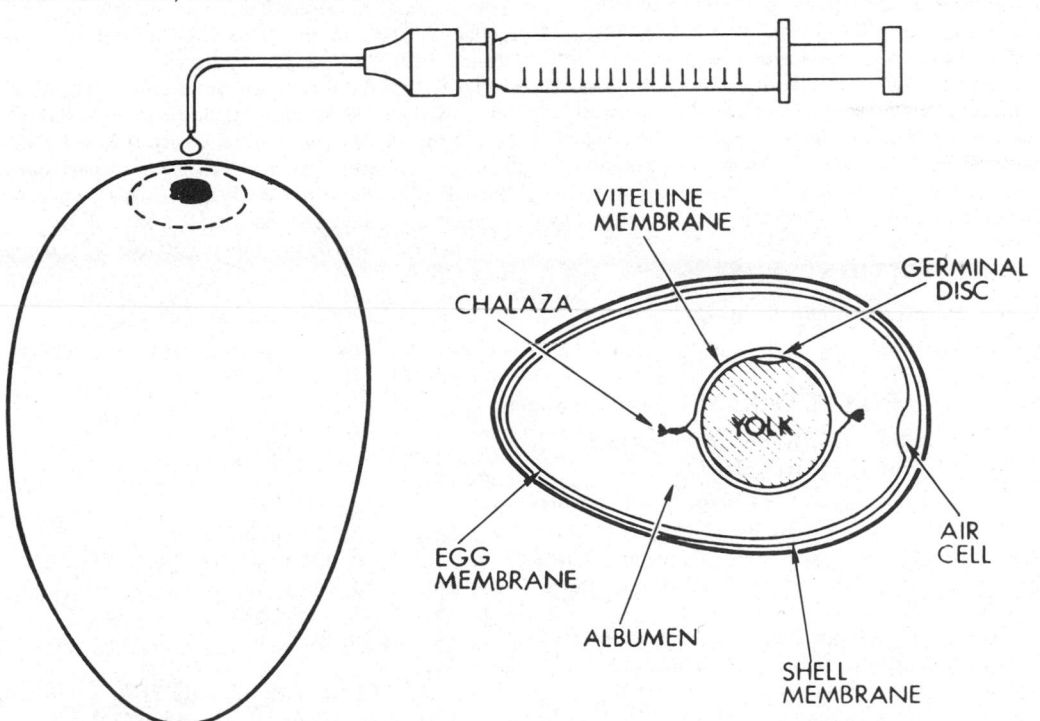

FIG. 26:2—Schematic showing parts of egg and modes of test material introduction

be assayed in absolute alcohol to obtain final aflatoxin B_1 concn of 10 $\mu l/ml$ (test soln), based on
chemical analysis. Set up protocol, based on dose
response obtained in **26.060**, according to Table 26:1.

Table 26:1—Complete protocol

No. of Eggs	Quantity Injected[a] ml	Quantity Injected[a] μg	Expected Mortality, %	Material Injected
≥ 20	0.020	0.20	100	Test soln
≥ 20	0.010	0.10	100	Test soln
≥ 20	0.005	0.05	90	Test soln
≥ 20	0.0025	0.025	50	Test soln
≥ 20	0.020	0.20	100	B_1 std soln, 10 $\mu g/ml$
$\geq 20^b$	0.010	0.10	100	B_1 std soln, 10 $\mu g/ml$
$\geq 20^b$	0.005	0.05	90	B_1 std soln, 10 $\mu g/ml$
≥ 20	0.02		≤ 20	Absolute alcohol
$\geq 20^b$	0.01		≤ 10	Absolute alcohol
$\geq 20^b$	0.005		≤ 10	Absolute alcohol
≥ 30			≤ 20	Non-injected controls

[a] Figures given are examples, based on *JAOAC* **47**, 1003(1964)).
[b] See (b).

(b) *Routine protocol.*—After complete protocol is
performed several times to assure system is func-
tioning properly, levels of std and solv. indicated by
[b] in Table 26:1 may be omitted. Complete procotol
must be performed when there is any change in
experimental conditions.

(c) *Lower level protocol.*—If insufficient material is
available for complete protocol, reduce number of
eggs per level and number of levels. Use min. of 2
levels: highest level, to assure some toxic response
even if chemical analysis is higher than true value,
and 1 of 2 lowest levels. Besides mortality, presence
of aflatoxin B_1 is also demonstrated by teratogenic
effects occurring in Single Comb White Leghorn
embryo after 12 days, severe growth retardation
(e.g., 21-day embryo may be as small as normal 12-
day embryo), short feet, edema, and hemorrhaging.

MARINE TOXINS

26.062   Paralytic Shellfish Poison

See **18.049–18.056.**

PHYTOTOXINS

Cyanogenetic Glucosides in Feeds and Similar Materials (12)

26.063   *Qualitative Test—Official Final Action*

Prep. Na picrate paper by dipping strips of filter
paper into 1% picric acid soln and drying; then
dipping into 10% Na_2CO_3 soln and drying. Store
these papers in stoppered bottle.

Finely chop small quantity of plant material and
place in test tube. Insert piece of moistened Na
picrate paper in tube, taking care that it does not
come in contact with sample. Add few drops $CHCl_3$
and stopper tube tightly. The Na picrate paper

gradually turns orange, then brick red, if plant tissue
contains cyanogenetic glucosides. (Test is delicate,
and rapidity of change in color depends upon quantity of free HCN present. This test works well with
fresh plant materials, but relatively dry substances,
particularly seeds of various plants, should be ground
and moistened with H_2O and allowed to hydrolyze in
stoppered test tube contg Na picrate paper. If necessary, small quantity of *emulsin* may be added.)

Hydrocyanic Acid Formed by Hydrolysis of Glucosides in Beans (13)— Official Final Action

26.064   *Acid Titration Method*

Place 10–20 g sample, ground to pass No. 20 sieve,
in 800 ml Kjeldahl flask, add 100 ml H_2O, and
macerate at room temp. 2 hr. Add 100 ml H_2O and
steam distill, collecting distillate in 20 ml 0.02N
$AgNO_3$ acidified with 1 ml HNO_3. Before distg, adjust app. so that tip of condenser dips below surface
of liq. in receiver. When 150 ml has passed over,
filter distillate thru gooch; wash receiver and gooch
with little H_2O; and titr. excess $AgNO_3$ in combined
filtrate and washings with 0.02N KCNS, using Fe
alum indicator.

1 ml 0.02N $AgNO_3$ = 0.54 mg HCN.

26.065   *Alkaline Titration Method*

Place 10–20 g sample, ground to pass No. 20 sieve,
in 800 ml Kjeldahl flask, add ca 200 ml H_2O, and let
stand 2–4 hr. (Autolysis should be conducted with
app. completely connected for distn.) Steam distill,
collect 150–160 ml distillate in NaOH soln (0.5 g in
20 ml H_2O), and dil. to definite vol.

To 100 ml distillate (it is preferable to dil. to 250
ml and titr. 100 ml aliquot) add 8 ml 6N NH_4OH
and 2 ml 5% KI soln and titr. with 0.02N $AgNO_3$,
using microburet. End point is faint but permanent
turbidity and may be easily recognized, especially
against black background.

1 ml 0.02N $AgNO_3$ = 1.08 mg HCN. (1 Ag equiv.
to 2 CN.)

SELECTED REFERENCES

(*1*) J. Am. Oil Chemists' Soc. **46**, 678(1969).
(*2*) JAOAC **53**, 96(1970).
(*3*) JAOAC **53**, 92(1970).
(*4*) JAOAC **51**, 67(1968).
(*5*) JAOAC **49**, 730(1966).
(*6*) JAOAC **53**, 104(1970).
(*7*) JAOAC **52**, 61(1969).
(*8*) JAOAC **52**, 1300(1969).
(*9*) JAOAC **50**, 354(1967); **51**, 485(1968).
(*10*) JAOAC **53**, 101(1970).
(*11*) JAOAC **47**, 1003(1964).
(*12*) JAOAC **19**, 94, 589(1936); **20**, 444(1937); **21**, 614(1938).
(*13*) J. Am. Chem. Soc. **37**, 601(1915); JAOAC **4**, 151(1920); **17**, 182(1934); **18**, 347(1935); **19**, 589(1936); **33**, 83(1950); **38**, 96(1955).

27. Nuts and Nut Products (1)

27.001 Preservation of Sample—Procedure

Store sample in air-tight container at 5–10°. Store meats in glass containers only.

27.002 Preparation of Sample—Procedure

(a) *Nuts in shell.*—Remove meats from shells, and sep. all shell particles from meats. Skin or spermoderm should be included with meat in all nuts, including peanuts and coconuts unless specifically excluded by description. Prep. sepd meats as in (b).

(b) *Nut meats, shredded coconut, or small pieces.*—Grind ≥250 g twice thru Enterprise No. 5 food chopper, equipped with revolving knife blade and plate with holes ca ⅛″ diam. (Other types of food choppers, graters, or comminuting devices that give smooth homogeneous paste without loss of oil may be used.) Mix sample well and store in air-tight glass container.

(c) *Nut butters and pastes.*—Transfer sample to container of convenient size and shape, warming semisolid products, and mix carefully with stiff-blade spatula or knife. (Elec. mixers or stirrers may be used instead if sample is of consistency to give uniform mixt.) Store sample in air-tight glass container.

27.003 Moisture (2)—Official First Action

(Not applicable to high sugar products or products contg glycerol or propylene glycol)

Dry sample representing ca 2 g dry material to constant wt (ca 5 hr) at 95–100° under pressure ≤100 mm Hg. Report loss in wt as moisture.

27.004 Crude Fat (3)—Official First Action

(*Caution: See* **46.011**, **46.039**, and **46.054**.)

(a) *Direct method.*—If large amts of sol. carbohydrates interfere with complete extn of fat, ext with H_2O before making detn. Ext ca 2 g sample with ether, dried as in **7.047**, 16 hr in Soxhlet-type extractor. Evap. ether, dry residue 30 min at 95–100°, cool in desiccator, and weigh; continue this alternate drying and weighing at 30 min intervals to constant wt (1–1.5 hr is usually required).

(b) *Indirect method.*—Proceed as in **27.003**; then ext dried substance 16 hr as in (a), and dry as in (a). Report loss in wt as ether ext.

27.005 Crude Protein (4)—Official First Action

Det. N as in **2.051**, and multiply result by 6.25. (It may be desirable to defat with pet ether.)

27.006 Crude Fiber—Official First Action—*See* **7.057**

27.007 Ash (5)—Official First Action—*See* **31.012**, or **31.013** if added chlorides are present.

27.008 Reducing Sugars (5)—Official Final Action—*See* **7.058**

27.009 Sucrose (5)—Official Final Action—*See* **7.059**

27.010 Sodium Chloride (5)—Official Final Action

To 2 g prepd sample, **27.002**, in Pt dish, add and thoroly incorporate 10 ml 10% $Ca(OAc)_2$ soln. For nut butters and pastes, disperse sample in 10 ml acetone before adding $Ca(OAc)_2$, and remove acetone at room temp. with air current. Dry on steam bath, and ash in muffle at lowest visible red heat (550°). (Complete ashing is not necessary.)

Dissolve ash in 25 ml HNO_3 (1 + 3), add known vol. 0.1N $AgNO_3$ more than enough to ppt all Cl, heat to boiling, cool, add 5 ml Fe indicator, **6.018(e)**, and titr. excess Ag with 0.1N NH_4SCN, **45.031(b)**, until soln turns permanent light brown. Calc. Cl as NaCl, after correcting for any Cl in the $Ca(OAc)_2$ soln.

27.011 Water-Insoluble Inorganic Residue—Official First Action—*See* **40.032**

27.012 Aflatoxins—*See* **Chap. 26**

PEANUT BUTTER

27.013 Preliminary Examination—Procedure

Make microscopic examination to detect addn of starch or any off-grade material not identifiable chemically.

27.014 Starch (6)—Official First Action

Weigh 4–5 g sample by difference into 250 ml centrf. bottle and ext twice with 50 ml portions pet ether, shaking 5 min each time. Wash down sides of bottle with pet ether, centrf., and pour off solv., disregarding opalescence. Warm bottle to drive off remaining solv., transfer residue to mortar, and grind. Return fine powder to bottle with aid of 100 ml 10%

NaCl soln. Shake bottle 15 min, wash down sides with NaCl soln, centrf. well, and pour off supernatant, disregarding opalescence. Repeat procedure twice.

Ext in same manner once with 70% alcohol and once with H_2O, shaking 1–2 min each time. Drain bottle several min, chill, and add from pipet 100 ml HCl (20.5–21.0 g HCl/100 ml) at temp. $\leq 15°$. Shake vigorously 3 min, centrf. well, and pour off soln thru cotton pledget in funnel stem. Cool soln to temp. at which the HCl was added, and pipet off 50 ml into nursing bottle contg 115 ml alcohol. Shake with whirling motion 1 min, let stand 2 min, centrf. 2 min, pour off thru weighed gooch contg thin asbestos pad, and add 50 ml 70% (v/v) alcohol to ppt. Stopper bottle, shake vigorously, wash down sides with the 70% alcohol, centrf. lightly, and pour off thru crucible. Repeat once with 70% alcohol and once with alcohol. Dry crucible and contents 1.5 hr at 130° in air, or 5 hr at 98–100° *in vacuo*. Cover crucible, place in desiccator contg efficient desiccant, and weigh when crucible reaches room temp.

SHREDDED COCONUT

27.015 Glycerol—Official First Action

Ext 4 times, with suction, 4 g shredded coconut (dried 5–6 hr *in vacuo* at 70°) on filter (fritted glass buchner is most convenient), using for each extn 50 ml pet ether (bp <65°), and allowing 3 min intervals between extns. Use flat-end glass rod for stirring. After removing fat, ext residue on filter with four 50 ml portions absolute alcohol, allowing 3 min intervals with stirring, as before. Dil. ext to 250 ml with absolute alcohol at room temp.

Pipet 100 ml into 500 ml erlenmeyer, and add 5 ml H_2O and paste made by adding hot H_2O to 2 or 3 g $Ba(OH)_2$ in small mortar. Heat mixt. on steam bath to boiling and boil ca 1 min; transfer to 250 ml centrf. bottle and centrf. at 2000 rpm ca 5 min. Transfer clear liq. to large porcelain dish and wash residue in centrf. bottle with 50–75 ml absolute alcohol, stirring with glass rod and centrfg as before. Evap. on steam bath at temp. <70° to few drops, or almost dryness.

Transfer to 50 ml g-s cylinder with 10 ml absolute alcohol and wash dish with two 5 ml portions absolute alcohol. Further wash dish with three 10 ml portions anhyd. ether, shaking g-s cylinder thoroly after each addn of anhyd. ether. Transfer to sediment tube and centrf. 10 min at 3200 rpm. Transfer clear soln in sediment tube to evapg dish, preferably Pt, and wash sediment tube with 25 ml of mixt. of absolute alcohol and anhyd. ether (2 + 3), stirring with glass rod and centrfg as before. Evap. on steam bath at 85–90° to ca 5 ml, add 20 ml H_2O, and evap. to ca 5 ml; repeat this operation twice. Transfer residue with hot H_2O to 50 ml vol. flask and proceed as in **30.077**.

SELECTED REFERENCES

(1) JAOAC **18**, 418(1935).
(2) JAOAC **8**, 295(1925); **31**, 521(1948); **32**, 527 (1949); **33**, 753(1950); **34**, 357(1951); **37**, 845 (1954).
(3) JAOAC **31**, 521(1948); **33**, 753(1950); **34**, 357 (1951); **37**, 845(1954).
(4) JAOAC **33**, 753(1950); **34**, 357(1951); **37**, 845 (1954).
(5) JAOAC **33**, 753(1950); **34**, 357(1951).
(6) JAOAC **37**, 845(1954).

28. Oils and Fats[★]

28.001 Preparation of Sample—Procedure

Melt solid fats and filter, using hot H_2O funnel or similar app. Make detns on samples of this melted, homogeneous mass. Filter oils that are not clear. To retard rancidity, keep oils and fats in cool place and protect from light and air.

Moisture and Volatile Matter (1)

28.002 Vacuum Oven Method—Official Final Action

Soften sample if necessary by gentle heat, taking care not to melt it. When soft enough, mix thoroly with mech. egg beater or other equally effective mech. mixer.

Weigh 5 ± 0.2 g prepd sample into Al moisture dish ca 5 cm diam. and 2 cm deep with tight-fit slip-over cover. Dry to constant wt in vac. oven at uniform temp. 20–25° above bp of H_2O at working pressure, which should be ≤100 mm Hg. Cool sample in efficient desiccator 30 min and weigh. Constant wt is attained when successive 1 hr drying periods show addnl loss of $\leq0.05\%$. Report % loss in wt as moisture and volatile matter.

Specific Gravity (Apparent) at 25/25°— Official Final Action

28.003 Standardization of Pycnometer

(*Caution:* CrO_3-H_2SO_4 can cause severe burns. *See* **46.023** and **46.030.**)

Carefully clean pycnometer by filling with satd soln of CrO_3 in H_2SO_4 and letting stand several hr. Empty pycnometer and rinse thoroly with H_2O; fill with recently boiled H_2O previously cooled to ca 20°, and place in constant temp. bath at 25°. After 30 min adjust H_2O level to proper point on pycnometer and stopper; remove from bath, wipe dry with clean cloth or towel, and weigh. Empty pycnometer, rinse several times with alcohol and then ether, let dry completely, remove ether vapor, and weigh. Det. wt of contained H_2O at 25° by subtracting wt pycnometer from its wt when filled with H_2O.

28.004 Determination

Fill clean, dry pycnometer with sample previously cooled to ca 20°, place in constant temp. bath 30 min at 25°, adjust oil level to proper point on pycnometer, and stopper. Remove from bath, wipe dry, and weigh as in **28.003**. Subtract wt empty pycnometer from its wt when filled with oil and divide difference by wt H_2O at 25°, as detd in **28.003**. Quotient is sp gr at 25/25° (apparent).

If sp gr at 20/20° is required, proceed as above and as in **28.003** but subtract 5° from each temp. specified.

28.005 Temperature Correction for Specific Gravity of Oils (2)—Official Final Action

If sp gr of oil is detd at other than std temp., approx. sp gr at 25/25° may be calcd as follows:

$$G = G' + 0.00064(T - 25°),$$

where
$\quad G = $ sp gr at 25/25°;
$\quad G' = $ sp gr at $T/25°$;
$\quad T = $ temp. at which sp gr was detd;

and $0.00064 = $ mean correction for 1°.

Index of Refraction—Official Final Action

28.006 General Directions

Det. index of refraction with any std instrument, reading oils at 20 or 25° and fats at 40°. Place instrument so that diffused daylight or some form of artificial light can be used for illumination. Circulate stream of constant temp. H_2O thru prisms. Approx. temp. corrections of butyrorefractometer readings may be made by following formula (Wiley, "Principles and Practice of Agricultural Analysis," 2nd ed., **3**, p. 414(1906–14); Conn. Agr. Expt. Sta. Rpt., 1900 (II), p. 142): $R = R' + K(T' - T)$, where $R = $ reading reduced to std temp., $R' = $ reading obtained at temp. T', $T = $ std temp., and $K = 0.55$ for fats and 0.58 for oils.

Readings of instruments that give index of refraction directly can be reduced to std temp. by substituting factor 0.000365 for 0.55 and 0.000385 for 0.58 in formula. As temp. rises, refractive index falls. Instrument used may be stdzd with H_2O at 20°, theoretical refractive index of H_2O at that temp. being 1.3330. Any correction found should be made on all readings. Index of refraction varies with density and in same direction.

28.007 By Means of Abbé Refractometer

To charge instrument, open double prism by means of screw head and place few drops sample on prism or, if preferred, open prisms slightly by turning screw head and pour few drops sample into funnel-shape aperture between prisms. Close prisms firmly by tightening screw head. Let instrument

---

[★] Methods so marked are surplus methods. *See* "Definitions of Terms and Explanatory Notes," item (29).

stand few min before reading, so that temp. of sample and instrument will be same.

Method of measurement is based upon observation of position of *border line of total reflection* in relation to faces of flint glass prism. Bring this border line into field of vision of telescope by rotating double prism by means of alidade in following manner: Hold sector firmly and move alidade backward or forward until field of vision is divided into light and dark portion. Line dividing these portions is "border line," and, as a rule, will not be sharp line but band of color. Colors are eliminated by rotating screw head of compensator until sharp, colorless line is obtained. Adjust border line so that it falls on point of intersection of cross hairs. Read refractive index of substance directly on scale of sector. Check correctness of instrument as in **28.006**, or with quartz plate that accompanies it, using monobromonaphthalene, and make necessary correction in reading.

28.008 *Butyrorefractometer Readings and Indices of Refraction*

Reading	Index of Refraction	Reading	Index of Refraction
40.0	1.4524	60.0	1.4659
40.5	1.4527	60.5	1.4662
41.0	1.4531	61.0	1.4665
41.5	1.4534	61.5	1.4668
42.0	1.4538	62.0	1.4672
42.5	1.4541	62.5	1.4675
43.0	1.4545	63.0	1.4678
43.5	1.4548	63.5	1.4681
44.0	1.4552	64.0	1.4685
44.5	1.4555	64.5	1.4688
45.0	1.4558	65.0	1.4691
45.5	1.4562	65.5	1.4694
46.0	1.4565	66.0	1.4697
46.5	1.4569	66.5	1.4700
47.0	1.4572	67.0	1.4704
47.5	1.4576	67.5	1.4707
48.0	1.4579	68.0	1.4710
48.5	1.4583	68.5	1.4713
49.0	1.4586	69.0	1.4717
49.5	1.4590	69.5	1.4720
50.0	1.4593	70.0	1.4723
50.5	1.4596	70.5	1.4726
51.0	1.4600	71.0	1.4729
51.5	1.4603	71.5	1.4732
52.0	1.4607	72.0	1.4735
52.5	1.4610	72.5	1.4738
53.0	1.4613	73.0	1.4741
53.5	1.4616	73.5	1.4744
54.0	1.4619	74.0	1.4747
54.5	1.4623	74.5	1.4750
55.0	1.4626	75.0	1.4753
55.5	1.4629	75.5	1.4756
56.0	1.4633	76.0	1.4759
56.5	1.4636	76.5	1.4762
57.0	1.4639	77.0	1.4765
57.5	1.4642	77.5	1.4768
58.0	1.4646	78.0	1.4771
58.5	1.4649	78.5	1.4774
59.0	1.4652	79.0	1.4777
59.5	1.4656	79.5	1.4780

28.009 *By Means of Zeiss Butyrorefractometer*

Place 2 or 3 drops filtered sample on surface of lower prism. Close prisms and adjust mirror until it gives sharpest reading. If reading is indistinct after running constant temp. H_2O thru instrument for some time, sample is unevenly distributed on prism surfaces. As index of refraction is greatly affected by temp., use care to keep temp. constant. Carefully adjust instrument, using std fluid supplied with it. Convert instrument reading to refractive indices from table, **28.008**.

Melting Point of Fats and Fatty Acids—Official Final Action

Wiley Method

28.010   *Reagent*

Alcohol-water mixture.—Sp gr should be same as that of fat to be examined. Prep. by sep. boiling H_2O and alcohol 10 min to remove gases held in soln. While still hot pour H_2O into test tube until it is almost half full. Nearly fill test tube with hot alcohol, pouring it down side of inclined tube to avoid too much mixing. If alcohol is added after the H_2O has cooled, air bubbles will make mixt. unfit for use.

28.011   *Determination*

Let melted and filtered fat fall 15–20 cm from dropping tube upon piece of ice or upon surface of cold Hg. Disks thus formed should be 1–1.5 cm diam. and weigh ca 200 mg. Remove disks when solid, and let stand 2–3 hr to obtain normal mp.

Alternatively, disks may be prepd using app. consisting of Al plate ca 3 mm thick and 100 mm square with perforations ca 10 mm in diam. and steel plate ca 10 mm thick and 150 mm square. Thoroly chill steel plate in refrigerator and place Al plate on top (surfaces should be flush). Pour melted and filtered fat into holes of Al plate and let stand in refrigerator ≥2 hr. Remove fat above surface of Al plate and remove disks.

Place 30 × 3.5 cm test tube, contg alcohol-H_2O mixt., in tall 35 × 10 cm beaker contg ice and H_2O, and leave until mixt. is cold. Drop disk of fat into tube. It will sink immediately to point where density of alcohol-H_2O mixt. is exactly equiv. to its own. Lower accurate thermometer, that can be read to 0.1°, into test tube until bulb is just above disk. To secure even temp. in all parts of alcohol-H_2O mixt. around disk, stir gently with thermometer. Slowly heat H_2O in beaker, constantly stirring with air stream or other suitable device.

When temp. of alcohol-H_2O mixt. rises to ca 6° below mp of fat, disk of fat begins to shrivel and gradually rolls up into irregular mass. Lower thermometer until fat particle is even with center of bulb. Rotate thermometer bulb gently and so regulate heat that ca 10 min is required for last 2° increase in temp. As soon as fat mass becomes spherical, read thermometer. This is Wiley mp. At this point temp. of bath must be ≤1.5° above mp of sample. Conduct 2 addnl detns exactly as above. Second and third results should agree closely.

If edge of disk touches side of tube, make new detn.

28.012 Capillary Tube Method (3)

Draw ca 10 mm melted and filtered fat into thin-wall capillary tube, 1 mm id. Seal end of tube with sample in small flame. Do not burn fat. Hold tubes contg fat overnight (ca 16 hr) in refrigerator at 4–10°. Attach tube to accurate thermometer graduated to 0.2°, so that lower end is even with bottom of Hg bulb. Suspend in 600 ml beaker half filled with H_2O so that thermometer is immersed ca 30 mm. Starting 8–10° below mp of sample, apply heat so as to increase bath temp. ca 0.5°/min, agitating H_2O in bath by small stream of air or with slow stirrer. Take as mp temp. at which substance becomes transparent. (Magnifying glass is useful to detect complete melting.) Report av. of 3 detns (should agree within 0.5°).

Titer Test (4)—Official Final Action

28.013 Specifications for Titer Test Thermometers

Type.—Etched stem, glass.
Liquid.—Mercury.
Range and subdivision.—Minus 2 to +68° in 0.2°.
Total length.—385–390 mm.
Stem.—Constructed of suitable thermometer tubing of either plain or lens front type. Diam., plain front type: 6–7 mm; diam., lens front type: cross section of stem must be such that it will pass thru 8 mm ring gage but not enter 5 mm slot gage.
Bulb.—Corning normal or equally suitable thermometric glass. Length, 15–25 mm; diam., 5.5 mm to not greater than that of stem.
Distance from bottom of bulb to −2° mark.—50–60 mm.
Distance to 68° mark from top of thermometer.—20–35 mm.
Length of unchanged capillary.—Between highest graduation and expansion chamber, 10 mm.
Expansion chamber.—To permit heating to at least 85°. Space above Hg to be evacuated or filled with N or other suitable gas.
Top finish.—Glass ring.
Graduation.—All lines, figures, and letters to be clear-cut and distinct. Each degree mark to be longer than remaining lines. Graduations to be numbered at zero and at each multiple of 2°.
Immersion.—45 mm.
Marking.—"A.O.A.C. Titer Test," serial number, and manufacturer's name or trademark must be etched on stem. Words "45 mm immersion" must also be etched on stem, as well as line extending around stem 45 mm above bottom of bulb.

Scale error.—Error at any point on scale must be ≤0.2°.
Standardization.—Thermometer must be stdzd at ice point and at intervals of ca 20°, for condition of 45 mm immersion, and for av. stem temp. of emergent Hg column of 25°.
Case.—Thermometer must be supplied in suitable case on which appears markings "A.O.A.C. Titer Test," "−2° to +68° in 0.2°."

Note: For interpreting these specifications, following definitions apply:

Total length is over-all length of finished instrument.

Diam. is that measured with ring gage or micrometer.

Length of bulb is distance from bottom to beginning of enamel backing.

Top of thermometer is top of finished instrument.

28.014 Apparatus

Stirring titer assembly, as shown in Fig. 28:1 consisting of 2 L beaker, wide-mouth bottle (capacity 450 ml, ht 190 mm, id of neck, 38 mm), titer test tube (25 × 100 mm), and stirrer (2–3 mm od, one end bent in form of loop, 19 mm diam.).

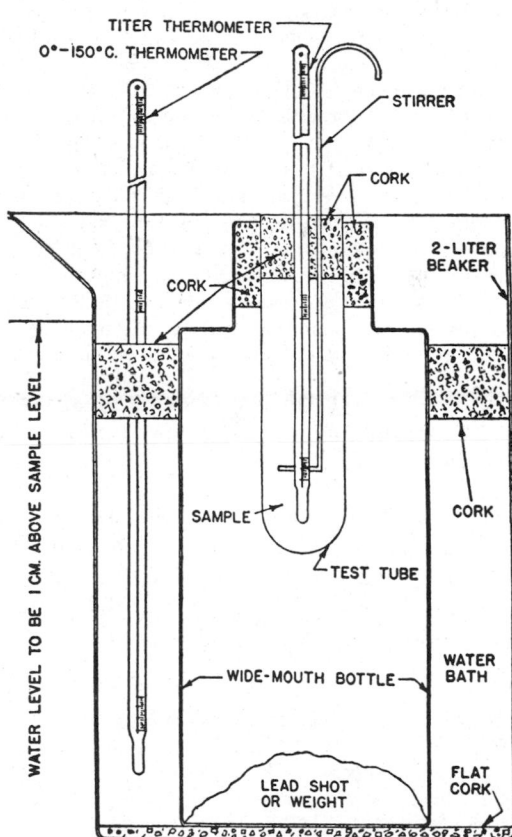

FIG. 28:1—Titer stirring assembly

28.015 *Determination*

Heat 110 g *glycerol-KOH soln* (25 g KOH in 125 g glycerol) to 150° in 800 ml beaker and add 50 ml of oil or melted fat, previously filtered if necessary to remove foreign substances. (Altho saponification often takes place almost immediately, continue heating and frequent stirring 15 min. Do not heat >150°.)

When saponification is complete, usually indicated by perfectly homogeneous soln, cool slightly and add 200–300 ml H_2O. After complete soln of the soap, add with stirring 50 ml dil. H_2SO_4 (16 ml H_2SO_4 in 70 ml H_2O). Heat soln, with frequent stirring and addn of H_2O if necessary, until layer of fatty acids is completely melted and clear. Siphon off aq. acid layer, add H_2O to fatty acids, boil 2–3 min, and again siphon off aq. layer. Repeat treatment with H_2O until wash H_2O is neut. to Me orange. Remove fatty acids so as not to include H_2O, and filter while melted thru rapid paper. Heat to 130° on hot plate to remove traces of H_2O and pour fatty acids into titer tube to ht of 57 mm from bottom. If H_2O is present in fatty acids, decant, refilter, and reheat.

Fill H_2O bath and adjust to 20° for all samples with titers 35° or higher, and to 15–20° below titer for samples with titers <35°. (H_2O level should be 1 cm above sample level.) Place test tube contg fatty acids in app., Fig. 28:1. Insert thermometer to immersion mark and equidistant from sides of tube. Stir vertically with stirring rod at rate of 100 complete up-and-down motions/min, starting agitation while temp. is ≥10° above titer point. (Stirrer should move thru vertical distance of ca 3.8 cm. If preferred, stirring may be performed mech.) Continue stirring until temp. remains constant 30 sec or begins to rise in <30 sec interval. Immediately discontinue stirring and observe rise in temp. Report as titer highest point reached by thermometer. Duplicate detns should normally agree within 0.2°.

28.016 ★ Acetyl Value (5)—Official Final ★ Action

See **26.016–26.017**, 10th ed.

Hydroxyl Value (6)—Official Final Action

American Oil Chemists' Society Method

(Hydroxyl value is number of mg KOH equiv. to hydroxyl content of 1 g sample. Applicable to fatty oils and derivatives such as fatty alcohols, mono- and diglycerides, and hydroxystearic acid.)

28.017 *Reagents*

(a) *Pyridine.*—Reagent grade, redistd at 114–115°.

(b) *Acetic anhydride.*—ACS, fresh.

(c) *Pyridine-acetic anhydride reagent.*—Mix 3 vols reagent (a) with 1 vol. (b) just before use.

(d) *n-Butyl alcohol.*—Reagent grade. Neutze with 0.5N KOH to faint pink phthln end point.

(e) *Alcoholic potassium hydroxide std soln.*—0.5N. (Should be ≥0.5N so that blank titers do not require refilling of 50 ml buret.)

28.018 *Determination*
(*Caution: See* **46.018** *and* **46.022**.)

According to expected hydroxyl value, weigh following amts of sample into 250 ml g-s erlenmeyers to nearest mg for acetylation:

Hydroxyl Value	Weight (g)
0– 20	10±0.1
20– 50	5
50–100	3
100–200	2

Weigh 9.0–11.0 g sample into another flask for acidity detn. (For fatty acids such as hydroxystearic acid, take 0.9–1.1 g.)

Pipet 5.0 ml reagent (c) into flask contg acetylation sample. For samples with 0–20 hydroxyl value, add addnl 5 ml pyridine. Mix thoroly by gentle swirling. Pipet 5.0 ml reagent (c) (and 5.0 ml pyridine, if used in acetylation) into another flask for reagent blank. Place flasks on steam bath under reflux condenser and heat 1 hr. (*Do not* use hot plate or mantle.) Add 10 ml H_2O thru condenser and heat addnl 10 min. Let flasks cool with condenser attached. Add 25 ml *n*-butyl alcohol, ca half thru condenser, remove condenser, and use rest to wash down sides of flask. Add 1 ml phthln and titr. to faint pink end point with 0.5N alc. KOH.

Add 10 ml pyridine, neutzd to phthln, to acidify sample. Swirl gently to mix, add 1 ml phthln, and titr. to faint pink end point with 0.5N alc. KOH.

Hydroxyl Value = $[B + (W \times A/C) - S]$ × Normality × 56.1/W,

where A = ml KOH for acidity titrn, B = ml KOH for reagent blank, C = g sample for acidity titrn, S = ml KOH for acetylated sample, W = g sample used for acetylation.

Iodine Absorption Number— Official Final Action
(All reports should specify method used)

Hanus Method

28.019 *Reagent*

Hanus iodine soln.—Dissolve 13.2 g pure I in 1 L HOAc (99.5%) that shows no reduction with dichromate and H_2SO_4. Add enough Br to double halogen content as detd by titrn (ca 3 ml). The I may be dissolved by heating, but soln should be cold when Br is added.

Convenient procedure for prepg Hanus I soln is as follows: Measure 825 ml HOAc and dissolve 13.615 g I in it with aid of heat. Cool, and titr. 25 ml with 0.1N $Na_2S_2O_3$, **45.038–45.039**. Measure another portion of 200 ml HOAc and add 3 ml Br. To 5 ml of this soln add 10 ml 15% KI soln, and titr. with the 0.1N $Na_2S_2O_3$. Calc. quantity of Br soln required to double halogen content of remaining 800 ml I soln as follows:

$A = B/C$, where A = ml Br soln required; B = 800 × thiosulfate equiv. of 1 ml I soln; and C = thiosulfate equiv. of 1 ml Br soln. If necessary, reduce mixed soln to proper concn by diln with HOAc.

28.020 *Determination*

Weigh ca 0.5000 g fat, or 0.2500 g oil (0.1000–0.2000 g of oils that have high absorbent power), into 500 ml g-s flask or bottle and dissolve in 10 ml $CHCl_3$. With pipet add 25 ml Hanus I soln, draining pipet definite time, and let stand 30 min in dark, shaking occasionally. (For accurate results use exact time. Excess I should be ≥60% of quantity added.)

Add 10 ml 15% KI soln, shake thoroly, and add 100 ml freshly boiled and cooled H_2O, washing down any free I on stopper. Titr. I with std 0.1N $Na_2S_2O_3$, adding it gradually, with constant shaking, until yellow soln turns almost colorless. Add few drops starch indicator, **2.129**(c), and continue titrn until blue entirely disappears. Toward end of titrn, stopper bottle and shake violently, so that any I remaining in soln in $CHCl_3$ may be taken up by KI soln.

Conduct 2 blank detns along with detn on sample. Number of ml 0.1N $Na_2S_2O_3$ required by blank (B) minus number of ml used in detn (S) gives $Na_2S_2O_3$ equiv. of I absorbed by the fat or oil. Calc. % by wt of I absorbed (I number, Hanus method).

I number = $[(B - S) \times N \times 12.69]/g$ sample, where N is normality of $Na_2S_2O_3$ soln.

Wijs Method (7)

28.021 *Reagents*
(*Caution: See* **46.018, 46.022,** and **46.047.**)

Wijs iodine soln.—(*1*) Dissolve 13 g resublimed I in 1 L HOAc (99.5%), and pass in dried (thru H_2SO_4) Cl until original $Na_2S_2O_3$ titrn of soln is not quite doubled. (Characteristic color change at end point indicates proper amt of Cl. Convenient procedure is to reserve some of original I soln, add slight excess of Cl to bulk of soln, and bring to desired titer by readdns of reserved portion.) Or: (*2*) Dissolve 16.5 g ICl in 1 L HOAc.

Store in amber bottle sealed with paraffin until ready for use. Wijs solns are sensitive to temp., moisture, and light. Store in dark at <30°. Det. I/Cl ratio as follows:

Iodine content.—Pipet 5 ml Wijs soln into 500 ml erlenmeyer contg 150 ml satd Cl-H_2O and some glass beads. Shake, heat to boiling, and boil briskly 10 min. Cool, add 30 ml H_2SO_4 (1 + 49) and 15 ml 15% KI soln, and titr. immediately with 0.1N $Na_2S_2O_3$.

Total halogen content.—Pipet 20 ml Wijs soln into 500 ml erlenmeyer contg 150 ml recently boiled and cooled H_2O and 15 ml 15% KI soln. Titr. immediately with 0.1N $Na_2S_2O_3$.

I/Cl = 2A/(3B − 2A), where A = ml 0.1N $Na_2S_2O_3$ required for I content and B = ml required for total halogen content. I/Cl ratio must be 1.10±0.1.

28.022 *Determination*

Use sample wt calcd as 26/expected I value, or from following table:

I Value	g Sample[a]	Accuracy, mg
3	10.58–8.46	±5.
10	3.17–2.54	0.2
20	1.59–1.27	0.2
40	0.79–0.63	0.2
80	0.40–0.32	0.2
120	0.26–0.21	0.2
160	0.20–0.16	0.2
200	0.16–0.13	0.2

[a] For 100 and 150% excess, resp.

Weigh melted and filtered sample into clean, dry, 500 ml g-s flask contg 20 ml CCl_4. With pipet add 25 ml I soln, draining pipet definite time. Excess of I should be 50–60% of quantity added, that is, 100–150% of quantity absorbed. Swirl, and let bottle stand in dark 30 min at 25±5°. Let samples with I values >150 (linseed and perilla) stand 1 hr.

Add 20 ml 15% KI soln and 100 ml recently boiled and cooled H_2O. Titr. the I with 0.1N $Na_2S_2O_3$, **45.038–45.039,** added gradually, shaking constantly until yellow soln turns almost colorless. (Vigorous magnetic stirring is convenient.) Add few drops starch indicator, **2.129**(c), and continue titrn until blue entirely disappears. Toward end of reaction, stopper bottle and shake violently so that any I remaining in soln in CCl_4 may be taken up by KI soln.

Conduct 2 detns on blanks in same manner as sample, but without fat. Slight variations in temp. appreciably affect titer of I soln, as HOAc has high coefficient of expansion. It is essential, therefore, that blanks and detns on sample be made at same time. ml Std $Na_2S_2O_3$ soln required by blank (B) minus quantity used in detn (S) gives $Na_2S_2O_3$ equiv. of I absorbed by sample taken. Calc. % by wt of I absorbed as in **28.020** and report as I number, Wijs method.

Peroxide Value—Official Final Action

American Oil Chemists' Society Method (8)

28.023 *Reagents*

(a) *Acetic acid-chloroform soln.*—Mix 3 vols HOAc with 1 vol. $CHCl_3$, NF.

(b) *Potassium iodide soln, saturated.*—Dissolve excess KI in freshly boiled H_2O. Excess solid must remain. Store in dark. Test daily by adding 0.5 ml to 30 ml HOAc-$CHCl_3$, (a); then add 2 drops 1%

starch soln, **2.129**(c). If soln turns blue, requiring >1 drop $0.1N$ $Na_2S_2O_3$ to discharge color, prep. fresh soln.

(c) *Sodium thiosulfate std solns.*—0.1 and $0.01N$. Prep. and stdze as in **45.038–45.039**. For $0.01N$, dil. $0.1N$ with freshly boiled and cooled H_2O.

28.024   *Determination*

(a) *Fats and oils.*—Weigh 5.00 ± 0.05 g sample into 250 ml g-s erlenmeyer. Add 30 ml HOAc-$CHCl_3$, (a), and swirl to dissolve. Add 0.5 ml satd KI soln, (b), from Mohr pipet, let stand with occasional shaking 1 min, and add 30 ml H_2O. Slowly titr. with $0.1N$ $Na_2S_2O_3$ with vigorous shaking until yellow is almost gone. Add ca 0.5 ml 1% starch soln, **2.129**(c), and continue titrn, shaking vigorously to release all I from $CHCl_3$ layer, until blue just disappears. If <0.5 ml $0.1N$ $Na_2S_2O_3$ is used, repeat detn with $0.01N$ $Na_2S_2O_3$.

Conduct blank detn daily (must be ≤0.1 ml $0.1N$ $Na_2S_2O_3$). Subtract from sample titrn.

Peroxide value (milliequiv. peroxide/kg sample) $= S \times N \times 1000/g$ sample, where $S =$ ml $Na_2S_2O_3$ (blank corrected) and $N =$ normality $Na_2S_2O_3$ soln.

(b) *Margarine.*—Melt sample by heating with constant stirring on hot plate at low heat, or heat in air oven at 60–70°. (Avoid excessive heat and long exposure >40°.) When completely melted, hold in warm place until aq. portion and most of solids have settled. Decant oil into clean beaker and filter thru Whatman No. 4 or equiv. paper. Do not reheat unless necessary to obtain clear filtrate. Proceed as in (a).

28.025   ★   Thiocyanogen Number—   ★
Official First Action

(*Caution:* Thiocyanogen is toxic. *See* **46.018, 46.022, 46.047,** and **46.050.**)

See **26.026–26.027,** 10th ed.

Saponification Number (Koettstorfer Number) —Official Final Action
28.026   *Reagent*

Alcoholic potassium hydroxide soln (JAOAC **19,** 427(1936)).—(*1*) Reflux 1.2 L alcohol 30 min in distg flask with 10 g KOH and 6 g granulated Al (or Al foil). Distill and collect 1 L after discarding first 50 ml. Dissolve 40 g KOH in this 1 L alcohol, keeping temp. <15° while dissolving alkali. Keep soln in g-s bottle. Or, (*2*) crush 40 g KOH in 7 or 8" mortar. Add 45 g granulated CaO and grind mixt. to powder. From 1 L alcohol add 100 ml to mortar and transfer to flask, rinsing mortar with several more portions. Add remainder of alcohol to flask, shake mixt. ≥5 min, and invert beaker over neck of flask. Repeat shaking several times during day. Next morning filter soln into clean, dry, g-s bottle.

28.027   *Determination*

Accurately weigh ca 5 g filtered sample into 250–300 ml erlenmeyer. Pipet 50 ml alc. KOH soln into flask, draining pipet definite time. Connect flask with air condenser and boil until fat is completely saponified (ca 30 min). Cool, and titr. with $0.5N$ HCl, **45.012–45.013**, using phthln. Conduct blank detn along with that on sample, using same pipet for measuring KOH soln and draining same time. Subtract ml $0.5N$ HCl required in detn on sample from ml required on blank to obtain ml $0.5N$ HCl equiv. to KOH used in saponification of sample taken. Calc. and report as saponification number (mg KOH required to saponify 1 g fat).

28.028   ★   Soluble Acids—Official   ★
Final Action

See **26.030,** 10th ed.

28.029   ★   Insoluble Acids (Hehner   ★
Number)—Official Final Action

See **26.031,** 10th ed.

Free Fatty Acids in Crude and Refined Oils
28.030   *National Cottonseed Products Association Method—Official Final Action*

(a) *In crude oils.*—Weigh 7.05 g well-mixed oil into 250 ml flask or 4 oz bottle. Add 50 ml alcohol, previously neutzd by adding 2 ml phthln soln and enough $0.1N$ NaOH to produce faint permanent pink. Titr. with $0.25N$ NaOH, **45.035–45.036**, with vigorous shaking until permanent faint pink appears and persists ≥1 min. Report as % free fatty acids expressed as oleic acid; ml $0.25N$ NaOH used in titrn corresponds to this %.

(b) *In refined oils.*—Put ca 50 ml alcohol into clean, dry 150 ml flask, and add few drops of the oil and 2 ml phthln. Place flask in H_2O at 60–65° until warm, and add enough $0.1N$ NaOH to produce faint permanent pink. Weigh 56.4 g oil into the neutzd alcohol and titr. with $0.1N$ NaOH, **45.035–45.036**, occasionally warming and violently shaking mixt. until same faint permanent pink appears in supernatant alcohol. Multiply ml $0.1N$ NaOH by 0.05 and report as % free fatty acids expressed as oleic acid.

Free fatty acids may also be expressed in terms of acid value (mg KOH necessary to neutze 1 g sample). Acid value = % free fatty acids (as oleic) $\times$ 1.99.

Soluble and Insoluble Volatile Acids (Reichert-Meissl and Polenske Values) (9)—Official Final Action
28.031   *Reagents*

(a) *Sodium hydroxide soln.*—(1 + 1). Protect soln from contact with CO_2. Let soln settle and use only clear liq.

(b) *Glycerol-soda soln.*—Add 20 ml 1 + 1 NaOH soln to 180 ml pure glycerol.

(c) *Silicon carbide.*—Grit No. 6. Carborundum Co.

28.032 *Determination*

Accurately weigh 5±0.1 g sample into clean, dry 300 ml r-b flask. Add 20 ml glycerol-soda soln and heat with swirling over flame or asbestos-covered hot plate until completely saponified, as shown by mixt. becoming perfectly clear. No oil should remain on surface; walls of flasks are wet by soln. Let flask cool to ca 100° (ca 5 min) and *dissolve* contents in 135±1 ml recently boiled H_2O with min. loss of H_2O vapor. (135 ml H_2O is conveniently measured from 125 ml erlenmeyer previously calibrated to deliver 134.6±1.0 g H_2O at 25°.) Add 6 ml H_2SO_4 (1 + 4) and 15 pieces of SiC. Distill, using app. with dimensions given in Fig. 28:2. (Adapter may be used for distg into 110 ml vol. flask.) Rest flask on piece of asbestos board with center hole 5 cm diam., and regulate flame so as to collect 110 ml distillate in 30±2 min (measure time from passage of first drop of distillate from condenser to receiving flask), letting distillate drip into receiving flask at temp. of ca 20°.

When 110 ml has distd, substitute 25 ml cylinder for receiving flask, remove flame, and disconnect distn head from condenser. Mix without violent shaking, immerse flask contg distillate almost completely in 15° H_2O 15 min, filter thru dry 9 cm moderately retentive paper (S&S No. 589 White Ribbon is satisfactory), and titr. 100 ml filtrate with 0.1N NaOH, **45.035–45.036**, using phthln.

Soln should remain pink 2–3 min. Reichert-Meissl value is ml 0.1N NaOH used, corrected for titrn of blank detn, ×1.1, calcd to 5.00 g sample.

Remove remainder of sol. acids from insol. acids on filter by washing with three 15 ml portions 15° H_2O, each previously passed thru condenser, 25 ml cylinder, and 110 ml receiving flask. Dissolve insol. acids by passing three 15 ml portions neut. alcohol thru filter paper, each portion having previously passed thru condenser, 25 ml cylinder, and 110 ml receiving flask. Titr. combined alc. washings with 0.1N NaOH, using phthln. Polenske value is ml 0.1N NaOH required for titrn, corrected for titrn obtained in blank detn, and calcd to 5.00 g sample.

Note: Unless these directions are followed in every detail, satisfactory results cannot be obtained.

Mole Per Cent Butyric Acid in Fat
Chromatographic Method (10)—Official Final Action

28.033 *Apparatus*

Chromatographic tube.—Fuse 15 cm section of 38 mm od tubing to 20 cm of 22 mm tubing, which in turn is fused to 5 cm of 7 mm tubing, with drip tip.

28.034 *Reagents*

(a) *Silicic acid.*—Mallinckrodt Chemical Works No. 2847. Heat in shallow pan or evapg dish 18 hr at 175°. Store in desiccator or tightly sealed container.

(b) *Bromocresol green-glycol soln.*—Dissolve 700 mg bromocresol green in 700 ml ethylene glycol by

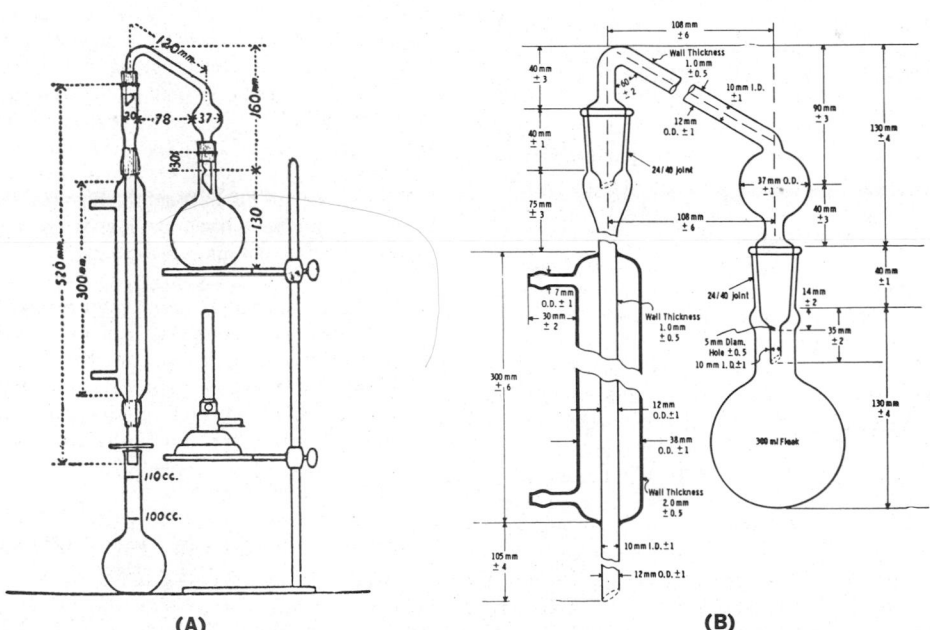

(A)   **(B)**

FIG. 28:2—Apparatus for determining Reichert-Meissl and Polenske values; (A) with rubber stoppers, (B) with glass joints

warming on steam bath. Cool, and add ca 200 ml
H_2O. Prep. $0.1N$ NH_4OH by dilg ca 6.6 ml NH_4OH
to 1 L with H_2O. Add 40 ml of this soln to indicator
soln and addnl H_2O to make 1 L. Store this ink-blue
soln in stoppered bottle.

(c) *Packing material.*—Mix H_2SiO_3, (a), in ratio
of 100 g to ca 95 ml bromocresol green-glycol soln,
(b), until homogeneous olive-green powder is obtained. Small batches may be mixed in mortar;
larger batches, in mech. mixer. Prepd packing material may be stored in tightly stoppered container
several months.

(d) *Hexane-butanol mixture.*—Add 1 vol. *n*-buta-
nol to 100 vols *n*-hexane (com. grade; Phillips Petroleum Co. or equiv.).

(e) *Isopropanol-KOH soln.*—Dissolve 25 g KOH
pellets in 400 ml isopropanol by warming and swirling on steam bath. Decant supernatant alc. soln
from the small amt of aq. soln clinging to bottom of
flask. Cool and decant supernatant isopropanol-
KOH soln, which contains ca 50 mg KOH/ml.
Store in refrigerator.

(f) *Potassium hydroxide soln.*—Approx. $0.05N$.
Dil. 60 ml isopropanol-KOH soln, (e), with 440 ml
isopropanol and 500 ml MeOH. Store in amber or
"Life-time Red" Pyrex bottle.

(g) *Thymol blue soln.*—Dissolve 300 mg thymol
blue in 25 ml $0.05N$ alc. KOH soln, (f), and add 75
ml isopropanol.

28.035   *Preparation of Fatty Acid Solution*

(a) *Saponification.*—Transfer 0.5–0.7 g well-
mixed, melted fat to 20×150 mm test tube with
lip, and add 5 ml isopropanol-KOH soln, (e), and
boiling chip. Place tube to depth of 2″ in boiling
H_2O bath 20 min to saponify fat, and evap. isopropanol, leaving solid soap. Stopper, and analyze
within 48 hr.

(b) *Determination of quantity of acid required to
hydrolyze soap.*—Add 5 ml isopropanol-KOH soln,
(e), to 10 ml H_2O and 2 drops thymol blue soln,
(g), in small beaker or flask. Add H_2SO_4 $(2 + 1)$
dropwise, with constant stirring, until initial blue
color turns to yellow, orange, and finally red. This
vol. H_2SO_4, measured with same dropper, is subsequently used to hydrolyze the soap. (If top of
chromatgc column turns blue on addn of fatty acid
soln, use of more H_2SO_4 to hydrolyze soap is indicated; top of chromatgc column should be yellow.)

(c) *Hydrolysis of soap and extraction of fatty
acids.*—Add to soap, while cooling tube in cold H_2O,
number of drops H_2SO_4 $(2 + 1)$ indicated in (b).
Break up lumps in bottom of tube with glass stirring
rod. After mass in tube is thoroly mixed, yellow
mixt. of fatty acids clinging to viscous aq. layer of
K_2SO_4 should be obtained. Add 10 ml hexane-
butanol soln to tube and thoroly mix with glass rod.
Aq. phase should cling to white ppt of K_2SO_4, allowing easy decantation of hexane-butanol soln of
fatty acids. This soln of acids is ready for chromatgy.

28.036   *Preparation of Chromatographic
Column*

Overlay 35 g packing material with hexane-
butanol mixt. in mortar. Mix with pestle to form
slurry. Place small glass wool plug loosely in constricted end of column and gently tamp into place
with glass rod. Place finger over constricted end of
column and add hexane-butanol mixt. until reservoir
is half full. Using teaspoon, underlay prepd slurry
beneath solv. Jiggle spoon up and down along side
of reservoir, and let flocculent slurry settle to bottom
of column.

After adding all packing material, remove finger
and let solv. flow out and packing material settle.
Apply 5–10 lb air pressure to top of column to speed
up flow of solv. and facilitate uniform packing of
slurry. Release pressure just before last portion of
solv. sinks into column. If column looks uniformly
packed, it is ready for use; if not, add more hexane-
butanol soln to reservoir and again apply pressure
as before. Prepd column should have flow rate of ca
3.5 ml/min without use of pressure. If flow rate is
<3 ml/min, add more bromocresol green-glycol
soln to packing material, and remix. If flow rate is
>4 ml/min, add more H_2SiO_3 to packing material,
and remix. Hexane-butanol mixt., recovered during
prepn of column, may be used subsequently to prep.
other columns or for chromatgy.

28.037   *Chromatography of Fatty Acids*

Decant hexane-butanol soln of fatty acids onto
top of packed column and immediately start collecting eluate in 250 ml erlenmeyer. As soon as fatty
acid soln completely settles into packing, wash down
inside of reservoir with three 5 ml portions hexane-
butanol mixt. Let each washing sink into packing
before refilling reservoir. Yellow band should always
be observed at very top of column; this band contains inorg. acids (H_2SO_4 and acid sulfate) and will
not move.

If sample contains butter fat, second distinct yellow band due to butyric acid appears and slowly
migrates down column, breaking away from top
band. Long-chain fatty acids, $\geq C_6$, pass rapidly
thru column and do not form yellow bands. Eluate
vol. between elution of last traces of long-chain
acids and first traces of butyric acid will be 20–30
ml. When lower edge of yellow butyric acid zone is
1 cm from lower end of chromatgc column, change
fraction collector. First fraction contains long-chain
acids and is usually 100 ± 10 ml. Next 120 ml fraction
contains butyric acid.

28.038   *Titration of Fatty Acid Fractions*

Add 1 drop thymol blue soln for each 10 ml eluate
being titrd. Titr. each fraction to first permanent
appearance of purple-blue end point, using ca $0.05N$
KOH, (f), dispensed from 50 ml buret for first fraction and from 5 ml buret, graduated in 0.01 ml, for

second fraction. End point for each fraction is sharp but is subject to fading because of CO_2 absorption. The CO_2 effect is negligible if titrn is conducted rapidly with little agitation. If necessary, titrn may be carried out in CO_2-free atmosphere which tends to make titrn values more reproducible. (Pass air thru 20% aq. KOH soln, then thru H_2O, and finally into titrn flask.)

Blank corrections are not required. Alkali added to thymol blue soln takes care of blank.

Express butyric acid titrn as % of sum of the 2 titrns, calcd to nearest 0.1%. *Example:* Long-chain acid titrn = 26.1 ml; butyric acid titrn = 2.83 ml; sum = 28.93. Mole % butyric acid = 2.83 × 100/ 28.9 = 9.8.

★ Saturated and Unsaturated ★ Fatty Acids

28.039 *Lead Salt-Ether Method (11)—Official Final Action*

(Not applicable to fats and oils that contain erucic, elaeostearic, chaulmoogric, hydnocarpic, or similar acids; to hydrogenated products that contain appreciable quantities of iso-oleic acid; nor to coconut or palm kernel oils that contain appreciable quantities of lower fatty acids that give ether-sol. Pb salts. *Caution: See* **46.001, 46.011, 46.039,** and **46.054.**)

Accurately weigh 10 (for plant fats used in common household cooking oils) or 20 g sample into 200 ml erlenmeyer. Add 30 ml alcohol and 8 ml KOH soln (1 + 1). Mix thoroly and heat on steam bath ca 30 min. Add slight excess of HOAc (1 + 2), using phthln, and then add enough 15% KOH soln, while rotating flask, to produce distinct pink. Heat to boiling in 1 L flask 60 ml (120 ml for 20 g sample) 20% Pb(OAc)₂ soln and same quantity of H_2O. Add the neutzd soap soln cautiously to avoid any loss, rinsing saponification flask with 5 ml alcohol, then with small portions hot H_2O. Boil mixt. gently ca 5 min, shake thoroly, and cool under running H_2O, rotating flask so that all pptd Pb soaps adhere to sides and bottom of flask. When mixt. is cold, pour off aq. soln into large beaker and examine soln for particles of Pb soap. (Usually soln is slightly turbid due to some basic Pb(OAc)₂ and no particles or globules of Pb soap are seen.) Wash flask and Pb soap twice with cold H_2O and let flask drain 10 min. Remove last drops of H_2O, using thin roll of filter paper held by forceps, being careful to press paper only lightly against ppt. Add ca 120 ml ether and shake by rotating flask ca 5 min.

Connect flask with reflux condenser and boil gently until Pb soap is completely disintegrated or dissolved. Remove flask and rinse down sides with enough ether to make final vol. ca 150 ml. Invert close-fitting beaker over neck of flask and refrigerate ≥15 hr. Place 7 cm filter paper in 7.5 cm buchner, apply full suction, and fit hardened filter paper cut to 8 cm diam. as snugly as possible to sides of funnel. Decant ether soln from sepd Pb soaps, using only

enough suction to draw ether thru filter. (Too much suction causes ether to evap. so rapidly that filter may become clogged with sepd unsatd acids, Pb soaps, or ice.) Reserve ether filtrate (contains ether-sol. Pb soaps).

Transfer ppt to filter by rinsing flask with small portions ether. During filtration keep funnel covered as much of time as possible to prevent evapn of ether. If at any time filtration proceeds so fast as to cause mass of Pb soap to crack, close cracks by pressing with small spoon or spatula; otherwise ppt cannot be properly washed. Rinse spoon free of ppt and wash ppt 8 or 10 times with ether, finally letting suction continue until ppt cracks into numerous pieces. Without delay, sep. with spoon as much of ppt as possible and transfer it without loss to 500 ml separator contg ca 50 ml ether, washing off any ppt adhering to spoon and neck of separator with ether. Transfer filter paper to 1 L flask. Thoroly shake separator to disintegrate lumps of Pb salt and let stand ca 20 min.

Add 20 ml HCl previously dild with 10 ml H_2O and shake thoroly 2 min to decompose all Pb soap. Add 5–10 ml HCl (2 + 1) to 1 L flask contg filter paper; shake thoroly to decompose any ppt adhering to flask and filter; then wash into separator with small alternate portions ether and H_2O until all fatty acids and $PbCl_2$ are removed from flask. Again shake separator with rotary motion and let stand 10 min.

Drain lower aq. soln slowly, taking precautions not to remove any emulsion or undecomposed Pb soap. When Pb soap is present (shown in form of lumps that float on top of aq. soln), add 10 ml HCl and shake again; add ca 20 ml H_2O, shake, and let mixt. stand until layers sep. Drain aq. soln and wash ether with successive 25 ml portions H_2O until washings are HCl-free (no ppt with $AgNO_3$). Dehydrate ether with ca 2 g anhyd. Na_2SO_4 and transfer soln to weighed 300 ml erlenmeyer. Rinse separator and Na_2SO_4 with several small portions ether to remove all fatty acids, taking care not to let any Na_2SO_4 fall into weighed flask. Distill ether, avoiding any loss of fatty acids, and heat over steam bath to constant wt under controlled flow of N to prevent oxidn of fatty acids. Cover steam bath with towel to prevent splashing H_2O into erlenmeyer. Obtain wt satd acids and save them for later investigation.

Transfer reserved ether soln of sol. Pb soaps to 500 or 1000 ml separator, rinsing buchner and filter flask with small quantities of ether. Add mixt. of 30 ml HCl and 75 ml H_2O, and shake with rotary motion 2 min. Let mixt. stand 10 min; then slowly drain aq. soln into beaker. Repeat HCl hydrolysis until no more $PbCl_2$ is pptd. If drops of ether soln are entrapped by the $PbCl_2$ ppt and are removed with it, decant soln from pptd $PbCl_2$ that has settled into separator. Rinse beaker and ppt with small amts of ether, adding washings to separator. Rotate contents of separator and let stand 10 min.

Drain aq. soln and wash ether with successive 50 ml portions H_2O until HCl is removed (no ppt in wash H_2O with $AgNO_3$). Dehydrate ether with ca 2 g Na_2SO_4 and transfer ether soln to weighed 300 ml erlenmeyer. Distill ether and place flask in oven heated to ca 110° ca 1 hr, while passing stream of CO_2 into flask to prevent oxidn of unsatd acids. Cool in atm. of CO_2. When cold, remove the CO_2 and weigh. Repeat treatment until constant wt is obtained.

Det. in duplicate I numbers of 0.2–0.3 g oil from unsatd fatty acid fraction and from entire satd fatty acid fraction. (I number of satd acid fraction is due to presence of some unsatd acid.)

To correct for unsatd acids present in fraction of satd acids use following formula:

$$\frac{\text{I No. of satd acid fraction}}{\text{I No. of unsatd acid fraction}} \times 100$$

$$= x \ (\% \text{ unsatd acids in satd acid fraction}).$$

Obtain correct value by formula $x \times y/100$, where y is % impure satd acids (as found by analysis). Subtract this correction from % impure satd acids and add it to % unsatd acids actually detd.

Polyunsaturated Acids (12)—Official Final Action

American Oil Chemists' Society Method

28.040   *Principles*

Natural conjugated constituents are detd by measuring UV absorption at specified wavelengths in purified solv. Nonconjugated polyunsatd constituents are partially conjugated by heating in KOH-glycol soln and absorptions of conjugated constituents are redetd. The % conjugated diene, triene, tetraene, and pentaene acids are calcd from predetd a by simultaneous equations.

Method is applicable to detn of polyunsatd acids, dienoic thru pentaenoic, in animal and vegetable fats contg only natural or cis isomers, only small amts of preformed conjugated material, and only small amts of pigments whose absorption may undergo considerable change during the alkali isomerization. Method is not applicable, or is applicable only with specific precautions, to hydrogenated oils, or other fats contg trans isomers of unsatd fatty acids, to fish oils or similar fats contg acids more highly unsatd than pentaenoic, to crude oils or samples contg pigments whose absorption undergoes changes during alkali isomerization, or to fats and oils contg large quantities of preformed conjugated fatty acids.

28.041   *Apparatus*

(a) *Isomerization apparatus.*—(See Fig. 28:3.) (1) *Constant temperature bath.*—180±1°. Capacity sufficient to immerse 25 × 250 mm Pyrex test tubes to depth of 4½″ (114 mm). (Westinghouse or equiv.

household deepfat fryer has been found satisfactory.) For bath liq. use Fisher Scientific Co. No. B-219 bath wax or DC 550 fluid, Dow Corning Corp. Place bath in insulated box with insulated cover having holes for stirrer and cork supports for test tubes.

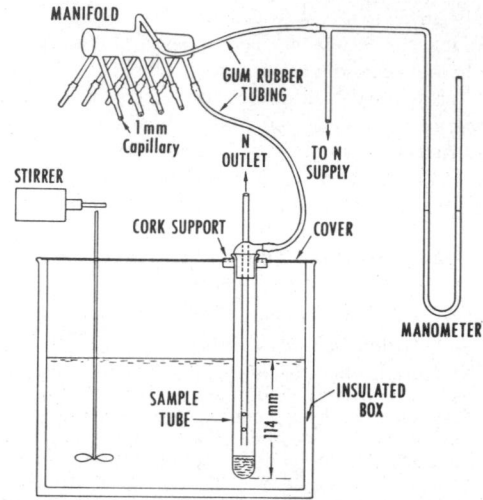

FIG. 28:3—Constant temperature bath and accessories

(2) *Test tubes.*—Pyrex, lipped, 25 × 250 mm.

(3) *Distributing heads.*—To fit test tubes snugly. Tubing in center of head has both ends open and two small holes 25 and 38 mm, resp., from bottom. (See Fig. 28:4, right.)

(4) *Manifold.*—With 10 outlets each connected to 50 mm long capillary tube, 1 mm bore. Cap unused outlets. (See Fig. 28:4, left.)

(5) *Nitrogen manometer.*—Construct from 6 mm od tubing bent in shape of U-tube, ht ca 380 mm, width ca 30 mm. Fill manometer ca half full with H_2O contg 1 drop Me orange and 1 drop H_2SO_4. To adjust flow of N, attach ca 3′ rubber tubing to one of N outlets on distributing head. Fill 100 ml graduated cylinder with H_2O and invert in container of H_2O. Insert end of rubber tubing under cylinder. Turn on N supply and measure rate of displacement of H_2O in cylinder. Rate of flow should be 50–100 ml/min. Mark level of liq. in manometer at this flow rate.

(b) *Spectrophotometer.*—Covering range of 220–360 nm with wavelength scale readable to 0.1 nm. Beckman Model DU is satisfactory. Adjust H lamp with no cell in beam so meter balances at lowest possible wavelength (usually ≤211 nm). Slit widths are critical for absorption measurements at 262, 268, 274 nm where, at final balancing, adjustments must be 0.8–0.9 mm.

(c) *Absorption cells.*—Quartz, matched pairs in lengths 1.000±0.005 cm. When filled with H_2O or isooctane, must match within 0.01 A unit.

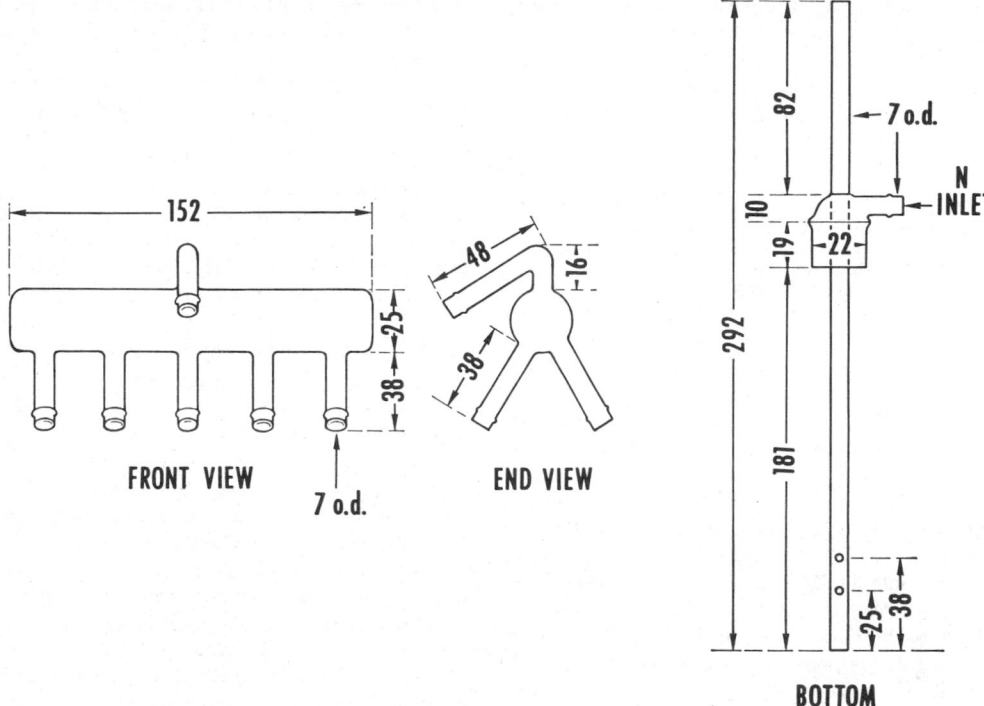

FIG. 28:4—Right, distribution heads. Left, manifold. All dimensions are in mm

28.042   *Reagents*

(a) *Methanol, absolute.*—Check A of 1 cm layer of MeOH against H₂O at 220 nm and thru range of wavelengths used in analysis. A at 220 nm must be <0.4 and curve should be smooth in range 262–322 nm. Otherwise purify as follows, and recheck A:

Place 2 L MeOH from new drum or glass bottles into 3 L double-neck ₮ distg flask; add 10 g KOH and 25 g Zn dust. Stopper one outlet and place reflux condenser in other, and reflux on steam bath 3 hr. Remove from steam bath; replace reflux tube with distg trap, 75° connecting tube, and condenser. Place flask in H₂O bath or elec. heating mantle and distill, collecting distillate in 2 L erlenmeyer. Store in g-s bottle. Absolute alcohol is satisfactory if of comparable purity (as obtained or purified).

(b) *Isooctane (2,2,4-trimethylpentane).*—NBS certified grade or spectral grade, Phillips Petroleum Co., Bartlesville, OK 74003. Hexane or cyclohexane is satisfactory if A requirements are met. Purify as follows: Place ca 3.5″ glass wool above stopcock at lower end of 32 × 1.75″ filter tube. Add ca 12″ silica gel (Grade 12, 28–200 mesh, Fisher No. S-157, or equiv.). Pour isooctane slowly into tube, filling ca ¾ full. Insert cork stopper covered with Al foil loosely in top of tube and let isooctane filter thru silica gel, collecting in 2 L erlenmeyer. Renew silica gel as often as necessary to yield isooctane conforming to A limit. Check A of 1 cm layer of the isooctane against H₂O thru range of wavelengths used

in analysis. A compared with H₂O set at 0 must be ≤0.070 at all wavelengths and the resultant A versus wavelength curve must be smooth. Otherwise refilter and recheck A.

(c) *Potassium hydroxide-glycol soln.*—6.6% KOH for 25 min isomerization. Weigh ca 750 g ethylene glycol into 1 L r-b Pyrex flask. Close with hollow stopper contg short outlet tube and inlet tube reaching to bottom of flask. Connect inlet tube to O-free N supply (<0.01% O) and bubble N thru liq. during all stages of prepn to exclude all air and to agitate liq. slightly. Place in oil bath at 100–150°; raise bath temp. to 190° and hold 10 min to dry glycol. Remove bath and let bath temp. drop to 120°. Slowly and carefully add 60 g 85% KOH, keeping soln under N. Return to oil bath; reheat bath to 190° and hold at this temp. 10 min. Remove from bath, and cool. Remove hollow stopper and close with solid stopper. Store in refrigerator at ca 40°F under N.

Check KOH content by adding 10.00 g KOH-glycol soln to ca 90 ml MeOH, neutzd with 1N HCl to phthln end point. Titr. with stdzd 1N HCl until pink just disappears. % KOH = ml × normality × 5.61/wt soln. If % KOH is not 6.5–6.6, dry some glycol by heating under N at 190° as above, and adjust to 6.6% KOH.

(d) *Potassium hydroxide-glycol soln.*—21% KOH for 15 min isomerization. Prep. as in (c) except use 210 g 85% KOH. Titr., and adjust to 21±0.1% KOH, if necessary.

(e) *Nitrogen gas.*—Pre-purified grade, <0.01% O.

28.043   *Preparation of Sample*

Melt sample carefully on steam bath, stir thoroly, and filter if not clear.

28.044   *Determination*

(The 6.6% KOH method is preferred when samples contain only linoleic and linolenic acids; the 21% KOH method is preferred when samples contain linoleic, linolenic, and arachidonic acids. When pentaenoic acids are present, 21% KOH method must be used.)

(a) *For conjugated polyunsaturated acids.*—Weigh into 1 ml Pyrex cup (diam. 14 mm, ht 10 mm) enough sample to give A reading of ≥ 0.2 (ca 200 mg). Drop cup into 75 ml isooctane in 150 ml beaker, and rotate beaker to dissolve sample, warming if necessary. Cool to room temp., transfer to 100 ml g-s vol. flask, dil. to vol. with solv., and mix thoroly. Measure A in UV region against matched cell contg solv., dilg soln (and/or using other cell lengths if necessary so that observed A is 0.2–0.8). Also take readings on both sides of specified wavelengths to det. that max. is present. Component is considered absent if max. is not found in characteristic region and no further calcns are made in this region. Measure at: Dienoic, *233* nm; trienoic, 262, *268*, 274 nm; tetraenoic, 308, *315*, 322 nm; pentaenoic, *346* nm.

(b) *For nonconjugated polyunsaturated acids, 6.6% KOH, 25 min isomerization.*—Weigh 100 mg (to nearest 0.5 mg) sample into 1 ml Pyrex glass cup. Weigh 11.0±0.1 g of the 6.6% KOH-glycol soln into 10 × 1″ Pyrex test tube. Conduct ≥ 2 blank detns with sample. Cover tube with distributing head and connect to a capillary tube on manifold. Adjust flow of N to permit ≥ 50–100 ml N to pass thru tube/min. Let N sweep thru tube 1 min to remove air; then immerse to depth of 4.5″ in bath at 180±1°. Check temp. frequently and stdze thermometer at frequent intervals.

After 20 min remove distributing head and drop 1 ml cup contg weighed sample into tube, note exact time, and replace head. Drop clean 1 ml cup into blanks. Keeping distributing head in place, remove tube from bath, swirl vigorously few sec, and return to bath. After 1 min in bath, examine soln; if clear, return to bath. If not clear, indicating incomplete saponification, swirl tube 2–3 times and return to bath. At 1 min intervals, repeat swirling until saponification is complete. Keep bath temp. at 180±1°.

Exactly 25 min after dropping sample into tube, remove from bath, wipe clean, and place in 3 L beaker to cool, continuing to pass N over soln. Cold H_2O bath may also be used. After cooling, remove head, and wash lower tubing with 20 ml purified MeOH, collecting washings in test tube. Wash with MeOH from beaker; do not use wash bottle.

Insert glass stirring rod 12″ long with curved end at bottom into test tube and move cup up and down to mix soln. Transfer soln to 100 ml g-s vol. flask, dil. to vol. with purified MeOH, and mix thoroly. Measure A as in (a), using KOH-glycol blank as ref. If diln of sample soln is required, make similar dilns of blank. If blanks do not check, repeat tests, increasing flow of N.

(c) *For nonconjugated polyunsaturated acids, 21% KOH, 15 min isomerization.*—Proceed as in (b), except use 80 mg sample and 21±0.1% KOH-glycol soln, and isomerize exactly 15 min.

28.045   *Spectrophotometric Readings*

If polyunsatd fatty acid constituent is known to be absent, or its absence is confirmed during analysis (no max. detected at its analytical wavelength), no spectrophtric reading is required in region of its absorption and no a at that region need be included in equations. For example, cottonseed oil is known to contain no polyunsatd constituents more highly unsatd than dienoic (linoleic acid). Hence in analysis of this oil, measurements are required only at 233 nm, and equation to calc. linoleic acid content requires a only at this wavelength.

Correction for background absorption is used only when measuring very small traces of fatty acids. When fatty acid is present in more than trace, background corrections are not required and their use may lead to erroneous results. When a of any polyunsatd constituent after isomerization, at its analytical wavelength, is >1.0, no backgound correction should be made. No background corrections are to be made after isomerization with 21% KOH.

28.046   *Calculations*

(a) *Absorptivity for conjugated constituents.*—Calc. a for each wavelength recorded in detn, **28.044**(a), using subscripts, 233, 268, 315, 346, to designate each individual a. $a = A/bc$, where A = observed absorbance, b = cell length in cm, and c = g sample/L final diln used for A measurement.

In following equations, subscripts 2, 3, 4, and 5 refer to diene, triene, tetraene, and pentaene constituents, resp.

Absorptivity at 233 nm corrected for absorption by acid or ester groups = $a_2 = a_{233} - a_0$ where $a_0 = 0.07$ for esters and 0.03 for soaps and fatty acids.

Absorptivity at 268 nm corrected for background absorption = $a_3 = 2.8 [a_{268} - \frac{1}{2}(a_{262} + a_{274})]$.

Absorptivity at 315 nm corrected for background absorption = $a_4 = 2.5 [a_{315} - \frac{1}{2}(a_{308} + a_{322})]$.

Absorptivity at 346 nm = $a_5 = a_{346}$.

(b) *Conjugated acids.*—If quantities within brackets of a_3 or a_4 are 0 or neg., no characteristic absorption maxima are present and corresponding constituent is reported as absent. As preformed constituents are usually present in small amts, background absorption corrections are usually required. If large amts of preformed constituents are present, this method is not applicable. However, no background corrections are to be applied to readings in pentaenoic region, 346 nm.

% Conjugated diene = $C_2 = 0.91a_2$.
% Conjugated triene = $C_3 = 0.47a_3$.
% Conjugated tetraene = $C_4 = 0.45a_4$.
% Conjugated pentaene = $C_5 = 0.39a_5$.

(c) *Absorptivities for nonconjugated constituents, 6.6% KOH, 25 min isomerization.*—Calc. a' for each wavelength in detn, (b). $a' = A/bc$.

Absorptivity at 233 nm corrected for conjugated diene acids originally present = $a'_2 = a'_{233} - a_2 - 0.03$.

Absorptivity at 268 nm corrected for background absorption and for undestroyed conjugated triene = $a'_3 = 4.03[a'_{268} - \frac{1}{2}(a'_{262} + a'_{274})] - a_3$.

Absorptivity at 315 nm corrected for background absorption and for undestroyed conjugated tetraene = $a'_4 = 2.06[a'_{315} - \frac{1}{2}(a'_{308} + a'_{322})] - a_4$.

(d) *Nonconjugated acids, 6.6% KOH, 25 min isomerization.*—(1) Without background corrections:

% Linoleic acid = $X = 1.086a'_2 - 1.324(a'_{268} - a_{268}) + 0.40(a'_{315} - a_{315})$.
% Linolenic acid = $Y = 1.980(a'_{268} - a_{268}) - 4.92(a'_{315} - a_{315})$.
% Arachidonic acid = $Z = 4.69(a'_{315} - a_{315})$.

(2) When background corrections are required:
% Linoleic acid = $X = 1.086a'_2 - 1.324a'_3 + 0.40a'_4$.
% Linolenic acid = $Y = 1.980a'_3 - 4.92a'_4$.
% Arachidonic acid = $Z = 4.69a'_4$.

(e) *Absorptivities for nonconjugated constituents, 21% KOH, 15 min isomerization.*—Calc. a' for each wavelength 233, 268, 315, and 346 nm. (If no max. is found, report component as 0 without further measurement or calcn.)

Absorptivity at 233 nm = $a'_2 = a'_{233} - a_2$.
Absorptivity at 268 nm = $a'_3 = a'_{268} - a_{268}$.
Absorptivity at 315 nm = $a'_4 = a'_{315} - a_{315}$.
Absorptivity at 346 nm = $a'_5 = a'_{346} - a_{346}$.

(f) *Nonconjugated acids, 21% KOH, 15 min isomerization.*—(Spectrophtric method will not differentiate between acids with same number of double bonds but different chain length, e.g., between C_{20} and C_{22} pentaenes. First 2 sets of equations below are for samples contg C_{20} pentaene acid and for samples contg C_{22} pentaene acid, resp. If chain length is unknown, assume that these pentaene acids are present in equal amts, and apply third set of equations.)

(1) *Samples contg C_{20} pentaene acid:*
% Linoleic acid = $X = 1.09a'_2 - 0.57a'_3 - 0.26a'_4 + 0.002a'_5$.
% Linolenic acid = $Y = 1.10a'_3 - 0.88a'_4 + 0.31a'_5$.

% Arachidonic acid = $Z = 1.65a'_4 - 1.55a'_5$.
% Pentaenoic acids = $P = 1.14a'_5$.

(2) *Samples contg C_{22} pentaene acid:*
% Linoleic acid = $X = 1.09a'_2 - 0.57a'_3 - 0.26a'_4 - 0.12a'_5$.
% Linolenic acid = $Y = 1.10a'_3 - 0.88a'_4 - 0.02a'_5$.
% Arachidonic acid = $Z = 1.65a'_4 - 1.86a'_5$.
% Pentaenoic acids = $P = 1.98a'_5$.

(3) *Samples contg pentaene acids of unknown chain length (calcd as 50% C_{20}–50% C_{22} pentaenoic acids):*
% Linoleic acid = $X = 1.09a'_2 - 0.57a'_3 - 0.26a'_4 - 0.03a'_5$.
% Linolenic acid = $Y = 1.10a'_3 - 0.88a'_4 + 0.19a'_5$.
% Arachidonic acid = $Z = 1.65a'_4 - 1.67a'_5$.
% Pentaenoic acids = $P = 1.45a'_5$.

(g) *Total composition:*
% Total conjugated polyunsaturated acids = $C_2 + C_3 + C_4 + C_5$.
% Total nonconjugated polyunsatd acids = $X + Y + Z + P$.
% Oleic acid = ${I$ value (Wijs) of sample $- [1.811(C_2 + X) + 2.737(C_3 + Y) + 3.337(C_4 + Z) + 4.014*(C_5 + P)]}/0.899$.
% Satd acids = % total fatty acid $-$ (% oleic acid + % conjugated acid + % nonconjugated acid).

(% total fatty acid of most naturally occurring oils is 95.6. To calc. to fatty acid basis, multiply the % value by 100/% total fatty acid.)

Isolated Trans Isomers (13)—Official First Action

(Applicable to margarines and shortenings contg <5% total conjugates)

28.047 *Principles*

Unsatd constituents of most vegetable fats and oils contain only nonconjugated (isolated) double bonds in *cis* configuration; these may isomerize to *trans* form during extn and processing due to oxidn or partial hydrogenation. Animal and marine fats may naturally contain some *trans* isomers. In long-chain fatty acids, esters, and glycerides, isolated *trans* bonds show absorption at ca 10.3 μm that can be measured with IR spectrophtr. *Cis* double bonds and satd compds do not show this band.

Long-chain fatty acids also show band at ca 10.6 μm (carboxyl). Correction for this band and any background is made by baseline technic. But if isolated *trans* content is small, correction may greatly affect absorption at 10.3 μm. Therefore, long-chain fatty acids contg <15% isolated *trans* isomers must be converted to their Me esters before making IR measurements.

---

* Corresponding constant for sample contg all C_{20} pentaene acids is 4.197; for all C_{22} pentaene acids it is 3.841.

Triglycerides give isolated *trans* values which are ca 2–3% high and Me esters give isolated *trans* values which are ca 1.5–3% low. Factors are applied to correct for these errors.

Do not apply method to samples contg >5% conjugated unsatn (tung oil), materials contg functional groups which modify absorption of C–H deformation around *trans* bond (castor oil contg ricinoleic or ricinelaidic acids), mixed glycerides with long and short-chain moieties (diacetostearin), or any materials where specific groups may absorb close to 10.3 μm.

28.048 *Apparatus*

Infrared spectrophotometer and accessories.—Covering region ca 9–11 μm, wavelength readable to 0.01 μm, holding fixed thickness cells 0.2–2.0 mm with NaCl or KBr windows. Most convenient are split-beam automatic recording instruments (Perkin-Elmer Model 21 or 221, Beckman Models IR-4, IR-5A, or IR-7, Baird Atomic Model 4-55) or memory type recorders such as Beckman Models IR-3 or IR-2-T. Smaller instruments of these companies, or nonrecording or null type instruments (Beckman IR-2 or Perkin-Elmer 12-C) may also be used. All instruments must be checked for accuracy of wavelength and photometric scales by manufacturer's instructions. Absorptivities of stds (reagents **28.049**(b) and (c)) must be established for each instrument, and re-checked periodically. With split-beam instruments, cells filled with CS_2 solv. must balance to 0.01 A. With null type instruments, matched pairs of cells must balance to this figure. Chart paper must be linear in either wavelength or wave no. (depending upon instrument) and calibrated in either T or A.

28.049 *Reagents*

(a) *Carbon disulfide.*—Dry, ACS grade. Use with adequate ventilation.

(b) *Primary stds.*—Elaidic acid, Me elaidate, and trielaidin, highest possible purity, >99% (Hormel Institute, 801 16th Ave NE, Austin MN 55912).

(c) *Secondary stds.*—If reagents (b) are not available, acid, ester, and triglyceride stds contg known proportion of *trans* isomer calibrated against primary std can be used. (Available from Chairman of Spectroscopy Committee, AOCS, 35 E. Wacker Drive, Chicago, IL 60601.)

28.050 *Preparation of Samples and Standards*

Melt solid fats on steam bath and mix; filter if cloudy. If *dild* sample is cloudy due to H_2O, add little anhyd. Na_2SO_4 to melted sample, mix, and let settle before taking portion for analysis.

Accurately weigh (±0.2 mg) ca 0.2000 g std or sample into 10 ml vol. flask, dil. to vol. with CS_2, and mix thoroly. T at *trans* absorption max. should

be 20–70%; if not, use different sample wt or cell thickness.

28.051 ★ *Preparation of Methyl Esters* ★

(*Caution: See* **46.011** *and* **46.073**.)

See **26.052**, 10th ed., H_2SO_4-MeOH method.

Boron Trifluoride Method (14)—Official First Action

28.052 *Principles*

Me esters of long-chain fatty acids are prepd with BF_3 catalyst for further analysis by IR, **28.056**, or GLC, **28.060**.

Method is applicable to common fats, oils, and fatty acids. Unsaponifiables are not removed and, if present in large amts, may interfere with subsequent analyses.

Method is not suitable for prepn of Me esters of fatty acids contg epoxy, hydroperoxy, cyclopropenyl, cyclopropyl, and possibly hydroxyl because of partial or complete destruction of these groups.

28.053 *Apparatus*

(a) *Reaction flasks.*—50 ml and 125 ml flat-bottom boiling flasks or erlenmeyers with ⊤ 19/38 or 24/40 outer necks.

(b) *Water-cooled condenser.*—Liebig or West design, 20 or 30 cm jacket, with ⊤ 19/38 or 24/40 inner joint.

28.054 *Reagents*

(a) *Boron trifluoride-methanol reagent.*—125 g BF_3/L MeOH. Available com. or prep. as follows: Weigh 2 L flask contg 1 L MeOH. Cool in ice bath, and with flask still in bath, bubble BF_3 from cylinder thru glass tube into MeOH until 125 g BF_3 is absorbed. Perform operation in fume hood. BF_3 must be flowing thru glass tube before it is placed in and until it is removed from MeOH to prevent liq. from being drawn into gas cylinder valve system. Gas should not flow so fast that white fumes emerge from flask. Reagent is stable 2 years. (*Caution: See* **18.035**(c).)

(b) *Alcoholic sodium hydroxide.*—0.5N in MeOH.

(c) *Heptane.*—Pure, as detd by GLC.

(d) *Methyl red indicator.*—0.1% in 60% alcohol.

(e) *Nitrogen gas.*—High purity.

28.055 *Preparation*

(*Caution: See* **46.011** *and* **46.073**.)

(Analyze Me esters as soon as possible after prepn. They may be kept in N atm. in screw cap vial 24 hr at 2°. For longer storage seal in glass ampule under vac. and place in freezer.)

Accurate weighing is not required. Sample size need be known only to det. size of flask and amts of reagents that should be used according to following tabulation:

Sample, mg	Flask, ml	NaOH, 0.5N ml	BF₃-MeOH Reagent, ml
100–250	50	4	5
250–500	50	6	7
500–750	125	8	9
750–1000	125	10	12

(a) *For fatty acids.*—Introduce fatty acids into 50 or 125 ml reaction flask. Add specified amt of BF₃-MeOH reagent, attach condenser, and boil 2 min. Add 2–5 ml heptane thru condenser and boil 1 min longer. Remove from heat, remove condenser, and add enough satd aq. NaCl soln to float heptane soln of Me esters into neck of flask. Transfer ca 1 ml heptane soln into test tube and add small amt of anhyd. Na₂SO₄. Dry heptane soln may then be injected directly into gas chromatograph.

To recover dry esters, transfer aq. and heptane phases to 250 ml separator. Ext twice with 50 ml portions of redistd pet ether (bp 30–60°). Wash combined exts with 20 ml portions H₂O until acid-free (test H₂O with Me red), dry with Na₂SO₄, and evap. solv. under stream of N on steam bath.

There is danger of losing some of more volatile esters if solv. removal step is prolonged or if too vigorous stream of N is used. For IR spectroscopy, terminate this step as soon as all solv. is removed. For GLC, method may be extended to fatty acids with 8-C atoms if solv. is not completely removed.

(b) *For fats and oils.*—Introduce fat into 50 or 125 ml reaction flask. Add specified amt 0.5N methanolic NaOH and add boiling chip. Attach condenser and heat mixt. on steam bath until fat globules dissolve (5–10 min). Add specified amt BF₃-MeOH reagent thru condenser and proceed as in (a).

28.056 *Determination*

Fill cell with CS₂ solv. and matching cell with prepd sample of std soln, 28.050. Use hypodermic syringe with blunted needle, and with cell upright, inject from bottom so bubbles pass up thru cell. Measure T or A from 9 to 11 μm.

(Programming of instruments depends upon type, but once basic curve for primary std is derived, all samples must be read on same instrument with controls at identical positions. Proper technics of slit width, scanning speed, etc., must be used (*see* "Proposed Recommended Practices for General Techniques of Infrared Quantitative Analysis," ASTM, 1916 Race St, Philadelphia, PA 19103). If instrument requires adjustment or replacements (glower, detector, etc.) and exact settings cannot be duplicated, calibration curve of std *must* be re-run and new values used in calcns.)

28.057 *Calculations*

Acids, methyl esters, and triglycerides.—Compare curve of sample (acid, ester, triglyceride) with its appropriate std, 28.049(b) or (c). Note A at 10.36 μm peak or convert T at this point to A, and calc. a. On charts, draw baseline from 10.10 to 10.65 μm for acids, from 10.02 to 10.59 μm for Me esters, or from 10.05 to 10.67 μm for triglycerides. For charts registering T, draw vertical line at peak (ca 10.3 μm) connecting 0 line of chart, x; peak, b; and baseline, c. Fractional $T = xb/xc$. Convert this value to A and then to background-corrected a as below. For charts registering A, subtract A at baseline from A at peak to obtain A of sample.

Absorptivity, $a = A/bc$, where A = corrected absorbance, b = cell thickness in cm, and c = concn of soln (g/L).

% *Trans* as elaidic acid, Me elaidate, or trielaidin = [a (sample, background corrected)/a (appropriate std, background corrected)] $\times$ 100.

Corrected trans values.—Triglycerides with 0 or low *trans* content read ca 2–3% high; their derived Me esters, 28.055, read 1.5–3% low or neg. Oils similar to test samples but contg no *trans* isomers may be analyzed to det. suitable correction factors to be used, or following equations may be used to correct approx. for pos. triglyceride or neg. Me ester errors:

For fats and oils contg primarily long-chain fatty acids (peanut oil, cottonseed oil, etc.):

Triglycerides, % *trans* (corrected) = (% *trans* (calcd) − 2.5)/0.975.

Me esters, % *trans* (corrected) = (% *trans* (calcd) + 1.5)/1.015.

For fats and oils contg large proportions of lower and medium-chain fatty acids (coconut oil, etc.):

Triglycerides, % *trans* (corrected) = (% *trans* (calcd) − 3.0)/0.970.

Me esters, % *trans* (corrected) = (% *trans* (calcd) + 3.0)/1.030.

Absence of peak at 10.3 μm, regardless of baseline A, indicates no *trans* isomers in sample.

Methyl Esters of Fatty Acids
American Oil Chemists' Society–AOAC Gas Chromatographic Method (15)—Official First Action

28.058 *Principles*

Me esters of fatty acids from animal and vegetable fats having 8–24 C atoms are sepd and detd by gas chromatgy. Method is not applicable to epoxy, oxidized, or polymerized fatty acids.

28.059 *Apparatus*

(a) *Gas chromatograph.*—With 5–10′ × ⅛ or ¼″ glass, stainless steel, Al, or Cu tube packed with polyester liq. phase on acid-washed Chromosorb W, or equiv. Maintain column temp. to ±1.0° between

170 and 210° and inlet port ca 50° higher than column temp. Perform detns on 2 columns with polyesters of different polarity to check for presence of coincident peaks. Polyethylene glycol succinate is recommended liq. phase, altho other liq. phases may be used for specific sepns.

(1) Flame ionization detector.—Use ⅛″ od tube packed with 8–12% polyester liq. phase on 80–100 mesh acid-washed Chromosorb W, or equiv. *(2) Thermal conductivity detector.*—Use ¼″ od tube packed with 15–20% polyester liq. phase on 60–80 mesh acid-washed Chromosorb W, or equiv.

(b) *Detector.*—Thermal conductivity or flame ionization. If sep. thermostated, maintain at column temp. or up to 50° higher.

(c) *Recorder.*—0–1, 2.5, or 5.0 mv range, 1 sec full scale deflection with chart speed of 0 5–1.0″/min; with attenuator switch to change recorder range. Use 0–1 mv recorder only when thermal conductivity detector is employed.

(d) *Gases.*—*(1) Carrier.*—For thermal conductivity detection, use He, min. purity 99.95 mole %; for flame ionization detection, use He, N, or Ar, min. purity 99.95 mole %. *(2) Other:* For flame ionization detector, use H, min. purity 99.95 mole %, and dry air, breathing quality (<2 ppm hydrocarbons equiv. to CH_4).

(e) *Syringe for injecting sample.*—1 or 5 µl, with known and reproducible vol. (7000 series, Hamilton Co. or equiv.).

(f) *Soap bubble flow meter.*—Construct from side arm, pinchcock 50 ml buret such as Kimble Products No. 17024, by adding rubber bulb contg soap soln at bottom and attaching side arm to outlet of gas chromatograph. Force film of soap soln into buret from bulb; gas carries film to top of buret. Measure rate of gas flow by observing time of travel of film thru definite vol. in buret.

28.060   *Determination*

With carrier gas flowing thru app., adjust to operating temp. and record baseline to check for stability of instrument. With flame ionization detector, operate app. at medium rather than max. sensitivity. Condition new column by holding ca 10° above operating temp. with carrier gas flowing 24 hr, or until stable. Disconnect column from detector during conditioning.

Proper gas flow rate and temp. permits elution of Me linolenate, other C_{18} esters, and shorter chain length esters in ≤30 min. When esters of fatty acids of greater chain length are present, increase gas flow and/or temp. so that retention time of last component is reduced. In addn, use largest sample size consistent with attenuation requirements to better detect and quantitate slower moving esters. Maintain constant gas flow thruout analysis as measured at exit with soap bubble flow meter or other suitable device.

Measure 0.5–4 µl Me ester sample, **28.055**, in syringe for thermal conductivity detection. With flame ionization detector, dil. Me esters with isooctane, hexane, or other suitable solv., so that injection of 0.5–4 µl contains 0.01–0.1 µl Me esters. Pierce septum of sample inlet port and quickly discharge sample. Withdraw needle and note on recorder chart small peak due to air or solv., marking sample introduction ref. point. Adjust sample size so major peak is not attenuated more than 8×, preferably less.

Change setting of attenuator as necessary to keep peaks on chart paper. Mark attenuator setting on chart.

After all peaks have been traced and pen has returned to baseline, remove chart for calcn.

28.061   *Calculations*

Det. area of each peak by drawing lines tangent to sides of peak and intersecting baseline. Calc. area of resulting triangle by multiplying ht (corrected for any change in attenuation) by half base. For automatically attenuated peak, obtain peak width by drawing tangents to outer sides of peak (these must be full chart span, and upper ⅔ of peak must be used) and intersecting baseline. Calc. area by multiplying ht (corrected for attenuation) by half base. If instrument is equipped with electromech. or electronic integrator, measure peak area following manufacturer's instructions. When integrator is employed, baseline must remain constant or integrator must be equipped with baseline corrector. Divide area of each component by its calibration factor. Sum areas of all peaks and calc. % by wt represented by each. Report this value as % of each component.

Identify peaks by relative position on chart. Esters appear in order of increasing number of C atoms and of increasing unsatn for same number of C atoms. C_{16} is ahead of C_{18}, and C_{18} Me esters appear in order: Stearate (18:0), oleate (18:1), linoleate (18:2), and linolenate (18:3). The C_{20} satd ester (arachidic, 20:0) usually appears after 18:3 ester but may be reversed on some columns, or positions may change with column use. Establish identity with known mixts. At constant gas flow, ratios of times (chart distances) from air or solv. peak to sample component peaks can be used for identification of peaks. Compare these ratios with those calcd from known mixts run periodically on same column under same conditions.

Det. calibration factors relative to Me palmitate (16:0) to correct for nonlinearity of instrument response and for molecular wt differences. Det. factors by analyzing known mixts having composition similar to that of unknown sample. Divide area of each peak by true wt % of that component; then divide each value by value for Me palmitate to obtain calibration factor. Ref. mixts simulating most fats and oils may be obtained from Applied Science Laboratories, Inc.; Supelco, Inc., Supelco Park, Bellefonte, PA 16823; Lipids Preparation Laboratory, Hormel Institute, Austin, MN 55912; and Analabs, Inc., 80 Republic Drive, North Haven, CT 06473.

Monitor instrument and column performance by noting sepn of 18:1 and 18:0 Me ester peaks, expressed as peak resolution. Peak resolution = $2Y/(S + O)$, where: Y is distance between peak max. for 18:0 and 18:1 Me esters, S is base width of 18:0 peak, and O is base width of 18:1 peak.

Det. these values on sample contg approx. equal quantities of 18:0 and 18:1 Me esters, using sample size such that these peaks are 25–50% of chart width. If peak resolution is ≥ 1.0, column and instrument are in satisfactory condition. All columns will show gradual loss in peak resolution with use; when value becomes < 1.0, install new column.

28.062 *Precision*

Two single detns of major components ($> 5\%$) performed in 1 laboratory shall not differ by > 1.0 percentage unit. Two single detns performed in different laboratories shall not differ by > 3.0 percentage units.

28.063 Unsaponifiable Residue (16)—Official Final Action

(*Caution: See* **46.011, 46.039,** and **46.054.**)

Accurately weigh 2–2.5 g fat into saponification flask (200 ml erlenmeyer with $\mathbf{\underline{\Phi}}$ 24/40 outer joint is recommended). Add 25 ml alcohol and 1.5 ml KOH soln (3 + 2). Saponify by boiling, with occasional swirling, on steam bath 30 min under reflux air condenser. (No loss of alcohol should occur during saponification.) Transfer alc. soap soln while still warm to 250 ml separator, using total of 50 ml H_2O. Rinse saponification flask with 50 ml ether and add ether to separator. Shake vigorously and let layers sep. and clarify. Drain lower layer and pour ether layer thru top into second separator contg 20 ml H_2O. Rinse pouring edge with ether, adding rinsings to second separator. Make 2 addnl extns of soap soln with 50 ml portions ether in same manner. Make total of 4 extns in case of marine oils or other oils of high unsaponifiable content.

Rotate combined ether exts gently with the 20 ml H_2O (violent shaking at this stage may cause troublesome emulsions). Let layers sep. and drain aq. layer. Wash with two addnl 20 ml portions H_2O, shaking vigorously. Then wash ether soln 3 times with alternate 20 ml portions ca $0.5N$ aq. KOH and H_2O, shaking vigorously each time. If emulsion forms during washing, drain as much aq. layer as possible, leaving emulsion in separator with ether layer, and proceed with next washing. After third KOH treatment, wash ether soln successively with 20 ml portions H_2O until washings are no longer alk. to phthln.

Transfer ether soln to 250 ml lipped, conical beaker, rinse separator and its pouring edge with ether, and add rinsings to main soln. Evap. to ca 5 ml and transfer quant., using several small portions ether, to 50 ml fat flask or erlenmeyer previously dried and weighed with similar flask as tare. Evap. ether. When nearly all ether has been removed, add 2–3 ml acetone, and while heating on steam or H_2O bath, completely remove solv. in gentle current of air. Dry at 100° for 30 min periods to constant wt.

Dissolve contents of flask in 2 ml ether, add 10 ml neutzd (phthln) alcohol and titr. with $0.1N$ alc. NaOH (or KOH). (≤ 0.10 ml is usually required.) Correct wt residue for free fatty acid present (1 ml $0.1N$ alkali = 0.0282 g oleic acid).

Correct wt residue for reagent blank obtained by conducting detn similarly but omitting fat.

Squalene (17)—Official Final Action

28.064 *Reagents*

(**a**) *Concentrated potassium hydroxide soln.*—Dissolve 60 g KOH in 40 ml H_2O.

(**b**) *Dilute potassium hydroxide soln.*—Dissolve 28 g KOH in H_2O and dil. to 1 L.

(**c**) *Petroleum ether.*—Skellysolve B (bp 63–70°) or equiv.

(**d**) *Aluminum oxide adsorbent, 80–200 mesh.*—Adsorption alumina for chromatgic analysis, Fisher A-540, or equiv. Keep in tightly closed container, away from moisture.

(**e**) *Pyridine sulfate bromide soln.*—$0.1N$. (*Caution: See* **46.047, 46.072,** and **46.081.**) Dissolve 8 g Br in 20 ml HOAc (99.5%). Prep. another soln by gradually adding, with cooling, 5.45 ml H_2SO_4 to mixt. of 20 ml HOAc and 8.15 ml pyridine. Mix 2 solns, cool, and dil. to 1 L with HOAc.

(**f**) *Sodium thiosulfate std soln.*—$0.05N$. Prep. daily by dilg $0.1N$ soln, **45.038–45.039.**

28.065 *Apparatus*

Adsorption column.—Prep. fresh column for each detn immediately before use. Place small wad of cotton in constricted end of glass tube, 8 mm id and 30 cm long. (For convenience, column may have Teflon stopcock in stem and top reservoir of ≥ 40 ml capacity.) Add alumina adsorbent in ca 10 small portions until column is ca 10 cm high. Apply gentle suction and tamp each portion alumina lightly with flattened end of heavy glass rod. Place small wad of cotton on top of column and tamp lightly. Wash column with ca 15 ml pet ether, remove suction, and keep top of column covered with shallow layer of pet ether until ready for use.

28.066 *Determination*

(*Caution: See* **46.011, 46.039,** and **46.073.**)

Accurately weigh (± 20 mg) ca 5 g sample into 125 ml erlenmeyer with $\mathbf{\underline{\Phi}}$ joint, add 3 ml concd KOH soln and 20 ml alcohol, and boil mixt. under air condenser 30 min, shaking occasionally. Cool somewhat, and while still warm, add 50 ml pet ether; mix, and transfer to separator. Rinse flask with 20 ml alcohol and then with 40 ml H_2O, adding rinsings to soln in separator. Shake vigorously, let sep. completely, and slowly drain soap soln. Pour pet ether ext from top of separator into another separator contg 20 ml H_2O. Repeat extn of soap soln with 50 ml pet ether. Rotate combined exts gently with the 20 ml H_2O and, after letting layers sep., discard wash H_2O. Repeat washing by shaking vigorously with 20 ml H_2O and again discard lower layer after sepn. Wash pet ether soln with 20 ml dil. KOH soln and then with successive 20 ml portions H_2O until wash liq. is alkali-free, shaking vigorously each time. After final washing, drain last drops of H_2O brought down by swirling separator. Pour pet ether soln from top of separator into lipped conical beaker. Rinse separator with pet ether and add rinsings to beaker. Add few pieces of broken porcelain or SiC and evap. almost all of solv. on steam bath. Remove last traces of solv. in current of CO_2 or other inert gas while warming beaker. To avoid oxidn of residue, do not expose to air while still warm.

Dissolve unsaponifiable matter in 5 ml pet ether and transfer to adsorption column. (Filtrate, which is caught in 250 ml g-s I flask, should emerge dropwise, ca (but $\leq$) 1 ml/min, gentle pressure being used if necessary.) When soln has been nearly drawn into column, add ca 5 ml pet ether previously used to rinse beaker. Continue adding solv. in 5–10 ml portions previously used to rinse beaker, always keeping surface of column covered with liq., until total of 50 ml has passed thru column. (If column with Teflon stopcock and top reservoir is used, proceed as above thru addn of 5 ml rinse; then rinse beaker with remaining 40 ml pet ether, add to reservoir, and let pass thru column.)

Add few pieces of broken porcelain or SiC and remove most of solv. on steam bath. Finally pass current of CO_2 or other inert gas thru heated flask until last traces of solv. are expelled. Cool residue to room temp. under inert atm. (All traces of solv. must be removed before detn is continued.)

Dissolve unadsorbed residue in 5 ml $CHCl_3$ and add enough pyridine sulfate bromide soln to provide $\geq 50\%$ excess (10 ml is usually adequate). Let mixt. remain in dark 5 min and then add 5 ml 10% KI soln, together with 40 ml H_2O. Mix thoroly, wash down any free I on stopper, and titr. with $0.05N$ $Na_2S_2O_3$. Toward end of titrn add starch indicator, **2.129**(c), shake vigorously, and continue titrn to disappearance of blue. Conduct blank detn on pyridine sulfate bromide soln similarly and calc. ml $0.05N$ $Na_2S_2O_3$ equiv. to absorbed halogen. Blank detn on all reagents used should show practically no halogen consumption. 1 ml $0.05N$ $Na_2S_2O_3$ = 1.71 mg squalene. Report results as mg squalene/100 g sample.

Vegetable Fats in Butterfat
Sterol Acetate Melting Point Method
(18)—Official Final Action

28.067   *Apparatus*

(a) *Special micro filter.*—See Fig. 28:5. Fisher Scientific Co. No. 20-680 is also satisfactory.

(b) *Platinum spatula.*—Heavy Pt wire, hammered flat, to ca 3 mm wide $\times$ 15 mm long, on one end. Mount in dissecting needle holder.

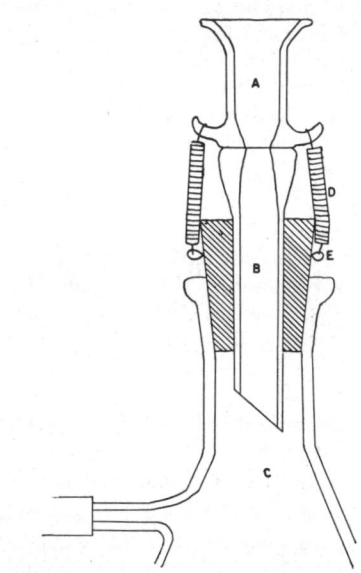

FIG. 28:5—Glass micro filter for sterol acetate precipitates
A: Top portion of filter, capacity 1 ml. **B:** Lower portion of filter. Ground surfaces between **A** and **B** hold filter pad. **A** and **B** are held together by springs, **D. C,** filter flask. **E,** wire twisted around stopper to hold lower end of springs.

28.068   *Determination*

To 15 g filtered fat in 150 ml beaker add 4 g KOH dissolved in 4 ml H_2O. Add 20 ml 95% alcohol, cover with watch glass, and heat 0.5 hr on steam bath, stirring occasionally.

Add 60 ml H_2O, mix, and pour into 400 ml beaker contg 180 ml 95% alcohol. Warm to ca $40°$ and add 40 ml *1% digitonin in alcohol*. (Heat may be necessary to dissolve digitonin.) Stir and let stand overnight in refrigerator.

Filter cold mixt. with strong suction on rapid qual. 11 cm paper in buchner. When liq. has passed thru paper, pour 50 ml H_2O over paper without stopping suction. Swirl occasionally. Continue to apply strong suction (H_2O passes thru paper rather slowly) until all H_2O has passed thru paper to wash out most of soaps. Pour 50 ml alcohol over paper and continue suction until all liq. has passed thru. Finally wash paper with four 50 ml portions ether, letting each portion pass thru completely before adding next portion.

Dry paper and ppt 15 min at 100°. Sep. ppt from paper. Crush or crumble ppt, and place it in 18×150 mm test tube. Add 2 ml Ac₂O and heat in 130° glycerol bath 15 min. (Ppt should dissolve in ca 5 min; do not use direct heat, since spattering may occur and material may be lost.) Cool to ca 70°.

Carefully add 4 ml alcohol and mix. Filter hot soln by gravity thru pledget of cotton in micro filtering tube (Pregl type), receiving filtrate in 20 ml beaker. Place beaker on small hot plate and carefully bring liq. to gentle boil. Add H₂O drop by drop until sterol acetate is just about to ppt but still remains in soln at bp.

Let cool, stirring occasionally with Pt spatula, for 15–20 min or longer. Filter on small disk of paper in micro buchner (ca 15 mm diam.). Suck dry and sep. ppt from paper. Place ppt in 5 ml beaker and heat with 1 ml 95% alcohol to dissolve completely. Cool beaker by setting in petri dish of ice-H₂O. When thoroly chilled, material usually sets to semisolid cryst. slurry.

Transfer slurry to special micro-filter, using Pt spatula, and apply suction. As liq. is drawn thru filter, compact ppt by tamping with flat end of glass rod of suitable size. (Ppt can then be cleanly and completely removed from paper in form of small button or tablet.) Redissolve ppt in same 5 ml beaker with addnl 1 ml hot alcohol (or 0.5 ml if ppt is very small), and after chilling to recrystallize, filter second time on micro-filter. Repeat recrystn and filtration third and fourth time; then dry ppt 1 hr at 100°.

Det. mp of recrystd, dried sterol acetates (temp. at which liq. first starts to run, detd when heated at rate of 0.5–1.0°/min). If mp is ≥2° higher than that of pure butter similarly treated, vegetable fat is indicated.

28.069   *Microcrystal Test*

Dissolve sterol acetate remaining from mp detn in 2 ml alcohol in 20 ml beaker and add 3 drops 40% aq. KOH. Heat on steam bath 5 min. Add 10 ml H₂O and transfer liq. to 125 ml separator. Add 25

ml ether and shake. Let layers sep.; then drain and discard aq. layer. Wash ether with three 5 ml portions H₂O and evap. ether to dryness in 50 ml beaker.

Add 10 ml 70% alcohol to residue and heat to dissolve. Cool, place drop of clear soln on slide, and examine drop microscopically at 100–200× for typical crystals of phytosterol or phytosterol-cholesterol mixt. (*see* Fig. 28:6).

28.070   Digitonin Recovery—Procedure

Combine filtrates from digitonide pptns and add enough *cholesterol* dissolved in alcohol to combine with all digitonin present. Let mixt. stand 3 hr or overnight. Filter off ppt and wash with H₂O, alcohol, and ether; then suck dry. Crush ppt and tamp it lightly into paper extn thimble. Suspend thimble in Ŧ erlenmeyer closed by reflux condenser and contg small amt of *xylene*. Heat xylene to boiling and let thimble and contents hang in hot vapors of boiling xylene 16 hr.

Remove thimble and dry at 100° until xylene has evapd. Remove digitonin residue, weigh, and transfer to beaker. Dissolve residue in enough H₂O to make ca 2% digitonin soln. Add ca ½ vol. alcohol and heat on steam bath. Add 1 ml *n-amyl alcohol* (reagent grade), cool, and filter off digitonin compd on buchner of suitable size. Suck dry and transfer ppt to watch glass. Dry at 100° until all amyl alcohol is volatilized. Digitonin may then be pulverized and is ready for re-use.

Gas Chromatographic Method (Sterol Acetates) (19)—Official First Action

28.071   *Preparation of Sample*

Obtain fat from butter by **16.167**. Weigh 5–10 g filtered fat into 150 ml beaker and proceed as in **28.068**, beginning "add 4 g KOH . . ." (Sterol acetate need not be recrystd unless mp is also desired.)

28.072   *Reagents*

(a) *GLC column packing.*—(1) *Stationary phase.*— JXR or OV–1 dimethylpolysiloxane or OV–17

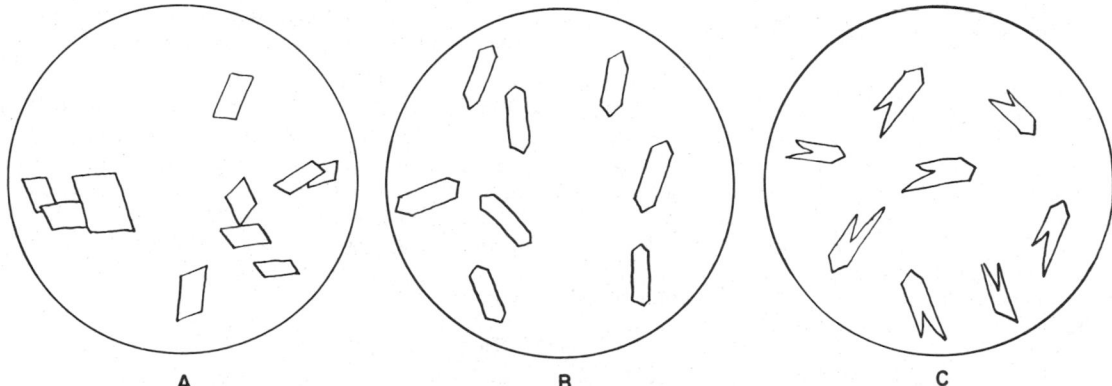

A   **B**   **C**

FIG. 28:6—Crystalline forms of free sterols. A: Cholesterol. B: Phytosterol. C: Mixed cholesterol-phytosterol

methylphenylpolysiloxane. *(2)* *Support.*—100–120 mesh Gas-Chrom Q. Com. prepd packing of 1–3% stationary phase available from Applied Science Laboratories, Inc., or Supelco, Inc., Bellefonte, PA 16823.

(b) *Ethyl acetate.*—Distd in glass (Burdick and Jackson Laboratories, Inc., or equiv.).

(c) *Cholestane std soln.*—0.4 μg/μl. Weigh 40.0 mg cholestane std (Applied Science Laboratories, Inc.) into 100 ml vol. flask and dil. to vol. with EtOAc.

(d) *Cholestane internal std soln.*—0.2 μg/μl. Dil. 10.0 ml std soln, (c), to 20.0 ml with EtOAc.

(e) *β-Sitosterol acetate std soln.*—2.0 μg/μl. Weigh 22.2 mg β-sitosterol acetate std (Nutritional Biochemicals Corp., ca 90% pure) into 10 ml vol. flask and dil. to vol. with EtOAc. Com. β-sitosterol acetate is mixt. of campesterol acetate (earlier eluting minor component) and β-sitosterol acetate. Det. concn of β-sitosterol acetate in std by chromatographing 2–3 μl std soln. Det. area of campesterol acetate and β-sitosterol acetate peaks by drawing lines tangent to sides of peak and intersecting baseline. Det. areas of resulting triangles by multiplying ht by ½ base. Concn β-sitosterol acetate = $(C_s \times P_s)/(P_s + P_c)$, where C_s = mg sterol acetate std/ml, P_s = area β-sitosterol acetate peak, and P_c = area campesterol peak.

(f) *Cholestane-β-sitosterol acetate std mixture.*—0.2 μg cholestane and 1.0 μg β-sitosterol acetate/μl. Mix equal vols (c) and (e).

28.073 *Apparatus*

(a) *Gas chromatograph.*—Barber-Colman Co. Model 5000, or equiv., with H flame ionization detector and 1 mv strip chart recorder. Temps: column, 220–260°; flash heater and detector, 240–270°; flow rates: N (ultra high purity grade), 20–25 psi to elute β-sitosterol acetate in 16–20 min; H, ca 40–45 ml/min; air, 300–340 ml/min.

Adjust electrometer sensitivity so that 2.5 μg β-sitosterol acetate gives ca 50% deflection (10^{-9}–10^{-10} amp full scale deflection with 1 mv recorder). Repeat injections until constant peak hts are obtained on successive injections of identical vols of std mixt.

(b) *Preparation of column.*—(*Caution: See* **46.039** and **46.040**.) Pack glass column, 6' × 4 mm id, with com. 1–3% stationary phase on 100–120 mesh Gas Chrom Q or dissolve 0.4–1.2 g polysiloxane in 200 ml toluene or CH_2Cl_2-toluene (1 + 1). Heat to dissolve (polysiloxane dissolves slowly in solv. mixt.). (*Caution:* Siloxanes are toxic. Wear disposable gloves and use effective fume removal device when handling.) Add soln to 40 g Gas-Chrom Q and let stand 10 min with occasional gentle stirring. Dry in rotary evaporator held in 50° bath or heat on steam bath with occasional gentle stirring and remove residual solv. in vac. oven at 50°.

Carefully wash inside of column and small amt glass wool with 5% soln dimethyldichlorosilane in toluene, rinse with MeOH until rinsings are neut.

to indicator paper, and air-dry. Plug column exit with small plug of silanized glass wool and thru-hole septum, and plug injection side arm with ½ hole septum. Add coated packing material thru injection port, using funnel and plastic tubing and tapping column very gently during addn. Add ¼ packing material at time, remove funnel, and apply ca 5–10 psi N to injection port while tapping gently to settle packing. Pack to 2.5 cm below injection side arm and plug with silanized glass wool.

(c) *Conditioning of column.*—Heat ≥8 hr at 260° with ca 5–10 psi N flowing thru column. Shut off pressure, raise temp. to 290°, and continue heating ≥8 hr. Reduce temp. to 260°, adjust N to 5–10 psi, and heat addnl 8–12 hr.

(d) *Performance.*—Chromatograph ca 2 μl β-sitosterol acetate std soln to det. retention times and resolution of column. Min. of 1600 theoretical plates is required for β-sitosterol acetate peak. Theoretical plates = $(L/B)^2 \times 16$, where L = mm β-sitosterol acetate peak from injection point and B = mm triangulated base width of β-sitosterol acetate peak.

28.074 *Determination*

Pipet 1.0 ml cholestane internal std soln into 3 dram vial contg sterol acetates, rotate vial to wash down sides, and swirl to dissolve. Inject 2–3 μl sample soln and 2–3 μl std mixt., (f), at least in duplicate. Identify β-sitosterol acetate peak in sample from retention time in std mixt. If ht of sample peak is >60% full scale, add addnl 1.0 ml internal std soln to sample soln, and rechromatograph sample and std mixt. solns. Measure peak hts of cholestane and β-sitosterol acetate peaks in mm.

mg β-sitosterol acetate/100 g sample = $(H_i/H_x) \times (C_x/C_i) \times (S_x/S_i) \times (Q_i/Q) \times 100$, where H_i and H_x = ht (mm) cholestane and β-sitosterol acetate peaks, resp., in std mixt.; S_x and S_i = ht (mm) β-sitosterol acetate and cholestane peaks, resp., in sample; C_x and C_i = μg β-sitosterol acetate and cholestane/μl, resp., in std mixt.; Q_i = μg cholestane/μl in sample; and Q = mg sample/μl.

β-Sitosterol in Butter Oil (20)—Official First Action

(Applicable to samples contg ≥4 mg free β-sitosterol/100 mg butter oil)

28.075 *Principle*

Free 3-β-OH sterols are removed from butter oil by complexing with digitonin, and sterols are then removed from digitonide-Celite column by elution with dimethyl sulfoxide (DMSO). Butter oil has apparent range of 0–1 mg β-sitosterol/100 g and ice cream has apparent value of ca 4 mg/100 g fat from emulsifiers.

28.076 *Reagents*

(a) *Diatomaceous earth.*— Celite 545, or equiv.

(b) *Digitonin.*—(Mann Research Laboratories, Mountain View Ave, Orangeburg, NY 10962.)

(c) *β-Sitosterol std soln.*—2 µg β-sitosterol/µl CHCl₃. Prep. from Aldrich Chemical Co., 2371 N 30th St, Milwaukee, WI 53210, reagent (64% β-sitosterol, 36% campesterol) or Applied Science Laboratories, Inc., reagent (90% β-sitosterol, 10% campesterol).

(d) *n-Hexane.*—Distill pure grade over KOH. (*Caution: See* **46.011, 46.037, 46.039,** and **46.061.**)

28.077 *Apparatus*

(a) *Gas chromatograph.*—Operating conditions: temps, column 225–245° and injection port and flame ionization detector 265–285°. Adjust N carrier gas flow (ca 50–60 ml/min) to obtain following retention times: cholesterol 16–18 min, campesterol 22–24 min, and β-sitosterol 28–30 min. Use 6′ × 4 mm id column contg 3% JXR silicone on 100–120 mesh Gas-Chrom Q and condition column 24 hr at 250° with 15–20 psi N.

(b) *Performance.*—Monitor performance of gas chromatograph by noting sepn of campesterol and sitosterol expressed as peak resolution = $2D/(C + B)$, where D = distance between the 2 peak maxima, C = campesterol peak base width, and B = β-sitosterol peak base width. Peak resolution should be ≥1.6.

(c) *Injection technic.*—With 10 µl Hamilton microsyringe, draw 1 µl air into barrel, insert needle into soln, and draw desired amt into barrel. Remove needle from soln and draw 1 µl air into barrel. Note vol. on scale and adjust to desired vol., if necessary.

(d) *Preparation of std curve.*—Prep. std soln of 2 µg β-sitosterol/µl CHCl₃. (Det. composition of std as in **28.072(e).**) Obtain std curves daily covering range 1–10 µg β-sitosterol, using ≥3 points. Plot area of β-sitosterol peak against µg β-sitosterol.

28.078 *Preparation of Column*

Dissolve, with heating, 300 mg digitonin in 5 ml H₂O, add to mortar and pestle contg 10 g Celite, and mix thoroly. (Packing material can be kept several months if stored at 5° in tightly closed container.) Transfer 3 g Celite-digitonin mixt. to 2 × 12 cm tube with ca 5 mm id outflow tube and small pad glass wool at bottom, and closed with short length of gum rubber tubing and pinchcock. Pack firmly, using packing rod. (Flow rate of tightly packed column is 0.5–0.75 ml/min.) Sat. column with 5 ml n-hexane and let flow thru packing until n-hexane reaches top of packing material. Use column immediately. Do *not* let dry.

28.079 *Preparation of Sample*

Dissolve 900 mg butter oil in 3 ml n-hexane. Quant. transfer soln, using disposable pipet, to digitonin-Celite column and let pass thru column until soln has entered packing material. Wash sample beaker twice with 2 ml n-hexane and add each wash to column, rinsing sides of tube. Wash column with five 2 ml portions n-hexane. After all hexane has en-

tered column, wash with five 2 ml portions benzene. When last portion benzene reaches ca 1 cm above top of packing material, remove rubber tubing and wash inner and outer surface of column tip thoroly with benzene to remove traces of fat. (Failure to wash column sides and column tip with solv. will result in poor chromatograms due to interference from triglycerides.) Discard hexane and benzene. Begin elution with 10 ml DMSO before benzene falls below top of packing material. Collect DMSO eluate in 15 ml screw-cap centrf. tube.

Add 3 ml n-hexane to eluate, shake, and centrf. Transfer upper layer contg sterols to second screw-cap centrf. tube. Repeat extn of DMSO layer in first tube with two 4 ml portions n-hexane-benzene (1 + 1), carefully transferring upper layer to second tube each time. Vigorously shake pooled upper layers with 3 ml H₂O and centrf. until clear. Remove upper layer and evap. under N or filtered air in 30 ml beaker on steam bath. Transfer residue to 0.5 dram screw-cap vial with two 0.8 ml portions CHCl₃. After evapg solv. with N or filtered air over steam bath, redissolve sterols in 0.1 ml CHCl₃ for GLC analysis.

28.080 *Determination*

Inject 2–8 µl extd sample and calc. β-sitosterol by converting peak area to wt, using daily std curve. Calc. mg β-sitosterol/100 g butter oil = (µg from curve/1000) × (100/µl injected) × (100/g sample).

Identify peaks from butter oil samples by comparing their retention times to retention times of known compds. Relative retention times are cholesterol 1.0, campesterol 1.4, β-sitosterol 1.7.

Animal Fats in Vegetable Fats and Oils (Determination of Cholesterol) (21)—Official First Action

28.081 *Preparation of Sample*

Saponify and ext unsaponifiable matter from 2.5±0.01 g fat as in par. 1 and 2, **28.063.** Discard aq. solns. Transfer ether ext to 250 ml beaker and evap. to dryness on steam bath under N. Dissolve unsaponifiable matter in 4–5 ml CHCl₃, transfer to 4 dram vial, and evap. to dryness. Rinse beaker with three 3 ml portions CHCl₃, taking special care to dissolve any material on sides of beaker. Transfer rinsings to vial and evap. to dryness under N. Store samples in freezer.

Isolation of Sterols by Thin Layer Chromatography

28.082 *Reagents and Apparatus*

(a) *Silica gel.*—PF 254 + 366 (Brinkmann Instruments, Inc., or equiv.).

(b) *Chloroform.*—Distd in glass (Burdick and Jackson Laboratories, Inc., or equiv.)

(c) *Ethyl ether.*—Anhyd., ≤0.01% alcohol (Fisher Scientific Co. E-138, or equiv.).

(d) *Petroleum ether.*—Distd in glass, bp 30–60° (Burdick and Jackson Laboratories, Inc., or equiv.).

(e) *β-Sitosterol std soln.*—3 µg/µl. Weigh 30.0 mg β-sitosterol std (Aldrich Chemical Co., 2371 N 30th St, Milwaukee, WI 53210) into 10 ml vol. flask and dil. to vol. with EtOAc. Com. material is mixt. of campesterol (earlier eluting component) and β-sitosterol.

(f) *Thin layer chromatographic apparatus.*—*See* **26.001(k)**.

(g) *Thin layer plate scraper.*—Optional; adapt from sealing tube with fritted disk (Corning Glassworks 39580, 30M). *See* Fig. 26:1.

28.083   Preparation of Plates

Align 5 matching 20 × 20 cm glass plates on mounting board, and just before coating, wipe plates with tissue dampened with alcohol to remove any dust or fingerprints. Adjust applicator to deliver 0.5 mm thick layer. Weigh 45 g silica gel into 500 ml erlenmeyer, add 130 ml H_2O, shake vigorously 25–30 sec, and pour into applicator. Immediately coat plates with silica gel suspension and let plates rest undisturbed until gelled (0.5–1 hr). Dry coated plates ≥2 hr at 110° and store in desiccating cabinet until just before use.

28.084   Thin Layer Chromatography
(*Caution: See* **46.016, 46.040,** and **46.056.**)

Line developing chamber with blotting paper and add 100 ml ether-pet ether (1 + 1) to chamber. Cover chamber and equilibrate 2 hr.

Draw line across plate 17 cm from bottom and ca 1 cm from each side. Spot 10 µl β-sitosterol std soln, (e), at point 2 cm from bottom edge and 3 cm from 1 side of plate. Dissolve unsaponifiable matter, **28.081,** in 200 µl $CHCl_3$ and spot entire sample in 10 µl portions on imaginary line 2 cm from bottom edge of plate so that spot centers are 0.75 cm apart. Rinse vial with ca 100 µl $CHCl_3$ and spot rinse soln in equal portions on top of sample spots.

Immediately insert plate into equilibrated chamber (position plate to expose coated surface to max. chamber vol.); cover chamber and seal with tape. Withdraw plate from chamber when solv. front reaches 17 cm stop line. Evap. solv. and view plate under long wave UV light in darkened room. Mark off sterol band (same R_f, 0.2–0.3, as β-sitosterol std) with needle, and remove sterol band as follows (do *not* remove β-sitosterol std): Scrape off sterol band with square end of stainless steel spatula (Fisher No. 14-375-10, or equiv.) into 100 ml beaker and transfer with 20 ml $CHCl_3$ to 70 mm top diam. funnel contg folded 12.5 cm diam. filter paper (S&S No. 588, or equiv.). Ext sterols with five 10 ml portions $CHCl_3$ and evap. combined filtrate to near dryness on steam bath under N. Transfer residue to 3 dram vial (screw-cap with Al liner) with $CHCl_3$ and evap. to dryness under N. (Alternatively remove sterol band with TLC plate scraper, elute sterols from silica gel with 70 ml $CHCl_3$ (fourteen 5 ml portions), and evap. solv. to near dryness on steam bath under N.)

Gas Chromatography of Sterols

28.085   Reagents

Use reagents **28.072(a)**, **(b)**, **(c)**, and **(d)** and following:

(a) *Cholesterol std soln.*—1.2 µg/µl. Weigh 60.0 mg cholesterol std (Applied Science Laboratories, Inc.) into 50 ml vol. flask and dil. to vol. with EtOAc.

(b) *Cholestane-cholesterol std mixture.*—0.2 µg cholestane and 0.6 µg cholesterol/µl. Mix equal vols cholestane, **28.072(c)**, and cholesterol std solns.

(c) *Cholesterol-β-sitosterol std mixture.*—0.6 µg cholesterol and 1.5 µg β-sitosterol/µl. Mix equal vols cholesterol and β-sitosterol, **28.082(e)**, std solns.

(d) *Cholesteryl acetate std soln.*—0.6 µg/µl. Weigh 30.0 mg cholesteryl acetate std (Nutritional Biochemicals Corp.) into 50 ml vol. flask and dil. to vol. with EtOAc.

28.086   Apparatus

(a) *Gas chromatograph.* — Barber-Colman Co. Model 5000, or equiv., with H flame ionization detector and 1 mv strip chart recorder. Temps: column, 220–250°; detector and flash heater, 240–270°; flow rates: N (ultra high purity grade), 20–25 psi to elute cholesterol in 8–12 min; H, ca 40–45 ml/min; air, 300–340 ml/min. Electrometer sensitivity 1×10^{-9} amp full scale deflection with 1 mv recorder.

Adjust electrometer sensitivity so that 1.5 µg cholesterol gives ca 50% deflection. Repeat injections until constant peak hts are obtained on successive injections of identical vols of std mixt.

(b) *Preparation of column.*—*See* **28.073(b)**.

(c) *Conditioning of column.*—Heat 12–24 hr under conditions specified in **28.073(c)**.

(d) *Performance.*—Chromatograph ca 2 µl cholesterol-β-sitosterol std mixt. to det. retention times and resolution of column. Min. of 1600 theoretical plates is required for cholesterol peak; theoretical plates = $(L/B)^2 \times 16$, where L = cm cholesterol peak from injection point, and B = cm triangulated base width of cholesterol peak. In addn, sepn of cholesterol and campesterol peaks, expressed as peak resolution, should be ≥2.2. Peak resolution = $2D/(B + P)$ where D = distance in cm between cholesterol and campesterol peak max.; B = triangulated base width of cholesterol peak; and P = triangulated base width of campesterol peak. Det. peak resolution on sample having ca equal quantities cholesterol and campesterol (ca equal peak areas); sample injected should give peak hts 25–50% of chart width.

28.087   Determination

Pipet 1.0 ml cholestane internal std soln into 3 dram vial contg extd sterols, rotate vial to wash down sides with internal std soln, and swirl to dissolve sterols. Inject 2 µl sample at least in duplicate. Repeat with 2 µl cholestane-cholesterol std mixt. Identify cholesterol peak in sample from its retention time in std mixt. If cholesterol peak ht in sample is

>60% full scale deflection, add addnl 1.0 ml cholestane internal std soln to sample and chromatograph sample and std mixt. as above. Measure peak hts cholestane and cholesterol in mm.

Calc. mg cholesterol/100 g sample, correcting for internal std, as follows:

$$\text{mg cholesterol}/100\ g\ =\ (H_i/H_x)\ \times\ (C_x/C_i)\ \times\ (S_x/S_i)\ \times\ (Q_i/Q)\ \times\ 100,$$

where H_i and H_x = ht (mm) cholestane and cholesterol peaks, resp., in std mixt.; S_x and S_i = ht (mm) cholesterol and cholestane peaks, resp., in sample; C_x and C_i = μg cholesterol and cholestane/μl, resp., in std mixt; Q_i = μg cholestane/μl in sample; and Q = mg sample/μl.

28.088   Confirmatory Test

Presence of cholesterol may be confirmed by GLC of sterol acetates. After detg cholesterol by GLC, evap. sample to dryness on steam bath under N. Cool and add 3 ml pyridine and 1 ml Ac_2O. Cap vial, swirl on steam bath until sterols dissolve, and continue heating on steam bath 1 hr. Evap., using N stream, until no odor of pyridine is detected. Chromatograph sterol acetates and cholesteryl acetate std solns and compare retention times of sample and cholesteryl acetate peaks.

Rosin Oil

28.089 Qualitative Test—Procedure

Polarize pure oil, or definite diln with pet ether, in 200 mm tube. Rosin oil has polarization in 200 mm tube of +30 to +40°S, while most oils read between +1° and −1° (Lewkowitsch, "Chemical Technology and Analysis of Oils, Fats, and Waxes," 6th Ed., 1, 350(1921)).

Cottonseed Oil

28.090 Halphen Test (22)—Official
Final Action

(Caution: See 46.039, 46.040, and 46.048.)

Mix CS_2 contg 1% S in soln with equal vol. amyl alcohol. Mix equal vols of this reagent and sample under examination, and heat in bath of boiling satd NaCl soln 1–2 hr. Presence of as little as 1% cottonseed oil produces pronounced characteristic red or orange-red soln. Depth of color is proportional, to certain extent, to amt of cottonseed oil present, and comparative tests with known mixts of cottonseed oil give approx. amt.

Different oils react with different intensities. Oils that have been heated to 200–210° (Allen, "Commercial Organic Analysis," 5th Ed., 2, 177(1924)) and hydrogenated oils (Jamieson, "Vegetable Fats and Oils," 2nd Ed. (1943)) react with greatly diminished intensity. Heating 10 min at 250° renders cottonseed oil incapable of giving reaction (Abs. J. Soc. Chem. Ind. 18, 711(1899)). Fat of animals fed on cottonseed meal or other cottonseed products may give pos. reaction by this test.

Peanut Oil

28.091 Modified Renard Test (23)—Official
Final Action

(Caution: See 46.011, 46.039, and 46.054.)

Weigh 20 g oil into erlenmeyer. Saponify with alc. KOH soln, 28.026; neutze exactly with HOAc (1 + 3), using phthln; and wash into 800–1000 ml flask contg boiling mixt. of 100 ml H_2O and 120 ml *20% Pb(OAc)₂ soln*. Boil 1 min and then cool pptd soap by immersing flask in H_2O, swirling flask occasionally to cause soap to stick to sides. After flask cools, decant H_2O and excess $Pb(OAc)_2$ soln, and wash Pb soap with cold H_2O and alcohol, 90% by vol. Add 200 ml ether, cork, and let stand until soap disintegrates; heat on H_2O bath, using reflux condenser, and boil ca 5 min. With oils, most of soap will be dissolved; with lards, which contain much stearin, part of soap will be left undissolved. Cool ether soln of soap to 15–17° and let stand until all insol. soaps sep. (ca 12 hr).

Filter on buchner and thoroly wash insol. Pb soaps with ether. Wash ether-insol. Pb soaps into separator with jet of ether, alternating with HCl (1 + 3) at end of operation if little of soap sticks to paper. Add enough HCl (1 + 3) so that total vol. of acid is ca 200 ml and enough ether to make its total vol. 150–200 ml, and shake vigorously several min. Let layers sep., drain off acid layer, and wash ether once with 100 ml HCl (1 + 3) and then with several portions of H_2O until H_2O washings are no longer acid to Me orange. If few undecomposed lumps of Pb soap remain (indicated by solid particles remaining after third washing with H_2O), break up by running off almost all H_2O layer, adding little HCl, and shaking; then continue washing with H_2O as before.

Distill ether from soln of insol. fatty acids and dry latter in flask by adding little absolute alcohol and evapg on steam bath. Dissolve dry fatty acids by warming with 100 ml 90% alcohol by vol. Cool slowly to 15°, shaking to aid crystn. Let stand 30 min at 15°.

In presence of peanut oil, crystals of arachidic acid sep. from soln. Filter, wash ppt twice with 10 ml alcohol, 90% by vol., and then with alcohol, 70% by vol., taking care to keep arachidic acid and wash solns at definite temp. in order to apply solubility corrections given below. Dissolve arachidic acid on filter with boiling absolute alcohol, evap. to dryness in weighed dish, dry, and weigh. To this wt add 0.0025 g/10 ml of 90% alcohol used in crystn and washing, if conducted at 15°; if conducted at 20°, add 0.0045 g/10 ml.

Mp of arachidic acid thus obtained is 71–72°. 20 times wt arachidic acid gives approx. quantity peanut oil present. Arachidic acid has characteristic appearance and may be identified under microscope. As little as 5–10% peanut oil can be detected by this method.

Modified Bellier Test (24)—Official
Final Action

(Applicable only in presence of olive, cottonseed, corn, and soybean oils)

28.092 *Reagents*

(a) *Alcoholic potassium hydroxide soln.*—1.5N. Dissolve 10 g KOH in purified alcohol, **28.026**, and dil. to 100 ml with purified alcohol.

(b) *Hydrochloric acid.*—Sp gr 1.16. Dil. 83 ml concd acid (sp gr 1.19) to 100 ml with H_2O. Check with sp gr spindle.

(c) *Alcohol.*—70%. Dil. 700 ml alcohol to 950 ml with H_2O. Check by sp gr or refractive index and adjust if necessary.

28.093 *Test*

Weigh 0.92 g or measure 1 ml sample into 125 ml erlenmeyer with $\overline{\text{S}}$ outer joint. If oil is measured, use short Mohr pipet with fairly large opening at tip, drain to lower mark, hold until meniscus stops rising in pipet, and drain to mark again. Add 5 ml alc. KOH soln, and heat 5 min on steam bath, using air condenser to avoid loss of alcohol. Swirl once or twice during saponification. Add 50 ml 70% alcohol and 0.8 ml of the HCl. Warm to dissolve any ppt that may form.

Insert thermometer and cool with continuous agitation so that temp. falls ca 1°/min. Observe turbidity temp. or clouding point, which is temp. at which definite ppt first appears. (If temp. of soln is above room temp., cooling may be accomplished in air or by occasionally immersing soln in H_2O bath of temp. ≤5° below that of soln. Do not immerse flask below level of contents, and agitate continuously to prevent premature formation of turbidity by local cooling. Soln may be agitated by stirring with thermometer or by swirling flask. Observe turbidity temp. by looking thru soln toward good light, or toward dark background with good light coming from one side.)

If turbidity appears before temp. reaches 9° (olive oil) or 13° (cottonseed, corn, or soybean oils) presence of peanut oil is indicated. Confirm by **28.091**.

28.094   Cold Test (25)—Procedure

(Applicable to refined winterized salad oils)

Fill 4 oz oil sample bottle with oil at 25°, cork tightly, and seal with paraffin. Completely submerge bottle in bucket contg finely cracked ice and add H_2O until it rises to top of bottle. Keep bucket filled solidly with ice by removing any excess H_2O and adding ice when necessary. After 5.5 hr remove bottle and examine oil. If it is properly wintered, sample will be brilliant, clear, and limpid.

28.095   Tea Seed Oil in Olive Oil (26)—
Official Final Action

For preliminary qual. test use following room temp. method: Measure into test tube (18 × 150 mm is convenient) exactly 0.8 ml Ac_2O, 1.5 ml $CHCl_3$, and 0.2 ml H_2SO_4. Mix, and cool to room temp. Add 7 drops of oil to be tested directly to reagents, mix, and cool again. (To measure test oil use glass tubing, 4 mm od, and ca 2 mm id; 7 drops should weigh ca 0.22 g.) If soln of oil in reagents is cloudy after mixing and cooling, add Ac_2O dropwise, shaking after each addn until soln suddenly clears. Appreciable deviations from these quantities, particularly in H_2SO_4, cause distinct variations in color intensities. Since mixed reagent deteriorates slowly, do not mix in advance of testing.

After 5 min, add 10 ml absolute ether from cylinder and mix immediately by inverting once. Tea seed oil forms brown soln changing to intense red within min or so. This red reaches max. and then fades slowly within few min. Olive oil forms initial green soln on addn of ether. This color fades slowly to brown-gray, occasionally passing thru faint pink stage. Both olive oil and tea seed oil eventually fade to permanent light brown. Mixts of tea seed oil and olive oil show characteristic tea seed oil colors proportional in intensity to quantity of tea seed oil present.

For approx. quant. estns drop oil into reagents as described above and let remain at room temp. 5 min. In meantime, cool 10 ml portion absolute ether in ice-H_2O. After 5 min, place test tube contg oil and reagents in ice-H_2O 1 min, add cold ether (taking care that no H_2O falls into test tube), and mix. Return tube to ice-H_2O bath and let colors develop while it is immersed in ice-H_2O. Colors develop slowly and reach max. within ca 5 min.

Use deepest red colors produced as basis for comparison, and because of short period of stable max. intensity do not test more than 3 oils at one time. Stds contg known quantities of tea seed oil in olive oil that give little or no pink with this test should be run simultaneously with sample. Preliminary room temp. test gives indication of stds to be used in ice-H_2O method.

Sesame Oil

28.096   *Modified Villavecchia Test (27)—*
Official Final Action

Add 2 ml furfural to 100 ml alcohol. Thoroly mix 0.1 ml of this soln with 10 ml HCl and 10 ml sample by shaking in test tube 15 sec. Let mixt. stand 10 min, observe color, add 10 ml H_2O, shake, and again observe color. If crimson color disappears, sesame oil is absent. (As furfural gives violet tint with HCl, it is necessary to use the very dil. soln specified.)

28.097   Foreign Fats Containing Tristearin in
Lard (28)—Official First Action

Weigh 5 g melted and filtered lard into g-s cylinder and add 20 ml warm acetone. Mix well, taking care that soln is clear and has temp. >30°. Let stand 16–18 hr at constant temp. of 30°. Fine mass of crystals occupying ≤3 ml should then be found at bottom of cylinder. Should vol. of crystals materially exceed 3 ml, take smaller quantity of lard (3–4 g) for new test. Should no crystals be deposited, as may be case with soft or oily lard, tristearin is probably absent.

Decant supernatant acetone soln from crystd glycerides. Add three 5 ml portions warm (30–35°) acetone from small wash bottle, taking care not to break up deposit in washing, and decant first 2 portions. Actively agitate third portion in cylinder and by quick movement transfer crystals to small filter paper. Using wash bottle, wash crystals with 5 successive small portions of the warm acetone and remove excess acetone by suction. Spread out paper and its contents, breaking up any large lumps, and dry in air at room temp.

Thoroly comminute mass and take mp of crystals in closed 1 mm tube, using app. similar to that of Fig. 28:7. Heat H₂O in beaker rapidly to ca 55° and maintain this temp. until thermometer carrying mp tube registers 50°; then heat again and raise temp. of outer bath rather quickly to 67°. Remove burner. Mp is reached when fused substance becomes perfectly clear and transparent.

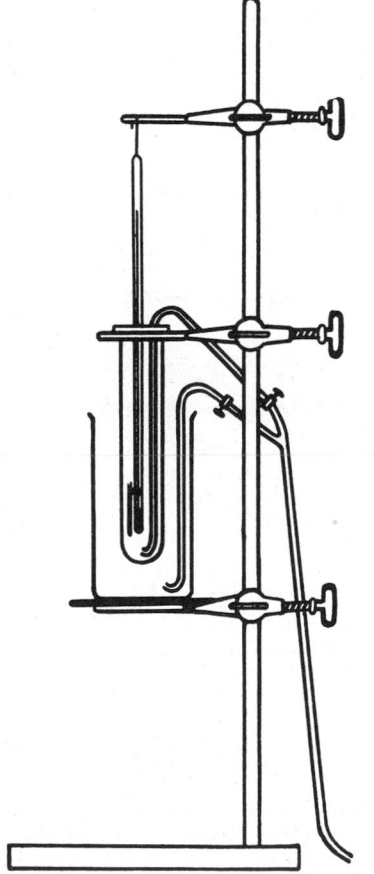

FIG. 28:7—Apparatus for determining melting point

When mp of glycerides obtained by this method is <63.6°, presence of beef fat or other fat contg tristearin should be suspected, and mp of ≤63.2° is evidence that sample is not pure lard. Conduct detn with control sample of pure lard.

Conclusion indicated by mp may be confirmed by taking mp of fatty acids prepd from glycerides. After detg mp, transfer crystd glycerides to 50 ml beaker, add 25 ml ca 0.5N alc. KOH, and heat on steam bath until saponification is complete. Pour soln into separator contg 200 ml H₂O, acidify, add 75 ml ether, shake, and let stand. Drain aq. acid layer and wash ether soln ≥3 times with H₂O. Transfer ether soln to clean, dry 50 ml beaker, evap. ether on steam bath, and finally dry acids at 100°. Let acids remain at room temp. ca 2 hr and det. mp. If mp of glycerides, plus twice difference between mp of glycerides and mp of fatty acids, is <73°, the lard is regarded as adulterated.

Conclusions may be confirmed further by precise detns of mean molecular wt of sepd fatty acids. Dissolve acids in colorless, redistd alcohol carefully neutzd immediately before use, and titr. with 0.5–0.2N KOH, using phthln. Mean molecular wt = wt fatty acids × 1000/ml × normality KOH used. If sample is pure lard, mean molecular wt of fatty acids should correspond closely to that of fatty acids of α-palmito-distearin, 275.14. If sample is impure, mean molecular wt should approach that of fatty acids from tristearin, 284.49.

Fish Oil and Marine Animal Oils in Presence of Vegetable Oils and in Absence of Metallic Salts

28.098 *Qualitative Test—Procedure*

Dissolve ca 6 g sample in 12 ml mixt. of equal parts CHCl₃ and HOAc in test tube. Add Br, dropwise, until slight excess is indicated by color, keeping soln at ca 20°. Let mixt. stand ≥15 min and place test tube in boiling H₂O. If only vegetable oils are present, soln is perfectly clear, but fish oils remain cloudy due to presence of insol. bromides.

Mineral Oil in Fats (29)

28.099 *Qualitative Test—Procedure*

Place 1 ml oil or melted fat in erlenmeyer; add 1 ml KOH soln (3 + 2) and 25 ml alcohol. Boil under reflux air condenser, shaking occasionally, until saponification is complete (ca 5 min). Add 25 ml H₂O and mix. In presence of >0.5% mineral oil, distinct turbidity appears.

28.100 *Quantitative Method—Official Final Action*

(*Caution: See* **46.011, 46.039,** and **46.073.**)

Treat unsaponifiable residue, **28.063,** with H₂SO₄ as below. When very small quantities of mineral oil are present, enough unsaponifiable residue for test may be obtained as follows:

Saponify 100 g fat by refluxing under air condenser 2 hr with 55 ml KOH soln (3 + 2) and 240 ml alcohol, occasionally shaking flask. Cool, add 300 ml pet ether (bp 35–60°), and transfer to separator. Rinse flask with 240 ml alcohol and add rinsings to separator. Add 480 ml H_2O and shake vigorously. Let layers sep., drain lower layer, and transfer upper layer to another separator. Repeat extn of saponified fat with 300 ml pet ether and combine exts. Wash ext twice with 60 ml portions H_2O, using gentle agitation. Repeat washing with 60 ml 0.5N KOH, followed by vigorous agitation with successive 60 ml portions H_2O until washings are alkali-free. Evap. ext to small vol. and dry with anhyd. Na_2SO_4.

Filter pet ether soln thru small cotton plug into Babcock milk-test bottle, **16.053**(a), add few small pieces broken porcelain, and remove solv. by heating on steam bath while passing current of air thru bottle. Cool, add 5 ml H_2SO_4, mix, and keep bottle in boiling H_2O bath 30 min, shaking occasionally. Remove bottle from bath, cool, and fill with H_2SO_4 until surface rises well into graduated neck. Centrf. 5 min at 1200 rpm and read vol. of unreacted residue. If enough mineral oil is available, obtain density as in **28.004,** using small Sprengel tube. Wt mineral oil can be closely approximated by multiplying vol. by 0.88. Refractive index of colorless residue should be <1.500 at 20°.

Hydrocarbons and Mineral Oil (30)— Official Final Action AOCS–AOAC Method

(Applicable to satd hydrocarbons in glycerides)

28.101   *Apparatus and Reagents*

(a) *Chromatographic tube.*—With Teflon stopcock, 25–35 mm diam. and 400 mm long.

(b) *Aluminum oxide.*—Activated alumina, Alcoa, grade F-20, 80–200 mesh (Aluminum Co. of America, Alcoa Bldg., Pittsburgh, PA 15219, or equiv.). Dry alumina ≥4 hr at 200° before using. Store in sealed bottles in desiccator. Alumina must have moisture content of 0–3% to retain glycerides.

28.102   *Determination*

(*Caution: See* **46.011, 46.039,** and **46.073.**)

Weigh 10±0.01 g melted, well mixed sample into 125 ml erlenmeyer, and dissolve in 50–100 ml pet ether, warming gently, if necessary.

Prep. column by tamping plug of glass wool into bottom of tube so that some of glass wool is in constricted portion above stopcock. Fill tube ca ⅔ full with pet ether (Fisher Scientific Co. No. E139, or equiv.) and add 200 g alumina thru powder funnel. Tap side of tube to aid in packing. Cover with ca ½″ anhyd. Na_2SO_4. Elute at rate of 80–90 drops (3.0–3.5 ml)/min, using stopcock for control.

When solv. head drops to ca 1 cm, add sample soln. Let solv. layer drop to ca 1 cm above alumina, collecting eluate in 500 ml erlenmeyer. Rinse sample

flask with 50 ml pet ether and add to column. Repeat 3 times, adding each rinse to column when solv. head drops to ca 1 cm, and wash down sides of column on transferring. Continue adding pet ether to column until total of 400 ml has passed thru. (Inverted vol. flask can serve as convenient reservoir for final addn of solv.)

Evap. eluate on steam bath to 50–75 ml. Stirring rod placed in flask will help prevent superheating and consequent boiling over. Gentle air stream will aid solv. removal. Transfer to weighed 250 ml Soxhlet flask, rinsing with three 20 ml portions pet ether. Remove remaining solv. by evapn on warm surface with gentle air stream, keeping soln below bp. Cool to room temp. in desiccator and weigh.

Repeat with addnl heating periods of 20 min, cooling, and weighing until change in wt is <0.5 mg.

Conduct blank detn without sample.

% Hydrocarbons = $(S - B) \times 100/C$, where S = g sample residue, B = g blank residue, and C = g sample.

28.103   *Precision*

Following 95% confidence limits may be expected:

	% Hydrocarbon Content at Level of			
	0.0	0.05	0.5	5.0
Two single detns in 1 laboratory should differ ≤		0.06	0.09	0.14	0.33
Single detns in different laboratories should differ ≤		0.06	0.10	0.14	0.40

Confirm presence of hydrocarbons or mineral oil by comparison of IR spectrum of residue with that of pure hydrocarbons or mineral oil, USP.

Chick Edema Factor

Bioassay Method (31)—Official Final Action

28.104   *Reagents*

(a) *Assay ration.*—

Component	Level % (w/w)
Casein, crude	19.4
Sucrose	18.8
Starch	18.7
Gelatin	13
Cottonseed oil, USP[a]	2
Control fat[b]	16 − x
Test fat	x
Salt mixt. (b)	6
Vitamin mixt. (c)	2.2
Sodium chloride (iodized)[c]	1.2
Celluflour (Alphacel)	2
DL-Methionine	0.9
Procaine penicillin (1000 units/mg)[d]	0.1

[a] Addn of this amt of cottonseed oil improves physical form of diet which may contain 16% of solid test fat.

[b] Use cottonseed oil, USP, as diluent for test fat. For negative controls, total fat content will be 18% of cottonseed oil.

[c] Addn of this NaCl gives level of 2.04% in ration.

[d] If penicillin prepn is of lower potency, add the addnl amt to ratio at expense of equal portions of starch and sucrose.

(b) *Salt mixture.*—(Jones Foster.) Available from number of com. sources.

	g/2 kg salt mixt.	g/100 g salt mixt.	g/kg diet
KH_2PO_4	816.6	38.89	23.334
$CaCO_3$	800.8	38.14	22.884
NaCl	292.5	13.93	8.358
$MgSO_4$	120.3	5.73	3.438
$FeSO_4.7H_2O$	56.6	2.70	1.620
$MnSO_4.2H_2O$	9.35	0.45	0.270
KI	1.66	0.08	0.048
$CuSO_4.5H_2O$	0.999	0.048	0.0288
$ZnCl_2$	0.545	0.026	0.0144
$CoCl_2.6H_2O$	0.476	0.023	0.0138

(c) *Vitamin mixture.*—Vitamin diet fortification mixt. available from Nutritional Biochemicals Corp. *with vitamin D_3 substituted for D_2* has been found satisfactory.

	Amount/kg diet
Vitamin A, stabilized[a]	19,000 USP units
Vitamin D_3, stabilized[a]	2,200 IC units
Choline chloride	1650 mg
Ascorbic acid	990
α-Tocopheryl acetate	110
p-Aminobenzoic acid	110
Inositol	110
Niacin	99
Ca pantothenate	66
Menadione	49
Riboflavin	22
Pyridoxine.HCl	22
Thiamine.HCl	22
Folic acid	1.98
Biotin	0.44
Vitamin B_{12}	29.7 μg

[a] Prepns of small particle size coated with gelatin, albumin, etc.

28.105 *Treatment of Experimental Animals*

Use day-old white leghorn, single comb cockerels. On day of receipt of chicks, tag individually, record body wts, and place in brooder cages equipped with heater. Use room with controlled temp. and humidity.

Offer control ration contg 18% cottonseed oil as fat and H_2O *ad libitum*. After 48 hr, weigh chicks and do not use any chick that is outside limit of mean body wt by ±5 g. Place 12 chicks in each brooder cage, and record body wt and date of beginning feeding regimen.

28.106 *Assay Period*

Continue 1 group on control ration contg 18% cottonseed oil and substitute test fats for all or part of 18% cottonseed oil in assay rations. Check chicks daily for fatalities and for presence of adequate food and H_2O. Record all deaths and cause of deaths. For each death due to other than accidental cause, autopsy and record presence of hydropericardium, hydroperitoneum, subcutaneous edema, and amt of heart fluid to 0.01 ml. Autopsy remaining chicks on 21st day and record findings as above.

28.107 *Postmortem Examination for Quantity of Heart Fluid*

(a) *Sacrifice of chicks.*—Sacrifice by means of cervical dislocation and proceed as follows:

(b) *Exposure of heart.*—With dissecting scissors make small transverse cut in skin over full diam. of abdomen. Peel skin toward head and lay skin fold over head. This cutaneous incision permits wide field exposure of subcutaneous area over thoracic and abdominal cavities for examination for subcutaneous edema. Skin may be reflected caudally to afford wider field of vision. Record (+ or −) evidence of subcutaneous edema.

Insert blunt tip of scissors thru body wall, and make transverse incision of musculature to lower rim of rib cage, avoiding cutting into organs of peritoneal cavity.

Lift breastbone with fingers, insert blunt tip of scissors, and carefully enlarge incision by cutting on each side of chest cavity thru rib joints up to clavicles. (Do not cut into subclavian vessels.) With sufficiently wide cut, fingers may be used to protract incised chest cavity and thus permit clear observation of substernal attachment of pericardium. Firmly clasp pericardial attachment with fingers and reflect flap of sternum so as to expose heart with pericardium intact.

Est. visually and record severity of pericardial edema according to following table:

Absent	0
Slight	+
Moderate	++
Severe	+++
Very severe	++++

(c) *Withdrawal of heart fluid.*—*(1) For volumes estimated as <1.0 ml.*—Firmly clasp apex of pericardium with small forceps and make small incision in heart sac. Insert small spatula into incision of pericardium and push heart to one side. Carefully aspirate fluid into 1.0 ml tuberculin syringe. Blunt-end 18 gage needle permits more complete aspiration of small vols. To reduce formation of air bubbles during aspiration, prerinse needle and syringe with *n*-butyl alcohol. Do not include vol. of *n*-butyl alcohol in measurement of fluid.

(2) For volume estimated as >1.0 ml.—Insert sharp hypodermic needle on 10 ml syringe into intact pericardium. Aspirate as much as possible of heart fluid (*n*-butyl alcohol rinse is unnecessary). Collect and measure remainder with blunt-end tuberculin syringe. Record total vol. heart fluid to nearest 0.01 ml.

(d) *Other observations.*—Observe and record other obvious changes such as peritoneal edema (ascites), liver changes, kidney changes, etc.

28.108   *Interpretation*

Calc. mean of logarithms of pericardial fluid vols of test group and of concurrent neg. control group, $\bar{x}_t$ and $\bar{x}_c$, resp. Calc.

$$ t = \frac{\bar{x}_t - \bar{x}_c}{\sqrt{\dfrac{s_t^2}{n_t} + \dfrac{s_c^2}{n_c}}} $$

where n_t and n_c are the number of chicks in the test and control groups and s_t^2 and s_c^2 are variances of test and control groups, resp.; $s^2 = [n(\Sigma x^2) - (\Sigma x)^2]/n(n - 1)$, where Σx is sum of logarithms of pericardial fluid vols and (Σx^2) is sum of squares of logarithms of pericardial fluid vols for either test, t, or control, c, group data.

Test sample contains chick edema factor if t is $> +1.3$ and mean logarithm of ($100 \times$ pericardial fluid vol.) is >1.1461, provided mean logarithm of neg. control is <1.1460.

Gas Chromatographic Method (32)— Official First Action

(Caution: See **46.011, 46.015, 46.030, 46.039, 46.040,** and **46.073.***)*

28.109   *Principles*

Fat, oil, fatty acid, or lipid is treated with H_2SO_4 and extd with pet ether. Ext is purified on Al_2O_3 column, further treated with H_2SO_4, and examined by electron capture GLC. Peaks with retention times relative to aldrin (R_a) between 8 and 45 indicate presence of chick edema factors (hexa-, hepta-, and octachlorodibenzo-*p*-dioxins).

28.110   *Reagents and Apparatus*

(Rinse all glassware with appropriate solvs before use. Do not store solvs in polyethylene containers.)

(a) *Petroleum ether.*—Distd in glass, bp 30–60° (available from Burdick and Jackson Laboratories, Inc.).

(b) *Ethyl ether for alumina chromatography.*—Ether ($\leq 2\%$ alcohol) or absolute ether ($\leq 0.01\%$ alcohol) (available from Burdick and Jackson Laboratories, Inc.).

(c) *Carbon tetrachloride.*—Distd in glass (available from Burdick and Jackson Laboratories, Inc.).

(d) *Isooctane.*—Distd in glass (available from Burdick and Jackson Laboratories, Inc.).

(e) *Aldrin std soln.*—0.05 μg/ml isooctane.

(f) *Chick edema factor low positive reference sample.* —1.5% ref. toxic fat (available from Division of Pesticide Chemistry and Toxicology, Food and Drug Administration, Washington, DC 20204) in USP cottonseed or other vegetable oil. (*Caution:* Do not contact toxic fat.)

(g) *Activated alumina.*—Fisher Scientific Co. No. A-540; do not substitute. Activate 100 g portions by heating 4 hr at 260°. Transfer without cooling to dry container and close tightly. Check activity of Al_2O_3 by analysis of low pos. ref. sample, **(f)**, examining Al_2O_3 fractions 2 and 3. With sufficiently

activated Al_2O_3, chick edema factor elutes predominantly or entirely in fraction 3 as indicated by gas chromatograms. (Chromatograms should show series of peaks with R_a between ca 8 and 45.)

(h) *Alumina chromatographic column.*—To dry tube, 17 mm od $\times$ 250 mm long, fitted at bottom with coarse porosity fritted glass disk and Teflon stopcock (tube without disk but with glass wool plug at bottom may also be used), add redistd pet ether, dried before use with anhyd. Na_2SO_4, until tube is $\frac{2}{3}$ full. Transfer 15 g Al_2O_3 to tube in small portions, tapping to settle. After last portion has settled and air bubbles stop rising to surface of solv., add 5 g anhyd. Na_2SO_4. Drain excess pet ether until it is just above surface of Na_2SO_4.

(i) *Gas chromatographic column.*—Glass, 7–9′ $\times$ $\frac{1}{4}$″, packed with 2.5% SE 52 silicone gum rubber on 60–80 mesh Gas-Chrom Q (Applied Science Laboratories). Coat support with substrate as follows: Dissolve 2.5 g silicone gum rubber in 300 ml CH_2Cl_2-toluene (1 + 1) with heat. Add 97.5 g Gas-Chrom Q and let stand 10 min with occasional gentle stirring. Dry in rotary evaporator held in 50° bath. Apply vac. to chromatgc tube and add small amts of coated support while tapping tube at packing level after each addn. Fill to within 1″ on exit side and 3″ on entrance side and fill remaining space with silanized glass wool. Condition column at operating pressure 2–5 days at 250°.

(j) *Gas chromatograph.*—With tritium source concentric-type electron capture detector. Operate instrument in accordance with instructions of manufacturer. Obtain stable baseline before use. Choose operating voltage that will cause between 0.6 and full scale deflection for 0.1 ng aldrin (2 μl std aldrin soln) at sensitivity setting of 1×10^{-9} amp full scale. Keep column temp. at 200 ± 1° and adjust N flow so that aldrin elutes in 1–1.5 min (0.25–0.33″/ min chart speed). Inject 2 μl aldrin std soln before each ref. or test sample.

28.111   *Determination*

(a) *Analysis of reference toxic fat.*—Dissolve 2.5 g of ref. 1.5% toxic fat in 10 ml CCl_4 in 500 ml g-s erlenmeyer and proceed as in **(b)**, **(c)**, and **(d)**. Dissolve residue in 250 μl isooctane and inject 5 μl (equiv. to 50 mg original sample) into gas chromatograph. Resulting chromatogram should exhibit series of peaks with R_a ca 8–45. Peaks at 8–13 are due to hexachlorodibenzo-*p*-dioxin isomers; 2 peaks at 17–22 to the 2 hepta-isomers; and peak at 35–45 to octa-isomer.

(b) *Preliminary sulfuric acid cleanup.*—Dissolve 2.5 g sample in 10 ml CCl_4 in 500 ml g-s erlenmeyer. Add 10 ml H_2SO_4, stopper, and shake 30 sec. Add 125 ml pet ether, stopper, and shake vigorously ca 1 min. Let sep. and decant upper layer into 500 ml erlenmeyer, avoiding transfer of lower layer. Repeat extn with addnl 125 ml portion pet ether. Evap. combined pet ether exts to 5 ml.

(c) *Alumina chromatography.*—Before use, dry all solvs by shaking with anhyd. Na₂SO₄. Transfer evapd pet ether ext to Al₂O₃ column, (h), using total of 10 ml pet ether. Let drain to just above level of Na₂SO₄. Keeping liq. level above Na₂SO₄ at all times, elute with 100 ml pet ether (fraction 1), 50 ml 5% Et ether in pet ether (fraction 2), and 100 ml 25% Et ether in pet ether (fraction 3). (Flow rates of 8–9 ml/min are satisfactory.) Discard fractions 1 and 2 and collect fraction 3 in 125 ml erlenmeyer. Add several boiling chips and evap. to ca 2 ml on steam bath. Transfer residue with small portions pet ether to 10 ml g-s graduated cylinder and further evap. to 3 ml under N.

(d) *Additional sulfuric acid cleanup.*—Add 2 ml H₂SO₄ to pet ether soln, stopper, and shake vigorously 30 sec. Let sep. and decant upper layer into 10 ml beaker, avoiding transfer of any H₂SO₄. Add 2 ml pet ether to cylinder, swirl vigorously, let sep., and decant upper layer into beaker. Add 0.5 g solid NaHCO₃ to beaker and stir ca 0.5 min. Let stand 5 min and decant pet ether layer into 2 or 4 dram vial. Wash NaHCO₃ with 2 ml pet ether and decant washings into vial. Evap. solv. just to dryness at room temp. in vial under N.

(e) *Gas chromatography.*—Dissolve residue in 250 μl isooctane, stopper vial, and rotate to wet sides with solv. Inject 1 μl soln (equiv. to 10 mg sample) into gas chromatograph, (j). Peaks with R_a of 8–45 indicate presence of chick edema factor. Compare R_a values with those from ref. toxic fat, (a). If peaks indicative of chick edema factor are not observed, inject 5 μl soln (equiv. to 50 mg sample). (Types of samples found by experience to be free of components characteristic of toxic fats may be examined by initial injection of 5 μl.)

Perform reagent blank detn with each set of samples. Smooth baseline should be obtained in region R_a 8–45.

Synthetic Colors (33)—Official Final Action

28.112 *Reagents*

(a) *Acid soln A.*—Mix 1 L HOAc with 200 ml HCl and 100 ml H₂O.

(b) *Acid soln B.*—Cautiously add 400 ml H₂SO₄ to 100 ml H₂O. When cool, add 900 ml HOAc and mix.

(c) *Sodium hydroxide soln.*—Approx. 25%. Dissolve 250 g NaOH in H₂O and dil. to 1 L.

28.113 *Separation and Identification*

(*Caution: See* **46.011, 46.039,** *and* **46.073.**)

Place 125 ml oil and 250 ml pet ether in each of 6 separators. Shake contents of first with 50 ml Soln A and, as soon as layers sep., transfer lower layer to flask contg 250 ml H₂O. Mix, and immediately ext this dild acid soln by passing successively thru two 500 ml separators, each contg 75 ml pet ether. Shake vigorously, let layers sep., and discard lower aq. layer. Repeat this procedure with each of other 5 separators, using same pet ether to re-ext colors from the dild acid solns. Combine the 2 pet ether exts, wash with three 25 ml portions H₂O, and filter.

Ext combined pet ether soln with two 25 ml portions Soln A. Treat each acid ext sep. by mixing with 150 ml H₂O and re-extg quickly by passing thru two 250 ml separators, each contg 50 ml pet ether. Combine these pet ether solns, wash acid-free with 15 ml portions H₂O, and evap. to dryness on steam bath. Do not heat dish after removal of solv. Residue may contain Ext. D&C Yellow No. 9 or No. 10 (formerly FD&C Yellow No. 3 or No. 4, resp.) and possibly trace of Ext. D&C Orange No. 4 (formerly FD&C Orange No. 2) if latter dye was originally present in large amts. Identify color spectrophtric as in Chap. **34.**

Shake first separator contg dild oil with 25 ml Soln B, let sep. 20 min, and transfer lower layer to flask contg 200 ml 25% NaOH. Mix, and add 200 ml H₂O. Cool, and remove color from this alk. soln by passing successive 100 ml portions thru two 250 ml separators, each contg 75 ml pet ether. Discard extd alk. soln. Continue this Soln B treatment of oil in other 5 separators, and finally combine the 2 pet ether exts. Wash with three 50 ml portions H₂O and ext with two 20 ml portions Soln B, letting layers sep. 5 min. Drain lower layers into flask contg 300 ml 25% NaOH, mix, and add 300 ml H₂O. Cool, and remove color from this alk. soln by passing successive 100 ml portions thru 2 separators, each contg 75 ml pet ether. Combine pet ether solns, wash free from alkali with H₂O, transfer to evapg dish, and remove solv. on steam bath. Residue may contain Ext. D&C Orange No. 4 and D&C Green No. 6. Remove former by dissolving in 3–5 ml portions 60% alcohol and filtering each portion thru small paper. Identify color spectrophtric as in Chap. **34.**

Dissolve residue on paper in 2–5 ml portions pet ether, collecting filtrate in original evapg dish. Remove solv. on steam bath. Blue residue indicates D&C Green No. 6. Dissolve residue in 15 ml alcohol and 10 ml H₂O, and add 0.5 ml HOAc. Identify color spectrophtric as in Chap. **34.**

Pink color in the various acid exts usually indicates synthetic dye. However, corn oil sometimes produces faint pink color in these exts. This is readily differentiated from synthetic colors spectrophtric. Chlorophyll may appear as green scum at interface in acid exts and as green residue on papers after filtration of pet ether solns.

MONO- AND DIGLYCERIDES

Glycerides in Monoglyceride Concentrates (34)—Official Final Action

28.114 *Apparatus*

(a) *Chromatographic tube.*—Reservoir, 250 ml, with Teflon stopcock attached thru ₮ 19/22 drip tip inner joint to column 290 mm long × 19 mm diam. with outer ₮ 19/22 joint at top and with coarse fritted glass disk and inner ₮ 19/22 joint at bottom.

Bottom joint connects to adapter consisting of outer ⨍ 19/22 joint connected to Teflon stopcock. (Available from Scientific Glass Apparatus Co., from Print No. 580241-12.)

(b) *Mixer*.—Patterson-Kelley Twin Shell Blender or equiv. for mixing adsorbent. (Available from Patterson-Kelley Co., 105 Warren St, E. Stroudsburg, PA 18301.)

28.115   *Preparation of Silica Gel*

Place ca 10 g silica gel (Fisher Scientific Co. No. S-679, grade 923, 100–200 mesh) in tared weighing bottle and cap immediately. Weigh to nearest mg and subtract tare wt. Remove cap and dry 2 hr at 200°. Remove from oven, cap immediately, and let cool 30 min at room temp. Raise cap momentarily to equalize internal pressure with atm. Weigh, reheat 5 min at 200°, cool, and reweigh. Repeat 5 min drying cycle until 2 consecutive wts agree within 10 mg. Calc. H_2O content as follows:

% H_2O in original silica gel = x = (loss in wt) × 100/sample wt. Adjust H_2O content of original silica gel to 5% as follows:

H_2O to be added = g original silica gel × $(5 - x)$/95.

Weigh silica gel to be adjusted in blender and add calcd amt H_2O to give final H_2O content of 5±0.1%. Blend 1 hr to insure complete H_2O distribution and store in sealed container. Det. H_2O content of adjusted silica gel as above, and readjust if necessary.

28.116   *Preparation of Sample*

(To avoid rearrangement of partial glycerides, use extreme caution in applying heat to samples. Do not heat >50°.)

(a) *Samples melting below 50°*.—Melt by warming at <50° for short periods (30 min max.).

(b) *Samples melting above 50°*.—Grind ca 10 g in mortar and pestle. If necessary, chill samples in solid CO_2.

Weigh 0.9–1.1 g prepd sample to 1 mg in 100 ml beaker. Add 15 ml $CHCl_3$ and warm if necessary for complete soln. Use only min. heat and do not heat >40°.

28.117   *Preparation of Column*

Assemble chromatgc tube but without reservoir. Do not grease joints. Weigh 30 g prepd silica gel into 150 ml beaker and add 50–60 ml pet ether. Stir slowly with glass rod until all air bubbles are expelled. Place powder funnel in tube and transfer slurry. Open stopcock and let liq. level drop to ca 2 cm above silica gel. To transfer any silica gel slurry remaining in beaker, invert beaker over powder funnel at 45° and wash into tube with wash bottle, using min. amt pet ether. Rinse funnel and sides of tube; when solv. level drops to 2 cm above silica gel, close bottom stopcock. Remove powder funnel and carefully add sample. Open stopcock and adjust

flow rate to 2 ml effluent/min. Rinse beaker with 5 ml $CHCl_3$ and add rinse to column when level drops to 2 cm above silica gel.

(Keep temp. of work area below bp of most volatile solv. used, Et ether (34.6°). Higher temp. will cause sepn of column packing and permit solv. to channel.

Never let column become dry on top, and maintain 2 ml/min flow rate thruout elution. If necessary to interrupt elution, do so when very little glyceride is passing thru bottom stopcock. Avoid such interruptions, since solv. above bottom stopcock may cause pressure buildup and result in leakage thru stopcock or cracks in silica gel packing.)

28.118   *Separation of Glycerides*
(*Caution: See* 46.011, 46.039, 46.040, 46.045, and 46.054.)

Attach reservoir to column, add 200 ml benzene, and collect effluent in tared 250 ml flask (triglyceride fraction). When all benzene has been added from separator and level in column drops to 2 cm above silica gel, add 200 ml 10% (v/v) ether in benzene and collect effluent in second tared 250 ml flask (diglyceride + free fatty acid (FFA) fraction). When all benzene-ether soln. has been added from separator and level in column drops to 2 cm above silica gel, add 200 ml ether, change to third tared 250 ml flask, and collect monoglyceride fraction.

(Addn of Et ether to column often creates internal pressure, resulting in increased effluent flow rate and cracks in silica gel packing before fraction is completely eluted. Avoid by slightly sepg reservoir from column for ca 30 sec and letting solv. flow into column at same rate as effluent is collected.)

To ensure quant. sepn of fractions, rinse tip of column into receiver with same solv. used in elution just before changing flasks for next eluate.

Evap. collected tri-, di- plus FFA, and monoglyceride fractions on steam bath under stream of N or dry air. Let flasks cool at room temp. ≥15 min and weigh. Reheat samples on steam bath 5 min under N or dry air, let cool 15 min, and reweigh. Repeat 5 min evapn, cooling, and reweighing until 2 consecutive wts agree within 2 mg.

Any free fatty acid present is eluted with diglyceride fraction. To det. free fatty acid content of weighed diglyceride, add 25 ml warm neut. alcohol and 1 drop phthln indicator, and titr. with 0.05N NaOH.

28.119   *Calculations*

% FFA (as oleic) = ml NaOH × Normality × 28.2/g diglyceride

% Triglyceride = g triglyceride × 100/g sample

% Diglyceride = (g diglyceride × 100/g sample) − % FFA

% Monoglyceride = g monoglyceride × 100/g sample.

1-Monoglycerides (35)—Official First Action

American Oil Chemists' Society Method

28.120 *Principles*

1-Monoglycerides are detd from HIO_4 consumed in the oxidn of adjacent hydroxyl groups. 2-Monoglycerides are not oxidized by HIO_4. Method is applicable to fats, oils, monoglycerides, and blends; not applicable to samples contg $CHCl_3$-sol. substances with 2 or more adjacent hydroxyl groups.

28.121 *Reagents*

(a) *Periodic acid soln.*—Reagent grade (available from G. Frederick Smith Chemical Co.). Test as follows: To 0.5–0.6 g glycerol in 50 ml H_2O add 50 ml HIO_4 soln from pipet. Prep. blank contg 50 ml H_2O. Let stand 30 min and titr. as in **28.123**. Titer of soln contg glycerol/titer of blank = 0.75–0.76 if reagent is satisfactory.

Dissolve 5.4 g HIO_4 in 100 ml H_2O, add 1900 ml HOAc, and mix thoroly. Store in g-s bottle in dark.

(b) *Starch indicator soln.*—Make homogeneous paste of 1.0 g sol. starch with H_2O. Add to 100 ml boiling H_2O, stir rapidly, and cool. Salicylic acid, 0.125 g/100 ml, may be added as preservative. Soln keeps longer if stored in refrigerator. Color of 2 ml starch soln dild with 100 ml H_2O contg 0.05 ml 0.1N I must be discharged by 0.05 ml 0.1N $Na_2S_2O_3$. Discard if end point from blue to colorless is no longer sharp.

(c) *Chloroform.*—Reagent or NF. Blanks on HIO_4 soln with and without $CHCl_3$ must check within 0.5 ml.

28.122 *Preparation of Samples*

(Do not subject samples to excessive temps or monoglyceride content may be reduced.)

(a) *Solids in flake form.*—Mix without melting.

(b) *Solids not in flake form.*—Melt at $\leq 10°$ above mp, mix thoroly, and take sample. Do not test samples contg so much free glycerol that it seps on solidification.

(c) *Semi-solids and liquids.*—Proceed as in (b).

28.123 *Determination*

Accurately weigh 0.3–10 g sample calcd from equation: g = 30/% monoglyceride in sample (10 g for $\leq 3\%$), dissolve in $CHCl_3$, and transfer to 100 ml g-s vol. flask. Dil. to vol. with $CHCl_3$ and mix. Transfer entire soln to 500 ml g-s erlenmeyer (do not rinse) and add 100 ml H_2O. Stopper, and shake vigorously 1 min. Let stand until layers sep. and $CHCl_3$ layer is clear or only slightly cloudy (1–3 hr). If emulsions form, causing poor sepn, repeat detn, using 100 ml HOAc (5 + 95) instead of H_2O.

Pipet 50 ml HIO_4 soln into series of 400 ml beakers. Add 50 ml $CHCl_3$ to 2 and 50 ml H_2O to third as blanks (**28.121**(c)). Pipet 50 ml $CHCl_3$ sample soln into fourth, avoiding any aq. phase, and shake

gently. (Solns must be cooled to $<95°F$, if necessary.) Cover with watch glass and let stand 30 min.

Add 20 ml 15% KI soln, mix by gentle shaking, and let stand ≥ 1 min but ≤ 5 min, away from strong sunlight. Add 100 ml H_2O, and titr. with stdzd 0.1N $Na_2S_2O_3$, stirring continuously with mech. stirrer. After I color disappears from aq. layer, add 2 ml starch soln and continue titrn to disappearance of blue from aq. layer. Vigorous stirring is necessary to remove I from $CHCl_3$ layer.

If titer of sample is <0.8 titer of blanks, repeat detn, using smaller aliquot of $CHCl_3$ soln or smaller sample wt, to assure adequate excess of HIO_4. If titer of blank minus titer of sample is <4 ml, repeat detn, doubling sample wt to max. of 10 g.

% Monoglyceride as monostearin = $(B - S) \times N \times 17.927/W$, where B = titer of $CHCl_3$ blank, S = titer of sample, N = normality of $Na_2S_2O_3$, W = g sample in $CHCl_3$ aliquot, and 17.927 = molecular wt monostearin/20.

If content is to be calcd to monoglyceride other than monostearin, substitute for 17.927 molecular wt of other monoglyceride/20. Alternatively, det. molecular wt as follows: Sep. fatty acids as in first 2 par. of **28.015**. Accurately weigh ca 2 g fatty acids into 250 ml erlenmeyer and add 20–30 ml hot alcohol neutzd to faint pink of phthln. (SDA formula 30 or 3A is satisfactory.) Add 0.5 ml phthln and titr. immediately while shaking with 0.5N NaOH to pink that persists 30 sec. Calc. acid number (mg *KOH* required to neutze fatty acids in 1 g sample) = ml NaOH $\times$ normality $\times$ 56.1/g sample. Av. molecular wt of fatty acids = 56104/acid number = M. Molecular wt monoglyceride = $(M + 92.09) - 18.02$.

Duplicate detns made on same day by 1 analyst should not differ (95% confidence limits) by more than ca 0.1, 0.5, and 1.2% 1-monoglyceride at 3, 40, and 90% levels; single detns and av. of duplicate detns made in 2 different laboratories should not differ by more than ca 0.5, 1.2, and 3.2%, and 0.5, 1.1, and 3.1%, resp., at same levels.

Revised Miner Method (36)

28.124 *Principle*

Periodic acid oxidizes vicinal hydroxyl groups. Compds with $=O$, $-OH$, $-NHR$, and $-NH_2$ attached to adjacent C atoms will be oxidized by H_5IO_6; phospholipids can interfere. Such substances are absent from usual fat samples.

Samples are dissolved in $CHCl_3$ contg 5% dimethylformamide (to assure soln of glycerol) and aliquots are oxidized with excess H_5IO_6. H_5IO_6-H_2O soln exts and oxidizes free glycerol and H_5IO_6-MeOH soln oxidizes monoglyceride plus glycerol. Unused H_5IO_6 is detd iodometrically by reacting with KI and titrg with 0.05N std arsenite soln.

Calcn of monoglyceride is based on amt of H_5IO_6 consumed in oxidn of monoglyceride plus glycerol corrected for amt consumed in oxidn of free glycerol alone.

28.125   *Reagents and Apparatus*

(a) *Periodic acid stock soln.*—Dissolve 12.0 g H_5IO_6 (G. Frederick Smith Chemical Co., reagent grade) in 100 ml H_2O. Store at room temp. in brown g-s bottle.

(b) *Periodic acid in 95% methanol.*—Mix 25 ml stock soln with 475 ml MeOH. Store at room temp. in brown g-s bottle and prep. fresh every 3–5 days.

(c) *Periodic acid in water.*—Mix 50 ml stock soln, (a), with 950 ml H_2O.

(d) *Potassium iodide soln.*—Dissolve 75 g KI and 50 g $NaHCO_3$ in H_2O.

(e) *Sodium arsenite.*—0.05N. See **45.005–45.006.**

(f) *Starch indicator.*—Make homogeneous paste of 0.50 g potato starch with 5 ml H_2O. Add to 200 ml boiling H_2O and boil 15 min, stirring constantly. Cool and store in g-s bottle. Prep. fresh daily.

(g) *Chloroform.*—I absorption should be <0.1 ml 0.1N $Na_2S_2O_3$/30 ml solv.

(h) *N,N-Dimethylformamide (DMF).*—25% soln in $CHCl_3$ (g). *Caution:* This material is toxic. Avoid contact with skin or inhalation of vapors.

(i) *Hot plate.*—Thermolyne, Model HP 1915B, or equiv.

28.126   *Preparation of Samples*

See **28.122.**

28.127   *Determinations*

(*Caution: See* **46.018, 46.040, 46.053,** and **46.056.**)

Weigh sample into 100 ml beaker, calcg g required as:

$S = K/(M' + 8G) = 50/(M' + 8G) = 4W_1 = 2W_2$;

where M' = % monoglyceride expected; G = % free glycerol expected; K = constant which dets % excess reagent [100 $T_1/(B_1 - T_1)$]; W_1 = aliquot wt for monoglyceride; W_2 = aliquot wt for free glycerol; B_1 = blank titrn for monoglyceride plus glycerol; B_2 = blank titrn for free glycerol; T_1 = sample titrn for monoglyceride plus glycerol; and T_2 = sample titrn for free glycerol.

For 20% excess, $K = 70$; 50% excess, $K = 50$ (preferred); and 100% excess, $K = 42$. Max. S should be 40 g/100 ml or, if preferred, 10 g can be weighed directly into reaction vessel.

(a) *Monoglyceride plus glycerol.* — Dissolve weighed sample in 20 ml 25% DMF. Use $CHCl_3$ to transfer quant. to 100 ml vol. flask and dil. to vol. Aliquots can be used for analysis of both monoglyceride plus glycerol and free glycerol.

Pipet 25 ml aliquot into 500 ml erlenmeyer and record sample wt in aliquot as W_1. Prep. 2 blanks in similar flasks by adding 5 ml 25% DMF and 20 ml $CHCl_3$ to each.

Pipet exactly 25 ml H_5IO_6-MeOH into the 25 ml aliquot and into each blank. (For samples low in monoglyceride, such as triglyceride fat or oil, vol.

H_5IO_6-MeOH may be reduced from 25 ml to 10, 5, or even 3 ml; use same amt of reagent for blanks.) Add 2–3 glass beads to each sample and heat just to boiling on hot plate, swirling several times during heating. (Do *not* heat blanks.) Let stand 30 min to cool, protected from sunlight or other strong illumination. Add 200 ml H_2O to each blank and sample, and swirl several times. Let sample stand 5 min (up to 45 min is permissible). Blanks may be analyzed immediately. Add 40 ml KI soln from graduate and swirl to mix. Let stand 1 min; then titr. with Na arsenite. After I color fades to pale yellow, add 2–3 ml starch indicator and continue titrn until starch-I color disappears. Record av. titrn of 2 blanks as B_1 and of sample as T_1. When >1 sample is run on same day with same reagents, av. titrn of 2 blanks which check within 0.1 ml can be used in all calcns. If 2 blanks do not check within 0.1 ml, third blank must be run. Excess H_5IO_6 must be 20–100%. If 100 $T_1/(B_1 - T_1)$ is <20%, repeat with smaller sample; if excess is much >100%, repeat with larger sample or use less H_5IO_6-MeOH. To complete H_5IO_6 oxidn, min. of 20% excess is required. If excess H_5IO_6-MeOH is much >100%, high apparent monoglyceride may result.

(b) *Free glycerol.*—Free glycerol must be extd completely from DMF layer into aq. layer. If glycerol is not in aq. layer when H_5IO_6-H_2O is added, or during standing time, results may be low.

Pipet 50 ml aliquot of weighed sample from (a) into 500 ml erlenmeyer. Record sample wt in aliquot as W_2. Prep. 2 blanks in similar flasks by adding 10 ml 25% DMF and 40 ml $CHCl_3$.

Add ca 100 ml H_2O to sample and blanks. Swirl ca 1 min, reversing direction several times. Pipet exactly 25 ml H_5IO_6-H_2O into each flask. Let stand at room temp. 30 min, swirling vigorously ≥30 sec at beginning and every 5 min during this period. Add 40 ml KI soln from graduate, swirl, and let stand 1 min. Titr. with 0.05N Na arsenite to starch-I end point as in (a), including blank titrns. Record sample titrn as T_2 and av. of blank titrn as B_2. Any excess >20% is permissible for H_5IO_6-H_2O.

28.128   *Calculation*

% Monoglyceride =

$$\frac{\left[(B_1 - T_1) - \dfrac{W_1}{W_2}(B_2 - T_2)\right] \times N \times MW \times 100}{W_1 \times 2 \times 1000},$$

where N is normality of Na arsenite soln, and MW is molecular wt of monoglyceride.

Monoglyceride content can be calcd as monostearin. Using exactly 0.05N Na arsenite, 358 as molecular wt of monostearin, and sample wt of free glycerol equal to twice amt used for monoglyceride plus glycerol, following formula can be applied:

% Monoglyceride (as monostearin) =
   $[(B_1 - T_1) - \tfrac{1}{2}(B_2 - T_2) \times 0.895]/W_1$.

Glycerides in Shortening (37)—Official Final Action

(Not generally applicable when emulsifiers other than mono- and diglycerides are present. *Caution: See* **46.011, 46.039, 46.040, 46.045,** and **46.054.**)

28.129 *Apparatus*

See **28.114.**

28.130 *Preparation of Silica Gel*

See **28.115.** Check each new lot of adsorbent for satisfactory sepn of glycerides. Collect last 15 ml portion of each eluate in weighed flask. If residue after evapn is >2 mg, increase amt of eluate until last 15 ml portion collected contains <2 mg. Once amts of eluates needed for complete sepn of glyceride fractions are established, only occasional checking of each lot of silica gel is required.

28.131 *Preparation of Sample*

Melt entire sample in hot H_2O at 50° to avoid overheating, and mix well. Weigh 4.9–5.1 g prepd sample to 1 mg in 100 ml beaker. Add 10 ml benzene and warm if necessary for complete soln. Use only min. heat and do not heat >50°.

28.132 *Preparation of Column*

Prep. column as in **28.117** and adjust flow rate to 2 ml effluent/min. Begin collecting effluent in weighed 400 ml beaker. Rinse beaker with 10 ml benzene and add to column when level drops to 2 cm. Repeat rinsing with 10 ml portions benzene, using total of 40 ml.

Observe precautions of last 2 par. of **28.117.**

28.133 *Separation of Glycerides*

Attach reservoir separator to column, add 300 ml benzene, and collect effluent in weighed 400 ml beaker (triglyceride fraction). When all benzene has been added and level in column drops to 2 cm above silica gel, add 250 ml 10% (v/v) ether in benzene and collect effluent in second weighed 400 ml beaker (diglyceride fraction). When all benzene-ether solv. has been added and level in column drops to ca 2 cm above silica gel, add 200 ml ether and collect effluent in third weighed 400 ml beaker (monoglyceride fraction). Observe precaution of second par., **28.118.**

To ensure quant. sepn of fractions, rinse tip of column into receiver before changing beakers for next eluate. (Weighed 300 ml Soxhlet flasks can be used for collecting fractions, but 2 will be required for triglyceride eluate.)

Evap. tri-, di-, and monoglyceride fractions on steam bath under stream of clean N or dry air. Let beakers cool at room temp. ≥15 min and weigh. Replace beakers on steam bath 5 min, remove, cool 15 min, and reweigh. Repeat 5 min evapn, cooling, and reweighing until 2 consecutive wts agree within 2 mg.

28.134 *Calculations*

% Triglyceride = g triglyceride × 100/g sample
% Diglyceride = g diglyceride × 100/g sample
% Monoglyceride = g monoglyceride × 100/g sample

High free fatty acid contents will give high results, since approx. 20% of free fatty acid is eluted with each of the tri- and monoglyceride fractions and 60% with diglyceride fraction. With most shortenings, effect is insignificant, since level of free fatty acids is <0.2%.

Nonhydroxy derived glycerides as may be formed by thermal exposure may interfere. This material is found primarily in diglyceride fraction. Significant amts are not present in fresh shortenings. On used fats, diglyceride content of that fraction can be obtained from hydroxyl value.

FLAXSEED

28.135 ★ Oil by Refraction (38)— ★ Official Final Action

(*Note:* Halogenated naphthalene may be harmful. *Caution: See* **46.084.**)

See **26.111–26.115,** 10th ed.

SELECTED REFERENCES

(1) Ind. Eng. Chem. **18,** 1347(1926); JAOAC **14,** 247(1931); **15,** 560(1932).

(2) Lewkowitsch, "Chemical Technology and Analysis of Oils, Fats and Waxes," 6th ed., **1,** 312(1921); J. Soc. Chem. Ind. **26,** 513(1907).

(3) USDA Bur. Chem. Bull. **13** (IV), p. 448; Lewkowitsch, "Chemical Technology and Analysis of Oils, Fats and Waxes," 6th ed., **1,** 325(1921); Wiley, "Principles and Practice of Agricultural Analysis," 2nd ed., **3,** 309(1906–14).

(4) JAOAC **25,** 726(1942).

(5) Compt. rend. **172,** 984(1921); Bull. soc. chim. (4), **29,** 745(1921); J. Am. Chem. Soc. **44,** 392 (1922); JAOAC **10,** 323(1927).

(6) Ber. **34,** 3354(1901); J. Biol. Chem. **104,** 627 (1934); Ind. Eng. Chem., Anal. Ed. **17,** 394 (1945); AOCS Method Cd 13–60.

(7) JAOAC **48,** 127(1965).

(8) J. Am. Oil Chemists' Soc. **26,** 345(1949); AOCS Method Cd 8–53.

(9) JAOAC **13,** 255(1930); **38,** 319(1955); **39,** 355 (1956); **40,** 61, 509(1957).

(10) JAOAC **39,** 88, 212(1956); **40,** 531(1957).

(11) Cotton Oil Press **6,** No. 1, 41(1922); JAOAC **11,** 301(1928); **12,** 203(1929); **51,** 20(1968).

(12) JAOAC **40,** 487(1957); **42,** 42, 354(1959); AOCS Method Cd 7–58.

(13) JAOAC **48,** 437(1965); AOCS Method Cd 14–61.

(14) J. Am. Oil Chemists' Soc. **45,** 103(1968).

(15) J. Am. Oil Chemists' Soc. **41,** 158(1964); AOCS Method Ce 1–62.

(16) Analyst **58,** 203(1933); JAOAC **28,** 282(1945); **29,** 248(1946).

(17) JAOAC **26,** 499(1943); **28,** 282(1945); **29,** 247 (1946).

(18) Netherlands Milk and Dairy J. **9,** 261(1955); JAOAC **38,** 338(1955); **41,** 40, 268(1958).

(19) JAOAC **53,** 623(1970).

(20) J. Dairy Sci. **50,** 1764(1967); JAOAC **52,** 600 (1969); **53,** 535(1970).

(21) JAOAC **52,** 774, 778(1969); **53,** 441(1970).

(22) J. Pharm. chim. 6th ser., **6,** 390(1897); Abs. Analyst **22,** 326(1897); Allen, "Commercial Organic Analysis," 5th ed., **2,** 177(1924); Conn. Agr. Expt. Sta. Rpt., **1900** (II), p. 143; Nature **178,** 372(1956); Chem. Rev. **64,** 497(1964).

(23) Compt. rend. **73,** 1330(1871); Lewkowitsch, "Chemical Technology and Analysis of Oils, Fats and Waxes," 6th ed., **2,** 316(1922).

(24) Analyst **62,** 96(1937); JAOAC **28,** 293(1945); **32,** 363(1949).

(25) JAOAC **12,** 203(1929).

(26) JAOAC **19,** 496(1936); **20,** 418(1937).

(27) J. Soc. Chem. Ind. **12,** 67(1893); **13,** 69(1894); JAOAC **6,** 441(1923).

(28) USDA Bur. Animal Ind. Circ. **132;** JAOAC **3,** 432(1920); **4,** 195(1920); **19,** 417(1936); Analyst **65,** 623(1940).

(29) JAOAC **28,** 282(1945).

(30) JAOAC **49,** 71, 232(1966).

(31) JAOAC **44,** 146, 449, 456(1961); **45,** 210, 231, 739(1962); **46,** 406(1963).

(32) JAOAC **46,** 384(1963); **48,** 433(1965); **50,** 216, 874, 1338(1967); **51,** 940(1968); **53,** 628(1970); Nature **220,** 702(1968).

(33) JAOAC **25,** 726(1942); **34,** 235(1951).

(34) J. Am. Oil Chemists' Soc. **35,** 325(1958); JAOAC **48,** 444(1965).

(35) J. Am. Oil Chemists' Soc. **34,** 301(1957); AOCS Method Cd 11–57; JAOAC **49,** 816 (1966).

(36) J. Am. Oil Chemists' Soc. **31,** 466(1954); JAOAC **49,** 816(1966); **52,** 409, 602(1969).

(37) JAOAC **49,** 232, 812(1966).

(38) USDA Bull. **1471**(1927); JAOAC **20,** 421 (1937).

SPECIAL REFERENCES

AMERICAN OIL CHEMISTS' SOCIETY, "Official and Tentative Methods," Chicago (1946 and revisions).

"BAILEY's Industrial Oil and Fat Products," 3rd ed., edited by Swern, Interscience Publishers, Inc., New York (1964); "Cottonseed and Cottonseed Products," Interscience Publishers, Inc., New York (1948).

BAILEY, "Marine Oils with Particular Reference to Those of Canada," Bull. **89,** Fisheries Research Board of Canada, Ottawa (1952).

BOEKENOOGEN, "Analysis and Characterization of Oils, Fats, and Fat Products," Vol. 1 (1964), Vol. 2 (1968), John Wiley and Sons, Inc., New York.

BRITISH STANDARDS INSTITUTION, "Methods of Analysis of Oils and Fats," British Standard **684,** London (1950).

COCKS AND VAN REDE, "Laboratory Handbook for Oil and Fat Analysis," Academic Press, New York (1966).

DEUEL, "The Lipids," Vol. 1, Interscience Publishers, Inc., New York (1951).

DEUTSCHE GESELLSCHAFT FÜR FETTWISSEN-SCHAFT E.V., "Deutsche Einheitsmethoden zur Untersuchung von Fetten, Fettprodukten und verwandten Stoffen," Wissenschaftliche Verlagsgesellschaft, Stuttgart (1950–).

ECKEY, "Vegetable Fats and Oils," Reinhold Publishing Co., New York (1954).

GUNSTONE, "An Introduction to the Chemistry and Biochemistry of Fatty Acids and Their Glycerides," 2nd ed., Chapman and Hall Ltd., London (1967).

HILDITCH AND WILLIAMS, "The Chemical Constitution of Natural Fats," 4th ed., John Wiley and Sons, Inc., New York (1964).

HOLMAN, "Progress in the Chemistry of Fats and Other Lipids," Vols. 1– (1952–) Pergamon Press, New York.

INTERNATIONAL UNION OF PURE AND APPLIED CHEMISTRY, "Standard Methods for the Analysis of Oils, Fats and Soaps," Butterworths, London (1964).

JAMIESON, "Vegetable Fats and Oils," 2nd ed., Reinhold Publishing Co., New York (1943).

KAUFMANN, "Analyse der Fette und Fettprodukte," 2 Vol., Springer-Verlag, Berlin (1958).

KIRSCHENBAUER, "Fats and Oils," 2nd ed., Reinhold Publishing Co., New York (1960).

LUNDBERG, "Autoxidation and Antioxidants," Vol. 1 (1961); Vol. 2 (1962), Interscience Publishers, Inc., New York.

MARKLEY, "Fatty Acids, Their Chemistry, Properties, Production, and Uses," 2nd ed., Part 1 (1960); Part 2 (1961); Part 3 (1964); Part 4 (1967); Part 5 (1968); Interscience Publishers, Inc., New York.

MEHLENBACHER, "The Analysis of Fats and Oils," The Garrard Press, Champaign, Ill. (1960).

PATTISON, "Fatty Acids and Their Industrial Applications," Marcel Dekker, Inc., New York (1968).

RALSTON, "Fatty Acids and Their Derivatives," John Wiley and Sons, Inc., New York (1948).

SCHULTZ, "Lipids and Their Oxidation," The Avi Publishing Co., Inc., New York (1962).

WILLIAMS, "Oils, Fats and Fatty Foods," 4th ed., American Elsevier Publishing Co., New York (1966).

29. Pesticide Residues[★]

MULTIPLE RESIDUES

GENERAL METHOD FOR CHLORINATED AND PHOSPHATED PESTICIDES (1)

Table 29:1—Pesticides and crops to which general method applies

Pesticide	Official First Action	Official Final Action
Aldrin		apples, apricots, beets, bell peppers, broccoli, cabbage, canta-
BHC	dairy products	loupes, cauliflower, celery, collard greens, corn silage, cu-
p,p'-DDE	dairy products	cumbers, eggplant, endive, grapes, green beans, kale, mus-
p,p'-DDT	dairy products	tard greens, peaches, pears, peas, plums, potatoes, radishes,
Endrin		radish tops, spinach, squash, strawberries, sugar beets,
Heptachlor		sweet potatoes, tomatoes, turnips, turnip greens
Lindane	dairy products	
Methoxychlor	dairy products	
p,p'-TDE (DDD)	dairy products	
o,p'-DDT	dairy products	
Dieldrin		dairy products, vegetable oils
Heptachlor epoxide		dairy products, vegetable oils
Carbophenothion		
Diazinon		
Ethion		
Malathion	apples, lettuce	
Me parathion		
Parathion		
Ronnel		

29.001   *Principles*

Thoroly mixed sample is extd with CH₃CN. Aliquot of CH₃CN is dild with H₂O and pesticide residues are extd into pet ether. Residues are purified by chromatgy on Florisil column, eluting with mixt. of pet and Et ethers. Residues in concd eluates are measured by gas chromatgy and identified by combinations of gas, thin layer, or paper chromatgy.

29.002   *General Reagents*

Solvs must be purified and final distn conducted in all-glass app. (*Caution: See* **46.011, 46.039, 46.040, 46.043, 46.054, 46.061,** and **46.073.**) Suitable products are available from Burdick and Jackson Laboratories, Inc., and other manufacturers.

Purity test.—Electron capture gas chromatgy requires absence of substances causing detector response as indicated by following test: Place 300 ml reagent in Kuderna-Danish concentrator fitted with 3-ball Snyder column and calibrated collection vessel, and evap. to 5 ml. Inject 5 µl conc. from 10 µl syringe into gas chromatograph, using conditions described in **29.008.** Conc. must not cause recorder

deflection >1 mm from baseline for 2–60 min after injection.

(a) *Acetonitrile.*—*See Purity test.* Purify tech. CH₃CN as follows: To 4 L CH₃CN add 1 ml H₃PO₄, 30 g P₂O₅, and boiling chips, and distill in all-glass app. at 81–82°. Do not exceed 82°.

Some lots of reagent grade CH₃CN are impure and require distn. Generally vapors from such lots will turn moistened red litmus paper blue when held over mouth of storage container. Pronounced amine odor is detectable.

(b) *Acetonitrile saturated with petroleum ether.*—Sat. CH₃CN, (a), with redistd pet ether, (m).

(c) *Alcohol.*—USP, reagent grade, or MeOH, ACS.

(d) *Alcoholic alkali soln.*—2%. Dissolve 2 g NaOH or KOH in alcohol, and dil. to 100 ml.

(e) *Eluting solvent, 6%.*—Dil. 60 ml Et ether, (h), to 1 L with redistd pet ether, (m).

(f) *Eluting solvent, 15%.*—Prep. as in (e), using 150 ml Et ether.

(g) *Eluting solvent, 50%.*—Prep. as in (e), using 500 ml Et ether.

(h) *Ethyl ether.*—Redistd at 34–35°, and stored under N. Add 2% alcohol. Must be peroxide-free by test in *Definitions of Terms and Explanatory Notes,* item (3). *See also Purity test* above.

[★] Methods so marked are surplus methods. *See* "Definitions of Terms and Explanatory Notes," item (29).

(i) *Florisil.*—60/100 PR grade, activated at 1250°F (650°C), available from Floridin Co. When 1250°F activated Florisil is obtained in bulk, transfer immediately after opening to ca 1 pt glass jars, or bottles, with g-s or foil-lined, screw-top lids, and store in dark. Heat $\geq$5 hr at 130° before use. Store at 130° in g-s bottles or in desiccator at room temp. and reheat at 130° after 2 days.

Prep. mixed pesticide std soln in hexane contg 1, 4, 1, 2, 1, 2, and 4 µg/ml, resp., of ronnel, ethion, heptachlor epoxide, parathion, dieldrin, endrin, and malathion.

Test each batch of activated Florisil by placing 1 ml mixed pesticide std on prepd column and eluting as in *Cleanup*, **29.014.** Conc. eluates from Florisil column to 10 ml. Inject aliquot (*see* **29.008**) of appropriate eluate into gas chromatograph and det. quant. recovery of each compd as in **29.017.** Florisil that quant. elutes heptachlor epoxide, ronnel, and ethion in 6% eluate, dieldrin, endrin, and parathion in 15% eluate, and malathion in 50% eluate is satisfactory.

(j) *Hexane.*—Reagent grade, redistd in all-glass app. *See Purity test.*

(k) *Magnesium oxide.*—Sea Sorb No. 43 (Fisher Scientific Co. No. S-120). Treat as follows: Slurry ca 500 g with H_2O, heat on steam bath ca 30 min, and filter with suction. Dry overnight at 105–130° and pulverize to pass No. 60 sieve. Store in closed jar.

(l) *Magnesia-Celite mixture.*—Mix treated MgO, (**k**), with Celite 545, 1 + 1 by wt. Pet ether ext of Celite should be free of electron capturing substances.

(m) *Petroleum ether.*—*See Purity test.* Reagent grade, redistd in all-glass app. at 30–60°.

(n) *Sodium sulfate.*—Anhyd., granular.

29.003   *Reagents for Thin Layer Chromatography*

(a) *Aluminum oxide.*—Neutral Al_2O_3 G (E. Merck, Darmstadt, W. Germany; Brinkmann Instruments, Inc.), or equiv., for TLC.

(b) *Developing solvents for chlorinated pesticides.*— (*1*) n-Heptane, com. grade. (*2*) n-Heptane contg 2% reagent grade acetone.

(c) *Chromogenic agent for chlorinated pesticides.*— Dissolve 0.100 g $AgNO_3$ in 1 ml H_2O, add 20 ml 2-phenoxyethanol (Practical, Eastman Kodak Co.), dil. to 200 ml with acetone, add very small drop 30% H_2O_2, and mix. Store in dark overnight and decant into spray bottle. Discard after 4 days.

(d) *Developing solvents for phosphated pesticides.*— (*1*) *Immobile.*—15 or 20% N,N-dimethylformamide (DMF) in ether. Dil. 75 or 100 ml DMF to 500 ml with ether and mix. (*2*) *Mobile.*—Methylcyclohexane.

(e) *Chromogenic agents for phosphated pesticides.*— (*1*) *Stock dye soln.*—Dissolve 1 g tetrabromophenolphthalein Et ester (Eastman No. 6810) in 100 ml acetone. (*2*) *Dye soln.*—Dil. 10 ml stock dye soln (*1*) to 50 ml with acetone. (*3*) *$AgNO_3$ soln.*—Dissolve

0.5 g $AgNO_3$ in 25 ml H_2O and dil. to 100 ml with acetone. (*4*) *Citric acid soln.*—Dissolve 5 g granular citric acid in 50 ml H_2O and dil. to 100 ml with acetone.

29.004   *Reagents for Paper Chromatography*

(a) *Aqueous system.*—(*1*) *Immobile solvents.*— Mineral oil, USP heavy (corn, cottonseed, tung, or soya oil may also be used). Dissolve 25 ml in Et ether and dil. to 500 ml. (*2*) *Mobile solvents.*— Acetone, 2-methoxyethanol (Me Cellosolve), or MeOH, dil. 75 ml to 100 ml with H_2O; pyridine, dil. 40 ml to 100 ml with H_2O.

(b) *Nonaqueous system.*—(*1*) *Immobile solvents.*— Dil. 175 ml N,N'-dimethylformamide to 500 ml with Et ether; or dil. 50 ml 2-phenoxyethanol to 500 ml with ether. (*2*) *Mobile solvents.*—2,2,4-Trimethylpentane; mixed octanes.

(c) *Chromogenic agent.*—Place 1.7 g $AgNO_3$ in 200 ml vol. flask, dissolve in 5 ml H_2O, add 10 ml 2-phenoxyethanol, and dil. to vol. with reagent grade acetone (add 1 small drop 30% H_2O_2 soln to flask just before dilg to mark).

(d) *Pesticide std solns.*—1 mg/ml in EtOAc or hexane. (1 µl = 1 µg.)

29.005   *General Apparatus*

(a) *High speed blender.*—Waring Blendor, or equiv.

(b) *Chromatographic tube.*—With Teflon stopcocks and coarse fritted plate or glass wool plug; 22 mm id × 300 mm.

(c) *Chromatographic tubes without stopcocks.*—22 mm id × 300 or 400 mm.

(d) *Filter tubes.*—Approx. 22 mm id × 200 mm with short delivery tube and coarse fritted plate or glass wool plug.

(e) *Kuderna-Danish concentrators.*—500 ml with 5 or 10 ml vol. receiving flasks or graduated tubes (Kolmer or Mills type; Kontes Glass Co. No. K-570000, K-621400, or equiv.).

(f) *Separators.*—1000 and 125 ml with Teflon stopcocks.

(g) *Micro-Snyder column.*—2-ball (Kontes Glass Co., No. K-569000, or equiv.).

(h) *Micro-Vigreaux column.*—Kontes Glass Co. No. K-569250, or equiv.

29.006   *Apparatus for Thin Layer Chromatography*

(a) *Desaga/Brinkmann standard model applicator, or equiv.*

(b) *Desaga/Brinkmann standard mounting board, or equiv.*

(c) *Desaga/Brinkmann drying rack.*—Accommodates ten 8 × 8″ plates, or equiv.

(d) *Desaga/Brinkmann model 51 stainless steel desiccating cabinet, or equiv.*

(e) *Window glass.*—8 × 8″, double strength window glass plates of uniform width and thickness; smooth off corners and edges with file or other tool.

(f) *Chromatographic tank and accessories.*—Available from Arthur H. Thomas Co. No. 3106-F05, or equiv., with metal instead of glass troughs.

(g) *Dipping tank and accessories.*—Stainless steel, $8\frac{1}{2} \times 8\frac{1}{2} \times \frac{1}{4}-\frac{3}{16}$″ inside width with metal supports and close-fitting U-shaped cover ca $9 \times \frac{1}{2}$″. Capacity ca 300 ml (Arthur H. Thomas Co. No. 3106-H50, or equiv.).

(h) *Spotting pipets.*—1 μl (Kontes Glass Co. No. K-422520).

(i) *Spray bottle.*—8 oz (Arthur H. Thomas Co. No. 9186-R2 or Scientific Glass Apparatus Co. No. JC 2850, 250 ml).

(j) *Chromatography spray flask.*—250 ml (Microchemical Specialties Co., 1825 Eastshore Hwy, Berkeley, CA 94710, No. S-4530-D).

(k) *Tank liner.*—Cut two pieces, $12\frac{1}{4} \times 8\frac{3}{4}$″, from desk blotter, white or colored, and bend into L-shape to fit tank.

29.007 Apparatus for Paper Chromatography

(a) *Chromatographic chamber.*—For ascending chromatgy with 8 × 8″ sheets. Construct tanks, 9″ long × 9″ high × $3\frac{1}{2}$″ wide, from light stainless steel. From $\frac{1}{4}$″ strips of the metal, form 2 supports and suspend flush with top from notches on sides at corners of tank. (Arthur H. Thomas Co. No. 3106-F10 has been found suitable.)

(b) *Pipets.*—Graduated 0.1 ml Mohr, and 1 μl spotting pipet long enough to reach bottom of conical centrf. tubes (Kontes Glass Co. No. K-422520).

(c) *Strong ultraviolet light source.*—Such as germicidal lamps (General Electric Co., 24400 Highland Rd, Richmond Hts, OH 44143), either (1) two 30 watt, 36″ tubes, mounted in reflectors ca 8″ above papers; or (2) two 15 watt, 18″ tubes, mounted in desk lamp fixture ca 4″ above papers. Must be shielded. Protect eyes and skin at all times.

(d) *Chromatographic paper.*—Whatman No. 1, 8 × 8″ sheets. With hard pencil rule origin line 1″ from bottom edge and make dot at 8–10 evenly spaced positions, with end dots 1″ from sides of paper. With pencil, mark test number or other identification below each dot. Wash papers for aq. systems several times with *distd* H_2O and dry before use. (Papers for nonaq. systems need not be washed.) Any of following technics has been found satisfactory for washing papers:

(1) Hang paper clipped to glass rod in chromatgy tanks with lower edge in trough filled with distd H_2O; when H_2O rises to top of paper, hang paper in hood and let dry. Repeat. Two papers may be clipped to each side of rod (4 papers per rod, 8 per tank).

(2) Wash by adaptation of continuous ascending paper chromatgy, using slit cover for box with 1 sheet per slit (JAOAC **40**, 1013(1957)). Let washing continue overnight; air-dry papers without removing from cover.

(3) Place 10–12 papers on shallow pan, cover with distd H_2O, and let soak ca 15 min; then carefully pour off H_2O. Repeat 8–10 times. Dry papers, and weight pile with glass plate during storage.

(4) Place 10–25 papers in inclined shallow pan and let distd H_2O run slowly in one end and out other 2–3 hr; dry papers.

(5) Place papers in $8\frac{1}{4}$″ square stainless steel funnel with 8″ square perforated removable plate at bottom, let soak in distd H_2O 15–30 min, and drain off H_2O into suction flask; repeat several times, press papers between two 9 × 9″ glass or stainless steel plates, and dry overnight in forced-draft oven at 100–110°.

Paper, especially washed paper, must be dry. (All air-dried papers should be further dried 30 min at 100–110° before use.) If appreciable amt of moisture is in paper, it cannot absorb enough immobile solv. soln, and high R_f values result, as well as faint, indistinct chromatograms. Apparent air dryness is not enough; drying in forced-draft oven is necessary. Once dried, paper may be kept in ordinary dry storage without adverse result. This moisture effect is most critical with nonaq. systems.

29.008 Apparatus for Gas Chromatography

(*See also* Burke and Giuffrida, JAOAC **47**, 326–342 (1964), and Giuffrida, Ives, and Bostwick, *ibid.* **49**, 8–21 (1966).)

Gas chromatgc system when operated with column, (b), and approx. conditions described in *Gas Chromatography*, 29.017, should be capable of producing ca $\frac{1}{2}$ scale deflection for 1 ng heptachlor epoxide by electron capture detection and for 2 ng parathion by KCl-thermionic detection, and should resolve mixt. of heptachlor, aldrin, heptachlor epoxide, ethion, and carbophenothion into sep. peaks. Retention time for aldrin should be ca 4.5 min. Independent power supply, electrometer, and 5 mv recorder are required for each detection system. Other app. and column may be used if they provide equiv. performance.

(a) *Gas chromatograph.*—Barber-Colman Model 5000, or equiv., with electron capture and thermionic detectors, complete with independent power supply, electrometer, and 5 mv recorder for each detector.

(b) *Column.*—Glass, 6′ × 4 mm id packed with 10% DC-200 (w/w) on solid support: (1) 80–100 mesh Chromosorb W HP (Johns-Manville Products, manufacturer, but available thru many GLC distributors); (2) 80–100 mesh Gas-Chrom Q (Applied Science Laboratories, Inc.); (3) Anakrom ABS.

Weigh 2 g Dow Corning 200 silicone fluid (12,500 centistokes) into beaker. Dissolve in $CHCl_3$ and transfer to 300 ml Morton-type flask, using total of ca 100 ml CHCl₃. Add 18 g solid support, (*1*), (*2*) or (*3*), to flask. Swirl, and let stand ca 10 min. Place flask on rotary evaporator and remove solv. slowly with intermittent rotation, using 50° H₂O bath and slight vac. (Foaming may occur initially.) When solids appear damp, increase vac. Remove last traces of CHCl₃ without rotation or by air-drying. Use only free-flowing material for prepn of 4 mm id × 6′ glass column. Use care at all stages of column prepn to prevent fracturing solid support. Condition column at 250–260° with N flow of ca 100 ml/min ≥48 hr or until endrin exhibits single peak.

(c) *Electron capture detector (ECD)*.—For use with gas chromatograph, concentric design, and tritium source (ca 150 mc tritium) (Packard Instrument Co., 2200 Warrenville Rd, Downers Grove, IL 60515, or equiv.). Det. detector operating characteristics as follows: Apply dc voltage to detector. After system becomes stable (overnight), det. current-voltage relationship at various voltages between 200 and 0 v. (Current measurements at voltages of 200, 150, 100, 75, 50, 40, 30, 25, 20, 15, 10, 8, 6, 4, 2, and 1 provide points for smooth curve.) Slightly lower, stable, standing current may be obtained after detector has been at operating temp. several hr. This is probably due to loss of some easily removed radioactive material. Det. and plot response-voltage relationship at 1 × 10⁻⁹ amp full scale sensitivity for 1 ng injections of heptachlor epoxide at same voltages used in obtaining current-voltage curve. Select as operating voltage that voltage at which heptachlor epoxide causes ca 40–50% full scale recorder deflection. Check linearity of system from 0.2 to 2.0 ng heptachlor epoxide.

(d) *Potassium chloride thermionic detector (KClTD)*. — Barber-Colman flame detector, or equiv., modified to incorporate coil with KCl coating prepd as in (*1*) or (*2*). Detector voltage is 300 v dc. Used in dual arrangement with electron capture detector.

All dual detector systems described are capable of comparable performance. In-series, (**h**), arrangement is preferred because of simplicity and ease of operation.

(*1*) *Coil with potassium chloride for in-series dual detector*.—*See* Fig. 29:1 (may be used with all detector arrangements). Wind Pt-Ir wire (B&S gage 26) on 7 mm diam. rod into 2 turn helix so that turns are touching. Approx. 5 mm below helix, continue to wind wire on ⅛″ rod, or rod with same outside diam. as flame jet, making 3-turn spiral. Cut wire so that 7 mm helix is supported 4 mm above flame jet when ⅛″ spiral is slipped over jet. Fill 30 ml size tall-form Pt crucible ca ¼ full with KCl (ACS). Heat with Meker burner until all salt melts. Continue heating until bottom of crucible glows red, imparting pink glow to melt. Remove heat and begin dipping the 2-turn helix of coil into melt at 5 sec intervals as melt cools. (Make sure only 2-turn helix touches melt and

do not raise coil above top of crucible.) When melt is at proper temp., salt clings to coil. Remove coil from melt. Place probe in center of coil while salt is molten. This causes crystn around probe tip. Remove center of coil. Remove any rough edges on coil coating by holding coil in burner flame 1 sec; id of properly coated coil is 5 mm. Position coil over flame jet.

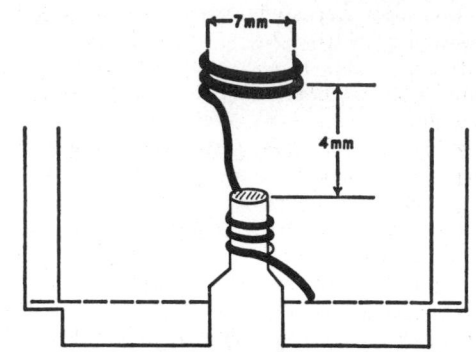

FIG. 29:1—KCl thermionic detector coil for in-series dual detection system

(*2*) *Coil with potassium chloride for parallel and in-series split dual detectors*.—*See* Fig. 29:2. Wind Pt-Ir wire (B&S gage 26) on 5 mm diam rod into 5 turn helix so that turns are close together or touching. Continue to wind wire on ⅛″ rod, or rod having same outside diam. as flame jet, making 3-turn spiral. Cut wire so that 5 mm helix is supported 2 mm above flame jet when ⅛″ spiral is slipped over jet. Grasp formed wire by end opposite 5 mm helix with forceps. Dip 5 mm helix into satd KCl (recrystd twice from H₂O) soln, or apply KCl soln with dropper. Fuse in flame. (*Caution:* Use safety glasses; spattering occurs.) Repeat application of KCl soln 3–4 times until helix is coated with fused KCl. Coating should appear almost crystal clear. Position coil over flame jet.

(e) *Hydrogen*.—From generator or cylinder of compressed H gas (cylinder preferred). Equip cylinder with pressure drop of stainless steel capillary tubing (0.020″ id) to restrict H flow to ca 30 ml/min

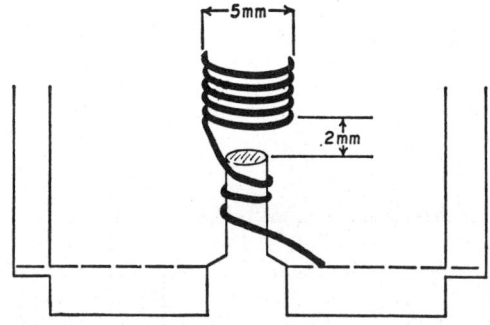

FIG. 29:2—KCl thermionic detector coil for *parallel* and *in-series split* dual detection systems

at 20 lb delivery pressure. Place H source close to detector and use gas lines with min. dead vol. to reduce out-gassing time in lines. (For fine precise control of H flow, insert Nupro Very Fine Metering Valve, "S" series (Nupro Co., 15635 Saranac Rd, Cleveland, OH 44110; Part Number B-15) between exit end of capillary tubing pressure drop and inlet of detector H line. *Caution:* Do not use Nupro valve as shut-off valve. Repeated tightening damages needle.) Use Swagelok fittings for all connections.

(**f**) *Air.*—Min. air requirement for thermionic detector is 300 ml/min. Cylinder of compressed air or aquarium air pump is recommended.

(**g**) *Capillary T-tube.*—(*See* Figs. 29:4 and 29:5.) Prep. 1:1 stream splitter (*B*) for parallel and in-series split dual detection systems. Fit two 1¾″ lengths of stainless steel capillary tubing, 0.010″ id, 1⁄16″ od, into ½″ length of std wall, 1⁄8″ stainless steel tubing. Fit 1″ length of No. 16 hypodermic tubing at right angles in hole drilled into the piece of 1⁄8″ tubing. Silver braze all connections. Prep. capillary T-tube (*E*) for introducing purge gas to parallel system. Fit two 1″ lengths of No. 16 hypodermic tubing into ½″ length of std wall, 1⁄8″ stainless steel tubing. Fit 1″ length of No. 16 hypodermic tubing at right angles in hole drilled into piece of 1⁄8″ tubing. Silver braze as above.

(**h**) *Assembly of in-series dual detection system.*—Assemble as in Fig. 29:3. Introduce column effluent (*A*) of 120 ml/min directly to ECD inlet. Connect ECD outlet directly to KClTD inlet, using No. 16 std wall Teflon tubing.

Note: For in-series (**h**) and in-series split (**i**) operation, thoroly check ECD for gas leaks, particularly at Teflon insulator.

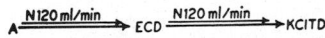

FIG. 29:3—In-series dual detection system

(**i**) *Assembly of in-series split dual detection system.*—Assemble as in Fig. 29:4. Introduce column effluent (*A*) of 120 ml/min directly to ECD inlet. Connect 1:1 stream splitter (*B*) between ECD outlet and KClTD inlet so that only 60 ml N/min enters KClTD and remaining 60 ml N/min exits to atm. Use No. 16 std wall Teflon tubing for all connections. *See Note* in (**h**).

(**j**) *Assembly of parallel dual detection system.*—Assemble as in Fig. 29:5. Split column effluent (*A*) of 120 ml/min by passing thru 1:1 stream splitter

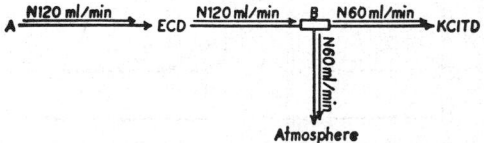

FIG. 29:4—In-series split dual detection system

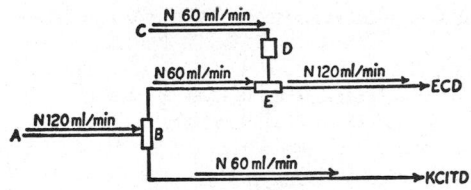

FIG. 29:5—Parallel dual detection system

(*B*) so that each detector receives 60 ml effluent/min. Increase flow to ECD by introducing 60 ml N/min from second N source (*C*) thru capillary T-tube (*E*). Preheat N from *C* by passing thru stainless steel capillary tube (*D*) (0.040″ id) which extends 48″ into column bath and returns to detector bath where addnl 14″ of tubing is coiled into small helix. Connect capillary tubes and splitters to detectors with No. 16 std wall Teflon tubing. Measure flow at each end of splitter (*B*) to ensure exact 1:1 split.

(**k**) *Potassium chloride thermionic detector operation.*—Zero recorder with zero control before detector flame is ignited (no signal). Turn on H (ca 30 ml/min) and ignite flame. Adjust H with flame burning to give baseline current (BLC) of 0.2–0.8 × 10⁻⁸ amp. (Sensitivity to P compds is directly related to KCl temp., which depends on H concn in flame.) Select operational electrometer setting and adjust H concn to obtain 40–50% full scale recorder deflection for 2 ng parathion entering detector. When baseline has stabilized, measure BLC precisely, at electrometer setting of 1×10^{-8} amp full scale. Return to operational electrometer setting and zero recorder pen using current balance control to "buck out" current generated by detector. Check linearity of system from 0.4 to 4.0 ng parathion. Monitor BLC frequently during operation. If drift occurs, readjust H concn to maintain some BLC. *For accurate quantitation, BLC must be identical during chromatography of sample and std.*

Preparation of Sample

29.009 *Fruits and Vegetables*
(*Caution:* See 46.004, 46.011, 46.039, 46.040, 46.043, and 46.073.)

(**a**) *Leafy and cole-type vegetables, firm fruits, and roots.*—Chop or blend representative sample, mix thoroly, and proceed as in (**b**).

(**b**) *Soft fruits.*—Pit, if necessary, and blend representative sample. Weigh 100 g chopped or blended sample into high-speed blender jar, add 200 ml CH₃CN and ca 10 g Celite, and blend 2 min at high speed. Filter with suction thru 12 cm buchner fitted with sharkskin paper into 500 ml suction flask. Transfer filtrate to 250 ml graduated cylinder and record vol. (*F*). Transfer measured filtrate to 1 L separator.

(**c**) *Fruits and other products containing 5–15% sugar.*—Add 200 ml CH₃CN and 50 ml H₂O to 100 g sample in blender and proceed as in (**b**). Transfer

≤250 ml filtered ext (record vol. (*F*)) to 1 L separator.

(d) *Fruits and other products containing 15–30% sugar, e.g., grapes.*—Heat mixt. of 200 ml CH₃CN and 50 ml H₂O to 75°, add to 100 g sample in blender, and immediately proceed as in (b). Before filtered ext cools, transfer ≤250 ml (record vol. (*F*)) to 1 L separator. Let cool to room temp.

Carefully measure 100 ml pet ether and pour into separator. Shake vigorously 1–2 min and add 10 ml satd NaCl soln and 600 ml H₂O. Hold separator in horizontal position and mix vigorously 30–45 sec. Let sep., discard aq. layer, and gently wash solv. layer with two 100 ml portions H₂O. Discard washings, transfer solv. layer to 100 ml g-s cylinder, and record vol. (*P*). Add ca 15 g anhyd. Na₂SO₄ and shake vigorously. Do not let ext remain with Na₂SO₄ >1 hr or losses of chlorinated pesticides by adsorption may result. Transfer soln directly to Florisil column or conc. to 5–10 ml in Kuderna-Danish concentrator for transfer.

29.010   *Fat-Containing Foods*

(After isolation of fat, proceed with CH₃CN partitioning, 29.011.)

(a) *Animal and vegetable fats and oils.*—If solid, warm until liq. and filter thru dry filter.

(b) *Butter.*—Warm at ca 50° until fat seps and decant fat thru dry filter.

(c) *Milk.*—(*Caution: See* **46.011, 46.039, 46.054,** and **46.073.**) To 100 ml fluid milk (dil. evapd milk 1 + 1 with H₂O) in 500 ml centrf. bottle, add 100 ml alcohol or MeOH and ca 1 g Na or K oxalate, and mix. Add 50 ml ether and shake vigorously 1 min; then add 50 ml pet ether and shake vigorously 1 min. Centrf. at ca 1500 rpm ca 5 min. Blow off solv. layer with wash bottle device, **16.177,** *Notes,* into 1 L separator contg 500–600 ml H₂O and 30 ml satd NaCl soln. Re-ext aq. residue twice, shaking vigorously with 50 ml portions ether-pet ether (1 + 1); centrf. and blow off solv. layer into separator after each extn. Mix combined exts and H₂O cautiously. Drain and discard H₂O. Rewash solv. layer twice with 100 ml portions H₂O, discarding H₂O each time. (If emulsions form, add ca 5 ml satd NaCl soln to solv. layer or include with H₂O wash.) Pass ether soln thru column of anhyd. Na₂SO₄, 25 od × 50 mm, and collect eluate in 400 ml beaker. Wash column with small portions pet ether and evap. solv. from combined exts at steam bath temp. under air current to obtain fat.

(d) *Cheese.*—Place 25–100 g (to provide 3 g fat) diced sample, ca 2 g Na or K oxalate, and 100 ml alcohol or MeOH in high-speed blender and blend 2–3 min. (If experience with product indicates emulsions will not be broken by centrfg, add 1 ml H₂O/2 g sample before blending.) Pour into 500 ml centrf. bottle, add 50 ml ether, and shake vigorously 1 min; then add 50 ml pet ether and shake vigorously 1 min

(or divide between two 250 ml bottles and ext each by shaking vigorously 1 min with 25 ml each ether). Proceed as in (c), beginning "Centrf. at ca 1500 rpm ca 5 min."

29.011   *Acetonitrile Partitioning*

(*Caution: See* **46.011, 46.039,** and **46.073.** Different fats and oils may show varying tendencies to emulsion formation.)

Weigh ≤3 g fat into 125 ml separator, and add pet ether so that total vol. of fat and pet ether in separator is 15 ml. Add 30 ml CH₃CN satd with pet ether, **29.002(b),** shake vigorously 1 min, let layers sep., and drain CH₃CN into 1 L separator contg 650 ml H₂O, 40 ml satd NaCl soln, and 100 ml pet ether. Ext pet ether soln in 125 ml separator with 3 addnl 30 ml portions CH₃CN satd with pet ether, shaking vigorously 1 min each time. Combine all exts in the 1 L separator. Hold separator in horizontal position and mix thoroly 30–45 sec. Let layers sep. and drain aq. layer into second 1 L separator. Add 100 ml pet ether to second separator, shake vigorously 15 sec, and let layers sep. Discard aq. layer, combine with pet ether in original separator, and wash with two 100 ml portions H₂O. Discard washings and draw off pet ether layer thru 25 od × 50 mm column of anhyd. Na₂SO₄ into 500 ml Kuderna-Danish concentrator. Rinse separator and then column with three ca 10 ml portions pet ether. Evap. combined ext and rinses to ca 10 ml in Kuderna-Danish concentrator for transfer to Florisil column.

Concentration Technics

29.012   *Purified Extracts*

(Never evap. purified exts to dryness.)

(a) *To approximately 5 ml or more.*—Evap. in Kuderna-Danish concentrator fitted with 3-ball Snyder column and vol. flask or graduated collection tube; 20-mesh boiling chip is necessary.

(b) *To less than 5 ml.*—Evap. to ca 5 ml as in (a). Remove calibrated tube from concentrator and fit tube with 2-ball micro-Snyder or micro-Vigreaux column. Evap. to slightly less than desired vol., permit condensate to drain into tube, and remove column. Min. attainable vol. is 0.2–0.4 ml.

29.013   *Extracts Containing Fats, Oils, or Plant Extractives*

(a) *Kuderna-Danish concentrator.*—Fitted with 3-ball Snyder column and vol. flask or graduated collection tube. Use on steam bath.

(b) *Flash evaporator.*—Keep flask in H₂O bath at room temp.

(c) *Beaker.*—Evap. in beaker on H₂O bath at 35–40° under stream of clean, dry air. Remove from heat and air stream as soon as last of solv. evaps. Let residual H₂O evap. spontaneously. Solvs may be evapd from fats on steam bath for short periods.

Cleanup Technics

29.014 *Florisil Cleanup*

(Caution: See 46.011, 46.039, 46.040, 46.054, and 46.073.)

Prep. 22 mm id Florisil column, 29.005(b), contg 4″, after settling, of activated Florisil topped with ca 0.5″ anhyd. Na_2SO_4. Prewet column with 40–50 ml pet ether. Place Kuderna-Danish concentrator with vol. or graduated collection flask under column to receive eluate. Transfer pet ether ext or conc. to column, letting it pass thru at ≤ 5 ml/min. Rinse containers and Na_2SO_4 with two ca 5 ml portions pet ether, pour rinsings onto column, rinse walls of tube with addnl small portions pet ether, and elute at ca 5 ml/min with 200 ml 6% eluting solv., 29.002(e). Change receivers and elute with 200 ml 15% eluting solv., 29.002(f), at ca 5 ml/min. Change receivers and elute with 200 ml 50% eluting solv., 29.002(g), at ca 5 ml/min.

Conc. each eluate to suitable definite vol. in Kuderna-Danish evaporator app. When vol. <5 ml is needed, use 2-ball micro-Snyder or micro-Vigreaux column.

First eluate (6%) contains *chlorinated pesticides* (aldrin, BHC, DDE, DDD (TDE), *o,p'*- and *p,p'*-DDT, heptachlor, heptachlor epoxide, lindane, and methoxychlor) and *phosphated pesticides* (carbophenothion, ethion, and ronnel) and is usually suitable for GLC directly. If further cleanup is necessary, repeat Florisil cleanup, using new column. Second eluate (15%) contains *chlorinated pesticides* (dieldrin and endrin) and *phosphated pesticides* (Diazinon, Me parathion, and parathion). If further cleanup is necessary, det. phosphated pesticides by GLC and TLC; then proceed with *Magnesia Cleanup*, 29.015, and/or *Saponification*, 29.016, which are applicable only to chlorinated pesticides in 15% eluate (phosphated pesticides are degraded). Third eluate (50%) contains *phosphated pesticide* malathion.

Calculation for fruits and vegetables.—Calc. g sample in eluate as $S \times (F/T) \times (P/100)$; where S = g sample taken; F = vol. filtrate; T = total vol. (ml H_2O in sample + ml CH_3CN added − correction in ml for vol. contraction); P = ml pet ether ext; and 100 = ml pet ether into which residues were partitioned. When 50 ml H_2O is added to CH_3CN for extn of high sugar products, total vol., T, is increased by 45, *i.e.*, T = 325 instead of 280 for samples contg 85% H_2O.

Example: 100 g sample contains 85 g H_2O; 200 ml CH_3CN is added; vol. contraction is 5 ml. Total vol., T, is 280 ml. If vol. filtrate is 235 ml, vol. pet ether ext is 85 ml, and residue is transferred to 100 ml pet ether, then $100 \times (235/280) \times (85/100) = 75$ g sample in concd eluate.

Consult refs on food composition for av. H_2O content. Water content of most fresh fruits and vegetables may be assumed to be 85%.

29.015 *Magnesia Cleanup*

(Applicable only to chlorinated pesticides in 15% eluate when addnl cleanup is necessary.)

Transfer ca 10 g MgO-Celite mixt., 29.002(l), to chromatgc tube without stopcock, 29.005(c), using vac. to pack. Prewash with ca 40 ml pet ether, discard prewash, and place Kuderna-Danish receiver under column. Transfer 15% Florisil eluate, concd to ca 5 ml, to column, rinsing with small portions pet ether. Force pet ether into column with slight vac. or pressure. Then elute with 100 ml pet ether. Conc. eluate to suitable vol. Proceed with detn, or saponification, if required.

29.016 *Saponification*

(Applicable only to chlorinated pesticides in 15% eluate if MgO-Celite eluate is not substantially free from oily materials.)

Transfer concd eluate to 125 ml g-s flask, rinsing with pet ether, and evap. just to dryness. Add 20 ml 2% alc. NaOH or KOH, 29.002(d), and reflux 30 min under air condenser. Transfer to 125 ml separator and rinse flask with three 10 ml portions pet ether, transferring each to separator. Add 20 ml H_2O and shake vigorously. Drain aq. layer into second separator contg 20 ml pet ether, shake vigorously, let sep., discard aq. layer, and add pet ether to first separator. Wash combined pet ether exts with three 20 ml portions aq. alcohol (1 + 1). (If initial aq. alcohol wash causes heavy emulsions, use H_2O only for addnl washes.) Discard aq. alcohol and dry pet ether layer thru 25 od × 50 mm column of anhyd. Na_2SO_4, rinsing with pet ether. Conc. solv., and rechromatograph on MgO-Celite column.

Detection Methods

29.017 *Gas Chromatography—Tentative Identification and Quantitative Measurement*

Inject suitable aliquot (3–8 μl) of concd eluate from Florisil or MgO-Celite column contg quantity of pesticide within linear range into gas chromatograph, 29.008, using 10 μl syringe. Tentatively identify residue peaks on basis of retention times. Measure area under pesticide residue peak and compare to area obtained from known quantity of appropriate std pesticide. For most accurate measurement, residue and std peaks should be of similar size. Chromatograph std pesticide immediately after sample analysis.

(a) *Recommended operating conditions for 10% DC-200 column.*—Glass column, 4 mm id × 6'. Injection temp., 225°; column temp., 200°; detector bath temp., 210° max.; carrier gas flow, 120 ml N/min.

(b) *Electron capture detection (ECD).*—(Use for detn of chlorinated pesticides in fruits, vegetables, and food contg fats.) Select as operating voltage that voltage (ca 50 v dc) at which 1 ng heptachlor epoxide produces 40–50% full scale recorder deflection at 1×10^{-9} amp full scale sensitivity.

(c) *Potassium chloride thermionic and electron capture dual detection.*—(Use one of the 3 dual detection systems specified in **29.008**(h), (i), (j), for detn of phosphated and chlorinated pesticides in fruits and vegetables. In-series system, (h), is preferred because of simplicity and ease of operation.) (*1*) *In-series dual detection.*—Operate ECD as in (b). For KClTD, adjust H flow producing $0.2–0.8 \times 10^{-8}$ amp baseline current and select electrometer setting at which 2 ng parathion produces 40–50% full scale recorder deflection. (*2*) *In-series split dual detection.*—Same as (*3*), *Parallel*, except ECD receives entire injection and KClTD receives one-half amt injected into column. (*3*) *Parallel dual detection.*—Same as (*1*), *In-series dual*, except column effluent is split; therefore, inject twice as much sample to obtain desired examination sensitivity.

Thin Layer Chromatography—Confirmation of Identity

Method I

(Applicable to chlorinated and phosphated pesticides except where indicated)

29.018　　　　*Preparation of Adsorbent Layer*

Before coating, wash plates in hot soapy water and thoroly rinse with distilled H_2O. Press plates snugly into position on mounting board that has retaining ledge on one side and one end. Plastic board is mounted so that long side with raised ledge faces operator while short side with ledge is to right of operator. Before coating, wipe plates with few ml alcohol. Position applicator, trough open, with left edge $\frac{1}{4}''$ in from edge of first plate to be coated.

To coat 5 plates, weigh 30 g Al_2O_3 G, **29.003**(a), into 250 ml $\overline{S}$ erlenmeyer. Add 50 ml H_2O, stopper, and shake moderately 45 sec. Violent shaking produces bubbles, resulting in "pock-marked" layer.

Suspensions that contain adsorbents with binders set rapidly, and entire operation from prepn of slurry to final coating must be completed within 2 min.

After shaking, immediately pour slurry into applicator chamber. Rotate chamber by turning large lever handle thru 180°. After few sec, slurry begins to flow out of exit slit. Grasp applicator with both hands and pull it manually with steady motion across series of plates. Approx. 5 sec is required for actual coating operation. Immediately after application, tap edge of mounting board or shake entire board gently to smooth out slight ripples or imperfections in wet coating.

Let coated plates dry in position on mounting board 15 min. Then dry plates in forced-draft oven 30 min at 80°. Remove plates and cool.

Examine plates carefully in transmitted and reflected light for imperfections or irregularities in coating. Discard any plates showing extensive rippling or mottling of layer.

Prep. 5 more plates while first set is drying. Be sure applicator is thoroly cleaned and dried before reusing. The 10 coated and dried plates may be prewashed immediately.

29.019　　　　*Prewashing of Adsorbent Layer*

Scrape $\frac{1}{2}''$ of adsorbent off edge of plate with razor blade. Pour 15 ml 50% aq. acetone into metal trough inside chromatgc tank. Cut out $\frac{3}{4} \times 8''$ strip of Whatman No. 1 filter paper, wet with solv., and place over scraped off portion with $\frac{1}{4}''$ overlapping adsorbent layer. Place plate in chromatgc tank, seal tank with masking tape, and develop with 50% aq. acetone to within 1.5″ from top of plate (75–90 min). Remove plate from tank, remove filter paper wick, invert plate, and dry in hood 5 min. Dry plate 45 min at 80°. Remove plate from oven, cool, and store in desiccator until needed. Use prepd plates within 1 week after prepn.

29.020　　　　*Sample Spotting*

Make pencil mark 1.5″ from bottom of plate at both sides. Imaginary line between the two points indicates sample spotting or origin "line." Draw line (which removes coating) completely across plate 5.5″ from bottom edge; this line represents solv. front after development. On lower edge of adsorbent starting 0.75″ in from left edge of plate, make 18 marks with pencil at 6/16″ intervals. (Fewer marks with longer intervals may be used, if desired. Marks serve as horizontal guides to sample application. Identity of samples and stds may be etched directly into adsorbent layer above these marks above solv. front line.)

Imaginary spotting "line" is actually shadow line cast by strong light source from wooden ruler supported 1″ above plate. Align ruler shadow on the two 1.5″ marks on either edge of plate. Shadow line and 18 marks, resp., serve as vertical and horizontal guides for sample application.

For optimum semiquant. detn, spot aliquot of sample as follows:

(a) *Chlorinated pesticides.*—Adjust aliquot to give residue spot within range 0.005–0.1 μg. Spot stds and std mixts at 0.002, 0.005, 0.01, 0.02, 0.05, 0.1, and 0.2 μg. Sample spots >0.2 μg are difficult to det. quant. and <0.005 μg may be difficult to distinguish. Spot all 6% Florisil eluates on one plate and 15% Florisil eluates on another plate.

(b) *Phosphated pesticides.*—Adjust aliquots of sample and stds to give spot within range 0.1–0.5 μg. Spot 6, 15, and 50% Florisil eluates on same plate. Ronnel, ethion, and carbophenothion are not resolved; spot each std sep. Spot Diazinon, Me parathion, and malathion sep. or as mixt.

Vol. of sample ext spotted should be ≤10 μl, if possible, and spotting should be done repeatedly with 1, 2, or 3 μl Kontes spotting pipet. Spot std and sample solns with same pipet. For best results, keep size of spotted sample as small as possible.

29.021 *Development*

(a) *Chlorinated pesticides.*—Place liners and metal trough in tank, **29.006**(f). Presat. liner by pouring 75 ml developing solv., **29.003**(b), into bottom of tank ≥30 min before developing plate. Presatn decreases development time and improves uniformity of R_f values.

For plates spotted with 6% Florisil eluates, pour 50 ml *n*-heptane into trough. Place lower edge of plate in metal trough with top of plate leaning against side of tank. Place glass cover plate on tank and seal with masking tape.

For plates spotted with 15% Florisil eluates, use acetone-*n*-heptane (2 + 98) as developing solv.

(b) *Phosphated pesticides.*—Prep. chromatgc tank, **29.006**(f), after samples and stds have been spotted on plate. Place liners and metal trough in tank. Pour 50 ml methylcyclohexane, **29.003**(d)(*2*), into trough, and 75 ml into bottom of tank. Quickly fill dipping tank, **29.006**(g), to within 1.5–2″ from top with immobile solv., **29.003**(d)(*1*). Invert plate and dip with uncoated side touching back wall of tank to prevent front wall from scraping the adsorbent layer during dipping operation. Dip plate *just* to spotting line, remove, and immediately place in metal trough, with top portion of plate leaning against side of tank. Place glass cover plate on tank and seal with masking tape.

When solv. front in (a) or (b) *just* reaches pencil line 10 cm above spotting "line," remove plate and dry in hood 5 min.

29.022 *Spraying*

(Caution: See **46.017**.)

(a) *Chlorinated pesticides.*—Support plate on one side and spray fairly heavily with chromogenic agent, **29.003**(c), using lateral motions of spray bottle perpendicular to direction of solv. flow. Spray until plate appears translucent or soaked with reagent. Underspraying will result in poor sensitivity. After spraying, dry plate in hood 15 min; then immediately place under UV light source and proceed as in **29.023**.

(b) *Phosphated pesticides.*—Immediately spray plate moderately heavily and uniformly with dye soln, **29.003**(e)(*2*), using lateral motions of spray flask, **29.006**(j), perpendicular to direction of solv. flow. Plate should be vivid blue after spraying. Using spray bottle, **29.006**(i), overspray plate lightly and uniformly with AgNO₃ soln, **29.003**(e)(*3*) (at this point plate should be bluish purple and spots should be discernible).

After 2 min, overspray plate moderately and uniformly with citric acid soln, **29.003**(e)(*4*), using spray bottle, **29.006**(i). After spraying, thiophosphate pesticides should immediately appear as vivid blue or purple spots against yellow background. Color of spots reaches max. intensity ca 5–10 min after citric acid spraying. After ca 10 min, background begins to change from yellow to greenish blue, masking spots. At this point, respraying plate with citric acid soln changes background back to yellow and makes spots stand out as well as or better than originally. Evaluate chromatogram ≤10 min after respraying. Blue spots fade completely and irreversibly after 30–40 min from time of original citric acid spraying.

29.023 *Exposure*

(Caution: See **46.016**.)

Expose plate to UV light until spot for std of lowest concn appears; 5 ng of most chlorinated org. pesticides should be visible after 15–20 min exposure with equipment described under **29.007**(c). Exposure times >30 min will not harm plates. For best results, place plates 3″ from bottom edge of lamps.

Method II
(Applicable only to chlorinated pesticides)

29.024 *Preparation of Adsorbent Layer*

Weigh 40 g Al₂O₃ G, **29.003**(a), into 500 ml centrf. bottle. Add 80 ml 0.2% HNO₃, shake well, and centrf. at ca 1200 rpm 1–2 min. Decant supernatant into 100 ml graduated cylinder, and record vol. (35–40 ml should be recovered). Add 80 ml H₂O, breaking up material on bottom of centrf. bottle with glass rod, if necessary. Shake well and centrf. as before. Decant and record vol. supernatant recovered (60–70 ml). Add 2 addnl 80 ml portions H₂O, shake well, centrf., and decant.

Weigh the Al₂O₃ and H₂O that has been retained. (Wt should be ca 100 g.) Add 10 ml 1% AgNO₃ soln and enough H₂O to make total wt 120–130 g. Shake well, place in applicator, and prep. plates as in **29.018**. Let plates air-dry in position on mounting board 15 min. Place in metal drying rack, in vertical position, 30 min at 100°.

29.025 *Sample Spotting*

Spot as in **29.020**. Draw line across plate 1.5″ from top (which removes coating). Next, scrape 0.25″ of coating from each side of plate. (Irregularities in thickness of coating on these outer edges cause uneven flow of mobile solv.) Make pencil mark at each side of layer 1″ from bottom of plate; imaginary line between these 2 points indicates sample spotting line. Spot samples and stds at ⁵⁄₁₆″ intervals.

29.026 *Development and Exposure of Plates*
(Caution: See **46.016**.)

Develop plates as in **29.021**, except use only 25–30 ml mobile solv. in trough, since spotting line has been lowered to 1″. Use *n*-heptane to develop 6% eluates, and acetone-*n*-heptane (2 + 98) for 15% eluates.

Plates may be exposed to UV light after short drying period (ca 5 min) after removal from tank. Spots of aldrin, DDE, and isomers of DDT will appear within 5–10 min after exposure; lindane, endrin, dieldrin, and all others will require more time. Plates may be exposed 1.5–2 hr without appreciable darkening of background.

Paper Chromatography
29.027   *Technic (2)*

(Once paper chromatgy is started, spot, develop, spray with chromogenic agent, and expose to UV light without delay; do not interrupt overnight. *Caution: See* **46.016**.)

Transfer 10 ml aliquot from column cleanup to 15 ml conical centrf. tube. (With most pesticides upper limit for good spots is ca 10 μg and optimum is ca 2 μg.) Evap. under gentle air stream at room temp. just to dryness (caution). Wash down sides of tube with 0.5 ml ether, evap., and again wash down with 0.1–0.2 ml ether. Evap., take up residue (usually not visible) with 0.03–0.04 ml ether, and transfer to one of dots on origin line of chromatogram, **29.007**(d), using 1 μl pipet repeatedly, until all residue is placed on 1 spot. Let spot dry after each application to restrict its size. Wash tube again with 0.03–0.04 ml ether and transfer to same spot.

Transfer std solns of known pesticides to other dots on same paper, adjacent to sample spots. (1 full μl pipet contains 1 μg compd. Use addnl pipetfuls to increase quantity of pesticide on 1 spot.) For identification place several compds on sep. dots on same paper as unknown. For semiquant. estn place different quantities of same compd, varying by 1–2 μg intervals, on sep. dots. (Experience and preceding analyses are guide to pesticide residues to be expected and thus to choice of pesticides to be used as stds for identification. If R_f values differ enough, several different pesticides may be placed on same dot; use 2–5 μg per pesticide.)

After samples and stds are spotted on paper, put 50 ml mobile solv. in trough; then fill dipping tank, **29.006**(g), with immobile solv. Hold paper by bottom, using spring clip, immerse it top down into soln of immobile solv. just to origin line, and immediately remove it. For aq. system, hang paper to dry 2–3 min; while paper is drying, clip glass rod, which supports paper in tank, to top of paper (opposite origin line). In nonaq. system, when paper is dipped in immobile solv., place in mobile solv. in chromatgc tanks as quickly as possible, allowing no time for drying. (As ether evaps, it may condense moisture on paper, which interferes with ability of pesticides to dissolve in immobile solv. *Excessive humidity and temp. tend to result in high R_f values and faint indistinct chromatograms*.) Hang paper in tank so that origin end dips ca ½″ into trough filled with mobile solv. Place glass plate on top of tank and seal with masking tape.

When mobile solv. has risen thru paper to within 1″ of top (1.5–4 hr, depending on solv. system used), unseal tank, mark solv. front, and hang paper up until it appears dry. Uniformly spray dry paper with chromogenic agent (do not spray so heavily that it

runs down paper). Dry paper until most of solv. is removed, and expose both sides to UV light until reduced Ag spots are developed. (Darkening of chromatogram background during storage may be largely prevented by washing finished chromatogram, after exposure to UV light, as follows: Suspend paper from glass rod with 3 or 4 clips, and thoroly play gentle stream of distd H_2O on both sides of sheet. Let suspended papers hang until dry (papers are very fragile when wet).)

It is advisable to evaluate chromatograms before washing them. Compare location, size, and intensity of spots from unknown with those from stds for identification and semiquant. estn of pesticides. Always chromatograph knowns and unknowns on same paper.

MULTIPLE RESIDUE METHOD FOR PHOSPHATED PESTICIDES (3)— OFFICIAL FIRST ACTION

(Sweep codistillation cleanup for parent organophosphate residues of carbophenothion, O,O-diethyl-O-(2-isopropyl-4-methyl-6-pyrimidinyl) phosphorothioate (Diazinon®), ethion, malathion, Me parathion, and parathion in kale, endive, carrots, lettuce, apples, potatoes, and strawberries (fresh or non-sugared frozen); this cleanup is not adequate for electron capture gas chromatgc detector. Use only with KCl thermionic detector.)

29.028   *Reagents*

(a) *Ethyl acetate.*—Redistd from glass (available from Burdick and Jackson Laboratories, Inc.). Check suitability of reagent by concg 100 ml to 2 ml. Inject 5 μl into GLC (KCl thermionic detector) with operating conditions specified in **29.029**(h). Chromatogram should show no peaks to 20 min with chart speed of 1″/2 min.

(b) *Pesticide std soln.*—Prep. EtOAc soln contg 1 μg/ml of each of following: carbophenothion, Diazinon, ethion, malathion, Me parathion, and parathion.

29.029   *Materials and Apparatus*

(a) *Glass wool.*—Silanized (available from Applied Science Laboratories, Inc.).

(b) *Anakrom ABS.*—80–90 mesh. Remove fines by stirring with EtOAc, decanting several times, and drying.

(c) *Teflon tubing.*—AWG No. 16, std, natural.

(d) *Disposable glass capillary pipets.*—145 mm long, 6 mm id, with capillary stem (Arthur H. Thomas Co. No. 8216-D, or equiv.).

(e) *Syringes.*—1 ml Tuberculin Luer-Lok and 2 ml Luer-Lok with Luer-Lok 2″ No. 25G needles.

(f) *High-speed blender.*—400 ml capacity. Omnimixer (available from Ivan Sorvall, Inc., Pearl St, Norwalk, CT 06852, or equiv.).

(g) *Sweep co-distillation apparatus.*—See Fig. 29:6. Following tubes are required: (*1*) *Storherr tube.*—24.5 cm long, 6 mm id (Kontes Glass Co., No. F-1423A, or equiv.). (*2*) *Concentrating tube.*—10 ml calibrated to 0.5 ml, ⚵ 19/22 Mills tube (Kontes Glass Co., No. K-570050, 1025, or equiv.). (*3*) *Adapter for extension of concentration tube.*—7 cm long, ⚵ 19/22 (Kontes No. K-57010 (K-50075 part 355), or equiv.). Complete app. available from Kontes Glass Co. as No. K-500500.

(**h**) *Gas chromatograph with potassium chloride thermionic detector.*—Barber-Colman Co. Model 5000, or equiv., with thermionic detector and 5 mv detector.

Following conditions are important in operation of GLC and KCl thermionic detector:

(*1*) Every day before starting work change silanized glass wool plug insert in injection port of GLC column. Remove and replace only that portion affected by syringe.

(*2*) Every week before starting work reheat KCl spiral over gas burner and reinsert into detector. Detector must then equilibrate ca 2 hr before use.

(**i**) *Column.*—10% DC 200 on 60–100 mesh Chromosorb W HP in glass column 6' × 4 mm id; *see* **29.008**(b). Recommended operating conditions: N flow 60 ml/min; temps: injection 225°, column 205°, detector 210°. Adjust column temp. to give retention time for parathion of ca 5 min.

(**j**) *Potassium chloride thermionic detector* (*KClTD*).—*See* **29.008**(d)(*1*) or (*2*), (**e**), (**f**), and (**k**).

29.030   *Preparation of Apparatus*

App. is constructed in 3 parts: removable Storherr tube, permanent heating coil, and sampling collector (*see* Fig. 29:6). Com. model is available from Kontes Glass Co.

(**a**) *Preparation of removable Storherr tube.*—Pack Storherr tube with silanized glass wool. Use silanized glass wool as received. Do not pack glass wool too tightly; otherwise removal for cleaning is difficult. Only 5–6" portion from injection end requires packing. Insert injection septum and two 1-hole septums. Tube is now ready for use. Use clean tube for each sample. Clean tubes thoroly with soap and H_2O after use, rinse with acetone, and dry. Soak tubes difficult to clean in $K_2Cr_2O_7$-H_2SO_4 soln before cleaning with soap and H_2O.

(**b**) *Preparation of permanent heating coil.*—Attach bimetallic wires of calibrated pyrometer directly to outside middle area of Cu tube (length 8" × $\frac{7}{16}$" id). (Thermometer with stem covered with Al foil may also be used for temp. measurement.) Wrap heating tape (2' × 0.5") uniformly around outside of

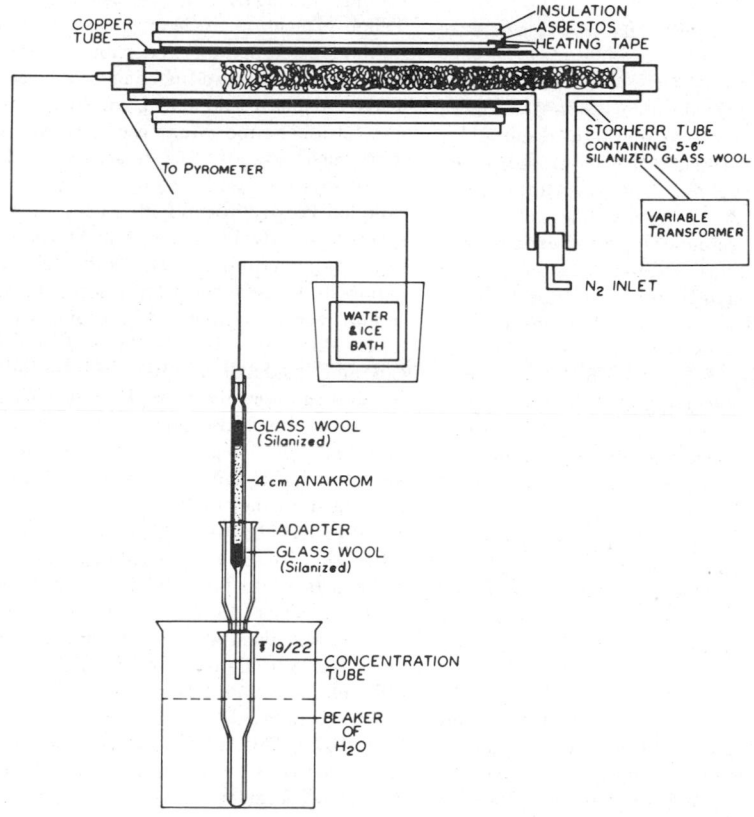

FIG. 29:6—Sweep co-distillation apparatus

Cu tubing and over bimetallic wires or thermometer, and secure ends. Cover heating tape with asbestos tape and secure with glass tape or glass thread. Cover asbestos with several layers of Al foil and secure with tape.

Place heating assembly on ring stand, using asbestos-covered 3-prong clamp. Orient and use heating coil in near horizontal position. Attach heating tape leads to variable transformer. Adjust transformer so pyrometer reads 180–185°. Use this setting or temp. for all crop cleanup.

Add N flow, 600 ml/min, to sidearm of Storherr tube. (For N pressure gage to give meaningful readings, add stainless steel capillary tube to reduce gas flow. Connect capillary tube directly to 1-hole septum in sidearm of tube with short length Teflon tubing.) Measure N flow with gas flow gage, and calibrate pressure regulator gage by this means.

(c) *Sample distillate collector.*—Construct in 3 parts: cooling coil, scrubber tube, and concn tube with extended adapter.

(1) *Cooling coil.*— Cut 120 cm length of Teflon tubing. Form this tubing into three 7 cm diam. loops having 2 arms of ca 20 cm lengths. Attach Teflon cooling coil and 1-hole septum directly to Storherr tube. Place coils in 250 ml beaker contg ice and H₂O. Place 250 ml beaker inside 400 ml beaker for insulation.

(2) *Scrubber tube.*—Insert silanized glass wool plug in constricted end of disposable pipet. On outside of pipet place marks 4 and 6 cm above top of glass wool plug. Add Anakrom ABS to 6 cm mark and pack Anakrom to 4 cm mark by compressing with 3 mm rod. Place silanized glass wool plug on top of packed Anakrom and 1-hole septum in pipet top. Connect exit arm of Teflon cooling coil directly into 1-hole septum in scrubber tube and extending ca ¾" below septum. Secure scrubber tube on sep. ring stand with 3-prong clamp. Scrubber tube must be lower than cooling bath, especially in rinsing step.

(3) *Concentration tubes.*—Use 10 ml calibrated Mills tubes. Adapter, (g)(3), is needed for insertion into concn tube to prevent splash during sweep and rinsing steps. Place tip of scrubber thru adapter and into concn tube. If possible, place scrubber tip against wall of concn tube. Hold tube in place with clamp.

Adjust heat to 180–185° and N flow to 600 ml/min (measure before entering Storherr tube). Flush several 0.5 ml EtOAc injections thru entire system, using 2 ml syringe (used for all rinsings). Replace concn tube with clean tube and insert adapter; assembly is ready for use.

29.031   *Extraction*

Ext all crops with EtOAc in *exact* order as follows: To high-speed blender, add 25 g chopped sample, 125 ml EtOAc from pipet, and 25 g anhyd. granular Na₂SO₄. Blend 5 min at slow speed; then 5 min at high speed with mixer cup immersed in ice-H₂O

bath. Decant liq. thru 1" silanized glass wool plug contained in short glass column. (Do not add solids to glass wool plug.) Collect EtOAc ext (ca 100 ml) in 125 ml flask or bottle. Remove 50 ml aliquot (equiv. to 10 g original sample) and place in Kuderna-Danish concentrator with Snyder column, calibrated Mills tube, or 5 ml receiving flask, and conc. to ca 5.0 ml. Adjust vol. to exactly 5.0 ml, using air jet or adding EtOAc. Use 1 ml aliquots (2 g sample) for sweep co-distn cleanup.

Store all stds and crop solns at 0° or below when not in use. Warm to room temp. ca 1 hr prior to use.

29.032   *Sweep Co-Distillation Cleanup*

Assemble app. as in Fig. 29:6, except position Storherr tube and heating unit so exit end of Storherr tube is ca 10° below horizontal to avoid backup of sample into N inlet arm. If sample backs up, *discard detn.* Check temp. (180–185°), N flow (600 ml/min), and receiver tube. Inject 1 ml (2 g) sample, using 1 ml Luer-Lok tuberculin syringe. Immediately follow sample with injection of 0.5 ml EtOAc sweeping solv. and repeat 0.5 ml EtOAc injection every 3 min for 21 min. After last injection wait 1 min until solv. has cleared cooling coil and scrubber tube; then disconnect cooling coil arm with septum from Storherr tube. Disconnect septum with attached cooling coil arm from scrubber tube and rinse ¾" Teflon projection, collecting rinse in scrubber tube (still in position in concn tube). With septums in place on disconnected cooling coil arms, *reverse* coil arms and place that end formerly in Storherr tube into scrubber tube. Make certain that Teflon tubing in this arm extends ¾" into scrubber tube below inserted septum (similar to position when cleaning up sample). Slowly inject 1 ml EtOAc rinse from 2 ml syringe directly into open end of cooling coil arm formerly in scrubber tube. Gently force rinse, using N flow from disconnected Storherr tube, thru cooling coil into scrubber tube and into concn tube. Repeat 1 ml EtOAc rinse 1–2 addnl times. Rinse scrubber tip end and inside of adapter, remove scrubber, disconnect adapter, and rinse ⚗ joint. Collect all rinses in concn tube. Rinse down sides of concn tube and conc. to 1 ml, using N or air jet. Prevent H₂O condensation inside tubes by placing tube in room temp. H₂O bath during this step. If cleaned up soln is too concd for GLC detn (>2 µg/ml), dil. soln to 5 or 10 ml mark with EtOAc. If calibrations of Mills tube are incorrect (most usually are except for 1 ml mark), quant. transfer the concd soln to 5 or 10 ml vol. flask, using disposable pipet with attached rubber bulb. Rinse inside of tube with EtOAc and transfer rinse in same pipet. Repeat this rinse of tube and pipet several times; then rinse inside of pipet into flask, using EtOAc. Dil. to vol. Further diln with EtOAc or concn may be necessary to bring concn within measurement range.

Anakrom scrubber tube is used repeatedly without change. Final EtOAc rinses after each run keep it clean. However, if Anakrom becomes discolored, prep. new tube.

29.033 Determination by Gas-Liquid Chromatography

Operate chromatograph under conditions specified for column, 29.029(i). Inject 3–8 μl aliquot concd cleaned up soln contg amt pesticide within linear range of gas chromatgc system, (h), using 10 μl syringe. Tentatively identify residue peaks on basis of retention times. Det. amt of pesticide by comparing area under peak with that from known amt of appropriate std pesticide. For accurate detn, baseline current of sample and std must be identical during chromatgy.

Injections <3 μl are difficult to reproduce; injections >8 μl may cause flame blow-out. Sample wt is not critical—use <1 mg or several hundred mg injections. Inject appropriate std immediately after every sample. Peak ht also may be used for detn, but only if ht of ref. std is ca same ht as sample unknown (width of base should then be same).

Single Sweep Oscillographic Polarographic Confirmatory Method (4)—Official First Action

(Applicable to Diazinon, malathion, Me parathion, and parathion)

29.034 Apparatus

(Wash all glassware with hot HNO_3 (1 + 1) and rinse with H_2O.)

(a) *Polarograph.*—Fast sweep instrument such as Polarotrace K1000, Davis Differential Cathode-Ray Polarotrace A1660, or equiv., with necessary accessories (cells, electrodes, Hg, capillaries, etc.).

(b) *Silver wire electrode.*—Deposit very thin coating of AgCl on No. 20 or 22 gage Ag wire as follows: Dip wire in 10% HNO_3, rinse in H_2O, and then let stand 10 min in $1N$ HCl.

29.035 Reagents

(Burdick and Jackson Laboratories, Inc. solvs have been found satisfactory without addnl distn.)

(a) *Acetonitrile.*—Distd in glass at 82±1°.

(b) *Acetone.* — Distill at 56.5° with 0.25 g $KMnO_4$/L. Distn must be performed as directed.

(c) *Ethyl acetate.*—Distd in glass at 77±1°.

(d) *Petroleum ether.*—Distd in glass at 30–60°.

(e) *Nitrogen.*—Prepurified, H_2O-pumped.

(f) *Tetramethyl ammonium bromide.*—Eastman White Label No. 670, or equiv.

(g) *Electrolyte solns.*—(1) For Diazinon.—Dissolve 7.7 g Me_4NBr in 300 ml H_2O. Add 115 ml HOAc and dil. to 500 ml with H_2O. (2) For malathion.—Dissolve 15.4 g Me_4NBr in 300 ml H_2O. Add 0.2 g LiCl and 4.1 ml HCl, and dil. to 500 ml with H_2O. (3) For methyl parathion and parathion.—Dissolve 2.2 g $NaOAc.3H_2O$ and 1.17 g NaCl in 100 ml H_2O and adjust to pH 4.8 with HOAc, using pH meter.

(h) *Pesticide std solns.*—(1) Stock solns.—Prep. individual solns contg 1.00 mg pesticide/ml EtOAc.

Store at 0°. (2) *Intermediate solns.*—0.2 mg/ml. Transfer 5 ml stock soln to 25 ml vol. flask and dil. to vol. with pet ether for Diazinon, MeOH for malathion, and acetone for Me parathion and parathion.

29.036 Preparation of Standard Curves

(a) *Diazinon.*—Transfer 0.0, 1.0, 2.0, 3.0, 4.0, and 5.0 ml intermediate std soln of Diazinon to individual 100 ml vol. flasks and dil. to vol. with pet ether. Transfer 1.0 ml of each soln to sep. 50 ml erlenmeyers and evap. to incipient dryness under gentle jet of dry air. Evap. remaining solv. with warmth of hand. Dissolve residue in 5.0 ml electrolyte soln (g)(1). Transfer soln to polarographic cell, adjust to 25±1°, and bubble N thru soln 5 min. Polarograph between −0.70 and −1.2 v against either Hg pool or Ag wire ref. electrode.

Peak potential for Diazinon at 25° is −0.90±0.05 v against either electrode. Plot μg diazinon/ml cell soln against peak ht in units × sensitivity factor.

(b) *Malathion.*—Transfer 0.0, 1.0, 2.0, 3.0, 4.0, and 5.0 ml intermediate std soln of malathion to individual 25 ml vol. flasks and dil. to vol. with MeOH. Transfer 2.0 ml of each soln to sep. 50 ml erlenmeyers and add 1.0 ml 0.1N KOH. After 3 min, add 2.0 ml electrolyte soln (g)(2), mix well, and let stand 5 min. Transfer to polarographic cell, adjust to 25±1°, and bubble N thru soln 5 min. Polarograph between −0.5 and −1.0 v against either Hg pool or Ag wire electrode.

Peak potential for malathion at 25° is −0.82 ±0.05 v against Ag wire and −0.85±0.05 v against Hg pool ref. electrodes. Plot μg malathion/ml cell soln against peak ht in units × sensitivity factor. (*Note:* Compd actually polarographed is fumaric acid resulting from basic hydrolysis of malathion.)

(c) *Parathion and methyl parathion.*—Transfer 0.0, 1.0, 2.0, 3.0, 4.0, and 5.0 ml intermediate parathion (or Me parathion) std soln to individual 100 ml flasks and dil. to vol. with acetone. Transfer 5.0 ml aliquots of each soln to sep. 50 ml erlenmeyers, add 5.0 ml electrolyte soln (g)(3), mix well, and transfer ca 5 ml to polarographic cell. Adjust to 25±1°, bubble N thru soln 5 min, and polarograph between −0.4 and −0.9 v against either Hg pool or Ag wire ref. electrode.

Peak potential for parathion and Me parathion at 25° is −0.68±0.05 v against Hg pool and −0.70 ±0.05 v against Ag wire ref. electrodes. Plot μg pesticide/ml cell soln (10 ml) against peak ht in units × sensitivity factor. Cell soln vol. = 5 ml sample soln + 5 ml electrolyte soln.

29.037 Preparation of Sample Solution

Prep., ext, and clean up samples as in 29.009–29.014. Conc. 15% and 50% eluates from Florisil column to suitable definite vol. in Kuderna-Danish evaporator app. All eluting solvs must be peroxide-free by test in *Definitions and Explanatory Terms*, item (3).

29.038 *Determination*

(a) *Parathion and/or methyl parathion.*—Transfer aliquot of concd eluate from 15% elution, equiv. to 5 g crop, to 50 ml erlenmeyer. Carefully evap. to dryness under gentle jet of dry air at room temp. Dissolve residue in 3.0 ml acetone. (*Note:* Since good polarotraces can be obtained by using as little as 0.5 ml soln in cell, min. of 0.25 ml acetone can be used to dissolve residue.) Add 3.0 ml electrolyte soln, (g)(3), mix well, transfer to polarographic cell, and adjust to 25±1°. Bubble N thru soln 5 min and polarograph as in **29.036**(c). Measure ht of wave whose peak potential corresponds to that of parathion, and det. concn from freshly prepd std curve or by comparing wave hts of sample soln with those of std soln polarographed immediately before or after sample. (Latter method is recommended for greater accuracy.)

Calculate μg/ml as follows:

$$C_{sample} = [(WH_{sample}) \times (SF_{sample}) \times (C_{std})]/ [(WH_{std}) \times (SF_{std})]$$

where C = concn of pesticide/ml cell soln; WH = wave ht; SF = sensitivity factor.

ppm = C_{sample}/g sample.

Limit of quant. detn is 0.01 ppm based on 1 g crop in 1 ml cell soln.

Me parathion, parathion, and paraoxon polarograph at ca same peak potential. If any one of these pesticides is present as indicated by multiple residue methods, it should be polarographed against that std. If these pesticides are present together, use mixed std contg ratio of pesticides as estd from analysis by multiple residue method. (Paraoxon will not be recovered by cleanup specified.)

Other pesticides known to give polarographic peak potential similar to parathion are pentachloronitrobenzene (PCNB), 1,2,4,5-tetrachloro-3-nitrobenzene (TCNB), and O-ethyl O-p-nitrophenyl phenylphosphonothioate (EPN). PCNB and TCNB are eluted in 6% eluate and will not interfere. Verify presence or absence of EPN by GLC or TLC.

(b) *Diazinon.*—Transfer aliquot of concd eluate from 15% elution, equiv. to 5 g crop, to 50 ml erlenmeyer. Carefully evap. just to dryness, using gentle jet of dry air at room temp. Dissolve residue in 5.0 ml electrolyte soln, (g)(1). Transfer soln to polarographic cell and adjust to 25±1°. Bubble N thru soln 5 min and polarograph as in **29.036**(a). Calc. amt of Diazinon present as in (a).

Limit of quant. detn is 0.2 ppm based on 1 g crop sample in 1 ml cell soln.

(c) *Malathion.*—Transfer aliquot of concd eluate from 50% elution, equiv. to 5 g crop, to 50 ml erlenmeyer. Carefully evap. just to dryness under gentle jet of dry air at room temp. Dissolve residue in 2.0 ml MeOH, add 1.0 ml 0.1N KOH, and let stand 3 min. Add 2.0 ml electrolyte soln, (g)(2), mix well, and let stand 5 min. Transfer to polarographic cell,

adjust to 25±1°, and polarograph as in **29.036**(b). Calc. amt of malathion present as in (a).

Limit of quant. detn is 0.3 ppm based on 1 g crop in 1.0 ml cell soln.

Note 1: If polarotrace cannot be obtained because of high residual currents, check concd eluate for peroxides. If peroxides are present, transfer 5 ml concd eluate to small separator contg 25 ml 3% FeSO₄ soln; shake well and discard aq. layer. Transfer 1.0 ml ether layer to 50 ml erlenmeyer and proceed as in (a), (b), or (c).

Note 2: All glassware used for polarographic detns should be thoroly washed with hot HNO₃ (1 + 1) and rinsed with distd H₂O.

Cholinesterase Inhibition Method (5)— Official First Action

(Nonspecific measure of H₂O-sol., cholinesterase inhibiting substances; applicable to alpha isomer of 2-carbomethoxy-1-methylvinyl dimethyl phosphate (Phosdrin®).)

29.039 *Reagents*

(a) *Petroleum ether or Skellysolve B.*—Boiling range 60–70°, redistd.

(b) *Acetylcholine stock soln.*—10 mg/ml. Dissolve 1.38 g acetylcholine bromide in 100 ml 0.001M NaOAc soln. Soln should keep 2 months if stored in refrigerator. (Bromide is hygroscopic and must be handled rapidly.)

(c) *Acetylcholinesterase stock soln.*—100 units/ml. Dissolve 20,000 unit vial purified bovine cholinesterase (Winthrop Laboratories, 90 Park Ave, New York, NY 10016) in sterile H₂O and dil. to 200 ml. Store in brown bottle in refrigerator. (Should keep 2 months, but will change slowly. Stdze every 2 weeks.)

(d) *Buffer soln.*—pH 7.2. Dissolve 16.72 g Na₂HPO₄.12H₂O and 2.72 g KH₂PO₄ in 1 L H₂O. Add drop of toluene to preserve.

(e) *Dilute hydrochloric acid.*—(1 + 2).

(f) *Ferric chloride soln.*—Dissolve 10 g FeCl₃ .6H₂O in 100 ml 0.1N HCl.

(g) *Hydroxylamine hydrochloride soln.*—2M. Dissolve 13.9 g NH₂OH.HCl in H₂O and dil. to 100 ml. Store in refrigerator and discard after 2 weeks.

(h) *Alkaline hydroxylamine soln.*—Prep. daily by mixing equal vols NH₂OH.HCl soln with 14% NaOH soln.

(i) *Paraffin wax soln.*—6% (w/v) in pet ether, (a).

(j) *Phosdrin std solns.*—(1) *Stock soln.*—0.5 mg/ml. Dil. 1.0 g analytical grade Phosdrin (60.2% alpha isomer; Shell Chemical Co.) to 2 L in vol. flask. (2) *Working soln.*—0.5 μg/ml. Using vac., pipet 1 ml stock soln into 1 L vol. flask and dil. to vol. (*Caution:* Phosdrin is volatile and highly toxic. Never pipet by mouth, and wash hands thoroly with soap and warm water after handling solns.) Store solns in refrigerator; discard after 1 month.

29.040 *Apparatus*

(a) *Constant temp. bath.*—Regulated at 35°.

(b) *Evaporator.*—Two-hole cork, fitting into

25 × 200 mm test tube, carrying outlet tube connected to water-pump in one hole, and in other, constricted tube which may be pushed down to follow surface of soln as it evaps.

29.041 Preparation of Sample

Chop sample of fruits or vegetables into small pieces, weigh 250 g into high-speed blender, and add 500 ml $CHCl_3$. Blend 3–5 min (lesser time for watery products such as berries and spinach, which may emulsify) until mixt. is uniform. Filter thru Whatman No. 12 or equiv. folded paper contg layer of anhyd. Na_2SO_4. Store soln in g-s bottle in refrigerator until ready for analysis.

29.042 Standardization of Acetylcholine Substrate

Pipet 6.0, 7.0, 8.0, and 9.0 ml portions of acetylcholine soln into 25 ml vol. flasks and dil. to vol. with H_2O. Pipet 1 ml aliquots of these solns into 30 ml g-s centrf. tubes. Add 3 ml H_2O and 4 ml alk. NH_2OH .HCl soln, and shake *vigorously*. Let stand at least 1 min, add 2 ml HCl (1 + 2), and mix. Add 2 ml $FeCl_3$ soln, (f), and shake *vigorously*. Transfer immediately into 1 cm spectrophtr cells and det. A at 540 nm against H_2O ref. (Soln will fade at room temp., so read at once. If cooled to 3–5°, color is stable 18 hr.) Plot A against ml acetylcholine stock soln/25 ml. From std curve select diln giving A of 1.30±0.01 (ca 7.6 ml). Use this diln to prep. acetylcholine substrate soln.

29.043 Standardization of Acetylcholinesterase Reagent

Pipet 2.5, 3.0, 3.5, 4.0, and 5.0 ml acetylcholinesterase soln into 100 ml vol. flasks and dil. to vol. with pH 7.2 buffer. Pipet 2.0 ml aliquots of these dilns into 30 ml g-s centrf. tubes and add 1 ml H_2O to each. Temper in 35° water bath; then add 1 ml selected acetylcholine substrate soln, **29.042**, previously brought to 35°. Add to one tube at time at 1 min intervals, and mix thoroly. Hold tubes at 35° *exactly* 60 min to hydrolyze acetylcholine.

Pipet 4.0 ml alk. NH_2OH.HCl soln into each tube and shake vigorously; then add 2.0 ml HCl (1 + 2) and shake. Add 2 ml $FeCl_3$ soln and shake vigorously. Transfer *immediately* into 1 cm cells and det. A at 540 nm against H_2O. Plot A of each diln against ml stock cholinesterase soln. From plot, select diln giving A of 0.20. Use this diln to prep. acetylcholinesterase reagent.

29.044 Preparation of Standard Curve

(*Caution: See* **46.018** *and* **46.041**.)

Pipet duplicate 0, 0.1, 0.2, 0.3, and 0.4 ml portions Phosdrin working std soln into 30 ml g-s centrf. tubes and dil. to 1.0 ml with H_2O. Temper in 35° bath; then add 2.0 ml acetylcholinesterase soln, previously

warmed to 35°, to each tube at 1 min intervals. Shake tubes, and hold at 35° exactly 30 min. Add 1.0 ml selected acetylcholine substrate soln, **29.042**, previously brought to 35°, to each tube, mix, and proceed as in **29.043**, beginning "Hold tubes at 35° *exactly* 60 min to hydrolyze acetylcholine."

Calc. % inhibition in each tube:

$$\% \text{ inhibition} = 100 - 100 \times (1.30 - B)/(1.30 - C),$$

where $B = A$ of tubes contg Phosdrin, and $C = A$ of blank tube (no Phosdrin).

Plot % inhibition against μg Phosdrin. (Curve may not be straight.)

29.045 Determination

Transfer 10 ml $CHCl_3$ ext (equiv. to 5 g sample) to 25 × 200 mm test tube. Evap. to ca 3 ml in H_2O bath at 50–60°, using evaporator. Add 8.0 ml pet ether and 0.5 ml paraffin wax soln and mix. Pipet 10 ml H_2O into tube and shake thoroly. Return to evaporator and remove nonaq. phase at 50–60°, shaking at 10 min intervals until all org. solvs are removed. Wash down sides of tube 3 times with 3 ml portions pet ether, shaking and evapg off after each wash. Chill tube in ice-H_2O 5 min; then filter cold aq. ext thru No. 40 Whatman or equiv. paper into small beaker. Transfer 1.0 ml aq. ext (0.5 g sample) into 30 ml g-s centrf. tube and proceed as in **29.044**, beginning, "Temper in 35° bath; . . ."

Calc. % inhibition and compare against Phosdrin std curve to obtain μg Phosdrin.

Phosdrin, ppm = μg Phosdrin in aliquot/g sample in aliquot. (For best accuracy carry equiv. ext of Phosdrin-free check crop thru method and subtract net A ($A - A$ of 0 Phosdrin std) from sample reading. Prep. complete std curve at least weekly, preferably with each set of samples. If >0.4 ppm Phosdrin is indicated, take smaller aliquot of $CHCl_3$ soln.)

INDIVIDUAL RESIDUES

Benzene Hexachloride (Hexachlorocyclohexane, BHC)— Official Final Action

29.046 Principles

(a) *Multiple residue method.*—See **29.001–29.027**.

(b) ★*Colorimetric method (6)*★—BHC is removed from sample by extg with CCl_4. After removal of solv., BHC is dechlorinated to benzene by action of Zn and HOAc in presence of malonic acid which slowly liberates CO_2, sweeping benzene formed into nitrating mixt. Benzene is converted in constant but not quant. (ca 85%) proportion to *m*-dinitrobenzene. After extn, *m*-dinitrobenzene is treated with butanone-2 and alkali, and A of magenta colored compd formed is measured at 565 nm.

See **24.101–24.105**, 10th ed. (*Caution: See* **46.011**, **46.039**, and **46.054**.)

★ **Distinction Between Lindane** ★
and Technical BHC (7)—
Official First Action

29.047   *Principles*

BHC is extd with *n*-hexane. Ext is refluxed over fuming H₂SO₄ and BHC is extd with acetonitrile. Purified ext is chromatographed on paper to sep. and identify pesticides. (*Caution: See* **46.004, 46.011, 46.016, 46.030, 46.031, 46.039,** and **46.061.**)

See **24.107–24.110**, 10th ed.

Biphenyl (8)—Official Final Action
(Applicable to citrus fruit)

29.048   *Principle*

Biphenyl is extd from blended peel or pulp by steam-liq.-liq. extn. Ext is subjected to TLC and biphenyl zone is completely scraped from developed plate. Biphenyl is eluted from adsorbent with alcohol for spectrophtric detn.

29.049   *Reagents*

(a) *Silica gel.*—GF 254 (Brinkmann Instruments, Inc. No. 7730).

(b) *Biphenyl std solns.*—(*1*) *Stock soln.*—Approx. 0.5 mg/ml. Dissolve ca 50 mg accurately weighed biphenyl in *n*-heptane and dil. to 100 ml with *n*-heptane. (*2*) *Limit soln.*—Approx. 0.01 mg/ml. Dil. 5 ml stock std to 250 ml with *n*-heptane.

Use stock std soln for spectrophtric quantitation after TLC step. Limit std soln aids in locating biphenyl zone and in estg small amts.

29.050   *Apparatus*

(a) *Thin layer apparatus.*—*See* **19.040**; use 8 × 8″ glass plates.

(b) *Spotting pipet.*—100 µl (Kontes Glass Co. No. K-763800, or equiv.).

(c) *Tank liner.*—Whatman 3MM paper cut to fit tank.

(d) *Moisture test apparatus.*—Similar to lighter-than-H₂O volatile oil trap, **30.017**(a), Fig. 30:1, with cold finger condenser (Scientific Glass Apparatus Co. No. JM-8590, or equiv.).

29.051   *Preparation of TLC Plates*

Mix 40 g silica gel with 80 ml H₂O, shaking vigorously few sec, and finally swirling ca 30 sec to eliminate air bubbles. Spread slurry 0.3 mm thick over 5 plates. Let plates air-dry in place ca 1 hr. Put plates in drying rack and place in 100° oven 2 min. Remove plates and store in desiccator over silica gel or CaCl₂ until used. Plates may be stored up to 30 days.

29.052   *Preparation of Sample*

Sort out and discard rotten units. Completely peel 6 or more whole fruits (include all white material under peel in peel portion). Weigh peelings and peeled fruit, and calc. wt ratio of peelings to peeled fruit.

(a) *Peel.*—Grind combined peel in food grinder. Blend 200 g ground peel with 400 g H₂O at high speed 5 min (or in five 1 min increments if blender becomes very warm), using high-speed blender. (Larger batches may be blended with large blender as long as peel-H₂O ratio is same.)

(b) *Peeled fruit.*—Cut peeled fruit into small pieces and blend at high speed 5 min (or in five 1 min increments if blender becomes very warm).

29.053   *Extraction*

Accurately weigh ca 300 g recently blended peel slurry or ca 100 g recently blended peeled fruit, and transfer to 1 L r-b ℥ 29/42 flask with enough H₂O to yield total vol. of ca 500 ml; add few boiling chips (6 mesh granular SiC is convenient). Connect extn unit of moisture test app. to flask and fill side arm with H₂O to overflowing. Place ca 3 ml *n*-heptane on top of H₂O layer and insert cold finger cooled with very rapid flow of cold H₂O. Gradually heat flask with mantle (controlled by variable transformer) until even boiling is obtained, then intensely enough to maintain vigorous boiling. Continue extn 3 hr from time mixt. starts boiling. (Wrap exposed portion of flask and connector arm between flask and extn unit with Al foil.) Initial carry-over of froth does not interfere. After 3 hr, discontinue heat and drain entire contents of extractor into 125 ml separator. Discard lower layer and drain heptane ext thru 1″ column of granular anhyd. Na₂SO₄ (8–10 mm id column) into 10 ml vol. flask. Rinse separator with 1 ml *n*-heptane and add rinse to column. Rinse cold finger and extn unit with five 2 ml portions alcohol, collecting successive rinses in separator. Add 5 ml *n*-heptane to separator and shake vigorously few sec; add 50–75 ml H₂O and shake moderately few sec. Let layers sep. (lower layer may remain slightly cloudy) and discard lower layer. Pass heptane layer thru same Na₂SO₄ column into vol. flask. Rinse separator and column with enough *n*-heptane to dil. to vol.

29.054   *Thin Layer Chromatography*

Pre-sat. tank contg liner with *n*-heptane ≥1 hr before use. Establish imaginary spotting line 3 cm from bottom edge of plate. For each intended spot, use tip of 100 µl pipet to scratch mark in adsorbent layer just size of pipet tip. (Space spots evenly with max. of 7 spots including blank.) Spot 100 µl each stock and limit std solns on extreme spots (one on far right and one on far left of plate). Spot 100 µl *n*-heptane as blank and 100 µl sample between std spots. Use same pipet for all spots, rinsing thoroly with *n*-heptane between applications. Keep size of spots uniform at 1.5–2 cm diam. by using following technic: Fill 100 µl pipet past mark with soln to be spotted. Carefully drain excess into absorbent towel until soln is at exact vol. mark. Press pipet tip against exposed glass in center of spotting mark on plate (hold pipet in vertical position at all times).

Regulate size of spot by holding finger over top of pipet and pressing tip tightly against plate. Blow across spot (orally) only when necessary to regulate size of spot and never lift pipet from place once spotting is begun.

Pour 10–15 ml n-heptane in tank trough, insert plate, and seal tank. Develop until solv. is within 1″ from top of plate (ca 30 min). Remove plate, air-dry few min, and view under UV light. Biphenyl appears as bright blue spot on yellow background.

If no biphenyl appears in sample, end analysis at this point. If biphenyl is found, remove spots from plate without delay. Score upper and lower extremes of biphenyl zone horizontally across plate. Score vertical lines in adsorbent between biphenyl spots to include approx. equal area in each rectangle, scribing same area for ref. spot. Use razor blade to scrape off, and discard all adsorbent below biphenyl zone and outside extreme vertical lines. Use absorbent tissue and alcohol to clean exposed glass thoroly. Carefully scrape adsorbent from one extreme rectangular zone onto glazed paper and transfer to funnel inserted in 10 ml vol. flask; do *not* use solv. to rinse paper. Rinse off razor blade into funnel with small portion of alcohol. Tip plate at angle to facilitate rinsing of scraped area into funnel and rinse with several small portions alcohol. Rinse funnel and finally dil. to vol. with alcohol. Shake mixt. vigorously and let stand 5 min, shaking occasionally. Remove each biphenyl spot same way, working inward from each side of plate and cleaning and drying each previously removed zone. Filter each mixt. thru Whatman No. 44 paper, or equiv., and store filtrate in stoppered vessel for spectrophtric detn.

29.055 *Spectrophotometry*

Det. A of each soln at 248 and 300 nm in 1 cm cell with alcohol as ref.

ppm Biphenyl = (net A_{248} sample/net A_{248} std) $\times$ (μg std spotted/g sample spotted), where net A_{248} = A_{248} − [A_{300} $\times$ (A_{248} blank/A_{300} blank)]

2-(p-*tert*-Butylphenoxy)-1-Methylethyl 2-Chloroethyl Sulfite (Aramite®) (9)— Official Final Action

29.056 *Principles*

Aramite is stripped from sample with benzene, soln is concd, and Aramite is hydrolyzed with KOH-isopropanol to form ethylene oxide. Evolved ethylene oxide is converted to HCHO with KIO_4 and HCHO is reacted with acetylacetone to form colored compd.

29.057 *Reagents*

(a) *Isopropanol.*—Redistill and store over anhyd. Na_2SO_4.

(b) *Periodic acid soln.*—Dissolve 0.5 g HIO_4 .$2H_2O$ in H_2O and dil. to 100 ml with H_2O. Dil. 1 vol. with 2 vols 0.1N HCl.

(c) *Sodium arsenite soln.*—Dissolve 2 g Na_2AsO_2 in H_2O and dil. to 100 ml with H_2O.

(d) *Acetylacetone reagent.*—Dissolve 25 g NH_4OAc in H_2O, add 3 ml HOAc and 0.2 ml redistd acetylacetone, and dil. to 100 ml with H_2O.

(e) *Aramite std solns.*—(1) *Stock soln.*—ca 5 mg/ ml. Accurately weigh ca 250 mg (ca 0.25 ml) std Aramite (available from Uniroyal Chemical), dissolve in benzene, and dil. with benzene to 50 ml. (2) *Intermediate soln.*—50 μg/ml. Dil. aliquot of stock soln contg 5 mg to 100 ml with benzene. (3) *Working solns.*—Dil. aliquots of intermediate soln with benzene to obtain lower concns. Solns as dil. as 10 or 25 μg/ml remain unchanged 2–3 weeks. Store std solns in refrigerator.

29.058 *Isolation Apparatus*

Lead air or N at ca 1 lb pressure into surge tank consisting of 2 L bottle fitted with inlet and outlet. Connect outlet to 500 ml gas washing bottle contg H_2SO_4, connected thru capillary bubble counter (constructed from thermometer tubing) filled with light mineral oil, and then to reaction tube (25 $\times$ 100 mm over-all length with ℥ 19/22 joint) with gas inlet tube equipped with inner ℥ 19/22 joint to fit into reaction tube. Attach ≥80 mm 8 mm od thin wall tubing above inlet before attachment to 2–5 mm id capillary delivery tube. (Gas inlet tube, Corning Glass Works No. 96800, ℥ 19/38, may be used by connecting a ℥ 19/38 inner joint to capillary delivery tube.) Construct scrubber at lower end of delivery tube with 4 expanded rings in 50 mm, which just fits inside 11 mm id test tube, upper portion of which is enlarged to 16 mm id to increase its vol. (See Fig. 29:7.)

29.059 *Preparation of Samples*

(*Caution: See* **46.039, 46.040,** *and* **46.045.**)

(a) *Leafy vegetables.*—Chop into small pieces. Weigh 500 g into 2 qt tumble jar, add 500 ml benzene, and roll or tumble ca 10 min. Pour off solv., sep. any H_2O, dry benzene with anhyd. Na_2SO_4, and filter.

(b) *Small fruits.*—Weigh 500 g into 2 qt tumble jar and strip with 500 ml benzene as above.

(c) *Large fruits.*—Weigh 10 whole fruits (1–2 kg) into 2 gal. tumble jar, add 500 ml benzene, and roll or tumble ca 10 min. Pour off benzene, dry, and filter as above.

29.060 *Determination*

(*Caution: See* **46.011, 46.039, 46.040,** *and* **46.045.**)

Conc. aliquot of filtered strip soln (100–400 ml) to 3 ml in reaction tube. (Entire strip soln may be concd in beaker under gentle air current and dild to definite vol. (50 or 100 ml). Aliquots of this concn can then be measured directly into reaction tube for final evapn to 3 ml. Soln must *never* be evapd to dryness.) Place premixed reagent, (b), in scrubber. Use 3 ml for residues <0.5 ppm or 5 ml for residues ≥0.5 ppm. (Two std curves are required, 1 for 3 ml vol. in

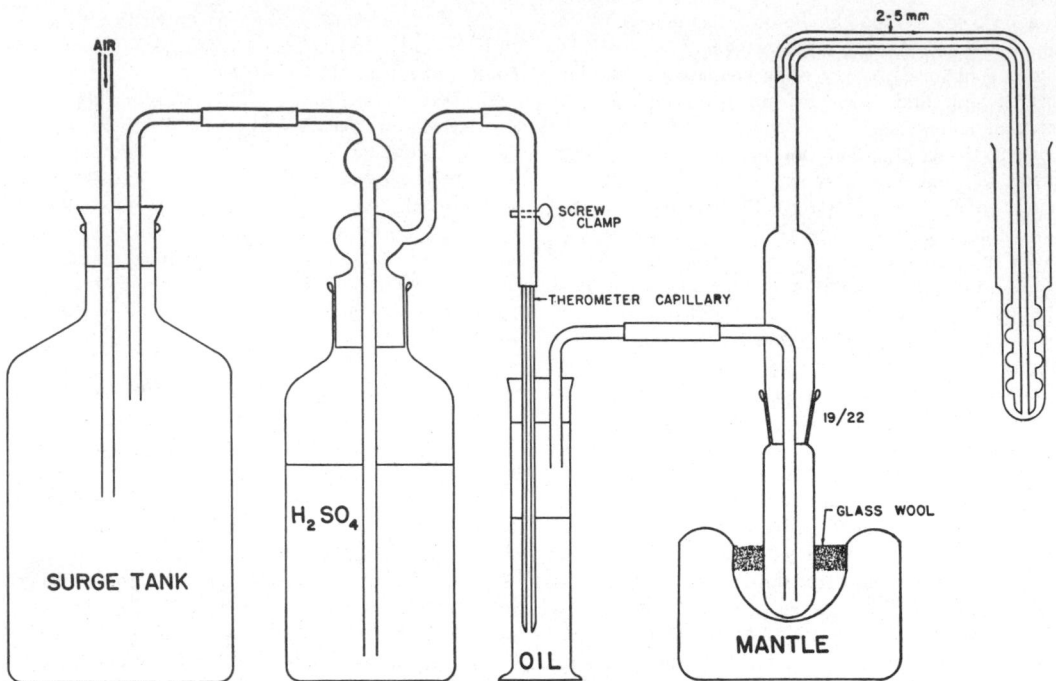

FIG. 29:7—Apparatus for determining Aramite

scrubber and other for 5 ml.) To sample in reaction tube add 5 ml isopropanol and 3 pellets KOH. Attach to app. without delay.

Pass current of dry air or N thru gas inlet tube at rate of 4–6 ml/min, and heat reaction tube, maintaining *gentle* refluxing 30 min. Remove scrubber tube and heat in 50° constant temp. bath 15 min. Cool to room temp. Pipet 2 ml into small test tube, add 0.5 ml 2% sodium arsenite, let stand for moment, shake, and let stand until colorless. Add 0.5 ml acetylacetone reagent, mix, and heat in boiling H_2O or live steam 6 min. Remove from heat and let stand $\geq$10 min in air. Cool to room temp., transfer to cell, and det. A at 412 nm. Color is stable for $\geq$2 hr. Det. μg from std curve, and calc. to ppm.

Prep. std curve by measuring quantities of std soln contg 0–150 μg into reaction tube with enough benzene to total 3 ml, and carry thru entire detn as for samples. Plot A against μg Aramite.

Captan (N-(Trichloromethylthio)-4-Cyclohexene-1,2-Dicarboximide) (10)—Official Final Action

(Applicable to firm fruits such as apples, pears, peaches, and plums and to green vegetables)

29.061   *Principles*

Captan is extd from crop with benzene; H_2O, color, and appreciable amts of waxes are removed, and red color is developed by fusion of captan with resorcinol at 135°; color changes to yellow on addn of HOAc.

29.062   *Reagents*

(a) *Resorcinol.*—Must be free of discoloration and pass following tests: Fuse 0.5 g and dissolve in 25 ml HOAc. A at 425 nm is $\leq$0.015, against HOAc. 1.00 g should not lose >2 mg in 4 hr over H_2SO_4; if more is lost, dry over H_2SO_4 until test is satisfactory.

(b) *Cleanup mix.*—10 parts Nuchar, 5 parts Hyflo Super-Cel, and 5 parts anhyd. Na_2SO_4.

(c) *Captan std solns.*—(1) *Stock soln.*—3 mg/ml. Transfer 150 mg pure captan (available from Chevron Chem. Co., 940 Hensley St, Richmond, CA 94804) to 50 ml vol. flask and dil. to vol. with benzene. (2) *Intermediate soln.*—300 μg/ml. Pipet 10 ml stock soln into 100 ml vol. flask and dil. to vol. with benzene. (3) *Working soln.*—30 μg/ml. Pipet 10 ml intermediate std soln into 100 ml vol. flask and dil. to vol. with benzene.

29.063   *Preparation of Sample*

(*Caution: See* **46.039, 46.040,** *and* **46.045.**)

(a) *Fruits.*—Accurately weigh ca 500 g sample into clean, dry jar with screw cap faced with sheet cork gasket covered with wet filter paper, or other solv.-tight lid, and add 500 ml benzene. Multiples of sample to benzene ratio can be used. Agitate 15 min, drain benzene into container, and transfer to separator. (Transfer to separator may be omitted where there is no separable aq. layer.)

Transfer ca 100 ml sepd benzene layer to 250 ml g-s flask, and decolorize and dehydrate with 3–4 g cleanup mix, (b), by shaking vigorously ca 5 min. Filter thru folded paper, rejecting first 10–15 ml.

(b) *Green vegetables.*—Chop sample in food chopper such as Hobart Food Cutter, mix, and transfer 100 g to explosion-proof blender. Add 200 ml benzene and blend 2 min; add 20 g anhyd. Na$_2$SO$_4$ and blend 2 min more. Pour mixt. into 500 ml centrf. bottle, stopper with *cork*, and centrf. at ca 1400 rpm 5–10 min. Decant benzene layer into 250 ml g-s erlenmeyer, add ca 6 g cleanup mix, **(b)**/100 ml benzene, and shake vigorously ca 5 min. Filter thru folded paper, discarding first 10 ml. If water-white soln does not result, repeat cleanup treatment. Pipet 50 ml into 100 ml vol. flask and dil. to vol. with benzene.

29.064 *Determination*

(*Caution: See* **46.018, 46.040, 46.041,** and **46.045.**)

Pipet 5 ml filtrate, **29.063**(a), or aliquot, **(b)**, into 25 × 200 mm test tube and add 0.5±0.1 g resorcinol. Heat 20 min in oil bath at 135±5°, cautiously at first to evap. benzene; then immerse reaction tubes to depth of ca 2″, but do not let them touch bottom of bath. Remove, and immediately add 10–15 ml HOAc, followed by rapid immersion in H$_2$O at room temp. Transfer quant. to 25 ml vol. flask, using HOAc, dil. to vol. with HOAc, and mix.

Det. *A* at 425 nm in 1 cm cell against HOAc within 1 hr. Calc. ppm from std curve.

29.065 *Preparation of Standard Curve*

Prep. std curve simultaneously with samples. Pipet 0, 2, 4, and 5 ml aliquots of working std soln into 25 × 200 mm test tubes and add benzene to make total vol. of 5 ml in each tube. Add 0.5±0.1 g resorcinol and continue as in detn, beginning "Heat 20 min in oil bath . . ."

Note: One drop H$_2$O in reaction tube will cause apparent loss of ca 20% captan. Do not leave benzene aliquots in unstoppered reaction tubes where condensation of moisture will take place.

Carbaryl (1-Naphthyl N-Methylcarbamate) (Sevin®) (*11*)—Official Final Action

29.066 *Reagents*

(a) *Acetone.*—Redistd.

(b) *Coagulating soln.*—Dissolve 0.5 g NH$_4$Cl in 400 ml H$_2$O contg 1 ml H$_3$PO$_4$.

(c) *Color reagent.*—Dissolve 25 mg *p*-nitrobenzenediazonium fluoborate in 5 ml MeOH and add 20 ml HOAc. Prep. just before use.

(d) *Methylene chloride.*—Redistd CH$_2$Cl$_2$.

(e) *Alcoholic potassium hydroxide soln.*—0.1*N* in MeOH.

(f) *Polyethylene glycol soln.*—Dil. 1 ml polyethylene glycol to 100 ml with CH$_2$Cl$_2$.

(g) *Carbaryl std solns.*—Ref. std material is available from Union Carbide Corp., Chemicals Div., Technical Center, South Charleston, WV 25921. (*1*) *Stock soln.*—0.5 mg/ml. Place 50.0 mg in 100 ml vol. flask and dil. to vol. with CH$_2$Cl$_2$. (*2*) *Intermediate soln.*—50 µg/ml. Transfer 10 ml stock soln to 100 ml vol. flask and dil. to vol. with CH$_2$Cl$_2$. (*3*)

Working soln.—5.0 µg/ml. Transfer 10 ml intermediate soln to 100 ml vol. flask and dil. to vol. with CH$_2$Cl$_2$.

29.067 *Apparatus*

Evaporative concentrator.—*See* Fig. 29:8. Vac. manifold connected thru stopcock to antisurge column, 250 × 19 mm od, contg glass marble, or Snyder column, attached to ⨎ 24/40 erlenmeyer. Use surgical tubing wherever contact with sample is likely.

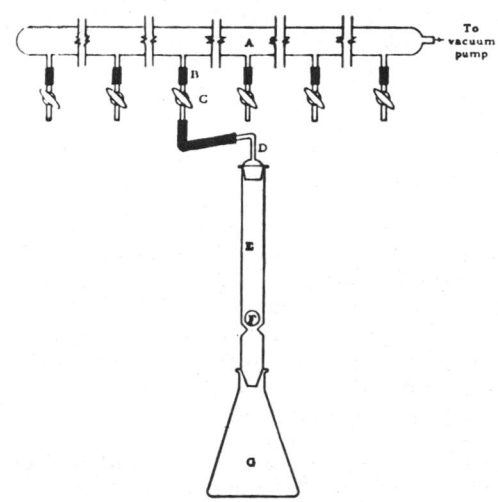

FIG. 29:8—Evaporative concentrator. A, glass manifold. B, pressure tubing. C, stopcock. D, adapter, ⨎ 24/40. E, antisurge column, 25 cm × 19 mm od. F, glass marble. G, erlenmeyer, ⨎ 24/40, 250 ml.

29.068 *Preparation of Sample Solution*

Transfer 50 g sample to high-speed blender and add 150 CH$_2$Cl$_2$ and 100 g powd anhyd. Na$_2$SO$_4$. Blend at high speed 2 min and let settle 1 min. Decant solv. into 9 cm buchner fitted with Whatman No. 1 or equiv. paper covered with thin coat of Hyflo Super-Cel or equiv. filter aid. Cautiously apply vac. until all solv. has filtered. Repeat extn with two 100 ml portions CH$_2$Cl$_2$. Treat combined filtrates as in (a) or (b):

(a) Transfer combined filtrates to 500 ml ⨎ erlenmeyer and add 1 ml polyethylene glycol soln. Connect to evaporative concentrator, place flask in H$_2$O bath at 25–30°, and carefully reduce pressure to ca 20 mm. After solv. evaps, immediately disconnect antisurge column from manifold. Rinse down walls of column and flask with 5 ml acetone from pipet, swirl flask, and warm gently under hot H$_2$O tap 30 sec. Add 50 ml coagulating soln thru column, and swirl. Remove column, let mixt. stand 30 min, and filter with vac. thru ⅛″ layer of Super-Cel in No. 1 buchner. Wash flask and pad with two 15 ml portions coagulating soln.

Transfer filtrate to 125 ml separator, add 25 ml CH$_2$Cl$_2$, shake well, and let sep. completely. Drain lower layer into $\bar{\textbf{S}}$ 250 ml erlenmeyer. Repeat extn of aq. layer with 25 ml CH$_2$Cl$_2$, adding ext to same 250 ml erlenmeyer. If combined exts are cloudy, add 5–10 g granular anhyd. Na$_2$SO$_4$, and shake. Decant solv. into clean 250 ml $\bar{\textbf{S}}$ erlenmeyer, rinsing with small portion CH$_2$Cl$_2$. (If residue is expected to be >2 ppm, dil. exts to vol. in 100 ml vol. flask, and use appropriate aliquot.)

(b) Add 1 ml polyethylene glycol. Stopper, carefully reduce pressure to ca 150 mm, and warm on steam bath. When vol. is ca 5 ml, remove from steam bath and swirl until dry. Release vac., remove stopper, and let cool. Continue as in (a), beginning "Rinse down walls ..." except column is not present.

29.069   Determination

To soln in erlenmeyer add 1 ml polyethylene glycol soln and connect to column and evaporator. Evap. solv. as before, immediately disconnect, and remove column. Rinse down walls of flask with 2 ml 0.1N KOH in MeOH from pipet, rotating to ensure complete contact. Let stand 5 min, add exactly 17 ml HOAc, and with swirling add 1 ml color reagent. Let stand exactly 1 min and det. A in 1 cm cell at 475 nm against reagent blank processed along with sample as ref. Det. μg from std curve; ppm carbaryl = μg/g sample ($\times$ diln factor if aliquot was used).

29.070   Preparation of Standard Curve
(Caution: See **46.018** and **46.041**.)

Pipet 0.0, 1.0, 3.0, 5.0, and 10.0 ml aliquots working std soln to 500 ml $\bar{\textbf{S}}$ erlenmeyers, add 300 ml CH$_2$Cl$_2$ to each, and proceed as in **29.068**, beginning "Treat combined filtrates as in (a) or (b):"

Plot A against μg carbaryl to obtain std curve.

Qualitative and Semiquantitative Method
(12)—Official First Action
(Applicable to apples and spinach)

29.071   Reagents

(a) *Adsorbent.*—Al$_2$O$_3$ G (contains 10% CaSO$_4$). Manufactured by E. Merck, Darmstadt, W. Germany; available from Brinkmann Instruments, Inc.

(b) *Coagulating soln.*—See **29.066**(b).

(c) *Chromogenic spray soln.*—Sat. diethylene glycol-alcohol soln (1 + 9) with *p*-nitrobenzenediazonium fluoborate (practical grade, ca 25 mg/100 ml) by stirring ca 2 min. Filter, keep cold during use, and store in refrigerator. Do *not* use after 3 days.

(d) *Diethylene glycol soln.*—Dil. 10 ml diethylene glycol to 100 ml with redistd CH$_2$Cl$_2$.

(e) *Carbaryl std.*—Mp 141–142°. See **29.066**(g). Recrystallize from alcohol and H$_2$O, if necessary.

29.072   Apparatus

(a) *TLC apparatus.*—App. suitable for 8 × 8″ plates. See **29.006**.

(b) *Evaporative concentrator.*—Two chambers, $\bar{\textbf{S}}$ joint 24/25, micro-Snyder column (Kontes Glass Co.

K-569000); 10 ml Mills tube, graduated (Kontes K-570050).

29.073   Extraction and Cleanup of Sample

Transfer 25 g sample to blender. Add 150 ml CH$_2$Cl$_2$ and 100 g powd (150 g granular) anhyd. Na$_2$SO$_4$. Blend 2 min at low speed and let settle. Attach 9 cm buchner contg rapid paper to 500 ml filter flask. Cover paper with thin coat of Hyflo Super-Cel prepd as slurry in CH$_2$Cl$_2$. Decant ext into buchner and cautiously apply vac. Rinse blender with 50 ml CH$_2$Cl$_2$ and filter. Return residue to blender. (Complete sepn of residue from Super-Cel is unimportant.) Add 150 ml CH$_2$Cl$_2$, re-ext, filter, and rinse again with 50 ml CH$_2$Cl$_2$. Add 1 ml diethylene glycol soln to filter flask. Place flask with buchner contg original filter pad attached on steam bath and apply vac. When vol. in flask is ca 5 ml, remove flask from steam bath and swirl until dry. Release vac., remove buchner, and let flask cool.

Rinse down side of flask with 3 ml acetone from pipet and swirl to dissolve residue. While gently swirling flask, add 15 ml coagulating soln and let stand >10 min with occasional swirling. Filter, using vac., thru small fritted glass funnel, medium porosity, contg ca ¼″ layer of Hyflo Super-Cel and receive filtrate in 30 ml test tube. Wash ppt with three 2 ml portions acetone-H$_2$O soln (1 + 9), letting each washing remain in contact with ppt ca 15 sec before applying vac. Transfer filtrate and washings to 25 ml vol. flask, dil. to vol. with acetone-H$_2$O soln (1 + 9), and mix.

29.074   Determination
(Caution: See **46.017**.)

Transfer 10 ml sample soln to 125 ml separator. Ext soln with two 5 ml portions CH$_2$Cl$_2$, shaking 5–10 sec each time. Combine exts in Mills tube, add small SiC chip (<0.01 ml vol.), fit with micro-Snyder column, and evap. to 0.1 ml on steam bath.(*Caution:* Samples may be lost by vigorous ebullition.)

Prepare 8 × 8″ TLC plates coated with 250 μm layer Al$_2$O$_3$ adsorbent. Dry plates in forced-draft oven 30 min at 80°. Store in desiccator cabinet. Using 1 μl pipet, spot aliquots equiv. to 2 g sample and carbaryl stds (in CH$_2$Cl$_2$) to cover expected range.

Place trough in chromatgc tank lined with blotting paper. Add ca 50 ml acetone-benzene soln (1 + 4) to bottom of tank to sat. atm., and then add 50 ml same soln to trough. Place plate in trough and seal tank with masking tape. Develop plate until solv. front just reaches line drawn 10 cm from origin. Dry plate ca 15 min in hood. Spray moderately with 1.0N alc. KOH soln. Then spray moist plate with chromogenic soln. Blue spot with R_f value same as std carbaryl spot indicates carbaryl (R_f range, 0.52–0.60). Compare size and intensity of sample and std spots for semiquant. estn of amt of pesticide. It is possible to distinguish, for example, between 0.2 and 0.4 μg, but not between 0.3 and 0.4 μg. Optimum range for quant. estn is ca 0.1–0.4 μg. For quantities >0.4 μg, spot smaller aliquot of remaining 80 μl soln. Then spot same vol. of std soln for valid comparison.

★ p-Chlorophenyl Phenyl Sulfone ★ (Sulphenone®) (13)— Official Final Action

29.075 Principles

Tech. grade Sulphenone contains ca 80% p-chlorophenyl phenyl sulfone (p-ClDPS); the remainder consists almost entirely of related sulfones, bis(p-chlorophenyl) sulfone (p,p'-ClDPS) and diphenyl sulfone (DPS).

Hexane strip solns are extd with CH$_3$CN which seps Sulphenone components from bulk of waxes, coloring matter, and to some extent from other pesticides. The CH$_3$CN residue is chromatographed on Magnesol column with hexane-anhyd. ether. The residue of fraction contg p-ClDPS is dissolved in isooctane for detn of UV A.

Magnesol column seps p,p'-ClDPS, p-ClDPS, and DPS in that order. DDT, TDE, methoxychlor, and other highly absorbing pesticides are eluted within threshold vol. for p-ClDPS. A few pesticides (phenothiazine and malathion), when present in amts well over their tolerances, show slight interference.

29.076 Apparatus

(a) Chromatographic tube.—Std wall Pyrex glass tubing 2.5 cm od × 60 cm long ending in ca 45° taper sealed to stopcock with 2 mm bore. Seal medium porosity fritted disk in place just above taper. Lubricate stopcock with starch-glycerol gel or glycerol.

(b) Pressure source.—See 6.247(a). Three-way stopcock between column and pressure source permits convenient release of pressure. Connect to column with rubber stopper but avoid wetting stopper with solvs.

(c) Solvent evaporator.—Bent glass tubes in support, connected to filtered air source.

(d) Spectrophotometer.—Suitable for measuring A between 230 and 260 nm; with 2 matched, 1 cm cells.

(e) Glassware. — Avoid contamination, taking special care with flasks for receiving chromatgc fractions. Rinse successively in small groups with acetone and follow with ≥3 rinsings with hexane or isooctane, according to use. All acetone must be removed. Clean heavily contaminated glassware with chromic acid cleaning soln followed by thoro rinsing and drying.

29.077 Reagents

(a) Hexane.—Bp 60–70° (Skellysolve B or equiv.).

(b) Isooctane. — Pure grade, 2,2,4-trimethylpentane (Phillips Petroleum Co., or Enjay Co., Inc., 60 W. 49th St, New York, NY 10020). A at 230, 240, and 250 nm against H$_2$O should be ≤0.100; other-

wise purify by shaking 15 min with 5 g silica gel (28–200 mesh) for each 100 ml in g-s bottle. Keep in dark; filter when needed. Sample and std A are detd against isooctane blank. Solv. in both cells must be from same batch of filtered solv.

(c) Ethyl ether, anhydrous.—(Mallinckrodt A. R. or equiv.). Evap. 20 ml at 40–50° and dissolve residue in 20 ml isooctane. A at 230, 240, and 250 nm against isooctane should be ≤0.020. Differential A, A_{240} − $0.5(A_{230} + A_{250})$, should be ≤±0.003.

(d) Hexane-ether solvent mixture.—Distill hexane, rejecting first 5% and last 10%. Mix 700 ml hexane with 300 ml anhyd. ether. Store in g-s bottle.

(e) Acetonitrile.—Practical grade.

(f) Magnesol.—Industrial regular grade (FMC Corp., Inorganic Chemicals Div., 633 3rd Ave, New York, NY 10017). Mix batch by tumbling in large jar. Keep in small, tightly closed containers.

(g) Sulphenone std soln.—0.5 mg/ml. Dissolve 50 mg tech. grade Sulphenone (Stauffer Chemical Co., Richmond Research Lab., Richmond, CA 94804) in ca 60 ml hexane in 100 ml vol. flask on steam bath, cool, and dil. to vol.

(h) p-Chlorophenyl phenyl sulfone (p-ClDPS).—Suitable for std (Stauffer Chemical Co.).

29.078 Standardization of Chromatographic Column

(Caution: See 46.018 and 46.041.)

Pipet 1 ml (0.5 mg) Sulphenone std soln into 125 ml Phillips conical beaker and evap. to dryness with gentle air current. Add 5 ml hexane-ether solv. to residue. Form close-fitting metal foil cover over top of beaker, warm to ca 45°, swirl to insure soln, and set aside while prepg chromatgc column.

Clamp chromatgc tube in ring stand, in vertical position, and place 100 ml graduated cylinder under outlet. Pour 25 ml hexane-ether solv. into tube, add 15.0 g Magnesol thru powder funnel, and wash down tube walls with 50 ml hexane-ether. Stir thoroly with glass rod until no more bubbles rise and mixt. is uniform; remove rod and let settle ca 1 min. Loosen clamp holding tube and tap end on folded towel while slowly rotating tube back and forth to achieve evenly packed and smooth surface adsorbent bed.

Replace tube in stand, clamping near surface of Magnesol to minimize motion at this point, and force solv. into adsorbent with ca 1–2 lb pressure. (When liq. is being forced into adsorbent, release pressure when level approaches adsorbent surface and let flow continue by gravity until liq. layer has practically disappeared. Have filled pipet ready and make next addn to column. Except as otherwise indicated, rinsing of column or transfer of liqs to column is always by pipet with tip circling in contact with tube near top. If vol. delivered is ≥10 ml, add first few ml slowly, as full flow may impair adsorbent surface. Maintain contact of tip with tube to avoid dripping on adsorbent.)

Rinse down tube walls with 10 ml hexane-ether solv. and force into adsorbent. Transfer prepd Sulphenone soln to column with 2 ml pipet. Rinse down walls of conical beaker with 3 ml hexane-ether solv. from pipet and transfer to column. Repeat rinsing with second 3 ml portion solv. and then force combined soln and rinsings into adsorbent. Rinse tube with 10 ml hexane-ether solv., and force into adsorbent. Replace 100 ml cylinder with 10 ml graduated cylinder. Transfer 10–20 ml hexane-ether solv. to column, and slowly pour in ca 200 ml addnl. Apply 1–2 lb pressure to maintain elution rate of ca 5 ml/min. Collect twenty 10 ml fractions, alternating two 10 ml graduated cylinders. Pour fractions and drain well into clean 50 ml erlenmeyers, numbered consecutively. After 20th fraction is collected, release pressure and close stopcock. Reserve column for collection of addnl fractions, if required. All fractions should be collected same day.

Evap. the 20 fractions, and also 10 ml hexane-ether solv. for ref., to dryness with gentle air current in shallow H_2O bath at 40–45°. Add 10 ml isooctane to each flask and swirl at intervals during ca 10 min to insure complete soln of residue.

Det. A of initial fractions (*Note 1*) at 248 nm (p,p'-ClDPS max.) and 242 nm (p-ClDPS max.) and locate leading fraction for p-ClDPS (*Note 2*). Sulfones are eluted in following order: p,p'-ClDPS, p-ClDPS, DPS. In satisfactory column, threshold vol. for p-ClDPS will usually be ca 80–100 ml and eluate vol. ca 80–100 ml also. If threshold vol. is too low, sepn from other pesticides and p,p'-ClDPS may not be satisfactory. In such case, prep. new column, using more Magnesol, and recalibrate. If threshold vol. is high, recalibrate, if desired, using less Magnesol. If column is satisfactory, det. A of remaining fractions contg p-ClDPS. Det. A of trailing fractions at 242 and 234 nm (DPS max.) to locate final fraction for p-ClDPS.

Note 1.—First few fractions normally show little A; considerable A in these fractions indicates absorbing impurities in the Magnesol. Prewashing columns with addnl 50 or 100 ml hexane-ether solv. may suffice to remove impurities. All subsequent columns should then be prewashed with equal amt of solv. mixt.

Note 2.—Slight overlap in elution patterns of p,p'-ClDPS and p-ClDPS generally occurs, i.e., A of ca 0.050 for min. in-between fraction. Recovery of p-ClDPS is not materially affected.

29.079   *Preparation of Sample*
(*Caution: See* **46.011, 46.039, 46.040,** *and* **46.045.**)

(a) *Apples and firm pears that can withstand "free" tumbling without breakdown.*—Proceed as in **29.142** (a). Pipet aliquot of strip soln equiv. to ca 50–70 g fruit into 125 ml Phillips beaker and evap. benzene on steam bath with air current to ca 5 ml. Complete evapn in shallow H_2O bath at 40–45° with air current. Add 25 ml hexane, heat on steam bath to dissolve waxy residue, cool, and transfer to 125 ml separator. Rinse beaker with 10 ml CH_3CN, warm on

steam bath to dissolve remaining residue, cool, and transfer to separator. Proceed as in **29.081**, first par., beginning "... shake ca 1 min ..."

(b) *Peaches and relatively soft pears.*—Proceed as in **29.142**(a), except use hexane instead of benzene, and strip 15 min. To minimize breakdown, choose sample or jar of such size as to allow limited movement of fruit. Filter ext thru folded paper and keep in tightly closed container. Proceed as in **29.081**.

29.080   *Determination of Absorbances of Standard*

Dissolve 100 mg p-ClDPS, accurately weighed, in ca 60 ml isooctane in 100 ml vol. flask on steam bath. Cool, and dil. to vol. Prep. diln contg 1 mg/100 ml and det. A at 230, 240, and 250 nm against isooctane. Refill ref. and std cell, repeat readings at above wavelengths, and obtain av. reading for each wavelength.

Also det. A at enough points between 220 and 260 nm to establish A-wavelength curve.

29.081   *Separation and Determination of p-ClDPS*
(*Caution: See* **46.011, 46.040,** *and* **46.043.**)

Pipet aliquot of strip soln equiv. to ca 50–70 g fruit into 125 ml separator and dil. to 25 ml with hexane. (Lubricate stopcock with film of silicone or petrolatum.) Add 10 ml CH_3CN, shake ca 1 min, let sep., and drain into second separator. Repeat extn with 2 addnl 10 ml portions CH_3CN and discard hexane. Shake combined CH_3CN ext well with 5 ml hexane and drain lower layer into 125 ml Phillips beaker. Ext hexane with 5 ml CH_3CN and drain into Phillips beaker. Evap. CH_3CN on steam bath with air current to ca 5–10 ml. Complete evapn in shallow H_2O bath at 40–45° with gentle air current, leaving in H_2O bath ca 3–5 min after solv. evaps.

Add 5 ml hexane-ether solv. to sample residue and prep. column as in **29.078**. Follow with chromatgc sepn of p-ClDPS and collect, in graduated cylinder, eluate found in calibration to contain p-ClDPS. Transfer to 125 ml g-s flask, rinse cylinder with small portions of the mixed solv., and evap. on steam bath with air current to ca 10–15 ml. Complete evapn in shallow H_2O-bath at 40–45° with gentle air current, leaving in H_2O-bath ca 3–5 min after evapn of solv. Pipet 50 ml isooctane into flask, stopper, and let stand ca 10 min, rotating frequently to insure soln. Det. A for sample and A' for std, at 230, 240, and 250 nm against isooctane. Calc., for sample, corrected $A_{samp.} = A_{240} - 0.5(A_{230} + A_{250})$. Calc., for std, corrected $A'_{std} = A'_{240} - 0.5(A'_{230} + A'_{250})$.

ppm Sulphenone $= (C \times 50/W) \times (A_{samp.}/A'_{std})$, where C = concn of std in mg/ml, W = wt fruit represented by aliquot of strip soln in kg, and 50 = diln factor. If diln is necessary to obtain readings, multiply by this addnl diln factor.

Det. A at enough points between 220 and 260 nm to det. shape of curve.

Dichlorodiphenyltrichloroethane (DDT)
(1,1,1-Trichloro-2,2-bis(chlorophenyl)ethane)
—Official Final Action

Colorimetric Method (14)

29.082 *Principles*

Com. DDT consists essentially of 2 isomers, p,p' and o,p' DDT, in proportion of ca 3:1. Dry isomers of DDT can be nitrated to tetranitro DDT, which can be extd by ether, dried, and taken up in measured vol. benzene. Treating this soln with stdzd anhyd. NaOMe soln produces reasonably stable colors —blue for p,p' and reddish-purple for o,p' isomer. This reaction (Schechter-Haller) is fairly specific for DDT. Exceptions are nitrated or dehalogenated decomposition products of DDT and certain close analogs that can produce yellow to red and sometimes blue colors with NaOMe. If distinctly "off" colors are produced on samples of unknown spray history and cannot be removed from solv. by careful washing with alkali, analogs may be present, and special methods for their detection must be applied.

Principal known interfering insecticides are TDE (1,1-dichloro-2,2-bis(p-chlorophenyl)ethane), methoxychlor (1,1,1-trichloro-2,2-bis(p-methoxyphenyl) ethane), DNB and DNP (2-nitro-1,1-bis(p-chlorophenyl)butane and propane analogs of DDT). Other insecticidal compds, as well as limited amt of benzene-sol. plant extractives, are oxidized or degraded in nitration and are then removed from ether or pet ether soln by washing with alkali, or they do not react under conditions of method. Other org. material does not seriously interfere, but if >100 mg of extraneous org. matter is present, as in fats, special sepns must be made.

29.083 *Preparation of Sample*

(*Caution: See* **46.004, 46.011, 46.039, 46.040, 46.043, 46.045,** and **46.073.**)

(**a**) *For all fresh or frozen fruits and vegetables, meat, and canned food except milk, and for all soft or wet materials generally: Beans (green), broccoli, brussels sprouts, cauliflower, cabbage, cherries, cranberries, grapes, lettuce, pea pods, spinach, squash, tomatoes, silage, etc.*—Finely chop 1 kg sample or entire contents of small unit package in suitable food chopper (powered mech. food chopper such as Hobart is satisfactory) and transfer well-mixed 100 g portion to high-speed blender. Add 100 ml isopropanol and blend 2 min. Add 200 ml hexane or benzene and blend again 2 min. (To avoid splashing and possible loss of sample, regulate blending speed with rheostat or autotransformer when necessary.)

Pour mixt. as completely as possible into 600–800 ml beaker and let solids settle. Pour solv. layer equally into two 250 ml centrf. bottles. With aid of stirring rod and funnel, distribute solid material equally between the 2 bottles. Stopper and centrf. 5 min at ca 1500 rpm. If solids pack firmly, decant supernatant directly into 500 ml vol. flask. If solids

pack loosely, transfer liq. thru siphon tube, **16.177,** *Notes.* Wash blender cup, cap, and beaker with two 100 ml portions isopropanol-hexane or -benzene $(1 + 2)$. Distribute washings equally between the 2 bottles. Break up solid material with stirring rod, stopper bottles, and shake vigorously 2 min. Centrf. as before and add solv. layer to vol. flask. Dil. to vol. with isopropanol-hexane or -benzene $(1 + 2)$. (Final soln should be clear.)

(**b**) *For hay, cured (dry).*—Chop 1 kg sample and mix well. Grind portion in Wiley or other mill to ca 20 mesh.

Measure 500 ml extg solvent (350 ml H_2O dild to 1 L with CH_3CN, **29.002**(**a**), and mixed in graduated cylinder). Pour ca 350 ml into high-speed blender, add 50 g sample, and blend 2 min. Add remainder of extg solv. (total 500 ml) and blend addnl 3 min at highest speed attainable without splashing. Filter with vac. thru powder funnel contg wad of glass wool and press out free liq. with back of large spoon or other means. Measure and record vol. filtrate, and transfer to 2 L separator. Add 200 ml pet ether (boiling range 30–60°), and shake vigorously 1–2 min. Add ca 20 ml satd NaCl soln and ca 1200 ml H_2O, and mix gently but thoroly. Re-ext aq. layer with two 100 ml portions pet ether. Discard aq. layer, swirl combined pet ether, drain off any aq. phase closely, and transfer exts to beaker. Evap. just to dryness on steam bath with aid of gentle air current.

Wt sample represented in analysis = wt sample taken $\times$ vol. filtrate/vol. extg solv. added.

(**c**) *For flour, cereals, feeding stuffs, or other comparatively fine dry materials.*—Ext 25 g sample with ether or benzene in Soxhlet app. or shake larger samples with suitable amts of solv. in centrf. bottle, centrf., and decant solv. Repeat extn once or twice, according to size sample. If necessary, sep. fat and DDT as in **29.087**(**b**), and det. DDT in ext by colorimetric method.

(**d**) *For milk, cream, cheese, butter, oils or fats, etc.*—As DDT is dissolved in fat phase of dairy products, first sep. fats as in **29.010**; then isolate DDT as in **29.011**; and det. by colorimetric method (3 g fat is upper limit). Proceed as in **29.087**(**b**).

29.084 *Reagents*

(*Caution: See* **46.011** and **46.039.**)

(**a**) *Ether.*—Peroxide- and aldehyde-free.

(**b**) *Redistilled ether-petroleum ether.*—$(1 + 4)$.

(**c**) *Benzene.*—(*Caution: See* **46.045.**) Redistd. Distill until no more H_2O comes over, and discard distillate; replace condenser with dry one, and collect balance of distillate.

(**d**) *Nitrating mixture.*—(*Caution: See* **46.026, 46.030,** and **46.031.**) Mix fuming HNO_3 (sp gr 1.49–1.50) with equal vol. H_2SO_4. Chill before using.

(**e**) *Sodium methylate soln.*—$1.74N$. 40 g Na/L MeOH. (*Caution: See* **46.034** and **46.038.**) Prep. anhyd. MeOH as follows: Place 75 ml "absolute"

MeOH in flask provided with reflux condenser and add 5 g clean Mg turnings. Add 0.5 g I and warm gently, if necessary, until vigorous evolution of H sets in; then reflux until most of Mg has been converted to $Mg(OMe)_2$. Add mixt. to ca 900 ml untreated MeOH, reflux 30 min, and distill with exclusion of atm. H_2O. Preserve in tightly stoppered bottles. (Or dehydrate by refluxing 2–4 hr with 25 g CaH_2/L and then distg.)

Place 20.0 g freshly cut Na in flask provided with reflux condenser and add portionwise thru condenser enough purified MeOH to dissolve all the Na, warming and refluxing if necessary. Rinse into 500 ml vol. flask with addnl purified MeOH, cool, dil. to vol., and mix thoroly. Chill, centrf. down any carbonate turbidity, and decant clear supernatant into dispensing system that excludes atm. H_2O and CO_2. Adjust batches of NaOMe soln to std concn by titrn with std acid, and prep. new std curve for each batch as made.

Store in dispensing system with all outlets trapped against CO_2 and H_2O and with inner delivery tube to buret packed with dry, alkali-treated asbestos to filter soln immediately before use.

(f) *Pure p,p′ (mp 108–109°) and o,p′ (mp 74–74.5°) DDT.*—ESA Ref. Std p,p′-isomer available from City Chemical Corp., 132 W. 22nd St, New York, NY 10011. p,p′-Isomer may be prepd from 200 g tech. DDT by recrystg 2 or 3 times from alcohol, and o,p′-DDT from mother liquors by concn, fractional crystn from n-pentane, and recrystn from MeOH. o,p′-DDT may be synthesized as in Haller, *et al.*, J. Am. Chem. Soc. **67**, 1591(1945).

(g) *DDT std solns.*—(1) *Pure soln.*—0.2 mg total DDT (0.15 mg p,p′ and 0.05 mg o,p′)/ml. Weigh 50 mg of the 2 pure isomers into 2 sep. 50 ml vol. flasks and dil. to vol. with benzene. Pipet 15 ml p,p′ soln and 5 ml o,p′ soln into 100 ml vol. flask and dil. to vol. with benzene. (2) *Technical soln.*—0.2 mg tech. DDT/ml benzene.

29.085 *Preparation of Standard Curves*

(a) *For 0–1.0 mg range.*—Measure 0, 1.00, 2.00, 3.00, 4.00, and 5.00 ml of either std DDT soln into 50 ml erlenmeyers and evap. solv. on steam bath. Remove residual vapors with gentle air current, weight flasks (small Pb rings are convenient), and immerse in pan of ice-H_2O. (Use pan shelved so that vessels do not rest directly on bottom; porcelain desiccator platform in pan of proper size makes convenient bath.) Thoroly chill flasks and to each slowly add 5 ml chilled nitrating mixt. Rotate flasks to wet all portions of residue; then place pan on hot plate or steam bath and heat so that solns reach ca 85° in 20–30 min. Remove flasks from pan, place directly upon active steam bath, and nitrate 30 min. Remove flasks and cool under tap or leave overnight.

Slowly pour chilled acid mixt. from each flask into separator contg ca 25 ml ice-cold H_2O, rinse flask with several portions of ice-H_2O, and pour rinsings

into separator. Rinse again with 25 ml ether-pet ether (1 + 4), and finally with second 15 ml portion ether-pet ether (1 + 4), pouring last rinse into second separator. Ext by shaking first separator vigorously 1 min; then drain aq. layer into second separator and repeat extn. Discard aq. layer and drain second separator into first, rinsing with small portions of ether mixt. Bleed off any residual aq. layer as completely as possible, add 10 ml 10% KOH soln, and shake vigorously 30 sec. Drain off closely and wash with two 15 ml portions satd NaCl soln. Drain well and filter ext thru 0.5″ layer of washed and dried glass wool previously wetted with ether mixt., held in filter tube, into 125 ml erlenmeyer contg glass bead. Rinse separator and filter with few small portions of ether mixt., evap. off ether on steam bath (gentle air current speeds evapn and controls bumping), and heat 1 hr at 100°.

Cool flask, making sure interior is thoroly dry, and take up residue with exactly 25 ml redistd benzene. Stopper flask and swirl 1 min to ensure complete soln of residue. (Procedure may be interrupted overnight at this stage.)

Transfer 5.00 ml aliquot to small flask and develop characteristic DDT color by adding exactly 10.0 ml NaOMe soln. Mix well, let stand 15 min, and then det. A at 600 nm in cell of appropriate length against benzene-NaOMe soln (1 + 2). (Readings in blue at 450 nm and in green at 510 nm should also be made to check presence of extraneous yellow and red colors when actual samples are read later.) If instrument used records in terms of T, convert to A ($-\log T$).

Measure all colors of series in same (or similar) cells and plot A against μg DDT on linear coordinate paper to obtain std curve. Stopper cells with glass covers or stoppers. If test tubes are used, close with clean cork stoppers. Either cells with optically fused ends or cells constructed with alkali-resistant cement may be used, but if cemented cells are used, do not leave alk. solns in cells longer than necessary to make measurements, and clean cells immediately after use.

(b) *For 0–50 μg range.*—Add 0, 10, 20, 30, 40, and 50 μg DDT, in benzene soln, to series of 50 ml erlenmeyers, each contg 10 mg oleic acid in benzene soln, and evap. to dryness. (Small Pb rings are convenient for weighting flasks. Oleic acid serves as inert buffer material to prevent loss of micro amts of DDT.) Nitrate as in (a) and ext with redistd pet ether. Wash ext 3 times with 10% KOH soln, shaking vigorously 2 min each time. Heat final washed residues 1 hr at 100°, take up in 3.00 ml redistd benzene, and develop color with 6.00 ml of the NaOMe soln. Plot A against μg DDT as in (a).

29.086 *Removal of Coloring Matter*
(*Caution: See* **46.011, 46.030, 46.031, 46.039, 46.040, 46.045, 46.049,** *and* **46.054.**)

(a) *Applicable to extracts of fruits, vegetables, and most other low fat products.*—Evap. 200 ml aliquot prepd soln, **29.083**(a), or suitable aliquot of **29.083** (c), just to dryness in 400 ml beaker on steam bath with aid of small air current. Dissolve residue in 10 ml CCl_4 and transfer to column prepd as follows:

Grind 10 g Celite 545 thoroly with 3 ml 15–20% fuming H_2SO_4 in mortar, add 3 ml H_2SO_4, and grind well. Transfer at once to fritted glass funnel or tube (funnel: 40 mm id, 60 ml capacity, coarse porosity; tube: 30 mm disk, 130 ml capacity, coarse porosity (sulfur absorption tube, Arthur H. Thomas Co. No. 9327-V is satisfactory)). Pack adsorbent to firm level surface with flat-end glass rod. Add CCl_4 to column to wet adsorbent and let solv. drain until ca 2 mm layer remains on top of column.

Transfer 10 ml CCl_4 sample soln to column. Rinse sample beaker with three 10 ml portions CCl_4 and add rinsings to column. Collect eluate in 125 ml g-s flask. Let solv. drain until level just reaches surface of adsorbent and rinse walls of tube with 10 ml CCl_4. Repeat with second 10 ml portion CCl_4. After solv. drains to surface level, add 25 ml CCl_4 and let drain completely. At no time permit solv. to sink entirely into column (go dry) until this point is reached. Tamp surface of column with flat-end glass rod to remove all free liq.

(b) *Applicable to extracts of hay.*—Proceed as in (a), except use 20 g Celite 545 with 6 ml 15–20% fuming H_2SO_4 and 6 ml H_2SO_4 for column, and 170 ml CCl_4 for elution.

(c) *Applicable to extracts of fatty materials containing maximum of 3 g fat.*—Proceed as in (a), except use 30 g Celite 545 with 9 ml 15–20% fuming H_2SO_4 and 9 ml H_2SO_4, and 250 ml CCl_4 for elution.

29.087 **Determination**
(*Caution: See* **46.011, 46.039, 46.040, 46.049,** and **46.054.**)

(a) *Applicable to extracts of fruits, vegetables, and other low fat products.*—Evap. solv. just to dryness on steam bath with aid of small air current. Carefully nitrate residue as in **29.085**(a). To ensure thoro removal of interfering oxidn byproducts, wash ether mixt. with six 10 ml portions 10% KOH soln.

If quantity DDT is unknown, develop exploratory color with 5 ml aliquot and 10 ml NaOMe soln. If A is <0.20, check by taking 10–15 ml aliquot, evapg to dryness, redissolving in 5 ml benzene, and developing color; if A is >0.80, check by taking smaller aliquot, dilg to 5 ml with benzene, and developing color. In all cases, even if exploratory A reading falls in range 0.20–0.80, develop color on another aliquot of nitrated sample as check.

Det. A of final soln at 600 nm and also take readings at 510 and 450 nm to det. if gross amts of interfering red or yellow are present. Obtain total DDT in aliquot from std curve and calc. total DDT in sample in ppm.

(b) *Applicable to extracts of fatty materials containing maximum of 3 g fat.*—Proceed as in (a), except use all of nitrated sample to develop color, and use 0–50 μg std curve method, **29.085**(b).

Dichlone (2,3-Dichloro-1,4-naphthoquinone) (Phygon®) (*15*)—Official Final Action

29.088 **Reagents**

(a) *Dichlone std soln.*—0.2 mg/ml. Dissolve and dil. 40 mg dichlone (Eastman Kodak Co. No. 3836, or equiv.) to 200 ml with benzene.

(b) *Dimethylamine.*—25% aq. soln (Eastman Kodak Co. P 601 or equiv.).

(c) *Florisil.*—60/100 mesh, PR Grade, activated at 1250° F (Floridin Co.). Heat ≥4 hr at 130° and store in stoppered flasks in desiccator prior to use.

29.089 **Preparation of Standard Curve**

Place 0, 1.00, 2.00, 3.00, 4.00, and 5.00 ml dichlone std soln in 25 ml g-s graduated cylinders and dil. each to 10 ml with benzene. To each cylinder add isopropanol to 20 ml mark and mix. Add 1 ml 25% Me_2NH soln, dil. to 25 ml with isopropanol, and mix.

Read A of stds against blank in covered 1 cm cells (color remains stable >1 hr) at 495 nm, and plot A against mg dichlone (0–1.0 mg range).

29.090 **Preparation of Column**

Fill 15 × 300 mm chromatgc tube fitted with fritted glass disk or glass wool plug with Florisil to ca ⅓ its length. (No stopcock is required.) Prewet Florisil with 30 ml benzene.

29.091 **Determination**
(*Caution: See* **46.011, 46.039, 46.040,** and **46.045.**)

Strip weighed sample (ca 1 kg) with 500 ml benzene by gently turning or tumbling 10 min in suitable container (ca 1 gal.). (Avoid breaking plant tissue.) Drain benzene into 1 L flask thru folded paper (ca 32 cm) contg ca 50 g anhyd. Na_2SO_4.

Add 200 ml dried benzene strip soln to prepd chromatgc column. Discard benzene eluate. Elute dichlone from column with 100 ml acetone-benzene eluting mixt. (1 + 99). Collect eluate in beaker and evap. to ca 15 ml. (Do not let sample overheat or go to dryness.) Rinse sample into graduated cylinder and dil. to 20 ml with benzene. Develop color in 10 ml of this soln as in **29.089.** mg Dichlone from std curve × 5 = ppm dichlone.

If visible color is present in benzene eluate, simultaneously develop color in remaining 10 ml aliquot, omitting Me_2NH and adding 1 ml H_2O. Subtract this blank A from that of developed sample to correct for sample blank.

O,O-Dimethyl S-(4-Oxo-1,2,3-benzotriazin-3-(4H)-yl Methyl) Phosphorodithioate (Guthion®) (*16*)—Official First Action

(Applicable to cole-type crops and to apples, plums, peaches, grapes, apricots, and cherries. For cherries and highly pigmented cole-type vegetables, carry recovery run along with detn. "*(Stop)*" indicates points in method where sample may be held for short periods or overnight without loss.

29.092   *Principles*

Guthion is extd from crop with acetone and re-extd with $CHCl_3$ from acetone after diln with H_2O. Solv. is removed by evapn; residue is dissolved in isopropanol and cleaned up on chromatgc column. Guthion is hydrolyzed in alk. soln to anthranilic acid, which is diazotized and coupled with *N*-(1-naphthyl)ethylenediamine.$2HCl$ to form colored compd. Omission of alk. hydrolysis reveals presence of interfering materials except Et homolog of Guthion.

29.093   *Reagents*

(a) *Potassium hydroxide in isopropanol soln.—* $0.5N$. Dissolve 28.5 g KOH in absolute (99.5%) isopropanol.

(b) *Alumina.*—Acid-wash 0.5 lb Merck chromatgc grade Al_2O_3 in 1 L flask by adding 400 ml H_2O and 2.5 ml HCl and mixing thoroly. Let stand 2 hr, wash by decantation 4 times with H_2O, filter thru buchner, and wash until filtrate is only faintly acid. Finally wash with two 200 ml portions alcohol, evap. last traces of alcohol on steam bath, and dry in oven at 140° overnight. Store in tightly closed container or desiccator.

(c) *Ammonium sulfamate soln.*—2.5%. Prep. every 3 days.

(d) *Guthion std soln.*—80 µg/ml. Dissolve 80 mg Guthion (available from Chemagro Corp., PO Box 4913, Kansas City, MO 64120) in acetone and dil. to 100 ml with acetone. Dil. 10 ml to 100 ml with acetone. (*Caution:* Guthion is extremely poisonous. Avoid contact with skin and inhalation of dust.)

(e) *Coupling reagent.*—1% soln of *N*-(1-naphthyl) ethylenediamine.$2HCl$. Prep. every 3 days.

(f) *Magnesium oxide.*—Sea Sorb 43 (Westvaco), Fisher Scientific Co. No. S-120.

(g) *Sodium nitrite soln.*—0.2%. Prep. fresh daily.

29.094   *Preparation of Sample*

(*Caution: See* **46.004, 46.039,** and **46.046.**)

Remove stems, stones, or pits from fruits. Chop sample into small pieces, using Hobart food cutter or equiv., and weigh 200 g sample into high-speed blender. Blend at high speed 5 min with 200 ml acetone. Add 200 ml addnl acetone and blend 5 min at low speed. Cool to room temp. and transfer to 1 L graduated cylinder with dil. acetone (2 + 1). Dil. to 700 ml with dil. acetone (2 + 1) and mix. Filter thru plug of glass wool in funnel. Refilter thru same plug, if necessary, to obtain clear filtrate. (*Stop*)

29.095   *Purification*

(*Caution: See* **46.011, 46.040,** and **46.056.**)

Place 350 ml clear filtrate in 1 L separator, add 3.0 ml HCl and 300 ml H_2O, and mix. Add 100 ml $CHCl_3$ and shake gently 1 min. Let sep., and drain $CHCl_3$ thru column contg 100 g anhyd. Na_2SO_4, collecting filtrate in 600 ml beaker. Ext with 6 addnl 50 ml por-

tions $CHCl_3$, avoiding emulsions. Filter each portion with suction thru Na_2SO_4 column to remove droplets of H_2O. Evap. combined $CHCl_3$ exts to dryness on steam bath in air current.

Prep. 2 × 40 cm column with fritted glass plate contg successive layers of 2 g Hyflo Super-Cel, 5 g well-mixed mixt. of 2 parts Super-Cel and 1 part Sea Sorb MgO, 10 g Al_2O_3, and 20 g anhyd. Na_2SO_4. Add each layer under suction and after each layer is added, remove suction and tamp on wood block to liberate trapped air. Equilibrate column with 50 ml isopropanol.

Dissolve residue from $CHCl_3$ extn in 25 ml isopropanol, boiling gently if necessary. Cool and pour sample soln onto column as last of equilibrating solv. passes into top layer of column. Rinse beaker with 25 ml isopropanol and transfer to column. Collect 200 ml isopropanol eluate, using suction to maintain flow. (*Stop*)

29.096   *Determination*

Evap. eluate or aliquot to dryness on steam bath in air current and remove from bath. (*Stop*) Dry residue 30 min in 50–60° oven. Dissolve dry residue in 10 ml benzene, add 10 ml alc. $0.5N$ KOH, (a), and mix. After 20 min, acidify with 8 ml $3N$ HCl. Transfer mixt. to 250 ml separator, using 15 ml H_2O and 50 ml benzene to rinse beaker. Shake vigorously 1 min, let sep., and drain aq. layer into 50 ml g-s graduated cylinder. Rinse beaker with addnl 15 ml H_2O, transfer to separator, shake vigorously, and let sep. Drain aq. layer into cylinder and discard benzene layer.

Dil. aq. soln to 50 ml with H_2O and mix. Add 0.2 g Zn dust and let react 15 min, mixing 2–3 times. (Zn reduction is not necessary for fruits.) Filter thru Whatman No. 12 paper or equiv., and place 20 ml aliquot filtrate in 25 ml g-s graduated cylinder or vol. flask. Add 1 ml $NaNO_2$ soln, mix, and let stand 10 min. Add 1 ml NH_4 sulfamate soln, mix, and let stand 10 min. Add 2 ml coupling reagent, mix, dil. to vol. with H_2O, and mix thoroly. Let stand 30 min and read *A* at 555 nm against blank prepd with 3 ml $3N$ HCl, 17 ml H_2O, and other reagents used in diazotization. Det. µg Guthion from std curve.

29.097   *Preparation of Standard Curve*

Add 1.0, 2.0, 3.0, 4.0, and 5.0 ml Guthion std soln to 50 ml beakers and evap. to dryness on steam bath in current of air. Proceed as in **29.096,** beginning "Dissolve dry residue in 10 ml benzene . . ." Plot *A* at 555 nm against µg Guthion.

Dodine (Cyprex®) (Dodecylguanidine Acetate) (DDGA) (17)—Official Final Action

(Applicable to apples, peaches, pears, pecans, and strawberries)

29.098   *Reagents*

(a) *Bromocresol purple soln.*—Recrystallize indicator-grade bromocresol purple from boiling toluene (ca 2 g/100 ml). (Material from Harleco, 60th &

Woodland, Philadelphia, PA 19143, has been satisfactory without purification.) Dissolve 0.4 g recrystd material in 75 ml 0.01N NaOH; if necessary, add addnl 0.01N NaOH to bring pH to 6.0–6.1. Filter, if necessary, and dil. to 500 ml with CO₂-free H₂O. Store in brown bottle.

(b) *Buffer soln.* — pH 5.5. Dissolve 15.2 g Na₂HPO₄.7H₂O and 74.0 g NaH₂PO₄.H₂O in CO₂-free H₂O and dil. to 1 L.

(c) *Dodecylguanidine acetate (DDGA) std solns.*— (1) *Stock soln.*—130 μg/ml. Dissolve 32.5 mg in MeOH and dil. to 250 ml with MeOH. (2) *Working soln.*—13 μg/ml. Dil. 25 ml aliquot stock soln to 250 ml with MeOH.

29.099   Preparation of Sample

Grind sample in high-speed blender with MeOH-CHCl₃ (2 + 1) in ratio of 400 ml solv./100 g sample. Filter with suction thru 2 Whatman No. 1, or equiv., papers in buchner, and wash pulp with MeOH-CHCl₃ (2 + 1), using 100 ml/100 g sample. Det. vol. of ext and transfer portion equiv. to 50 g sample to 400 ml beaker.

29.100   Determination

Add several glass beads and 1 ml HCl to beaker, and evap. to 50 ml on steam bath. Add 30 ml 30% NaCl soln and 100 ml MeOH. Cool, transfer to 500 ml separator, and ext *gently* with 50 ml CCl₄ by inverting separator 6–8 times. Let phases sep. and discard CCl₄ layer. Repeat with 50 ml CCl₄, inverting separator ca twice as many times. Discard CCl₄; then ext with 50 ml CCl₄, shaking gently 30 sec. Finally, ext with 50 ml CCl₄, shaking vigorously 1 min, and again discard CCl₄.

Adjust pH of soln to ca 5.5 with 4N NaOH (pH meter), and add 20 ml pH 5.5 buffer and 20 ml bromocresol purple soln. Re-adjust pH to 5.5 and ext complex with two 50 ml portions CHCl₃, shaking 2 min each time. Shake combined ext 30 sec with 25 ml pH 5.5 buffer, and transfer CHCl₃ layer to another separator. Shake 1 min with 25 ml pH 5.5 buffer, let stand 10 min, and transfer CHCl₃ to another separator. Shake with 20 ml 0.05N NaOH to remove all combined indicator and any org. acids which may persist. Recomplex dodecylguanidine (in CHCl₃ as free base) by shaking 3 min with 5 ml bromocresol purple soln and 20 ml pH 5.5 buffer. Wash CHCl₃ with three 15 ml portions pH 5.5 buffer, shaking 1 min each time. Transfer CHCl₃ to dry 250 ml separator and shake 2 min with 20 ml 0.05N NaOH, measured by pipet. Read A of indicator in aq. soln at 590 nm, using Beckman spectrophtr or equiv. Obtain quantity DDGA from std curve.

29.101   Preparation of Standard Curve

Add 0.5, 1.0, 2.0, 3.0, 4.0, and 5.0 ml std soln to series of separators contg 100 ml MeOH, 50 ml H₂O, 30 ml 30% NaCl soln, 20 ml bromocresol purple soln, and 20 ml pH 5.5 buffer. Adjust pH of each soln to

5.5 and continue as in **29.100**, beginning "... and ext complex with two 50 ml portions CHCl₃, shaking 2 min each time." Read A of each aq. soln at 590 nm and plot against μg DDGA. No blank correction is necessary for stds.

ppm DDGA = μg DDGA in aliquot/g sample in aliquot.

2-Heptadecyl Glyoxalidine Acetate (Glyodin)
(18)—Official Final Action

(Applicable to apples and pears. Not applicable to fruits with extensive softening or decomposition. All glassware must be free of soap or detergent.)

29.102   Reagents

(a) *Bromophenol blue soln.*—Prep. just before use. Transfer 50 mg bromophenol blue powder into 500 ml vol. flask with small amt H₂O. Add 2 ml HOAc and swirl until dye is completely dissolved. Dil. to vol. with H₂O, and mix.

(b) *Glyodin std solns.*—Prep. from 2-heptadecyl glyoxalidine, purified grade (available from Union Carbide Corp.). (1) *Stock soln.*—1 mg/ml. Dissolve 100.0 mg 2-heptadecyl glyoxalidine in CHCl₃ in 100 ml vol. flask, dil. to vol. with CHCl₃, and mix. (2) *Working soln.*—0.05 mg free base/ml. Transfer 5 ml stock soln to 100 ml vol. flask, dil. to vol. with CHCl₃, and mix.

29.103   Preparation of Standard Curve

Add 0, 2, 4, 6, 8, and 10 ml working std soln to six 50 ml vol. flasks. Add exactly 1 ml HOAc to each flask and dil. to vol. with CHCl₃. Place 25 ml of each std, measured in graduated cylinder or fast-flow pipet, in 125 ml separator. Add 25 ml bromophenol blue soln, (a), from graduated cylinder or fast-flow pipet to each separator, and shake vigorously 1 min. Let sep. ≥20 min. Filter CHCl₃ layer thru pledget of glass wool in stem of separator into small g-s erlenmeyer. Det. A at 415 nm in spectrophtr, using 1 cm cells and 0 std as ref. Plot A against mg 2-heptadecyl glyoxalidine.

29.104   Preparation of Sample

Fill tared wide-mouth gal. glass jar with whole fruit so that little or no slack is present (to prevent battering of fruit). Weigh, and add 250 ml isopropanol. Screw cap on tightly with double thickness of cellophane placed over mouth of jar before cap is screwed on to help prevent leakage. Tumble or shake 10 min. Filter into 500 ml vol. flask thru small layer of glass wool in funnel. Drain off as much liq. as possible. Repeat stripping with second 250 ml portion of isopropanol, and filter into vol. flask. Wash glass wool and funnel with small portions of isopropanol and dil. to vol.

29.105   Determination

Transfer 25 ml aliquot of strip soln to 50 ml beaker and evap. to dryness on steam bath under air jet. To residue add exactly 1 ml HOAc, allowing acid to drip slowly down sides of beaker so that all residue is wetted. Cover beaker with watch glass and heat gently on steam bath with swirling, until residue at bottom loosens and disintegrates. Thoroly rinse down sides with few ml CHCl₃ and transfer to 50 ml vol. flask. Rinse beaker 4 more times with small portions CHCl₃, and transfer to vol. flask. Dil. to vol. with CHCl₃ (disregard turbidity and slight color in soln).

Transfer 25 ml CHCl₃ soln, measured in cylinder or fast-flow pipet, to 125 ml separator. Proceed as in **29.103**, beginning, "Add 25 ml bromophenol blue soln, (a), . . ."

Perform detns along with prepn of std curve, using 0 std as ref. when detg sample A. Det. quantity of 2-heptadecyl glyoxalidine in aliquot from std curve.

Glyodin (2-heptadecyl glyoxalidine acetate) = 2-heptadecyl glyoxalidine × 1.195.

Malathion (S-[1,2-bis(Ethoxycarbonyl)ethyl] O,O-Dimethyl Phosphorodithioate) (19)— Official First Action

29.106   *Principles*

Malathion is extd with either CCl₄ or mixt. of CCl₄ and isopropanol and decomposed by alkali in CCl₄-alcohol soln into Na O,O-dimethyl phosphorodithioate, Na fumarate, and alcohol. Na O,O-dimethyl phosphorodithioate is converted to cupric salt which is sol. in CCl₄ with formation of intense yellow color. Color intensity is proportional to concn of O,O-dimethyl phosphorodithioic acid and is measured photometrically at 418 nm.

29.107   *Reagents*

(a) *Malathion std solns.*—(1) *Stock soln.*—0.4 mg/ml. Dissolve 0.1 g purified material (obtainable from American Cyanamid Co.) in absolute alcohol and dil. to 250 ml with absolute alcohol. Mix well. (2) *Working soln.*—40 μg/ml. Dil. 25 ml stock soln to 250 ml with absolute alcohol.

(b) *Carbon tetrachloride.*—Reagent grade; or tech. grade distd from all-glass app. at steam bath temp. and stored in amber bottles, which meets following test: Evap. ca 500 ml on steam bath to 100 ml with aid of air jet. Add known amt of malathion (ca 0.5 mg) in alcohol and det. malathion, using reagent grade CCl₄, as in prepn of std curve. A found should agree closely with A of same amt of malathion carried thru prepn of std curve, when reagent grade CCl₄ is used.

(c) *Carbon disulfide soln.*—0.5%. Dissolve 1 ml CS₂ in 200 ml reagent grade CCl₄.

(d) *Ferric chloride soln.*—5%. Dissolve 5 g FeCl₃ .6H₂O in 100 ml 1N HCl.

(e) *Copper sulfate soln.*—Dissolve 3.5 g CuSO₄ .5H₂O in 100 ml H₂O.

(f) *Sodium sulfate soln.*—Dissolve 90 g anhyd. Na₂SO₄ in H₂O and dil. to 1 L.

29.108   *Preparation of Sample*

Where possible, use sample size and vol. CCl₄ such that 100 ml of the CCl₄ ext contains 0.1–1.0 mg malathion. To det. 0.2 ppm malathion, use vol. ext equiv. to at least 500 g sample. Conc. larger vol. CCl₄ to 100 ml by evapn on steam bath with aid of air jet.

For firm fruits such as apples, pears, peaches, and plums and for fresh or frozen vegetables and soft or wet materials generally.—Finely chop ca 1 kg sample or entire contents of small unit package in suitable food chopper (powered mech. chopper, such as Hobart, is satisfactory) and transfer well-mixed 100 g portion to high-speed blender. Add 100 ml isopropanol and blend 2 min. Add 200 ml CCl₄ and blend addnl 2 min. Centrf., and pour CCl₄-isopropanol layer into separator. Wash with four 50 ml portions H₂O to remove isopropanol (if emulsions occur, use 2% aq. Na₂SO₄ soln for washing). Use 100 ml washed CCl₄ ext for detn.

29.109   *Preparation of Standard Curve*
(*Caution: See* **46.018** *and* **46.041**.)

Pipet 0, 2.5, 5, 10, 15, 20, and 25 ml aliquots working std soln into sep. 250 ml separators contg 100 ml CCl₄ and 1 ml 0.5% CS₂ soln, (c), and add absolute alcohol until total vol. of alcohol is 25 ml. Mix by gentle swirling, add 75 ml Na₂SO₄ soln, (f), which has been acidified with 2.5 ml HCl, and shake vigorously 1 min. Let layers sep. and filter CCl₄ layer thru 12 cm fluted paper into dry 250 ml separator. Do not let any of aq. layer run into filter paper and do not wash paper. Add 25 ml absolute alcohol to separator contg filtered CCl₄ soln and mix by swirling. Add 1.0 ml 6N NaOH and shake exactly 1 min. Immediately add 75 ml Na₂SO₄ soln cooled to 15° and shake vigorously 1 min. Let sep.; drain CCl₄ layer and discard it.

Add 25 ml CCl₄ to separator, shake vigorously 30 sec, let sep., and discard CCl₄ layer. Add to separator 25 ml CCl₄, 2 drops phthln, and 6N HCl, dropwise with swirling until pink disappears; then add 1 ml 5% FeCl₃ soln. Shake vigorously 30 sec, let sep., and discard CCl₄ layer. Again add 25 ml CCl₄, shake vigorously 30 sec, let sep., and discard CCl₄ layer. Repeat extn of aq. layer third time with 25 ml CCl₄ and discard it. Pipet in 25 ml CCl₄ and 1 ml CuSO₄ soln, (e); shake vigorously exactly 1 min and let sep. Immediately filter CCl₄ layer thru small plug of cotton, placed loosely in funnel stem, into 1 cm cell. Det. A of yellow soln (stable only 5–10 min) at 418 nm, against reagent grade CCl₄. Prep. std curve by plotting A of each std against μg malathion.

29.110   *Determination*
(*Caution: See* **46.018, 46.040,** *and* **46.049**.)

Transfer 100 ml of the CCl₄ ext contg ≤1.0 mg malathion, to 250 ml separator; add 1 ml 0.5% CS₂ soln, (c), and 25 ml absolute alcohol; and mix well by swirling. Proceed as in prepn of std curve, beginning

"... add 75 ml Na$_2$SO$_4$ soln, (f) ...", discarding small amt of emulsion layer and suspended solids that may have formed after shaking with FeCl$_3$ soln. After this extn, repeat extn of aq. phase, using 25 ml portions CCl$_4$ until colorless (measure A at 418 nm). After final CCl$_4$ extn, drain CCl$_4$ as completely as possible and discard.

To aq. phase in separator add by pipet 25 ml CCl$_4$ and then 1 ml CuSO$_4$ soln. Immediately shake 1 min and let sep. Immediately filter CCl$_4$ layer thru small plug of cotton, placed loosely in funnel stem, into 1 cm cell. Measure A of yellow soln (stable only 5–10 min) at 418 nm, against reagent grade CCl$_4$.

From std curve read amt of malathion corresponding to the A and calc. ppm malathion in sample. ppm Malathion in sample = μg malathion found/g sample in aliquot analyzed. Det. crop blank by carrying same amt of malathion-free crop thru method.

Note: For apples use 1 ml 5% CS$_2$ in CCl$_4$ in place of 1 ml 0.5% CS$_2$ reagent used for other products. In subsequent neutzn of alk. aq. layer with HCl solns, flocculent white ppt forms. Retain ppt with aq. layer when CCl$_4$ washings are drained. On final washing drain small amt of suspended solids at CCl$_4$-aq. layer interface.

Maleic Hydrazide (20)—Official Final Action

(Applicable to whole, dehydrated mashed, and frozen french fried potatoes, and potato chips; whole cranberries, onions, and peaches; and tobacco dust)

29.111   *Principles*

Sample is boiled in alk. soln to drive off volatile basic interferences. Distn with Zn with N sweep expels hydrazine liberated from maleic hydrazide. Hydrazine is reacted in acid soln with p-dimethyl-aminobenzaldehyde to form yellow compd.

29.112   *Apparatus*

(a) *Distillation apparatus.*—See Fig. 29:9. Flask is 300 ml capacity, flat-bottom, double thickness, with thermometer well. Thermometer is 90–220° (Tinius Olsen No. 718636 "Yellow Bak," or equiv. in temp. range and length; available from H. G. Graff Co., 1237 Highland Ave, Boston, MA 02192). Use 5″ wire gauze with 4″ diam. asbestos center. Centrf. tube receiver (50 ml) is graduated in 1 ml divisions.

(b) *Spectrophotometer.* — Beckman Instruments Model DU or equiv.

29.113   *Reagents*

(a) *p-Dimethylaminobenzaldehyde soln.*—Dissolve 2 g in 100 ml 1N H$_2$SO$_4$. Soln is stable.

(b) *Zn granules.*—"10 mesh."

(c) *Maleic hydrazide std soln.*—10 μg/ml. Dissolve 0.0100 g maleic hydrazide in 100 ml 0.1N NaOH and dil. to 1 L. Soln is stable.

29.114   *Preparation of Sample*

Grind sample to soup-like consistency in high-speed blender, adding measured wt of H$_2$O if necessary. Prepd samples may be frozen for storage.

29.115   *Determination*

Transfer 2 g ground sample to 300 ml distn flask. Dry socket neck joint, and add 50 g NaOH pellets, 1 ml *refined vegetable oil,* as anti-foam, and 40 ml H$_2$O. Add 1 ml high bp oil to thermometer well and insert thermometer. Heat flask on high-temp. hot-plate and swirl ca every 20 sec until pellets dissolve and gentle boiling begins. When temp. reads 160°, remove flask and let cool 5 min. Wipe socket joint clean and dry; add 0.5 g *ferrous chloride* and 5 ml (equiv. to ca 5 g) Zn.

Quickly grease socket joint with light film of high-vac. silicone grease and attach flask to app. (Fig. 29:9). Center flask firmly on asbestos pad. Place 4 ml p-dimethylaminobenzaldehyde soln in 50 ml centrf. tube (ice-cooled) and immerse condenser tip. Adjust N flow (*dry N*) to 3 bubbles/sec in receiver. With rapid flow of condenser H$_2$O, heat flask with Bunsen burner, centering tip of outer cone of flame on asbestos pad. When boiling begins, adjust distance of burner so foaming contents fill ca ¾ of flask. Distill until temp. reads 173°, *slowly* add H$_2$O from reservoir until temp. drops to 168°, turn off H$_2$O, and distill to 173°. Continue H$_2$O addn and distn at these temps until receiver contains ca 40 ml. Remove receiver. (If during distn receiver soln becomes turbid or ppt appears, add 2 drops H$_2$SO$_4$ and shake.)

Record vol. of distillate and det. A at 430, 460, and 490 nm, using 1 cm cells and 4 ml p-dimethylamino-benzaldehyde soln dild to 40 ml as ref.

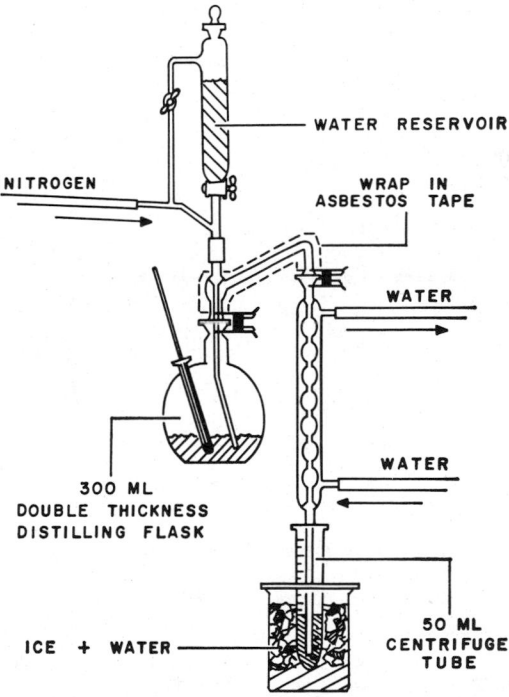

WATER RESERVOIR

NITROGEN

WRAP IN ASBESTOS TAPE

WATER

300 ML DOUBLE THICKNESS DISTILLING FLASK

WATER

WATER

ICE + WATER

50 ML CENTRIFUGE TUBE

FIG. 29:9—Distillation apparatus for maleic hydrazide determination

After distn, remove hot distg flask from app. with heat-resistant gloves, remove thermometer, and seal well with small cork. Rinse N-H2O inlet tube free of caustic with HCl from plastic squeeze bottle followed by H2O. Then (with gloves and safety glasses) pour molten contents of distg flask into Fe can in sink to trap Zn granules. Rinse flask 3 times with H2O and 2 times with HCl to remove encrusted caustic and Zn granules. Fill flask with HCl (1 + 9) to remain until next use. Rinse 3 times with H2O before reuse. (Careful removal of *all* Zn granules with HCl is essential because residual Zn would cause premature destruction of maleic hydrazide in precook of next sample. Because of corrosion by the caustic soln, flasks may last for only ca 30 detns.)

29.116   Preparation of Standard Curve

To clean 300 ml distn flasks add 50 g NaOH pellets, 40 ml H2O, and std soln equiv. to 0, 5, 10, 20, 30, 50, 100, 150, and 200 μg maleic hydrazide. Precook, distill, and measure A as in **29.115**. Det. net A for each std as follows:

$$A_{net} = \left[A_{460} - \frac{(A_{430} + A_{490})}{2} \right] \times \frac{\text{vol. color soln}}{40}$$

Plot net A of each std against μg maleic hydrazide to obtain std curve. If desired, derive simple factor from curve slope, K, converting net A to μg maleic hydrazide; thus, μg maleic hydrazide = $A_{net} \times K$.

29.117   Calculations

Multiply net A of sample by K to derive μg maleic hydrazide; ppm = μg/sample wt (g).

Methoxychlor (2,2-Bis(*p*-Methoxyphenyl) 1,1,1-Trichloroethane) (*21*)— Official Final Action

(Applicable to firm fruits such as apples, pears, peaches, and plums)

29.118   Principles

(a) ★*Colorimetric method.*★—Pet ether soln of ext of sample is extd with acetonitrile to sep. methoxychlor from fats and plant waxes. Methoxychlor in concd ext is dehalogenated and converted by alk. hydrolysis to dehydrochloride which is sepd by pet ether extn and reacted with 85% H2SO4 to produce red soln. *See* **24.149–24.152**, 10th ed. (*Caution: See* **46.011, 46.039,** and **46.073.**)

(b) *Multiple residue method.*—See **29.001–29.027.**

Monofluoroacetic Acid (Sodium Salt, "1080") (*22*)

Qualitative Test—Official First Action

(Monochloroacetic acid also responds to this test. Confirm presence of org. F by **29.121–29.127.**)

29.119   Reagents

(a) *Decolorizing carbon.*—See **16.027**(b).

(b) *Thiosalicylic acid soln.*—Dissolve 300 mg thiosalicylic acid (Eastman's tech. grade is suitable) in mixt. of 2 ml 1N NaOH and 18 ml H2O.

(c) *Potassium ferricyanide soln.*—Dissolve 1 g K3Fe(CN)6 in H2O and dil. to 50 ml with H2O.

29.120   Test

Prep. sample and ext as in **29.124–29.125.** If convenient, ext large enough sample to obtain 2–10 mg 1080. With very low levels of 1080, *e.g.*, 1–5 ppm, ext large enough sample to obtain $\geq$0.5 mg 1080.

Sep. ether ext from any aq. sludge which may have been carried over in extn, add ca 5 g anhyd. Na2SO4 and 0.5 g decolorizing C/100 ml ether, and shake vigorously. Let stand ca 15 min at room temp. with occasional shaking, and decant thru fluted paper into separator. Add ca 25 ml H2O and enough NaOH soln (ca 1N) to make aq. layer alk. after vigorous shaking (outside test paper). Drain aq. layer into 125 ml erlenmeyer and aerate to remove dissolved ether. Using pH test paper and ca 1N solns of H2SO4 and NaOH, adjust to pH 4–6. Add 0.5 g C and place on steam bath for 15 min.

Cool under tap and filter thru fluted paper into ca 25 × 150 mm test tube. Add 1 ml thiosalicylic acid soln and 2 drops NaOH (1 + 1), and mix. Conc. soln to small vol. by placing on steam bath under gentle air current. Completely dry residue in oven at 130° or, if time is not factor, in 100° oven. (When convenient, overnight drying is satisfactory, with or without prior concn of soln.)

Dissolve *thoroly* dry residue in 2–3 ml H2O, add 1 ml K3Fe(CN)6 soln, and mix. Red ppt, which forms at once when $\geq$1 mg 1080 is present, or upon standing when only fraction of mg is present, is pos. test for 1080.

Employ chromatgc instead of C purification in following cases:

(*1*) With pineapple juice when <2 mg 1080 can be extd.

(*2*) With grape juice even when $\geq$2 mg of 1080 can be conveniently extd.

(*3*) With any food or material when 1080 is strongly suspected and neg. test is obtained using C purification technic.

For chromatgc purification, follow **29.126** for sepg 1080 from other acids. Discard forerun, which may contain HOAc and other extraneous materials. Collect percolate fraction large enough to contain all the 1080 as detd by preliminary detn. Ext fluoroacetic acid from chromatgc percolate with 25 ml H2O and enough alkali to cause aq. layer to retain alky after vigorous shaking (outside test paper). Drain org. layer and discard. Drain aq. layer into 125 ml erlenmeyer and aerate to remove CHCl3. Pour soln into test tube and continue as above, beginning "Add 1 ml thiosalicylic acid soln . . ."

Quantitative Method—Official Final Action

29.121   Principles

After suitable sample prepn, acid is extd with ether and sepd from inorg. fluorides (partially ether-sol.)

by partition chromatgy on silicic acid, using $0.5N$ H_2SO_4 as immobile solv. and $CHCl_3$ contg 10% *tert*-amyl alcohol or *n*-butyl alcohol as mobile solv. Monofluoroacetic acid in eluate is converted to its Na salt, and quantity is estd by micro F detn, **25.033(a)**, **25.034**, and **25.035**.

29.122 *Apparatus*

(a) *Chromatographic tubes.*—18 mm od × 250 mm long, prepd from Pyrex tubing.

(b) *Pressure source.*—Compressed air or cylinder of N or CO_2, and means of keeping pressure constant, such as Hg column or diaphragm-type pressure regulator.

(c) *Mixer.*—High-speed blender.

29.123 *Reagents*

(a) *Silicic acid.*—Mallinckrodt analytical reagent grade pptd powder, or equiv.

(b) *Mobile solvent.*—Add 100 ml *tert*-amyl alcohol or *n*-butyl alcohol to 900 ml $CHCl_3$, and mix.

(c) *Phosphotungstic acid soln.*—Dissolve 20 g in H_2O and dil. to 100 ml.

29.124 *Preparation of Sample*

This will vary with type of material. Dissolve sugars in H_2O, acidify with H_2SO_4, and ext directly. Following methods for different type materials will be suggestive. Simple H_2O wash may be adequate to prove contamination of certain foods.

(a) *Sugar.*—Dissolve 100 g sample in enough H_2O to give ca 350 ml.

(b) *Flour.*—Place 100 g sample in mixer, add 400 ml H_2O and 5 g *pancreatin*, and comminute ca 2 min. Adjust to pH 7–8, using satd $Na_3PO_4.12H_2O$ soln and suitable indicator paper. Transfer comminuted material to tared 1 L erlenmeyer, washing mixer 3 times with 25 ml portions H_2O. Incubate mixt. at 35–40° $\geq$3 hr. Add 5 ml H_2SO_4 (1 + 1) and swirl. Add 20 ml phosphotungstic acid soln and swirl again. Dil. to 750 g with H_2O, stopper, and shake vigorously ca 2 min. Filter thru fluted paper or with suction thru buchner (16 cm size is convenient). Or, more quickly, centrf. and decant supernatant. Use $\geq$375 g aliquot of filtrate. (Since sp gr of filtrate is very close to 1, measuring out aliquot in graduated cylinder is satisfactory.)

(c) *Wheat.*—Grind sample finely in suitable mill, such as Wiley mill. Proceed as in (b).

(d) *Corn meal.*—Proceed as in (b), except omit pancreatic digestion.

(e) *Corn.*—Grind sample and proceed as in (d).

(f) *Peanuts.*—Grind sample finely (like peanut butter) and proceed as in (d), except use 100 ml phosphotungstic acid soln. If necessary, refilter thru folded paper to remove oil.

(g) *Cheese.*—Proceed as in (d), except use 40 ml phosphotungstic acid soln.

(h) *Other foods such as chili peppers, cacao beans,* *etc.*—Treat in manner similar to one of preceding foods.

(i) *Biological tissue.*—If material is tough or fibrous, grind it twice thru food chopper. (Soft tissues, *e.g.*, brain and liver, need not be ground.) Place 100 g ground tissue in 800 ml beaker, add ca 300 ml H_2O, cover with watch glass, and boil gently ca 30 min. Transfer material to mixer, rinsing beaker with two 25 ml portions H_2O, and comminute thoroly (ca 2 min). Transfer comminuted material to tared 1 L erlenmeyer, rinsing mixer with two 25 ml portions H_2O. Add 5 ml H_2SO_4 (1 + 1) and mix. Add enough phosphotungstic acid soln (50–75 ml) to ppt all proteins, then H_2O to make 600 g. Shake vigorously ca 2 min, and filter thru fluted paper or with suction thru buchner. If material does not filter rapidly, return mixt. to flask, add ca 10 ml addnl phosphotungstic acid soln, shake vigorously, and refilter.

Alternative method.—Place 100 g ground tissue in mixer, add 300 ml H_2O and 15 g pancreatin, and comminute thoroly (ca 2 min). Adjust to ca pH 8 with satd $Na_3PO_4.12H_2O$ soln, using suitable indicator paper. Transfer comminuted material from mixer to tared erlenmeyer, washing mixer with two 25 ml portions H_2O and incubate ca 3 hr at 35–40°. Ppt proteins and make to wt as directed previously.

29.125 *Extraction*

Transfer soln (of sugar) or wt-aliquot of protein-free filtrate (of protein-contg materials) to 200 ml continuous extractor, Fig. 16:1, page 246. (Tube is 115–120 cm long and 33–34 mm od; side arm, attached ca 63 cm from bottom, is 15–16 mm od. Inner tube is 12–13 mm od flared at top to ca 25 mm diam. 1.5 L Extractors of this type have been used successfully. Extra coarse fritted filter tip on bottom end of inner tube aids in getting smaller droplets of extg solv.) For each 50 g soln, add 1 ml H_2SO_4 (1 + 1). Ext with ether until all fluoroacetic acid has been extd (detd by preliminary experiment; usually 3–4 hr with 400 ml extractor). Transfer ether ext to separator of appropriate size.

To extn flask add ca 20 ml H_2O, 2 drops phthln, and enough $1.0N$ NaOH from buret to give strong alk. color of indicator after swirling. Pour rinse soln into separator and add addnl alkali until alk. color of indicator persists in aq. phase after vigorous shaking. Record vol. alkali required. Drain aq. layer into 100 ml beaker and wash ether with two 10 ml portions H_2O, rinsing extn flask each time with the H_2O before pouring it into separator. Add washings to beaker. Carefully adjust alky of ext just to alk. color of phthln with $0.1N$ H_2SO_4 and NaOH solns. Evap. neutzd ext to dryness on steam bath (current of air hastens evapn). If during evapn alk. color of indicator should disappear, add just enough $0.1N$ NaOH to give alk. color again. Do not continue heating after residue is apparently dry. Slightly moist residue is permissible.

29.126 *Chromatography*

To 5 g silicic acid, (a), in mortar add max. amt of 0.5*N* H₂SO₄ that it will hold without becoming sticky (50–80% of its wt). Mix well with pestle; then add ca 35 ml of the mobile solv. and work up into smooth slurry. (If SiO₂ agglomerates in solv., too much H₂SO₄ was used.) Place small cotton plug in bottom of chromatgc tube and pour in slurry, tilting tube slightly to avoid air bubbles. Let silicic acid pack down under 2–10 lb pressure applied thru gas pressure regulator. When excess solv. has drained thru (column firm and viscous enough to resist pouring when tipped), column is ready for use. In prepg column take care to avoid cracking or drying out of the gel caused by leaving pressure on after column packs down and all solv. sinks into gel.

To dry or slightly moist residue in 100 ml beaker add enough H₂SO₄ (1 + 1) (ca 18*N*), usually 0.5–1.0 ml, to give excess of ca 0.25 ml over quantity necessary to convert all salts to free acid, as calcd from amt of 1*N* NaOH required to neutze acid extd by the ether. Wet salts *thoroly* with the acid, using small, narrow blade spatula (steel or monel metal) to loosen salts from glass, and using flat-end glass rod to break up solid particles and mix resulting slurry. Add 5–10 g anhyd. granular Na₂SO₄ to take up excess liq. Stir well with tamping rod, breaking up any lumps. Add 10 ml mobile solv., (b), stir thoroly, and decant solv. carefully onto column.

Catch percolate in graduate. Apply pressure until all solv. sinks into gel; then release pressure. Add 5 ml mobile solv. to beaker and again stir thoroly. Carefully decant solv. onto column and, with aid of narrow-blade spatula, transfer bulk of material in beaker, mostly Na₂SO₄, to column. Renew pressure. When solv. passes ca halfway thru Na₂SO₄, release pressure. Rinse out beaker with addnl 5 ml solv. and transfer to column. After this washing sinks ca halfway into Na₂SO₄, fill tube with mobile solv. and complete collection, under pressure, of enough percolate to obtain all monofluoroacetic acid, as detd by test run on silicic acid used (ca 50 ml). Collect dropwise; 3–4 ml/min is convenient rate.

Transfer percolate to 125 ml separator; add ca 20 ml H₂O and enough 1.0*N* NaOH to give alk. color of phthln (phthln is present in percolate and no further addn is required) in aq. phase, after vigorous shaking. Drain aq. layer into 125 ml erlenmeyer and return solv. layer to separator. Wash solv. twice with 10 ml portions H₂O and add washings to erlenmeyer. Aerate soln with current of air to remove traces of CHCl₃. (If excess CHCl₃ is not removed, excessive Cl may complicate F distn in next step.)

29.127 *Determination*

Transfer aq. ext to Pt dish with little H₂O and mix with ca 20 ml lime suspension, **25.032**(a), evap. to *dryness*, and ash 15–20 min at 600°. (Little C in ash will not interfere in detn.) Proceed as in **25.033**

(a), beginning "When clean ash is obtained . . ." and **25.034–25.035** (100 ml Nessler tubes are preferable). Convert F results to fluoroacetic acid (× 4.11) or to Na monofluoroacetate (1080) (× 5.26) as desired, and correct for aliquot taken, if any, in extn. Ignore vol. occupied by insol. solids.

Naphthaleneacetic Acid (NAA) (23)— Official First Action

29.128 *Apparatus*

(a) *Spectrophotometer.*—Cary 15 (Cary Instruments, 2724 S. Peck Rd, Monrovia, CA 91016), or equiv., with 5 cm cells.

(b) *Chromatographic tube.*—Glass, 22 mm id × 200 mm.

(c) *Food chopper.*—Hobart No. 84141 (Hobart Mfg. Co., 711 Pennsylvania Ave, Troy, OH 45373), or equiv.

(d) *Blender cups.*—Stainless steel, 1 L capacity, with air-tight screw cover (Scientific Products No. S8390) for high-speed blender.

29.129 *Reagents*

(a) *Sodium phosphate soln.*—0.5*M*. 134 g Na₂HPO₄.7H₂O or 70.5 g anhyd. salt/L.

(b) *Permanganate soln.*—0.02*M*. 31.6 g KMnO₄/L.

(c) *Florisil.*—60–100 mesh PR grade activated at 1250° (Floridin Co.); use as received.

(d) *Naphthyleneacetic acid (NAA) soln.*—0.1 mg α-NAA/ml CHCl₃.

29.130 *Extraction*

Chop sample in food chopper and transfer 200 g to blender cup. Add 20 ml 1*N* H₂SO₄ and 400 ml CHCl₃, screw top on blender, and blend 2 min at low speed. Pour blend into 500 ml centrf. bottle and centrf. 10 min at 1600 rpm. Take 200 ml aliquot from CHCl₃ layer.

29.131 *Cleanup*

(a) *Apples.*—Place glass wool plug into chromatgc tube, add 4″ Florisil, and top Florisil with glass wool plug. Transfer 200 ml CHCl₃ ext to column with min. amt CHCl₃. Rinse inside of column twice with ca 5 ml CHCl₃. Elute column, in order, with 100 ml portions of CH₃CN, ether, NH₃-satd CHCl₃, and CHCl₃ and discard eluates. Using 500 ml separator as receiver, elute NAA with 100 ml 1% HOAc in CHCl₃ followed by 100 ml CHCl₃. Discard column, add 50 ml 1*N* H₂SO₄ to separator, and shake vigorously. Transfer CHCl₃ layer to 250 ml separator contg 50 ml H₂O and shake vigorously. Transfer CHCl₃ layer to 250 ml separator contg exactly 50 ml 0.5*M* Na₂HPO₄, shake vigorously, and discard CHCl₃ layer.

(b) *Potatoes.*—Proceed as in (a). Add 2 ml 85% H₃PO₄ and 2 ml 0.02*M* KMnO₄ to separator contg Na₂HPO₄ phase, mix, and let stand exactly 5 min.

Ext NAA with two 25 ml portions CHCl₃, transfer CHCl₃ exts to 125 ml separator contg exactly 50 ml 0.5*M* Na₂HPO₄, shake vigorously, and discard CHCl₃ layer.

29.132 *Determination*

(**a**) *Apples.*—Transfer 1 ml NAA std soln to 125 ml separator, add exactly 50 ml 0.5*M* Na₂HPO₄ and 50 ml CHCl₃, and shake vigorously. Let layers sep. and discard CHCl₃ layer. Obtain UV spectra (230–330 nm) of cleaned up apple ext and NAA std ext, using 5 cm cells, against 0.5*M* Na₂HPO₄. Use peak at 283 nm to compare apple ext and NAA std ext, correcting for baseline *A*, and calc. ppm NAA present.

(**b**) *Potatoes.*—Transfer 1 ml NAA std soln to 125 ml separator, add 50 ml 0.5*M* Na₂HPO₄ and 50 ml CHCl₃, and shake vigorously. Let layers sep. and discard CHCl₃ layer. Add 2 ml 85% H₃PO₄ and 2 ml 0.02*M* KMnO₄ to separator, mix, and let stand exactly 5 min. Ext NAA with two 25 ml portions CHCl₃, transfer CHCl₃ exts to 125 ml separator contg exactly 50 ml 0.5*M* Na₂HPO₄, shake vigorously, let layers sep., and discard CHCl₃ layer. Obtain UV spectrum and calc. ppm NAA as in (**a**). (If there is excessive interference in sample spectra, repeat 5 min oxidation for both sample and std, beginning with "Add 2 ml 85% H₃PO₄ . . .")

Nicotine (24)—Official Final Action
(Applicable to apples, cabbage, and spinach)

29.133 *Reagents*

(**a**) *Dilute hydrochloric acid.*—Approx. 0.05*N*. Dil. 4.1 ml HCl to 1 L.

(**b**) *Nicotine std solns.*—(*1*) *Stock soln.*—1 mg/ml. Dil. 100 mg nicotine (Eastman Kodak Co. No. 1242, or equiv.) to 100 ml in vol. flask with ca 0.05*N* HCl. (*Caution:* nicotine is very toxic.) (*2*) *Working soln.*— 0.01 mg/ml. Pipet 1 ml stock soln into 100 ml vol. flask and dil. to vol. with ca 0.05*N* HCl.

(**c**) *Stripping soln.*—Dil. 20 ml NH₄OH to 2 L in vol. flask. Prep. at time of use.

Leafy Crops

29.134 *Preparation of Sample*
(*Caution: See* **46.040, 46.045,** and **46.056.**)

Weigh 500 g chopped sample (spinach, cabbage) into clean, dry jar (3–5 gal.). Add 800 ml benzene, 200 ml CHCl₃, and 10 ml NH₄OH. Close, tumble or roll ca 10 min, and drain soln as completely as possible into 1 L beaker. Filter thru folded 38.5 cm paper into flask and proceed immediately with detn.

29.135 *Determination*

Place 400 ml filtered soln in 500 ml separator. Add 25 ml ca 0.05*N* HCl and 2 ml HCl, and shake vigorously. Let phases sep. (ca 5 min) and drain lower layer into 250 ml separator. Swirl large separator, let stand ca 2 min, and drain any addnl ext into 250 ml separator. Repeat several times. Then ext soln with 25, 25, 15, and 10 ml portions ca 0.05*N* HCl, repeating swirling as above. Drain all acid exts into 250 ml separator. Make exts just alk. to litmus with 10% NaOH. Ext with two 50 ml and four 25 ml portions CHCl₃, combining exts in 250 ml separator.

Add 2 ml HCl to exts and make sure soln is acid to litmus. Ext with 25, 25, 20, 10, and 5 ml portions ca 0.05*N* HCl, combining all exts in short-stem 125 ml separator. Wash exts with 15 ml pet ether. Drain aq. layer into second 125 ml separator and wash pet ether with 5 ml ca 0.05*N* HCl, adding wash to combined acid soln. Ext soln with another 15 ml pet ether, drain aq. layer into 100 ml vol. flask, and wash pet ether with 5 ml ca 0.05*N* HCl. Drain acid into vol. flask and dil. to vol. with ca 0.05*N* HCl. Mix, pour portion into 50 ml beaker, and let stand 10–15 min. Det. *A* at 236, 259, and 282 nm with ca 0.05*N* HCl as ref. Confirm presence of nicotine by reading at 2 nm intervals and plot absorption curve, or use recording spectrophtr. Det. *A* of std nicotine soln against ca 0.05*N* HCl as ref.

Waxy Crops

29.136 *Preparation of Sample*

Weigh 2–2.5 kg apples into clean, dry, jar (3–5 gal.). Add 1 L stripping soln, tumble or roll ca 10 min, and drain carefully into 1 L beaker. Filter thru folded 38.5 cm paper into flask and proceed immediately with detn.

29.137 *Determination*

Place 400 ml filtered soln in 500 ml separator. Add 50 ml CHCl₃, invert separator back and forth gently ca 2 min, and let phases sep. Drain clear portion of ext into 250 ml separator. (With fruits, emulsions may be formed which are very hard to break. Break emulsions by drawing CHCl₃ layer into *dry* 125 ml separator and shaking vigorously. Separator must be dry.) Let phases sep. and drain clear portion into the 250 ml separator. Add 35 ml CHCl₃ to the 125 ml separator, shake gently, and drain into the 500 ml separator. Ext as above and combine clear ext in the 250 ml separator. Ext with 35, 35, and 10 ml CHCl₃, combining exts in the 250 ml separator. Add 1 ml or more HCl to exts until definitely acid to litmus. Then ext with three 15 ml portions ca 0.05*N* HCl, combining acid exts in a 125 ml separator. Wash the 250 ml separator with 10 ml ca 0.05*N* HCl after each extn and add to 125 ml separator used to break emulsions. Shake, but do not attempt to break any emulsions in this separator. Combine all acid exts in 125 ml separator and shake with 15 ml pet ether. Let stand ca 5 min and drain aq. layer into another 125 ml separator. Wash pet ether with 5 ml ca 0.05*N* HCl (do not shake vigorously) and add washings to separator. Repeat washing with 15 ml pet ether and drain aq. ext into 100 ml vol. flask. Wash pet ether as before, add washings to flask, and let stand 10–15 min. Dil. to vol. with ca 0.05*N* HCl and det. *A* at 236, 259, and

282 nm, against ca $0.05N$ HCl as ref. Confirm presence of nicotine as in **29.135.**

29.138 *Calculations*

Take A of std soln as:

$$A_{std} = A'_{259} - 0.5(A'_{236} + A'_{282})$$

and A of sample soln as:

$$A_{samp.} = A_{259} - 0.5(A_{236} + A_{282}).$$

Then·

$$mg\ Nicotine = (A_{samp.}/A_{std}) \times 2.5.$$

★ **Parathion (25)—Official Final Action** ★
(*Caution: See* 46.004, 46.011, 46.039, 46.040, and 46.045.)

(*See* also multiple residue methods, **29.001–29.027, 29.028–29.033,** and **29.034–29.038.**)

29.139 *Principles*

Parathion is extd with benzene or isopropanol-benzene and the strip soln is clarified. Parathion is brought into aq. soln and simultaneously reduced to its amine with Zn-HCl. The amine is diazotized and coupled with N-(1-naphthyl)ethylenediamine to form colored compd.

29.140 *Reagents*

(a) *Benzene.*—Redistd. Discard first 5% of distillate (which contains azeotropic H_2O), dry condenser, and resume distn, leaving ca 20% of benzene in still.

(b) *Adsorbent mixture.*—10 parts anhyd., powd Na_2SO_4, 5 parts Attaclay, 5 parts Filter-Cel, 2 parts Nuchar.

(c) *Parathion std solns.*—(1) *Stock soln.*—1 mg/ml. Weigh exactly 100 mg pure parathion (available from American Cyanamid Co.) onto watch glass or glass boat, rinse into 100 ml vol. flask, and dil. to vol. with redistd benzene. Store in cold when not in use, and prep. fresh monthly. (2) *Working soln.*—20 μg/ml. Dil. 5 ml stock soln to 250 ml with the redistd benzene. Prep. fresh weekly. (*Caution: Parathion is extremely poisonous.* Avoid contact with the skin and breathing of vapors.)

(d) *Dilute hydrochloric acid.*—Approx. $0.5N$. Dil. 44.2 ml HCl to 1 L.

(e) *Sodium nitrite soln.*—0.25%. Dissolve 250 mg in H_2O and dil. to 100 ml. Prep. weekly.

(f) *Ammonium sulfamate soln.*—2.5%. Dissolve 1.25 g in H_2O and dil. to 50 ml. Prep. weekly.

(g) *N-(1-naphthyl)ethylenediamine dihydrochloride soln.*—1.0%. Prep. daily. Weigh 200 mg into beaker and dissolve in 20 ml H_2O added from pipet. Filter into dark bottle.

29.141 *Apparatus*

Spectrophotometer or filter photometer.—Max. absorption of developed color is at ca 555 nm. Use spectrophtr set at this wavelength or photometer with monochromatic filter centering at approx. this point. With 1 cm cell, A for 100 μg parathion is ca 0.33.

Practical working range for Beckman Model DU spectrophtr is 0–200 μg parathion. For more precise results use longer cells and more restricted std ranges.

29.142 *Preparation of Sample*

(a) *Firm, relatively tough-skinned fruits, such as apples, pears, etc.*—Weigh 2–3 kg fruit into clean dry jar (ca 3 gal.), so mounted that it can be turned with end-over-end tumbling action by hand crank or motor (JAOAC **26,** 150(1943)). Add 500 ml benzene and stopper with tight-fitting cork, wooden bung, or plastic screw-cap faced with gasket of sheet cork or other suitable solv.-resisting material. (ACS quality benzene is satisfactory.) Turn jar 5 min at 75–100 rpm. (Since apples treated for longer periods become swollen and soft, limit time of stripping; on firmer products time factor is not so important.) Open jar and drain off benzene as completely as possible into 1 L erlenmeyer.

(b) *Soft fruits, such as peaches, plums, tomatoes, berries, etc.*—Use 1–2 kg sample with 300–500 ml redistd benzene, and strip by shaking gently by hand for 5 min in suitable size jar.

(c) *Fresh, leafy vegetables, such as cabbage, lettuce, greens, etc.*—Finely chop ca 1 kg sample or entire contents of small unit package in suitable food chopper (powered mech. chopper such as Hobart is satisfactory) and transfer well-mixed 100–200 g portion to high-speed blender. Add equal wt H_2O and blend ca 2 min. Add vol. redistd benzene equal in ml to wt sample in g, and blend 4–5 min in covered blender. Pour into large centrf. bottles, stopper, and centrf. ca 5 min. If emulsion has not broken, stir in 50 g powd anhyd. Na_2SO_4 and recentrf. (Sometimes aq. layer, overlaid with emulsion, forms at bottom of centrf. bottle; if so, siphon off aq. layer, mix addnl anhyd. Na_2SO_4 into emulsion, and recentrf.) Or:

Blend 100 g sample with 100 ml isopropanol 2 min in high-speed blender. Add 200 ml benzene and blend again 2 min. Pour mixt. into centrf. bottles and centrf. ca 5 min. Transfer supernatants to 1 L separator. Wash blender with two 50 ml portions benzene and transfer to centrf. bottles. Break up solids with stirring rod, stopper, and shake vigorously ca 2 min. Centrf. as before and add solv. layer to separator. Wash ext with ca equal vol. H_2O to remove isopropanol. Dry benzene layer with ca 30 g anhyd. Na_2SO_4, and dil. to suitable vol. with benzene.

(d) *Other products.*—Handle in manner similar to (c). Grind dried products, such as alfalfa, dried leaves, etc., in Wiley mill and ext with benzene in large Soxhlet-type extractor 1–2 hr. Satisfactory extn may be achieved in many cases by letting ground material steep overnight in stoppered jars with measured vol. redistd benzene.

In all cases, treat benzene ext by shaking 5 min with adsorbent mixt., (b), in proportion of ca 10 g to 100 ml ext. Finally, filter thru rapid, folded paper.

29.143 *Preparation of Standard Curve*

For 0–200 μg range, add 2.0, 4.0, 6.0, 8.0, and 10.0 ml parathion working std soln, (c)(*2*), to series of 250 ml, ⊺ 24/40 erlenmeyers, preferably lipped. Add redistd benzene to 25 ml total vol., and provide blank flask with 25 ml redistd benzene. Add 20 ml 0.5*N* HCl and ca 200 mg *finely powd Zn dust*. Connect to condenser by all-glass adapter fitted with thermometer, place on hot plate at medium heat, and rapidly distill off benzene. (Vapor temp. is ca 70°; ebullition stops after benzene is eliminated, and vapor temp. falls.) Do not let aq. soln boil; at this point, disconnect flask, add 10 ml alcohol, and reconnect to reflux condenser. Reflux 5 min, remove from hot plate, and cool flask under tap. Treat flasks in succession (time can be saved by distg benzene from one flask while preceding one is refluxing).

Add ca 100 mg Filter-Cel to each flask and filter into 50 ml vol. flasks thru 9 cm quant. papers (Whatman No. 44, or equiv.). Use long, thin stirring rods in transfer of solns and washings to papers and take care not to exceed vol. of 45 ml in flasks. (*Caution:* Vol. wash H₂O that may be used is limited to ca 15 ml and must be used judiciously if flask and filter are to be properly washed. Let filter drain thoroly between addns. Use small jets of H₂O to rinse down interior walls of flask, and let final portions of rinse H₂O drip over upper portions of paper.)

Add 1 ml NaNO₂ soln to each flask, mix, and let stand 10 min. Add 1 ml NH₄ sulfamate soln to each flask, mix, and let stand 10 min. Then add 2.0 ml reagent (**g**), dil. to vol., mix, and let stand 10 min before reading in spectrophtr at 555 nm. Colors should be stable ≥1 hr.

Read colors in succession, using "blank" std as ref. and plot A against μg parathion to obtain std curve. (A of "blank" std should not change appreciably during course of 1 day but check it at intervals against H₂O. With 1 cm cells it should read ca 0.017; this figure may vary for different batches of reagent (**g**).)

29.144 *Determination*

Place aliquot of clarified soln obtained in **29.142** in 250 ml ⊺ erlenmeyer. (Aliquot size, usually 10–200 ml, will depend on wt/vol. relationship of sample and solv., upon possible interference from excess unremoved waxy materials in case of large aliquots, and upon expected residue content.) If aliquot <25 ml is taken, dil. to 25 ml with redistd benzene. Add 20 ml 0.5*N* HCl and 200 mg finely powd Zn dust, and proceed as in **29.143**.

Some azeotropic H₂O distills with benzene; ignore this amt for 25 ml aliquot, but add 4, 8, and 16 ml H₂O to erlenmeyer (in addn to the 20 ml 0.5*N* HCl) for 50, 100, and 200 ml aliquots, resp.

After reduction, chill *thoroly* under tap, add Filter-Cel, and swirl vigorously to coagulate unremoved waxy material. Let stand few min with occasional

swirling and filter into 50 ml vol. flask. If filtrate is not perfectly bright and colorless, repeat with smaller aliquot.

Develop color, read A against std "blank," and det. μg parathion from std curve. From wt/vol. relationship of original sample and vol. benzene used as extractant, calc. parathion content of sample in ppm.

Piperonyl Butoxide (*26*)—
Official Final Action

(Applicable to Alaska peas, barley, hulled rice, oats, pinto beans, and wheat)

Principles

Strong H₂SO₄ liberates HCHO which is detd colorimetrically with chromotropic acid.

29.145 *Reagents*

(**a**) *Chromotropic acid reagent.*—Dissolve 100 mg Na 1,8-dihydroxynaphthalene-3,6-disulfonate/ml of H₂O, filter, and keep in dark. Prep. daily. (1 ml required for each detn.)

(**b**) *Dilute sulfuric acid.*—Mix carefully 5 vols H₂SO₄ with 3 vols H₂O. Cool to room temp. and store in tight g-s container.

(**c**) *Methanolic potassium hydroxide.*—Dissolve 1.4 g KOH in 5 ml H₂O and add 95 ml MeOH (HCHO-free).

(**d**) *Methanol.*—If necessary, purify as follows: Reflux 1 L MeOH 1 hr with ca 10 g powd Al and ca 10 g NaOH and distill ca 800–900 ml.

(**e**) *Hexane.*—Redistd.

(**f**) *Chloroform.*—Reagent or redistd (for wheat extn).

(**g**) *Piperonyl butoxide std solns.*—(*1*) *Stock soln.*— 1 mg/ml. Dissolve 0.1000 g in 100 ml benzene. (*2*) *Intermediate soln.*—100 μg/ml. Dil. 10 ml stock soln to 100 ml with benzene. (*3*) *Working soln.*—20 μg/ml. Dil. 20 ml intermediate soln to 100 ml with benzene.

29.146 *Preparation of Standard Curve*

Add 0, 20, 40, 60, 80, and 100 μg piperonyl butoxide, resp., to each of 6 g-s test tubes (15 × 150 mm) (25–50 ml g-s centrf. tubes are also satisfactory) and evap. on steam bath with small air jet. Evap. last 1–2 ml benzene without heat.

Into each of tubes pipet both 1 ml chromotropic acid reagent and 5 ml dil. H₂SO₄, (**b**). Stopper loosely and place tubes in beaker of boiling H₂O 45 min, remove, and cool in beaker of cold H₂O. When cool, pipet 5 ml H₂O into each test tube, mix well, and read A in spectrophtr set at 575 nm against reagent blank prepd similarly. Plot μg piperonyl butoxide against A.

29.147 *Determination*

Ext sample as in **29.083**(c), using CHCl₃. With current of air, evap. 25 ml (or suitable size aliquot) ext in small beaker just to dryness. Add 5 ml methanolic

KOH. Warm gently just enough to melt wax (do not boil). Let stand 30 min, swirling vigorously at ca 10 min intervals. Transfer to small separator, rinse beaker with two 5 ml portions of H_2O, and add to separator. Add 15 ml hexane to separator, shake vigorously 1 min, and let sep. Drain aq. layer and discard. Quant. transfer hexane layer to g-s test tube or centrf. tube and evap. to dryness with air jet. Small amt of heat may be used, but evap. last 1–2 ml with air alone. (Warmth of hand at this point is enough.)

Into dried residue pipet both 1 ml chromotropic acid reagent and 5 ml of the dil. H_2SO_4. Swirl vigorously to ensure that reagent contacts all of sample and place test tube in boiling H_2O bath. Stopper tube, lightly at first and then tighten. After 45 min in H_2O bath, remove, and cool to room temp. in beaker of cold H_2O. Pipet in 5 ml H_2O, mix well, and measure A in spectrophtr at 575 nm against reagent blank prepd similarly. From std curve calc. piperonyl butoxide in aliquot.

Thiram (Tetramethylthiuram Disulfide) (27)—Official Final Action

29.148   Principles

Thiram is extd from sample with $CHCl_3$. Treatment with solid CuI results in formation of brown, $CHCl_3$-sol. Cu dimethyldithiocarbamate, and its A is measured at 440 nm. Other commonly used pesticides do not interfere, with exception of metal dithiocarbamates sol. in $CHCl_3$, such as ferbam or ziram. Moderate amts of color, waxes, and other extd plant matter do not interfere.

29.149   Reagents

(a) *Chloroform.*—Either reagent or tech. grade may be used.

(b) *Thiram std solns.*—(1) *Stock soln.*—500 μg/ml Dissolve 50.0 mg thiram (available from E. I. du Pont de Nemours & Co., Industrial and Biochemicals Dept., Wilmington, DE 19898) in $CHCl_3$ and dil. to 100 ml with $CHCl_3$. (2) *Working soln.*—25 μg/ml. Dil. 5 ml stock soln to 100 ml with $CHCl_3$.

(c) *Cuprous iodide.*—If not available, prep. as follows: To soln of 10 g $CuSO_4 \cdot 5H_2O$ in ca 100 ml H_2O, slowly add excess of KI soln. Remove liberated I by adding $Na_2S_2O_3$ soln in slight excess. Filter and wash thoroly with H_2O and with alcohol. Dry at room temp. and crush to fine powder.

(d) *Attapulgus clay.*—Available from Engelhard Minerals and Chemicals Corp., Menlo Park, Edison, NJ 08817.

29.150   Apparatus

(a) *Spectrophotometer.*—Suitable for measuring A in UV and at 440 nm.

(b) *Glassware.*—Avoid contamination by rinsing with $CHCl_3$ and drying before use. Rinse app. that may have contained CuI from previous detns with dil. acid, H_2O, alcohol, and $CHCl_3$.

29.151   Preparation of Standard Curve

(To minimize errors due to evapn of solv., keep flasks closed as much as possible, and cover funnels with watch glasses during filtrations.)

Using buret, add 2.0, 5.0, 10.0, and 15.0 ml working std soln to 25 ml vol. flasks. Dil. to vol. with $CHCl_3$, and mix. Solns contain 2, 5, 10, and 15 μg thiram/ml, resp.

Transfer ca 10 ml portions of std solns to 125 ml g-s erlenmeyers, add 10 mg CuI to each, stopper, and let stand 1 hr with occasional mixing. Filter, using 9 cm quant. paper, and read A at 440 nm against $CHCl_3$ as ref. Plot A against thiram concn in μg/ml.

29.152   Isolation

(Avoid contact of solv with rubber.)

(a) *Corn.*—Ext 200 g by shaking with 100 ml $CHCl_3$ 5 min in 500 ml g-s erlenmeyer. Decant ext thru small funnel (to retain corn kernels) into flask.

(b) *Apples, pears, and similar firm fruits.*—Weigh 2–3 kg into clean, dry jar (ca 3 gal.). Add 500 ml $CHCl_3$ and stopper with tight-fitting cork, wooden bung, or plastic screw cap faced with gasket of sheet cork or other suitable solv.-resisting material. Ext 5 min by tumbling or other agitation. Decant ext into flask.

(c) *Tomatoes, berries, and similar soft fruits and vegetables.*—Weigh 1–3 kg into suitable container. Add 500 ml $CHCl_3$ and stopper with solv.-resisting closure. Ext 5 min by gentle shaking and decant into g-s erlenmeyer thru loose plug of glass wool.

(d) *Celery.*—Cut 2–3 kg into 1–3″ pieces. Mix thoroly and ext 500 g sample with 500 ml $CHCl_3$ as above.

Add anhyd. Na_2SO_4, ca 5 g/100 ml, to decanted ext. Stopper flask, shake 5 min, and filter thru folded Whatman No. 12 or equiv. paper.

29.153   Determination

(Thiram in $CHCl_3$ soln, particularly in presence of plant extractives, may decompose. Make detns as soon as possible.)

Transfer ca 10 ml filtered ext to g-s erlenmeyer and develop color as in **29.151,** beginning "add 10 mg CuI ...." As ref., use another portion of filtered ext., untreated with CuI. From std curve obtain thiram concn in μg/ml. If developed color is too intense, dil. with $CHCl_3$, making similar diln of ref. ext, and multiply thiram value found by appropriate diln factor.

ppm Thiram = (μg thiram/ml) $\times$ ml $CHCl_3$ used for extn/g sample.

29.154   Qualitative Test

Adjust concn of ext, **29.152,** if necessary, to 10–15 μg thiram/ml by evapn on steam bath or by diln with $CHCl_3$. Add 0.25–1.0 g Attapulgus clay, depending on color of ext, to 50 ml of adjusted ext in beaker. Mix well and filter thru Whatman No. 12 folded paper or equiv. Transfer 25 ml filtrate to g-s erlenmeyer, add 0.2 ml ca 0.1N AgNO$_3$ to ppt thiram and other CHCl$_3$-sol. dithiocarbamates, stopper, and shake vigorously 30 sec. Add ca 1 g anhyd. Na$_2$SO$_4$ and shake 30 sec. Let settle and decant carefully into 1 cm quartz cell and *use as ref. soln*, adjusting to 0 A at 350 nm. Det. UV absorption curve on clarified and filtered ext untreated with AgNO$_3$ over range 250–350 nm. Thiram gives curve with plateau at 270–283 nm, dropping sharply after peaking at ca 283. Ferbam and ziram give characteristic curves distinguishable from thiram.

SELECTED REFERENCES

(*1*) JAOAC **44**, 171(1961); **48**, 668(1965); **49**, 84, 460, 463, 468(1966); **50**, 575, 1205(1967); **51**, 311, 666(1968); **52**, 1280(1969); **53**, 152(1970).

(*2*) JAOAC **40**, 999(1957).

(*3*) JAOAC **51**, 662(1968).

(*4*) JAOAC **52**, 811(1969).

(*5*) JAOAC **47**, 272(1964).

(*6*) Anal. Chem. **24**, 544(1952); JAOAC **39**, 700 (1956).

(*7*) JAOAC **41**, 560(1958).

(*8*) JAOAC **50**, 934(1967).

(*9*) JAOAC **42**, 534(1959).

(*10*) JAOAC **40**, 219(1957); **46**, 143, 241(1963).

(*11*) JAOAC **47**, 283(1964); **48**, 676(1965).

(*12*) JAOAC **51**, 679(1968).

(*13*) JAOAC **41**, 572(1958).

(*14*) Ind. Eng. Chem., Anal. Ed. **15**, 383(1943); **17**, 704(1945); **19**, 51, 54(1947); JAOAC **29**, 112, 188(1946); **30**, 337(1947); **31**, 355(1948); **33**, 585(1950); **51**, 892(1968).

(*15*) JAOAC **48**, 759(1965).

(*16*) JAOAC **46**, 229(1963).

(*17*) JAOAC **47**, 300(1964).

(*18*) JAOAC **46**, 238(1963).

(*19*) JAOAC **40**, 230 (1957); J. Sci. Food Agr. **20**, 4(1969).

(*20*) JAOAC **46**, 261(1963); **48**, 744(1965); **49**, 87 (1966).

(*21*) JAOAC **40**, 235(1957).

(*22*) JAOAC **32**, 788(1949); **33**, 608(1950); **34**, 828 (1951); **37**, 581(1954).

(*23*) JAOAC **53**, 149(1970).

(*24*) JAOAC **47**, 303(1964).

(*25*) Anal. Chem. **20**, 753(1948); JAOAC **38**, 673 (1955).

(*26*) JAOAC **43**, 707(1960); **46**, 244(1963).

(*27*) JAOAC **42**, 545(1959); **45**, 410(1962).

30. Spices and Other Condiments[*]

SPICES

30.001 Preparation of Sample—Procedure

Grind sample to pass thru sieve with circular openings 1 mm diam. and mix thoroly. Since most spices lack uniformity and have tendency to stratify, use extreme care in weighing out portion for analysis. Stir material thoroly and weigh out the 2 g samples, using spoon with ca 2 g capacity. Dip spoonful from center of material, being careful to take ca required quantity so as to avoid adding to or taking from portion on scale pan. In detn of starch in spices by diastase method, further reduce subsample as nearly as possible to impalpable powder.

30.002 Moisture (1)—Official Final Action

Clean distg tube receiver and condenser described in **7.004** with $K_2Cr_2O_7$-H_2SO_4 mixt., rinse thoroly with H_2O and then with ca 0.5N alc. KOH, and drain 10 min. Before cleaning, remove connecting stopper from condenser, so that it remains dry. Place 40 g spice in distg flask and proceed as in **7.005.**

30.003 Ash (1)—Official Final Action

(a) *Most spices.*—Accurately weigh ca 2 g sample in flat-bottom dish, preferably Pt. Place dish in entrance of open muffle so that sample fumes off without catching fire. Then ignite in muffle 30 min at 550°, break up ash with several drops H_2O, evap. carefully to dryness, and heat in muffle 30 min. If previous wetting showed ash to be C-free, remove dish to desiccator contg fresh efficient desiccant (H_2SO_4 or anhyd. $Mg(ClO_4)_2$ is satisfactory), let cool to room temp., and weigh soon. If first wetting showed C, repeat wetting and heating until no specks of C are visible; then heat 30 min after disappearance of C. If C persists, leach ash with hot H_2O, filter thru quant. paper, wash paper thoroly, transfer paper and contents to ashing dish, dry, and ignite in muffle at 550° until ash is white. Cool dish, add filtrate, evap. to dryness on steam bath, and heat in muffle 30 min. Cool, and weigh as previously.

(b) *Nutmeg, mace, ginger, and cloves.*—Proceed as in (a), but heat at 600°.

(c) *Ground mustard or mustard flour.*—Ignite as in (a) and heat 30 min at 550°. Leach ash with hot H_2O, filter, and wash thoroly. Transfer paper and contents to ashing dish, dry, and heat in muffle 30 min. Remove dish, let cool, add 5–10 drops HNO_3, evap. to dryness, and heat in muffle 30 min. Repeat HNO_3 and heating treatment until residue is white. Add filtrate, evap. to dryness, and heat in muffle 30 min. Cool, and weigh as in (a).

30.004 Soluble and Insoluble Ash— Official Final Action

Proceed as in **31.015,** using ash obtained in **30.003.**

30.005 Ash Insoluble in Acid— Official Final Action

Boil H_2O-insol. residue, **30.004,** or total ash, **30.003,** with 25 ml HCl (1 + 2.5) 5 min, covering dish with watch glass to prevent spattering; collect insol. matter on gooch or ashless filter, wash with hot H_2O until washings are acid-free, ignite until C-free, cool, and weigh.

30.006 Calcium in Ash—Official Final Action

Ignite 2–4 g sample as in **30.003,** digest with hot HCl (1 + 2.5), evap. to dryness, moisten dry residue with dil. HCl, and again evap. to dryness to make SiO_2 insol. Treat residue with 5–10 ml HCl, add ca 50 ml H_2O, let stand on H_2O bath few min, filter, and wash insol. residue with hot H_2O. Det. CaO in combined filtrate and washings as in **3.011.**

30.007 Nitrogen—Official Final Action

Proceed as in **2.051.** Use 1 g sample for black or white pepper.

30.008 Nitrogen in Nonvolatile Ether Extract—Official Final Action

(For black and white peppers)

(*Caution: See* **46.009, 46.011, 46.039,** and **46.054.**)

Ext 10 g pepper 20 hr in continuous extn app. with absolute ether, collecting ext in weighed 250 ml flask. Evap. ether, and dry first at 100° and finally to min. wt at 110°. Det. N in weighed ext as in **2.051,** digesting in same flask used for extn. Crude piperine = N × 20.36.

30.009 Volatile and Nonvolatile Ether Extract (2)—Official Final Action

(Not suitable for detn of volatile ether ext in spices high in volatile oils, such as cloves)

(*Caution: See* **46.009, 46.011, 46.039,** and **46.054.**)

Ext 2 g ground material 20 hr in continuous extn app. with anhyd. ether. Transfer ethereal soln to weighed capsule and let evap. at room temp. Store 18 hr over H_2SO_4 and weigh total ether ext. Heat ext gradually and then to min. wt at 110°. Loss is volatile ether ext; residue is nonvolatile ether ext.

---

[*] Methods so marked are surplus methods. *See* "Definitions of Terms and Explanatory Notes," item (29).

30.010 Alcohol Extract (3)— Official Final Action

Place 2 g sample in 100 ml vol. flask and fill to mark with alcohol. Stopper, shake at 30 min intervals during 8 hr, and let stand 16 hr longer without shaking. Filter ext thru dry paper, evap. 50 ml aliquot filtrate to dryness in flat-bottom dish on steam bath, and heat to min. wt at 110°.

30.011 Copper-Reducing Substances by Direct Acid Hydrolysis— Official Final Action

Ext 4 g sample with five 10 ml portions ether on filter that will completely retain smallest starch granules. Let ether evap. from residue and wash with 150 ml alcohol, 10% by vol.

To avoid clogging of filter by glutinous mass that may result from washing with H_2O or dil. alcohol, omit all preliminary washings with cassia buds and cinnamon.

Carefully wash residue from paper into 500 ml flask with 200 ml H_2O, using small wash bottle and gently rubbing paper with tip of finger. Hydrolyze and det. Cu-reducing material as in **8.017.** Express results in terms of starch.

Starch—Official Final Action
30.012 Method I

Ext 4 g finely pulverized sample with ether and 500 ml 10% alcohol as in **30.011,** and det. starch by diastase method, **31.110.**

30.013 Method II

(Applicable to dry mustard)

Treat 2–3 g dry mustard flour as in **30.038.**

30.014 Crude Fiber—Official Final Action

Proceed as in **7.057,** and before drying the crude fiber remove all ether extractives by successive washings with ether.

Tannin (4)—Official Final Action

(For cloves and allspice)

30.015 Reagents

(a) *Oxalic acid soln.*—0.1N. 1 ml = 0.006235 g quercitannic acid or 0.0008 g O absorbed.

(b) *Potassium permanganate std soln.*—Dissolve 1.333 g $KMnO_4$ in 1 L H_2O and stdze against (a).

(c) *Indigo soln.*—Dissolve 6 g Na indigotin disulfonate in 500 ml H_2O by heating; cool, add 50 ml H_2SO_4, dil. to 1 L, and filter.

30.016 Determination

(*Caution: See* **46.009, 46.011, 46.039,** and **46.054.**)

Ext 2 g sample 20 hr with anhyd. ether. Boil residue 2 hr with 300 ml H_2O, cool, dil. to 500 ml, and filter. Measure 25 ml of this infusion into 2 L porcelain dish; add 20 ml indigo soln and 750 ml H_2O.

Add std $KMnO_4$ soln, 1 ml at time, until blue soln changes to green; then add few drops at time until soln becomes golden yellow. Similarly titr. mixt. of 20 ml indigo soln and 750 ml H_2O. Multiply difference between 2 titrns by desired factor to obtain quercitannic acid or O absorbed.

Volatile Oil (5)—Official Final Action
30.017 Apparatus

(a) *Volatile oil traps.*—Clevenger type with $\overline{\mathrm{S}}$ joints: (*1*) For oils with densities near or less than that of H_2O; and (*2*) for oils with densities greater than that of H_2O. (*See* Fig. 30:1.)

(b) *Flask with magnetic stirrer.*—1 L r-b, short neck with $\overline{\mathrm{S}}$ 29/42 joint; heavy duty magnetic stirrer with egg-shaped stirring bar.

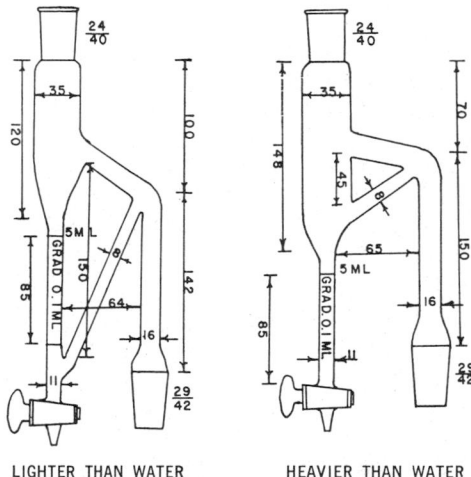

LIGHTER THAN WATER   HEAVIER THAN WATER

FIG. 30:1—Apparatus for volatile oil in spices. (Dimensions in mm)

30.018 Determination

Prep. sample as in **30.001,** except use No. 20 sieve. Take precautions to prevent loss of volatile oil from heating during grinding.

Transfer enough weighed sample to 1 L flask to yield 2–4 ml volatile oil. Add H_2O to fill flask ca half full. Insert stirring bar and place flask in heating mantle set over magnetic stirrer. Add antifoam agent, such as Dow Corning Antifoam Emulsion, ca size of pea. Clean trap and condenser with cleaning soln just before use and fill trap with H_2O. Set app. so that condensate will not drop directly on surface of liq. in trap but will run down side. Start stirrer and heat mantle thru variable transformer set at 90 volts ($\leq$3 amps).

If oil seps in graduated portion of trap or clings to walls, add several drops satd aq. detergent soln thru top of condenser. Repeat, if necessary (usually once is enough). Distill 10 min after adding detergent to wash it out of trap. When density of oil is nearly 1, as in cassia, or if oil seps into 2 fractions in trap, as in nutmeg and allspice, add 1 ml xylene, accurately measured, to lighter-than-H_2O trap.

Distill until 2 consecutive readings taken at 1 hr intervals show no change in oil content (≥ 6 hr). Cool, and read vol. collected oil. If xylene was added, subtract its vol., and report oil as ml/100 g spice.

If required for further examination, drain oil into g-s tube or graduate, sepg from aq. layer. Let oil stand until clear, or dry with min. quantity anhyd. Na_2SO_4, and let settle before detg chemical and physical characteristics. Store in refrigerator.

30.019   Specific Gravity of Volatile Oil— Official Final Action

Det. sp gr at $25/25°$ as in **28.003** and **28.004**, using 1 ml Sprengel tube.

30.020   Refractive Index of Volatile Oil— Official Final Action— See 28.007 and 28.009

30.021   Eugenol in Volatile Oil— Official Final Action

Measure 2 ml volatile oil (transfer pipet) into Babcock milk bottle, **16.053**(a). Add 20 ml 3% KOH soln, shake mixt. 5 min, heat 10 min in boiling H_2O bath, remove, and cool to room temp. When liqs sep. completely, add enough KOH soln to bring residual oil within graduated portion of neck and note vol. Calc. % by vol. from difference between vol. sample used and residual oil.

30.022   Volatile Oil and Resin in Ginger (6)— Official Final Action

(*Caution: See* **46.011, 46.039,** and **46.054.**)

Place 50 g ground ginger in Soxhlet extractor and ext completely with ether (ca 4 hr). Transfer ext to 300 ml flask and evap. ether on steam bath until solv. is no longer detected. Add 50 ml H_2O to residue and det. yield of volatile oil (using trap for oils lighter than H_2O), sp gr, and refractive index, as in **30.018–30.020.**

Transfer residue in flask to separator and ext resin with ether. Transfer to tared beaker, evap. ether on steam bath, and dry to constant wt in vac. desiccator.

Volatile Oil in Mustard Seed (7)— Official First Action

30.023   *Apparatus and Reagents*

(a) *Gas chromatograph.*—Equipped with flame ionization detector. Approx. parameters are: column temp. 145°, detector temp. 200°, injector temp. 160°, N flow rate 100 ml/min. Optimum conditions are obtained when at least 4″ peak is obtained for 8 μl std soln injection.

(b) *Column and packing.*—12′, 4 mm id, 5% Carbowax 4000 on Fluoropak 80, 20–40 mesh.

(c) *Allyl isothiocyanate std soln.*—30.5 mg/100 ml. Measure 30 μl allyl isothiocyanate in 50 μl syringe with ±0.5% accuracy. Add to 50 ml of 10% alcohol in 100 ml vol. flask and shake intermittently until dissolved. Dil. to vol. with H_2O.

30.024   *Determination*

Grind ≥ 15 g seed to pass thru No. 20 sieve. Immediately weigh 6.0 g into 300 ml erlenmeyer, add 150 ml 5% alcohol, stopper tightly, and stir with magnetic stirring bar 90±5 min in 37° H_2O bath.

(a) *Gas chromatographic method.*—Distill ca 70 ml into 100 ml vol. flask contg 20 ml 5% alcohol, taking care that end of condenser dips below surface of soln. Dil. to vol. with H_2O. Inject 4–10 μl into gas chromatograph. Compare peak ht of sample with that from same vol. std soln.

(b) *Titration method.*—Distill ca 60 ml into 100 ml vol. flask contg 10 ml NH_4OH (1 + 2), taking care that end of condenser dips below surface of soln. Add 20 ml 0.1N $AgNO_3$ to distillate, let stand overnight (*Caution: See* **46.044**), heat to boiling on H_2O bath (boil behind safety barrier) in order to agglomerate Ag_2S, cool, dil. to 100 ml with H_2O, and filter. Acidify 50 ml filtrate with ca 5 ml HNO_3 and titr. with 0.1N NH_4CNS, using 5 ml 10% $FeNH_4(SO_4)_2.12H_2O$ soln as indicator. 1 ml 0.1N $AgNO_3$ = 0.004958 g allyl isothiocyanate.

Note: Before discarding Ag_2S and filter paper, treat with 25 ml 1N $Na_2S_2O_5$ in 1N NaOH.

Microscopic Examination—Procedure

30.025   *General (8)*

Adulterants of vegetable origin in spices are best detected microscopically. General knowledge of vegetable histology and microscopic appearance of spices and spice adulterants is essential. Some std works on these subjects (8) are listed in Selected References.

30.026   *Reagents*

(a) *Acidified chloral hydrate-glycerol soln.*—Dissolve 270 g chloral hydrate crystals in 150 ml H_2O, 19 ml HCl, and 60 ml glycerol.

(b) *Chloral hydrate soln.*—Dissolve 8 parts by wt chloral hydrate crystals in 5 parts H_2O.

(c) *Ferric acetate or chloride soln.*—Freshly prepd 1% aq. soln.

(d) *Iodine-potassium iodide soln (iodine soln).*—Dissolve 0.5 g I and 1.5 g KI in very small amt of H_2O and dil. to 25 ml.

(e) *Iodine-potassium iodide in zinc chloride soln.*—Dissolve 100 g $ZnCl_2$ in 60 ml H_2O in g-s bottle and add 20 g KI and 0.5 g I. Leave few I crystals in bottle to insure satn and let soln stand few hr before use. Soln keeps for months. If color developed in tissue is too deep blue, dil. reagent slightly.

(f) *Millon reagent.*—See **7.100**(g).

(g) *Potassium chlorate macerating soln.*—Mix 0.5 g $KClO_3$ with 50 ml HNO_3 (1 + 1) as needed.

(h) *Potassium hydroxide soln.*—Dissolve 5 g KOH in H_2O and dil. to 100 ml.

(i) *Sudan IV, saturated alcoholic soln.*—Approx. 0.09%.

30.027 *Apparatus*

(a) *Wide-field stereoscopic microscope.*—Instrument with ca 10 to 60× magnification is useful for preliminary sepn.

(b) *Compound microscope.*—Instrument with ca 100 to 400× magnification. Eyepiece micrometer, mech. stage, and polarizing microscope are desirable for special types of work.

(c) *Sieves.*—Series of std mesh sieves from No. 10 to 100, and sieve with circular openings 1 mm diam.

(d) *Slides, cover glasses, needles, forceps, etc.*

30.028 *Preparation of Sample*

Reduce one portion to fine powder in mortar. Sep. another portion into several grades of fineness by sieves of different mesh or by jarring on sheet of paper. In coarser grades, fragments of suspicious nature may often be seen with naked eye or under simple microscope; these should be picked out for subsequent examination under compd microscope.

30.029 *Examination*

Mount small amt ground sample in H_2O and examine under compd microscope with both ordinary and polarized light. This gives general information as to nature of material and serves for detection and identification of starch granules and various tissues. Place small drop of I-KI soln at edge of cover-glass, draw it into prepn by means of piece of filter paper placed at opposite edge of cover-glass, and examine again. Starch granules are colored blue or blue-black; cellulose, yellow; and proteins, either brown or yellow.

In manner described draw little KOH soln under cover-glass and again examine. This treatment gelatinizes starch granules, dissolves proteins, saponifies fats, and in other ways clears prepn. It also imparts reddish color to tannins. If this treatment does not clear tissues satisfactorily, treat fresh portion for short time with acidified chloral hydrate-glycerol soln, heating gently, if necessary, or for some hrs with the chloral hydrate soln.

Also examine crude fiber obtained in chemical analysis, as stone cells and other tissues are shown distinctly in this material.

To isolate stone cells, bast fibers, and other thick-wall cells, macerate portion of sample in $KClO_3$ macerating soln, varying proportions of $KClO_3$ and HNO_3 and heating long enough to secure desired results.

To distinguish cellulose from infiltrated substances (lignin, suberin, etc.), add freshly prepd I-KI in $ZnCl_2$ soln to H_2O mount. Cellulose is colored blue, and infiltrated substances are yellow.

To distinguish fats, oils, essential oils, resins, latex, and wax from other cell contents, place small amt of tissue on slide, add 2 drops Sudan IV soln and 2 drops glycerol or acidified chloral hydrate-glycerol soln, and heat gently; these substances are stained red. Treat sep. portion of tissue with ether, pet ether, or alcohol. Ether and pet ether dissolve fats, oils, essential oils, resins, latex, and wax. Alcohol dissolves essential oils and resins but usually affects fats, oils, latex, and wax slowly or not at all.

Test for proteins by warming cautiously on slide with drop of Millon reagent. Proteins are partially decomposed, gradually acquiring brick red color. If it is desired to study form of aleurone (protein) granules, which in some plants are quite as characteristic as starch granules, prep. mount in pure glycerol or oil.

Test for tannins and tissues impregnated with them by adding $Fe(OAc)_3$ or $FeCl_3$ soln. Both reagents give green or blue color with tannins, but $Fe(OAc)_3$ acts more slowly and is preferred.

Crystals of Ca oxalate (J. Am. Pharm. Assoc. **12,** 301(1923)) are recognized by their characteristic forms and by behavior to polarized light. To distinguish Ca oxalate from $CaCO_3$, treat with HOAc, which does not affect oxalate but dissolves carbonate with effervescence. Both are sol. in HCl.

Powd charcoal and charred shells resist bleaching action of KOH, chloral hydrate, and $KClO_3$ macerating soln.

PREPARED MUSTARD

30.030 Preparation of Sample—Procedure

Transfer entire contents of container to dish large enough to permit thoro stirring and make whole mass homogeneous. Preserve in g-s bottle. Stir well each time before removing portion for analysis.

30.031 Solids—Official Final Action

Weigh 5 g sample into flat-bottom Pt dish; distribute evenly over bottom of dish with little H_2O, place on steam bath until mixt. appears dry, and heat in oven at 100° to min. wt.

30.032 Total Chlorides (9)— Official Final Action

Weigh 3–4 g sample from weighing bottle, place in 300 ml erlenmeyer, and add excess std $0.1N$ $AgNO_3$ (usually 30 ml is enough). Mix thoroly, add 15 ml HNO_3, and bring to boil on hot plate. Add to boiling mixt. 15 ml 5% $KMnO_4$ soln, 5 ml at time, rotating flask after each addn to mix contents. Add ca 50 ml H_2O and filter into 200 ml vol. flask. Wash filter free of $AgNO_3$ and dil. to vol. with H_2O. Mix thoroly and titr. 100 ml aliquot with $0.1N$ KCNS, using 2 ml satd Fe alum soln as indicator. Calc. chlorides as NaCl.

30.033 Ether Extract—Official Final Action

(*Caution: See* **46.009, 46.011, 46.039,** and **46.054.**)

Weigh 10 g sample into SiO_2, Al, or porcelain drying dish and mix with ca 30 g sand. Heat on H_2O bath until mixt. appears dry; then finish drying in H_2O oven. Grind until all lumps are broken up, and det. ether ext by extg 16 hr with anhyd. ether in Soxhlet extractor with Whatman single thickness or other close-texture thimble. Dry ext 30 min at 100°, cool, and weigh.

30.034 Total Nitrogen—Official Final Action

Det. N as in **2.051,** using 5 g sample.

30.035 Acidity—Official Final Action

Weigh 10 g sample into 200 ml vol. flask, dil. to vol. with H_2O, shake, filter thru dry paper, and det. acidity in 100 ml by titrn with $0.1N$ alkali, using phthln. Express result as HOAc. 1 ml $0.1N$ alkali = 0.0060 g HOAc.

30.036 ★ Sucrose—Official First Action ★

See **28.036–28.037,** 10th ed.

Starch—Official Final Action

30.037   *Reagents*

(**a**) *Calcium chloride soln.*—30 g/100 ml soln adjusted to $0.01N$ alky.

(**b**) *Alcoholic sodium hydroxide soln.*—70 ml alcohol + 30 ml $0.1N$ NaOH.

(**c**) *Iodine-potassium iodide soln.*—2 g I + 6 g KI in 100 ml H_2O.

30.038   *Determination*

Place 5 g prepd mustard in 500 ml erlenmeyer and pipet in 100 ml $CaCl_2$ soln, swirling flask gently until all lumps are broken. Add calcd quantity $1N$ NaOH to neutze acid in wt prepd mustard taken for analysis. Add glass beads. Connect to reflux condenser, first wetting inside of condenser and stopper with H_2O and draining 1 min. Heat gently (on asbestos board with center hole) to avoid initial foaming, and boil 15 min.

Leaving condenser connected, cool flask to room temp. in pan of cold H_2O. Remove flask, stopper, and shake vigorously. Pour contents into centrf. bottle and centrf. at 1500 rpm 5 min. Withdraw as much as possible of partially clarified middle layer (ca 75 ml) and filter thru 11 cm circle of absorbent cotton ca 5 cm thick placed in 60° funnel. Pipet 50 ml filtrate into second centrf. bottle contg 150 ml alcohol, stopper, and shake vigorously several min. Centrf. at 1500 rpm until clear (ca 5 min).

Decant liq. thru asbestos pad in Caldwell crucible, using suction, without transferring starch to crucible. Transfer pad to same centrf. bottle, and rinse all particles adhering to crucible into bottle with H_2O. Add several glass beads and H_2O to ca 100 ml. Stopper and shake vigorously until ppt is as finely dispersed as possible. Add slight excess I-KI soln (2–3 ml) and 30 ml satd $(NH_4)_2SO_4$ soln. Stopper and shake bottle. Rinse particles adhering to stopper into bottle, and centrf. until clear.

Decant supernatant, with suction, thru asbestos pad in Caldwell crucible. Add 50 ml alc. NaOH soln to ppt in centrf. bottle. Stopper and shake vigorously. Wash stopper with 70% alcohol. Centrf. and decant supernatant thru same pad as before. Repeat treatment with the NaOH soln until practically all blue disappears (usually 2–3 treatments). Without centrfg, transfer contents of bottle to Caldwell crucible, using 70% alcohol. Aspirate until pad is dry; then transfer pad to 500 ml Kjeldahl flask. Rinse bottle and crucible with 10 ml HCl (sp gr 1.1029) followed by five 10 ml portions H_2O, carefully removing all adhering particles. Attach Kjeldahl flask to reflux condenser, first adding glass beads to lessen bumping. Place on asbestos board with center hole and boil 1 hr. Cool, neutze with NaOH $(1 + 1)$ (Me orange), and filter into 200 ml vol. flask; rinse flask and filter thoroly, and dil. to vol. with H_2O. Mix well, and det. glucose in 50 ml aliquot by **31.039.** (Blank on Fehling soln should be ≤ 0.3 mg.)

$$\% \text{ starch} = [\text{g glucose} \times 0.9(100 + V + W) \times 8]/\text{wt sample},$$

where $V =$ ml $1N$ NaOH used to neutze acidity, **30.035,** and $W =$ g H_2O in sample taken (calcd from solids, **30.031**).

30.039 Crude Fiber (*10*)—Official Final Action

Weigh 10 g sample and transfer to 8 oz nursing bottle with 50 ml alcohol, stopper, and shake vigorously. Add 40 ml ether, shake, and let stand ca 5 min, shaking occasionally. Centrf. and decant alcohol-ether mixt. Treat twice more with 40 ml portions ether, shaking, centrfg, and decanting as before. Rest bottle on its side for short time, without heat, to let most of ether evap. Transfer material to 500 ml erlenmeyer, using 200 ml boiling H_2SO_4, **7.054**(a), and proceed as in **7.057,** but in addn wash fiber with successive portions of ether before drying and weighing.

If preferred, treat sample with alcohol and ether in small beaker, transfer to hardened 11 cm filter paper, wash several times with ether, and transfer to 500 ml erlenmeyer with 200 ml boiling H_2SO_4.

30.040 Preservatives—Official Final Action— *See* Chap. 20

DRESSINGS FOR FOODS (*11*)

30.041 Preparation of Sample—Procedure

(**a**) *Semisolid and emulsified dressings.*—Before removing any portion of sample for analysis, transfer to suitable container, such as glass fruit jar, of larger capacity than vol. of sample, and mix with spatula until homogeneous (2–3 min should be enough). Repeat mixing before each subsequent portion is removed for analysis if sample has stood for any appreciable time. For various detns, take ca quantity directed and weigh. (Light 100 ml flask fitted with straight glass tube and oversized rubber bulb makes suitable weighing bottle.)

(b) *Separable dressings, small containers.*—Weigh bottle contg sample. Shake bottle 1 min, empty contents into high-speed blender, and let bottle drain 1 min. Weigh empty bottle to det. wt sample. Add 0.20 g egg albumen powder/100 g sample, cover blender, and stir 5 min; then transfer to suitable container of capacity larger than sample vol. Shake sample ca 20 times and stir with spatula or spoon ca 20 times before each portion is removed for analysis. Make all weighings immediately after sample prepn. Correct results for added emulsifier.

(c) *Separable dressings, large containers.*—Stir contents thoroly, adding 0.20 g egg albumen powder/100 g sample. Mech. stirrer of double-beater type is satisfactory. Continue stirring until powder is well dispersed thruout sample. Add sample in portions to high-speed blender and stir each portion ca 5 min. Transfer emulsified portions to jar of ca same size as original container and stir entire contents of sample to ensure uniform mixt. Transfer portion of prepd sample to suitable jar (ca 1 pt). Proceed as in (b), beginning "Shake sample ca 20 times . . ."

30.042 Total Solids—Official Final Action

Use 2 g sample and proceed as in 17.006(a).

30.043 Reducing Sugars Before Inversion— Official Final Action

Weigh 20 g sample into wide-mouth 4 oz bottle and ext oil by adding ca 80 ml pet ether, shaking, and centrfg. Draw off as much as possible of pet ether soln (conveniently done by using suction and short-stem pipet), and repeat treatment with pet ether until all oil is removed (indicated by absence of color in solv.; usually 4 extns are required). Reserve ether soln for identification of oil. Remove pet ether from residue with air current and transfer residue with H_2O to 100 ml vol. flask. Add 5–10 ml *fresh soln of HPO_3* (remove any white coating on HPO_3 by rinsing with H_2O; dissolve 5 g transparent lumps or sticks in cold H_2O, and dil. to 100 ml), mix thoroly, dil. to vol., and filter. Transfer 80 ml filtrate, or as large aliquot as possible, to 100 ml vol. flask; neutze with NaOH soln (1 + 1), using phthln; cool, dil. to vol., and det. reducing sugars on aliquot as in 31.039. Calc. to invert sugar.

With dressings, particularly those contg starch, that cannot be clarified by above method, remove oil as in 16.052, using 1 ml NH_4OH and 5 ml alcohol/g sample; transfer residue to 250 ml vol. flask with alcohol, 50% by vol., and proceed as in 7.058 and 31.039.

30.044 Reducing Sugars After Inversion— Official Final Action

Invert aliquot of soln, 30.043, as in 31.026(b) or (c), nearly neutze with NaOH soln (1 + 1), and det. reducing sugars in inverted soln as in 31.039. Calc. to invert sugar from 47.019.

30.045 Sucrose—Official Final Action

Subtract % invert sugar obtained before inversion, 30.043, from that obtained after inversion, 30.044, and multiply difference by 0.95.

30.046 Total Acidity—Official Final Action

Weigh ca 15 g sample into 500 ml erlenmeyer, dil. to ca 200 ml, and shake until all lumps are thoroly broken up. Titr. with 0.1N NaOH, using phthln, and calc. as HOAc. In order to recognize end point, have duplicate sample at hand so that, by comparison, first change of color may be noted.

30.047 Total Nitrogen—Official Final Action

Weigh ca 15 g sample into 500 ml Kjeldahl flask and place on steam bath until egg is thoroly cooked and oil seps readily. Cool, and add ca 50 ml pet ether; mix, and pour off pet ether thru small filter. Repeat pet ether treatment twice, rinsing out as much oil as possible. Wash filter with pet ether and add filter paper to sample in flask. Det. N, using 50 ml H_2SO_4 (more, if necessary) for digestion, as in 2.051.

30.048 Total Phosphorus— Official Final Action

Use 10 g sample and proceed as in 17.022(a) and 17.023, except use Pt dish in place of beaker and burn off oil before ashing in muffle.

30.049 Total Fat—Official Final Action

(*Caution: See* 46.011, 46.039, 46.054, *and* 46.073.)

Mix sample thoroly and accurately weigh ca 1 g, by difference, into Mojonnier tube. Add 10 ml HCl, shake, set tube in H_2O bath heated to 70°, and bring to boiling. Boil 30 min, shaking tube thoroly every 5 min. Remove from H_2O bath, add H_2O to fill lower bulb of tube (but not neck), and cool to room temp.

To mixt. in Mojonnier tube add 25 ml ether and shake vigorously $\geq$1 min. Add 25 ml pet ether and again shake vigorously $\geq$1 min. To break emulsion centrf. 5–10 min at ca 300 rpm. Pour off ether-fat soln into flask, contg porcelain chips or glass beads, that has been dried at 100°, allowed to cool in air to constant wt, and weighed against similar flask similarly treated as counterpoise. Rinse off mouth of tube with small quantity ether after each decantation, letting ether run into flask. Repeat ether extns twice, using only 15 ml of each ether for second and third extns. Again shake vigorously after addn of each ether and centrf. If necessary in order to pour off all ether-fat soln after first extn, add more H_2O prior to second decantation.

Slowly evap. combined ether solns in flask, dry ca 90 min at 100° (placing counterpoise in oven at same time), cool in air to constant wt, and weigh.

30.050 Identification of Oil— Official Final Action

Proceed as in Chap. 28, using oil obtained by evapg pet ether exts from detn of reducing sugars, 30.043. (*Caution: See* 46.011 and 46.073.)

30.051 Gums in Mayonnaise and French Dressing (*12*)—Official Final Action

(Not applicable in presence of starch)

(*Caution: See* 46.082.)

Transfer 100 g sample to 250 ml beaker, add 35–40 ml hot H_2O, and mix thoroly. Heat to 65–70° in H_2O bath, add 10 ml *50% trichloroacetic acid soln*, and maintain at 65–70° until emulsion shows signs of breaking (never >10 min). Transfer mixt. to 8 oz nursing bottle and insert pipet guard (JAOAC **20**, 529(1937)) (wide-bore glass tube long enough to reach almost to bottom of centrf. bottle, with lower end loosely stoppered; tube is held in place by slotted rubber stopper). Centrf. 15–20 min at ca 1200 rpm. (This should sep. mixt. into lower aq. layer and upper oily layer, with layer of curd between. If sepn does not occur, add 30–40 ml toluene, mix, and repeat centrfg.) Using pipet inserted thru pipet guard, remove as much aq. layer as possible and filter it into 600 ml beaker. Add 5 vols alcohol and let mixt. stand overnight to ppt gums.

Decant or pipet off enough alcohol to leave ≤225 ml, transfer contents of beaker to 8 oz nursing bottle, centrf. until gum settles to bottom, and decant supernatant alcohol as completely as possible. Dissolve residue in ≤50 ml hot H_2O, add 1 or 2 ml HOAc, and ppt by adding alcohol to 8 oz mark on nursing bottle. Let stand overnight, or until ppt flocculates, centrf. at 1200 rpm, and decant alcohol. (Heavy flocculent ppt at this point indicates presence of significant quantity of gum. Slight ppt should not be considered positive test for gums, as spices present in most mayonnaises and french dressings usually give such ppt.) Confirm presence of gums as follows:

Add 35 ml hot H_2O to ppt in nursing bottle, transfer to small beaker, add 5 ml HCl, and boil gently 2 min to hydrolyze gums to sugars. This soln may now be used for various qual. tests for monosaccharide sugars, as follows:

(**a**) *Copper reduction test.*—Transfer 1 ml hydrolyzed gum soln to test tube, neutze to litmus paper with ca 2*N* NaOH, and remove paper. Add 5 ml Benedict qual. soln, **16.211**(a), and boil vigorously 1–2 min. Let cool spontaneously. Voluminous ppt, which may be green, yellow, or red, indicates reducing sugars.

(**b**) *Molisch test.*—Transfer 5 ml hydrolyzed gum soln to test tube, and add 2 drops *15% alc.* α-

naphthol soln. Incline tube and slowly pour 3–5 ml H_2SO_4 down inner side so that 2 layers do not mix. Reddish-violet zone at point of contact indicates carbohydrates. (5% alc. thymol soln may be substituted for α-naphthol.)

Gums in Salad Dressing (*13*)— Official Final Action

(Applicable in presence of starch)

30.052   *Reagents*

(**a**) *Calcium chloride soln.*—Sp gr 1.2 at 20°. If cloudy, let soln stand so insol. matter may ppt, and then filter.

(**b**) *Iodine soln.*—See **30.037**(c).

30.053   *Separation of Gums from Starch*

Defat 50 g salad dressing by heating on steam bath in 250 ml beaker until fat seps, cool, and ext with pet ether until last ether ext is colorless. Make alk. with $MgCO_3$ (2–2.5 g), testing with pH test paper. Heat mixt. in H_2O bath at 80° until residual ether and CO_2 are expelled. Then add 100 ml $CaCl_2$ soln and heat in boiling H_2O bath 30 min, stirring occasionally. Pour into 250 ml Pyrex centrf. bottle, centrf., and decant as much of supernatant as possible into 250 ml separator. Add 10 ml $CaCl_2$ soln to residue in bottle and shake well. Centrf. and decant supernatant as before into separator. Swirl funnel gently and let oil sep. Drain all material below oil into another 250 ml Pyrex centrf. bottle. Centrf. and filter supernatant thru 11 cm buchner fitted with Whatman No. 1 or equiv. paper precoated with layer of Celite filter-aid or equiv. Collect filtrate in beaker within bell jar or in large test tube in suction flask. Add 10 ml $CaCl_2$ soln to residue in centrf. bottle, shake well, centrf., and decant supernatant onto filter in buchner. Wash filter with enough $CaCl_2$ soln so that total vol. filtrate is ca 110 ml.

Add slowly, with stirring, 20 ml I soln to clear ext to ppt starch-iodide. I should be present in considerable excess over amt required to react quant. with the starch. Considerable amts of reducing substances are present, which must be satisfied before starch can be quant. sepd. Add small quantity of Celite filter-aid and let starch-iodide, which seps in finely divided condition, stand ca 1 hr. Filter by suction thru 11 cm Whatman No. 1 or equiv. paper, precoated with adequate layer of Celite. Use wire screen under paper to aid filtration. Do not wash pad. Test for excess I in filtrate with starch-iodide paper or starch soln. This test must be pos. to ensure removal of all starch. To brown filtrate add 4 vols alcohol and let stand overnight.

Centrf. off pptd crude gum. Wash twice with 70% alcohol. If possible, gum should be transferred into centrf. bottle, but in some cases gum adheres so firmly to wall of beaker that it can only be rinsed until washings are clear.

Heat on steam bath or in oven at 100° until alcohol is removed. Dissolve residue in 20 ml H_2O by heating in H_2O bath until no more material dissolves. Use rubber policeman to assist soln. (Be sure gum is dissolved or it will be lost here.) Centrf. to remove any insol. material. Decant supernatant into another 250 ml centrf. bottle; add 1 drop HOAc and 1 drop $CaCl_2$ soln; and reppt with 4 vols alcohol. Let stand at least 1 hr or overnight. Centrf. and wash ppt twice with 70% alcohol by shaking well and centrfg.

Again drive off alcohol with aid of gentle air stream by heating in hot H_2O bath and dissolve ppt in 10 ml hot H_2O, using rubber policeman. (Heed warning in preceding par.) Centrf. to remove any insol. material and decant into 50 ml heavy duty Pyrex centrf. tube. (Short cone type is less liable to break.) Adjust vol. to 10 ml; add 1 drop HOAc and 1 drop $CaCl_2$ soln; and reppt with 40 ml alcohol. Let stand 1 hr, centrf., and wash with 70% alcohol as before. Heavy flocculent ppt at this point indicates presence of gums. Very small quantity of ppt adhering to walls of centrf. tube or appearing as mere turbidity is to be disregarded, as spice gums present in most salad dressing usually give such ppt.

30.054 — *Detection of Gum*

To confirm presence of gums, remove residual alcohol by gentle heating in hot H_2O bath, dissolve residue in 10 ml hot H_2O, and centrf. to remove any insol. material. Decant supernatant into 10 ml graduated cylinder, dil. to 10 ml with H_2O, and mix. To 1 ml of this soln add 1 or 2 drops basic $Pb(OAc)_2$ reagent, **31.021**(a), 1 drop at time. Immediate flocculent, curdy, or gelatinous ppt is confirmation of presence of gums. Ppt may form on standing but this is to be disregarded.

Alginates (*14*)—Official First Action
(Applicable to mayonnaise, salad dressing, and french dressing)

30.055 — *Preparation of Sample*

Weigh directly into 250 ml centrf. bottle 2 g or enough sample to give 10–20 mg alginate (ca 2 g at 0.5% level). Disperse in 50 ml H_2O and fill bottle with acetone-alcohol (1 + 2). Shake vigorously and let stand until ppt begins to settle; then centrf. at 1600–1700 rpm ca 10 min. Decant, discard liq., disperse in 50 ml H_2O, and reppt 2 more times. To ppt add 50 ml dioxane, shake well, and filter thru asbestos-matted gooch with suction. Transfer ppt to gooch, rinse bottle and ppt with several portions dioxane, and suck dry. Return ppt and asbestos mat to centrf. bottle, add 50 ml H_2O, disperse ppt, and adjust to pH 8–9 with 3% NaOH. (With french dressing add 0.25 g Celite 545, shake, and let stand 10 min, shaking several times. Centrf. 10 min at 1600–1700 rpm. Decant supernatant, filtering if necessary to remove suspended particles.) To 10 ml aliquot in 50 ml centrf. tube, add 40 ml acetone-alcohol (1 + 2), stir vigorously, and let stand until

ppt forms. If necessary, add 1 drop satd NaCl soln to start pptn. Centrf., discard liq., and dry ppt on steam bath.

30.056 — *Detection*

(Start detection at beginning of day so color changes can be observed.)

Moisten ppt with 3 drops $0.1N$ NaOH, rubbing thoroly with glass rod. Add 2 ml $Fe-H_2SO_4$ reagent, **13.057**, and let stand. Formation of purple-red color indicates presence of alginate. If brown color forms, repeat detection, using smaller aliquot for final pptn. Alginates are absent if no color develops on standing overnight.

Starch—Official Final Action
30.057 — *Reagents—See* **30.037**

30.058 — *Determination*

Det. total acidity of prepd sample as in **30.046**. Place 4–5 g prepd sample in 500 ml erlenmeyer and add calcd quantity $0.1N$ NaOH, V, to neutze acid in wt sample taken. Pipet in 100 ml $CaCl_2$ soln, stopper flask, and swirl gently until all large lumps of dressing are broken up. Continue as in **30.038**, line 5, beginning "Add glass beads." Calc. % starch from formula:

$$\% \text{ starch} = [\text{g glucose} \times 0.9(100 + V + W) \times 8]/\text{wt sample},$$

where $W = $ g H_2O in sample taken (calcd from solids, **30.042**.)

VINEGARS (*15*)
(Unless otherwise directed, express results as g/100 ml.)

30.059 Organoleptic Examination—Procedure

Note appearance, color, odor, and taste. Neutze portion of sample with NaOH soln and note odor and taste. Ext neutzd vinegar with ether, evap. ether ext, and note odor and taste of residue. (Spices and pungent materials are indicated by characteristic odors and tastes.) Evap. portion of sample on H_2O bath. Odor of material as last of volatile matter evaps and appearance and taste of residue give information as to source and character of vinegar.

30.060 Preparation of Sample—Procedure

Mix thoroly and filter thru rapid paper.

30.061 Solids—Official Final Action

Measure 10 ml sample into weighed 50 mm diam., flat-bottom Pt dish, evap. on boiling H_2O bath 30 min, and dry exactly 2.5 hr in H_2O oven at temp. of boiling H_2O. Cool in desiccator and weigh. (To obtain concordant results it is necessary to use dish of size and shape stated and to dry exactly time specified.)

30.062   Ash—Official Final Action

Measure 25 ml sample into weighed Pt dish, evap. to dryness on H_2O or steam bath, and heat in muffle 30 min at 500–550°. Break up charred mass in Pt dish, add hot H_2O, filter thru ashless paper, and wash *thoroly* with H_2O. Return paper and contents to dish, dry, and heat 30 min at ca 525°, or until all C is burned off. Add filtrate, evap. to dryness, and heat 15 min at ca 525°. Cool in desiccator and weigh (wt x). Reheat in muffle 5 min at ca 525°, and cool ≤1 hr in desiccator contg efficient desiccant. Put ≤2 dishes (preferably only 1) in desiccator at a time. Place wt x on balance pan before removing dish from desiccator, and weigh rapidly to mg. Calc. total ash from last wt.

30.063   Soluble and Insoluble Ash— Official Final Action

Treat ash, **30.062**, as in **31.015**.

30.064   Alkalinity of Soluble Ash— Official Final Action

Proceed as in **31.016**, using sol. ash obtained in **30.063**. Express result as number ml $1N$ acid required to neutze sol. ash from 100 ml vinegar. If relationship of ash to alky of sol. ash is abnormal, study composition of ash, especially as to content of chlorides, sulfates, phosphates, and alkalies (J. Am. Chem. Soc. **22**, 218(1900)).

30.065   Soluble Phosphorus (16)— Official Final Action

Proceed as in **2.031** or **8.027**, or **22.039**, using soln obtained in **30.064**. If either volumetric or colorimetric method is used, stdze with sample of known phosphate content. Express results as mg P_2O_5/100 ml vinegar.

30.066   Insoluble Phosphorus (16)— Official Final Action

Dissolve H_2O-insol. ash, **30.063**, in ca 50 ml boiling HNO_3 $(1 + 8)$ (use 25 ml H_2SO_4 $(1 + 9)$ for colorimetric method) and proceed as in **2.031** or **8.027**, or **22.039**. If either volumetric or colorimetric method is used, stdze with sample of known phosphate content. Express result as mg P_2O_5/100 ml vinegar.

30.067   Total Phosphorus (16)— Official Final Action

Dissolve ash, **30.062**, or both sol. and insol. ash, **30.063**, in ca 50 ml boiling HNO_3 $(1 + 8)$ (use 25 ml H_2SO_4 $(1 + 9)$ for colorimetric method) and proceed as in **2.031** or **8.027**, or **22.039**. If either volumetric or colorimetric method is used, stdze with sample of known phosphate content. Express result as mg P_2O_5/100 ml vinegar. If desired, digest vinegar as in **22.038**, instead of using ash from **30.062**.

30.068   Total Acids—Official Final Action

Dil. 10 ml sample with recently boiled and cooled H_2O until it appears only slightly colored and titr. with $0.5N$ alkali, using phthln. 1 ml $0.5N$ alkali = 0.0300 g HOAc.

30.069   Nonvolatile Acids—Official Final Action

Measure 10 ml vinegar into 200 ml porcelain casserole, evap. just to dryness, add 5–10 ml H_2O, and again evap.; repeat until at least 5 evapns have been made. Add ca 200 ml recently boiled and cooled H_2O, and titr. with $0.1N$ alkali, using phthln. 1 ml $0.1N$ alkali = 0.00600 g HOAc.

30.070   Volatile Acids—Official Final Action

Subtract quantity nonvolatile acids, **30.069**, from quantity total acids, **30.068**.

30.071   Total Reducing Substances Before Inversion—Official Final Action

Measure 25 ml sample into 50 ml vol. flask and add enough NaOH soln $(1 + 1)$ to nearly neutze acid. Cool, dil. to vol. with H_2O, and det. reducing substances in 20 ml soln as in **31.039**. If quantity of reducing substances is very small, use 40 ml. Calc. result as invert sugar (for malt vinegar as glucose).

30.072   Total Reducing Substances After Inversion—Official Final Action

Invert 25 ml sample in 50 ml vol. flask with 5 ml HCl, as in **31.026(b)** or **(c)**. Nearly neutze with NaOH soln $(1 + 1)$ and det. reducing substances as in **31.039**.

30.073   Nonvolatile Reducing Substances (Sugar)—Official Final Action

(Useful in calcg nonsugar solids)

Evap. 50 ml sample on steam or H_2O bath to sirupy consistency, add 10 ml H_2O, and evap. again. Repeat with 10 ml H_2O. Transfer residue to 100 ml vol. flask with ca 50 ml warm H_2O. Cool; invert with 10 ml HCl as in **31.026(b)** or **(c)**; nearly neutze with NaOH soln $(1 + 1)$; cool, dil. to vol. with H_2O, and det. reducing substances in 20 ml or 40 ml, depending on quantity present, as in **31.039**. Calc. result as invert sugar (for malt vinegar as glucose). If results for total reducing substances before and after inversion show absence of sucrose, inversion may be omitted here.

30.074   Volatile Reducing Substances (17)— Procedure

When sucrose is absent, subtract quantity of nonvolatile reducing substances, **30.073**, from mean of total reducing substances before inversion, **30.071**, and after inversion, **30.072**. When sucrose is present, subtract quantity of nonvolatile reducing substances, **30.073,** from quantity of total reducing substances after inversion, **30.072.**

30.075 Alcohol—Official Final Action

Measure 100 ml sample into r-b distn flask. Make faintly alk. with NaOH soln (1 + 1), distill almost 50 ml, dil. to 50 ml at temp. of sample, and det. sp gr at 20/20° with pycnometer, **9.011.** Obtain % by vol. from **47.003.** Undue foaming may be obviated by adding small piece of paraffin, free from volatile constituents.

Glycerol (*18*)—Official Final Action

30.076   *Reagents*

(**a**) *Strong potassium dichromate soln.*—1 ml = 0.01 g glycerol. Dissolve 74.55 g dry, recrystd $K_2Cr_2O_7$ in H_2O; add 150 ml H_2SO_4; cool, and dil. with H_2O to 1 L at 20°. Because of high coefficient of expansion of this concd soln it is necessary to make all volumetric measurements of soln at same temp. as that at which it was dild to vol.

(**b**) *Dilute potassium dichromate soln.*—Measure 25 ml (**a**) at 20° into 500 ml vol. flask and dil. to vol. with H_2O at room temp. 20 ml of this soln = 0.01 g glycerol.

(**c**) *Ferrous ammonium sulfate soln.*—Dissolve 30 g $FeSO_4 \cdot (NH_4)_2SO_4 \cdot 6H_2O$ in H_2O, add 50 ml H_2SO_4, cool, and dil. with H_2O to 1 L at room temp. 1 ml of this soln = ca 1 ml (**b**). As its value changes slightly from day to day, stdze against (**b**) whenever used.

(**d**) *Diphenylamine indicator.*—Dissolve 1 g diphenylamine in 100 ml H_2SO_4. (Diphenylamine may be harmful. *Caution: See* **46.084.**)

(**e**) *Retarder.*—Dil. 150 ml H_3PO_4 with 600 ml H_2O, and add 250 ml H_2SO_4.

(**f**) *Milk of lime.*—Place 150 g CaO, selected from clean hard lumps, prepd preferably from marble, in large porcelain or iron dish; slake with H_2O, cool, and add enough H_2O to make 1 L.

(**g**) *Silver carbonate.*—Dissolve 0.1 g Ag_2SO_4 in ca 50 ml H_2O, add excess of Na_2CO_3 soln, let ppt settle, and wash with H_2O several times by decantation until washings are practically neut. Prep. immediately before use.

30.077   *Determination*

Make evapns on H_2O bath held at 85–90°. Area of dish exposed to bath should not be greater in circumference than that covered by liq. inside.

Evap. 100 ml vinegar to 5 ml, add 20 ml H_2O, and again evap. to 5 ml to expel HOAc. Treat residue with ca 5 g 40-mesh sand and 15 ml milk of lime, and evap. almost to dryness with frequent stirring, avoiding formation of dry crust or evapn to complete dryness. Treat moist residue with 5 ml H_2O; rub to homogeneous paste; slowly add 45 ml absolute alcohol, washing down sides of dish to remove adhering paste; and stir thoroly. Heat mixt. on H_2O

bath, with constant stirring, to incipient boiling; transfer to suitable vessel and centrf.

Decant clear liq. into porcelain dish and wash residue with several small portions hot alcohol, 90% by vol., by centrfg. (If centrf. is not available, decant liq. thru folded paper into porcelain dish. Wash residue repeatedly with small portions hot 90% alcohol, twice by decantation, and then by transferring all material to filter. Continue washing until filtrate equals 150 ml.) Evap. to sirupy consistency, add 10 ml absolute alcohol to dissolve residue, and transfer to 50 ml g-s cylinder, washing dish with successive small portions absolute alcohol until vol. of soln is 20 ml. Add three 10 ml portions anhyd. ether, shaking thoroly after each addn. Let stand until clear, pour off thru filter, and wash cylinder and filter with mixt. of 2 vols absolute alcohol and 3 of anhyd. ether. If heavy ppt forms in cylinder, centrf. at low speed, decant clear liq., and wash with three 20 ml portions of the alcohol-ether mixt., shaking mixt. thoroly each time and sepg ppt by centrfg. Wash paper with the alcohol-ether mixt. and evap. filtrate and washings on H_2O bath to ca 5 ml; add 20 ml H_2O, and again evap. to 5 ml; again add 20 ml H_2O and evap. to 5 ml; finally add 10 ml H_2O and evap. to 5 ml. These evapns are necessary to remove all ether and alcohol, and when conducted at 85–90° they result in no loss of glycerol if concn of latter is <50%.

Transfer residue with hot H_2O to 50 ml vol. flask, cool, add Ag_2CO_3 prepd from 0.1 g Ag_2SO_4, shake, and let stand 10 min. Add 0.5 ml basic $Pb(OAc)_2$ soln, **31.021**(**a**); shake occasionally, and let stand 10 min. Dil. to vol., shake well, and filter, rejecting first portion of filtrate. Pipet 25 ml clear filtrate into 250 ml vol. flask.

Add 1 ml H_2SO_4 to ppt excess Pb and then 30 ml strong $K_2Cr_2O_7$ soln. Carefully add 24 ml H_2SO_4, rotating flask gently to mix contents and avoid violent ebullition, and then place in *boiling* H_2O bath exactly 20 min. Remove flask from bath, dil., cool, and dil. to vol. at room temp. Enough strong $K_2Cr_2O_7$ soln should have been used to leave excess of ca 12.5 ml at end of oxidn; 30 ml is enough for ordinary vinegar contg ≤0.35 g glycerol/100 ml.

Stdze $Fe(NH_4)_2(SO_4)_2$ soln by pipetting 20 ml into 250 ml beaker and adding 20 ml retarder, 4 drops indicator, and ca 100 ml H_2O. Titr. with dil. $K_2Cr_2O_7$ soln until liq. turns dark green; then slowly add dropwise, stirring continuously, until blue-gray changes to deep violet. Designate ml dil. $K_2Cr_2O_7$ soln used as x. In place of $K_2Cr_2O_7$ soln, substitute buret contg oxidized glycerol and excess strong $K_2Cr_2O_7$ soln, and titr. 20 ml $Fe(NH_4)_2(SO_4)_2$ soln as before, designating ml used as y. From figures obtained calc. glycerol by following formula:

$$G = [D - (250x/20y)]0.02$$

where G = g glycerol/100 ml vinegar, and D = ml strong $K_2Cr_2O_7$ soln used to oxidize glycerol.

30.078 Color—Official Final Action

Det. depth of color in Lovibond tintometer by good reflected daylight, using $\frac{1}{2}$ or $1''$ cell and brewer's scale. Report result in terms of $\frac{1}{2}''$ cell and so state.

30.079 Polarization (19)—Official Final Action

Whenever possible, polarize in 200 mm tube without decolorizing. Report result on basis of 200 mm tube in °S, **31.020(a)**. When necessary, decolorize as follows:

(a) To 50 ml sample add measured quantity of satd neut. Pb(OAc)₂ soln, avoiding excess of Pb; filter, remove Pb with powd anhyd. K oxalate, and filter. Polarize and correct for diln with Pb(OAc)₂ soln.

(b) To 50 ml sample add decolorizing C, avoiding excessive quantity or length of treatment. Filter thru double paper and polarize.

30.080 Sulfates—Official Final Action

To 100 ml sample add 2 ml ca $1N$ HCl, heat to boiling, and add 10 ml hot BaCl₂.2H₂O soln (1 g/100 ml), dropwise. Continue boiling 5 min, keeping vol. ca constant by adding hot H₂O as required. Let mixt. stand until supernatant is clear (overnight is convenient, but this time should not be exceeded). Filter on ashless paper or weighed Munroe crucible (Z. Anal. Chem. **2**, 241(1888); J. Am. Chem. Soc. **31**, 456, 928(1909)). Wash Cl-free with hot H₂O, dry, ignite at low red heat (700–800°), cool, and weigh. Express result as mg SO₃/100 ml vinegar.

30.081 Dextrin (Qualitative Test)— Procedure

Evap. 100 ml sample to ca 15 ml. Add slowly, and with constant stirring, 200 ml alcohol and let stand overnight. Sep. ppt, preferably by centrfg, and wash with 80% alcohol. Dissolve in min. quantity H₂O and det. optical rotation. Distinct optical rotation indicates dextrin. Treat soln with several drops I soln of ca same color intensity. Formation of reddish-brown color indicates dextrin.

30.082 Preservatives—Official Final Action— See Chap. 20

Permanganate Oxidation Number (20)— Official Final Action

(For differentiating between vinegar and com. HOAc)

30.083 *Reagents*

(a) *Potassium permanganate soln.*—31 g/L. Prep. according to **45.026**; stdzn is unnecessary.

(b) *Sodium thiosulfate.*—0.5N. Accurately stdze against K₂Cr₂O₇ as in **45.039**, except use ca 0.5 g K₂Cr₂O₇, 10 g KI, 10 ml HCl, and 90 ml H₂O.

(c) *Potassium iodide soln.*—Dissolve 50 g KI in 100 ml H₂O and filter. Do not use unless colorless.

30.084 *Determination*

Adjust sample to 4 g/100 ml acidity as HOAc. Steam distill 50 ml adjusted sample and collect 50 ml distillate. Regulate distn so that ca 45 ml remains in distg flask when 50 ml distillate has been collected. All-glass app. is preferable; if not available, cover cork or rubber stoppers with Sn or Al foil. App. illustrated in Fig. 18:1, **18.026(a)**, is convenient. Keep distillate and reagents at 25°.

Transfer 50 ml distillate to 500 ml g-s erlenmeyer. Add 10 ml H₂SO₄ (1 + 1) and 25 ml of KMnO₄ soln. Accurately measure KMnO₄ soln, draining pipet definite time. Hold at 25°, preferably in H₂O bath, exactly 1 hr. Then immediately add 20 ml KI soln and mix well. Titr. liberated I with 0.5N Na₂S₂O₃.

Conduct blank detn at same time, using 50 ml H₂O, 10 ml H₂SO₄ (1 + 1), and 25 ml KMnO₄ soln.

(ml 0.5N Na₂S₂O₃ required by blank − quantity used in detn) ÷ 2 = permanganate oxidation number of vinegar. Report on basis of adjusted vinegar (4% acid).

If permanganate oxidation number is >15, repeat detn, using 25 ml adjusted vinegar + 25 ml H₂O. Repeat this reduction by $\frac{1}{2}$ until ml KMnO₄ soln used is <15. Calc. permanganate oxidation number to basis of 50 ml adjusted vinegar.

SELECTED REFERENCES

(1) JAOAC **24**, 667(1941).

(2) USDA Bur. Chem. Bull. **13**, (II), p. 165; JAOAC **23**, 581(1940).

(3) Conn. Agr. Expt. Sta. Rpt., 1898 (II), p. 187.

(4) USDA Bur. Chem. Bull. **13**, (II), p. 167; Anal. Chem. **27**, 1159(1955).

(5) JAOAC **17**, 70, 371(1934); **18**, 611(1935); **21**, 435(1938); **22**, 598(1939); **25**, 700(1942); **33**, 575(1950); **36**, 750(1953); **37**, 390(1954); **38**, 548(1955); **41**, 252(1958); **42**, 312(1959); **45**, 212, 562(1962).

(6) JAOAC **19**, 98, 411(1936).

(7) JAOAC **4**, 525(1921); **53**, 1(1970).

(8) Winton, "Microscopy of Vegetable Foods," 2nd ed., 1916; Winton, "Structure and Composition of Foods," vol. IV, 1939; Youngken, "Textbook of Pharmacognosy," 6th ed., 1948; Food, Apr. 1956–Mar. 1957, inclusive, "Food Microscopy," parts 4–15; Claus, "Pharmacognosy," 4th ed., 1961; Parry, "Spices," 1962.

(9) JAOAC **24**, 703(1941); **25**, 98(1942).

(10) JAOAC **7**, 71(1923).

(11) JAOAC **5**, 248(1921); **7**, 138(1923); **16**, 77, 548(1933); **24**, 83, 695(1941); **34**, 267(1951); **35**, 231(1952); **36**, 758(1953); **37**, 393(1954).

(12) JAOAC **20**, 527(1937); **21**, 110(1938); **22**, 607(1939).

(13) Ind. Eng. Chem., Anal. Ed. **7**, 311(1935);

JAOAC **24,** 700(1941); **25,** 705(1942); **27,** 260(1944); **28,** 249(1945); **29,** 250(1946); **35,** 358(1952).

(14) JAOAC **46,** 623(1963); **47,** 389(1964).

(15) JAOAC **8,** 150(1924); **9,** 440(1926); **10,** 490 (1927); **11,** 499(1928); **14,** 507(1931); **15,** 535 (1932); **16,** 536(1933); **17,** 360(1934); **21,** 430 (1938); **23,** 586(1940); **25,** 702(1942); **26,** 233 (1943); **29,** 304(1946); **32,** 336(1949); **37,** 391 (1954); **38,** 548(1955); **42,** 316(1959); **45,** 562 (1962).

(16) JAOAC **24,** 684(1941).

(17) J. Am. Chem. Soc. **39,** 309(1917); J. Ind. Eng. Chem. **5,** 845(1913).

(18) USDA Bur. Chem. Bull. **137,** p. 61; JAOAC **3,** 411(1920); **15,** 535(1932); **18,** 82(1935).

(19) JAOAC **5,** 245(1921); **8,** 151(1924); **14,** 507 (1931).

(20) JAOAC **27,** 263(1944); **32,** 336(1949); **34,** 262(1951); **35,** 229(1952).

31. Sugars and Sugar Products [*]

SUGARS AND SIRUPS

31.001 Preparation of Sample— Official Final Action

(a) *Solids (sugars, etc.).*—Grind, if necessary, and mix to uniformity. Thoroly mix raw sugars with spatula in min. time. Break up any lumps either on glass plate with glass or iron rolling pin, or in large, clean, dry mortar, with pestle.

(b) *Semisolids (massecuites, etc.).*—Weigh 50 g sample, dissolve crystals of sugar in min. quantity of H_2O, wash into 250 ml vol. flask, dil. to vol., and mix thoroly; or weigh 50 g sample and dil. with H_2O to 100 g. If insol. material remains, mix uniformly by shaking before taking aliquots or weighed portions for detns.

(c) *Liquids (molasses, sirups, etc.).*—Mix materials thoroly. If crystals of sugar are present, dissolve them by heating gently (avoiding loss of H_2O by evapn), or by weighing whole mass, then adding H_2O, heating until completely dissolved, and after cooling, reweighing. Calc. all results to wt original substance.

Color of Raw Cane Sugars (1)— Official First Action

31.002 Reagent

Filter-aid.—Celite, or equiv., analytical filter-aid.

31.003 Apparatus

Fractionator.—Construct fractionator of 35 mm id, heavy-wall Pyrex tubing, 145 mm long from top to bottom shoulder where it is sealed to ⊤ stopcock with 3 mm bore and 9 mm od tubing. Leave 55 mm stem below stopcock. Seal tube, 9 mm od, 45 mm long, to body of fractionator 45 mm below top. Connect to buchner and source of vac. thru "T" tube as shown in Fig. 31:1. (Dimensions are not critical.)

31.004 Determination

Place 60 g sample in flask, add 40 g boiling H_2O, and rotate flask until all sugar dissolves. Add 3 g Celite and shake mixt. vigorously 1 min. Assemble special filtration app., and connect to constant vac. of 24″. With stopcock open, place paper, S&S No. 589 blue ribbon, 7 cm diam., in buchner, wet with H_2O, and suck excess H_2O thru filtering tube into flask. Close stopcock and pour well-shaken mixt. of sugar soln and Celite evenly over paper. Collect ca

10 ml of first filtrate, which is somewhat turbid, in filtering tube and run into flask by opening stopcock. Close stopcock, collect another 10 ml filtrate in filtering tube, and run into flask as before to wash inner walls of tube free from any small particles of turbidity. Keep bed of Celite well covered with sugar soln during entire filtration. *Do not let it run dry.* Collect final clear filtrate in filtering tube, transfer to small bottle or to small, g-s erlenmeyer, and mix thoroly. Det. refractometer Brix on portion of soln and calc. concn, *c* (g dry substance/ml soln), by multiplying Brix by corresponding true density and dividing by 100.

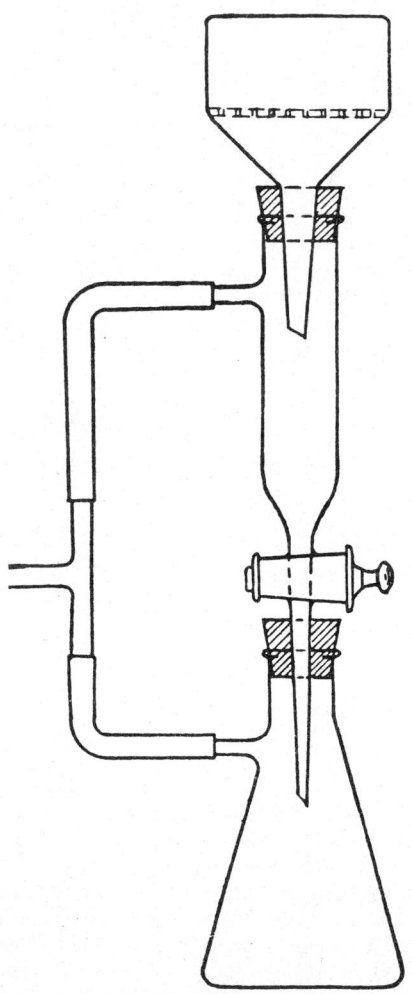

FIG. 31:1—Fractionator

Det. % T at 560 nm on spectrophtr with wavelength and T scales that have been checked, preferably with std glass filter supplied by NBS. Use distd H_2O as the 100% T std. Cell thickness, b (in cm), used should be such that readings are within range 25–75% T.

Calc. attenuation index, $a_c^* = -(\log T)/bc$.

Moisture

31.005 Vacuum Drying—Official Final Action

(Applicable to cane and beet, raw and refined sugars)

Dry 2–5 g prepd sample, **31.001**(a), in flat dish (Ni, Pt, or Al with tight-fit cover), 2 hr at ≤70° (preferably 60°), under pressure ≤50 mm Hg. Bleed oven with current of air (dried by passing thru anhyd. $CaSO_4$, P_2O_5, or other efficient desiccant) during drying to remove H_2O vapor. Remove dish from oven, cover, cool in desiccator, and weigh. Redry 1 hr and repeat process until change in wt between successive dryings at 1 hr intervals is ≤2 mg.

31.006 Drying at Atmospheric Pressure— Procedure

(Applicable to cane and beet, raw and refined sugars)

Dry ca 5 g prepd sample, **31.001**(a), in flat dish (Ni, Pt, or Al with tight-fit cover), 3 hr at 100°. Remove dish, cover, cool in desiccator, and weigh. Redry 1 hr and repeat process until change in wt between successive dryings at 1 hr intervals is ≤2 mg. For large-grain sugars, increase temp. to 105–110° in final heating periods to expel last traces of occluded H_2O. Report loss in wt as H_2O.

31.007 Drying upon Pumice Stone— Official Final Action

(Applicable to massecuites, molasses, and other liq. and semiliq. products)

Prep. pumice stone of 2 grades of fineness, one to pass thru 1 mm sieve, other thru 6 mm but not 1 mm sieve. Digest each 8 hr with H_2SO_4 (1 + 4) on steam bath. Wash acid-free and heat to 525°. Make detn in flat metal dish 60 mm diam. Place 3 mm layer of the fine pumice stone on bottom of dish, then 6–10 mm layer of coarse pumice stone; dry and weigh. Dil. sample with weighed portion of H_2O so that dild material contains 20–30% solid matter. Weigh into prepd dish quantity of dild sample to yield ca 1 g dry matter. If this weighing cannot be made rapidly, use weighing bottle provided with cork thru which pipet passes. Dry at 70° under pressure ≤50 mm Hg, bleeding with dry air as in **31.005**. Make trial weighings at 2 hr intervals toward end of drying period until change in wt is ≤2 mg. Report loss in wt as H_2O. Substances contg little or no fructose or other readily decomposable substance may be dried in oven at 100°.

31.008 Drying upon Quartz Sand (2)— Official Final Action

(Applicable to massecuites, molasses, and other liq. and semiliq. products)

Digest pure quartz sand that passes No. 40 but not No. 60 sieve with HCl, wash acid-free, dry, and ignite. Preserve in stoppered bottle. Place 25–30 g prepd sand and short stirring rod in dish ca 55 mm diam. and 40 mm deep, fitted with cover. Dry thoroly, cover dish, cool in desiccator, and weigh immediately. Add enough dild sample of known wt to yield ca 1 g dry matter and mix thoroly with sand. Heat on steam bath 15–20 min, stirring at 2–3 min intervals, or until mass becomes too stiff to manipulate readily. Dry at <70° (preferably 60°) under pressure ≤50 mm Hg, bleeding with dry air as in **31.005**. Make trial weighings at 2 hr intervals toward end of drying period (ca 18 hr) until change in wt is ≤2 mg.

For materials contg no fructose or other readily decomposable substance, dry 8–10 hr at atm. pressure in oven at 100°, cool in desiccator, and weigh, repeating heating and weighing until loss in 1 hr heating is ≤2 mg. Report loss in wt as H_2O.

As dry sand, as well as dried sample, absorbs appreciable quantity of moisture on standing over most desiccating agents, make all weighings as quickly as possible after cooling in desiccator.

Solids

31.009 By Means of Spindle— Official Final Action

(Accurate only when applied to pure sucrose solns, but extensively used for approx. results with liq. sugar products contg invert sugar and other non-sucrose solids.)

(a) *Direct.*—Density of juices, sirups, etc., is conveniently detd with Brix or Baumé hydrometer, preferably former as scale graduations agree closely with % total solids. Table for comparison of degrees Brix (% by wt of pure sucrose in pure solns), degrees Baumé (modulus 145), sp gr at 20/4°, and sp gr at 20/20° is given in **47.008**.

Use Brix spindle graduated in tenths and of appropriate range, and cylinder of sufficient diam. (at least 12 mm larger than spindle bulb) to permit spindle to come to rest without touching sides. Soln should be at room temp. If this varies >1° from temp. at which spindle was graduated (20°), apply correction according to **47.010**. Before taking reading, let soln stand in cylinder until all air bubbles escape and all fatty or waxy materials come to top and are skimmed off. (Air bubbles may be conveniently removed by applying vac. to cylinder by means of tube passing thru stopper inserted in top of cylinder.) Lower spindle slowly into sirup; do not let sirup on spindle reach above sirup level.

(b) *Double dilution.*—If sample is too dense to det. density directly, dil. weighed portion with weighed quantity of H_2O, or dissolve weighed portion and dil. to known vol. with H_2O. In first instance, % total solids is calcd by following formula:

% solids in undild material = WS/w, in which S = % solids in dild material; W = wt dild material; and w = wt sample taken for diln.

When diln is made to definite vol., use following formula:

% solids in undild material = VDS/w, where V = vol. dild soln at given temp.; D = sp gr of dild soln at same temp.; S = % solids in dild soln at same temp.; and w = wt sample taken for diln.

Calcn is simplified by mixing equal wts sugar product and H_2O, and multiplying Brix of soln by 2.

31.010 By Means of Pycnometer (3)—
Official Final Action

(a) *Specific gravity (in vacuo or in air).*—Det. sp gr of soln at 20/4°, 20/20° *in vacuo*, or 20/20° in air as in **9.011**, using either pycnometers described in **9.009(b)** or other suitable type. Det. % by wt of solids as sucrose from appropriate table, **47.008** or **47.020**. When density of substance is too high for direct detn, dil. and then calc. sucrose content of original material as in **31.009(b)**.

(b) *Specific gravity of molasses.*—Use special calibrated 100 ml vol. flask with neck ca 8 mm id. Weigh empty flask and then fill with molasses, using long-stem funnel reaching below graduation mark, until level of molasses is up to lower end of neck of flask. (Flow of molasses may be stopped by inserting glass rod of suitable size into funnel so as to close stem opening.) Carefully remove funnel to prevent molasses from coming in contact with neck, and weigh flask and molasses. Add H_2O almost to graduation mark, running it down side of neck to prevent mixing with molasses. Let stand several hr or overnight for bubbles to escape. Place flask in constant temp. H_2O bath, preferably at 20°, and leave until it reaches bath temp. Dil. to vol. at that temp. with H_2O. Weigh. Reduce wt molasses to *in vacuo* and calc. density. Ascertain corresponding Brix or Baumé reading from **47.008**.

Example: grams
A, wt H_2O content of flask at 20°
in vacuo   = 99.823
B, wt molasses at 20° *in vacuo*   = 132.834
C, wt molasses and H_2O at 20°
in vacuo   = 137.968
$A - (C - B)$ = wt H_2O occupying space
of molasses *in vacuo*   = 94.689

$$\frac{132.834}{94.689} = 1.403 \text{ sp gr} \left(\frac{20°}{20°}\right) \text{ molasses.}$$

31.011 By Means of Refractometer (4)—
Official Final Action

(Applicable only to liq. samples contg no undissolved solids)

Det. refractometer reading of soln at 20° and obtain corresponding % dry substance from either direct reading, if sugar refractometer is used, or from **47.012**, if instrument gives readings in terms of refractive index. Circulate H_2O at constant temp., preferably 20°, thru jackets of refractometer or thru trough of immersion instrument, long enough to let temp. of prisms and of sample reach equilibrium, continuing circulation during observations and taking care that temp. is held constant.

If detn is made at temp. other than 20°, or if humidity causes condensation of moisture on exposed faces of prisms, make measurements at room temp. and correct readings to std temp. of 20° from **47.015**. If soln is too dark to be read in instrument, dil. with concd sugar soln; never use H_2O for this purpose. Mix weighed quantities of soln under examination and soln of pure sugar of about same strength, and obtain quantity of dry substance in former by following formula: $x = [(A + B)C - BD]/A$, in which x = % dry substance to be found; A = wt (g) sample mixed with B; B = wt (g) sugar soln used in diln; C = % dry substance in mixt. $A + B$ obtained from refractive index; and D = % dry substance in pure sugar soln obtained from its refractive index.

For liq. products contg invert sugar, correct % solids obtained from **47.012** by adding 0.022 for each % invert sugar in sample.

Ash—Official Final Action
31.012 Method I

Heat sample of appropriate wt for product being examined (usually 5–10 g) in 50–100 ml Pt dish at 100° until H_2O is expelled; add few drops pure olive oil and heat slowly over flame or under IR lamp until swelling stops. Place dish in muffle at ca 525° and leave until white ash is obtained. Moisten ash with H_2O, dry on steam bath and then on hot plate, and re-ash in muffle at 525° to constant wt.

31.013 Method II

Carbonize sample of appropriate wt for product being examined (usually 5–10 g) in 50–100 ml Pt dish at ca 525° and treat charred mass with hot H_2O to dissolve sol. salts. (In case of low-purity products, addn of few drops pure olive oil, as in **31.012**, may be desirable.) Filter thru ashless paper, ignite paper and residue to white ash, add filtrate of sol. salts, evap. to dryness, and ignite at ca 525° to constant wt.

31.014 Sulfated Ash—Official Final Action

Weigh 5 g sample into 50–100 ml Pt dish, add 5 ml 10% (by wt) H_2SO_4, ignite until sample is well carbonized, and then ash in muffle at ca 550°. Cool, add 2–3 ml 10% H_2SO_4, evap. on steam bath, dry on hot plate, and again ignite at 550° to constant wt. Express result as % sulfated ash.

31.015 Soluble and Insoluble Ash—
Official Final Action

Ash sample as in **31.012** or **31.013**. Add 10 ml H_2O to ash in the Pt dish, heat nearly to boiling, filter thru ashless paper, and wash with hot H_2O until combined filtrate and washings measure ca 60 ml. Return paper and contents to Pt dish, ignite carefully, cool, and weigh. Calc. % H_2O-sol. and H_2O-insol. ash.

31.016 Alkalinity of Soluble Ash— Official Final Action

Cool filtrate from **31.015** and titr. with 0.1N HCl, **45.012–45.013**, using Me orange, **6.004(g)**. Express alky in terms of ml 1N acid/100 g sample.

31.017 Alkalinity of Insoluble Ash— Official Final Action

Add excess 0.1N HCl (usually 10–15 ml) to ignited insol. ash in Pt dish, **31.015**, heat to incipient boiling on asbestos plate, and cool. Transfer quant. to erlenmeyer and titr. excess HCl with 0.1N NaOH, using Me orange. Express alky in terms of ml 1N acid/100 g sample.

31.018 Mineral Adulterants in Ash (5)— Official First Action

In large porcelain evapg dish, mix 100 g sample with ca 35 g H_2SO_4 and evap. to sirupy consistency. Pass elec. current thru it while stirring by placing one Pt electrode in bottom of dish near one side and attaching other to lower end of glass rod with which contents are stirred. Begin with current of ca 1 amp and gradually increase to 4. In 10–15 min mass is reduced to fine, dry char that may be readily burned to white ash in original dish over free flame or in muffle.

Note: This method is preferred to ordinary method of heating with H_2SO_4, especially in case of molasses, because, if properly manipulated, material comes quickly into form of very finely divided char or powder that is especially adapted for subsequent quick ignition.

If elec. current is not available, treat 100 g sample in large porcelain dish, evap. to sirupy consistency with enough H_2SO_4 to carbonize mass thoroly, and ignite in usual manner.

Following adulterants may be present: salts of Sn, used in molasses to bleach; mineral pigments, such as $PbCrO_4$ in yellow confectionery; oxides of Fe, sometimes used to simulate color of chocolate; and Cu. These elements may be detected by usual qual. tests.

31.019 Nitrogen—Official Final Action

Det. N in 5 g sample as in **2.051**, using larger quantity of the H_2SO_4 if necessary for complete digestion.

Sucrose—Polarimetric Methods

31.020 General Procedure

(Rules of International Commission for Uniform Methods of Sugar Analysis (ICUMSA) (6))

(a) *Standardization of Saccharimeter Scale (Official Final Action).*—Saccharimeter scale must be graduated in conformity with International Sugar Scale adopted by ICUMSA. Rotations on this scale are designated as degrees sugar (°S).

Basis of calibration of 100° point on International Sugar Scale is polarization of normal soln of pure sucrose (26.000 g/100 ml) at 20° in 200 mm tube, using white light and dichromate filter defined by Commission, (b). This soln, polarized at 20°, must give saccharimeter reading of exactly 100°S. Temp. of sugar soln during polarization must be kept constant at 20°.

Following rotations hold for normal quartz plate of International Sugar Scale: Normal Quartz Plate = 100°S = 40.690°±0.002° (λ = 5461 Å) at 20°

$$1° (\lambda = 5461 \text{ Å}) = 2.4576°S$$

Normal Quartz Plate = 100°S = 34.620°±0.002° (λ = 5892.5Å) at 20°

$$1° (\lambda = 5892.5 \text{ Å}) = 2.8885°S$$

For existing saccharimeters graduated on Herzfeld-Schönrock scale, either change saccharimeter scale or use wt w of 26.026 g in 100 ml.

(b) *Directions for Raw Sugars (Official Final Action).*—In general, make all polarizations at 20°. For countries where mean temp. is >20°, saccharimeters may be adjusted at 30° or any other suitable temp., under conditions specified above, provided sugar soln is dild to final vol. and polarized at this same temp.

In detg polarization of substances contg sugar, employ only half-shade instruments, either single or double wedge, and either 200 or 400 mm instruments. During observation keep app. in fixed position and so far removed from source of light that polarizing nicol is not warmed. As sources of light, employ lamps that give strong white illumination or Na lamp. Whenever there is any irregularity in source of light, place thin ground-glass plate between source of light and polariscope so as to render illumination uniform.

Before and after each set of observations, det. correct adjustment of saccharimeter, using stdzd quartz plates; use calibrated wts, polarization flasks, and observation tubes and cover glasses. (Scratched or strained cover glasses must not be used.) Make several readings and take mean thereof but do not reject any reading.

Quartz plates are stdzd to second decimal place. Instrument and plate must be at same temp. (preferably 20°). Different points of scale, preferably 20°, 50°, 80°, and 100°S, should be tested against the plates.

In detg polarization, use whole normal wt (26± 0.002 g) for 100 ml or multiple for any corresponding vol. Bring soln exactly to mark at proper temp. and after wiping out neck of flask with filter paper, add min. quantity of *dry basic Pb(OAc)₂*, **31.021(c)**, shake to dissolve, and pour all clarified sugar soln on rapid, air-dry filter. Cover funnel at start of filtration. Reject first 25 ml filtrate and use remainder (must be perfectly clear) for polarization. In no case return whole soln or any part to filter. If filtrate is cloudy after 25 ml has been rejected, begin new detn. Polarize in 200 mm tube. If, after all means have been used to effect proper decolorization, soln is too dark to read, use 100 mm tube and multiply reading by 2.

Other permissible clarifying and decolorizing agents are alumina cream, **31.021**(b), or concd alum soln. Do not use boneblack or decolorizing powders.

Whenever white light is used, it must be filtered thru soln of $K_2Cr_2O_7$ of such concn that % $K_2Cr_2O_7 \times$ length of column of soln in cm = 9. Double this concn in polarizing carbohydrate materials of high rotation dispersion, such as com. glucose, etc.

(c) *Normal Weights and Conversion Factors of Different Saccharimeter Scales.*—(1) *Herzfeld-Schönrock Scale.*—Normal wt = 26.026 g/100 ml soln. 1° = 0.34657° Angular Rotation D.*

(2) *International Sugar Scale.*—Normal wt = 26.000 g/100 ml soln. 1° = 0.34620° Angular Rotation D.*

(3) *French Sugar Scale.*—Normal wt = 16.269 g/100 ml soln. 1° = 0.21667° Angular Rotation D.*

31.021   Preparation and Use of Clarifying Reagents (7)—Official Final Action
(Caution: See 46.084.)

(a) *Basic lead acetate soln.*—Activate litharge by heating 2.5–3 hr at 650–670° in muffle (cooled product should be lemon color). Boil 430 g neut. $Pb(OAc)_2.3H_2O$, 130 g freshly activated litharge, and 1 L H_2O 30 min. Let mixt. cool and settle; then dil. supernatant to sp gr of 1.25 with recently boiled H_2O. (Solid basic $Pb(OAc)_2$ may be substituted for the normal salt and litharge in prepn of soln. Because of error caused by vol. of ppt this reagent is not recommended for clarifying products of low purity.)

(b) *Alumina cream.*—Prep. cold satd soln of alum in H_2O. Add NH_4OH with constant stirring until soln is alk. to litmus, let ppt settle, and wash by decantation with H_2O until wash H_2O gives only slight test for sulfates with $BaCl_2$ soln. Pour off excess H_2O and store residual cream in g-s bottle. (Alumina cream is suitable for clarifying light-colored sugar products or as adjunct to other agents when sugars are detd by polariscopic or reducing sugar methods.)

(c) *Dry basic lead acetate ACS.*—$3Pb(OAc)_2$.$2PbO$. Of this salt, ca ⅓ g = 1 ml basic $Pb(OAc)_2$ soln, (a). In making clarification, add small quantity of dry salt to sugar soln after dilg to vol., and shake; then add more salt and shake again, repeating addn until pptn is complete, but avoiding any excess. When molasses or any other substance producing

heavy ppt is being clarified, add some dry, coarse sand to break up pellets of basic $Pb(OAc)_2$ and ppt. (Unless in excess, dry basic $Pb(OAc)_2$ does not cause vol. error.)

(d) *Neutral lead acetate soln.*—Prep. satd soln of neut. $Pb(OAc)_2$ and add to sugar soln before dilg to vol. (This reagent may be used for clarifying light-colored sugar products when sugars are detd by polariscopic methods, and its use is imperative when reducing sugars are detd in soln used for polarization.)

To remove excess Pb used in clarification, add to clarified filtrate anhyd. K or Na oxalate in small quantities until test for Pb in filtrate is neg.; then refilter.

31.022   Temperature Corrections for Polarization of Sugars (8)— Official First Action

(a) *Refined sugars.*—Polarizations of sugars testing ≥99, when made at temp. other than 20°, may be calcd to polarizations at 20° by following formula:
$P_{20} = p_t[1 + 0.0003 (t - 20)]$, where p_t = polarization at temp. read, and t = temp. at which polarization is read. (May be applied to beet sugar and raw cane sugars polarizing ≥96°S without appreciable error.)

(b) *Raw sugars.*—Polarization of raw cane sugars <96°S when made at temps other than 20°, may be calcd to polarizations at 20° by following formula:
$P_{20} = p_t + 0.0015 (p_t - 80) (t - 20)$, where p_t and t are same as in (a).

When % fructose in the sugar is known (in case of honeys and sugar cane products = ca ½ reducing sugars), use following formula:
$P_{20} = p_t + 0.0003S (t - 20) - 0.00812F (t - 20)$, where p_t and t are same as in (a); S = % sucrose; and F = % fructose.

These formulas give results agreeing closely with polarizations obtained at 20° if sugar is of av. normal composition.

31.023   Mutarotation—Procedure

Products, such as honey and com. glucose, that contain glucose or other reducing sugars in cryst. form or in soln at high density may show mutarotation under conditions prevailing during analysis. Only constant rotation should be used in polarimetric methods. To obtain this, let soln prepd for polarization stand overnight before making reading. If it is desired to make reading immediately, heat neut. soln (pH ca 7.0) to boiling or add few drops NH_4OH, before dilg to vol.; or, if soln has been made to vol., add dry Na_2CO_3 until just distinctly alk. to litmus paper. (Do not let slightly alk. solns stand at such high temps or for such lengths of time as to cause destruction of fructose.) Det. completion of mutarotation by making readings at 15–30 min intervals until constant.

---

* Designation D refers to Na light of 589.2 nm.

Sucrose in Absence of Raffinose

By Polarization Before and After Inversion with Invertase (9)—Official Final Action

31.024 *Reagent*

Invertase soln.—Com. invertase prepns are available (Wallerstein Co.; Mann Research Laboratories, 136 Liberty St, New York, NY 10006). If it is desired to prep. soln in laboratory, method described in (1) may be used. In either case, prepn may be further purified and concd by ultrafiltration method described in (3). Com. prepns may also be purified by dialysis and then reconcd by evapg *in vacuo* at temp. ≤40°.

(1) *Crude invertase soln.*—Mix yeast with H₂O in proportion of 10 lb compressed bakers' yeast to 5 L H₂O. Add 2 L toluene and stir thoroly at frequent intervals during first 24 hr. Let stand 7 days with occasional stirring, and filter by gravity thru large fluted papers. Mix residue with 2 L H₂O, filter, and combine filtrates. Purify (J. Ind. Chem. **16**, 562 (1924)) by adding 15 g neut. $Pb(OAc)_2.3H_2O$ to each L of ext and filtering on paper after all $Pb(OAc)_2$ dissolves. Complete purification immediately by dialysis or by washing on ultrafilter as in (3).

(2) *Collodion ultrafilter (10).*—Dissolve 6 g sol. (in alcohol and ether mixt.) pyroxylin or nitrocellulose in mixt. of 50 ml absolute alcohol and 50 ml absolute ether by adding the alcohol to the cotton, letting mixt. stand in stoppered flask 10 min, adding the ether, and shaking. Let soln stand overnight. Pour ca 100 ml into 2 L cylinder, and coat entire inside surface of cylinder with the collodion. Drain, and dry 10 min. Fill cylinder with H₂O, let stand 10–15 min, pour out H₂O, and remove collodion sack. Test for leaks by filling with H₂O. Slit open longitudinally and cut out circular piece 7–8″ diam. Cut bottom from 2 L bottle or erlenmeyer and grind edge smooth. Place it upon still moist collodion disk, fold edge of disk up around bottle, and cement it thereto with collodion that contains increased proportion of ether. Place 3 or 4 thicknesses of wet filter paper in 8″ buchner. Place bottle with collodion membrane upon filter paper. Pour melted white petrolatum to depth of 1″ between bottle and inside of funnel. Provide bottle with small mech. stirrer.

(3) *Washing and concentrating of invertase soln by ultrafiltration.*—Filter 4 L partially purified soln thru the ultrafilter, stirring continuously, until ca 1 L remains. Wash with distd H₂O added from constant level device until filtrate is colorless (3 or 4 L of wash H₂O is required). Discard filtrate and transfer invertase soln to stoppered bottle. During entire process and in storage preserve invertase soln with toluene.

(4) *Activity of invertase soln.*—Following test for activity of invertase soln is usually adequate: Dil. 1 ml invertase prepn to 200 ml. Transfer 10 g sucrose (granulated sugar) to sugar flask graduated at 100 and 110 ml, dissolve in ca 76 ml H₂O, add 2 drops HOAc, and dil. to 100 ml mark. To the 100 ml sugar soln add 10 ml dil. invertase soln and mix thoroly and rapidly, noting exact time at which solns are mixed. After exactly 60 min, make portions of soln just distinctly alk. to litmus paper with anhyd. Na_2CO_3 and polarize in 200 mm tube at 20°. If invertase soln is sufficiently active, alk. soln will polarize ca 31°S without correcting for diln to 110 ml and optical activity of invertase soln.

If more exact information concerning activity of invertase prepn is desired, det. its velocity constant as follows: Dil. 1 ml invertase soln to 200 ml at 20°; place in constant temp. bath at 20°; and when soln reaches this temp., pipet 20 ml into flask contg 200 ml sucrose soln (10 g/100 ml concn) previously made distinctly acid to Me red (corresponding to pH ca 4.6) by addn of HOAc and also brought to temp. of 20° in same bath. Mix thoroly and promptly, and note time at which invertase soln was added. Keep sucrose-invertase mixt. in constant temp. bath; remove portions after 15, 30, and 45 min; immediately after removing make each portion just distinctly alk. to litmus paper with anhyd. Na_2CO_3; and polarize at 20°. Correct all polarizations for polarization of invertase soln. Calc. velocity constant, k, for each of polarizations (at time t) subsequent to initial polarization by following formula:

$$k = [\log_{10} 1.32\, R_0 - \log_{10} (R_t + 0.32\, R_0)]/t,$$

where k = unimolecular reaction velocity constant; t = number of min elapsing from time invertase and sucrose solns were mixed until inversion was stopped by addn of Na_2CO_3; R_0 = initial polarization (calcd by multiplying polarization of sucrose soln by 10/11 and correcting for polarization of invertase soln); and R_t = polarization at time t.

Invertase soln of sufficient activity (JAOAC **11**, 168(1928); **16**, 79(1933); **17**, 74(1934)) should yield av. value for k (for various time periods) of at least 0.1, after multiplying k value directly obtained by 200 in order to correct for initial diln of invertase soln. Diln of invertase soln mentioned above is made solely for purpose of detg its activity; original, undild invertase soln is used as inverting reagent in detn of sucrose, **31.025**, unless activity of original invertase soln greatly exceeds k value of 0.1, and it is desirable to conserve invertase. In this case, dil. to k value of 0.1, which is done in same manner as dilg other solns to std strength. Activity of invertase prepn required for rapid inversion, **31.025(c)**, is same as that needed for overnight inversion, **31.025(b)**, but proportion of invertase prepn used in former case is twice that used in latter instance.

31.025 *Determination*

(a) *Direct reading.*—Dissolve double normal wt of sample (52 g), or fraction thereof, in H₂O in 200 ml vol. flask; add necessary clarifying agent, **31.021**(a), (b), or (d), avoiding excess; shake, dil. to vol. with H_2O, mix well, and filter, keeping funnel covered with watch glass. Reject first 25 ml filtrate.

If Pb clarifying agent was used, remove excess Pb from soln when enough filtrate collects by adding anhyd. Na_2CO_3, little at time, avoiding excess; mix well and filter again, rejecting first 25 ml filtrate. (Instead of weighing 52 g into 200 ml flask, two 26 g portions may be dild to 100 ml each, and treated exactly as described. Depending on color of product, multiples or fractions of normal wt may be used, and results calcd to basis of 26 g/100 ml.)

Pipet one 50 ml portion Pb-free filtrate into 100 ml vol. flask, dil. to vol. with H_2O, mix well, and polarize in 200 mm tube. Result, multiplied by 2, is direct reading (P of formula given below) or polarization before inversion. (If 400 mm tube is used, reading equals P.) If there is possibility of mutarotation, proceed as in **31.023**.

(b) *Invert reading.*—First det. quantity of HOAc necessary to make 50 ml of the Pb-free filtrate distinctly acid to Me red; then to another 50 ml Pb-free soln in 100 ml vol. flask add requisite quantity of acid and 5 ml invertase soln, fill flask with H_2O nearly to 100 ml, and let stand overnight (preferably at $\geq 20°$).

Cool, and dil. to 100 ml at 20°. Mix well and polarize at 20° in 200 mm tube. If in doubt as to completion of hydrolysis, let portion of soln remain several hr and again polarize. If there is no change from previous reading, inversion is complete. Carefully note reading and temp. of soln. If it is necessary to work at temp. other than 20°, which is permissible within narrow limits, complete vols and make both direct and invert readings at same temp. Correct polarization for optical activity of invertase soln and multiply by 2. Calc. % sucrose by following formula:

$$S = \frac{100(P - I)}{132.1 - 0.0833(13 - m) - 0.53(t - 20)},$$

where $S = \%$ sucrose; $P =$ direct reading, normal soln; $I =$ invert reading, normal soln; $t =$ temp. at which readings are made; and $m =$ g total solids in 100 ml inverted soln (total solids in 50 ml original soln). For liqs, det. total solids in original sample as % by wt, as in **31.011**, and multiply this figure by wt original sample in 100 ml invert soln.

(c) *Rapid inversion at 55–60°* (*11*).—If more rapid inversion is desired, proceed as follows: Prep. sample as in (a) and to 50 ml Pb-free filtrate in 100 ml vol. flask add enough HOAc to render soln distinctly acid to Me red, **31.024**(*4*). Det. quantity of HOAc required before pipetting 50 ml portion as in (b). Add 10 ml invertase soln, mix thoroly, place flask in H_2O bath at 55–60°, and let stand at that temp. 15 min, shaking occasionally.

Cool, add Na_2CO_3 until distinctly alk. to litmus paper, dil. to 100 ml at 20°, mix well, and det. polarization at 20° in 200 mm tube. Let soln remain in tube 10 min and again det. polarization. If there is no change from previous reading, mutarotation is complete. Carefully note reading and temp. of soln. Cor-

rect polarization for optical activity of invertase soln and multiply by 2. Calc. % sucrose by formula given in (b).

If soln has been made so alk. as to cause destruction of sugar, polarization, if neg., will in general decrease, since decomposition of fructose ordinarily is more rapid than that of other sugars present. If soln has not been made alk. enough to complete mutarotation quickly, polarization, if neg., will in general increase. As analyst gains experience he may omit polarization after 10 min if he has satisfied himself that he is adding enough Na_2CO_3 to complete mutarotation at once without causing any destruction of sugar during period intervening before polarization.

31.026 By Polarization Before and After Inversion with Hydrochloric Acid (*12*)—Official Final Action

(a) *Direct reading.*—Prep soln as in **31.025**(a). Pipet 50 ml Pb-free filtrate into 100 ml vol. flask; add 2.315 g NaCl and 25 ml H_2O. Dil. to vol. with H_2O at 20° and polarize in 200 mm tube at 20°. Multiply reading by 2 to obtain direct reading.

(b) *Invert reading.*—Pipet 50 ml portion Pb-free filtrate into 100 ml vol. flask and add 20 ml H_2O. Add, little by little, while rotating flask, 10 ml HCl (sp gr 1.1029 at 20/4° or 24.85° Brix at 20°). Heat H_2O bath and adjust burner to keep bath at 60°. Place flask in H_2O bath, agitate continuously ca 3 min, and leave flask in bath exactly 7 min longer. Plunge flask at once into H_2O at 20°.

When contents cool to ca 35°, dil. almost to mark. Leave flask in bath at 20° at least 30 min longer and finally dil. to mark. Mix well and polarize soln in 200 mm tube provided with lateral branch and H_2O jacket, keeping temp. at 20°. This reading must also be multiplied by 2 to obtain invert reading. If it is necessary to work at temp. other than 20°, which is permissible within narrow limits, vols must be completed and both direct and invert polarizations must be made at exactly same temp.

Calc. sucrose by following formula:

$$S = \frac{100(P - I)}{132.56 - 0.0794(13 - m) - 0.53(t - 20)},$$

where $S = \%$ sucrose; $P =$ direct reading, normal soln; $I =$ invert reading, normal soln; $t =$ temp. at which readings are made; and $m =$ g total solids in 100 ml inverted soln (total solids in 50 ml original soln). For liqs, det. total solids in original sample as % by wt as in **31.011**, and multiply this figure by wt original sample in 100 ml invert soln.

(c) *Inversion at room temperature.*—Inversion may also be accomplished as follows: (*1*) Pipet 50 ml Pb-free filtrate into 100 ml vol. flask, add 20 ml H_2O and 10 ml HCl (sp gr 1.1029 at 20/4° or 24.85° Brix at 20°), and set aside 24 hr at $\geq 22°$; or (*2*) set aside 10 hr if $> 28°$. Dil. to 100 ml at 20° and polarize as in (b). Under these conditions formula must be changed to following:

$$S = \frac{100(P - I)}{132.66 - 0.0794(13 - m) - 0.53(t - 20)}.$$

Sucrose and Raffinose (13)

By Polarization Before and After Treatment with Two Enzyme Preparations—Official Final Action

31.027   *Reagents*

(a) *Invertase soln (top yeast extract).*—See **31.024**. This soln should be free from enzyme melibiase. Its invertase activity should be at least as great as that used for detn of sucrose in absence of raffinose, **31.024**(*4*). Com. available.

(b) *Invertase-melibiase soln (bottom yeast extract).* —Prep. as in **31.024**, using bottom fermenting brewers' yeast instead of bakers' yeast. Invertase activity should be at least as great as in (a). Obtainable only from brewers as a liq. Compress by filtering on buchner.

Test melibiase activity of soln as follows: Add 2 ml soln to be tested to 20 ml weakly acid melibiose soln polarizing +20.0°S and let stand 30 min at ca 20°. Add enough Na₂CO₃ to make soln slightly alk. to litmus paper. Prepn suitable for overnight hydrolysis of solns contg ≤0.2 g raffinose in 100 ml should have hydrolyzed 35% of melibiose present under conditions mentioned; prepn suitable for overnight hydrolysis of solns contg ≤0.65 g raffinose in 100 ml should have produced 50% hydrolysis of melibiose; and prepn suitable for overnight hydrolysis of solns contg 0.65–1.3 g raffinose in 100 ml should have hydrolyzed at least 70% of melibiose present under above conditions. Prepns of melibiose soln that polarize +20°S before hydrolysis will polarize +16.4°, +14.9°, and +12.9°S after 35, 50, and 70% hydrolysis, resp.

31.028   *Determination*

With sugar beet products, weigh material specified in table, **31.029**, transfer to 300 ml vol. flask, add quantity of basic Pb(OAc)₂ soln, **31.021**(a), indicated in table, and dil. to vol. at 20°. Mix thoroly and filter thru fluted paper in closely covered funnel, rejecting first 25 ml filtrate. When enough filtrate collects, remove Pb from soln by adding NH₄H₂PO₄ in as small excess as possible, **31.029**. This condition is readily detd after little practice by appearance of Pb₃(PO₄)₂ ppt, which usually flocculates and settles rapidly in presence of slight excess of the salt. Mix well and filter, again rejecting at least first 25 ml filtrate.

Make direct polarization in 200 mm tube at 20° unless soln contains appreciable quantity of invert sugar, in which case pipet 50 ml portion Pb-free filtrate into 100 ml flask, dil. with H₂O to vol., mix well, and polarize at 20°, preferably in 400 mm tube. This reading, calcd to normal wt of 26 g in 100 ml and 200 mm tube length, is direct reading (*P*) of formula given below for polarization before inversion.

Transfer two 50 ml portions of the Pb-free filtrate to 100 ml vol. flasks. To one add 5 ml invertase soln (top yeast ext) and to other 5 ml invertase-melibiase soln (bottom yeast ext), let stand overnight at room temp. (preferably ≥20°), dil. to vol., mix well, and polarize at 20°, preferably in 400 mm jacketed tube.

If rapid hydrolysis is desired, add 10 ml of each of the enzyme solns to 50 ml portions Pb-free filtrate in 100 ml vol. flasks and place in H₂O bath 40 min at 50–55°. Then add Na₂CO₃ until soln is slightly alk. to litmus paper, dil. to vol. at 20°, mix well, and polarize at 20°, preferably in 400 mm tube. Correct invert readings for optical activity of enzyme soln and calc. polarization to that of normal wt soln of 26 g/100 ml; also calc. reading to 200 mm tube length, if necessary.

Calc. % of anhyd. raffinose and sucrose from following formulas:

$$R = 1.354(A - B); \quad S =$$
$$\frac{(P - 2.202A + 1.202B)100}{132.12 - 0.00718[132.12 - (P - 2.202A + 1.202B)]},$$

where R = % anhyd. raffinose; S = % sucrose; P = direct polarization, normal soln; A = corrected polarization after top yeast hydrolysis, normal soln; and B = corrected polarization after bottom yeast hydrolysis, normal soln.

Quantities A and B are treated algebraically.

31.029   (*See table at top of next page*)

31.030   **By Polarization Before and After Inversion with Hydrochloric Acid— Official Final Action**

(Of value chiefly in analysis of beet products)

If direct reading is >1° higher than % sucrose as calcd by formula given in **31.026**(b), raffinose is probably present. Calc. sucrose and raffinose by following formulas (J. Ind. Eng. Chem. **13**, 793 (1921)).

When polarizations are made at 20°:

$$S = (0.514P - I)/0.844, \text{ and}$$
$$R = (0.33P + I)/1.563,$$

where P = direct reading, normal soln; I = invert reading, normal soln; S = % sucrose; and R = % anhyd. raffinose.

Following formulas (J. Ind. Eng. Chem. **13**, 793 (1921)) are applicable to all temps other than 20°:

$$S = \frac{P(0.478 + 0.0018t_2) - I(1.006 - 0.0003t_1)}{(0.908 - 0.0032t_2)(1.006 - 0.0003t_1)},$$

and

$$R = \frac{P(0.43 - 0.005t_2) + I(1.006 - 0.0003t_1)}{(1.681 - 0.0059t_2)(1.006 - 0.0003t_1)},$$

where P = direct reading, normal soln; I = invert reading, normal soln; S = % sucrose; R = % anhyd. raffinose; t_1 = temp. of direct polarization; and t_2 = temp. of invert polarization.

31.031   **Sucrose by Double Dilution Method (14)—Official Final Action**

(Applicable to substances in which vol. of combined insol. matter and ppt from clarifying agents is >1 ml from 26 g)

31.029   *Quantities of Sample and Reagents Required for Clarification and*
Deleading of Beet Sugar-House Products

Material	Quantity per 100 ml	Basic Lead Acetate (55° Brix)	Ammonium Dihydrogen Phosphate
	gram	ml	gram
Cossettes[a]	13	3	0.2
Pulp	100 ml[b]	2–4	0.2
Lime cake or sewer[c]	26.5	1.5	. . . .[d]
Thin juice	52	2	0.2–0.3
Thick juice	26	4	0.3–0.4
White massecuite	13 or 26	3 or 6	0.3–0.7
High wash sirup	13 or 26	3 or 6	0.3–0.7
High green sirup	13 or 26	5 or 10	0.3–0.7
Raw or remelt massecuite	13	6	0.3–0.4
Raw or remelt sugar	26	3–4	0.3–0.4
Sugar melter	26	2–3	0.3–0.4
Low wash sirup	13	8–10	0.4–0.5
Low green sirup or molasses	13	10	0.4–0.5
Saccharate cakes and milk (carbonated)	26	4–6	0.3–0.4
Steffen waste and wash waters[c]	78 or 50 ml	2–3	0.2

[a] Usual method of extn, 26 g in 201.2 ml.
[b] Dil. to 110 ml.
[c] Neutze with HOAc before adding basic Pb(OAc)$_2$.
[d] As Ca in soln will be partly pptd by the phosphate, it is necessary to add enough phosphate to complete pptn of both Pb and Ca salts, and no definite quantity can be specified.

Weigh 13 g sample and dil. soln to 100 ml, using appropriate clarifier (basic Pb(OAc)$_2$ for dark-colored confectionery or molasses, and alumina cream for light-colored confectionery). Also weigh 26 g sample and dil. this second soln with clarifier to 100 ml. Filter both solns, and obtain direct polariscopic readings. Invert each soln as in **31.025(b)** or **(c)** or **31.026(b)** or **(c)** and obtain respective invert readings.

True direct polarization of sample = 4 times direct polarization of dild soln minus direct polarization of undild soln. True invert polarization = 4 times invert polarization of dild soln minus invert polarization of undild soln. Calc. sucrose from true polarizations thus obtained, using formula in **31.025(b)** or **31.026(b)** or **(c)** corresponding to method of inversion used.

Sucrose—Chemical Methods

31.032   From Reducing Sugars Before and
After Inversion—Official Final Action

Det. reducing sugars as in **31.039** (clarification having been effected with neutral Pb(OAc)$_2$ as in **31.021(d)**) and calc. to invert sugar from **47.019**. Invert soln as in **31.025(b)** or **(c)**, or **31.026(b)** or **(c)**; exactly neutze acid; and again det. reducing sugars, but calc. them to invert sugar from table referred to above, using invert sugar column alone. Deduct % invert sugar obtained before inversion from that obtained after inversion and multiply difference by 0.95 to obtain % sucrose. Dil. solns in both detns so that ≤230 mg invert sugar is present in quantity taken for reduction. It is important that all Pb be removed from soln with anhyd. powd K oxalate before reduction.

Commercial Glucose (Approximate) Polarimetric Methods—Procedure

31.033   Substances Containing Little or
No Invert Sugar

Com. glucose cannot be detd accurately, since quantities of dextrin, maltose, and dextrose present vary. However, in sirups in which quantity of invert sugar is too small to appreciably affect result, com. glucose may be estd approx. by following formula:

$$G = (a - S)100/211,$$

where G = % com. glucose solids; a = direct polarization, normal soln; and S = % cane sugar.

Express results in terms of com. glucose solids polarizing +211°S. (This result may be recalcd in terms of com. glucose of any polarization desired.)

31.034   Substances Containing Invert Sugar

Prep. inverted half-normal soln of substance as in **31.026(b)**, except cool soln after inversion, make neut. to phthln with NaOH soln, slightly acidify with HCl (1 + 5), and treat with 5–10 ml alumina cream, **31.021(b)**, before dilg to vol. Filter, and polarize at 87° in 200 mm jacketed metal tube. Multiply reading by 200 and divide by factor 196 to obtain quantity of com. glucose solids polarizing +211°S. (Result may be recalcd in terms of com. glucose of any polarization desired.)

Invert Sugar—Chemical Methods

I. Lane-Eynon General Volumetric Method
(15)—Official Final Action

31.035   *Reagents*

Soxhlet modification of Fehling soln.—Prep. by mixing equal vols of **(a)** and **(b)** immediately before use.

(a) *Copper sulfate soln.*—Dissolve 34.639 g $CuSO_4.5H_2O$ in H_2O, dil. to 500 ml, and filter thru glass wool or paper. Det. Cu content of soln (preferably by electrolysis, 31.045) and so adjust that it contains 440.9 mg Cu/25 ml.

(b) *Alkaline tartrate soln.*—Dissolve 173 g KNa tartrate.$4H_2O$ (Rochelle salt) and 50 g NaOH in H_2O, dil. to 500 ml, let stand 2 days, and filter thru prepd asbestos, 31.038.

(c) *Invert sugar std soln.*—1%. To soln of 9.5 g pure sucrose, add 5 ml HCl and dil. with H_2O to ca 100 ml. Store several days at room temp. (ca 7 days at 12–15° or 3 days at 20–25°); then dil. to 1 L. (Acidified 1% invert sugar soln is stable for several months.) Neutze aliquot with ca 1N NaOH and dil. to desired concn immediately before use.

31.036   *Standardization*

Accurately pipet 10 or 25 ml mixed Soxhlet reagent, or 5 or 12.5 ml each of Soxhlet solns 31.035(a) and (b), into 300–400 ml erlenmeyer. (Quantity of Cu taken differs slightly between two methods of pipetting, and method used must be consistent in stdzn and detn.) Prep. std soln of pure sugar of such concn that >15 ml and <50 ml is required to reduce all the Cu. Dispense from buret with offset tip to keep tube out of steam. mg Sugar required to completely reduce Cu at different concns is given in 47.017 and 47.018. Add sugar soln within 0.5–1.0 ml of total required, heat cold mixt. to boiling on wire gauze over burner, and maintain moderate boiling 2 min (coarse grains of C or other suitable inert material may be used to prevent bumping). Without removing flame add 1 ml *0.2% aq. methylene blue soln* (or 3–4 drops 1% soln) and complete titrn within total boiling time of ca 3 min by small addns (2–3 drops) of sugar soln to decoloration of indicator. (Maintain continuous emission of steam to prevent reoxidn of Cu or indicator.) After complete reduction of Cu, methylene blue is reduced to colorless compd and soln resumes orange Cu_2O color which it had before addn of indicator.

Multiply titer by mg/ml std soln to obtain total sugar required to reduce the Cu. Compare with tabulated value in 47.017 or 47.018 to det. correction, if any, to be applied to table. Small deviations from tabulated values may arise from variations in individual procedure or composition of reagents. If only approx. results (within 1%) are required, stdzn may be omitted, provided specifications of analysis are rigidly observed.

31.037   *Determination*

(a) *Incremental method.*—If approx. concn of sugar in sample is unknown, proceed by incremental method of titrn. To 10 or 25 ml mixed Soxhlet soln, add 15 ml sugar soln and heat to boiling over wire gauze. Boil ca 15 sec and rapidly add further quantities of sugar soln until only faintest perceptible blue remains. Then add 1 ml 0.2% aq. methylene blue soln (or 3–4 drops 1% soln) and complete titrn by adding sugar soln dropwise. (Error resulting from this titrn will generally be ≤1%.)

(b) *Standard method.*—For higher precision repeat titrn, adding almost entire sugar soln required to reduce all Cu and proceed as in 31.036. In 47.017 or 47.018 find total reducing sugar corresponding to titer and apply correction previously detd. Calc. as follows: total reducing sugar required × 100/titer = mg sugar in 100 ml.

II. Munson-Walker General Method (16)— Official Final Action

31.038   *Reagents*

Asbestos.—Digest asbestos, amphibole variety, with HCl (1 + 3) 2–3 days. Wash acid-free, digest similar period with 10% NaOH soln, and then treat few hr with hot alk. tartrate soln, 31.035(b) (alk. tartrate solns that have stood for some time may be used for this purpose). Wash asbestos alkali-free; digest several hr with HNO_3 (1 + 3); and after washing acid-free, shake with H_2O into fine pulp. In prepg gooch, make film of asbestos ¼″ thick and wash thoroly with H_2O to remove fine particles. If pptd Cu_2O is to be weighed as such, wash crucible with 10 ml alcohol and then with 10 ml ether; dry 30 min at 100°, cool in desiccator, and weigh.

Other reagents and solns used are described in 31.035. Solns may be clarified by neut. $Pb(OAc)_2$ soln, 31.021(d) (never basic $Pb(OAc)_2$). Remove excess Pb with dry $Na_2C_2O_4$.

31.039   *Precipitation of Cuprous Oxide*

Transfer 25 ml each of $CuSO_4$ and alk. tartrate solns to 400 ml beaker of alkali-resistant glass and add 50 ml reducing sugar soln; or if smaller vol. of sugar soln is used, add H_2O to make final vol. 100 ml. Heat beaker on asbestos gauze over Bunsen burner, regulate flame so that boiling begins in 4 min, and continue boiling exactly 2 min. (It is important that these directions be strictly observed. To regulate burner for this purpose it is advisable to make preliminary tests, using 50 ml reagent and 50 ml H_2O, before proceeding with actual detn. Elec. heater may be used instead of burner.) Keep beaker covered with watch glass during heating.

Filter hot soln at once thru asbestos mat in porcelain gooch, using suction. Wash ppt of Cu_2O thoroly with H_2O at ca 60° and either weigh directly as Cu_2O, 31.040, or det. quantity of reduced Cu by one of methods described in 31.041–31.045. Conduct blank detn, using 50 ml reagent and 50 ml H_2O, and if wt Cu_2O obtained is >0.5 mg, correct result of reducing sugar detn accordingly. Alk. tartrate soln deteriorates on standing, and quantity of Cu_2O obtained in blank increases.

Determination of Reduced Copper

31.040   By Direct Weighing of Cuprous Oxide

(Use only for detns in solns of reducing sugars of comparatively high purity. In products contg large quantities of mineral or org. impurities, including sucrose, det. Cu in the Cu_2O by one of methods described in **31.041–31.045**, since the Cu_2O is likely to be contaminated with foreign matter.)

Prep. gooch as in **31.038**. Collect pptd Cu_2O on mat as in **31.039**; wash thoroly with hot H_2O, then with 10 ml alcohol, and finally with 10 ml ether. Dry ppt 30 min in oven at 100°, cool, and weigh. Obtain wt invert sugar equiv. to wt Cu_2O from **47.019**.

Number of mg Cu_2O reduced by given quantity of reducing sugar varies, depending upon whether or not sucrose is present. In table, absence of sucrose is assumed except in entries under invert sugar and lactose, where, in addn to columns for these alone, columns are given for their mixts with sucrose in specified ratios in the case of lactose and in specified amts of total sugar in 50 ml soln in the case of invert sugar.

(Later Hammond table has replaced original Munson-Walker table, where applicable.)

By Titration with Sodium Thiosulfate (17)

31.041   Reagent

Thiosulfate std soln.—Prep. soln contg 39 g $Na_2S_2O_3 \cdot 5H_2O$/L. Accurately weigh 0.2–0.4 g pure electrolytic Cu and transfer to 250 ml erlenmeyer roughly marked at 20 ml intervals. Dissolve Cu in 5 ml HNO_3 (1 + 1), dil. to 20 or 30 ml, boil to expel red fumes, add slight excess satd $Br-H_2O$, and boil until Br is completely removed. Cool, and add 10 ml NaOAc soln (574 g trihydrate/L). Prep. 42 g/100 ml KI soln made very slightly alk. to avoid formation and oxidn of HI. Add 10 ml of the KI soln and titr. with $Na_2S_2O_3$ soln to light yellow. Add enough starch indicator, **6.004(f)**, to produce marked blue. As end point nears, add 2 g KCNS and stir until completely dissolved. Continue titrn until ppt is perfectly white. 1 ml $Na_2S_2O_3$ soln = ca 10 mg Cu.

It is essential for $Na_2S_2O_3$ titrn that concn of KI in soln be carefully regulated. If soln contains <320 mg Cu, at completion of titrn 4.2–5 g KI should have been added for each 100 ml total soln. If greater quantities of Cu are present, add KI soln slowly from buret with constant agitation in quantities proportionately greater.

31.042   Determination

Wash pptd Cu_2O, cover gooch with watch glass, and dissolve the Cu_2O with 5 ml HNO_3 (1 + 1) directed under watch glass with pipet. Collect filtrate in 250 ml erlenmeyer roughly marked at 20 ml intervals, and wash watch glass and gooch Cu-free. Proceed as in **31.041**, beginning, "boil to expel red fumes ..." Obtain wt reducing sugar equiv. to wt Cu from **47.019**.

By Titration with Potassium Permanganate (18)

31.043   Reagents

(a) *Potassium permanganate std soln.*—Approx. $0.1573N$, and contg 4.98 g/L. Prep. and stdze as in **45.026–45.027**, using 0.35 g Na oxalate.

(b) *Ferric sulfate soln.* — Dissolve 135 g $FeNH_4(SO_4)_2 \cdot 12H_2O$ or 55 g anhyd. $Fe_2(SO_4)_3$ in H_2O, and dil. to 1 L. Det. $Fe_2(SO_4)_3$ in stock supply by strong ignition to Fe_2O_3. Titr. 50 ml $Fe_2(SO_4)_3$ soln, acidified with 20 ml $4N$ H_2SO_4, with $KMnO_4$ soln, and use this titer as zero-point correction.

(c) *Ferrous phenanthroline indicator.*—Dissolve 0.7425 g o-phenanthroline.H_2O in 25 ml $0.025M$ $FeSO_4$ soln (6.95 g $FeSO_4 \cdot 7H_2O$/L).

31.044   Determination

Filter the Cu_2O thru gooch, and wash beaker and ppt thoroly. Transfer asbestos pad to beaker with glass rod. Add 50 ml $Fe_2(SO_4)_3$ soln and stir vigorously until Cu_2O is completely dissolved. Examine for complete soln, holding beaker above eye level. Cu_2O must be quant. transferred; if necessary, immerse crucible in soln and make sure adhering Cu_2O is dissolved. Remove crucible with glass rod and wash with H_2O. Add 20 ml $4N$ H_2SO_4 and titr. with std $KMnO_4$ soln. As end point approaches, add 1 drop ferrous phenanthroline indicator. At end point, brownish soln changes to green. Obtain wt reducing sugar equiv. to wt Cu from **47.019**.

31.045   By Electrolytic Deposition from Nitric Acid Solution (19)

Decant hot soln, **31.039**, thru asbestos mat in gooch, and wash beaker and ppt thoroly with hot H_2O. Transfer asbestos mat from crucible to beaker with glass rod and rinse crucible with 14 ml HNO_3 (1 + 1), letting rinsings flow into beaker. After Cu_2O dissolves, dil. to 100 ml, heat to boiling, and continue boiling ca 5 min to remove oxides of N. Cool, filter, transfer to 250 ml beaker, and dil. to 200 ml. Add 1 drop $0.1N$ HCl and mix thoroly.

For electrolysis use cylindrical electrodes of Pt gauze, ca 1.5″ and 2″ diam., resp., and ca 1.75″ high, thoroly cleaned, ignited, cooled in desiccator, and weighed. Insert electrodes in Cu soln so that surface of cathode clears anode by at least 5 mm and both electrodes almost touch bottom of beaker. Cover with split watch glass to avoid loss by spattering. Electrolyze with current of 0.2–0.4 amp until deposition is complete, usually overnight. (Wash down sides of beaker and watch glass with H_2O, thus raising level of soln and exposing new surface of cathode; if new surface shows deposit of Cu, electrolysis is not complete.)

Without interrupting current, slowly lower beaker and at same time wash electrodes with stream of H_2O. Immediately immerse electrodes in another beaker of H_2O and break current. (Siphon can be used for washing, adding H_2O as soln is removed. Displacement of HNO_3 soln is complete when current ceases to flow.) Rinse cathode with alcohol and dry few min in oven at 100°. Cool in desiccator and weigh.

Electrolyte may be stirred by rotating anode or mech. stirrer. In this case, current may be increased to 1–2 amp, thus shortening time required for complete deposition of Cu to ca 1 hr.

If extreme care is taken to avoid spattering, Cu_2O can be dissolved by letting HNO_3 flow down walls of crucible. Keep crucible covered as much as possible with small watch glass. Collect filtrate in beaker, and wash watch glass and tip of pipet with jet of H_2O. Continue as above, beginning "dil. to 100 ml ..." Obtain wt reducing sugars equiv. to wt Cu from **47.019.**

31.046 ★ III. Ofner Volumetric Method ★ (20)—Official Final Action

(For materials contg small quantities of invert sugar in presence of sucrose)

See 29.046–29.047, 10th ed.

31.047 ★ IV. Meissl-Hiller Gravimetric ★ Method—Official Final Action

(For materials contg >1.5% invert sugar and <98.5% sucrose)

See 29.048, 10th ed.

★ V. Quisumbing-Thomas Method (21)— ★ Official First Action

31.048 *Reagents*

(a) *Copper sulfate soln.*—Dissolve $CuSO_4.5H_2O$ in hot H_2O to make satd soln, and filter. Det. Cu electrolytically and dil. soln so that 25 ml contains 525 mg Cu (41.2 g $CuSO_4.5H_2O$/500 ml soln).

(b) *Alkaline tartrate soln.*—Dissolve NaOH in equal wt H_2O and let stand several days until insol. carbonates and other impurities settle out. Siphon off clear soln and det. its alky by titrn with std acid. Dissolve 173 g highest purity KNa tartrate.$4H_2O$ (Rochelle salt) in H_2O in 500 ml vol. flask and add calcd quantity NaOH soln so that 500 ml of this alk. tartrate soln contains exactly 65 g NaOH. Dil. to vol. with H_2O.

(c) *Ferric ammonium sulfate soln.*—Add 200 ml H_2SO_4 to ca 500 ml H_2O and cool. Dissolve 240.9 g $FeNH_4(SO_4)_2.12H_2O$ in the dil. H_2SO_4 and dil. to 1 L.

(d) *Indicator soln.*—Dissolve 0.15 g o-phenanthroline.H_2O and 0.07 g $FeSO_4$ in 10 ml H_2O.

31.049 *Determination*

Measure exactly 25 ml each of $CuSO_4$ and alk. tartrate solns into 400 ml Pyrex beaker, diam. ca 9 cm. Add 50 ml sugar soln contg preferably 50–150 mg sugar. Cover beaker with watch glass and place in H_2O bath held at 80°.

After digesting exactly 30 min, filter Cu_2O by suction thru mat of asbestos in gooch. Wash ppt with H_2O; then with aid of stirring rod transfer asbestos mat and Cu_2O back into beaker in which reduction took place. Rinse inside of crucible and lip of beaker with 10 ml $FeNH_4(SO_4)_2$ soln from pipet. Receive rinsings in beaker contg the Cu_2O. Holding crucible over beaker, stir contents of beaker thoroly with stirring rod until Cu_2O dissolves. Wash crucible with ca 25 ml hot H_2O (80°), receiving washings in beaker. Stir contents of beaker and then raise beaker to see if any undissolved particles of Cu_2O are resting on bottom. If so, press each one with point of stirring rod until all dissolve. Add ca 125 ml addnl hot H_2O and 1 drop indicator soln. Titr. at once, with continual stirring, with $0.05N$ $KMnO_4$. (In long titrn, preferably add indicator just before end point is reached.) Stdze $KMnO_4$ as in **45.027.** Calc. wt sugar from table, **47.024.**

VI. Berlin Institute Method (22)— Official First Action

(Applicable to dark colored solns without defecation)

31.050 *Reagent*

Müller's soln.—Dissolve 35 g $CuSO_4.5H_2O$ in 400 ml boiling H_2O. Sep. dissolve 173 g KNa tartrate .$4H_2O$ (Rochelle salt) and 68 g Na_2CO_3 in 500 ml boiling H_2O. Cool, mix the 2 solns, and dil. to 1 L. Shake with small amt of C and filter. If ppt forms on storage, refilter.

31.051 *Determination*

Select quantity of sample (10 g or less) contg ≤30 mg invert sugar. Pipet 10 ml Müller's soln and 100 ml sugar soln into 300 ml flask and cover. Mix thoroly and heat exactly 10 min in H_2O bath boiling so vigorously that immersion of flask does not interrupt boiling. Place flask so that H_2O level is at least 2 cm above surface of liq. in flask. After heating period, cool flask rapidly without agitation. Add 5 ml $5N$ HOAc to cooled soln, mix, and immediately add excess $0.0333N$ I soln (20–40 ml) from buret. After all Cu_2O ppt dissolves, titr. excess I with $0.0333N$ $Na_2S_2O_3$.

Apply following corrections to ml I soln consumed: (1) ml I required in blank with H_2O instead of sugar soln; (2) ml I required by sugar soln in detn conducted without heating; (3) 2.0 ml I for reducing action of 10 g sucrose or proportionate correction for smaller amt sucrose. After these corrections 1 ml $0.0333N$ I = 1 mg invert sugar.

Glucose—Chemical Methods

31.052 Lane-Eynon General Volumetric Method—Official Final Action

Proceed as in **31.037,** referring titer to **47.017** or **47.018.**

**31.053 *Munson-Walker General Method—*
*Official Final Action***

Proceed as in **31.039** and obtain wt glucose from **47.019**.

Shaffer-Somogyi Micro Method—
Official Final Action

31.054   Reagents

(a) *Shaffer-Somogyi carbonate 50 reagent, 5 g KI.*—Dissolve 25 g each of anhyd. Na_2CO_3 and KNa tartrate.$4H_2O$ (Rochelle salt) in ca 500 ml H_2O in 2 L beaker. Add thru funnel with tip under surface, with stirring, 75 ml of soln of 100 g $CuSO_4.5H_2O$/L. Add 20 g $NaHCO_3$, dissolve, and add 5 g KI. Transfer soln to 1 L vol. flask, add 250 ml 0.100N KIO_3 (3.567 g dissolved and dild to 1 L), dil. to vol., and filter thru fritted glass. Age overnight before use.

(b) *Iodide-oxalate soln.*—Dissolve 2.5 g KI and 2.5 g $K_2C_2O_4$ in H_2O and dil. to 100 ml. Prep. fresh weekly.

(c) *Thiosulfate std soln.*—0.005N. Prep. daily from stdzd stock 0.1N soln, **45.038–45.039**.

(d) *Starch soln.*—Rub 2.5 g sol. starch and ca 10 mg HgI_2 in little H_2O. Dissolve in ca 500 ml boiling H_2O.

31.055   Determination

Pipet 5 ml soln contg 0.5–2.5 mg glucose into 25 × 200 mm test tube. Add 5 ml reagent, (a), and mix well by swirling. Prep. blank, using 5 ml H_2O and 5 ml reagent. Place tubes, capped with bulb or funnel, in boiling H_2O bath 15 min. Carefully remove

tubes without agitation to running H_2O cooling bath 4 min. Remove caps and add down side of each tube 2 ml KI-$K_2C_2O_4$ soln and then 3 ml 2N H_2SO_4 (56 ml/L). (Do not agitate solns while alk.) Mix thoroly to ensure that all Cu_2O is dissolved, and let stand in cold H_2O bath 5 min, mixing twice during that time. Titr. with 0.005N $Na_2S_2O_3$, using starch indicator, (d). Subtract titrn of test soln from that of blank and det. amt glucose in 5 ml soln from **31.056**.

Make control detns with known amts of glucose and apply corrections for any deviations from tabulated equivs.

31.056   (*See table below*)

Folin and Wu Micro Method (23)—
Official First Action

31.057   Reagents

(a) *Phosphomolybdic acid soln.*—Add 200 ml 10% NaOH soln and 200 ml H_2O to 35 g molybdic acid and 5 g Na tungstate in 1 L beaker. Boil vigorously 20–40 min. Cool, dil. to ca 350 ml, add 125 ml H_3PO_4 (85%), dil. to 500 ml, and mix.

(b) *Alkaline copper soln.*—Dissolve 40 g Na_2CO_3 in ca 400 ml H_2O and transfer to 1 L vol. flask. Dissolve 7.5 g tartaric acid in this soln and then 4.5 g $CuSO_4.5H_2O$; mix, and dil. to vol. If sediment forms on standing, decant and use clear supernatant.

(c) *Glucose std solns.*—(1) *Stock soln.*—10 mg/ml. Dissolve 1.0 g highest purity anhyd. glucose in ca 50 ml filtered 0.25% benzoic acid soln and dil. to vol. in

31.056   ***Shaffer-Somogyi Dextrose-Thiosulfate Equivalents***

mg glucose = (0.1099) (ml 0.005N $Na_2S_2O_3$) + .048

ml 0.005N $Na_2S_2O_3$	Tenths ml 0.005N Thiosulfate									
	0	0.1	0.2	0.3	0.4	0.5	0.6	0.7	0.8	0.9
	mg Dextrose in 5 ml of Soln									
3	.378	.389	.400	.411	.422	.432	.444	.455	.466	.477
4	.488	.499	.510	.521	.532	.543	.554	.565	.576	.587
5	.598	.608	.619	.630	.641	.652	.663	.674	.685	.696
6	.707	.718	.729	.740	.751	.762	.773	.784	.795	.806
7	.817	.828	.839	.850	.861	.872	.883	.894	.905	.916
8	.927	.938	.949	.960	.971	.982	.993	1.004	1.015	1.026
9	1.037	1.048	1.059	1.070	1.081	1.092	1.103	1.114	1.125	1.136
10	1.147	1.158	1.169	1.180	1.191	1.202	1.213	1.224	1.235	1.246
11	1.257	1.268	1.279	1.290	1.301	1.312	1.323	1.334	1.345	1.356
12	1.367	1.378	1.389	1.400	1.411	1.422	1.433	1.444	1.455	1.466
13	1.477	1.488	1.499	1.510	1.521	1.532	1.543	1.554	1.565	1.576
14	1.587	1.598	1.609	1.620	1.631	1.642	1.653	1.664	1.675	1.686
15	1.697	1.707	1.718	1.729	1.740	1.751	1.762	1.773	1.784	1.795
16	1.806	1.817	1.828	1.839	1.850	1.861	1.872	1.883	1.894	1.905
17	1.916	1.927	1.938	1.949	1.960	1.971	1.982	1.993	2.004	2.015
18	2.026	2.037	2.048	2.059	2.070	2.081	2.092	2.103	2.114	2.125
19	2.136	2.147	2.158	2.169	2.180	2.191	2.202	2.213	2.224	2.235
20	2.246	2.257	2.268	2.279	2.290	2.301	2.312	2.323	2.334	2.345
21	2.356	2.367	3.378	3.389	2.400	2.411	2.422	2.433	2.444	2.455
22	2.466	2.477	2.488	2.499	2.510	2.521	2.532	2.543	2.554	2.565

J. Biol. Chem. **100**, 695 (1933); **160**, 61 (1945); JAOAC **42**, 341 (1959); **43**, 645 (1960).

100 ml vol. flask with the benzoic acid soln. Soln keeps indefinitely.

(2) *Dilute std soln.*—0.2 mg/ml. Transfer 2.0 ml stock soln to 100 ml vol. flask, dil. to vol. with H_2O (or 0.25% benzoic acid soln if soln is to be kept for any length of time), and mix well.

31.058 *Determination*

Transfer 2 ml sample soln to Folin-Wu blood sugar test tube. Add 2 ml alk. Cu soln. Surface of mixt. must reach constricted part of tube. Transfer tube to boiling H_2O bath and heat 6 min. Transfer to cold H_2O bath and cool without shaking 2–3 min. Add 2 ml phosphomolybdic acid soln. When Cu_2O dissolves, dil. soln to 25 ml mark with phosphomolybdic acid soln dild $1 + 4$, insert rubber stopper, and mix. Let stand 10–15 min, transfer to colorimeter tube, and read within 15 min in photoelec. colorimeter at 420 nm.

Make parallel detns on 2 ml H_2O as blank and on 2 ml dil. std glucose soln. Express reading as function o fA ($-\log T$) and calc. unknown concn, $c = c' \times A/A'$, where c' is concn of std; A refers to unknown and A' to std.

Fructose—Chemical Methods—
Official Final Action
31.059 *Lane-Eynon General Volumetric Method*

Proceed as in **31.037**, referring titer to **47.017** or **47.018**.

31.060 *Munson-Walker General Method*

Proceed as in **31.039** and **31.045**, and obtain wt fructose equiv. to wt Cu from **47.019**.

Jackson-Mathews Modification of Nyns Selective Method (24)
31.061 *Reagent*

Ost soln.—Dissolve 250 g anhyd. K_2CO_3 in ca 700 ml hot H_2O, add 100 g pulverized $KHCO_3$, and agitate mixt. until completely dissolved. Cool, and add, with very vigorous agitation, soln of 25.3 g $CuSO_4 \cdot 5H_2O$ in 100–150 ml H_2O. Dil. to 1 L and filter.

31.062 *Determination*

Transfer 50 ml Ost soln to 125 ml erlenmeyer and pipet in vol. sample soln contg ≤ 92 mg fructose or its equiv. of fructose-glucose mixt. (glucose has ca $\frac{1}{12}$ reducing power of fructose). Add H_2O to 70 ml. Immerse in H_2O bath, regulated at 55° preferably within 0.1°. Digest exactly 75 min, swirling at 10 or 15 min intervals.

Filter pptd Cu_2O on closely packed asbestos-mat gooch, and wash flask and ppt thoroly without attempting to transfer ppt quant. Det. Cu by one of methods described in **31.041–31.045**. As it is usually difficult to transfer Cu ppt quant. from erlenmeyer,

select method of Cu analysis in which total Cu is dissolved in HNO_3 and detd by electrolysis or $Na_2S_2O_3$ titrn, or in $Fe_2(SO_4)_3$ soln followed by $KMnO_4$ titrn as in **31.044**.

See **31.063** for fructose equiv. If sample contained glucose in addn to fructose, analytical result is not true but "apparent" fructose, as glucose has appreciable reducing action under conditions of analysis. To det. correction for glucose, analyze sample also for total reducing sugars and compute true glucose and fructose by series of approximations. Calc. % reducing sugars in original sample and similarly % "apparent" fructose. Difference between these 2 percentages is "apparent" glucose. Divide apparent glucose by factor 12.4 and deduct result from apparent fructose to obtain new approximation to true fructose. Deduct new fructose % from total reducing sugar % to obtain more nearly correct value for true glucose and again divide by 12.4. Deduct quotient from original value of "apparent" fructose and continue approximation in same manner until % fructose remains essentially unaltered by 2 successive approximations.

If original sample contained sucrose, det. by means of Clerget procedure, **31.026**. Correct Cu for reducing action of sucrose before referring to table, **31.063**. 1, 2, 3, 4, and 5 g sucrose under conditions of analysis ppt 3.3, 5.7, 7.4, 8.5, and 9.0 mg Cu, resp.

31.063 *Copper-Fructose Equivalents According to Jackson and Mathews Modification of Nyns Selective Method for Fructose; Values Expressed in mg*

(Linear interpolation yields accurate results)

Cu	Fructose	Cu	Fructose
5	2.5	130	39.3
10	4.5	140	42.0
15	6.2	150	44.7
20	7.9	160	47.4
25	9.5	170	50.0
30	11.0	180	52.6
35	12.5	190	55.2
40	13.9	200	57.9
45	15.4	210	60.6
50	16.8	220	63.4
55	18.3	230	66.4
60	19.7	240	69.4
65	21.2	250	72.5
70	22.5	260	75.7
80	25.4	270	79.0
90	28.1	280	82.4
100	30.9	290	85.9
110	33.7	300	89.5
120	36.5	310	93.2

Maltose—Chemical Methods—
Official Final Action
31.064 *Lane-Eynon General Volumetric Method*

Proceed as in **31.037**, referring titer to **47.017** or **47.018**.

31.065 *Munson-Walker General Method*

Proceed as in **31.039** and **31.040,** and obtain wt maltose equiv. to wt Cu_2O from **47.019.**

Lactose—Chemical Methods—
Official Final Action

31.066 *Lane-Eynon General Volumetric Method*

Proceed as in **31.037,** referring titer to **47.017** or **47.018.**

31.067 *Munson-Walker General Method*

Proceed as in **31.039** and **31.040,** and obtain wt lactose equiv. to wt of Cu_2O from **47.019.**

31.068 **Arabinose, Galactose, and Xylose and Other Sugars—Official First Action**

Proceed as in **31.055,** using appropriate heating time and equation for calcn from **31.069.** Make control detns with known amts of sugar and apply corrections for any deviations from equations.

31.069 *Shaffer-Somogyi Sugar-Thiosulfate Equivalents*

y = mg sugar in 5 ml; x = ml 0.005N $Na_2S_2O_3$.

Sugar	Heating Time, min	Equation
L-Arabinose	30	$y = 0.1234x + 0.060$
Fructose	15	$y = 0.1113x + 0.079$
D-Galactose	30	$y = 0.1332x + 0.033$
Glucose	15	$y = 0.1099x + 0.048$
Lactose	35	$y = 0.2031x + 0.030$
Maltose	30	$y = 0.2199x + 0.0725$
D-Mannose	35	$y = 0.1148x + 0.084$
D-Ribose	25	$y = 0.1381x + 0.098$
L-Sorbose	15	$y = 0.1244x + 0.116$
D-Xylose	30	$y = 0.1103x + 0.044$

MOLASSES AND
MOLASSES PRODUCTS (25)

31.070 *Sampling—Procedure*

(a) *Liquid molasses.*—(*1*) *Molasses in barrels.*— Det. number of barrels to be sampled as follows: From lots of 1–10 barrels, sample all barrels; from lots of 11 barrels or more, sample 10 barrels. Take uniform amt from each barrel. Prep. composite from individual samples by mixing in container. Reduce composite to amt required and fill two ≥ 1 pt glass, stainless metal, or plastic jars. Close jars air-tight. Place one sample in cold storage (do *not* freeze) and put at disposal of second party as soon as possible. Send second sample to testing laboratory immediately after sampling.

(*2*) *Molasses in small retail containers.*—Content of intact and unopened container constitutes sample.

(*3*) *Molasses in tank cars, tank trucks, or storage tanks.*—(1) *Continuous drip sampling.*—Draw drip sample from pipe line as molasses is being pumped from vessel. From lot <5000 gal., collect ≥ 1 qt; from lot >5000 gal., draw 1 pt from each 5000 gal., but ≥ 1 qt.

(2) *Bacon bomb or thief sampling.*—Draw 2 similar complete samples of ca 1 qt each consisting of continuous portion of core extending from top to bottom of tank. When for any reason such core cannot be obtained, draw three 1 qt samples as follows: 1 portion from top just below surface of liq., 1 from center, and 1 from bottom of tank. Make composite for tank by combining samples from different levels as shown below.

Sample	Vessels of uniform cross section	Horizontal cylindrical tank (full)
Upper	1 part	1 part
Middle	3 parts	8 parts
Lower	1 part	1 part

Reduce composite to amt required and fill two ≥ 1 pt glass, stainless metal, or plastic jars. Close jars air-tight. Store and send for testing as in (a)(*1*).

(b) *Dried molasses.*—Proceed as in **7.001.** Divide composite into 2 equal portions and place each portion into sep. air-tight jar. Store and send for testing as in (a).

31.071 *Transport of Samples*

Transport samples to laboratory as quickly as possible after sampling. Do not expose to direct sunlight or high temp. during transit.

31.072 *Preparation of Sample*

Let samples come to ca room temp. before opening containers.

(a) *Dried products.*—Do not grind. Pass samples contg lumps thru No. 8 sieve and crush retains on glass plate with glass or metal rolling pin, or in clean, dry mortar, using pestle. Mix entire sample thoroly and place in air-tight container.

(b) *Liquids.*—See **31.001**(c).

31.073 *Moisture—Official Final Action*

(a) *Dried products.*—See **31.005.**

(b) *Liquids.*—See **31.007** or **31.008.**

Water in Molasses (26)—
Official Final Action

31.074 *Apparatus*

Buret with automatic zero; reservoir for reagent; magnetic stirring device; titrn vessel (300 ml Berzelius beaker with stopcock attached to side at bottom for withdrawing excess soln is recommended), electrodes, and circuitry for deadstop end point detection. All openings must be tightly closed or protected with drying tubes to prevent contamination from atm. H_2O. Various titrn assemblies may be obtained com. or one may be assembled.

Assemble titrn app. and follow manufacturer's instructions, set for direct titrn. Set timer to give 30 sec end point. Add enough dry MeOH to cover electrodes on electrode probes and turn on stirrer. Adjust speed to obtain good stirring without splashing. Do not let stirrer bar contact electrodes. Titr. until satisfactory end point is reached. App. newly assembled or not recently used may require repetition of this step to dry out system.

31.075 Reagents

(*Caution: See* **46.066, 46.072,** and **46.081.**)

(a) *Karl Fischer reagent.*—Available com. or prep. as follows: Dissolve 133 g I in 425 ml dry pyridine in dry g-s bottle. Add 425 ml dry MeOH or ethylene glycol monomethyl ether. (Less trouble with stopcock leakage is obtained with ethylene glycol monomethyl ether.) Cool to <4° in ice bath and bubble in 102–105 g SO_2. Mix well and let stand 12 hr. Reagent is reasonably stable, but restdze for each series of detns.

(b) *Anhydrous methanol.*—Reagent grade MeOH contg <0.1% H_2O. Prep. by distg over Mg.

31.076 Determination

Add ca 120 mg H_2O from weighing pipet or other suitable device and titr. with Karl Fischer reagent. Calc. C = mg H_2O/ml reagent.

For titrn of molasses, C = ca 5 mg/ml. Weigh molasses estd to give 20–40 ml titer into titrn app. and titr.

% H_2O = (C × ml reagent)/(g sample × 10).

Drain excess liq. and repeat with succeeding samples. If time lapse occurs between titrn of samples, adjust liq. in titrn vessel to end point by titrn with reagent before adding next sample.

31.077 Specific Gravity—Official Final Action
See **31.010(b).**

31.078 Ash—Official Final Action
See **31.012, 31.013,** or **31.014.**

31.079 Soluble and Insoluble Ash—Official Final Action
See **31.015.**

31.080 Mineral Adulterants in Ash—Official Final Action
See **31.018.**

31.081 Nitrogen—Official Final Action
See **31.019.**

31.082 Sucrose—Official Final Action
Polarimetric methods (when required by law). *See* **31.020–31.031.**

Total Sugars Expressed as Invert Sugar—Official Final Action
Lane-Eynon Constant Volume Volumetric Method

31.083 Apparatus

(a) *Electric heater.*—With white top and continuous temp. control over range 110–600°; attaining max. temp. within 5 min.

(b) *Buret.*—50 ml, graduated in 0.1 ml, with stopcock or pinchcock and offset delivery tube.

31.084 Reagents

(a) *Soxhlet modification of Fehling soln.*—Prep. as in **31.035(a)** and **(b).**

(b) *Invert sugar std solns.*—(*1*) *Stock soln.*—10 mg/ml. Prep. as in **31.035(c),** using 5 ml HCl (sp gr 1.18 at 20/4°) and letting stand 3 days at room temp. (20–25°). (*2*) *Working soln.*—5 mg/ml. Pipet 100 ml stock soln into 200 ml vol. flask, add few drops phthln, and neutze with 20% NaOH. Dil. to vol. and mix well. Prep. fresh daily.

31.085 Preparation of Sample Solution

(a) *Dried products containing not less than 30% total sugars.*—Weigh 8.00 g sample and transfer with 250 ml H_2O, preheated to 60±5°, into 500 ml vol. flask. Shake flask 30 min mech. Let stand addnl 30 min and cool to 20°. Dil. to vol. with H_2O. Mix well and filter, using filter aid (Hyflo Super-Cel, or equiv.) and loose texture paper (Whatman No. 1, or equiv.). Discard first 25 ml filtrate. Cover funnel during filtration with watch glass to prevent evapn.

(b) *Liquids.*—Weigh 8.00 g sample and transfer with H_2O to 500 ml vol. flask. Dissolve, and dil. to vol. with H_2O. Proceed as in (a), beginning "Mix well ..."

31.086 Standardization of Soxhlet Reagent

Fill 50 ml buret with working std soln contg 5 mg invert sugar/ml.

Accurately pipet 10 ml each Soxhlet soln, (a) and (b), into 300 ml erlenmeyer, mix, and add 30 ml H_2O. Add from buret almost all std working soln (ca 19 ml) necessary to reduce the Cu. Add few boiling chips. Place cold mixt. on heater, regulate heat so that boiling will begin in ca 3 min, and maintain at moderate boil exactly 2 min, reducing heat, if necessary, to prevent bumping. Without removing flask from heater, add ca 4 drops *1% aq. methylene blue soln* and complete titrn within total boiling time of ca 3 min by dropwise addn of std working soln at intervals of ca 10 sec until boiling mixt. resumes bright orange appearance which it had before indicator was added. Maintain continuous emission of steam to prevent reoxidn by air. Repeat stdzn several times. Factor F is av. number ml std sugar soln required to completely reduce 20 ml Soxhlet soln. Use av. of ≥3 titrns.

31.087   *Inversion with Acid at Room Temperature*

Pipet 100 ml filtrate, **31.085**, into 200 ml vol. flask, and add 5 ml HCl (sp gr 1.18 at 20/4°). Let stand 24 hr at 20–25° or 10 hr at >25°. Add few drops phthln and neutze with 20% NaOH. Add few drops 0.5N HCl until red disappears. Dil. to vol. with H_2O and mix well.

31.088   *Approximation Titration of Sample*

Det. approx. sugar content of sample as follows: Accurately pipet 10 ml each Soxhlet soln, (a) and (b), into 300 ml erlenmeyer, mix, and add 10 ml aliquot inverted sample soln. Add 40 ml H_2O so that vol. H_2O plus vol. sample soln is 50 ml, as in **31.086**. Mix in cold by swirling. Add few boiling chips. Place flask on heater, regulating heat so that boiling begins in ca 3 min. After liq. boils 10–15 sec, observe change in color of soln. If blue color persists, add working std sugar soln 0.5–1.0 ml at time, with few sec actual boiling after each addn until unsafe to add more without risk of passing end point. Add 3–4 drops methylene blue soln and continue adding sugar soln ca 1 ml at time, at intervals of ca 10 sec, until indicator is completely decolorized. Calc. approx. % invert sugar in sample.

31.089   *Titration of Sample*

Pipet 10 ml each of Soxhlet soln, (a) and (b), into 300 ml erlenmeyer, mix, and add aliquot inverted sample soln as indicated in **31.090**. Add ml H_2O specified in table so that vol. H_2O plus vol. sample soln is 50 ml, as in **31.086**, and mix in cold by swirling. Add few boiling chips. Place flask on heater, regulate heat so that boiling begins in ca 3 min, and during boiling, rapidly add working std invert sugar soln from buret, so that 0.5–1.0 ml is required to complete titrn. Continue as in **31.086**, beginning "Without removing flask . . ." Maintain moderate boiling. Calc. % sugar as invert = $(F - M) \times I \times 100/W$, where F is Cu factor (ml std sugar soln required to reduce 20 ml mixed Soxhlet reagent); M is ml std sugar soln used in back-titrn of sample; I is g invert sugar in 1 ml working std sugar soln; and W is g sample in aliquot used. Report total sugars, expressed as invert.

31.090   *Aliquots for Cane Sirups and Molasses*

ml H_2O	ml Aliquot	g Sample in Aliquot	Total Sugar as Invert, %	
			Max.	Min.
40	10	0.08		73.00
35	15	0.12	82.00	58.00
30	20	0.16	61.00	41.00
25	25	0.20	49.00	35.00
20	30	0.24	41.00	29.00

Invert Sugar—Official Final Action

31.091   *Preparation of Sample Solution*

Proceed as in **31.085**. Then pipet 100 ml filtrate into 200 ml vol. flask, dil. to vol. with H_2O, and mix well.

31.092   *Titration of Sample*

Proceed as in **31.088–31.089**, except use aliquot of prepd sample soln without inversion as indicated in **31.093**.

31.093   *Aliquots for Cane Sirups and Molasses (Without Inversion)*

ml H_2O	ml Aliquot	g Sample in Aliquot	Total Sugar as Invert, %	
			Max.	Min.
40	10	0.16	61.00	40.00
35	15	0.24	40.00	30.00
30	20	0.32	30.00	24.00
25	25	0.40	24.00	20.00
20	30	0.48	20.00	15.00
10	40	0.64	15.00	12.00
—	50	0.80	12.00	8.00

Unfermentable Reducing Substances (27)— Official Final Action

(Applicable to molasses)

31.094   *Reagents*

(a) *Bakers' yeast, free from starch.*—Fleischmann, sold in 1 lb units by Standard Brands, Inc., is suitable. May be stored for few days in refrigerator.

(b) *Neutral lead acetate soln.*—Dissolve 20 g $Pb(OAc)_2.3H_2O$ in H_2O and dil. to 100 ml.

(c) *Soxhlet soln.*—See **31.035**(a) and (b).

(d) *Potassium iodide soln.*—Dissolve 20 g KI in H_2O and dil. to 100 ml.

(e) *Thiosulfate std soln.*—0.1N. See **45.038–45.039**.

31.095   *Fermentation*

Transfer 12 g blackstrap molasses (or 8 g hightest molasses) to 500 ml vol. flask, using 75 ml H_2O in all. Add 25 g fresh yeast, coarsely chopped, and mix thoroly with molasses soln. Close flask with stopper provided with delivery tube, other end of which dips ca 1 cm below surface of H_2O in beaker; or use any other type of fermentation trap. Place flask in H_2O bath kept at 30° and let ferment at least 4 hr, shaking occasionally. (Incubator may be used and flask left overnight.)

When fermentation is complete, dil. mixt. with H_2O, clarify with 15 ml neut. $Pb(OAc)_2$ soln, dil. to vol. at 20°, add teaspoonful of Filter-Cel, shake well, and filter, discarding first few ml. Delead entire filtrate with ca 0.5 g anhyd. $K_2C_2O_4$ and filter again with aid of Filter-Cel. Test filtrate for Pb. If necessary add addnl $K_2C_2O_4$ and refilter.

31.096   *Determination*

Transfer 25 ml final filtrate to 250 ml erlenmeyer, mix with 20 ml combined Soxhlet soln, and wash down wall of flask with 5 ml H_2O, making 50 ml total. Add few pieces of ignited pumice stone and place flask on wire gauze covered with asbestos plate that has center hole slightly smaller than bottom of flask. Heat with Bunsen burner, or, preferably, elec. heater with temp. control. Heat to boiling in 3 min and boil gently exactly 2 min longer. Immediately close flask with stopper provided with Bunsen valve and cool quickly under H_2O tap to prevent reoxidn. Add 15 ml KI soln and then 10 ml H_2SO_4 (1 + 3). Titr. liberated I at once with $0.1N$ $Na_2S_2O_3$, adding starch indicator toward end of titrn.

Det. blank with 75 ml H_2O instead of molasses soln, adding yeast, etc., as above. Deduct titer of sample from titer of blank, and find mg invert sugar corresponding to difference from table, **31.097.** Result, divided by 6 (in case of high-test molasses, by 4) gives directly % unfermentable reducing substances in the molasses, in terms of invert sugar.

31.097   *Milligrams Invert Sugar Corresponding to 0.1N Thiosulfate*

0.1N Thiosulfate	Invert Sugar	0.1N Thiosulfate	Invert Sugar
ml	*mg*	*ml*	*mg*
1	3.2	14	47.3
2	6.4	15	50.8
3	9.7	16	54.3
4	13.0	17	58.0
5	16.4	18	61.8
6	19.8	19	65.5
7	23.2	20	69.4
8	26.5	21	73.3
9	29.9	22	77.2
10	33.4	23	81.2
11	36.8	24	85.2
12	40.3	25	89.2
13	43.8	—	—

CONFECTIONERY

31.098 Preparation of Sample— Official Final Action

If composition of entire sample is desired, grind and mix thoroly. If sample is composed of layers or of distinctly different portions and it is desired to examine these individually, sep. with knife or other mech. means as completely as possible, and grind and mix each portion thoroly.

31.099 Moisture—Official Final Action— See 31.005, 31.006, 31.007, or 31.008

31.100 Ash—Official Final Action— See 31.012 or 31.013

31.101 Soluble and Insoluble Ash— Official Final Action—See 31.015

31.102 Alkalinity of Soluble Ash— Official Final Action—See 31.016

31.103 Alkalinity of Insoluble Ash— Official Final Action—See 31.017

31.104 Mineral Adulterants in Ash— Official First Action—See 31.018

31.105 Nitrogen—Official Final Action

Det. N in 2–5 g sample as in **2.051,** using larger quantity of H_2SO_4 if necessary for complete digestion.

Sucrose—Polarimetric Methods

31.106 *In Absence of Raffinose—Official Final Action—See 31.025, 31.026, or 31.031*

Sucrose—Chemical Methods

31.107 *By Reducing Sugars Before and After Inversion—Official Final Action— See 31.032*

31.108 *Commercial Glucose—Procedure— See 31.033 or 31.034*

Starch—Official First Action

31.109   *Reagent*

Malt extract.—Use clean, new barley malt of known efficacy and grind only as needed. Grind well, but not so fine that filtration is greatly retarded. Prep. infusion of freshly ground malt just before use. For every 80 ml malt ext required, digest 5 g ground malt with 100 ml H_2O, at room temp. 2 hr, or 20 min if mixt. can be stirred by elec. mixer. Filter to obtain clear ext, refiltering first portions of filtrate if necessary. Mix infusion well.

31.110   *Determination*

Measure 25 ml of soln of uniform mixt. (representing 5 g sample) into 300 ml beaker, or add to beaker 5 g finely ground sample (previously extd with ether if sample contains much fat); add enough H_2O to make 100 ml; heat to ca 60° (avoiding, if possible, gelatinizing starch); and let stand ca 1 hr, stirring frequently to secure complete soln of sugars. Transfer to wide-mouth bottle, rinse beaker with little warm H_2O, and cool. Add equal vol. alcohol, mix, and let stand at least 1 hr.

Centrf. until ppt is closely packed on bottom of bottle and decant supernatant thru hardened filter. Wash ppt with successive 50 ml portions of alcohol, 50% by vol., by centrfg and decanting thru filter until washings are sugar-free by following test: Add to test tube few drops of washings, 3 or 4 drops *20%* *alc. α-naphthol soln*, and 2 ml H_2O. Shake well, tip tube, let 2–5 ml H_2SO_4 flow down side of tube, and then hold tube upright. If sugar is present, interface of 2 liqs is colored faint to deep violet; on shaking, whole soln becomes blue-violet. Transfer residue from bottle and hardened filter to beaker with 50 ml H_2O.

Immerse beaker in boiling H_2O, and stir constantly 15 min, or until all starch is gelatinized; cool to 55°, add 20 ml malt ext, and hold at this temp. 1 hr. Heat again to boiling few min, cool to 55°, add 20 ml malt ext, and hold at this temp. 1 hr, or until residue treated with I soln shows no blue tinge upon microscopic examination. Cool, dil. to 250 ml, and filter.

Place 200 ml filtrate in flask, add 20 ml HCl (sp gr 1.125), connect with reflux condenser, and heat in boiling H_2O bath 2.5 hr. Cool, nearly neutze with 10% NaOH soln, finish neutzn with Na_2CO_3 soln, and dil. to 500 ml. Mix soln thoroly, pour thru dry filter, and det. glucose in aliquot as in **31.039**. Conduct blank detn on same vol. of malt ext as used with sample and correct wt glucose accordingly. Wt glucose obtained $\times$ 0.90 = wt starch.

Ether Extract—Official First Action

(*Caution: See* **46.011, 46.039, 46.054,** and **46.073.**)

31.111 *Continuous Extraction Method*

Measure 25 ml 20% mixt. or soln into very thin, readily breakable glass evapg shell, or thin Pb or Sn foil contg 5–7 g freshly ignited asbestos fiber; or, if possible to obtain uniform sample, weigh 5 g mixed finely divided sample into dish and wash with H_2O onto asbestos in evapg shell, using small portion of asbestos fiber on stirring rod to transfer last traces of sample from dish to shell.

Dry to constant wt at 100°, cool, wrap glass dish loosely in smooth paper, crush into rather small fragments between fingers, and carefully transfer crushed mass, including paper, to extn tube or fat extn cartridge. If metal dish is used, cut into small pieces and place in extn tube. Ext with anhyd. ether or pet ether (bp 45–60° and without weighable residue) in continuous extn app. at least 25 hr. In most cases it is advisable to remove substance from extractor after first 12 hr, grind with sand to fine powder, and re-ext remaining 13 hr. Transfer ext to weighed flask, evap. solv., and dry to constant wt at 100°.

31.112 *Roese-Gottlieb Method*

Introduce 4 g sample, or amt of uniform soln equiv. to this wt dry substance, into Mojonnier fat extn tube or similar app.; dil. to 10 ml with H_2O, add 1.25 ml NH_4OH, and mix thoroly. Add 10 ml alcohol

and mix; then add 25 ml ether and shake vigorously ca 30 sec; and finally add 25 ml pet ether (bp <60°) and shake again ca 30 sec. Let stand 20 min or until sepn of liqs is complete.

Draw off as much as possible of ether-fat soln (usually 0.5–0.8 ml is left) into weighed flask thru small, rapid filter. (Weigh flask with similar one as counterpoise.) Again ext liq. remaining in tube, this time with 15 ml each of ether and pet ether; shake vigorously ca 30 sec with each solv. and let settle. Proceed as above, washing mouth of tube and filter with few ml of mixt. of equal parts of the 2 solvs (previously mixed and freed from deposited H_2O).

For greater degree of accuracy, repeat extn. If previous solv.-fat solns have been drawn off closely, third extn usually yields $\leq$1 mg fat, or ca 0.02% on 4 g charge. Slowly evap. solv. on steam bath and then dry fat in boiling H_2O oven to constant wt. Test purity of fat by dissolving in little pet ether. If residue remains, wash fat out completely with pet ether, dry residue, weigh, and deduct wt.

31.113 Paraffin—Official First Action

To solv. ext in flask, **31.111** or **31.112**, add 10 ml alcohol and 2 ml NaOH soln (1 + 1); connect flask with reflux condenser; and heat 1 hr on H_2O bath, or until saponification is complete. Remove condenser and keep flask on bath until alcohol evaps and residue is dry. Dissolve residue as completely as possible in ca 40 ml H_2O and heat on bath, shaking frequently. Wash into separator, cool, and ext with 4 successive portions of pet ether, collecting exts in weighed flask or capsule. Evap. pet ether and dry to constant wt at 100°. Any phytosterol or cholesterol present in fat would be extd with the paraffin but quantity is so insignificant that it may generally be disregarded.

31.114 Shellac (*28*)—Official Final Action

(*Caution: See* **46.011, 46.040,** and **46.045.**)

Place 50 g candy in 400 ml beaker. Add 50 ml mixt. of benzene and absolute alcohol (1 + 1), and cover with watch glass. Place beaker on steam bath, heat to boiling, and simmer few min, stirring occasionally. Decant liq. into tared, round 100 ml glass dish with flat bottom ca 2¾″ diam. Ext once more with benzene-alcohol mixt., and finally rinse with two 25 ml portions absolute alcohol, simmering and stirring each time. With moist sugar candy, avoid overheating to prevent pieces from sticking together.

Add each ext to glass dish previously placed on steam bath. Evap. until alcohol is just removed, rotating dish as it goes to dryness in order to spread ext uniformly over bottom surface. Avoid baking shellac on dish. If fat appears to be present, wash with three 15 ml portions pet ether, stirring and warming. Decant thru rapid filter.

Add mixt. of 25 ml *isoamyl alcohol* (bp 129–132°)

and 25 ml benzene to filter, and filter back into dish. Heat on steam bath with stirring, cool somewhat, and transfer soln with suspended matter to 125 ml separator. Rinse dish with 25 ml hot (ca 60°) H_2O, and add to separator; shake well and filter wash H_2O if necessary. Repeat washing with H_2O *twice* (or until washings are colorless), rinsing dish well around sides with first portions of liq. Finally, filter soln of shellac into tared dish, rinsing separator and filters with little absolute alcohol. Evap. to dryness on steam bath, rotating dish to give uniform film.

If much fat was extd in original benzene extn, wash final shellac residue with 25 ml pet ether, warming and stirring. Decant, dry on steam bath and in 100° oven, and weigh. After weighing, check for complete removal of sugars by thoroly rinsing dish and surface of shellac with hot H_2O, warming on steam bath, decanting, rinsing down with alcohol, and evapg with care to give uniform film on dish. Dry and reweigh.

31.115 Alcohol in Sirups Used in Confectionery ("Brandy Drops")— Official Final Action

Collect in beaker sirup from enough pieces of sample to yield 30–50 g, strain into weighed beaker, and weigh. Place sirup in 250–300 ml distg flask, dil. with half its vol. of H_2O, attach flask to vertical condenser, and distill almost 50 ml, or as much of liq. as possible without causing charring. Foaming may be prevented by adding little *tannin*, or piece of *paraffin* ca size of pea. Cool distillate, dil. to vol. with H_2O, and mix well. Det. sp gr as in **9.011.** Calc. % alcohol by wt in candy filling, using tables **47.003** and **47.005.**

HONEY

31.116 Preparation of Sample— Official Final Action

(a) *Liquid or strained honey.*—If sample is free from granulation, mix thoroly by stirring or shaking before weighing portions for detns; if granulated, place closed container in H_2O bath without submerging, and heat 30 min at 60°; then, if necessary, heat at 65° until liquefied. Occasional shaking is essential. Mix thoroly, cool rapidly as soon as sample liquefies, and weigh portions for detns. Do not heat honey intended for diastatic detn. If foreign matter, such as wax, sticks, bees, particles of comb, etc., is present, heat sample to 40° in H_2O bath and strain thru cheesecloth in hot H_2O funnel before weighing portions for analysis.

(b) *Comb honey.*—Cut across top of comb, if sealed, and sep. completely from comb by straining thru No. 40 sieve. When portions of comb or wax pass thru sieve, heat sample as in (a) and strain thru cheesecloth. If honey is granulated in comb, heat until wax is liquefied; stir, cool, and remove wax.

Color Classification (29)—Official First Action
31.117 Apparatus

(a) *Containers.*—French square bottles, screw finish, clear glass, 1.5 × 1.5″, 2⅞₂ oz. (Available from Phoenix Precision Instrument Co., 3803 N. 5th St, Philadelphia, PA 19140.)

(b) *Comparator.*—All-metal boxes, approx. 8 × 2 × 3″, divided by thin partitions into 5 square compartments, each of which has 2 windows, front and back, ca 1.2″ square. The 3 lighter glass stds (water white, extra white, and white) are mounted in 1 of comparator boxes on shelf against front windows in compartments 1, 3, and 5. The 3 darker stds (extra light amber, light amber, and amber) are mounted similarly in second comparator box. Place containers, (a), filled with H_2O (blanks) behind glass stds. With turbid honeys substitute containers filled with suspensions of diat. earth (Hyflo Super-Cel) designated as "Cloudy 1," "Cloudy 2," and "Cloudy 3," contg 100, 200, and 400 mg/L H_2O, resp.

(c) *Glass stds.*—Use selected colored glasses tested and stdzd by USDA to correspond with color stds for honey.

Complete grading set is available from Phoenix Precision Instrument Co.

31.118 Determination

Place clear blanks or cloudy suspensions in back of glass stds in compartments 1, 3, and 5 of 1 or both comparators. Pour sample (must be free from granulation) into clean, dry container, **31.117**(a). Place sample container in compartment 2 or 4 of either comparator. Hold comparator at convenient distance from eye and view by diffused light (e.g., north or overcast sky, diffused light from W lamp, or white or daylight fluorescent lamp). Move sample from compartment to compartment, interchanging blanks with cloudy suspensions if necessary. Det. classification as follows: If sample is equal to water white std in hue, or not as red (i.e., yellower), classify as water white; if perceptibly redder than water white std in hue but not redder than extra white std, classify as extra white, etc. If redder in hue than amber std, classify as dark amber. Hue (amber quality or redness) is attribute of color in classification.

Moisture—Official Final Action
31.119 Direct Drying

Proceed as in **31.007** or **31.008,** using weighed quantity of sample sufficient to yield ca 1 g solids. Add, if necessary, few ml H_2O to incorporate sample thoroly with the sand. Dry at <70° (preferably 60°) under pressure ≤50 mm Hg.

31.120 By Means of Refractometer (30)

Det. refractometer reading of honey at 20° and obtain corresponding % moisture from **31.121.** If detn is made at temp. other than 20°, correct reading to std temp. of 20° according to footnote.

31.121 Relationship Between Refractive Index and Water Contents of Honeys[a]

Water Content, %	Refractive Index			Water Content, %	Refractive Index		
	20°C[b]	60°F[c]	40°C		20°C[b]	60°F[c]	40°C
13.0	1.5044	1.5053	1.4998	19.0	1.4890	1.4900	1.4845
13.2	1.5038	1.5048	1.4993	19.2	1.4885	1.4895	1.4840
13.4	1.5033	1.5043	1.4988	19.4	1.4880	1.4890	1.4835
13.6	1.5028	1.5038	1.4983	19.6	1.4875	1.4885	1.4829
13.8	1.5023	1.5033	1.4978	19.8	1.4870	1.4880	1.4824
14.0	1.5018	1.5027	1.4973	20.0	1.4865	1.4875	1.4819
14.2	1.5012	1.5022	1.4968	20.2	1.4860	1.4870	1.4814
14.4	1.5007	1.5017	1.4962	20.4	1.4855	1.4865	1.4809
14.6	1.5002	1.5012	1.4957	20.6	1.4850	1.4860	1.4804
14.8	1.4997	1.5007	1.4952	20.8	1.4845	1.4855	1.4799
15.0	1.4992	1.5002	1.4947	21.0	1.4840	1.4850	1.4794
15.2	1.4987	1.4997	1.4942	21.2	1.4835	1.4845	1.4788
15.4	1.4982	1.4992	1.4937	21.4	1.4830	1.4840	1.4783
15.6	1.4976	1.4986	1.4932	21.6	1.4825	1.4835	1.4778
15.8	1.4971	1.4981	1.4927	21.8	1.4820	1.4830	1.4773
16.0	1.4966	1.4976	1.4922	22.0	1.4815	1.4825	1.4768
16.2	1.4961	1.4971	1.4916	22.2	1.4810		
16.4	1.4956	1.4966	1.4911	22.4	1.4805		
16.6	1.4951	1.4961	1.4906	22.6	1.4800		
16.8	1.4946	1.4956	1.4901	22.8	1.4795		
17.0	1.4940	1.4951	1.4896	23.0	1.4790		
17.2	1.4935	1.4946	1.4891	23.2	1.4785		
17.4	1.4930	1.4940	1.4886	23.4	1.4780		
17.6	1.4925	1.4935	1.4881	23.6	1.4775		
17.8	1.4920	1.4930	1.4876	23.8	1.4770		
18.0	1.4915	1.4925	1.4870	24.0	1.4765		
18.2	1.4910	1.4920	1.4865	24.2	1.4760		
18.4	1.4905	1.4915	1.4860	24.4	1.4755		
18.6	1.4900	1.4910	1.4855	24.6	1.4750		
18.8	1.4895	1.4905	1.4850	24.8	1.4745		
				25.0	1.4740		

[a] Values for 20°C and 60°F are Wedmore's calculations (Bee World **36**, 197 (1955)); 40°C values are calcd from Auerbach and Borries equation (Z. Nahr. Genussm. **22**, 353–358 (1924)). Values >22.0% were extended by FAO/WHO Codex Committee on Methods of Analysis and Sampling (1968).

[b] If refractive index is measured at temp. above (below) 20°C, add (subtract) 0.00023/°C above (below) 20°C before using table.

[c] If refractive index is measured at temp. above (below) 60°F, add (subtract) 0.00013/°F above (below) 60°F before using table.

31.122 Ash (31)—Official Final Action

Weigh 5–10 g honey into ignited and weighed Pt dish. Place under 375 watt IR lamp with variable voltage input and slowly increase applied voltage until sample is black and dry and there is no danger of loss by foaming. Heat in muffle at 600° to constant wt (overnight). Cool and weigh.

31.123 Soluble Ash—Official Final Action— See 31.015

31.124 Alkalinity of Soluble Ash— Official Final Action—See 31.016

31.125 Nitrogen (31)—Official First Action

Det. N as in **42.014–42.016**, using 300 mg sample, 3.0±0.1 ml H_2SO_4, and 1 hr digestion after acid comes to true boil. Titr. with 0.01N HCl and calc. % N.

31.126 Direct Polarization— Official First Action

(a) *Immediate direct polarization.*—Transfer 26 g honey to 100 ml vol. flask with H_2O, add 5 ml alumina cream, **31.021**(b), dil. to vol. with H_2O at 20°, filter, and polarize immediately in 200 mm tube.

(b) *Constant direct polarization.*—Complete mutarotation as in **31.023**. If necessary to conserve sample, soln from tube used in immediate direct polarization, (a), may be returned to flask. Make final reading at 20° in 200 mm tube.

(c) *Mutarotation.*—Difference between (a) and (b) is measure of mutarotation.

(d) *Direct polarization at 87°.*—Polarize soln obtained in (b) at 87° in jacketed 200 mm metal tube.

31.127 Invert Polarization— Official First Action

(a) *At 20°.*—Invert 50 ml soln, **31.126**(a), as in **31.025**(b) or (c) or **31.026**(b) or (c), and polarize at 20° in 200 mm tube.

(b) *At 87°.*—Polarize soln (a) at 87° in jacketed 200 mm metal tube.

31.128 Reducing Sugars— Official Final Action

(a) *Munson-Walker method.*—Dil. 10 ml soln, **31.126**(a), to 250 ml and det. reducing sugars in 25 ml of this soln by **31.039.** Calc. result to % invert sugar.

(b) *Lane-Eynon method.*—Dil. 10 ml soln, **31.126**(a), to 500 ml and det. reducing sugars by constant vol. method:

Stdze Fehling solns, **31.035,** so that 5.00 ml soln (a) and 5 ml soln (b) will react completely with 50 mg invert sugar std soln, **31.035**(c), added as 25 ml of diln to 2 g/L.

Pipet 5 ml of each Fehling soln into 250 ml erlenmeyer. Add 7 ml H_2O, little antibumping agent, and 15 ml dild honey soln from buret with offset tip. Heat to boiling over wire gauze, and maintain moderate boil 2 min. Add 1 ml 0.2% methylene blue soln while still boiling and complete titrn within total boiling time of 3 min by repeated small addns of dild honey soln until indicator is decolorized. (Observe color of supernatant.) Note vol. honey soln used (x ml).

Repeat titrn, using 5 ml of each Fehling soln, $(25 - x)$ ml H_2O, and all but 1.5 ml dild honey soln (from buret) detd in preliminary titrn. Add honey soln to end point within 3 min and note vol. dild honey soln used (y ml). Duplicate titrns should agree within 0.1 ml.

% Invert sugar $= 2000/($g honey sample $\times y)$.

31.129 Sucrose—Official Final Action

(a) Calc. from data given in **31.126**(b) and **31.127**(a) if inversion is conducted as in **31.025**(b) or (c). Use formula given in **31.025**(b).

(b) Proceed as in **31.032.** To det. reducing sugars after inversion, dil. 10 ml soln, **31.127**(a), with small amt of H_2O, neutze with Na_2CO_3, and dil. to 250 ml with H_2O. Use 50 ml of this soln, making detn as in **31.128**(a).

31.130 Fructose—Official First Action

Multiply direct reading at 87°, **31.126**(d), by 1.0315 and from product subtract constant direct polarization at 20°, **31.126**(b); divide difference by 2.3919 to obtain g fructose in normal wt honey. From this figure calc. % fructose in original sample, or det. fructose selectively by **31.062.**

31.131 Glucose—Official First Action

To obtain approx. % glucose, subtract % fructose, **31.130,** from % invert sugar, **31.128.**

To det. glucose more closely, multiply % fructose, **31.130,** by factor 0.915, which gives its glucose equiv. in Cu reducing power. Subtract figure obtained from that of reducing sugars, **31.128,** calcd as glucose, to obtain % glucose in sample. Because of difference in

reducing powers of different sugars, sum of glucose thus found and fructose, **31.130,** will be greater than quantity of invert sugar obtained in **31.128.**

31.132 Dextrin (Approximate)—Procedure

Using ≤ 4 ml H_2O, transfer 8 g sample (4 g for dark-colored honeydew honey) to 100 ml vol. flask by letting sample drain from weighing dish into flask and then dissolving residue in 2 ml H_2O. Add this soln to flask, and rinse weighing dish with two 1 ml portions H_2O, adding few ml absolute alcohol each time before decanting. Fill flask to vol. with absolute alcohol, shaking constantly. Set flask aside until dextrin collects on sides and bottom and liq. is clear.

Decant clear liq. thru filter paper and wash residue in flask with 10 ml alcohol, pouring washings thru same filter. Dissolve dextrin in flask with boiling H_2O and filter thru paper already used, receiving filtrate in weighed dish prepd as in **31.008.** Rinse flask and wash filter number of times with small portions of hot H_2O, evap. on H_2O bath, and dry to constant wt at 70° under pressure ≤ 50 mm Hg.

Dissolve weighed alcohol ppt in H_2O and dil. to definite vol., using 50 ml H_2O for each 0.5 g ppt or part thereof.

Det. reducing sugars in soln both before and after inversion as in **31.032,** expressing results as invert sugar. Calc. sucrose from results thus obtained and subtract sum of reducing sugars before inversion and sucrose from wt total alcohol ppt to obtain wt dextrin.

Chromatographic Separation of Sugars (32)— Official First Action

31.133 *Principle*

By adsorption of honey sample on charcoal column, followed by elution into monosaccharide, disaccharide, and higher sugar fractions, interference of disaccharides in glucose and fructose detns is eliminated. Elution is by progressively higher alcohol concns, followed by detn of individual monosaccharides, sucrose, and reducing disaccharides collectively as maltose, and trisaccharides and higher sugars collectively after hydrolysis.

31.134 *Preparation and Standardization of Adsorption Column*

Column is 22 mm od $\times$ 370 mm long, with 1 L spherical section and 35/20 $\overline{\underline{\text{S}}}$ spherical joint at top. Adsorbent is $1 + 1$ mixt. of Darco G-60 charcoal and rapid filter-aid (Celite 545 or Dicalite 4200). Insert glass wool plug, wet from below, and add enough dry adsorbent to dry tube (23–26 cm) to compress to 17 cm when vac. is applied with *gentle* tapping of column. Remove excess charcoal from walls of column, and add filter-aid layer at top with *gentle* packing (1–1.5 cm). Wash column with 500 ml H_2O and 250 ml 50% alcohol, and let stand overnight with 50% alcohol on it. Flow rate should be 5.5–8.0

ml/min with H_2O at 9 lb/sq in. pressure. Slower flow rates delay analyses excessively.

Alcohol content of eluting solns must be adjusted to retentive power of charcoal used. Wash column alcohol-free with 250 ml H_2O, quant. add 10 ml soln of 1.000 g anhyd. glucose to top, and draw it into column with suction (do not let dry). Add 300 ml H_2O to top, break suction, apply pressure (10 lb/sq in. max.), and collect eluate in five 50 ml portions in tared beakers. Include 10 ml from sample introduction in first 50 ml fraction. Evap. fractions on steam bath, dry in vac. oven at 80–100°, and weigh.

Decant remaining H_2O from top of column, pass 50 ml 50% alcohol and then 250 ml H_2O thru column, and repeat chromatgy, using 1.000 g anhyd. glucose in 10 ml 1% alcohol, washing with 250 ml 1% alcohol as above. Select as *solv. A* that which removes glucose in 150 ml. Repeat chromatgy with 2% alcohol if necessary.

Wash column with 250 ml H_2O and then 20 ml 5% alcohol. To top, add 10 ml 5% alcohol soln contg 100 mg maltose and 100 mg sucrose. Elute as above with 250 ml 5% alcohol, weighing evapd 50 ml portions of filtrate. Repeat, if necessary, with 7, 8, and 9% alcohol to find *solv. B* that will elute ≥98% disaccharides in 200 ml. *Solv. A* previously selected must not elute disaccharides. Combinations found satisfactory with various charcoals are 1%, 7%; 2%, 8%; 2%, 9%. At conclusion, pass 100 ml 50% alcohol thru column, and store under layer of this solv.

31.135   *Preparation of Fractions*

Wash column with 250 ml H_2O and decant any supernatant. Pass 20 ml *solv. A* thru column, and discard. Dissolve 1 g sample in 10 ml *solv. A* in 50 ml beaker. Transfer sample (using long-stem funnel) onto column, and force into column. Use 15 ml *solv. A* to rinse beaker and funnel, and add to column. Collect all eluate, beginning with sample introduction, in 250 ml vol. flask. Add 250 ml *solv. A*, and collect exactly 250 ml total (fraction *A*, monosaccharides). Decant excess solv. from top, add 265–270 ml *solv. B*, and collect 250 ml in vol. flask (fraction *B*, disaccharides). Decant excess, add 110 ml 50% alcohol (*solv. C*), and collect 100 ml in vol. flask (fraction *C*, higher sugars). Mix each fraction thoroly. Column may be stored indefinitely, outlet closed, under 50% alcohol. Discard after 8 uses.

Fructose

31.136   *Reagents*

Use reagents in **31.054** and following:

(a) *Iodine soln.*—0.05N. Dissolve 13.5 g pure I in soln of 24 g KI in 200 ml H_2O, and dil. to 2 L. Do not stdze.

(b) *Sodium sulfite soln.*—1%. Dissolve 1 g Na_2SO_3 in 100 ml H_2O. Make fresh daily.

(c) *Bromocresol green soln.*—Dissolve 150 mg bromocresol green in 100 ml H_2O.

31.137   *Determination*

Pipet 20 ml fraction *A* into 200 ml vol. flask. Add 40 ml 0.05N I soln by pipet; then with vigorous mixing add 25 ml 0.1N NaOH over 30 sec period, and immediately place flask in $18\pm0.1°$ H_2O bath. Exactly 10 min after alkali addn, add 5 ml 1N H_2SO_4 and remove from bath. Exactly neutze I with Na_2SO_3 soln, using 2 drops starch soln near end point. Back-titr. with dil. I if necessary. Add 5 drops bromocresol green and exactly neutze soln with 1N NaOH; then make just acid to indicator. Dil. to vol. and det. reducing value of 5 ml aliquots by Shaffer-Somogyi method, **31.055**.

Make duplicate blanks and detns. Deduct titrn from that of blank and calc. fructose:

$$\% \text{ fructose} = \frac{500[(\text{titer} \times 0.1150) + 0.0915] \times 100}{\text{mg sample}}$$

Fructose correction for glucose detn = f.c. = [(titer $\times$ 0.1150) + 0.0915] $\times$ 40. Bracketed quantity is mg fructose in 5 ml aliquot, valid between 0.5 and 1.75 mg fructose.

Glucose

31.138   *Reagents*

Sodium thiosulfate soln.—0.05N. Prep. from stdzd stock 0.1000N soln **45.038–45.039**.

31.139   *Determination*

Pipet 20 ml fraction *A* into duplicate 250 ml erlenmeyers. Evap. to dryness on steam bath in air current. Add 20 ml H_2O, pipet in 20 ml 0.05N I, and slowly add 25 ml 0.1N NaOH, as in fructose detn. Immediately place in $18\pm0.1°$ H_2O bath. Exactly 10 min after alkali addn, add 5 ml 2N H_2SO_4, remove from bath, and titr. with 0.05N $Na_2S_2O_3$, using starch soln.

Make duplicate blanks, using H_2O, subtract titrn value from that of blank, and calc. glucose:

$$\% \text{ glucose} = \frac{56.275[\text{titer} - (0.01215 \times \text{f.c.})] \times 100}{\text{mg sample}},$$

where f.c. = fructose correction from fructose detn. Equation is valid over range 10–15 mg glucose in 20 ml. In presence of glucose, 1 mg fructose requires 0.01215 ml 0.05N $Na_2S_2O_3$, in range 15–60 mg fructose.

Reducing Disaccharides as Maltose

31.140   *Determination*

Pipet 5 ml aliquots of fraction *B* into 25×200 mm test tubes, and det. reducing value as in **31.055**, except boil tubes 30 min. Value for 15 min H_2O blank may be used here. Calc. % reducing disaccharides as maltose:

$$\% \text{ "maltose"} = \frac{50[(\text{titer} \times 0.2264) + 0.075] \times 100}{\text{mg sample}}$$

Maltose correction for sucrose detn = m.c. = maltose titer $\times$ 0.92. Bracketed quantity is mg maltose in 5 ml aliquot, valid between 0.15 and 3.80 mg maltose. Reducing value of maltose at 15 min is 92% of final value.

Sucrose

31.141   *Determination*

Pipet 25 ml fraction *B* into 50 ml vol. flask. Add 5 ml 6*N* HCl and 5 ml H_2O. Mix, let stand in 60° H_2O bath 17 min, cool, and neutze to bromocresol green with 5*N* NaOH (103 g/500 ml). (Polyethylene squeeze bottle is excellent for holding and delivering alkali.) Adjust to acid color of indicator, using 2*N* H_2SO_4 to correct over-run. Dil. to vol. and det. reducing value of 5 ml aliquots by Shaffer-Somogyi detn, **31.055**. Subtract titrn from blank, and calc. sucrose by ref. to curve constructed from following table:

Sucrose in 5 ml Aliquot Oxidized, mg	0.005N $Na_2S_2O_3$ Required, ml
0.255	1.75
0.502	3.95
1.004	8.72
1.260	11.28

From curve obtain S_1 = sucrose equiv. to maltose correction, **31.140**, and S_2 = sucrose equiv. of sucrose titer.

$$\% \text{ sucrose} = \frac{50(2S_2 - S_1) \times 100}{\text{mg sample}}$$

Higher Sugars or "Dextrin"

31.142   *Determination*

Pipet 25 ml aliquots of fraction *C* into 50 ml vol. flasks. Add 5 ml 6*N* HCl and 5 ml H_2O, and heat in boiling H_2O bath 45 min. Cool, neutze as for sucrose, dil. to vol., and det. reducing value by Shaffer-Somogyi detn, **31.055**. Subtract titrn value from blank and obtain glucose equiv. from curve constructed from following table:

Glucose, mg	Titer, ml
0.05	0.20
0.10	0.60
0.25	1.85
0.50	4.00
1.00	8.50
2.00	17.60

$$\% \text{ higher sugars} = \frac{40(\text{glucose equiv.}) \times 100}{\text{mg sample}}$$

Notes: For most accurate work, Shaffer-Somogyi values must check within 0.04 ml. Calibration of all operations, including column, using known synthetic mixts of glucose, fructose, sucrose, maltose, and raffinose (corrected for moisture) is recommended for critical work. Sugar:ml $Na_2S_2O_3$ relations [(titer × 0.1150) + 0.0915] in equation for % fructose, and [(titer × 0.2264) + 0.075] in equation for % maltose, are obtained by analyzing known mixts of glucose and fructose for fructose, and known amts of maltose, resp., by method.

Efficiency of column sepn may be checked by paper chromatgy of fractions *A*, *B*, and *C* as in **31.145**.

Commercial Glucose

Qualitative Test (33)—Official Final Action

31.143   *Reagent*

Aniline-diphenylamine chromogenic reagent.—Dissolve 500 mg diphenylamine.HCl and 0.55 ml redistd aniline in 50 ml acetone. Add 5 ml 85% H_3PO_4. Prep. fresh daily.

31.144   *Preparation of Sample*

Dil. sample with equal vol. H_2O. To 0.5 ml in small centrf. tube (11 × 100 mm test tube) add 4 ml absolute alcohol, shake, and centrf. Decant clear or slightly cloudy supernatant, dissolve ppt in 0.5 ml H_2O, reppt with 4 ml absolute alcohol, and centrf. Decant, and dissolve ppt in 0.1 ml H_2O. Apply 2 μl to origin of paper chromatogram, as well as control spots of authentic honey and/or honeydew and corn sirup treated as above.

31.145   *Chromatography*

For details of performing paper chromatgy *see* **29.027** and JAOAC **40**, 999(1957).

Ascending or descending is satisfactory. Suitable solv. for latter is *n-propanol-EtOAc-H_2O*, 7 + 1 + 2. Equilibrate 45 min and irrigate ≥40 hr, letting solv. drip from serrated lower edge of paper. For shorter ascending use (ca 6 hr) roll paper into cylinder, staple edges, and set in cylindrical jar, using *isoamyl alcohol-pyridine-H_2O*, 7 + 7 + 6. To obtain increased resolution, dry paper and repeat irrigation 1 or more times.

Irrigate with suitable solv., remove, and dry paper chromatogram. Dip in chromogenic reagent, let acetone evap., and heat at 85–95° ca 5–8 min until control spots of corn sirup treated as above become blue. Honey or honeydew sample contg 5% of com. glucose shows series of blue maltodextrin spots of low R_F, converging to origin. Honey and honeydew dextrin spots are distinctly brown or gray, not blue. If paper is heated excessively, both honey dextrin spots and maltodextrin spots will approach same shade of gray.

31.146   *Quantitative Estimation—*
             Procedure

Approx. detn can be made by Browne's formula as follows: Multiply difference in polarizations of invert soln at 20° and 87°, **31.127**, by **77** and divide this product by % invert sugar found in sample after inversion. Multiply quotient by 100 and divide product by 26.7 to obtain % honey in sample; 100% − % honey = % glucose (USDA Bur. Chem. Bull. 110).

Commercial Invert Sugar (34)

Resorcinol Test (35)—Procedure

31.147   *Reagent*

Resorcinol soln.—Dissolve 1 g resublimed resorcinol in 100 ml HCl (sp gr 1.18–1.19).

31.148 *Test*

Dissolve 2 g honey in 10 ml H_2O and ext rapidly with washed ether 30 min in continuous extractor, Fig. 36:3. Conc. ether to ca 5 ml and transfer to test tube. Add 2 ml freshly prepd resorcinol soln, shake, and note color. Cherry red color appearing within 1 min indicates presence of com. invert sugar. Yellow to salmon shades have no significance.

Note: Resorcinol test, when neg., may not be regarded as conclusive evidence of absence of com. invert sugar sirup in honey.

Diastatic Activity of Honey (36)— Official First Action

(Do not heat sample for this detn.)

31.149 *Principle*

Buffered sol. starch-honey soln is incubated and time required to reach specified end point is detd by photoelec. photometer. Results are expressed as ml 1% starch hydrolyzed by enzyme in 1 g honey in 1 hr.

31.150 *Apparatus*

(a) *Reaction vessel.*—Attach sealed side arm, 18 × 60 mm, to 18 × 175 mm test tube. Lower side of side arm is attached 100 mm from bottom of tube, making 45° angle with lower portion of tube.

(b) *Photoelectric photometer.*—Equipped with 660 nm red filter or 600 nm interference filter and 1 cm cells.

31.151 *Reagents*

(a) *Iodine stock soln.*—Dissolve 8.80 g resublimed I in 30–40 ml H_2O contg 22.0 g KI, and dil. to 1 L with H_2O.

(b) *Iodine soln.*—0.0007N. Dissolve 20 g KI and 5.00 ml I soln, (a), in H_2O and dil. to 500 ml. Prep. fresh every second day.

(c) *Acetate buffer soln.*—pH 5.3 (1.59M). Dissolve 87 g NaOAc.3H₂O in 400 ml H_2O, add ca 10.5 ml HOAc in H_2O, and dil. to 500 ml. Adjust pH to 5.30 with NaOAc or HOAc, if necessary.

(d) *Sodium chloride soln.*—0.5M. Dissolve 14.5 g NaCl in H_2O and dil. to 500 ml.

(e) *Starch soln.*—Weigh 2.000 g sol. starch (Pfanstiehl Labs, 1219 Glen Rock Ave, Waukegan, IL 60086, reagent grade, Improved Lintner Method, or equiv.) and mix with 90 ml H_2O in 250 ml erlenmeyer. Rapidly bring to boil, swirling soln as much as possible. Reduce heat and boil gently 3 min, cover, and let cool to room temp. Transfer to 100 ml vol. flask and dil. to vol. Observe details closely to limit variation in starch-I A values of blank.

31.152 *Standardization*

Pipet 5 ml starch soln into 10 ml H_2O and mix well. Pipet 1 ml of this soln into several 50 ml graduated cylinders contg 10 ml dil. I soln. Mix well, and det. H_2O diln necessary to produce A value of 0.760

±0.02. This is std diln for starch prepn used. Repeat when changing starch source.

31.153 *Determination*

Weigh 5 g sample into 20 ml beaker, dissolve in 10–15 ml H_2O and 2.5 ml buffer soln, and transfer to 25 ml vol. flask contg 1.5 ml NaCl soln. Dil. to vol. (Soln must be buffered before addn to NaCl soln.)

Pipet 5 ml starch soln into side arm of reaction tube and 10 ml sample soln into bottom of tube, with care not to mix. Place tube in H_2O bath 15 min at 40±0.2°; then mix contents by tilting tube back and forth several times. Start stopwatch. At 5 min, remove 1 ml aliquot with 1 ml serological pipet and add rapidly to 10.00 ml dil. I soln in 50 ml graduated cylinder. Mix, dil. to previously detd vol., and det. A in photoelec. photometer. Note time from mixing of starch and honey to addn of aliquot to I as reaction time. (Place 1 ml pipet in reaction tube for reuse when later aliquots are taken.) Continue taking 1 ml aliquots at intervals until A value of <0.235 is obtained.

The 5 min value gives approximation of end point as follows:

Absorbance	End Point, min
0.7	>25
0.65	20–25
0.6	15–18
0.55	11–13
0.5	9–10
0.45	7–8

31.154 *Calculation*

Plot A against time (min) on rectilinear paper; draw straight line thru starting A and as many points as possible. From graph det. time dild reaction-I mixt. reaches A of 0.235. Divide 300 by this time to obtain diastase no. (DN).

Notes: A 5-min reading is sufficient for approximating end point of sample of high DN (>35) if another value is taken soon enough to obtain A of ca 0.20. For accurate results, repeat detn, taking samples each min from start. With samples of low DN, another reading at 10 min will permit prediction of end point by plotting the data. No addnl readings need be taken until within few min of end point. Only 2 such readings are needed. The 5 min value will not accurately predict low DN.

31.155 Free, Lactone, and Total Acidity (37)—Official First Action

Dissolve 10 g sample in 75 ml CO_2-free H_2O in 250 ml beaker. Stir with magnetic stirrer, immerse electrodes of pH meter in soln, and record pH. Titr. with 0.05N NaOH at rate of 5.0 ml/min. Stop addn of NaOH at pH 8.50. Immediately pipet in 10 ml 0.05N NaOH and immediately back-titr. with 0.05N HCl from 10 ml buret to pH 8.30. Calc. as milliequiv./kg: Free acidity = (ml 0.05N NaOH from buret − ml blank) × 50/g sample; lactone = (10.00 − ml 0.05N

HCl from buret) $\times$ 50/g sample; total acidity = free acidity + lactone.

MAPLE PRODUCTS (38)

31.156 Preparation of Sample—Procedure

(a) Maple Sirup

(1) *For solids determination.*—If sample contains no sugar crystals or suspended matter, decant enough clear sirup for detn. If sugar crystals are present, redissolve by heating at ca 50°. If suspended matter is present, filter sample thru cotton wool.

(2) *For other determinations.*—If sugar crystals are present, redissolve by heating. If other sediment is present, distribute it evenly thru sirup by shaking. Transfer ca 100 ml sirup, with its suspended sediment, to casserole or beaker, add $\frac{1}{4}$ vol. H_2O, and evap. over flame. When temp. of boiling sirup approaches 104°, draw small amt into thin-wall, ca 1 ml pipet, and cool to room temp. in running H_2O. Wipe outside of pipet, let possibly dild sirup in point escape, transfer some of remaining sirup to refractometer, and det. solids content of cooled sirup. Repeat operation from time to time until reading is obtained corresponding to 64.5% solids (n_{20} = 1.4521), or to such other value as in experience of analyst will give filtered sirup of 65.0% solids. Filter sirup thru filter that will let the 100 ml pass within 5 min and adjust filtrate to 65.0±0.5% solids (refractometric) by thoro mixing with appropriate amt of H_2O.

(b) Maple Sugar and Other Solid or Semisolid Products

(1) *For moisture and solids determination.*—Grind in mortar, if necessary, and mix thoroly.

(2) *For other determinations.*—To prep. sirup dissolve ca 100 g sample in 150 ml hot H_2O, boil until temp. approaches 104°, and complete prepn of resulting sirup as in (a)(2), beginning "draw small amt into thin-wall, ca 1 ml pipet, . . ."

Color Classification (39)—Official Final Action

31.157   Apparatus

(a) *Containers.*—See 31.117(a). Internal thickness 1.24 $\times$ 1.24″ (31.5 mm).

(b) *Comparator.*—See 31.117(b). Only 1 box is required with 3 glass color stds (light amber, medium amber, and dark amber). Place containers, (a), filled with H_2O behind each glass std.

(c) *Glass stds.*—Use selected colored glasses tested and stdzd by USDA to correspond with color stds for maple sirup.

Complete grading set is available from Phoenix Precision Instrument Co., 3803 North 5th St, Philadelphia, PA, 19140.

31.158   Determination

Proceed as in 31.118. Det. classification as follows: If sample is equal to light amber std in hue, or not as red (*i.e.*, yellower), classify as light amber; if perceptibly redder than light amber std in hue but not redder than medium amber std, classify as medium amber; if perceptibly redder than medium amber std, but not redder than dark amber std, classify as dark amber; if redder in hue than dark amber std, classify as "unclassified." Hue (redness or yellowness) is attribute of color in classification.

Moisture or Solids—Official Final Action

31.159 Maple Sugar

Proceed as in 31.006, or preferably 31.005, using sample prepd as in 31.156(b)(1).

31.160 Maple Sirup, Maple Cream, etc.

Proceed as in 31.005, 31.007, or 31.011, using prepd sample, 31.156(a)(1).

31.161 Ash (40)—Official First Action

Prep. sirup as in 31.156(a)(2) or (b)(2). Using eye dropper, transfer 5–10 g sample into tared Pt dish (weigh to nearest 0.1 mg). Add few drops pure olive oil and place in oven 1 hr at 110°. Remove and heat slowly over low flame or under IR lamp until all H_2O is expelled and swelling ceases. Place in muffle $\geq$3 hr at 600°. Reweigh and report % ash.

31.162 Soluble and Insoluble Ash—Official Final Action—See 31.015

31.163 Alkalinity of Soluble Ash—Official Final Action—See 31.016

31.164 Alkalinity of Insoluble Ash—Official Final Action—See 31.017

31.165 Alkalinity of Total Ash—Official Final Action

Add alkalinities of sol. and insol. portions from 31.163 and 31.164.

Polarization—Official Final Action

31.166 Direct Polarization—See 31.025(a)

31.167 Invert Polarization

(a) *At 20°.*—Proceed as in 31.025(b) or (c) or 31.026(b) or (c).

(b) *At 87°.*—Proceed as in 31.034.

31.168 Sucrose—Polarimetric Methods—Official Final Action

Proceed as in 31.025 or 31.026, or calc. from results of 31.166 and 31.167(a), using appropriate formula from 31.025 or 31.026.

Sucrose—Chemical Methods—Official Final Action

31.169 By Reducing Sugars Before and After Inversion—See 31.032

31.170   Reducing Sugars as Invert Sugar—
Official Final Action

(a) *Before inversion.*—Proceed as in **31.037** or **31.039**, using aliquot of soln used for direct polarization, **31.166**. If soln is clarified, only neut. $Pb(OAc)_2$ soln may be used, and excess of Pb must be removed with dry $Na_2C_2O_4$.

(b) *After inversion.*—Proceed as in **31.037** or **31.039**, using aliquot of soln used for invert polarization, **31.167**(a). If soln is clarified, only neut. $Pb(OAc)_2$ soln may be used, and excess of Pb must be removed with dry $Na_2C_2O_4$.

31.171   Commercial Glucose—Procedure—
See 31.033 or 31.034

Lead Number

31.172   ★   Canadian Lead Number   ★
(Fowler Modification)(41)—
Official Final Action

See **29.147–29.148**, 10th ed.

Winton Lead Number (42)—
Official Final Action

31.173   Reagent

(a) *Basic lead acetate std soln.*—(*Caution: See* **46.084**.) Activate litharge by heating 2.5–3 hr to 650–670° in muffle (cooled product should be lemon color). In 500 ml erlenmeyer provided with reflux condenser, boil 80 g neut. $Pb(OAc)_2.3H_2O$ and 40 g freshly activated litharge with 250 g H_2O 45 min. Cool, filter off any residue, and dil. with recently boiled H_2O to density of 1.25 at 20°.

(b) *Dilute basic lead acetate std soln.*—To measured vol. reagent, (a), add 4 vols H_2O, and filter. Conduct blank with each set of detns.

31.174   Determination of Lead in Blank

Transfer 25 ml dil. std basic $Pb(OAc)_2$ soln to 100 ml vol. flask, add few drops HOAc, and dil. to vol. with H_2O. Shake, and det. $PbSO_4$ in 10 ml soln as in **31.175**. Use of HOAc is imperative to retain all Pb in soln when reagent is dild with H_2O.

31.175   Determination

Transfer 25 g sample with H_2O to 100 ml vol. flask. Add 25 ml dil. std basic $Pb(OAc)_2$ soln and shake. Fill to mark, shake, and let stand ≥ 3 hr before filtering. Pipet 10 ml clear filtrate into 250 ml beaker, add 40 ml H_2O and 1 ml H_2SO_4, shake, and add 100 ml alcohol. Let stand overnight, filter on weighed gooch, wash with alcohol, dry in 100° oven, and ignite in muffle at 550°, or over Bunsen burner, placing crucible in larger crucible, applying heat gradually at first and heating until outside of crucible is barely visible red. Cool and weigh. Subtract wt $PbSO_4$ so found from wt $PbSO_4$ found in blank,

31.174, and multiply by factor 27.33. Use of this factor gives Pb number directly (without various calcns otherwise required).

Conductivity Value (43)—Official Final Action
31.176   Apparatus

(a) *Conductivity bridge.*—Use any com. available conductivity bridges, which are usually self-contained instruments with 2 external connections, one for connection to power source, usually 110 volt AC, and other to conductivity cell. In addn, some models have means for making adjustment for temp. and cell constant. Leeds and Northrup Bridge No. 4961 and cell No. 4924 are commonly used and conductivity read directly, corrected to 20° when in "SC" position. "RC" type instruments, manufactured by Beckman Instruments, Inc., 89 Commerce Rd, Cedar Grove, NJ 07009, do not have compensator circuit to adjust instrument for temp. Consequently sirup soln must be read at exact temp. specified to be comparative. RD-15 conductivity meter, manufactured by Beckman Instruments, corrects all readings to conductivity at 25°.

Calibrate scale (slide wire) of conductivity bridge by use of external fixed resistor with external leads. This should have resistance of 1000 ohms which will approx. that of conductivity cell. Resistor is attached to bridge connections for conductivity cell and slide wire set to same value as that of resistor. Bridge should give 0 reading or response.

(b) *Conductivity cell.*—Made of resistance glass with platinized electrodes firmly fixed and adequately protected from displacement. Cell may be of dipping type, for immersing cell into test soln, or of vessel type, into which soln may be run and subsequently drained.

(c) *Constant temperature bath.*—To maintain or supply H_2O at $25\pm0.1°$ for controlling temp. of test soln and cell.

31.177   Determination of Cell Constant

Dry 2–3 g KCl at 110° to constant wt. Weigh 2 portions dried KCl, one 0.3728 ± 0.0002 g and other 0.7456 ± 0.0002 g, transfer to two 500 ml flasks, and dil. to vol. with H_2O at 20°. These solns will be 0.01 and $0.02M$ KCl, resp. Transfer portion of $0.01M$ KCl soln to beaker and adjust temp. to $25\pm0.1°$.

If conductivity bridge has temp. compensating device, set it at 25°, the temp. of KCl solns. With leads of conductivity cell attached to conductivity bridge, place dipping conductivity cell in $0.01M$ KCl, taking care to completely immerse electrodes. Adjust slide wire of bridge to give null-point reading. Repeat until 3 successive and concordant slide wire values (ohms resistance) are obtained. Replace KCl soln with fresh portion before making next measurement, taking care to shake adhering drops of liq. from electrodes before immersing them.

Repeat, using $0.2M$ KCl.

Calc. cell constant by multiplying observed resistances (scale readings in ohms) by 141.2 (specific conductivity of $0.01M$ KCl), and by 276.1 (specific conductivity of $0.02M$ KCl), resp. Average the 2 results.

31.178 *Determination*

Add 70 ml H_2O to 100 ml g-s graduated cylinder and fill to vol. with maple sirup to be tested. Stopper, mix thoroly, adjust temp. to $25\pm0.1°$, and measure resistance of dil. sirup with conductivity cell in same manner as used to calibrate cell. Repeat until 3 concordant observed scale readings (ohms) are obtained. Conductivity value

$$= \text{cell constant} \times 100,000/\text{ohms}.$$

Malic Acid (44)—Official Final Action

31.179 *Apparatus*

(a) *Ion exchange tubes.*—Std wall Pyrex glass tubing, 10 mm id $\times$ 30 cm long, with 5 cm capillary tip.

(b) *Spectrophotometer.*—Suitable for measuring A at 390 nm, with matched 1 cm cells or matched test tubes.

31.180 *Reagents*

(a) *Ion exchange resins.*—(1) *Cation exchanger.*—Dowex-50 (60–80 mesh). (2) *Anion exchanger.*—AG1-X8 (50–100 mesh) (Bio-Rad Labs, 32nd & Griffin Ave, Richmond, CA 94804 or Amberlite CG 400, Type I (100–200 mesh) (Mallinckrodt).

(b) *Ammonium carbonate soln.*—0.25N. Dissolve 14.26 g $(NH_4)_2CO_3.H_2O$ in enough H_2O to make 1 L.

(c) *Ammonium carbonate soln.*—1.0N. Dissolve 57.05 g $(NH_4)_2CO_3.H_2O$ in enough H_2O to make 1 L.

(d) *Sodium carbonate soln.*—1.0N. Dissolve 5.3 g Na_2CO_3 in enough H_2O to make 100 ml.

(e) *Hydrochloric acid soln.*—5%. Dil. 12 ml HCl with 88 ml H_2O.

(f) *2,7-Naphthalenediol.*—1 g dissolved in 100 ml H_2SO_4.

(g) *Malic acid std soln.*—Dry Eastman white label L-malic acid 18 hr at $40°$. Dissolve 0.2000 g in 500 ml H_2O. Dil. known vol. of this soln (ca 10 ml) to 100 ml so that final soln gives A, after reaction with color reagent as in detn, of 0.2–0.8.

31.181 *Preparation of Ion Exchange Columns*

For each column add enough H_2O to 10 ml dry resin to make thin slurry and pour slurry into tube contg small plug of glass wool. Let H_2O drain to level of settled resin and wash with 2 ml portions H_2O to condition resins. To cation exchange resin (Dowex-50) add three or four 10 ml portions 5% HCl, letting acid drain to top of resin between each addn. Wash resin acid-free with 10 ml portions H_2O

until effluent gives no test for chlorides. (Approx. 4 bed vols of H_2O are required.)

Treat anion exchanger resin with three or four 10 ml portions 5% NaOH soln, draining liq. to top of resin between addns. Remove excess alkali with H_2O by washing with 10 ml portions until effluent gives neg. alkali test with indicator paper. Transform resin into carbonate form by addn of three or four 10 ml portions 1.0N Na_2CO_3 soln. Wash carbonate-free with 10 ml portions H_2O until effluent is neut. to indicator test paper. Mount conditioned columns vertically with cation resin column directly above anion resin column, connecting tubes with 1-hole rubber stopper mounted in top of anion column. No stopcocks are required; close packing of fine resins prevents liq. from draining below surface of resins. Any portion of resin that becomes dry will be inactivated.

31.182 *Separation of Malic Acid*

Transfer ca 10 ml sirup sample to tared 100 ml vol. flask and weigh to ±0.2 mg. Dil. to vol. with H_2O and transfer aliquot contg 6–20 mg malic acid (ca 15 ml) to cation exchange resin and let eluate pass onto anion exchange resin. Wash cation resin (upper column) with three 10 ml portions H_2O, again letting effluent pass directly onto anion resin. Remove upper column and wash anion resin column with three 10 ml portions H_2O to remove sugars and any loosely held acids present that might interfere with test. Elute column with five 10 ml portions 0.25N $(NH_4)_2CO_3$ to quant. remove all glycolic, glyceric, or lactic acids possibly present in original test soln. Elute malic acid from anion resin with five 10 ml portions 1N $(NH_4)_2CO_3$; after 45–48 ml eluate collects in 250 ml vol. flask, remove flask and dil. to vol. with H_2O.

31.183 *Determination*

Transfer 1 ml malic acid-$(NH_4)_2CO_3$ eluate to 18×150 mm culture tube and slowly add 6 ml 96% H_2SO_4 from buret, adding first 2 ml down walls of tube to avoid excessive evolution of CO_2. Add 0.1 ml 2,7-naphthalenediol reagent and mix thoroly. Cap tubes with metal culture tube closures and heat in boiling H_2O bath (deepfat fryer is satisfactory) 25 min to develop color. Cool tubes, and measure A of colored solns within 30 min in 1 cm cell at 390 nm against blank of 1 ml H_2O, 6 ml H_2SO_4, and 0.1 ml reagent also heated 25 min in boiling H_2O bath.

Color developed follows Beer's law in which $a = A/Cb$, where a is absorptivity, C is concn in mg/ml, and b is cell thickness. Absorptivity may vary from day to day because of differences in blank; therefore a must be established daily with duplicate portions of fresh std malic acid soln. Calc. a from A at 390 nm of colored soln resulting from reaction of soln of std malic acid and color reagent. Calc. amt of malic acid in sample from: $C = (A/ab) \times$ diln factor. Express value for malic acid in maple sirup in terms of std density (65.5° Brix) sirup.

Formaldehyde (45)—Official Final Action

31.184   *Apparatus*

(a) *Distillation apparatus.*—30 ml micro Kjeldahl flask fitted with 19/38 $\bar{\mathbb{S}}$ outer joint and 4″ water-cooled West condenser with 19/38 $\bar{\mathbb{S}}$ inner joint bent at 90° angle. *See* Fig. 31:2.

(b) *Spectrophotometer.*—Suitable for measuring A at 415 nm; with matched 1 cm cells or matched test tubes.

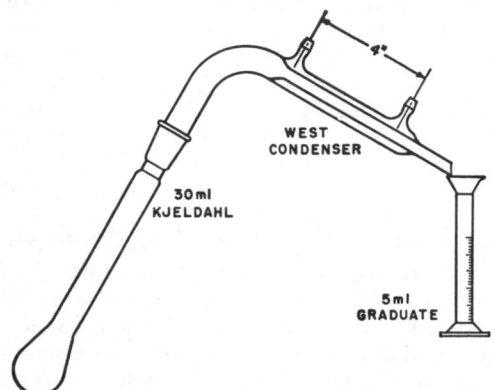

FIG. 31:2—Formaldehyde distillation apparatus

31.185   *Reagents*

(a) *Nash's Reagent "B".* — Dissolve 150 g NH_4OAc, 3 ml HOAc, and 2 ml acetylacetone in 200–300 ml H_2O in 1 L flask and dil. to vol.

(b) *Formaldehyde.*—Approx. 37% by wt. Assay by **6.117.**

31.186   *Preparation of Standard Solutions*

(a) *Soln A.*—1000 ppm. Weigh 5.35 g 37.4% CH_2O soln (for other concns, g CH_2O soln required = 200/% CH_2O) into 2 L vol. flask contg H_2O and dil. to vol. with H_2O.

(b) *Soln B.*—50 ppm. Pipet 10 ml *Soln A* into 200 ml vol. flask and dil. to vol. with H_2O.

(c) *Soln C.*—100 ppm. Pipet 10 ml *Soln A* into 100 ml vol. flask and dil. to vol. with H_2O.

(d) *Soln D.*—200 ppm. Pipet 10 ml *Soln A* into 50 ml vol. flask and dil. to vol. with H_2O.

(e) *Formaldehyde std solns.*—Prep. 1, 2, and 4 ppm std solns by pipetting 10 ml *Solns B, C, and D*, resp., into 500 g sirup and stirring mech. 15 min.

31.187   *Determination*

Weigh 20±0.20 g sample into tared 30 ml micro Kjeldahl flask. Add 2 drops antifoam agent, and connect West condenser. Mount app. at oblique angle and heat flask with micro heater (preferably elec.) previously adjusted to distill 3 ml H_2O from sirup in 12–14 min. Collect 3 ml distillate in 5 ml graduate with funnel top. Using transfer pipets, place 1 ml distillate in 13 mm id test tube, and add 1 ml H_2O and 2 ml Nash's reagent. Heat 30 min in H_2O bath at 37±1° to develop color. Transfer

colored soln to 1 cm spectrophtric cell and measure A at 415 nm against H_2O.

31.188   *Blanks*

To det. A due to reagents, substitute 1 ml H_2O (from same source as used in detn) for 1 ml sample distillate. Subtract A of blank from that for sample to obtain A due to CH_2O. Or, as simpler operation, measure A of sample with instrument adjusted to zero A for blank.

Obtain concn of CH_2O in sirup from A, using std curve.

31.189   *Preparation of Standard Curve*

Construct std curve by plotting A obtained for sirups contg 1, 2, and 4 ppm CH_2O against concn of added CH_2O in ppm.

Straight line relationship is obtained for std curve. Project this line to Y axis (A); Y intercept indicates blank for sirup. Since sirup used to construct curve from A values may be atypical, draw and use parallel curve with zero intercept. Correct ppm values obtained from this curve for av. sirup blank (ca 0.9 ppm).

Yeast Count (46)—Official Final Action

31.190   *Apparatus*

(a) *Water bath.*—Constant temp., capable of holding H_2O temp. at 27±1°.

(b) *Electric stirrer.*—Non-aerating (Kraft Apparatus, Inc., 125–19 Liberty Ave, S. Richmond Hill, NY 11419, Model S-25-25A, or equiv.).

(c) *Beakers.*—Tall-form, 300 and 500 ml. Cover with Al foil before sterilizing.

(d) *Hypodermic syringe.*—5 ml (Luer-Lok), or equiv. with hypodermic needle, 14 gage (Luer-Lok), 2″ long.

(e) *Dilution bottles.*—160 ml, 45 × 140 mm.

(f) *Pipets, serological.*—To deliver 1.0 ml with 0.1 ml graduations.

(g) *Petri dishes.*—100 × 15 mm.

Sterilize apparatus (c), (d), (f), and (g) 1 hr in hot air oven at 160°. Items (f) and (g) do not have to be sterilized when obtained as "single use" sterile plastic.

31.191   *Culture Medium*

Wort agar culture medium.—Boil 15.00 g malt ext, 0.78 g peptone, 2.75 g dextrin, 2.35 g glycerol, 1.00 g K_2HPO_4, 1.00 g NH_4Cl, 12.75 g maltose, and 20.00 g agar in 1 L H_2O until dissolved. Sterilize by autoclaving 15 min at 121°.

31.192   *Reagents*

(a) *Phosphate buffer stock soln.*—pH 7.2, 0.25M. *See* **4.023** (e).

(b) *Phosphate buffer dilution water.*—*See* **4.023** (f).

(c) *Hypochlorite germicide soln.*—200 ppm available Cl. Add 5 ml 5.25% NaClO soln to 1 gal. H_2O.

31.193 *Preparation of Sample Culture*

Sterilize stirrer head by submerging in 400 ml germicide soln in 500 ml tall-form beaker for ≥ 10 min. Rinse by immersing in three 450 ml portions sterile H_2O in 500 ml tall-form beakers.

Warm bottle contg sirup to 80°F in H_2O bath set at 80 ± 1.0°F. Transfer sirup to 300 ml sterile tall-form beaker, place in 80°F constant temp. H_2O bath, and insert sterilized stirrer. Position stirrer near bottom of beaker and off center to prevent forming vortex. Cover beaker with Al foil while stirring. Stir sirup 10 min at ca 500 rpm. If gas bubbles form, let sirup stand in H_2O bath until gas bubbles rise to surface.

Assemble sterile 14 gage needle and 5 ml syringe. Remove cover from sirup sample and with needle held at least 1″ below surface of sirup, slowly draw 5.5–6.0 ml sirup into syringe. Invert syringe, holding needle vertically. Wipe excess sirup from needle with gauze pad wetted with alcohol. Holding pad around tip of needle, bring syringe plunger exactly to 5.0 ml graduation, expelling excess sirup and any air bubbles into sterile pad.

Make 10^{-1} diln of sirup by expelling 5 ml sirup completely from syringe into 45 ml sterile phosphate buffer diln blank, (b). Shake inoculated diln blank vigorously 10 sec, transfer 1 ml to petri dish with 1 ml pipet for 10^{-1} diln plate, and transfer 0.1 ml 10^{-1} diln with 1 ml pipet to petri dish for 10^{-2} diln plate. Transfer 1 ml of 10^{-1} diln to 99 ml sterile diln blank, (b), for 10^{-3} diln. Prep. 10^{-3} and 10^{-4} diln plates by using 1 and 0.1 ml vol. 10^{-3} sirup diln, resp. Transfer 1 ml 10^{-3} diln to 99 ml sterile diln blank, (b), to make 10^{-5} sirup diln. Prep. 10^{-5} and 10^{-6} diln plates by using 1 and 0.1 ml 10^{-5} diln, resp.

Pour 10–12 ml liquefied wort agar at 42–44° into each plate and mix with dild culture. After agar has solidified, invert plates and incubate 5 days at 21–25°. Count plates on 5th day, using Quebec Colony Counter, or equiv.

SUGAR BEETS
Sucrose

31.194 *Hot Water Digestion Method I (47)—*
Official First Action

(*Caution: See* 46.015.)

Pass sample (usually in form of cossettes) thru meat grinder fitted with plate having ¼″ perforations and mix thoroly. Weigh 26 g prepd sample and rinse into 201.0 ml Kohlrausch flask, using ca 100 ml H_2O. Place flask under good vac. 5–10 min to remove air, carefully avoiding mech. loss when vac. is first applied. Add H_2O to ca 175 ml, and digest in H_2O bath at 80°, supporting flask so that body is entirely immersed but is not in contact with heating element. Remove flask 2 or 3 times during digestion, swirl contents, and after each agitation wash down pulp adhering to walls of flask with little H_2O at 80°.

After exactly 30 min digestion, fill flask to within 2–5 ml of mark with H_2O at 80° and continue digestion exactly 10 min longer. Cool to room temp. in H_2O bath. Add 6 ml basic $Pb(OAc)_2$ soln, 31.021(a), and H_2O to fill to mark. (Previous addns of H_2O and reagents should be so adjusted that ≤ 4 ml H_2O is required to make to vol.) Mix well by shaking, let stand 5 min, shake again, and filter. After soln stands near saccharimeter at least 5 min, polarize in 400 mm glass tube. If vol. adjustment and polariscopic observation are made at 20°, reading gives % sucrose directly; if at other temps, apply formula in 31.022 (a).

Notes: The 1 ml >200 ml vol. is the detd vol. of marc for beets grown in Colorado and neighboring states. It should be detd for other localities. Beets of abnormally low purity may require 8–10 ml basic $Pb(OAc)_2$ soln for clarification. If trouble is experienced with foam, flask may be put under vac. second time after cooling, or few drops ether or 1 drop *amyl alcohol* may be added before soln is dild to vol.

31.195 *Hot Water Digestion Method II (48)—*
Official First Action

Use Ni-plated sheet Fe vessels, 11 cm high, 6 cm body diam., and 4 cm mouth diam.; use stoppers covered with Sn foil to fit.

Weigh 26 g prepd beet pulp, 31.194, on watch glass (small enough to go into neck of beaker) and transfer to metal beaker; add 177 ml dil. basic $Pb(OAc)_2$ soln (5 parts basic $Pb(OAc)_2$ soln, 31.021(a), to 100 parts H_2O); shake, and stopper lightly. Submerge beaker in H_2O bath 30 min at 75–80°, shaking intermittently. When all air is expelled (generally after 5 min), tighten stopper. After 30 min, shake, cool to std temp., filter, add drop HOAc to filtrate, and polarize in 400 mm tube. Reading is % sugar in beet pulp.

STARCH CONVERSION PRODUCTS

31.196 **Preparation of Sample—**
Official First Action—*See* 31.001

Moisture—Official First Action

31.197 *Method I*

(Applicable to refined corn sugars)—*See* 31.005

Method II (49)

(Applicable to corn sirups and crude corn sugars)

31.198 *Apparatus*

(a) *Filter paper.*—Strip of Whatman No. 1 filter paper, 4.375 × 50 cm.

(b) *Separator.*—Corrugated strip of phosphor-bronze, No. 36 B&S, 1.25 × 40 cm.

(c) *Weighing bottle.*—Medium form, 40 × 65 mm, with ꚍ 40/20 stopper.

31.199 *Determination*

Place separator on filter paper strip and roll together to form cylinder ca 30 mm diam., fasten with paper clip, and place in weighing bottle. Dry in air oven at 100° ca 6 hr. Cool and weigh. Remove coil and weigh ca 1 g sirup in weighing bottle, add 1 or 2 ml H_2O, and mix, using heat if necessary. Replace coil, shaking until all soln is absorbed on paper. Dry to constant wt in vac. oven at 100° for corn sirups or 70° for crude corn sugars (ca 6 hr).

Method III (50)

(Applicable to corn sirups and crude corn sugars)

31.200   *Material and Apparatus*

(a) *Diatomaceous earth.*—Filter-Cel. Preferably analytical grade. If com. grade is used, wash with HCl, then with H_2O to remove acid, and dry in oven at ca 105°. (Material should give no test for acid when moistened.)

(b) *Moisture dish.*—Al dish 25 mm high × 75 mm diam., with cover.

(c) *Pestle.*—Flat-end glass stirring rod ca 60 mm long.

31.201   *Determination*

Place 10 g Filter-Cel in moisture dish contg pestle and dry to constant wt. Weigh ca 5 g corn sirup or sugar in nickel scoop, dil. with ca 5 ml H_2O, and add to Filter-Cel. Wash scoop with three 2 ml portions H_2O and add washings to Filter-Cel. Thoroly incorporate soln with Filter-Cel by means of pestle, yielding *damp* workable mass. Dry to constant wt in vac. oven at 100° for corn sirup or 70° for crude corn sugars.

Dry Substance—Official First Action

Method I—By Hydrometer (51)

31.202   *Apparatus*

(a) *Water bath.*—Insulated H_2O bath with stirrer and thermostatic control, held at 60°.

(b) *Cylinders.*—Pyrex, 15 × 2¼″, without lip.

(c) *Stopper seal.*—Consisting of 2 rubber stoppers that fit snugly into cylinder, sepd on metal rod by ca 3″. Rod is fixed in lower stopper but does not extend thru it. Top stopper is free to move on rod, altho tight enough to maintain predetd position, preventing evapn during heating.

(d) *Baumé hydrometers.*—Streamlined type, modulus 145, stdzd at 15.56° with range 35–45° Bé in 0.1° Bé; length over-all 12–13″; body diam. 0.77–0.79″; scale length 147–155 mm.

31.203   *Determination*

Fill cylinder with sirup to within 4″ of top, taking care that sides are free from sirup. Seal cylinder with stopper seal, placing bottom stopper within ½″ of sirup surface and closing cylinder with top stopper. Immerse cylinder in H_2O bath at 60° (140°F) so that level of sirup is ca 2″ below level of H_2O. Immerse hydrometer in H_2O bath. When sirup in cylinder is free of air and has reached temp. of bath (ca 90 min), raise cylinder until surface of sirup is at eye level. Remove stopper seal and insert previously dried hydrometer. After ca 10 min, read hydrometer. To obtain com. Baumé, add 1° Bé. to observed reading of hydrometer:

Com. Baumé = Bé. (140°F/60°F) + 1° Bé.

Det. corresponding dry substance from **31.205.**

31.204 *Method II—By Refractometer (52)*

(Applicable only to liq. samples contg no undissolved solids)

Det. refractometer reading at 45°. Circulate H_2O thru jackets of refractometer long enough to let temp. of prisms and of sample reach equilibrium, continuing circulation during observation, and taking care that temp. is held constant. From **31.206** obtain com. Baumé corresponding to observed refractive index. From **31.205** obtain corresponding dry substance.

31.205   *Commercial Table for Dry Substance in Corn Sirup and Corn Sugar Sirup*
(Commercial Baumé = Bé. 140°F/60°F + 1° Bé.)

Commercial Baumé	Dextrose Equivalent and Ash							
	30.00 0.28	42.00 0.28	55.00 0.30	82.00 0.41	87.00 0.61	89.00 0.61	91.2 0.61	90.7 1.22
	Dry Substance (per cent)							
40.00	73.66	74.39	75.16	76.82	77.12	77.24	77.37	77.10
41.00	75.58	76.34	77.14	78.86	79.18	79.30	79.44	79.17
42.00	77.51	78.30	79.13	80.92	81.25	81.38	81.52	81.25
43.00	79.45	80.27	81.14	83.00	83.35	83.48	83.63	83.33
44.00	81.39	82.25	83.17	85.10	85.46	85.60	85.75	85.44
45.00	83.36	84.25	85.20	87.21	87.58	87.72	87.88	87.56
46.00	85.34	86.26	87.26	89.33	89.71	89.86	90.03	89.69
47.00	87.33	88.29	89.34	91.47	91.87	92.03	92.21	91.84

31.206 *Commercial Table of Refractive Indices of Corn Sirups and Corn Sugar Sirups at 45°C*
(Commercial Baumé = Bé. 140°F/60°F + 1° Bé.)

Commercial Baumé	Dextrose Equivalent and Ash									
	30.00 0.28	35.00 0.28	42.00 0.28	45.00 0.28	50.00 0.30	55.00 0.30	60.00 0.30	65.00 0.30	82.00 0.41	89.00 0.61
	Refractive Index at 45°									
40.00	1.4774	1.4773	1.4771	1.4770	1.4769	1.4768	1.4767	1.4766	1.4762	1.4760
41.00	1.4825	1.4824	1.4822	1.4821	1.4820	1.4820	1.4818	1.4817	1.4813	1.4811
42.00	1.4878	1.4877	1.4875	1.4874	1.4873	1.4873	1.4871	1.4869	1.4865	1.4863
43.00	1.4933	1.4931	1.4929	1.4928	1.4927	1.4926	1.4924	1.4923	1.4919	1.4916
44.00	1.4986	1.4985	1.4983	1.4982	1.4981	1.4980	1.4978	1.4977	1.4973	1.4971
45.00	1.5041	1.5040	1.5038	1.5037	1.5036	1.5036	1.5034	1.5033	1.5029	1.5027
46.00	1.5098	1.5097	1.5095	1.5094	1.5093	1.5092	1.5090	1.5089	1.5085	1.5083
47.00	1.5155	1.5154	1.5152	1.5151	1.5150	1.5149	1.5148	1.5147	1.5143	1.5142

31.207 Ash—Official First Action—*See* 31.012

(For most corn sugars and sirups it is unnecessary to re-ash.)

31.208 Sulfated Ash—Official First Action— *See* 31.014

31.209 Acidity—Official First Action

Weigh 50 g sample, dissolve in 200 ml H_2O, and titr. with 0.1N NaOH, using phthln, to faint pink end point. (This corresponds to electrometric pH of 8.3.) Calc. acidity as HCl.

31.210 Hydrogen-Ion Concentration— Official First Action

Prep. soln of sample contg 40% total solids and det. pH electrometrically. (Buffer capacity of product is normally such that no special provision need be made with regard to H_2O used for diln. If glass electrode is used, stdze against ref. buffer within 1.0 of detd pH.)

31.211 Nitrogen—Official First Action— *See* 2.051

31.212 Total Reducing Sugars— Official First Action

(a) *Lane-Eynon General Volumetric Method.*— *See* **31.037.** Use glucose as std.

(b) *Munson-Walker General Method.*—*See* **31.039.** Prep diln contg ca 1% reducing sugar.

Glucose by Steinhoff Methods— Official First Action
Zerban-Sattler Modification (53)

31.213 *Reagents*

(a) *Soxhlet modification of Fehling copper soln.*— *See* **31.035**(a).

(b) *Sodium acetate soln.*—Dissolve 500 g NaOAc .3H_2O in ca 800 ml hot H_2O, cool, and dil. to 1 L.

(c) *Potassium iodide-iodate soln.*—Dissolve 5.4 g KIO₃ and 60 g KI in H_2O, add 0.25 g NaOH dissolved in little H_2O, and dil. to 1 L.

(d) *Sulfuric acid.*—Approx. 2N. Dil. 57 ml H_2SO_4 to 1 L.

(e) *Saturated potassium oxalate soln.*—Dissolve 165 g $K_2C_2O_4 . H_2O$ in 500 ml hot H_2O, and cool.

(f) *Sodium thiosulfate std soln.*—0.1N. Use std soln, **45.038–45.039.** 1 ml 0.1N $Na_2S_2O_3$ = 6.354 mg Cu.

(g) *Sugar soln.*—Dissolve amt of sample contg ca 10 g solids in H_2O and dil. to 1 L.

31.214 *Determination*

Transfer 10 ml Soxhlet soln, 20 ml NaOAc soln, 10 ml sugar soln, and 10 ml H_2O to 250 ml erlenmeyer. Mix, close flask with rubber stopper provided with Bunsen valve, and immerse in briskly boiling H_2O bath exactly 20 min. Immerse in cold running H_2O, venting valve to prevent boiling caused by vac. Cool, add 25 ml KI-KIO₃ soln by pipet, and mix by gentle shaking. Rapidly add 40 ml 2N H_2SO_4 from graduated cylinder; then add 20 ml $K_2C_2O_4$ soln from graduated cylinder. Shake until ppt completely dissolves, and titr. excess I with 0.1N $Na_2S_2O_3$.

Det. blank, substituting H_2O for sugar soln. Difference between titer of blank and that of sample is direct measure of Cu_2O pptd. From **31.215** obtain dextrose equiv. corresponding to titer of 0.1N $Na_2S_2O_3$.

Correction for reducing effect of maltose.—If maltose is present, correct observed titer of 0.1N $Na_2S_2O_3$ for reducing effect of maltose by subtracting correction obtained from **31.215** by interpolation.

31.215 (See table at top of next page)

Sichert-Bleyer Modification (54)

31.216 *Reagents*

(a) *Ferric ammonium sulfate soln.*—Dissolve 120 g $Fe_2(SO_4)_3 . (NH_4)_2SO_4 . 24H_2O$ and 100 ml H_2SO_4 in H_2O and dil. to 1 L.

(b) *Potassium permanganate soln.*—0.1N. Prep. as in **45.026.**

31.215   ***Zerban-Sattler Table for Determination of Glucose with Copper Acetate Reagent****

| | Glucose (mg) | | | | | | | | | | Maltose Corrections (Subtract from Observed Titer) | | |
| | | | | | | | | | | | Maltose Present (mg) | | |
Titer	0.0	0.1	0.2	0.3	0.4	0.5	0.6	0.7	0.8	0.9	200	100	50
10	25.7	26.0	26.3	26.6	26.9	27.2	27.5	27.8	28.1	28.4	2.5	1.4	0.6
11	28.7	29.0	29.3	29.6	29.9	30.3	30.6	30.9	31.2	31.5	2.3	1.2	.4
12	31.8	32.2	32.5	32.9	33.2	33.6	34.0	34.3	34.7	35.0	2.2	1.1	.4
13	35.4	35.8	36.1	36.5	36.8	37.2	37.6	37.9	38.3	38.6	2.0	1.0	.3
14	39.0	39.4	39.9	40.3	40.7	41.2	41.6	42.0	42.4	42.9	1.9	1.0	.3
15	43.3	43.8	44.2	44.7	45.1	45.6	46.1	46.5	47.0	47.4	1.8	1.0	.3
16	47.9	48.4	49.0	49.5	50.1	50.6	51.1	51.7	52.2	52.8	1.7	1.0	.3
17	53.3	53.9	54.5	55.2	55.8	56.4	57.0	57.6	58.3	58.9	1.6	0.9	.3
18	59.5	60.2	60.9	61.6	62.3	63.1	63.8	64.5	65.2	65.9	1.4	.8	.3
19	66.6	67.4	68.2	69.0	69.8	70.6	71.4	72.2	73.0	73.8	1.2	.7	.3
20	74.6	75.6	76.5	77.5	78.4	79.4	80.3	81.3	82.2	83.2	1.0	.6	.2
21	84.1	85.2	86.3	87.4	88.5	89.6	90.6	91.7	92.8	93.9	0.6	.4	.2
22	95.0										.4	.3	.1

* Table may be interpolated for each .01 ml, but should *not* be extrapolated.

31.217   ***Standardization***

To obtain factor for 0.1N KMnO$_4$ make analysis as in **31.218** on 10 ml soln contg 50 mg pure glucose. From **31.219**, titer of 15.38 ml corresponds to 50 mg glucose; 15.38 divided by titer obtained gives correction factor for KMnO$_4$ soln. Multiply all titers by this factor before referring to **31.219**. Redet. factor each day analyses are made.

31.218   ***Determination***

Proceed as in **31.214** thru "... immerse in briskly boiling H$_2$O bath exactly 20 min." Filter Cu$_2$O ppt thru gooch prepd as in **31.038**, and wash flask and crucible 3 times with hot H$_2$O. (It is not necessary to remove all ppt from flask.)

Transfer asbestos mat and crucible to 150 ml beaker marked at 60 ml. Wash flask with exactly 20 ml FeNH$_4$(SO$_4$)$_2$ soln in 3 portions and transfer quant. to beaker contg crucible. (All ppt must be dissolved.) Finally wash flask and crucible with hot H$_2$O and remove crucible. Add hot H$_2$O to 60 ml mark. Heat soln to boiling on hot plate, let stand 3 min, and titr. with 0.1N KMnO$_4$. Addn of 1 ml H$_3$PO$_4$ toward end of titrn facilitates reading of end point. Pink-gray end point persists ca 20 sec. Multiply titer by factor and obtain mg glucose from **31.219**.

31.219   ***Sichert-Bleyer Table for Determination of Glucose****

Titer 0.1N Permanganate	Glucose (mg)									
	0	0.1	0.2	0.3	0.4	0.5	0.6	0.7	0.8	0.9
ml										
10	26.5	26.8	27.1	27.4	27.8	28.1	28.4	28.7	29.0	29.3
11	29.7	30.0	30.4	30.7	31.1	31.5	31.8	32.2	32.6	32.9
12	33.3	33.7	34.1	34.5	34.9	35.4	35.8	36.2	36.6	37.0
13	37.4	37.9	38.4	38.8	39.3	39.8	40.3	40.7	41.2	41.7
14	42.2	42.7	43.2	43.8	44.3	44.9	45.4	46.0	46.5	47.0
15	47.6	48.2	48.8	49.4	50.1	50.7	51.3	51.9	52.5	53.2
16	53.8	54.5	55.2	55.9	56.6	57.3	58.0	58.7	59.4	60.2
17	60.9	61.7	62.5	63.3	64.1	64.9	65.7	66.5	67.4	68.2
18	69.0	69.9	70.9	71.9	72.8	73.8	74.8	75.7	76.7	77.6
19	78.6	79.6	80.7	81.7	82.7	83.7	84.8	85.8	86.8	87.8
20	88.9	90.0	91.2	92.3	93.5	94.7	96.0	97.2	98.5	99.7

* Table may be interpolated for each .01 ml, but should *not* be extrapolated.

Glucose by Glucose Oxidase Method (55)— Official Final Action

31.220 *Principle*

Glucose is enzymatically oxidized with glucose oxidase to form H_2O_2, which reacts with a dye in presence of peroxidase to give stable colored product proportional to glucose concn.

31.221 *Reagents*

(a) *Glucose test soln.*—Consists of (*1*) *Glucose oxidase.*—1000 glucose oxidase units/ml; purified (Miles Laboratories, Inc., or equiv.). (*2*) *Horseradish peroxidase.*—Available from Worthington Biochemical Co., Freehold, NJ 07728. (*3*) *Chromogen.*—o-Dianisidine.2HCl. (*4*) *Acetate buffer soln.*—pH 5.5, 0.1*M*. Dissolve 13.608 g NaOAc.3H_2O and dil. to 1 L with H_2O. Add 2.7 ml HOAc and adjust pH with NaOAc or HOAc, if necessary.

Dissolve 40 mg chromogen, 40 mg horseradish peroxidase, and 0.4 ml glucose oxidase in 0.1*M* acetate buffer and dil. to 100 ml with buffer soln.

Bottle contg glucose oxidase, horseradish peroxidase, buffer, and chromogen in proper proportions is available from Fermco Laboratories, Box 5110, Chicago, IL 60680. Reconstitute by adding H_2O directly to bottle; e.g., for 125 test size add 125 ml H_2O. Mix and store unused portion at 5°. Do *not* freeze.

(b) *Glucose std soln.*—1 mg/ml. Dissolve 1.000 g NBS anhyd. glucose (previously dried 4 hr at 70° under vac.) in H_2O and dil. to 1 L in vol. flask. Mix and let stand 2 hr to permit mutarotation to occur. Prep. fresh on day of use.

31.222 *Apparatus*

(a) *Spectrophotometer.* — Beckman Instruments Model B or equiv. with matching 1 cm cells.

(b) *Water bath.*—Capable of maintaining temp. at 30±1°.

31.223 *Preparation of Standard Curve*

Pipet 1, 2, 3, and 4 ml aliquots std glucose soln into sep. 50 ml vol. flasks and dil. to vol. with H_2O. Mix and pipet 2 ml of each dild std into 18 × 150 mm test tubes (0.04, 0.08, 0.12, 0.16 mg glucose). Use 2 ml H_2O as blank. Place all tubes in 30° H_2O bath 5 min. At 0 time, start reaction by adding 1.0 ml glucose *test* soln to first tube. Allow 30–60 sec interval between enzyme addn to each subsequent tube. Mix tubes and let react exactly 30 min at 30°. Immediately stop reaction (30–60 sec intervals) by pipetting 10 ml H_2SO_4 (1 + 3) into each tube. Mix, cool to room temp., and measure *A* against reagent blank at 540 nm, using 1 cm cells. Plot *A* at 540 nm against mg glucose on linear coordinate paper.

31.224 *Determination*

Weigh 1–5 g sirup sample to nearest 0.1 mg, using weighing bottle to prevent moisture loss during weighing. Dil. successively with H_2O to concn of 2.5–7.5 mg glucose/100 ml. Pipet 2 ml dild sample into 18 × 150 mm test tube. Proceed as in **31.223**, beginning "Place all tubes in 30° H_2O bath 5 min." Det. mg glucose from std curve and calc. % glucose in sample.

For results on dry substance basis, det. sample dry substance as in **31.202–31.203** or **31.204**.

SELECTED REFERENCES

(*1*) JAOAC 37, 292(1954).

(*2*) JAOAC 8, 255(1925).

(*3*) JAOAC 15, 195(1932); 18, 83(1935).

(*4*) JAOAC 15, 79(1932); 16, 81(1933); 17, 74 (1934); 41, 621(1958).

(*5*) Leach, 32nd Ann. Rept. Mass. Board Health, 1900, p. 563; Leach-Winton, "Food Inspection and Analysis," 4th ed., 1920, p. 654.

(*6*) Z. Ver. deut. Zucker-Ind. 50, (N. F. 37), 357 (1900); 63, (N. F. 50), 25(1913); J. Ind. Eng. Chem. 5, 167(1913); JAOAC 18, 162(1935); NBS Circular C 440, 1942, pp. 768, 774; Int. Sugar J. 35, 19(1933); 39, 32S(1937).

(*7*) JAOAC 16, 78(1933); 17, 74(1934).

(*8*) Browne and Zerban, "Sugar Analysis," 1941, p. 395.

(*9*) JAOAC 8, 256(1925).

(*10*) J. Ind. Eng. Chem. 16, 170(1924).

(*11*) JAOAC 8, 258(1925).

(*12*) JAOAC 8, 400(1925).

(*13*) JAOAC 9, 33(1926).

(*14*) Analyst 21, 182(1896).

(*15*) J. Soc. Chem. Ind. 42, 32T(1923); JAOAC 9, 35(1926); 12, 38(1929); 25, 99(1942).

(*16*) J. Am. Chem. Soc. 28, 663(1906); 29, 541 (1907); J. Research Natl. Bur. Standards 24, 589(1940); JAOAC 26, 101(1943).

(*17*) JAOAC 12, 38(1929); 18, 83(1935); J. Am. Chem. Soc. 57, 845(1935); Anal. Chem. 21, 975(1949).

(*18*) J. Research Natl. Bur. Standards 15, 493 (1935); 19, 691(1937); RP1057.

(*19*) JAOAC 23, 558(1940); J. Research Natl. Bur. Standards, 22, 697(1939); RP1213.

(*20*) Z. Zuckerind Cechoslovak Rep. 59, 52, 63 (1934); JAOAC 26, 463(1943); 30, 124(1947).

(*21*) J. Am. Chem. Soc. 43, 1503(1921); JAOAC 15, 71(1932).

(*22*) JAOAC 38, 594(1955).

(*23*) J. Biol. Chem. 41, 367(1920); JAOAC 35, 635 (1952).

(*24*) JAOAC 15, 79, 198(1932).

(*25*) JAOAC 51, 755(1968); 52, 564(1969); 53, 347 (1970).

(*26*) JAOAC 49, 551(1966).

(*27*) "Methoden van Onderzoek bij de Java-Suikerindustrie," 6th Ed., 1931, p. 365; JAOAC 31, 109(1948); 32, 102(1949).

(*28*) JAOAC 32, 102(1949).

(*29*) USDA, Eastern Regional Research Lab., AIC-307, May 1951; JAOAC 39, 919(1956).

(*30*) JAOAC **52**, 729(1969).

(*31*) JAOAC **45**, 548(1962).

(*32*) JAOAC **37**, 466(1954); **39**, 1016(1956); **42**, 341 (1959); **43**, 774(1960).

(*33*) JAOAC **42**, 341(1959); **43**, 638(1960).

(*34*) USDA Bur. Chem. Bull. **110** and **154**.

(*35*) USDA Bur. Chem. Bull. **154**, p. 15; JAOAC **15**, 78(1932); **45**, 213(1962).

(*36*) Food Research **23**, 446(1958); JAOAC **42**, 341 (1959); **47**, 486(1964).

(*37*) JAOAC **45**, 548(1962); **46**, 148(1963).

(*38*) J. Am. Chem. Soc. **26**, 1523(1904); JAOAC **15**, 79(1932); **16**, 79(1933); **17**, 73(1934); **18**, 83 (1935); Trans. Roy. Soc. Can. 1919, sec. 111, 221.

(*39*) JAOAC **44**, 330(1961).

(*40*) JAOAC **52**, 554(1969).

(*41*) JAOAC **4**, 437(1921); **16**, 80(1933); **17**, 74 (1934).

(*42*) J. Am. Chem. Soc. **28**, 1204(1906); JAOAC **16**, 80, 158(1933); **17**, 74, 157(1934).

(*43*) JAOAC **49**, 508(1966).

(*44*) JAOAC **42**, 349(1959).

(*45*) JAOAC **47**, 548(1964).

(*46*) JAOAC **50**, 747(1967); **51**, 586(1968); **52**, 414 (1969).

(*47*) JAOAC **25**, 98(1942).

(*48*) USDA Bur. Chem. Bull. **146**, p. 19.

(*49*) Ind. Eng. Chem., Anal. Ed. **13**, 855(1941).

(*50*) Ind. Eng. Chem., Anal. Ed. **13**, 858(1941).

(*51*) Ind. Eng. Chem., Anal. Ed. **15**, 193(1943).

(*52*) Ind. Eng. Chem., Anal. Ed. **16**, 161(1944).

(*53*) Ind. Eng. Chem., Anal. Ed. **10**, 669(1938); Z. Spiritusind. **56**, 64(1933).

(*54*) Z. Anal. Chem. **107**, 328(1936); Z. Spiritusind. **56**, 64(1933).

(*55*) JAOAC **52**, 556(1969).

32. Vegetable Products, Processed[*]

CANNED PRODUCTS
Drained Weight—Procedure

32.001   *Sieves*

One-half inch and No. 8.—See *Definition of Terms and Explanatory Notes*, item (15). Use 8″ diam. (for No. 3 or smaller cans) or 12″ diam. (for cans larger than No. 3).

32.002   *Determination*

Weigh full can, open, and pour entire contents on No. 8 sieve (use 0.5″ sieve for canned tomatoes). Without shifting product, incline sieve at ca 17–20° angle to facilitiate drainage. Drain 2 min, directly weigh either drained solids or free liq. and weigh dry empty can. From wts obtained det. % liq. and % drained solid contents.

32.003   Preparation of Sample—Procedure

(a) *Products composed of solid and liquid portions.* —If only solid portion is required for analysis or examination, thoroly grind drained vegetables in mortar or food chopper. If composite of solid and liq. portion is required, thoroly grind entire contents of can in mortar or food chopper. In all cases, thoroly mix portion used and store balance in g-s container. Unless analysis is to be completed in reasonably short time, det. H_2O in portion of sample prepd as above. To prevent decomposition, dry remainder, grind, mix thoroly, and store in g-s container. (Second H_2O detn is required in this procedure.)

(b) *Comminuted products (tomato juice, tomato catsup, strained vegetables).*—Thoroly shake unopened container to incorporate any sediment. Transfer entire contents to large glass or porcelain dish, and mix thoroly, continuing stirring at least 1 min. Transfer well-mixed sample to g-s container and shake or stir thoroly each time before removing portions for analysis.

32.004   Total Solids (*1*)—Official Final Action

To flat-bottom metal dish with tight-fitting cover, add ca 15 mg diat. earth filter aid/sq cm, dry ca 30 min at 110°, cool in desiccator, weigh, and to each dish add sample of such size that dry residue will be ≥9 but ≤30 mg/sq cm. Weigh as rapidly as possible to avoid moisture loss. Mix with filter aid and distribute uniformly over bottom of dish, dilg with H_2O if necessary to facilitate distribution. Bring sample

to apparent dryness (remaining moisture not >ca 50% dry solids) by one of following methods:

(1) Place sample on boiling H_2O bath and remove when samples reach apparent dryness.

(2) Place sample in forced-draft oven at 70°. Oven must have rapid air circulation and enough interchange of outside air to rapidly remove moisture. Examine dishes at intervals of ≤30 min, and remove as soon as they reach apparent dryness.

(3) Place sample in vac. oven at 70° with release cock left partly open to allow rapid flow of air thru oven at ≥310 mm Hg pressure. Examine dishes at 30 min intervals and remove any that reach apparent dryness.

Place partially dried samples in vac. oven with bottoms of dishes in direct contact with shelf. Measure temp. of oven by thermometer in direct contact with shelf. Oven must be so constructed that temp. variation from one part of shelf to another does not exceed ca 2°. Admit dry air to oven at rate of 2–4 bubbles/sec by bubbling through H_2SO_4. Dry samples 2 hr at 69–71° (oven may be as low as 65° at start of drying, but must reach 69–71° before end of first hr) at pressure ≤50 mm Hg. As dried sample will absorb appreciable amt of moisture on standing over most desiccating agents, cover quickly, and weigh as soon as possible after sample reaches room temp.

32.005   Insoluble Solids (*2*)—Official Final Action

Wash 20 g sample repeatedly with hot H_2O, centrfg after each addn of H_2O and pouring clear supernatant thru weighed filter paper on buchner. (Filter used is 1 of 2 such papers dried 2 hr at 100° and weighed in covered dish. Use second paper, if necessary, when first becomes clogged.) After 4 or 5 washings, transfer remaining insol. matter to filter, dry in uncovered dish 2 hr at 100°, cover, cool in desiccator, and weigh.

32.006   Alcohol-Insoluble Solids in Canned Peas (*3*)—Official Final Action

Pour sample on No. 8 screen, using 8″ size for container of <3 lb net wt and 12″ for larger quantities. Spread peas evenly and let drain. Transfer peas to white pan and remove any foreign material. Add vol. H_2O equal to double vol. original sample.

Pour peas back on screen, spreading evenly, tilt screen as much as possible without shifting peas, and drain 2 min. With cloth wipe surplus moisture from

★ Methods so marked are surplus methods. *See* "Definitions of Terms and Explanatory Notes," item (29).

lower surface of screen. Grind drained peas in food chopper until cotyledons are reduced to smooth homogeneous paste, stir, and weigh 20 g ground material into 600 ml beaker. Add 300 ml 80% alcohol, stir, cover beaker, and bring to boil. Simmer slowly 30 min.

Fit into buchner filter paper of appropriate size (previously prepd by drying in flat-bottom dish 2 hr at temp. of boiling H_2O, covering with tight-fit cover, cooling in desiccator, and weighing at once). Apply suction and transfer contents of beaker to buchner so as to avoid running over edge of paper. Suck dry and wash material on filter with 80% alcohol until washings are clear and colorless.

Transfer paper and alcohol-insol. solids to dish used in prepn of paper, dry uncovered 2 hr at temp. of boiling H_2O, place cover on dish, cool in desiccator, and weigh at once. From this wt deduct wt dish, cover, and paper. Calc. % by wt of alcohol-insol. solids.

32.007　Soluble Solids—Official Final Action

% Total solids, **32.004** − % insol. solids, **32.005** = % sol. solids.

Soluble Solids in Tomato Products (4)—
Official First Action

32.008　　　　　*Apparatus and Reagents*

(a) *Filters.*—Cut stems off 75 mm id glass or plastic funnels ca 1 cm from apex at 90° angle and firepolish ends. Set funnels in 150 ml jars, ca 55 mm id. If 150 ml beakers are used, close pouring spout with tape to prevent evapn. Insert folded paper, Whatman No. 2V, 12.5 cm, or equiv., in funnel.

(b) *Refractometer.*—Sensitive to 0.0001 n.

(c) *Pectic enzyme.*—(1) *Dry preparation.*—In diat. earth base, e.g., Pectinol 10R (Rohm and Haas), Klerzyme® analytical (Wallerstein Co.), or Pectinase conc. (Miles Laboratories, Inc). (2) *Soln.*—Prep. 0.4–1% aq. soln of (1); mix thoroly and let settle. Use clear supernatant.

32.009　　　　　*Preparation of Sample*

(a) *Without dilution.*—Weigh 100 g sample at room temp. and add weighed amt (0.2–1.0 g) dry enzyme prepn. Immediately mix with spoon or spatula to avoid evapn and transfer to filter. Tamp so sample is in close contact with paper and cover with petri dish (top or bottom portion) to have loose seal with top of funnel. Discard samples that do not filter in reasonable length of time (<1 hr). Mix 0.2–1.0 g dry enzyme prepn with 100 g fresh sample, seal in closed container, and incubate 30–60 min at ca 40°. Cool nearly to room temp. before opening container, remix sample, and transfer to filter. For samples that still do not filter within 1 hr, proceed as in (b).

(b) *With dilution.*—(Applicable to samples contg ≥35% solids that will not filter when treated as in (a)). Add 100 g enzyme soln to 100 g sample and immediately mix with spoon or spatula to avoid evapn. (Mech. mixer (e.g., Osterizer) with sealed blending container may be used.) Alternately blend and shake to dislodge and break up lumps sticking to container. Examine mixt. carefully for lumps and continue mixing until homogeneous. Transfer to filter and cover with petri dish.

32.010　　　　　　　*Determination*

Adjust refractometer for refractive index (n) of 1.3330 with H_2O at 20°. Let sample filter into jar or beaker until filtrate is clear (some color and turbidity may be tolerated). Quickly remove funnel and transfer large drop of filtrate directly from funnel to refractometer prism. (Tip of funnel may touch refractometer prism but should not scratch prism.) Replace funnel in jar. Read refractometer preferably at 20°, but if humidity causes condensation of moisture on prism, make measurements at room temp. and correct readings to std temp. as in **47.015.** Read n or % sucrose on refractometer. If n is read, convert to % sucrose from **47.012.**

Let sample filter several min more. Repeat reading by removing funnel and transferring drop of filtrate to refractometer prism. The 2 readings should agree within 0.0002 n or 0.1% sucrose. If not, repeat readings on successive portions of filtrate until agreement is obtained. Erratic readings indicate evapn of sample or faulty mixing and/or filtration technic.

Read clear supernatant of 1% soln of dry enzyme on refractometer and convert to % sucrose. Subtract $1.15 \times B \times C$ from direct reading on sample (as % sucrose); where 1.15 = correction for insol. solids in weighed sample, assuming 12.5% total solids to be insol. solids; B = % enzyme prepn added to sample, and C = reading as sucrose obtained on 1% soln.

If dild sample is used, subtract $0.55 \times D \times C$ from reading on sample (as % sucrose); where 0.55 = correction for insol. solids, as above, and D = % enzyme prepn added to diln H_2O. Multiply corrected reading for dild sample by 2 and add addnl correction according to following table:

Natural Tomato Sol. Solids as % Sucrose Corrected for Enzyme × 2	Correction
25.0	0.3
30.0	0.4
35.0	0.5
40.0	0.7
45.0	0.8
50.0	0.9

Correction for added salt.—(Use only when sample contains added salt and $R > S$.) Correct refractometer reading expressed as % sucrose at 20° for added salt by following formula: $S = (R - N) \times 1.016$ = total sol. solids as sucrose exclusive of added salt; where S = refractometer reading as sucrose corrected for added NaCl, R = total sol. solids as sucrose, and N = % total chlorides expressed as NaCl (detd by **32.017**).

32.011 Specific Gravity (5)—Official Final Action

(Applicable to comminuted tomato products)

Det. sp gr at 20/20°, using Gay-Lussac or similar small-neck bottle without cap. Clean and calibrate bottle at 20° as in 9.010, strike off excess H_2O with straight edge, wipe bottle dry, and weigh immediately. Cool sample to 16–18°, fill bottle with the pulp, and centrf. 1 min at ca 1000 rpm. Add enough pulp to fill bottle to top and centrf. again. Remove bottle and take temp. of pulp, inserting thermometer so that no air is introduced. When temp. is just 20°, remove thermometer, add enough pulp at same temp. to have bottle slightly over full, and strike off even with straight edge. Clean outside of bottle and weigh at once to nearest 0.01 g. Sp gr = wt pulp in bottle ÷ wt H_2O at 20° that bottle holds.

32.012 Ash—Official Final Action—See 31.012 or 31.013

32.013 Alkalinity of Ash—Official Final Action

Proceed as in 22.021. Express result as ml $1N$ acid required to neutze ash from 100 g sample.

Calcium (6)—Official Final Action

(Applicable to canned lima beans, potatoes, and tomatoes)

32.014 Reagents and Apparatus

See 36.305 and 36.306.

32.015 Preparation of Sample

Thoroly comminute entire contents of can (representative portion if larger than No. 303 size can) in high-speed blender. Weigh 50 g sample (100 g in absence of declaration of added Ca) into Pt or porcelain dish. Evap. to dryness, using forced-draft oven, IR radiation, or other convenient means. Ash and treat as in 36.307.

32.016 Determination

Transfer 100 ml aliquot prepd sample soln to 250 ml beaker and adjust to pH 3.5 with 10% KOH soln added dropwise, using pH meter and magnetic stirrer. Pass sample soln thru resin column (column is in chloride form), collecting effluent in 400 ml beaker at flow rate of 2–3 ml/min. Wash column with two 50 ml portions H_2O, passing first portion thru at same rate as sample soln and second at 6–7 ml/min. Finally pass enough H_2O freely thru column to make 250–300 ml final vol. Adjust to pH 12.5–13.0, using pH meter and magnetic stirrer, with KOH–KCN soln, 1.021(b). Add 0.100 g ascorbic acid and 200–300 mg hydroxynaphthol blue indicator. Titr. immediately with 0.01M EDTA soln thru pink to deep blue end point, using magnetic stirrer.

% Ca = ml EDTA × (0.01/molarity EDTA soln) × 0.4008 × 2 × 100/mg sample.

Sodium Chloride—Official Final Action

32.017 Method I

Proceed as in 3.068 or 3.070, using HNO_3 soln of ash, 3.067. Calc. and report results as % NaCl.

32.018 Method II (Rapid Method) (7)

Weigh ca 5 g material, transfer with 80% alcohol to 100 ml vol. flask, and add enough 80% alcohol to give vol. of ca 50 ml. Shake well to suspend all insol. material. Add 1 ml HNO_3 and with pipet add excess of 0.1N $AgNO_3$ soln. Dil. to 100 ml with alcohol. Transfer mixt. to centrf. bottle and centrf. 5 min at ca 1800 rpm. Pipet 50 ml supernatant into 300 ml erlenmeyer, add 2 ml satd $FeNH_4(SO_4)_2$ soln and 2 ml HNO_3, and titr. to permanent light brown with 0.1N NH_4CNS. Divide ml 0.1N $AgNO_3$ used by 2 and subtract ml NH_4CNS soln used. Multiply difference by 0.005844 to obtain g NaCl present.

32.019 Reducing Sugars Before Inversion—Official Final Action

Weigh 20 g sample into 200 ml vol. flask, dil. with ca 100 ml H_2O, clarify with slight excess of neut. $Pb(OAc)_2$ soln, 31.021(d), dil. to vol., and filter. Remove excess of Pb with anhyd. Na_2SO_4 or with dry Na or K oxalate. Filter, and det. reducing sugars as in 31.039. Express result as % invert sugar.

32.020 Reducing Sugars After Inversion—Official Final Action

Transfer 50 ml filtrate, 32.019, to 100 ml vol. flask, add 5 ml HCl, and let stand overnight, as in 31.026(c). Nearly neutze with NaOH soln, cool, dil. to vol., and det. reducing sugars in aliquot as in 31.039. Express result as % invert sugar.

32.021 Sucrose—Official Final Action— See 31.032

32.022 Total Acids—Official Final Action

Proceed as in 22.058 or 22.059, using 5 g sample. Express result as ml $1N$ alkali required to neutze 100 g sample.

Lactic Acid—Official Final Action

32.023 Preparation of Solution

Weigh 50 g ground and mixed sample into tared centrf. bottle and add 100 ml H_2O. Make acid to Congo red paper with $1N$ H_2SO_4. Adjust wt of contents of bottle to 200 g by addn of H_2O, shake vigorously, and centrf. Decant supernatant and weigh 100 g into 100–110 ml vol. flask. Dil. to 110 ml mark with H_2O, shake, and pipet 50 ml into continuous extractor (Fig. 16:1). Add 0.5 ml H_2SO_4 (1 + 1) and 2 ml 20% $Na_2WO_4 \cdot 2H_2O$ soln, and proceed as in 16.030.

If sample contains HOAc added in course of manufacture (e.g., catsup), transfer extd material, after evapn of ether, to beaker, add ca 50 ml H_2O, and evap. to 20 ml. Again add 50 ml H_2O and evap. to 20 ml. Neutze with satd Ba(OH)$_2$ soln and proceed as in **16.031.**

**32.024 ★   Field Corn in Canned Mixtures ★
of Field and Sweet Corn (8)—
Official Final Action**

See **30.016,** 10th ed.

DRIED VEGETABLES
Water (9)—Official Final Action
(Dry all glassware in oven.)

32.025   Preparation of Sample

Grind sample to pass No. 30 sieve and store in tightly sealed container.

Near-Infrared Spectrophotometric Method
32.026   Apparatus

Spectrophotometer.—Beckman Instruments DK2A, or equiv., near-IR recording instrument.

32.027   Preparation of Standard Curve

Accurately weigh 200, 300, 400, 500, and 600 mg H$_2$O into sep. 125 ml g-s erlenmeyers. Pipet 100 ml *N,N-dimethylformamide* into each flask. Record *A* of solns in matched quartz or silica cells from 1.8 to 2.1 μm, using for ref. same lot dimethylformamide as used for prepn of std solns. Draw baseline between minima at ca 1.82 μm and 2.0 μm. *A* of std soln at max., ca 1.92 μm = total *A* at max. − baseline *A* at max. Plot corrected baseline *A* against mg H$_2$O/100 ml dimethylformamide.

32.028   Determination

Accurately weigh sample contg ca 70–100 mg H$_2$O into 50 ml g-s erlenmeyer. Pipet in 20 ml N,N-dimethylformamide. Tape stopper securely to flask and heat 60±1 min at 90±1° in oven. Shake flask mech. 10 min. Cool to room temp. Decant soln into g-s centrf. tube and centrf. at 1500 rpm until soln is clear (ca 5 min). Record *A* of soln and calc. *A* at max. as in **32.027.**

$$\% \text{ H}_2\text{O} = \text{(mg H}_2\text{O from std curve} \times 100)/(5 \times \text{mg sample)}$$

Karl Fischer Method
32.029   Apparatus

Titrimeter.—Fisher Scientific Co. Model 36, or equiv., with 2 Pt electrodes. See **31.074.**

32.030   Reagents

(a) *Karl Fischer reagent std.*—Stabilized, with H$_2$O equiv. of ca 5 mg H$_2$O/ml reagent. Available com. or prep. as in **31.075**(a), using ethylene glycol monomethyl ether. Place 50 ml formamide, practical grade, into 200 ml Berzelius beaker contg stirrer magnet. Place in titrimeter and titr. (Titr. slowly near end point until 0.1 ml addn causes meter to deflect to right of zero and remain 60 sec.) Quickly add accurately weighed quantity (0.250–0.350 g) diso-

dium tartrate.2H$_2$O. Titr. immediately to same end point. Repeat detn and calc. av.

mg H$_2$O/ml reagent = (mg Na$_2$C$_4$H$_4$O$_6$. 2H$_2$O × 0.1566)/ml reagent.

(b) *Sodium tartrate dihydrate.*—"60 mesh."   ·

32.031   Determination

Accurately weigh 2.0–2.5 g sample into 50 ml g-s erlenmeyer. Pipet in 20 ml *N,N-dimethylformamide.* Ext and centrf. as in **32.028.**

Place 50 ml formamide into 200 ml Berzelius beaker and titr. to end point as in stdzg Karl Fischer reagent. Quickly pipet 10 ml sample soln into beaker and titr. to same end point. Det. blank by titrg 10 ml dimethylformamide in same manner as sample. Repeat blank detn and calc. av.

% H$_2$O in sample = [200 (ml reagent for sample − blank titer) mg H$_2$O/ml reagent]/mg sample.

FROZEN VEGETABLES
Net Contents of Frozen Food Containers
(10)—Procedure
32.032   Apparatus

(a) *For packages up to 5 pounds.*—Use scale of adequate capacity with sensitivity of 0.01 oz.

(b) *For packages over 5 pounds.*—Use scale of adequate capacity with sensitivity of 0.025 oz.

32.033   Procedure

Set scale on firm support and level. Adjust zero load indicator or rest point and check sensitivity.

(a) *Unglazed frozen foods.*—Remove package from low temp. storage, remove frost and ice from outside of package, and weigh immediately (*W*). Open package; remove contents, including any product particles and frost crystals. Air-dry empty package at room temp. and weigh (*E*). Wt contents = *W* − *E*.

(b) *Glazed frozen foods.*—See **18.001**(a).

Aldehydes as Acetaldehyde (11)—Official First Action
32.034   Apparatus

Steam distilling apparatus.—Consists of 500 ml Kjeldahl flask, spray trap, and condenser, preferably all-glass with ⚎ joints (Cat. No. JD 1710, Scientific Glass Apparatus Co., is satisfactory). App. with rubber stoppers and connections is suitable if satisfactory blanks are obtained. (Some rubber yields neg. blanks.)

32.035   Reagents

(a) *Sodium thiosulfate std soln.*—0.05*N*. Prep. daily by dilg 0.1*N* soln, **45.038–45.039.** 1 ml 0.05*N* Na$_2$S$_2$O$_3$ = 1.1 mg AcH.

(b) *Iodine std soln.*—0.05–0.0515*N*. Prep. as in **45.019,** stdze against Na$_2$S$_2$O$_3$ soln, (a), and adjust concn, if necessary.

(c) *Sodium bisulfite std soln.*—0.05*N* in ca 10% alcohol. Dissolve 2.60 g NaHSO$_3$ in 500 ml H$_2$O in 1 L vol. flask. Add 100 ml alcohol, mix, and dil. to vol. with H$_2$O. Stdze against I soln, (b), and adjust concn, if necessary, so as to be slightly weaker than that of the I soln, but not $<0.0485N$. Prep. fresh daily.

(d) *Aldehyde-free alcohol.*—Use alcohol contg <2 ppm AcH; if greater, purify as in **19.066**(a). Det. aldehydes as in **32.036,** using 300 ml freshly boiled and cooled H_2O and 35 ml of the alcohol, beginning "Pipet in 25 ml $NaHSO_3$ soln ..." Det. blank similarly but without alcohol. Difference in titrns $\times$ 31 = ppm aldehydes as AcH.

32.036 *Determination*

Sharply strike package of frozen vegetable on surface or edge of table to break up block. Mix well and grind ca 150 g thru food chopper.

Transfer 50 g sample to Kjeldahl flask with ca 150 ml H_2O. Add 1–2 drops *DC Antifoam,* or equiv., and steam distill into 500 ml erlenmeyer, immersed in ice bath and contg 100 ml chilled, freshly boiled H_2O to cover end of delivery tube. Collect ca 200 ml within 12–15 min. To distillate add 35 ml aldehyde-free alcohol. Pipet in 25 ml $NaHSO_3$ soln and let stand 30 min, shaking occasionally. Pipet in 25 ml I soln, and titr. with $Na_2S_2O_3$ soln, using 5 ml starch indicator, **32.037**(g). Det. blank on 300 ml freshly boiled and cooled H_2O. Difference in ml $\times$ 1.1 = mg AcH; mg AcH $\times$ 1000/wt sample = ppm.

Catalase (12)—Official First Action

32.037 *Reagents*

Relatively Stable Reagents

(a) *Phosphate buffer soln.*—0.1M, pH 6.95±0.15. Dissolve 15.22 g K_2HPO_4.$3H_2O$ and 4.54 g KH_2PO_4 in H_2O and dil. to 1 L.

(b) *Sulfuric acid containing molybdate.*—$2N$. Add 55 ml H_2SO_4 to ca 800 ml H_2O, cool, add 0.1 g finely ground $(NH_4)_6Mo_7O_{24}$.$4H_2O$, agitate until completely dissolved, and dil. to 1 L with H_2O.

(c) *Sodium thiosulfate (ca 0.01N) in 10% potassium iodide soln.*—Dissolve 100 g KI, 2.50 g $Na_2S_2O_3$.$5H_2O$, and ca 1 g Na_2CO_3 in 500 ml H_2O and dil. to 1 L. (Need not be stdzd.)

(d) *Iodine std soln.*—0.01N. Prep. as in **45.019.** Stdze against std $Na_2S_2O_3$ *soln,* **45.038–45.039.** (Avoid exposure to excessive light even while in buret.)

Relatively Unstable Reagents

(e) *Hydrogen peroxide.*—0.1N. Dil. 0.58 ml 30% H_2O_2 to 100 ml with cold H_2O. Keep in refrigerator or ice bath when not in use. *Prep. daily.*

(f) *20% soln of glucose in buffer soln.*—Dissolve 20 g glucose in 100 ml phosphate buffer soln, (a). Keep refrigerated and prep. weekly.

(g) *Starch indicator.*—Add 1.0 g sol. starch to 100 ml cold H_2O, stir thoroly, and heat to boiling. Prep. biweekly.

32.038 *Preparation of Extract*

To avoid contamination with oxides of heavy metals, handle samples *only* with nonmetallic or stainless steel spatulas.

(a) *Undried or frozen vegetables.*—Comminute 50 g portions in high-speed blender 3 min with ca 1 g $CaCO_3$ and enough H_2O to make total vol. 200 ml. Remove larger particles by filtering thru 6″ gauze-backed cotton milk filter. Assay filtrate within 30 min.

(b) *Dried vegetables.*—Rehydrate 5 g sample and ext as in (a).

32.039 *Determination*

(a) *To demonstrate presence or absence of catalase.* —To 10 ml ext (or less, depending on activity) add H_2O to total vol. of 43 ml and 5 ml glucose soln, (f). Mix, and add 2 ml 0.1N H_2O_2. *Immediately* after addn of H_2O_2, thoroly mix and quickly remove "zero-time" aliquot of completed reaction mixt. with rapid-flow pipet and blow it into 125 ml erlenmeyer contg 10 ml H_2SO_4-molybdate soln. Count "zero time" from time delivery of aliquot from pipet is started. Remove 10 ml aliquots at 5 and 10 min. (Temp. of reaction mixt. must remain at $<20°$.) At any time within 1 hr add, to each flask, 5 ml $Na_2S_2O_3$-KI soln and mix. Let stand 3–5 min; then titr. excess $Na_2S_2O_3$ with 0.01N I, using ca 10 drops starch indicator.

Perform blank in exactly same manner, except add H_2O instead of H_2O_2, and do not remove 5 and 10 min aliquots. Differences between titer value of blank and of values obtained in presence of H_2O_2 are I soln equivs of H_2O_2 present at respective times. "Zero-time" titer value should be 0.5–2 ml I soln; differences between blank-titer value and "zero-time" titer value should be 3.0–4.5 ml 0.01N I. Difference of <3.0 ml (*i.e.,* I titer values >2 ml) indicates that the H_2O_2 was too weak or that catalase activity was so high that large amt of H_2O_2 was decomposed before "zero-time" aliquot was removed. In latter case, differences corresponding to 5 and 10 min may be nearly 0, even when large amts of catalase are present. In such case catalase content of ext can be detd by method (b) if desired. If 10 ml aliquots of ext are used, blank-titer value is 4–6 ml, and "zero-time" titer value is <2 ml, catalase is indicated to be absent (within experimental error) when titer values for 5 and 10 min do not differ from "zero-time" titer value by >0.20 ml and 0.40 ml, resp.

(b) *To accurately determine catalase activity of sample in terms of K_f.*—"Katalase Fähigkeit," K_f, is k, first order reaction constant (log base 10) detd at 0°, divided by g sample/50 ml reaction mixt. That is, $K_f = k/g$, and is therefore expression of catalase activity of prepn. Pure catalase has K_f of 40,000–60,000, depending on source. If K_f is to be detd, make assay exactly as in (a), except maintain reaction mixt. at 0°. It is generally desirable to obtain 15 min titer value in addn to those described in (a). If sample is enzyme prepn of high activity rather than a vegetable, dissolve suitable quantity in dil. buffer, pH 6.5–7.5, preferably contg 2% glucose.

32.040 *Calculation of K_f*

Value for K_f for 0–5 min and 5–10 min periods should check at 0°, but at higher temps K_f (5–10 min) may be $< K_f$ (0–5 min), because catalase is inactivated by H_2O_2 at significant rate at higher temps. K_f is given by following formula:

$$K_f = \frac{\left(\dfrac{1}{t_b - t_a}\right) \log \left(\dfrac{\text{blank titer} - \text{titer at } t_a}{\text{blank titer} - \text{titer at } t_b}\right)}{\text{g sample/50 ml reaction mixt.}},$$

where t_a and t_b are initial and final times for 2 titer values under consideration. For exts of undried vegetables prepd as in **32.038**, the g sample in reaction mixt. is obtained with enough accuracy by multiplying ml ext used by 0.25. For most nearly accurate results, enzyme concn should be adjusted so that difference between blank titrn and t_0 titrn is 3–4 ml, and difference between blank titrn and t_{10} titrn is 0.5–1 ml I soln.

Peroxidase (13)—Official Final Action
32.041 *Reagents*
Relatively Stable Reagents

(a) *Phosphate-oxalate buffer soln.*—$0.1M$, pH 6.0. Dissolve 14.2 g Na_2HPO_4 (or 26.81 g Na_2HPO_4 .$7H_2O$) and 12.6 g $H_2C_2O_4$.$2H_2O$ in H_2O with heat, cool, adjust pH to 6.0 with $1N$ NaOH, and dil. to 1 L.

(b) *Oxalic acid soln.*—$1M$. Dissolve 126 g $H_2C_2O_4$.$2H_2O$ in H_2O and dil. to 1 L.

(c) *Sodium chloride soln.*—2.0%. Dissolve 20 g NaCl in H_2O and dil. to 1 L. Cool to 0° and store at 0°.

Relatively Unstable Reagents

(d) *Hydrogen peroxide soln.*—$0.1N$. Dil. 0.58 ml 30% H_2O_2 to 100 ml with cold H_2O. Stdze iodometrically as follows: To 25 ml $0.1N$ H_2O_2 add 10 ml $4N$ H_2SO_4, 6 ml $1N$ KI, and 3 drops $1N$ $(NH_4)_2Mo_7O_{24}$. Titr. soln with $0.1N$ $Na_2S_2O_3$ to starch end point. Store in refrigerator when not in use. Prep. fresh weekly.

(e) *Indophenol soln.*—$0.001N$. Dissolve 200 mg 2,6-dichlorophenolindophenol (La Motte Chemical Products Co., Chestertown, MD 21620) or 175 mg Na salt (Eastman Kodak Co.), or equivs, in H_2O and dil. to 1 L. Stdze against $0.01N$ $Na_2S_2O_3$ by titrg I liberated by 50 ml dye after addn of 10 ml $1N$ KI and 10 ml $4N$ H_2SO_4. Store in refrigerator. Prep. fresh weekly.

(f) *Ascorbic acid soln.*—$0.05M$. Dissolve 880 mg L-ascorbic acid in $0.1M$ buffer, (a), and dil. to 100 ml. Prep. fresh daily.

32.042 *Preparation of Extract*

Comminute 50 g portions fresh or frozen vegetable tissue in high-speed blender with 200 ml cold 2% NaCl soln. Remove larger particles by filtering thru 6″ gauze-backed cotton milk filter. Assay filtrate within 30 min.

32.043 *Determination*

Into 400 ml beaker place 75 ml buffer, **32.041**(a), 50 ml dye, 5 ml ascorbic acid, and enough H_2O to make total vol. of 250 ml after addn of tissue ext and H_2O_2. Adjust to $25\pm0.5°$ by warming or cooling as necessary. Place beaker on magnetic stirrer (Precision Scientific Co., 3737 W. Cortland St, Chicago, IL 60647, Mag-Mix is suitable) and stir mixt. 30 sec at speed just below that which would cause excessive aeration. From pipet add 1–3 ml ext (equiv. to 0.2–0.4 g tissue) and rapidly add 5 ml H_2O_2 from blow-out pipet. Start stopwatch immediately on addn of H_2O_2. Continue mixing during addn of H_2O_2 and until first aliquot is removed.

Within 15–30 sec after adding H_2O_2, remove 25 ml aliquot of reaction mixt. with 25 ml rapid-flow pipet adjusted to empty by blowing out in 5 sec, and discharge into 5 ml oxalic acid soln in 125 ml erlenmeyer. Take 4–5 subsequent samples at 1 min intervals and blow out into other 125 ml flasks each contg 5 ml oxalic acid soln. Record time as time pipet is emptied. Titr. residual ascorbic acid with dye soln and calc. first order reaction rate constant. Adjust enzyme activity so that constant is of order of magnitude of $15–20 \times 10^{-2}$ and express peroxidase activity, K_f, as K_1/g tissue used. Perform all titrns beyond fading end point to clearly visible pink, permanent 1 min. Adjust all titrns to same end point by comparison with first flask of each series. Add dye rapidly at first and more slowly later.

32.044 *Calculation of K_1 and K_f*

Under optimal conditions, initial titrn value is 35–40 ml dye and subsequent titrn values decrease to 20–25 ml in 5 min. Calc. first order reaction rate constant as for catalase, **32.040**, or take from slope of plot of log ml dye against time. Divide av. K_1 value for several intervals of time (0–1, 1–2, 2–3 min) by wt of vegetable tissue corresponding to vol. of ext in reaction mixt.

SELECTED REFERENCES
(1) JAOAC **47**, 492(1964).
(2) USDA Bur. Chem. Bull. **152**, 118(1911).
(3) JAOAC **21**, 244(1938); **22**, 370(1939).
(4) JAOAC **52**, 1050(1969).
(5) N.C.A. Bull. **27**–L, Revised 1950, p. 26; JAOAC **19**, 254(1936).
(6) JAOAC **49**, 287(1966); **50**, 787(1967); **51**, 796 (1968).
(7) JAOAC **22**, 765(1939); **23**, 353(1940); **24**, 424 (1941); **25**, 466(1942).
(8) JAOAC **11**, 136(1928); **12**, 39(1929); **15**, 167 (1932).
(9) JAOAC **50**, 701(1967); **52**, 416(1969).
(10) JAOAC **46**, 30(1963).
(11) JAOAC **39**, 282(1956).
(12) JAOAC **30**, 76, 413(1947).
(13) JAOAC **46**, 712(1963).

33. Waters, Mineral; and Salt[*]

MINERAL WATERS[*]

33.001 Specific Gravity—Official Final Action

Det. sp gr at 20/20°, using pycnometer, as in **9.011.**

33.002 Total Solids—Official Final Action

Thoroly shake sample, and pipet 100 ml unfiltered sample into weighed Pt dish. If sample contains much suspended matter, shake, pour rapidly into 100 ml graduate, and immediately transfer to weighed Pt dish. Evap. to dryness and heat to constant wt at 100°.

33.003 Solids in Solution—Official Final Action

Let sample stand until all sediment settles and filter if necessary to secure perfectly clear liq. (Occasionally, clear filtrate can be obtained only by use of alumina cream, **31.021(b)**; avoid if possible.) Evap. 100–250 ml to dryness in weighed Pt dish. Heat to constant wt at 100°.

33.004 Ignited Residue—Official Final Action

Ignite residue from **33.002** at 525–550° in muffle or over burner until dish shows dull red glow and ash is white or nearly so. Note any odor or change in color produced during ignition. Record wt ignited residue and calc. loss on ignition.

Nitrogen in Form of Nitrate (1)—Official Final Action
Phenoldisulfonic Acid Method
(For water of low Cl content)

33.005 Reagents

(a) *Phenoldisulfonic acid soln.*—(*Caution: See* **46.030** and **46.031**.) Dissolve 25 g pure white phenol in 150 ml H_2SO_4, add 75 ml fuming H_2SO_4 (13–15% SO_3), and heat 2 hr at 100°.

(b) *Nitrate std soln.*—Dissolve 0.607 g pure $NaNO_3$ in 1 L NO_3-free H_2O. Evap. 50 ml of this soln to dryness in porcelain dish; when cool, treat with 2 ml phenoldisulfonic acid soln, grind and stir with glass rod to ensure intimate contact, and dil. to 500 ml. 1 ml = 0.01 mg N (0.044 mg NO_3). (This soln is permanent.) Prep. stds for comparison by adding NH_4OH to measured vols of std soln in 100 ml Nessler tubes as in detn.

(c) *Silver sulfate std soln.*—Dissolve 4.398 g Ag_2SO_4, NO_3-free, in 1 L H_2O. 1 ml = 1 mg Cl.

33.006 Determination

To 100 ml sample, or quantity contg ≤0.05 mg N, add enough std Ag_2SO_4 soln to ppt all but ca 0.5 mg of the Cl. Heat to boiling and let settle, or add little alumina cream, **31.021(b)**, filter, and wash with small quantities of hot H_2O. Evap. filtrate to dryness in porcelain dish on steam bath; when cool, treat with 2 ml phenoldisulfonic acid soln as in **33.005(b)**. Dil. with H_2O and slowly add NH_4OH until max. color is developed. Filter if necessary, transfer to 100 ml Nessler tubes, and compare with stds in usual manner. Record result as mg N or nitrate/L.

Reduction Method (2)
(For water of high Cl content)

33.007 Reagents

(a) *Aluminum foil.*—Purest obtainable. Cut into ca 10 cm strips, weighing ca 0.5 g each.

(b) *Nessler reagent.*—Dissolve 143 g NaOH in 950 ml H_2O and filter thru asbestos. Add 50 g red HgI_2 to filtrate and dil. with H_2O to 1 L. Mix thoroly, let settle, and use supernatant.

(c) *Sodium hydroxide soln.*—Dissolve 250 g pure NaOH in 1250 ml H_2O. Add 2 or 3 strips Al foil and let stand ca 12 hr. Conc. soln to 1 L by boiling.

(d) *Ammonium chloride std soln.*—0.01 mg N/ml. Dissolve 3.819 g NH_4Cl in NH_3-free H_2O and dil. to 1 L. Dil. 10 ml of this soln to 1 L.

33.008 Determination

To 100 ml sample, or quantity contg ≤0.1 mg nitrate N in 300 ml casserole, add 2 ml NaOH soln and conc. by boiling to ca ⅓ original vol. Transfer to 100 ml test tube, using N-free H_2O, and dil., if necessary, to ca 75 ml. Prep. blank (preferably several blanks, since N impurity in Al is often distributed unevenly) by placing ca 75 ml N-free H_2O and 2 ml NaOH soln in 100 ml test tube. Place strip of Al foil in each tube. Close ends of test tubes with rubber stoppers connected by bent glass tubes to other test tubes contg ca 50 ml slightly acidified NH_3-free H_2O. (These latter tubes serve as traps to prevent escape of NH_3 and at same time permit free evolution of H.) Let sample and blank stand at room temp. 12 hr or until reduction is complete.

Nesslerize contents of trap tubes by addn of 2 ml Nessler reagent. If high in NH_3, indicating frothing over of sample, discard detn. Disregard traps if they contain only 0.01–0.02 mg each of N as NH_3.

---

[*] Methods so marked are surplus methods. *See* "Definitions of Terms and Explanatory Notes," item (29).

[*] The official methods for nitrogen, **2.051** and **2.052**, conform with the recommendations made by the Joint Committee on Uniformity of Methods for Water Examination, 1959.

Transfer sample and blank to distn flasks, using 250 ml NH₃-free H₂O for each; distill at rate of ca 1 tubeful in 10 min into 50 ml Nessler tubes until NH₃ ceases to be given off (4 or 5 tubes are usually enough). Add to each tube 2 ml Nessler reagent and let stand 10 min. From small buret measure into Nessler tubes definite amts of std NH₄Cl soln, dil. contents of each tube to 50 ml with NH₃-free H₂O, add 2 ml Nessler reagent, and compare depth of color with Nesslerized distillate. Report as mg N or nitrate/L.

Chloride—Official Final Action

33.009   *Reagents*

(a) *Potassium chromate indicator.*—Dissolve 5 g K_2CrO_4 in H_2O, add satd $AgNO_3$ soln until slight permanent red ppt forms, filter, and dil. to 100 ml.

(b) *Silver nitrate std soln.*—Dissolve 4.792 g $AgNO_3$ in H_2O and dil. to 1 L. 1 ml = 1 mg Cl. Stdze as in **45.030.**

33.010   *Determination*

To 100 ml sample add few drops of phthln. If soln turns pink, titr. CO_3 thus indicated to bicarbonate with $0.05N$ H_2SO_4. If sample is acid to Me orange, add $0.05N$ Na_2CO_3 to neutze acidity. Add 1 ml K_2CrO_4 indicator and titr. with std $AgNO_3$ soln. Correct for amt of $AgNO_3$ soln necessary to give, in 100 ml Cl-free H_2O with 1 ml K_2CrO_4 soln, shade obtained at end of titrn of sample. If iodides and bromides are found in interfering amts, make equiv. correction.

If Cl is present in very small amts, conc. 500 or 1000 ml in porcelain dish to 100 ml, carefully rub down sides of dish, add 1 ml K_2CrO_4 indicator, and titr. with std $AgNO_3$ soln. If enough Cl is present in 100 ml water to consume >25 ml std $AgNO_3$ soln, det. by pptn and weigh AgCl as in **3.068.**

Fluorides (3)—Official Final Action

33.011   *Reagents*

(a) *Fluoride std soln.*—0.01 mg F/ml. Dissolve 2.21 g NaF (min. purity 98%) in 1 L H_2O. Dil. 10 ml of this soln to 1 L.

(b) *Thorium nitrate soln.*—Dissolve 0.25 g $Th(NO_3)_4.12H_2O$ or 0.2 g $Th(NO_3)_4.4H_2O$ in 1 L H_2O.

(c) *Alizarin red indicator.*—0.01% aq. soln Na alizarin sulfonate (alizarin red S).

(d) *Hydrochloric acid.*—Exactly $0.05N$.

(e) *Sodium hydroxide soln.*—Exactly $0.05N$.

(f) *Hydroxylamine hydrochloride soln.*—1.0 g/100 ml.

33.012   *Apparatus*

(a) *Claisen flask.*—250 ml.

(b) *Nessler tubes.*—6 long-form 50 ml tubes with double optically plane disks fused to tubes. Match tubes for length and test for optical similarity as follows: Add ca 40 ml H_2O, 1 ml indicator, 2 ml $0.05N$ HCl, and H_2O to mark on tube. To 1 tube add such amt of $Th(NO_3)_4$ soln that, after dilg to mark and mixing, color is barely changed to faint pink. Note amt of $Th(NO_3)_4$ soln used. Add same amt of $Th(NO_3)_4$ soln to each of remaining 5 tubes. Reject tubes showing detectable differences in shade or intensity.

See also **25.031.**

33.013   *Preparation of Sample*

If sample has odor of H_2S, oxidize with 0.1 ml 30% H_2O_2 soln before evapn.

Place 100 ml sample in porcelain or Pt dish, make alk. to phthln with 10% NaOH soln (avoid excess), and evap. to 20 ml over burner at temp. just below bp. During evapn keep sample alk. by adding small quantities $0.05N$ NaOH soln from time to time. Transfer the 20 ml evapd sample to Claisen flask contg glass beads or boiling tube previously rinsed with boiling 10% NaOH soln to eliminate all traces of gelatinous SiO_2 accumulating in flask.

Place flask contg sample on asbestos board (6″ × 6″ × ¼″ with 1″ center hole) over burner adjusted for medium flame. Close straight neck of flask with 2-hole rubber stopper thru which pass thermometer and stem of small separator with outlet constricted to 2 mm diam. (Adjust thermometer and outlet tube of separator to extend almost to bottom of flask.) Close other neck of flask with solid rubber stopper. (Alternatively, all-glass distn assembly may be used.)

Connect flask with H_2O condenser, add 20 ml 60% $HClO_4$ (*Caution: See* **46.028**(a) *and* (d)) to flask, rinsing evapg dish and separator; then add amt of satd $AgClO_4$ soln that will ppt chlorides (detd previously by titrn with std $AgNO_3$ soln), and distill at 132±3°, adding H_2O dropwise thru separator to maintain temp. during distn. Collect nearly 200 ml distillate. Dil. to vol. (200 ml) and mix well. To det. acidity use 40 ml distillate, add 1 ml indicator, mix thoroly, and note ml $0.05N$ NaOH required for neutzn.

Repeat prepn and distn, using 100 ml H_2O in place of sample, to det. blank.

33.014   *Determination*

Prep. one std, one color comparison tube, and one or more sample tubes as follows:

(a) *Color comparison tube.*—To 40 ml H_2O add 2 ml $0.05N$ HCl, 1 ml alizarin red indicator, 1 ml $NH_2OH.HCl$ soln, and enough $Th(NO_3)_4$ soln to give faint but definite pink end point. Compare all end point colors with this color.

(b) *Sample tube.*—To sample tube contg 40 ml distillate add 1 ml indicator, 1 ml $NH_2OH.HCl$ soln, and such amt of $0.05N$ HCl that total amt of acid in tube (acidity previously detd plus amt of $0.05N$ HCl added) equals 2 ml $0.05N$ HCl. Dil. to vol. and mix. If in preliminary acidity detn it is found that the 40 ml distillate requires >2 ml 0.05N NaOH soln for neutzn, do not add the HCl soln to sample tube, but add to std tube same amt of acid as was found present in sample tube. If 40 ml distillate requires >5 ml 0.05N NaOH, repeat distn under conditions favorable to low acidity. From 10 ml buret, graduated to 0.05 ml, add Th(NO$_3$)$_4$ soln with frequent mixing until faint pink appears, comparable to comparison tube, (a). Note vol. Th(NO$_3$)$_4$ soln used.

(c) *Std tube.*—To std tube contg 40 ml H$_2$O add 1 ml indicator, 1 ml NH$_2$OH.HCl soln, and ≥2 ml 0.05N HCl, as was required in sample tube in (b). If aliquot chosen for detn already contains 2–5 ml 0.05N acid, add exactly same amt to std tube. Add exactly same amt of Th(NO$_3$)$_4$ soln as was added to sample tube. To std tube (now more highly colored than sample tube) add std F soln from 10 ml buret with mixing until color matches that of sample tube. Dil. contents of both std and sample tubes to same vol. Mix soln in each tube and let all air bubbles escape before making color comparisons. Check end point by adding 1–2 drops std F soln to std tube. Distinct color change should develop.

33.015 *Calculation*

Subtract ml F soln required by blank from ml F soln required by sample.

$$\frac{\text{ml F soln} \times \text{ml total distillate} \times 10}{\text{ml aliquot titrd} \times \text{wt sample taken}} = \text{F (ppm)}.$$

Example: 100 ml sample, evapd and distd to 200 ml, of which 40 ml aliquot corresponds to 5 ml F soln, gives:

$$(5 \times 200 \times 10)/(40 \times 100) = 2.5 \text{ F (ppm)}.$$

★ Hydrogen Sulfide (4)—Official ★ Final Action

33.016 *Iodometric Method*

See **31.016–31.017**, 10th ed.

33.017 Carbonate and Bicarbonate— Official Final Action

To 100 ml sample add few drops phthln, and if pink is produced, titr. with 0.05N HCl or H$_2$SO$_4$, adding drop every 2–3 sec until color disappears. Multiply buret reading by factor 3 to obtain mg CO$_3$ ion in 100 ml. To colorless soln from this titrn, or to original soln if no color is produced with phthln, add 1–2 drops Me orange, continue titrn without refilling buret, and note total reading. If CO$_3$ is absent, multiply total buret reading by factor 3.05 to obtain value of HCO$_3$ ion in mg/100 ml. If CO$_3$ is present, multiply reading with phthln by 2 and subtract from total reading of buret. Multiply difference by 3.05 to obtain HCO$_3$ ion in mg/100 ml. Express results as mg/L.

33.018 Silica—Official Final Action

Make preliminary examination, using 100–250 ml sample, to det. approx. amt of Ca and Mg present, in order to det. amt of sample to be evapd for final analysis.

Evap. amt of sample equiv. to 0.1–0.6 g CaO or 0.1–1 g Mg$_2$P$_2$O$_7$ (usually 1–5 L). Acidify sample with HCl and evap. on steam bath to dryness in Pt dish. Continue drying ca 1 hr. Thoroly moisten residue with 5–10 ml HCl. Let stand 10–15 min and add enough H$_2$O to bring sol. salts into soln. Heat on steam bath until salts dissolve. Filter to remove most of SiO$_2$ and wash thoroly with hot H$_2$O. Evap. filtrate to dryness and treat residue with 5 ml HCl and enough H$_2$O to dissolve sol. salts, as before. Heat, filter, and wash thoroly with hot H$_2$O. Designate filtrate as *Soln A*.

Transfer the two residues to Pt crucible, ignite, heat over blast lamp, and weigh. Moisten contents of crucible with few drops H$_2$O, add few drops H$_2$SO$_4$ and few ml HF, and evap. on steam bath under hood. Repeat treatment if all SiO$_2$ is not volatilized. Dry carefully on hot plate, ignite, heat over blast lamp, and weigh. Difference between the two wts is wt SiO$_2$. Add wt residue (Fe$_2$O$_3$ + Al$_2$O$_3$) to that of Al$_2$O$_3$ and Fe$_2$O$_3$ obtained in **33.019**. (If residue weighs >0.5 mg, BaSO$_4$ may be present in sample. If so, make necessary correction and add to wt Fe$_2$O$_3$ and Al$_2$O$_3$ in **33.019**.)

33.019 Iron and Aluminum—Official Final Action

Conc. *Soln A*, **33.018**, to 200 ml; while still hot, slowly add NH$_4$OH, stirring constantly, until alk. to Me orange. Boil, filter, and wash 3 times with hot H$_2$O. Dissolve ppt in hot HCl (1 + 1). Dil. to ca 25 ml, boil, and again ppt with NH$_4$OH. Filter, wash thoroly with hot H$_2$O, dry, ignite, and weigh as Al$_2$O$_3$ and Fe$_2$O$_3$. (In presence of H$_3$PO$_4$, wt of this residue must be corrected for P$_2$O$_5$ equiv. to H$_3$PO$_4$ found in **33.032**, allowing for difference in vols of the water used for these detns.) Designate filtrate as *Soln B*.

Iron—Official Final Action

33.020 *Colorimetric Method*

(Iron <1 mg; not applicable in presence of phosphates)

Fuse, in Pt crucible, ignited ppt of Fe$_2$O$_3$ and Al$_2$O$_3$, **33.019**, with fused KHSO$_4$, dissolve in H$_2$O, and ppt Fe and Al with NH$_4$OH. Filter, dissolve ppt on filter paper in HCl and HNO$_3$, dil. soln, add 3 ml 5% NH$_4$CNS soln, dil. to suitable vol., and compare color developed with that of calibrated color disks or stds contg known amts of Fe treated similarly.

33.021 *Volumetric Method*

(*Caution: See* **46.059**.)

Fuse residue of Fe$_2$O$_3$ and Al$_2$O$_3$, **33.019**, in Pt crucible with ca 1 g fused KHSO$_4$. (Fusion takes only few min, and must not be continued beyond time actually needed.) When fusion is complete, set crucible aside to cool. Add H_2SO_4 $(1 + 4)$ and heat crucible until fused mass dissolves. Evap. on steam bath as far as possible; then heat gradually until copious fumes of SO_3 evolve. Dissolve in H_2O and let stand on steam bath. Cool, transfer to erlenmeyer, and dil. to such vol. that soln contains $\leq 2.5\%$ free H_2SO_4.

Pass H_2S thru soln to reduce Fe and ppt any Pt contaminating residue from fusion. (Zn may be used instead of H_2S for reducing Fe.) Filter, wash, and again pass H_2S thru soln to reduce all Fe. Expel H_2S by boiling, at same time passing current of CO_2 thru soln. Test escaping gas with $Pb(OAc)_2$ paper to confirm complete removal of H_2S. Discontinue boiling and let flask cool without discontinuing current of CO_2. Titr. reduced Fe with std $KMnO_4$ soln (1 ml = 1 mg Fe) and calc. as Fe.

33.022   Aluminum—Official Final Action

To obtain wt Al_2O_3, in absence of phosphates, subtract from wt Fe_2O_3 and Al_2O_3, 33.019, the Fe, 33.020 or 33.021, calcd to Fe_2O_3. Calc. to Al.

33.023   Calcium—Official Final Action

Conc. *Soln B*, 33.019, to 150–200 ml, and to this soln, contg equiv. of ≤ 0.6 g CaO or 1 g $Mg_2P_2O_7$, add 1–2 g $H_2C_2O_4 \cdot 2H_2O$ and enough HCl $(1 + 1)$ to clear soln. Heat to boiling and neutze with NH_4OH, stirring constantly. Add NH_4OH in slight excess and let stand 3 hr in warm place. Filter supernatant and wash ppt once or twice by decantation with 1% $(NH_4)_2C_2O_4$ soln. Dissolve ppt in HCl $(1 + 1)$, dil. to 100–200 ml, add little more $H_2C_2O_4$, and ppt as above. After letting ppt stand 3 hr, filter, wash with 1% $(NH_4)_2C_2O_4$ soln, dry, ignite, heat over blast lamp at $\geq 950°$, and weigh as CaO and SrO. From this wt subtract wt SrO equiv. to the Sr, 33.024. Difference is wt CaO. Calc. to Ca. Designate combined filtrates and washings as *Soln C*.

As check on CaO, evap. to dryness filtrate from the $Sr(NO_3)_2$ in 33.024, beginning "Filter, and wash with ether-alcohol mixt. . . ." Dissolve the $Ca(NO_3)_2$ in H_2O, ppt as oxalate, filter, wash, ignite at 950°, and weigh as CaO. CaO $\times$ 0.7147 = Ca.

33.024   Strontium (5)—Official Final Action

Dissolve oxides, 33.023, in HNO_3 $(1 + 1)$ and test with spectroscope for Sr. If Sr is present, transfer HNO_3 soln to small erlenmeyer. Evap. nearly to dryness over low flame, and heat 1–2 hr at 150–160° after H_2O is evapd. Break up dried material with stirring rod and add 10–15 ml mixt. of absolute alcohol and ether $(1 + 1)$ to dissolve the $Ca(NO_3)_2$. Cork flask and let stand with frequent shaking 2 hr or longer. Decant soln thru 5.5 cm filter, reserving filtrate. Wash residue several times by decantation with small portions of the ether-alcohol mixt. Dry residue and paper, and repeatedly wash paper with small portions of hot H_2O, collecting filtrate in flask contg main portion of $Sr(NO_3)_2$ residue. Add 1 or 2

drops HNO_3 $(1 + 1)$, evap., dry, pulverize, and treat with 10–15 ml ether-alcohol mixt. Cork flask and let stand ca 12 hr, shaking occasionally.

Filter, and wash with ether-alcohol mixt. until few drops filtrate evapd on watch glass leave practically no residue. Dry paper and ppt. Dissolve $Sr(NO_3)_2$ in few ml hot H_2O. Add few drops H_2SO_4 and then add vol. alcohol equal to vol. soln and let stand 12 hr. Filter, ignite, weigh as $SrSO_4$, and calc. to Sr. Test spectroscopically for Ca and Ba. If these elements are present, det. quantity and make necessary correction.

33.025   Magnesium—Official Final Action

Conc. *Soln C*, 33.023, to 200 ml, acidify with HCl $(1 + 1)$, and add 2–3 g $(NH_4)_2HPO_4$ and enough HCl $(1 + 1)$ to produce clear soln when all $(NH_4)_2HPO_4$ is dissolved. When cold, make slightly alk. with NH_4OH, stirring constantly. Add 2 ml excess of NH_4OH and let stand ca 12 hr. Filter supernatant and wash 4 times by decantation with NH_4OH $(1 + 10)$. Dissolve ppt in HCl $(1 + 1)$, dil. to ca 150 ml, add little $(NH_4)_2HPO_4$, and ppt with NH_4OH as before. Let stand 12 hr, filter, wash Cl-free with NH_4OH $(1 + 10)$, place in porcelain crucible, ignite, heat over blast lamp, and weigh as $Mg_2P_2O_7$. Calc. to Mg. $Mg_2P_2O_7 \times 0.21842 = Mg$.

33.026   Sulfate—Official Final Action

Make preliminary examination, using 100–250 ml sample, to det. approx. quantity of sulfates. (Alkali salts present can be approximated by calcg quantity of Na necessary to combine with excess of acids—HCl, H_2SO_4, and H_2CO_3—over Ca and Mg.)

Take enough sample (usually 1–5 L) to yield ≤ 1 g $BaSO_4$ and ≤ 0.5 g mixed chlorides. Acidify with HCl $(1 + 1)$, evap. to dryness in Pt dish, and remove SiO_2 by 2 evapns as in 33.018, using ≤ 2 ml HCl for final soln. Combine filtrate and washings from SiO_2 detns and conc. to 150–200 ml. Heat to boiling and ppt with slight excess of 10% $BaCl_2 \cdot 2H_2O$ soln, added very slowly and with constant stirring. Cover, and let stand on steam bath ca 12 hr. Filter, thoroly wash ppt of $BaSO_4$ with hot H_2O until Cl-free, dry, ignite over Bunsen burner, and weigh.

If sulfate content of sample is unusually large, proceed as far as concn of SiO_2 filtrates, as above, Add 50 ml HCl, heat to boiling, and ppt with $BaCl_2$ soln as before. Evap. to dryness, take up in H_2O and few drops HCl, digest till ppt settles, wash by decantation, filter, ignite, and weigh. Calc. to SO_4 ion. Designate filtrate as *Soln D*.

Sodium, Potassium, and Lithium

Ether-Alcohol Method (6)—Official Final Action

33.027   *Preparation of Mixed Chlorides*

Evap. *Soln D*, 33.026, to dryness in Pt dish, and ignite residue to faint redness to remove all traces of

NH_4 salts. Dissolve residue in dish in ca 200 ml H_2O and ppt with satd $Ca(OH)_2$ soln or satd $Ba(OH)_2$ soln. Boil, let stand 30 min, and filter off insol. $Mg(OH)_2$ and undissolved $Ca(OH)_2$. Thoroly wash ppt with hot H_2O and combine filtrate and washings. If ppt of Mg is large, dissolve in small amt of HCl, evap. to dryness, take up with H_2O, and ppt as before.

Conc. the two filtrates and washings to 200–250 ml. Add NH_4OH and enough solid $(NH_4)_2CO_3$ to ppt Ca and Ba. Let stand on steam bath 1–2 hr. Filter off supernatant, dissolve ppt in HCl, again ppt as above, and wash thoroly with hot H_2O. Evap. combined filtrates and washings to dryness and drive off NH_4 salts by gentle heat. Treat residue with H_2O, pass thru small filter, using as little wash H_2O as possible, evap. to small vol., and again ppt with 1 or 2 drops NH_4OH and 2 or 3 drops satd solns of $(NH_4)_2CO_3$ and $(NH_4)_2C_2O_4$. If any ppt appears, filter and repeat process.

Evap. filtrate to dryness and drive off all NH_4 salts by heating to faint redness in Pt dish. Treat residue with little H_2O, filter into small Pt dish, add few drops HCl $(1 + 1)$, and evap. to dryness. Dry in oven; heat to faint redness; cool in desiccator; and weigh combined chlorides of K, Na, and Li. Repeat heating to constant wt (x). Dissolve mixed chlorides in hot H_2O, filter, and wash. Return filter paper and residue to dish, dry, ignite, and weigh (y). $(x) - (y)$ = wt mixed chlorides.

33.028 Determination

(*Caution: See* **46.011, 46.039,** and **46.054.**)

Dissolve mixed chlorides, **33.027,** in min. amt of cold H_2O (ca 1.5 ml is more than enough for 0.5 g salts), in tall 200 ml beaker. Add 1 drop HCl, and then gradually add 20 ml absolute alcohol, dropping alcohol into center of beaker (not on sides) while rotating soln. (NaCl and KCl should be pptd in perfectly uniform granular condition.) In similar manner add 60 ml ether (sp gr 0.716–0.717 at 25°) and let mixt. stand ca 5 min or until ppt is well agglomerated and supernatant is almost clear, rotating mixt. occasionally. Filter with suction thru weighed gooch into erlenmeyer, using bell jar arrangement, washing beaker thoroly with mixt. of alcohol and ether $(1 + 5)$, and collecting all ppt on gooch with aid of policeman. Thoroly wash ppt on gooch, set crucible aside, and rinse funnel with alcohol-ether mixt. to wash any adhering Li soln into flask contg filtrate. Evap. filtrate to dryness on steam bath, using air current.

Treat residue with 10 ml absolute alcohol, warming if necessary, so that practically all residue dissolves. If slight film remains on bottom and sides of flask, remove with policeman. Then, while rotating soln in flask, add 50 ml ether (sp gr 0.716–0.717 at 25°), followed by 1 drop HCl. Let stand 30 min, rotating soln frequently. When fine ppt has agglomer-

ated (only very small amt is usually pptd), filter into tall beaker with suction thru gooch contg first ppt. Wash combined ppts with the ether-alcohol mixt., taking same precautions as in first pptn. Air-dry gooch and contents; then dry in oven, ignite gently, cool, and weigh to obtain combined wt NaCl and KCl. Reserve crucible and contents for K detn.

Evap., on steam bath, ether-alcohol filtrate and washings contg the Li. Dissolve residue in little H_2O, add slight excess of H_2SO_4 $(1 + 1)$, and transfer to weighed porcelain or Pt dish. Evap. as far as possible on steam bath and then gently ignite residue over flame. (By placing dish on triangle over asbestos gauze and using low flame, soln can be evapd without spattering.) Finally ignite carefully over full flame, cool, and weigh. If charring has occurred, repeat ignition with H_2SO_4. Calc. to Li, using factor 0.1262.

Remove KCl and NaCl from gooch by washing with 25–50 ml hot H_2O, using suction, and collecting filtrate in porcelain dish. Add enough Pt soln, **2.076(b),** to convert KCl and NaCl to K_2PtCl_6 and Na_2PtCl_6, and evap. to dryness. Treat residue with 80% alcohol by vol., filter, and wash until excess of H_2PtCl_6 and Na_2PtCl_6 is removed. Dry filter and ppt, dissolve residue in hot H_2O, and transfer to weighed Pt dish. Evap. on steam bath, dry 30 min in oven at 100°, cool, and weigh as K_2PtCl_6. Calc. to KCl, using factor 0.3068, and to K, using factor 0.1609.

Det. wt NaCl by subtracting wt KCl from wt combined KCl and NaCl. Calc. to Na, using factor 0.3934.

Barium—Official Final Action

(It is not necessary to look for Ba if sulfate is present in appreciable amt unless sample contains large amt of bicarbonate or chloride, which may hold in soln small amts of both sulfate and Ba.)

Gravimetric Method (7)

33.029 Reagents

(a) *Ammonium dichromate soln.*—Dissolve 100 g of the SO_4-free salt in H_2O and dil. to 1 L.

(b) *Ammonium acetate soln.*—Dissolve 300 g of the salt in H_2O, neutze with NH_4OH, and dil. to 1 L.

(c) *Dilute ammonium acetate wash soln.*—Dil. 20 ml (b) to 1 L.

(Reaction of acetate solns should be alk. rather than acid.)

33.030 Determination

Acidify 1–5 L portion of sample with HCl and conc. to ca 200 ml. (If ppt forms, filter off and test for Ba.) Add ca 0.5 g NH_4Cl, and ppt Fe and Al with NH_4OH. Boil, filter, and wash. To filtrate add excess (10 ml) NH_4OAc soln, (b), keeping total vol. ca 200 ml. Heat to boiling and add, with stirring, ca 5 ml $(NH_4)_2Cr_2O_7$ soln. Let settle and cool. Decant clear liq. thru filter and wash ppt by decantation with dil. NH_4OAc soln until filtrate is no longer perceptibly colored (ca 100 ml wash soln).

Place beaker under funnel, dissolve ppt on paper with warm HNO_3 $(1 + 1)$, using as little as possible, and wash paper. Add little more acid to dissolve ppt in beaker, and then NH_4OH until ppt that forms no longer redissolves. Heat to boiling; add, with stirring, 10 ml NH_4OAc soln, (b), and 2 ml $(NH_4)_2Cr_2O_7$ soln; let cool slowly, and wash ppt free of chromate with dil. NH_4OAc soln by decantation and filtration. Dry ppt, ignite moderately to constant wt, and weigh as $BaCrO_4$. Calc. as Ba, using factor 0.5421.

33.031 *Volumetric Method*

Proceed as in **33.030** thru "wash ppt free of chromate with dil. NH_4OAc soln." (after second pptn). Dissolve ppt in ca 10 ml HCl $(1 + 1)$ and hot H_2O. Wash filter, dil. soln to ca 400 ml, and add ca 50 ml freshly prepd 10% KI soln. Mix carefully and titr. liberated I after 3 or 4 min with $0.1N$ $Na_2S_2O_3$. 1 ml $0.1N$ $Na_2S_2O_3$ = 4.578 mg Ba.

33.032 Phosphate—Official Final Action

Treat 500 ml sample, or larger quantity if necessary, with ca 10 ml HNO_3 and evap. in porcelain dish nearly to dryness to drive off HCl. Treat residue with H_2O and filter if necessary. Add NH_4OH to alky and then just enough HNO_3 to restore acidity. Add some solid NH_4NO_3 and heat in 45–50° H_2O bath. Add freshly prepd molybdate soln, **2.029**(b), and keep 30 min at 45–50°. If more than trace of yellow ppt is present, filter and wash with recently boiled and cooled H_2O until entirely acid-free. Transfer ppt and filter to beaker, add little H_2O, and beat paper and contents to pulp. Dissolve yellow ppt in small amt of std KOH soln, **2.029**(c), add phthln, and titr. with the std acid. ml $0.1N$ KOH $\times$ 0.4130 $\times$ 1000/ml sample = mg PO_4/L.

33.033 Preparation of Sample—Manganese, Iodine, Bromine, Arsenic, and Boric Acid—Official Final Action

Evap. 0.5–2 L sample to dryness after addn of small amts of solid Na_2CO_3. Boil residue thus obtained with H_2O, transfer to filter, and wash thoroly with hot H_2O. Use residue remaining on filter for detn of Mn. Dil. alk. filtrate to definite vol. and use for detn of I, Br, As, and H_3BO_3.

Manganese—Official Final Action
Persulfate Method

33.034   *Reagents*

(a) *Silver nitrate soln.*—Dissolve 2 g $AgNO_3$ in H_2O and dil. to 1 L.

(b) *Manganese std soln.*—0.1 mg/ml. Dissolve 0.2877 g pure $KMnO_4$ in ca 100 ml H_2O, acidify soln with H_2SO_4 $(1 + 1)$, and slowly heat to boiling. Slowly add enough 10% $H_2C_2O_4 \cdot 2H_2O$ soln to discharge color. Cool, and dil. to 1 L.

33.035   *Determination*

Dissolve insol. residue, **33.033**, in excess HNO_3 $(1 + 1)$, evap. to dryness, treat with H_2O, and add ca 1 ml HNO_3 and little of the $AgNO_3$ soln. If ppt of AgCl appears, add addnl $AgNO_3$ soln until all Cl is pptd. Add excess of ca 10 ml $AgNO_3$ soln for each mg Mn present in sample. Filter, add 1 g $(NH_4)_2S_2O_8$ to filtrate, and place beaker or flask contg soln on steam bath until pink color develops (ca 20 min). Compare color developed with stds similarly prepd by treating solns contg known amts of std Mn soln with dil. HNO_3, $AgNO_3$ soln, and $(NH_4)_2S_2O_8$.

33.036 ★ *Bismuthate Method (8)* ★
See **31.037–31.038**, 10th ed.

Iodide and Bromide—Official First Action

(This method is qual. and approx. quant. For accurate quant. methods for iodides, *see* **33.058**.)

33.037   *Determination*

(*Caution: See* **46.039, 46.040, 46.047,** and **46.048**.)

Evap. aliquot of alk. filtrate, **33.033**, to dryness; add 2–3 ml H_2O to dissolve residue and enough alcohol to make ca 90% alcohol. (This ppts chlorides.) Heat to boiling, filter, and repeat soln and pptn once or twice. Add 2 or 3 drops 10% NaOH soln to combined alc. filtrates and evap. to dryness. Dissolve last residue in 2–3 ml H_2O and repeat pptn with alcohol, heating, and filtering. Add drop of 10% NaOH soln to this alc. filtrate and evap. to dryness.

Dissolve residue in little H_2O; acidify with H_2SO_4 $(1 + 5)$, using 3 or 4 drops excess; and transfer to small flask. Add 4 drops *0.2% $NaNO_2$ soln* and ca 5 ml CS_2. Shake until all I is extd and filter off acid soln from CS_2. Wash flask, filter, and contents with cold H_2O and transfer CS_2 contg the I in soln to Nessler tube, using ca 5 ml CS_2. In washing filter, make contents of tube to definite vol., usually 12–15 ml, and compare color with that of other tubes contg known amts of I dissolved in CS_2. Prep. these std tubes by treating measured amts of soln of known KI content as described above, beginning "acidify with H_2SO_4 $(1 + 5)$ ..."

Sep. transfer acid soln of sample and stds from which I has been removed to small flasks. To stds add definite measured amts of bromide soln of known concn, and to each flask contg sample and stds add 5 ml CS_2. Add *satd and freshly prepd Cl-H_2O*, 1 ml at time, shaking after each addn until all Br is set free. Avoid large excess of Cl, as a bromo-chloride may form and spoil color reaction.

Filter off aq. soln from CS_2 thru moistened filter, wash contents of filter 2 or 3 times with H_2O, and then transfer to Nessler tube with ca 1 ml CS_2. Repeat extn of filtrate twice, using 3 ml CS_2 each time. Combined CS_2 exts usually total 11.5–12 ml. Add enough CS_2 to tubes to make definite vol., usually 12–15 ml, and compare sample with stds. If, when using this method near its upper limit, amts of CS_2

recommended do not ext all Br, make 1 or 2 addnl extns with CS₂, transfer exts to another tube, and compare color with some of lower stds. Add readings thus obtained to others.

Results closely approximating true values for I and Br can be obtained in shorter time on most samples by omitting extns with alcohol and comparing color of CS₂ solns directly in extn flasks.

33.038 ★ Bromide in Presence of ★ Chloride but Not Iodide (9)—Official First Action

See **31.040–31.043**, 10th ed.

33.039 ★ Bromide in Presence of ★ Chloride and Iodide (10) —Official Final Action

See **31.044–31.046**, 10th ed.

Arsenic—Official Final Action

33.040 *Reagents and Apparatus— See 25.006 and 25.007*

33.041 *Determination*

Take portion of alk. filtrate, **33.033**, contg ≤0.03 mg As₂O₃. If amt taken is >10 ml, evap. soln to ca that vol. on steam bath. Transfer soln into generator of app., **25.007**, with aid of ca 10 ml H₂O, add 20 ml H₂SO₄ (1 + 2), and proceed as in **25.010**, beginning "add 5 ml KI reagent ..."

★ Boric Acid ★

33.042 Qualitative Test—Procedure

See **31.049**, 10th ed.

33.043 Quantitative Method (11)—Official First Action

Titrn with NaOH in presence of mannitol. See **31.050–31.051**, 10th ed.

33.044 Lead—See 25.044–25.048

33.045 Method of Reporting Results (12)—Procedure

Report radicals and anhyd. salts in mg/L or, in case of highly concd waters, in g/L. For benefit of physicians, in case of medicinal waters, also report salts in terms of grains/qt, using factor 0.014600 to convert mg/L to grains/qt. In reporting salts in terms of grains/qt, convert salts that have H₂O of crystn to hydrated form as expressed in USP and in NF, and convert Mg(HCO₃)₂ to MgCO₃ and Ca(HCO₃)₂ to CaCO₃. Use following factors in these calcns:

$$Na_2SO_4 \times 2.2684 = Na_2SO_4.10H_2O$$
$$MgSO_4 \times 2.0477 = MgSO_4.7H_2O$$
$$CaSO_4 \times 1.2647 = CaSO_4.2H_2O$$
$$Mg(HCO_3)_2 \times 0.5762 = MgCO_3$$
$$Ca(HCO_3)_2 \times 0.6174 = CaCO_3.$$

When complete analysis is made, report error of analysis and state how it is distributed. Report only significant figures.

Report Fe and Al together when present in unimportant quantities and in calcns consider them as Fe. When Fe and Al are present in larger amts, make sepn and report each sep.

In calcg hypothetical combinations of acidic and basic ions, join NO₂, NO₃, BO₃, and AsO₄ to Na; I and Br to K; and PO₄ to Ca. Assign residual basic ions in following order: NH₄, Li, K, Na, Mg, Ca, Sr, Mn, Fe, and Al; to residual acid ions in following order: Cl, SO₄, CO₃, and HCO₃. When not enough HCO₃ is present to join with all Ca, residual Ca is joined to SiO₂ to form CaSiO₃, and Mn, Fe, and Al are calcd to oxides Mn₃O₄, Fe₂O₃, and Al₂O₃, resp.

Use equiv. combining wts or their reciprocals in uniting radicals and, when necessary for purpose of comparison, in reducing salts to radicals and reuniting radicals in order specified above.

Equiv. combining wt of radical is obtained by dividing its wt by its valence. Equiv. combining wt of salt is obtained by dividing its molecular wt by product of valency of basic element and number of atoms of basic element in the salt.

Procedure in calcg hypothetical combinations by use of equiv. combining wts and their reciprocals is as follows:

Multiply wts obtained, expressed in mg/L, or, for highly concd waters, in g/L, for each radical to be combined, by corresponding reciprocal of equiv. combining wts. If Na and K are to be detd by calcn, as is frequently the case, subtract sum of values obtained (reacting values) for basic radicals from sum of reacting values for acid radicals. Difference represents reacting value of undetd Na and K.

When all constituents in water have been detd, sums of reacting values of acid and basic radicals should be very nearly same. In this case, if difference is reasonable and well within limit of accuracy of methods used, it may be distributed equally among all radicals detd, or among those believed to be less accurately detd than others. If difference is unreasonably great, repeat analysis in whole or in part. Sums of reacting values of acid and basic radicals must be equal before calcn is made. Obtain reacting values of the salts by subtracting in succession reacting values of radicals in specified order. To convert these values to mg/L of respective salts multiply each of them by the equiv. combining wt of respective salt.

33.046 *(See table at top of next page)*

SALT (13)

33.047 Preparation of Sample—Procedure

If sample is coarser than "20 mesh," grind so that all will pass No. 20 sieve, but avoid undue grinding so that as much as possible will be retained on No. 80

33.046   *Equivalent Combining Weights and Their Reciprocals Based On International Atomic Weights, 1969*

Neg. Radicals	Equiv. Combining Wts	Reciprocals of Equiv. Combining Wts	Pos. Radicals	Equiv. Combining Wts	Reciprocals of Equiv. Combining Wts
NO_3	62.0049	0.01613	NH_4	18.0386	0.05544
BO_2	42.810	0.02336	Li	6.941	0.14407
AsO_4	46.3064	0.02160	K	39.102	0.02557
I	126.9045	0.00788	Na	22.9898	0.04350
Br	79.904	0.01252	Mg	12.153	0.08228
PO_4	31.6571	0.03159	Ca	20.04	0.04990
HS	33.07	0.03024	Sr	43.81	0.02283
S	16.03	0.06238	Ba	68.67	0.01456
SiO_3	38.042	0.02629	Mn	27.4690	0.03640
O	7.9997	0.12500	Fe^{++}	27.924	0.03581
Cl	35.453	0.02821	Fe^{+++}	18.616	0.05372
SO_4	48.03	0.02082	Al	8.9938	0.11123
CO_3	30.005	0.03333	Cu	31.773	0.03147
HCO_3	61.017	0.01639			

Salts	Equiv. Combining Wts	Reciprocals of Equiv. Combining Wts	Salts	Equiv. Combining Wts	Reciprocals of Equiv. Combining Wts
NH_4Cl	53.492	0.01869	$MgCl_2$	47.606	0.02101
LiCl	42.394	0.02359	$MgSO_4$	60.18	0.01662
Li_2SO_4	54.97	0.01819	$MgCO_3$	42.157	0.02372
Li_2CO_3	36.946	0.02707	$Mg(HCO_3)_2$	73.170	0.01367
$LiHCO_3$	67.958	0.01471	$Mg(NO_3)_2$	74.157	0.01348
KCl	74.555	0.01341	$CaCl_2$	55.49	0.01802
K_2SO_4	87.13	0.01148	$CaSO_4$	68.07	0.01469
K_2CO_3	69.106	0.01447	$CaCO_3$	50.04	0.01998
$KHCO_3$	100.119	0.00999	$Ca(HCO_3)_2$	81.057	0.01234
KI	166.007	0.00602	$CaSiO_3$	58.08	0.01722
KBr	119.006	0.00840	$Ca_3(PO_4)_2$	51.70	0.01934
NaCl	58.443	0.01711	$SrSO_4$	91.84	0.01089
NaBr	102.895	0.00972	$SrCO_3$	73.81	0.01355
NaI	149.8943	0.00667	$Sr(HCO_3)_2$	104.82	0.00954
Na_2SO_4	71.02	0.01408	$BaSO_4$	116.70	0.00857
Na_2CO_3	52.9944	0.01887	$Ba(HCO_3)_2$	129.69	0.00771
$NaHCO_3$	84.0070	0.01190	$MnSO_4$	75.50	0.01325
$NaNO_2$	68.9953	0.01449	$MnCO_3$	57.474	0.01740
$NaNO_3$	84.9957	0.01177	$Mn(HCO_3)_2$	88.486	0.01130
$NaBO_2$	65.800	0.01520	$FeSO_4$	75.95	0.01317
Na_3AsO_4	69.2962	0.01443	$Fe_2(SO_4)_3$	66.64	0.01501
NaF	41.9882	0.02382	$FeCO_3$	57.928	0.01726
NaHS	56.06	0.01784	$Fe(HCO_3)_2$	88.940	0.01124
Na_3PO_4	54.6469	0.01830	Fe_2O_3	26.615	0.03757
Na_2S	39.02	0.02563	$Al_2(SO_4)_3$	57.02	0.01754
Na_2SiO_3	61.031	0.01639	Al_2O_3	16.9935	0.05885

sieve. Mix sample by quartering and weigh all needed portions as nearly at same time as possible.

33.048 Moisture—Official First Action

Place ca 10 g sample in dry, weighed 200 ml erlenmeyer. Weigh flask and sample. Spread sample evenly over bottom of flask by shaking gently and insert small funnel in neck. Heat flask and sample for periods of 1 hr each at ca 250° until 2 consecutive weighings agree within 5 mg. Occasionally shake flask so that sample will dry evenly. Report loss of wt as H_2O.

33.049 Matters Insoluble in Water—Official First Action

Place 10 g sample in 250 ml beaker, add 200 ml H_2O at room temp., and let stand 30 min, stirring frequently. Filter thru weighed gooch with asbestos mat dried at 110°. Transfer residue to gooch with aid of policeman, using total of ≤ 50 ml H_2O. Wash residue with ca ten 10 ml portions H_2O, until 10 ml filtrate shows only faint opalescence upon addn of few drops $AgNO_3$ soln. Dry crucible and contents to constant wt at 110°. Report increase in wt gooch as "matters insol. in H_2O" and report results in % on

H_2O-free basis. If matters insol. in H_2O are $>0.1\%$ det. their nature.

33.050 Matters Insoluble in Acid (14)—Official First Action

Treat 10 g sample with 200 ml HCl $(1 + 19)$, boil 2–3 min, and let stand 30 min, stirring frequently. Filter thru gooch with mat dried at 110°. Wash, dry at 110°, cool, and weigh. Express results in %.

33.051 Preparation of Solution for Sulfate, Calcium, and Magnesium—Procedure

Weigh ca 20 g sample, transfer to 400 ml beaker, and dissolve in 200 ml HCl $(1 + 3)$. Cover beaker, heat to boiling, and continue boiling gently 10 min. Filter thru paper and wash residue with small amts hot H_2O until filtrate is Cl-free. Unite filtrate and washings, cool, and dil. to 500 ml (*Soln A*).

33.052 Sulfate—Official First Action

Place 250 ml *Soln A*, 33.051, in 400 ml beaker, heat to boiling, and add slight excess hot 10% $BaCl_2$ soln dropwise while stirring. Conc. by heating gently and finally evap. to dryness on steam bath. Facilitate removal of free acid by stirring partly dried residue. Wash ppt by decantation with small amts hot H_2O, finally transferring ppt to close-grain filter paper with aid of policeman and stream of hot H_2O. Test filtrate for presence of Ba. Wash ppt on paper until filtrate is Cl-free. Dry and ignite paper contg ppt over Bunsen flame. Report $\%$ SO_4 in sample on H_2O-free basis.

33.053 Calcium—Official First Action

Place remainder of *Soln A* in 400 ml beaker. Add excess of 10% $H_2C_2O_4.2H_2O$ soln (10 ml usually is enough). Add few drops Me orange; neutze while hot by adding NH_4OH dropwise, stirring constantly. Add ca 1 ml excess NH_4OH, stir, and let stand in warm place 3 hr. Decant supernatant thru filter, reserving filtrate for detn of Mg. Test filtrate for Ca with $(NH_4)_2C_2O_4$ soln. Wash ppt in beaker once with 10 ml 1% $(NH_4)_2C_2O_4$ soln, decanting thru filter paper. Combine filtrate and washings. Dissolve ppt on paper with hot HCl $(1 + 1)$, using same beaker; dil. to 100 ml, add little more $H_2C_2O_4$ soln, and ppt as before. Let stand 3 hr, filter, and wash with 1% $(NH_4)_2C_2O_4$ soln as before, reserving filtrate and washings. Transfer ppt to crucible, dry, ignite, and heat over blast lamp to constant wt (CaO). Report as $\%$ Ca on H_2O-free basis.

33.054 Magnesium—Official First Action

Combine filtrates and washings from Ca detn, conc. if necessary by boiling gently to ca 150 ml, and proceed as in 33.025. Report as $\%$ Mg on H_2O-free basis.

33.055 Lead—*See 25.044–25.048*

Iodine in Iodized Salt (15)—Official Final Action

33.056 Reagents

(a) *Bromine water.*—(*Caution: See* **46.047.**) For alternative procedure, **33.058**(b), det. approx. concn (mg Br/ml) by adding measured vol. from buret to flask contg 50 ml H_2O, 5 ml 10% KI soln, and 5 ml H_2SO_4 $(1 + 9)$, and titrg liberated I with $0.1N$ $Na_2S_2O_3$.

(b) *Sodium thiosulfate.*—$0.005N$. Prep. daily by dilg $0.1N$ soln, **45.038–45.039.**

(c) *Starch soln.*—1% (freshly prepd). *See* **2.129**(c).

(d) *Potassium iodide control soln.*—0.3270 g KI/ 250 ml. Dil. 50 ml to 250 ml, and use 5 ml (= 1.0 mg I and 1.308 mg KI) for control.

.26 mg/ml

33.057 Preparation of Sample

Dissolve 50 g sample in H_2O and dil. to 250 ml in vol. flask. Take 25, for **33.058**(a), or 50 ml, for **33.058**(b), aliquot for analysis.

33.058 Determination

(a) *Applicable when $Na_2S_2O_3$ content is $\leq 0.5\%$.*— Place sample aliquot in 600 ml beaker and dil. to ca 300 ml. Neutze to Me orange with H_3PO_4 and add 1 ml excess. Proceed as in **7.091**, third par.

(b) *Alternative procedure. Not applicable in presence of $Na_2S_2O_3$.*—Pipet 50 ml sample soln into 200 ml erlenmeyer. Neutze to Me orange with $2N$ H_2SO_4. Add Br-H_2O dropwise from buret in amt equiv. to 20 mg Br. After few min destroy greater portion of remaining free Br by adding 1% Na_2SO_3 soln *dropwise while mixing*. Wash down neck and sides of flask with H_2O and complete removal of Br by adding 1 or 2 drops 5% phenol soln. Add 1 ml $2N$ H_2SO_4 and 5 ml 10% KI soln, and titr. liberated I with $Na_2S_2O_3$ soln, adding 1 ml starch indicator near end of titrn. Correct detn for blank on reagents and make one or more control detns, using 50 ml 20% reagent-grade NaCl soln to which has been added appropriate amts of dil. control KI soln. 1 ml $0.005N$ $Na_2S_2O_3$ = 0.1058 mg I and 0.1384 mg KI.

33.059 Method of Reporting Results—Procedure

(In absence of added drying agents such as $MgCO_3$, Ca phosphate, etc.)

Convert sulfate to $CaSO_4$ and unused Ca to $CaCl_2$, unless sulfate in sample exceeds amt necessary to combine with Ca, in which case convert Ca to $CaSO_4$ and unused sulfate first to $MgSO_4$ and remaining sulfate, if any, to Na_2SO_4. Convert unused Mg to $MgCl_2$. Add percentages of $CaCl_2$ and $MgCl_2$. Report on H_2O-free basis $\%$ of matter insol. in H_2O, of SO_4, of Ca, of Mg, of $CaSO_4$, of $CaCl_2$, and of $MgCl_2$. Report also results of qual. examination of matters insol. in H_2O, if quantity is $>0.1\%$ on H_2O-free basis.

SELECTED REFERENCES

(*1*) J. Am. Chem. Soc. **31**, 922(1909); **32**, 630 (1910); **33**, 381(1911).

(*2*) Univ. of Illinois Bull. **7**, No. 2 (1909); Water Survey Ser., No. 7, p. 14; JAOAC **4**, 92(1920).

(*3*) JAOAC **22**, 482(1939).

(*4*) JAOAC **9**, 29(1926).

(*5*) Chem. Ztg. **35**, 337(1911); JAOAC **1**, 97, 458 (1915); **2**, 113(1916).

(*6*) J. Am. Chem. Soc. **38**, 2326(1916); USDA Bur. Chem. Bull. **153**; JAOAC **3**, 368(1920).

(*7*) Morse, "Exercises in Quantitative Chemistry," p. 417; JAOAC **4**, 86(1920).

(*8*) J. Am. Chem. Soc. **34**, 1379(1912); JAOAC **4**, 85(1920).

(*9*) J. Ind. Eng. Chem. **11**, 954(1919).

(*10*) J. Ind. Eng. Chem. **12**, 358(1920); JAOAC **5**, 29(1921).

(*11*) Ind. Eng. Chem., Anal. Ed. **4**, 38(1932); Methods of Analysis used in Rubidoux Laboratory, USDA Bur. Plant Ind., 5th Ed., 22(1947).

(*12*) JAOAC **5**, 385(1922).

(*13*) JAOAC **5**, 384(1922).

(*14*) JAOAC **5**, 385(1922); **6**, 129(1923).

(*15*) Biochem. Z. **138**, 383(1923); **174**, 364(1926); JAOAC **26**, 440(1943).

34. Color Additives *

(Number in brackets following name of a color represents number of that color as listed in Society of Dyers and Colourists' "Colour Index," second edition, 1956.

In conformity with common usage, thruout this chapter the reagent designated as "amyl alcohol" is actually "isoamyl alcohol.")

SEPARATION AND IDENTIFICATION OF COLOR ADDITIVES IN FOODS, DRUGS, AND COSMETICS

34.001 ★ PIGMENTS AND LAKES— ★ PROCEDURE

Sep. insol. pigments, ultramarine, lampblack, etc., that are most commonly used as facings, by washing sample with H_2O and letting washings settle. Identify particles of coloring matter by microscopic examination and treat residue or purified coloring matter with chemical reagents.

Pigments occasionally encountered are charcoal or other form of C, ultramarine blue (principally Al, S), Prussian blue (principally Fe), and talcum (principally SiO_2). Charcoal is indifferent towards usual chemical reagents and can be burned. Ultramarine blue is stable towards alkalies, but is decomposed by dil. HCl with evolution of H_2S. Prussian blue is unaffected by dil. HCl, but is decomposed by alkalies. Talcum can be confirmed by purple color obtained by fusing with $Co(NO_3)_2$ (test for Al).

Lakes are products formed by combining org. coloring matters with metallic salts. They can be prepd from animal or vegetable coloring matters or from synthetic dyes. As a rule they are insol. in H_2O but are readily decomposed by acids with liberation of the coloring matter.

Large proportions of common pigments other than lakes, such as yellow, brown, and red ochres and umbers, are derivatives of heavy metals and contain Fe, Mn, etc. Others, such as green and blue compds, including certain green chlorophyll derivatives, may contain Cu. These pigments may be identified by usual tests for respective metals.

★ Methods so marked are surplus methods. *See* "Definitions of Terms and Explanatory Notes," item (29).

SOLUBLE COLOR ADDITIVES AND THEIR LAKES: SEPARATION BY IMMISCIBLE SOLVENTS (*1*)

34.002 ★ Synthetic Organic Color ★ Additives in General—Official Final Action

Use of immiscible solvs to sep. mixts of coloring matters generally requires systematic fractionation, since many dyes do not differ very greatly in their solubilities in various solvs. These sepns may also be accomplished by column and paper chromatgy.

34.003 ★ Oil-Soluble Dyes (*2*)— ★ Official First Action

Ext oil or fat with pet ether and treat pet ether ext as follows:

(a) Ext with 10–25 ml portions HCl-HOAc mixt. (H_2O, HCl, HOAc; $0.5 + 1 + 5$) until colorless or nearly so. Make acid exts alk. with ca 25% NaOH soln and re-ext with pet ether of low bp. Wash pet ether ext free of excess alkali, and evap. Take up residue in 70% alcohol and identify. Dyes present may be aniline yellow, butter yellow, aminoazotoluene, sudan G or sudan I, yellow AB or OB, orange SS, or oil red XO.

(b) If pet ether soln is not colorless after extn with HCl-HOAc mixt., ext with 5–15 ml portions H_2SO_4-HOAc mixt. (H_2O, H_2SO_4, HOAc; $1 + 4 + 9$) until colorless. Make combined H_2SO_4-HOAc exts alk. with the NaOH soln, re-ext with pet ether, evap. pet ether ext, and take up residue in 70% alcohol as in (a). Dyes present may be sudan III or IV, oil red OS, or quinizarine green SS.

In all cases test 2 small portions of alc. soln by mixing one with equal vol. HCl and other with equal vol. 40% $SnCl_2$ soln. Common oil-sol. dyes are made redder or bluer with acid and are decolorized by $SnCl_2$. Most natural coloring matters become slightly paler with acid and are little changed by $SnCl_2$.

★ Water-Soluble Dyes (*1*)— ★ Official Final Action

34.004 *Preparation of Solution*

(a) *Water-soluble colors.*—Obtain aq. soln as free as practicable from suspended matter, alcohol, acids, alkalies, and salts. Liqs require no prepn except removal of alcohol.

(b) *Water-insoluble lakes.*—If sample is in solid form, treat well-divided material with enough H_2O to form paste.

34.005   *Separation of Basic Dyes*

Most basic dyes may be sepd from mixts by making prepd soln, **34.004**, alk. with 10% NaOH soln and shaking with ether. Sep. ether layer, which may or may not be colored; wash twice with few ml H_2O to remove excess alkali; and shake with HOAc $(1 + 18)$, which takes up any dye present and forms colored soln. Altho this treatment may, to some extent, alter common basic colors, it can be used to detect Me violet B [42535], magenta [42510], bismarck brown [21000], malachite green [42000], and rhodamine B [45170]. With care auramine [41000] also may be sepd in this way, tho it quickly decomposes on standing in alk. soln.

34.006   *Separation of Acid Dyes*

Following short procedure is often convenient for examination of mixts of acid dyes: Make prepd sample, **34.004**, strongly acid by adding ½ its vol. of HCl, and shake with amyl alcohol. Sep. amyl alcohol soln and wash by shaking with successive portions of ½ its vol. of H_2O, reserving portions in sep. test tubes or beakers. Because of varying acid content of the amyl alcohol these washings will show regular decrease in acidity, and coloring matters will appear in max. quantity in different fractions according to their respective solubilities.

Ponceau 6R [16290] is washed out chiefly while acidity is still high, ca $1N$. Amaranth [16185], brilliant scarlet [16255], tartrazine [19140], sunset yellow FCF [15985], orange G [16230], and sol. blue [42755] appear when washings have acidity of ca $0.25N$, and palatine scarlet [14900], ponceau 2R [16150] and 3R [16155], ponceau SX [14700], naphthol yellow S [10316], cochineal [75470], crystal ponceau [16250], and azorubine A [14720], between $\frac{1}{16}N$ and $\frac{1}{256}N$.

When practically all acid is removed, orange I [14600], orange II [15510], and croceine orange [15970] begin to wash out, and, less readily, orange IV [13080] and metanil yellow [13065]. Finally unsulfonated coloring matters, such as erythrosine G [45425], erythrosine B [45430], and the rose bengals [45435] and [45440] are removed very slowly by H_2O or not at all unless solv. is dild with pet ether and dyes are removed with H_2O contg few drops of NH_4OH.

Acid yellow [13015] and brilliant yellow S [13085] are not uniform in composition. They are partially taken up by amyl alcohol from acid soln and appear chiefly in first washings. Indigotine [73015] behaves somewhat similarly.

When it appears probable that only synthetic dyes presently or previously listed in regulations for enforcement of Federal Food, Drug, and Cosmetic Act

(Federal Security Agency, S.R.A., F.D.C. 3 (1940); Compilation of Regulations for Color Certification, U.S. Dept. Health, Education, and Welfare (1959)) for use in food products are present, following abridged method may be used for their sepn:

SYNTHETIC ORGANIC COLOR ADDITIVES IN FOODS (3)

(Amaranth, ponceau 3R, ponceau SX, erythrosine, orange I*, light green SF yellowish, fast green FCF, guinea green B, brilliant blue FCF, indigotine, naphthol yellow S**, sunset yellow FCF, tartrazine, yellow AB**, yellow OB**, orange SS*, and oil red XO*.)

34.007 ★ Preparation of Solution— ★ Official First Action

(a) *For foods containing oil-soluble dyes.*—Shake oil or melted fat with equal vol. alcohol, 90% by vol., wash alc. ext with several portions of pet ether to free coloring matter from fats, and then evap. alc. ext to dryness in casserole. Treat residue with 40 ml pet ether, and shake pet ether soln with two or three 5 ml portions 2–4% NaOH soln (to remove annatto, turmeric, etc., if present). Pet ether soln will contain yellow OB, yellow AB, orange SS, and oil red XO.

(b) *For foods containing no oil-soluble dyes or from which these dyes have been removed.*—Obtain aq. soln as free as possible from suspended matter, alcohol, acids, alkalies, and salts. Dye soln should preferably be 0.01–0.05%. Soln obtained in examination of colored food products rarely requires further diln, but with com. food colors care must be taken that concn is not too great.

34.008 ★ Separation—Official Final Action ★

(a) *Yellow AB and yellow OB.*—Ext pet ether soln of these dyes, **34.007**(a), 3 times with ½ its vol. $13N$ H_2SO_4. Shake each acid ext successively with 2 portions (equal vols) of pet ether, using same 2 portions of pet ether for each acid portion. Ext each of 2 latter pet ether portions with 20 ml $13N$ H_2SO_4, using same acid portion successively for both pet ether portions. Finally ext second of these pet ether portions with another 20 ml portion $13N$ H_2SO_4. (Original pet ether soln has now been shaken with acid 3 times, next pet ether portion 4 times, and third 5 times.) Combine acid exts, dil. with H_2O, re-ext with pet ether, and evap. solv. Yellow AB will be found in practically pure state.

Combine pet ether solns (original and subsequent solns left after acid washings), wash with small portions of H_2O to remove excess acid, and evap. solv. Yellow OB will remain as residue. (This method is not absolutely quant., but it is accurate enough to sep. either dye with comparatively little contamination from other.) Following color tests may be applied to sepd dyes to confirm identity:

---

* Not permitted in United States as of Feb. 16, 1956.

** Not permitted in United States as of May 6, 1959.

(*1*) Shake 5 ml neut. pet ether soln of dye in test tube with 5 ml mixt. of 1 part 40% HCHO soln and 4 parts Ac_2O. Both coloring matters are extd by Ac_2O, yellow AB giving red soln in few sec, and yellow OB, under same conditions, giving orange soln.

(*2*) To 1 ml alc. soln of dye (0.005–0.01%), add 0.1 ml HCHO, 0.1 ml H_2SO_4, and finally 8.0 ml H_2O. Yellow AB yields red soln, unaltered by addn of excess NH_4OH and somewhat intensified by further addn of excess HOAc. Yellow OB gives yellow or orange soln.

(*3*) To 1 ml alc. soln of dye (0.005–0.01%), add 0.1 ml *Cu-pyridine soln* (5 g $CuSO_4.5H_2O$ and 10 ml pyridine dild to 100 ml with H_2O) and 8.0 ml H_2O. Yellow AB yields pink soln, becoming purple on addn of excess NH_4OH. Yellow OB gives colorless or bluish soln.

(**b**) *Amaranth, ponceau 3R, ponceau SX, erythrosine, orange I, light green SF yellowish, fast green FCF, guinea green B, brilliant blue FCF, indigotine, naphthol yellow S, sunset yellow FCF, and tartrazine.* —To soln obtained in **34.007(b)** add enough 25% NaCl soln to make concn ca 10%, and 1 part HOAc to every 7 parts soln. Ext with three 50 ml portions amyl alcohol. Drain lower layer and reserve for further treatment. Wash amyl alcohol ext in rotation with 25 ml portions 5% NaCl soln until washings are colorless or nearly so. Add washings to original aq. soln. Dil. amyl alcohol ext with equal vol. pet ether and wash with 25 ml portions H_2O until all color is extd. Coloring matters obtained are orange I and guinea green B. For their sepn see (*1*) below.

Treat amyl alcohol-pet ether soln with 10 ml portions 0.1N NaOH or with 10 ml portions NH_4OH (1 + 9), to remove erythrosine. Acidify original soln and washings (from which 3 named dyes were removed) with HCl (1 vol. acid to 40 vols soln) and ext in 50 ml vols with three 50 ml portions amyl alcohol. Reserve lower aq. layer for further treatment. Wash amyl alcohol ext with 25 ml portions 0.25N HCl until washings are colorless or nearly so. Combine washings with aq. soln above. Ext amyl alcohol with several 25 ml portions H_2O until all color is extd. Coloring matters obtained are ponceau 3R, ponceau SX, and naphthol yellow S. For their sepn see (*2*).

Treat original soln and washings (from which 6 named dyes were removed) in 50 ml vol. with three 50 ml portions *glycerol dichlorohydrin*. Reserve upper aq. layer for further treatment. Wash dichlorohydrin ext in rotation with several 20 ml portions 25% NaCl soln. Combine washings with aq. soln above. Dil. dichlorohydrin ext with 2 vols CCl_4 and ext with several 25 ml portions H_2O until all color is extd. Coloring matters obtained are light green SF yellowish, fast green FCF, and brilliant blue FCF. For their sepn see (*3*).

Further acidify original soln and washings (from which the 9 named dyes were removed) with HCl (1 vol. acid to 40 vols soln) and ext in 50 ml vols with three 50 ml portions amyl alcohol. (If color intensity of soln was not too strong, all coloring matter should have been extd by solv.) Discard lower colorless or nearly colorless layer and wash out dyes from amyl alcohol ext in rotation with several 25 ml portions H_2O until all color is extd. Coloring matters obtained are indigotine, amaranth, tartrazine, and sunset yellow FCF. For their sepn see (*4*).

(*1*) *Orange I and guinea green B.* —Ext combined colors with two 20 ml portions glycerol dichlorohydrin. Discard colorless upper aq. layer, dil. solv. with 2 vols CCl_4, and ext orange I in rotation with several 10 ml portions H_2O, and guinea green B with several 10 ml portions 25% alcohol.

(*2*) *Ponceau 3R, ponceau SX, and naphthol yellow S.* —Acidify combined colors with HCl (1 part acid to 10 parts soln) and ext naphthol yellow S with two 20 ml portions washed EtOAc or amyl acetate. (Ponceau 3R and ponceau SX are not extd appreciably and remain in aq. layer.) Wash solv. with 5 ml portions 1N HCl to remove traces of ponceaus. Remove naphthol yellow S from combined EtOAc or amyl acetate exts with 5 ml portions NH_4OH (1 + 9). Ext remaining ponceau soln with 20 ml portions amyl alcohol and wash out excess of acid twice with few ml portions H_2O. Dil. amyl alcohol with equal vol. pet ether and remove color with small vols H_2O.

Treat 10 ml of this soln with 1 ml HCl, 2 ml satd $Br-H_2O$ (*Caution: See 46.047*), and lastly 3 ml *satd hydrazine sulfate soln;* immediately pour into test tube contg 10 ml 2N Na_2CO_3 and 2 drops *1% alc. α-naphthol.* (Light orange soln indicates ponceau 3R; deep brownish-red soln indicates ponceau SX.) Add 5 ml ether to soln, mix well, and drain lower aq. layer which, if colored, contains ponceau SX. To ether ext add equal vol. HCl; formation of purplish soln confirms presence of ponceau 3R.

(*3*) *Light green SF yellowish, fast green FCF, and brilliant blue FCF.* —Treat combined colors with equal vol. 2N Na_2CO_3 and ext in 25 ml vols with two 50 ml portions *n-butyl alcohol.* Drain lower aq. layer contg fast green FCF and wash out last traces from solv. with 25 ml portions 2N Na_2CO_3. Reserve washings and add to aq. soln for confirmatory tests. Light green SF yellowish is colorless in the solv. while brilliant blue FCF imparts bluish-green color.

To prove presence of light green SF yellowish in presence of brilliant blue FCF proceed as follows: Dil. solv. with equal vol. pet ether and remove color with small portions H_2O. Treat 20 ml soln with 4 ml 10% NaOH soln and boil 5 min. Brilliant blue FCF is changed to red; light green SF yellowish is changed to yellow. Acidify with 10 ml HOAc, which changes brilliant blue FCF to violet and light green SF yellowish to green. Treat with ca 3 g Zn dust and heat until soln is decolorized. Filter, make slightly alk. with NH_4OH and then acid with HOAc, and bring to boil. In presence of light green SF yellowish, deep green soln is formed while brilliant blue FCF remains colorless.

(*4*) *Indigotine, amaranth, tartrazine, and sunset*

yellow FCF.—To sep. indigotine, heat to boiling small portion of soln, which should be neut. or faintly acid, and add few crystals of $Na_2S_2O_4$ until all dyes are reduced. On adding few drops HOAc and shaking with air, indigotine is quickly restored, while amaranth, tartrazine, and sunset yellow FCF are destroyed.

If pos. test for indigotine is obtained, add several decigrams *urea* to remainder of mixed dye soln, heat, and while mixt. is boiling add 1 or 2 drops *10% $NaNO_2$ soln*. Indigotine is converted to pale yellow isatine sulfonate, while amaranth, tartrazine, and sunset yellow FCF are little affected. Acidify resultant mixt. with H_2SO_4 (1 + 4), using 1 part dil. acid to 10 parts soln. Ext in 25 ml portions with three 50 ml portions *n*-butyl alcohol. Drain lower layer and pass successively thru all separators. Reserve aq. layer if colored; if not colored, discard.

Prep. following soln: 13.5 ml H_2SO_4, 100 g anhyd. Na_2SO_4, and enough H_2O to make 1 L. Ext the butyl alcohol successively with 25 ml portions of this soln until washings are colorless. Reserve them for amaranth and tartrazine. Dil. the butyl alcohol with equal vol. pet ether and remove sunset yellow FCF with H_2O. Confirm spectrophtric.

Acidify reserved soln with HCl (1 vol. acid to 20 of soln) and ext with two 30 ml portions amyl alcohol. (This exts both amaranth and tartrazine while isatine compd, being less readily extd, remains in lower layer and is discarded.) Remove coloring matter with several 10 ml portions H_2O. To portion of soln add 5 drops NH_4OH and few $Na_2S_2O_4$ crystals. (This treatment completely destroys amaranth, leaving tartrazine practically unaltered.)

Add excess of HCl and speedily ext dye with small vol. amyl alcohol, from which soln tartrazine can be removed with $0.25N$ HCl. Treat another 10 ml portion of neut. dye soln in test tube with 2 ml 20% NH_4Cl soln and 1 ml *25% KCN soln* (*Caution: See* **46.050**), and heat in boiling H_2O bath 5 min. Cool rapidly, acidify with 2 ml HCl, and ext with 10 ml amyl alcohol (*Caution*). Drain lower layer and discard. Remove tartrazine with 5 ml portions $0.25N$ HCl; amaranth is converted to lower sulfonated dye and is not removed at this acid concn. Dil. solv. with equal vol. pet ether and ext dye with small vols H_2O (amaranth is modified to brownish-red dye).

34.009   Identification—Procedure

(a) *Oil-soluble dyes.*—Prep. soln of the isolated dye of suitable concn in $CHCl_3$. Det. spectrophtric curve of this soln and compare curve with those of known dyes in $CHCl_3$ solns detd on same instrument under same conditions. If spectrophtric data cannot be correlated with that of known color, unknown color may be mixt. In such cases, proceed as in **34.012–34.016**.

(b) *Water-soluble dyes.*—Prep. ca neut. soln of the dye in concn suitable for spectrophtric analysis with cells and instruments available. Divide soln into 3

portions and to 1 portion add few crystals of NH_4OAc. To second portion add HCl to make ca $0.1N$. To third portion add NaOH soln to make ca $0.1N$. Det. spectrophtric curves of the 3 solns and compare with corresponding curves of known dyes detd under same conditions on same instrument.

If spectrophtric data of unknown color cannot be correlated with that of a known color, unknown color may be mixt. In such cases subject unknown color soln to chromatgy. For oil-sol. colors, paper chromatgc procedure of Tilden (JAOAC **35**, 423(1952); **36**, 802(1953)), or following column chromatgc method may be used.

34.010   *Preparation of Column*

Lightly tamp glass wool plug into constricted end of chromatgc tube ca 40″ long × 1″ diam. Prep. thin aq. slurry of ca 40 g *powd cellulose*, such as Solka-Floc BW 40, and pour into column. Let liq. drain as cellulose settles and add more slurry as needed until all is added. When liq. level drops almost to top of adsorbent bed, add wash of 20% NaCl soln. Just before last of this soln enters adsorbent, close constricted end of column. Column may be used immediately or may be stored for several weeks before use. (Column described is adequate for 0.5–2.0 mg total dye. Column size may be varied if more or less dye is present.)

34.011   *Chromatographic Separation*

To neut. aq. soln of the color add enough NaCl to make 20% soln. Pour soln into column so that adsorbent bed is not disturbed; then open constricted end of tube. When last of soln is ready to pass into adsorbent bed, add few ml 20% NaCl soln. If any color moves down column at moderate rate, continue washing with 20% NaCl soln. If all color remains at or near top of column, change to 10% NaCl soln. If this soln fails to move any color down column, change to 5% NaCl soln. Continue lowering NaCl concn by half until concn is found which moves color down column at moderate rate.

Continue adding appropriate concn of NaCl soln until color is eluted and collected. If color seps into 2 or more bands as it progresses down column, collect each band sep. In some cases it may be necessary to change to still more dil. NaCl soln to elute upper bands of color. If 2 or more bands of color are found, examine each spectrophtric as in **34.009(b)**. If this procedure gives no indication that more than 1 color is present, it may be assumed that color is not mixt.

Chromatographic Separation of
Oil-Soluble Color Additives
(4)—Official First Action

34.012   *Principles*

Eleven oil-sol. color additives are sepd chromatgc. Colors in fractions are identified spectrophtric. Steps are given in Table 34:1.

34.013   *Apparatus*

Chromatographic tubes.—20 mm id × 300 mm, with stopcock and fritted glass plate (or glass fiber disk over glass wool plug). With device to deliver air pressure at top.

34.014   *Adsorbents*

(a) *Florisil.*—60–100 mesh. Activated at 650° (1200°F) by manufacturer (Floridin Co). Store at 130° in g-s bottle. For use, add 1.5 ml H_2O to 100 g Florisil in g-s bottle, shake to break up lumps, and mix thoroly. Let stand overnight before use.

(b) *Alumina.*—80–200 mesh. Adsorption, for chromatgc analysis. Heat 100–200 g 1 hr at 400°. Store in tightly stoppered bottle in desiccator.

(c) *Sea Sorb 43.*—Fisher Scientific Co. No. S-120.

(d) *Celite 545.*—Johns-Manville.

(e) *Silicic acid.*—100 mesh. For chromatgy (Mallinckrodt Chemical Co. No. 2847, or equiv.).

(f) *Solvents.*—Reagent grade. Pet ether, ether, alcohol, $CHCl_3$, n-hexane, benzene, and acetonitrile. Redistill acetonitrile from H_3PO_4 and P_2O_5, if necessary.

34.015   *Preparation of Columns*

(Place plug of glass wool or piece of Teflon-coated nylon on top of each column.)

(a) *Florisil column.*—Fill tube to ht of 4″, tapping to pack and remove air. Wash with pet ether and drain to top level of column.

(b) *Alumina column.*—Add 50 ml pet ether to closed tube, add 18 g alumina, and work plunger to break lumps and remove air. Drain to top level.

(c) *Magnesia column.*—Mix equal wts of magnesia and Celite 545. Prep. as for (b), using 9 g of mixt. Compress column with slight air pressure.

(d) *Silicic acid column.*—Add ca 4″ of mixt. of equal wts silicic acid and Celite 545 to column, using suction. Tamp and smooth upper surface, and wash with n-hexane, using pressure.

34.016   *Determination*

(*Caution: See* **46.011, 46.039, 46.040, 46.043, 46.045, 46.054, 46.056, and 46.061.**)

Dil. 10 ml oil-based sample with 10 ml pet ether and place on Florisil column. Elute with pet ether. Discard colorless portion and begin collection when color appears. Continue elution until eluate (No. 1) is colorless. Set eluate aside, change receivers, and elute with ether until eluate (No. 2) is colorless. Set eluate No. 2 aside, start elution with alcohol-ether (1 + 3), and watch eluting colors. Change receivers when eluate color changes. (Identify receivers by position in scheme. Usually first eluate is yellow from natural color of base oil and has no distinctive spectrophtric curve. Discard this eluate.) Next eluate is D&C Violet No. 2 (if present); then D&C Yellow No. 11.

When alcohol-ether eluate is colorless, begin elution with acetonitrile. (This will elute last trace of D&C Yellow No. 11; also D&C Red No. 35.)

Evap. individual alcohol-ether and acetonitrile eluates to dryness, dissolve residues in $CHCl_3$, and dil. to vols suitable for spectrophtr. Scan between 350–700 nm, and compare against curves of known colors. (Sepn of D&C Violet No. 2 and D&C Yellow No. 11 may not be complete but colors can be identified because absorption peaks are widely sepd. These colors may be sepd by extg D&C Yellow No. 11 with 70% alcohol from soln of their mixt. in pet ether.) Evap. original ether eluate (No. 2) to remove all ether, add pet ether eluate (No. 1), and evap. to ca 15 ml.

Table 34:1—Scheme for separation and identification of oil-soluble color additives

A Florisil column	Pet ether	Colorless (discard)
	Ether	Colored⎫ To column **B** Colored⎭
	Alcohol-ether	Yellow (Natural color, discard) D&C Violet No. 2 [60725] D&C Yellow No. 11 [47000]
	Acetonitrile	Traces of D&C Yellow No. 11 D&C Red No. 35 [12120]
B Alumina column	Pet ether	Discard
	$CHCl_3$	Colorless (Discard)
	Alcohol-$CHCl_3$	Colored⎫ To column **C** Colored⎭
C Magnesia column	Pet ether	Discard
	$CHCl_3$	D&C Green No. 6 [61565] ⎫ To column **D** Ext. D&C Blue No. 5 [Hexyl Blue]⎭ Ext. D&C Orange No. 4 [15510] Ext. D&C Red No. 14 [12140]
	Alcohol-$CHCl_3$	D&C Red No. 18 [26125] Ext. D&C Yellow No. 9 [11380] and 10 [11390] D&C Red No. 17 [26100]
D Silicic acid column	n-Hexane-benzene	D&C Green No. 6
	Benzene	Ext. D&C Blue No. 5

Transfer carefully to alumina column. When all soln enters column, wash with 50 ml pet ether and discard eluate. Add two 10 ml portions CHCl₃. If CHCl₃ eluate is green or blue, add it to following alcohol-CHCl₃ eluate; if CHCl₃ eluate is colorless, discard it. Continue elution with alcohol-CHCl₃ (1 + 3) until eluate is colorless. Evap. solv. completely and dissolve residue in pet ether.

Carefully add soln to magnesia column, dropwise at side of tube, with pipet. Apply slight pressure until soln just passes into adsorbent; then wash column with 25 ml pet ether, and discard pet ether wash. Elute with CHCl₃ and watch for colors, collecting individual fractions. (First fraction may contain D&C Green No. 6 and Ext. D&C Blue No. 5. Second may contain Ext. D&C Orange No. 4 and Ext. D&C Red No. 14.) Continue to colorless eluate and change receivers; then elute with alcohol-CHCl₃ (1 + 3), changing receivers as different colors appear (D&C Red No. 18, Ext. D&C Yellow Nos. 9 and 10, and D&C Red No. 17). Evap. individual solns, dissolve each in CHCl₃, and scan from 350 to 700 nm. Compare curves with those from known colors. If curve for blue-green portion does not conform to known color, use following sepn:

Evap. CHCl₃ and dissolve residue in *n*-hexane. Put on silicic acid column, and elute with *n*-hexane-benzene (1 + 1). Collect eluate until colorless and continue elution with benzene until eluate is colorless.

(If curve for D&C Red No. 17 has min. at 385 nm, Ext. D&C Yellow Nos. 9 and 10 may be present. Sep. yellows from Red No. 17 as follows: Evap. CHCl₃. Dissolve residue in min. vol. pet ether. Put on magnesia column, and elute with alcohol-CHCl₃ (1 + 3). Collect individual fractions as color changes.)

Det. color present by evapg solv. in fraction, dilg to vol. with CHCl₃, and scanning from 350 to 700 nm. Compare curves with known color on same chart.

★ NATURAL COLORING MATTERS— ★ OFFICIAL FIRST ACTION

34.017   Properties

As a class, natural coloring matters show much less tendency to dye animal fiber than do common synthetic colors. Many crude products contain number of colored substances, and complete sepn is not practicable. As dil. solns of most of natural coloring matters are sensitive to alkalies and some are sensitive to acids, such reagents must be used with care. Relatively few good tests are known for common natural colors. (*See* **22.102–22.112.**)

34.018   Separation

(a) *By extraction with ether from neutral solns.*— From neut. solns ether exts carotene, xanthophyll (pigments found in leaves, fats and oils, egg yolk, carrots, etc.), coloring matter of tomatoes and paprika, and green chlorophyll. Coloring matter re-

mains in the ether soln on shaking with 1N NaOH or 1N HCl, no apparent change taking place, altho the substances may be altered chemically by this treatment.

(b) *By extraction with ether from acid solns.*— From slightly acid solns ether very readily and completely exts coloring matter of alkanet, annatto, turmeric, and red dyewoods, sandalwood, camwood, and barwood. It exts, in large proportions, flavone coloring matters of fustic, Persian berries, and quercitron (after hydrolysis), as well as coloring matter of brazilwood and green derivatives formed from chlorophyll by alk. treatment. It exts, in relatively small amt, coloring matters of logwood, orchil, saffron, and cochineal. Coloring matters of this group are readily removed from ether by shaking with alk. solns, but in most cases they rapidly undergo chemical change.

(c) *By extraction with amyl alcohol from acid solns.* —From slightly acid solns amyl alcohol exts major part of coloring matters of logwood, orchil, saffron, and cochineal. Amyl alcohol exts relatively small proportions of caramel and anthocyans constituting red coloring matter of most common fruits.

Identification

34.019   *By Color Changes Produced with Various Reagents*

Evap. to dryness ether solns obtained in **34.018**(a) and (b) (*Caution: See* **46.011** and **46.054**), warm residue with little alcohol, and dil. with H₂O. Dil. amyl alcohol soln obtained in **34.018**(c) with pet ether and ext with H₂O. To portions of these somewhat purified solns of coloring matter apply reagents as follows:

Hydrochloric acid.—Add to soln, first, 1 or 2 drops HCl; then excess equal to 3–4 times vol. soln.

Sodium or potassium hydroxide.—Make soln slightly alk. by adding 1 drop 10% NaOH or KOH soln. (Red changing to yellow, especially on warming, may be due to presence of gallate antioxidants.)

Sodium hyposulfite.—Add small Na₂S₂O₄ crystal.

Ferric chloride.—Very carefully add small amt of freshly prepd 0.5% FeCl₃ soln, small drop at time. (Colors are not always obtained when excess is used.)

Alum.—To test soln add ⅕ its vol. of 10% K- or NH₄-alum soln.

Uranium acetate.—Add 5% UO₂(OAc)₂.2H₂O soln dropwise. (*Caution: See* **46.083** and **46.084.**)

Sulfuric acid on dry color.—Evap. small amt of soln or of coloring matter in porcelain dish. Cool thoroly and treat dry residue with 1 or 2 drops cold H₂SO₄. Colors are sometimes extremely transitory, and may be observed only instant acid wets residue.

Table 34:2 shows behavior of certain natural coloring matters when treated in manner described above.

34.020   *By Special Tests*

(a) *Chlorophyll.* — "Brown phase reaction" (Molisch, Ber. botan. Ges. **14**, 16(1896)) may be

Table 34:2—Reaction of certain natural coloring matters to common reagents

Coloring Matter	Hydrochloric Acid	10% Sodium Hydroxide Solution	Sodium Hyposulfite	0.5% Ferric Chloride Solution	10% Alum Solution	5% Uranium Acetate Solution	Sulfuric Acid on Dry Color
Logwood	Deep red with excess of acid	Violet to violet-blue	Almost decolorized, color returning imperfectly by reoxidn	Dark shades of violet, brown, or black (the first hue often evanescent)	Rose-red (change rather slow)	Violet, quickly fading	Red, changing to yellow
Red woods (brazilwood, sandalwood, camwood, and barwood)	Deep red with excess of acid	Violet-red		As above	Rose-red (change rather slow)		
Anthocyans of red fruit colors		Change to green, dull blue, or slate color, usually very quickly becoming browner by oxidn	Anthocyanidins derived by hydrolysis, almost completely decolorized				
Alkanet		Deep blue				Yellowish green	Violet-blue
Orchil	Little or no change	Blue	Decolorized, color returning when shaken with air; more easily seen in alk. soln				Violet-blue
Cochineal	Little or no change	Violet	No marked change	Slightly darker		Green	
Annatto	Remains orange. Little change		Little affected	No marked change. Perhaps browner			Blue
Turmeric (soln in ether or alcohol characterized by pure yellow color and light green fluorescence)	Orange-red or carmine-red on addn of several vols of concd acid	Orange-brown	Little affected	No marked change. Perhaps somewhat browner	Little change	Somewhat browner	Red
Flavone colors of fustic, Persian berries, quercitron, etc.	Becomes intensely yellow with 2-4 vols concd acid	Bright yellow	Little affected	Olive-green or black colorations	More strongly yellow; fustic, developing green fluorescence	Orange colorations	Yellow to orange
Saffron	Little or no change	Remains yellow	Little affected	No marked change. Perhaps browner	Little change	Not affected	Blue
Carotene and xanthophyll	Little change. Perhaps slightly paler	Little or no change	Little affected				Blue, reaction obtained with difficulty
Chlorophyll	More brownish	"Brown phase reaction" 34.020(a)					
Caramel	Little or no change	Little change or slightly browner	Slightly paler	No change			

useful to characterize chlorophyll, when it has not been previously treated with alkalies. Treat green ether or pet ether soln of coloring matter with small amt of 10% soln KOH in MeOH. Color becomes brown, quickly returning to green.

(b) *Annatto* (Leach-Winton, "Food Inspection and Analysis," 4th ed., 1920, pp. 161, 558).—Pour on moistened filter alk. soln of color obtained by shaking out oil or melted and filtered fat with warm 2% NaOH soln. If annatto is present, paper absorbs color, so that when washed with gentle stream of H_2O it remains dyed straw color. Dry paper, add drop of 40% $SnCl_2$ soln, and again dry carefully. If color turns purple, presence of annatto is confirmed.

(c) *Turmeric.*—Treat aq. or dil. alc. soln of color with HCl until shade just begins to appear slightly orange. Divide mixt. into 2 parts and add some H_3BO_3 powder or crystals to one portion. Marked reddening is quickly apparent, best seen by comparison with portion to which H_3BO_3 has not been added. Test may also be made by dipping piece of filter paper in alc. soln of coloring matter, drying at 100°, and then moistening with weak soln of H_3BO_3 to which few drops HCl have been added. On drying again, paper becomes cherry-red.

(d) *Cochineal.*—When presence of cochineal is suspected, acidify mixt. with ⅓ its vol. HCl and shake with amyl alcohol. Wash amyl alcohol soln of coloring matter 2–4 times with equal vols H_2O to reremove HCl, etc. Dil. amyl alcohol with 1–2 vols pet ether and shake with few small portions of H_2O to remove color. Divide combined aq. exts into 2 portions.

To first add, dropwise, 5% $UO_2(OAc)_2.2H_2O$ soln, shaking thoroly after each addn. In presence of cochineal, soln turns characteristic emerald-green. (Girard, "Analyse des Matières Alimentaires et Recherche de leurs Falsifications," 2nd ed., 1904.) U salts do not turn green in presence of much free acid. Therefore, add little NaOAc before making this test, or correspondingly larger amt of $UO_2(OAc)_2$ soln must be added.

To second portion add 1 or 2 drops NH_4OH; in presence of cochineal, soln turns violet. This, however, is not so characteristic as first test, as many fruit colors give almost identical reactions. Cochineal is not decolorized by $Na_2S_2O_4$ in either acid, neut., or alk. soln (differs from orchil).

As cochineal lakes often contain Sn, always make further examination for this metal when H_2O-insol. cochineal compds seem to be present.

(e) *Orchil.*—This coloring matter is either sulfonated or unsulfonated. Unsulfonated orchil is readily extd by amyl alcohol from weak acid soln, while extn of sulfonated color is incomplete even from strongly acidified soln. Behavior of color towards acids and alkalies is similar to cochineal, *e.g.*, HCl produces yellow shade and alkalies produce bluish shade. $Na_2S_2O_4$ reduces orchil, but color is restored by air oxidn (differing from cochineal). Characteristic property of orchil is to dye, strip, and redye wool readily.

(f) *Caramel.*—Number of tests have been developed for this coloring matter, most of them based upon insolubility in ether, $CHCl_3$, or amyl alcohol. Probably most sensitive test is Woodman-Newhall (Mass. Inst. Tech. Quart. **21**, 280(1908)) modification of Amthor test with slight deviation.

To 10–20 ml neut. soln of color in small centrf. tube add 2 ml 5% $ZnCl_2$ soln and 2 ml 2% KOH soln, stir well, and centrf. Pour off liq., and add 25 ml boiling H_2O to magma. Mix, centrf., and pour off liq. Repeat this operation until aq. wash liq. is colorless. Dissolve ppt with 15 ml 10% HOAc, conc., neutze carefully, and filter. Divide into 2 portions. To one add 3–5 vols *paraldehyde* in 50 ml g-s cylinder, and just enough absolute alcohol to form homogeneous soln (avoid excess). Caramel is indicated by formation of brownish ppt on standing. To other portion of caramel soln add equal vol. *freshly prepd reagent* consisting of phenylhydrazine.HCl, 2 parts; $NaOAc.3H_2O$, 3 parts; H_2O, 20 parts. Dark brown ppt is formed in presence of caramel.

ANALYSIS OF COMMERCIAL SYNTHETIC ORGANIC COLOR ADDITIVES

34.021 Specifications for Certifiable Synthetic Organic Color Additives

Color Additive Amendment of 1960 to Federal Food, Drug, and Cosmetic Act provides for listing of color additives that are safe for use in foods, drugs, or cosmetics, and for certification or exemption from certification of batches of those colors. "Code of Federal Regulations," Title 21, Part 9, Color Certification, provides listings of such color additives. Certifiable color additives and detns that must be made on each to establish compliance with specifications are listed below. Methods to be used for these detns are noted by section numbers.

Methods and specifications applicable to colors previously certifiable will be found in the 9th and 10th eds. of *Official Methods of Analysis*. (*See also* (e) and (f).)

(a) *Determinations To Be Made on All Straight Colors*

Det. Pb as in **34.097–34.099, 34.100–34.102,** or **34.103.**

(b) *Straight Colors—Foods, Drugs, and Cosmetics*

	Method		Method
FD&C Blue No. 1		**Citrus Red No. 2**	
(Brilliant Blue FCF)		Volatile matter (100°)	**34.037**
Volatile matter (135°)	**34.037**	H₂O-sol. matter	**34.127**
NaCl + Na₂SO₄	**34.118 & 34.122**	Matter insol. in CCl₄	**34.040**
H₂O-insol. matter	**34.039**	Uncombined intermediates	—
Leuco base	—	Subsidiary colors	—
o, m, and p-sulfobenzaldehydes	**34.059**	Pure dye	—
N-ethyl, N-(m-sulfobenzyl)sulfanilic			
acid	**34.059**		
Subsidiary colors	—	**FD&C Violet No. 1**	
Chromium	—	**(Wool Violet 5BN)**	
Total color	—	Volatile matter (135°)	**34.037**
		H₂O-insol. matter	**34.039**
		Ether exts	**34.053**
FD&C Blue No. 2		NaCl + Na₂SO₄	**34.118 & 34.122**
(Indigotine)		Mixed oxides	**34.105**
Volatile matter (135°)	**34.037**	Pure dye	**34.025(c)**
H₂O-insol. matter	**34.039**		**or (e)**
Ether exts	**34.053**		
NaCl + Na₂SO₄	**34.118 & 34.122**		
Mixed oxides	**34.105**	**FD&C Yellow No. 5**	
Pure dye	**34.025(c)**	**(Tartrazine)**	
		Volatile matter (135°)	**34.037**
		NaCl + Na₂SO₄	**34.118 & 34.122**
FD&C Green No. 3		H₂O-insol. matter	**34.039**
(Fast Green FCF)		Phenylhydrazine-p-sulfonic acid	—
Volatile matter (135°)	**34.037**	Other uncombined intermediates	—
H₂O-insol. matter	**34.039**	Subsidiary colors	**34.086**
Ether exts	**34.052**	Total color	—
NaCl + Na₂SO₄	**34.118 & 34.122**		
Mixed oxides	**34.105**		
Pure dye	**34.025(c)**		
		FD&C Yellow No. 6	
		(Sunset Yellow FCF)	
FD&C Red No. 2		Volatile matter (135°)	**34.037**
(Amaranth)		H₂O-insol. matter	**34.039**
Volatile matter (135°)	**34.037**	Ether exts	**34.052**
H₂O-insol. matter	**34.039**	NaCl + Na₂SO₄	**34.118 & 34.122**
Ether exts	**34.052**	Mixed oxides	**34.105**
NaCl + Na₂SO₄	**34.118 & 34.122**	Subsidiary dye	**34.088 & 34.090**
Mixed oxides	**34.105**	Pure dye	**34.025(a)**
Pure dye	**34.025(a)**		
FD&C Red No. 3			
(Erythrosine)		**Orange B**	
Volatile matter (135°)	**34.037**		
NaCl + Na₂SO₄	**34.123 & 34.122**	Volatile matter (135°)	**34.037**
H₂O-insol. matter	**34.039**	H₂O-insol. matter	**34.039**
NaI	**34.123**	NaCl + Na₂SO₄	**34.118 & 34.122**
Unhalogenated intermediates	—	1-(4-Sulfophenyl)-3-ethylcarboxy-5-	
Triiodoresorcinol	—	hydroxypyrazolone and 1-(4-Sulfo-	
2-(2′,4′-Dihydroxy-3′,5′-diiodobenzoyl)		phenyl)-3-carboxy-5-hydroxypyrazolone	—
benzoic acid	—	Naphthionic acid	—
Monoiodofluoresceins	—	Phenylhydrazine-p-sulfonic acid	—
Other lower iodinated fluoresceins	—	Trisodium salt of 1-(4-sulfophenyl)-3-	
Total color	—	carboxy-4-(4-sulfonaphthylazo)-5-	
		hydroxypyrazole	—
		Other subsidiary dyes	—
FD&C Red No. 4		Pure dye	—
(Ponceau SX)			
Volatile matter (135°)	**34.037**		
H₂O-insol. matter	**34.039**	**Lakes**	
Ether exts	**34.052**		
NaCl + Na₂SO₄	**34.118 & 34.122**	Ether exts	**34.049**
Mixed oxides	**34.105**	Sol. chlorides + sulfates	*See individual colors*
Pure dye	**34.025(c)**	(as Na salts)	

(c) *Straight Colors—Drugs and Cosmetics*

	Method		Method
D&C Blue No. 4		**D&C Orange No. 10**	
(Alphazurine FG)		(Diiodofluorescein)	
Volatile matter (135°)	34.037	Volatile matter (135°)	34.037
H_2O-insol. matter	34.039	Insol. matter (alk. soln)	34.048
Ether exts	34.052	Ether ext (alk. soln)	34.054
$NH_4Cl + (NH_4)_2SO_4$	34.118 & 34.122	NaCl	34.123
Mixed oxides	34.105	Mixed oxides	34.105
Pure dye	34.025(c)	Organically combined I in pure dye	34.107
		Pure dye	34.026(b)
D&C Blue No. 6			
(Indigo)		**D&C Orange No. 11**	
Volatile matter (135°)	34.037	(Erythrosine Yellowish NA)	
Sulfated ash	34.104	Volatile matter (135°)	34.037
Ether exts	34.049	H_2O-insol. matter	34.039
Pure dye	34.025(g)	Ether exts	34.053(a) & (b)
		$NaCl + Na_2SO_4$	34.123 & 34.122
D&C Blue No. 9		Mixed oxides	34.105
(Carbanthrene Blue)		Organically combined I in pure dye	34.107
Volatile matter (135°)	34.037	Pure dye	34.026(a)
Sulfated ash	34.104		
Matter extractable by alc. HCl	34.050		
Organically combd Cl in pure dye	34.110	**D&C Orange No. 17**	
Pure dye	34.029	(Permatone Orange, Permanent Orange)	
		Volatile matter (135°)	34.037
D&C Green No. 5		Sulfated ash	34.104
(Alizarin Cyanine Green F)		Matter insol. in toluene	34.043
Volatile matter (135°)	34.037	β-Naphthol	34.071(c)
H_2O-insol. matter	34.039	Pure dye ($CHCl_3$)	34.036
Ether exts	34.053		
$NaCl + Na_2SO_4$	34.118 & 34.122		
Mixed oxides	34.105	**D&C Red No. 6**	
Pure dye	34.025(b)	(Lithol Rubin B)	
		Volatile matter (135°)	34.037
D&C Green No. 6		H_2O-insol. matter	34.039
(Quinizarin Green SS)		Ether ext (isopropyl ether)	34.049
Volatile matter (135°)	34.037	$NaCl + Na_2SO_4$	34.118 & 34.122
H_2O-sol. matter	34.127	Mixed oxides	34.105
Matter insol. in CCl_4	34.046	Pure dye	34.025(c)
Intermediates	—		
Total color ($CHCl_3$)	34.036		
		D&C Red No. 7	
D&C Green No. 8		(Lithol Rubin BCA)	
(Pyranine Concentrated)		Volatile matter (135°)	34.037
Volatile matter (135°)	34.037	Ether ext (isopropyl ether)	34.049
H_2O-insol. matter	34.039	Chlorides and sulfates	34.118 & 34.122
$CHCl_3$ sol. matter	34.128	(as Ca salts)	
Pyrene	34.075	$Fe_2O_3 + Al_2O_3$	34.105
$NaCl + Na_2SO_4$	34.118 & 34.122	Pure dye	34.025(f)
Mixed oxides	34.105		
Pure dye	34.030 or 34.032		
		D&C Red No. 8	
D&C Orange No. 4		(Lake Red C)	
(Orange II)		Volatile matter (135°)	34.037
Volatile matter (135°)	34.037	Ether ext (isopropyl ether)	34.049
H_2O-insol. matter	34.039	β-Naphthol	34.071(c)
Ether ext	34.052	$NaCl + Na_2SO_4$	34.118 & 34.122
β-Naphthol	34.071(a)	Mixed oxides	34.105
$NaCl + Na_2SO_4$	34.118 & 34.122	Lake Red C Amine	34.066
Mixed oxides	34.105	Pure dye	34.025(f)
Pure dye	34.025(c)		
D&C Orange No. 5		**D&C Red No. 9**	
(Dibromofluorescein)		(Lake Red CBA)	
Volatile matter (135°)	34.037	Volatile matter (135°)	34.037
Insol. matter (alk. soln)	34.048	Ether ext (isopropyl ether)	34.049
Ether ext (alk. soln)	34.054	β-Naphthol	34.071(c)
NaCl	34.123	$NaCl + Na_2SO_4$	34.118 & 34.122
Mixed oxides	34.105	$Fe_2O_3 + Al_2O_3$	34.105
Free Br	34.115	Lake Red C Amine	34.066
Organically combined Br in pure dye	34.109	Pure dye	34.025(f)
Pure dye	34.026(b)		

(Continued)

(c) Straight Colors—Drugs and Cosmetics—(Continued)

	Method		Method
D&C Red No. 10		**D&C Red No. 22**	
(Lithol Red)		**(Eosin YS)**	
Volatile matter (135°)	34.037	Volatile matter (135°)	34.037
Ether ext (isopropyl ether)	34.049	H_2O-insol. matter	34.039
β-Naphthol	34.071(c)	Ether exts	34.053(a) & (b)
NaCl + Na₂SO₄	34.118 & 34.122	NaCl + Na₂SO₄	34.123 & 34.122
Mixed oxides	34.105	Mixed oxides	34.105
Pure dye	34.025(f)	Free Br	34.115
		Organically combined Br in pure dye	34.109
D&C Red No. 11		Pure dye	34.026(a)
(Lithol Red CA)			
Volatile matter (135°)	34.037	**D&C Red No. 27**	
Ether ext (isopropyl ether)	34.049	**(Tetrachlorotetrabromofluorescein)**	
β-Naphthol	34.071(c)	Volatile matter (135°)	34.037
Chlorides & sulfates	34.118 & 34.122	Insol. matter (alk. soln)	34.048
(as Ca salts)		Ether ext (alk. soln)	34.054
Fe₂O₃ + Al₂O₃	34.105	NaCl	34.123
Pure dye	34.025(f)	Mixed oxides	34.105
		Free halogens	34.115
D&C Red No. 12		Organically combined Br in pure dye	34.109
(Lithol Red BA)		Organically combined Cl in pure dye	34.111
Volatile matter (135°)	34.037	Pure dye	34.026(b)
Ether ext (isopropyl ether)	34.049		
β-Naphthol	34.071(c)	**D&C Red No. 28**	
NaCl + Na₂SO₄	34.118 & 34.122	**(Phloxine B)**	
Fe₂O₃ + Al₂O₃	34.105	Volatile matter (135°)	34.037
Pure dye	34.025(f)	H_2O-insol. matter	34.039
		Ether exts	34.053(a) & (b)
D&C Red No. 13		NaCl + Na₂SO₄	34.123 & 34.122
(Lithol Red SR)		Mixed oxides	34.105
Volatile matter (135°)	34.037	Free halogens	34.115
Ether ext (isopropyl ether)	34.049	Organically combined Br in pure dye	34.109
β-Naphthol	34.071(c)	Organically combined Cl in pure dye	34.111
NaCl + Na₂SO₄	34.118 & 34.122	Pure dye	34.026(a)
Fe₂O₃ + Al₂O₃	34.105		
Pure dye	34.025(f)	**D&C Red No. 30**	
		(Helindone Pink CN)	
D&C Red No. 17		Volatile matter (135°)	34.037
(Toney Red)		Matter insol. in xylene	34.047
Volatile matter (135°)	34.037	NaCl	34.118
Insol. matter (in toluene)	34.043	Mixed oxides	34.105
Aniline	34.057	Pure dye	34.025(g)
β-Naphthol	34.071(b)		
NaCl	34.118	**D&C Red No. 31**	
Mixed oxides	34.105	**(Brilliant Lake Red R)**	
Pure dye	34.025(e)	Volatile matter (135°)	34.037
(CHCl₃)	or 34.036	Ether ext (isopropyl ether)	34.049
		Aniline	34.057
D&C Red No. 19		Chlorides & sulfates	34.118 & 34.122
(Rhodamine B)		(as Ca salts)	
Volatile matter (135°)	34.037	Fe₂O₃ + Al₂O₃	34.105
H_2O-insol. matter	34.039	Pure dye	34.025(f)
Ether ext (acid soln)	34.053(c)		
NaCl + Na₂SO₄	34.120 & 34.122	**D&C Red No. 33**	
Mixed oxides	34.105	**(Acid Fuchsin D, Naphthalene Red B)**	
Pure dye (H_2O)	34.036	Volatile matter (135°)	34.037
		H_2O-insol. matter	34.039
D&C Red No. 21		Ether exts	34.052
(Tetrabromofluorescein)		Aniline	34.057
Volatile matter (135°)	34.037	NaCl + Na₂SO₄	34.118 & 34.122
Insol. matter (alk. soln)	34.048	Mixed oxides	34.105
Ether ext (alk. soln)	34.054	Pure dye	34.025(c)
NaCl + Na₂SO₄	34.123 & 34.122		
Mixed oxides	34.105	**D&C Red No. 34**	
Free Br	34.115	**(Deep Maroon, Fanchon Maroon)**	
Organically combined Br in pure dye	34.109	Volatile matter (135°)	34.037
Pure dye	34.026(b)	Ether ext (isopropyl ether)	34.049
		Chlorides & sulfates (as Ca salts)	34.118 & 34.122
		Fe₂O₃ + Al₂O₃	34.105
		Pure dye	34.025(f)

(Continued)

(c) *Straight Colors—Drugs and Cosmetics—(Continued)*

	Method		Method
D&C Red No. 36 (Flaming Red)		**D&C Yellow No. 8** (Uranine)	
Volatile matter (135°)	34.037	Volatile matter (135°)	34.037
Sulfated ash	34.104	H_2O-insol. matter	34.038
Matter insol. in toluene	34.043	Ether exts	34.053(a) & (b)
o-Chloro-p-nitroaniline	34.058	$NaCl + Na_2SO_4$	34.118 & 34.122
β-Naphthol	34.071(c)	Mixed oxides	34.105
Pure dye ($CHCl_3$)	34.036	Pure dye	34.025(e)
		(H_2O)	or 34.036
D&C Red No. 37 (Rhodamine B Stearate)			
Volatile matter (80°)	34.037	**D&C Yellow No. 10** (Quinoline Yellow WS)	
Sulfated ash	34.104	Volatile matter (135°)	34.037
Matter insol. in benzene	34.042	H_2O-insol. matter	34.038
Pure dye (H_2O)	34.036	Ether exts	34.052
		$NaCl + Na_2SO_4$	34.118 & 34.122
D&C Red No. 39 (Alba Red)		Mixed oxides	34.105
Volatile matter (135°)	34.037	Pure dye	34.029(a)
Matter insol. in acetone	34.044		or 34.032
Anthranilic acid	—		
N,N-(β,β'-Dihydroxy-diethyl)aniline	—	**D&C Yellow No. 11** (Quinoline Yellow SS)	
Subsidiary colors	—	Volatile matter (135°)	34.037
Total color	—	Sulfated ash	34.104
		Matter insol. in alcohol	34.045
D&C Violet No. 2 (D&C Blue No. 3, Alizurol Purple SS)		Pure dye ($CHCl_3$)	34.036
Volatile matter (135°)	34.037	Mp	34.131
Sulfated ash	34.104		
Matter insol. in CCl_4	34.046	**Phthalocyaninato (2-) Copper**	
p-Toluidine	34.057	Volatile matter (135°)	34.037
Pure dye ($CHCl_3$)	34.036	Salt content (as NaCl)	34.118
Mp	34.131	Alcohol sol. matter	—
		Org. chlorine	34.110
D&C Yellow No. 7 (Fluorescein)		Aromatic amines	—
Volatile matter (135°)	34.037	Total color	—
Insol. matter (alk. soln)	34.048		
Ether ext (alk. soln)	34.054	**Lakes**	
$NaCl + Na_2SO_4$	34.118 & 34.122	Ether ext (isopropyl ether)	34.049
Mixed oxides	34.105	Sol. chlorides and sulfates (as Na salts)	*See individual colors*
Pure dye	34.025(e)	Intermediates	*See individual colors*
(alk. aq. soln)	or 34.036		

(d) *Straight Colors—Externally Applied Drugs and Cosmetics*

	Method		Method
Ext. D&C Green No. 1 (Naphthol Green B)		**Ext. D&C Yellow No. 7** (Naphthol Yellow S)	
Volatile matter (135°)	34.037	Volatile matter (135°)	34.037
Ether exts	34.052	H_2O-insol. matter	34.039
H_2O-insol. matter	34.039	Ether exts	34.052
$NaCl + Na_2SO_4$	34.118 & 34.122	$NaCl + Na_2SO_4$	34.118 & 34.122
Pure dye	34.025(c)	Mixed oxides	34.105
		Martius Yellow	34.084
Ext. D&C Yellow No. 1 (Metanil Yellow)		Pure dye	34.025(c)
Volatile matter (135°)	34.037		
H_2O-insol. matter	34.039	**Lakes**	
$CHCl_3$-sol. matter	34.128	Ether exts (isopropyl ether)	34.049
$NaCl + Na_2SO_4$	34.118 & 34.122		
Mixed oxides	34.105		
Pure dye	34.025(c)		

(e) *Specifications and Applicable Methods for Following Previously Listed Colors Appear in Ninth Edition:*

FD&C Designation	C.I. No.	Common Name
FD&C Red No. 1	16155	Ponceau 3R
D&C Blue No. 5	61530	Alizarin Astrol B
D&C Blue No. 8	42052	Patent Blue CA
D&C Green No. 4	42095	Light Green CF Yellowish
D&C Green No. 7	42100	Fast Acid Green B
D&C Orange No. 3	16230	Orange G
D&C Orange No. 6	45370	Dibromofluorescein NA
D&C Orange No. 7	45370	Dibromofluorescein K
D&C Orange No. 8	45365	Dichlorofluorescein
D&C Orange No. 9	45365	Dichlorofluorescein NA
D&C Orange No. 12	45425	Erythrosine Yellowish K
D&C Orange No. 13	45455	Erythrosine Yellowish NH
D&C Orange No. 14	45456	Orange TR
D&C Orange No. 15	58000	Alizarin
D&C Orange No. 16	45371	Diiododibromofluorescein
D&C Red No. 14	15500	Lake Red D
D&C Red No. 15	15500	Lake Red DBA
D&C Red No. 16	15500	Lake Red DCA
D&C Red No. 18	26125	Oil Red OS
D&C Red No. 20	45170	Rhodamine B Acetate
D&C Red No. 23	45380	Eosin YSK
D&C Red No. 24	45366	Tetrachlorofluorescein
D&C Red No. 25	45366	Tetrachlorofluorescein NA
D&C Red No. 26	45366	Tetrachlorofluorescein K
D&C Red No. 29	45457	Bluish Orange TR
D&C Red No. 35	12120	Toluidine Red
D&C Red No. 38	12350	Toluidine Maroon
D&C Yellow No. 9	45350	Uranine K
Ext. D&C Black No. 1	26370	Coomassie Fast Black B
Ext. D&C Blue No. 1	52015	Methylene Blue
Ext. D&C Blue No. 2	52015	Methylene Blue-Zinc Dichloride
Ext. D&C Blue No. 3	42080	Erioglaucine X
Ext. D&C Blue No. 4	63010	Alizarin Saphirol
Ext. D&C Blue No. 5	61555	Hexyl Blue
Ext. D&C Orange No. 1	11725	Hansa Orange
Ext. D&C Orange No. 2	45395	Indelible Orange
Ext. D&C Orange No. 4	12100	Orange SS
Ext. D&C Red No. 1	18055	Amidonaphthol Red 6B
Ext. D&C Red No. 2	16105	Pigment Scarlet NA
Ext. D&C Red No. 3	45190	Violamine R
Ext. D&C Red No. 4	45435	Dichlorotetraiodofluorescein
Ext. D&C Red No. 5	45435	Rose Bengale TD
Ext. D&C Red No. 6	45435	Rose Bengale TDK
Ext. D&C Red No. 7	58005	Alizarin Carmine
Ext. D&C Red No. 9	14830	Bordeaux Red
Ext. D&C Red No. 10	14720	Azo Rubin Extra
Ext. D&C Red No. 11	18050	Fast Crimson GR
Ext. D&C Red No. 12	15570	Royal Scarlet
Ext. D&C Red No. 13	27290	Croceine Scarlet MOO
Ext. D&C Red No. 14	12140	Oil Red XO
Ext. D&C Violet No. 1	61710	Wool Violet 5BN
Ext. D&C Yellow No. 2	13065	Metanil Yellow CA
Ext. D&C Yellow No. 4	18950	Polar Yellow 5G
Ext. D&C Yellow No. 5	11680	Hansa Yellow
Ext. D&C Yellow No. 6	14010	Dupont Yellow
Ext. D&C Yellow No. 8	10316	Naphthol Yellow S Potassium Salt
Ext. D&C Yellow No. 9	11380	Yellow AB
Ext. D&C Yellow No. 10	11390	Yellow OB

(f) *Specifications and Applicable Methods for Following Previously Listed Colors Appear in Tenth Edition:*

FD&C Designation	C.I. No.	Common Name
FD&C Green No. 1	42085	Guinea Green B
FD&C Green No. 2	42095	Light Green SF Yellowish
D&C Black No. 1	20470	Naphthol Blue Black
D&C Blue No. 7	42052	Patent Blue NA
D&C Brown No. 1	20170	Resorcin Brown
D&C Red No. 5	16150	Ponceau 2R
Ext. D&C Orange No. 3	14600	Orange 1
Ext. D&C Red No. 8	15620	Fast Red A
Ext. D&C Red No. 15	16155	Ponceau 3R
Ext. D&C Red No. 24	14700	Ponceau SX
Ext. D&C Violet No. 2	60730	Alizurol Purple
Ext. D&C Yellow No. 3	18820	Fast Light Yellow

34.022   Preparation of Sample—Official Final Action

Thoroly mix and promptly weigh portion required. If weighing cannot be made directly into dish in which detn is to be made, use weighing bottles, placing in each bottle amt approximating wt required, and weighing immediately.

Pure Dye

By Titration with Standard Titanous Chloride Solution—Official Final Action

34.023   *Apparatus—See Fig. 34:1*

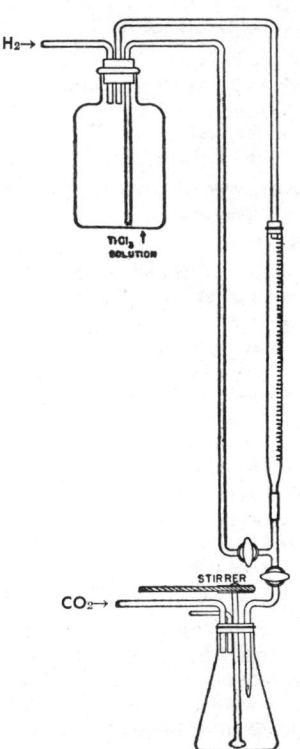

FIG. 34:1—Titanous chloride titration apparatus

34.024   *Reagents*

(a) *Titanous chloride std soln.*—0.1N. See **45.043–45.044**. *See* Tables 34:3 and 34:4 for factors.

(b) *Potassium dichromate std soln.*—*See* **45.025**.

(c) *Indicator.*—For many dyes TiCl₃ titrn end point is indicated by sharp decoloration. For some dyes change is so gradual that excess of TiCl₃ (≤ 0.3 ml ca 0.1N soln) is required, and suitable std soln of some other dye must be used for back-titrn (methylene blue serves well). In other cases it is better to use indicator that is reduced after original dye has reacted with the TiCl₃. Known quantity of FD&C Green No. 2 serves well for this purpose.

34.025   *Determination*

(a) Prep. 1.0% soln of sample in H₂O and place quantity of soln equiv. to ca 20 ml 0.1N TiCl₃ in 500 ml wide-mouth erlenmeyer. Add 15 g Na citrate and H₂O to bring vol. to 150–200 ml. Heat to boiling and titr. with std TiCl₃ soln.

(b) Prep. 0.5% soln of sample in alcohol. Proceed as in (a), substituting 50% alcohol for H₂O.

(c) *Proceed as in* (a), substituting 15 g Na acid tartrate for Na citrate.

(d) Proceed as in (c), using as indicator vol. FD&C Green No. 2 soln (freshly prepd) contg ca 10 mg dye. Det. TiCl₃ soln equiv. to vol. indicator soln used and deduct this quantity from total required for titrn.

(e) Prep. 0.5% soln of sample in alcohol. Proceed as in (d), substituting 50% alcohol for H₂O.

(f) (JAOAC **24**, 904(1941); **32**, 644(1949)). In wide-mouth erlenmeyer dissolve 0.2 g sample in 5 ml H₂SO₄, using stirring rod to break up any lumps, and mix well. Dil. with 100 ml alcohol and heat, with stirring, until all dye is in soln. Dissolve 20 g Na acid tartrate in 100 ml boiling H₂O and add 20 ml 30% NaOH soln. Stirring rapidly, add this soln to alc. dye soln. Titr. resulting soln with std TiCl₃ soln.

(g) Place sample equiv. to ca 20 ml 0.1N TiCl₃ in 50 ml beaker, and pour 2 ml *fuming H₂SO₄* (20% free SO₃) down side of beaker. Stir well with glass rod and place on steam bath. After 30 min pour sulfonated product into 500 ml wide-mouth erlenmeyer contg 100 g ice. Add few g cracked ice to material remaining in beaker and wash all color into flask. Add 50 ml alcohol and 20 g Na acid tartrate, heat, and titr. in usual manner.

(h) Proceed as in (g), but sulfonate at room temp.

Table 34:3—TiCl₃ titration factors

Color	Molecular wt	g Color/ml 0.1N TiCl₃	ml 0.1N TiCl₃/g Color
FD&C Blue No. 1	792.8	0.03965	25.2
FD&C Blue No. 2	466.4	0.02332	42.9
FD&C Green No. 3	808.9	0.04045	24.7
FD&C Red No. 2	604.5	0.01511	66.2
FD&C Red No. 4	480.4	0.01201	83.3
FD&C Violet No. 1	733.9	0.03670	27.3
FD&C Yellow No. 5	534.4	0.01336	74.9
FD&C Yellow No. 6	452.4	0.01131	88.4
D&C Blue No. 4	783.0	0.03915	25.5
D&C Blue No. 6	262.3	0.01312	76.3
D&C Blue No. 7	706.8	0.03534	28.3
D&C Brown No. 1	448.4	0.00561	178.4
D&C Green No. 5	622.6	0.03113	32.1
D&C Green No. 6	418.5	0.02093	47.8
D&C Orange No. 4	350.3	0.00876	114.2
D&C Red No. 6	430.3	0.01076	92.9
D&C Red No. 7	424.5	0.01061	94.2
D&C Red No. 8	398.8	0.00997	100.3
D&C Red No. 9	444.5	0.01111	90.0
D&C Red No. 10	400.4	0.01001	99.9
D&C Red No. 11	397.4	0.00994	100.6
D&C Red No. 12	446.1	0.01115	89.7
D&C Red No. 13	421.2	0.01053	95.0
D&C Red No. 17	352.4	0.00441	227.0
D&C Red No. 19	479.0	0.02395	41.8
D&C Red No. 30	393.3	0.01967	50.8
D&C Red No. 31	311.3	0.00778	128.5
D&C Red No. 33	467.4	0.01169	85.6
D&C Red No. 34	460.5	0.01151	86.9
D&C Red No. 36	327.7	0.00328	305.1
D&C Red No. 37	727.0	0.03635	27.5
D&C Red No. 39	329.4	0.00824	121.4
D&C Yellow No. 7	332.3	0.01662	60.2
D&C Yellow No. 8	376.3	0.01882	53.2
Ext. D&C Green No. 1	878.5	0.00732	136.6
Ext. D&C Yellow No. 1	375.4	0.00939	106.6
Ext. D&C Yellow No. 7	358.2	0.00299	335.0

Table 34:4—Conversion factors—precipitated color acids to specified salts

Color	Factor
FD&C Red No. 3	1.074ᵃ
D&C Red No. 22	1.068
D&C Red No. 28	1.056
D&C Yellow No. 11	1.075

ᵃ Includes 1 molecule H₂O of crystn.

34.026   *Gravimetrically—Official Final Action*

(a) Prep. 1.0% soln of sample in H₂O. Transfer 50 ml aliquot to 500 ml beaker, heat to boiling, add 25 ml HCl (1 + 49), and again bring to boil. Wash down sides of beaker with little H₂O, cover with watch glass, and keep on steam bath several hr or overnight. Cool to room temp., transfer ppt to weighed gooch with HCl (1 + 199), and wash with two 10–15 ml portions H₂O. Dry crucible and ppt 3 hr at 135°, cool in desiccator, and weigh. Calc. pure dye as follows:

$$\% \text{ pure dye} = \frac{\text{wt ppt} \times \text{conversion factor} \times 100}{\text{wt sample}}$$

(b) Prep. 1.0% soln of sample in ca 0.1N NaOH and proceed as in (a). No factor is required since colors for which this method is specified are not salts.

★ *From Nitrogen Content—* ★
Official Final Action

34.027   *Apparatus—See 42.015*

34.028   *Reagents*

(a) *Hydriodic acid.*—To 9 vols 50% HI add 1 vol. 50% H₃PO₂ (clear soln should result).

(b) *Cigaret papers.*—Trim off glued edge and cut into 3 parts, each ca 23 × 40 mm.

(c) *Indicator.*—Dissolve 0.3 g Me red in 60 ml alcohol and dil. to 100 ml with H₂O. Dissolve 0.2 g methylene blue in 100 ml 50% alcohol and add this soln to Me red soln.

34.029   *Determination*

(a) *Colors requiring reduction prior to digestion.*— On tared cigaret paper, accurately weigh quantity of sample expected to contain ca 2 mg N (10–25 mg). (Suitable aliquot of soln may be used if dye is H₂O-sol.) Place paper and sample in 30 ml Kjeldahl flask, add 0.5 ml HI mixt., and reflux gently 5–10 min, turning flask if necessary to ensure soln and reduction. Distill most of liq., remove flask from heater, cool, add 5 ml H₂SO₄ (1 + 1), and evap. to fumes. (If considerable I remains, add 1–2 ml H₂O and again take to fumes.) Remove flask from heater, cool, wash down with 0.5 ml H₂O, and add 0.6 g Na₂SO₄ and 0.5 ml *20% Hg(OAc)₂* soln. Place flask on digester and heat 1 hr after clearing (2.5 hr for dyes having ring N; add more H₂SO₄ if needed). Remove flask, cool, and add 10–12 ml H₂O to dissolve salts.

Set elec. controller connected to steam generator of micro-Kjeldahl distg app. so that 20 ml will distill in ca 10 min. Transfer soln from digestion flask with ca 10 ml H₂O. Add 5–6 ml NaOH soln (1 + 1) and 3 ml 21% Na₂S₂O₃ soln.

Arrange 50 ml erlenmeyer contg 5 ml 2% H₃BO₃ soln and 3 drops indicator soln so that outlet from condenser dips below level of liq. Steam distill 5 min. Lower receiving flask so that condenser outlet is above liq. in receiver and distill 1–2 min to wash out condenser tube.

Titr. the NH_3 with std acid. 1 ml 0.02N acid = 0.28 mg N. Det. blank on all reagents used.

mg N found × 100/mg sample = % N.

% N × 100/% N calcd from formula of color
$$= \% \text{ pure dye.}$$

(b) *Colors that do not require reduction prior to digestion.*—Weigh sample and transfer to digestion flask as in (a). Add 2 ml H_2SO_4 or 5 ml H_2SO_4 (1 + 1). Heat until thoroly charred, remove from heater, cool, and add 0.6 g Na_2SO_4 and 0.5 ml *20% $Hg(OAc)_2$* soln. Wash down any material adhering to side of flask with smallest possible vol. H_2O. Proceed as in (a).

★ *From Sulfur Content* ★

34.030　　*Fusion Method—Official Final Action*
(*Caution: See* **46.013.**)

Place ca 0.2 g accurately weighed sample in Parr calorimetric bomb and mix with ca 14 g Na_2O_2. Add ca 1 g sugar and ca 0.1 g $KClO_3$ to aid in igniting mass. Close bomb and ignite. Cool, unscrew cover, and place cup contg melt in beaker. Cover beaker with watch glass and add H_2O until cup is completely covered. After mass dissolves, remove cup and wash thoroly, adding washings to soln.

Cautiously acidify soln with HCl. After heating to near boiling few min, filter, and wash filter with hot H_2O. Make filtrate neut. to litmus and add 1 ml HCl. Dil. to ca 400 ml and heat to boiling. Slowly add, with stirring, slight excess hot 2% $BaCl_2$ soln. Digest ppt 1–2 hr on steam bath, let settle, and filter thru tared gooch. Wash ppt by decantation with three 25 ml portions hot HCl (1 + 99) and then transfer to crucible, using ca 250 ml hot HCl (1 + 99) in all. Finally wash with ca 15 ml hot H_2O and dry at 135° to constant wt.

% total S = 0.1373 × g $BaSO_4$ × 100/wt sample;

Total S − inorg. S (calcd from Na_2SO_4 found)
$$= \text{org. S;}$$

% org. S × 100/% S calcd from formula of color
$$= \% \text{ pure dye.}$$

Caution: Do not lean over bomb when mixing with sugar and stay at distance when igniting!

Perchloric Acid Digestion Method (5)—
Official First Action

34.031　　　　　　　　　　　　　　**Reagents**

(a) *Nitric-perchloric acid mixture.*—Mix 2 vols 70% HNO_3 and 1 vol. 72% $HClO_4$. (*Caution: See* **46.026** and **46.028**(a) and (d).)

(b) *Boric acid soln.*—Satd (ca 5 g H_3BO_3/100 ml H_2O).

(c) *Tetrahydroxyquinone indicator.*—May be obtained as "THQ Prepared Sulfate Indicator" from Betz Labs, Inc., 4636 Somerton Rd, Trevose, PA 19047.

(d) *Barium chloride std soln.*—0.02M. Dissolve 4.886 g $BaCl_2.2H_2O$ in 1 L H_2O. Stdze by pptn as $BaSO_4$.

34.032　　　　　　　　　　　　*Determination*

Caution: Some substances react with explosive violence when digested with $HClO_4$. Altho following method has been found to be safe with wide variety of compds, make trial digestion of small sample before analyzing substance not previously investigated. *See* **46.026** and **46.028**.

Weigh sample contg 2–6 mg S and transfer to bottom of 30 ml Kjeldahl flask. (Aliquot of aq. soln may be used.) Add 3–5 ml H_2O, 1 ml HCl (1 + 1), 3 ml HNO_3–$HClO_4$ mixt., and 2 or 3 glass beads. Place flask on digestion stand and boil gently until all HNO_3 is removed and boiling $HClO_4$ condenses ca ⅔ up neck of flask. If soln is not clear at this point, continue to heat until it clears and then heat 5–10 min at bp of $HClO_4$.

Remove flask from digestion stand, cool, dil. mixt. to 8–10 ml with H_2O, and transfer to 200 ml erlenmeyer. Rinse digestion flask with three 5 ml portions H_2O and add to main soln. Add 3 drops phthln, and neutze soln with NH_4OH. Place flask on hot plate and boil 2–3 min after soln is no longer pink. (Soln should be colorless; yellow or brown color indicates incomplete digestion.) Adjust vol. soln to 25±5 ml by further boiling or by addn of H_2O.

Cool to room temp. and add ca 0.05N NH_4OH until soln is faint pink. Add 2 ml satd H_3BO_3 soln to discharge color. If color persists, add ca 0.05N $HClO_4$ until soln is colorless. Add 25 ml alcohol, 1 ml 10% NH_4Cl soln, and ca 0.2 g tetrahydroxyquinone indicator, and shake until indicator dissolves. Slowly add std $BaCl_2$ soln until 1–2 ml from expected end point; then add 3 drops 10% $AgNO_3$ soln and continue titrn, adding $BaCl_2$ soln dropwise. Agitate thoroly thruout titrn. End point is appearance of rose-pink thruout soln. (Change from yellow to pink is usually very sharp and is readily detected after few practice titrns. It is preferable to perform titrn in natural light, altho end point can be observed in strong artificial light.)

Conduct blank detn by digesting same amts of reagents as in sample detn. Wash digestion mixt. into flask contg known amt of sulfate and continue as in regular detn; ml $BaCl_2$ soln required in excess of calcd amt is combined reagent and titrn blank.

1 ml 0.02M $BaCl_2$ = 0.642 mg S.

% total S = Net ml 0.02M $BaCl_2$ × 0.642
$$× 100/\text{mg sample;}$$

total S − inorg. S = org. S;

% org. S × 100/% S calcd from formula of color
$$= \% \text{ pure dye.}$$

By Spectrophotometric Measurement (6)—
Official Final Action

34.033   *Apparatus*

(a) *Spectrophotometer.* — Capable of accurate measurement of solns in region 400–750 nm; preferably with effective slit width of ≤ 10 nm.

(b) *Two or more matched absorption cells.*

34.034   *Reagents*

(a) *Std sample of dye to be determined.*—Std samples should be carefully prepd and of highest attainable purity. Pure dye content of std samples must be accurately known for quant. results.

(b) *Solvents.*—Free from suspended matter.

34.035   *Standardization*

Prep. series of solns of known concns of std sample and det. A [log $(1/T)$] of solns, corrected for A due to solv. and cell, at suitable wavelength. (Wavelength at which A is max. is usually selected.) Adjust concns of solns to give A values of 0.4–1.0 with instrument and cells used. Plot or tabulate data obtained.

34.036   *Determination*

Prep. sample soln in solv. used in stdzn. (Soln must be of such concn that A obtained will be in range covered by stds examined.) Det. A of this soln under same conditions used in stdzn.

Calc. "pure dye" content of sample from A of sample soln and stdzn data as follows:

$$\text{Pure dye} = \frac{A_{\text{samp}}/\text{concn sample}}{A_{\text{std}}/\text{concn std}}$$
$$\times \text{ purity of std.}$$

If straight line does not result when A and concn data obtained from examination of std soln are plotted, *i.e.*, if Beer's law does not hold, det. concn of "unknown" soln by comparison with data obtained from known soln of very nearly same concn.

34.037 Volatile Matter—Official Final Action

Accurately weigh ca 2 g sample into tared weighed bottle ca 1.5″ diam., and dry in air oven at temp. prescribed, **34.021**, 6 hr or overnight. Cool over efficient desiccant and reweigh. Report loss in wt as volatile matter.

INSOLUBLE MATTER
Water-Insoluble Matter—
Official Final Action

34.038   *Apparatus*

Prepared gooch crucible.—Digest good grade of retentive asbestos with HCl (1 + 3), wash free from acid, and decant to remove fine particles. Prep. well-packed asbestos mat of suitable thickness in gooch, wash with hot H_2O, dry, ignite, rewash, dry at 135°, cool in desiccator, and weigh. Repeat washing, heating, and drying to constant wt.

34.039   *Determination*

Dissolve 2 g sample in 200 ml hot H_2O and let soln cool to room temp. Filter thru tared gooch, **34.038**, wash with cold H_2O until washings are colorless, dry 3 hr at 135°, cool in desiccator, and weigh. Report increase in wt as H_2O-insol. matter.

34.040 Carbon Tetrachloride-Insoluble
Matter—Official Final Action
(*Caution: See* **46.040** and **46.049.**)

Mix 2 g sample with 100 ml CCl_4 in 250 ml beaker, stir, and heat to boiling. Filter hot soln thru weighed gooch, transfer residue in beaker to filter, and wash with 10 ml portions CCl_4 until washings are colorless. Dry 3 hr at 100–105° and weigh. Report increase in wt as matter insol. in CCl_4.

34.041 Toluene-Insoluble Matter—
Official Final Action

Proceed as in **34.040,** but use 1 g sample in 150 ml toluene.

34.042 Benzene-Insoluble Matter—
Official Final Action
(*Caution: See* **46.039, 46.040,** and **46.045.**)

Proceed as in **34.040,** but substitute benzene for CCl_4.

34.043 Toluene-Insoluble Matter—
Official First Action

Place 1 g sample in weighed gooch and place weighed cotton pad on top of sample. Support crucible in Soxhlet extn app. so that bottom of crucible is slightly above top of siphon tube. Ext with toluene until no more dye can be removed. Remove crucible, warm on steam bath until all toluene evaps, and dry 3 hr at 100–105°. Increase in wt − wt cotton pad = toluene-insol. matter.

34.044 Acetone-Insoluble Matter—
Official First Action

Proceed as in **34.043,** but substitute acetone for toluene.

34.045 Alcohol-Insoluble Matter—
Official First Action

Proceed as in **34.043,** but substitute alcohol for toluene.

34.046 Carbon Tetrachloride-Insoluble
Matter—Official First Action

Proceed as in **34.043,** but substitute CCl_4 for toluene.

34.047 Xylene-Insoluble Matter—
Official First Action

Proceed as in **34.043,** but substitute xylene for toluene.

34.048　Insoluble Matter (Alkaline Solution) —Official First Action

Proceed as in **34.039**, but use 1% NaOH soln or NH₄OH (1 + 14) instead of H₂O.

EXTRACTS

34.049　★　Isopropyl Ether Extract (7)—　★ Official Final Action

(*Caution:* Isopropyl ether is very flammable and forms explosive peroxides readily. *See* **46.039** and **46.070**.)

Transfer 5 g sample to cellulose thimble and ext with peroxide-free isopropyl ether, **34.051**, 2 hr in Soxhlet extn app. Pour ext into weighed flat-bottom 100 ml dish, rinse extractor with 10 ml isopropyl ether, and drain into same dish. Let ether evap. and dry residue over H₂SO₄ to constant wt (±0.5 mg). Increase in wt represents isopropyl ether ext plus small amt of color.

To det. blank, including dissolved color, re-ext original sample 2 addnl hr and subtract wt thus found from first ether ext. Difference is isopropyl ether ext.

34.050　★　Matter Extractable by Alcoholic　★ Hydrochloric Acid—Official First Action

Place 2 g sample in 100 ml vol. flask and add 50 ml alcohol and 0.1 ml (2–3 drops) HCl. Shake ca 2 min. Dil. to vol. with alcohol, mix, and filter. Place 50 ml filtrate in weighed dish, evap. to dryness on steam bath, dry at 98–100°, and weigh.

★　Ether Extracts—Official Final Action　★

By Extraction in Separator

34.051　　　　　　　　　　　　　Reagent

Isopropyl ether.—Wash 1 L isopropyl ether with two 100 ml portions ca 0.5N NaOH, and then with three 100 ml portions H₂O. (*See Caution,* **34.049**.)

34.052　　　　　　　　　　　Determination

(a) *Neutral ether extract.*—Place aq. soln contg 10 g sample in separator and dil. to 200 ml. Ext with two 100 ml portions washed isopropyl ether, shaking 1 min during each extn. Decant ether into clean separator and rinse first separator with 10 ml of the ether, decanting into second separator. Reserve aq. color soln for (b). Wash combined exts with 20 ml portions H₂O until washings are colorless. Decant ether into beaker, rinse separator with 10 ml isopropyl ether, and decant into same beaker. Place beaker on H₂O bath or steam bath in dust-free atm., let ether evap. to 50 ml, and transfer to weighed flat-bottom 200 ml crystg dish previously dried to constant wt over efficient desiccant. Rinse beaker with 10 ml isopropyl ether and drain into same dish. Evap. remaining ether and dry to constant wt (±0.5 mg) in desiccator. Increase in wt = neut. ether ext.

Caution: Do not fill beaker or dish more than ⅓ full; do not let isopropyl ether boil.

(b) *Alkaline ether extract.*—To reserved aq. color soln, (a), add 2 ml 10% NaOH soln and proceed as in (a), except wash ether ext with ca 0.1N NaOH instead of H₂O. Reserve aq. color soln for (c). Increase in wt = alk. ether ext.

(c) *Acid ether extract.*—To color soln reserved from (b), add 3 ml HCl (1 + 1) and proceed as in (a), except to wash the ether with HCl (1 + 199) instead of H₂O. Discard color soln. Increase in wt = acid ether ext.

34.053　*By Extraction in Continuous Extractor*

(a) *Neutral ether extract.*—Dissolve 5 g sample in vol. H₂O suitable for use in 250 ml continuous extractor and ext with ca 100 ml isopropyl ether, **34.051**, 5 hr. Transfer ext to separator, rinse flask with 10 ml of the ether, and add to main ext. Proceed as in **34.052**(a), beginning "Wash combined exts . . ."

(b) *Alkaline ether extract.*—To aq. soln in extractor add 2 ml 10% NaOH soln and proceed as in (a), except wash the ether with ca 0.1N NaOH instead of H₂O.

(c) *Acid ether extract.*—Add 3 ml HCl (1 + 1) to alk. aq. soln of sample in extractor and proceed as in (a), except wash the ether with HCl (1 + 199) instead of H₂O.

34.054　★　Ether Extracts from Alkaline　★ Solution—Official Final Action

Dissolve 5 g sample in vol. 0.5N NaOH suitable for use in 250 ml continuous extractor and proceed as in **34.053**(b).

34.055　Petroleum Ether Extract (7)— Official Final Action

(*Caution: See* **46.011** and **46.073**.)

Transfer 5 g sample to cellulose thimble and ext with pet ether 1 hr in Soxhlet extn app. Transfer ext to tared 100 ml crystg dish, rinse extractor with 10 ml pet ether, drain into same dish, and let evap. spontaneously. Dry in desiccator overnight and weigh. Increase in wt = pet ether ext.

INTERMEDIATES

★　Volatile Amines (8)—　★ Official Final Action

34.056　　　　　　　　　　　　　Reagents

(a) *Sodium nitrite soln.*—Dissolve 79 g NaNO₂ in 1 L H₂O.

(b) *Sulfamic acid soln.*—Dissolve 97 g NH₂HSO₃ in 1 L H₂O.

(c) *Coupling soln.*—In 500 ml wide-mouth flask dissolve 0.1 g 1-(4-sulfophenyl)-3-methyl-5-pyrazolone in 2 ml ca 2.5N NaOH, and add 50 ml H₂O and 10 g Na citrate. Cool, and store at 10° or below until used. Prep. just before use.

34.057　　　　　　　　　　　Determination

Place 10 g sample, 200 ml H₂O, and 5 g Na citrate in 500 ml r-b flask with ⊥ neck. Connect flask to condenser with suitable connecting tube. Distill 100 ml into 100 ml graduated cylinder contg 1 ml HCl, regulating distn rate to require ca 1 hr.

Place distillate in 500 ml erlenmeyer (washing out graduate into flask with few ml H_2O), cool in ice to <10°, and add 1 ml $NaNO_2$ soln. Mix well and let stand in ice bath 30 min. Then add 2 ml NH_2HSO_3 soln, mix well, and wash down sides of flask with few ml ice-H_2O. Let stand in ice 2–3 min; then pour into flask contg coupling soln. Let stand ≥1 hr, heat on steam bath 30 min, then heat to boiling, and titr. yellow soln with 0.1N $TiCl_3$ as in **34.025(a)**. If 1% soln of FD&C Green No. 2 is used as indicator, make correction for indicator blank. 1 ml 0.1N $TiCl_3$ = 2.3 mg aniline, 2.6 mg toluidine, 3.0 mg xylidine, or 3.3 mg pseudocumidine.

34.058 ★ Nonvolatile Unsulfonated ★ Amines (9)—Official Final Action
(*Caution: See* **46.011, 46.039,** and **46.073.**)

Place 10 g sample in Soxhlet extn thimble and ext with pet ether ≥4 hr or until ext siphoning over is colorless. (*Note:* Use ether for detn of *p*-nitroaniline.) Transfer solv. to 500 ml separator, rinse extn flask with two 10 ml portions fresh solv., and add washings to main ext. Wash combined exts with 30 ml H_2O and transfer ether layer to 500 ml wide-mouth erlenmeyer. Add 50 ml H_2O to ext and evap. on steam bath with gentle air stream until all volatile solv. is driven off.

Remove flask from steam bath, cool to room temp., transfer contents to 110 ml vol. flask, and dil. to 110 ml with H_2O. Filter soln thru retentive paper and transfer 100 ml aliquot from filtrate to 500 ml wide-mouth erlenmeyer. Add ca 15 g Na tartrate to soln and heat to boiling. Titr. with std 0.1N $TiCl_3$ as in **34.025(a)** until yellow disappears. End point is more readily detected when 1 ml std soln of FD&C Green No. 2 (Light Green SF Yellowish) is added as indicator near end of titrn.

One ml 0.1N $TiCl_3$ = 2.3 mg *p*-nitroaniline, 2.5 mg 3-nitro-4-aminotoluene or 2-nitro-4-aminotoluene, 2.8 mg 2-nitro-4-methoxyaniline, or 2.9 mg 2-chloro-4-nitroaniline.

Intermediates in FD&C Blue No. 1 (10)— Official Final Action

34.059 Principle
FD&C Blue No. 1 (C.I. No. 42090) is more strongly adsorbed on cellulose from concd $(NH_4)_2SO_4$ soln than are dye intermediates. Benzaldehyde sulfonic acids (SB), i.e., composite of *ortho* (OSB), *meta* (MSB), and *para* (PSB) isomers, and *N*-ethyl-*N*-(3-sulfobenzyl) sulfanilic acid (ESBSA) can be estd from UV absorption spectra of eluate fractions between 350 and 230 nm.

34.060 Apparatus
(**a**) *Chromatographic tube.*—400 mm long × 24 mm id with sealed-in coarse fritted disk. Attach short length of clean, rubber tube with pinchcock.

(**b**) *Spectrophotometer.*—Suitable for use in quartz UV region. (Recording spectrophtr is preferred.)

34.061 Reagents
(**a**) *Eluant.*—Dissolve 400 g $(NH_4)_2SO_4$ in H_2O and dil. to 1 L. Eluant should be free of Fe and other UV absorbing impurities. Test for purity as follows: Slurry eluant with ⅕ its wt of cellulose powder and filter. *A* should be ≤0.08 in the 350–230 nm region when measured in 1 cm cell against H_2O.

(**b**) *Cellulose powder.*—Whatman "Ashless Powder Chemically Prepared, Standard Grade," or equiv.

(**c**) *Ammonium sulfate.*—Grind to fine powder.

34.062 Preparation of Chromatographic Column
Slurry 24 g cellulose powder in 140 ml eluant. Close pinchcock and pour slurry into tube. Open pinchcock and let eluate drain at ≤5 ml/min until liq. is only 1–2 mm above level of packed cellulose. Shut off cock.

34.063 Separation of Intermediates
Place 0.200 g sample in 50 ml beaker. Add 10 ml H_2O and stir to dissolve. Add 2 g cellulose powder and mix. Add 7 g $(NH_4)_2SO_4$ powder and mix well. Transfer mixt. to top of column. Rinse beaker with 5 ml eluant and add washings to column. Let column drain until flow nearly ceases. Add eluant to column and adjust flow rate to ≤5 ml/min. Immediately collect 10.0±0.05 ml fractions. Collect as many 10.0 ml fractions as necessary to remove compds from column; 30 fractions should be enough, but exact number can be detd by inspection of fractions. Record spectra from 350 to 230 nm against eluant in 1.00 cm fused silica absorption cells, dilg fractions with eluant if necessary.

34.064 Calculations
Examine spectra to det. compds present. Calc. to nearest 0.01%, with min. report of "<0.05%."

OSB, MSB, and PSB elute together and generally appear between fractions 7 and 15 with absorption max. near 252, 246, and 251 nm, resp. Calc. as SB at 252 nm, i.e., isoabsorptive point of OSB and MSB.

If *o*-chlorobenzoic acid and/or *o*-sulfobenzoic acid are present in sample they will be eluted just ahead of SB; resolution may not be complete. Benzoic acids are identified by small max. or shoulders near 270 nm, but are not estd by this method. To calc. fraction as SB, ratio A_{252}/A_{274} must be ≥2.0.

ESBSA generally appears between fractions 15–30 and has absorption max. near 274 nm.

Any fraction whose absorption cannot be attributed to above compds should be noted and *A* at peak reported.

% SB = 0.0969 × ΣA_{252}, where ΣA_{252} = sum of *A* (corrected for diln if dild) of all fractions contg SB, and 0.0969 = 100/(51.6 × 20.0 × 1), where 100 = factor for conversion to %, 51.6 = *A* at 252 nm of mixt. of 92% (OSB + MSB) + 8% PSB, 20.0 = effective sample concn, g/L, and 1 = path length in cm.

% ESBSA = $0.0806 \times \Sigma A_{274}$, where ΣA_{274} = sum of A of all fractions contg ESBSA; and 0.0806 = 100/(62.0 × 20.0 × 1), where 100 = factor for conversion to %, 62.0 = ESBSA A at 274 nm, 20.0 = effective sample concn in g/L, and 1 = path length in cm.

% Other absorbers = $0.10 \times \Sigma A_x$, where ΣA_x = sum of A at wavelength max. of detected absorber; and 0.10 = 100/(50 × 20.0 × 1), where 100 = factor for conversion to %, 50 = assumed a, 20.0 = effective sample concn in g/L, and 1 = path length in cm.

★ Lake Red C Amine in D&C Red Nos. 8 ★ and 9 (11)—Official Final Action

34.065 Reagent

Std soln of Lake Red C Amine.—10 mg/L. Dry purified sample of Na salt of Lake Red C Amine 4 hr at 105°. Transfer 100 mg to 200 ml vol. flask and add ca 150 ml H_2O. When all amine dissolves, dil. to vol. with H_2O and mix well. Transfer 10 ml aliquot to 500 ml vol. flask, dil. to ca 450 ml with H_2O, and make slightly alk. (pH ca 8) with NH_4OH (1 + 1). Dil. to vol. with H_2O and mix thoroly.

34.066 Determination

Transfer 1.0 g sample to 500 ml tall beaker. Wet sample with 5 ml acetone and then add 100 ml 2% $BaCl_2$ soln. Boil mixt. 10 min and filter hot thru Whatman No. 12 folded paper into 500 ml Pyrex separator. Return paper and dye slurry to original beaker, repeat boiling H_2O extn, and filter as before. Make third hot H_2O extn in same manner. Discard paper and dye slurry.

Cool combined filtrates, acidify with 5 ml HCl (1 + 1), and ext with three 20 ml portions benzene. Wash combined benzene exts with 20 ml portion H_2O and add wash H_2O to combined filtrates. Insert cotton plug into separator stem and filter soln into 500 ml beaker. Add boiling chips and boil 15–20 min to remove benzene. Cool soln and adjust pH to ca 8.0 with NH_4OH (1 + 1). Transfer alk. soln to 500 ml vol. flask, dil. to vol. with H_2O, and mix thoroly.

Det. A of sample and of std, A', at 247 nm. Calc. % Lake Red C Amine in sample from following equation:

% Lake Red C Amine = $A \times 0.91 \times C' \times 100/A' \times W$, where C' is concn std (mg/L) and W is wt sample (mg).

★ β-Naphthol—Official Final Action ★ Method I

34.067 Reagent

Diazotized sulfanilic acid soln.—Approx. 0.05N. Dissolve 4.779 g sulfanilic acid in 500 ml H_2O to which has been added 5 ml HCl. Prep. ca 0.05N

$NaNO_2$ by dissolving 1.04 g $NaNO_2$ in 300 ml H_2O. Place 40 ml sulfanilic acid soln in 100 ml vol. flask, cool to 5°, add 44 ml $NaNO_2$ soln, and let diazotize, testing for excess HNO_2 with starch-iodide paper. Destroy any excess with few mg sulfamic acid. Dil. to vol. with H_2O.

34.068 Determination

(*Caution: See* **46.011, 46.039,** and **46.073.**)

Weigh 10 g sample into 25 × 80 mm seamless extn thimble, place in Soxhlet extn app. of suitable size, and ext with pet ether (bp 35–60°) 8 hr. (Some dye extd along with β-naphthol may collect on sides of flask.)

Disconnect extractor, add 150 ml HCl (1 + 10) to extn flask, gently boil off ether on hot plate, and filter thru glass wool. Rinse flask several times with small amts of the HCl, filtering each rinse thru glass wool, and dil. to 250 ml with H_2O in vol. flask. Mix thoroly and divide into 2 equal portions. Adjust pH of each portion to neutrality with dil. NaOH soln, using phthln. Reserve 1 soln for blank.

Add 10 g $NaOAc \cdot 3H_2O$ to other portion and cool to 5° in ice bath. Slowly add 25 ml diazotized sulfanilic acid soln, stir 5 min, and test for excess reagent with alk. β-naphthol soln on spot paper. If test is neg., add addnl reagent until pos. test is obtained. Let stand 1 hr (or longer).

Heat on H_2O bath 30 min to decompose excess reagent and test with β-naphthol soln on spot paper for complete decomposition. To each of coupled and uncoupled portions add 10 g Na bitartrate dissolved in 50 ml hot H_2O. Titr. uncoupled blank with 0.1N $TiCl_3$ to direct and colorless end point. Titr. coupled portion until dye reduces to yellow. Add 1–2 ml excess $TiCl_3$ soln and back-titr. *immediately* with stdzd methylene blue, or other suitable dye soln. (Back-titrn is necessary for coupled portion.)

Subtract ml required for blank from ml required for coupled portion, and calc. as % β-naphthol. 1 ml 0.1N $TiCl_3$ = 0.0036 g β-naphthol.

Method II

34.069 Apparatus

Spectrophotometer suitable for measurements at 490 nm.—See **34.033**(a).

34.070 Reagents

(a) *1 - (4 - Nitrophenylazo) - 2 - hydroxynaphthalene std soln.*—Dissolve 0.100 g pure 1-(4-nitrophenylazo)-2-hydroxynaphthalene in 200 ml $CHCl_3$. Make suitable dilns with $CHCl_3$ to give solns contg 5 and 10 mg/L, resp.

(b) *Isopropyl ether.*—Wash once with 0.1N NaOH.

(c) *p-Nitrobenzenediazonium chloride soln.*—Dissolve 20 mg p-nitroaniline in 2 ml HCl and dil. to 200 ml with H_2O. Add 100 g crushed ice and stir until temp. of soln is 5–10°. Add 2 ml 10% $NaNO_2$ soln and stir 10–15 min. Then add small portions 10% sulfamic acid soln until soln gives neg. test with starch-iodide paper.

34.071   *Determination*

(a) *Colors soluble in H₂O.*—Dissolve 2.0 g sample in 250 ml H_2O. Make soln acid with 5 ml $6N$ HCl and ext with six 30 ml portions isopropyl ether. Wash combined ether exts with 20 ml $0.1N$ HCl (discard) and ext with six 30 ml portions $0.1N$ NaOH.

Cool combined alk. β-naphthol exts to 5–10° with crushed ice and slowly add p-nitrobenzenediazonium chloride soln with constant stirring. Stir reaction mixt. 15 min, heat to 90° on steam bath, remove from steam bath, cool to room temp., and ext with 20 ml portions $CHCl_3$ until $CHCl_3$ exts are colorless. Wash combined $CHCl_3$ exts with 30 ml $0.1N$ NaOH. Filter $CHCl_3$ soln thru cotton pledget into 500 ml vol. flask and dil. to vol. with $CHCl_3$. Det. A of sample and of std, A', at 490 nm.

$$\% \ \beta\text{-Naphthol} = (A/A')$$
$$\times \ (\text{concn std soln in mg/L})$$
$$\times \ (144/293) \times (1/40).$$

(b) *Colors soluble in isopropyl ether.*—Dissolve 2.0 g sample in 250 ml isopropyl ether, warming on steam bath to aid soln, and ext with six 30 ml portions $0.1N$ NaOH. Wash combined alk. exts with 30 ml isopropyl ether and proceed as in (a), beginning "Cool combined alk. β-naphthol exts ..."

(c) *Colors insoluble in H₂O or isopropyl ether.*— Ext 10 g sample with isopropyl ether 8–10 hr in Soxhlet extn app. (*Caution: See* **46.011, 46.039**, and **46.070.**) Transfer ether ext to 1 L separator. Rinse extn flask with two 20 ml portions isopropyl ether and add to main ext. Ext isopropyl ether with six 30 ml portions $0.1N$ NaOH and wash combined alk. exts with 30 ml isopropyl ether.

Dil. alk. soln to exactly 500 ml with $0.1N$ NaOH, place 100 ml aliquot in beaker, and proceed as in (a), beginning "Cool combined alk. β-naphthol exts ..."

★ **α-Naphthol in Ext. D&C Orange No. 3—** ★
Official Final Action

34.072   *Apparatus—See* **34.033(a)**

34.073   *Reagent*

4-(4-Nitrophenylazo)-1-hydroxynaphthalene std soln. —2 mg/L. Dissolve 10 mg 4-(4-nitrophenylazo)-1-hydroxynaphthalene in 100 ml warm acetone, cool, transfer to 500 ml vol. flask, and dil. to vol. with $CHCl_3$. Dil. 10 ml aliquot to 100 ml with $CHCl_3$.

34.074   *Determination*

Place 5 g Ext. D&C Orange No. 3 in cellulose extn thimble and ext in Soxhlet extn app. with ether ≥ 4 hr. Transfer ext to 500 ml separator, wash extn flask with two 10 ml portions ether, and add washings to main ext. Wash combined exts once with 20 ml H_2O and ext with six 30 ml portions $0.1N$ NaOH. Dil. combined alk. exts to 500 ml with $0.1N$ NaOH.

Couple 100 ml aliquot of this soln with p-nitrobenzenediazonium chloride as in **34.071**(a). After coupling mixt. has been warmed on steam bath, make soln acid to litmus with $6N$ HCl, cool, and ext with 20 ml portions $CHCl_3$ until aq. layer is colorless. Wash combined $CHCl_3$ exts with 20 ml H_2O, filter thru cotton pledget into 500 ml vol. flask, and dil. to vol. with $CHCl_3$. Det A of sample and of std, A', at 464 nm.

$$\% \ \alpha\text{-Naphthol} = (A/A')$$
$$\times \ (\text{concn std soln in mg/L})$$
$$\times \ (144/293) \times (1/20).$$

34.075   Pyrene in D&C Green No. 8—
Official First Action

(*Caution: See* **46.011, 46.039**, and **46.054.**)

H_2O-insol. matter, **34.039**, contains all of pyrene as well as other H_2O-insol. material. Ext this residue with 50 ml ether, filter into weighed dish, wash filter with ether, and add washings to filtrate. Evap. ether at 40–50°, dry over H_2SO_4 in desiccator 3 hr, and weigh. Increase in wt is pyrene.

★   **Phthalic Acid Derivatives (12)—**   ★
Official Final Action

(Applicable to FD&C Red No. 3; D&C Orange Nos. 5, 10, 11, and 17; D&C Red Nos. 21 and 22; D&C Yellow Nos. 7 and 8.)

35.076   *Reagents*

(a) *Ethyl acetate.*—Absolute, reagent grade.

(b) *Phthalic acid std soln.*—Accurately weigh 0.130–0.135 g K acid phthalate, dissolve in H_2O, and dil. to 500 ml. Dil. 10 ml of this soln to 200 ml with ca $0.1N$ HCl. Calc. concn phthalic acid (mg/100 ml) = mg $KHC_8H_4O_4 \times 0.00813$.

34.077   *Determination*

(a) *Water-soluble salts.*—Wash 2 g sample, accurately weighed, into 250 ml beaker with ca 100 ml H_2O. Heat nearly to boiling and add HCl $(1 + 9)$ slowly, with stirring, until pptn appears complete. Add addnl 8.5 ml HCl $(1 + 9)$, dil. to ca 150–160 ml, and digest on steam bath 1–2 hr. Cool to room temp., wash into 200 ml vol. flask, and dil. to vol. with H_2O. Filter thru dry paper.

Pipet 50 ml filtrate into 125 ml separator (use no grease on stopcocks) and ext with 30 ml EtOAc. Transfer aq. phase to another separator and ext with 25 ml EtOAc. Again transfer aq. phase to third separator and ext with 20 ml solv. Pass three successive 50 ml portions H_2O thru funnels in same order that extns were made. Discard EtOAc, combine aq. exts, and evap. to dryness. (It is convenient to reduce to small vol. on hot plate with aid of air jet and then evap. to dryness on steam bath.)

Dissolve residue in H_2O and transfer to 100 ml vol. flask. Add 8.5 ml HCl $(1 + 9)$ and dil. to vol. Filter thru dry paper and det. A of soln at 230, 262, and 276 nm in spectrophtr, **34.033(a)**, against $0.1N$ HCl as blank. (If soln is too concd for accurate readings, dil. aliquot to more suitable concn with 0.1N HCl and multiply final result by diln factor.)

Measure A of std phthalate soln at same wavelengths.

(b) *Color acids.*—To 2 g sample add 6 ml 10% NaOH and few ml H₂O, and mix until color dissolves. Dil. to ca 100 ml and proceed as in **(a)**, beginning "Heat nearly to boiling ..."

34.078   *Calculations*

Calc. quantity Y for both sample and std as follows:

$$Y = [A_{230} - (A_{230} - 0.7A_{276})] - A_{262};$$

then: % phthalic acid = (Y_{sample}/Y_{std}) × (concn std soln in mg/100 ml) × 0.2.

34.079   *Applicable to D&C Yellow No. 10*

Dissolve 1 g sample in H₂O and wash into continuous extractor. Add ca 1 ml HCl/100 ml soln and ext 8 hr with ca 250 ml ether. Transfer ether to separator. Rinse extn flask with 2 small portions ether and add washings to main ext. Wash ether ext with four 10 ml portions HCl (1 + 199). Combine washings in separator and ext with 50 ml ether. Combine ether solns and ext with four 10 ml portions 1% NaOH soln. Collect alk. exts in beaker and evap. to dryness. Dissolve residue in H₂O and transfer to 200 ml vol. flask. Add 2 ml HCl and dil. to vol. Proceed as in **34.077**(a), third par., beginning "Filter thru dry paper and det. ..."

34.080   *Applicable to D&C Red No. 19 and D&C Yellow No. 11*

(a) *D&C Red No. 19.*—Weigh 0.5 g sample into beaker and dissolve in 20 ml hot H₂O. Cool to room temp. and transfer to 125 ml separator. Rinse beaker with 5 ml H₂O and add wash H₂O to separator. Add 80 ml CHCl₃ and 2 ml 10% NaOH soln, and shake vigorously 1 min. Drain CHCl₃ layer and wash aq. phase with two 30 ml portions CHCl₃, discarding CHCl₃. Add 7 ml HCl (1 + 9) and wash with two 30 ml portions CHCl₃, discarding CHCl₃. Transfer aq. soln to beaker, rinse funnel with 10 ml H₂O, and transfer to same beaker. Evap. to dryness on steam bath with aid of air jet. Proceed as in **34.077**(a), third par., beginning "Dissolve residue in H₂O ..."

(b) *D&C Yellow No. 11.*—Wash 0.5 g sample into 125 ml separator with 80 ml CHCl₃. Add 20 ml 1% NaOH soln and proceed as in **(a)**, beginning "... shake vigorously 1 min."

SUBSIDIARY AND LOWER SULFONATED DYES

★ **Orange II in Ext. D&C Orange No. 3** ★
(13)—Official Final Action

34.081   *Apparatus—See 34.033(a)*

34.082   *Reagents*

Prep. following solns, using 0.1N NaOH as solv.:
(a) Soln contg 5–10 mg sample/L.

(b) Soln contg 5–10 mg Ext. D&C Orange No. 3/L, recrystd twice from alcohol (1 + 1) and dried at 135°.

(c) Soln contg 10–20 mg D&C Orange No. 4/L, recrystd twice from alcohol and dried at 135°.

(All concns should be accurately known.)

34.083   *Determination*

Det. A of each soln at 455 and 515 nm and calc. A (mg/L) of solns of the purified colors at each wavelength.

Calc. quantity of D&C Orange No. 4 present in sample from equations:

$$Cx + Ey = A_{455} \quad \text{and} \quad Dx + Fy = A_{515},$$

where
$C = A$ (mg/L) of soln of purified D&C Orange No. 4 at 455 nm;
$D = A$ (mg/L) of soln of purified D&C Orange No. 4 at 515 nm;
$E = A$ (mg/L) of soln of purified Ext. D&C Orange No. 3 at 455 nm;
$F = A$ (mg/L) of soln of purified Ext. D&C Orange No. 3 at 515 nm;
$x =$ Concn (mg/L) of D&C Orange No. 4 in sample;
$y =$ Concn (mg/L) of Ext. D&C Orange No. 3 in sample;
$A_{455} = A$ of sample soln at 455 nm; and
$A_{515} = A$ of sample soln at 515 nm.

x × 100/concn soln, **34.082**(a) = % D&C Orange No. 4.

34.084   **Martius Yellow—Official First Action**

Dissolve 5 g sample in 150 ml H₂O, add 5 ml HCl, and shake vigorously in separator 1 min with 50 ml pet ether (sp gr 0.65). Sep. solns and again ext aq. liq. with 25–30 ml solv. Combine pet ether portions, decant into clean separator, and wash with 25 ml portions 0.25N HCl until washings are colorless. Remove Martius Yellow by shaking with few portions 5% NaOH soln. Neutze alk. dye soln with *tartaric acid*, add 5 g Na tartrate, and titr. with std TiCl₃ soln, using as indicator ca 10 mg FD&C Green No. 2 from freshly prepd soln. Det. blank on tartrate, FD&C Green No. 2, and H₂O.

1 ml 0.1N TiCl₃ = 0.002134 g Martius Yellow.

★ **Subsidiary Dyes in FD&C Yellow No. 5** ★
(14)—Official Final Action
Lower Sulfonated Dyes

34.085   *Spectrophotometric Standard*

Either **(a)** purified disodium salt of 3-carboxy-5-hydroxy-1-p-sulfophenyl-4-phenylazopyrazole or **(b)** purified FD&C Yellow No. 5 (recrystd twice from alcohol (1 + 1); dried at 135°) may be used as std.

Dissolve 100 mg of **(a)** or **(b)** in 1 L H₂O. Transfer 10 ml aliquot to 100 ml vol. flask, add ca 1 g NH₄OAc, and dil. to vol. with H₂O.

34.086 *Determination*

Dissolve 200 mg sample in 100 ml H_2O, heating on steam bath if necessary. To 50 ml of this soln add 1 ml HCl and ext lower sulfonated dye by successively shaking soln in 3 separators, each contg 50 ml amyl alcohol. Wash amyl alcohol exts by successively shaking with 50 ml portions 0.25N HCl, until washings are practically colorless, passing each acid portion thru funnels in same order as original amyl alcohol extn. Dil. amyl alcohol exts in each funnel with 1–2 vols pet ether and remove lower sulfonated dye by washing with several 10–20 ml portions H_2O, passing each portion thru the 3 funnels in reverse order to that previously followed. Transfer extd color to 100 ml vol. flask, add ca 1 g solid NH_4OAc, dil. to vol. with H_2O, and measure A of sample and of std, A', in spectrophtr, **34.033**(a), at 434 nm, using 1 cm cells.

Using std (a): % subsidiary = A/A'.
Using std (b): % subsidiary = $A/1.1A'$.

★ **Subsidiary Dyes in FD&C Yellow No. 6** ★
Lower Sulfonated Dyes (15)—
Official First Action

34.087 *Reagent*

D&C Orange No. 4 std soln.—Dissolve 0.100 g pure D&C Orange No. 4 in 500 ml H_2O. To 5 ml of this soln add 1–2 ml 2N NH_4OAc and dil. to 100 ml.

34.088 *Determination*

To soln of 0.2 g sample in 20 ml H_2O add 1 ml HCl and dil. to 50 ml. Ext by shaking soln successively in 3 separators, each contg 50 ml amyl alcohol. Wash amyl alcohol exts successively with 50 ml portions 5% NaCl soln until washings are colorless. Dil. amyl alcohol in each separator with 100 ml portions pet ether (sp gr 0.65) and remove lower sulfonated dye by washing with several 10 ml portions H_2O, passing each portion thru the 3 separators in reverse order to that previously followed.

Transfer combined aq. exts to 100 ml vol. flask, add 1 ml 2N NH_4OAc, dil. to vol. with H_2O, and measure A of sample and of std, A', at 485 nm.

% subsidiary dye = 0.5A/A'.

Higher Sulfonated Dyes (16)—
Official Final Action

34.089 *Preparation of Standard Solutions*

Dissolve 17.3 g anhyd. sulfanilic acid and 5.5 g Na_2CO_3 in 100 ml H_2O. Add 25 ml HCl, cool to ≤10°, and add 35 ml 20% $NaNO_2$ soln slowly, with stirring. Stir 10 min and then destroy excess nitrite with sulfamic acid.

(a) *R-salt std.*—Couple diazonium compd suspension obtained above with suspension of 34.8 g R-salt in 150 ml aq. soln contg 10 g NaOH and 10 g Na_2CO_3. Filter off product, crystallize from aq. alcohol (1 + 1), and dry at 135°.

(b) *G-salt std.*—Proceed as in (a) but use 34.8 g G-salt instead of R-salt.

Det. pure dye content of each product as in **34.025**(a). 1 ml 0.1N $TiCl_3$ = 0.01386 g pure dye. Prep. std solns in HCl (1 + 25) contg 4.0 mg pure dye/L.

34.090 *Determination*

Dissolve 100 mg sample in 100 ml HCl (1 + 25). Dil. 10 ml of this soln with 40 ml HCl (1 + 25) and ext by shaking soln successively thru 5 separators, each contg 50 ml amyl alcohol. Transfer acid layer to 100 ml vol. flask. Wash amyl alcohol exts with two 25 ml portions HCl (1 + 25), passing each portion thru separators in same order as used for original extn. Add washings to acid soln of subsidiary and dil. to vol. with H_2O.

(a) *R-salt isomer.*—Det. A of extd soln at max. (ca 490 nm) in 5 cm cell. Det. A' (mg/L) of std soln, **34.089**(a), at same wavelength and in same cell.

(b) *G-salt isomer.*—Proceed as in (a), using std soln, **34.089**(b), but det. A at 476 nm.

(c) *Mixtures of G- and R-salt isomers.*—Proceed as in (a), using std soln, **34.089**(a). Det. A at 476 nm where both isomers have ca same a.

% subsidiary = A/A'.

★ **Subsidiary Dyes in D&C Red Nos. 6** ★
and 7—Official First Action

34.091 *Reagents*

(a) *Potassium bromide-bromate soln.*—0.05N. Dissolve 1.3920 g $KBrO_3$ and 10 g KBr in 1 L H_2O.

(b) *Sodium thiosulfate std soln.*—Dissolve 12.5 g $Na_2S_2O_3 \cdot 5H_2O$ in 1 L H_2O and stdze against KBr-$KBrO_3$ soln as follows: Place 100 ml H_2O, 25 ml HCl, and 100 g crushed ice in 500 ml I flask. Add ca 20 ml KBr-$KBrO_3$ soln from buret as rapidly as possible. Stopper flask, and let stand in ice bath 10 min. Continue as in **34.092**, beginning "Add 2–3 g KI, ..." Calc. value of $Na_2S_2O_3$ soln in terms of KBr-$KBrO_3$ soln.

34.092 *Determination*

Weigh 2.0 g sample into 1 L r-b flask of distn app., and add few antibumping pellets, 100 ml 10% NaOH soln, 25 ml ethylene glycol monomethyl ether, and 10 g $Na_2S_2O_4$. Attach adapter to condenser, leading tip below surface of 25 ml HCl (1 + 4), and heat mixt. to effect simultaneous reduction and distn.

When ca 50 ml distillate collects, let 150 ml H_2O drip into heated flask at rate ca equal that of distn. Continue distn until 300 ml collects in receiving vessel. Transfer liq. to 500 ml I flask, and conc. to 100 ml. Cool, and add 20 ml HCl and 100 g crushed ice.

Add KBr-$KBrO_3$ soln to iced soln from buret until soln remains yellow ≥30 sec. Then add ca 5 ml more. Stopper flask and let stand in ice bath 10 min. Add 2–3 g KI, and titr. immediately with $Na_2S_2O_3$ soln, using 0.5% starch soln as internal indicator near end point. 1 ml 0.05N KBr-KBrO$_3$ = 4.10 mg subsidiary dye.

34.093 4-Toluene-azo-2-naphthol-3-carboxylic Acid in D&C Reds Nos. 6 and 7 (*17*)—Official First Action

Place 0.25 g sample in 125 ml acetylation flask and add 80 ml ethylene glycol monomethyl ether. Acidify with 5 ml HCl, attach air condenser, and reflux ca 15 min to dissolve. Transfer soln to separator and rinse flask with four 10 ml portions isopropyl ether and two 75 ml portions H$_2$O. Let sep., and drain lower acid phase into second separator. Ext with 40 ml isopropyl ether, combine isopropyl ether exts, and discard residual aq. soln.

Ext isopropyl ether ext with 20 ml portions H$_2$O until aq. ext is colorless. Filter ether soln thru pledget of cotton, rinse cotton and funnel with isopropyl ether, and dil. to 100 ml with isopropyl ether. Det A of this soln at wavelength of max. (ca 507 nm) and compare with A' of std soln obtained under same conditions.

Prep. std soln by refluxing 25 mg 4-toluene-azo-2-naphthol-3-carboxylic acid with 80 ml ethylene glycol monomethyl ether and 5 ml HCl ca 15 min. Transfer soln to 100 ml vol. flask and dil. to vol. with ethylene glycol monomethyl ether. Add 5 ml aliquot (equiv. to 0.5% subsidiary dye) to separator contg 80 ml isopropyl ether and 100 ml H$_2$O. Shake and discard aq. phase. Proceed as above, beginning "Ext isopropyl ether ext with 20 ml portions H$_2$O ..."

% Subsidiary dye = $A \times 0.5/A'$.

34.094 ★ Subsidiary Dyes (1-(6-(and 8)- ★ sulfo-2-naphthyl)-azo-2-naphthol) in D&C Red Nos. 10–13 (*18*)— Official First Action

Reflux 0.25 g sample with 50 ml HOAc and 25 ml 8N HCl 3 hr in hood. Cool to room temp. and transfer to separator, rinsing with small portions ether.

Add 100 ml ether, shake, and add 200 ml H$_2$O. Transfer lower layer to another separator and ext with 100 ml ether. Transfer lower layer to third separator and ext residual isomeric colors with 40 ml isoamyl alcohol. Discard aq. phase and reserve isoamyl ext.

Wash ether exts with 40 ml portions H$_2$O in same order as in original extns until washings are colorless. Combine washings and ext dye with retained isoamyl alcohol. Wash isoamyl alcohol twice with 30 ml H$_2$O, and transfer colored solv. phase to beaker, rinsing with 5 ml isoamyl alcohol. Heat on steam bath to remove dissolved ether, and filter thru cotton plug into 50 ml vol. flask. Rinse with isoamyl alcohol and dil. to vol. Det A at 495 nm, increasing diln if necessary.

Reflux 25 mg either pure 6- or 8-isomeric compd as above. Transfer to 100 ml vol. flask and dil. to

vol. with HOAc-8N HCl (2 + 1). Dil. 5 ml aliquot to 70 ml with HOAc-8N HCl (1 + 1), ext as above, and det. A' at 495 nm.

% Isomeric compds = $A \times V \times 0.5/A' \times V'$; where V and V' are vols final solns of sample and std, resp.

★ Subsidiary Dyes in D&C Red No. 35— ★ Official First Action
Spectrophotometric Method (*19*)

34.095   Reagents

(a) *Chloroform.*—Redistd.

(b) *Alcohol.*—SDF No. 1 is satisfactory.

(c) *4-Toluene-azo-2-naphthol.*—Recrystd from alcohol. Dissolve 10 mg in alcohol and dil. to 1 L.

(d) *D&C Red No. 35.*—Recrystd from CHCl$_3$.

34.096   Determination

Ext 2 g sample with CHCl$_3$ in Soxhlet app. until leachings are colorless. Cool, filter, and thoroly wash residue (D&C Red No. 35) and paper with alcohol. Evap. CHCl$_3$-alcohol filtrate to dryness (avoid spattering), and heat residue with 25 ml alcohol. Cool, transfer to 50 ml vol. flask, and dil. to vol. Remove insol. matter by filtration and dil. 5 ml aliquot to 250 ml with alcohol. Det. A at 486 nm. Repeat detn, substituting 2 g D&C Red No. 35. Also det. A' of std 4-toluene-azo-2-naphthol soln.

Total mg subsidiary dye = $25A/A'$.

(Total mg subsidiary dye − mg apparent subsidiary dye in D&C Red No. 35) $\times$ 1/20 = % subsidiary dye.

METALS
Lead—Official Final Action
Method I (*20*)
(Applicable to colors not contg Ca, Ba, or Sr)

34.097   Reagents

(a) *Lead std solns.*—See **25.043**(a).

(b) *Dilute nitric acid.*—1%. See **25.043**(b).

(c) *Citric acid soln.*—50%. Special grade—low in Pb. See **25.043**(d).

(d) *Diphenylthiocarbazone (dithizone) soln.*—Stock soln of purified dithizone in CHCl$_3$ contg 1.00 mg/ml. Also working soln contg 20 mg/L. See **25.043**(e).

(e) *Potassium cyanide soln.*—10%. Dissolve 50 g phosphate-free KCN in H$_2$O and dil. to 500 ml. (*Caution: See* **46.050**.)

(f) *Hydroxylamine hydrochloride soln.*—10%. Dissolve 10 g NH$_2$OH.HCl in 20 ml H$_2$O and make slightly alk. with NH$_4$OH. Ext Pb with dithizone. Remove excess dithizone with CHCl$_3$ and boil off any CHCl$_3$ remaining in aq. phase. Acidify with HCl and dil. to 100 ml.

(g) *Thymol blue indicator.*—0.1%. Dissolve 0.1 g thymol blue in H$_2$O, add enough 0.1N NaOH to change color to blue, and dil. to 100 ml.

34.098   *Preparation of Sample*

(Caution: See 46.019, 46.026, 46.028, and 46.030.)

Transfer 5.00 g sample to 500 ml Kjeldahl flask, add 10 ml H_2SO_4 and 10 ml HNO_3, and heat. When SO_3 fumes begin to evolve, add 5 ml HNO_3 and heat until SO_3 again evolves. Repeat addn of HNO_3 each time SO_3 fumes appear until dye is completely in soln and digest is yellow. Then add 10 ml of mixt. of HNO_3 and 60–70% $HClO_4$ (1 + 1), and continue heating until digest is colorless or pale yellow and bulk of H_2SO_4 is evapd.

Cool flask under running H_2O and neutze soln by addns of small portions of NH_4OH. Add 20 ml citric acid soln and adjust to pH 8.5–9 with NH_4OH, using 4 drops thymol blue indicator. Add 5 ml 10% KCN soln.

Transfer alk. soln to 250 ml Pyrex separator. Ext Pb with 20 ml portion dithizone soln contg 20 mg/L. (*Note:* If enough Fe is present to cause excessive oxidn of dithizone as indicated by yellow color in $CHCl_3$ layer, add 10 ml 10% $NH_2OH.HCl$ soln to reduce the Fe.) Let $CHCl_3$ layer settle and drain into another separator. Wash down floating globules of $CHCl_3$ with two 5 ml portions of less concd dithizone soln (4 mg/L) and add to receiving separator. Repeat extns with the more concd dithizone soln until no more red Pb dithizonate is observed. Make 2 more extns with 10 ml portions less concd dithizone soln.

Add 25 ml 1% HNO_3 to separator contg combined dithizone exts. Shake, let settle, and drain green dithizone layer into another separator contg addnl 25 ml 1% HNO_3. Shake, let layers sep., and discard $CHCl_3$ fraction. Combine 1% HNO_3 exts.

34.099   *Determination*

Det. Pb in combined 1% HNO_3 exts as in **25.048.**

Method II (21)
(Applicable to Al lakes)

34.100   *Apparatus*

See Fig. 34:2. Pptn tube *B* is fitted with inlets for addn of sample and of H_2S and for release of H_2S and transfer of pptd PbS to filter in *C* (fine porosity fritted glass covered with Celite or other similar filter-aid). For 20–300 μg Pb, ca 0.5 g filter-aid is enough to allow rapid filtration with complete retention of ppt. Filter must be thoroly washed with HNO_3 followed by H_2O before use.

Wash all glassware successively with scouring powder, H_2O, HNO_3, and again with H_2O. Wash pptn app. with HNO_3 and H_2O between detns.

34.101   *Reagents*

All reagents should be Pb-free. *See* **25.043.** Any source of H_2S may be used. Scrub gas first with H_2SO_4 (1 + 1), and then with H_2O before passing into soln.

34.102   *Determination*

(Caution: See 46.019, 46.026, 46.028, 46.030, and 46.059.)

Weigh 2 g sample into 500 ml Kjeldahl flask, add 10 ml H_2SO_4 and 10 ml HNO_3, and digest over low flame until SO_3 fumes appear. Add 5 ml portions HNO_3 (waiting until SO_3 fumes appear before adding each succeeding portion) until all org. matter is in soln. Slowly add 5–10 ml mixt. of HNO_3 and 60–70% $HClO_4$ (1 + 1), and continue digestion until white ppt formed shows first signs of spattering. Let flask cool, and cautiously add 5 ml H_2O and then few drops NH_4OH. Vigorously swirl flask and cool under running H_2O. Add 20 ml citric acid soln, **34.097**(c), and adjust to pH 3.0–3.4 (bromophenol blue) with NH_4OH. Add 1 ml $CuSO_4$ *soln* (1 mg Cu/ml) and transfer soln to pptn tube, *B*, of sulfiding app., Fig. 34:2. Bubble H_2S thru soln 3–5 min at rate of ca 2 bubbles/sec and filter resulting suspension thru *C* at rate of ca 1 drop/sec. When filtration

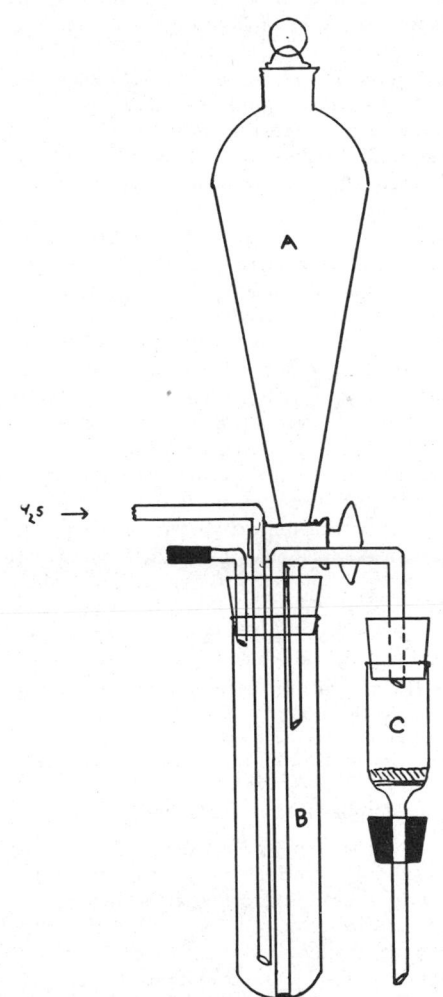

FIG. 34:2—Sulfiding apparatus (full scale)

is complete, remove receiver contg filtrate and attach suction test tube.

Add 3 ml hot HNO_3 thru separator *A* and draw thru filter; follow with 2 ml hot H_2O. Detach filter and pass addnl 3 ml hot HNO_3 thru filter, wetting all sides. Again follow with 2 ml hot H_2O. If filter is still colored with PbS, wash again with hot HNO_3 and H_2O. Wash dissolved sulfides into pptn tube *B*, wetting all sides to take up any residual PbS and then into 50–100 ml g-s erlenmeyer. Stopper, and shake few sec; remove stopper and boil until soln clears, to remove last traces of H_2S and to coagulate any free S present.

Transfer soln to 250 ml separator. Wash flask with two 5 ml portions H_2O and add washings to main soln. Add 10 ml citric acid soln, 5 ml 10% KCN soln, and few drops of $NH_2OH.HCl$ soln, **34.097**(f), to prevent oxidn of dithizone; adjust pH to 8.5–9.5 (thymol blue) with NH_4OH.

Immediately ext with 20 ml portions dithizone, **34.097**(d), using the more dil. soln unless exceptionally large amts of Pb are present. Shake 20–30 sec, let layers sep., and note color of $CHCl_3$ phase. (Pb dithizone complex is red, but color may be masked by excess green dithizone, giving intermediate hues of purple and crimson. Color of $CHCl_3$ ext gives first indication of quantity of Pb present, and progress of extn can be followed by noting color of successive exts.)

Drain $CHCl_3$ layer into 125 ml short-stem separator contg 25–30 ml H_2O made ammoniacal with *one drop* NH_4OH (sp gr 0.90). Continue extn until 2 successive exts with small portions of more dil. dithizone solns show the neg. color (green, not bluish or purple), combining exts in smaller separator. Shake, let layers sep., drain $CHCl_3$ fraction into another small separator, and repeat washing process as before. Drain $CHCl_3$ fraction as cleanly as possible into 100 or 150 ml beaker, and pass small portion of dil. dithizone soln thru separators in succession so as to wash out small portions of ext persisting in aq. fraction. Add to beaker and evap. $CHCl_3$ with gentle heat on steam bath. Take up dry residue with 3–4 ml HNO_3, and heat by swirling over low flame. Dil. to ca 25 ml and continue heating 1–2 min to expel oxides of N. Add small piece of litmus paper, neutze with NH_4OH, and dil. to 50 ml. Add 0.5 ml HNO_3 and proceed as in **25.048**.

34.103 *Method III (21)*

(Applicable to Ca, Ba, and Sr lakes)

Place 2 g sample, 4 g Na_2CO_3, 6 g K_2CO_3, and 0.5 g $NaNO_3$ in Pt crucible and mix thoroly. Heat carefully until sample is carbonized; then heat to ca 850° and hold at that temp. 15 min. (If temp.-controlled furnace is available, it is only necessary to place fusion mixt. in cold furnace and raise temp. gradually to 850° over 2 hr period. Usually 15 min heating at 850° will complete fusion.)

Let crucible and contents cool to <100°; then add 2 or 3 ml H_2O and heat over low flame, using care to prevent spattering, until contents can be sepd from crucible. Transfer fused mixt. to 150 ml beaker with aid of ca 25 ml hot H_2O. Boil until caked material is completely disintegrated, and filter thru retentive paper. Wash residue on filter with two 15 ml portions hot 5% Na_2CO_3 soln. Pb will be in both filtrate and residue. Transfer filtrate to separator and ext Pb from filtrate as in **34.102**.

Dissolve residue on filter in 10–20 ml HCl (2 + 5), wash filter with H_2O, and add washings to filtrate. Boil soln to expel CO_2; then transfer to separator and ext Pb as above. Combine with $CHCl_3$ exts from sol. portion of fusion products and det. total Pb as in **34.102**.

34.104 ★ Sulfated Ash—Official Final ★ Action

Accurately weigh ca 5 g sample in weighing bottle and transfer to Pyrex Kjeldahl flask or tall beaker, washing out weighing bottle with little H_2O. Destroy org. matter by digestion, using 15 ml H_2SO_4 and adding HNO_3 as required. As bulk of HNO_3 is driven off, lower flame to avoid reaction on glass.

Transfer mixt. to weighed Pt dish and heat carefully over ring burner to avoid spattering. At first use low flame at safe distance below dish; then increase flame, and gradually bring it closer to dish. Continue heating until acid fumes decrease. If C remains, remove flame, let mass cool, and add H_2SO_4 dropwise until mass is moistened. Repeat treatment until all C is burned off and ash is white or reddish. Heat carefully with blast lamp until fusion takes place with production of clear liq. free from bubbles. Cool in desiccator and weigh. After deducting wt Na_2SO_4 equiv. to inorg. Na salts (chlorides, sulfates, carbonates, etc.) found in other detns, calc. % Na combined in dye.

34.105 ★ Mixed Oxides (Fe, Al, Ca, and ★ Mg)—Official Final Action
(*Caution: See* 46.059.)

Moisten sulfated ash obtained in **34.104** with 2–3 ml HCl and evap. to dryness on steam bath. Warm residue with 20 ml HCl (1 + 19) until all sol. material dissolves, transfer to 100 ml vol. flask, dil. to 100 ml with H_2O, mix, and filter thru dry paper.

To 40 ml aliquot filtrate add 5 g NH_4Cl and neutze with NH_4OH (1 + 1), boiling to drive off any excess. If ppt is very slight, disregard it; otherwise filter thru quant. paper, wash with H_2O contg trace of NH_4OH (reserving filtrate and washings), and ignite paper and ppt in weighed crucible. Weigh mixt. of Fe_2O_3 and Al_2O_3.

Place mixed oxides in 500 ml erlenmeyer and dissolve in aqua regia (HNO_3 + HCl (1 + 3)), boiling to drive off Cl. Add H_2O to ca 75 ml and add NH_4OH to incipient pptn. Dissolve ppt with as little HCl as possible, cool, and titr. ferric Fe present with 0.1N

TiCl$_3$, **45.043**, using 5 g NH$_4$CNS as indicator. Calc. Fe as Fe$_2$O$_3$. To calc. Al$_2$O$_3$, deduct wt Fe$_2$O$_3$ from total wt mixed oxides. From wt Al$_2$O$_3$, calc. % Al.

Pass washed stream of H$_2$S into alk. filtrate from Fe and Al hydroxides. White ppt indicates presence of Zn.

To second 40 ml aliquot filtrate add 250 ml H$_2$O to ensure low concn of Mg, if present. Heat to boiling and add 3.5 g NH$_4$Cl and enough NH$_4$OH soln (1 + 99) to make soln barely alk. Filter off pptd hydroxides of Fe and Al. Wash and discard ppt. Heat combined filtrate and washings to boiling and add 1 g NH$_4$ oxalate. Let cool and stand 1 hr, filter thru asbestos mat prepd on small Witt plate in glass funnel, and wash with very little H$_2$O, reserving combined filtrate and washings. Place mat in beaker, add 100 ml H$_2$O and 2 ml H$_2$SO$_4$, heat gently until CaC$_2$O$_4$ dissolves, and titr. with 0.1N KMnO$_4$. Calc. as Ca.

Heat reserved filtrate and washings to boiling and add 1N NaNH$_4$HPO$_4$ soln until there is no further pptn. While stirring add ca ⅓ the vol. of NH$_4$OH soln (1 + 9). Let stand 3 hr, filter thru ashless paper, and wash with NH$_4$OH soln (1 + 49). Ignite filter and ppt in weighed crucible, cool in desiccator, and weigh the Mg$_2$P$_2$O$_7$. Calc. as Mg.

★ HALOGENS IN PURE COLORS ★
Iodine (22)—Official Final Action
34.106 *Reagents*

(**a**) *Saturated potassium permanganate soln.*—Dissolve 7 g KMnO$_4$ in 100 ml H$_2$O.

(**b**) *Sodium thiosulfate std soln.*—0.1N or 0.05N, depending on size of sample taken. Use std soln, **45.038–45.039**, or prep. 0.05N daily by dilg 0.1N soln.

(**c**) *Starch soln.*—0.5%. Weigh 1 g sol. starch. Make into thin paste with several ml cold H$_2$O, pour into 200 ml hot H$_2$O, and while still hot add 2–3 small crystals HgI$_2$ as preservative.

34.107 *Determination*

Place accurately weighed sample contg ca 50 mg I in 500 ml tall beaker. Dissolve sample in ca 2 ml 30% NaOH soln, dil. to 100 ml, and add few glass beads and 15 ml satd KMnO$_4$ soln. Cover with watch glass, boil 5 min, and remove from heat. When boiling ceases, carefully add 10 ml HNO$_3$ and boil 5 min more.

Remove beaker from heat and wash down cover glass and sides (excess KMnO$_4$ must be present). Add 5 ml 10% NaNO$_2$ soln quickly with swirling. (KMnO$_4$ color is destroyed, and brown suspension of MnO$_2$ is left.) Continue addn of NaNO$_2$ soln dropwise until suspension begins to clear; then cautiously add NaNO$_2$ soln, letting each drop react before next is added. When soln appears colorless by transmitted light, but some particles of solid MnO$_2$ remain, do not attempt to destroy these, but imme-diately add 1% KMnO$_4$ soln in 1 ml portions until soln becomes pink.

Note: If >2 ml is required or if brown color appears, at once add 10 ml of the dil. KMnO$_4$ soln and again heat to boiling. Repeat dropwise addn of NaNO$_2$ soln and again add dil. KMnO$_4$ soln until soln becomes pink.

Filter soln rapidly with suction thru medium porosity fritted glass filter into wide-mouth 500 ml flask. Thoroly wash beaker with H$_2$O. (Soln must remain pink after filtration.) Add NaNO$_2$ soln dropwise with shaking until 1 drop has been added in excess of that required to decolorize soln. Add 5 ml *10% sulfamic acid soln*, wash down sides of flask, and swirl contents. Cool soln to room temp., add 2–3 g solid KI, and titr. liberated I with std Na$_2$S$_2$O$_3$ soln, using starch indicator, (**c**). Det. blank on reagents used. 1 ml 0.1N Na$_2$S$_2$O$_3$ = 0.002115 g I.

Total I − inorg. I = organically combined I.

Bromine (23)—Official Final Action
34.108 *Apparatus (Fig. 34:3)*

Consists of 100 ml r-b flask with 24/40 ⚥ inner joint; condenser with jacket ca 130 mm long; and absorption flask with 2 bulbs. Condenser is equipped with 12/30 and 24/40 ⚥ inner joints. Small dropping funnel is fused to tube above jacket. Absorption flask has outer 12/30 ⚥ joint. Small springs (not shown) are attached to hooks on joints to keep app. tightly connected during use.

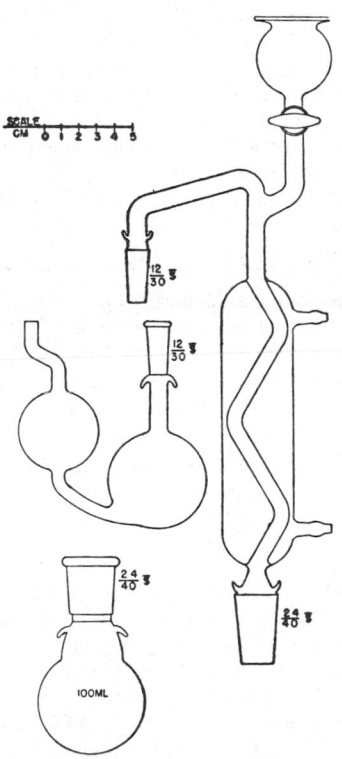

FIG. 34:3—Bromine apparatus

34.109   *Determination*

Place sample calcd to contain 40–60 mg Br in oxidn flask and dissolve in 2 ml 10% NaOH soln and 8 ml H_2O, or use 10 ml aliquot of suitable soln of dye. Lubricate joints of app. with H_3PO_4 and connect flask to condenser. Place ca 15 ml *1% $N_2H_4.H_2SO_4$ soln* and 5 ml 10% NaOH soln in absorption flask and connect to app.

Add 5 ml CrO_3 soln (1 + 1) thru addn tube, wash down with 2–3 ml H_2O, and then slowly add 10 ml H_2SO_4. If vigorous reaction begins, let it subside before heating flask; if reaction does not begin as acid is added, heat gently with small flame, but remove flame before reaction becomes too vigorous, otherwise reaction mixt. may foam up into condenser. When reaction subsides and most of dye is in soln, heat mixt. to boiling. When foaming subsides, add 5 ml H_2SO_4 thru dropping funnel, boil 10 min, add another 5 ml H_2SO_4, and boil again 10 min. Drain H_2O from condenser and boil reaction mixt. until 2–3 drops H_2O distill into absorber.

Disconnect absorption flask, wash contents into 500 ml I flask, and dil. to ca 100 ml with H_2O. Add ca 12 ml H_3PO_4, 5 ml 3% KCN soln, and 15 ml 3% $KMnO_4$ soln, wetting sides of flask with each reagent as it is added. Stopper flasks and mix by gentle swirling, wetting entire inside surface. Let stand ≥7 min; then add ca 2 g solid $FeSO_4.(NH_4)_2SO_4.6H_2O$. Wash down sides of flask and mix. (Clear, nearly colorless soln should result.) If any $KMnO_4$ or MnO_2 remains, add more $Fe(NH_4)_2(SO_4)_2$ (2 g excess does no harm).

Add ca 2 g KI and immediately titr. liberated I with 0.05N $Na_2S_2O_3$, using starch indicator. (End point is disappearance of starch-I color; avoid overtitrn as color of soln remains light blue.) 1 ml 0.05N $Na_2S_2O_3$ = 0.001998 g Br.

Total Br − inorg. Br = organically combined Br.

34.110   Chlorine (24)—Official Final Action

Proceed as in **34.109** until Cl has been driven into halogen absorber. Disconnect absorbing flask, wash contents into 500 ml beaker, and ppt Cl with $AgNO_3$ as in **35.021**. AgCl × 0.24737 = Cl.

Total Cl − inorg. Cl = organically combined Cl.

Chlorine in Presence of Bromine (22)—
Official Final Action

34.111   *Method I*

Proceed as in **34.109** until halogens have been driven into absorbing soln. Disconnect absorption flask, wash contents into 110 ml vol. flask, and dil. to vol. with H_2O. Pipet 50 ml aliquot into 500 ml I flask and det. Br as in **34.109**. Ppt total halogens in another 50 ml aliquot as in **34.110**.

Calc. wt AgBr equiv. to Br found in first aliquot and subtract from wt ppt obtained from second aliquot. From difference (wt AgCl) calc. Cl present.

Br × 2.35 = AgBr; total AgCl − AgBr = AgCl; and AgCl × 0.24737 = Cl.

Multiply results obtained by 2.2 to obtain Cl and Br in the 110 ml soln.

Method II (25)

34.112   *Reagent*

Silver iodate.—Suitable for detn of Cl. (Obtainable from Merck & Co., Rahway, NJ 07065.)

34.113   *Determination*

Accurately weigh sample contg ≥15 mg Cl or 30 mg Br. Oxidize sample and absorb evolved halogen in mixt. of 15 ml *1% $N_2H_4.H_2SO_4$ soln* and 5 ml 10% NaOH soln as in **34.109**.

Transfer absorbing soln to 200 ml beaker and wash absorption flask with two 5–10 ml portions H_2O. Complete washing with 5 ml 10% $NaNO_2$ soln and 10 ml H_2SO_4 (1 + 5), and add these reagents to beaker. Thoroly mix resulting soln and let stand ≥2 min. Wash down sides of beaker with 10 ml *10% sulfamic acid soln* and stir mixt. 2 min. Add excess (0.4–0.8 g) of solid $AgIO_3$, and mix vigorously ≥2 min. Transfer mixt. to 100 ml vol. flask, cool to room temp., and dil. to vol. with H_2O. Mix thoroly and filter thru dry fluted paper. Discard first few ml filtrate.

Dil. aliquot of filtrate to ca 100 ml with H_2O, add 2 g KI, and titr. liberated I with std $Na_2S_2O_3$ soln, **34.106(b)**, using starch soln as indicator. 1 ml 0.1N $Na_2S_2O_3$ = 0.591 mg Cl, or 1.332 mg Br.

If sample contains both Br and Cl, dil. soln to exactly 100 ml before adding $AgIO_3$. Neutze aliquot of this soln, using at least half the soln, with 30% NaOH soln and det. Br as in **34.109**. To remaining soln add solid $AgIO_3$, shake vigorously ≥2 min, filter, and titr. aliquot of filtrate as above to obtain total halide content (mols).

Calc. Br and Cl content of sample as follows:

$$Br \ (mg) = (T_1 \times N_1 \times 39.96 \times 100)/X$$

and

$$Cl \ (mg) = [(T_2 \times N_2 \times 100/Y)$$
$$- (3 \times T_1 \times N_1 \times 100/X)] \times 5.91,$$

where T_1 = titrn for Br detn; T_2 = titrn for total halide detn; N_1 = normality of $Na_2S_2O_3$ used in T_1; N_2 = normality of $Na_2S_2O_3$ used in T_2; X = aliquot used for Br detn; and Y = aliquot used for total halide detn.

FREE HALOGENS—OFFICIAL
FIRST ACTION
★ **Free Chlorine or Bromine** ★

34.114   *Apparatus*

Two gas-washing bottles (ca 4 × 25 cm).

34.115   *Determination*

Place layer of glass beads in first gas-washing bottle so that top of layer is ca 5 cm above tip of inlet tube, and place 50.0 g sample on top of beads.

Place 5–10 cm layer of glass wool in outlet of bottle to prevent mech. carry-over of dye.

Place ca 100 ml 1% KI soln contg few drops H_2SO_4 in second gas-washing bottle and connect outlet tube of first bottle to inlet tube of second bottle. Pass steady stream of air thru app. 15–20 min. (*Caution*: Before passing air thru app. be sure that inlet tube of first bottle is not plugged with dye.) Titr. liberated I in second bottle with $0.1N$ $Na_2S_2O_3$, **34.106**(b), using starch indicator. 1 ml $0.1N$ $Na_2S_2O_3$ = 3.5 mg Cl or 8.0 mg Br.

★ INORGANIC SALTS—OFFICIAL ★
FINAL ACTION
Sodium Chloride in Acid Dyes (26)

34.116 *Reagents*

(a) *Silver nitrate std soln.*—1 ml = ca 0.005 g NaCl. Stdze gravimetrically.

(b) *Ammonium thiocyanate std soln.*—Stdze by titrn against $AgNO_3$ soln.

(c) *Ferric alum indicator.*—To satd aq. soln $Fe(NH_4)(SO_4)_2$ add just enough HNO_3 to discharge red color.

(d) *Activated carbon.*—Norit SG No. 2 (American Norit Co., 6301 Glidden Way, Jacksonville, FL 32208) or other activated C practically free of Cl and SO_4.

34.117 *Preparation of Solution*

Add 10 g activated C to soln of 2 g sample in ca 100 ml H_2O, and boil gently 2–3 min. Cool to room temp., add 1 ml ca $6N$ HNO_3, and stir vigorously. Transfer mixt. to 200 ml vol. flask, dil. to vol. with H_2O, mix, and filter thru dry paper. If filtrate is colorless, proceed with detn of NaCl and Na_2SO_4. If dye is not completely adsorbed, add 2 g C, and stir. Test for complete adsorption by dipping corner of piece of filter paper into soln and observing color of liq. that rises in paper. Continue adding C in 2 g portions until test paper no longer shows color (indicating complete adsorption); then filter thru dry paper. Save filtrate for detn of NaCl and Na_2SO_4.

34.118 *Determination*

To 50 ml aliquot filtrate in 250 ml g-s flask add 2 ml ca $6N$ HNO_3, 10 ml $AgNO_3$ soln (more if amt of Cl is large), and ca 5 ml *nitrobenzene*. Shake vigorously until AgCl coagulates, add 1 ml Fe alum indicator, and titr. excess $AgNO_3$ with NH_4CNS soln. Take as end point first definite color that persists after shaking 1 min. Calc. NaCl from net $AgNO_3$ titrn on basis of 195 ml total vol., since 10 g C occupies 5 ml.

Net ml $AgNO_3$ × NaCl equiv. × 195 = % NaCl.

Sodium Chloride in Basic Dyes (26)

34.119 *Preparation of Solution*

Dissolve 2 g sample in exactly 200 ml H_2O. Add 10 g activated C, **34.116**(d), stir 1 min, and test for complete adsorption as in **34.117**. Add C in 2 g portions, with stirring, until test paper shows no color; then filter thru dry paper.

34.120 *Determination*

Evap. 50 ml aliquot filtrate to dryness, and heat to volatilize any NH_4Cl. Transfer residue to 250 ml flask with ca 50 ml H_2O, and det. NaCl as in **34.118**. Net ml $AgNO_3$ × NaCl equiv. × 200 = % NaCl.

Sodium Sulfate (26)

34.121 *Reagents*

(a) *Barium chloride soln.*—1 ml = ca 0.0025 g Na_2SO_4. Stdze gravimetrically.

(b) *Tetrahydroxyquinone indicator.*—See **34.031** (c). (In neut. soln contg equal vols alcohol and H_2O, indicator changes from yellow to red when Ba ions are present, and end point is observed by transmitted light. After some practice, results can be reproduced to ±0.05 ml $BaCl_2$ soln. Blank of ca 0.1 ml should be deducted.)

(c) *Phenolphthalein indicator.*—0.5% soln in 50% alcohol.

34.122 *Determination*

Acid or basic dyes.—Place 25 ml filtrate, **34.117** or **34.119**, in 125 ml erlenmeyer, add 1 drop phthln, and make alk. by dropwise addn of ca $0.05N$ NaOH; then add ca $0.002N$ HCl dropwise until indicator is decolorized. Add 25 ml alcohol and ca 0.2 g tetrahydroxyquinone indicator. Titr. slowly with $BaCl_2$ soln, shaking constantly, to red end point. Det. blank on reagents. From net titrn calc. as follows: Acid dyes: Net ml $BaCl_2$ × Na_2SO_4 equiv. × 390 = % Na_2SO_4; Basic dyes: Net ml $BaCl_2$ × Na_2SO_4 equiv. × 400 = % Na_2SO_4.

34.123 Sodium Halides in Halogenated Fluorescein Colors

Place 5 g sample in 400 ml beaker and add ca 150 ml H_2O. (If sample is a color acid, add just enough 10% NaOH soln to give complete soln.) Heat soln nearly to boiling and add 5 ml H_3PO_4. Digest soln until ppt of color acid is well coagulated, cool to room temp., transfer to 250 ml vol. flask, and dil. to vol. Mix thoroly, filter thru dry fluted paper, and discard first few ml filtrate.

(a) *Sodium iodide.*—Transfer 100 ml aliquot filtrate to 500 ml tall beaker; add 2.5 ml 30% NaOH soln, few glass beads, and 15 ml satd $KMnO_4$ soln, **34.106**(a). Proceed as in **34.107**, beginning "boil 5 min . . ."

1 ml $0.1N$ $Na_2S_2O_3$ = 0.002498 g NaI.

(b) *Sodium bromide.*—Place 100 ml aliquot filtrate in 500 ml I flask and proceed as in **34.109**, beginning "Add ca 12 ml H_3PO_4 . . ."

1 ml $0.05N$ $Na_2S_2O_3$ = 0.00257 g NaBr.

(c) *Sodium chloride.*—Place 100 ml aliquot filtrate in 400 ml beaker, heat to boiling, and add enough

10% AgNO₃ soln to ppt halides. Digest soln until ppt is well coagulated, cool, and transfer ppt to weighed gooch. Thoroly wash ppt with H_2O and alcohol. Dry crucible and contents at 135°, cool, and weigh.

If sample contains no NaBr or NaI, NaCl content can be calcd directly from wt ppt. If other halides are present, deduct wt Ag halide equiv. to I or Br found, (a) or (b), from wt ppt before calcg NaCl content.

AgCl × 0.4078 = NaCl; NaI × 1.566 = AgI; and NaBr × 1.825 = AgBr.

★ Sodium Acetate ★

34.124 *Apparatus*

App., Fig. 34:4, can be assembled from stock items. Distg flask is 125 ml acetylation flask with ⊤ 24/40 joint. Receiver is 300 ml flask.

34.125 *Reagents*

(a) *p-Toluenesulfonic acid.*—Dry *p*-toluenesulfonic acid. H_2O overnight at 110°, cool, and grind to powder.

(b) *Silver toluenesulfonate.*—Dissolve Ag₂O or Ag₂CO₃ in ca 10% excess of *p*-toluenesulfonic acid soln, evap. to dryness, and dry 8 hr at 135°.

(c) *m-Cresol purple indicator.*—Triturate 0.5 g *m*-cresolsulfonphthalein with 13 ml 0.1N NaOH and dil. with H_2O to 100 ml.

34.126 *Determination*

To 500 ml erlenmeyer add 100 ml H_2O, 1 drop *m*-cresol purple indicator, and enough 0.1N NaOH or

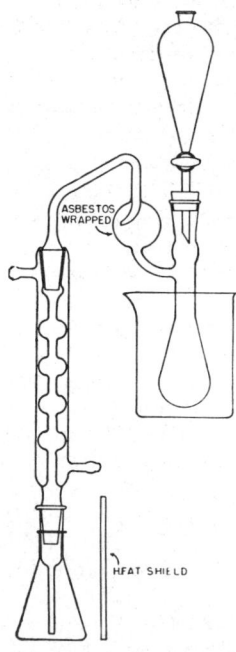

FIG. 34:4—Sodium acetate apparatus

0.1N HCl to turn color of soln just yellow; place flask under condenser.

Transfer 30 ml absolute alcohol to distn flask and add thru powder funnel 5.00 g sample, 5 g *p*-toluenesulfonic acid, and 1 g Ag toluenesulfonate. Add 3–4 pieces Alundum or other antibumping agent and mark level of liq. in distn flask. Wash funnel and neck of flask with 25 ml absolute alcohol. Shake flask to mix contents thoroly and attach it to condenser.

Immerse distn flask as far as possible in beaker of hot H_2O and heat H_2O to boiling. After ca 25 ml distillate collects, remove heat source and slowly add 25 ml absolute alcohol to distn flask. When contents of flask again begin to distill gently, replace heat source and collect second 25 ml distillate. Make third addn of alcohol and distill in similar manner. Finally boil until distn rate is slow (ca 30 min for total time from beginning of first distn).

Wash 50 ml H_2O down condenser into receiver, and add 50.0 ml 0.1N NaOH. Add 3–4 pieces Alundum or other antibumping agent and connect to reflux condenser fitted with absorption tube contg Ascarite or other CO_2-absorbing material. Reflux 10 min, cool to room temp., add few drops *m*-cresol purple indicator, and titr. with 0.1N HCl to yellow-green that does not change in hue on further addn of acid. Det. blank by repeating detn, omitting sample.

Calc. NaOAc from net vol. std NaOH soln required. 1 ml 0.1N NaOH = 0.0082 g $C_2H_3O_2Na$.

SOLUBLE MATTER—OFFICIAL FIRST ACTION

34.127 Water-Soluble Matter

Place 5 g well-powd sample in 500 ml erlenmeyer or wide-mouth bottle, add 200 ml H_2O, stopper, and shake vigorously. Repeat mixing several times during 2 hr period. Filter, and evap. 100 ml filtrate in weighed Pt dish on steam bath. Dry in oven at 100–105°, cool in desiccator, and weigh. Report increase in wt as H_2O-sol. matter. Test small portions of remainder of filtrate for chlorides, sulfates, and nitrates. If more than traces are present, make proper analyses on aliquot portions of filtrate.

34.128 Chloroform-Soluble Matter

Weigh 5 g sample into cellulose thimble and ext in Soxhlet app. with CHCl₃ 16 hr. Transfer ext to separator and wash with 30 ml portions H_2O until washings are practically colorless. Ext combined washings with ca 30 ml CHCl₃ and add washings to main ext. Drain CHCl₃ ext into weighed dish. Wash separator with few ml CHCl₃ and add washings to dish. Evap. at room temp., dry in desiccator to constant wt (±0.5 mg), and weigh. Report as CHCl₃ ext.

34.129 ★ Matter Soluble in One Per ★ Cent Aqueous Hydrochloric Acid

To 2 g sample in 300 ml beaker add 100 ml 1% HCl (1 + 99). Boil gently 5 min, stirring continuously, cool, and filter thru dry paper. Place 50 ml filtrate in previously weighed dish, evap. nearly to dryness, dry in oven 2 hr at 105°, cool in desiccator, and weigh. Increase in wt is matter sol. in 1 % HCl.

MISCELLANEOUS

★ **Melting Point—Official Final Action** ★

34.130 *Apparatus—See Fig. 34:5*

34.131 *Determination*

To capillary tube 1 mm or smaller id, sealed at one end, transfer small portion of sample by inserting open end of tube into sample, removing tube, inverting, and gently tapping until loosely packed substance fills bottom of tube to ht of 2–4 mm. Attach tube to thermometer so that sample is placed at ca middle of Hg bulb. Raise temp. of bath rapidly to within 5° of approx. mp of sample; then raise slowly until melting is observed. When temp. rises to ca

0.5° of mp, substance usually darkens; true melting is indicated by formation of meniscus on upper surface. When this condition is observed, record temp., and consider this temp. as mp of sample. Keep temp. as nearly constant as possible until entire sample liquefies; then record temp. again.

34.132 ★ **Free Acid—Official First Action** ★

Dissolve 1 g sample in exactly 10 ml H_2O, and det. pH of soln. If pH is ≥ 4.7, no free H_2SO_4 is present.

SELECTED REFERENCES

(1) USDA Bur. Chem. Bull. **448**; USDA Bur. Chem. Circs. **25** and **63**; Allen, "Commercial Organic Analysis," 4th ed., 1911, Vol. 5; Leach-Winton, "Food Inspection and Analysis," 4th ed., 1920; Girard, "Analyse des Matières Alimentaires et Recherche de leurs Falsifications," 2nd ed., 1904; USDA Bur. Animal Ind. Circ. **180**; J. Ind. Eng. Chem. **8**, 1123(1916); **9**, 955(1917).

(2) USDA Bur. Chem. Bull. **65**, p. 152; Ann. fals. **3**, 293(1910); USDA Bur. Chem. Circs. **25** and **63**; Abs. Chem. Centr. **69**, (2) 943(1898); J. Ind. Eng. Chem. **8**, 614(1916); **10**, 436(1918).

(3) USDA Bull. **1390**, Supplement 1 (1930).

(4) JAOAC **49**, 674(1966).

(5) JAOAC **26**, 182(1943).

(6) JAOAC **27**, 576(1944); **30**, 522(1947); **31**, 598, 674(1948); **32**, 130, 635(1949).

(7) JAOAC **25**, 936(1942).

(8) JAOAC **31**, 592(1948); **32**, 613(1949).

(9) JAOAC **31**, 594(1948); **32**, 624(1949).

(10) JAOAC **50**, 526(1967).

(11) JAOAC **35**, 419(1952).

(12) JAOAC **33**, 398(1950); **34**, 407(1951).

(13) JAOAC **32**, 640(1949).

(14) JAOAC **33**, 937(1950).

(15) JAOAC **32**, 672(1949).

(16) JAOAC **37**, 805(1954).

(17) JAOAC **46**, 344(1963).

(18) JAOAC **44**, 56(1961).

(19) JAOAC **35**, 754(1952); **37**, 803(1954); **38**, 357(1955).

(20) JAOAC **30**, 552(1947); **32**, 622(1949).

(21) JAOAC **31**, 677(1948); **32**, 621(1949).

(22) JAOAC **25**, 755(1942); **32**, 680(1949).

(23) JAOAC **26**, 433(1943); **28**, 757(1945).

(24) JAOAC **26**, 433(1943); **32**, 609(1949).

(25) JAOAC **32**, 680(1949).

(26) JAOAC **25**, 958(1942).

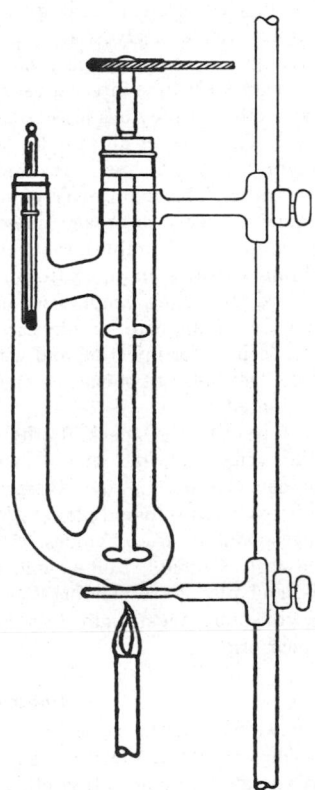

FIG. 34:5—Melting point apparatus

35. Cosmetics★

GENERAL METHODS
Water and Ethyl Alcohol (1)—
Official First Action

35.001 *Principles*

Sample is dissolved or dispersed in ethylene glycol monomethyl ether, which also serves as internal std, and H_2O and alcohol are detd by GLC, using relatively inert column, perfluorocarbon substrate coated with high molecular wt polyethylene glycol, to minimize tailing.

35.002 *Apparatus*

Gas chromatograph.—With thermal conductivity detector operated at following temps: Detector, ca 250°; injection port, ca 260°; oven, ca 100°; He flow rate, 50 ml/min; bridge current, as directed by manufacturer.

35.003 *Standard Solutions*

Prep. 3 std solns in 125 ml g-s flasks contg H_2O and absolute alcohol, weighed to 0.1 mg, in ethylene glycol monomethyl ether weighed to 10 mg, as follows:

H_2O, mg	Alcohol, mg	Ethylene Glycol Monomethyl Ether, g
125	375	24.50
250	250	24.50
375	125	24.50

H_2O content of ethylene glycol monomethyl ether should be <0.05%. If same batch is used for stds and samples, small amts of H_2O should not greatly affect accuracy of results. Com. product is usually satisfactory, but because of hygroscopicity *expose solns to air as little as possible.*

35.004 *Preparation of Column*

Weigh 10 g polyethylene glycol 20000 (Carbowax 20M) into 800 ml beaker, dissolve completely in ca 400 ml warm CH_2Cl_2, and cool to ca 0°. Slurry cold soln with 190 g precooled (ca 0°) Fluoropak 80, 40–60 mesh (Applied Science Laboratories). Transfer to 6″ crystg dish, place in hood, and evap. to dryness at room temp. with occasional stirring. Re-cool to ca 0° and screen thru No. 40 on No. 60 precooled screen. Pack fraction remaining on No. 60 in 15′ × ¼″ precooled Cu column, using vibrator. (Use of cooled column packer (Press-Pak, available from Alltek Associates, PO Box 498, Arlington Hts, IL 60006) at 35

lb/sq in. N pressure allows packing of cooled, precoiled column.)

35.005 *Standardization*

Inject 3 μl of one of std solns with 10 μl syringe and det. elution time of ethylene glycol monomethyl ether. (Order is alcohol, H_2O, and glycol ether.) Adjust oven temp., if necessary, so latter elutes in 15–20 min. With satisfactory column, pen will return to within 1% of recorder zero between alcohol and H_2O peaks. Det. sample size for each std soln such that response for smallest peak is at least ¼ full scale on ×1 attenuation. Det. all attenuations necessary to keep all peaks on chart scale. (Too large samples will overload column and skew glycol ether peak.)

With some gas chromatographs, alcohol peak response will vary with time interval between emergence of glycol ether of previous injection and injection of sample. Thus, inject all samples (std curves and actual detns) at same time interval after emergence of glycol ether. This requires use of preliminary sample. If time sequence is broken, inject another preliminary sample to re-establish sequence.

Obtain chromatograms, in duplicate, and on same day, for each std soln, using sample sizes and attenuations detd above. Duplicate sample sizes to 0.1 μl and use same technic for injecting and withdrawing syringe needle. Det. peak ht of each component, correcting for attenuation.

Calc. ratios: peak ht H_2O/peak ht ethylene glycol monomethyl ether (R_{PW}), and wt H_2O/wt ethylene glycol monomethyl ether (R_{WW}). Average the two R_{PW} values for each std soln and plot av. R_{PW} values against corresponding R_{WW} values. Draw best straight line thru 3 points. Make same calcns for alcohol stds, and plot corresponding R_{PA} and R_{WA} values. (Curves should be straight lines intersecting x or y axis near origin.)

35.006 *Determination*

Accurately weigh sample contg ca 100–400 mg H_2O and/or alcohol into 125 ml g-s flask, add 24.50 ±0.1 g ethylene glycol monomethyl ether, and mix thoroly. (Complete soln is unnecessary but glycol ether phase should contain all the H_2O and alcohol.) Det. proper sample size as in **35.005**, recording necessary attenuations. From good chromatogram, calc. R_{PW} and R_{PA} values. Read R_{WW} and R_{WA} values from std curves. From latter values prep. *final std soln* of 24.50 g ethylene glycol monomethyl ether plus H_2O and/or alcohol which approximates (within 10%) curve of sample. Det., in sequence, (*a*) curve of proper size sample, (*b*) curve of adjusted *final std*

---

soln, and repeat (*a*) and (*b*), in that order. Det. av. R_{PW} and R_{PA} values of unknown and final std solns, then R_{WW} and R_{WA} of std soln.

For H_2O: R_{WW} (sample) = R_{PW} (sample) $\times$ R_{WW} (std)/R_{PW} (std); wt H_2O (sample) = wt ethylene glycol monomethyl ether (sample) $\times$ R_{WW} (sample), and % H_2O (sample) = (wt H_2O/wt sample) $\times$ 100.

For alcohol: R_{WA} (sample) = R_{PA} (sample) $\times$ R_{WA} (std)/R_{PA} (std); wt alcohol (sample) = wt ethylene glycol monomethyl ether (sample) $\times$ R_{WA} (sample), and % alcohol (sample) = (wt alcohol/wt sample) $\times$ 100.

Propylene Glycol (2)—
Official First Action
(Applicable to all types of cosmetics)

35.007 *Apparatus*

(a) *Distillation apparatus.*—All-glass, with ⚙ 20/40 joints: 250 ml r-b flask, elec. heating mantle, 20 ml Barrett H_2O trap with ⚙ stopper, and driptip condenser.

(b) *Gas chromatograph.*—With H flame detector and capable of operating at ca 200°.

(c) *GLC column.*—6' $\times$ ¼″ od Cu or Al column packed with 80–100 mesh Chromosorb 101. Pack resin in column, using vibrator and column packer (Press-Pak, Alltek Associates, PO Box 498, Arlington Hts, IL 60006) operated at 25–35 lb pressure. Heat column overnight at 240° with He flow rate ca 100 ml/min. Condition column with propylene glycol as in **35.010**. Inject enough aq. soln of propylene glycol-trimethylene glycol (1 + 1) to give at least ½ full scale response. If column is satisfactory, two symmetrical peaks will be obtained. Reject batches of Chromosorb 101 which give unsymmetrical peaks.

35.008 *Reagents*

(a) *Propylene glycol.*—Eastman Kodak Co. No. 1321, or equiv.; assay by periodate oxidn as in **19.007**(a).

(b) *Trimethylene glycol.*—Propylene glycol-free.

(c) *Isooctane (2,2,4-trimethylpentane).*—Bp 99–100°.

(d) *Propylene glycol and trimethylene glycol std solns.*—10 mg/ml. Prep. sep. std solns. Accurately weigh ca 1.0 g std, dissolve in H_2O, transfer to 100 ml vol. flask, and dil. to vol.

35.009 *Separation of Propylene Glycol by Co-distillation*

(*Caution: See* **46.011, 46.039,** *and* **46.062.**)

Accurately weigh sample contg ca 2–40 mg propylene glycol into 250 ml r-b flask. Add 8–10 ml H_2O and few boiling chips. Connect flask to distn app. and add, thru condenser, enough isooctane to fill H_2O trap and provide 25–40 ml isooctane in distn flask. Adjust voltage on heating mantle so that isooctane distills at 5–10 ml/min. Continue distn 30 min after all H_2O appears to be collected in trap. Drain as much H_2O as possible (leave ca 0.25 ml in

H_2O trap) into small g-s container. (Stoppered 25 ml graduated cylinder is convenient.) Remove heat from distn flask and, when boiling stops, disconnect flask from app. and add 5 ml H_2O. Re-connect to app. and distill as before. Drain distillate into container contg first H_2O distillate. Repeat with second 5 ml portion H_2O. Mix combined distillates.

35.010 *Preparation of Instrument*

With Chromosorb 101 column in gas chromatograph, set column temp. at ca 180°, injection port and detector temps at ca 300°, and He flow rate near 70 ml/min. If necessary, adjust column temp. to elute propylene glycol in ca 6 min. Condition column by initial 0.5 μl injection of propylene glycol. Column must be conditioned in this manner once a day before use for detg propylene glycol. Use 5 μl aq. test soln contg ca 1 mg propylene glycol/ml and adjust H and air flow to flame detector until max. response is obtained. (*See* manufacturer's directions.) Note range and attenuation settings needed to keep peak on scale.

Establish rough calibration curve of peak ht response against wt propylene glycol by injecting known amts propylene glycol and observing response.

35.011 *Determination*

Det. approx. propylene glycol content of aq. soln, obtained by co-distn of sample with isooctane, by injecting known amt distillate into chromatograph. To sample soln add known aliquot of std trimethylene glycol soln (preferably sample soln should contain approx. equal wts propylene glycol and trimethylene glycol). Prep., from accurately measured aliquots of stds, soln contg approx. same wt propylene glycol and trimethylene glycol as prepd sample and dil. to approx. same vol. as sample soln.

Det., by trial injections, resp. vols of sample and std solns required to give nearly equal responses of ca 75% full scale for propylene glycol. Alternately inject these vols sample and known solns, making at least 2 injections of each soln. Det. sample and its corresponding std at same range and attenuation settings.

35.012 *Calculations*

From chromatograms calc. following peak ht ratios:

R_u = peak ht propylene glycol/peak ht trimethylene glycol

R_s = peak ht propylene glycol/peak ht trimethylene glycol, where R_u and R_s refer to sample and std ratios, resp. Using av. values of R_u and R_s, calc. amt propylene glycol in sample.

mg Propylene glycol = $(R_u/R_s) \times$ mg propylene glycol (std) $\times$ [mg trimethylene glycol (sample)]/[mg trimethylene glycol (std)]

(If same aliquot of trimethylene glycol is used for prepd sample and std, last factor = 1.)

DEODORANTS AND ANTI-PERSPIRANTS

Aluminum and Zinc (3)—Official Final Action

35.013   Reagents

(a) *8-Hydroxyquinoline soln.*—Dissolve 5.0 g 8-hydroxyquinoline in 12 ml HOAc, dil. to 100 ml with H_2O, and filter if not clear. Prep. fresh soln at least every 2 weeks.

(b) *Ammonium acetate soln.*—Approx. 2N. Dissolve 150–160 g NH_4OAc in 1 L H_2O and filter if not clear.

(c) *Hydrochloric acid.*—Approx. 2N.

(d) *Ammonium hydroxide.*—Approx. 2N. (Quantity of NH_4OH required to neutze 20 ml 2N HCl, (c), should be known to within ±2 ml.)

35.014   Preparation of Sample

(a) *Liquids.*—Dil. 5 ml sample to 250 ml with H_2O in vol. flask. If perfume oils sep., filter before taking aliquot for analysis.

(b) *Creams and pastes.*—Accurately weigh 2–3 g sample into 250 ml beaker. Add 5 ml HCl (HNO_3 if chlorides are to be detd) and ca 50 ml H_2O, and heat until oils liquefy and sep.; cool until oils solidify, and decant aq. layer thru fluted paper into 250 ml vol. flask. Return filter to original beaker and macerate thoroly. Repeat above extn twice, decant as before, and finally thoroly wash residue and paper with H_2O. (It is unnecessary to return filter paper to beaker after these extns.) Cool combined exts to room temp., dil. to vol. with H_2O, and mix.

(c) *Solids.*—Accurately weigh 2–3 g sample into 250 ml beaker, add 5 ml HCl (HNO_3 if chlorides are to be detd) and ca 50 ml H_2O, and heat to boiling. Cool, and filter thru fluted paper into 250 ml vol. flask. If filtrate is cloudy, refilter thru fine quant. paper. Thoroly wash beaker and paper with H_2O. Cool flask and contents to room temp., dil. to vol. with H_2O, and mix.

35.015   Determination

(a) *Interfering metals absent.*—Take aliquot of sample soln contg 12–25 mg Al or 20–60 mg Zn. Add 1–2 drops phthln, and then add 2N NH_4OH until neut. or until faint permanent turbidity results. Add 5 ml HOAc (1 + 9), dil. to ca 100 ml, and heat to 70–90°. Add 10 ml 8-hydroxyquinoline soln and then slowly add NH_4OAc soln until 20 ml (*see Note*) in excess of quantity required to produce permanent ppt has been added. If permanent ppt forms on addn of 8-hydroxyquinoline, add only 20 ml NH_4OAc soln. Heat below bp 2–5 min and set aside 30–60 min. (Moderate excess of 8-hydroxyquinoline is required for complete pptn. If enough reagent has been added, soln will be yellow at this point; if it is not, repeat detn, using larger quantity of 8-hydroxyquinoline soln.) Filter thru tared gooch, wash thoroly with H_2O, dry 1–2 hr at 130–140°, cool, and weigh. Dry again 30 min, cool, and weigh. Repeat to constant

wt (±0.3 mg). (Alternatively, ppt may be dried overnight.)

$$Wt\ ppt \times 0.05871 = Al;$$
$$Wt\ ppt \times 0.1848 = Zn$$

Note: Final pH of soln from which metals are pptd should be 4.9–5.1. Quantity of NH_4OAc soln required to produce this pH should be detd experimentally each time new set of reagents is prepd. If NH_4OAc is of usual purity, ca 20 ml of soln will be required.

(b) *In presence of magnesium.*—Ppt as in (a) and set aside ca 30 min. Decant most of liq. thru quant. paper (part or all of ppt may be transferred to paper if necessary) and discard filtrate. Place beaker used for pptn under funnel and dissolve ppt on paper in hot 2N HCl (20 ml is usually enough if added in several small portions). Wash paper and funnel with 20–30 ml H_2O. Add 2 ml 8-hydroxyquinoline soln, 5 ml HOAc (1 + 9), and quantity of 2N NH_4OH equiv. to 2N HCl used to dissolve ppt (do not use excess). Dil. to ca 100 ml, heat to 70–90°, and proceed as in (a), beginning "slowly add NH_4OAc soln ..."

Zinc (4)—Official Final Action

35.016   Reagent

8-Hydroxyquinaldine soln.—Dissolve 5.0 g 8-hydroxyquinaldine in 12 ml HOAc, dil. to 100 ml with H_2O, and filter if soln is not clear. (Soln is stable ca 1 week; if only tech. grade base is available, purify by recrystn from alcohol (2 + 1), using 6 ml solv. for each g base, before prepg soln.)

35.017   Determination

Pipet aliquot of sample soln, **35.014**, contg 20–50 mg Zn, into 400 ml beaker. Adjust soln to slight acidity, add 1 g NH_4 tartrate if Al is present, and then add 2 ml 8-hydroxyquinaldine soln for each 10 mg Zn present; dil. to 200 ml and heat to 60–80°. Neutze excess acid by adding NH_4OH (1 + 4) until Zn complex salt that forms on addn of each drop just redissolves on stirring. Slowly add, with stirring, 45 ml NH_4OAc soln, **35.013**(b), and let mixt. come to room temp.

Det. pH of soln; if pH is not 5.7–5.9, adjust with the NH_4OH soln, and let mixt. stand 10–20 min to achieve equilibrium. Decant thru tared gooch and wash ppt in beaker twice with hot H_2O, decanting each washing into crucible. Finally transfer ppt to crucible and again wash with hot H_2O. (Total vol. washings should be >200 ml.) Dry crucible and ppt 2 hr at 130–140°, cool, and weigh. Reheat 30 min at 130–140°; cool, reweigh, and repeat heating, cooling, and weighing to constant wt. Wt ppt × 0.1712 = wt Zn.

35.018 Aluminum—Official Final Action

Multiply wt Zn found, **35.017**, by 5.411 to obtain equiv. wt 8-hydroxyquinoline salt, multiply by appropriate factor for aliquot taken, and subtract from wt combined Al and Zn salts, **35.015**. Difference × 0.05871 = wt Al.

Boric Acid (5)—Official Final Action

35.019 Preparation of Ion Exchange Column

Provide glass tube 23″ long × 0.75″ diam. with stopcock and outlet tube. Tamp 1″ glass wool plug into bottom of tube, fill tube with H_2O, and add Amberlite IR-120(H) ion exchange resin slowly to form 8″ column. Wash with HCl (1 + 9) and then with 50 ml portions H_2O until effluent gives neg. Cl test.

Regenerate after use by transferring accumulated resin from number of detns to large glass tube and washing with HCl (1 + 9) until effluent gives neg. test for adsorbed cations, e.g., Zn, Al. Then remove HCl from resin by washing with H_2O until effluent gives neg. Cl test.

35.020 Determination

Place sample contg 50–200 mg H_3BO_3 in 250 ml casserole, add 2 drops phthln, and make alk. with 10% NaOH soln. Evap. to dryness on steam bath under gentle air current, dry residue 1 hr at 140° in oven, and ash 1 hr at 550°. Cool to room temp., add ca 50 ml hot H_2O, acidify cautiously with HCl, and filter hot soln thru quant. paper into 250 ml beaker. Wash paper with little hot H_2O and reserve filtrate (may be slightly cloudy).

Transfer paper to same casserole and make alk. by wetting with ca 10 ml H_2O and few drops 10% NaOH soln. Evap. to dryness on steam bath, dry 1 hr at 140°, and ash 2 hr at 550°. Cool, add ca 50 ml hot H_2O, acidify with HCl, and filter into reserved filtrate. Wash casserole and paper thoroly with hot H_2O, and discard paper. (Total vol. soln should be ca 200 ml.)

Cool soln; add NH_4OH until barely alk. to litmus paper or until flocculent ppt appears. Reacidify with HCl until slightly acid to litmus paper or until ppt just redissolves. Pass soln thru ion exchange column into 1 L flask at rate requiring 10–15 min for passage. Follow sample soln with several 50 ml portions H_2O until effluent is only slightly acid to pH test paper. Add 5 drops Me red, 2.084(b), make alk. with freshly prepd 10% NaOH soln, and then barely acid with HCl.

Connect flask to H_2O-cooled reflux condenser and boil 5 min. Wash down condenser with little H_2O and cool soln to room temp. under running H_2O. Neutze to Me red with 0.1N NaOH, 45.035; add 4–5 g mannitol and ca 0.5 ml phthln. Titr. with 0.1N NaOH to pink color, add more mannitol, and if pink disappears, continue titrn until it reappears. Repeat addn of mannitol until there is no further change in color.

Det. blank as follows: To ca 350 ml H_2O add quantity freshly prepd 10% NaOH soln equal to that required to neutze sample after passing thru column. Barely acidify with HCl and proceed as above, beginning "Connect flask to H_2O-cooled reflux condenser ..." Subtract blank titrn from sample titrn

and calc. H_3BO_3 content of sample. 1 ml 0.1N NaOH = 0.00618 g H_3BO_3.

35.021 Chlorides (6)—Official Final Action

Pipet aliquot of sample soln, 35.014, contg ca 100 mg Cl into 250 ml beaker. Dil. to 150 ml with H_2O, neutze to litmus with NH_4OH (1 + 1), and acidify with 1 ml HNO_3 (1 + 1). If any undissolved ppt remains, add more HNO_3 (1 + 1) until clear soln is obtained. Add dropwise, stirring constantly, slight excess of 0.1N $AgNO_3$. (Excess should be ≤5 ml.) Pptn and succeeding operations must be carried out in subdued light. Heat mixt. to 90–95° and stir until ppt coagulates. Let ppt settle; add 1–2 drops 0.1N $AgNO_3$ to supernatant to assure presence of excess Ag. Let mixt. stand 1–2 hr in dark.

Decant thru tared gooch, wash ppt 2–3 times with 0.01N HNO_3 by decantation, and finally transfer ppt to gooch with 0.01N HNO_3. Continue washing ppt with 0.01N HNO_3 until washing gives neg. test for Ag when 1 drop 0.1N HCl is added. Complete washing by removing most of the HNO_3 with two 10 ml portions H_2O. Dry crucible 2 hr at 120–130° and weigh. Repeat drying to constant wt (0.2 mg). Wt AgCl × 0.2474 = wt Cl.

35.022 Sulfates (6)—Official Final Action

Pipet aliquot of sample soln, 35.014, contg ca 100 mg sulfate into 600 ml beaker. Dil. to 350 ml with H_2O, neutze to litmus with NH_4OH (1 + 1), and acidify with 2 ml HCl. If any undissolved ppt remains, add more HCl until soln is clear.

Heat 50 ml 1% $BaCl_2$ soln almost to boiling and add rapidly with stirring to sulfate soln which has also been heated to near bp. Let ppt settle, and add little $BaCl_2$ soln to assure excess of Ba. Let mixt. stand 1–2 hr on steam bath. Decant thru tared gooch, wash ppt 4–5 times with small portions of warm H_2O by decantation, and finally transfer ppt to gooch with warm H_2O. Continue washing ppt with warm H_2O until washing gives neg. test for Cl. Dry crucible 2 hr at 110–120° and weigh. Repeat drying to constant wt (0.2 mg). Wt $BaSO_4$ × 0.4116 = wt sulfate.

Methenamine (7)—Official Final Action

35.023 Reagent

Borax-carbonate soln.—Dissolve 5.0 g Na_2CO_3 and 4.0 g $Na_2B_4O_7 \cdot 10H_2O$ in 100 ml H_2O.

35.024 Determination

Pipet aliquot of sample soln, 35.014, contg 150–200 mg methenamine into 500 ml r-b flask and dil. to 30 ml with H_2O. Neutze to litmus with either NaOH soln or dil. H_2SO_4; then acidify with 1 ml H_2SO_4. Connect flask to H_2O-cooled condenser and reflux 30 min to hydrolyze methenamine. Dil. to 175 ml by adding H_2O thru top of condenser, and disconnect condenser. Connect flask thru Kjeldahl trap to efficient straight-wall condenser and distill into 200 ml vol. flask contg 10 ml freshly prepd 10% NaHSO₃ soln. Continue distn until residual vol. is ca 5 ml, taking care to avoid charring.

Wash down condenser with little H_2O and cool distillate to room temp. Dil. distillate to vol. with H_2O, mix well, and let stand 30 min. Pipet 20 ml aliquot into wide-mouth 250 ml erlenmeyer, add 3–4 ml starch indicator, **6.004**(f), and destroy excess bisulfite with ca $1N$ I soln. Carefully adjust to starch-I end point with 0.5% NaHSO₃ soln and $0.05N$ I. Dil. to 50 ml with H_2O, add 10 ml borax-carbonate soln, and titr. with $0.05N$ I to permanent blue. 1 ml $0.05N$ I consumed in alk. titrn = 0.5841 mg methenamine.

Phenolsulfonates—Official Final Action

★ Bromination Method (7) ★

35.025　　　　　　　　　　　　　*Reagent*

Potassium bromate.—$0.1N$. Dissolve 2.8 g KBrO₃ in 1 L H_2O. Stdze against $0.1N$ Na₂S₂O₃.

35.026　　　　　　　　　　*Determination*

Pipet aliquot of sample soln, **35.014**, contg 60–125 mg phenolsulfonic acid into 250 ml I flask and dil. to ca 75 ml with H_2O. Add 2–3 ml HCl and 2–3 g KBr, and titr. slowly with $0.1N$ KBrO₃ until 1–3 ml excess is present. (In early stages of titrn, Br formed disappears rapidly but near end point some time is required for Br to react.) Stopper flask and let stand 10 min. If color disappears, add more $0.1N$ KBrO₃ and let stand addnl 10 min. Add 2–3 g KI, shake thoroly, and titr. liberated I with $0.1N$ Na₂S₂O₃, using starch indicator, **6.004**(f). I liberated is equiv. to excess KBrO₃ soln added. From net vol. KBrO₃ soln required in bromination, calc. amt of phenolsulfonic acid in sample. 1 ml $0.1N$ KBrO₃ = 0.004354 g phenolsulfonic acid.

Spectrophotometric Method (8)

35.027　　　　　　　　　　　　*Apparatus*

Spectrophotometer.—Capable of isolating wave band of 5 nm or less in region 220–350 nm.

35.028　　　　　　　　　　　　　*Reagent*

Zinc phenolsulfonate std soln.—10 mg/L in ca $0.1N$ NaOH. Dissolve 100 mg Zn phenolsulfonate, NF XI (equiv. to 62.67 mg phenolsulfonic acid) in 100 ml H_2O. Dil. 10 ml aliquot to 100 ml with H_2O. Pipet 10 ml aliquot into 100 ml vol. flask, add 4 ml freshly prepd 10% NaOH soln, and dil. to vol. with H_2O.

35.029　　　　　　　　　　*Determination*

(a) *In presence of sulfated surface active agents.*— Accurately weigh sample contg 5–10 mg phenolsulfonic acid into 250 ml erlenmeyer. Add 10 ml H_2O and 2 ml HCl, connect to H_2O-cooled condenser, and reflux 0.5 hr. Cool to room temp., transfer to 100 ml separator with aid of 20 ml H_2O, and proceed as in (b), beginning "ext with three 30 ml portions CHCl₃."

(b) *In absence of sulfated surface active agents.*— Accurately weigh, in weighing bottle, sample contg 5–10 mg phenolsulfonic acid. Transfer to 100 ml separator with aid of 30 ml H_2O. Acidify with HCl and ext with three 30 ml portions CHCl₃. Discard CHCl₃ exts. Filter aq. soln thru moistened quant. paper into 100 ml vol. flask and dil. to vol. with H_2O. Pipet 10 ml aliquot into 100 ml vol. flask, neutze to litmus paper with freshly prepd 10% NaOH soln, add 4 ml excess, and dil. to vol. with H_2O. Det. A of sample soln and A' of std soln at 253 nm in 1 cm cells, using $0.1N$ NaOH as blank. Calc. % phenolsulfonic acid as follows:

% phenolsulfonic acid = $C \times A/[10A' \times$ (g sample)], where C = concn phenolsulfonic acid (mg/L) in std soln.

35.030　Urea (6)—Official Final Action

Pipet aliquot of sample soln, **35.014**, contg 50–100 mg urea into 100 ml r-b flask with ♄ 24/40 female joint. Acidify with HCl, adding 0.5 ml excess. Immerse flask in steam bath and evap. to dryness. Add 10 g cryst. MgCl₂.6H₂O and 1 ml HCl, and connect flask to reflux condenser. Carefully heat mixt. with small flame until MgCl₂ dissolves in its H_2O of crystn, and reflux slowly 2 hr so that rate of return of liq. from condenser is 9–14 drops/min.

Let soln cool, add H_2O thru top of condenser, disconnect flask, and if necessary, heat to dissolve solids. Transfer soln to 1 L flat-bottom flask, dil. to ca 400 ml with H_2O, make alk. with 10% NaOH soln, and distill ca 275–300 ml into suitable portion of $0.1N$ H₂SO₄ contg several drops of Me red, **45.015**(a). Titr. excess acid with ca $0.1N$ NaOH, using more indicator if necessary. Stdze the $0.1N$ NaOH against the std $0.1N$ H₂SO₄, using Me red as indicator.

Correct for blank by refluxing 10 g cryst. MgCl₂ .6H₂O and 1 ml HCl and proceeding as above. 1 ml $0.1N$ H₂SO₄ = 3.003 mg urea.

DEPILATORIES

35.031　Sulfides in Powders (9)—
Official Final Action

(*Caution: See* **46.018** *and* **46.078**.)

Pipet 50 ml $0.1N$ As₂O₃ soln, **45.006**, into 250 ml g-s vol. flask. Weigh sample contg <0.12 g sulfide calcd as H₂S and transfer to flask, washing down any material on sides of flask with H_2O. Add 20 ml HCl (1 + 1), stopper immediately, and shake vigorously until sample decomposes. (If sample contains CaCO₃, slowly add the 20 ml acid thru dropping funnel fitted with rubber stopper to fit flask. Shake gently, letting liberated CO_2 bubble up thru acid. When reaction subsides, drain remainder of acid into flask, remove funnel, stopper flask, and shake vigorously.)

Cool to room temp. and dil. to vol. with H_2O. Filter thru dry paper into dry flask. Pipet 100 ml filtrate into 300 ml erlenmeyer; add 5 ml starch soln,

2.129(c), and enough I soln to form blue soln. Make alk. with $NaHCO_3$, adding 1–2 g excess. Titr. to permanent blue with $0.1N$ I, **45.019.** Subtract ml $0.1N$ I consumed in alk. titrn from ml $0.1N$ As_2O_3 present in aliquot. 1 ml $0.1N$ As_2O_3 = 0.005411 g CaS or 0.01271 g BaS.

★ FACE POWDERS (10) ★

35.032 ★ **Fats and Fatty Acids as** ★
Stearic Acid—Official Final Action
(Caution: See **46.011, 46.039, 46.040, 46.045,**
and **46.073.**)

Weigh ca 2 g sample into 250 ml g-s erlenmeyer. Add 30 ml benzene and swirl to mix thoroly. Add 10 ml HCl and swirl, removing stopper frequently to let CO_2 escape from carbonates. When pressure is spent, add 50 ml pet ether, and shake cautiously, periodically removing stopper until pressure again subsides. Then shake vigorously ca 50 times.

Decant ether layer thru cotton pledget into flask contg few glass beads previously weighed with similar flask as counterpoise. (This decanting involves no danger of loss; particles of powder are tenaciously retained in acid layer.) Again add 50 ml pet ether and repeat shaking and decanting. Repeat with third 50 ml portion pet ether. Evap. solv. soln to dryness on steam bath under hood. Place in forced-draft oven 1 hr at 100°, heating flask used as counterpoise at same time. Remove flask, cool, and weigh as stearic acid.

35.033 ★ **Boric Acid—Official Final Action** ★

(a) *Starch absent.*—Accurately weigh ca 4 g sample and transfer to 500 ml g-s erlenmeyer. Add 50 ml H_2O, stopper flask, and shake vigorously. With stopper out, heat flask just to boiling, and when cool enough to handle, stopper, shake, and filter thru 12.5 cm medium quant. paper. Quant. transfer residue to paper by shaking with small portions H_2O. Wash residue with H_2O and reserve for detn of Zn. Acidify filtrate to Me orange with $0.5N$ H_2SO_4, adding ca 1 ml excess. Proceed as in **20.033**, beginning "Boil ca 1 min . . ." ($0.1N$ NaOH may be used in place of $0.2N$ NaOH specified.)

(b) *Starch present.*—Ext sample with 50 ml cold H_2O by vigorously shaking flask 100 times at 5 min intervals during 30 min. Filter, and proceed as in (a), beginning "Quant. transfer residue . . ."

★ **Total Zinc—Official Final Action** ★

35.034 *Reagents*

(a) *Wulfing precipitant.*—Dissolve 80 g finely ground $(NH_4)_2CO_3$ in mixt. of 90 ml NH_4OH and 375 ml H_2O, and add 475 ml alcohol, which may or may not cause pptn, depending on temp. Let any ppt settle, and use supernatant.

(b) *Wash soln.*—Mix equal vols. of the Wulfing precipitant and alcohol.

35.035 *Determination*

Weigh ca 2 g sample (or if H_3BO_3 is present, use residue from H_3BO_3 detn, **35.033**) into Pt dish and ignite to light gray ash at 600–650°. Heat no longer than necessary. With aid of wide-mouth funnel, transfer ash to 500 ml g-s erlenmeyer. Add 100 ml Wulfing precipitant so as to wash down funnel. Stopper flask and shake vigorously 1 min, pausing occasionally to remove stopper and relieve pressure. Let stand overnight.

Filter thru 12.5 cm medium quant. paper. Wash out flask with wash soln, pouring washings thru filter, but make no attempt to transfer residue completely. Reserve flask for later detn of acid-sol. constituents. Thoroly wash residue on paper with wash soln.

Det. Zn in filtrate as follows: Exactly neutze to Me red with HCl, add 200 ml H_2O, and bring nearly to boiling on hot plate. Add 60 ml 10% $(NH_4)_2HPO_4$ soln, and continue to heat at just below boiling 30 min. Remove and let cool slowly to room temp. Filter thru weighed gooch previously ignited 10 min at full heat of Fisher or equiv. burner. Wash with freshly prepd 1% $(NH_4)_2HPO_4$ soln, and finally with 50 ml 50% alcohol. Discard filtrate. Place gooch in porcelain crucible of suitable size, and dry over low flame; then ignite at full heat to constant wt. $Zn_2P_2O_7 \times 0.5341 = ZnO$.

35.036 ★ **Acid-Soluble Calcium—** ★
Official Final Action
(Caution: See **46.047.**)

Place paper contg residue from Zn sepn in Pt dish and burn off paper at <650°. Transfer ash to 250 ml beaker. Wash residue out of flask used in Zn sepn with 100 ml HCl (1 + 9), adding washings to beaker. If some residue still clings to inside of flask, wash out with stream of H_2O from wash bottle. Stir thoroly, let stand 10 min, and filter thru medium quant. paper. Disregard turbidity in filtrate. Wash residue on paper 3 times with H_2O. Place in Pt dish ≥ 6 cm diam. and ≥ 2 cm high, and hold pending addn of recovered acid-sol. Fe, Al, and $BaSO_4$.

Nearly neutze filtrate to Me red with NH_4OH. Add 200 mg $(NH_4)_2SO_4$ and enough $Br-H_2O$ to destroy indicator and distinctly color soln. Boil free of Br, add more Me red, and while still nearly boiling add NH_4OH dropwise to first distinct yellow, avoiding any excess. Let stand ca 3 min, and filter thru medium quant. paper. Wash with hot 2% NH_4Cl soln. Transfer paper and residue to the Pt dish contg acid-insol. constituents. Det. Ca in filtrate as in **6.047**, beginning "heat to boiling . . ."

35.037 ★ **Acid-Soluble Magnesium—** ★
Official Final Action

Det. Mg in filtrate from acid-sol. Ca as in **33.025**. $Mg_2P_2O_7 \times 0.3622 = MgO$.

★ **Barium Sulfate—Official Final Action** ★
35.038 *Apparatus*

Air bath.—On tripod over Fisher or equiv. burner place 3″ clay triangle holding ca 125 ml Ni or Fe crucible. On top of crucible place 2½″ clay triangle; Pt dish used for fusion rests on this triangle.

35.039 *Determination*
(Caution: See **46.025.**)

Ash residues reserved in Pt dish (acid-insol. portion and materials recovered prior to Ca pptn, **35.036**) at <650°. Pulverize ash with flat-end glass rod, and moisten with 4 ml H_2O. Add 4 ml H_2SO_4, place under hood, and fill dish to ca ¼ its depth with 48% HF. Evap. on air bath, swirling occasionally to mix contents, until only H_2SO_4 appears to remain; then cautiously heat over low flame of Fisher or equiv. burner to pasty consistency, but do not take to complete dryness. Add 15 g pulverized $K_2S_2O_7$, and heat to melting. Continue heating, gradually raising temp. until clear melt is obtained. (Achieved only when dish glows red-hot and melt is orange-red. Too rapid heating will cause spattering. Foaming will occur but is not to be feared. After fusion, clarity of melt may be marred by bubbles and possibly by few flakes of K_2SO_4 produced by the high temp., but these may be disregarded if melt is generally clear.) Set dish aside on asbestos board.

When cool, dislodge melt into 600 ml beaker, wash dish with successive portions of hot H_2SO_4 (1 + 19) to ca 150 ml, and boil until melt dissolves. $BaSO_4$ ppts at this point; if there is no ppt, dil. soln to 500 ml and proceed as in **35.041**. If there is ppt, digest soln on steam bath 1 hr, let cool, dil. to ca 400 ml, stir well, and let stand at least 2 more hr. Filter thru finest available quant. paper, catching filtrate in 500 ml vol. flask. Thoroly wash residue 3 times with H_2O, transfer to weighed porcelain crucible, burn off paper at low temp., and ignite at dull red heat (ca 700°). Weigh as $BaSO_4$. (Residues <0.5% should not be counted as $BaSO_4$, as they represent HF-resistant silicate or quartz originally present in talc or kaolin.)

Dil. filtrate from $BaSO_4$ detn to 500 ml and use for detn of Fe, Ti, and Al.

★ **Total Titanium and Iron—** ★
Official Final Action
35.040 *Apparatus*

Jones reductor.—With long glass rod, ram pledget of glass wool into the constricted lower end of 50 ml pinchcock buret (without pinchcock attachment). Fill buret to ca 15 ml mark with "20- or 30-mesh" amalgamated Zn. (Zn may be amalgamated by letting it fall into 200 ml H_2O contg 4 g dissolved $HgCl_2$ and 10 ml H_2SO_4. Wash several times with H_2O by decantation before placing in buret.) Fit constricted lower end of buret with 4″ piece of thick-wall rubber tubing with screw-clamp ca midway and terminating in glass tube thrust thru 1-hole No. 7 rubber stopper. Fit stopper to 500 ml vac. flask and adjust glass tube

to reach ca 2″ above bottom of flask. When not in use, keep Jones reductor filled with H_2O.

35.041 *Determination*

Pipet 100 ml aliquot filtrate from $BaSO_4$ detn, **35.039**, into beaker and add 5 ml H_2SO_4 with stirring. Place in vac. flask 10 ml *10% Fe alum soln* (free of ferrous Fe and other substances reducing $KMnO_4$). Fit flask to reductor, apply vac., and open screw-clamp enough to permit controlled passage of liq. into flask. When meniscus in buret nears level of the Zn, add more soln. (It is preferable never to expose amalgamated Zn to air.) When all soln has been added, add ca 100 ml H_2O in same manner. Close screw-clamp just before meniscus of last washing reaches level of Zn, release vac., and disconnect flask.

Transfer contents to 300 ml tall-form beaker and add 3 ml H_3PO_4. Using 10 ml microburet, titr. over white surface with $0.1N$ $KMnO_4$ to first pink. Prep. blank contg 3 g $K_2S_2O_7$ and 6.5 ml H_2SO_4 in 100 ml H_2O and treat identically as sample, finally titrg to same shade of pink. Subtract titer of blank from that of sample. 1 ml $0.1N$ $KMnO_4$ = 0.007988 g TiO_2 + Fe_2O_3 (these have practically same equiv. wt).

★ **Total Iron—Official Final Action** ★
35.042 *Reagent*

Titanous chloride std soln.—$0.05N$. Prep. and stdze as in **45.043** and **45.044**, but use only 100 ml 15% $TiCl_3$ soln. Soln may be stdzd in ordinary microburet, titrd in open beaker, kept in g-s bottle, and restdzd before each set of detns.

35.043 *Determination*

Pipet 100 ml aliquot filtrate from $BaSO_4$ detn, **35.039**, into 150 ml beaker. Add 1 g NH_4CNS. Slowly, and with thoro stirring, titr. with $0.05N$ $TiCl_3$ from microburet to disappearance of red. Det. blank on 3 g $K_2S_2O_7$ and 6.5 ml H_2SO_4 in 100 ml H_2O. (Blank is often nil.) Correct titer for blank. 1 ml $0.05N$ $TiCl_3$ = 0.003992 g Fe_2O_3.

35.044 ★ **Total Titanium—** ★
Official Final Action

% total (TiO_2 + Fe_2O_3) − % total Fe_2O_3 = % total TiO_2.

35.045 ★ **Total Oxides of Iron,** ★
Titanium, and Aluminum—
Official Final Action

Pipet 250 ml aliquot filtrate from $BaSO_4$ detn, **35.039**, into 600 ml beaker. Add few drops Me red and 5 g NH_4Cl, and bring to boil. Neutze by adding NH_4OH dropwise to first distinct yellow. Let stand ca 3 min and filter thru 12.5 cm medium quant. paper. Wash several times with hot 2% NH_4Cl soln. Reserve filtrate for acid-insol. Ca detn, **35.047**.

Place paper in weighed Pt crucible and dry in oven or air bath. Transfer crucible to muffle furnace at room temp., and raise temp. to ca 1100°. Ignite to constant wt. Wt residue is total Al_2O_3 + Fe_2O_3 + TiO_2.

35.046 ★ Total Aluminum— ★ Official Final Action

% Total $(Al_2O_3 + Fe_2O_3 + TiO_2)$ − % total $(Fe_2O_3 + TiO_2)$ = % total Al_2O_3.

35.047 ★ Acid-Insoluble Calcium— ★ Official Final Action

Det. Ca in filtrate from NH_4OH ppt, **35.045**, as in **6.047**, beginning "heat to boiling ..."

35.048 ★ Acid-Insoluble Magnesium— ★ Official Final Action

Det. Mg in filtrate from acid-insol. Ca as in **33.025**. $Mg_2P_2O_7 \times 0.3622 = MgO$.

35.049 ★ Silica—Official Final Action ★
(*Caution: See* **46.025** and **46.028**.)

Weigh ca 1 g sample into 250 ml beaker. Moisten with alcohol and add 100 ml HCl $(1 + 9)$. Stir, and let stand 10 min. Filter thru 12.5 cm medium quant. paper. Wash residue 3 times with H_2O. Transfer paper to Pt crucible and ash at <650°. Cool, and pulverize ash with flat-end glass rod. Add 6 g Na_2CO_3, portion at time, intimately mixing with same glass rod between addns. Use last portion Na_2CO_3 to sprinkle over top of mixt. Place in muffle at <800°, and raise temp. to bring contents into fusion. Heat 15 min at ca 1000°. Remove crucible and let cool.

Dislodge melt into dry 500 ml beaker. (Not always easy; it often helps to return crucible to hot furnace ½ min; then remove and immediately dip ca ⅔ its ht in beaker of H_2O. If repeated enough times, this treatment causes melt to crack away from Pt so that it can be removed by simply inverting crucible over beaker.)

Mix 15 ml HNO_3 with 5 ml H_2O in graduate, and wash crucible with successive small portions of mixt., adding washings to beaker. If soln of melt becomes slow, hasten disintegration by gentle pressure with glass rod. When Na_2CO_3 in melt dissolves, place beaker under hood and add, in order, 5 g NH_4Cl and 25 ml $HClO_4$ (60%). Cover beaker with watch glass and boil over moderate flame until oxides of N pass off and $HClO_4$ refluxes down sides of beaker. Slightly cool mixt., add 150 ml very hot H_2O, stir, and let stand until SiO_2 settles.

Decant thru 12.5 cm medium quant. paper; transfer residue to paper with hot H_2O, policing beaker. Wash thoroly 5 times with hot H_2O. Transfer to Pt dish, burn off paper, and ignite to constant wt at ca 1100°. Weigh as crude SiO_2.

To residue in dish add ca 2 ml H_2SO_4 $(1 + 9)$ and enough 48% HF to cover the SiO_2. Heat on steam bath under hood until SiF_4 and excess HF have evapd. Cautiously heat over nonreducing flame of Fisher or equiv. burner until fumes of SO_3 cease to be

evolved, and then heat strongly several min. Cool and reweigh. Difference between wt crude SiO_2 and this wt = wt SiO_2.

35.050 ★ Starch—Official Final Action ★

Weigh ca 5 g sample into 500 ml Florence flask (preferably ⚶). Moisten with 10 ml alcohol. Acid-wash as in **8.018**, hydrolyze starch as in **8.017** (but filter hydrolyzed mixt. before and not after dilg to vol.), and det. glucose as in **31.039** and **31.040**.

HAIR PREPARATIONS
2,5-Diaminotoluene in Hair Dyes and Rinses (*11*)—Official Final Action

35.051 ★ *Acetylation Method* ★
(*Caution: See* **46.011**, **46.039**, and **46.054**.)

Place in small separator 5–20 ml aliquot sample soln contg 0.05–0.15 g diamine. Add ca 0.05 g Na_2SO_3 and vol. NaOH soln $(1 + 1)$, **45.034(b)**, equal to 55% of previously measured vol. of sample soln. (It is convenient to add NaOH soln from wide-tip Mohr pipet.) Cool contents of separator as rapidly as possible, add 20 ml ether, and shake gently ca 30 sec. Let stand ca 1 min and drain NaOH layer into second separator, taking care to remove all aq. layer. (It does no harm to transfer 1–2 ml of ether layer also.)

Carefully decant ether layer thru cotton pledget in long-stem funnel into tared evapg dish in such way that none of aq. layer that drains from sides of funnel is transferred with ether. Wash first separator with 20 ml ether and drain ether into separator contg alk. layer. Make second extn as before, return aq. layer to first separator, and decant ether layer thru cotton pledget into evapg dish. Continue in this manner until 5 extns are made.

Wash funnel and cotton with little ether and evap. combined exts on steam bath to ca 10 ml. Add 1 ml Ac_2O (<0.003% nonvolatile material) and continue evapn to dryness. Add few ml alcohol and evap. until Ac_2O odor disappears. Dry residue 15 min at 100°, cool, and weigh diacetyl derivative of the diamine. Repeat drying to constant wt ($\pm$0.5 mg). Diacetyl 2,5-diaminotoluene $\times$ 0.5924 = 2,5-diaminotoluene.

Check purity of diacetyl derivative by detg its mp; mp diacetyl 2,5-diaminotoluene is 219–220°.

★ *Dichlorimide Method* ★
35.052 *Reagents*

(**a**) *Sodium hypochlorite soln.*—5% NF soln of NaOCl.

(**b**) *Sodium arsenite soln.*—10%. Dissolve 10 g $NaAsO_2$ in 100 ml H_2O; or dissolve by heating 8.5 g As_2O_3 and 1.5 g NaOH in 100 ml H_2O. (*Caution: See* **46.076** and **46.084**.)

35.053 *Determination*

To separator contg 5 ml NaOCl soln and ca 1 g $NaHCO_3$, add, from pipet or buret, aliquot of sample soln contg 0.01–0.08 g diamine. If insufficient NaOCl is indicated by presence of brown color while soln is being added, repeat operation, using more NaOCl or smaller aliquot. Thoroly mix soln during addn by gently swirling separator. Stopper separator and shake ca 10 sec. Add 10 ml NaAsO₂ soln, stopper separator, and shake again.

Ext dichlorimide with two 25 ml portions CHCl₃ and combine exts in second separator. Wash combined exts with 10 ml H₂O and filter thru cotton pledget into I flask. Make addnl extn, wash with the H₂O, and combine with major portion. Add 50 ml H₂O contg 1 g KI and 3 ml HCl to combined CHCl₃ exts, stopper flask, and shake vigorously 1 min. Titr. liberated I with 0.1N Na₂S₂O₃. Stopper flask and shake vigorously at intervals during titrn. (The I in CHCl₃ acts as indicator.) Toward end of titrn add starch soln, **2.129**(c), for final end point. 1 ml 0.1N Na₂S₂O₃ = 0.002036 g 2,5-diaminotoluene.

Paraphenylenediamine in Hair Dyes and Rinses—Official Final Action

★ *Acetylation Method (12)* ★

35.054 *Preparation of Sample*

(a) *Powders or dry mixtures.*—Place 1–2 g powder directly into 50 ml vol. flask, add 2 ml HCl (1 + 1), and dil. to vol. with H₂O.

(b) *Aqueous preparations.*—Dil. if necessary so that 5 ml aliquot contains 0.1–0.3 g *p*-phenylenediamine.

35.055 *Determination*

Pipet 5 ml aliquot prepd soln into continuous extractor such as that shown in Fig. 36:3C and add enough anhyd. Na₂CO₃ to render aq. layer alk. to litmus paper. Completely ext with CHCl₃, remove flask, and transfer CHCl₃ soln to 100 ml beaker, rinsing flask with few small portions CHCl₃. Evap. CHCl₃ to ca 25 ml and add 1 ml Ac₂O slowly, with stirring. Let stand 1 hr and filter on weighed gooch. Wash beaker and ppt with three or four 5 ml portions CHCl₃. *Carefully* remove last traces of ppt from beaker. Dry to constant wt at 120° and weigh ppt of diacetyl *p*-phenylenediamine, C₆H₄(NHCOCH₃)₂, mp 312–314°. Diacetyl derivative × 0.5626 = *p*-phenylenediamine.

Check purity of diacetyl derivative by detg mp.

35.056 ★ *Dichlorimide Method* ★ *(Benzoquinone Method) (13)*

Proceed as in **35.053**. 1 ml 0.1N Na₂S₂O₃ = 0.001802 g *p*-phenylenediamine.

Potassium Bromate and Sodium Perborate in Cold Wave Neutralizers—Official Final Action

35.057 *Qualitative Tests (14)*

(a) *General tests.*—KBrO₃ and NaBO₃ are white cryst. salts sol. in H₂O. Aq. soln of KBrO₃ is slightly acid; of NaBO₃, slightly alk. In flame test, using Pt wire in slightly darkened room, KBrO₃ gives reddish-

violet flame when viewed thru Co glass; NaBO₃, typical yellow Na flame. Both compds give following test: Dissolve 0.1 g sample in 10 ml H₂O, acidify with HCl, and add 0.5 g KI. Liberation of I indicates presence of oxidizing agent.

(b) *Confirmatory test for bromate.*—To 1 ml 5% soln of sample in test tube slowly add 2 ml H₂SO₄ with vigorous shaking. Note odor and color of liberated gas. (*Caution.*) Cool test tube, *carefully* add 2 ml CS₂, and shake. CS₂ layer becomes yellow or red if Br is present.

(c) *Confirmatory test for boron.*—Moisten 0.2 g sample in porcelain crucible with 1–2 drops H₂SO₄, add 2 ml MeOH, stir well, and ignite. Green flame indicates presence of B.

★ Pyrogallol in Hair Dyes (15)— ★ Official Final Action

35.058 *Qualitative Test*

Add 5–10 ml sample to separator contg ca 0.5 g NaHSO₃ and ext with two or three 30 ml portions ether. Filter ether exts thru cotton and evap. to dryness on steam bath. Dry 30–60 min at 100°. Pulverize residue, mix well, and take mp. If residue does not melt at 131–134°, sublime and again take mp, which should fall within this range. Mix small portion of residue with equal quantity of sublimed pyrogallol and det. mp, which should not change.

Quantitative Determination

35.059 *Reagents*

(a) *Ferrous tartrate reagent.*—Dissolve 1.00 g Na K tartrate (Rochelle salt) and 0.200 g FeSO₄.7H₂O in H₂O, and dil. to 100 ml in vol. flask. Prep. fresh daily.

(b) *Sodium acetate soln.*—Dissolve 15.00 g NaOAc.3H₂O in H₂O, bring to room temp., and dil. to 100 ml.

(c) *Pyrogallol std soln.*—0.2000 g/L.

35.060 *Preparation of Standard Curve*

To six 100 ml vol. flasks add, from buret, 2.50, 5.00, 7.50, 10.00, 12.50, and 15.00 ml std pyrogallol soln. Develop color as follows on ≤3 stds at time, and make readings within 15 min after color is developed:

Pipet 10 ml NaOAc soln and 10 ml Fe tartrate reagent into flasks, dil. to vol., and mix. Using 1 cm or ½″ cells, measure A of solns with photometer or spectrophtr at 540 nm.

With filter photometers obtain zero point by reading blank soln contg 10 ml NaOAc soln and 10 ml Fe tartrate reagent in 100 ml. Draw std curve, plotting concns pyrogallol against photometer readings, on large-scale graph paper so that concn can be read to 0.01 mg. Straight line should be obtained between concns of 1–6 mg/100 ml. With spectrophtr use freshly prepd blank as ref. soln. Draw std curve as above, or, if straight line passing thru origin is obtained, calc. av. value of $a = A/bc$, where b is cell length and c is concn pyrogallol. This value of a may be used to calc. concn of unknowns directly from A.

35.061 Determination
(*Caution: See* **46.001, 46.011, 46.039,** and **46.054.**)

(a) *Liquid dyes.*—Ext convenient aliquot of sample (usually 10 ml) by one of following methods with min. exposure to air, as pyrogallol is readily oxidized:

(*1*) *Continuous extraction.*—Pipet sample aliquot into suitable continuous extractor contg ca 0.3 g NaHSO₃. Ext with ether until pyrogallol is completely removed (3–7 hr, depending upon efficiency of extractor). (Det. time required for each extractor by extg aq. soln of known pyrogallol content or by testing for complete extn as follows: After extn is considered complete, remove flask contg ether, replace with one contg fresh ether, and continue extn 30–60 min. Treat this ext as below, and use 50 ml aliquot filtrate to develop color.) Evap. ether ext on steam bath to 8–10 ml and continue evapn at temp. ≤40° until odor of ether is completely gone.

Dissolve residue in 20 ml H₂O and wash completely into 100 ml vol. flask. Dil. to vol. and mix. (If liq. sample contains chlorophyll, treat residue from ether extn with alumina cream as in (b), beginning "Add 10 ml H₂O and loosen residue …") Filter thru dry paper and discard first 20 ml filtrate. (If detn cannot be completed same day extn is made, let ether ext stand overnight, preferably in refrigerator, before ether is evapd. Do not let aq. soln stand overnight.) Use suitable aliquots of filtrate to develop color as in **35.060,** beginning "Pipet 10 ml NaOAc soln …" If 5 ml aliquot contains >6 mg pyrogallol, make suitable diln in vol. flask and use aliquots of dild soln to develop color. For final calcn use av. of results obtained on ≥2 aliquots of different sizes, preferably contg 2–5.5 mg pyrogallol. Calc. to g/100 ml in original sample.

(*2*) *Extraction in separators.*—Pipet sample into 125 ml separator contg ca 0.3 g NaHSO₃ and ext 6 times with ether. For each extn use vol. ether equal to 3 or 4 times vol. sample and shake vigorously 1 min. Filter ether exts successively thru cotton wet with ether. (6 extns carefully made will completely remove pyrogallol, but seventh may be made and used to test for complete extn as in (*1*).) Evap. combined ether exts and proceed as in (*1*).

(b) *Henna powder mixture.*—Weigh 0.9–1.1 g thoroly mixed sample into paper extn thimble. Cover sample with small piece of cotton and place thimble in Soxhlet app. (If temp. and humidity are such that H₂O will condense on condenser, connect tube contg drying agent to outlet of condenser.) Ext 5 hr with EtOAc, 99% min. purity. Boil at such rate that solv. siphons off 15–20 times/hr.

If EtOAc ext is clear, evap. to dryness as below. If ext contains any sediment, evap. to ca 75 ml if necessary, cool to room temp., and completely transfer to 110 ml g-s vol. flask. Dil. to vol. and mix. Filter thru

dry paper, taking precautions to prevent evapn of solv. Pipet 100 ml filtrate into 250 ml beaker and evap. to ca 5 ml on hot plate or steam bath. Continue evapn to complete dryness at temp. ≤40°. Add 10 ml H₂O and loosen residue with stirring rod. Pour into 50 ml vol. flask. Rinse beaker 4 or 5 times with small vols H₂O and add rinsings to flask. Add 1.2 ml alumina cream, **31.021**(b), dil. to vol., mix, and filter thru dry paper. Ext 25 ml filtrate by one of methods given in (a). If extn cannot be started immediately, add ca 0.4 g NaHSO₃ to filtrate and hold no longer than overnight. Calc. to % pyrogallol in original sample.

★ Resorcinol in Hair Lotions (*16*)— ★
Official Final Action
35.062 Reagents
(a) *Potassium iodide soln.*—Dissolve 25 g KI in H₂O and dil. to 100 ml.

(b) *Sodium thiosulfate std soln.*—0.1N. Use std soln, **45.038–45.039.**

(c) *Potassium bromide-bromate std soln.*—0.1N. Prep. as in **45.021.** Stdze as in **36.208.**

35.063 Determination
(*Caution: See* **46.011, 46.039,** and **46.054.**)

Pipet 25 ml sample into 150 ml beaker. Dealcoholize as follows: Place beaker on covered surface of steam bath and under air jet. Evap. to ca 10 ml, add 15 ml H₂O, and again evap. to 10 ml. Transfer contents to separator with several small portions H₂O to final vol. of 30 ml. Complete transfer by washing beaker with several portions CHCl₃, totaling 25 ml. (Most of solid material remaining after dealcoholization is transferred by the CHCl₃ rather than by the H₂O.) Acidify with 1–2 ml HCl (1 + 9).

Ext with two addnl 25 ml portions CHCl₃. Wash each ext with same 5 ml portion H₂O. Discard CHCl₃, and add wash H₂O to residual acid aq. layer. Ext aq. layer with five 35 ml portions ether. Add 10 ml H₂O to combined ether exts. Evap. ether, at low temp., on surface of steam bath under air jet. Transfer aq. soln to 100 ml vol. flask, cool, dil. to vol., and mix.

Transfer portion of this soln (aliquot taken should require 20–40 ml 0.1N KBr-KBrO₃) to I flask. Add 50 ml KBr-KBrO₃ soln, dil. with 50 ml H₂O, and add 5 ml HCl. Immediately stopper and shake flask, and let stand 1 min. Remove stopper just enough to add 5 ml KI soln, taking care that no Br vapors escape. Immediately stopper and shake thoroly, remove stopper, and rinse it and neck of flask with 20 ml H₂O. Titr., *at once,* with Na₂S₂O₃ soln, using starch indicator, **2.129**(c). 1 ml 0.1N KBr-KBrO₃ = 0.001835 g resorcinol.

35.064 ★ Salicylic Acid in Hair Lotions ★
(*17*)—Official Final Action
Acidify 25 ml sample in 250 ml beaker with 2 ml HCl (1 + 3). Dealcoholize by heating at ≤70°—if

possible, by use of air current at room temp. Transfer to separator and dil. with H_2O to ca 25 ml. Since $CHCl_3$ is to be used later as extg solv., make transfer by washing from beaker to separator with 2 or 3 portions $CHCl_3$, totaling 25 ml, repeating washing with H_2O in portions totaling 25 ml, thus obtaining indicated aq. diln.

Ext with four 25 ml portions $CHCl_3$ (including 25 ml used in transfer of sample to separator). Wash each $CHCl_3$ ext with same 5 ml H_2O and filter into 150 ml beaker thru $CHCl_3$-satd cotton pledget. Wash the 5 ml H_2O with $CHCl_3$, filtering this $CHCl_3$ washing into same beaker. Evap. $CHCl_3$ on steam bath to 20–25 ml, and then evap. spontaneously to 5 ml.

Transfer remaining 5 ml to separator with enough $CHCl_3$ as rinse to total ca 30 ml in separator. Ext with three 5 ml portions 5% $NaHCO_3$ soln and one 5 ml portion H_2O. Wash combined aq. exts with 10 ml $CHCl_3$ and discard $CHCl_3$.

Filter combined $NaHCO_3$ solns thru paper into 100 ml vol. flask. Rinse separator and wash filter with H_2O until filtrate reaches 100 ml mark, and mix.

Proceed as in **36.209(b)**, line 4, beginning "Transfer aliquot of this soln ..." Before adding $0.1N$ KBr-$KBrO_3$, carefully neutze aliquot in I flask to liberate CO_2 from bicarbonate present; then make alk. with 1 drop 10% $NaOH$ soln and continue as directed. 1 ml $0.1N$ KBr-$KBrO_3$ = 0.002302 g salicylic acid.

Thioglycolate Solutions in Cold Permanent Waves (14)—Official Final Action

35.065 Qualitative Test

(*Caution: See* **46.018**. $Cd(OAc)_2$ is toxic.)

Dil. 2 ml sample to 10 ml with H_2O, acidify with 10% HOAc, add 5 ml excess, and shake well. Add 2 ml 10% $Cd(OAc)_2 \cdot 2H_2O$ soln, and shake. White gelatinous ppt forms if thioglycolic acid is present. Add excess of NH_4OH (2 + 3) and shake. Ppt of Cd thioglycolate will dissolve.

35.066 Quantitative Method

(Applicable in absence of reducing substances other than thioglycolates)

Pipet sample aliquot contg 250–300 mg thioglycolic acid into wide-mouth 250 ml erlenmeyer. Dil. to 50 ml with H_2O, add 2–3 drops Me red, **2.104(c)**, and make slightly acid with HCl. Add 3–4 ml starch indicator, **6.004(f)**, and titr. with $0.1N$ I to purple end point. 1 ml $0.1N$ I = 0.009212 g thioglycolic acid.

Dithiodiglycolic Acid (18)— Official First Action

35.067 Principle

Soln contg mixt. of thioglycolic (TGA) and dithiodiglycolic (DTDGA) acids is titrd with std $0.1N$ I soln, which selectively titrs TGA. DTDGA is reduced to TGA in Jones reductor. Resulting total TGA is titrd; increased TGA represents DTDGA.

35.068 Reagents

(a) *Zinc metal.*—20–30 mesh. Mallinckrodt Chemicals Analytical Reagent grade has been found suitable.

(b) *Mercuric salt soln.*—2% aq. soln of $Hg(NO_3)_2$ or $HgCl_2$. (*Caution: See* **46.079**.)

35.069 Apparatus

(a) *Jones reductor.*—Glass tube, 20–25″ long, ¾″ id, with stopcock, preferably Teflon, and delivery tip extending ca 3″ below stopcock.

(b) *Magnetic stirrer.*—With glass- or Teflon-covered stirring bar.

35.070 Preparation of Jones Reductor

Place 300 g Zn in 800 ml beaker; add 300 ml Hg soln and 2 ml HNO_3. Stir 10 min with glass rod. Decant supernatant and repeat amalgamation with fresh portion Hg soln and 2 ml HNO_3. Wash amalgamated Zn 3 times, by decantation, with H_2O. (Zn should have silvery luster.) Maintain H_2O layer over Zn thruout.

Fill column with H_2O; then slowly add prepd Zn, draining excess H_2O. Pass 500 ml H_2O thru column, maintaining H_2O layer over Zn.

Det. suitability of reductor as follows: Pass 20 ml H_2O thru column, followed by 200 ml H_2SO_4 (1 + 9), then 100 ml H_2O. Titr. combined washings as in **35.071(c)**. If titrn is >0.2 ml, wash column with addnl H_2O.

Det. reductor efficiency by treating ca 350 mg DTDGA, accurately weighed, in 5 ml H_2O as in **35.071(b)**. Recovery must be ≥97%. Lower recovery indicates unsuitable reductor.

Prepd reductor may be stored 3 months before use, provided amalgamated Zn is always kept covered with H_2O. Pre-wash column with 200 ml H_2SO_4 (1 + 9) before use after overnight storage.

35.071 Determination

(a) *Titration 1.*—Pipet sample aliquot contg 350–400 mg TGA and DTDGA into 500 ml Phillips flask contg magnetic stirring bar; dil. to 100 ml with H_2O, add 2 drops Me red indicator, **2.104(c)**, and just acidify with H_2SO_4 (1 + 1). Add starch indicator soln, **6.004(f)**, and titr. soln with $0.1N$ I std soln, **45.019**.

$$1 \text{ ml } 0.1N \text{ I} = 9.212 \text{ mg TGA.}$$

(b) *Reduction.*—Arrange reductor column to deliver into 1 L suction flask contg magnetic stirring bar. Connect flask to vac. outlet which can be regulated to desired flow rate.

Dil. sample aliquot equal to that used in Titration 1 with 200 ml H_2SO_4 (1 + 9).

Add 50 ml H_2SO_4 (1 + 19) to column, apply gentle suction, and elute at ca 10 ml/min. When liq. reaches top of amalgam, immediately add dild sample soln, increase vac., and elute at ca 17–20 ml/min. When liq. reaches top of amalgam, rinse sample container with 100 ml H_2SO_4 (1 + 19) in several portions and add to column. Follow with three 100 ml portions H_2O at ca 50 ml/min. Release vac., rinsing column tip into flask with H_2O.

(c) *Titration 2.*—Place suction flask contg reduced sample soln on magnetic stirrer; add 5 drops Me red indicator, **2.104(c)**, and set stirrer at medium speed. Add NH_4OH to yellow indicator color (ca 70 ml); then add H_2SO_4 (1 + 1) dropwise just to indicator red color. Stopper flask and place in ice bath. Cool sample soln with min. swirling to 25° or below. Add 5 ml starch indicator, **6.004(f)**, place on magnetic stirrer, and titr. with 0.1N I to purple end point.

Perform sep. blank detns for Titrations 1 and 2 and make appropriate corrections.

mg DTDGA in sample aliquot = 9.111 ($N - M$)

where M = ml 0.1N I from Titration 1 corrected for blank and N = ml 0.1N I from Titration 2 corrected for blank.

SUNTAN PREPARATIONS
Amyl p-Dimethylaminobenzoate (19)—
Official First Action

35.072   *Apparatus*

(a) *Spectrophotometer.*—Cary Model 11 recording spectrophtr, or equiv., with 1 cm quartz cells.

(b) *Chromatographic equipment.*—(*1*) Glass chromatgc tube, 22 × ⅛″ id with glass wool plug in constricted tip. (*2*) Brass tamper to fit chromatgc tube. (*3*) Source of variable air pressure to regulate column elution rate at ca 2 ml/min.

35.073   *Reagents*

(a) *Solvent.*—(*1*) *Immobile solvent.*—*n*-Heptane-CCl_4 (1 + 1). (*2*) *Mobile solvents.*—Acidified 50% and 60% alcohol, contg 2 ml HCl/500 ml.

(b) *Diatomaceous earth.*—Celite 545 (Johns-Manville), HCl-washed, silane-treated. Weigh ca 700 g Celite into 4 L beaker, add 3 L 20% HCl, and stir thoroly. Heat on steam bath several hr, stirring occasionally. Filter slurry thru buchner under vac. Wash filter thoroly with H_2O until washings are Fe- and chloride-free. Suck filter cake dry, transfer to beaker, and dry at 135° in oven overnight or longer. To coat Celite with silicone, transfer ca 150 g dried Celite to crystg dish and let stand in air 30 min. In well ventilated hood, pour 25 ml GE SC-77 Dri-Film (General Electric Co., 1 River Rd, Schenectady, NY 12305) into bottom of large glass desiccator. Place dish contg Celite on porcelain support in closed desiccator. After 2 hr, remove dish and let stand in open air until residual HCl vaporizes.

(c) *Amyl p-dimethylaminobenzoate.*—0.01 mg/ml. Dil. 10 mg std (available as Escalol 506 from Van Dyk and Co., Inc., Belleville, NJ 07109) to 1 L with NH_4OH-60% alcohol (1 + 99).

35.074   *Preparation of Samples*
(*Caution: See* **46.011, 46.040,** and **46.056.**)

In weighing bottle weigh sample contg 10–20 mg amyl *p*-dimethylaminobenzoate. Transfer sample to 250 ml separator with 50 ml H_2O, slightly acidify with HCl, using test paper, and ext with four 35 ml portions $CHCl_3$. Combine exts, wash with 10 ml H_2O, and filter thru $CHCl_3$-washed cotton plug fitted into powder funnel, collecting in 250 ml beaker. Wash cotton plug with 10 ml $CHCl_3$. Evap. to ca 1 ml on steam bath under air jet. Remove beaker from steam bath and continue evapn under air jet until all $CHCl_3$ has evapd. Reserve prepd residue for chromatgy.

35.075   *Chromatography*

(a) *Column preparation.*—Weigh two 12 g portions silanized Celite, add 7 ml *n*-heptane-CCl_4 (1 + 1) to one portion, and mix well. Pack gently but firmly into chromatgc tube in ca 4 g portions, using tamper. (Proper prepn of columns may be checked by eluting known amt std from column, noting recovery.) Dissolve prepd sample in 7 ml *n*-heptane-CCl_4 (1 + 1), add second portion Celite, mix well, and pack into chromatgc tube as before. Wipe beaker, stirring rod, and tamper with glass wool and place glass wool on top of column.

(b) *Elution.*—Elute column first with 100 ml acidified 50% alcohol at 2 ml/min, then with 350 ml acidified 60% alcohol at same flow rate. Collect eluates in consecutively numbered 50 ml vol. flasks. Add few drops NH_4OH to each flask, mix well, test for alkalinity, and dil. to vol.

35.076   *Determination*

Obtain UV spectra at 220–360 nm for each eluate. For blanks, use corresponding alcohol solns consisting of either NH_4OH-50% alcohol (1 + 99) or NH_4OH-60% alcohol (1 + 99). Dil. as necessary with NH_4OH-alcohol solns of proper concn. For quant. detn, obtain spectra of this compd in basic soln, not acid soln. Calc. amt material in each eluate by comparing A at 314 nm of sample with std amyl *p*-dimethylaminobenzoate soln in NH_4OH-60% alcohol (1 + 99), (c), using "straight-line" background correction.

VANISHING CREAM (20)
35.077 Test for Type of Emulsion—
Official Final Action

Dust small amts of finely ground oil-sol. and H_2O-sol. dyes on sep. portions of sample. If color of oil-sol. dye spreads rapidly, H_2O-in-oil emulsion is indicated; if color of H_2O-sol. dye spreads, oil-in-H_2O emulsion is indicated.

35.078 Water—Official Final Action

Transfer 5–20 g sample to erlenmeyer; add 50 ml toluene, few glass beads, and ca 2 g *lump rosin*. Connect flask to Dean and Stark distg tube receiver, and distill until no more H_2O collects in receiver. Cool, read vol. H_2O under the toluene at room temp., and from this vol. calc. $\% H_2O$.

35.079   Ash—Official Final Action

Place 2–10 g sample in flat-bottom Pt dish, and remove H_2O and volatile material by placing dish on steam bath or in 100° oven. Ignite sample at low temp. and finally at 600° to constant wt.

35.080   Chloroform-Soluble Material—Official Final Action

(*Caution: See* **46.011, 46.040,** and **46.056.**)

Place 2–10 g sample in separator, add 25–50 ml H_2O, acidify slightly with H_2SO_4 (1 + 9), and ext with successive portions $CHCl_3$, collecting all exts in second separator. (Usually 4–5 portions $CHCl_3$, each ca 35 ml, are enough to remove all $CHCl_3$-sol. material.) Wash combined $CHCl_3$ exts with 10 ml H_2O, filter thru cotton plug placed in separator stem, and collect filtrate in weighed dish. Shake aq. washing with small quantity of $CHCl_3$, and filter this $CHCl_3$ into dish. Evap. $CHCl_3$ on steam bath and dry residue for 15 min intervals at 100° to constant wt.

Glycerol—Official Final Action

35.081   *Reagents*

(a) *Potassium periodate soln.*—$0.02M$. Dissolve 4.6 g KIO_4 in ca 500 ml hot H_2O. Dil. to ca 900 ml with H_2O, cool to room temp., and dil. to 1 L.

(b) *Sodium hydroxide std soln.*—$0.02N$. See **45.036** or **45.037.**

(c) *Bromocresol purple indicator.*—Dissolve 0.1 g bromocresol purple in 100 ml alcohol.

(d) *Propylene glycol.*—Bp 85–86°/10 mm.

(e) *Arsenious oxide soln.*—$0.02N$. Dil. 100 ml $0.1N$ As_2O_3, **45.006,** to 500 ml with H_2O.

35.082   *Isolation and Oxidation of Glycerol*

(a) *Isolation of glycerol.*—Place 2–10 g sample in separator, add 25–50 ml H_2O, acidify slightly with H_2SO_4 (10 g/100 ml), and ext with successive portions $CHCl_3$. (Usually 4–5 portions, each ca 35 ml, remove all $CHCl_3$-sol. material.) Wash combined $CHCl_3$ exts with 10 ml H_2O. Filter aq. soln and wash H_2O thru cotton plug to remove droplets of $CHCl_3$, and collect filtrate in 250 ml vol. flask. Add 3 drops bromocresol purple indicator to filtrate and neutze with CO_2-free alkali ($0.1N$ NaOH is satisfactory), making final adjustment with $0.02N$ NaOH. Dil. almost to vol. with H_2O, and if necessary add more alkali to keep soln light but definite purple; then complete diln to vol. and mix.

(b) *Periodate oxidation.*—Transfer aliquot of the neut. soln, preferably contg 30–40 mg glycerol, to 100 ml vol. flask, and add 50 ml KIO_4 soln. Dil. to vol. with H_2O and let stand ca 1 hr. Test for excess periodate, which must be present in oxidn mixt., by adding $NaHCO_3$ and KI to test portion. If excess is present, I is liberated.

35.083   *Determination*

(a) *By titration of formic acid.*—(Applicable in absence of substances yielding acid on periodate oxidn.) Transfer 50 ml aliquot of oxidized mixt. to titrn flask, add 10 drops of propylene glycol (ca 0.5 ml), mix well, wash down sides of flask with H_2O, and let stand 10 min. Add 3 drops bromocresol purple indicator and titr. with NaOH soln to light purple end point. 1 ml $0.02N$ NaOH = 1.842 mg glycerol.

(b) *From periodate consumed.*—Transfer 20 ml aliquot of oxidized mixt., **35.082(b),** to titrn flask and dil. with ca 50 ml H_2O. Add ca 1.0 g $NaHCO_3$, 0.5 g KI, and 5 ml starch indicator, **2.129(c).** Titr. immediately with As_2O_3 soln to disappearance of blue. Stdze 10 ml KIO_4 similarly. Difference between the 2 titrns represents amt of periodate reduced in 20 ml aliquot taken. To obtain amt of periodate reduced in original aliquot obtained from 250 ml flask, multiply above difference by 5.

1 ml $0.02N$ As_2O_3 = 0.4605 mg glycerol.

SPECIAL REFERENCE

NEWBURGER, "A Manual of Cosmetic Analysis," AOAC, Washington, DC (1962).

SELECTED REFERENCES

(*1*) JAOAC **49**, 718(1966).
(*2*) JAOAC **53**, 82(1970).
(*3*) Ind. Eng. Chem., Anal. Ed. **10**, 212(1938); JAOAC **28**, 734(1945).
(*4*) Ind. Eng. Chem., Anal. Ed. **16**, 387(1944); JAOAC **33**, 371(1950).
(*5*) Anal. Chem. **24**, 182(1952); JAOAC **36**, 791 (1953).
(*6*) JAOAC **34**, 298, 299(1951).
(*7*) JAOAC **35**, 279(1952).
(*8*) JAOAC **37**, 798(1954).
(*9*) JAOAC **23**, 440(1940); **25**, 113(1942); **27**, 112 (1944).
(*10*) JAOAC **25**, 909(1942); **32**, 50, 601(1949); **33**, 359(1950).
(*11*) JAOAC **22**, 159(1939); **26**, 116(1943); **28**, 739 (1945); **33**, 374(1950).
(*12*) JAOAC **23**, 717(1940); **33**, 374(1950).
(*13*) JAOAC **22**, 159(1939); **25**, 113(1942); **27**, 112 (1944).
(*14*) JAOAC **35**, 285(1952).
(*15*) Analyst **48**, 2(1923); **50**, 49(1925); JAOAC **28**, 744(1945); **30**, 512(1947); **31**, 577(1948); **32**, 592(1949).
(*16*) JAOAC **25**, 897(1942); **30**, 517(1947).
(*17*) JAOAC **25**, 112(1942); **26**, 355(1943); **27**, 112 (1944).
(*18*) JAOAC **53**, 78(1970).
(*19*) JAOAC **53**, 84(1970).
(*20*) JAOAC **25**, 903(1942); **26**, 249(1943); **27**, 462 (1944); **30**, 507, 651(1947); **31**, 580(1948); **33**, 362, 367(1950).

36. Drugs★

GENERAL DIRECTIONS

36.001 Extraction with Lighter-Than-Water Solvents

Perform preliminary steps directed in method prior to extn. Ext aq. soln in separator with specified vols of solv. (ether, pet ether, etc.) by shaking $\geqslant 1$ min. Let sep. completely, swirl to remove H_2O droplets, transfer lower aq. layer to second separator, and decant solv. layer thru pledget of cotton in short-stem funnel inserted in neck of third separator. Wash mouth of separator with fine stream of solv. Repeatedly shake aq. soln with addnl portions of solvs until substance sought is extd, using second and first separators alternately for shaking, collecting solvs by filtering into third. If aq. soln is to be further examined, dry cotton pledget in funnel by drawing air thru stem and wash with 5 ml H_2O into main aq. ext.

Sampling (1)—Official Final Action
36.002 I. Tablets and Pills

(a) *Bulk lots.*—Mix lot thoroly without mutilating contents. Count, weigh, and thoroly powder $\geqslant 100$ units. Calc. av. wt/unit.

(b) *Containers of 1000 or more units.*—Open and cautiously mix contents without mutilation. Count, weigh, and powder $\geqslant 30$ units selected at random.

(c) *Containers of 100–500 units.*—Remove from one container $\geqslant 20$ units selected at random, weigh, and powder.

(d) *Small containers, e.g., tubes of hypodermic tablets.*—Choose enough containers to provide $\geqslant$ 20 units, weigh, and powder contents.

(e) *Tablets or pills of small dosages, e.g., 1/100 grain of active ingredient.*—Number of units necessary may be so large as to make powdering unnecessary. Half or whole bottleful may be required. Count units to be used but do not powder.

36.003 II. Soft Capsules

Count and weigh $\geqslant 20$ capsules and det. gross wt/capsule. Open capsules and transfer as much of contents as possible to weighing bottle. Clean capsules (cutting in 2 if necessary) and wash by agitating with alternate portions of alcohol and ether.

(Few drops of HOAc mixed with alcohol aids cleaning.) Remove ether before fan or air blast. Deduct wt cleaned, empty capsules from gross wt and calc. av. net contents.

36.004 III. Ampuls

Before opening ampuls dislodge any liq. in neck. With file, or other suitable instrument, mark level of liq. on necks of $\geqslant 1$ ampul if vol. is $\geqslant 10$ ml; $\geqslant 3$ if vol. is >3 ml but <10 ml; $\geqslant 5$ if vol. is $\leqslant 3$ ml. Open each near tip, transfer bulk of contents to small flask, and mix. To det. vol. contents, wash and dry empty ampuls, and fill to mark with H_2O from buret or graduated pipet.

SOLVENTS

Acetone and Isopropyl and Ethyl Alcohols— Qualitative Tests (2)—Official Final Action

Acetone (In Absence of Other Ketones)
36.005   *Reagent*

2,4-Dinitrophenylhydrazine soln.—Suspend 2 g 2,4-dinitrophenylhydrazine in 15 ml 2N HCl, add 10 ml HCl and then 600 ml 2N HCl, and filter.

36.006   *Test*

To 1 ml sample add 5 ml reagent; acetone gives ppt. To obtain enough material for identification, treat 5 ml sample with 50 ml reagent. Swirl mixt. and let stand 15 min. Filter thru gooch and dry at 100°. Dissolve hydrazone in hot alcohol and filter; conc. filtrate to ca 5 ml; and let cool and crystallize. Acetone 2,4-dinitrophenylhydrazone melts at 128°.

Isopropyl and Ethyl Alcohols
36.007   *Reagents*

(a) *3,5-Dinitrobenzoyl chloride.*—Eastman Kodak Co. cryst. material, mp 66–68°, can be used without further purification. If mp is $>70°$, indicating hydrolysis to 3,5-dinitrobenzoic acid, reconstitute to acid chloride as follows: Reflux 5 g material with 50 ml $SOCl_2$ (*Caution:* $SOCl_2$ is toxic; use effective fume removal device, rubber gloves, and eye protection when using, distg, or evapg) until completely dissolved. Remove excess $SOCl_2$ by evapn on steam bath with air current. (*Caution:* Do not purify acid chloride by distn.)

(b) *Ether-petroleum ether solvent.*—Mix 1 vol. ether with 5 vols pet ether. (3,5-Dinitrobenzoates are easily sol. in this solv., whereas 3,5-dinitro-benzoic acid is practically insol.)

(c) *Lanthanum nitrate soln.*—Dissolve 0.5 g $La(NO_3)_3.6H_2O$ in 10 ml H_2O.

36.008   Test I. Either Alcohol Present in at Least 5% Aqueous Solution

Transfer 100 ml sample to 150 ml Claisen flask with long side arm bent downward at right angle ca 4″ from end. (Test tube immersed in ice-NaCl mixt. is convenient receiver.) Place anti-bumping aid in flask fitted with thermometer, and immerse flask in beaker of H_2O. Heat H_2O to boiling and continue distn until temp. inside flask reaches 90°.

Add ca 1 g Na_2SO_4 to receiver and keep in re-frigerator 1–2 hr to finish drying the alcohol. Filter thru small funnel into second test tube contg ca 0.1 g 3,5-dinitrobenzoyl chloride. Immediately stopper tube and immerse lower end in H_2O at 75–80°. Shake gently and continue heating 30 min. Cool soln, scratching side of tube to induce crystn. Ext cryst. material with the ether-pet ether solv. by filling tube with solv. and shaking. Filter into separator. Repeat extn 4 or 5 times. Ext ether soln with 5% Na_2CO_3 soln, wash thoroly with H_2O, and filter thru funnel contg Na_2SO_4. Collect fil-trate in beaker, evap. solv., and det. mp of residue. Isopropyl 3,5-dinitrobenzoate melts at 122° and ethyl 3,5-dinitrobenzoate at 92°.

36.009   Test II. Either or Both Alcohols Present in Approximately 1% Aqueous Solution

Transfer ca 10 ml sample to 50 ml erlenmeyer and add 10 ml reagent, 36.005. Formation of floc-culent ppt of acetone 2,4-dinitrophenylhydrazone indicates presence of acetone. If acetone is present, proceed as in (a), and if absent, proceed as in (b).

(a) *Acetone present.*—Place 10 ml sample in 200 ml erlenmeyer and add 10 ml H_2O, 0.4–0.5 g *paraformaldehyde*, and 10 ml 5% NaOH soln. Heat to boiling under reflux. Continue heating until resin forms as indicated by appearance of ppt. While mixt. is still hot, add 50 ml *Fehling soln*, 31.035, thru top of condenser. (Excess should be present, indicated by characteristic blue color.) Let mixt. cool, transfer to 500 ml Kjeldahl flask, and distill ca 50 ml into another Kjeldahl flask.

To distillate add 50 ml 10% $K_2Cr_2O_7$ soln, fol-lowed by 100 ml H_2SO_4 $(1 + 3)$. Let stand 1 hr with occasional swirling; then add 100 ml 25% $FeSO_4.7H_2O$ soln and distill slowly. When 25 ml distillate collects, change receivers and collect addnl 50 ml.

Test first fraction with dinitrophenylhydrazine reagent; ppt indicates presence of isopropyl alco-hol. Test ca 5 ml second fraction for HOAc by adding 1 ml $La(NO_3)_3$ soln, followed by 1 ml $0.02N$ I and 1 drop NH_4OH. Heat over burner,

and if HOAc is present (indicating Et alcohol), deep blue develops.

(b) *Acetone absent.*—Transfer 10 ml sample to 50 ml erlenmeyer and add 10 ml $HgSO_4$ reagent, **9.068.** Place on steam bath and heat 15 min. White-yellow ppt indicates presence of isopropanol. If it is present, transfer 10 ml sample to Kjeldahl flask, add 50 ml H_2O, and proceed as in (a), be-ginning "add 50 ml 10% $K_2Cr_2O_7$ . . ."

If isopropanol is absent, test 10 ml sample by adding few drops 5% NaOH soln and excess of aq. I-KI soln, and warming. Odor of CHI_3 indi-cates presence of Et alcohol.

ALKALOIDS, OPIUM

36.010   Microchemical Tests—Official Final Action

See **36.525–36.528.**

36.011   General Titration Method (3)— Official Final Action

(*Caution: See* **46.011, 46.040,** and **46.056.**)

Det. av. wt/tablet or other unit and grind to fine powder. Accurately weigh sample equiv. to 100–200 mg alkaloid and transfer to separator with ca 20 ml H_2O. Add 1 ml H_2SO_4 $(1 + 9)$ and ext with three 25 ml portions $CHCl_3$. (Extn from acid soln is not necessary in absence of $CHCl_3$-sol. acidic or neut. components.) Add ca 1 ml NH_4OH (use excess solid $NaHCO_3$ for apomorphine or physostigmine) and ext with four 25 ml portions $CHCl_3$ (use CH_2Cl_2 for ephedrine and $CHCl_3$-isopropanol $(4 + 1)$ for morphine). Use corre-spondingly larger vols of solv. if larger vols aq. soln are required, as in case of sirups or with exces-sive amts of excipients. Check alky of soln after first extn by touching indicator paper to stopper. If not distinctly alk., add addnl NH_4OH. Check for complete extn by evapg 1 ml final ext to dry-ness; if more than trace of residue remains, ext with addnl portions solv. Filter ext thru plug of cotton or fine glass wool previously wet with $CHCl_3$ into 200 ml erlenmeyer. Complete detn by either of following methods ((a) must be used for arecoline and cocaine):

(a) Evap. combined exts on steam bath with air current to ca 10 ml. Add measured excess $0.02N$ H_2SO_4 and continue evapn to remove solv. Cool, add Me red, and titr. excess acid with $0.02N$ NaOH.

(b) Evap. combined exts on steam bath with air current to dryness. Dissolve residue in ca 2 ml MeOH, heating if necessary. Add Me red, and titr. with $0.02N$ H_2SO_4 to faint pink. If alkaloid is not completely dissolved, heat gently to complete soln. Add ca 40 ml freshly boiled, cooled H_2O, and com-plete titrn.

36.012   Titration Factors for Alkaloids

Alkaloid	Formula	mg/ml 0.02N H_2SO_4
Apomorphine hydrochloride	$C_{17}H_{17}O_2N.HCl.\frac{1}{2}H_2O$	6.25
Arecoline hydrobromide	$C_8H_{13}O_2N.HBr$	4.72
Atropine	$C_{17}H_{23}NO_3$	5.79
Atropine sulfate	$(C_{17}H_{23}NO_3)_2.H_2SO_4.H_2O$	6.95
Cocaine hydrochloride	$C_{17}H_{21}O_4N.HCl$	6.80
Codeine sulfate	$(C_{18}H_{21}O_3N)_2.H_2SO_4.5H_2O$	7.87
Codeine phosphate	$C_{18}H_{21}O_3N.H_3PO_4.1\frac{1}{2}H_2O$	8.49
Emetine hydrochloride	$C_{29}H_{40}O_4N_2.2HCl$	5.54
Ephedrine	$C_{10}H_{15}ON$	3.30
Ephedrine hydrochloride	$C_{10}H_{15}ON.HCl$	4.03
Ephedrine sulfate	$(C_{10}H_{15}ON)_2.H_2SO_4$	4.29
Ethylmorphine hydrochloride	$C_{19}H_{23}O_3N.HCl.2H_2O$	7.72
Homatropine hydrobromide	$C_{16}H_{21}O_3N.HBr$	7.13
Homatropine hydrochloride	$C_{16}H_{21}O_3N.HCl$	6.24
Hydrocodone hydrochloride	$C_{18}H_{21}O_3N.HCl.H_2O$	7.08
Hydrocodone bitartrate	$C_{18}H_{21}O_3N.C_4H_6O_6.2\frac{1}{2}H_2O$	9.89
Morphine hydrochloride	$C_{17}H_{19}O_3N.HCl.3H_2O$	7.52
Morphine sulfate	$(C_{17}H_{19}O_3N)_2.H_2SO_4.5H_2O$	7.59
Physostigmine salicylate	$C_{15}H_{21}O_2N_3.C_7H_6O_3$	8.27
Physostigmine sulfate	$(C_{15}H_{21}O_2N_3)_2.H_2SO_4$	6.49
Pilocarpine hydrochloride	$C_{11}H_{16}O_2N_2.HCl$	4.89
Pilocarpine nitrate	$C_{11}H_{16}O_2N_2.HNO_3$	5.43
Procaine hydrochloride	$C_{13}H_{20}O_2N_2.HCl$	5.46
Strychnine	$C_{21}H_{22}O_2N_2$	6.69
Strychnine sulfate	$(C_{21}H_{22}O_2N_2)_2.H_2SO_4.5H_2O$	8.57
Strychnine nitrate	$C_{21}H_{22}O_2N_2.HNO_3$	7.95

36.013   Apomorphine in Tablets—Official Final Action

See 36.011.

36.014   Codeine in Tablets—Official Final Action

See 36.011.

Codeine in Presence of Antihistamines (4)— Official Final Action

(Applicable to sirups contg codeine with pyrilamine, methapyrilene, prophenpyridamine, and similar antihistamines)

36.015   *Apparatus*

(a) *Chromatographic tubes.*—Fuse 6 cm length of 5–6 mm tubing to piece of 25 mm tubing ca 25 cm long (25 × 200 mm test tube may be used). Constrict stem slightly ca 2 cm below seal. Pack wad of Pyrex glass wool in base as support.

(b) *Tamping rod.*—Flatten end of glass rod to circular head with clearance of ca 1 mm in tube (a). Or use disk of stainless steel, Al, etc., of diam. ca 1 mm less than id of column (a), attached to 12–18″ rod.

36.016   *Reagents*

(a) *Triethylamine.*—If blank *A*, 36.018, is >0.010, purify as follows: Reflux 100 ml Et₃N with 20 ml H_2O and 2 g Na hydrosulfite ≥8 hr. Wash with H_2O, dry by distg into Dean-Stark trap, and then distill, collecting first 75 ml. Store

over anhyd. Na_2CO_3 or K_2CO_3. (*Caution: See* 46.011, 46.040, and 46.052.)

(b) *Chloroform.*—Use $CHCl_3$ satd with H_2O thruout.

(c) *Diatomaceous earth.*—Celite 545 or acid-washed Celite 545.

36.017   *Preparation of Sample*

Prep. following 3 columns (columns II and III need not be quant.):

(a) *Column I.*—Pipet 2.0 ml sample, draining thoroly, into small beaker. Add 0.5 ml 1N NaOH and 3 g Celite. Mix thoroly and transfer quant. to tube, 36.015(a). Dry-wash beaker with small portion Celite and few drops H_2O, and add to tube. Press Celite firmly with tamping rod, and press pad of glass wool over Celite.

(b) *Column II.*—Mix 3 g Celite and 2 ml 1N HNO_3, and prep. column as in (a).

(c) *Column III.*—Mix 3 g Celite and 2 ml 1N H_2SO_4, and prep. column as in (a).

36.018   *Determination*

Arrange columns so that effluent from I flows into II and then into III. Pass 100 ml $CHCl_3$ over columns. Discard column I which retains excipients.

Pass 50 ml $CHCl_3$ thru column II (which retains antihistamine) onto III; then pass 25 ml $CHCl_3$ over III. Remove column II.

To recover codeine, place 50 ml vol. flask contg 10 ml MeOH and 1 ml HCl under column III.

Pass 5 ml CHCl₃ contg 1 ml Et₃N over column followed by 32 ml 1% Et₃N in CHCl₃. Dil. to vol. with CHCl₃ and det. A at 287 nm against CHCl₃. (Film of Et₃N.HCl may adhere to walls of cells. Rinse cells carefully with H_2O and alcohol; then wipe clean before use.) Correct for blank A of mixt. of 10 ml MeOH, 1 ml Et₃N, and 1 ml HCl dild to 50 ml with CHCl₃. Also det. A' of std prepd by dilg 5 ml std soln contg 1 mg codeine salt/ml MeOH, to 50 ml with CHCl₃ and 5 drops HCl.

mg Codeine salt in sample $= 5AC/A'$, where $A =$ corrected A of sample and $C =$ mg codeine salt/ml std soln.

Codeine and Terpin Hydrate in Elixirs (5)— Official Final Action

36.019   *Reagents*

(a) *Color reagent.*—Either Folin-Denis reagent, 9.081(a), or phosphotungstic-phosphomolybdic acid reagent prepd as follows: To 100 g pure Na tungstate and 20 g phosphomolybdic acid (free from nitrates and NH₄ salts), add 100 g H₃PO₄ and 700 ml H_2O. Boil over free flame 1.5–2 hr, cool, filter if necessary, and dil. to 1 L with H_2O. Equiv. quantity of pure molybdic acid may be substituted for phosphomolybdic acid.

(b) *Terpin hydrate std soln.*—Accurately weigh ca 80 mg terpin hydrate, add 2 ml HOAc, and stir until terpin hydrate is almost dissolved. Add 10 ml alcohol, stir, and transfer to 100 ml vol. flask. Rinse dish with three 10 ml portions alcohol. Finally rinse few times with H_2O and dil. to vol. with H_2O. Soln keeps indefinitely.

(c) *Codeine std soln.*—Accurately weigh ca 100 mg codeine sulfate.5H₂O, dissolve in MeOH, transfer to 100 ml vol. flask, and dil. to vol. with MeOH. 1 ml = 0.8067 mg codeine.H₂O.

(d) *Water-saturated ether.*—Add 100 ml H_2O to 200 ml ether in separator, shake, and after 30 min standing discard H_2O.

(e) *Acidified water-saturated chloroform.*—Sat. 300 ml CHCl₃ with H_2O. After 30 min standing transfer CHCl₃ to flask contg 3 ml HOAc.

(f) *Diatomaceous earth.*—See 36.016(c).

36.020   *Determination of Terpin Hydrate*

Pipet 5 ml sample into distg flask and add 100 ml satd NaCl soln, 35 ml alcohol, 2 ml HOAc, and 10 ml H_2O. Distill, collecting 100 ml distillate.

Pipet 5 ml color reagent into 50 ml vol. flask. Cool under running H_2O while slowly adding 5 ml H₂SO₄. Let mixt. come to room temp. and then add exactly 2 ml sample distillate. Place flask in boiling H_2O 20 min. Cool under H_2O to room temp. and dil. to vol. with dil. alcohol (1 + 3). Shake every few min until soln is clear (10–15

min). (If soln fails to clear, phosphomolybdic acid used to prep. color reagent is unsatisfactory.)

Let stand 0.5 hr and det. A at 725 nm against reagent blank prepd without sample. Det A' of std soln prepd simultaneously with sample, beginning "Pipet 5 ml color reagent...". Terpin hydrate (g/100 ml elixir) $= A \times C \times 20/A'$; where $C =$ g terpin hydrate/100 ml std soln.

36.021   *Determination of Codeine*

Pipet 5 ml sample into 100 ml beaker, add 0.5 g *p-toluenesulfonic acid,* and stir with glass rod. Add 6 g Celite 545, mix to fluffy mass, and transfer to tube, 36.015(a), contg plug of glass wool at base. Tamp firmly, and cover with glass wool. Pass H_2O-satd ether over column and discard ether (column I).

Mix 2 g Celite 545 and 1 ml 1N NaHCO₃ (8.4 g/100 ml). Add to second tube (II), tamp, and cover with glass wool. Mount column I over column II and place 100 ml vol. flask contg 10 ml MeOH and 4 drops HCl under II. Add in 4 equal portions enough acidified H_2O-satd CHCl₃ to column I to fill vol. flask to mark. Completely drain each portion before adding next.

Prep. std codeine soln contg 10 ml std soln, (c), and 2 drops HCl dild to 50 ml with H_2O-satd CHCl₃.

Det. A at 287 nm of std and sample solns against mixt. of 10 ml MeOH and 2 drops HCl dild to 50 ml with H_2O-satd CHCl₃.

Codeine.H₂O, mg/100 ml elixir $= A_s \times C \times 20/A'$, where $A_s = A$ of sample, $A' = A$ of std, and $C =$ mg codeine.H₂O in 100 ml std soln.

36.022   ★   Diacetylmorphine (Heroin)   ★   in Tablets (6)—Official Final Action

(Caution: See 46.011, 46.040, and 46.056.)

Weigh, and transfer directly to small separator, number of tablets contg ca 0.15 g diacetylmorphine. Dissolve in 5 ml H_2O contg 1 drop HOAc. Add 1 ml NH₄OH and ext 5 times with CHCl₃, using 30, 20, 10, 10, and 5 ml, resp. Combine CHCl₃ exts in second separator which has cotton pledget wet with CHCl₃ in stem. Wash combined exts with 1 ml H_2O and evap. on H_2O bath, using elec. fan to prevent decrepitation of residue. When dry, remove immediately and complete detn by one of following methods:

(1) To alkaloidal residue add 2–3 ml MeOH, cover beaker with watch glass and heat on steam bath until residue, including any portions that may adhere to upper part of beaker, completely dissolves. Add 2 drops Me red and, without diln, carefully titr. with 0.02N H₂SO₄ to faint pink, avoiding excess. Cover beaker and digest on steam bath until all particles dissolve. If >2 ml MeOH

is added, evap. excess. Cool, and dil. with 50 ml boiled H_2O (soln should now be yellow). Finish titrn with the std acid to faint red.

(2) Dissolve residue in 2–3 ml MeOH on steam bath. Add 2 drops Me red. Then add 5–10 ml excess $0.02N$ H_2SO_4 from buret, noting total quantity used. Cover beaker with watch glass and heat on steam bath until 'residue, including any portions that may adhere to upper part of beaker, dissolves. Dil. with 50 ml cold, previously boiled H_2O. Back-titr. with $0.02N$ NaOH. The H_2O and alkali should be sufficiently CO_2-free to ensure sharp end point with Me red.

1 ml $0.02N$ H_2SO_4 = 0.00848 g diacetylmorphine hydrochloride, $C_{21}H_{23}O_5N.HCl.H_2O$.

Diacetylmorphine and Quinine—Official Final Action

36.023 Reagents

(a) *Sodium hydroxide-methanol soln.*—Dissolve 4 g NaOH in 200 ml MeOH and dil. to 1 L with H_2O.

(b) *Morphine std soln.*—100 μg as heroin.HCl/ ml (100 ppm). Dissolve 92.6 mg morphine.HCl.$3H_2O$ (USP XV) in ca 20 ml anhyd. MeOH and dil. to 100 ml with $0.1N$ NaOH. Dil. 10 ml of this soln to 100 ml with NaOH-MeOH soln.

(c) *Quinine std soln.*—50 μg quinine.HCl/ml (50 ppm). Dissolve 50 mg quinine.HCl in ca 20 ml anhyd. MeOH and dil. to 100 ml with $0.1N$ NaOH. Dil. 10 ml of this soln to 100 ml with NaOH-MeOH soln.

36.024 Preparation of Standard Curve

Det. A_H of std solns contg 0, 50, 100, 150 ppm heroin.HCl in NaOH-MeOH soln in matched silica cells on spectrophtr at 297.5 and 330 nm (A_H at 330 nm should be 0); det. A_Q of std solns contg 0, 25, 50, 75 ppm quinine.HCl in NaOH-MeOH solns in matched silica cells at same wavelengths. Plot the 3 std curves corrected for cell corrections, $A_{H,297.5}$, $A_{Q,297.5}$, and $A_{Q,330}$, against concn in ppm, and calc. the corresponding a (a = A/concn, mg/L (ppm), in 1 cm cells).

36.025 Determination

Dissolve 100 mg sample in 10 ml anhyd. MeOH, and filter thru fritted glass funnel contg ¼″ layer of H_2O- and MeOH-washed asbestos, using suction. Wash with several portions anhyd. MeOH to total vol. of ca 40 ml and combine alc. solns in 100 ml vol. flask. Dil. to vol. with $0.1N$ NaOH. Dil. 10 ml aliquot to 100 ml with NaOH-MeOH soln. Det. A of this soln at 297.5 ($A_{297.5}$) and 330 nm (A_{330}) in matched silica cells against NaOH-MeOH soln.

Calc. quinine.HCl concn in ppm (Q) from equation: $A_{330} = a_{Q,330} \times Q$. Calc. heroin.HCl concn in ppm (H) from equation: $A_{297.5} = (a_{H,297.5} \times H) + (a_{Q,297.5} \times Q)$.

36.026 Ethylmorphine (Dionine) in Sirups— Official Final Action

See 36.011.

Hydrocodone (Dihydrocodeinone)—Official Final Action

36.027 General Method

See 36.011.

In Presence of Antihistamines (7)

(*Caution: See* 46.011, 46.040, and 46.056.)

36.028 Apparatus and Reagents

(a) *Chromatographic tubes and tamping rod.*— See 36.015(a) and (b).

(b) *Column I.*—Thoroly mix 4 g acid-washed Celite 545 and 3 ml ca $2N$ HCl. Transfer to tube and tamp to uniform mass, using gentle pressure.

(c) *Column II.*—Mix and tamp layers as in (b). (1) *Lower layer.*—2 g Celite and 1 ml $1N$ $NaHCO_3$. (2) *Upper layer.*—4 g Celite and 3 ml 6% succinic acid.

(d) *Equilibrated sulfuric acid.*—Thoroly shake $1N$ H_2SO_4 with small vol. H_2O-satd $CHCl_3$.

(e) *Hydrocodone std soln.*—175 μg hydrocodone bitartrate/ml. Dissolve 17.5 mg hydrocodone bitartrate in equilibrated H_2SO_4 in 100 ml vol. flask and dil. to vol. with equilibrated H_2SO_4. Shake ca 20 ml std soln with ca 75 ml H_2O-satd $CHCl_3$. Det. A_{std} of aq. phase from 360 to 250 nm.

36.029 Determination

Mount Column I directly over Column II. Transfer 10.0 ml sample (or vol. contg ca 3–4 mg hydrocodone bitartrate) to separator. Add 5 ml H_2O and 1 ml ca $1N$ NaOH, and ext with four 30 ml portions of $CHCl_3$. Pass each ext thru columns; let individual exts drain completely into both columns. Wash with 50 ml H_2O-satd $CHCl_3$. Discard Column I. Wash Column II with addnl 100 ml H_2O-satd $CHCl_3$. Discard eluate.

Add mixt. of 3.5 g Celite and 3 ml NH_4OH to Column II, directly onto packing. Tamp. Pass 150 ml H_2O-satd $CHCl_3$ thru column. Evap. eluate to ca 75 ml or until NH_3 is completely removed (test vapors with moistened indicator paper). Quant. transfer to separator contg 20.0 ml equilibrated H_2SO_4 and shake thoroly. Det. A of aq. phase from 360 to 250 nm, using max. at ca 282 nm for calcn. Calc. mg hydrocodone bitartrate in ml sample taken = (A_{sample}/A_{std}) $\times$ C $\times$ V, where C = mg hydrocodone bitartrate/ml in std and V = vol. H_2SO_4 (20 ml).

36.030 Morphine in Sirups and Tablets— Official Final Action

See **36.011.**

Morphine in Opium and Paregoric (*8*)

(*Caution: See* 46.011, 46.039, 46.040, 46.052, 46.054, and 46.056.)

36.031 *Apparatus*

(a) *Chromatographic tubes.*—*See* **36.015.**

(b) *Diatomaceous earth.*—Celite 545, acid-washed.

36.032 *Reagents*

(a) *Triethylamine.*—Purified as in **36.016(a).**

(b) *Morphine std soln.*—0.08 mg anhyd. morphine/ml. Accurately weigh morphine base or salt equiv. to 4 mg anhyd. morphine into 50 ml vol. flask. Add 10 ml MeOH, 1 ml HCl, and 1 ml Et$_3$N and dil. to vol. with CHCl$_3$. Alternatively, prep. stock soln by dissolving accurately weighed std equiv. to ca 40 mg anhyd. morphine in 0.5 ml Et$_3$N in 100 ml vol. flask, and dil. to vol. with MeOH. Pipet 10 ml this stock soln into 50 ml vol. flask, add 1 ml Et$_3$N and 1 ml HCl, and dil. to vol. with H$_2$O-satd CHCl$_3$.

(c) *Citrate buffer.*—0.1*M*, pH 4.4. Mix equal vols 0.1*M* Na citrate (2.94 g Na$_3$C$_6$H$_5$O$_7$.H$_2$O/100 ml) with 0.1*M* citric acid (2.10 g H$_3$C$_6$H$_5$O$_7$.H$_2$O/100 ml).

36.033 *Preparation of Sample*

(a) *Opium (Official First Action).*—Accurately weigh ca 2 g opium into 100 ml vol. flask. Add 20 ml dimethyl sulfoxide (DMSO) and heat in beaker of boiling H$_2$O or in steam bath ca 15 min. Swirl gently to dissolve, keeping opium particles in contact with DMSO and not letting particles remain on flask walls. Inspect soln carefully. If undissolved material remains, continue heating. Small amt insol. material, such as fine leaf fragments, sand-like particles, and gelatinous particles, may remain undissolved; add more DMSO, if necessary. Cool, add H$_2$O to ca 90 ml, and mix. Let soln reach room temp., dil. to vol. with H$_2$O, and mix. (If foaming occurs on mixing, use 1 drop ether or alcohol to dispel foam.)

If sample is in pieces too large to fit in neck of vol. flask, accurately weigh into 100 ml beaker, add 20 ml DMSO, and heat in boiling H$_2$O or steam bath. Use stirring rod to disperse sample while heating. Decant into 100 ml vol. flask. If undissolved opium remains in beaker, heat with addnl 3 ml portions DMSO as needed until soln is complete as possible. (DMSO concn in final soln can vary over wide range without adverse effect.) Dil. to vol. with H$_2$O as above.

Filter prepd soln thru paper, rejecting first 20 ml filtrate. Use 2 ml aliquot for prepn of Column I.

(b) *Paregoric (Official Final Action).*—Evap. 10.0 ml paregoric, contg ca 4 mg morphine, to ca 2 ml on steam bath under stream of air. If evapn continues

beyond 2 ml, dil. to 2 ml with H$_2$O. Cool soln to room temp. and then use for prepn of Column I.

36.034 *Preparation of Columns*

(a) *Column I.*—(*1*) *Lower layer.*—Mix 3 g Celite and 2 ml citrate buffer; transfer to tube and tamp as in **36.017.** (*2*) *Upper layer.*—Add 0.5 ml citrate buffer to 2.0 ml aliquot of sample ext, **36.033**(a) or (b). Add 3 g Celite, mix, and transfer to tube. Dry-wash beaker with 1 g Celite and add to column; tamp and add glass wool pad.

(b) *Column II.*—Mix 3 g Celite and 2 ml 1.0*M* K$_2$HPO$_4$ (17.42 g/100 ml); transfer to tube, tamp, and add glass wool pad.

(c) *Column III.*—Mix 3 g Celite and 2 ml 0.5*M* NaOH; transfer to tube, tamp, and add glass wool pad.

36.035 *Determination*

(Use H$_2$O-satd solvs thruout. Rinse each column tip with CHCl$_3$ before discarding columns or changing receivers.)

Pass 100 ml ether, followed by 100 ml CHCl$_3$, thru Column I. Discard eluates. Mount Columns II and III in series below Column I. Pass thru columns 5 ml 20% (v/v) Et$_3$N in CHCl$_3$, followed by four 10 ml portions 1% Et$_3$N in CHCl$_3$. Let each portion pass thru completely before next addn. Continue elution without delay. Discard Column I, and pass three 5 ml portions 1% Et$_3$N in CHCl$_3$ thru remaining columns. Discard Column II. Wash Column III successively with 10 ml 1% Et$_3$N in CHCl$_3$, 50 ml CHCl$_3$, 2 ml 10% HOAc in CHCl$_3$, and 50 ml 1% HOAc in CHCl$_3$. Discard all eluates.

Place as receiver under Column III 50 ml vol. flask contg 10 ml MeOH and 1 ml HCl. (Remove metal leashes from vol. flasks to prevent contamination during transfer to cuvets.) Elute column with 5 ml 20% Et$_3$N in CHCl$_3$, followed by 33 ml 1% Et$_3$N in CHCl$_3$. Dil. eluate to vol. with CHCl$_3$.

Scan spectrum of eluate and morphine std from 360 to 255 nm, using CHCl$_3$ as ref. (Film of Et$_3$NHCl may adhere to walls of cuvets. Rinse cuvets carefully with H$_2$O and alcohol; then wipe clear before scanning.) Correct *A* at max. of ca 285 nm by extrapolating baseline from 340 to 310 nm to this wavelength. Calc. wt anhyd. morphine in aliquot taken from formula: $W = (W_s \times A_u/A_s) \times f$, where W_s = wt morphine in std soln, A_u and A_s = corrected *A* of sample and std, resp., and *f* = factor to convert wt std to its equiv. in anhyd. morphine (if hydrated morphine or morphine salt is used as std).

ALKALOIDS, OTHER THAN OPIUM, AND RELATED COMPOUNDS

36.036 ★ **Aconitine in Aconite Root— ★ Qualitative Test (*9*)—Procedure**

See **32.028,** 10th ed.

Amphetamine (*10*)—Official Final Action

36.037 Titrimetric Method

Accurately weigh $\geqslant 20$ tablets and det. av. wt/tablet. Grind tablets in mortar to pass No. 80 sieve. Accurately weigh enough powder to provide 125 mg amphetamine sulfate (or equiv. of other salt), transfer to 100 ml beaker, add 15 ml H_2O, and stir 15 min. Using rod or policeman, transfer as much of suspension as possible to fritted glass funnel (medium porosity, 40 mm disk is convenient) and filter with suction into suitable vessel. Break suction and, with portions of H_2O totaling 15 ml, rinse as much material as possible from beaker into funnel. Triturate mixt. in funnel to uniform paste and reapply suction. Make transfer and filtration quant. by repeating washing with 4 addnl 10 ml portions H_2O. Quant. transfer filtrate to 100 ml vol. flask with small portions of H_2O, dil. to vol., and mix.

Transfer 40 ml aliquot to separator, add 1 ml 10% NaOH soln, and ext with six 25 ml portions ether as in **36.001**. Wash combined ether exts with two 5 ml portions H_2O, and ext combined washings with two 10 ml portions ether. Combine ether washings with main ether ext, filter thru cotton pledget into 250 ml separator, thoroly rinse separator which contained unfiltered ether exts with ether, and filter these rinsings into filtered ether exts. Ext filtrate with exactly 20 ml $0.02N$ H_2SO_4 and drain acid ext into 200 ml erlenmeyer. Wash ether with 10, 5, and 5 ml portions H_2O, combine washings with acid ext and heat on steam bath until dissolved ether is expelled. Cool, and titr. soln with $0.02N$ NaOH, using Me red. Calc. % amphetamine sulfate in sample and quantity/tablet. 1 ml $0.02N$ H_2SO_4 = 3.685 mg amphetamine sulfate.

36.038 Confirmatory Gravimetric Determination

(*Caution: See* **46.011, 46.040,** and **46.056.**)

Combine titrd soln, **36.037**, in 250 ml separator with 50 ml aliquot of the 60 ml unused aq. ext remaining in vol. flask, acidify by dropwise addn of $0.1N$ H_2SO_4, and ext with three 10 ml portions CCl_4. Discard CCl_4 exts, sepg as much CCl_4 as practicable. Add 4.10 g $NaHCO_3$ to aq. soln, and swirl separator until most of salt dissolves. Rapidly add 1.0 ml Ac_2O by blowing in from 1 ml pipet. Immediately stopper separator securely and shake vigorously until evolution of CO_2 nearly ceases (frequently release pressure during shaking by opening stopcock). Add addnl 1.0 ml portion Ac_2O, and keep shaking separator until evolution of CO_2 ceases (5–10 min after addn of second portion of Ac_2O).

Let mixt. stand 5 min, and completely ext acetylamphetamine by shaking with 50 ml portions $CHCl_3$ (4 should be enough; test fifth for com-

plete extn). Filter exts thru cotton pledget, rinse filter with $CHCl_3$, evap. filtrate to small vol. on steam bath in air current, quant. transfer soln to tared 50 ml beaker by rinsing with small portions $CHCl_3$, and continue evapn until solv. is removed. Heat residue of acetylamphetamine in oven (not forced-draft type) 1 hr at 80°, cool in desiccator, and weigh. Calc. % amphetamine salt in sample and quantity/tablet. Acetylamphetamine $\times$ 1.0395 = amphetamine sulfate.

Induce crystn in residue, if it has not crystd spontaneously, by trituration, adding small seed crystal of racemic acetylamphetamine if necessary. Finely powder cryst. derivative, and mix well. Pure acetyl-*d*-amphetamine melts at 124.5–125°; racemic derivative melts at 93–93.5°.

Spectrophotometric Method (*11*)—Official First Action

(Applicable in presence of thyroid, phenobarbital, atropine, and aloin)

36.039 Apparatus

(a) *Spectrophotometer.*—Capable of isolating bands $\leqslant 1$ nm in 225–300 nm region; with 1 cm cells.

(b) *Distillation apparatus.*—Use following or equiv.: 500 ml Kjeldahl flask (Kontes Glass Co., No. K-742000) to which is fitted bulb-type distg head (K-517000). Attach connector (K-169500) from distg head to H_2O-cooled West condenser (K-452000). Attach adapter to bottom of condenser to dip below surface of liq. in 300 ml erlenmeyer. All joints are ⊤ 24/40. Lightly coat flask joint with Dow Corning high vac. grease to prevent freezing.

36.040 Preparation of Standard Solution

Accurately weigh 80–90 mg amphetamine sulfate of known purity, transfer to 100 ml vol. flask, and dissolve in $1N$ H_2SO_4. Dil. to vol. with $1N$ H_2SO_4 and mix well.

36.041 Preparation of Sample

Accurately weigh $\geqslant 20$ tablets or capsules and obtain av. wt/unit or unit contents. Grind tablets or capsule contents to pass No. 60 sieve without appreciable loss.

36.042 Determination

Accurately weigh portion prepd sample contg ca 20–22 mg amphetamine sulfate (or equiv. of other salt). Transfer to Kjeldahl flask, add 25 ml $1N$ H_2SO_4, ca 0.5 g granulated Zn, and 100 ml H_2O, and heat on steam bath ca 5 min. Swirl occasionally to completely disperse sample. Cool and wash down sides of flask with 75 ml H_2O contg small amt antifoam agent such as Dow Corning Antifoam A spray. Place 300 ml erlenmeyer contg

50 ml 0.5N H2SO4 under condenser so that adapter extends nearly to bottom of flask.

Place Kjeldahl flask on wire gauze square from which 1.5″ circle of asbestos has been removed. Add 25 ml 10% NaOH soln to flask and quickly connect distn app. Make sure all joints are tight. Begin heating with Bunsen burner and bring to rolling boil (shield receiver from excessive heat). Collect 150–175 ml distillate or enough so total vol. in receiver is 200–225 ml. Distill 60±15 min.

When distn is complete, remove connector first, then burner. Rinse condenser and adapter into receiver with few ml H2O. Transfer distillate to 500 ml separator, washing flask with few ml H2O, and add washing to separator. Make soln alk. with 25 ml 10% NaOH soln, immediately add 50 ml CHCl3, and shake cautiously but thoroly 2 min. Let layers sep. completely. Carefully drain CHCl3 ext into clean, dry 250 ml separator and re-ext alk. soln with 50, 25, 25, and 25 ml CHCl3. Add by pipet 25 ml 1N H2SO4 to separator contg combined CHCl3 exts and shake vigorously 2–3 min. Let layers sep. completely and discard CHCl3. Obtain UV spectrum of aq. phase in 1 cm cell between 225 and 300 nm against ref. soln of CHCl3-satd 1N H2SO4.

Shake 250 ml H2O and 175 ml CHCl3 in 500 ml separator 1–2 min. Withdraw clear CHCl3 layer into separator contg 25 ml std soln. Shake vigorously 2–3 min. Obtain UV spectrum of aq. phase in 1 cm cell as above.

36.043   Calculations

mg Amphetamine sulfate/g sample taken

$$= (A_u/A_s) \times (\text{mg std per ml/g sample}) \times 25,$$

where $A_u = A_{max}$. of sample at ca 257 nm $- (A_{min}$. at ca 254 nm $+ A_{min}$. at ca 262 nm)/2 and $A_s = A_{max}$. of std at ca 257 nm $- (A_{min}$. at ca 254 nm $+ A_{min}$. at ca 262 nm)/2.

Stereochemical Composition of Amphetamines (12)

36.044   Polarimetric Method

Accurately weigh 90 mg acetyl derivative, 36.038, transfer quant. to 5 ml vol. flask, and dil. to vol. with CHCl3. Det. optical rotation of soln in semimicro 2 dm (200 mm) tube (bore, ca 4.5 mm; vol., 3–4 ml) at same temp. as soln was dild to vol. Acetyl-d-amphetamine is levorotatory in CHCl3.

In measuring rotation with polariscope, take 10 readings on soln and calc. av. to 0.001°. Det. av. reading with same tube filled with CHCl3 similarly, and use av. zero-point reading thus obtained to correct av. reading given by soln. If saccharimeter is used instead of polariscope, est. all readings to 0.05 division, calc. av. to 0.01 division, correct for zero-point, and multiply value so obtained by appropriate factor, 31.020(c), or by 0.3462 (°S) to obtain rotation, α, in angular degrees.

Calc. specific rotation, $[\alpha]$, to 0.1° by equation $[\alpha] = 100\alpha/c \times l$, in which $c = $ acetylamphetamine concn in g/100 ml and $l = $ tube length in decimeters.

Det. % dextroamphetamine by equation: % $d = 50 + (50[\alpha]/44)$, in which $[\alpha] = $ specific rotation of acetyl derivative from sample, and $44 = $ specific rotation of pure acetyl-d-amphetamine; sign of rotation is ignored.

36.045   Confirmatory Thermal Analysis

In mp tube, 2–3 mm id at bottom and ca 70 mm long, place enough finely powd acetyl-dl-amphetamine (ca 8 mg) to form column 5–6 mm high after tube and contents have been tapped firmly several times on hard surface.

Select thermometer with 90–130° range, with graduations permitting readings to 0.5° with aid of low-power hand lens. (Anschütz-type thermometer is convenient but not necessary.) Thermometer need not be calibrated, but if not, same thermometer must be used in detg std mp curve and mp of derivative from sample.

Fix mp tube securely to thermometer by 2 small rubber bands, one near top of tube and other as far down as possible without letting liq. in bath touch band. (Bands may be cut from rubber tubing of proper size.) Adjust tube so that middle of column of specimen coincides approx. with middle of thermometer bulb.

Support assembly in mech.-stirred mp bath. (DC 200 Silicone fluid, viscosity grade 20 centistokes at 25°, made by Dow Corning Corp., is convenient bath liq.) Rapidly raise temp. of bath until it is ca 5° below anticipated mp (temp. at which specimen becomes entirely clear liq.); then regulate heating carefully so that rise in temp. is ≤0.5°/min. After specimen begins to melt, stir continuously with chromel wire (0.4 mm diam.; flatten ca 3 mm of lower end and bend flattened portion at right angle ca 1 mm from tip so as to form hoe-like stirrer) while carefully inspecting it with ca 10× hand lens. (Observation is facilitated by passing beam of light thru specimen from rear.) Note temp. at which last crystal disappears, and record this as mp. Remove tube and thermometer from bath, induce melt to solidify by stirring (seeding if necessary), and repeat detn. Replicate detns will not differ by >1° if carefully performed. Following same procedure, det. mp of pure acetyl-d-amphetamine.

Prep. series of std mixts of acetyl-d- and acetyl-l-amphetamine with following compositions, expressed in mg: $80d + 20dl$, $60d + 40dl$, $40d + 60dl$, and $20d + 80dl$. These mixts contain, resp., 90, 80, 70, and 60% d-isomer. In each case accurately weigh each component into small (18 × 55 mm) test tube, hold tube in bath heated to 130–135° until contents melt completely, stir molten contents with small stainless steel spatula until well mixed, and then withdraw tube from bath and continue to stir until melt solidifies completely. Transfer solidified material as completely as possible to small mortar, powder finely, and mix thoroly. Det. mp of each mixt. as above. In each mixt. beginning of fusion (softening, appearance of liq. phase) will be noted at ca same temp. (ca 93°), but temp. at which system becomes entirely liq. (mp) will depend on composition of mixt. Unlike mp detns of pure *dl-* and *d*-derivatives, it is not important to stir mixts continuously after first evidence of fusion. After considerable liq. phase forms, stir sample occasionally as solid phase diminishes. Stir continuously during ca last 2 min of detn, *i.e.*, during inspection in anticipation of disappearance of last portion of cryst. matter. Push down any solids adhering to walls of tube above melt into melt with wire stirrer.

Plot on coordinate paper av. mp (ordinate) of each specimen against composition (abscissa) expressed as % acetyl-*d*-amphetamine, and draw best smooth curve thru the 6 plotted points.

Det. mp of derivative obtained from sample and est. % *d*-isomer present from std curve.

36.046 Arecoline Hydrobromide—Official Final Action

See 36.011.

Atropine in Tablets—Official Final Action
36.047 Extraction Method

See 36.011.

Infrared Method (13)
36.048 Apparatus

IR spectrophtr for operation in 2–15 μm region, with 2 NaCl cells 1.0 mm thick, suitable for CS_2 solns. A of cells when filled with CS_2 should match to within 0.05; use cell having higher A for sample soln.

36.049 Determination

Transfer enough tablets to yield 5–10 mg atropine to small separator. Dissolve tablets in 5 ml H_2O, add 1 ml NH_4OH and 20 ml $CHCl_3$, and shake 1 min. Let sep. and filter $CHCl_3$ layer thru cotton pledget moistened with $CHCl_3$ into 50 ml g-s flask. Repeat extn with three 10 ml portions $CHCl_3$. Evap. combined $CHCl_3$ exts to dryness on steam bath with aid of air current.

Transfer ca 25 mg atropine, NF, accurately weighed, to 50 ml g-s flask. By pipet, add to sample and std flasks measured vols of CS_2 sufficient to produce concns of ca 3 mg/ml. Stopper flasks, mix well, and immediately det. A of sample and std solns relative to CS_2 at max. of 9.68 μm, using baseline between minima at 9.14 and 9.87 μm. Calc. atropine sulfate content of sample; atropine $\times$ 1.20

= atropine sulfate. Record spectra of sample and std solns from 2 to 15 μm and compare for identity of sample.

Belladonna and Stramonium Alkaloids in Ointments (14)—Official Final Action
36.050 ★ Method I ★

(*Caution: See* 46.011, 46.040, and 46.056.)
Solv. extn method. *See* 32.037, 10th ed.

36.051 ★ Method II ★

Acid extn method. *See* 32.038, 10th ed.

Benzocaine (15)—Official Final Action
36.052 Principle

Benzocaine is diazotized with $NaNO_2$, excess nitrite is removed with NH_4 sulfamate, and product is coupled with N-1-naphthylethylenediamine.2HCl. Colored soln has max. at 540 nm. Method is not applicable in presence of sulfanilamides. Benzocaine must be sepd from inorg. I to avoid interference. Antipyrine in 10-fold excess does not interfere.

36.053 Reagents

Benzocaine std solns.—(*1*) *Stock soln.*—0.25 mg/ml. Dissolve 25.0 mg benzocaine NF in 25–50 ml H_2O in 100 ml vol. flask. Add 3 ml HCl, shake gently, and dil. to vol. with H_2O. (*2*) *Working soln.*—5 μg/ml. Pipet 10 ml stock soln into 100 ml vol. flask and dil. to vol. with H_2O. Pipet 20 ml of this soln into 100 ml vol. flask and dil. to vol. with H_2O.

36.054 Preparation of Standard Curve

Pipet 0.0, 2.0, 6.0, and 10.0 ml working std soln into sep. 25 ml vol. flasks. To each flask add 1 ml HCl (1 + 1). Dil. to 15 ml with H_2O, add 1 ml 0.1% $NaNO_2$ soln, 36.476(c), mix, and let stand 5 min, swirling several times during standing. Add 1 ml 0.5% NH_4 sulfamate soln, 36.476(d), and let stand 5 min, swirling several times during standing. Add 1 ml colorless 0.1% N-1-naphthylethylenediamine.2HCl soln, 38.013(d), let stand 15 min, swirling several times during standing, and dil. to 25.0 ml with H_2O.

Det. A of each soln in matched 1 cm cells in spectrophtr at 540 nm against H_2O as ref. (Avoid collection of N bubbles on cell walls.) To obtain net ΔA, subtract reading of soln contg *no* std from each of other std readings. Plot ΔA against benzocaine concn.

36.055 Preparation of Samples

(a) *Liquid preparation in water-soluble bases.*—Weigh sample contg 100 mg benzocaine, transfer to 250 ml vol. flask, and add 75 ml alcohol. Add 3 ml HCl, dil. to vol. with H_2O, and mix well.

Pipet 10 ml into 100 ml vol. flask, dil. to vol. with H_2O, and mix well. Pipet 10 ml of diln into 100 ml vol. flask, dil. to vol. with H_2O, and mix well.

(b) *Solid tablets or troches.*—Weigh powd sample contg 7.5–10 mg benzocaine. Transfer to 100 ml beaker, wet with 2–3 ml alcohol, stir with glass rod to slurry, add 5 ml H_2O and 2 ml HCl, stir, and let stand at room temp. 5 min. Dil. with 25 ml H_2O, transfer quant. to 100 ml vol. flask, and dil. to vol. If soln is cloudy, filter thru dry paper, discarding first 10 ml filtrate. Pipet 10 ml clear filtrate into 100 ml vol. flask, dil. to vol. with H_2O, and mix well.

(c) *Suppositories in water-soluble bases.*—Weigh sample contg 50–100 mg benzocaine into 100 ml beaker, add 15 ml H_2O and 3 ml HCl, and let stand at room temp. 15 min, stirring occasionally with rod. Transfer quant. to 250 ml vol. flask, dil. to vol., and mix well. Pipet 10 ml into 100 ml vol. flask, dil. to vol., and mix well. Pipet 10 ml of diln into 100 ml vol. flask, dil. to vol., and mix well.

36.056 Determination

Pipet 2 aliquots of final diln specified in **36.055** contg 20–30 μg benzocaine into sep. 25 ml vol. flasks. Label one flask "sample" and the other "sample blank." Proceed as in **36.054**, beginning "To each flask add 1 ml HCl (1 + 1)." except do not add $NaNO_2$ to "sample blank."

Det. A at 540 nm for each soln against H_2O as ref. Subtract A of "sample blank" from "sample" reading. Det. μg benzocaine in aliquot from std curve. Calc. as follows:

% Benzocaine $= (B \times F)/(W \times 10)$, where $B = \mu$g benzocaine from std curve, $F =$ diln factor, and $W =$ mg sample.

Benzocaine and Antipyrine (16)—Official Final Action

(Applicable in presence of glycerol and propylene glycol bases)

36.057 Principle

Benzocaine and antipyrine are extd by column partition chromatgy. Antipyrine is retained on $FeCl_3$ column and benzocaine on HCl column. Max. A are detd in $CHCl_3$ eluates at 272 nm for antipyrine and 283 nm for benzocaine. To identify compds, IR spectra of KBr dispersions are compared to stds.

36.058 Apparatus and Reagents

(a) *Chromatographic column and tamping rod.* —See **36.015**.

(b) *Syringe.*—10 ml syringe with 14 gage 4″ laboratory cannula.

(c) *Ferric chloride.*—9%. Dissolve 9 g anhyd. $FeCl_3$ in H_2O and dil. to 100 ml.

(d) *Celite 545.*—Acid-washed.

(e) *Chloroform.*—Washed; shake 4 vols $CHCl_3$ with 1 vol. H_2O.

(f) *Mixed solvent.*—Mix H_2O-satd $CHCl_3$, ether, and isooctane (10 + 25 + 65).

(g) *Antipyrine std soln.*—1 mg/100 ml. Accurately weigh portion antipyrine std, previously dried 2 hr at 60°, and dil. with $CHCl_3$ to give concn of 0.1 mg/ml. Pipet 10 ml into 100 ml vol. flask contg 10 ml MeOH and 1.0 ml mixed solv., and dil. to vol. with washed $CHCl_3$.

(h) *Benzocaine std soln.*—0.4 mg/100 ml. Accurately weigh portion benzocaine std, previously dried 3 hr over P_2O_5, and dil. with $CHCl_3$ to concn of 0.04 mg/ml. Pipet 10 ml into 100 ml vol. flask contg 10 ml MeOH and 1.0 ml mixed solv., and dil. to vol. with washed $CHCl_3$.

(i) *Photometric blank.*—Pipet 10 ml MeOH and 1 ml mixed solv. into 100 ml vol. flask, dil. to vol. with washed $CHCl_3$, and mix.

(j) *Potassium bromide.*—Anhyd. spectrophtric grade.

36.059 Sample Density

(Altho sample is weighed because of viscosity of prepns, report results on wt/vol. basis.)

Slowly withdraw 10 ml sample with syringe, keeping air bubbles to min., and transfer to previously weighed 10 ml vol. flask without touching sides of flask above mark. Let any air bubbles present rise before filling to final vol. Weigh flask and contents, and calc. sample density.

36.060 Preparation of Chromatographic Columns

Loosely pack small amt glass wool uniformly in base of 3 chromatgc tubes to support Celite.

Bottom column.—Mix 3 g Celite with 2 ml $2N$ HCl to form uniform fluffy mixt. Transfer mixt. to column and tamp firmly to uniform mass.

Middle column.—Mix 5 g Celite with 3 ml $FeCl_3$ soln and transfer to column as above.

Top column.—Accurately weigh portion sample contg 20 mg antipyrine into 100 ml beaker. Add 2 ml H_2O and then 3 g Celite. Mix thoroly, transfer to column, and tamp firmly to uniform mass. Dry-wash beaker with 1 g Celite and tamp as above.

Place small loose plug of glass wool above each prepd column.

36.061 Determination

(*Caution:* See **46.011**, **46.040**, and **46.056**.)

(a) *Separation of antipyrine and benzocaine.*— Arrange 3 columns in series. Rinse beaker that contained sample with 50 ml mixed solv. and transfer to top column. Elute columns with 3 addnl 25 ml portions mixed solv. Discard eluate. (Middle column contains antipyrine and bottom column contains benzocaine.) Sep. columns, and elute middle and bottom columns sep. with four 25 ml portions washed CHCl₃, collecting eluates in 100 ml vol. flasks. Dil. to vol. with washed CHCl₃.

(b) *Determination of antipyrine.*—Pipet 5 ml from antipyrine flask into 100 ml vol. flask contg 10 ml MeOH and dil. to vol. with washed CHCl₃. Det. A of final diln against photometric blank, (i), at 272 nm with spectrophtr, using 1 cm cells. Similarly, det. A of std antipyrine soln and calc. amt of antipyrine in sample.

(c) *Determination of benzocaine.*—Pipet aliquot of eluate contg 0.4 mg benzocaine into 100 ml vol. flask contg 10.0 ml MeOH and dil. to vol. with washed CHCl₃. Det. A of final diln against photometric blank, (i), at 283 nm. Similarly, det. A of std benzocaine soln and calc. amt of benzocaine in sample.

(d) *Identification of antipyrine and benzocaine.* —Transfer remaining CHCl₃ eluates from antipyrine and benzocaine sepn to sep. 150 ml beakers. Place beakers in 30–40° H₂O bath and evap. to dryness with gentle air current. (*Caution:* Benzocaine is volatile.)

Prep. KBr disk of each residue, using 0.8 mg residue and 200 mg KBr. Record IR spectrum of each between 2 and 16 μm and qual. compare these spectra with IR spectra of antipyrine and benzocaine stds.

Butacaine Sulfate (*17*)—Official Final Action

36.062 *Reagents*

(a) *Potassium iodide soln.*—20%. Prep. fresh.

(b) *Starch indicator.*—Make 1.5 g sol. starch into paste with few ml H₂O, and add slowly, with stirring, to 300 ml boiling H₂O.

(c) *Picrolonic acid soln.*—2.5% in alcohol.

36.063 *Determination*

(*Caution: See 46.011, 46.040, and 46.056.*)

(a) *Ointments containing butacaine sulfate in petrolatum or other greasy base.*—Accurately weigh into 125 ml separator sample contg ca 50 mg butacaine sulfate. Add 25 ml benzene and swirl until ointment base dissolves; then add 10 ml HCl (1 + 7) and shake separator gently ca 1 min. Let layers sep., drain aq. phase into second separator, and repeat extn 4 times with 10 ml portions H₂O. Wash combined aq. exts with 5 ml CCl₄ and discard washing. Neutze soln with NH₄OH, add 2 ml excess, and ext butacaine base by shaking with five 15 ml portions CHCl₃. Filter each ext thru cotton pledget into 100 ml beaker, and evap. combined exts on steam bath under air current until no CHCl₃ odor remains.

Rinse down beaker wall with 2 ml alcohol delivered from pipet, warm until oily base dissolves completely, and add 1 drop HCl. Tilt and rotate beaker to wet with acidic soln any liq. on wall of beaker, and add 1 drop Me red. If soln does not react strongly acid, add enough HCl dropwise. Dil.

with few ml H₂O, and quant. wash into 500 ml I flask with more H₂O.

To soln add, from pipet, 10 ml KBr-KBrO₃ soln, **36.208**, dil. to 200 ml with H₂O, and add 10 ml HCl. Immediately stopper flask and swirl 5 min or until ppt coagulates. After 5 min add 5 ml KI soln to flask, stopper, and shake vigorously. Rinse stopper and neck of flask with little H₂O, and titr. soln with 0.1N Na₂S₂O₃, **45.038**, until color is discharged. Add 15 ml starch indicator and 20 ml CHCl₃, stopper flask, and shake vigorously. Continue titrn, vigorously shaking stoppered flask after each addn of Na₂S₂O₃ soln. Add Na₂S₂O₃ soln dropwise as end point approaches. (During titrn, mixt. passes thru series of color changes; at end point aq. phase is colorless and emulsified CHCl₃ layer is nearly so.) 1 ml 0.1N KBr-KBrO₃ = 0.00889 g (C₁₈H₃₀N₂O₂)₂.H₂SO₄.

To isolate bromination product for identification, transfer titrd mixt. to separator, make alk. with NH₄OH, and shake vigorously. Drain emulsified CHCl₃ layer, and to break emulsion, filter with suction thru 0.5 cm layer Hyflo Super-Cel (or similar filter-aid) supported on paper in buchner. Shake aq. phase remaining in separator with 25 ml CHCl₃, and pass CHCl₃ ext thru filter. Transfer combined filtrates to separator, filter CHCl₃ layer thru cotton pledget into beaker, and evap. on steam bath under air current.

To oily residue of dibromobutacaine add 2 ml picrolonic acid soln and stir. Filter ppt on Hirsch funnel, wash with 2–3 ml alcohol, dry at 105°, and det. capillary mp, alone and in admixt. with authentic dibromobutacaine picrolonate (mp 158–160° with decomposition). If ppt does not form on adding picrolonic acid soln to bromination product, seed with small crystal of dibromobutacaine picrolonate; if ppt still does not form, butacaine is absent.

(b) *Tablets.*—Accurately weigh 20 tablets and det. av. wt/tablet. To 125 ml separator add enough accurately weighed, finely powd tablet mixt. to provide ca 200 mg butacaine sulfate, add 25 ml H₂O, and swirl separator until sample dissolves. Add 2 ml NH₄OH and ext with six 15 ml portions CHCl₃. Shake each ext with 5 ml H₂O in second separator, and then filter thru cotton pledget into beaker. (If emulsion forms in aq. phase in first separator, more than 6 extns may be required. Test for complete extn by evapg seventh ext on steam bath; if appreciable residue is obtained, dissolve it in CHCl₃, combine with previous exts, and continue extns until complete. If aq. phase in first separator tends to emulsify, break emulsion by addn of Na₂SO₄ or by other means.) Evap. filtrate to small vol. on steam bath and complete detn by one of following methods:

(*1*) Quant. transfer concd soln of butacaine base to tared 50 ml beaker with CHCl₃, remove solv. by heating on steam bath in air current, dry 30 min at 105°, cool in desiccator, and weigh. Wt residue × 1.160 = wt butacaine sulfate, $(C_{18}H_{30}N_2O_2)_2$ $.H_2SO_4$.

Gravimetric detn may be checked acidimetrically as follows: Rinse down wall of beaker with 2 ml neut. alcohol delivered from pipet, warm beaker on steam bath until butacaine base dissolves completely, add 1 drop Me red, and rinse down beaker wall with another 2 ml alcohol. Titr. soln with 0.1 N H_2SO_4, 45.041 or 45.042, almost to point of color change; rinse down wall of beaker with H_2O, dil. to ca 45 ml, and complete titrn. 1 ml 0.1N $H_2SO_4 = 0.0355$ g $(C_{18}H_{30}N_2O_2)_2$ $.H_2SO_4$.

(2) Det. gravimetrically as in (1); then proceed as in (a), beginning "Rinse down wall of beaker with 2 ml alcohol..." except to use 50 ml instead of 10 ml KBr-KBrO_3 soln.

(3) Completely remove solv. on steam bath, and proceed as in (1), second par. Then wash titrd soln into 500 ml I flask, pipet in 50 ml KBr-KBrO_3 soln, 36.208, dil. to 200 ml with H_2O, add 10 ml HCl, and proceed as in (a), beginning "Immediately stopper flask..."

(c) *Crystals.*—Accurately weigh ca 200 mg sample into 125 ml separator, add 25 ml H_2O, and swirl separator until sample dissolves. Continue as in (b), beginning "Add 2 ml NH_4OH..."

(d) *Solns.*—Transfer to 125 ml separator aliquot contg ca 200 mg butacaine sulfate, and if necessary dil. to 25 ml with H_2O. Proceed as in (b), completing detn by (b)(1), (2), or (3) if chlorobutanol is absent, and only by (b)(3) if chlorobutanol is present.

36.064   Cocaine—Official Final Action
See 36.011.

36.065   Emetine Hydrochloride in Tablets—Official Final Action
See 36.011.

36.066   ★ Ephedra, Alkaloids in (18)— ★ Official Final Action
(*Caution: See* 46.011, 46.039, and 46.054.)
See 32.047, 10th ed.

★ Ephedrine in Inhalants— ★ Official Final Action
36.067   *Method I (19)*
(*Caution: See* 46.011, 46.039, and 46.054.)
Accurately weigh 5–10 g sample into small tared beaker. Add 10 ml H_2SO_4 (1 + 90), stir, and let stand ca 15 min. Transfer to small separator, rinsing beaker with small portions ether. Shake gently, and transfer acid layer to second separator. Shake ether with three 10 ml portions H_2SO_4 (1 + 90). Test for complete removal of alkaloid.

Neutze combined acid solns in separator with

NH_4OH and add 5 ml excess. Ext soln with 30 ml washed ether (automatic extractor optional), transfer aq. layer to second separator, and wash ether ext with 1 ml H_2O, adding washings to main aq. soln. Swirl ether to remove H_2O adhering to side of separator. After all H_2O has been removed, filter mixt. into erlenmeyer thru cotton pledget wet with ether inserted in small funnel. Repeat extn with liberal portions washed ether ≥4 times, or until alkaloid is removed completely, washing each portion with same 1 ml H_2O. Evap. ether to 10 ml in air current. Add bromothymol blue, 6.116(e), measured excess 0.02N H_2SO_4, and ca 40 ml CO_2-free H_2O; cover with watch glass, heat on steam bath to dissolve alkaloid on sides of flask, and evap. all ether. Cool, and titr. excess acid with 0.02N NaOH, using indicator std, pH 6.0, 45.011, for comparison. 1 ml 0.02N $H_2SO_4 = 0.00330$ g ephedrine.

36.068   *Method II (20)*
(*Caution: See* 46.011, 46.040, and 46.056.)

(a) *Oily inhalants containing oxazolidines (products of reaction of ephedrine with carbonyl compounds).*—Accurately weigh or otherwise measure sample contg ca 100 mg ephedrine. (With most inhalants, sample size will be ca 10 ml. Altho sample contg as little as 20 mg of the drug may be used if necessary, larger sample should be employed when practicable.) Quant. rinse sample into 125 ml erlenmeyer with portions reagent-grade benzene totaling ca 5 ml, add 10 ml H_2SO_4 (1 + 35), and boil gently 10 min with frequent agitation and swirling. (Boiling is best done on hot plate, taking care to avoid superheating, bumping, and loss of sample.)

Cool flask, transfer contents to 125 ml separator, and rinse erlenmeyer with portions benzene totaling ca 1.5 times vol. sample to remove all oily matter from flask. (Preferably use lipped flask to facilitate quant. transfer to separator.) Shake separator contg the acid and benzene rinsings, drain acid layer into second separator, and vigorously swirl first separator to force down addnl acid and ensure more nearly complete phase sepn. Drain into second separator any acid layer that further seps, and ext benzene-oil phase with the three 5 ml portions H_2O previously used to rinse flask. Swirl first separator each time after main portion of H_2O has been drained into second separator. (In transfer of ephedrine from org. solv. to aq. phase, and *vice versa*, shake ≥1 min and as vigorously as possible without causing troublesome emulsions.)

Wash acid soln of ephedrine sulfate with 3 ml CHCl_3 and discard CHCl_3 washings. Make soln alk. to litmus with 20% NaOH soln (ca 2.5 ml); then add 0.5 ml excess and ext ephedrine by shaking *vigorously* with six 15 ml portions CHCl_3. If >50 mg ephedrine is present, filter exts thru cotton pledget into tared 100 ml beaker previously dried at 110° and cooled in desiccator. After fourth extn, rinse filter funnel and its tip with CHCl₃ (letting rinsings drain into beaker), float 5 drops (0.2 ml) HCl onto surface of combined exts, and evap. on steam bath in air current until beaker can easily accommodate remaining exts. To test for complete extn, shake alk. phase with seventh and eighth 15 ml portions CHCl₃, filter these thru cotton into small beaker, float 2 drops HCl on surface, and evap. to dryness on steam bath in air current. If *cryst.* residue results, combine it with main exts, using little MeOH for transfer, and repeat test if considered necessary.

Continue evapn of main exts to 1 or 2 ml. Then cautiously heat on bath, but without air current, until no HCl odor remains and residue of ephedrine.HCl is apparently dry. Heat beaker 30 min at 110°, cool in desiccator, and weigh. Wt residue × 0.8192 = wt ephedrine base.

If <50 mg ephedrine is present in sample, carry out extn to completion as described above, and evap. filtered exts in untared beaker until CHCl₃ (but not excess HCl) has been removed. Direct fine stream redistd MeOH around inside of beaker to dissolve ephedrine salt, and immediately repeat process with stream of CHCl₃. Transfer MeOH-CHCl₃ soln to tared 20 ml beaker, previously dried at 110° and cooled in desiccator, and repeat MeOH and CHCl₃ rinsings until ephedrine.HCl has been quant. transferred. Evap. soln on steam bath, in air current, until the salt begins to crystallize. Continue solv. removal by cautious heating alone, to avoid loss from decrepitation, until residue is apparently dry and there is no odor of HCl. Dry and weigh as above.

(b) *Oily inhalants or petroleum jelly preparations containing free ephedrine only.*—If product is oil, quant. transfer suitable sample, (a), to 125 ml separator with portions benzene totaling ca 1.5 times vol. sample, and ext mixt. with 5 ml H₂SO₄ (1 + 16) and then with four 5 ml portions H₂O, swirling separator each time as in (a), and continue assay as in (a), beginning "Wash acid soln of ephedrine sulfate..." If product is petroleum jelly prepn, dissolve sample in enough benzene to obtain soln of suitable fluidity (30 ml should be enough for 10 g sample) and proceed as for oily inhalants.

36.069   Ephedrine in Water-Soluble Jellies, Sirups, and Solutions of Ephedrine Salts—Official Final Action

(a) *Water-soluble jellies.*—If product is thin jelly of viscosity similar to that of NF XII prepn, accurately weigh ca 10 g sample. If it is thick jelly, reduce size of sample (which should contain 20–100 mg alkaloid) to ca 5 g to diminish possibility of emulsion formation during ether extns. Transfer

quant. to separator with aid of H₂O, and dil. with H₂O until vol. jelly and H₂O is ca 20 ml. Make mixt. slightly alk. to litmus with 20% NaOH soln, add addnl 0.5 ml, and quant. ext ephedrine with ether, using 3-separator technic as in **36.001**. In each extn use vol. ether equal to that of aq. phase, and swirl separator vigorously after draining bulk of aq. layer to obtain efficient phase sepn. If equilibrium is attained in each extn, 5 or 6 will be enough. Ext ether with 5 ml H₂SO₄ (1 + 16) and four 5 ml portions H₂O as in **36.068**(b), and continue assay as in **36.068**(a), beginning "Wash acid soln of ephedrine sulfate..."

(b) *Sirups.*—Use 10 ml sample, measured by vol. flask, and proceed as in (a).

(c) *Solns of ephedrine salts.*—Use accurately measured sample contg ca 100 mg ephedrine and proceed as in (a), but if sample is <20 ml, diln to this vol. before extg is unnecessary.

Ephedrine in Tablets and Capsules— Official Final Action

36.070   Method I
See **36.011**.

36.071   Method II (20)

Accurately weigh sample of capsule contents or finely powd tablets (preferably contg ca 100 mg drug). Transfer to separator contg 20 ml H₂O and make alk. with ca 0.5 g anhyd. Na₂CO₃. Continue as in **36.069**(a), beginning with ether extns, but make acid ext alk. with anhyd. Na₂CO₃ instead of 20% NaOH soln. Use ca 0.5 g excess of that required to make soln alk. to litmus.

Ephedrine With or Without Antihistamines and Barbiturates (21)—Official First Action

36.072   Reagents

(a) *Hydrochloric acid.*—1.2N. Dil. 10.0 ml HCl to 100.0 ml in vol. flask with H₂O and stdze as in **45.013**. Use normality to calc. amt concd acid needed to make eluting solns (b)(2).

(b) *Alcoholic hydrochloric acid solns.*—(1) *Washing soln.*—6N. Dil. 50 ml HCl to 100 ml with alcohol (normality not critical). (2) *Eluting solns.* —2.50N, 0.60N, 0.270N, and 0.055N. Add 500 ml alcohol to sep. 1 L vol. flasks and add enough HCl to each to give exact normality when dild to vol. Cool to room temp., dil. to vol. with H₂O, and mix.

(c) *Alkaline borate buffer.*—pH 9. (1) *Concd soln.*—See **38.019**(a). pHydrion buffers (Micro Essential Laboratory, Inc., Brooklyn, NY 11210), USP alk. borate buffer, or equiv., may be used. (2) *Dild soln.*—Dil. 5 ml concd soln with 95 ml isopropanol (1 + 1).

(d) *Cationic exchange resin.*—Bio-Rad AG 50W-X4, 100–200 mesh, in H-form (Bio-Rad Laboratories, 32nd and Griffin Ave, Richmond, CA

94804), or equiv. (This is washed and sized Dowex 50W-X4 resin with max. impurities (ppm): Fe 1.00, Cu 0.8, Ni 0.05, Pb 0.2, and Al 15.)

(e) *Anion exchange resin.*—Bio-Rad AGI-X2, 200–400 mesh, in Cl-form, or equiv. (This is washed and sized Dowex 1-X2 resin with max. impurities (ppm): Fe 0.5, Cu 0.2, Ni 0.05, Pb 0.005, and Al 5.)

36.073 ***Apparatus***

(a) *Chromatographic tubes.*—250 and 150 mm long × 12 mm id Chromaflex (Kontes Glass Co. K-422281, sizes 25-12 and 15-12), with 125 ml glass reservoir (K-422450), two replaceable coarse fritted glass disks (K-952050, 12 mm size), two Teflon stopcock adapters (one each of K-422380 and K-42240, 12 mm size), and two clamps (K-67500, 12 mm size); or equiv.

(b) *Recording spectrophotometer.*—Beckman Instruments DK-2A, or equiv., with 1 cm and 5 or 10 cm cells.

36.074 ***Preparation of Columns***

(a) *Column I.*—Place fritted glass disk over small glass wool pad in ₮ adapter (Kontes Glass Co. K-422400). Seal adapter to 250 mm column with Buna-N "O" ring. Hold in place with metal clamp and tighten thumb screw on clamp. Mix 3.0 g cation exchange resin with 15 ml H_2O in beaker. Add slurry to 250 mm tube contg some H_2O. Rinse beaker with H_2O and add wash to column.

Before using column, pretreat by adding five 10 ml portions 6*N* alc. HCl. Stir gently few sec with each addn and let soln pass to level of resin before further addn to column. Follow with H_2O, stirring gently few sec until eluate is pH 4–7. Condition resin by washing with 200 ml, followed by 10 ml, 2.5*N* alc. HCl. Collect each eluate sep. and mix each. Scan 200 ml eluate against 10 ml eluate, using 1 cm cells, at 360–220 nm to det. whether any adsorbing material is being eluted from resin bed. If A is $>$0.05 at 258 and 310 nm, repeat conditioning. Pass H_2O thru column until neutzd to pH 4–7. Drain to level of resin. Column is ready for use.

(b) *Column II.*—Place fritted glass disk over small glass wool pad in non-₮ adapter (Kontes Glass Co. K-422380). Seal adapter to 150 mm length tube with Buna-N "O" ring. Hold in place with metal clamp and tighten thumb screw on clamp. Mix 1.5 g anion exchange resin with 15 ml H_2O in beaker. Add slurry to 150 mm length tube contg some H_2O. Rinse beaker with H_2O and add to column.

Before using column, pretreat as in (a) and wash until eluate is pH 4–7. Condition resin by washing with 50 ml isopropanol (1 + 1). Drain to level of resin. Column is ready for use.

No flow rate adjustment is necessary. Use max. gravity flow with stopcock fully opened.

(c) *Regeneration (both columns).*—(Repeat after each analysis.) Add five 10 ml portions 6.0*N* alc. HCl. Stir gently for few sec after each addn. Let soln pass to level of resin before further addn to column. Follow with H_2O, stirring gently until eluate is pH 4–7. Store with H_2O on each column. Drain H_2O to level of resin for use.

36.075 ***Preparation of Standard Solutions***

(Use all stds within 8 hr of prepn.)

(a) *Barbital sodium.*—0.01 mg/ml. Weigh 1.0 mg barbital Na (K & K Laboratories, Inc.) into 100 ml vol. flask contg 5.0 ml concd pH 9 buffer and dil. to vol. with isopropanol (1 + 1).

(b) *Ephedrine sulfate.*—0.15 mg/ml. Weigh 15 mg ephedrine sulfate (Matheson Coleman & Bell) into 100 ml vol. flask and dil. to vol. with 0.60*N* HCl.

(c) *Methapyrilene hydrochloride.*—0.025 mg/ml. Weigh 2.5 mg methapyrilene.HCl (K & K Laboratories, Inc.) into 100 ml vol. flask and dil. to vol. with 2.50*N* alc. HCl.

(d) *Phenobarbital.*—0.01 mg/ml. Prep. as in (a), using USP Phenobarbital.

(e) *Pyrilamine maleate.*—0.025 mg/ml. Prep. as in (c), using NF Pyrilamine Maleate.

(f) *Tripelennamine citrate.*—0.025 mg/ml. Prep. as in (c), using USP Tripelennamine Citrate.

36.076 ***Preparation of Sample***

(a) *Ephedrine sulfate alone or with barbiturate and/or antihistamine.*—(Following directions are for use with 5 cm UV cells. If sample size is limited, use ½ stated amts and 10 cm cells.)

(*1*) *Tablets.*—Weigh and pulverize 20 tablets. Accurately weigh portion equiv. to ca 19 mg amphetamine sulfate or ephedrine sulfate into 50 ml Florence flask (vol. flask can be substituted) contg ca 25 ml isopropanol (1 + 1). Warm on steam bath 5 min and mix until thoroly dispersed. Filter into 50 ml vol. flask thru Whatman No. 541 dry paper and rinse with four 5 ml portions warm isopropanol (1 + 1). Cool, dil. to vol. with isopropanol (1 + 1), and mix. Pipet 40 ml sample soln onto column I (equiv. to ca 15 mg amphetamine sulfate or ephedrine sulfate).

(*2*) *Powders.*—Proceed as in (*1*), beginning with "Accurately weigh portion ..."

(*3*) *Capsules.*—Completely transfer contents of ≥20 capsules to 200 ml vol. flask. Place emptied capsules in beaker, add ca 50 ml cold H_2O to cover, and let stand 10 min with frequent agitation. Add soln to vol. flask and rinse beaker with four 5 ml portions cold H_2O, adding rinses to flask. Add 75 ml undild isopropanol to vol. flask and mix. Warm on steam bath 5 min and mix until thoroly dispersed. Filter into 200 ml vol. flask thru Whatman No. 541 dry paper and wash paper with four 5 ml portions warm isopropanol (1 + 1). Cool, dil.

to vol. with isopropanol (1 + 1), and mix. Pipet aliquot equiv. to 15 mg amphetamine sulfate or ephedrine sulfate onto column I.

(*4*) *Individual tablet assay.*—Crush tablet and completely transfer with ca 25 ml isopropanol (1 + 1) into 50 ml Florence flask. Warm on steam bath 5 min and mix until thoroly dispersed. Filter thru Whatman No. 541 dry paper onto column I and rinse flask and paper with four 5 ml portions isopropanol (1 + 1).

(**b**) *Antihistamine.*—Proceed as in (**a**), except weigh portion of powder contg ca 6.25 mg antihistamine.

(**c**) *Barbiturate.*—Proceed as in (**a**), except weigh portion of powder contg ca 2.0 mg barbiturate.

(**d**) *Ephedrine sulfate sirup.*—Transfer 25 ml aliquot Ephedrine Sulfate Sirup NF XII (contg ca 100 mg ephedrine sulfate) to 100 ml vol. flask, using "to contain" pipet (draw sirup just to meniscus). Wash pipet with alcohol (1 + 1) and add wash to vol. flask. Dil. soln to vol. with alcohol (1 + 1) and mix. Transfer 15.0 ml aliquot to column I. Perform diln and analysis same day. Proceed as in **36.077(c)**.

36.077 *Determination*

(Complete detn within single day.)

(**a**) *Ephedrine sulfate with barbiturate and antihistamine.*—Arrange columns so eluate from column I flows thru column II and into 200 ml vol. flask. Let sample soln pass thru columns until it sinks into resin. Pass ca 150 ml isopropanol (1 + 1) thru columns. (To prevent resin disturbance establish ca 5 ml solv. head on column II before each elution as follows: Break seal between columns. Turn column II stopcock off and let eluate from column I drain onto column II until 5 ml is added. Turn column I stopcock off. Reestablish seal between columns and turn both stopcocks on. Each eluate should pass completely thru resin in both columns I and II before next eluate is added.)

Add 10.0 ml concd pH 9.0 buffer to vol. flask, dil. to vol. with isopropanol (1 + 1), and mix. This flask contains barbital Na or phenobarbital. Dil. sample solns with dild pH 9.0 buffer to give final concn ca 1 mg/100 ml. Scan sample and std solns from 350 to 220 nm against dild pH 9.0 buffer. Det. *A* at max. (ca 240 nm) and calc. sample soln concn.

Remove column II and wash column I with 50 ml 0.055*N* alc. HCl. Follow with 10.0 ml 0.27*N* alc. HCl to elute excipients and any remaining color. Discard wash. Place 100 ml vol. flask beneath column and elute ephedrine sulfate with 100 ml 0.60*N* alc. HCl. Scan spectra of sample and std solns between 350 and 220 nm in 5 cm cells against 0.60*N* alc. HCl. Calc. sample soln concn by drawing baseline between min. at ca 265 and 255 nm. Measure distance between max. and baseline at ca 258 nm.

For methapyrilene.HCl, pyrilamine maleate, or tripelennamine citrate, place 250 ml vol. flask beneath column I and elute antihistamine with 250 ml 2.50*N* alc. HCl and mix. Dil. sample with 2.5*N* alc. HCl to give concn ca 2.5 mg/100 ml. Scan sample and std solns from 360 to 220 nm against 2.50*N* alc. HCl. Det. *A* at max. (ca 310 nm) and calc. sample soln concn.

(**b**) *Ephedrine sulfate alone or with barbiturate.*—Proceed as in (**a**), except 2.50*N* alc. HCl used to remove antihistamine is not needed.

(**c**) *Ephedrine sulfate and antihistamine.*—Let sample soln pass thru column I until sample reaches resin level. Proceed as in (**a**), beginning "...wash column I with 50 ml 0.055*N* alc. HCl."

(**d**) *Antihistamine.*—Proceed as in (**c**), except 0.60*N* alc. HCl used to remove ephedrine sulfate is not needed.

(**e**) *Barbiturate.*—Place 200 ml vol. flask beneath column II and let sample soln pass thru column II. Proceed as in (**a**), beginning "Pass ca 150 ml isopropanol (1 + 1) ..." except 0.27*N*, 0.6*N*, and 2.5*N* alc. HCl eluates are not needed.

Ergotamine (22)—Official Final Action

(Applicable in presence of caffeine, acetophenetidin, phenobarbital, and belladonna alkaloids)

36.078 *Reagents*

(**a**) *Tartaric acid soln.*—1%. Dissolve 10 g tartaric acid in H_2O and dil. to 1 L.

(**b**) *Alcoholic tartaric acid soln.*—Mix equal vols tartaric acid soln, (**a**), with alcohol. Prep. fresh daily.

(**c**) *Sodium bicarbonate soln.*—10%. Dissolve 100 g $NaHCO_3$ in H_2O and dil. to 1 L.

(**d**) *Citric acid soln.*—(1 + 1). Mix equal wts of citric acid and H_2O.

(**e**) *Alum soln.*—0.25*M*. Dissolve 12 g $KAl(SO_4)_2.12H_2O$ in H_2O and dil. to 1 L. pH should be 3.5±0.2.

(**f**) *Color reagent.*—Dissolve 1.25 g *p*-dimethylaminobenzaldehyde in cooled mixt. of 650 ml H_2SO_4 and 350 ml H_2O. Add 0.5 ml 9% $FeCl_3$ soln.

(**g**) *Diatomaceous earth.*—See **36.016(c)**. If Celite 545 is used, acid-wash as follows: Boil 150 g with 1 L HCl (1 + 1) 10 min and cool. Wash with H_2O to remove acid and dry in oven at ca 100°. Dried product should give neg. test for acid when moistened.

(**h**) *Ergotamine tartrate std soln.*—50 µg/ml. Dissolve 25 mg ergotamine tartrate, USP, in enough tartaric acid soln, (**a**), to make 500 ml.

36.079 *Preparation of Chromatographic Column*

Chromatographic tube.—Prep. chromatgc tube as in **36.015(a)**. Fit with packing rod, **36.015(b)**. Place small wad of glass wool in bottom of tube.

Ergotamine-retaining layer.—Add ca 4 g Celite to 3 ml citric acid soln in beaker. Mix thoroly with scoop-shaped spatula until mixt. appears fluffy and uniform, and transfer to chromatgc tube. Tap side of tube gently to settle mixt. Press down firmly with packing rod.

Ergonovine-retaining layer.—Add ca 2 g Celite to 2 ml alum soln, mix, and transfer to tube on top of citric acid layer. Press down firmly and evenly.

Water layer.—Add ca 2 g Celite to 2 ml H_2O, mix, and transfer to tube on top of alum layer. Press down firmly and evenly. Place wad of glass wool on top of column.

36.080   *Preparation of Sample*

(a) *Tablets.*—Weigh counted number $\geqslant 10$ and reduce to fine powder. Weigh portion equiv. to 2.5 mg ergotamine tartrate into beaker. Mix thoroly with 5 ml 1% tartaric acid soln and let stand 30 min. Add 5 ml $CHCl_3$ and 1 ml 10% $NaHCO_3$ soln, and mix. (Aq. phase must be alk.) Add ca 7 g Celite and stir thoroly until mass appears uniform and does not stick to beaker. (It may be necessary to wash down sides of beaker with small amts of $CHCl_3$.) Add and mix more Celite as may be necessary to make mixt. workable. Quant. transfer mixt. to another chromatgc tube fitted with glass wool plug, in several portions, pressing down firmly with packing rod. Wash packing rod, spatula, and sides of beaker with small amt (ca 5 ml) $CHCl_3$. Add enough Celite to make mixt. workable. Scrub sides of beaker and add mixt. to tube. Again rinse rod, spatula, and beaker with $CHCl_3$ and pour wash onto column.

(b) *Suppositories.*—Place suppositories equiv. to 3–5 mg ergotamine tartrate in 125 ml separator. Add 10 ml 0.2N H_2SO_4 and 75 ml ether. Shake until sample dissolves and then 1 min more. Drain acid layer into second separator. Complete extn with three 10 ml portions acid. Discard ether layer. Combine exts and make alk. with NH_4OH. Promptly ext alkaloids with four 10 ml portions $CHCl_3$. Pass each $CHCl_3$ ext directly onto prepd column, **36.079**. Let column drain completely between addn of successive exts. Proceed as in **36.081**, second par.

36.081   *Separation of Ergotamine*

Place tube contg sample so that effluent will flow directly onto water layer of second column. Add 50 ml H_2O-satd ether to top column and receive eluate from bottom column in 250 ml erlenmeyer. Follow with 50 ml H_2O-satd $CHCl_3$. (Since effluent may flow faster thru sample column than thru second column, do not add too much $CHCl_3$ at a time.) Rinse tip of sample column with $CHCl_3$ from wash bottle and discard sample column.

Let column drain completely and then rinse down sides with small amt of $CHCl_3$. Pass thru addnl 25 ml H_2O-satd $CHCl_3$ into same flask and rinse tip of column with alcohol. Discard effluent if ergotamine was properly retained. (*See Note.*)

Inspect column for proper retention of ergotamine and for presence of H_2O-sol. alkaloids by holding column under UV light *very briefly.* (*Caution: See* **46.016.**) Blue fluorescent band must not be at bottom of column. (*See Note.*) Extrude column into 400 ml beaker. Rinse tube with H_2O. Add 8 g $NaHCO_3$ and ca 25 ml H_2O to form aq. liq. layer. Break up column with spatula and mix. Wash mixt. with H_2O from wash bottle into 250 ml separator. Add 10 ml $CHCl_3$ and shake. Check aq. layer to assure that it is alk. Be sure that layers are well sepd. It may be necessary to break $CHCl_3$ bubbles with wire. Drain $CHCl_3$ layer thru glass wool filter into 100 ml vol. flask. Ext aq. layer with four 10 ml portions $CHCl_3$ and filter solv. layers into the 100 ml vol. flask. Dil. to vol. with $CHCl_3$, and mix.

36.082   *Determination*

Evap. 10 ml aliquot $CHCl_3$ soln in 50 ml erlenmeyer to dryness with air current. Do not heat. (Ergotamine is easily decomposed. If assay cannot be completed in 1 day, dried residue after evapn of $CHCl_3$ may be stored in refrigerator overnight.) Dissolve residue, equiv. to 0.25 mg ergotamine tartrate, in 5.0 ml alc. tartrate soln. Pipet 5.0 ml std soln into 50 ml erlenmeyer. Add, to each, 10 ml color reagent dropwise while swirling continuously in ice-H_2O bath. After 30, but <60 min, det. *A* of sample and of std, *A′*, at 550 nm relative to blank prepd by mixing 5 ml H_2O and 10 ml reagent.

mg Ergotamine tartrate in sample weighed $= (A/A') \times 2.5$.

Note: Ergot alkaloids fluoresce bright blue when exposed to UV light at ca 360 nm. If fluorescent band has reached bottom of trap layer, sample must be discarded. If desired, sample can be salvaged by combining column and effluent, shaking with $CHCl_3$, and passing thru another acid trap. Use of eluant which is not H_2O-satd will cause loss of ergotamine from column. Blue fluorescent ring at top of alum layer indicates presence of H_2O-sol. ergot alkaloids. If detn of H_2O-sol. alkaloid content is desired, repeat detn on new portion of sample, changing citric acid trap to one prepd by mixing 3 g Celite with 3 ml alum soln. Cover alum layer with mixt. of 2 g Celite and 2 ml H_2O.

Paper Chromatographic Identification (23)—
Official Final Action

36.083   *Reagents*

(a) *Mobile solvent.*—Dissolve 7.1 g Na citrate in H_2O and dil. to 100 ml. Adjust pH to ca 4.7 with 2N HCl and transfer to separator. Add 70 ml formamide and 9 ml dimethylphthalate. Shake vigorously, let sep., and drain and discard lower layer. Adjust to pH 5.2 with 2N HCl or NaOH.

(b) *Immobile solvent.*—Mix 1 vol. dimethylphthalate with 9 vols CHCl₃ immediately before use.

(c) *Ergotamine std solns.*—Accurately weigh 10 mg ergotamine tartrate, USP, into small separator contg 5 ml 1% tartaric acid soln and mix gently. Make alk. with few drops 10% NaHCO₃ soln, add 2.0 ml CHCl₃, and shake vigorously. Draw off CHCl₃ layer (*std soln 1*). Dil. 1.0 ml *std soln 1* to 25 ml with CHCl₃ (*std soln 2*).

36.084 Identification

For details of app. and technic *see* 29.007 and 29.027. Blotter paper liners must be used in tank and tank must be sealed.

Equilibrate mobile solv. in sealed tank ≥3 hr with liners dipping into solv. Just before use, quickly dip marked 8 × 8″ paper once in freshly prepd immobile solv. and let dry 15 min. Prep. soln of ergotamine in CHCl₃, as in 36.081, contg 2.5 mg/0.5 ml (remainder of CHCl₃ soln from assay may be evapd to this concn). Spot 0.010 ml each of sample and std solns on paper and let solv. evap. Place paper in tank and let chromatogram develop until solv. front is ca 1″ from top (ca 3 hr). Let paper dry overnight in hood and examine under UV light. There should be one yellow primary spot (and there may be a "tail," probably as result of ergotamine changing to ergotaminine during developing) corresponding to 50 μg ergotamine spot (*std 1*) in position and intensity. If any other spot is more intense than that of *std 2*, >2 μg other ergot alkaloids, expressed as ergotamine tartrate, are present.

Note: Ergot alkaloids produce blue fluorescence which on overnight contact with formamide and air changes to yellow fluorescence. Paper must be completely dry and *std 2* spot clearly visible. In humid weather it may be necessary to dry developed paper 2–3 days in well ventilated hood.

36.085 Homatropine in Tablets—Official Final Action

See 36.011.

★ Ipecac Alkaloids in Fluidextract ★ (24)—Official Final Action

36.086 Preparation of Solution

See 32.061, 10th ed.

Determination

(*Caution:* See 46.011, 46.039, and 46.054.)

36.087 Automatic Extraction Method

See 32.062, 10th ed.

36.088 Hand Extraction Method

See 32.063, 10th ed.

Lysergic Acid Diethylamide (LSD) (25)— Official First Action

(*Caution:* LSD is strong psychotomimetic agent. Use rubber gloves and effective fume removal device to avoid skin contact and breathing dusts of materials suspected or known to contain LSD.)

36.089 Reagents and Apparatus

(a) *Indicator paper.*—Sat. filter paper (Whatman No. 1, or equiv.) with 2% *p*-dimethylaminobenzaldehyde in alcohol, air-dry, and cut into strips 1.5–2″ wide. Store in tightly capped amber glass bottles.

(b) *Chromatographic paper saturated with immobile solvent.*—Sat. 8 × 8″ Whatman No. 1 chromatgc paper with MeOH soln of 25% formamide (stabilized reagent grade or recently distd) and 1% benzoic acid. Place wet paper between 2 Whatman No. 1 sheets and remove excess solv. by blotting lightly; then suspend paper from glass rod for ca 15 min to let MeOH evap. (paper remains slightly moist with formamide).

(c) *Chromatographic mobile solvent.*—Sat. ether with formamide by shaking in separator. Let reagents sep. and discard lower formamide layer.

(d) *Reference stds.*—LSD-25 (Sandoz, Ltd., *d*-lysergic acid diethylamide tartrate. CH₃OH) and USP Ref. Std Ergonovine Maleate.

(e) *Spectrophotometer.*—Preferably capable of recording spectrum continuously from 400 to ca 200 nm.

36.090 Presumptive Test

Ext LSD (ca 40 μg) from ground powder with enough MeOH to provide ca 5 drops liq. ext. Decant clear liq. into beaker. Transfer 1 or 2 drops liq. (contg ca 5–10 μg LSD) to prepd indicator paper with eye dropper and let MeOH evap. Add 1 drop HCl and let paper stand, supported so that HCl does not touch any surface. If LSD is present, violet-red or violet-blue spot develops and slowly diffuses to edge of ring to form colored ring. Compare test with MeOH blank and LSD ref. soln in MeOH.

Test is sensitive to 1 μg LSD. Larger amt LSD gives faster reaction and more pronounced and more stable color ring.

36.091 Paper Chromatography

(Spot solns from (a) and (b) and chromatograph simultaneously on same chromatgc paper.)

Arrange chromatgc chamber for ascending chromatgy. To mobile solv. trough in chamber, add enough mobile solv. to develop chromatogram and equilibrate chamber with solv. vapor. Cover chamber and let equilibrate ca 15 min.

(a) *Paper chromatography of LSD.*—Prep. sample soln by extg ca 60 μg LSD from ground sample with 5 ml MeOH and filtering. Evap. ca one-half filtrate to dryness in 10–15 ml centrf. tube by warming on steam bath under gentle air stream. Wash sides of tube with 10 µl MeOH. Spot sep. 3 µl (10 µg LSD) concd sample soln and equiv. (10 µg) LSD ref. std MeOH soln on prepd chromatgc paper. Apply soln in portions (ca 0.5 µl) and let dry before reapplication; spot size should be <10 mm diam. Altho method is applicable to as much as 100 µg LSD, vol. ext spotted must be minimal.

After spotting is complete and spot is dry, apply enough immobile solv. (ca 5–10 µl) to cover spot. Spotting removes immobile solv.; it must be replenished to prevent streaking. Check adequacy of sample spot by comparing intensity of fluorescence with that of std under UV light. If sample spot fluoresces weakly, indicating insufficient LSD, overspot more sample ext from centrf. tube as above.

Place spotted paper in equilibrated chromatgc chamber and seal with tape. Develop chromatogram until mobile solv. reaches within ca 2″ of top of paper (ca ½ hr). Withdraw paper and let air-dry. Observe under UV light (long and short wavelength).

(b) *Paper chromatography of products of partial racemization of LSD by base.*—In 25 ml erlenmeyer, add remaining filtered sample soln from (a) and adjust vol. to ca 5 ml. Treat equiv. LSD ref. std soln similarly. Add equal vol. 1N NaOH, cover, and heat on steam bath 5 min. Remove from steam bath, cool, transfer to separator, and dil. with ca 20 ml H_2O. Ext LSD with 15 ml $CHCl_3$, wash $CHCl_3$ with 15 ml H_2O, and discard H_2O wash. Evap. $CHCl_3$ to dryness and dissolve residue in 10 µl MeOH as in (a). Spot and develop MeOH soln and degraded LSD ref. std soln as in (a).

Racemization, which produces iso-LSD, causes 2 spots to appear on paper. Iso-LSD has lower R_f value than LSD.

36.092 Determination

(Carry out assay as rapidly as possible and away from direct sunlight. Use freshly prepd std soln.)

Place accurately weighed portion powd sample in 50.0 ml alcohol and shake. Filter to remove insol. material, discarding first few ml filtrate. Take aliquot of filtrate contg ca 0.2 mg LSD and evap. almost to dryness under air current on steam bath with min. heat. Dissolve residue in several ml 0.1N HCl and transfer to separator with several portions 0.1N HCl to make total vol. ca 25 ml. Make soln alk. with NH_4OH. Ext LSD with four 15 ml portions $CHCl_3$. Evap. combined $CHCl_3$ ext to dryness with min. heat in air current. Dissolve residue in 10 ml 1% HOAc in alcohol.

Prep. std soln by accurately weighing LSD-25 std and dilg to 20 µg/ml with 1% alc. HOAc.

Scan sample and std solns from 400 to 200 nm and compare A_{max} (ca 312 nm), using 1% alc. HOAc as blank. Calc. as follows:

$$LSD\text{-}25 \ (mg/g) = (A/A') \times (C/W) \times 10$$

where A and A' are A_{max} of sample and std solns, resp.; C is concn of std in mg/ml; and W is g sample powder in aliquot filtrate taken.

Accurately weigh ≥5 mg (microbalance) USP Ergonovine Maleate Ref. Std, dissolve in 1% alc. HOAc, and dil. with 1% alc. HOAc to ca 20 µg/ml. Measure A between 400 and 200 nm. Calc. LSD concn, using A_{max} at ca 312 nm and following formula:

$$LSD\text{-}25 = (A/A') \times (C/W) \times 0.937 \times 10$$

Meperidine (Demerol®, Pethidine) (26)— Official Final Action

★ *Distillation Method* ★

36.093 *Apparatus*

500 ml r-b, short-neck flask to which is fitted adapter with attached separator (Ace Glass, Inc. No. 5270). Connect distg head (Scientific Glass Apparatus Co. No. J-1148), fitting this adapter to straight inner-tube, H_2O-cooled condenser by another adapter (Ace No. 5125). Third adapter attached to bottom of condenser dips below surface of liq. in 1 L erlenmeyer. All joints are ⊤ 24/40.

36.094 *Preparation of Sample*

Weigh ≥20 tablets and reduce to fine powder without appreciable loss.

36.095 *Determination*

Accurately weigh powder contg ca 100 mg meperidine and wash into 500 ml r-b flask with ca 25 ml H_2O. Add ca 1 g powd $CaCO_3$ to flask and connect to distn app. Place 1 L erlenmeyer contg 20 ml 0.02N H_2SO_4 under condenser so that adapter on end of condenser is below surface of acid. Add 100 ml H_2O to flask thru separator, and distill until ca 25 ml remains in flask. Without interrupting distn, add second 100 ml H_2O slowly enough so that distillate does not suck back into distn flask. Continue distn until this portion has distd over. Similarly, distill over third 100 ml H_2O. Then add 10 ml alcohol thru separator. When most of alcohol distills, add and distill 10 ml portion H_2O.

Disconnect condenser from distn app. and rinse inside of condenser and adapter that dipped into std acid, catching rinsings in receiving flask. Bring collected distillate to vigorous boil to remove any dissolved CO_2, cool, and titr. excess acid with 0.02N NaOH, using Me red. 1 ml 0.02N H_2SO_4 = 0.005676 g meperidine·HCl, $C_{15}H_{21}O_2N \cdot HCl$.

36.096   Extraction Method

Accurately weigh portion of powder, prepd as in 36.094, contg ca 0.1 g meperidine, and macerate 2 hr with 10 ml H_2O and 1 ml $1N$ H_2SO_4. Decant liq. thru small filter into separator. Macerate residue 20 min with 5 ml H_2O, filter thru same filter, and wash residue and filter with small portions of H_2O.

Sat. soln with NaCl; then add 5 ml $1N$ NaOH and ext with 25 ml and six 20 ml portions ether as in 36.001. Wash combined ether exts with two 5 ml portions H_2O; ext this H_2O with 10 ml ether and add this ether to main ether ext. Ext ether soln first with 20.0 ml $0.02N$ H_2SO_4, and then successively with 10 and 5 ml H_2O. Combine H_2SO_4 and H_2O exts in beaker and warm on H_2O bath until no ether odor is detected. Cool soln, and titr. excess acid with $0.02N$ NaOH, using Me red. 1 ml $0.02N$ $H_2SO_4 = 0.005676$ g meperidine.HCl, $C_{15}H_{21}O_2N.HCl$.

Methapyrilene in Expectorants (27)— Official Final Action

36.097   Reagent

Methapyrilene hydrochloride std soln.—0.015 mg methapyrilene.HCl/ml. Transfer 60 mg methapyrilene.HCl, accurately weighed, to 200 ml vol. flask. Dissolve in ca $0.1N$ H_2SO_4 and dil. to vol. with ca $0.1N$ H_2SO_4. Transfer 5 ml aliquot to 100 ml vol. flask and dil. to vol. with ca $0.1N$ H_2SO_4.

36.098   Determination

Pipet 10 ml sample into separator, make alk. with NH_4OH, and ext with four 20 ml portions $CHCl_3$. Combine $CHCl_3$ exts in 100 ml vol. flask and dil. to vol. with $CHCl_3$. Transfer aliquot contg 1–3 mg methapyrilene to small beaker and evap. just to dryness on steam bath with air current. Dissolve residue in ca $0.1N$ H_2SO_4, transfer to 100 ml vol. flask, and dil. to vol. with ca $0.1N$ H_2SO_4. Det. A of this soln and of std against ca $0.1N$ H_2SO_4 blank at 315 nm.

mg Methapyrilene.HCl/100 ml sample = $(A \times 1.5 \times 100 \times 10)/(A' \times$ vol. aliquot$)$, where A refers to sample and A' to std.

36.099   Neostigmine (Prostigmine®) (28)— Official Final Action

Weigh portion of powd sample equiv. to ca 0.06 g neostigmine bromide into 500 ml Kjeldahl flask. Add 200 ml H_2O, 25 ml NaOH $(1 + 1)$, few crystals of $Ba(OH)_2$ to prevent foaming, and several glass beads. Distill dimethylamine formed by alk. hydrolysis into 25.0 ml $0.02N$ H_2SO_4, collecting ≥ 150 ml distillate. Titr. excess H_2SO_4 with $0.02N$ NaOH, using Me red.

1 ml $0.02N$ $H_2SO_4 = 0.00606$ g neostigmine bromide, $C_{12}H_{19}BrO_2N_2$.

Norepinephrine (Arterenol) in Preparations of Epinephrine (Adrenalin) (29)—Official Final Action

36.100   Apparatus

(a) Chromatographic tube and tamping rod.—See 36.015.

(b) Hypodermic syringe.—1 ml without needle, graduated in 0.01 ml.

36.101   Reagents

(a) Diatomaceous earth.—See 36.016(c).

(b) Glass wool.—Pyrex No. 3950.

(c) Benzene.—Distill reagent grade benzene in all-glass app. Shake distillate with H_2O 2–3 min and filter benzene layer thru paper. Use this H_2O-satd solv. unless dry benzene is specified. (Caution: See 46.011, 46.039, 46.040, and 46.045.)

(d) Concentrated phosphate buffer.—pH 6. Dil. 50.0 ml $0.2M$ KH_2PO_4 soln, 45.010(b), and 5.64 ml $0.2M$ NaOH, 45.010(d), to 100 ml with H_2O.

(e) Iodine-potassium iodide soln.—Dissolve 2 g I and 6 g KI in H_2O, and dil. to 100 ml.

(f) Norepinephrine std soln.—0.100 mg norepinephrine base/ml. Dissolve 19.9 mg l-norepinephrine (levarterenol) bitartrate.H_2O in exactly 100 ml H_2O. Discard after 8 hr.

36.102   Preparation of Sample

(a) Aqueous solns of epinephrine.HCl containing bisulfite and chlorobutanol.—If soln is 0.1% with respect to "total epinephrine" (epinephrine + norepinephrine), pipet 30 ml sample into 125 ml separator provided with tightly fitting stopper and stopcock. If soln is more concd, use sample contg 30 mg "total epinephrine," and dil. to 30 ml with H_2O.

(b) Suspensions of epinephrine in oil.—Mix suspension by gentle swirling and agitation; add to separator accurately measured vol. contg ca 30 mg epinephrine and 25 ml pet ether, and swirl until oily base dissolves. Add 10 ml $0.05N$ H_2SO_4 and ext epinephrine by shaking 1 min. Drain aq. layer into 125 ml separator, and wash pet ether layer with two 10 ml portions H_2O. Add washes to acid ext, wash combined aq. layers with two 10 ml portions CCl_4, and discard CCl_4. Rinse stopper and mouth of separator with few drops H_2O and let rinsings drain into separator. Proceed as in 36.103, beginning "Add 2.10 g $NaHCO_3$ ..."

(c) Ointments of epinephrine bitartrate (petrolatum base).—Transfer to separator accurately weighed sample contg ca 60 mg epinephrine bitartrate. Add 25 ml benzene and swirl until ointment base dissolves. Proceed as in (b), beginning "Add 10 ml $0.05N$ H_2SO_4 ..." except if bisulfite is present, it must be removed with I as below before proceeding with acetylation.

36.103   *Acetylation*

(Caution: See **46.011, 46.040,** and **46.056.**)

Add 25 ml CCl_4 and shake vigorously to ext chlorobutanol. After layers sep. completely, drain and discard solv., and repeat extn with two 25 ml portions CCl_4. After each extn, drain as much solv. as possible. Rinse stopper and mouth of separator with few drops of H_2O, and let rinsings drain into separator. Add 4 drops starch indicator, **36.062(b)**; then, while swirling, destroy $NaHSO_3$ by adding I-KI soln, **(e)**, *dropwise* until soln remains blue. Immediately discharge blue color by adding $0.1N$ $Na_2S_2O_3$ dropwise. Add 2.10 g $NaHCO_3$ (prevent it from contacting wet mouth of separator) and swirl few sec to dissolve most of $NaHCO_3$. Immediately, using hypodermic syringe, rapidly inject into separator exactly 1 ml Ac_2O (prevent reagent from contacting mouth of funnel). Stopper separator at once and shake vigorously until evolution of CO_2 stops (ca 7–8 min). Release pressure as necessary by momentarily inverting separator and cautiously opening stopcock.

Let mixt. stand 5 min; then ext with six 30 ml portions $CHCl_3$. Filter each ext thru $CHCl_3$-washed compact pledget of absorbent cotton into beaker, and evap. combined exts to small vol. or to dryness on steam bath under air current. Quant. transfer residue with small portions $CHCl_3$ to tared 50 ml beaker and continue evapn until solv. is removed. Dry 30 min at 105°, let cool in desiccator, and weigh. Wt mixed amorphous triacetyl derivatives of epinephrine and norepinephrine $\times$ $0.5923 = E =$ "total epinephrine."

36.104   *Chromatographic Separation*
                        of Acetylation Product

(Caution: See **46.011, 46.039, 46.040,**
             46.045, and **46.056.**)

Place wad of glass wool in chromatgc tube and compress it tightly at juncture of tube and stem, using packing rod.

Place 10 g Celite 545 and ca 175 ml benzene in 250 ml beaker. While stirring vigorously and continuously, add 7.0 ml H_2O, drop by drop, to produce uniform solid phase. Transfer to chromatgc tube ca $\frac{1}{10}$ of the solid, under benzene, and compress it firmly and evenly with packing rod. While keeping column of benzene above solid in tube, add remainder of solid in beaker in ca 5 equal portions and compress each portion firmly and evenly before adding next. Properly prepd column is ca 65 mm high and permits flow of ca 2–4 ml benzene/min under head of 8 cm solv. With wad of absorbent cotton affixed to stiff wire, remove any solid adhering to tube above column. Keep layer of benzene above column until used.

To beaker contg mixt. of triacetyl derivatives add exactly 6 ml *dry* benzene. Warm gently and dissolve residue completely by stirring and swirling. Cover beaker with watch glass to retard evapn, and cool to room temp.

Remove supernatant benzene from tube by careful aspiration, pipet onto top of column accurately measured aliquot of soln of derivative equiv. to 20–25 mg total epinephrine, and immediately place graduated cylinder under tube. As soon as last of benzene soln is absorbed by column, rinse down wall of tube with three 2 ml portions benzene, delivered conveniently from pipet. Let each rinse be completely absorbed before adding next portion. Then carefully add benzene into tube to ht of ca 8 cm above top of column, and maintain level of the benzene with suitable constant level device. After 160 ml effluent (contg triacetylepinephrine) collects, thoroly rinse tip of tube with $CHCl_3$ and discard effluent and rinsings, or reserve for qual. tests.

Remove layer of benzene above column by aspiration, place clean receiver under tube, and let $CHCl_3$ pass thru column until 100 ml effluent (contg triacetylnorepinephrine) collects. Evap. effluent to dryness and transfer to 50 ml beaker, confining residue near bottom of beaker.

36.105   *Determination of Norepinephrine*

Add exactly 10 ml $0.50N$ HCl to residue of triacetylnorepinephrine, warm gently, and dissolve by stirring and rubbing with rubber policeman. Pour soln into g-s test tube (15 $\times$ 150 mm is convenient), place tube in boiling H_2O bath, and stopper loosely. After 5 min, stopper tightly and maintain 30 addnl min at 100°. Remove tube and cool to room temp., lifting stopper slightly from time to time to keep vac. from forming.

Mix contents thoroly and transfer 1 ml aliquot to another g-s test tube. Neutze acid by adding exactly 42 mg $NaHCO_3$. (Ensure that *all* $NaHCO_3$ is delivered to bottom of tube, and that none adheres to wall above acid layer.) After effervescence stops, add 1.5 ml H_2O and 2.5 ml buffer, **(d)**. Mix by swirling, and add 4 drops $0.1N$ I. Swirl, and after exactly 3 min (timed by stopwatch) from addn of I, add 6 drops $0.1N$ $Na_2S_2O_3$, stopper, and mix thoroly. Measure A at 520 nm, 3 ± 0.5 min after addn of $Na_2S_2O_3$ soln, in 1 cm cells against the pH 6 buffer blank in Beckman Model DU (or equiv.) spectrophtr.

Transfer 1.5 ml aliquot std soln to g-s test tube. Add 1 ml H_2O and 2.5 ml pH 6 buffer, **(d)**, and swirl. Develop color and measure A at 520 nm as above.

Calc. amt norepinephrine in sample originally taken for analysis, and from this value and E, **36.103**, calc. % norepinephrine in "total epinephrine."

Pamaquine (Plasmochin®) *(30)* —
Official Final Action

36.106   *Reagent*

Bromocresol purple soln.—Triturate 0.1 g bromocresol purple in agate mortar with 9 ml $0.02N$

NaOH. When dissolved, dil. with H_2O to 200 ml, and filter if necessary. Soln should be deep orange to red. If it is purple, addn of $\leqslant 0.5$ ml $0.02N$ acid should make it red. If it is yellow, addn of $\leqslant 0.5$ ml $0.02N$ alkali should make it red.

36.107 *Determination*

Weigh powd sample equiv. to ca 0.2 g pamaquine naphthoate and transfer to 100 ml beaker. Add 10 ml H_2O and 5 ml HCl $(1+3)$, and stir until powder is thoroly wet. Add 20 ml H_2O and stir again. Filter thru Selas crucible or gooch, and wash with several portions H_2O until filtrate is colorless.

Completely transfer filtrate to separator, make alk. with NH_4OH, and ext with several portions $CHCl_3$. (Test for complete extn by evapg sep. ext to dryness and adding $1N$ acid; yellow color should not appear. If ext is yellow, return it to separator and re-ext.) Wash $CHCl_3$ exts with several ml H_2O, filter thru cotton, evap. to ca 5 ml, and then add 25 ml $0.02N$ acid. Continue heating, and when bulk of $CHCl_3$ evaps, stir with glass rod to facilitate removal of last droplets $CHCl_3$, avoiding prolonged heating of soln. Cool, and titr. to purple tint with $0.02N$ alkali, using bromocresol purple. 1 ml $0.02N$ acid = 0.01408 g pamaquine naphthoate, $C_{19}H_{29}ON_3.C_{23}H_{16}O_6$, or 0.00631 g pamaquine base, $C_{19}H_{29}ON_3$.

★ **Phenylephrine Hydrochloride (31)—** ★
Official First Action

36.108 *Apparatus*

(a) *Spectrophotometer.*—Suitable for measurement in range 250–350 nm.

(b) *Chromatographic tube.*—20 × 400 mm or similar dimensions equipped with glass or Teflon stopcock, and medium or coarse porosity fritted glass disk or glass wool plug. Do not use stopcock grease to lubricate.

36.109 *Reagents*

(a) *Washed chloroform.*—Wash $CHCl_3$ with H_2O to remove alcohol. Remove excess H_2O by filtration thru cotton or paper.

(b) *Acetylating soln.*—Mix 2 ml Ac_2O with 25 ml $CHCl_3$, (a). (*Caution:* Prep. just prior to use. Acetic anhydride decomposes on standing in moist air. Use fresh bottle of Ac_2O or bottle of known quality.)

(c) *Diatomaceous earth.*—See **36.016(c)**. If Celite 545 is used, acid-wash as follows: Wash with HCl $(1+2)$ until no more yellow appears in eluate; then wash with H_2O until eluate is neut., followed by alcohol, and dry at 105° until odor of alcohol is no longer present.

(d) *Sodium borate.*—Powd $Na_2B_4O_7.7H_2O$ or $Na_2B_4O_7.10H_2O$.

(e) *Alcoholic potassium hydroxide.*—Colorless; ca $1N$. Dissolve 5.6 g KOH in 100 ml alcohol.

(f) *Phenylephrine hydrochloride std soln.*—Prep. ca 1 mg/ml aq. soln, accurately detd, using phenylephrine.HCl, USP, previously dried 2 hr at 105°. For working std, dil. 5 ml std soln to 100 ml by adding 5 ml ca $1N$ alc. KOH and dilg to vol. with H_2O.

36.110 *Preparation of Sample*

(a) *Tablets or powder.*—Dissolve portion of finely ground material in enough H_2O to give final concn of 1 mg phenylephrine.HCl/ml. Filter thru S&S 589 Blue Ribbon paper or equiv. into g-s erlenmeyer, discarding first 5 ml filtrate. Proceed as in **36.111**, beginning, "Prep. layered column..."

(b) *Solutions.*—Dil. aliquot of soln with H_2O to final concn of 1 mg phenylephrine.HCl/ml. Proceed as in **36.111**, beginning, "Prep. layered column..." Remove any alcohol present in soln by evapn from 5 ml aliquot taken for analysis.

36.111 *Determination*
(*Caution: See* **46.011, 46.040,** *and* **46.056.**)

Prep. layered column with tamped layer of 5 g Celite on bottom. (Celite may be wet with few ml $CHCl_3$, (a), to facilitate packing.) Thoroly mix 5 ml sample soln with 1 g Na borate in 250 ml beaker, using flat spatula. Add 5 g Celite and mix again. Add mixt. in portions to column and tamp after each addn. Scrub beaker with Celite-H_2O $(1+1)$ until clean and add to column. Tamp column and add glass wool overlay. (*Caution:* Once column is prepd, do not stop detn until acetylated derivative is eluted.)

Pass 150 ml washed $CHCl_3$ thru column. Collect last 25 ml eluate in sep. beaker and evap. to dryness to det. if all $CHCl_3$-sol. compds have been completely eluted. Continue washing until no residue is obtained. (Appearance of residue after column has been washed with 200 ml $CHCl_3$ may be due to Celite. Check by washing 10 g Celite with 200 ml $CHCl_3$ and evapg last 50 ml eluate to dryness. If residue is found to be due to Celite, stop analysis, and repeat analysis with acid-washed Celite prepd as in (c).) Let $CHCl_3$ drain into glass wool overlay and stop column flow. Place clean 250 ml beaker under column and collect all column eluate from this point on. Add 25 ml acetylating soln to column and let drain thru into glass wool overlay. Stop column flow 10 min; then elute acetylated phenylephrine from column with 150 ml $CHCl_3$.

Evap. eluate to small vol. on steam bath with aid of air current and transfer quant. to 100 ml beaker, using $CHCl_3$. Evap. to dryness. If residue appears to be wet, add small portions ether and evap. to dryness several times. Add 5 ml ca $1N$ alc. KOH to dry residue, cover beaker with watch glass, and heat on steam bath 30 min. Cool, and wash watch glass with H_2O into beaker. Quant.

transfer contents to 100 ml vol. flask with H_2O, and dil. to vol. with H_2O.

Record A of std and sample solns between 350 and 250 nm against ref. soln of 5 ml ca $1N$ alc. KOH dild to 100 ml with H_2O. Det. net A of each soln at ca 291 nm, using baseline technic as follows: Draw perpendicular from peak at 291 nm to zero A line and draw straight line between minima at ca 318 and ca 262 nm; distance between peak ht and intersection of perpendicular with line joining two minima = net A.

(Net A of sample soln/net A of std soln) $\times$ mg phenylephrine.HCl in 100 ml working std = mg phenylephrine.HCl in sample aliquot.

Colorimetric Method (32)—Official Final Action

(Not applicable in presence of tetracycline, acetaminophen, salicylamide, phenolic compds, and Zn salts)

36.112   Reagents

Prep. (a), (b), and (d)(2) fresh on day of use.

(a) *4-Aminoantipyrine hydrochloride soln.*—(Eastman) 3% in H_2O.

(b) *Potassium ferricyanide soln.*—4% $K_3Fe(CN)_6$ in H_2O.

(c) *Sodium borate soln.*—2% $Na_2B_4O_7.10H_2O$ in H_2O.

(d) *Phenylephrine hydrochloride std solns.*—(1) *Stock soln.*—Approx. 0.25 mg/ml. Weigh ca 125 mg phenylephrine.HCl to nearest 0.1 mg into 50 ml vol. flask and dil. to vol. with H_2O. Soln is stable several months under refrigeration. (2) *Working std soln.*—Approx. 0.025 mg/ml. Dil. 5 ml stock soln to 50 ml with H_2O.

36.113   Preparation of Samples

(a) *Tablets and capsules.*—Weigh $\geqslant$20 tablets or capsules and det. av. wt/unit. Grind tablets to powder and mix, or mix contents of capsules. Weigh aliquot contg ca 12.5 mg phenylephrine.HCl into 50 ml vol. flask, add ca 30 ml H_2O, and shake vigorously. Dil. to vol., shake again, and filter if soln is not clear.

(b) *Powders for oral suspensions, oral suspensions, sirups, solns, etc.*—Reconstitute powders for oral suspension as directed on label or use solns, sirups, and oral suspensions as is. Transfer aliquot contg ca 12.5 mg phenylephrine.HCl into 50 ml vol. flask and proceed as in (a).

36.114   Determination

(Reaction is time dependent; assay samples one at a time.)

Transfer 2 ml aliquot sample soln to 50 ml vol. flask (omit sample for reagent blank), add 1.0 ml 4% $K_3Fe(CN)_6$ soln, and swirl. Dil. to ca 48 ml with $Na_2B_2O_7$ soln and add 1.0 ml aminoantipyrine soln. Immediately dil. to vol. with $Na_2B_2O_7$

soln and shake vigorously. Immediately det. A of soln at 490 nm against reagent blank, in matched 1 cm cells.

Calc. sample concn, $S = CFA/A'$, where C = mg std/ml, F = diln factor, and A and A' refer to sample and std, resp.

Report mg phenylephrine.HCl/tablet, capsule, or vol. liq. dose.

Ion-Pair Column Partition Method (33)— Official First Action

(Not applicable in presence of phenolic nitrogenous bases)

36.115   Apparatus and Reagents

(a) *Recording spectrophotometer.*—With matched 1 cm cells.

(b) *Chromatographic tubes.*—Chromaflex (Kontes, or equiv.) 20 cm $\times$ 22 mm id, and tamping rod.

(c) *Phosphate buffer.*—pH 5.80$\pm$0.05. Mix 1 vol. $1M$ K_2HPO_4 (174 g/L) and 9 vols $1M$ KH_2PO_4 (136 g/L) and adjust pH with either component.

(d) *Phosphate-citrate buffer.*—pH 5.10$\pm$0.05. Mix 2 vols $1M$ K_2HPO_4 and 1 vol. $1M$ citric acid (192 g $C_6H_8O_7$ or 210 g $C_6H_8O_7.H_2O/L$) and adjust pH with either component.

(e) *Diatomaceous earth.*—Celite 545, acid-washed.

(f) *Di-(2-ethylhexyl) phosphoric acid (DEHP) soln.*—Reagent grade (K & K Laboratories, Inc). 2.4% v/v in H_2O-satd ether. Prep. fresh daily.

(g) *Sulfuric acid.*—0.1N, ether-satd. Prep. fresh daily.

(h) *Chloroform and ether.*—H_2O-satd. Prep. fresh daily and use thruout detn.

(i) *Phenylephrine hydrochloride std solns.*—(1) *Stock soln.*—1 mg/ml. Accurately weigh ca 100 mg phenylephrine.HCl USP Ref. Std in 100 ml vol. flask and dil. to vol. with H_2O. (2) *Working soln.*—0.04 mg/ml. Dil. 2 ml stock soln to 50 ml with 0.1N NaOH and use to obtain spectrum between 200 and 400 nm (or as far as instrument permits) along with sample detn.

36.116   Preparation of Samples

(a) *Samples containing about 1 mg phenylephrine.HCl/ml sirup.*—Pipet 4.0 ml pH 5.8 buffer into 10 ml vol. flask. Carefully add sirup to vol. Do *not* wet flask above mark.

(b) *Samples containing more than 1 mg phenylephrine.HCl/ml sirup.*—Dil. to 1 mg/ml and proceed as in (a).

(c) *Tablets.*—Weigh ground sample contg ca 2 mg phenylephrine into 50 ml beaker. If components of tablets are H_2O-sol., add 2 ml H_2O, warm slightly to dissolve, and add 1 ml pH 5.8 buffer. If some components are not H_2O-sol. (e.g., acetaminophen), add 1 ml dimethylsulfoxide, warm to dissolve, and then add 2 ml pH 5.8 buffer. For tablets contg antacids (e.g., $Mg(OH)_2$ and $Al(OH)_3$) heat powd sample contg ca 2 mg phenylephrine with 5 ml alcohol and 1 ml HCl to dissolve alk. material; add 10 ml *n*-butanol and evap. to dryness. Dissolve residue in 1 ml dimethylsulfoxide and add 2 ml pH 5.8 buffer.

(d) *Capsules.*—Take portion of contents contg ca 2 mg phenylephrine and proceed as in (c). Grind sample if necessary.

36.117 *Determination*

Pack small glass wool plug in base of chromatgc tube as support. Transfer mixt. of 1 g Celite with 0.8 ml pH 5.1 buffer to tube and tamp to uniform mass. Mix 4 g Celite with 3.0 ml aliquot prepd sample and carefully transfer directly above pH 5.1 layer, tamping gently. Dry-wash beaker with 1 g Celite, add to column, and tamp. Cover with small glass wool plug. Pass 75 ml $CHCl_3$ thru column followed by 125 ml ether and discard eluates. Place 125 ml separator contg ca 20 ml $0.1N$ H_2SO_4 as receiver under column. Elute column with 50 ml DEHP-ether soln and then with 25 ml ether, collecting in same separator. Shake separator and transfer aq. phase to 50 ml vol. flask contg 6 ml $1N$ NaOH. Re-ext ether with 15 ml $0.1N$ H_2SO_4. Combine exts and dil. to vol. with H_2O. Obtain spectrum between 200 and 400 nm on same day as elution.

36.118 *Calculations*

Det. corrected A (ΔA) on both std and sample as follows: Construct baseline representing background A extension obtained from 400 to ca 250 nm. (Constructed baseline A value at wavelength of max. A (ca 290 nm) is designated as A_B.) Subtract A_B from total A_{max} observed at wavelength peak. For std, calc. $a = \Delta A/bc$, where b = cell pathlength (1 cm), and c = concn in g/L.

For samples, calc. $c = (\Delta A \times F)/ab$, where F = diln factor.

Report mg phenylephrine.HCl/tablet, capsule, or vol. liq. dose.

Phenylephrine Hydrochloride, Chlorpheniramine Maleate, and Codeine (34)—Official First Action

36.119 *Standard Solutions*

(a) *Codeine std soln.*—Prep. soln of codeine salt in ca $0.1N$ HCl contg 84 μg codeine/ml. If codeine salt of known purity is not available, ext codeine from its salt as in **36.011**.

(b) *Phenylephrine std soln.*—Prep. soln of phenylephrine.HCl in ca $0.1N$ HCl contg 40 μg phenylephrine/ml.

(c) *Chlorpheniramine std soln.*—Prep. soln of chlorpheniramine maleate in ca $0.1N$ HCl contg 16 μg base/ml.

36.120 *Preparation of Sample*

Prep. sample and columns as in **36.017**, except use $1N$ HCl in place of $1N$ HNO_3 in prepg column II.

36.121 *Determination*

(Use H_2O-satd $CHCl_3$ thruout where $CHCl_3$ is specified. *Caution: See* **46.011, 46.022, 46.040, 46.052, 46.056.**)

Arrange columns so that effluent from I flows into II and then into III. Pass 150 ml $CHCl_3$ over columns. Discard $CHCl_3$ and sep. columns.

(a) *Phenylephrine.*—Remove phenylephrine from column I (NaOH column) with 2 ml Ac_2O in 5 ml $CHCl_3$, followed by 95 ml of 1% soln of Ac_2O in $CHCl_3$. Evap. eluate to dryness, add several small portions $CHCl_3$, and evap. to remove Ac_2O. Add 5 ml colorless $0.5N$ alc. KOH, cover beaker with watch glass, and saponify acetylphenylephrine by heating 15 min on steam bath. Acidify with HCl, dissolve residue with warming, and dil. with H_2O to calcd concn of ca 40 μg/ml in vol. flask. Filter if not clear. Det. phenylephrine.HCl spectrophtric at wavelength of max. A (ca 272 nm). Compare with std. Scan spectrum from 320 to 230 nm.

Alternatively, dil. alk. saponified soln with H_2O to calcd concn of ca 40 μg/ml in vol. flask. Det. phenylephrine.HCl spectrophtric at wavelength of max. A (ca 291 nm). Compare with std contg ca 40 μg/ml in H_2O and alc. KOH. Make alc. KOH concn same as that of sample. Scan spectrum from 350 to 250 nm.

(b) *Chlorpheniramine.*—Remove chlorpheniramine from column II (HCl column) with 2 ml redistd triethylamine, **36.016(a)**, in 5 ml $CHCl_3$, followed by 95 ml 1% soln of triethylamine in $CHCl_3$. Evap. eluate just to dryness, take up residue in ca $0.1N$ HCl, and dil. to calcd concn of ca 16 μg/ml with ca $0.1N$ HCl. Det. chlorpheniramine maleate spectrophtric at wavelength of max. A (ca 265 nm). Compare with std. Scan spectrum from 320 to 230 nm.

(c) *Codeine.*—Remove codeine from column III (H_2SO_4 column) with 2 ml redistd triethylamine, **36.016(a)**, in 5 ml $CHCl_3$, followed by 95 ml 1% soln of triethylamine in $CHCl_3$. Evap. eluate just to dryness. Dissolve residue in ca $0.1N$ HCl with warming, and dil. to calcd concn of ca 84 μg/ml with ca $0.1N$ HCl. Det. codeine salt spectrophtric at wavelength of max. A (ca 285 nm). Compare with std. Scan spectrum from 320 to 250 nm.

Phenethylamines (35)—Official Final Action

(Applicable to amphetamine, methamphetamine, mephentermine, phenylpropylmethylamine (Vonedrine®), and ephedrine)

36.122 *Apparatus*

Spectrophotometer.—Capable of isolating bands ⩽1 nm in region 250–270 nm; with 1 cm cells of quartz or fused Si (preferably matched pair).

36.123 *Preparation of Standard Solution*

Accurately weigh 500–700 mg phenethylamine salt of known purity, transfer to 100 ml vol. flask, and dissolve in 0.1N H_2SO_4. Dil. to vol. with the H_2SO_4 and mix well.

36.124 *Determination*

Accurately weigh powd sample contg 25–50 mg amine base and transfer to 40–50 ml g-s centrf. tube contg 3–3.5 g NaCl and 6–7 glass beads. Dissolve sample by adding 5 ml 1N H_2SO_4, and swirl gently to aid escape of any liberated CO_2. Test for acidity with litmus paper, adding more acid if necessary. Pipet in 25 ml $CHCl_3$ and 4 ml 2N NaOH, stopper securely, and shake 3–5 min. To second 40–50 ml centrf. tube contg 3–3.5 g NaCl and 6–7 glass beads add 10 ml std soln, **36.123**. Swirl to dissolve salt, pipet in 25 ml $CHCl_3$ and 1 ml 2N NaOH, stopper securely, and shake 3–5 min.

Centrf. tubes at 1500–1800 rpm 3–5 min. Withdraw 10 ml clear $CHCl_3$ layer by closing upper end of 10 ml pipet with index finger while lowering tip thru aq. layer. Wipe off outer portion of pipet, and transfer 10 ml $CHCl_3$ layer to second 40–50 ml centrf. tube contg 25 ml 0.1N H_2SO_4 and 6–7 glass beads. Stopper securely, shake, and centrf. as above.

Prep. acid blank soln by shaking 25 ml 0.1N H_2SO_4 with 3–5 ml $CHCl_3$ and centrfg to obtain clear acid soln. Read *A* of portions of clear acid soln obtained from aliquot of std and sample soln against acid blank prepd above in ref. cell, using 1 cm cells at 0.5 nm intervals in range 252–255 for first minima, 256–258 for maxima, and 260–262 for second minima. (Use same slit width for sample and std solns. Best results are obtained with slit widths of 0.4–0.7 mm when using Beckman DU.)

36.125 *Calculations*

Calc. *A* difference (Δ*A*) between *A* at maxima and *A* of 2 minima: $\Delta A = A_{max} - 0.5(A_{min\,1} + A_{min\,2})$.

Calc. absorptivity differential (Δ*a*) produced by 1 g/L (1 mg/ml) of std amine base or salt: $\Delta a_{std} = \Delta A_{std} \times 100/wt\ std$, where $\Delta A_{std} = A$ difference for std soln; 100 = ml std soln measured; and wt = mg std in aliquot measured.

Mg amine/unit of sample

$$= \frac{(\Delta A_{sample} \times 25 \times 25 \times av.\ wt\ of\ unit\ in\ mg)}{(\Delta a_{std} \times 10 \times wt\ sample\ in\ mg)}$$

**Phenylpropanolamine Hydrochloride—
Official Final Action
*Chromatographic Method (36)***

36.126 *Apparatus*

See **36.015**.

36.127 *Reagent*

(a) *Chloroform.*—*A* at 258.5 nm, measured against H_2O blank, <0.200.

(b) *Diatomaceous earth.*—See **36.016(c)**.

36.128 *Preparation of Tube with Wash Layer*

Fix pledget of glass wool in stem of chromatgc tube above constriction. Clamp tube vertically. In small beaker mix 3 g Celite No. 545 and 2 ml H_2O. Transfer to tube with metal spatula and press down evenly with packing rod.

36.129 *Determination*

(a) *Capsules and tablets.*—To 150 ml beaker transfer accurately weighed amt of powd sample contg ca 50 mg phenylpropanolamine.HCl. Add 5 ml NH_4OH (1 + 4) and mix by gentle swirling. Add 5 g Celite and mix with metal spatula. Transfer to tube without loss thru powder funnel, in 4 or more portions, pressing down each portion evenly with packing rod. When removing funnel from tube each time, tap it lightly in tube to remove loosely adhering particles; then hang it in beaker of such size that it does not touch bottom. After using packing rod, scrape off most of adhering material into tube with spatula, and tap rod and spatula over mouth of tube. When laying down implements, place them in such position that their ends do not touch anything. Finally use smooth, intact rubber policeman to sweep material from beaker and funnel into tube. Rub beaker, spatula, and packing rod with three ca 1 g portions Celite, sweeping each portion thru funnel into tube, using rubber policeman. Press down each portion with packing rod.

Place 100 ml vol. flask in receiving position. Wash down inside of tube with $CHCl_3$, adding enough (ca 20 ml) to moisten column and produce only few drops of eluate. Elute with 95 ml $CHCl_3$, wash tip of tube with little $CHCl_3$, and dil. to vol. with $CHCl_3$. Measure *A* at 258.5 nm, 2–5 min after pouring into silica cell, against portion of same $CHCl_3$ used for elution.

To 150 ml beaker transfer ca 50 mg pure phenylpropanolamine.HCl, accurately weighed. Proceed as with sample, beginning "Add 5 ml NH_4OH (1 + 4) ...." Det. *A* of sample and std eluates at ca same time, on same setting of wavelength dial. Use same cell for both eluates, and same cell for both blanks. Calc. phenylpropanolamine.HCl content.

(b) *Aqueous solns.*—Prep. tube with wash layer as in **36.128**. Into 150 ml beaker pipet vol. sample contg ca 50 mg phenylpropanolamine.HCl, or pipet 10 ml, whichever is less. Add 1 ml NH_4OH and mix by gentle swirling. Add number of g Celite equal to total number ml of liq. and mix with metal spatula. Proceed as in (a), beginning "Transfer to tube without loss ..."

Extraction Method (37)

36.130 *Determination*

Proceed as in **36.124–36.125**.

36.131 ★ **Physostigmine (Eserine) in** ★ **Ointments (38)—Official Final Action**

See 32.089, 10th ed.

36.132 Physostigmine Salicylate in Tablets— Official Final Action

See 36.011.

36.133 Pilocarpine Hydrochloride in Tablets —Official Final Action

See 36.011.

Procaine—Official Final Action

36.134 *Qualitative Tests*

See Microchemical Tests, 36.525–36.528.

Quantitative Methods

36.135 *Method I (39)*

(Dets as procaine any *p*-aminobenzoic acid formed by decomposition)

Dissolve amt sample contg ca 0.1 g procaine.HCl in 5 ml H_2O in 50 ml beaker. Add 25 ml $0.1N$ NaOH and heat on steam bath 25 min. Cool and transfer soln to 500 ml g-s flask. Add 50 ml std KBr-KBrO$_3$ soln, **36.208**, dil. with H_2O to 250 ml, add 10 ml HCl, and stopper immediately to avoid loss of Br. Shake occasionally and let stand 2 hr at room temp., keeping flask tightly stoppered. (Large excess of Br, as shown by bright yellow soln, must be present.) Quickly add 10 ml 20% KI soln, stopper, and shake flask. Let stand 15 min, shaking occasionally. Titr. excess I with $0.1N$ Na$_2$S$_2$O$_3$, using starch indicator, **6.004(f)**. Titr. to disappearance of blue, disregarding color that reappears on standing. 1 ml $0.1N$ KBr-KBrO$_3$ = 0.00455 g procaine.HCl, $C_{13}H_{20}O_2N_2$.HCl.

36.136 *Method II*

(Dets only undecomposed procaine)

See 36.011.

36.137 ★ ***Method III (40)*** ★

(Applicable in presence of chlorobutanol, cocaine, codeine, heroin, lactose, and morphine)

Distn into excess std acid and back-titrn. *See* 32.096, 10th ed.

Pyrilamine in Cough Sirup (27)— Official Final Action

36.138 *Reagent*

Pyrilamine std soln.—0.015 mg pyrilamine maleate/ml. Transfer 150 mg pyrilamine maleate to 500 ml vol. flask, dissolve in ca $0.1N$ H_2SO_4, and dil. to vol. with ca $0.1N$ H_2SO_4. Transfer 5 ml aliquot to 100 ml vol. flask and dil. to vol. with ca $0.1N$ H_2SO_4.

36.139 *Determination of Pyrilamine*

Proceed as for detn of methapyrilene, **36.098**, but measure A at 314 nm. mg Pyrilamine maleate/

100 ml sample = $(A \times 100 \times 1.5 \times 10)/(A' \times$ vol. aliquot), where $A = A$ of sample and $A' = A$ of std.

Quinacrine Hydrochloride (Atabrine®)

Volumetric Method (41)—Official Final Action

36.140 *Reagents*

(a) *Sodium acetate-acetic acid mixture.*—Dissolve 2.5 g NaOAc.3H$_2$O and 1 ml HOAc in enough H_2O to make 45 ml.

(b) *Dilute hydrochloric acid.*—Dil. 15 ml HCl to 80 ml with H_2O.

(c) *Potassium iodide soln.*—Dissolve 16.5 g KI in H_2O and dil. to 100 ml.

36.141 *Determination*

Transfer accurately weighed sample contg ca 0.25 g quinacrine.HCl to 100 ml vol. flask with aid of 45 ml NaOAc-HOAc mixt. Shake thoroly to dissolve quinacrine.HCl. Let settle and add 50.0 ml $0.1N$ K$_2$Cr$_2$O$_7$. Dil. to vol. with H_2O and mix well. Let stand 10–15 min and filter thru dry paper, rejecting first 15 ml filtrate. Measure 50.0 ml filtrate into g-s flask. Add 80 ml dil. HCl and 20 ml KI soln. Stopper flask and mix by gentle swirling. Let stand 5 min and titr. liberated I with $0.1N$ Na$_2$S$_2$O$_3$, adding starch indicator as end point nears. 1 ml $0.1N$ K$_2$Cr$_2$O$_7$ = 0.00848 g C$_{23}$H$_{30}$OClN$_3$.2HCl.2H$_2$O.

Fluorometric Method (42)—Official First Action

(*Caution: See* **46.008**.)

36.142 *Apparatus*

Spectrophotofluorometer.—(Aminco-Bowman, or equiv.) with 1 cm cell path, Xe lamp, slit position 3, excitation wavelength 420 nm, meter multiplier 0.01, and sensitivity to produce 80% fluorescence intensity (F) for std soln.

36.143 *Reagent*

Quinacrine hydrochloride std soln.—0.00050 mg/ml. Weigh 5.0 mg USP Quinacrine.HCl in 1 L vol. flask and dil. to vol. with H_2O. Mix well and dil. 10.0 ml to 100 ml with $0.1N$ HCl. Alternatively, weigh 50.0 mg quinacrine.HCl into 1 L vol. flask and dil. to vol. with H_2O. Mix well and dil. 10.0 ml to 1 L with $0.1N$ HCl. Prep. fresh daily.

36.144 *Preparation of Sample*

(a) *Tablets and powders.*—Weigh amt of well mixed or well ground sample contg 100 mg quinacrine.HCl into 200 ml vol. flask. Dil. to vol. with $0.1N$ HCl, mix 2 min, and filter if necessary. Dil. 10.0 ml clear sample soln to 1 L with H_2O and mix. Finally dil. 10 ml to 100 ml with $0.1N$ HCl to obtain sample soln.

(b) *Liquids.*—Pipet accurately measured sample contg ca 100 mg quinacrine.HCl into 200 ml vol. flask. Proceed as in (a), beginning "Dil. to vol. with $0.1N$ HCl, . . ."

36.145   *Determination*

Adjust spectrophotofluorometer to ca 80% fluorescence intensity (F) at 500 nm with std soln. Transfer ca 3 ml sample soln to 10×10 mm clean cell and read $\% F$, using 0.1N HCl as blank.

Calc. as follows:

Liqs: $200{,}000 \times C \times (F_u/F_s) \times (1/V) = $ mg quinacrine.HCl/ml.

Solids: $200{,}000 \times C \times (F_u/F_s) \times (100/W) = \%$ by wt quinacrine.HCl, where $C = $ mg/ml std soln; F_u and F_s, resp., = fluorescence of sample and std solns at 500 nm, each corrected for blank; $W = $ mg sample; and $V = $ ml sample.

36.146   *Identification*

Set emission wavelength monochromator at wavelength of max. fluorescence, i.e., 500 nm. Scan std and sample solns used for quantitation with excitation wavelength monochromator from 200 to 750 nm.

Use same instrument parameters as for quantitation except set sensitivity at ca 40. Sample and std spectra exhibit identical max. and min.

Quinine—Official Final Action
Spectrophotometric Method (43)

36.147   *Reagent*

Quinine std soln.—Recrystallize quinine twice from benzene and dry to constant wt at 100°. Prep. soln contg 5.0 mg of this anhyd. quinine in 100 ml 0.1N HCl. (Keeps indefinitely.)

36.148   *Determination*

(a) *In presence of compounds which have no absorption in HCl soln at 347.5 nm.* (These compds include strychnine, atropine, ephedrine, caffeine, acetylsalicylic acid, acetanilid, acetophenetidin, camphor, phenolphthalein, glycerol, alcohols; most green, blue, and red dyes; and sugars; all of which are frequently found in prepns contg quinine.)— Accurately weigh or measure sample contg ca 0.1 g quinine and transfer to 1 L vol. flask. Dissolve in 25 ml HCl $(1 + 2)$ and dil. to vol. so that final concn is ca 0.1N in HCl. Filter soln if not perfectly clear. Pipet aliquot contg 2–5 mg quinine into 100 ml vol. flask and dil. to vol. with 0.1N HCl. Det. A relative to blank of 0.1N HCl at 347.5 nm, and A' of std soln relative to same blank.

mg Quinine (anhyd.) in aliquot $= 5.0A/A'$.

(b) *Applicable in presence of ferric compounds, such as elixir of iron, quinine, and strychnine.*— Proceed as in (a), but add 10 ml H_3PO_4 to soln in 100 ml flask before dilg to vol. Std soln should contain 10 ml H_3PO_4/100 ml, and blanks should consist of 0.1N HCl contg 10 ml H_3PO_4/100 ml.

(c) *Applicable in presence of interfering substances.*—Before detg quinine by A at 347.5 nm, sep. it from following compds: Aloin, podophyllin, anthraquinone derivatives, other cinchona alkaloids, and yellow dyes. These absorb light in region of 347.5 nm.

36.149   Quinine Ethylcarbonate (44)—
Official Final Action

(*Caution: See* **46.011, 46.040,** and **46.056.**)

Weigh amt powd sample equiv. to ca 0.065 g alkaloid and transfer to 125 ml erlenmeyer. Add 5 ml alcohol and 15 ml 0.5N NaOH. Place small funnel in neck of flask and heat on steam bath 10 min. Transfer soln to separator. Rinse flask with small portions H_2O, followed by small portions HCl $(1 + 3)$, and add rinsings to soln in separator. Acidify soln with the HCl and then make alk. with NH_4OH. Ext with four 25 ml portions $CHCl_3$. Wash combined $CHCl_3$ exts with 5 ml H_2O and filter thru cotton pledget into weighed beaker. Evap. to dryness on steam bath, add 5 ml alcohol, and evap. alcohol. Dry 1 hr at 100° and weigh. Dissolve amorphous alkaloid in 5 ml neut. alcohol, and titr. with 0.02N H_2SO_4 to yellow color, using 2 drops bromocresol purple, **36.106.** Heat on steam bath until most of alcohol is expelled, adding, if necessary, enough 0.02N H_2SO_4 to maintain acid reaction. 1 ml 0.02N $H_2SO_4 = $ 0.00649 g anhyd. quinine, $C_{20}H_{24}O_2N_2$.

Elixirs of Iron, Quinine, and Strychnine
Method I (45)—Official Final Action

36.150   *Apparatus*

(a) *Chromatographic tube.*—Corning Glass Works No. 38450, or equiv., 20×400 mm, with coarse fritted disk. If unavailable, use plain chromatgc tube of similar dimensions with retentive cotton pad.

(b) *Packing rod.*—See **36.015(b).**

(c) *Test tube.*—25×200 mm, Corning No. 7940 or equiv., accurately marked at 25 ml.

36.151   *Reagents*

(a) *Diatomaceous earth.*—See **36.016(c).**

(b) *Washed ether.*—Vigorously shake equal vols H_2O and ether 2 min and discard H_2O. Repeat washing twice and filter ether thru cotton.

(c) *Washed chloroform.*—Prep. in same manner as washed ether. Do not use washed $CHCl_3$ after 1 week. Keep in dark, or in amber bottles.

(d) *Purified cotton.*—Purify absorbent cotton by washing with several portions each of ether and $CHCl_3$, and drying.

(e) *Amalgamated zinc.*—Mix 20 g "30-mesh" Zn with 8 g $HgCl_2$ and then quickly add 20 ml H_2O. Intermittently stir mixt. ca 5 min, pour off aq. phase, and wash amalgam with H_2O until most of soft amalgam is washed off as fine dark suspension. Dry amalgamated Zn in air, break up any clumps, and mix.

(f) *Strychnine std soln.*—10 µg/ml. Accurately weigh 50 mg strychnine previously dried 1 hr at 100° and dissolve and dil. to 250 ml with ca 0.1N HCl. Transfer 10 ml to 200 ml vol. flask, slowly add 10 ml HCl, cool, and dil. to vol. with HCl (1 + 1). (Strychnine soln in 0.1N HCl will keep ⩾1 year; diln in HCl (1 + 1) should not be used after 3 days.)

(g) *Quinine std soln.*—50 µg/ml. Accurately weigh 100 mg pure quinine previously dried 1 hr at 125° and dissolve and dil. to 200 ml with ca 0.1N HCl. To 10 ml of this soln, add 10 ml H_3PO_4, and dil. to 100 ml with 0.1N HCl.

36.152   Preparation of Chromatographic Column

Cover fritted disk with ca ¼–⅜″ layer (after tamping) purified cotton (ca 0.4 g). Prep. "wash" layer by mixing 1 g Celite and 1 ml H_2O until all H_2O is absorbed and powder is fluffy. Transfer to chromatgc tube and press down lightly with packing rod. Prep. "trap" layer by mixing 3 g Celite and 3 ml 2N HCl until uniform, and transfer in ca 2 equal portions, pressing down each portion lightly with packing rod.

36.153   Preparation of Sample

Evap. 10 ml Elixir of Iron, Quinine, and Strychnine in 250 ml beaker on steam bath. (Evap. elixirs contg nonvolatile solvs—glycerol, propylene glycol, etc.—to sirupy residue; evap. elixirs contg volatile solvs to dryness and dissolve residue in 4 ml H_2O instead of 3 ml.) Add 3 ml H_2O, stir, add 2 ml 6N HCl, stir, and mix thoroly with 6 g Celite. Transfer to chromatgc tube in 4 or 5 portions, pressing down each portion lightly with packing rod. "Wash" beaker by rubbing with 1 g Celite and add dry "washings" to tube; repeat twice. (It is convenient to use rubber policeman and powder funnel for washing and transferring operation.) Press wad of purified cotton on top of column. Over-all ht of column, with ca 20 mm id tube, should be 130–150 mm.

36.154   Determination of Strychnine

(*Caution: See* **46.011, 46.040,** *and* **46.056.**)

Add 135 ml washed ether to column and let percolate thru, without pressure. Discard ether soln. Elute strychnine.HCl without pressure, using 150 ml washed $CHCl_3$, collecting eluate in beaker. Reserve column for quinine detn. Evap. eluate to dryness on steam bath with aid of air current, avoiding prolonged heating. Dissolve residue in 10 ml 0.1N HCl with warming. Cool, transfer to 50 ml vol. flask with H_2O, dil. to vol., and mix thoroly.

Transfer aliquot contg 0.1–0.2 mg strychnine (but <12.5 ml) to marked test tube. (Use 5 ml with Elixir of Iron, Quinine, and Strychnine, NF XI.) Slowly add equal vol. HCl with mixing,

and dil. to 25 ml with HCl (1 + 1). Add 1.5 g amalgam, place test tube in 25 mm opening on steam bath, and heat 12 min. Remove from steam bath and cool quickly in cold H_2O. Add H_2O to make 25 ml and decant mixed soln as completely as possible into 50 ml erlenmeyer. Add 6 drops (0.3 ml) 0.1% $NaNO_2$, freshly prepd, while gently swirling flask, and mix well. Measure A within 15 min at 530 nm, using 1 cm cell and HCl (1 + 1) as ref. soln.

Prep. std curve by adding 5, 10, 15, 20, and 25 ml std strychnine soln in HCl (1 + 1) to test tubes and dil. to 25 ml with HCl (1 + 1). Proceed as above, beginning: "Add 1.5 g amalgam ...." If approx. strychnine content is known, use aliquot contg 0.10–0.20 mg strychnine and prep. std at that concn.

mg Strychnine in aliquot

$$= (A \times \text{mg strychnine in std})/A',$$

where A refers to sample and A' to std.

36.155   Determination of Quinine

Add 15 ml H_2O to chromatgc tube, apply gentle air pressure, and collect eluate in 250 ml separator. Repeat with five 15 ml portions H_2O. (5 ml of sixth portion should give no test for Cl.) Sep. $CHCl_3$ and wash it in second separator with 20 ml H_2O. Combine aq. layers, filter thru gooch (*Caution:* possible initial foaming) into 200 ml vol. flask, wash, dil. to vol., and det. quinine as in **36.148(b).** For Elixir of Iron, Quinine, and Strychnine, NF XI, use 10 ml aliquot for diln to 100 ml.

Method II (46)—Official Final Action
36.156   Apparatus

See **36.015.**

36.157   Reagents

(a) *Strychnine sulfate std solns.*—(*1*) *Stock soln.* —250 µg/ml. Dissolve 25.0 mg strychnine sulfate in MeOH and dil. to 100 ml with MeOH. (*2*) *Working soln.*—50 µg/ml. To 10 ml stock soln add 5 drops HCl and dil. to 50 ml with $CHCl_3$.

(b) *Triethylamine.*—See **36.016(a).**

36.158   Preparation of Sample and Columns

Sample.—Pipet 10 ml sample into 100 ml beaker, add 0.2 g p-toluenesulfonic acid, and heat on steam bath under gentle air current to remove alcohol.

Column I.—Add 2 ml 2N NaOH to 3 g Celite 545. Mix thoroly by kneading with flexible spatula, transfer to column, and tamp, using gentle pressure, to uniform mass. Add 8 g Celite 545 to alcohol-free sample. (If sample is too sirupy from excess evapn of H_2O, add small amt of H_2O.) Mix thoroly, transfer to column above NaOH layer, and tamp. Dry-wash with ca 1 g Celite for quant. transfer.

Column II.—Mix 3 g Celite 545 and 2 ml 2*N* NaOH, and tamp as above. Mix 8 g Celite 545 and 7 ml 1*N* HCl, transfer to column above NaOH layer, and tamp.

Column III.—Mix 3 g Celite 545 and 2 ml 1*N* tartaric acid, and tamp as above.

Place small wad of glass wool above each column.

36.159 Determination

(Use H_2O-satd solvs thruout.)

Pass 100 ml ether thru column I, discarding eluate contg aromatic flavoring components and bulk of transformation product of quinine which forms in aged prepns.

Mount columns so that eluate from I passes thru II onto III. Pass 100 ml $CHCl_3$ thru columns and discard column I. Pass 50 ml $CHCl_3$ thru column II onto III and finally pass 50 ml $CHCl_3$ thru column III. Discard eluate. Column II may be used for quinine detn as in **36.155.**

Place 50 ml vol. flask contg 10 ml MeOH and 1 ml HCl under column III which contains strychnine. Pass thru column 5 ml $CHCl_3$ contg 1 ml triethylamine, followed by 32 ml 1% triethylamine in $CHCl_3$. Dil. to vol. with $CHCl_3$. Det. *A* at 350, 320, and 288 nm against $CHCl_3$ or preferably record spectrum over this region. (Film of $Et_3N.HCl$ may adhere to walls of cells. Rinse cells carefully with H_2O and alcohol; then wipe clean before use.) Background *A* at 310–360 nm should be <0.02. Deduct av. reading at 320 and 350 nm from reading at inflexion at 288. (Max. *A* of strychnine is at ca 255 nm but nature of solvs makes it undesirable to use this wavelength.)

Deduct *A* of blank of 10 ml MeOH, 1 ml triethylamine, and 1 ml HCl dild to 50 ml with $CHCl_3$. Compare net *A* with that of dild strychnine sulfate std soln and calc. strychnine content.

Reserpine
Method I (47)—Official Final Action
36.160 Reagents

(a) *Sulfamic acid soln.*—2.5%. Prep. fresh every 2–3 days.

(b) *Alcoholic sodium nitrite soln.*—Dissolve 10 g $NaNO_2$ in 100 ml H_2O. Store in refrigerator. Mix 1 ml of this aq. soln with 50 ml alcohol.

(c) *Reserpine std soln.*—50 μg/ml. Dissolve 25 mg cryst. reserpine std in ca 40 ml boiling alcohol, cool, and dil. to 100 ml with alcohol. Dil. 10 ml of this stock soln to 50 ml with alcohol. When stored in tightly stoppered brown bottle in dark, solns are stable for weeks.

36.161 Determination

(a) *Crystalline reserpine.*—Accurately weigh ca 25 mg reserpine, dissolve in ca 40 ml boiling alcohol, cool, and dil. to 100 ml with alcohol. Transfer 10.0 ml to separator contg 50 ml 1% $NaHCO_3$ soln. Ext with 20, 10, and 10 ml $CHCl_3$, washing each $CHCl_3$ ext in second separator with 50 ml *2% citric acid soln*. Filter $CHCl_3$ exts thru cotton into 50 ml vol. flask contg 5 ml alcohol, dil. to 50 ml with $CHCl_3$, and mix.

Transfer duplicate 5.0 ml aliquots to 25 ml vol. flasks contg 15 ml alcohol. Transfer duplicate 5.0 ml aliquots dil. reserpine std soln to 25 ml vol. flasks contg 10 ml alcohol and 4.5 ml $CHCl_3$. Add 1.0 ml alc. $NaNO_2$ soln to 1 std and 1 sample soln. Add 10 drops HCl to all flasks, swirl, and let stand 30 min. Add 1.0 ml sulfamic acid soln, dil. with alcohol to 25 ml, and mix. Let stand 15 min and det. *A* in matched 1 cm cells at 390 nm against alcohol. mg Reserpine in sample weighed = $25 \times (A - A_0)/(S - S_0)$, where *A* and A_0 refer to nitrite-treated and untreated sample, resp., and *S* and S_0 refer to corresponding std aliquots.

(b) *Tablets.*—Accurately transfer weighed portion powd tablets equiv. to ca 5 mg reserpine to 100 ml beaker. Add 20 ml alcohol, cover with watch glass, and heat to simmering. Boil gently 20 min, stirring occasionally, adding small portions alcohol to maintain vol. Cool to <50°, add 10 ml $CHCl_3$, and mix. Filter thru pledget of cotton, and collect filtrate in 50 ml vol. flask. Wash filter and solids with several portions $CHCl_3$. Cool, dil. to 50 ml, and mix. Transfer 25 ml aliquot to separator contg 50 ml 1% $NaHCO_3$. Add 5 ml $CHCl_3$ and shake vigorously. Transfer $CHCl_3$ layer to separator contg 50 ml *2% citric acid soln*, and shake. Repeat extns with two 10 ml portions $CHCl_3$. Filter exts thru cotton and collect in 50 ml vol. flask contg 5 ml alcohol. Proceed as in (a), second par. after dilg to vol. with $CHCl_3$.

mg Reserpine in portion powd tablets weighed = $5 \times (A - A_0)/(S - S_0)$.

Method II (48)—Official First Action
36.162 Reagents

(Prep. std, sample, and blank solns from same bottles of $CHCl_3$ and MeOH.)

(a) *Treated fiberglass.*—Soak Pyrex fiberglass, Corning Glass Works No. 3950, in $CHCl_3$, rinse several times with $CHCl_3$, and air-dry on filter paper or dry in forced-draft oven.

(b) *Dimethylsulfoxide (DMSO).*—Spectral grade or equiv. Available from Crown Zellerbach, Camas, WA 98607; Fisher Scientific Co.; or Matheson Coleman & Bell, Cat. No. MX 1457.

(c) *Sodium nitrite in dilute methanol soln.*—0.3% in MeOH (1 + 1). Stable ≥1 month when stored in refrigerator. Bring to room temp. before use.

(d) *Methanolic hydrochloric acid soln.*—Dil. 6.0 ml HCl to 100 ml with MeOH.

(e) *Reserpine std soln.*—20 μg/ml. Dissolve 25.0 mg accurately weighed USP Reserpine Ref. Std, previously dried 3 hr at 60°, in 0.25 ml CHCl₃. Mix with ca 30 ml MeOH, previously warmed to 50°; transfer mixt. to 250 ml vol. flask with warm MeOH. Cool soln to room temp., dil. to vol. with MeOH, and mix. Protect soln from light. Just prior to use pipet 10 ml into 50 ml vol. flask, add 36 ml CHCl₃, and dil. to vol. with MeOH.

(f) *Diatomaceous earth.*—Celite 545, acid-washed.

36.163 *Preparation of Column*

Place small pledget of treated glass wool in base of 200 × 22 mm id tube. *Lower layer:* Mix 1 g acid-washed Celite with 0.5 ml freshly prepd 2% NaHCO₃, transfer to column, and tamp to uniform mass. *Acid layer:* Mix 1 g acid-washed Celite with 0.5 ml freshly prepd 0.5% citric acid soln, transfer to column, and tamp. *Water layer:* For every two columns mix 1 g acid-washed Celite with 0.5 ml H₂O; transfer ½ mixt. to column, and tamp.

Proceed with entire assay *quickly,* without interruption, avoiding exposure of sample to direct light. Read UV spectrum immediately after column elution is completed.

36.164 *Chromatography*

Weigh and powder ≥20 tablets and pass thru No. 60 sieve. Transfer accurately weighed amt, contg ca 1 mg reserpine, to 150 ml beaker. Add 1 ml DMSO and wet by thoroly mixing with spatula. Let stand, with spatula remaining in beaker, 5 min. Add ca 2 g acid-washed Celite and mix immediately until mixt. is uniformly fluffy. Quant. transfer to column thru wide-mouth funnel. Dry-wash beaker with ca 1 g acid-washed Celite and transfer to column. Wipe beaker, spatula, and funnel with small pledget of treated glass wool. Tamp sample, Celite dry-wash, and glass wool firmly. Pass ca 45 ml CHCl₃ thru sample column. Collect eluate in 50 ml vol. flask contg 14 ml MeOH, rinsing tip of column with CHCl₃, and dil. sample to vol. with CHCl₃.

Prep. and elute blank column exactly as above, replacing sample layer with 1 ml DMSO + 2 g Celite.

36.165 *UV Assay*

Scan UV absorption spectrum of sample eluate from 250 to 350 nm, against column blank eluate. Likewise, scan spectrum of std soln in same range against ref. blank of 3.6 parts CHCl₃ and 1.4 parts MeOH. Calc. mg reserpine in sample portion = $(A_u/A_s) \times (C_s \times 50)$, where A_u and $A_s = A$ of sample and std, resp., at 268 nm and C_s = mg reserpine/ml in std soln (0.02).

36.166 *Colorimetric Assay*

Pipet duplicate 5.0 ml aliquots of sample eluate and std soln into sep. 10 ml vol. flasks. Add 2.0 ml

methanolic HCl soln to each flask and swirl. To one std and one sample flask, add 1.0 ml MeOH (1 + 1) (blanks). To remaining std and sample flasks, add 1.0 ml 0.3% NaNO₂ soln and mix. Let stand exactly 30 min. Add 0.5 ml freshly prepd 5% *NH₄ sulfamate* soln to each flask, dil. with MeOH, and let stand ≥10 min. Read A from 450 to 350 nm for each soln against blank of 3.6 parts CHCl₃, 5.4 parts MeOH, and 1 part H₂O. Calc. mg reserpine in sample portion = $[(A_u - A_{ou}) \times (C_s \times 50)]/(A_s - A_{os})$, where A_u, A_{ou}, A_s, and $A_{os} = A$ of sample, sample blank, std, and std blank, resp., at 390 nm and C_s = mg reserpine/ml in std soln (0.02).

Reserpine-Rescinnamine Group Alkaloids in *Rauwolfia serpentina* (49)—Official Final Action

36.167 *Reagents*

(a) *1,1,1-Trichloroethane.*—(*Caution:* Trichloroethane is toxic. *See* **46.040.**) Redistill in all-glass app., collecting fraction boiling at 73–76°.

(b) *Reserpine std soln.*—20 μg/ml. Dissolve 20.0 mg cryst. reserpine std in 25 ml hot alcohol, cool, and dil. to 50 ml with alcohol. Dil 5 ml of this soln to 100 ml with alcohol.

(c) *Dilute sulfuric acid.*—0.5N. Dissolve ca 30 ml H₂SO₄ in 2 L H₂O.

(d) *Sulfamic acid soln.*—5% aq. soln. Prep. fresh every 2–3 days.

36.168 *Apparatus*

Soxhlet extraction apparatus.—Medium size extractor with 250 ml flask and 35 × 80 mm thimble is most convenient, although smaller app. may be used.

36.169 *Determination*

Ext 2–3 g finely powd *Rauwolfia serpentina* root or equiv. in powd tablets in Soxhlet extn app. 4 hr, using ca 100 ml vigorously boiling alcohol. Protect flask and thimble, and all solns of rauwolfia alkaloids, from strong or direct light.

Wash ext into 100 ml vol. flask with alcohol, cool, dil. to vol., and mix. Transfer 20 ml aliquot to separator contg 200 ml 0.5N H₂SO₄, mix, and ext with three 25 ml portions trichloroethane. Drain lower solv. phase as completely as possible. Wash each trichloroethane ext in second separator contg 50 ml 0.5N H₂SO₄, and discard.

Ext main aq. soln with 25, 15, 15, 10, 10, and 10 ml CHCl₃. Wash each CHCl₃ ext with the acid in second separator, and then with two 10 ml portions 2% NaHCO₃ soln in third and fourth separators. Filter CHCl₃ exts thru cotton into 100 ml vol. flask contg 10 ml alcohol. Dil. to 100 ml with CHCl₃ and mix.

Transfer duplicate 10.0 ml aliquots to 18 × 150 mm test tubes and mix each with 4 ml alcohol.

Add two or three "20-mesh" SiC boiling chips, and heat to boiling in H_2O bath at ca 70°. Gradually raise bath temp. to 100°, or until boiling in tube *just* stops (avoid prolonged heating in absence of solv.). Wipe outsides of warm tubes, place in vac. desiccator, and evap. to dryness under vac. Dissolve residues by agitating with 5.0 ml alcohol.

Take duplicate 5 ml aliquots reserpine std soln, and add 2.0 ml 0.5N H_2SO_4 to one sample tube and to one std tube (blanks). To other tubes add 1.0 ml 0.5N H_2SO_4 and 1.0 ml 0.3% $NaNO_2$ soln. Mix contents of each tube, and warm in H_2O bath 20 min at 50–60°. Cool, add 0.5 ml sulfamic acid soln to each tube, and mix. Let stand 15 min and det. A in matched 1 cm cells at 390 nm against alcohol–H_2O $(2 + 1)$. mg Reserpine-rescinnamine alkaloids in sample weighed $= 5 \times (A - A_0) / (S - S_0)$, where A and A_0 refer to nitrite-treated and untreated samples, resp., and S and S_0 are corresponding A for std soln aliquots.

Rescinnamine (50)—Official Final Action

36.170   *Reagents*

(a) *Ammonium sulfamate soln.*—2.5%. Prep. fresh every 2–3 days.

(b) *Alcoholic sodium nitrite soln.*—See **36.160(b)**.

(c) *Rescinnamine std soln.*—40 μg/ml. Dissolve 20.0 mg NF Ref. Std rescinnamine in 0.5 ml $CHCl_3$, transfer to 50 ml vol. flask, and dil. to vol. with alcohol. Protect all rescinnamine solns from direct or strong light. Alc. soln is stable several weeks in dark. Dil. 5.0 ml std soln to 50 ml with $CHCl_3$.

36.171   *Determination*

(a) *Crystalline rescinnamine.*—Accurately weigh ca 20 mg sample, dissolve in 0.5 ml $CHCl_3$, transfer to 50 ml vol. flask, and dil. to vol. with alcohol. Pipet 5 ml aliquot into separator contg 50 ml 0.5N H_2SO_4, add 22 ml $CHCl_3$ and 3 ml alcohol, and shake vigorously 2 min. Transfer $CHCl_3$ layer to second separator contg 50 ml 1% $NaHCO_3$ soln, and shake again. Filter $CHCl_3$ layer thru cotton previously washed with $CHCl_3$ into 50 ml vol. flask contg 5.0 ml alcohol. Ext acid and alk. solns with 2 addnl 10 ml portions $CHCl_3$, filter into vol. flask, and dil. to vol. with $CHCl_3$.

Transfer duplicate 10 ml aliquots prepd sample soln and 40 μg/ml std soln to 25 ml vol. flasks, each contg 10 ml alcohol. Add 1 ml alc. $NaNO_2$ soln, **36.160(b)**, to 1 flask of each set; to remaining flasks add 1 ml alcohol. Add 10 drops HCl to all flasks, swirl, and let stand 30 min. Add 1 ml 2.5% NH_4 sulfamate soln, dil. to vol. with alcohol, mix, and let stand 10 min.

Det. A in matched 1 cm cells at 390 nm against mixt. of 9 vols $CHCl_3$, 15 alcohol, and 1 H_2O as ref.

mg Rescinnamine in sample weighed $= 20 \times (A - A_0) / (S - S_0)$, where A and A_0 refer to nitrite-treated and untreated sample, resp., and S and S_0 are A of corresponding std aliquots.

(b) *Tablets.*—Transfer accurately weighed portion powd tablets contg ca 2.5 mg rescinnamine to 50 ml beaker. Insert small glass rod and cover with watch glass. Add 10 ml alcohol, mark vol., and boil gently 20 min with occasional stirring, maintaining original vol. by adding alcohol when necessary. Cool to <50°, add 5 ml $CHCl_3$, and filter thru pledget of cotton previously washed with $CHCl_3$ into 25 ml vol. flask. Wash filter and solids with $CHCl_3$, cool, and dil. to vol. Mix, and let settle ca 10 min. (If soln is not clear, transfer to g-s graduated cylinder and let settle 10 min more.)

Pipet 20 ml aliquot into separator contg 50 ml 0.5N H_2SO_4, add 10 ml $CHCl_3$, and shake vigorously 2 min. Transfer $CHCl_3$ to second separator contg 50 ml 1% $NaHCO_3$ soln, and shake again. Filter $CHCl_3$ layer thru cotton previously washed with $CHCl_3$ into 50 ml vol. flask contg 5.0 ml alcohol. Ext acid and alk. solns with two 10 ml portions $CHCl_3$, filter into vol. flask, and dil. to vol. with $CHCl_3$.

Proceed as in (a), second par.

mg Rescinnamine in sample weighed $= 2.5 \times (A - A_0) / (S - S_0)$.

36.172   *Determination of Total Alkaloids*

Transfer 10 ml aliquot prepd sample soln and 10 ml std soln to sep. 25 ml vol. flasks, and dil. to vol. with alcohol. Det. absorption spectrum of each soln in region 250–360 nm against blank of 9 ml $CHCl_3$ dild to 25 ml with alcohol.

mg Total alkaloids in sample weighed $= 2.5 \times T/S$, where T and S are A of sample and std solns at max. near 304 nm, resp.

Presence of other alkaloids is indicated by difference between the 2 spectra; presence of reserpine in particular is indicated by discrepancy between HNO_2 and UV detns.

36.173 Strychnine in Liquid Preparations (51)—Official Final Action

(Other alkaloids absent. *See* also **36.150–36.159.**)

Measure into evapg dish 50 ml sample, or enough to yield ⩾0.065 g strychnine, and remove alcohol by evapn. Transfer to separator, add 1 ml NH_4OH, or enough to render soln alk., and proceed as in **36.011**, beginning "... ext with four 25 ml portions $CHCl_3$ (use ..."

36.174 Strychnine in Tablets—Official Final Action

(Other alkaloids absent)

See **36.011**.

Theobromine in Theobromine-Calcium Salicylate (52)—Official Final Action

36.175   Method I

Dry ca 0.5 g sample at 110° to constant wt. Weigh 0.2 g dried substance into g-s 100 ml vol. flask, add 2 ml HOAc, and warm on steam bath. Add 10 ml boiling H_2O and shake until dissolved, adding more boiling H_2O if necessary. Cool soln to room temp. (Soln should be clear or nearly so.) Add 50 ml $0.1N$ I, 20 ml satd NaCl soln, and 2 ml HCl. Shake well and dil. to vol. with H_2O. Shake again and let stand overnight. Filter, discarding first 10 ml filtrate. Titr. 50 ml filtrate with $0.1N$ $Na_2S_2O_3$, using starch soln, 6.004(f), as indicator. 1 ml $0.1N$ I = 0.00450 g theobromine, $C_7H_8O_2N_4$.

Method II—In Tablets (53)

36.176   Indicator

Phenol red indicator.—Triturate 0.1 g phenol red in agate mortar with 15 ml $0.02N$ NaOH until dissolved and dil. soln to 200 ml with recently boiled H_2O.

36.177   Determination

Place 0.5 g powd tablets, 0.4 g powder, or 0.2 g theobromine alkaloid in 300 ml beaker and add 100 ml H_2O. Warm moderately over flame and add 15 ml ca $0.1N$ H_2SO_4. Heat to boiling to ensure complete soln and to remove CO_2. Cool to room temp. Add 1.5 ml phenol red indicator and make slightly alk. with ca $0.1N$ NaOH (violet-red); then titr. carefully to acid reaction with $0.1N$ H_2SO_4 (yellow). To this soln add 25 ml (an excess) neut. $0.1N$ $AgNO_3$, 45.028, and immediately titr. liberated HNO_3 with $0.1N$ NaOH to distinct violet-red. Cautiously titr. dropwise with constant stirring near end point. 1 ml $0.1N$ NaOH = 0.01802 g $C_7H_8O_2N_4$.

36.178   Theophylline (54)—Official Final Action

(Applicable to solns and tablets. *Caution: See* 46.011, 46.040, and 46.056.)

Weigh 0.2–0.3 g theophylline (or equiv. of powd tablets), or measure equiv. quantity of soln, into separator. Add 5 ml $0.5N$ NaOH and shake gently until alkaloid dissolves. Add strip of litmus paper and enough $0.5N$ HCl from buret to produce distinct acid reaction; then add 0.5 ml excess. Add 30 ml $CHCl_3$-isopropanol (3 + 1) and shake 1 min. Let settle, and drain lower layer into second separator contg 10 ml H_2O acidified with HCl. Shake well, let settle, and filter solv. into weighed flask thru cotton pledget placed in stem of funnel.

Repeat extn with 6 more 20 ml portions $CHCl_3$-isopropanol mixt., wash each portion thru second separator, and pass solv. thru filter into weighed flask. Ensure complete extn by seventh shaking with 10 ml solv. mixt. and evapn of washed solv.

mixt. in sep. container. Recover most of solv. and evap. remainder on steam bath while rotating container in inclined position. Add 2 ml absolute ether to residue and evap. (cautiously to avoid spattering). Dry residue at 80° to constant wt and weigh as anhyd. theophylline. $C_7H_8O_2N_4 \times 1.10 = C_7H_8O_2N_4 \cdot H_2O$.

ANTIPYRETIC DRUGS

Acetaminophen (55)—Official First Action

36.179   Reagents

(a) *Bicarbonate-carbonate buffer.*—pH 10.1. Weigh 1.0 g $NaHCO_3$ and 4.5 g Na_2CO_3 into 100 ml vol. flask and dil. to vol. with H_2O.

(b) *Acidic methanol.*—1.0 ml $0.1N$ HCl/100 ml MeOH. Prep. enough to ensure same MeOH is used thruout for std and sample.

(c) *Diatomaceous earth.*—Celite 545, acid-washed.

(d) *Acetaminophen std soln.*—0.008 mg acetaminophen/ml. Accurately weigh 40 mg acetaminophen std into 100 ml vol. flask. Dil. to vol. with acidic MeOH and mix well. Transfer 2.0 ml to 100 ml vol. flask and dil. to vol. with acidic MeOH.

36.180   Preparation of Chromatographic Column

Pack fine glass wool plug in base of chromatgc tube (25 × 250 mm) with aid of tamping rod ca 18″ long and having disk with diam. ca 1 mm less than tube. To 3.0 g Celite 545 add 2.0 ml buffer soln and mix until fluffy mixt. is obtained. Transfer mixt. to column and tamp gently to compress material to uniform mass. Transfer 2.0 ml sample soln to 100 ml beaker, add 1 drop HCl, and mix. Add 3.0 g Celite 545, mix thoroly, and transfer to column. Scrub beaker with 1 g Celite 545 and 2 drops H_2O. Transfer to column, tamp, and top column with fine glass wool pad.

36.181   Preparation of Sample

(a) *Sirup.*—Transfer 15.0 ml $0.1N$ NaOH to 25 ml vol. flask. Dil. to vol. with acetaminophen sirup, avoiding wetting flask neck above graduation mark while adding sirup, and mix. Transfer 10.0 ml of this diln to 100 ml vol. flask, dil. to vol. with H_2O, and mix.

(b) *Tablets.*—Weigh and finely pulverize ≥ 20 tablets. Accurately weigh portion of powder contg ca 240 mg acetaminophen and transfer to 250 ml vol. flask. Add 2 ml $1.0N$ NaOH and ca 100 ml H_2O. Shake, dil. to vol. with H_2O, and mix.

36.182   Determination

(*Caution: See* 46.011, 46.039, and 46.054.)

(Use H_2O-washed solvs thruout.)

Pass 100 ml $CHCl_3$ thru column and discard eluate. Elute acetaminophen with 150 ml ether, collecting eluate in 400 ml beaker. Evap. soln to dryness on steam bath under air stream. Dissolve residue in acidic MeOH, transfer quant. to 50 ml vol. flask, and dil. to vol. with same solv. Transfer 10.0 ml of this soln to 50 ml vol. flask, dil. to vol. with acidic MeOH, and mix. Scan spectrum of sample and std solns from 350 to 240 nm in 1 cm cells, using acidic MeOH as blank.

mg Acetaminophen in portion of sirup or tablet taken $= 31.25 \times C \times (A_u/A_s)$, where $C =$ mg/ml std soln, and A_u and $A_s =$ absorbances of sample and std, resp., at max. of ca 249 nm.

★ Acetanilid and Acetophenetidin ★ (Phenacetin) (56)

36.183　Qualitative Test for Acetophenetidin —Procedure

See **32.129**, 10th ed.

36.184　Quantitative Methods—Official Final Action

(a) *Acetophenetidin.*—(1) *Volumetric.* See **32.131(a)(1)**, 10th ed. (2) *Gravimetric.* See **32.131(a)(2)**, 10th ed.

(b) *Acetanilid.*—See **32.131(b)**, 10th ed. (*Caution: See* **46.011, 46.040,** and **46.056.**)

36.185　★ Acetanilid and Caffeine ★ (57)—Official Final Action

See **32.132–32.134**, 10th ed. (*Caution: See* **46.011, 46.040,** and **46.056.**)

36.186　★ Acetanilid, Caffeine, and ★ Codeine (58)—Official Final Action

See **32.135–32.136**, 10th ed. (*Caution: See* **46.011, 46.040,** and **46.056.**)

36.187　★ Acetanilid, Caffeine, and ★ Quinine (58)—Official Final Action

See **32.137–32.139**, 10th ed. (*Caution: See* **46.011, 46.040,** and **46.056.**)

36.188　★ Acetanilid, Caffeine, Quinine, ★ and Morphine (59)—Official Final Action

See **32.140–32.141**, 10th ed. (*Caution: See* **46.011, 46.040,** and **46.056.**)

36.189　★ Acetanilid and Sodium ★ Salicylate (60)—Official Final Action

See **32.142–32.143**, 10th ed. (*Caution: See* **46.011, 46.040,** and **46.056.**)

Acetophenetidin, Acetylsalicylic Acid, and Caffeine (APC)—Official Final Action

(For antihistamines in combination with APC—See **36.223**.)

36.190　★ Method I (For Acetylsalicylic ★ Acid Only) (61)

(*Caution: See* **46.011, 46.040** and **46.056.**)

Det. av. wt of number of tablets and reduce to fine powder. Weigh ca 0.2 g powder, transfer to separator with ca 25 ml H_2O, and ext with repeated portions $CHCl_3$; ca 6 extns with 30, 25, 20, 10, 10, and 5 ml are generally required. Test final extn by evapg small portion on steam bath to dryness.

Collect $CHCl_3$ fractions in separator and drain thru cotton pledget in stem into 200 ml erlenmeyer. Wash separator twice with 5 ml portions $CHCl_3$, passing this thru the cotton and leaving any H_2O that may have sepd in separator. Add $CHCl_3$ washings to flask and evap. $CHCl_3$ on steam bath to ca 2 ml. Add 10 ml H_2SO_4 $(1 + 9)$, connect with reflux condenser, and digest 30 min, partially immersing flask in boiling H_2O bath.

Cool, and transfer to separator, rinsing condenser with $CHCl_3$ and using min. amt of H_2O for transfer, so that final vol. does not greatly exceed 20 ml. Ext caffeine and salicylic acid with 6 portions $CHCl_3$, using 30, 25, 20, 15, 10, and 10 ml. Collect these fractions in separator, add 20 ml H_2O and 1 g Na_2CO_3, and shake thoroly. Drain $CHCl_3$ into another separator and wash twice more with 15 and 10 ml H_2O. Reject $CHCl_3$, and combine Na_2CO_3 soln and wash H_2O in 200 ml erlenmeyer. Heat on steam bath to expel traces of $CHCl_3$ and dil. to 100 ml with H_2O; then slowly add 25–40 ml strong I soln (ca $0.2N$), enough to ensure excess during digestion, and digest 1 hr on steam bath.

Remove free I with few drops of $Na_2S_2O_3$ soln. Decant clear soln thru weighed gooch, retaining most of ppt in flask. To latter add 50 ml boiling H_2O, digest 10 min on steam bath, filter, and gradually wash all ppt into the gooch, using total of ca 200 ml hot H_2O. Dry to constant wt at 100° and weigh ppt of tetraiodophenylenequinone $(C_6H_2I_2O)_2$. Wt ppt $\times$ 0.4016 = total salicylic acid. If free salicylic acid is present, **36.207**, deduct from total; difference $\times$ 1.304 = wt acetylsalicylic acid.

Method II (62)

36.191　Reagents

(a) *Dilute sulfuric acid soln.*—2%. Pour 6.0 ml H_2SO_4 into 500 ml H_2O.

(b) *Sodium bicarbonate soln.*—Freshly prepd. Add 3 g $NaHCO_3$ to 45 ml H_2O previously cooled to 15° or lower. Stir until dissolved and add 2–3 drops HCl $(1 + 3)$.

36.192　Determination

(*Caution: See* **46.011, 46.040,** and **46.056.**)

(a) *Acetylsalicylic acid.*—Make detn as soon as possible to prevent any hydrolysis in $NaHCO_3$ soln.

Weigh powd sample contg $\geqslant 0.04$ g caffeine,

transfer to separator contg ca 10 ml H_2O cooled to 15° or lower, and shake thoroly. Add 15 ml cooled $NaHCO_3$ soln slowly to prevent mech. loss due to effervescence and immediately ext with successive portions $CHCl_3$. Usually 5 extns with ca 30 ml portions $CHCl_3$ are enough. Extn is complete when final ext evapd to dryness leaves negligible residue.

Wash each portion $CHCl_3$ thru second separator contg 2 ml cold $NaHCO_3$ soln and filter thru cotton moistened with $CHCl_3$. Set aside combined $CHCl_3$ exts contg caffeine and acetophenetidin for later treatment. Transfer wash H_2O in second separator to soln in first separator, rinsing several times with small portions H_2O. Acidify combined $NaHCO_3$ solns with HCl $(1 + 1)$ and ext acetylsalicylic acid by shaking with successive portions $CHCl_3$, filtering each portion thru funnel contg cotton pledget moistened with $CHCl_3$ (usually 5 extns are enough).

Evap. combined $CHCl_3$ exts on steam bath with aid of fan or gentle air stream to ca 10 ml. Transfer to suitable small tared container with $CHCl_3$ and evap. to dryness with aid of fan or gentle air stream without heat. Dry in desiccator overnight and weigh as acetylsalicylic acid. Extd acetylsalicylic acid may be checked by Br method, **36.209(b)**, or by double titrn method, **36.212**.

(b) *Acetophenetidin and caffeine.*—Evap. $CHCl_3$ soln contg acetophenetidin and caffeine on steam bath and transfer, when vol. reaches 5–10 ml, to 100 ml beaker, using small portions $CHCl_3$. Evap. again to ca 5 ml and add 10 ml 2% H_2SO_4. Insert stirring rod and heat mixt. on bath until all $CHCl_3$ evaps, stirring occasionally. Cool to room temp. and decant without suction thru tared gooch previously dried to constant wt at 100°. Collect filtrate in 150 ml beaker, retaining as much acetophenetidin as possible in beaker. Rinse sides of beaker contg acetophenetidin with 5–10 ml $CHCl_3$, add 10 ml 2% H_2SO_4, and heat on bath as before until all $CHCl_3$ evaps. Cool, and decant thru same crucible as before. Repeat process with another 10 ml portion 2% H_2SO_4, and quant. wash acetophenetidin into crucible with H_2O. Wash beaker and crucible with H_2O until filtrate measures ca 75 ml. Dry crucible at 100° and weigh acetophenetidin.

To filtrate contg caffeine and small amt of acetophenetidin still in soln (ca 0.075 g), add 5 ml H_2SO_4 $(1 + 9)$ and evap. on steam bath to ca 10 ml. Transfer with small portions H_2O to 50 ml erlenmeyer previously marked for vols of 5 and 10 ml. Proceed as in **36.203(a)**; note that hydrolysis must be continued until no odor of HOAc is present. (Hydrolysis is hastened somewhat if flask is allowed to hang in the steam by wire wrapped around its neck so that mouth of flask is ca level with surface of bath (ca 3 evaps are usually enough).) Wt acetophenetidin obtained + wt ace-

tophenetidin collected in gooch = total acetophenetidin.

Chromatographic Method (63)

36.193 *Reagents*

(a) *Sodium bicarbonate soln.*—1*M*. Dissolve 4.2 g $NaHCO_3$ in 48 ml H_2O.

(b) *Washed ether.*—Wash USP ether with equal vol. H_2O in separator. Filter thru paper, rejecting first 15 ml. Use within 3 days. Approx. 70 ml required for each sample.

(c) *Chloroform.*—NF. A against H_2O at 276 nm ≤0.050. Use same lot thruout.

(d) *Washed chloroform.*—Wash $CHCl_3$ with equal vol. H_2O in separator. Filter thru paper, rejecting first 15 ml. Use within 3 days. Use same lot thruout. Approx. 700 ml is required for stds and 170 ml for each sample.

(e) *Isooctane.*—A against H_2O at 286 nm ≤0.050. Use same lot thruout.

(f) *Acetophenetidin std soln.*—7 mg/100 ml. Dissolve 70.0 mg pure acetophenetidin in $CHCl_3$ and dil. to 100 ml with $CHCl_3$. Dil. 10 ml aliquot to 100 ml with isooctane.

(g) *Caffeine std soln.*—1.4 mg/100 ml. Dissolve 140.0 mg caffeine in washed $CHCl_3$ and dil. to 100 ml. Dil. 10 ml aliquot to 100 ml; dil. 10 ml aliquot of this soln to 100 ml with washed $CHCl_3$.

(h) *Acetylsalicylic acid std soln.*—5 mg/100 ml. Dissolve 100.0 mg acetylsalicylic acid in washed $CHCl_3$ and dil. to 100 ml. To 5 ml aliquot add 1.0 ml HOAc and dil. to 100 ml with washed $CHCl_3$. Prep. fresh daily.

(i) *Salicylic acid std soln.*—2.5 mg/100 ml. Dissolve 100.0 mg salicylic acid in washed $CHCl_3$ and dil. to 100 ml. Dil. 25 ml aliquot to 100 ml; to 10 ml aliquot of this soln, add 1.0 ml HOAc and dil. to 100 ml with washed $CHCl_3$.

36.194 *Apparatus*

See **36.015**.

36.195 *Preparation of Sample*

Weigh powd sample contg ca 100 mg acetylsalicylic acid and transfer to 100 ml vol. flask. Add 60 ml $CHCl_3$ and shake well. Add 0.2 ml HOAc and dil. to vol. with $CHCl_3$.

36.196 *Preparation of Chromatographic Column*

Loosely pack small amt of fine glass wool in base of chromatgc tube so as to support Celite, but not cause irregularity in thickness of Celite layer.

To 2.0 g Celite 545 in 100 ml beaker, or glass mortar, add 2.0 ml H_2SO_4 $(1 + 9)$. Mix well with metal spatula. Transfer to chromatgc tube, and with packing rod compress lightly to uniform mass. Mix 2.0 g Celite with 2.0 ml 1*M* $NaHCO_3$ and place in column above acid layer. Wash column with 15–20 ml washed ether and discard washings.

36.197 *Separation*

(Use washed ether and washed CHCl₃ thruout, except for dissolving acetophenetidin residue.)

(a) *Acetophenetidin.*—Dil. 5 ml aliquot prepd sample soln with 20 ml ether and pass thru column, receiving eluate in 100 or 150 ml beaker. After soln has passed into adsorbent, wash with five 5 ml portions ether, letting each portion pass into adsorbent before adding next. Wash tip of outlet with CHCl₃ and evap. total eluate to dryness by gentle heating on steam bath with air current. Dissolve acetophenetidin residue in 5 ml NF CHCl₃ and dil. with isooctane to 50 ml.

(b) *Caffeine.*—Immediately after passage of last portion of ether thru column, replace beaker with 50 ml vol. flask. Pass 48 ml CHCl₃ thru column, wash tip with CHCl₃ and dil. eluate to vol.

(c) *Acetylsalicylic acid and salicylic acid.*—Immediately replace receiver with 100 ml vol. flask. Pass soln of 0.5 ml HOAc in 5 ml CHCl₃ thru column, followed by 90–92 ml 1% soln of HOAc in CHCl₃. Wash tip with CHCl₃ and dil. eluate to vol.

36.198 *Determination*

Immediately det. A of acid fraction and of acetylsalicylic and salicylic acid std solns at 280 and 310 nm against 1% HOAc in CHCl₃. Det A of acetophenetidin fraction and std at 286 nm against isooctane-NF CHCl₃ (9 + 1) and that of caffeine fraction and std at 276 nm against washed CHCl₃ blank.

Calc. quantity of each ingredient in sample. Acetylsalicylic and salicylic acids may be calcd by successive approximations as follows: Attributing entire A at 310 nm to salicylic acid, use ratio of salicylic acid std readings at the 2 wavelengths to calc. A due to salicylic acid at 280 nm, and deduct from total A at 280 nm. Attributing remainder to acetylsalicylic acid, use ratio of acetylsalicylic acid std readings to calc. A due to acetylsalicylic acid at 310 nm. Deduct this A from total at 310 nm. Use remainder to calc. quantity of salicylic acid in sample and also to recalc. A due to salicylic acid at 280 nm. Deduct latter from total A at 280 nm and use remainder to calc. quantity acetylsalicylic acid in sample. Alternatively, calc. these two ingredients by simultaneous equations. Amt of acetylsalicylic acid hydrolyzed may be calcd by multiplying amt of salicylic acid by 1.3044.

36.199 ★ Acetophenetidin, Acetylsali- ★ cylic Acid, and Salol (Phenyl Salicylate) (*64*)—Official Final Action

See **32.153**, 10th ed. (*Caution: See* **46.011**, **46.040**, and **46.056**.)

36.200 ★ Acetophenetidin, Amino- ★ pyrine, and Caffeine (*65*)— Official Final Action

See **32.154**, 10th ed. (*Caution: See* **46.011**, **46.040**, and **46.056**.)

36.201 ★ Acetophenetidin, Amino- ★ pyrine, Caffeine, and Pheno- barbital (*66*)—Official Final Action

See **32.155**, 10th ed.

★ Acetophenetidin (Phenacetin) and ★ Caffeine (*67*)—Official Final Action

(*Caution: See* **46.011**, **46.040**, and **46.056**.)

36.202 *Preparation of Solution*

(a) *Solid samples.*—Weigh 0.3–0.5 g powd sample or, if preferred, amt equal to, or multiple of, av. unit dose (previously detd by weighing collectively ≥20 such doses). Transfer to separator, add 50 ml CHCl₃ and 20 ml H₂O, shake vigorously, and after clearing, drain lower layer thru small dry filter into 250 ml beaker. Repeat extn with two addnl 50 ml portions CHCl₃. Recover any caffeine-acetophenetidin mixt. seen around apex of delivery tube of separator, edge of filter, and tip of separator by careful washing with CHCl₃, and add these washings to main portion. Evap. combined CHCl₃ exts to ca 10 ml.

If caffeine is present as free alkaloid or in other readily extractable form, extn may be made on filter paper by washing with successive 5–10 ml portions CHCl₃ (30–50 ml is usually enough) until extn is complete, as indicated by absence of any residue after evapn of small portion of last washing.

(b) *Liquid samples.*—With dil. alc. solns, evap. measured amt on steam bath until most of alcohol is expelled, or take aliquot of residue from an alcohol detn and transfer to separator by pouring and rinsing with min. amt of H₂O so that final vol. does not greatly exceed 20 ml. To avoid loss of acetophenetidin by hydrolysis during evapn, add little solid NaHCO₃ and drop Ac₂O. If prepn contains other alkaloids, acidify with few drops H₂SO₄ (1 + 9) immediately after acetylation to retain such basic material in aq. soln. Add 50 ml CHCl₃, shake vigorously, and after clearing, drain CHCl₃ layer thru filter into 250 ml beaker. Repeat extn with two addnl 50 ml portions CHCl₃ and evap. combined CHCl₃ washings to ca 10 ml.

36.203 *Determination*

(a) *Caffeine.*—Treat CHCl₃ ext, **36.202**, with 10 ml H₂SO₄ (1 + 9) and digest on steam bath to ca 5 ml. Dil. with 10 ml H₂O and continue digestion until vol. is again reduced to 5 ml; again add 10 ml H₂O and continue heating to 5 ml. Repeat dilg and evapg until odor of HOAc can no longer be detected in vapors. If, during digestion, particles of acetophenetidin remain on sides of flask, rinse them into soln with few drops CHCl₃. (*Note:* Special care must be given to degree of evapn. Should aq. acid soln and suspension of caffeine-acetophenetidin be concd much beyond limits indicated, phenetidin sulfonate is likely to be formed, which later resists acetylation and conversion to acetophenetidin.)

Cool, and transfer with H_2O to separator so that final vol. does not greatly exceed 20 ml. Add 50 ml CHCl₃, ext, and after clearing, drain lower layer thru small dry filter into 200 ml erlenmeyer. Repeat extn with two 50 ml portions CHCl₃. Evap. combined exts to ca 10 ml, finally transferring residual liq., by washing with CHCl₃, to weighed beaker or crystg dish. Let soln evap. spontaneously, or by gentle heat and air current, to apparent dryness. Cool, and let stand in open until wt becomes constant.

From prepns contg powd cinnamon, celery seed, ginger, or other vegetable products, CHCl₃ exts certain oils, fats, waxes, resins, pigments, and other substances, in addn to caffeine and acetophenetidin. After caffeine-acetophenetidin mixt. has been digested, these oils, etc., appear either in suspension or soln and contaminate the caffeine. Remove any suspended impurities by filtering thru small moistened filter immediately after hydrolysis and before extn with CHCl₃.

If recovered caffeine is deeply colored or contaminated with foreign matter, purify as follows: Dissolve in H_2SO_4 (ca 5 ml $0.2N$ acid/100 mg caffeine); filter, if necessary, thru moistened filter; add 1 ml $9N$ H_2SO_4 and enough I reagent, **36.101(e)**, to color supernatant deep claret; stir, and let stand 1 hr, preferably in refrigerator. Filter and wash periodide with few ml I soln; transfer both filter and ppt to separator, using ⩽20 ml H_2O; and decolorize with crystal of Na_2SO_3. Ext with three 50 ml portions CHCl₃ and proceed as above.

(b) *Acetophenetidin.*—Wash filter used to dry the CHCl₃ with 5 ml H_2O, receiving washings in separator contg soln of phenetidin sulfate. Treat with successive small portions solid NaHCO₃ until, after compléte neutzn of free acid, excess of NaHCO₃ remains. Add 50 ml CHCl₃, and for each 0.1 g acetophenetidin known or believed to have been present, add 5 drops Ac₂O. Shake vigorously, let clear, and drain CHCl₃ into second separator contg 5 ml H_2O. Shake this mixt., and after clearing, pass solv. thru small, dry filter into 250 ml erlenmeyer. Repeat extn twice with 50 ml portions CHCl₃, washing each portion with the 5 ml H_2O in second separator.

Evap. combined CHCl₃ exts to ca 10 ml, transfer residual soln with enough fresh solv. to weighed

50 ml beaker or crystg dish, evap. on steam bath to apparent dryness, and finally remove any considerable excess of Ac₂O by repeated addns and evapns of 1 ml CHCl₃ and drop of alcohol. (Reformed acetophenetidin should finally appear as whitish, cryst. mass with faint acetous odor that disappears completely on standing several hr in open or over CaO in vac. desiccator.) Weigh at intervals until final wt differs from preceding by ⩽0.5 mg.

★ Acetophenetidin (Phenacetin) and ★ Salol (Phenyl Salicylate) (*68*)—Official Final Action

36.204 *Acid Hydrolysis Method*

See **32.158**, 10th ed.

36.205 *Alkaline Hydrolysis Method*

See **32.159**, 10th ed.

Acetylsalicylic Acid (*69*)—Official Final Action

36.206 ★ *Melting Point* ★

If excipients are present, treat 0.2–0.3 g with small portions CHCl₃ and filter into beaker or evapg dish. Evap. bulk of CHCl₃ on steam bath and complete evapn at room temp. Det. mp of cryst. residue by USP method.

36.207 ★ *Free Salicylic Acid* ★

(a) *Qualitative test.*—Shake 0.5 g sample in small erlenmeyer with ca 10 ml CHCl₃ and filter. Evap., treat residue with 10 ml cold H_2O, and filter. Add 1 drop 10% FeCl₃ soln. Violet color indicates free salicylic acid.

(b) *Determination.*—In each of 2 colorimeter tubes mix 48 ml H_2O and 1 ml freshly prepd $FeNH_4(SO_4)_2$ soln (1 ml $1N$ HCl and 2 ml 8% $FeNH_4(SO_4)_2.12H_2O$ soln/.00 ml). Shake 2.5 g powd sample (prepd as in **36.002**) with exactly 25 ml alcohol and filter if necessary. Immediately add 1 ml filtrate to one of colorimeter tubes and 1 ml std salicylic acid soln (0.01 g/100 ml alcohol) to other, and mix. Immediately and rapidly make color comparisons and calc. free salicylic acid on basis of acetylsalicylic acid present. If color is too intense for satisfactory comparison, repeat entire detn, using smaller wt powd sample.

★ Total Salicylate ★

36.208 *Reagent*

Potassium bromide-bromate soln.—$0.1N$. Prep. as in **45.021**. Stdze as follows: Transfer 30 ml to I flask, and add 25 ml H_2O, 5 ml 20% KI soln, and 5 ml HCl. Shake thoroly and titr. with $0.1N$ $Na_2S_2O_3$, using starch indicator, **6.004(f)**.

36.209 *Determination*

(a) *Iodine method.*—Weigh sample contg 0.1–0.2 g acetylsalicylic acid into beaker, add 20 ml H_2O

and 1 g Na_2CO_3, and heat on steam bath 15 min. Filter, if necessary, to remove talc. Dil. to 60–75 ml, heat nearly to boiling, slowly add excess (50–80 ml) of ca $0.1N$ I (enough to ensure excess during digestion), and digest 1 hr on steam bath.

Remove free I with few drops $Na_2S_2O_3$ soln and decant clear liq. thru weighed gooch, retaining most of ppt, tetraiodophenylenequinone $(C_6H_2I_2O)_2$, in flask. To latter add 50 ml boiling H_2O, digest 10 min on steam bath, filter, and gradually wash all ppt into gooch, using ca 200 ml hot H_2O for this purpose and final washings. Dry ppt to constant wt at 100°. Multiply wt ppt by 0.4016 to obtain total salicylic acid and deduct free salicylic acid, **36.207(b)**. Remainder $\times$ 1.304 = wt acetylsalicylic acid.

(b) *Bromine method.*—Saponify 0.5 g sample with 10 ml 2% NaOH soln by heating 15 min on steam bath. Dil. with H_2O in vol. flask to 500 ml. Transfer aliquot of this soln, contg 0.04–0.05 g but ⩽0.05 g acetylsalicylic acid, to 500 ml I flask, and add 30 ml std KBr-$KBrO_3$ soln. Add 5 ml HCl and immediately insert stopper. Shake frequently during 30 min and let stand 15 min. Remove stopper just enough to quickly add 5 ml 20% KI soln, taking care that no Br vapors escape, and immediately stopper flask. Shake thoroly, remove stopper, and rinse it and neck of flask with little H_2O so that washings flow into flask. Titr. with $0.1N$ $Na_2S_2O_3$, using starch indicator, **6.004(f)**. 1 ml $0.1N$ KBr-$KBrO_3$ = 0.00230 g salicylic acid, or 0.00300 g acetylsalicylic acid.

36.210 ★ *Combined Acetic Acid (70)* ★

(*Caution: See* **46.011**, **46.040**, and **46.056**.)

If excipients are present, accurately weigh 2 g powd sample and transfer to separator, using ca 25 ml H_2O. Ext completely with $CHCl_3$, testing last extn by evapg small quantity of the $CHCl_3$ to dryness. (Usually 6 extns with 30, 25, 20, 10, 10, and 5 ml portions $CHCl_3$ are enough.) Filter $CHCl_3$ fractions thru cotton pledget into beaker. Wash original beaker, funnel, and cotton with $CHCl_3$ and add these washings to $CHCl_3$ soln in beaker. Evap. $CHCl_3$ on steam bath and dry residue 15 min at 80°.

Treat $CHCl_3$ ext, or if no excipients are present, 2 g powd sample, in 150 ml beaker with 30 ml $1N$ NaOH and evap. on steam bath nearly to dryness. Transfer to separator, using 10 ml H_2O, 20 ml 10% H_2SO_4, and finally two 5 ml portions H_2O. Ext with successive portions $CHCl_3$, using first 50 ml portion to rinse beaker used for saponification. Continue extns with $CHCl_3$ until all salicylic acid is removed (ca 6 extns). Keep stopper in separator during these extns to guard against loss of HOAc by evapn. Collect $CHCl_3$ fractions in second separator, wash with 25 ml H_2O, and wash this H_2O

once with 5 ml $CHCl_3$. Discard $CHCl_3$ exts and return wash H_2O to acid H_2O in first separator.

Transfer acid H_2O contg HOAc and H_2SO_4 to 200 ml vol. flask, wash separators thoroly with H_2O, add to flask, dil. to vol., and mix thoroly. Pipet two 50 ml aliquots, using same pipet and draining same length of time. Place one portion in receptacle suitable for titrn and other in large Pt dish. Titr. first portion at once with $0.5N$ alkali, using phthln. Evap. portion in Pt dish on steam bath to dryness, take up in 10 ml H_2O, and again evap., repeating this process twice more. (During evapn guard against contact with NH_3 vapors.) Take up residue in H_2O and titr. with $0.5N$ alkali, using phthln. Subtract second titrn reading from first and calc. % HOAc in 0.5 g sample. 1 ml $0.5N$ alkali = 0.0300 g HOAc.

Double Titration Method (71)
36.211   *Preparation of Solution*

(a) *Dry extraction method (applicable in all cases).*—Treat weighed quantity of sample contg ⩾0.3 g acetylsalicylic acid with small portions $CHCl_3$, filter into beaker, and wash residue with $CHCl_3$ until completely extd. Evap. bulk of $CHCl_3$ on steam bath, finishing with aid of elec. fan without heat.

(b) *Wet extraction method (applicable in absence of acids and alkalies, or alkaline earth carbonates).*—Transfer accurately weighed sample to small separator contg ca 20 ml H_2O. Ext repeatedly with $CHCl_3$, using 30, 25, 20, 15, 10, and 5 ml portions, and test for completeness of extn by evapg portion of final ext on watch glass. Filter combined $CHCl_3$ portions thru cotton, and wash funnel and cotton with $CHCl_3$. Evap. bulk of $CHCl_3$ on steam bath, finishing with aid of elec. fan without heat.

(c) *Acetylsalicylic acid and uncoated tablets containing no excipient.*—Dissolve sample directly in 10 ml neut. alcohol.

36.212   *Determination*

Dissolve the dry $CHCl_3$ ext in 10 ml neut. alcohol, and immediately and rapidly titr. with $0.1N$ alkali, using phthln. Use first persistent pink as end point, since any slight excess of alkali tends to hydrolyze ester quickly. Add vol. of the $0.1N$ alkali equal to that used in first titrn and then add 5 ml more. Heat on steam bath 15 min. Back-titr. with $0.1N$ acid. If product is pure, total quantity of alkali consumed will be twice that of first titrn. 1 ml $0.1N$ alkali consumed in 2 titrns = 0.0090 g acetylsalicylic acid.

Acetylsalicylic Acid and Phenobarbital (72)— Official Final Action
36.213   *Apparatus*

(a) *Spectrophotometer.*—Capable of isolating spectrum of 2 nm or less in region 230–300 nm.

(b) *Chromatographic tube and tamping rod.*—See **36.015**.

36.214 Reagents

(a) *Dibasic potassium phosphate soln.*—Approx. $2M$. Dissolve 35 g K_2HPO_4 in H_2O, cool to room temp., and dil. to 100 ml.

(b) *Diatomaceous earth.*—Celite 545.

(c) *Washed chloroform.*—Wash NF $CHCl_3$ with ½ vol. H_2O in separator.

(d) *Acetylsalicylic acid std soln.*—5 mg/100 ml. Dissolve 100 mg acetylsalicylic acid in $CHCl_3$ and dil. to 100 ml with $CHCl_3$. Dil. 5 ml aliquot to 100 ml with $CHCl_3$.

(e) *Phenobarbital std soln.*—1 mg/100 ml. Dissolve 100 mg phenobarbital in NH_4OH $(1 + 27)$ and dil. to 500 ml with NH_4OH $(1 + 27)$. Dil. 5 ml aliquot to 100 ml with NH_4OH $(1 + 27)$.

36.215 Preparation of Sample Solution

Transfer accurately weighed portion of finely ground tablets contg 60–120 mg phenobarbital to 100 ml vol. flask. Dissolve in $CHCl_3$ by shaking vigorously and dil. to vol. with $CHCl_3$.

36.216 Preparation of Chromatographic Column

Pack small pledget of glass wool in constricted portion of stem of tube and place pad of glass wool ca 5 mm thick in bottom of large portion of tube. Fasten piece of rubber tubing with attached screw clamp to outlet to limit flow during packing. Clamp tube in vertical position.

To 10 g Celite 545 in mortar add 50 ml $CHCl_3$, and mix with pestle to form slurry. Distribute 10 ml $2M$ K_2HPO_4 soln, (a), over surface of slurry and mix thoroly until homogeneous, adding more $CHCl_3$ if necessary. Add this slurry to tube, ca ⅓ at time, alternately packing and forming flocculent suspension by working packing rod up and down. Celite must be covered with $CHCl_3$ at all times.

After column is packed, remove rubber tube from stem and rinse stem with $CHCl_3$. Check flow rate of column with $CHCl_3$ level ca 5 cm above surface of column. Adjust rate of flow to 2–5 ml/min by tightening or loosening glass wool pledget in constricted portion of stem. When level of solv. just reaches surface of Celite, place 100 ml vol. flask under stem.

36.217 Determination of Phenobarbital

Add 5 ml prepd sample soln, **36.215**, from pipet to side of tube near Celite surface. When level of sample soln reaches surface of column, add 5 ml washed $CHCl_3$, let sink into column, and repeat with another 5 ml washed $CHCl_3$. After last rinse enters column, add washed $CHCl_3$ to tube and keep level of 4–8 cm $CHCl_3$ above column during elution.

Collect 95 ml eluate in the 100 ml vol. flask. Dil. to vol. with $CHCl_3$, mix, and transfer 20 ml aliquot to 100 ml beaker. Evap. to dryness on steam bath under air current. Dissolve residue in NH_4OH $(1 + 27)$ and transfer to 100 ml vol. flask. Rinse, and dil. to vol. with NH_4OH $(1 + 27)$. Det. A at 240.5 nm against blank prepd by passing 5 ml $CHCl_3$ thru column as with sample soln.

$$\text{g phenobarbital in sample} = 10A/a,$$

where A is A of soln at 240.5 nm, and a is a of phenobarbital at 240.5 nm obtained by dividing A of std phenobarbital soln in 1 cm cell at 240.5 nm by its concn (0.01 g/L).

36.218 Determination of Acetylsalicylic Acid

Dil. 5 ml original sample soln, **36.215**, to 100 ml with $CHCl_3$ in vol. flask. Dil. 10 ml aliquot of this soln to 100 ml with $CHCl_3$. Det. A of final diln on spectrophtr at 278 nm against $CHCl_3$ blank.

$$\text{g acetylsalicylic acid in sample} = 20A'/a',$$

where A' is A of soln at 278 nm, and a' is a of acetylsalicylic acid at 278 nm obtained by dividing A of std acetylsalicylic acid soln in 1 cm cell at 278 nm by its concn (0.05 g/L).

36.219 Acetylsalicylic Acid and Phenolphthalein in Tablets (73)—Official Final Action

(Caution: See **46.011, 46.039, 46.040, 46.054, and 46.056.)**

Accurately weigh powd sample, prepd as in **36.002**, contg 0.05–0.1 g phthln. Ext repeatedly with 20 ml portions ether, and filter into separator. Test for complete extn (5–8 extns required).

(a) *Acetylsalicylic acid.*—Shake ether soln, ⩾1 min each time, with two 20 ml portions 4% $NaHCO_3$ soln (temp. ⩽20°). Transfer soln to second separator. Wash ether with two 10 ml portions H_2O and add to $NaHCO_3$ soln. Ext $NaHCO_3$ soln with 20 ml ether. Drain lower aq. layer into 100 ml vol. flask. Wash ether with small portions H_2O, rinse into flask, and dil. to vol. Add wash ether to bulk of solv. in original separator. Reserve ether soln for detn of phthln.

Transfer aliquot $NaHCO_3$ soln contg ⩾0.3 g acetylsalicylic acid to separator. (Acid must be sepd from $NaHCO_3$ soln as rapidly as possible to prevent hydrolysis.) Acidify with HCl $(1 + 3)$ and ext liberated acetylsalicylic acid with 30, 20, 20, 10, and 10 ml portions $CHCl_3$-ether $(3 + 2)$. Wash each ext with 2 ml H_2O in second separator and filter thru cotton pledget, moistened with $CHCl_3$-ether mixt., into counterpoised weighed beaker. Test for complete extn. Evap. filtrate to 10–15 ml on H_2O bath, and complete evapn without heat. Dry residue to constant wt at room temp. Wt may be checked by double titrn method, **36.212**.

(b) *Phenolphthalein.*—Ext original ether soln

with 20 ml portions 3% NaOH soln until all phthln is removed (indicated by color). Transfer these alk. exts to second separator, acidify with HCl (1 + 3), and ext with CHCl₃-ether (3 + 2). Wash each ext in third separator with 2 ml H_2O to which has been added 1 or 2 drops HCl (1 + 3). Filter exts into counterpoised weighed beaker, using cotton pledget moistened with the CHCl₃-ether mixt. in stem of funnel. Evap. on H_2O bath and dry to constant wt at 120°. Wt may be checked by tetraiodo method, **36.467**.

Aminopyrine (Pyramidon®)—
Official Final Action
36.220   Qualitative Tests (74)

(a) Dissolve 0.01 g sample in 2 ml H_2O and add few drops of yellow HNO_3 (contg HNO_2). Purplish-blue soln is produced.

(b) Dissolve 0.01 g sample in 2 ml H_2O and add 1 ml 10% $FeCl_3$ soln. Purple to violet color develops, which becomes red on addn of H_2SO_4 (1 + 9).

(c) Dissolve 0.1 g sample in 2 ml H_2O and add few drops of 5% $AgNO_3$ soln. After few sec purple to violet color is produced, and on standing, deposit of metallic Ag results (useful for detecting aminopyrine in antipyrine).

(d) Dissolve 0.1–0.2 g sample in 2 ml H_2O, add 1 or 2 drops 0.2% $NaNO_2$ soln and few drops of H_2SO_4 (1 + 9), and shake few sec. Purplish-blue color develops and then gradually fades, leaving colorless soln. Excess $NaNO_2$ destroys aminopyrine color. On addn of few more drops of $NaNO_2$ soln and dil. H_2SO_4, yellowish-green color remains after purple disappears if antipyrine is present. (Useful for detecting antipyrine in presence of aminopyrine.)

36.221   Quantitative Method (75)

(*Caution: See* **46.011**, **46.040**, and **46.056**.)

Place 1 g powd sample in 100 ml vol. flask, add 60 ml 1N H_2SO_4, and shake several min to ensure complete soln of aminopyrine. Dil. to vol. with 1N H_2SO_4. Filter, if not clear, thru dry filter, rejecting first part of filtrate. Pipet 20 ml aliquot of soln or filtrate into separator; make distinctly alk. with either NH_4OH or 5% NaOH; and ext with 20, 15, 10, 10, and 5 ml portions CHCl₃. Combine CHCl₃ exts in second separator and wash with 2 ml H_2O. Filter CHCl₃ soln into weighed beaker thru cotton pledget satd with CHCl₃. Ext wash H_2O with 5 ml CHCl₃ and add this to combined CHCl₃ exts. Evap. combined CHCl₃ exts just to dryness on H_2O bath with aid of elec. fan and dry residue 10 min at 100°. Cool in desiccator, and weigh as aminopyrine. Identify aminopyrine by its mp, 106.5–109°, or qual. tests, **36.220**, or microchemical tests, **36.536**.

Antihistamines in Presence of Acetophenetidin, Acetylsalicylic Acid, and Caffeine (APC)
(76)—Official Final Action

(Applicable to thonzylamine.HCl, pheniramine maleate, and chlorpheniramine maleate in combination with APC)

36.222   Preparation of Standard Solutions

Prep. sep. std solns of thonzylamine.HCl, pheniramine maleate, and chlorpheniramine maleate by dissolving 250 mg antihistamine salt, accurately weighed, in 50.0 ml H_2O. Pipet 5 ml of each soln into 100 ml vol. flasks and dil. to vol. with ca 0.1N H_2SO_4. Transfer 10 ml of each acid soln to sep. 100 ml vol. flasks and dil. to vol. with ca 0.1N H_2SO_4. (Concn = 2.5 mg/100 ml.) Det. A_{std} of thonzylamine.HCl at 314 nm, pheniramine maleate at 265 nm, and chlorpheniramine maleate at 264 nm.

36.223   Determination

Place accurately weighed powd sample contg ca 10 mg antihistamine in 125 ml separator. Add 15 ml H_2O and ca 0.5 ml H_2SO_4 (1 + 1). Ext with CHCl₃, using 30, 20, 20, and 20 ml portions. Re-ext by passing CHCl₃ exts successively thru 2 separators, each contg 10 ml ca 0.1N H_2SO_4, shaking vigorously each time. Discard CHCl₃ and combine aq. solns.

Make combined solns alk. with 10% NaOH and ext with 30, 20, 20, and 20 ml portions CHCl₃. Again pass CHCl₃ exts successively thru 2 separators, each contg 20 ml ca 0.1N H_2SO_4, shaking vigorously each time. Discard CHCl₃, combine acid aq. solns, and dil. to vol. with ca 0.1N H_2SO_4 in 100 ml vol. flask. Transfer 25 ml aliquot to 100 ml vol. flask and dil. to vol. with ca 0.1N H_2SO_4. Det. A at wavelength of max. absorption against ca 0.1N acid as ref.

% Antihistamine
$$= (A \times 2.5 \times 4 \times 100)/(A_{std} \times mg\ sample).$$

36.224   Antipyrine and Benzocaine—Official Final Action

See **36.057–36.061**.

★ **Antipyrine and Caffeine (77)—** ★
Official Final Action
36.225   Preparation of Sample

(*Caution: See* **46.011**, **46.040**, and **46.056**.)

(a) Weigh amt of finely powd sample equal to, or multiple of, av. unit dose; transfer to filter or beaker and ext with CHCl₃. Evap. CHCl₃ on steam bath.

(b) With alc. prepns, remove alcohol from measured amt by heating on steam bath. Ext residue with three 50 ml portions CHCl₃ in separator. Evap. CHCl₃ on steam bath.

36.226 Determination

(a) *Antipyrine.*—Transfer residue obtained, **36.225**, which should weigh ca 0.25 g, to 125 ml separator, using two 5 ml portions alcohol-free (washed) $CHCl_3$, followed by 10 ml H_2O. (Use of alcohol-free $CHCl_3$ for iodination of antipyrine is necessary to preclude formation of CHI_3, presence of which in residue X would vitiate result.) Add 1 g $NaHCO_3$ and 10–15 ml $0.2N$ I (or double quantity of $0.1N$ I), adding latter in small portions and shaking vigorously after each addn. (I should then be in excess of that required to convert all antipyrine to monoiodo derivative; if it is not, add little more I and shake mixt. again.)

Remove free I with small crystal of $Na_2S_2O_3$.$5H_2O$ and add 15 ml washed $CHCl_3$, shaking vigorously 1 min. After clearing, drain $CHCl_3$ into second separator; wash with 5 ml H_2O, filter thru small, dry filter into weighed 50 ml beaker, and evap. to apparent dryness on steam bath, using air current. Repeat extn with 2 (3, if $0.1N$ I has been used) 25 ml portions washed $CHCl_3$, washing, filtering, and evapg each portion as before. Recover any cryst. product sepg around tip of delivery tube, funnel, and edge of filter by careful washing with $CHCl_3$. Dry nearly colorless cryst. residue of caffeine and iodoantipyrine 30 min at 100°, cool, and weigh. Designate this wt as X.

Dissolve residue in 5 ml HOAc, add 10 ml *satd SO_2 soln,* and wash with hot H_2O into 400–500 ml beaker until final vol. is ca 200 ml. Add enough $AgNO_3$ soln to ppt all the I (ca 0.3 g $AgNO_3$) and few drops of HNO_3, heat nearly to boiling, and stir to agglomerate AgI. Add 15 ml HNO_3, cover beaker with watch glass, and boil gently 5 min. Decant thru weighed gooch; wash ppt once with little alcohol and then with two 100 ml portions boiling H_2O; and finally transfer AgI to crucible. Wash several times with hot H_2O and again with alcohol to remove traces of org. matter, dry 30 min at 110°, cool, and weigh. Wt AgI $\times$ 0.8018 = wt antipyrine.

(b) *Caffeine.*—Multiply wt AgI by 1.3380 and subtract product from wt X, in (a).

In analysis of mixt. contg caffeine, antipyrine, acetanilid, and Na salicylate, following steps are essential to effect sepn: (1) Extn of caffeine, acetanilid, and antipyrine from aq. alk. soln with $CHCl_3$; (2) hydrolytic treatment with H_2SO_4 of 3 substances thus sepd, preliminary to detn of caffeine and antipyrine as in (a).

Cinchophen—Official Final Action
In Presence of Salicylates (78)
36.227 Reagents

(a) *Sodium carbonate soln.*—Dissolve 12.5 g $Na_2CO_3.H_2O$ in enough H_2O to make 100 ml.

(b) *Iodine std soln.*—$0.1N$. Prep as in **45.019** and stdze against std $Na_2S_2O_3$ soln, **45.039**.

(c) *Sodium thiosulfate soln.*—$0.02N$. Dil. 200 ml stdzd $0.1N$ $Na_2S_2O_3$, **45.039**, to 1 L with H_2O.

36.228 Determination

If product is solid, accurately weigh into 50 ml beaker finely powd sample contg ca 0.15 g cinchophen. Treat with 5, 3, and 3 ml portions Na_2CO_3 soln, (a), and filter thru 5 cm paper into 50 ml beaker, finally washing first beaker and paper with little H_2O. Evap. filtrate and washings to complete dryness on steam bath with aid of air current.

If product is clear soln, transfer measured portion to beaker, and evap. to dryness.

In either case, dissolve hot residue in 5 ml HOAc, and transfer to 100 ml vol. flask, using $\leqslant 10$ ml HOAc to complete transfer. Heat to ca 90° on steam bath. Slowly add 25 ml $0.1N$ I from pipet with constant agitation, and immediately stopper flask. Let cool, dil. to 100 ml with H_2O, stopper, and let stand 30 min with occasional thoro agitation. Filter thru small, rapid filter, rejecting first 15 ml filtrate, and immediately titr. 50 ml aliquot with std $Na_2S_2O_3$ soln, adding starch indicator, **6.004(f)**, as end point approaches. 1 ml $0.1N$ I = 0.0166 g cinchophen, $C_{16}H_{11}O_2N$.

In Presence of Sodium Bicarbonate (79)
36.229 Reagents

(a) *Solvent.*—Mix 50 ml alcohol and 50 ml ether with 100 ml $CHCl_3$.

(b) *Neutral alcohol.*—Neutze to phthln with $0.1N$ NaOH.

36.230 Determination

Accurately weigh powd sample contg 0.3–0.4 g cinchophen, transfer to separator, and add 10 ml 4% NaOH soln to dissolve the cinchophen. Neutze with HCl $(1 + 3)$ and add 2 ml excess. Ext with five 25 ml portions solv., (a), collecting exts in second separator. Wash with 25 ml H_2O and filter exts into beaker. Ext wash H_2O with 15 ml solv. and filter into same beaker. Test for complete extn. Evap. solv. to dryness on steam bath. Dissolve residue in 60 ml neut. alcohol. Titr. with $0.1N$ NaOH to permanent pink, using phthln. 1 ml $0.1N$ NaOH = 0.02493 g cinchophen.

36.231 ★ Salicylic Acid in Presence of ★ Other Phenols (80)—Official Final Action

See **32.184–32.185**, 10th ed. (*Caution: See* **46.011**, **46.040**, and **46.056**.)

HORMONES AND RELATED COMPOUNDS
Diethylstilbestrol (81)—Official Final Action
36.232 Reagent and Apparatus

Diethylstilbestrol std soln.—Accurately weigh suitable amt of USP Ref. Std Diethylstilbestrol, dissolve in alcohol, and prep. soln contg 20.0 μg/ml by accurate stepwise diln with alcohol. Prep. working std soln by mixing 25 ml of this soln with 25 ml 1.8% K_2HPO_4 soln.

Irradiation containers.—Quartz cells $\geqslant$4 ml capacity with clear sides, or 18 × 150 mm Vycor test tubes, held in rack that does not obstruct effective light beam of cylindrical 15 watt germicidal lamp, may be used conveniently.

36.233   *Preparation of Assay Solution*

(a) *Oil solns containing 2 mg or less diethylstilbestrol/ml.*—Using accurately calibrated hypodermic syringe, transfer vol. sample contg 2 mg diethylstilbestrol to separator contg 50 ml isooctane. Shake mixt. with 10 ml 1N NaOH and transfer well-defined aq. layer as completely as possible to second separator contg 50 ml isooctane. Shake vigorously and transfer clear aq. layer to third separator. Repeat extn of the 2 isooctane layers successively with two 10 ml portions 1N NaOH, collect aq. layers in third separator, and discard extd isooctane layers.

Acidify combined aq. exts with 3 ml H_2SO_4 (1 + 1), cool, and ext diethylstilbestrol with three 30 ml portions $CHCl_3$. Wash $CHCl_3$ exts successively in 2 separators, first contg 20 ml 1% $NaHCO_3$ and second 20 ml H_2O.

Filter washed $CHCl_3$ exts thru cotton pledget moistened with $CHCl_3$ into 100 ml vol. flask, dil. to vol. with $CHCl_3$, and mix.

Transfer 10.0 ml $CHCl_3$ soln, contg 200 μg diethylstilbestrol, to small erlenmeyer and evap. just to dryness on steam bath with aid of air current. Cool in vac. desiccator 10 min. Add 10.0 ml alcohol, stopper, and dissolve residue by swirling. After 15 min, mix with 10.0 ml 1.8% K_2HPO_4 to prep. assay soln.

(b) *Oil solns containing more than 2 mg diethylstilbestrol/ml.*—Dil. convenient accurately measured vol. oil soln with $CHCl_3$ to obtain soln contg 0.5 mg diethylstilbestrol/ml. Transfer 4 ml aliquot to separator contg 50 ml isooctane and proceed as in (a), beginning "Shake mixt. with 10 ml 1N NaOH . . ."

(c) *Tablets.*—Transfer accurately weighed portion powd material contg 2 mg diethylstilbestrol to separator contg 30 ml $CHCl_3$. Add 10 ml H_2O and 1 ml H_2SO_4 (1 + 1) and shake vigorously. Drain $CHCl_3$ layer into second separator, wash with 5 ml H_2O, and filter thru cotton pledget moistened with $CHCl_3$ into 100 ml vol. flask. Repeat extn with three 20 ml portions $CHCl_3$, dil. combined exts to 100 ml, and mix.

Proceed as in (a), fourth par.

36.234   *Irradiation*

(*Caution:* Protect eyes from direct rays of UV light.)

Test transparency of several irradiation containers as follows: Transfer convenient vols of working std soln to tubes, place them ca 7 cm from 15 watt germicidal lamp, and irradiate soln transversely ca 10 min. Measure A of yellow solns at 418 nm in suitable spectrophtr in matched 1 cm cells, against H_2O. Re-irradiate for 1–3 min intervals, and note irradiation time required for max. A. Repeat irradiation process, varying distance of tubes from lamp, and det. most convenient conditions for developing stable, repeatable colors of max. A (ca 0.7 at 418 nm).

Transfer portions of working std soln and assay soln to clean, dry irradiation containers, and irradiate under optimum conditions previously detd. Calc. quantity of diethylstilbestrol in sample.

36.235   *Total Phenols*

Transfer to beaker 20 ml $CHCl_3$ ext, 36.233, contg 400 μg diethylstilbestrol. Transfer alc. soln contg 400.0 μg USP Ref. Std Diethylstilbestrol to similar beaker, and treat both solns as follows: Evap. to dryness on steam bath with aid of air current. Dissolve residues in 2.0 ml HOAc with gentle warming. Cool to room temp., add 10 drops H_2SO_4 (1 + 1), and mix. Cool, add 5 drops *10% $NaNO_2$ soln,* and let stand 45 min with occasional mixing. Wash quant. into 25 ml vol. flask with ca 20 ml alc. NH$_4$OH soln, prepd by mixing equal vols alcohol and dil. NH$_4$OH (4 + 6). Cool in ice bath, and let stand at room temp. 1 hr. Dil. to vol. with the alc. NH$_4$OH soln, and mix. If ppt forms, filter thru dry paper, rejecting first few ml filtrate. Det. A of clear, yellow alk. solns at 420 nm in tightly stoppered 1 cm cells, in suitable spectrophtr, against alcohol (1 + 2). Calc. % total phenols, as diethylstilbestrol, in sample.

Ethisterone (17α-Ethynyltestosterone) (82)— Official First Action
KBr Disk Method

36.236   *Apparatus*

(a) *Pipets.*—Calibrated to deliver 0.10 and 0.20 ml.

(b) *Mechanical vibrator.*—Such as Crescent Amalgamator, 3275 rpm, with steel capsules, ⁵⁄₁₆ × 1″, and steel balls ⅛″ diam.

(c) *Die.*—Suitable for prepg disks 12.7 mm diam.

(d) *Hydraulic press.*—20,000–40,000 lb capacity.

(e) *Micrometer.*—Calibrated in in. or mm.

(f) *Ruler or drafting divider.*—Graduated in mm.

(g) *Recording double-beam infrared spectrophotometer.*—With holder for disks.

36.237   *Reagents*

(a) *Adsorbent.*—Celite 545, acid washed, rinsed to neutrality, and dried. Celite 545, acid-washed, neut., may be used as received.

(b) *Potassium bromide.*—200-325 mesh, IR

quality (Harshaw Chemical Co., 6801 Cochran Rd, Solon, OH 44039, or equiv.), dried ≥16 hr at 105° before use.

36.238 Chromatography

(*Caution: See* **46.011, 46.040, and 46.056.**)

Thoroly mix 10 g adsorbent and 5 ml H_2O. Place pledget of glass wool in stem and base of chromatgc tube, 200 × 22 mm with 40 × 5 mm stem, add Celite-H_2O mixt. in 3 equal portions, and tamp down after each addn. (Ht of 1 cm/g Celite gives suitable flow rate.)

Transfer weighed amt of ground tablets contg 25 mg ethisterone to 100 ml beaker contg 2 g adsorbent. Add 1 ml H_2O, mix thoroly, and add mixt. to prepd column. Rinse beaker with 0.5 g adsorbent, add rinse to column, and tamp down. Place small glass wool pledget on top of column. Rinse beaker with ca 2 ml redistd isooctane, and add rinse to column.

Immediately support stoppered separator contg 200 ml redistd isooctane at ht to maintain 1″ of solv. above column, open stopcock, and elute, collecting ca 175 ml eluate (discard). Rinse sample beaker with two 5 ml portions $CHCl_3$ and add rinses to column. Completely elute column with 400 ml $CHCl_3$, collecting eluate. Stabilize eluate by adding 5 ml absolute alcohol. Evap. to dryness at <50° under vac. or with stream of dry air at 35–40°. (Needles that form are light and fluffy; therefore remove final traces of solv. with very gentle air stream.) Add 15 ml absolute MeOH to residue and dissolve by warming. Quant. transfer soln to 25 ml vol. flask, rinsing with two 3 ml portions warm MeOH, and dil. to vol. (Final concn is ca 1.0 mg/ml.)

36.239 Spectrophotometry

Transfer duplicate 0.20 ml aliquots sample and std solns contg 1.0 mg NF ethisterone/ml absolute MeOH to steel capsules contg 1 steel ball, 200 mg KBr, and 0.1 ml benzene. Touch pipet tip to inner side of cylinder to complete transfer. Use same pipet for sample and std. Evap. solns to dryness with very gentle stream of dry air or N at ca 30–35° (evapn time, ca 5 min/0.1 ml). Evap. samples and std simultaneously. Wash down sides of cylinders with 0.1 ml absolute MeOH and evap. solv. as above in ca 5 min. Dry residues 30 min at 105°, and cool to room temp.

Break up residues and free steel balls with dry microspatula. Add 0.005 ml absolute MeOH to each cylinder just before grinding (within 5 sec). Vibrate stoppered cylinder on mech. vibrator exactly 60 sec. Dry residues 15 min at 105°, cool to room temp., remove steel balls, and transfer residue to 0.5″ die. Evacuate 1 min at ca 1 mm pressure under ca 2000 lb force, and press mixt. 3 min at 20,000–25,000 lb under continued vac. Use same

force for both std and sample. Place disks in vials, heat 20 min at 105°, and cool to room temp.

Place disks in holder and outline area exposed to sample beam. Obtain duplicate spectra of disks between 5.3 and 6.7 µm, using quant. instrument settings. Dct. av. thickness of exposed disk area from 6 micrometer readings. Measure baseline A of 6.03 µm peak, using 5.45 and 6.6 µm min. Det. band width, H, at ½ the ht (baseline to peak) with ruler or calibrated divider. Calc. absorptivity coefficient,

$$a = (A_s \times H \times 0.99)/(C \times L_s),$$

where A_s = baseline A of std band; C = ratio of wt std to wt KBr; L_s is av. thickness (mm) of std disk area in beam; H is half band width in mm; and 0.99 = correction factor for recovery of std.

Calc. mg ethisterone/tablet =

$$(A_u \times H \times M \times 25 \times T)/(a \times L_u \times 0.2 \times W),$$

where subscript u indicates corresponding value of sample; M = wt KBr in mg; T = av. wt/tablet; and W = wt sample (in same units as T).

Prove identity of sample by comparing spectrum of sample in 2–15 µm region with that of std. Relative intensities of bands in std and sample spectra should be same.

Hexestrol (4,4'-(1,2-Diethylethylene Diphenol)) (83)—Official Final Action

36.240 Determination

Grind representative number of tablets (≥20) to fine powder.

Weigh portion powd tablets contg ca 5 mg hexestrol into 125 ml separator contg 25 ml H_2O and 1 ml HCl (1 + 9). Ext with 25, 15, 10, and 10 ml $CHCl_3$. Drain each ext thru $CHCl_3$-satd cotton pledget into 100 ml beaker. Evap. combined exts to ca 25 ml on steam bath in air current. Check for completeness of extn by evapg addnl 10 ml ext to dryness.

Quant. transfer concd $CHCl_3$ exts to 125 ml separator contg 10 ml isooctane. Ext with 25, 15, 15, and 10 ml ca 0.1N NaOH, rolling or shaking separator gently 90 sec each time; emulsions may form. Drain lower org. layer into second 125 ml separator, each time including any small emulsion layer present. Continue alk. extn of org. phase, draining it alternately into two 125 ml separators and combining alk. exts by pouring each time into original separator. Discard org. phase.

Make combined alk. exts acid with HCl. Ext with 25, 15, 15, and 10 ml $CHCl_3$, collecting combined exts in 125 ml separator. Wash $CHCl_3$ exts with two 15 ml portions H_2O. Discard H_2O washes.

Pass combined $CHCl_3$ exts thru 1 cm column of granular anhyd. Na_2SO_4 in coarse fritted glass funnel, ca 3.5 cm id, into 100 ml vol. flask. Rinse column and stem tip with small portions $CHCl_3$.

Dil. to vol. with CHCl₃. Place 50.0 ml aliquot in g-s flask and evap. just to dryness on steam bath, with aid of air current. Remove last traces of CHCl₃ with air current and without heat. Pipet 50.0 ml alcohol onto dry residue; shake 1 min to dissolve. This is sample soln.

Prep. std soln by dissolving pure hexestrol in enough alcohol to make concn ca 2.5 mg/50.0 ml. Use alcohol as ref. blank with sample and std solns.

Det. baseline A of sample and std solns at 280 nm with spectrophtr. If recording UV spectrophtr is used, record spectra between 320 and 240 nm. Adjust instrument to begin at 320 nm with zero A, and record spectra to 240 nm.

Calc. mg hexestrol in assay sample = (A/A') × (mg/ml std soln) × total ml sample soln, where A refers to sample and A' refers to std soln at 280 nm.

36.241   Qualitative Identification

(a) *Ultraviolet spectra.*—Dil. alc. soln of sample and std previously used for quant. assay to ca 20 μg/ml with alcohol. Compare UV spectrum from 215 to 320 nm with similar spectrum from authentic hexestrol.

(b) *Infrared spectra.*—Prep. KBr disk contg 0.3–0.6% hexestrol from residue obtained by evapg portion of remaining CHCl₃ sample soln from assay. Compare IR spectrum from 2 to 16 μm with similar spectrum from authentic hexestrol. (Extraneous peak at 5.85 μm appears in spectra of tablet prepns that does not appear in std.)

Ketosteroids (84)—Official First Action
36.242   Apparatus

(a) *Spectrophotometer or photometer.*—Capable of isolating spectral band 2 nm or less at 400–700 nm. Beckman quartz spectrophtr fitted with matched 1 cm cells is suitable.

(b) *Separators.*—125 ml, with well-fitting stopcocks lubricated *only with* H_2O.

36.243   Reagents

(a) *Benzenesulfonyl chloride.*—Reagent grade redistd under vac. in all-glass app. (*Caution:* May be harmful. Use effective fume removal device and protect skin and eyes when handling. See **46.015.**)

(b) *BQC reagent.*—Prep., just before use, 0.5% soln of cryst. dibromoquinonechloroimide in alcohol. Soln deteriorates progressively, yielding undesirable background colors. Store solid reagent in brown glass bottle in desiccator. (*Caution: See Note,* **16.082(d).**)

(c) *Buffer soln.*—pH 5.2–5.4. Dissolve 220 g NaOAc.3H₂O (or 133 g anhyd. salt) in 600 ml H₂O. Add 20.0 ml HOAc, dil. to 1 L, and mix.

(d) *Ether.*—USP, freshly washed twice with equal vol. H₂O.

(e) *Girard reagent T* (*trimethylacethydrazide ammonium chloride*).—Recrystallize com. samples twice from absolute alcohol and dry under vac. at room temp. Recrystd material should be white and practically odorless. Store in tightly stoppered bottle in desiccator.

(f) *Modified iron-Kober reagent.*—Dil. 10 ml stock iron-Kober reagent, **36.250(a)**, to 100 ml with H₂SO₄ (2 + 1) just before use, shaking vigorously to homogeneity.

(g) *Pyridine.*—Redistd over solid KOH in all-glass app. (*Caution:* May be harmful. Use effective fume removal device and protect skin and eyes when handling. See **46.011** and **46.072.**)

(h) *Silicon carbide.*—"20 mesh" (Carborundum Co.).

(i) *Skellysolve C or high-boiling petroleum ether.*—Boiling range 65–110°, 90–100°, etc.

36.244   Standard Solutions

(a) *Estrone std soln.*—50 μg/ml. Dissolve 25 mg NF Ref. Std estrone, accurately weighed, in alcohol, and dil. to 500 ml with alcohol.

(b) *Equilin std solns.*—(1) 50 μg/ml. Dissolve 25 mg equilin, accurately weighed, in alcohol, and dil. to 500 ml with alcohol. (2) Prep. dild (10 μg/ml) std in alcohol, required in estrone detn, from aliquot of this soln.

(c) *Equilenin std soln.*—50 μg/ml. Dissolve 25 mg equilenin, accurately weighed, in alcohol, and dil. to 500 ml with alcohol.

Stored in tightly stoppered containers in dark, std solns keep for months. Equilin and equilenin available from K&K Laboratories, Inc.

36.245   Isolation of Ketosteroids

(*Caution: See* **46.011**, **46.039**, and **46.054.**)

(a) *Tablets.*—Weigh counted number of tablets and reduce to fine powder without appreciable loss. Accurately weigh sample contg: (1) 5–10 mg ketosteroids; (2) 0.2–0.5 mg estradiol; or (3) 50,000–100,000 International Units estrogens. Transfer to 125 ml separator contg 25 ml H₂O and 2 ml H₂SO₄ (1 + 1). Ext with four 20 ml portions CHCl₃. Evap. combined CHCl₃ exts to ca 5 ml, add 25 ml Skellysolve C, transfer to 125 ml separator with several small portions CHCl₃, and proceed as in (c), beginning "Add 10 ml ca 2N NaOH . . ."

(b) *Aqueous suspensions.*—Measure portion of sample contg quantity of estrogens specified in (a), and transfer to 125 ml separator. Ext with six 25 ml portions ether (samples contg polyoxyethylene sorbitol monoöleate, or similar compds, should be extd with CHCl₃, as ether frequently forms emulsions difficult to break). Combine ether exts and evap. to ca 5 ml. Add 25 ml Skellysolve C, transfer to 125 ml separator with aid of several small portions CHCl₃, and proceed as in (c), beginning "Add 10 ml ca 2N NaOH . . ."

(c) Oil solns.—Measure portion of sample contg quantity of estrogens specified in (a), and transfer to 125 ml separator contg 25 ml Skellysolve C. Add 10 ml ca 2N NaOH, shake vigorously 2 min, and let layers sep. completely. Transfer aq. layer to second 125 ml separator. Repeat extn with 2 addnl 10 ml portions 2N NaOH soln, adding each ext to second separator. (Alk. extn should be completed as quickly as possible; long standing in strongly alk. soln may cause some decomposition of keto-steroids.) Discard Skellysolve soln.

Add H_2SO_4 (1 + 1) to combined alk. solns until permanent opalescence or ppt forms (acid to lit-mus). Cool thoroly, add 25 ml washed ether, shake carefully 1 min, and let sep. Transfer acid layer to second 125 ml separator and repeat extn with 25 ml washed ether. Discard acid layer. Ext ether layers successively with two 5 ml portions 10% Na_2CO_3 soln and two 5 ml portions H_2O. Discard aq. layers. Transfer ether solns to small beaker and carefully evap. to dryness on steam bath in air current, adding few ml alcohol if necessary to aid in removal of residual H_2O.

Dissolve ether ext in small amt of $CHCl_3$, warming if necessary, and transfer with few ml $CHCl_3$ to 18 × 150 mm test tube. Carefully evap. $CHCl_3$ on steam bath in air current. Add 100 mg Girard reagent T and 0.5 ml HOAc to test tube, stopper loosely with foil-covered cork, and heat in boiling H_2O bath 5 min.

Cool in ice bath, dissolve reaction mixt. in few ml ice-H_2O, and transfer to 125 ml separator contg ca 25 ml ice-H_2O. Make soln neut. to litmus paper by addn of ca 2N NaOH and ext *at once* with three 15 ml portions $CHCl_3$. Successively drain each portion of $CHCl_3$ into second separator contg 5 ml H_2O, wash, and filter thru cotton pledget wet with $CHCl_3$ into 50 ml vol. flask. Dil. to 50 ml with *alcohol* and retain for estimation of β-estradiol.

Add the 5 ml wash H_2O to aq. soln in first sepa-rator. Acidify aq. soln with 2 ml H_2SO_4 (1 + 1) and let remain 1 hr at room temp. Add 15 ml $CHCl_3$, shake vigorously 1 min, and let sep. Trans-fer $CHCl_3$ layer to second separator. Repeat extn with three addnl 15 ml portions $CHCl_3$. Wash combined $CHCl_3$ exts with 5 ml H_2O, filter thru cotton pledget wet with $CHCl_3$ into beaker, evap. to small vol., and transfer with $CHCl_3$ to tared 25 ml beaker previously dried in vac. desiccator to constant wt. Carefully evap. to dryness on steam bath in air current, adding few ml alcohol if neces-sary to aid in removal of residual H_2O. Weigh (residue may be dried in vac. desiccator for semi-quant. est. of ketosteroids). Dissolve residue in enough alcohol for soln to contain 90–120 μg ketosteroids/ml.

Note: Isolation must be completed promptly once started. It may be interrupted after obtain-ing dry residue from ether ext.

36.246   *Determination of Equilenin*

Transfer 5 ml aliquot alc. sample soln, **36.245(c)**, to separator. Prep. alcohol blank and stds, one contg 200 μg equilenin and other 250 μg equilin, and each dild to 5 ml with alcohol in separators. Add 5 ml buffer soln and 1 ml BQC reagent to each separator. Mix, and let stand 2 hr. From buret add 10 ml $CHCl_3$ and mix by careful shak-ing. Add 20 ml ca 2N NaOH and shake vigorously ≥1 min. Drain $CHCl_3$ ext and filter rapidly thru dry, folded paper. Det. A of sample and std solns at 535 nm relative to blank. Correct sample read-ing for equilin content, **36.247**, and calc. quantity of equilenin present.

Note: If A of sample is less than that equiv. to 25 μg equilin, ketonic residue may be presumed to consist entirely of estrone.

36.247   *Determination of Equilin*

Transfer 5 ml aliquot alc. sample soln, **36.245(c)**, to 16 × 150 mm g-s test tube. Add chip of SiC, **(h)**, and evap. *just* to dryness by immersing in steam bath. Similarly treat 5 ml alcohol blank and aliquots of equilin std contg, resp., 100 and 200 μg equilin. Cool in vac. desiccator 1 hr. Dissolve resi-due in 2 ml dry pyridine, add 0.2 ml benzenesul-fonyl chloride, stopper, and let stand overnight.

Mix with 10–15 ml H_2O and wash into separator. Rinse tube with several 10 ml portions H_2O and then with 15 ml $CHCl_3$, and add each to separator. Shake vigorously ≥1 min and drain $CHCl_3$ layer into 50 ml g-s erlenmeyer. Repeat extn with 15 ml portion $CHCl_3$, combine exts, and evap. to dry-ness. Dissolve residue in 2 ml alcohol by gently warming in the stoppered flask, cool, and mix with 4 ml buffer soln and 2 ml BQC reagent. Let stand 4 hr (rapid development of pink color indicates incomplete esterification of equilenin).

Add 5 ml $CHCl_3$ from pipet and mix carefully. Add 20 ml ca 2N NaOH and shake vigorously ≥1 min. Sep. $CHCl_3$ phase and filter rapidly thru dry, folded paper. Det. A of sample and std solns rela-tive to blank at 570 nm, and calc. equilin content.

36.248   *Determination of Estrone*

Dil. 5 ml alc. sample soln, **36.245(c)**, with 5 ml alcohol. To 1 ml aliquot of this soln in 16 × 150 mm g-s test tube add 10 ml modified iron-Kober reagent with thoro mixing. Stopper, and mix vig-orously. Similarly treat 1 ml alcohol blank, 1 ml aliquot estrone std soln, and 1 ml each of equi-lenin and the 2 equilin std solns. Immerse loosely stoppered tubes in hot H_2O bath above level of their contents, heat to 75–80°, and keep at that temp. 2 hr.

Cool tubes rapidly in cold H_2O, mix by invert-ing, and let stand at room temp. 15 min. Det. A of sample and stds relative to blank at 510 nm (max. for estrone). Calc. and apply A corrections due to equilin and equilenin, using 10 μg/ml equilin std for quantities up to 10 μg equilin in aliquot and 50 μg/ml std for greater quantities. Calc. estrone content of sample.

★ Beta-Estradiol (84)—Official First Action ★

36.249 *Apparatus*

(a) *Spectrophotometer or photometer.*—See 36.242(a).

(b) *Separators.*—See **36.242(b)**.

(c) *Glass-stoppered test tubes.*—18 × 150 mm.

(d) *Burets.*—Stopcocks lubricated only with reagent. Orifice of one buret should be enlarged, if necessary, to deliver 1 ml Reagent A in 30 sec or less. Protect reagents in burets from moisture with suitable guard tubes.

(e) *Chromatographic tube.*—Select 25 × 200 mm test tube of 3.85–4.00 sq cm cross-sectional area by measuring ht of 50 ml column of H_2O in it. Fuse 6 cm length of 5–6 mm tubing to bottom of tube and slightly constrict this stem ca 2 cm below seal.

(f) *Benzene reservoir.*—500 ml separator with 3 mm or larger bore stopcock lubricated only with H_2O. Stem should be ca 10 cm long.

(g) *Packing rod.*—Flatten end of glass rod to circular head to provide clearance of ca 1 mm in chromatgc tube.

(h) *Leveling rod.*—Sharp-edged rod ca 1.5 cm diam.

36.250 *Reagents*

(a) *Reagent A (stock iron-Kober reagent).*—Dissolve 1.054 g $FeSO_4.(NH_4)_2SO_4.6H_2O$ (Mohr salt) in ca 20 ml H_2O; add 1 ml H_2SO_4 and 1 ml 30% H_2O_2. Mix, heat until effervescence ceases, and dil. to exactly 50 ml. To 3 vols of the Fe soln in vol. flask add H_2SO_4, with cooling, to make 100 vols.

Redistill phenol, discarding first 10% and last 5%. (*Caution:* Phenol may be harmful. Avoid contact with skin and eyes and breathing vapors.) Collect distillate with exclusion of moisture in dry, tared g-s flask of ca twice vol. of the phenol. Place stoppered flask in ice bath to solidify phenol, breaking top crust with glass rod to ensure complete crystn. Dry and weigh flask.

Add to phenol 1.13 times its wt of Fe-H_2SO_4 soln, stopper flask, and let stand without cooling but with occasional mixing until phenol is liquefied (ca 30 min or less). Shake mixt. vigorously until homogenous and let stand in dark 16–24 hr. Add to mixt. 23.5% its wt of H_2SO_4 (10 + 11). Shake vigorously to homogeneity. Transfer to dry g-s bottles. Stored in dark and protected from absorption of moisture, this reagent is stable for months.

(b) *Reagent B.*—To measured vol. Reagent A in g-s graduated cylinder add 0.45 vol. H_2O, mix,

cool, and transfer to dry g-s bottles. Store in dark and protect from absorption of moisture. Inspect before use and disperse any flocculent ppt by vigorous swirling of reagent. With this precaution, reagent may be used satisfactorily for weeks.

(c) *Reagent C.*—To carefully measured vol. Reagent A in g-s graduated cylinder add 0.45 vol. 1N HCl, mix vigorously, and place at once in H_2O bath at 25–28°. Use reagent preferably 1 hr and ≤3 hr after prepn.

(d) *Packing material.*—Celite 545 (Johns-Manville diat. earth).

(e) *Sodium hydroxide soln.*—0.400N (carbonate-free).

(f) *Benzene.*—Reagent grade, redistd in all-glass app.

36.251 *Standard Solutions*

(a) *Beta-estradiol std soln.*—20 μg/ml. Dissolve exactly 10 mg pure β-estradiol in alcohol and dil. with alcohol to 100 ml in vol. flask. Pipet 10 ml of this soln into 50 ml vol. flask and dil. to vol. with alcohol.

(b) *Alpha-estradiol std soln.*—20 μg/ml. **Prep.** as in (a) from pure α-estradiol.

(c) *Beta-dihydroequilin std soln.*—10 μg/ml. Prep. as in (a) from 5 mg pure β-dihydroequilin.

Stored in dark in tightly stoppered containers, std solns keep for months.

36.252 *Preliminary Determination*

Apply Methods A and B, 36.254, directly to aliquots of $CHCl_3$ soln of diols obtained from **36.245**. (Very turbid solns sometimes resulting from these aliquots should be filtered, along with blank and std solns, thru pledget of fine glass wool packed tightly in lower end of stem of funnel.) Calc. β-estradiol content, disregarding presence of β-dihydroequilin. If wt β-estradiol so detd is ≤1% of wt ketosteroids, report β-estradiol as "Not >1% of ketosteroid content." If β-estradiol content is >1% of wt ketosteroids, repeat detn on aliquot of the $CHCl_3$ soln, using chromatgc sepn, **36.254**.

36.253 *Preparation of Chromatographic Column*

(*Caution: See* **46.039, 46.040,** *and* **46.045.**)

Pack fine glass wool into constricted stem of chromatgc tube so that when tube is filled with benzene, rate of flow is 2.5–3.0 ml/min. Before packing column, fasten piece of rubber tubing with attached screw-clamp to outlet to control flow during packing.

Cover 1 g Celite in small beaker with benzene. Pipet in 0.5 ml H_2O and mix vigorously with stirring rod until Celite is uniformly wet. With tube ca ¼ filled with benzene, place pad of glass wool (ca 1 cm high when gently compressed) at bottom of tube and then transfer Celite mixt. to tube. Form flocculent suspension by slowly working packing rod up and down as piston thru Celite mixt. Gently compress Celite with packing rod and finish off edges with leveling rod to form level, sharply defined surface on uniform pack ca 1 cm high.

Cover 8 g Celite in mortar with ca 40 ml benzene and distribute exactly 5 ml $0.400N$ NaOH over Celite from pipet. Carefully mix several min with pestle until Celite appears uniformly wet. Open screw-clamp enough to permit slow drainage during packing of tube. Transfer Celite to tube with spatula in ca 5 portions, suspending each portion and gently packing as above. Finish off top of column, scraping down any Celite on upper wall of tube to form sharply defined, level surface on column of ca 30 ml vol. over initial pack. (Packing too tightly may cause loss of estradiol in forerun, particularly at room temp. much $>25°$. Celite must be covered with benzene at all times.)

Nearly fill reservoir with benzene and seal stopper with film of H_2O to prevent air leaks. Insert stem of funnel into benzene over the Celite, open stopcock fully, and adjust level of benzene to produce flow rate of 2.0–2.5 ml/min with screw-clamp fully open. Mark level of benzene on tube, close stopcock, and remove benzene reservoir.

36.254   *Determination*

(*Caution:* See **46.039, 46.040,** and **46.045.**)

Carefully evap., to just short of dryness, aliquot $CHCl_3$ ext, **36.245,** contg 100–250 μg total diols calcd as β-estradiol. If necessary, add few ml alcohol near end of evapn to help remove any residual H_2O. Remove last portions of solv. in efficient desiccator connected to vac. for $\geqslant 1$ hr.

Dissolve dry ext in 5 ml benzene by warming gently; then cool soln to room temp. or below. Remove rubber tubing from partition tube and when benzene *just* stops dropping from tube, transfer diol soln at once to tube, letting it flow down wall near top of Celite (5 ml pipet is convenient for this purpose). When benzene just stops dropping from tube, complete transfer in like manner with 3 addnl 5 ml portions benzene, discarding effluent. Immediately place 50 ml graduated cylinder under tube, add benzene to level marked on tube, and replace benzene reservoir, supporting it at ht to maintain that level when stopcock is fully opened. When 30 ml effluent collects in cylinder, replace cylinder as receiver with dry 250 ml beaker previously marked at 170 ml level. (Decrease 30 ml forerun by 2 ml for each 1° that room temp. is $>25°$.) Collect 170 ml effluent in beaker, conc. soln to 30–40 ml, transfer to 50 ml vol. flask, and dil. to vol.

Det. β-estradiol in soln by Methods *A, B,* and, if necessary, *C.*

Method A.—Transfer to dry 18×150 mm g-s test tubes: (1) Aliquot of sample soln contg 10–25 μg total estradiols; (2) 1 ml α-estradiol std; (3) 1 ml β-estradiol std; and (4) if necessary from Method *B,* 1 ml β-dihydroequilin std (see *Note*). Add several pieces of SiC, **36.243(h),** to each tube and rapidly evap. solv. in steam bath (do not use air current) until ebullition from boiling stones just stops. Instantly remove tube, quickly wipe dry, and transfer to efficient vac. desiccator. Keep connected to vac. $\geqslant 1$ hr.

To each tube and to blank tube add glass bead, and measure 1 ml Reagent *A* into each tube from buret, quickly wiping outside of tip with piece of absorbent paper before each addn. Stopper immediately and let stand 30 min, vigorously shaking tubes at 5 min intervals. Place in boiling H_2O bath 35 min, removing and shaking each tube few sec after first 5 min. Transfer to ice bath 2 min; then remove and add exactly 4 ml H_2SO_4 (7 + 13) from buret. Let stand 5 min; then mix by shaking, first gently, then vigorously, to homogeneity.

Measure *A* of sample and stds relative to blank at 525 nm (midpoint between max. for α-estradiol and β-estradiol) and at 420 nm, making any necessary corrections for cell variations.

μg total estradiols in aliquot (calcd as β-estradiol)

$$= T_a = 20$$
$$\times \frac{A_{525 \text{ nm (sample)}} - [(A_{420 \text{ nm (sample)}})/2]}{A_{525 \text{ nm } (\beta\text{-estradiol std})} - [(A_{420 \text{ nm } (\beta\text{-estradiol std})})/2]}$$

g α-estradiol in aliquot (calcd as β-estradiol)

$= B_a = \mu$g α-estradiol in aliquot (from Method *B*)
$$\times \frac{A_{525 \text{ nm } (\alpha\text{-estradiol std})} - [(A_{420 \text{ nm } (\alpha\text{-estradiol std})})/2]}{A_{525 \text{ nm } (\beta\text{-estradiol std})} - [(A_{420 \text{ nm } (\beta\text{-estradiol std})})/2]}$$

μg β-dihydroequilin (DHQ) in aliquot (calcd as β-estradiol)

$= D_a = \mu$g DHQ in aliquot (from Method *C*)
$$\times \frac{2A_{525 \text{ nm (DHQ std)}} - A_{420 \text{ nm (DHQ std)}}}{A_{525 \text{ nm } (\beta\text{-estradiol std})} - [(A_{420 \text{ nm } (\beta\text{-estradiol std})})/2]}$$

μg β-estradiol in aliquot

$$= T_a - (B_a \text{ or } D_a \text{ or both}),$$
depending on composition of aliquot.

Note: If β-dihydroequilin in aliquot is >10 μg, use correspondingly higher std in detg correction for β-dihydroequilin and correct calcn accordingly.

Method B.—Transfer to dry 18×150 mm g-s test tubes: (1) Aliquot of sample soln contg 10–25 μg total estradiols; (2) 1 ml α-estradiol std; and (3) 1 ml β-dihydroequilin std (see *Note*). Add several pieces of SiC to each tube, evap. solv., and dry residue as in Method *A.* To each tube and to blank tube, add 1 ml Reagent *B* from buret, quickly wiping outside of tip with absorbent paper before each addn. Stopper immediately and place in boiling H_2O bath exactly 2 min, shaking tube after 30 sec for few sec without removing from bath. Transfer to ice bath 2 min; then remove and add from buret exactly 4 ml H_2SO_4 (7 + 13). Mix by shaking vigorously to homogeneity. Promptly measure A of sample and std relative to blank at 526 nm (max. for α-estradiol), at 468 nm (max. for β-dihydroequilin), and 420 nm, making any necessary corrections due to cell variation. If

$$A_{468 \text{ nm (sample)}}$$

$$- \left(A_{526 \text{ nm (sample)}} \times \frac{A_{458 \text{ nm (α-estradiol std)}}}{A_{526 \text{ nm (α-estradiol std)}}} \right)$$

does not exceed 20% of $A_{468 \text{ nm ($\beta$-dihydroequilin std)}}$, then disregarding presence of β-dihydroequilin in like aliquot will result in $\leqslant 0.8$ μg apparent β-estradiol in Method A. This is normally negligible quantity, in which case calc. α-estradiol as follows and omit dihydroequilin std in Method A:

μg α-estradiol in aliquot = 20

$$\times \frac{A_{526 \text{ nm (sample)}} - (A_{420 \text{ nm (sample)}})/2}{A_{526 \text{ nm (α-estradiol std)}} - (A_{420 \text{ nm (α-estradiol std)}})/2}$$

Otherwise det. β-dihydroequilin by Method C and calc. α-estradiol as follows, where DHQ = β-dihydroequilin:

$A_{526 \text{ nm (sample)}}$ (corrected)

$$= A_{526 \text{ nm (sample)}}$$
$$- (A_{526 \text{ nm (DHQ std)}} \times \mu\text{g DHQ in aliquot}/10)$$

$A_{420 \text{ nm (sample)}}$ (corrected)

$$= A_{420 \text{ nm (sample)}}$$
$$- (A_{420 \text{ nm (DHQ std)}} \times \mu\text{g DHQ in aliquot}/10)$$

μg α-estradiol in aliquot = 20

$$\times \frac{A_{526 \text{ nm (sample)}} \text{ (corr.)} - (A_{420 \text{ nm (sample)}} \text{ (corr.)})/2}{A_{526 \text{ nm (α-estradiol std)}} - (A_{420 \text{ nm (α-estradiol std)}})/2}$$

Note: If β-dihydroequilin in aliquot is >10 μg, use correspondingly higher std in detg correction for β-dihydroequilin and correct calcn accordingly.

Method C.—Transfer to 18×150 mm g-s test tubes: (1) Aliquot of sample soln contg $\leqslant 20$ μg β-dihydroequilin; and (2) 2 ml β-dihydroequilin std. Add several pieces of SiC to each tube, evap. solv., and dry residue as in Method A. Place tubes in H_2O bath at 25–28° and rapidly add 5 ml Reagent C near bottom of each. Using long stirring rod, mix residue vigorously with reagent at least 1 min. Leave rod in tube. Measure A of sample and std relative to reagent (also held in bath at 25–28°) at 472 nm just 30 min after addn of reagent, and repeat measurement at 5–10 min intervals until max. A is reached (usually 35–55 min after mixing).

g β-dihydroequilin in aliquot
$$= 20 \times A_{472 \text{ nm (sample)}}/A_{472 \text{ nm (std)}}.$$

Conjugated Estrogens (85)—Official First Action

36.255   *Reagents*

(a) *Iron-Kober reagent.*—See **36.250(a)**.

(b) *Dicyclohexylamine acetate.*—Dissolve 50 g dicyclohexylamine in 150 ml acetone, cool in ice bath, and add, with stirring, 18 ml HOAc dissolved in 150 ml acetone. Filter ppt on buchner, wash with small amt acetone, and air dry.

(c) *Girard reagent T.*—See **36.243(e)**.

(d) *Estrone std soln.*—50 μg/ml. Dissolve ca 5.0 mg NF Ref. Std estrone, accurately weighed, in benzene, and dil. to 100 ml with benzene.

(e) *Equilin std soln.*—20 μg/ml. Dissolve ca 2.0 mg equilin, **36.244(b)**, accurately weighed, in benzene, and dil. to 100 ml with benzene.

36.256   *Preparation of Sample*

(*Caution:* See **46.011, 46.039, 46.040, 46.045,** and **46.056**.)

Weigh 20 tablets and reduce to fine powder without loss. Weigh sample contg ca 7 mg Na estrone sulfate and transfer to 250 ml beaker. Add 6 g Celite and mix thoroly. Add 4 ml H_2O and mix until uniform. Transfer quant., with aid of small amt of dry Celite, to 25×150 mm chromatgc tube. Tamp moderately tight and wash column with 100 ml H_2O-satd ether, discarding ether wash. Add 100 mg dicyclohexylamine acetate, (b), dissolved in 5 ml $CHCl_3$, to column, and collect eluate in 250 ml g-s flask. Wash column with several 5 ml portions $CHCl_3$ and finally with enough solv. to produce 150 ml total eluate. Evap. to dryness on steam bath with aid of air current.

Dissolve residue in 25 ml absolute MeOH, add 1 ml HCl and few boiling chips, stopper loosely, and boil 5 min. Cool, transfer to 125 ml separator with 70 ml H_2O, and ext with four 25 ml portions $CHCl_3$. Evap. combined $CHCl_3$ exts just to dryness on steam bath with aid of air current.

Dissolve residue in 5 ml $CHCl_3$ and transfer, using $\leqslant 5$ ml $CHCl_3$, to 125 ml separator contg 50 ml isooctane. Add 10 ml 10% NaOH soln and shake 1 min. Transfer aq. layer to second 125 ml separator. Ext with two addnl 10 ml portions 10% NaOH soln, adding each to second separator. Discard $CHCl_3$-isooctane soln. Acidify alk. ext with dil. H_2SO_4, cool, add 25 ml benzene, and shake 1 min. Transfer aq. layer to second separator contg 25 ml benzene, shake 1 min, and drain and discard aq. layer. Wash each benzene layer successively with 10 ml 10% Na_2CO_3 soln and two 10 ml portions H_2O. Filter benzene layers thru cotton plug previously washed with benzene into 100 ml vol. flask. Wash separators and funnel with benzene, filter washings into vol. flask, dil. to vol., and mix (*Soln A*).

Evap. 50 ml aliquot *Soln A* to ca 5 ml and transfer to 25 ml g-s erlenmeyer with small vol. $CHCl_3$. Evap. to dryness on steam bath with air current. Reserve remainder of *Soln A* for detn of total estrogens. Add 100 mg Girard Reagent T and 0.5 ml HOAc to flask, stopper loosely, and heat on steam bath 5 min, swirling several times to ensure complete mixing. Cool, and transfer to 125 ml separator with ca 25 ml ice-H_2O. Add 5 ml 5% NaOAc soln and ext immediately with three 10 ml portions $CHCl_3$. Combine $CHCl_3$ exts in second separator, wash with 5 ml ice-H_2O, and discard $CHCl_3$. Add H_2O wash to aq. soln in first separator. Add 3 ml H_2SO_4 $(1+2)$, mix well, and let stand 30 min. Ext aq. soln with three 25 ml portions $CHCl_3$, combine exts in second separator, wash with 5 ml H_2O, and filter thru cotton plug previously washed with $CHCl_3$ into 150 ml beaker. Wash separator and filter with little $CHCl_3$, and add to main ext. Evap. $CHCl_3$ soln to dryness on steam bath with air current. Dissolve residue in little benzene, transfer quant. to 50 ml vol. flask, and dil. to vol. with benzene (*Soln B*).

36.257 Determination of Total Estrogens as Sodium Estrone Sulfate

Transfer duplicate 1 ml aliquots *Soln A* and estrone std soln, using same pipet, to 16×150 mm g-s test tubes. Add few boiling chips to each tube, evap. to dryness in steam bath, and cool in vac. desiccator. To each tube and to blank tube, add 1.0 ml Fe-Kober reagent, 36.255(a), stopper, and place in boiling H_2O bath. Heat ca 1 min, shake tubes to mix, and release pressure by removing stopper for moment. Heat 90 min, cool in H_2O bath, add 10.0 ml H_2SO_4 $(1+2)$, and mix.

Det. A of std and sample solns against blank between 400 and 700 nm, and det. baseline A at 520 nm, drawing baseline between min. at ca 400 and 700 nm.

Total estrogens as Na estrone sulfate, mg/g = $(A_B/S_1) \times (C_1/w) \times 138 + d/2$ where A_B = baseline-corrected A of sample soln, S_1 = baseline-corrected A of std soln, C_1 = mg estrone in std aliquot, w = g sample, and d = Na equilin sulfate in mg/g from 36.258. Conversion factors are Na estrone sulfate:estrone = 1.38 and Na equilin sulfate:equilin = 1.38.)

36.258 Determination of Equilin as Sodium Equilin Sulfate

Transfer duplicate 1 ml portions *Soln B* and equilin std soln (larger aliquots may be used for samples low in equilin; do not exceed 25–30 μg equilin), using same pipet, to 16×150 mm g-s test tubes. Add few boiling chips to each tube, evap. to dryness in steam bath, and cool. To each tube and to blank tube add 0.10 ml alcohol and rotate tube to dissolve ketosteroids. Add 1.0 ml Fe-Kober reagent, 36.255(a), to each tube, mix thoroly, stopper, and heat in boiling H_2O bath 25 min. Cool, add 3.00 ml H_2SO_4 $(1+2)$ to each tube, and mix thoroly. Det. A against blank at 620 nm.

Na equilin sulfate, mg/g = $(A_2/S_2) \times (C_2/w) \times 138$; where $A_2 = A$ of sample soln, $S_2 = A$ of std soln, C_2 = mg equilin in std aliquot, and w = g sample.

36.259 Determination of Estrone as Sodium Estrone Sulfate

Transfer duplicate 1 ml aliquots *Soln B*, estrone std soln, and equilin std soln to 16×150 mm g-s test tubes. Proceed as in 36.257, beginning, "Add few boiling chips..." except heat 2 hr instead of 90 min. Det. A against blank at 520 nm. Correct A of sample soln for equilin A as follows: A_3 (corr.) = $A_3 - (S_4 \times A_2)/S_2$.

Na estrone sulfate, mg/g = $(A_3(corr.)/S_3) \times (C_1/w) \times 138$; where $A_3 = A$ of sample soln, $S_3 = A$ of estrone std soln, $S_4 = A$ of equilin std soln, C_1 = mg estrone in std aliquot, and w = g sample.

HYPNOTIC DRUGS

36.260 Barbiturates (86)—Official Final Action

(Applicable in absence of stearic acid. *Caution: See* 46.011, 46.040, and 46.056.)

Accurately weigh 0.3–0.5 g sample into separator, add 10 ml H_2O, and shake well. Add 5 ml $0.5N$ NaOH and shake again. Acidify to litmus paper with HCl $(1+3)$, added dropwise, and add ca 1 ml excess. Ext with successive 40, 30, 20, 20, and 10 ml portions $CHCl_3$. Test for complete extn by shaking with addnl 10 ml solv. and evapg in sep. beaker.

Combine solv. in second separator and wash with 2 ml H_2O acidified with 1 drop HCl. Filter solv. thru cotton pledget into small weighed beaker. Evap. on steam bath with aid of elec. fan, heat 10 min at 80–90°, cool in desiccator, and weigh. Add 2 or 3 ml anhyd. ether and evap. solv. (Usually 2 treatments with 2 ml each of anhyd. ether are enough to remove last traces of $CHCl_3$ and to produce cryst. residue.) Dry at 80–90°, cool, and weigh. Repeat treatment with anhyd. ether and evapn to constant wt. Det. mp to check purity of residue.

36.261 Alternative Method (87)—Official Final Action

(Applicable in presence of stearic acid)

Dissolve residue obtained in 36.260 in 10 ml alcohol, add 20 ml satd $Ba(OH)_2$ soln, and stir well. Filter into separator, and wash residue and filter with two or three 10 ml portions of the $Ba(OH)_2$ soln. Acidify filtrate with HCl $(1+3)$ and proceed as in 36.260, beginning "Ext with successive..."

36.262 Microcrystal Tests—Official Final Action

See 36.529–36.531, 36.536, and 36.541–36.543.

Amobarbital Sodium and Secobarbital Sodium (88)—Official Final Action

36.263 Reagents

(a) *Sodium secobarbital std.*—Assay by 36.260.

(b) *Phosphate buffer soln.*—pH 6.85–6.90. Dissolve 6.80 g KH_2PO_4 in ca 500 ml H_2O in 1 L vol.

flask. Add 23.6 ml 1.00N NaOH soln and dil. to vol. with H₂O.

36.264   Preparation of Standard Curve

Accurately weigh ca 100 mg Na secobarbital, transfer to 25 ml vol. flask, dil. to vol. with H₂O, and mix well. Calc. equiv. barbituric acid/ml std soln as follows:

$$\text{mg Barbituric acid/ml} = \frac{\text{mg Na secobarbital}}{25}$$

$$\times \frac{\text{\% Na secobarbital (from assay)}}{100} \times \frac{128.09}{260.27}.$$

Pipet 0.5, 1.0, and 2.0 ml aliquots into 50 ml vol. flasks, dil. to vol. with buffer soln, and mix. Det. A of each soln at 237 nm against buffer soln. Plot A against mg barbituric acid.

Include 1 or 2 stds with each set of detns.

36.265   Determination of Total Barbiturates

Accurately weigh sample contg ca 400 mg total Na amobarbital and Na secobarbital, transfer to 100 ml vol. flask, and dil. to vol. with H₂O. Mix, and let stand 10 min with occasional shaking. Filter thru quant. paper sufficiently retentive to produce clear soln, discarding first 10–15 ml filtrate. Pipet 2 ml filtrate into 50 ml vol. flask, dil. to vol. with buffer soln, and mix well. Det. A at 237 nm against buffer soln. Det. total barbituric acid in aliquot by ref. to std curve and calc. to mg total barbituric acid in sample.

36.266   Determination of Sodium
Secobarbital

Pipet 50 ml filtrate into I flask and add 10.0 ml 0.1N KBr-KBrO₃, **45.021.** Add 5 ml HCl, stopper at once, and let stand 5 min, shaking occasionally. Add 10 ml 10% KI soln, stopper, and shake. Rinse stopper and neck of flask with H₂O, add starch indicator, and titr. liberated I with 0.1N Na₂S₂O₃, **45.038,** using 10 ml buret. 1 ml 0.1N KBr-KBrO₃ consumed = 13.01 mg Na secobarbital. Calc. to mg Na secobarbital in sample.

36.267   Determination of Sodium
Amobarbital (by Difference)

mg Na amobarbital in sample
= [mg total barbituric acid
− (mg Na secobarbital × 0.492)] × 1.94.

Phenobarbital and Aminophylline (89)—
Official Final Action
36.268   Reagents

(a) *Dilute ammonium hydroxide soln.*—0.1% NH₃. Dil. 4 ml NH₄OH to 1 L with H₂O.

(b) *Phenobarbital std soln.*—10 μg/ml. Dissolve 100.0 mg phenobarbital in the dil. NH₄OH soln in 500 ml vol. flask, dil. to vol. with the dil. NH₄OH, and mix. Transfer 5 ml aliquot to 100 ml vol. flask, dil. to vol. with the dil. NH₄OH, and mix.

(c) *Theophylline std soln.*—10 μg/ml. Dissolve 100.0 mg theophylline in HCl (1 + 18) in 500 ml vol. flask. Dil. to vol. with the dil. HCl and mix. Transfer 5 ml aliquot to 100 ml vol. flask, dil. to vol. with H₂O, and mix.

36.269   Separation of Aminophylline and
Phenobarbital

Transfer weighed portion of powd sample contg ca 15 mg phenobarbital to separator contg 25 ml HCl (1 + 1). Add 60 ml ether, shake, and let stand to clear. Pass aq. soln successively thru 2 other separators, each contg 50 ml ether, shake, and let stand to clear. Transfer ether-washed aq. soln to 500 ml vol. flask. Wash the 3 ether solns successively with three 10 ml portions HCl (1 + 1) and one 10 ml portion H₂O, and add these washes to the vol. flask. Reserve for detn of theophylline.

36.270   Determination of Phenobarbital
(*Caution: See* **46.011, 46.039,** and **46.054.**)

Combine ether solns and evap. to dryness. Dissolve residue in ca 100 ml of the dil. NH₄OH and transfer to 200 ml vol. flask. Dil. to vol. with the dil. NH₄OH and mix. Filter, if necessary, transfer 10 ml aliquot to 100 ml vol. flask, dil. to vol. with the dil. NH₄OH, and mix. Det. A_P at 240.5 nm against solv. blank. Read this soln same day it is prepd.

Det. A_P' of std phenobarbital soln, **(b),** at 240.5 nm, using the dil. NH₄OH as blank. Calc. $a_P = A_P'/cb$, where $c = 0.01$ g/L, and $b =$ cell length in cm. Phenobarbital (g/L sample soln) $= A_P/a_P$.

If stearates are present, proceed as above, dissolving residue in ca 100 ml of the dil. NH₄OH and dilg to ca 190 ml with the dil. NH₄OH. Acidify with HCl, testing with litmus paper. Dil. to vol. with H₂O, mix, and filter. Transfer 10 ml aliquot to 100 ml vol. flask, add 1 drop NH₄OH (1 + 1), dil. to vol. with the dil. NH₄OH, and det. A_P at 240.5 nm.

36.271   Determination of Theophylline

Dil. aq. soln in vol. flask to vol. with H₂O and mix. Transfer 5 ml aliquot, or aliquot contg 0.5–1.0 mg theophylline, to 100 ml vol. flask, dil. to vol. with H₂O, and mix. Det. A_T at 271 nm against blank soln contg same quantity HCl. Det. A_T' of std theophylline soln, **(c),** and calc. a_T as in **36.270.** Theophylline (g/L sample soln) $= A_T/a_T$. Aminophylline, $C_{16}H_{24}N_{10}O_4 \cdot 2H_2O = 1.267 \times$ theophylline.

Phenobarbital and Diphenylhydantoin (90)—
Official Final Action
36.272   Reagents

(a) *Water-saturated soln of 15% n-amyl alcohol in CHCl₃.*—Sat. 500 ml 15% n-amyl alcohol in CHCl₃ with 25 ml H₂O and let stand 30 min. Det. suitability of reagent by passing 80 ml thru prepd column followed by 25 ml H_2O-satd $CHCl_3$, evapg to dryness on steam bath with air current, dilg to 25.0 ml with alcohol, and reading A in 1 cm cell on recording spectrophtr from 320 to 250 nm. For any A difference up to 0.190 between 258 and 263 nm, make blank correction accordingly. Higher A indicates better grade reagent must be used.

(b) *Acetic acid-chloroform soln.*—1% HOAc in H_2O-satd $CHCl_3$.

36.273 Preparation of Standards

(a) *Phenobarbital std soln.*—Weigh and transfer 20 mg phenobarbital, USP, to 50 ml vol. flask; dissolve and dil. to vol. with alcohol. Pipet 10 ml into 125 ml g-s erlenmeyer and evap. to dryness on steam bath with air current (4 mg/100 ml 0.1N NaOH has A of ca 1.30 at 253 nm in 1 cm cell).

(b) *5,5-Diphenylhydantoin std soln.*—Weigh and transfer 90 mg diphenylhydantoin (Eastman), to 50 ml vol. flask; dissolve and dil. to vol. with alcohol. Pipet 10 ml into 125 ml g-s erlenmeyer and evap. to dryness on steam bath with air current (18 mg/25 ml alcohol has A of ca 1.90 at 258 nm in 1 cm cell).

36.274 Preparation of Sample

Accurately weigh powd sample contg ca 90 mg diphenylhydantoin and transfer to 50 ml vol. flask. Add 1.5 ml alcohol, 0.1 ml HOAc, and ca 25 ml reagent 36.272(a). Heat on steam bath with swirling until $CHCl_3$ boils. Remove from heat and swirl 5 min. Heat to boiling as before, remove, and let stand 15 min with frequent agitation. Let cool and dil. to vol. with reagent (a). (Diphenylhydantoin dissolves with difficulty. Turbidity of soln may persist because of insol. excipients.)

36.275 Preparation of Column

Use glass tube 25 mm diam. $\times$ 15–30 cm long, with stem plugged with glass wool, and glass tamping rod weighing ca 32 g and having 20–22 mm ram head.

(a) *Column packing.*—(1) *Bottom layer.*—Mix 2 g acid-washed Celite 545 and 1 ml *12% BaCl$_2$ soln.* (2) *Top layer.*—Mix 4 g acid-washed Celite 545 and 3 ml *satd Na$_3$PO$_4$ soln.*

(b) *Packing technic.*—*Column must be packed exactly as follows:* Transfer sep. bottom and top packing layers to tube in 1–2 g portions and tamp 10–15 times with tamping rod after addn of each portion by dropping rod from 1″ above packing surface.

Place glass wool plug over Celite mixt. and pass 25 ml reagent (a) thru column at 5–10 ml/min, discarding eluate.

36.276 Determination

(*Caution: See* **46.011, 46.022, 46.040, and 46.056.**)

Place 125 ml g-s erlenmeyer under column and pipet 10 ml sample soln directly over glass wool pledget. Let drain into column, and wash column with three 10 ml portions reagent (a), letting each drain into column. Add addnl 40 ml reagent (a). Pass 25 ml H_2O-satd $CHCl_3$ thru column, wash stem with $CHCl_3$, and evap. eluate to dryness on steam bath with air current. (Odor of *n*-amyl alcohol must be absent.) Residue is diphenylhydantoin.

Place 125 ml g-s erlenmeyer under column and add to column 5 ml HOAc in $CHCl_3$ (1 + 4). Let drain into column. Add 20 ml reagent 36.272(b), let drain into column, and add 70 ml more. Wash stem with $CHCl_3$ and evap. eluate to dryness on steam bath with air current. Residue is phenobarbital.

Add 25 ml alcohol by pipet to both sample and std diphenylhydantoin residues. Stopper and warm with swirling. Let stand, swirling occasionally, until solid matter is completely dissolved. Det. A of solns on recording spectrophtr from 320 to 250 nm in 1 cm cell.

Calc. mg diphenylhydantoin/capsule

$$= C \times (K/W) \times (A_{258} - A_{263})/(S_{258} - S_{263}),$$

where A_{258} and A_{263} = max. and min. A of sample soln at 258 and 263 nm, resp.; S_{258} and S_{263} = max. and min. A of std soln at 258 and 263 nm, resp.; C = mg std diphenylhydantoin; K = av. capsule content wt (mg); and W = mg sample. Diphenylhydantoin $\times$ 1.087 = Na diphenylhydantoin.

Add 100 ml 0.1N NaOH by pipet to both sample and std phenobarbital residues. Stopper and shake vigorously 2 min. *Immediately* read A of solns on recording spectrophtr from 350 to 230 nm in 1 cm cell. Calc. mg phenobarbital/capsule = $C \times (K/W) \times (A_{253}/S_{253})$, where A_{253} and S_{253} = max. A of sample and std solns, resp., at 253 nm; C = mg std phenobarbital; K = av. capsule content wt (mg); W = mg sample.

Phenobarbital and Theobromine (91)— Official Final Action

36.277 Reagents

(a) *Theobromine std soln.*—1.00 mg/100 ml. Dissolve 100 mg theobromine in H_2SO_4 (1 + 4), and dil. to 100 ml with this acid. Transfer 5.0 ml aliquot to 500 ml vol. flask, add 200 ml 5% NaOH soln, and cool to room temp. Dil. to vol. with H_2O and mix thoroly.

(b) *Phenobarbital std soln.*—1.50 mg/100 ml. Dissolve 75.0 mg phenobarbital in $CHCl_3$ and dil. to 100 ml with $CHCl_3$. Dil. 10 ml aliquot to 50 ml with $CHCl_3$. Transfer 10 ml aliquot of latter soln to 100 ml vol. flask, dil. to vol. with $CHCl_3$, and mix.

36.278 Separation of Theobromine and Phenobarbital

(*Caution: See* **46.011, 46.039, and 46.054.**)

Transfer portion of well-mixed sample contg $\geqslant$15 mg phenobarbital to 125 ml separator, add 15 ml 5% NaOH soln, and ext with three 30 ml portions CHCl₃. Wash each CHCl₃ ext with 10 ml 5% NaOH soln in second separator. Discard CHCl₃.

Add 30 ml H₂SO₄ (1 + 4) to alk. mixt. in first separator, cool thoroly, and shake with 50 ml ether. Transfer aq. layer contg dissolved theobromine to second separator, cool, and shake with 40 ml ether. Remove lower phase to third separator and wash with another 40 ml portion ether. Repeat extn thru the 3 separators, using two 40 ml portions H₂SO₄ (1 + 4) and two 20 ml portions H₂O. Collect aq. exts in 250 ml vol. flask, dil. to vol. with H₂O, and mix. Reserve for theobromine detn.

Filter ether solns thru cotton pledget into beaker, washing the 3 separators and filter successively with three 5 ml portions ether. Evap. carefully to dryness, and dissolve residue in CHCl₃.

36.279   *Spectrophotometric Determinations*

(a) *Theobromine.*—Pipet aliquot contg 4–8 mg theobromine into 500 ml vol. flask, add 200 ml 5% NaOH soln, and cool to room temp. Dil. to vol. with H₂O and mix. Det. A at 274 nm of this soln and of std theobromine soln, (a), A', relative to soln prepd by dilg 10 ml 5% NaOH soln to 25 ml. Calc. theobromine content of sample.

mg Theobromine in aliquot = $5.0 \, A/A'$.

(b) *Phenobarbital.*—Transfer CHCl₃ soln to vol. flask and dil. with CHCl₃ to obtain soln contg 20–40 mg phenobarbital/100 ml. Place 5.0 ml in 100 ml vol. flask, dil. to vol. with CHCl₃, and mix. Transfer 20 ml aliquot of latter soln to separator contg 25 ml NH₄OH (1 + 24). Similarly treat 20 ml aliquot std phenobarbital soln, (b), and 20 ml portion CHCl₃ as blank. Shake vigorously ≥1 min, sep., and discard CHCl₃. Let aq. ext stand 30 min. Det. A at 241 nm of clear aq. solns of sample, and of std, A', relative to blank, using same cell for std and sample. Calc. phenobarbital content of sample.

mg Phenobarbital in final aliquot = $0.30A/A'$.

In presence of salicylates, proceed as in (c):

(c) *Phenobarbital in presence of salicylates.*— Prep. chromatgc column as in **36.216,** and adjust flow to 2–4 ml/min.

When CHCl₃ just stops flowing from tube, pipet 5 ml original CHCl₃ soln, (b), (equiv. to 1–2 mg phenobarbital) into tube, and collect eluate in 100 ml vol. flask. As level of CHCl₃ soln reaches top of Celite column, add ca 5 ml CHCl₃, and repeat with second CHCl₃ wash. Add enough CHCl₃ to keep column of solv. 2–5 cm high, and collect ca 95 ml eluate. Wash outside surface of stem with stream of CHCl₃ and collect washings in vol. flask. Dil. to vol. with CHCl₃ and mix thoroly. Det. phenobarbital in eluate as in (b), beginning "Transfer 20 ml aliquot of latter soln ..."

Acetylcarbromal and Bromisovalum (92)— Official Final Action

36.280   *Principle*

Acetylcarbromal is eluted with heptane-CCl₄ and bromisovalum with H₂O-satd CHCl₃ from Celite column. Eluates are dried; acetylcarbromal residue is dissolved in CCl₄ and bromisovalum residue in CHCl₃. Concns are detd by IR spectrometry at 5.8 µm. Identification is made from residues in KBr disks.

36.281   *Apparatus*

(a) *Infrared spectrophotometer.*—Beckman IR-5, or equiv., with 1 mm liq. cells.

(b) *Chromatographic tube.*—25 × 200 mm test tube to which is fused 5 cm length of 6–8 mm glass tubing.

36.282   *Reagents*

(a) *Diatomaceous earth.*—Celite 545, acid-washed, or equiv.

(b) *Reference std solns.*—Completely dissolve 50.0 mg acetylcarbromal (mp 109°) in CCl₄ in 50 ml vol. flask and dil. to vol. with CCl₄. Completely dissolve 50.0 mg bromisovalum (mp 148–149°) in CHCl₃ in 50 ml vol. flask and dil. to vol. with CHCl₃.

36.283   *Column Chromatography*

(*Caution: See* **46.011, 46.040, 46.049,** and **46.056.**)

Pack small wad of fine glass wool into bottom of tube. Thoroly mix 4 g Celite with 5 ml HCl (2 + 1), transfer to tube, and tamp to uniform mass with tamping rod. Finely powder 20 tablets, accurately weigh portion of powder contg 10–30 mg acetylcarbromal, and mix in beaker with 1 g Celite and 1 ml H₂O. Transfer to tube, dry-rinse beaker with small portion of Celite, and tamp to uniform mass. Wash beaker with few portions H₂O-satd CCl₄-heptane (1 + 1) and pour thru column. Elute acetylcarbromal with CCl₄-heptane mixt., collecting 50 ml eluate in beaker. Immediately, without letting column go dry, elute bromisovalum with 100 ml H₂O-satd CHCl₃, collecting eluate in beaker. Evap. both eluates to complete dryness on steam bath with air current.

Dissolve acetylcarbromal residue with several portions of CCl₄ (dried with anhyd. Na₂SO₄) and dil. to concn of 1 mg/ml. Dissolve bromisovalum residue in several portions of CHCl₃ (dried with anhyd. Na₂SO₄) and dil. to concn of 1 mg/ml. Using their resp. solvs as ref. solns, det. IR spectrum at 5–7 µm. For calcn, use A of max. at ca 5.8 µm, using baseline technic:

$$\% = (100 \times A \times C_s \times V)/(A' \times W),$$

where A refers to sample soln, A' refers to std soln, C_s = concn of std soln (mg/ml), V = final vol. sample soln, and W = mg sample.

36.284 Identification

Evap. 1 ml each of std and sample soln, and prep. KBr disk from each of residues, using ca 200 mg KBr. Scan IR spectra for identification.

36.285 Carbromal (93)—Official Final Action

Weigh 0.25–0.40 g sample and proceed as in **34.109.** 1 ml 0.05N $Na_2S_2O_3$ = 0.00593 g carbromal.

Note: Use <20 ml absorbing soln (15 ml hydrazine sulfate soln and 5 ml 10% NaOH soln) if app. has smaller absorption bulbs than those described in **34.108.**

36.286 Carbromal and Pentobarbital (93)—Official Final Action

(*Caution: See* **46.011, 46.040,** and **46.056.**)

Transfer 0.5–0.7 g sample to separator, and add 15 ml H_2O and 0.5 ml 1N NaOH from pipet. Ext carbromal with at least five 25 ml portions $CHCl_3$, washing each portion in second separator contg 10 ml H_2O and 2 drops 0.1N NaOH. Filter $CHCl_3$ thru cotton and transfer to tared flask or beaker. Test for complete extn. Evap. $CHCl_3$ soln of carbromal nearly but not quite to dryness on steam bath in air current. Remove container and let stand in air to constant wt.

Combine aq. solns and proceed as in **36.260,** beginning "Acidify to litmus paper . . ." Wt pentobarbital × 1.097 = wt Na pentobarbital in portion taken for assay. Det. mp of dried exts. Carbromal melts at 116–119° and pentobarbital at 126–130°.

Chloral Hydrate (94)—Official Final Action
36.287 Principle

Quinaldine ethyl iodide reacts with chloral hydrate to produce stable blue cyanine dye with A max. at ca 605 nm. Other polychlorinated compds do not interfere.

36.288 Reagents

(a) *Quinaldine ethyl iodide soln.*—1.5%. Dissolve 1.5 g quinaldine ethyl iodide in H_2O and dil. to 100 ml. Filter if necessary.

(b) *2-Aminoethanol soln.*—0.1N. Dissolve 6.1 g 2-aminoethanol in H_2O and dil. to 1 L.

(c) *Chloral hydrate std soln.*—100 μg/ml. Dissolve 0.2500 g chloral hydrate USP in H_2O and dil. to 250 ml. Dil. 10 ml aliquot to 100 ml with H_2O.

36.289 Apparatus

Recording spectrophotometer.—400–800 nm range with matched 1 cm cells.

36.290 Preparation of Sample

(a) *Capsules.*—Place counted number of capsules contg ca 2.5 g chloral hydrate in g-s 250 ml flask, add 25 ml H_2O, stopper, and heat on steam bath with frequent swirling until dissolved. Cool, and transfer quant. to 250 ml vol. flask with H_2O.

Dil. to vol., mix, and dil. stepwise to ca 100 μg/ml with H_2O.

(b) *Solns.*—Prep. soln contg ca 100 μg chloral hydrate/ml by stepwise diln with H_2O.

36.291 Determination

Pipet 10 ml sample soln contg ca 1 mg chloral hydrate into 100 ml vol. flask and pipet 10 ml std chloral hydrate soln into second 100 ml vol. flask. Pipet 10 ml H_2O into third 100 ml vol. flask as blank. To each flask add 10 ml quinaldine ethyl iodide soln and 60 ml isopropanol, and mix. Add 5 ml 0.1N 2-aminoethanol and dil. to vol. with H_2O. Place in H_2O bath 1 hr at 60°. Cool, and record absorption spectra of sample and std from 400 to 800 nm against blank. Do not exceed 120 nm/min near max. Det. A max. at ca 605 nm, using baseline technic with ca 430 and ca 770 nm as base. Calc. amt of chloral hydrate in sample aliquot = (Net A of sample soln/net A of std soln) × mg chloral hydrate in 10 ml std soln.

36.292 ★ (2-Isopropyl-4-Pentenyl) ★ Urea (Sedormid®) (95)—Official Final Action

Direct $CHCl_3$ extn. *See* **32.237,** 10th ed.

36.293 ★ Sulfonmethane (Sulfonal®) ★ or Sulfonethylmethane (Trional®) (96)—Official Final Action

Direct ether extn. *See* **32.238,** 10th ed. (*Caution: See* **46.011, 46.039,** and **46.054.**)

INORGANIC DRUGS
Arsenic in Iron-Arsenic Tablets (97)—Official Final Action
36.294 Reagent

Std soln of potassium bromate (or of iodine).—Stdze against pure As_2O_3. (Concn of this soln is matter of choice. 0.5625 g $KBrO_3$ dissolved in H_2O and dild to 1 L gives soln that is 0.02021N, 1 ml = 1 mg As_2O_3.)

36.295 Apparatus

Use either Ramberg-Sjöström As flask, Fig. 36:1A, consisting of 300 ml Kjeldahl flask provided with special outlet tube connected with flask by means of ⚭ joint, or 300 ml Kjeldahl flask provided with 13 mm id outlet tube, with constricted tip ca 5 mm, connected with flask by means of rubber stopper, B.

36.296 Determination

(*Caution: See* **46.019, 46.026, 46.030,** and **46.078.**)

Weigh and place in flask 5–10 tablets or pills, add 10–15 ml H_2O, and let soak 30 min. Add, in small portions at time, 20 ml fuming HNO_3, cooling if necessary to prevent loss by frothing. When

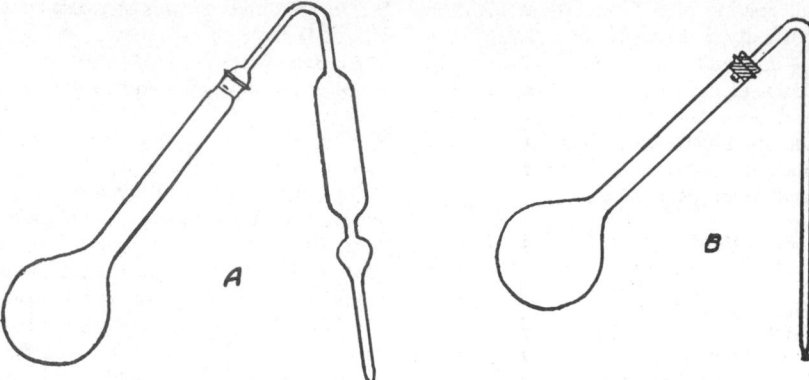

FIG. 36:1—Apparatus for determining arsenic in iron-arsenic tablets

reaction ceases, carefully add, in small portions at time, 25–28 ml H2SO4. Place flask in inclined position on asbestos mat and heat over small flame. When most of HNO3 is driven off, and while still heating, drop in 8 ml fuming HNO3 thru suitably placed separator and heat over larger flame until SO3 evolves. If after cooling, pptd sulfates are not colorless or pale yellow and are not free from gray or black particles, heat contents of flask further with addnl 10 ml fuming HNO3. (All org. matter must be destroyed.)

To cooled mixt. add 30 ml satd (NH4)2C2O4 soln; heat until fumes of SO3 evolve, and to ensure complete destruction of oxalic acid, for 10 min longer over low flame; cool, and add 20 ml H2O while gently swirling flask. Dry neck of flask over small flame and add 30 g NaCl, 5 g FeSO4.7H2O (or 1 g N2H4.H2SO4), 1 g NaBr, and 25 ml HCl. Mix, and connect delivery tube. If Ramberg-Sjöström app. is used, moisten ground-glass joint with 1 drop H2SO4. Fix flask in inclined position with tip of outlet tube ca 1 cm under surface of 150 ml H2O in erlenmeyer surrounded by ice or by cold H2O.

Distill at such rate that bend at top of tube becomes warm in 4 min and lower end in ca 8 min from time heat is applied. Discontinue distn after 10 min, but before removing flame lift distn flask until tip of outlet tube is above H2O in receiving flask. Let outlet tube drain, remove receiver, and either titr. with std KBrO3 soln, using 2 drops Me orange (red of indicator at end point may fade slowly, but color should persist ≥1 min upon addn of another drop of indicator); or nearly neutze with NaOH, add 4–5 g NaHCO3, and titr. with std I soln, **6.004(b)**, using starch indicator, **6.004(f)**.

36.297 Arsenic in Iron Methylarsenate (98) —Official Final Action

(*Caution: See* **46.078.**)

Transfer suitable quantity of sample (0.2 g, if practicable) to Kjeldahl flask. Add 10 g K2SO4,

0.3 g starch, and 20 ml H2SO4. Digest over low heat until frothing ceases and continue digestion over slightly higher flame until mixt. is colorless. Cool, and add 20 ml H2O. Dry neck of flask over small flame, cool contents, and add 30 g NaCl, 5 g FeSO4.7H2O, 1 g NaBr, and 25 ml HCl. Distill as in **36.296.** Conduct blank, using same quantities of reagents.

36.298 Arsenic in Sodium Cacodylate (99)— Official Final Action

Transfer 0.2 g sample, accurately weighed, to Kjeldahl flask. Add 10 g K2SO4, 0.3 g starch, and 20 ml H2SO4. Digest over low flame until frothing ceases. Continue digestion 4 hr or until mixt. is colorless. Cool, dil. with H2O, and transfer to 500 ml erlenmeyer. Slowly add NaOH soln (1 + 1) until alk. to litmus paper, and acidify with H2SO4. Place flask in H2O until thoroly cooled, add 5 g NaHCO3, and titr. with 0.1N I. Conduct blank, using same quantities of reagents. 1 ml 0.1N I = 0.00375 g As, or 0.00800 g anhyd. Na(CH3)2AsO2.

Bismuth Compounds

36.299 Gravimetric Method (100)—Official Final Action

(Applicable in absence of Pb. *Caution: See* **46.011, 46.026,** and **46.059.**)

Thoroly mix sample and weigh 0.5 g into 500 ml Kjeldahl flask. Ignite gently over small flame, using wire gauze under flask, and increase heat towards end. Let cool, add 15–20 ml HNO3, evap. to dryness, and ignite as before until yellow or orange Bi2O3 is formed. Cool residue and dissolve in 10–15 ml warm HNO3, using few ml 3% H2O2 if residue does not dissolve readily. Boil off excess H2O2 and wash into 400 ml beaker with H2O, rinsing flask well. Dil. to ca 200 ml, make just neut. to litmus with NH4OH, and add 5 ml HCl. Ppt with H2S completely.

Transfer ppt to filter paper and wash once with HCl (5 + 200) and then several times with H2O. Dissolve ppt of Bi2S3 on filter with hot HNO3

(1 + 2). Small residue of S (and HgS if Hg salts are present) usually remain. Neutze filtrate with NH₄OH (2 + 3) and ppt with 25 ml 20% (NH₄)₂CO₃ soln. Conc. to ca 150 ml (by boiling, if desired) and let stand on steam bath 1–2 hr. Collect ppt in previously ignited, weighed gooch, wash with small amt of H_2O, dry, ignite in muffle at ca 550°, and weigh as Bi_2O_3.

Colorimetric Method (101)—Official Final Action

36.300 Apparatus

Spectrophotometer or photometer.—Capable of isolating spectral band 2 nm or less in region of 420–500 nm. Beckman spectrophtr fitted with matched 1 cm cells is suitable.

36.301 Reagents

(a) *Thiourea soln.*—2.5%. Use white, cryst. powder with no perceptible odor of sulfide. Dissolve 5 g thiourea in 200 ml HNO_3 (1 + 9). Prep. just before use.

(b) *Bismuth subcarbonate.*—Assay Bi subcarbonate by 36.299 or by accurately weighing into tared crucible ca 1 g Bi subcarbonate, previously dried 3 hr at 105°, and igniting to constant wt (Bi_2O_3).

(c) *Bismuth std solns. (1) Stock soln.*—1 mg/ml. Accurately weigh portion Bi subcarbonate, previously dried 3 hr at 105°, equiv. to 100 mg Bi (124.2 mg if 100%). Transfer to 100 ml vol. flask, add 5 ml H_2O, and mix. From pipet add 10 ml HNO_3, mix, and heat on steam bath 15 min. Cool, and dil. to vol. with H_2O. (2) *Working soln.*—100 μg/ml. Dil. 10 ml stock soln to 100 ml with HNO_3 (1 + 9).

36.302 Preparation of Standard Curve

Pipet 1.0, 2.0, 3.0, 4.0, and 5.0 ml working std soln (100, 200, 300, 400, and 500 μg Bi) into 25 ml vol. flasks. Add enough HNO_3 (1 + 9) to make total vol. of 5 ml in each flask. For blank, pipet 5.0 ml HNO_3 (1 + 9) into 25 ml vol. flask. Dil. all solns to vol. with thiourea soln and mix thoroly. Det. A of each soln at 465 nm relative to blank, using matched 1 cm cells. Prep. std curve by plotting A against concn Bi in μg/25 ml.

36.303 Preparation of Sample

(a) *General.*—Weigh thoroly mixed sample contg 20–80 mg Bi and transfer to 100 ml vol. flask. Add 5 ml H_2O, mix, and slowly add 10 ml HNO_3. Mix, and heat on steam bath 15 min. Cool, and dil. to vol. with H_2O. Pipet 10 ml aliquot into 100 ml vol. flask and dil. to vol. with HNO_3 (1 + 9). Filter if necessary.

(b) *Bismuth subsalicylate oil suspensions.*—Shake vigorously ≥1 min before each sampling. Accurately weigh sample contg 10–45 mg Bi into tared 100 ml beaker. Pipet 20 ml HNO_3 into sus-

pension and mix by stirring. Heat on steam bath 15 min, stirring occasionally. Cool to room temp., and quant. transfer to 250 ml separator with four 20 ml portions H_2O. Wash beaker with three 25 ml portions ether, adding washings to separator. Rinse beaker with two addnl 5 ml portions H_2O, adding rinsings to separator.

Carefully mix contents of separator by gentle inversion and cool under tap H_2O. Shake ca 15–30 sec, let sep. completely, and drain aq. soln into 400 ml beaker. Wash ether with three 10 ml portions H_2O, adding washings to beaker. Add few boiling chips and evap. aq. soln on steam bath under air current 30–60 min to remove most of ether. (Slight odor of ether after 1 hr may be disregarded.) Cool to room temp., transfer to 200 ml vol. flask contg 10 ml HNO_3, rinsing with H_2O to vol., and mix well. Disregard faint turbidity; filter if definite cloudiness is present. Pipet 50 ml aliquot into 100 ml vol. flask, dil. to vol. with HNO_3 (1 + 9), and mix. Proceed as in 36.304 except that if >1 sample aliquot is assayed, use sep. blank for each.

36.304 Determination

Pipet 5 ml sample soln into 25 ml vol. flask and dil. to vol. with thiourea soln. Det. A at 465 nm relative to blank prepd by dilg 5.0 ml sample soln to 25 ml with HNO_3 (1 + 9). Det. Bi in sample aliquot from std curve. Bi in sample = Bi in aliquot × 200.

For Bi subsalicylate:

% Bi (w/w) = Bi in aliquot × 80 × 100/g sample.

Calcium and/or Magnesium (102)—Official Final Action

(Applicable to pharmaceuticals and vitamin-mineral prepns)

36.305 Reagents

Use H_2O redistd from glass (preferable) or deionized H_2O, reagents 1.021(a), (b), (c), and in addn:

(a) *Calcium carbonate.*—Primary std grade, dried 2 hr at 285°.

(b) *Hydroxy naphthol blue.*—Ca indicator (Mallinckrodt Chemical Works No. 5630 in dispenser bottle ready for use, or equiv.). Store in dark and replace after 1 year.

(c) *Calmagite.*—Ca + Mg indicator (Mallinckrodt No. 4283 in dispenser bottle ready for use, or equiv.). Store in dark and replace after 1 year.

(d) *Disodium dihydrogen ethylenediamine tetraacetate (EDTA) std soln.*—0.01M. Dissolve 3.72 g $Na_2H_2EDTA\cdot2H_2O$ (99+ % purity) in H_2O in 1 L vol. flask, dil. to vol., and mix. Accurately weigh enough $CaCO_3$ to give ca 40 ml titrn with 0.01M EDTA and transfer to 400 ml beaker. Add 50 ml H_2O and enough 10% HCl to dissolve $CaCO_3$. Dil. to ca 150 ml with H_2O and add 15 ml

1*N* NaOH, disregarding any ppt or turbidity. Add ca 200 mg hydroxy naphthol blue indicator and titr. from pink to deep blue end point, using magnetic stirrer. Add last few ml EDTA soln dropwise. Molarity EDTA soln = mg $CaCO_3$/(ml EDTA × 100.09).

36.306 *Apparatus*

(a) *Titration stand.*—Fluorescent illuminated, such as TitraLite, Precision Scientific Co., 3737 W. Cortland St, Chicago, IL 60647, or equiv.

(b) *Ion exchange column.*—Approx. 20 × 600 mm, fitted with coarse porosity fritted glass disk and Teflon stopcock. Place 30–40 g moist Amberlite IR-4B resin (anion exchange resin with high phosphate capacity) from fresh bottle in 600 ml beaker and exhaust with three 250 ml portions 5% Na_2CO_3 or NaOH. Wash with H_2O until excess base is removed. Treat resin with three 250 ml portions 5% HCl (3 + 22), mixing thoroly after each treatment. Rinse with H_2O until color is removed, and transfer with H_2O to column. Column is ready for use after draining H_2O to top of resin column. (Exchange capacity for phosphate is ca 1500 mg; therefore number of aliquots can be passed thru column before regeneration is necessary. Rinse column with ca 250 ml H_2O before each use until eluate is colorless.)

36.307 *Preparation of Sample*

Transfer 2 g well-mixed sample to 100 ml Pt or porcelain dish. Ash at temp. ≤525° until apparently C-free (gray to brown). Cool, add 20 ml H_2O, stir with stirring rod, and add 10 ml HCl cautiously under watch glass. Rinse off watch glass into dish and evap. to dryness on steam bath. Add 50 ml HCl (1 + 9), heat on steam bath 15 min, and filter thru quant. paper into 200 ml vol. flask. Wash paper and dish thoroly with hot H_2O. Cool filtrate, dil. to vol., and mix.

36.308 *Determination*

Transfer 50 ml aliquot prepd sample to 250 ml beaker and adjust to pH 3.5 with 10% KOH soln added dropwise, using pH meter and magnetic stirrer. Pass sample thru resin column (column is in chloride form), collecting effluent in 250 ml vol. flask and adjusting flow rate to 2–3 ml/min. Wash column with two 50 ml portions H_2O, passing first portion thru at same rate as sample soln and second at 6–7 ml/min. Finally, pass enough H_2O freely thru column to make to vol. Mix thoroly. Pipet two 100 ml aliquots into 400 ml beakers.

Titration A (calcium + magnesium).—Adjust first aliquot to pH 10 (using pH meter and magnetic stirrer) with pH 10 buffer soln, 1.021(a) (ca 5 ml). Add 2 ml 2% KCN soln, 1.021(c), and 200 mg Calmagite indicator, and titr. immediately with 0.01*M* EDTA soln thru red to deep blue end point, using magnetic stirrer.

Titration B (calcium).—Adjust second aliquot to pH 12.5–13.0 (using pH meter and magnetic stirrer) with KOH-KCN soln, 1.021(b) (ca 10 ml). Add 0.100 g ascorbic acid and 200–300 mg hydroxy naphthol blue indicator. Titr. immediately with 0.01*M* EDTA soln thru pink to deep blue end point, using magnetic stirrer.

% Ca = $B × F × 0.4008 × 10 × 100$/mg sample
% Mg = $(A − B) × F × 0.2431 × 10 × 100$/mg sample;

where A and B = ml EDTA soln from titrns A and B, and F = 0.01/molarity EDTA soln.

36.309 Calcium Gluconate (*103*)— Official Final Action

(Applicable to prepns whose aq. solns are neut. and which do not contain salts of other optically active hydroxy acids. *Caution: See* **46.083** and **46.084**.)

Weigh two 0.5 g portions Ca gluconate or two 1 g portions powd tablets contg ≤50% of the salt. If chocolate or fatty base is present, wash samples several times on hardened filter with absolute ether and warm residue until ether is driven off.

Transfer each portion to sep. 25 ml vol. flasks, add 15 ml H_2O, and warm until Ca salt dissolves. (Samples contg cocoa will have undissolved residue.) Cool mixt. to room temp.

To one flask (No. 1) add 3.5 g *finely pulverized uranyl acetate*, stopper, and shake mech. 1 hr. (If agitation is not vigorous enough, >1 hr of shaking may be required.) Let other flask (No. 2) stand. If sample contains chocolate, add little alumina cream, 31.021(b), to each flask. Cool to 20°; dil. contents of flask No. 1 to vol. with *uranyl acetate soln* (10 g shaken with 95 ml H_2O until satd and then filtered), and flask No. 2 with H_2O. Filter, and polarize each soln in 200 mm tube, using 50 mm tube contg 1.8% $K_2Cr_2O_7$ soln as light filter. If soln is too dark to read in 200 mm tube, make reading in 100 mm tube and multiply result by 2. If X = rotation in °S of Soln No. 2 and Y = rotation of Soln No. 1, with 1 g sample % $Ca(C_6H_{11}O_7)_2$ = 4.34 × (Y − X), and with 0.5 g sample % $Ca(C_6H_{11}O_7)_2$ = 8.52 × (Y − X).

36.310 Calcium, Phosphorus, and Iron in Vitamin Preparations (*104*)—Official Final Action

Transfer representative portion of well-mixed sample contg ≥10 mg P, 50 mg Ca, and 1 mg Fe to 100 ml Pt or porcelain dish. Ash at temp. ≤525° until apparently C-free (gray to brown). Cool, moisten with 20 ml H_2O, break up ash with stirring rod, and cautiously add 10 ml HCl under watch glass. Rinse off watch glass into dish and evap. to dryness on steam bath. Add 50 ml HCl (1 + 9), heat on steam bath 15 min, and filter thru quant. paper into 200 ml vol. flask. Thoroly wash filter and dish with hot H_2O, cool filtrate, dil. to vol., and mix.

(a) *Phosphorus.*—Using aliquot contg 2–5 mg P, proceed as in **22.036.**

(b) *Calcium.*—Transfer aliquot contg 20–40 mg Ca to beaker, dil. to 100 ml, and proceed as in **3.011.** Correct for $KMnO_4$ consumed in blank detn.

(c) *Iron.*—Transfer aliquot contg 0.2–0.5 mg Fe to 100 ml vol. flask, add enough HCl $(1 + 9)$ to yield 2 ml concd acid, and dil. to vol. Proceed as in **14.013(a),** beginning "Pipet 10 ml aliquot into 25 ml vol. flask ..." Det. Fe in sample by comparison with stds prepd as in **14.012.**

Effervescent Potassium Bromide with Caffeine (105)—Official Final Action
36.311 Preparation of Sample

Powder sample, transfer immediately to dry bottle, and seal tightly. Thoroly mix powder in bottle by rotating and shaking before removal of sample for analysis. Weigh all needed portions as nearly at same time as possible. Avoid extreme temps and humidities when opening and storing samples.

36.312 Determinations

(a) *Potassium bromide.*—Weigh 2.5–3 g sample and transfer to 250 ml erlenmeyer. Add 50 ml H_2O and swirl gently, avoiding loss of soln by spattering. Acidify soln with HNO_3 and add 5 ml excess. Add 30 ml $0.1N$ $AgNO_3$, **45.028–45.030,** and 2 ml ferric indicator, **36.372(b).** Let mixt. stand several min and swirl occasionally to aid in flocculating the AgBr. Titr. excess $AgNO_3$ with NH_4CNS soln, **36.372(a).** 1 ml $0.1N$ $AgNO_3$ = 0.0119 g KBr.

(b) *Caffeine.*—(*Caution: See* **46.011, 46.040,** and **46.056.**) Weigh 12–15 g sample, transfer to separator, and slowly add 50 ml H_2O, avoiding loss of soln by spattering. If soln is not alk. to litmus, make alk. with 5% NaOH soln. Add 50 ml $CHCl_3$, shake vigorously, and filter into beaker. Repeat extn with two 50 ml portions $CHCl_3$. Wash filter and funnel with few ml $CHCl_3$ to remove any adhering caffeine. Evap. combined $CHCl_3$ filtrates on H_2O bath to ca 10 ml, finally transferring residual liq. to small weighed beaker. Let soln evap. by gentle heat and air blast. Dry residue to constant wt at 80° and weigh.

Elixir of Five Bromides (106)— Official Final Action
36.313 Preparation of Dilution

Transfer 50 ml sample to 1 L vol. flask, dil. to vol., and mix. Measure aliquots of this diln at original temp. of sample.

36.314 Determinations

(a) *Ammonium bromide.*—Place 200 ml aliquot of diln in Kjeldahl flask; add small piece of *par-*

affin and excess 10% NaOH soln (ca 5 ml). Distill NH_3 into excess std acid (40 ml $0.1N$ usually is enough). Titr. excess acid with $0.1N$ NaOH, using Me red. 1 ml $0.1N$ acid = 0.00979 g NH_4Br.

(b) *Calcium bromide.*—Pipet 100 ml aliquot of diln into casserole or Pt dish and evap. to dryness. Ignite at dull red (ca 525°) until org. matter is thoroly charred. Cool, add 5 ml HCl $(1 + 3)$ to dissolve Ca salts, filter, and wash well with hot H_2O. Return filter and unoxidized C to casserole or dish and ignite at 600° until residue is white. Treat residue with 5 ml HCl $(1 + 3)$, filter, and wash with hot H_2O, combining filtrates.

Det. Ca as in **3.011,** and reserve filtrate for detn of Na, K, and Li. If $0.1N$ $KMnO_4$ is used, 1 ml = 0.0100 g $CaBr_2$.

(c) *Lithium bromide.*—Dil. filtrate and washings from Ca detn to 200 ml and mix. Evap. 100 ml aliquot to dryness and drive off all NH_4 salts by heating to faint red (ca 525°) in Pt dish. Treat residue with little H_2O, filter into Pt dish, add few ml HCl, and evap. to dryness.

Complete conversion of alkali bromides to chlorides by treating residue with $Cl-H_2O$ and evapg to dryness. Repeat addn and evapn of $Cl-H_2O$ twice more, or until there is no apparent darkening of soln due to liberation of Br. Proceed as in **33.027** and **33.028,** beginning "Dissolve mixed chlorides in hot H_2O, filter, and wash." (Since Na and K are to be detd directly, it is not necessary to weigh mixed chlorides.) $Li_2SO_4 \times 1.5800 = LiBr$.

(d) *Sodium bromide.*—Remove combined KCl and NaCl from gooch by washing with hot H_2O, dil. to 50 ml, and use 5 ml aliquot for detn of Na. Proceed as in **3.024,** beginning "add 100 ml Mg uranyl acetate soln ..." Calc. to NaBr, using factor 0.0688.

(e) *Potassium bromide.*—Use 25 ml aliquot of soln of KCl and NaCl and proceed as in **33.028,** fourth par., beginning "Add enough Pt soln, **2.076(b),** to convert KCl and NaCl to K_2PtCl_6 and Na_2PtCl_6, and evap. to dryness." Calc. to KBr, using factor 0.4897.

(f) *Total bromine.*—Transfer 20 ml of diln to 500 ml flask. Add 100 ml H_2O, 2 ml HNO_3, and excess of $0.1N$ $AgNO_3$ (usually 30 ml). Titr. excess $AgNO_3$ with $0.1N$ NH_4CNS, using Fe alum indicator. 1 ml $0.1N$ $AgNO_3$ = 0.00799 g Br.

Elixir of Three Bromides (106)— Official Final Action
36.315 Preparation of Dilution

Dil. 25 ml elixir to 250 ml. Measure aliquot of this diln at original temp. of sample.

36.316 Determination

(a) *Ammonium bromide.*—Transfer 50 ml of diln to Kjeldahl flask provided with trap and condenser; add 150 ml H_2O and excess 10% NaOH soln (ca 5 ml). Distill NH_3 into excess $0.1N$

H_2SO_4 (ca 50 ml), and titr. excess acid with $0.1N$ NaOH, using Me red. 1 ml $0.1N$ H_2SO_4 = 0.00979 g NH_4Br.

(b) *Potassium bromide.*—Evap. 10 ml of diln and ignite at dull red (ca 525°). Treat residue with hot H_2O, filter, and wash into porcelain evapg dish. Convert bromides to chlorides by treating residue with 2 portions Cl-H_2O, evapg between addns, and proceed as in **3.020**, beginning "acidify with few drops HCl..." $K_2PtCl_6 \times 0.4897$ = KBr.

(c) *Sodium bromide.*—Transfer 5 ml of diln to beaker and proceed as in **3.024**, beginning "add 100 ml Mg uranyl acetate soln..." Wt Na-Mg uranyl acetate $\times 0.0688$ = NaBr.

(d) *Total bromine.*—Transfer 10 ml of diln to flask and add slowly and with agitation 30 ml $0.1N$ $AgNO_3$, 2 ml HNO_3, and 2 ml $FeNH_4(SO_4)_2$ soln. Titr. excess $AgNO_3$ with $0.1N$ NH_4CNS. 1 ml $0.1N$ $AgNO_3$ = 0.00799 g Br.

Hypophosphites in Sirups (*107*)— Official Final Action

(Applicable in absence of phosphates; if phosphates are present, make suitable correction.)

36.317 Method I

(a) *Total hypophosphites.*—(*Caution: See* **46.011** and **46.026**.) Pipet 25 ml sample into 100 ml vol. flask, dil. to vol., and mix thoroly. Pipet 10 ml aliquot into flask. Add 25 ml HNO_3 and boil on hot plate to 2–3 ml; add 10 ml HNO_3 and boil again to 2–3 ml. Cool, and add 20 ml H_2O. Add NH_4OH in slight excess and barely dissolve ppt formed with few drops HNO_3, stirring vigorously. To hot soln add 70 ml molybdate soln, **2.029**(a), for each 0.1 g P_2O_5 present. Digest 1 hr at ca 65°, and test for complete pptn by addn of more reagent to clear supernatant. Filter, and wash with NH_4NO_3 soln, **8.025**(a).

Dissolve ppt on filter with NH_4OH (1 + 1) and hot H_2O, and wash into beaker to vol. of ≤100 ml. Nearly neutze with HCl, using litmus paper as indicator, and cool. From buret, slowly add (ca 1 drop/sec, stirring vigorously) 15 ml magnesia mixt., **8.025**(b), for each 0.1 g P_2O_5 present. After 15 min add 12 ml NH_4OH and let stand overnight. Filter, and wash ppt with dil. NH_4OH (1 + 9) until washings are practically Cl-free. Dry; ignite first at low temp. and finally to constant wt, preferably in elec. furnace at 950–1000°. Cool, and weigh as $Mg_2P_2O_7$. $Mg_2P_2O_7 \times 0.6377 = P_2O_5$.

(b) *Calcium.*—Using prepd soln, (a), first sentence, pipet 20 ml aliquot into 400 ml beaker and dil. to 100 ml. Add 2 ml HCl, 15 ml 10% NH_4OAc soln, and slight excess of satd $(NH_4)_2C_2O_4$ soln. Heat to boiling and let ppt settle at temp. just below boiling. Filter hot, wash with 1% NH_4OAc soln, dry, moisten with H_2SO_4, ignite gently, and weigh residue as $CaSO_4$. $CaSO_4 \times 0.2944$ = Ca.

Method II

(Not applicable in presence of other reducing agents or of phenolic compds)

36.318   Determination

Quant. transfer 50 ml sample, measured in 50 ml vol. flask, to 250 ml vol. flask, dil. to vol. with H_2O, and mix well. (This method is followed for sirup of $NH_4H_2PO_2$; for sirups contg larger amts of hypophosphites, dil. to 500 ml in vol. flask.)

Transfer 50 ml aliquot to 250 ml vol. flask, dil. to vol. with H_2O, and mix well. Transfer 50 ml aliquot (equiv. to 2 ml sirup) to 250 ml g-s flask; add 50 ml KBr-$KBrO_3$ soln, **36.208**, and 20 ml 10% H_2SO_4; stopper, shake well, and let stand 2 hr. Add 10 ml 20% KI soln, shake flask, and titr. liberated I with $0.1N$ $Na_2S_2O_3$ soln, **45.038–45.039**, to straw color; add 2 ml starch soln, **6.004**(f), and titr. until colorless. Conduct blank detn similarly. 1 ml $0.1N$ $Na_2S_2O_3$ = 0.00165 g H_3PO_2; 1 ml $0.1N$ $Na_2S_2O_3$ = 0.00208 g $NH_4H_2PO_2$.

36.319 Iodine (*108*)—Official Final Action

Transfer quantity of sample contg ≤0.1 g of the iodide (0.05 g is ample) to crucible, preferably Ni. If sample contains only slight amt of org. material, add 1 g starch. Add 2–3 g solid KOH. If sample is solid, add 10–15 ml alcohol before adding KOH. Alkali must be thoroly mixed with sample to prevent loss of I in muffle (either stir, leaving stirring rod in crucible, or heat and swirl on steam bath until KOH is in soln). Dry and char thoroly. (Use as low temp. as possible to prevent loss of I; not more than dull red.) Ext charred mass with hot H_2O, filter into erlenmeyer, and wash well with hot H_2O.

Neutze filtrate with H_2SO_4 (1 + 1), make alk. again with 4% NaOH soln, and add 1 ml excess. Heat to boiling and slowly add satd $KMnO_4$ soln until $KMnO_4$ color remains after several min of boiling. Then add ca 0.5 ml excess, continue boiling ca 5 min, and let cool. Add enough $KMnO_4$ to completely oxidize all iodide to iodate so that $KMnO_4$ color, not brown MnO_2 color, is present at end of boiling period. Add few ml alcohol and place on steam bath. ($KMnO_4$ color should be bleached; if it is not, add little more alcohol.) When ppt has settled, filter, and wash with hot 1% NH_4Cl soln. If filtrate is not clear, digest on steam bath until the MnO_2 can be retained on filter. After cooling, add 1–2 g KI, acidify with HCl, and titr. with $0.1N$ $Na_2S_2O_3$. 1 ml $0.1N$ $Na_2S_2O_3$ = 0.00277 g KI, 0.00250 g NaI, or 0.00212 g I.

36.320 Iodine Ointment (*109*)—Official Final Action

(a) *Free iodine.*—Weigh (to 1 mg) ca 2 g ointment, and transfer to 250 ml I flask. Melt on H_2O bath (≤70°), add 30 ml $CHCl_3$, mix well, and then add 30 ml H_2O. (All of base should be dissolved in $CHCl_3$ before H_2O is added.) Titr. with $0.1N$ $Na_2S_2O_3$, using starch indicator, **6.004(f)**. Approach end point dropwise, shaking flask vigorously to ensure that all I has been extd from $CHCl_3$ layer. 1 ml $0.1N$ $Na_2S_2O_3 = 0.01269$ g I.

(b) *Potassium iodide.*—Pour liqs from free I detn, (a), into 500 ml I flask, rinsing flask with 200 ml H_2O, added in several portions. (It is desirable to maintain this vol. within rather narrow limits.) Add 0.5 ml *0.2% alc. p-ethoxychrysoidin indicator* and 1–4 drops $0.1N$ NaOH (to neutze). (Aq. layer should now be clear yellow.) Titr. with $0.1N$ $AgNO_3$, approaching end point dropwise and swirling frequently. ($AgNO_3$ soln causes turbidity due to formation of colloidal AgI and development of reddish-brown color similar to that observed in over-titrd Volhard detn. End point, which is produced by 1 drop $AgNO_3$ soln, is characterized by flocculation of colloidal AgI and complete disappearance of reddish-brown tinge, leaving almost clear, pale yellow supernatant.) ml $0.1N$ $AgNO_3$ — ml $0.1N$ $Na_2S_2O_3$, (a) = ml consumed by iodide originally present. 1 ml $0.1N$ $AgNO_3 = 0.0166$ g KI.

Mercury (*110*)—Official Final Action

(Applicable to Hg in phenylmercuric chloride, HgI_2, nitromersol, HgO ointment, and calomel tablets. *Caution: See* **46.079.**)

36.321 *Reagents*

(a) *Strychnine sulfate soln.*—Approx. $0.01M$; 4.3 g/500 ml.

(b) *Valser's reagent.*—Dissolve 10 g KI in H_2O and dil. to 100 ml. Sat. with HgI_2 (ca 14 g) and filter.

36.322 *Apparatus*

(a) *Digestion flask.*—Acetylation or r-b; 100 ml capacity fitted to H_2O-cooled straight tube condenser with ⊤ joint.

(b) *Gooch crucibles.*—Fitted with 21 mm filter paper disks, covered with thin layer of asbestos, and dried at 105°. Use to filter and weigh ppt of strychnine.$HI.HgI_2$.

36.323 *Preparation of Samples*

(*Caution: See* **46.047.**)

Accurately weigh (avoid use of metal containers) or measure quantity of sample contg 20–100 mg Hg (optimal ca 50 mg) and treat as follows:

(a) *Solns of organic mercurials.*—Transfer sample to beaker and evap. just to dryness with low heat (60–70°) and air current. Dissolve residue in ca 5 ml 10% NaOH soln and transfer to digestion flask. Rinse beaker with four 3–4 ml portions H_2O and add rinsings to digestion flask. Add excess liq. Br to soln and connect flask to condenser. Boil 4–5 min and add 3 ml HCl thru top of condenser. Continue to heat soln until Br collects in con-

denser tube. Remove heat and cool until Br returns to soln in digestion flask.

Alternately heat and cool until Br has almost completely dissipated. (After 3 intervals of heating, flow of H_2O thru condenser may be discontinued to aid in removing Br.) Let flask cool, and rinse inside of condenser with ca 5 ml H_2O. Disconnect flask and rinse tip of condenser with small stream of H_2O from wash bottle. Filter thru 9 cm paper into 150 ml beaker, and rinse flask and filter with four 5 ml portions H_2O.

(b) *Ointments.*—Transfer sample to digestion flask and add 5 ml HCl $(1 + 3)$ followed by 5 ml satd Br-H_2O. Place small pieces of porcelain, SiC, or few glass beads in flask to prevent bumping. Connect flask to condenser and fit flask over hole cut in asbestos board so that bottom of flask extends just below undersurface of board. Heat over low flame, maintaining slow and continuous boiling ca 10 min, and then cool to room temp. Disconnect flask and decant aq. portion thru 9 cm paper into 150 ml beaker. Take precautions to retain all ointment base in flask. Rinse neck of flask into filter with few drops of H_2O from wash bottle. Add 1 ml HCl $(1 + 3)$, 1 ml satd Br-H_2O, and 8 ml H_2O to flask and reflux. Again cool contents of flask and decant aq. phase thru filter.

Repeat refluxing and decanting with two 10 ml portions H_2O and finally rinse condenser tube into flask with ca 5 ml H_2O. Disconnect flask, rinse condenser tip, and decant rinsings thru filter. Rinse filter with 2 small portions H_2O from wash bottle.

Test for complete removal of Hg by adding 5 ml H_2O and 2 drops HCl $(1 + 3)$ to digestion flask and refluxing as before. Pass this soln thru original filter into 50 ml beaker. To filtrate add 1 drop 10% KI soln and 1 drop strychnine sulfate soln. No turbidity should be produced. If extn is incomplete, repeat refluxings with H_2O until all Hg is removed. Reserve all test solns showing presence of Hg to add to major portion after pptn of Hg.

(c) *Calomel tablets.*—Weigh ≥20 tablets and det. av. wt. Grind to fine powder and transfer accurately weighed portion to digestion flask. Add 10 ml satd Br-H_2O and 5 ml HCl $(1 + 3)$. Connect flask to reflux condenser and gently boil contents until most of Br vapors collect in condenser. Discontinue heating until Br returns to soln in flask. Repeat alternate heating and cooling until Br vapors are dissipated. Cool flask and contents to room temp. and rinse condenser tube with ca 10 ml H_2O. Disconnect flask and rinse condenser tip into flask. Filter soln thru gooch into 150 ml beaker. Rinse flask with three 5 ml portions H_2O and pass rinsings thru crucible, and finally rinse crucible with fine stream of H_2O.

(d) *Tablets containing purgative drugs.*—If tablets contain purgative drugs, add 10 ml alcohol to weighed sample in flask. Heat on steam bath with gentle agitation until alcohol begins to boil. Remove flask, cool under tap, and filter supernatant thru gooch fitted with asbestos mat. Retain as much of insol. residue in flask as possible. Rinse flask and contents with three 10 ml portions alcohol and two 5 ml portions H_2O, and decant thru crucible as above. Remove asbestos mat with fine wire or needle and transfer to flask. Rinse crucible with 10 ml satd $Br-H_2O$ and 5 ml HCl $(1 + 3)$, and add rinsings to flask. Connect flask to condenser, and treat as in (c).

36.324   Determination

Add 10 ml 10% KI soln to filtrate, and if necessary, evap. on steam bath under air current to ca 50 ml. If soln has not previously been acidified, add 3 ml HCl $(1 + 3)$. Add 1% $NaHSO_3$ soln until I color is discharged, and keep soln free from I color by addn of $NaHSO_3$ soln until final filtration is made. Add strychnine sulfate soln slowly from buret or pipet until ppt coagulates and settles rapidly. (Strychnine sulfate soln may be added as rapidly as it will flow from buret if theoretical quantity is used, based on 1 ml soln for each 4 mg Hg expected to be present.) Avoid undue excess of strychnine because of slight solubility of its hydriodide.

Let ppt settle and test for complete pptn by adding 2–3 drops strychnine sulfate soln to clear supernatant. If pptn is incomplete, indicated by cloudiness around the drops, add strychnine sulfate soln in 1 ml increments until pptn is complete. Let ppt remain in beaker with occasional stirring 0.5–1 hr.

Decant supernatant thru weighed gooch, 36.322(b). Wash ppt into crucible with fine stream of H_2O. Completely transfer ppt to crucible, and wash residue and crucible with three 5 ml portions H_2O. Scrub beaker thoroly with policeman. Transfer crucible and holder to another small suction flask and wash residue with 2–3 ml H_2O. Test filtrate for complete removal of strychnine by addn of Valser's reagent. If necessary, continue washing ppt with small portions H_2O until last washings give no more than faint opalescence upon addn of Valser's reagent. Always test main filtrate by addn of ca 1 ml strychnine sulfate soln to assure complete pptn of Hg. If pptn was incomplete, repeat detn. Dry crucible 1 hr at 105°, cool in desiccator, and weigh. Calc. % Hg compd in sample on basis of mol. wt of 916.73 for ppt of strychnine.HI.HgI_2.

Merbromin (Mercurochrome®) (111)

36.325   Tests for Purity—Procedure

(a) Acidify portion of merbromin soln with 10% H_2SO_4 and filter off ppt. Filtrate is only slightly yellow.

(b) Pass H_2S (*Caution: See* **46.059**) into portion of filtrate. No ppt or coloring occurs.

(c) Add few ml 10% HNO_3 to another portion of filtrate and add $AgNO_3$ soln. No ppt forms.

36.326   Total Solids in Solution—Official Final Action

Pipet 10 ml merbromin soln into tared, extra-wide-form weighing bottle and evap. to dryness on steam bath. Let dry overnight in open bottle in desiccator contg H_2SO_4. Weigh.

36.327   Determination of Mercury—Official Final Action

(*Caution: See* **46.019, 46.030, 46.039, 46.040, 46.048, 46.049, 46.059,** and **46.080.**)

Pipet 10 ml ca 2% merbromin soln into 500 ml tall beaker and evap. to dryness on steam bath (or accurately weigh ca 0.2 g of the powder). Dissolve residue in 4 ml H_2O and slowly add, with constant mixing, 10 ml H_2SO_4. Incline beaker and cautiously add small portions finely pulverized $KMnO_4$, mixing after each addn, until deep purple color shows that considerable excess has been added. Let stand 30 min, mixing occasionally. Mixt. should still be purple.

Add 100 ml H_2O and mix thoroly. Add small portions finely pulverized oxalic acid, mixing after each addn, until soln is clear. Filter thru small filter into 400 ml beaker, wash original beaker and filter until filtrate measures ca 200 ml, and pass H_2S thru soln 20 min. Warm on steam bath until ppt of HgS settles quickly after stirring, and again pass H_2S thru warm soln 5 min. Immediately filter soln into weighed gooch; thoroly wash ppt on filter with H_2O, 3 times with alcohol, and then with 4 or 5 portions CCl_4 or CS_2, letting liq. run thru crucible without suction; finally wash with ether. Dry ppt to constant wt at 100° and weigh as HgS. $HgS \times 0.8622 = Hg$.

Qual. test dried ppt for Hg and other heavy metals. If slow filtration occurs during washing with H_2O, let ppt drain, and wash once with alcohol; then continue as directed.

36.328   Mercurous Chloride (Calomel) in Ointments (112)—Official Final Action

Accurately weigh ca 1 g ointment, transfer to 250 ml g-s erlenmeyer, and treat with ca 50 ml $CHCl_3$. When base is dissolved, decant thru dry, closely packed asbestos mat in Caldwell crucible, using light suction. Wash flask and contents several times with 20–30 ml portions $CHCl_3$, decanting thru crucible. Let any residual $CHCl_3$ in flask evap., and transfer asbestos mat and contents to flask, wiping sides of crucible and mouth of flask with damp piece of filter paper and adding it to flask. Add 2.5 g KI and 30 ml std 0.1N I, **45.019** (stdzd against $Na_2S_2O_3$), stopper, and mix well.

Let flask stand ca 1.5 hr or until soln of calomel is complete, agitating frequently and fairly vigorously. Titr. with $0.1N$ $Na_2S_2O_3$, **45.039**, adding 1 or 2 ml excess and using starch indicator, **6.004(f)**. When all traces of I disappear, back-titr. with std I soln to blue color. 1 ml $0.1N$ I = 0.02360 g Hg_2Cl_2.

36.329 Mercurous Chloride (Calomel) in Tablets (*113*)—Official Final Action

Count and weigh representative number of tablets. Pulverize quantity of tablets and accurately weigh well-mixed sample contg 0.19–0.26 g (3–4 grains) Hg_2Cl_2. Transfer to 200 ml g-s erlenmeyer, add ca 50 ml H_2O, acidify with HOAc, and after sol. fillers dissolve, decant with aid of suction thru tightly packed asbestos mat placed on plate of Caldwell crucible. Wash once with H_2O by decantation and then successively with alcohol and ether. Transfer removable plate holding mat and insol. material to original flask, washing into flask any insol. material adhering to sides of crucible. Add 2.5 g KI, 10 ml H_2O, and then 30 ml std $0.1N$ I soln, **45.019**. Complete detn as in **36.328**.

36.330 Mercurous Iodide in Tablets (*114*)— Official Final Action

Accurately weigh well-mixed powd sample contg 0.19–0.26 g (3–4 grains) Hg_2I_2. Transfer sample to 200 ml g-s flask, and proceed as in **36.329**, omitting addn of H_2O after the KI. 1 ml $0.1N$ I = 0.03275 g Hg_2I_2.

Note: Some com. tablets are difficult to filter thru asbestos mat without loss of Hg_2I_2. Placing few drops of alumina cream, **31.021(b)**, on mat before filtration is started (wash free from NH_3), satisfactorily prevents loss, tho it retards filtration.

36.331 Mercury in Mercurial Ointment (*115*)—Official Final Action

(*Caution: See* **46.011** and **46.026**.)

After mixing ointment thoroly with glass rod, avoiding contact with metals, weigh 1 g sample into erlenmeyer. Add 20 ml H_2O and 20 ml HNO_3, and heat gently over small flame until red fumes cease to evolve. Cool, and decant aq. soln from ointment base into separator. Wash ointment base with 50 ml boiling H_2O, cool, and decant into separator. Repeat washing until all Hg is removed.

Shake combined solns in separator with 50 ml ether. Transfer aq. soln to erlenmeyer. Wash ether soln with three 10 ml portions H_2O until Hg is removed, adding washings to flask. Add 3 ml $FeNH_4(SO_4)_2$ soln, **36.372(b)**, and titr. with $0.1N$ NH_4CNS. 1 ml $0.1N$ NH_4CNS = 0.01003 g Hg.

36.332 Mercury in Ointment of Mercuric Nitrate (*116*)—Official Final Action

(*Caution: See* **46.011** and **46.026**.)

Transfer, to 200–300 ml erlenmeyer, 3–5 g sample, accurately weighed, using glass or bone spatula.

Add 40 ml HNO_3 $(1 + 1)$ and few glass beads, and insert short-stem funnel into neck of flask. Boil gently 1–1.5 hr on hot plate or over low flame. (With latter, use piece of asbestos with circular hole under asbestos wire gauze.) Add 30 ml H_2O, using part to wash funnel. Cool enough (ca 20° or below) to cause solidification of unconsumed fat. Filter thru 11 cm paper into 200 ml vol. flask. Wash fat, flask, and filter, using ca 100 ml 1% HNO_3. Dil. to vol. and mix well. Reserve fat to test for complete extn as below.

Test for complete extn of Hg from fat and its removal from filter, etc., by repeating HNO_3 digestion ca 30 min on residual fat in flask or on filter, completing this as sep. detn, including $KMnO_4$ digestion. Add any titrn in excess of 1–2 drops (0.05–0.08 ml $0.1N$ NH_4CNS) resulting from this test portion to that obtained by titrg main ext.

Transfer 100 ml aliquot to 500 ml erlenmeyer. Add 7 ml HNO_3, 5 ml H_2SO_4, and 2 g powd $KMnO_4$, and rotate to dissolve. Heat just to boiling over low flame or on hot plate. Boil gently 45 min, maintaining excess of $KMnO_4$, indicated by dark purple color. (Excess is essential.) When adding $KMnO_4$ to boiling liq., use smaller portions (ca 0.5 g or less) to avoid loss due to frothing.

Caution: Use of greater excess of $KMnO_4$ than necessary is not objectionable, but proportionately more H_2O_2 is required to remove it and MnO_2 at end of digestion. Usually ca 10 g is required. Rate of consumption and total $KMnO_4$ consumed appear to vary with temp., org. matter present, and period of heating. Large amt of MnO_2 formed may lead to wrong conclusion concerning color indicative of excess of $KMnO_4$. Frequent examination of soln is necessary. Observation of this color is aided by looking thru supernatant toward white background while holding container in inclined position.

Remove excess $KMnO_4$ and dissolve MnO_2 by adding H_2O_2 (5–10% prepd from 30%) dropwise to hot soln. When colorless, add 2% $KMnO_4$ soln slowly until faint pink or brown persists ca 1 min. If large amt of MnO_2 forms at this point, again use H_2O_2 sparingly; then use $KMnO_4$ to discharge the H_2O_2. Discharge color from last addn of $KMnO_4$, including weak brown from MnO_2, by adding dropwise just enough 8% $FeSO_4.7H_2O$ soln. Cool to ca 20°, add 3 ml ca $0.5N$ $FeNH_4(SO_4)_2$.$12H_2O$, and titr. with std $0.1N$ NH_4CNS. 1 ml $0.1N$ NH_4CNS = 0.01003 g Hg.

Nitrites in Tablets—Official Final Action
Hydrazine Method (*117*)

(Applicable in presence or absence of nitrates or chlorides)

36.333 *Reagent*

Hydrazine sulfate std soln.—$0.1N$. Dissolve ca 3.25 g $N_2H_4.H_2SO_4$ in H_2O and dil. to 1 L. Stdze against $0.1N$ I, **45.019**, as in detn.

36.334 *Determination*

Weigh 20 tablets, reduce to fine powder, and mix well. Accurately weigh sample contg ca 130 mg $NaNO_2$, place in 100 ml vol. flask, dil. to vol. with H_2O, and mix well. Filter, discarding first few ml filtrate. Pipet 50 ml aliquot filtrate and 50 ml $0.1N$ $N_2H_4 \cdot H_2SO_4$ soln into 300 ml erlenmeyer, add 5 ml H_2SO_4 $(3 + 47)$, wash down flask with H_2O, mix (soln should be acid), and let stand 30 min with occasional swirling. Add $NaHCO_3$ in small amts, while tipping flask, until reaction ceases. Titr. excess $N_2H_4 \cdot H_2SO_4$ with $0.1N$ I to end point that remains 1 min. Starch indicator may be used in titrn of colored solns. 1 ml $0.1N$ $N_2H_4 \cdot H_2SO_4 =$ 2.300 mg $NaNO_2$.

Silver Proteinates (*118*)—Official Final Action

36.335 *Total Silver*

(*Caution: See* **46.011** and **46.026.**)

Place 1 g sample, accurately weighed, in 500 ml Kjeldahl flask; add 15 ml H_2SO_4 and then 10 ml HNO_3. Place on steam bath few min, with occasional rotation, to ensure homogeneous mixt., and boil to white fumes. Add more HNO_3, boil again to clear colorless soln, and cool. Add 100 ml H_2O and boil until free of N oxides. Cool, dil. to 300 ml, add 5 ml HNO_3 and 5 ml $FeNH_4(SO_4)_2$ soln, **36.372(b)**, and titr. with $0.1N$ NH_4CNS. 1 ml $0.1N$ $NH_4CNS = 0.01079$ g Ag.

36.336 *Ionizable Silver Compounds*

Weigh strip of com. dialyzing tubing 55 mm wide and ca 30 cm long, wet with H_2O until uniformly pliable, shake free of adhering H_2O, and partially dry by rolling in clean paper towel. Reweigh while still moist and place in 250 ml beaker. (Sheets of dialyzing parchment paper may be used in place of tubing. Over one end of glass tube 10 cm long and ca 2.5 cm od, fold and secure with rubber band square piece of parchment paper in form of sack large enough to hold sample soln. Dialyzing material should be kept in humid container to prevent breaking when handled.) Weigh 1 g sample, dissolve in 15 ml H_2O, and transfer to dialyzing tube. Calc., and add enough H_2O to beaker to make 100 ml (this ensures 20 ml in dialyzing tube and 80 ml in beaker). Adjust tubing to form "U" in beaker, cover with watch glass, and keep cool and in dark 24 hr.

(a) *Qualitative test.*—Test few ml clear, colorless soln from beaker for Ag ions by addn of few drops HCl $(1 + 3)$ and trace of HNO_3.

(b) *Determination.*—If Ag ions are present, remove 50 ml clear, colorless soln (representing 0.5 g sample) from beaker, dil. to 100 ml, and add 2 ml $FeNH_4(SO_4)_2$ soln, **36.372(b)**, and 2 ml colorless HNO_3. Titr. with $0.01N$ NH_4CNS and calc. to % by wt ionizable Ag. 1 ml $0.01N$ $NH_4CNS = 0.001079$ g Ag.

MISCELLANEOUS DRUGS

Aminacrine (9-Aminoacridine) (*119*)— Official First Action

(*Caution: See* **46.008.**)

36.337 *Principle*

Aminacrine is extd from basic soln with $CHCl_3$ and residue after evapn is dissolved in acid-alcohol. Aminacrine is detd fluorometrically and identified by TLC.

Fluorometric Method

36.338 *Apparatus*

Fluorometer.—Capable of measuring fluorescence of aminacrine. HCl by activation at 365 nm. (Aminco Fluoro-Microphotometer designed to accommodate 75×10 mm od cuvets with primary filter, Corning Glass Works No. CS 7-39 for excitation (365 nm) and second filter, Wratten 2A (415 nm cutoff), for emission wavelength, is suitable. Aperture plate, with 4 position sensitivity step in primary filter, is used in one-hole position with U-shaped 4W black-light as light source (max. energy at 365 nm).

36.339 *Reagent*

Aminacrine std soln.—1 µg/ml HCl-alcohol $(2 + 99)$. (Ref. grade aminacrine is available from K & K Laboratories, Inc.) Std should produce single yellow spot when chromatographed on thin layer plate as in **36.343**.

36.340 *Determination*

Weigh amt of well-mixed or well-ground sample contg ca 5 mg aminacrine in 100 ml vol. flask and dissolve in 20 ml warm alcohol. Cool, dil. to vol. with alcohol, mix well, and filter. Pipet 1 ml soln into separator, add 5 ml 5% NaOH, and ext with three 25 ml portions $CHCl_3$, draining each $CHCl_3$ ext into beaker thru pledget of glass wool previously moistened with $CHCl_3$. Evap. combined exts on steam bath with gentle air stream. (Do not evap. cloudy filtrate; refilter if cloudiness appears.) Dissolve residue in 15 ml alcohol, add 1 ml HCl, and dil. to vol. with alcohol in 50 ml vol. flask.

Adjust fluorometer to ca 55% T with std soln. Transfer ca 4 ml sample soln to cell and read, using HCl-alcohol $(2 + 99)$ as blank. Use same cell for each detn. (If solns appear too concd to read at 55% T, dil. to appropriate concn.)

36.341 *Calculation*

Calc. as follows:

$500 \ C \times (F_u/F_s) =$ mg aminacrine. HCl in sample, where C is final concn std soln, mg/ml; F_u and F_s are fluorescence of sample and std, resp., each corrected for blank.

Qualitative Thin Layer Chromatographic Method

36.342 Apparatus and Reagents

(a) *Thin layer chromatography plates.*—Microscope slides with 250 μm coating of silica gel G (E. Merck, Darmstadt, Germany; George Uhe Co., 76 Ninth Ave, New York, NY 10011). (Eastman Kodak Co. Chromagram sheets for TLC, No. 6060, silica gel with fluorescent indicator, cut to size, are suitable.)

(b) *Developing solvent.*—Benzene-MeOH (95 + 5).

(c) *TLC std soln.*—Prep. 0.1% soln of aminacrine.HCl in alcohol.

36.343 Test

(*Caution: See* 46.016.)

Place ca 10 ml developing solv. in 200 ml lipless beaker contg strip of solv.-satd filter paper. Cover beaker and let atm. sat. few min. Dissolve sample contg ca 100 mg aminacrine in alcohol, add 1 ml HCl, and dil. to 100 ml with alcohol. Mix well and filter. Spot 3 μl aminacrine std and sample soln on coated plate. Place slide in beaker opposite paper strip, cover, and let chromatogram develop 1 hr. Air-dry slide and examine spots under shortwave UV lamp. (Two well-defined spots appear for each soln spotted: intensely fluorescent spot at baseline and faintly fluorescent spot ca midway up slide.) Use faintly fluorescent spots for comparison, i.e., R_f values of samples are same as std.

36.344 Chlorobutanol (1,1,1-Trichloro-2-methyl-2-propanol) (*120*)—Official Final Action

(a) *Chlorobutanol crystals.*—Transfer to pressure bottle sample contg ca 0.3 g chlorobutanol and carefully add 25 ml alc. KOH soln, 36.355(a). Stopper bottle; swirl gently, taking care to prevent soln from contacting rubber washer; let stand 30 min or overnight. Place bottle in wire basket, and set basket in H$_2$O bath at room temp. Invert tin can over bottle and cover with towel to prevent injury in case bottle should burst. Heat bath to boiling and maintain this temp. 15 min. Cool gradually.

Add 25 ml H$_2$O, swirling gently, and transfer contents of pressure bottle to 400 ml beaker. Wash bottle with H$_2$O, draining washings into beaker. Add 15 ml HNO$_3$ and excess of 2% AgNO$_3$ soln, stir well, and let mixt. stand in dark 15 min. Collect ppt in gooch previously dried at 105° and weighed. Thoroly wash ppt with H$_2$O and then with 5 ml alcohol followed by 5 ml ether. Dry to constant wt at 105°. If reagents contain Cl, apply correction detd by blank test. 1 g AgCl = 0.4127 g C$_4$H$_7$OCl$_3$.

(b) *Aqueous ampul solns.*—Pipet into distg flask sample contg ca 0.1 g chlorobutanol. Add enough H$_2$O to bring vol. to 50 ml and distill ca 25 ml thru straight-bore condenser. Collect distillate in ca 100 ml pressure bottle contg 25 ml alc. KOH soln, 36.355(a), and surrounded by ice bath. Have delivery tube extend into alc. soln. (Use straight-bore condenser to assure complete soln of crystals of chlorobutanol in condenser.) Let cool, disconnect still head, and carefully wash condenser with 25 ml alcohol, letting alcohol drain into pressure bottle. Repeat washings, using ca 20 ml H$_2$O. Also wash receiving tube with H$_2$O. Stopper bottle and swirl gently, taking care to prevent soln from contacting rubber washer. Let stand 30 min or overnight. Complete detn of Cl as in (a).

Gas Chromatographic and Infrared Method (*121*)—Official Final Action

(*Caution: See* 46.039, 46.040, 46.048, and 46.049.)

36.345 Reagents

(a) *Diatomaceous earth.*—Celite 545, acid-washed.

(b) *Chlorobutanol.*—USP. Store over soln satd with both sugar and salt; product contains ½ mole H$_2$O of hydration.

(c) *Glass wool.*—Fine, washed with CS$_2$ and dried.

(d) *Dichlorodimethylsilane.*—Dissolve 5 ml in 100 ml toluene. (*Caution:* Dichlorodimethylsilane is toxic. Avoid contact with skin or eyes. Use effective fume removal device.)

36.346 Apparatus

(a) *Chromatographic tube.*—23 × 400 mm with drip tip small enough to fit into 10 ml vol. flask and with close-fitting tamping rod.

(b) *Infrared spectrophotometer.*—With matched 1 mm path length liq.-filled NaCl cells.

(c) *Gas chromatograph.*—With 6′ × 4 mm glass column, packed with Carbowax 6000 on 100–110 mesh Anakrom ABS, H flame ionization detector, and strip chart recorder.

36.347 Preparation of GLC Column

Carefully wash inside of column and small amt of glass wool with dichlorodimethylsilane soln, rinse with MeOH, and dry. Slowly sprinkle ca 25 g Anakrom ABS into 400 ml beaker almost filled with CCl$_4$. Remove fine particles remaining at surface with vac. line and trap. Decant solv., oven-dry support, and transfer 20.0 g to 500 ml filter flask fitted with trap and stopper. Dissolve 5.0 g polyethylene glycol (Carbowax 6000) in 100 ml toluene, warming if necessary. Add Carbowax soln to flask and apply vac. 5 min, swirling occasionally. Return to atm. pressure and let stand 5 min. Transfer slurry with rapid swirling to buchner fitted with coarse paper. Maintain reduced pressure on funnel 5 min; then dry coated support by spreading on smooth surface. Air-dry 1 hr. Oven-dry addnl hr at 90°.

Carefully plug column exit with small tuft fine glass wool and thru-hole septum. Apply vac. to exit port and slowly add coated support thru injection port, tapping very gently to pack firmly. Pack to within 1 cm of area heated by flash heater. Plug with fine glass wool and condition ca 3 days at 200° with slow N stream.

36.348   *Preparation of Standard Solutions*

Dissolve ca 0.5 g chlorobutanol.½H₂O, accurately weighed, in 1 ml alcohol and transfer to 100 ml vol. flask with 8 ml alcohol. Dil. to vol. with H₂O. Using 5 ml aliquots, prep. duplicate Celite columns with trap layers as in **36.350.** Prep. and elute columns individually. Calc. mg anhyd. chlorobutanol/ml CS₂ from equation $C_{anh} = C_{hyd} \times 0.9518$. (Chlorobutanol is appreciably volatile at room temp.; expose to atm. as little as possible.)

36.349   *Preparation of Trap Layer*

Weigh 3 g Celite, add 2 ml 1N HCl, and mix until uniform. Transfer to chromatgc tube plugged with small tuft glass wool and tamp moderately tight.

36.350   *Preparation of Sample*

Calc. vol. sample contg ca 25 mg chlorobutanol. Weigh Celite equal to 1 g/ml sample. Pipet sample into Celite and mix (ca 1 min) until uniform. Transfer quant. to same column with aid of small amt of dry Celite and tamp firmly. Pack as few portions as possible, each portion ⩽5 g Celite. Rinse beaker with small portions CS₂ and transfer to column until sample portion is wet with CS₂. Let each portion sink into column before adding next. Add 20 ml CS₂ to column and collect eluate in 10 ml vol. flask. Rinse column tip with few drops CS₂ (pipet) when 8–9 ml collects. Continue to collect eluate to vol., stopper flask, and mix. This should yield proper concn for either GLC or IR detns. (Tightly-stoppered solns of chlorobutanol in CS₂ may be stored overnight.)

36.351   *GLC Standard Curve*

Operating conditions: column temp., 135°; detector temp., 215°; flash heater temp., 230°; N flow rate, ca 35 ml/min to elute chlorobutanol in ca 6 min; and H flow rate, 30 ml/min.

Adjust electrometer sensitivity so that 12 μg chlorobutanol gives ca 50% deflection. Inject 4, 5, 6, 7, 8, and 9 μl of each std eluate from 10 μl syringe. Read vol. in syringe before and after injection; take difference as vol. injected. Plot net % deflection against μg anhyd. chlorobutanol injected.

36.352   *GLC Determination*

Inject, as above, 6 μl sample soln and est. concn from std curve.

36.353   *Preparation of Infrared Standard*

Record spectrum of each std eluate from 9 to 15 μm, using quant. instrument settings and CS₂ in ref. beam. Det. A of max. at 12.5–12.6 μm, using baseline technics with ca 9.5 and ca 14.2 μm as base. (Net A is linear from 0.5 to 4.5 mg chlorobutanol/ml CS₂.)

36.354   *Infrared Determination*

Det. A sample soln at 12.5–12.6 μm, as above.

mg Chlorobutanol in sample aliquot = (net A sample eluate/net A std eluate) × mg chlorobutanol in 10 ml CS₂ std.

★ Chloroform or Carbon Tetrachloride ★ (*122*)—Official Final Action

(*See also* **36.358–36.363.**)

36.355   *Reagents*

(**a**) *Alcoholic potassium hydroxide soln.*—Dissolve 35 g KOH (Cl-free) in MeOH to make 100 ml. Let stand several days and decant clear liq.

(**b**) *Ammonium or potassium thiocyanate std soln.*—0.05N. Adust after titrg against 0.1N AgNO₃.

(**c**) *Ferric ammonium sulfate indicator.*—Dissolve 8 g FeNH₄(SO₄)₂.12H₂O in enough H₂O to make 100 ml.

36.356   *Weighing of Sample*

(**a**) *Chloroform or carbon tetrachloride.*—Carefully transfer 30 ml alc. KOH soln to air-dried, 60–70 ml pressure bottle, and stopper. Do not moisten neck of bottle with reagent. Weigh stoppered bottle with contents (conveniently done by suspending bottle on balance with clamp that holds stopper).

Immediately after opening bottle, add ca 1 ml sample from 1 ml pipet, holding pipet just above top level of reagent in bottle. As level of reagent rises with draining of sample into bottle, raise pipet correspondingly so as to avoid contact with reagent. Avoid opening bottle longer than necessary (20 sec is convenient). Stopper bottle so as to assure tight fit and weigh. Det. wt by difference. Proceed as in **36.357.**

(**b**) *Carbon tetrachloride in capsules.*—Det. gross wt of representative number of capsules. Open capsules and transfer contents to g-s flask. Weigh dried empty capsules and det. av. net contents. Proceed as in (**a**), using composite sample.

(**c**) *Chloroform or carbon tetrachloride in drug mixtures.*—Proceed as in (**a**), using ⩽10 ml of mixt. contg 0.08–1.6 g CHCl₃ or CCl₄. Note temp. of mixts. Det. vol.-equiv. of weighed sample. (Weigh definite vol. of mixt. at same temp., using 50 or 100 ml vol. flask, and calc.)

Note: Sample may be measured directly with pipet instead of being weighed, or measured vol. may be dild with MeOH to some definite vol. and thoroly mixed, and suitable aliquot of this diln used.

36.357 *Determination*

If sample is mixt., mix contents of bottle by gentle swirling and let bottle stand ca 1 hr (30 min is enough for CHCl3, pure or nearly so). Place bottle in wire basket and set basket in H2O bath at room temp. Invert tin can over bottle and cover with towel to prevent injury in case bottle should burst. Heat bath to boiling and keep at this temp. 1 hr (15 min is enough for CHCl3, pure or nearly so). Gradually cool contents of pressure bottle, transfer to 200 ml vol. flask, and thoroly wash out bottle with H2O, draining washings into flask. Bring to room temp., dil. to vol. with H2O, and mix.

Transfer suitable aliquot to 100 ml vol. flask and acidify with HNO3, adding ca 2 ml excess. Add 25 or 50 ml 0.1N AgNO3 (an excess), shake thoroly, dil. to vol. with H2O, and mix. Filter mixt. thru dry filter into dry flask, rejecting first 20 ml filtrate. To 50 ml aliquot filtrate, add 3 ml FeNH4(SO4)2 indicator and titr. excess AgNO3, using 0.05N NH4 or K thiocyanate.

If original sample contains chloride, det. quantity and make correction. If original sample contains sugar or other org. material and (after saponification of the CHCl3 or CCl4 and diln of mixt. with H2O) is highly colored, thus interfering with titrn, transfer contents of pressure bottle to Ni crucible with H2O. Evap. to dryness and char residue. Let cool, treat with H2O, filter into suitable vol. flask, and wash residue and filter with H2O until Cl-free. Dil. to vol. with H2O, mix, and det. Cl as directed previously.

Det. blank, using in pressure bottle same quantities of solvs and reagents as for sample, and apply necessary correction. 1 ml 0.1N AgNO3 = 0.00398 g CHCl3 or 0.00385 g CCl4.

Chlorinated Hydrocarbons (123)—Official First Action

36.358 *Apparatus*

(a) *Infrared spectrophotometer.*—Double beam with wavelength range 2–16 μm with 1 mm sealed cells.

(b) *Device for filling pipet or buret by pressure.* —Fit 2-hole rubber stopper (No. 1 fits 8 oz medicine bottle) with 1 glass tube extending just thru stopper and with other end attached to tubing for application of pressure by mouth. Thru other hole fit straight glass tube extending to bottom of container and attach to other end short piece of rubber tubing to connect to delivery tip of buret or pipet. When not transferring, prevent evapn with pinch clamps.

36.359 *Reagents*

(*Caution: See* 46.011 *and* 46.040.)

(a) *Chloroform std soln.*—Wash CHCl3 3 times with H2O, and dry with Na2SO4. Pipet 10 ml dried CHCl3 into 200 ml vol. flask contg 185 ml alcohol,

dil. to vol. with alcohol, and mix. Using air pressure, transfer 20 ml of this soln to 200 ml vol. flask contg 170 ml alcohol (keep tip below surface), dil. to vol. with alcohol, and mix.

(b) *Carbon tetrachloride std soln.*—Prep. as in (a), using dilns of 5 to 200 and 10 to 200 ml.

(c) *Trichloroethylene std soln.*—Redistill CHCl= CCl2, collecting fraction boiling at 86–88°. Prep. as in (a), using dilns of 10 to 200 and 10 to 200 ml.

(d) *Tetrachloroethylene std soln.*—Redistill CCl2:CCl2, collecting fraction boiling at 119–121°. Prep. as in (a), using dilns of 10 to 200 and 10 to 200 ml.

(e) *Reference soln.*—Mix 10 ml alcohol with 75 ml 10% sucrose soln and ext with 10, 10, and 5 ml CS2. Combine exts in 25 ml vol. flask and dil. to vol. with CS2. (CS2 exts are sufficiently dry to be placed in NaCl cells.) Use in ref. cell for reading both stds and samples.

36.360 *Preparation of Standard Curves*

(Use air pressure to fill pipet or covered buret.)

Transfer 10–30 ml of each std soln to separators contg 5 vols 10% sucrose soln and 10 ml CS2, keeping delivery tip just below surface of liq. Quickly stopper separator and ext 1–2 min by very gently inverting 50–60 times/min. (Do not release pressure thru stopcock.) Let layers sep. and drain CS2 layer into 25 ml vol. flask or stoppered graduated cylinder. Repeat extn with 10 and 5 ml CS2, combine all exts, and dil. to vol. with CS2. (Exts may be held at room temp. overnight if tightly stoppered, but samples and stds must be read on same day.)

Obtain spectrum of each std soln from 2 to 16 μm against ref. soln, (e). (Thruout entire series of runs, gain and position of comb adjustments must not be altered.) If desired, obtain %T (or A) at wavelengths of interest, making shortened runs of remaining solns, and combining some of them on 1 chart. Det. %T (or A) of both peak and baseline; convert each to A; and plot A difference against ml std in aliquot taken for extn on linear paper. If %T is preferred, plot original values of %T on semilog paper.

36.361 *Infrared Wavelengths of Chlorinated Hydrocarbons*

Compound	Wavelength, μm	
	Peak	Baseline
Chloroform	8.25	7.70– 8.70
Carbon tetrachloride	12.80	12.10–13.90
Trichloroethylene	10.77	10.30–11.00
Tetrachloroethylene	11.10	10.50–11.50

36.362 *Preparation of Sample*

(a) *Encapsulated liquids.*—Prep. composite as in 36.356(b). Transfer 1 ml aliquot, using air pressure, to 200 ml vol. flask contg ca 195 ml alcohol (keep tip below surface), dil. to vol. with alcohol, and mix. For CHCl₃ use soln direct; for CCl₄, dil. 25 ml to 100 ml with alcohol; for tri- and tetrachloroethylene, dil. 50 ml to 100 ml with alcohol.

(b) *Preparations such as cough sirups.*—Shake well and let bubbles clear before opening container. Take aliquot contg chlorinated hydrocarbon vol. ca that of std, using alcohol for diln if necessary.

36.363   *Determination*

Transfer aliquot of sample or sample diln to separator contg 5 vols 10% sucrose soln and 10 ml CS₂ (keep tip beneath surface). Proceed as in **36.360**. Det. identity of chlorinated hydrocarbons present by comparison with std spectra and det. quantity from std curves.

36.364 ★   Cod Liver Oil in Emulsions ★
(124)—Official Final Action

See **32.299**, 10th ed.

Ethchlorvynol (1-Chloro-3-ethyl-1-penten-4-yn-3-ol) (125)—Official First Action

36.365   *Reagents*

(a) *Ethchlorvynol.*—(*Caution: See* **46.011** and **46.015.**) Purify by vac. distn (62° at ca 10 mm) or assay by titrn as follows: Transfer ca 110 mg ethchlorvynol, accurately weighed, to 250 ml erlenmeyer contg 50 ml 2.5% AgNO₃ soln in 70% alcohol. Immediately titr. with 0.05N NaOH, using 8–10 drops Me red-methylene blue, **34.028(c)**. Perform blank detn and make any necessary correction. 1 ml 0.05N NaOH = 7.230 mg ethchlorvynol. (*Caution:* Protect pure ethchlorvynol from excessive exposure to light and air.) Store at <10° in glass containers with polyethylene or Teflon stopper liners.

(b) *Ethchlorvynol stock soln.*—10 mg/ml. Accurately weigh ca 0.5 g ethchlorvynol and dissolve in 5 ml alcohol. Transfer quant. to 50 ml vol. flask with 10 ml alcohol. Dil. to vol. with H₂O.

(c) *Internal std soln.*—2.0%. Dissolve 2.0 g 1,3-dichloro-2-propanol in 10 ml alcohol and dil. to 100 ml with H₂O.

(d) *Dichlorodimethylsilane soln.*—Dissolve 5 ml dichlorodimethylsilane in 100 ml toluene. (*Caution:* Dichlorodimethylsilane causes severe burns. Vapor is harmful. Avoid contact with skin, eyes, or clothing. Use effective fume removal device. *See* also **46.040.**)

36.366   *Apparatus*

Gas chromatograph.—With 4′ × 4 mm glass column, packed with Carbowax 20M on 100–120 mesh Gas-Chrom Q, and H flame ionization detector. *Operating conditions:* temps—column 115°, detector 190°, injection port 200°; flow rates—N 50 ml/min, H 92 ml/min, air ca 500 ml/min. Adjust

column temp. to elute ethchlorvynol in 12–15 min (relative retention time of internal std is ca 0.8). Adjust H and air flow rates to give stable flame and good sensitivity. Adjust electrometer sensitivity so that 12 μg ethchlorvynol gives 50–70% deflection.

36.367   *Preparation of GLC Column*

Carefully wash inside of column and small amt of fine glass wool with dichlorodimethylsilane soln, rinse with alcohol, and dry thoroly. Dissolve 5.0 g Carbowax 20M in 100 ml CHCl₃. Add Carbowax soln to 10.0 g 100–120 mesh Gas-Chrom Q in 250 ml filter flask fitted with trap and stopper. Slowly apply vac. and maintain 5 min. Swirl slurry rapidly and transfer in small portions to buchner fitted with 9 cm Whatman No. 4 paper. Maintain vac. 5 min after last portion is added; then airdry coated support 1 hr by spreading on smooth surface. Oven-dry addnl hr at 100°.

Carefully plug column exit with small tuft of glass wool. Apply vac. to exit end and slowly add coated support thru inlet, tapping very gently to pack firmly. Pack to within 1 cm of area heated by injection port. Plug with glass wool and condition overnight at 220° with slow N stream.

36.368   *Preparation of Sample*

(a) *Capsules (200–500 mg).*—Place counted number of capsules contg ca 2.5 g ethchlorvynol in 250 ml vol. flask; add 75 ml H₂O and 30 ml alcohol, stopper, and heat on steam bath with frequent swirling until dissolved. Cool and dil. to vol. with H₂O.

(b) *Capsules (100 mg).*—Place 10 capsules in 100 ml vol. flask, add 50 ml H₂O and 15 ml alcohol, stopper, and heat on steam bath with frequent swirling until dissolved. Cool and dil. to vol. with H₂O.

(c) *Solutions.*—Prep. soln contg ca 10 mg ethchlorvynol/ml by stepwise diln with 20% alcohol.

36.369   *Determination*

Pipet 10 ml sample soln contg ca 100 mg ethchlorvynol into 50 ml vol. flask; pipet 10 ml ethchlorvynol stock soln in second 50 ml vol. flask. Pipet 10 ml internal std soln into each flask and dil. to vol. with H₂O.

Rinse 10 μl syringe with 50% alcohol and draw up 1 μl 50% alcohol. Draw in 1 μl air followed by 6 μl sample. Draw in 1 μl air and note sample vol. Insert needle thru septum of gas chromatograph, quickly depress plunger, and retract syringe needle. Inject 6 μl of each soln. Run std before and after sample. Calc. amt of ethchlorvynol in 10 ml sample aliquot as follows:

$C_u = C_s \times (X_u/X_s) \times (I_s/I_u)$, where C_u and C_s = mg ethchlorvynol in 10 ml sample aliquot and std stock soln, resp.; X_u = area ethchlorvynol peak in sample chromatogram; X_s = av. area ethchlor-vynol peak in std chromatograms; I_u = area internal std peak in sample chromatogram; and I_s = av. area internal std peak in std chromatograms.

36.370 ★ Ether (126)—Official Final ★ Action

(Not applicable in presence of essential oils)

Dichromate oxidn of aspirated sample. *See* 32.370–32.374, 10th ed.

36.371 Ethyl Aminobenzoate (127)— Official Final Action

(a) *In pure drug.*—Accurately weigh 0.12–0.15 g sample into I flask and dissolve in mixt. of 10 ml HCl and ca 200 ml H_2O. Add 0.1N KBr-KBrO₃, **36.208**, from buret until slight excess is present as shown by light yellow color. Stopper flask, shake, and let stand 5 min. Add 5 ml 20% KI soln, avoiding loss of Br, stopper flask, and shake. Titr. liberated I with 0.1N Na₂S₂O₃, stdzd as in **45.039**, using starch soln, **6.004(f)**, as indicator. From quantity of KBr-KBrO₃ soln used, calc. % Et aminobenzoate. 1 ml 0.1N KBr-KBrO₃ = 0.004127 g Et aminobenzoate.

(b) *In ointments.*—Accurately weigh 2.5–3 g ointment (enough to provide 0.12–0.15 g Et aminobenzoate) in small beaker, dissolve in benzene by warming on steam bath, and transfer to separator, using total of ca 50 ml benzene. Wash beaker with 50 ml HCl (1 + 19), pour into separator, shake, and transfer aq. layer to second separator. Add 20 ml pet ether to second separator, shake, and transfer aq. layer to I flask. Ext benzene soln with 3 addnl 50 ml portions HCl (1 + 19), washing each ext with the pet ether in second separator and then collecting it in the I flask. Treat combined acid exts as in (a), beginning "Add 0.1N KBr-KBrO₃ ..." and calc. % Et aminobenzoate.

Iodoform (128)—Official Final Action
36.372 *Reagents*

(a) *Ammonium thiocyanate std soln.*—0.05N. Stdze against 0.1N AgNO₃, using equal vol. alcohol and 3 ml FeNH₄(SO₄)₂ soln as indicator.

(b) *Ferric ammonium sulfate indicator.*—Dissolve 8 g FeNH₄(SO₄)₂.12H₂O in 100 ml H_2O.

36.373 *Determination*

Accurately weigh ca 0.25 g CHI₃ and transfer quant. to 200 ml erlenmeyer. Add 40 ml alcohol, swirl gently until CHI₃ dissolves, filter if necessary, and immediately add 40 ml 0.1N AgNO₃ and 10 ml HNO₃. Swirl gently ca 5 min, let stand at room temp. 2–3 hr, and then swirl occasionally as aid in flocculating the AgI. Titr. excess AgNO₃ with 0.05N NH₄CNS, using 3 ml of the FeNH₄(SO₄)₂ indicator. 1 ml 0.1N AgNO₃ =

0.01312 g CHI₃. Or: Proceed as in **36.374**, last par. beginning "Collect AgI on weighed gooch, ..."

36.374 Iodoform in Ointments (129)— Official Final Action

Transfer ca 2.5 g sample to tared 50 ml beaker and weigh. Add 5 ml CHCl₃, stir gently with glass rod, and transfer bulk of undissolved ointment and CHCl₃ soln to 250 ml g-s flask. Add 5 ml CHCl₃ to ointment remaining in beaker and stir until dissolved. Add soln to flask and finally wash beaker 3 times, using ≤5 ml CHCl₃ each time, and add washings to flask. Or: weigh sample in small, tared glass capsule, drop capsule with contents into 250 ml g-s flask, and add ≤20 ml CHCl₃. (Use glass capsule only in volumetric detn.) Swirl gently until all ointment dissolves. Add 40 ml 0.1N alc. AgNO₃ and swirl to wash down any CHI₃ that adheres to sides of flask. Slowly add 10 ml HNO₃ and let stand at room temp. ca 18 hr. Titr. excess of 0.1N alc. AgNO₃ with 0.05N NH₄CNS, **36.372(a)**, using 3 ml FeNH₄(SO₄)₂ indicator, **36.372(b)**, vigorously shaking mixt. near end of titrn. 1 ml 0.1N AgNO₃ = 0.01312 g CHI₃.

For gravimetric detn use ordinary erlenmeyer instead of g-s flask. Weigh ointment base into 100 ml beaker and add CHCl₃. After ointment base dissolves, filter thru gooch, using suction. Wash beaker and crucible once with alcohol. Wash crucible several times with CHCl₃ without suction. Collect filtrate in erlenmeyer and add 40 ml 0.1N AgNO₃ and 10 ml HNO₃ in small portions. Let mixt. stand 18 hr. Collect AgI on weighed gooch, using suction. Wash with H_2O and then with alcohol. Finally wash repeatedly with CHCl₃ without suction. Dry gooch and contents at ca 125° to constant wt. 1 g AgI = 0.5590 g CHI₃.

36.375 Iodoform on Gauze (130)— Official Final Action

Weigh, in tared g-s weighing bottle, sample of CHI₃ gauze contg ca 1 g CHI₃. (CHI₃ gauze is usually moist and loses wt rapidly when exposed to air.) Transfer to 150 ml beaker, add ca 75 ml alcohol, and stir until CHI₃ dissolves. Filter into 200 ml vol. flask, draining alc. soln by pressing on gauze. Wash with four or five 25 ml portions alcohol, filter washings, and finally dil. to vol. with alcohol. Pipet 40 ml aliquot into 200 ml erlenmeyer and immediately add 40 ml 0.1N AgNO₃ and 10 ml HNO₃. Proceed as in **36.374**, beginning "let stand at room temp. ca 18 hr."

Mandelic Acid (131)—Official Final Action
36.376 *Qualitative Tests*

(Applicable to free acid)

See Microchemical Tests, **36.536**.

36.377   *Determination*

(*Caution: See* 46.011, 46.039, 46.040, 46.054, and 46.056.)

(a) *Tablets.*—Wash quantity of powd sample contg 0.4–0.5 g mandelic acid and transfer to separator contg 10 ml H_2O. Acidify with HCl $(1 + 3)$ and add 2 ml excess. Ext with six 20 ml portions $CHCl_3$-ether $(2 + 1)$; wash each portion in second separator with 2 ml H_2O, and pass soln thru cotton plug, previously satd with solv., into 250 ml beaker. Wash outer surface of separator stem with few ml solv. and add to main portion. Test for complete extn with 15 ml addnl solv. and evap. in sep. beaker. Wash any residue thus obtained into beaker contg main ext with few ml solv. Evap. to dryness at $\leqslant 40°$ with aid of fan. Dissolve residue in 25 ml CO_2-free H_2O and titr. with 0.1N NaOH, using phthln. 1 ml 0.1N NaOH = 0.01522 g mandelic acid, $C_6H_5CHOHCOOH$; 0.01692 g NH_4 mandelate, 0.01741 g Na mandelate, 0.01712 g Ca mandelate, and 0.01633 g Mg mandelate.

After titrn, mandelic acid may be re-extd and ext used for mp detns or qual. tests.

(b) *Liquid preparations.*—Measure 1 ml sample, or aliquot of diln contg 0.4–0.5 g mandelic acid, into separator and acidify with HCl $(1 + 3)$. Proceed as in (a).

Mannitol Hexanitrate; Mannitol Hexanitrate and Phenobarbital (*132*)—Official Final Action

(*See also* 36.397–36.400.)

36.378   *Reagents*

(a) *Phenoldisulfonic acid.*—Heat 5 g colorless phenol, 30 ml H_2SO_4, and 15 ml fuming H_2SO_4 (ca 20% free SO_3) on steam bath 2 hr. (*Caution: See* 46.030 and 46.031.)

(b) *Nitrate std soln.*—Dissolve 100 mg KNO_3 or $NaNO_3$ in ca 1 ml H_2O and dil. to 100 ml with HOAc.

(c) *Phenobarbital std soln.*—In 100 ml vol. flask dissolve 100 mg phenobarbital and dil. to vol. with HOAc. Pipet 5 ml of this soln and 15 ml HOAc into 100 ml vol. flask, dil. to vol. with H_2O, and filter, discarding first 5 ml filtrate.

36.379   *Preparation of Sample*

Transfer accurately weighed sample contg ca 30 mg mannitol hexanitrate to 50 ml vol. flask, and dil. to vol. with HOAc. Shake well and filter, discarding first 5 ml filtrate.

36.380   *Determination of Mannitol Hexanitrate*

Treat 1.0 ml sample, 1.0 ml std, and 1.0 ml HOAc blank in identical manner. Transfer 1 ml soln and 2 ml phenoldisulfonic acid to 100 ml vol. flask and let stand 15 min. Dil. with H_2O to ca 60 ml, add NH_4OH (ca 10 ml) until max. yellow color appears, cool to room temp., dil. to vol. with H_2O, and mix. Det. A of sample and std relative to blank at 408 nm.

$(A \times R_2 \times k \times 50)/(A' \times R_1) = \%$ mannitol hexanitrate, where A and A' refer to sample and std, resp., R_1 is mg sample, R_2 is mg std/ml, and k is 88.66 for $NaNO_3$ and 74.56 for KNO_3 std.

36.381   *Determination of Phenobarbital*

Pipet 10 ml aliquot sample soln into 50 ml vol. flask, dil. to vol. with H_2O, shake, and filter, discarding first 5 ml filtrate. Prep. blank by dilg 10.0 ml HOAc to 50 ml with H_2O and filtering. Dil. sep. 20 ml aliquots of std, sample, and blank solns to 100 ml with NH_4OH $(1 + 9)$, adjusting to room temp. before dilg to vol. (Final pH of soln, 9.0–9.6.) Det. A of sample and std relative to blank at 240 nm, and calc. phenobarbital content.

Meprobamate (*133*)—Official Final Action
36.382   *Apparatus*

(a) *Spectrophotometer.*—Recording IR spectrophtr, effective over 0.75–3.5 µm range, with 1 cm matching near-IR silica cells. Peak at ca 2.91 µm for meprobamate must be resolved. (Beckman DK2A is suitable with following settings typical for quant. analysis: Sensitivity dial 2.00, gears 10 nm/cm, scanning time switch 10, time constant 0.2, range selector 0–100 (0–1), photomultiplier PbS cell mode.)

(b) *Chromatographic tubes.*—Glass, 20×300 mm.

36.383   *Reagents*

(a) *Alcohol-free chloroform.*—Thruout detn use only $CHCl_3$ prepd daily as follows: Ext alcohol by passing $CHCl_3$ successively thru three 500 ml separators, each contg 50–75 ml H_2O. Pack 2 chromatgc tubes half-full with alumina (80–200 mesh, Fisher No. A-540, or equiv.) activated by heating 2 hr at 300°. Mount one column above other and pass $CHCl_3$ thru both columns. Pass $\leqslant 500$ ml $CHCl_3$ at one time. If more $CHCl_3$ is needed, repeat purification with fresh alumina.

(b) *Meprobamate std soln.*—0.5 mg/ml. Accurately weigh ca 25 mg USP Ref. Std Meprobamate and transfer to 50 ml vol. flask. Dissolve in and dil. to vol. with $CHCl_3$. Absorptivity should be ca 1.0 if 2.91 µm peak is properly resolved.

36.384   *Preparation of Sample*

Finely pulverize $\geqslant 20$ tablets, accurately weigh portion contg 50 mg meprobamate, and transfer to dry 100 ml vol. flask. Add 50 ml $CHCl_3$, shake 15–20 min, and dil. to vol. with $CHCl_3$. Filter soln thru dry Whatman No. 1 paper, or equiv. Discard first 20–25 ml and collect remainder in dry g-s erlenmeyer.

36.385 *Determination*

Zero instrument at 2.914 μm with CHCl₃ in both cells. Scan IR spectra of sample and std solns against CHCl₃ between 3.000 and 2.790 μm. Measure baseline A values at max., ca 2.91 μm, from straight line drawn between minima at ca 2.980 and 2.875. Calc. mg meprobamate/tablet = A_{sample} × (C/A_{std}) × 100 × (T/W), where A refers to baseline values; C = mg meprobamate/ml std soln; T and W = av. wt/tablet and sample wt, resp., in mg.

36.386 Meprobamate and Pentaerythritol Tetranitrate

See **36.407–36.410.**

Methenamine (Hexamethylenetetramine) in Tablets (134)—Official Final Action

36.387 *Reagent*

Modified Nessler reagent.—(1) Dissolve 10 g HgCl₂, 30 g KI, and 5 g acacia in 200 ml H₂O, and filter thru cotton; (2) dissolve 15 g NaOH in 100 ml H₂O. Mix 20 ml soln (1) with 10 ml soln (2).

36.388 *Determination*

Weigh 0.5 g powder, prepd as in **36.002**, into r-b flask, and add 100 ml H₂O and 25 ml HCl (1 + 2.5). Connect with reflux condenser (preferably of worm type) and boil gently 15 min. Cool, wash condenser tube with little H₂O, transfer contents of flask to 250 ml vol. flask, and dil. to vol.

Chill 30 ml Nessler reagent and add 10 ml aliquot of hydrolyzed sample soln. Wash neck of container with jet of H₂O and let stand ≥1 min. Add 10 ml HOAc (1 + 1.5) so that inside of neck is completely washed by reagent, mix quickly and thoroly by rotating and tilting flask, and immediately add 20 ml 0.1N I from buret or pipet. Titr. excess I with 0.1N Na₂S₂O₃, adding 5–10 drops starch indicator, **6.004(f)**, toward end of titrn, until blue disappears. Final color of soln is pale straw-green. If preferred, end point may be detd by reappearance of faint blue when drop of the I soln is added. 1 ml 0.1N I = 0.00117 g methenamine.

Methyl Salicylate (135)—Official Final Action

36.389 *Reagents*

(a) *Salicylic acid std soln.*—20 μg/ml. Dissolve 0.2500 g reagent grade salicylic acid in 95 ml CHCl₃ in 250 ml vol. flask and dil. to vol. with alcohol. Dil. 2.00 ml to 100 ml with alcohol.

(b) *Sodium bicarbonate soln.*—Dissolve 5 g NaHCO₃ in 100 ml of H₂O to which 1 drop HCl has been added.

36.390 *Determination*

Pipet 5.00 ml sample into 50 ml ether-pet ether mixt. (1 + 1) in separator and wash with two 5 ml portions cold, freshly prepd NaHCO₃ soln. Discard unemulsified aq. phases. Ext org. layer with two 5 ml portions 5% NaOH soln followed by two 5 ml portions H₂O. Let phases sep. 5 min and drain unemulsified aq. layers into another separator. Wash combined exts with 10 ml pet ether and drain aq. phase into another separator. Acidify cautiously with HCl (litmus paper) and ext with four 20 ml and one 15 ml portions CHCl₃. Filter each ext thru CHCl₃-moistened plug of cotton into 250 ml vol. flask. Dil. to vol. with alcohol and transfer 2.00 ml aliquot to 100 ml vol. flask.

Dil. to vol. with alcohol and det. A at peak wavelength (ca 305 nm). Calc. as salicylic acid by comparison with A of std soln. Salicylic acid × 1.1016 = Me salicylate.

Methimazole (136)—Official First Action

(*Caution: See* **46.011, 46.040,** and **46.056.**)

36.391 *Apparatus*

(a) *Chromatographic tube.*—200 × 22 mm.

(b) *Spectrophotometer.*—Recording double-beam IR spectrophtr, with 2 mm cells and NaCl windows. (Perkin-Elmer Model 21 is suitable with following settings typical for quant. analysis: Resolution 984, gain 4, scanning speed 3 min/μm.)

36.392 *Reagents*

(a) *Diatomaceous earth.*—Celite 545. Acid-washed, rinsed to neutrality, and dried.

(b) *Methimazole std.*—Store in desiccator over P₂O₅ when not in use.

36.393 *Column Chromatography*

Transfer amt of freshly ground tablet mixt. contg 10 mg methimazole to 100 ml beaker, add 3 ml H₂O, and mix thoroly to wet sample. Add 4 g Celite and mix thoroly. Transfer in 2 equal portions to chromatgc tube contg pledget of glass wool and pack tightly. Rinse beaker with 0.5 g Celite and add to column; place pledget of glass wool on top of column. Rinse beaker with 150 ml H₂O-washed isooctane (redistd) and add rinses to column. Let last drops of isooctane drain from column before proceeding. Discard isooctane eluate.

Rinse beaker with three 5 ml portions H₂O-washed CHCl₃ and add rinses to column. Collect eluate. Elute methimazole with 200 ml H₂O-washed CHCl₃, maintaining solv. head ≤3″ during elution. Combine CHCl₃ eluates, and evap. at ca 40–60° with air stream to ca 10 ml, washing down sides of beaker with small portions CHCl₃ during evapn. Do not heat excessively, since methimazole may oxidize. Quant. transfer conc. to 30 ml beaker with several small portions CHCl₃. Evap. solv. at ca 30–40° under air stream. (Make certain all traces of isooctane are removed.) Dry residue in vac. over anhyd. P₂O₅ 30 min. (If necessary, store residue over desiccant in dark; methimazole oxidizes on standing.)

36.394   *Determination*

Add 5 ml CS_2 to residue in beaker, cover with watch glass, and warm to dissolve. Cool and quant. transfer soln to 10 ml vol. flask with CS_2. Repeat with two 2 ml portions CS_2, cool, transfer to flask, and dil. to vol.

Prep. std soln methimazole in CS_2, with warming, to contain exactly 1.00 mg/ml. Record quant. IR spectra of sample and std solns between 7.6 and 8.4 μm in 2 mm NaCl cells. Measure baseline A values of 7.83 μm max., using minima at 7.7 and 8.3 μm. Calc. mg methimazole in sample as follows:

mg Methimazole/tablet $= A_u \times (C_s/A_s) \times 10 \times (T/W)$, where A_u and $A_s =$ baseline values for sample and std, resp.; $C_s =$ mg/ml std soln; T and $W =$ av. wt/tablet and sample wt, resp., in mg.

Identify samples by comparing IR spectra of quant. solns with spectrum of std over 2–15 μm, using CS_2 as blank. Qual. conditions for Model 21 Perkin-Elmer spectrophtr: Resolution, 927; gain, 5–6; response, 1; suppression, 0; and scanning speed, 2–3 min/μm.

Methylene Blue (Methylthionine Chloride) (137)—Official Final Action

36.395   *Preparation of Solution*

(a) *Foreign material absent.*—Weigh into 50 ml beaker 0.1–0.14 g powd sample, **36.002**, and transfer to 200 ml vol. flask with 100–140 ml H_2O. Dissolve completely by heating 30 min on steam bath with frequent shaking.

(b) *Oils or water-insoluble material present.*—(*Caution:* See **46.040** and **46.049**.) Transfer to 50 ml beaker weighed quantity of prepd sample, **36.002**, contg 0.1–0.14 g methylene blue. Add 15 ml CCl_4, warm on steam bath few min, and stir with glass rod to dissolve oils. Transfer to 100 ml separator, using ca 50 ml hot H_2O and little CCl_4 if necessary. Cool, shake, and let sep. Transfer CCl_4 with undissolved material to second separator for further treatment. (Clear aq. soln of dye should now remain in first separator. If not clear, ext with another 15 ml portion CCl_4, transferring any remaining insol. material in similar manner to second separator.) Add ca 10 ml CCl_4 to second separator and remove methylene blue by shaking vigorously with 20–40 ml portions H_2O until practically no more dye is extd. (Few drops of HOAc hasten this extn.) To aq. exts in 400 ml beaker add main soln from first separator, cover with inverted watch glass on glass rods, and evap. to ca 50 ml. Proceed as in (c). CCl_4 soln may be reserved for qual. tests for oils.

(c) *Water-soluble material present.*—Either use aq. soln from (b), or weigh portion of sample

contg 0.1–0.14 g methylene blue into 150 ml beaker, add ca 50 ml H_2O, and heat 30 min on steam bath with occasional shaking. Transfer to 100 ml separator, keeping vol. as small as possible. Ext with α-*dichlorohydrin,* using 10, 5, 3, and 2 ml portions. Combine dichlorohydrin exts in 200–300 ml separator, add 3 or 4 times their vol. CCl_4, and ext dye with H_2O by repeated vigorous shaking with 30–50 ml portions. (Few drops of HOAc hasten removal.) From combined aq. exts remove any traces of dichlorohydrin by shaking once with ca 15 ml CCl_4 and draining after settling 5–10 min. Evap. aq. exts to ca 50 ml over flame, covering beaker as in (b) with inverted watch glass. Transfer to 200 ml vol. flask. Dissolve completely by heating 30 min on steam bath with frequent shaking.

36.396   *Determination*

Conduct blank as in detn, including filtration. Cool soln, **36.395**(a) or (c), add 50 ml HOAc, shake thoroly, and let stand $\geqslant$25 min. Add 30 ml 0.2N I, **45.019**, from buret, adding first 10 ml by fast drops with constant rotating of flask and remaining 20 ml at full speed, and continue shaking. Stopper flask and let stand 50 min, shaking thoroly 5 or 6 times during interval. Dil. to vol. with H_2O, shake, and let stand 10 min longer. Filter rapidly thru dry, folded, 12 cm paper. Titr. 100 ml aliquot with 0.1N $Na_2S_2O_3$, with or without starch indicator as desired. Correct for blank titrn. 1 ml 0.2N I = 0.01496 g methylene blue, $C_{16}H_{18}N_3ClS \cdot 3H_2O$; or 0.01279 g anhyd. methylene blue, $C_{16}H_{18}N_3ClS$.

Nitrate Esters—Official Final Action

Infrared Method (138)

(Applicable to mannitol hexanitrate, erythritol tetranitrate, or pentaerythritol tetranitrate)

36.397   *Apparatus*

(a) *Recording infrared spectrophotometer.*—With two 1.0 mm liq. absorption cells with NaCl windows, preferably matched or of known A difference, and KBr disk holder.

(b) *Chromatographic tube.*—25 × 200 mm with 5 × 40 mm stem.

(c) *Die and hydraulic press.*—Suitable for prepg KBr disks.

36.398   *Preparation of Standard Solution*

Ext ester from com. absorbate (usually 10% on lactose or other inert diluent) with ether, filter, and evap. to dryness with aid of air current at temp. $\leqslant$50°. Dry in vac. desiccator 1 hr. Prep. std soln contg 0.5 mg ester/ml $CHCl_3$.

Caution: Pure crystalline nitrate esters are very explosive, especially pentaerythritol tetranitrate. Do not use sample contg >5 mg pure compd.

36.399 *Preparation of Sample*

Weigh ⩾20 tablets and reduce to fine powder. Weigh sample contg ca 25 mg nitrate ester and transfer to 125 ml separator with ca 5 ml H_2O. Make distinctly acid with H_2SO_4 (1 + 9). Proceed as in (a) in absence of phenobarbital, or (b) in presence of phenobarbital.

(a) Add 10 ml $CHCl_3$ to separator, shake vigorously several min, and let sep. Transfer $CHCl_3$ layer to 50 ml vol. flask. Ext aq. soln with three addnl 10 ml portions $CHCl_3$ and transfer each ext to vol. flask. Dil. to vol. with $CHCl_3$, mix, and filter.

(b) Add 15 ml $CHCl_3$ to separator, shake vigorously several min, and let sep. Transfer $CHCl_3$ layer to chromatgc column contg 4 ml $1M$ K_3PO_4 soln adsorbed on 5 g Celite, collecting eluate in 50 ml vol. flask. Ext aq. soln with three addnl 10 ml portions $CHCl_3$, and pass each ext thru column, collecting eluate in vol. flask. Dil. to vol. with $CHCl_3$, mix, and filter.

36.400 *Determination*

(Store $CHCl_3$ to be used in IR measurements in stoppered flask.)

Transfer 5 ml aliquot $CHCl_3$ soln to 25 ml g-s erlenmeyer, evap. to dryness with aid of air current at temp. ⩽50°, and complete drying in vac. desiccator. Add 5.00 ml $CHCl_3$ to residue, stopper flask tightly, and let stand 30 min with occasional shaking to ensure complete soln. Det. A of std and sample solns against $CHCl_3$ at max. (ca 6.0 μm) and calc. amt of ester per tablet.

Evap. another portion $CHCl_3$ soln to dryness as above. Prep. KBr disk by grinding together in agate mortar 1 mg residue with 200 mg IR spectral grade KBr and pressing in die and hydraulic press. Record spectrum from 2 to 15 μm and compare with spectrum of std nitrate ester to det. identity of sample.

Nitroglycerin (Glyceryl Trinitrate)— Official Final Action
Reduction Method (139)

36.401 *Apparatus*

(a) *Connecting bulb.*—Hopkins style, ca 7.6 cm (3″) diam. This style has long inlet tube with opening on side of tube.

(b) *Condenser.*—Water-cooled, length 56 cm (22″), and preferably of Pyrex glass.

(c) *Adapter tube.*—Approx. 2.25 cm (⅞″) diam. at top and with narrow outlet.

(d) *Scrubber-trap.*—Any efficient trap in which all vapor is washed thoroly with H_2O before it leaves distg flask (*see* Fig. 36:2).

36.402 *Extraction*

(a) *Ether extraction.*—Place in 50 ml beaker weighed sample contg ca 0.0324 g nitroglycerin. If

sample consists of tablets, count those taken; if of powd material, mix thoroly before weighing. Add 10 ml ether, and to facilitate extn, reduce tablets to fine powder, using flat-end stirring rod. Stir thoroly. Decant ether thru dry 7 cm quant. paper into 250 ml beaker contg 10 ml alcohol. Hold paper in place in funnel with the stirring rod and pour ether down rod. Make 4 addnl extns in same way. Dissolve ether-insol. residue in small amt of H_2O, transfer soln to separator, and ext with two 10 ml portions ether. Filter these exts, add to first exts, and evap. combined soln to ca 10 ml with fan. Transfer soln to 800 ml Kjeldahl flask, rinsing beaker first with 10 ml alcohol and then with little H_2O. Dil. to ca 300 ml with recently boiled and cooled NH_3-free H_2O.

(b) *Alcohol extraction.*—Weigh into g-s erlenmeyer sample contg ca 0.065 g (1 grain) nitroglycerin. If sample consists of tablets, count those taken; if of powd material, mix thoroly before weighing portion taken for analysis. Pipet in 50 ml alcohol. To facilitate extn, reduce tablets to fine powder with flat-end rod. Stopper flask and shake. Let mixt. settle, transfer 25 ml aliquot of clear soln to 800 ml Kjeldahl flask, and dil. to ca 300 ml with NH_3-free H_2O.

36.403 *Determination*

Place flask on wire gauze with asbestos center. Add thru funnel 2 g *Devarda alloy*, ca 4 cm *heavy* (ca 16 gage) *Al wire*, and 10–15 ml alc. KOH soln (15 g KOH dild to 100 ml with alcohol).

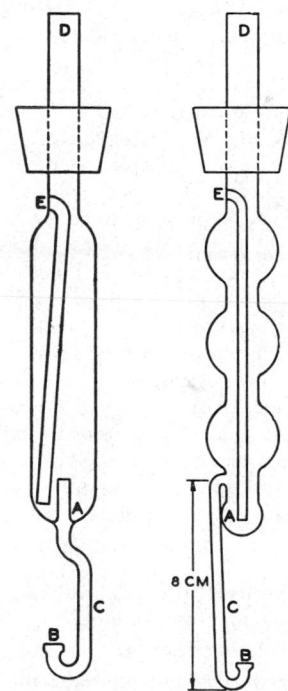

FIG. 36:2—Scrubber trap for ammonia distillation

Immediately after adding alkali, place little H_2O in scrubber trap (A and B, Fig. 36:2), and insert into neck of flask rubber stopper carrying scrubber trap and connecting bulb. Connect outlet tube of connecting bulb with upright condenser fitted with adapter tube dipping to bottom of 500 ml erlenmeyer contg measured vol. (ca 25 ml) $0.02N$ HCl or H_2SO_4 and 10–15 ml H_2O, and so inclined that tip of adapter is submerged as far as practicable under surface of liq. in flask.

Heat distn flask ca 1 hr, using small flame and regulating heat so that rapid evolution of H, but no appreciable distn, takes place. Gradually increase heat until distn begins; when active foaming ceases, continue distn with large flame until ca 40 ml liq. remains in distg flask. Lower flame toward end of distn to avoid cracking flask. Remove receiver contg distillate, add enough Me red to make soln red, and titr. excess acid with $0.02N$ NaOH soln. From difference between this excess and amt added, after making correction shown by blank with same amt or reagents distd in same manner, calc. % nitroglycerin in sample. 1 ml $0.02N$ acid = 0.001514 g nitroglycerin.

Infrared Method (13)

36.404   Reagent

Nitroglycerin std.—Absorbate on lactose contg ca 10% nitroglycerin. Stdze by **36.401–36.403**. This product is stable indefinitely in tightly stoppered bottle.

36.405   Determination

(*Caution:* See **46.011, 46.039, 46.040, and 46.048.**)

Transfer to small separator number of tablets contg ca 5 mg nitroglycerin. Dissolve or suspend in 5 ml H_2O, add 20 ml CS_2, shake 1 min, and let sep. Filter CS_2 layer thru pledget of cotton previously washed with CS_2 and collect in 100 ml beaker. Repeat extn with three 10 ml portions CS_2. Evap. combined exts to ca 3 ml, using gentle current of air, at temp. $\leqslant 50°$. Transfer quant. to 5 ml vol. flask and dil. to vol. with CS_2.

Accurately weigh quantity of std absorbate contg ca 5 mg nitroglycerin. Transfer to small separator and ext as above.

Det. baseline A_B of sample and std solns relative to CS_2 at 7.89 μm, drawing baseline between min. at 7.5 and 8.3 μm. Calc. nitroglycerin content of sample. Record spectra of sample and std solns from 2 to 15 μm and compare for identity of sample.

36.406   Pentaerythritol Tetranitrate (140)—Official Final Action

(Applicable in presence of meprobamate)

Accurately weigh powd sample contg ca 40 mg pentaerythritol tetranitrate into 50 ml g-s vol.

flask. Add ca 30 ml HOAc, shake ca 1 min, and dil. to vol. with HOAc. Filter, discarding first 5 ml filtrate. Proceed as in **36.380**.

% Pentaerythritol tetranitrate = $(A \times R' \times k \times 50)/(A' \times R)$, where A and A' refer to sample and std, resp.; R and R' are mg sample and mg std/ml, resp.; and k is 92.99 for $NaNO_3$ or 78.18 for KNO_3 std.

Pentaerythritol Tetranitrate (PETN) and Meprobamate (141)—Official First Action

(*Caution:* PETN may explode when heated strongly, even when dissolved.)

36.407   Apparatus

(a) *Recording infrared spectrophotometer.*—With two 1.0 mm liq. cells with NaCl windows, preferably matched or of known A difference, KBr disk holder, and equipment suitable for prepg KBr disk.

(b) *Chromatographic tube.*—25 $\times$ 200–250 mm with 5 $\times$ 40 mm stem.

(c) *Tamping rod.*—See **36.015(b)**.

36.408   Reagents

(*Caution:* See **46.011, 46.040, and 46.056.**)

(a) *Dilute phosphoric acid.*—3 + 1. Dil. 3 vols 85% H_3PO_4 with 1 vol. H_2O.

(b) *Water-washed benzene.*—Shake equal vols benzene and H_2O 1 min in separator. Discard lower phase. Use within 2 days of prepn.

(c) *Water-washed chloroform.*—Shake equal vols. $CHCl_3$ and H_2O 1 min in separator. Discard upper layer. Use within 2 days of prepn.

(d) *Anhydrous chloroform.*—Filter H_2O-washed $CHCl_3$ thru anhyd. Na_2SO_4.

(e) *Pentaerythritol tetranitrate (PETN) std soln.*—10 mg/50 ml. Ext PETN from com. PETN (usually 10% on lactose or other inert diluent) with $CHCl_3$ to give ca 20 mg pure PETN. Filter and evap. to dryness under air current with little or no heat. Dry in vac. desiccator 2 hr. Accurately weigh ca 10 mg, using microbalance, dissolve in anhyd. $CHCl_3$, and dil. to 50 ml with this solv. Destroy excess PETN by dissolving in acetone and burning in large vessel behind safety barrier, using effective fume removal device.

(f) *Meprobamate std soln.*—80 mg/100 ml. Dissolve 80 mg USP Meprobamate Ref. Std in anhyd. $CHCl_3$ and dil. to 100 ml with this solv.

(g) *Diatomaceous earth.*—Celite 545, acid-washed, or equiv.

36.409   Determination

(Use H_2O-washed solvs unless designated anhyd. *Caution:* See **46.011, 46.039, 46.040, 46.045, and 46.056.**)

Loosely pack small amt fine glass wool in base of chromatgc tube to support Celite. Weigh 3 g Celite into 100 ml beaker, add 2.0 ml $1N$ NaOH, mix with metal spatula until fluffy, and pack uniformly in tube. Weigh 5 g Celite into 250 ml beaker, add 7.0 ml dil. H_3PO_4, mix until fluffy, and pack uniformly on column. (Do *not* pack too tightly as column will elute too slowly.) Accurately weigh portion powd sample contg ca 10 mg PETN into 150 ml beaker. Add 4 ml benzene and heat gently with swirling ca 1 min. Cool, add 4 g Celite, mix until fluffy, transfer quant. to column, and pack uniformly. Dry-wash beaker with 1 g Celite and 0.5 ml benzene, transfer to column, and pack uniformly. Wipe sample beaker and all app. used in column prepn with glass wool, and pack on column.

Pass 75 ml benzene thru column and collect eluate in 150 ml beaker until elution ceases. Rinse column tip with small portions benzene into beaker and set aside. This fraction contains PETN.

Place 250 ml beaker under column. Add 4.0 ml H_2O to column and let it be absorbed. Pass 150 ml $CHCl_3$ thru column and collect eluate in 250 ml beaker. Rinse column tip with $CHCl_3$ into beaker. This fraction contains meprobamate.

Evap. each fraction on steam bath under gentle air current to ca 10 ml and take to dryness with little or no heat from steam bath. Place beakers in vac. oven 30 min at 30° and ≤15″ Hg. Remove from oven. Add ca 10 ml anhyd. $CHCl_3$ to PETN beaker and heat gently to dissolve residue. Quant. transfer with anhyd. $CHCl_3$ to 50 ml vol. flask and dil. to vol. with anhyd. $CHCl_3$.

Dissolve meprobamate residue with ca 20–25 ml anhyd. $CHCl_3$. If theoretical wt of meprobamate in sample wt taken is 100 mg, quant. transfer to 100 ml vol. flask with anhyd. $CHCl_3$ and dil. to vol. with this solv. If theoretical wt of meprobamate is ca 200 mg, use 250 ml vol. flask and proceed as above.

Scan sample and std solns in 1.0 mm cells from 5.0 to 6.5 μm (2000–1540 cm^{-1}) on IR spectrophtr, using anhyd. $CHCl_3$ as ref.

Calc. PETN by subtracting A at 5.5 μm (1818 cm^{-1}) from A at ca 6.02 μm (1660 cm^{-1}) and compare with std A. (*Note:* PETN sample solns may contain very small peak at ca 5.8 μm (1722 cm^{-1}). This is contaminant of meprobamate and does not interfere with PETN detn. Also, a peak may appear at ca 6.25 μm (1600 cm^{-1}). This is H_2O peak. Disregard this peak in calcg PETN net A.)

Calc. meprobamate by subtracting A at 5.5 μm (1818 cm^{-1}) from A at ca 5.82 μm (1718 cm^{-1}) and compare with std A.

36.410 *Identification*

(a) *PETN.*—Prep. both std and sample KBr disks from respective assay solns. Evap. 4–5 ml of each soln in small mortar, add 200 mg KBr, mix thoroly, and press. Scan spectrum from 2 to 15 μm (5000–667 cm^{-1}). Compare sample and std curves. (*Note:* Sample IR curve may deviate from std curve. This deviation is caused by meprobamate contaminant.

However, all major peaks in std and sample should be evident.)

(b) *Meprobamate.*—Prepare KBr disks as above from 1 ml sample and std assay solns. Scan and compare as in (a).

Phenaglycodol (*142*)—Official Final Action

36.411 *Apparatus*

Recording infrared spectrophotometer.—With two 1.0 mm liq. cells with NaCl windows (preferably matched) and KBr disk holder.

36.412 *Reagents*

(a) *Phenaglycodol std.*—Available from Eli Lilly & Co., or equiv.

(b) *Carbon disulfide.*—Spectral grade.

(c) *Cotton.*—Wash thoroly with $CHCl_3$ and dry.

36.413 *Determination*

(*Caution: See* **46.011, 46.040,** and **46.056.**)

Weigh ⩾20 tablets and reduce to fine powder or det. av. contents of ⩾20 capsules, grind, and sieve to obtain uniform sample. Accurately weigh sample contg ca 200 mg phenaglycodol and transfer to 125 ml separator with 50 ml $CHCl_3$. Add 15 ml $0.5N$ NaOH, shake 1 min, and filter sepd $CHCl_3$ layer thru cotton into 150 ml beaker. Ext alk. soln with two addnl 25 ml portions $CHCl_3$, filtering each sepd $CHCl_3$ layer into beaker. Evap. combined exts just to dryness, using gentle current of air, at temp. <50°. Dissolve residue in CS_2, transfer quant. to 50 ml vol. flask, and dil. to vol. with CS_2.

Accurately weigh ca 200 mg std phenaglycodol, transfer to 125 ml separator with 50 ml $CHCl_3$, and ext as above.

Det. baseline A of sample and std solns against CS_2 at ca 9.85 μm. Draw baseline between minima at ca 9.75 μm and ca 10.0 μm. Calc. phenaglycodol content of sample.

Prep. KBr disk by grinding 2 mg residue and 200 mg spectroscopic grade KBr in Mullite mortar and press in die with hydraulic press. Record spectrum at 2–15 μm and compare with spectrum of extd std residue to det. identity of sample.

Phenazopyridine Hydrochloride (Pyridium®, Mallophene®) (*143*)—Official Final Action

36.414 *Reagents*

(a) *Titanium trichloride std soln.*—Prep. as in **45.043** and stdze as in **45.044.**

(b) *Light green SF yellowish soln.*—Dissolve 1 g FD&C Green No. 2 in H_2O and dil. to 1 L.

36.415 *Preparation of Solution*

(*Caution: See* **46.011, 46.040,** and **46.056.**)

(a) *Solns.*—To vol. contg ca 0.1 g phenazopyridine.HCl add 10 ml $0.1N$ HCl and dil. to 100 ml.

(b) *Tablets and jelly.*—Accurately weigh sample (powd in case of tablets) contg ca 0.1 g phenazopyridine.HCl, add 10 ml 0.1N HCl, and dil. to 100 ml.

(c) *Ointments.*—Accurately weigh, in 100 ml beaker, sample contg ca 0.1 g phenazopyridine .HCl, stir with ether until ointment base dissolves, and wash into separator with ether and H_2O. Shake thoroly, and drain aq. layer into second separator contg 25 ml ether. Shake, and drain aq. layer into third separator contg 25 ml ether. Shake, and transfer aq. layer to 250 ml beaker. Wash ether layers with alternate 10 ml portions HCl (1 + 1) and H_2O until no more color is removed, successively passing each portion of the HCl or H_2O thru the 3 separators and finally into beaker. Nearly neutze combined acid exts with NH_4OH, cool, wash into separator, make ammoniacal, and ext with 25 ml portions $CHCl_3$ until no more color is removed, filtering $CHCl_3$ thru cotton pledget in stem of separator. Evap. combined $CHCl_3$ exts just to dryness, take up in 10 ml 0.1N HCl, and dil. to 100 ml.

36.416 *Determination*

Heat soln to boiling, add 15 g *Na acid tartrate,* and boil 2 min. Add 10 ml light green SF yellowish soln and titr. hot with std $TiCl_3$ soln in current of CO_2. End point is change from green to pale yellow. Perform blank titrn with 10 ml 0.1N HCl, 90 ml H_2O, 15 g Na acid tartrate, and 10 ml light green SF yellowish soln, and subtract from vol. $TiCl_3$ previously found. 1 ml 0.1N $TiCl_3$ = 0.00624 g phenazopyridine.HCl, $C_{11}H_{11}N_5$.HCl.

Phenothiazine (*144*)—Official Final Action

36.417 *Reagents and Apparatus*

(All $CHCl_3$ solns must be protected from light and the assay must be completed within 8 hr.)

(a) *Phenothiazine std soln.*—Dissolve phenothiazine in 10 parts toluene with heat. Add 0.1 g activated charcoal for each 4 g phenothiazine. Boil 10 min under reflux and filter while hot thru heated filter. Cool soln, and collect phenothiazine crystals on buchner or fritted glass filter. Dry crystals at 100° and then in vac. desiccator contg paraffin chips. Repeat recrystn, if necessary, until product melts at 184–185°. Dissolve 100.0 mg purified phenothiazine in $CHCl_3$ in 50 ml vol. flask and dil. to vol. with $CHCl_3$.

(b) *Internal std soln.*—Dissolve 125 mg promethazine.HCl in $CHCl_3$ in 25 ml vol. flask and dil. to vol. with $CHCl_3$.

(c) *Chromatographic column.*—Slurry 20 g Gas-Chrom Q (Applied Science Laboratories, Inc.), 100–120 mesh, with 100 ml $CHCl_3$ in 500 ml r-b flask. Add, with stirring, 1.0 g Apiezon L (James G. Biddle Co., Township Line and Jolly Rds,

Plymouth Meeting, PA 19462) dissolved in 50 ml $CHCl_3$. Evap. to dryness in 70° H_2O bath, using rotary vac. evaporator. Apply vac. (ca 20″ Hg) to one end of 4′ glass column (4 mm id) and, with gentle tapping only, fill tube with coated support. Condition column by heating 48 hr at 240° with N flow of ca 10 ml/min.

(d) *Gas chromatograph.*—Any gas chromatograph with H flame ionization detector capable of using specified column.

36.418 *Determination*

Grind representative sample portion to pass No. 60 sieve. Accurately weigh sample contg ca 200 mg phenothiazine and transfer to 100 ml vol. flask. Add 80 ml $CHCl_3$ and shake vigorously until phenothiazine is completely dissolved (ca 20 min). Dil. to vol. with $CHCl_3$, mix thoroly, and let stand 15 min. Pipet 5 ml aliquots of clear supernatant soln and phenothiazine std soln to individual 25 ml g-s erlenmeyers. Pipet 4 ml aliquots of promethazine.HCl internal std soln into each flask.

About 1 hr before initial injection adjust chromatgc conditions to following temps: column 215°, detector 230°, injector 230°. Set N carrier gas flow rate to give phenothiazine retention time of ca 8 min (ca 20 psig regulator outlet pressure). Retention time of internal std will be ca 17 min. Inject similar vol. of sample and std soln contg ca 10 μg phenothiazine, using sensitivity setting that gives 70–90% of full-scale deflection.

Calc. % phenothiazine in original sample as follows:

% Phenothiazine = $(M/W)(P_u/P_a) \times (P_b/P_p) \times 200$,

where M = mg phenothiazine used to prep. std soln, W = mg sample, P_u = phenothiazine sample soln peak area, P_a = promethazine.HCl sample soln peak area, P_b = promethazine.HCl std soln peak area, and P_p = phenothiazine std soln peak area.

Piperazine—Official Final Action
Chromatographic Method (145)
(Applicable to aq. solns)

36.419 *Apparatus*

Chromatographic tube.—40 × 300 mm, with stopcock and fritted glass disk or plug of glass wool as support.

36.420 *Determination*

(*Caution:* See **46.011, 46.040,** and **46.056.**)

Prep. layered column with tamped layer of 5 g Celite 545 on bottom; add layer of 5 g Celite 545 thoroly mixed with 5 ml H_2O, and tamp. Thoroly mix 25 g Celite 545 and 5 g $NaHCO_3$ in 600 ml beaker, add 25 ml aliquot of piperazine soln contg ca 100 mg piperazine, and again mix thoroly. Add 2 ml Ac₂O and mix 5 min, transferring to another beaker to ensure thoro mixing. Add mixt. to column, using large funnel to prevent loss, and tamp. Dry-clean the 2 beakers with 5 g Celite, add to column, and tamp. Place wad of glass wool on top.

Pass 200 ml CHCl₃ thru column, adjusting flow to ca 7 ml/min, and collect eluate in 250 ml beaker, previously dried at 80°, cooled in desiccator, and weighed. Evap. CHCl₃ on steam bath with air current, and dry to constant wt in convection oven at 80° (ca 3 hr). Piperazine = diacetylpiperazine × 0.5061.

Check for complete extn by passing another 100 ml portion CHCl₃ thru column, evapg to dryness, and noting if residue is present.

Det. mp of diacetylpiperazine, which should be ca 140°.

Near Infrared Method (146)

36.421 *Apparatus and Reagents*

(a) *Near-infrared spectrophotometer.*—With 5 cm Si cells.

(b) *Drying tube.*—Approx. 3.5 cm diam. × 9 cm long. Pack with glass wool and ca 6 cm granular anhyd. Na₂SO₄ prewetted with ca 30 ml reagent grade CHCl₃.

(c) *Piperazine dihydrochloride.*—53.8% piperazine base. (Available from Dow Chemical Co.) Store above Si gel.

36.422 *Preparation of Standard*

Accurately weigh std piperazine equiv. to ca 3.5-3.8 g anhyd. base, transfer to 100 ml vol. flask with H₂O, dil. to vol., and mix. Transfer 10.0 ml of this soln and exactly 5 ml H₂O to separator. Add 25 ml *NaOH soln* (1 + 1) and swirl. *Final concn of NaOH must be >30%.* Cool separator under tap, add 30 ml CHCl₃, and shake carefully ca 2 min. Drain CHCl₃ layer thru drying tube, (b), into 100 ml vol. flask. Ext with three 20 ml portions CHCl₃, draining thru drying tube into vol. flask. Rinse tube with CHCl₃ and dil. to vol. Prep. blank as above, using 15 ml H₂O.

36.423 *Preparation of Sample*

(a) *Powders.*—Transfer sample contg ca 250-300 mg piperazine base thru small funnel to separator contg exactly 5 ml H₂O. Rinse funnel with exactly 10 ml H₂O from pipet. Mix, and proceed as in **36.422**, beginning, "Add 25 ml *NaOH soln* ..." Dil. CHCl₃ exts to 100 ml.

(b) *Sirups.*—Transfer sample contg ca 500 mg piperazine base to separator. Add H₂O to total vol. of exactly 15 ml. Proceed as in **36.422**, beginning "Add 25 ml *NaOH soln* ..." *except* use 200 ml vol. flask to collect CHCl₃ exts, and ext with

three 50 ml portions CHCl₃, finally rinsing inside of separator with several 10-15 ml portions CHCl₃ before dilg to 200 ml.

36.424 *Determination*

Using 5 cm cells, scan from 1600 to 1450 nm against blank. (Max. is ca 1520 nm.) Draw baseline between min. at ca 1460 and 1565 nm and det. net A.

36.425 *Calculations*

$(A_{(sample)}/A_{(std)}) \times$ (mg base in std/ml CHCl₃) = (mg base in sample)/(ml final CHCl₃ soln)

Convert sample from base to known salt formula, if desired.

Propylene Glycol (147)—Official Final Action

36.426 *Reagents*

Use reagents in **19.005** except substitute following for heptane:

Cyclohexane.—Eastman Kodak Co. practical grade, or equiv., bp 81°.

36.427 *Determination*

Isolate propylene glycol as in **19.006**, using cyclohexane instead of heptane. Det. propylene glycol as in **19.007**(a). To correct for glycerol if present, transfer 25 ml aliquot of oxidized mixt. to erlenmeyer, add 1 drop bromocresol purple indicator, and titr. with 0.02N NaOH to light purple end point. Apply appropriate correction for any acidity in 0.02M KIO₄ soln by titrg 25 ml KIO₄ soln by same method. 1 ml 0.02N NaOH = 1.84 mg glycerol. Calc. as follows:

$A = 2$(ml KAsO₂ for blank − ml KAsO₂ for 50 ml oxidn aliquot);

$B = 4$[ml NaOH for 25 ml oxidn aliquot − 2(ml NaOH for blank correction)];

mg Propylene glycol in sample aliquot = ($A − 4B$) × 0.76.

36.428 Propylthiouracil (148)—Official Final Action

Start and complete detn on same day.

Transfer accurately weighed sample contg ca 150 mg propylthiouracil to 200 ml vol. flask, and transfer 150.0 mg pure propylthiouracil to another 200 ml vol. flask as std. To each flask add 150 ml NH₄OH (1 + 13), washing down necks. Shake flasks moderately and continuously 1 min to dissolve propylthiouracil. Dil. to vols with NH₄OH (1 + 13) and mix.

Filter sample soln, discarding first 25 ml filtrate. Dil. 20 ml aliquot clear filtrate to 200 ml with H₂O in vol. flask (or 25 ml aliquot to 250 ml) and mix. Dil. 20 ml aliquot of this soln to 200 ml in vol. flask (or 25 ml aliquot to 250 ml) and mix. Prep. same double diln of std soln to obtain final concn of 0.0075 mg/ml.

Det. *A* of final solns of std and sample against H_2O blank in silica cells in spectrophtr at 234 nm. Apply cell corrections unless same cell is used for both std and sample. Calc. propylthiouracil content of sample.

Sodium Fluorescein (*149*)—Official First Action

(Applicable to solns. *Caution: See* **46.008** and **46.016**.)

36.429   *Apparatus*

(a) *Fluorometric apparatus.*—(*1*) *Spectrophotofluorometer.*—(Aminco-Bowman, or equiv.), with cell path 1 cm, lamp Xe, slit position 3, excitation wavelength 460 nm, meter multiplier 0.1, and sensitivity to yield 85% *T* for most concd std soln. Warm lamp ≥20 min before making measurements. Or: (*2*) *Fluoro microphotometer.*—(Aminco-Bowman, or equiv.), with primary filters Aminco 4–7230 and 4–7201, secondary filter Aminco 4–7119, meter multiplier 0.03, lamp W, cells 8.5 mm cuvets, and sensitivity to yield 90% *T* with most concd std soln.

(b) *Thin layer sheets.*—Silica gel (100 μm) with fluorescent indicator (Eastman Kodak Co. Chromagram sheets for TLC, No. 6060, or equiv.).

36.430   *Reagents*

(a) *Acriflavine hydrochloride soln.*—Dissolve 5 mg salt (J. T. Baker Chemical Co., or equiv.) in 0.5 ml H_2O and dil. to 5 ml with alcohol.

(b) *Fluorescein diacetate.*—Mp 206–208° (Eastman Kodak Co. No. 1688, or equiv.). If material is impure, indicated by low mp or other evidence, recrystallize from alcohol.

(c) *Sodium fluorescein std solns.*—(*1*) *Stock soln.*—903.6 μg Na fluorescein/ml. Accurately weigh 100 mg fluorescein diacetate (equiv. to 90.36 mg Na fluorescein), dried 1 hr at 100°, and transfer to 100 ml vol. flask with ca 10 ml alcohol. Add 2 ml 10% NaOH and heat on steam bath at ca boiling temp. 20 min. Swirl frequently. After hydrolysis, cool flask, dil. to vol. with H_2O, and mix. (*2*) *Intermediate soln.*—0.9036 μg Na fluorescein/ml. Dil. 1 ml clear stock soln to 1 L with H_2O and mix. (*3*) *Working solns.*—0.000, 0.009, 0.018, 0.027, 0.036, and 0.045 μg Na fluorescein/ml. Transfer 0.0, 1.0, 2.0, 3.0, 4.0, and 5.0 ml intermediate soln to sep. 100 ml vol. flasks, add 20 ml pH 9 buffer to each, and dil. to vol. with H_2O.

(d) *Boric acid buffer.*—pH 9. Prep. ca 200 ml soln $0.05M$ in boric acid and $0.05M$ in KCl. Adjust to pH 9 with $0.2M$ NaOH.

(e) *Developing solvent.*—Butanol-alcohol-H_2O $(2+1+1)$.

36.431   *Preparation of Sample*

Quant. dil. sample with H_2O to obtain ca 1 μg Na fluorescein/ml and transfer 3.0 ml aliquot to 100 ml vol. flask contg 20 ml pH 9 buffer. Dil. to vol. with H_2O and mix.

36.432   *Determination*

Measure fluorescent intensity (*I*) of all working std solns and plot std curve (μg Na fluorescein against *I*). Det. *I* of sample soln and calc. concn of sample.

36.433   *Purity and Identification*

Dil. concd sample and hydrolyzed stock solns with alcohol to contain ca 1 mg Na fluorescein/ml.

Spot 10 μl each of above solns and acriflavine .HCl soln on fluorescent silica gel sheets and develop with *n*-butanol-alcohol-H_2O. Dry sheet and view under long wave UV light. Sample and std should exhibit only one spot, which has similiar R_f but different from spot obtained with acriflavine .HCl.

★ Tetrachloroethylene in Mixtures (*150*) ★ —Official Final Action

(*See also* **36.358–36.363**.)

36.434   *Reagent*

Metallic sodium.—Place 10 ml xylene (must be dry) and 2 g Na in small g-s erlenmeyer, adding more xylene if necessary to cover metal. Heat on hot plate until Na is melted. Shake to remove excess vapor, stopper, wrap in towel, and shake vigorously until Na is finely divided. Cool, remove xylene, and replace with 5 ml fresh xylene. (*Caution: See* **46.034**. Use Sn foil wrapped cork to stopper flask.)

36.435   *Determination*

Accurately weigh 125 ml cork-stoppered erlenmeyer. Remove from balance pan, open, and from graduated pipet add sample contg ca 0.16 g tetrachloroethylene. Stopper securely and weigh again. To contents of flask add 10 ml xylene and 2 g Na reagent. Connect flask to reflux condenser, using cork stopper protected by Sn foil, and heat to boiling on hot plate. Add ca 1 ml *amyl alcohol* thru condenser. Reflux gently 2 hr and at intervals add 1 ml portions amyl alcohol until total of 5 ml is added. Disconnect flask.

When cool, destroy excess Na by dropwise addn, with shaking, of 20 ml H_2O. After all action subsides, acidify with HNO_3 and transfer mixt. to separator. Wash xylene layer with three 10 ml portions H_2O and filter acid aq. solns into 200 ml vol. flask. Add 50 ml $0.1N$ $AgNO_3$ to flask and dil. to 200 ml. Shake thoroly, and pour thru dry filter, discarding first 20 ml filtrate. To 100 ml aliquot add 3 ml $FeNH_4(SO_4)_2$ indicator, **36.355**(c). Titr. excess $AgNO_3$, using $0.05N$ NH_4CNS. Make blank test for Cl. 1 ml $0.1N$ $AgNO_3 = 0.00415$ g C_2Cl_4.

Cl may also be detd gravimetrically as in **36.439**; 1 g AgCl = 0.2893 g C_2Cl_4.

36.436 ★ Thiouracil (151)—Official ★
First Action

Bromination method. *See* **32.394**, 10th ed.

★ Trichloroethylene (152)—Official ★
Final Action

(*See also* **36.358–36.363**.)

36.437 *Apparatus*

(a) *Pressure tubes.*—Start with clean, dry piece of soft glass tubing 16.5 cm long, 6–8 mm id, with wall 1–1.5 mm thick (1 mm is easier to work). Heat in center and draw out to make id 3–4 mm at narrow point. Seal both ends securely by heating. When cool, cut at narrow point to make 2 tubes, 8–10 mm long. Ends may be sealed after dividing. Leave narrow ends open.

(b) *Covered oil bath.*—Any oil bath is satisfactory if it permits heating of pressure tubes in ca upright position and protects analyst from burn or injury in case tube should burst. Chief risk to guard against is hot oil thrown out of bath. Following app. is suggested:

Wrap large Pyrex test tube, 38 × 300 mm, with sheet asbestos and wire, preferably so that tube may be slid in and out of wrapping. Leave round bottom exposed. Put heavy mineral oil in tube to depth of ca 10 cm, or enough to cover closed pressure tubes. Support bath in vertical position in hood, with round bottom set into circular hole in piece of asbestos board.

Suspend suitable thermometer from clamp above, with bulb immersed near tubes. Small cylindrical wire basket with attached wire for lowering and raising, fitting into bath tube, may be used to place tubes in bath. Basket and tubes may then be suspended in upper part of bath tube for cooling after reaction. Without basket, simply slip tubes into oil bath loose, and when cool, retrieve by looped wire or other device. In such bath several tubes may be heated at once. Smaller test tube may be used for bath if only one pressure tube is to be heated at time.

36.438 *Reagent*

Monoethanolamine.—Colorless and Cl-free. Com. monoethanolamine purified by distn is usually satisfactory.

36.439 *Determination*

Tare pressure tube with suitable support (such as small beaker or wire holder). Using fine-tip pipet, place 0.15–0.17 g sample in tube, gently wiping away any sample on rim or outside of tube. Wait until any sample in upper part of tube has evapd, and weigh. Immediately add 1.0–1.1 ml

monoethanolamine and immediately seal open end of tube securely in flame, without heating liq. in bottom. When tube has cooled, mix liqs completely and place in the covered oil bath at room temp. (Tube, or tubes, should rest in ca upright position and remain so until opened later.)

Suspend thermometer in bath with bulb near tubes, and heat bath to 210–240°, lowering hood window part way and observing temp. thru window. Keep in this temp. range 1 hr. Discontinue heating, and remove thermometer with tongs to avoid placing hands above bath. Remove tubes from oil, but keep safely covered until cool. (Use of wire basket as described above is convenient, but tubes may be cooled in the oil (slower procedure) and then removed. Precautions are not needed after tubes have cooled.)

Remove oil from outside of each tube. Open tube by filing above liq. and breaking cleanly. With aid of H_2O wash bottle, transfer contents without loss to 250–400 ml beaker, and dil. to 100–120 ml with H_2O. If necessary to remove glass particles, filter thru small cotton pledget into second beaker, washing thru entire soln. Neutze with HNO_3 (10–15 drops) and add 1–1.5 ml excess. Heat to 65–70° and add excess of $AgNO_3$ soln, 5% or less concd. Coagulate on steam bath with occasional stirring, filter thru gooch or fritted glass crucible, wash with hot H_2O, and dry at 130–140° (30 min is usually enough). 1 g AgCl = 0.30558 g C_2HCl_3.

MYDRIATICS AND MYOTICS

Cat-Eye Bioassay Method (153)—Official
Final Action

36.440 *Apparatus*

(a) *Mohr pipets.*—1 ml, graduated in 0.1 ml, with slender tips that deliver exactly 0.05 ml/drop.

(b) *Nitrogen-filled electric lamps.*—100-watt or equally intense illumination.

36.441 *Animals*

Adult cats.—In good physical condition, weighing >1500 g, and accustomed to being handled.

36.442 *Preparation of Sample*

Dissolve, in ca neut. H_2O, representative number of tablets, or enough powder, to make soln contg 1 mg alkaloid/ml. If alkaloids themselves are taken, add equiv. amts of acid to convert them to corresponding salts. Add 2 drops ca 0.02N acid/50 ml soln.

For greater accuracy, results of chemical assay upon sample should be followed in prepn of solns; when such accuracy is unnecessary, declaration of concn on label may be accepted as basis for prepn of soln.

One drop of respective concns of following drugs is min. effective dose:

Mydriatics

	mg/L
Atropine	12
Hyoscyamine	4
Scopolamine	0.4
Homatropine	200
Cocaine	60
Euphthalmin (Eucatropine)	50,000
Ephedrine (alkaloid)	2,500
Ephedrine salt (or synthetic ephedrine)	50,000
Pseudoephedrine (alkaloid)	2,500
Pseudoephedrine (salt)	80,000

Myotics

Pilocarpine	25,000
Physostigmine (eserine)	10
Arecoline	10,000

36.443   Determination of Cat's Threshold

Place cat ca 1 foot from 100-watt elec. lamp, and det. max. contractility of its pupils under this condition. Drop 0.05 ml freshly prepd std mydriatic or myotic soln, obtained by dilg 1 mg/ml soln, into outer margin of one eye, leaving other eye untreated as control. Compress inner canthus, while opening and closing lids, until fluid has apparently disappeared (10–30 sec). Return cat to cage.

One and 2 hr after application (for atropine, 3 and 4 hr also), place cat under same conditions, and note any differences in diam. between pupils of treated and untreated eyes. (Satisfactory reaction is produced when pupil of treated eye is just perceptibly wider or narrower (0.5–1.0 mm) than pupil of untreated eye.) Do not use same eye for another assay for ≥24 hr.

If concns given fail to produce satisfactory reaction, repeat test with more or less concd soln until min. effective concn is found. (This concn may vary somewhat for different cats, but it is essentially constant for same cat.)

36.444   Bioassay of Unknown Solutions

Dil. the 1 mg/ml soln to be tested to min. effective concn for cats to be used, and drop 0.05 ml of this diln into one eye of cat, following same technic as in detn of min. effective concn. Also prep. more or less concd solns and apply to one eye of each of other cats used. Test various concns until one is obtained that produces satisfactory mydriasis or myosis of same degree as std soln when tested on ≥2 cats.

To obtain mg alkaloid present in each ml original soln, multiply mg/ml found to be cat's min. effective concn by diln used. Knowing that original soln was made to contain 1 mg alkaloid/ml, calc. quantity of mydriatic or myotic present, and express as % total alkaloid.

PHENOLIC DRUGS

p-Aminosalicylic Acid (PAS) and Isonicotinylhydrazine (INH) (154)—Official
Final Action

36.445   Reagents

(a) *Benzaldehyde.*—NF or reagent grade.

(b) *Concentrated phosphate buffer.*—pH 7. Dissolve 34 g anhyd. KH_2PO_4 in 136 ml $1N$ NaOH and dil. to 1 L with H_2O.

36.446   Extraction of Tablets

(a) Accurately weigh sample of powd tablets contg 35–40 mg INH and transfer to 150 ml beaker. Stir with 20 ml H_2O, add 1.5 g $NaHCO_3$, and continue stirring until effervescence stops. Filter with suction thru medium porosity fritted glass filter (3.5 cm diam. is convenient) precoated with ca 3 mm layer of Celite 545. Rinse beaker thoroly with 5 ml H_2O, break suction, transfer rinsings to funnel, washing down inside wall, and reapply suction. Repeat washing of beaker and funnel with 3 addnl 5 ml portions H_2O. Quant. transfer filtrate to 50 ml vol. flask with aid of small portions H_2O, dil. to vol., and mix. Proceed immediately with detn of PAS. Det. IHN as soon as practicable, preferably ≤4 hr after prepn of $NaHCO_3$ soln.

(b) (*Applicable when filtration with suction is not feasible*).—Weigh sample as in (a), and transfer quant. to 40–50 ml r-b centrf. tube. Cautiously add, in small portions, freshly prepd soln of 1.5 g $NaHCO_3$ in 20 ml H_2O. Agitate well after each addn, avoiding loss from foaming by occasionally adding few drops of ether. After all $NaHCO_3$ soln is added, continue agitation until effervescence stops. Centrf. 5–10 min at ca 2000 rpm and decant supernatant into 50 ml vol. flask. Add 10 ml H_2O to tube, using rubber policeman to wash down wall, to disintegrate residual cake, and to secure uniform suspension. Centrf. as before, and combine supernatant wash with original ext. Repeat washing with three 5 ml portions H_2O, dil. combined aq. phases to vol., mix, and filter thru fluted paper. Proceed as in (a).

36.447   p-Aminosalicylic Acid (PAS)

From aq. $NaHCO_3$ ext, transfer aliquot contg ca 150 mg PAS to 500 ml vol. flask and dil. to vol. with H_2O. Transfer 10 ml aliquot to 250 ml vol. flask, add 12.5 ml concd pH 7 buffer, and dil. to vol. with H_2O. With Beckman Model DU spectrophtr (or equiv.) measure A of this diln in 1 cm cell at 299 (max.), 244 (min.), and 325 nm against 1 + 19 diln of the buffer. (With instruments suitable for A readings in range 1.0–1.5, use 2 cm cell thruout method or modify diln so that concn of substance is twice that specified.) Calc. baseline A:

$$A_B = A_{299} - (0.3210\,A_{244} + 0.6790\,A_{325}).$$

Accurately weigh ca 50 mg finely powd pure PAS, dissolve in 2 ml alcohol, add 5 ml 0.1N NaOH, and dil. with H_2O to exactly 500 ml. Transfer 25 ml aliquot to 200 ml vol. flask, add 10 ml concd pH 7 buffer, and dil. to vol. with H_2O. Det. A at 244, 299, and 325 nm as above. Det. A_B, and from this value and that obtained from sample soln, calc. quantity PAS in sample.

36.448   Isonicotinylhydrazine (INH)

(*Caution: See* **46.011, 46.040,** and **46.056.**)

Transfer 20 ml aliquot of the $NaHCO_3$ ext to 125 ml separator, add 0.5 ml benzaldehyde, shake 15 min, and let stand 10 min. Ext with six 20 ml portions $CHCl_3$, filter exts thru compact pledget of absorbent cotton into 150 ml beaker, and evap. filtrate on steam bath in air current until residue has only faint odor of benzaldehyde. Rinse down wall of beaker with little $CHCl_3$ to conc. residue at bottom, and evap. to dryness. Add 1–2 ml $CHCl_3$, evap. again to dryness on steam bath in air current, and heat residue few min. Repeat $CHCl_3$ and heating treatment until hot residue of benzylidine isonicotinylhydrazine (BINH) is odorless, or has at most very faint odor of benzoic acid (there must be no sweet odor or odor of benzaldehyde; take care to avoid loss from spattering).

Dissolve residue in $CHCl_3$ and transfer quant. to separator with addnl solv. Add $CHCl_3$ to vol. of 20–30 ml, shake with 10 ml freshly prepd 5% $NaHCO_3$, and filter $CHCl_3$ layer thru compact pledget of absorbent cotton. Wash aq. soln with three 10 ml portions $CHCl_3$, passing each wash thru filter, and evap. combined $CHCl_3$ exts to dryness on steam bath in air current.

Dissolve residue of BINH in alcohol without heat, and dil. to exactly 100 ml with alcohol. Dil. 5 ml aliquot of this soln to exactly 200 ml with alcohol, and det. A of diln (1 cm cell; alcohol blank) at 302 (max.) and 375 nm. Subtract reading at 375 (background A from impurities) from that at 302 nm. Difference represents A from BINH at 302 nm.

Dissolve ca 20 mg, accurately weighed, of pure BINH in alcohol and dil. to exactly 100 ml. Dil. 10 ml aliquot of this soln to exactly 250 ml with alcohol and det. A at 302 nm. Using this value and that due to BINH obtained from sample, calc. equiv. quantity of BINH in sample. BINH $\times$ 0.6088 = INH.

Benzoic and Salicylic Acids—Official Final Action
36.449   Titrimetric Method (155)

(Applicable to ointments. *Caution: See* **46.011, 46.039, 46.040, 46.054,** and **46.056.**)

Accurately weigh ca 2.5 g sample into separator, add ca 50 ml ether, and swirl until sample dissolves. Completely ext with satd $NaHCO_3$ soln,

using 15, 15, 10, and 10 ml portions, or more. Ext combined $NaHCO_3$ solns with 10 ml $CHCl_3$ and discard $CHCl_3$. Acidify with HCl and ext with $CHCl_3$-ether (2 + 1) until benzoic and salicylic acids are completely extd. Filter exts into 250 ml beaker thru filter moistened with $CHCl_3$. Evap. to ca 5 ml on steam bath, using air current; then complete evapn at room temp.

Dissolve residue in ca 20 ml dild alcohol (ca 50%); carefully titr. with 0.1N NaOH, using phthln; record vol., and add ca 2 ml excess. Completely evap. alcohol on steam bath, using air current. (Evapn from ca 50 ml vol. to 5 or 10 ml is sufficient. Alcohol consumes Br.)

Transfer remaining titrn liq. and washings to 100 ml vol. flask, cool to room temp., and dil. to vol. with H_2O. Mix thoroly. Pipet 25 ml aliquot into I flask; add 25 ml H_2O, exactly 25 ml 0.1N KBr-$KBrO_3$, **36.208**, and ca 5 ml HCl. Swirl mixt. frequently during 30 min. Carefully add 5 ml KI soln (ca 10%), shake well, and in ca 1 min titr. with 0.1N $Na_2S_2O_3$, using starch indicator.

Calc. salicylic acid from 0.1N KBr-$KBrO_3$ consumed; 1 ml 0.1N KBr-$KBrO_3$ = 0.0023 g salicylic acid. Calc. benzoic acid from difference between 0.1N NaOH titrn value and 0.1N NaOH equiv. of salicylic acid found. 1 ml 0.1N NaOH = 0.01221 g benzoic acid or 0.01381 g salicylic acid.

Chromatographic Method (156)
36.450   Apparatus

Prep. tube and rod as in **36.015(a)** and **(b)**. Place wad of fine glass wool (Pyrex Filtering Fibre, Corning Glass Works No. 3950) in tube as support.

36.451   Reagents

(a) *Ferric chloride-urea soln.*—Dissolve, without heating, 18 g reagent grade urea in 2.5 ml 60% $FeCl_3 \cdot 6H_2O$ (available from B&A Group, Allied Chemical Corp.) and 12.5 ml 0.05N HCl. Prep. fresh daily.

(b) *Phosphoric acid.*—30%. Dil. 30 ml 85% H_3PO_4 to 85 ml with H_2O.

(c) *Sodium bicarbonate.*—1N. Dissolve 2.5 g $NaHCO_3$ in 30 ml H_2O. Use only freshly prepd soln.

(d) *Diatomaceous earth.*—Celite 545, acid-washed.

(e) *Benzoic acid std soln.*—Accurately weigh 40–100 mg benzoic acid (depending on concn benzoic acid in sample), dissolve in $CHCl_3$, and dil. to 100 ml with $CHCl_3$. Shortly before use, transfer 5 ml to 50 ml vol. flask; add 4 drops HCl, 1 ml HOAc, 5 ml ether, and 7 ml MeOH; and dil. to vol. with $CHCl_3$.

(f) *Salicylic acid std soln.*—Dissolve 50 mg salicylic acid in $CHCl_3$ and dil. to 100 ml. Transfer 5 ml to 100 ml vol. flask; add 2 drops HCl, 2 ml HOAc, 10 ml MeOH, and 20 ml ether; and dil. to vol. with CHCl₃.

36.452   *Preparation of Sample*

(a) *Ointments.*—Dissolve ca 1 g sample, accurately weighed, in CHCl₃ and dil. to 100 ml. If necessary, dil. aliquot to prep. final soln contg 0.15–0.25 mg salicylic acid/ml CHCl₃.

(b) *Liquids.*—Dil. aliquot of liq. contg 150–250 mg salicylic acid to 100 ml with MeOH. Dil. 10 ml methanolic soln to 100 ml with CHCl₃.

36.453   *Columns*

Column A.—*Lower stage:* mix 1 g Celite with 0.5 ml 30% H₃PO₄ to form uniform fluffy mixt. Transfer to tube and tamp to uniform mass with gentle pressure. *Upper stage:* Similarly mix 5 g Celite with 3 ml FeCl₃-urea reagent. (Mix thoroly, as nonuniform column may cause difficulty in elution of salicylic acid.) Transfer to tube directly above H₃PO₄ layer. Cover with glass wool.

Column B.—Mix 2 g Celite with 1 ml freshly prepd 1N NaHCO₃ soln.

36.454   *Determination*

(Use H₂O-satd solvs.)

Mount *Column A* directly above *Column B.* Pipet 10 ml dild sample into small beaker. Pour onto upper column, washing beaker with 10 ml CHCl₃ in small portions. Let sample sink into column and wash column with 75 ml CHCl₃. If purple salicylic acid band reaches H₃PO₄ layer, repeat with smaller sample. Sep. columns and wash *Column B* with 50 ml ether. Discard wash. Elute *Column A* into 100 ml vol. flask (contg 10 ml MeOH and 2 drops HCl) with 2 ml HOAc in 20 ml ether followed by enough 1% HOAc in CHCl₃ to bring to vol. Measure *A* of eluate and salicylic acid std at max., ca 306 nm.

Elute *Column B* into 50 ml vol. flask (contg 7 ml MeOH and 4 drops HCl) with 0.5 ml HOAc in 5 ml CHCl₃ followed by enough 1% HOAc in CHCl₃ to bring to vol. Measure *A* of eluate and benzoic acid std at max., ca 275 nm.

36.455 ★   Dinitrophenol (or Its Sodium ★   Compound) (157)—Official   Final Action

Bromination method. *See* **32.331–32.332,** 10th ed.

Guaiacol (158)—Official Final Action
36.456   *Reagent*

Hydriodic acid.—Sp gr 1.7. Boil HI 30 min under reflux with excess of hypophosphorous acid. When cool, transfer to dark, g-s bottle. Do not leave bottle unstoppered more than few min.

36.457   *Apparatus*

Methoxyl apparatus.—*See* Fig. 42:6.

36.458   *Determination*

Place aliquot of alk. guaiacol soln (guaiacol dissolved in 1% NaOH) contg 0.03–0.06 g guaiacol in boiling flask and evap. soln just to dryness on steam bath in air current. For solid guaiacol compds, weigh 0.06–0.1 g and transfer directly to flask. Complete detn by method for methoxyl group, **42.037,** beginning "Add 2.5 ml melted *phenol* from wide-tip pipet..." Boil 30 min and use 0.1N Na₂S₂O₃ for titrn. 1 ml 0.1N I = 0.00207 g guaiacol; 0.00229 g guaiacol carbonate; 0.00404 g K guaiacol sulfonate.

Hexylresorcinol (159)—Official Final Action
36.459   *Reagents*

(a) *Sodium thiosulfate std soln.*—0.1N. Prep. as in **45.038.**

(b) *Purified methanol.*—Purify if necessary as follows: Add enough Br to com. MeOH to give bright yellow soln and heat to boiling on H₂O bath 5 min. Cool, and carefully decolorize by adding 10% NaHSO₃ soln dropwise until just colorless.

36.460   *Standardization of Thiosulfate*

Add 30 ml 0.1N KBr-KBrO₃, **36.208,** and 10 ml purified MeOH to 150 ml g-s flask. Wet stopper. Add 5 ml HCl, stopper flask, immediately place under running tap H₂O, and swirl until flask cools to room temp. Continue to shake flask 5 min after adding HCl. Cautiously loosen stopper and add 5 ml 20% KI soln. Swirl gently to liberate I, wash stopper, and titr. with Na₂S₂O₃ soln. Add starch paste when soln is pale yellow.

36.461   *Determination*

Transfer 0.07–0.09 g sample to 150 ml g-s flask. Add 10 ml MeOH, (b), and swirl gently to dissolve sample. Add 30 ml 0.1N KBr-KBrO₃. Moisten stopper, add 5 ml HCl, stopper flask, and immediately hold under running H₂O while swirling rather vigorously. When cooled to room temp. (ca 1 min), remove from tap and shake vigorously 5 min after adding HCl. Cautiously loosen stopper and add 5 ml 20% KI soln. Swirl gently, wash stopper with little H₂O, add 1 ml CHCl₃, and titr. with Na₂S₂O₃ soln while swirling flask gently. Near end point, stopper flask and shake vigorously to remove halogen from CHCl₃. When soln becomes pale yellow, add starch paste and continue titrn. End point is reached when starch-I color does not return during 30 sec of vigorous shaking. 1 ml 0.1N KBr-KBrO₃ soln = 0.00486 g hexylresorcinol.

8-Hydroxyquinoline Sulfate (Oxyquinoline) (160)—Official Final Action

(For quantities of hydroxyquinoline sulfate between 25 and 250 mg. Use this method whenever nature of sample permits.)

36.462 *Extraction*

(a) *Interfering substances absent.*—Dissolve sample in ca 75 ml H_2O and add 5 ml HCl.

(b) *Nonoily preparations.*—Ext preferably from soln alk. with $NaHCO_3$ or borax. If extn from such medium is impracticable, or if compds of NH_3 or heavy or alk. earth metals are present, add Me red, **45.015(a)**, and adjust with NaOH and/or HCl to slight acidity. Add $NaOAc.3H_2O$ in proportion of 1 g/100 ml soln. If heavy or alk. earth metals are present, also add 2 ml HOAc/100 ml soln.

Ext adjusted soln with enough 20 ml portions $CHCl_3$. For alk. or slightly acid soln, usually 6 extns suffice; when extra HOAc was added, 10–12 extns are needed. Test for complete extn by adding little HCl $(1 + 9)$ to last portion, evapg $CHCl_3$ on steam bath, adjusting to 70°, and adding drop of $0.01N$ KBr-$KBrO_3$ and then drop of Me red; Me red should be bleached immediately.

Ext combined $CHCl_3$ exts with five 10 ml portions HCl $(1 + 9)$. If salicylic acid, volatile oils, etc., are present, wash each acid portion with same 10 ml ether. If sample contains phenol or other volatile interfering substances not completely removed by preceding process, boil acid soln to remove them, keeping vol. ca constant by adding more H_2O.

(c) *Ointments, etc.*—Transfer sample to separator with 50 ml ether, and ext with five 10 ml portions HCl $(1 + 9)$. If salicylic acid, etc., is present, wash each acid portion with same 10 ml ether. Add Me red; make just alk. with 10% NaOH soln, then just acid with dil. HCl, and proceed as in (b), beginning "Add $NaOAc.3H_2O$ ..."

36.463 *Determination*

Adjust acid soln (a), (b), or (c) to 50° and keep at this temp. during titrn by reheating occasionally. Add drop (or more) Me red, **45.015(a)**, *from buret* and titr. with $0.1N$ KBr-$KBrO_3$, **36.208**. (Color of liq. gradually changes from brown-orange to yellow; add more indicator whenever soln becomes yellow. At slightly beyond halfway point, dibromohydroxyquinoline may crystallize and adsorb dye. Disregard color of ppt and judge by that of soln. By dilg to ≤0.1 g hydroxyquinoline sulfate/100 ml, formation of ppt can be avoided.) End point is reached when, after waiting 10 sec for absorption of last drop of KBr-$KBrO_3$ soln and adding drop of indicator, it is bleached almost immediately. Timing for addn of drop of indicator at end point is important, as proper conditions prevail only brief period.

Read vols of 2 solns consumed. Measure 10 ml Me red into erlenmeyer, add 2 ml HCl, and titr. with $0.1N$ KBr-$KBrO_3$. Correct main titrn for quantity of Br consumed by measured vol. indicator used in titrn. 1 ml $0.1N$ KBr-$KBrO_3$ = 0.00508 g $(C_9H_7NO)_2.H_2SO_4.H_2O$.

36.464 *Method II*

(For quantities between 2 and 10 mg)

Ext as in **36.462**. Start titrn as in **36.463**, using $0.01N$ KBr-$KBrO_3$, and dild Me red (1 vol. Me red, **45.015(a)**, 4 vols H_2O, and enough NaOH to dissolve dye) instead of stronger reagents. Use as little indicator as possible. When near end point, shown by more rapid consumption of indicator, heat to 70°, and complete titrn at this temp.

Phenolphthalein in Chocolate Preparations (161)—Official Final Action

36.465 *Reagents*

(a) *Potassium hydroxide soln.*—5±0.1N.

(b) *Iodine soln.*—0.5N. Dissolve 12.7 g KI in 10 ml H_2O, add 6.35 g I, and when dissolved add 12 ml KOH soln, (a). Dil. to 100 ml with H_2O.

(c) *Sodium sulfite soln.*—Dissolve 12.6 g anhyd. Na_2SO_3 in H_2O and dil. to 100 ml with H_2O.

36.466 *Preparation of Alcoholic Extract*

Chill sample until hard; then reduce to granules by grating, shaving, or grinding. Mix thoroly. Accurately weigh quantity of prepd sample contg ca 0.1 g phthln into gooch with thin asbestos mat or fritted glass disk. Ext fat with 5, 4, and 3 ml CCl_4, using slight suction towards end. Place crucible on bell jar app. Ext phthln from sample with several portions hot alcohol, collecting filtrate in 300 ml tall beaker. Wash underside of crucible free from phthln with hot alcohol (ca 50 ml is enough for extn and washings). Evap. combined alc. exts to dryness on steam bath.

36.467 *Determination*

Dissolve residue at room temp. in 1–1.5 ml KOH soln. (Alk. phthln soln is unstable in air, and phthln should be converted to tetraiodo compd within 1 hr.) Add piece of ice (ca 40 g) and 7–8 ml I soln. Add HCl dropwise from buret, using stirring rod, to complete pptn. If ppt and supernatant are not brown, add addnl I soln to ensure excess. Again dissolve ppt by adding KOH from buret dropwise, with stirring. Wash down any unreacted phthln adhering to sides of beaker with little H_2O. (Soln should now be blue to blue-purple.)

Repeat pptn with acid and re-soln with alkali 3 more times, adding small piece of ice if necessary. Then add 1–1.5 ml Na_2SO_3 soln to blue alk. soln and filter into 250 ml beaker thru gooch with *thin* asbestos mat or *coarse* fritted glass disk. Wash crucible several times with H_2O. Acidify filtrate with HCl, using few ml excess, and heat on steam bath 20–30 min, stirring occasionally. Decant hot supernatant thru weighed gooch (with asbestos mat or medium fritted glass disk). Wash white to cream-colored ppt in beaker by decantation with hot H_2O few times. Completely transfer ppt to the gooch and wash with hot H_2O until filtrate is clear and gives neg. test for Cl. When app. has cooled and ppt has been sucked fairly dry, wash ppt several times with pet ether, using suction toward end. Dry tetraiodophenolphthalein to constant wt at 110–130°. Wt ppt × 0.3873 = wt phthln.

36.468 Phenolphthalein in Emulsions (*162*) —Official Final Action

Shake sample well, preferably in mech. shaker, 10 min. Accurately weigh quantity of sample contg ca 0.1 g phthln from weighing buret directly into centrf. bottle. Add 100 ml alcohol-ether (1 + 3), stopper bottle, shake vigorously, and then centrf. until clear. Decant into separator. Wash residue in bottle twice with 10 ml portions solv. mixt., adding these washings to separator. Dissolve residue in bottle in few ml H_2O and reppt gums with 50 ml solv. mixt. Again shake and centrf. as before, decanting into separator. Wash residue and bottle with three 10 ml portions solv. mixt. and add these to separator. Dissolve residue in few ml H_2O and test for complete extn with NaOH.

Shake exts in separator repeatedly with 25 ml portions ca 0.1N NaOH until phthln is completely removed, as shown by absence of color. Combine alk. exts in another separator and acidify soln with dil. H_2SO_4 (1 + 15).

Ext phthln by shaking acid mixt. repeatedly with 10 ml portions ether. Test for complete extn with NaOH soln. Combine ether exts in 150 ml beaker, evap. to dryness, and det. phthln as in **36.467**, omitting filtration of alk. soln.

Phenolphthalein in Tablets
36.469 Ether Extraction Method (*163*)— Official Final Action

(Not applicable in presence of other ether extractives. *Caution: See* **46.011, 46.039,** and **46.054.**)

Weigh portion of powd sample, **36.002**, contg ca 0.2 g phthln, transfer to separator, using 10 ml 5% NaOH soln and little H_2O, and ext 3 or 4 times with ether as in **36.001**, using 25 ml for first and 20 ml for each subsequent extn. Transfer ether exts to second separator and wash with two 5 ml portions 5% NaOH soln. (Substances like quinine, acetanilid, and acetophenetidin as well as any unsaponified fatty material or mineral oil, if present, are removed by ether extn.) Combine alk. solns and acidify with HCl. Ext 4 or 5 times with ether

as before, until all phthln has been removed, as detd by testing portion of last ether ext with NaOH soln. Filter ether exts into weighed beaker, evap., dry residue at 100°, and weigh. Residue should be sol. in alcohol, showing absence of most oils. If titrd with 0.1N NaOH, alc. soln should be practically neut., showing absence of acid extractives such as fatty acids and salicylic or benzoic acid.

36.470 ★ Phenolsulfonates (*164*)— ★ Official Final Action

Bromination method. *See* **32.342,** 10th ed.

Thymol (*165*)—Official Final Action
36.471 Preparation of Solution

Weigh 2 g pulverized thymol, transfer to 500 ml vol. flask, and add 25 ml 25% NaOH soln. Agitate until thymol is dissolved and dil. to vol. at 20° with H_2O.

Determination
36.472 Method I

Transfer 25 ml aliquot thymol soln to 250 ml g-s erlenmeyer, add 20 ml hot HCl (1 + 1), and immediately add 1–3 ml less than theoretical quantity of 0.1N KBr-KBrO₃, **36.208**. Warm to 70–80°, add 2 drops 0.1% aq. Me orange, and titr. slowly with KBr-KBrO₃ soln, swirling vigorously after each addn. When red of Me orange has been bleached, add 2 drops titrg soln, stopper, shake vigorously 10 sec, add 1 drop Me orange, and again shake vigorously 10 sec. Continue addn of KBr-KBrO₃ soln, 2 drops at time, shaking each time until red disappears. Add 1 drop Me orange, shake vigorously, and if red does not disappear, repeat alternate addn of 2 drops KBr-KBrO₃ soln and 1 drop Me orange, shaking after each addn as before until red disappears. Calc. ml KBr-KBrO₃ soln used to % thymol. 1 ml 0.1N KBr-KBrO₃ = 0.003756 g thymol. Reserve mixt. in titrg flask for **36.473**.

36.473 Method II

To cooled mixt. from titrn, **36.472**, add 3–5 ml addnl KBr-KBrO₃ soln. (If sample has not been previously analyzed by **36.472**, approx. quantity of KBr-KBrO₃ soln to use may be detd by adding 20 ml HCl (1 + 1) to 25 ml soln, **36.471**, heating to ca 80°, and titrg slowly with KBr-KBrO₃ soln, while vigorously swirling flask, to yellow color maintained 1 min.) Stopper, shake, add 1 g solid KI, wash sides of flask and stopper with H_2O, and titr. I liberated by excess KBr-KBrO₃ soln with 0.1N $Na_2S_2O_3$, using starch soln, **6.004(f)**, as indicator. Calc. quantity of $Na_2S_2O_3$ soln used in terms of KBr-KBrO₃ soln, deduct from total quantity of KBr-KBrO₃ soln added, and calc. to % thymol.

36.474 Thymol in Antiseptics (166)— Official Final Action

(*Caution: See* 46.011, 46.039, and 46.054.)

If alc. content is not known, make preliminary alcohol detn.

Transfer 50 ml sample (or aliquot contg 0.05–0.10 g thymol) to Pt or porcelain evapg dish. Add 6–7 ml 50% NaOH soln, mix well, and carefully dealcoholize by placing dish on steam bath before elec. fan. Evap. vol. slightly more than quantity of alcohol present. (If >30% alcohol is present, dil. with H₂O to alc. content of 25%. In no case should evapn be carried beyond 70% of original vol.) Transfer soln to 125 ml separator, washing out evapg dish with enough H₂O to bring vol. to ca 75 ml.

Ext alk. soln with two 20 ml portions pet ether. Wash combined exts once with 5–10 ml 5% NaOH soln and add washings to aq. layer. Ext aq. soln contg thymol, together with Na salts of boric, benzoic, and salicylic acids, with ether as in 36.001, using 20, 15, 15, 10, and 10 ml. Use 8–10 extns if prepn contains glycerol. Combine ether exts, transfer to 250 ml g-s erlenmeyer, and add 5 ml recently prepd alc. KOH soln, 28.026. Evap. most of ether, using steam bath and elec. fan but do not evap. entirely to dryness. Leave 6–8 ml residue and add to it 75 ml hot H₂O (80–90°) and 10 ml HCl.

Immediately add 1–3 ml less than theoretical quantity of 0.1N KBr-KBrO₃, 36.208, swirling constantly. Add 2 drops aq. 0.1% Me orange and titr. slowly with KBr-KBrO₃ soln, shaking vigorously after each addn. When red of Me orange is bleached, add 2 drops titrg soln, stopper, shake vigorously 10 sec, add 1 drop Me orange, and again shake vigorously 10 sec. Continue addn of KBr-KBrO₃ soln, 2 drops at time, shaking after each addn until red disappears. Add 1 drop Me orange, shake vigorously, and if red does not disappear, repeat alternate addn of 2 drops KBr-KBrO₃ soln and 1 drop Me orange, shaking after each addn as above, until red disappears. 1 ml 0.1N KBr-KBrO₃ = 0.003756 g thymol.

Test for complete extn by shaking aq. layer with two 15–20 ml portions ether and titrg the thymol, if any, in ether exts. Add this titrn to that obtained for main ether ext.

If theoretical quantity of thymol present is not known, add 2 drops Me orange and titr. slowly, swirling constantly during addn of KBr-KBrO₃ soln until red color is bleached. Continue as above, beginning "add 2 drops titrg soln, stopper, shake vigorously . . ."

Caution: To avoid loss of thymol by volatilization, both evapn of alcohol and later evapn of ether must be done carefully.

SULFONAMIDE DRUGS

Mixtures of Sulfonamides

Paper Chromatographic Method (167)— Official First Action

36.475 Apparatus

(a) *Chromatographic chamber.*—See 29.006(f); equipped with trays approx. 1.5 × 8.5″, glass lid, and fasteners for ascending chromatography.

(b) *Chromatographic paper.*—8 × 8″ sheets, Whatman No. 1 or equiv.

(c) *Viewing apparatus.*—Use light source having intensity of ca 1.4 amp at 2537 Å suspended ≥9″ above paper. Chromato-Vue Model 3-C Black Light app. is convenient (Black Light Eastern Corp., 29 New York Ave, Westbury, NY 11590).

36.476 Reagents

(Reagent grade materials are used except as noted.)

(a) *Mobile solvent.*—50 ml methylene chloride.

(b) *Immobile solvent.*—Dissolve 30 ml redistd formamide in 70 ml acetone. Prep. fresh daily.

(c) *Sodium nitrite soln.*—0.1%. Prep. fresh daily.

(d) *Ammonium sulfamate soln.*—0.5%.

(e) *N-(1-naphthyl) ethylenediamine dihydrochloride.*—See 38.013(d).

(f) *Dilute hydrochloric acid.*—Approx. 0.12N. Dil. 10 ml HCl to 1 L.

(g) *Chromatographic rinse soln.*—Dil. 9 vols MeOH with 1 vol. NH₄OH (2 + 5).

(h) *Sulfadiazine, sulfamerazine, and sulfamethazine.*—USP Ref. Stds.

(i) *Sulfacetamide and sulfathiazole stds.*—NF XIII and XI grades resp., or equiv.

36.477 Preparation of Standards

(a) Prep. sep. std solns for each component of sample under test. Accurately weigh ca 10 mg Ref. Std, transfer quant. with MeOH rinses to 10 ml vol. flask contg 0.3 ml NH₄OH, dissolve, and dil. to vol. with MeOH. Transfer 1.0 ml of this soln to 100 ml vol. flask and dil. to vol. with 0.12N HCl. MeOH solns of stds are stable ≥1 week; acid solns, ≥1 month.

(b) Prep. mixed chromatgc std soln by transferring 1 ml of each MeOH soln of required stds to small g-s flask and mixing. This std is used to identify components of test sample on chromatogram.

36.478 Preparation of Sample

Weigh and finely powder 20 tablets. Accurately weigh quantity of powder contg ca 50 mg of each sulfonamide and transfer with MeOH rinses to 50 ml vol. flask contg 3 ml NH₄OH. Shake occasionally during 15 min and dil. to vol. with MeOH. Mix thoroly.

36.479   Determination

Draw pencil line parallel to and 1″ from bottom of paper. Mark line at points 1 and 2″ from each edge of paper. Impregnate paper by dipping it in immobile solv. 30 sec. (For convenience, roll paper and dip rolled sheet into 100 ml graduate contg immobile solv.) Remove paper, drain 10 sec, and blot between filter papers. Place impregnated paper on dry filter paper and air-dry 3–5 min. With 100 µl pipet and by repeated applications, streak sample soln along starting line, limiting delivery to ca 20 µl/streak. Evap. solv. with gentle air current between applications. Keep within marks 2″ from either edge, and make streak as narrow as possible by uniform motion of pipet along starting line. Rinse outside tip of pipet with drop (ca 10 µl) of chromatgc rinse soln, and streak rinse along starting line between 2″ and 1″ points at right edge. Repeat rinsing twice and finally blow out pipet. (Restricting application of rinse to sep. area prevents diffusion of major streak.) Apply 10 µl spot of mixed chromatgc std soln at mark 1″ from left edge. Dry paper 5 min before developing it.

Place mobile solv. in tray in chromatgc tank, cover tank, and let chamber equilibrate ca 15 min. Remove cover, and without delay, place 7–10 ml H_2O in second tray and suspend paper so that it dips into mobile solv. Seal edges of lid to tank with masking tape and develop chromatogram 1 hr. Remove paper from tank and air-dry 5 min.

Place chromatogram on dry sheet of filter paper and view it under short wave UV light. Sulfacetamide (lowest R_f) is light-sensitive and must be protected from excessive exposure. Circle sulfacetamide band and cover circled area with dry sheet of filter paper. Outline remaining bands and confirm identity of sample components by matching R_f values with those of spots from chromatgc stds.

Cut marked zones from paper. Cut each zone into 5 or 6 pieces and place in 50 ml g-s conical flask. Add 20.0 ml 0.12N HCl to each flask. Let stand 15–30 min; swirl each flask ⩾5 times. Filter solns thru dry glass wool into test tube, discarding first 4–5 ml filtrate. Pipet 5 ml aliquot of each sample soln into sep. 10 ml vol. flasks. Pipet 3 ml aliquot of each required std soln into sep. 10 ml vol. flasks. To each flask, and to blank flask contg 5 ml 0.12N HCl, add 1 ml $NaNO_2$ soln and 0.10 ml HCl. Let stand 5 min with frequent swirling. Then add 1 ml NH_4 sulfamate soln, swirl frequently, and let stand 5 min. Finally add 1 ml N-(1-naphthyl)ethylenediamine.2HCl soln, swirl, adjust to vol. with H_2O, mix, and let stand ⩾15 but ⩽60 min. Record spectra of sample and std solns between 440 and 700 nm relative to blank. Draw baseline, and det. corrected A at max. at ca 545 nm.

Calc. quantity of individual sulfonamides, in mg/g of sample taken, by formula: 2000 × (A/A')

× (C/W), where A and A' refer to sample and std solns, resp. (baseline-corrected), C is mg std in aliquot taken, and W is wt sample in g.

Sulfadiazine and Sulfamerazine (168)— Official Final Action

36.480   Reagents

(a) *Citrate buffer soln.*—Dissolve 37 g $Na_3C_6H_5O_7.2H_2O$ in H_2O, add 32 ml HCl, and dil. to 250 ml with H_2O.

(b) *2-Thiobarbituric acid soln.*—Recrystallize acid twice from H_2O. Dissolve 5 g recrystd acid in 20 ml 1N NaOH dild with 500 ml H_2O. Add 250 ml citrate buffer soln and adjust to pH 2.0. Reagent is stable when stored in g-s bottle in refrigerator.

36.481   Determinations

(a) *Sulfadiazine.*—To powd sample contg ca 0.1 g mixed sulfonamides add 50 ml 1N HCl. Shake intermittently 10 min, filter if necessary, and dil. filtrate and washings to 100 ml with H_2O. To 5 ml aliquot add 7.5 ml 1N HCl and dil. to 100 ml. Designate this soln (contg ca 5 mg mixed sulfonamides/100 ml 0.1N HCl) as *Soln X*. To 1.0 ml aliquot *Soln X* in g-s test tube add 10.0 ml 2-thiobarbituric acid soln, stopper, and heat 1 hr at 100°. Weigh tube before and after heating, and compensate for any loss by addn of H_2O. Similarly treat 1.0 ml std contg 25 µg sulfadiazine in 0.1N HCl and blank contg 0.1N HCl. Det. A of sample and of std, A', at 532 nm relative to blank.

mg Sulfadiazine in sample taken = 50 A/A'.

(b) *Sulfamerazine.*—Det. A_T of *Soln X*, and A_D' and A_M' of solns contg 5.0 mg pure sulfadiazine and sulfamerazine, resp., in 100 ml 0.1N HCl, at 305 nm relative to 0.1N HCl blank. Then A of *Soln X* due to sulfadiazine (A_D) = $A_D' ×$ (mg sulfadiazine in *Soln X*/5.0), and A due to sulfamerazine (A_M) = $A_T − A_D$.

mg Sulfamerazine in sample taken = 100 A_M/A_M'.

36.482   Sulfadiazine in Presence of Other Sulfonamides (167)—Official Final Action

Det. sulfadiazine as in **36.481**(a) from soln prepd to contain ca 25 µg sulfadiazine/ml 0.1N HCl.

36.483   Sulfanilamide (169)—Official Final Action

On 9 cm folded filter paper in funnel place portion of sample contg ca 0.5 g sulfanilamide. Wash sol. portion into 250 ml flask with fine stream of acetone, using total of ca 25 ml. Test for complete extn by evapg small portion of washings. Immerse flask in H_2O bath at ca 70° until acetone odor is no longer perceptible. Remove from bath and add

10–12 ml H_2SO_4 (3 + 1). Connect flask to reflux condenser with H_2O jacket, add few glass beads, and boil slowly 30 min. Wash down condenser with H_2O, dil. liq. in flask to ca 100 ml with H_2O, add excess of 50% alkali, distill, and collect NH_3 in distillate in excess of 0.1N H_2SO_4. Titr. excess acid with 0.1N NaOH, using Me red. 1 ml 0.1N $H_2SO_4 = 0.01722$ g $(NH_2)_2C_6H_4SO_2$.

VEGETABLE DRUGS AND THEIR DERIVATIVES NOT CONTAINING ALKALOIDS

36.484 Aloin (170)—Official Final Action

(Applicable to mixts contg cascara, rhubarb, senna, and other acid-hydrolyzable anthraglucosides, as well as to resins and phthln with aloin. Not applicable to aloes. *Caution: See* **46.011, 46.022, 46.040,** and **46.056.**)

Dry enough powd material 1 hr at 110° (or de-alcoholized soln if liq.) to provide ca 0.3 g aloin. Add 10 ml H_2O and few ml 5% NaOH soln. Transfer mixt. to 100 ml vol. flask, dil. to ca 75 ml, and immediately acidify with H_2SO_4, as aloin is attacked by alkali. Dil. to vol., and add few glass beads if much undissolved material is present. Shake occasionally during 1 hr to ensure soln of aloin. Filter, transfer 40 ml aliquot to continuous extn app. previously charged with $CHCl_3$ (A, Fig. 36:3), and add 10 ml 10% H_2SO_4 (by wt) to aliquot. Reflux to exhaustion (ca 2 hr).

Disconnect app. and transfer all aq. soln to separator, discarding $CHCl_3$. Sat. soln with NaCl and ext with five 30 ml portions $CHCl_3$-alcohol mixt. (3 + 1). Test for complete removal of aloin by evapg portion of sixth extn (more exts may be necessary). Shake violently. Combine exts, add 1 ml H_2O and 1 g $NaHCO_3$, or more if necessary to ensure excess, and shake. Filter solv., evap., add 5 ml $CHCl_3$, evap., dry 1 hr at 110°, cool, and weigh rapidly. Wt = aloin in aliquot taken.

As check, acetylate the aloin by dissolving in ca 10 ml Ac_2O, adding excess (ca 2 g) of powd anhyd. NaOAc, and boiling 5 min in acetylation flask placed in oil bath. Wash sample from flask with addnl Ac_2O and evap. to apparent dryness in hood with good draft. Add 10 ml H_2O and heat several min. Transfer with $CHCl_3$ to separator, washing flask with successive portions of $CHCl_3$, and ext with 2 addnl 10 ml portions $CHCl_3$ (aloin hexaacetate formed is sol. in $CHCl_3$). Combine $CHCl_3$ portions, filter, evap., add 10 ml $CHCl_3$, evap., dry 1 hr at 110°, cool, and weigh. Wt × 0.615 = aloin.

36.485 Camphor (171)—Official Final Action

(Not applicable to synthetic camphor)

Into 400 ml r-b Pyrex flask, accurately weigh powd sample contg ca 2 g camphor. Add 10 ml benzene and 10 ml H_2O, and connect flask with app. for steam distn. Use 8–12″ bulb condenser, well-cooled, outlet of which reaches to bottom of 200 ml flask. Steam distill, collecting benzene and ca 100 ml aq. distillate. Disconnect condenser and wash it slowly with 5 ml alcohol from pipet so as to wet entire inside of condenser. Wash condenser similarly with 10 ml benzene. Add both washings to contents of receiver.

Sat. distillate with NaCl, add enough H_2SO_4 (1 + 9) to ensure acidity, transfer to separator, shake, and sep. 2 layers. Rinse original receiver with 10 ml benzene and use rinsing to re-ext aq. soln. Sep. aq. layer and ext it once more with 10 ml benzene. Wash combined benzene exts with 10 ml satd NaCl soln rendered distinctly alk. with Na_2CO_3. Sep. layers and ext aq. layer with 10 ml benzene. Discard aq. solns, transfer benzene to 50 ml vol. flask, and dil. to vol. with benzene. Shake soln and filter into 200 mm polariscope tube, using H_2O-jacketed tube, if necessary, to keep constant temp. of 20°. Make 10 readings, using $K_2Cr_2O_7$ filter, **31.020(b)**, and take av. Calc. quantity of camphor, Q, in sample from av. reading in circular degrees, α, by formula: $Q = 0.6171\alpha - 0.0022\alpha^2$.

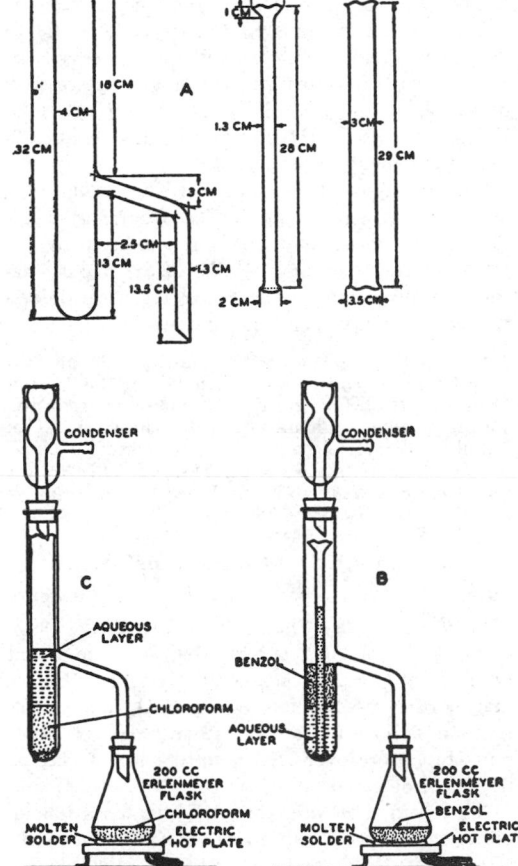

FIG. 36:3—Continuous extraction apparatus

Value of Q does not vary directly with length of tube. If longer or shorter tube than directed is used, correct value of α to 200 mm tube, and then make calcn by above formula.

Camphor in Spirits (172)—Official Final Action

36.486   *Reagent*

2,4-Dinitrophenylhydrazine reagent.—Dissolve 2 g 2,4-dinitrophenylhydrazine in 20 ml cold H_2SO_4 (1 + 1) by shaking in g-s flask; add 35 ml H_2O, mix, cool, and filter.

36.487   *Determination*

Dil. accurately measured quantity of spirit of camphor with *aldehyde-free alcohol* until soln contains ca 0.2 g camphor/10 ml. Pipet 10 ml diln into 125 ml pressure bottle contg 50 ml freshly prepd reagent, **36.486**. Close pressure bottle, immerse in beaker of H_2O, and heat on steam bath 4 hr, keeping temp. of pressure bottle at ca 75°. Cool to room temp.; then transfer contents to beaker, using 100 ml H_2SO_4 (1 + 11). Let stand overnight at room temp. Collect ppt on tared gooch; wash with 10 ml of the dil. H_2SO_4, and then with 75 ml cold H_2O to remove acid. Dry at 100°. Wt ppt $\times$ 0.458 = wt camphor.

Camphor, Monobromated, in Tablets (173)—Official Final Action

36.488   *Reagent*

Sodium amalgam.—Cut ca 1 g bright metallic Na into small pieces and dissolve in 100 g warm Hg, contained in small porcelain mortar, by impaling pieces successively on point of file and holding them submerged in the Hg until rather violent action is complete. Keep resulting amalgam in tightly stoppered bottle. (*Caution: See* **46.034** and **46.065.**)

36.489   *Determination*

Weigh portion of powd sample contg 0.1–0.2 g monobromated camphor and transfer with 20 ml alcohol and 10 ml H_2O to 100 ml r-b flask contg 15 g Na amalgam. Connect flask to reflux condenser. Gently boil mixt. over wire gauze $\geqslant$30 min. Cool slightly and wash out condenser tube with 5 ml alcohol and 5 ml H_2O, receiving washings in flask.

Place flask on steam bath and heat another hr, or until evolution of H has nearly or quite ceased. Toward latter part of this operation, to facilitate reduction, make liq. ca neut. with few drops of HOAc. Transfer contents of flask to separator, withdrawing Hg into second separator and washing it with at least two 50 ml portions H_2O. Pass the several aq. solns thru small filter, collecting clear filtrate in beaker. Ppt with 10% $AgNO_3$ soln, add ca 5 ml HNO_3, and filter, collecting AgBr in weighed gooch. Wash with H_2O and alcohol, dry at

100°, and weigh. Wt AgBr $\times$ 1.23 = wt monobromated camphor. Perform control detn on amalgam to det. if correction is necessary.

Chenopodium Oil (174)—Official Final Action

36.490   *Reagents*

(a) *Ferric ammonium sulfate std soln.*—0.1N. Dissolve 39.215 g pure, crystd $Fe(NH_4)_2(SO_4)_2$.$6H_2O$ in 200 ml H_2O in 1 L flask, add 30 ml H_2SO_4, and mix well. Weigh exactly 3.16 g $KMnO_4$, dissolve in 200 ml warm H_2O, and slowly add to soln in flask, with stirring. ($KMnO_4$ soln should be just enough to oxidize ferrous salt, but add last few ml in small portions.) Cool soln and dil. to 1 L with H_2O.

(b) *Titanium trichloride std soln.*—Prep. and stdze as in **45.043–45.044.**

36.491   *Determination*

Weigh 1 ml sample in 100 ml vol. flask and dil. to vol. with alcohol.

Place 50 ml $TiCl_3$ soln, (b), in erlenmeyer thru which passes current of CO_2. Fit flask with Bunsen valve, add 10 ml dild sample soln, close flask with Bunsen valve, and heat contents almost to boiling 2 min. (Prolonged heating has no effect if contents are not boiled vigorously.) If pale violet of $TiCl_3$ disappears, add more reagent to ensure excess. (Formation of white ppt does not interfere with detn.) Add 1 ml 5% NH_4CNS and titr. excess $TiCl_3$ with the $FeNH_4(SO_4)_2$ soln in CO_2 atm. to faint permanent brownish-red.

Subtract quantity of $FeNH_4(SO_4)_2$ soln used, expressed in equiv. mg $TiCl_3$, from mg $TiCl_3$ taken. Difference is mg $TiCl_3$ oxidized by oil taken. To convert mg $TiCl_3$ oxidized into ascaridole, divide by factor 1.284 (1 g ascaridole is reduced by 1.284 g $TiCl_3$).

Example: 0.9600 g oil was dild to 100 ml and 10 ml aliquot was heated with 50 ml $TiCl_3$ soln (1 ml contg 0.0034 g $TiCl_3$). Back-titrn required 5.9 ml reagent, each ml equiv. to 0.01543 g $TiCl_3$. Number of g $TiCl_3$ oxidized is numerically equal to (50 $\times$ 0.0034) − (5.9 $\times$ 0.01543), or 0.07896. Wt oil in aliquot was 0.0960 g. Hence % ascaridole = 0.07896 $\times$ 100/0.096 $\times$ 1.284 = 64.1.

Digitoxin (175)—Official Final Action

36.492   *Reagents*

(a) *Formamide.*—Shake 1 L $HCONH_2$ (99% grade) with ca 30 g anhyd. K_2CO_3 15 min and filter. Distill under vac. in all-glass app. Reject first portion of distillate contg H_2O, and collect fraction boiling at ca 101°/12 mm Hg (115°/25 mm Hg). Store over H_2SO_4 until odor of NH_3 is no longer detected.

(b) *Alkaline picrate reagent.*—Mix 20 ml 1% aq. picric acid soln with 10 ml 5% NaOH soln, dil. to 100 ml with H_2O, and mix. Reagent is stable 2–3 days.

(c) *Digitoxin std soln.*—0.04 mg/ml. Dissolve 20.0 mg USP Ref. Std Digitoxin in alcohol, and dil. to 50 ml with alcohol. Dil. 10.0 ml of this stock soln to 100 ml with alcohol.

(d) *Diatomaceous earth.*—See **36.016(c)**.

36.493 Preparation of Chromatographic Column

Chromatographic tube.—See **36.015(a)** and **(b)**.

Wash layer.—Add ca 2 g Celite to 1 ml H_2O in 100 ml beaker. Mix thoroly with stirring rod or scoop until the mixt. appears fluffy and uniform, and transfer to chromatgc tube. Press down lightly with packing rod. (Wash layer should be 15–20 mm thick.)

Trap layer.—Add 3 g Celite to 3 ml formamide-H_2O soln $(2 + 1)$ in 150 ml beaker, mix thoroly, and transfer to tube. Press trap layer down lightly and evenly.

36.494 Preparation of Sample

(a) *Crystalline digitoxin.*—Dissolve 20 mg digitoxin, accurately weighed, in 20 ml $CHCl_3$. Transfer to 100 ml vol. flask with several portions of benzene, dil. to 100 ml with benzene, and mix. Transfer 10.0 ml to chromatgc column. When liq. has passed into column, proceed as in **36.495**.

(b) *Tablets.*—Thoroly mix powd sample contg 2 mg digitoxin with 2 ml H_2O in 250 ml beaker. Add 4 ml formamide, stir thoroly, and cover beaker with watch glass. Heat mixt. 20 min on steam bath, with frequent stirring. Cool; add 2 ml H_2O and ca 8 g Celite. Stir thoroly until mass appears uniform and does not stick to beaker. Quant. transfer mixt. to chromatgc tube thru powder funnel in several portions, pressing it down with stirring rod. Use rubber policeman to sweep adhering particles from beaker and funnel into tube. Scrub beaker and stirring rod with ca 1 g Celite, and add dry washings to tube thru funnel. Repeat washing with 2 addnl portions Celite. Place cotton wad in tube and press it down on column with packing rod, sweeping Celite on sides of tube before it. (Over-all ht of column should be 120–150 mm.)

36.495 Separation of Digitoxin

Elute digitoxin with ca 240 ml benzene-$CHCl_3$ $(3 + 1)$, collecting eluate in 250 ml vol. flask at rate $\leqslant 4$ ml/min. Wash stem with stream of $CHCl_3$, dil. to 250 ml with $CHCl_3$, and mix.

Continue elution for **36.497**.

36.496 Colorimetric Determination

Transfer 25 ml aliquot eluate to small erlenmeyer and evap. to dryness on steam bath with aid of air current. Moisten residue with ca 0.5 ml alcohol, and again evap. to dryness. Add 5.0 ml alcohol to cooled flask, stopper, and let stand 15 min with occasional shaking.

Transfer 5.0 ml aliquot dild std digitoxin soln to small flask and 5 ml alcohol to another flask as blank. Add 3.0 ml alk. picrate reagent to each flask, and mix by swirling. Protect soln from intense light. After 10 min, det. *A* of std and sample solns relative to blank at 495 nm, repeating measurements at 2 min intervals until max. values are attained. Calc. digitoxin content of sample.

36.497 Tests for Other Digitoxosides

(Caution: See **46.011**, **46.040**, *and* **46.056**.*)*

After digitoxin seps, elute other digitoxosides with 200 ml $CHCl_3$, collecting eluate in separator. Shake with 100 ml H_2O. Transfer lower layer to beaker, ext H_2O with 30 ml $CHCl_3$, and add $CHCl_3$ washings to beaker. Evap. to dryness. Pipet 5 ml dild digitoxin std soln into second beaker and evap. to dryness. Add 4 ml Keller-Kiliani reagent, **36.498(b)**, to each of the cooled residues and mix thoroly. After 15 min, filter thru glass wool if necessary, and det. *A* of *clear* sample and std relative to reagent blank, at 590 nm; repeat measurements at 5 min intervals until max. values are attained. Calc. content of other digitoxosides in sample as digitoxin.

Digoxin and Total Digitoxosides (176)— Official Final Action

36.498 Reagents

(a) *Alkaline dinitrobenzene soln.*—(*1*) Prep. 5% soln *m*-dinitrobenzene in benzene, and store in g-s brown glass bottle. (*2*) Mix 1 ml 10% tetramethylammonium hydroxide soln with 140 ml absolute alcohol, titr. with 0.01*N* HCl, using Me red, and adjust to 0.008*N* with absolute alcohol. Just before use, mix 60 ml (*1*) with 40 ml (*2*).

(b) *Keller-Kiliani reagent.*—Mix 60 ml HOAc with 1 ml 9% $FeCl_3.6H_2O$ soln and 5 ml H_2SO_4, and cool.

(c) *Digoxin std soln.*—25.0 μg/ml. Dissolve 25.0 mg USP Ref. Std Digoxin, $C_{41}H_{64}O_{14}$, in hot alcohol, cool, dil. to 100 ml, and mix. Dil. 10.0 ml of this soln to 100 ml with alcohol and mix.

36.499 Preparation of Sample

(a) *Crystalline digoxin.*—Prep. alc. soln contg 125 μg digoxin/ml. Transfer 10.0 ml to separator, add 50 ml H_2O and 1 ml 2*N* H_2SO_4, and ext with three 30 ml portions $CHCl_3$. Wash each $CHCl_3$ ext in second separator by shaking with 10 ml H_2O and 1 g powd *anion-cation exchange resin* (Amberlite MB-1, analytical grade, indicator-free, has been found satisfactory; available as Mallinckrodt Cat. No. 3325), and filter thru pledget of cotton moistened with $CHCl_3$ into 100 ml vol. flask. Dil. to vol. with $CHCl_3$ and mix well. This soln is *Assay Soln.*

(b) *Elixirs and injections.*—Transfer aliquot contg 1.25 mg digoxin to separator, and proceed as in **(a)**, beginning: "add 50 ml H₂O and 1 ml 2N H₂SO₄ ..."

(c) *Tablets.*—Accurately weigh, into 100 ml beaker, portion of powd tablets contg 1.25 mg digoxin. Add 10 ml alcohol, cover with watch glass, and heat to simmering on steam bath. Let simmer 20 min with frequent stirring. Cool, wash quant. into separator with 30 ml CHCl₃ and 50 ml H₂O, add 1 ml 2N H₂SO₄ and proceed as in **(a)**, beginning: "ext with three 30 ml portions CHCl₃."

36.500 Determination

(a) *Digoxin.*—Pipet 5.0 ml digoxin std soln and 10.0 ml assay soln into similar erlenmeyers, and evap. to dryness on steam bath with aid of air current. Cool, and to each flask add 5.0 ml freshly prepd alk. dinitrobenzene reagent. Let stand 5 min at temp. ≤30°, with frequent mixing. Det. A of developing blue colors relative to reagent blank at 620 nm at 1 min intervals, using matched 1 cm cells and spectrophtr. Record max. A of aliquot of assay soln and that of digoxin std soln, A'. Digoxin (mg in assay soln) = 1.25 A/A'.

(b) *Other digitoxosides.*—Pipet 20.0 ml assay soln and 10.0 ml digoxin std soln into sep. beakers and evap. to dryness on steam bath with aid of air current. Cool, add 4.0 ml Keller-Kiliani reagent at temp. ≤30° to each beaker, and mix thoroly. After 15 min, det. A of sample and std at 590 nm relative to reagent blank at 5 min intervals. Record max. A of sample and that of std, A'. Total digitoxosides calcd as digoxin (mg in sample soln) = 1.25 A/A'. Difference between this value and that obtained in **(a)** is quantity of other digitoxosides in sample soln.

Gums, Identification (177)—Official Final Action
(See also 16.231–16.237.)
36.501 Reagents

(a) *Iodine-potassium iodide in zinc chloride soln.*—To 100 ml 60% ZnCl₂ soln, sp gr 1.8, add soln of 10 g KI and 0.15 g I in 10 ml H₂O. Keep few crystals of I in the soln.

(b) *Alcoholic iodine soln.*—Dissolve 7 g I and 5 g KI in 5 ml H₂O and dil. to 100 ml with alcohol.

(c) *Ruthenium red soln.*—To few ml 10% Pb(OAc)₂.3H₂O soln, add enough ruthenium red, [Ru(NH₃)₄OHCl]Cl.2H₂O (available from K&K Laboratories, Inc.), to produce wine-red color.

(d) *Alcoholic methylene blue soln.*—0.1% soln in alcohol.

(e) *Aqueous methylene blue soln.*—0.1% soln in H₂O.

36.502 Preparation of Samples

(a) *Controls.*—Moisten 1 g dry gum with alcohol, add 100 ml H₂O with constant stirring, and

bring to boil. To 5 or 10 ml resulting liq. or jelly add 4 vols alcohol, mix, and centrf. to bring ppt together as compact mass. (Some gums, notably acacia and agar, may fail to be thrown down by this treatment. Addn of few drops of satd NaCl soln should cause rapid flocculation and settling.)

(b) *Jellies or lotions.*—Stir, and add H₂O if necessary to produce fluid mass. Treat portion of sample with alcohol to ppt the gum as in **(a)**. Remove fatty or oily material, if present, by washing pptd gum with ether; then redissolve in H₂O and reppt.

36.503 Determination

With clean towel squeeze small lump of the alcohol ppt against slide to form mat 4–8 mm diam. on slide. Note character of resulting mat as possible index to type of gum. Quince and Irish moss form thin and rather translucent films, while agar, starch, and acacia are white and opaque. Cover mat with large drop I-KI-ZnCl₂ soln and observe carefully both with and without magnification. For direct examination place slide upon white surface. For microscopic examination use magnification of ca 90×. If no characteristic color is produced within 1–2 min, proceed with fresh mat to examine for the next group, 36.504. Continue similarly, using fresh mat for each test thru all group tests until identified.

36.504 Characteristics of Tests for Gums
See page 705.

Ipomea (178)—Official Final Action
36.505 Determination of Resin

Place 10 g sample, as "60-mesh" powder, in 250 ml erlenmeyer and add 50 ml alcohol. Fit flask with stopper thru which is inserted glass tube ca 1 m long to act as condenser, and heat on gently simmering steam bath 30 min, shaking occasionally. Transfer contents of flask to small percolator and percolate slowly with warm alcohol until ca 95 ml tincture collects.

To det. whether extn is complete, collect 10 ml more percolate and pour few drops into cold H₂O; if more than faint cloudiness appears, continue percolation with warm alcohol until test for resin fails. Conc. the addnl percolate by evapn and add to flask before dilg to vol. Cool percolate to room temp. and dil. to 100 ml with alcohol. Mix well.

Evap. 25 ml of the prepd tincture (representing 2.5 g drug) on H₂O bath in beaker or flask of suitable size and dry residue until alcohol-free. Add 15 ml H₂O, bring mixt. to boiling, let cool ca 3 min, and stir well with flat-end rod 2 min to ensure thoro washing of resin. Cool mixt. by placing container in jar of ice-cold H₂O and decant wash H₂O onto 9 cm filter. Repeat washing of resin with another 15 ml portion H₂O, boiling and cooling mixt., kneading resin as before, and decanting

36.504   *Characteristics of Tests for Gums*

Gum	Original Alcohol ppt	Group Reaction	Confirmatory Test	Remarks
Group I.—Reagent: Iodine-potassium iodide in zinc chloride soln				
Tragacanth	Stringy Bluish Translucent	Blue	Warm with 10% NaOH soln on steam bath. Yellow	Certain gums, *e.g.*, Irish moss, may yield dull yellow with NaOH; tragacanth, bright yellow
Starch	White Compact	Blue-black	Iodine, 0.1*N*. Blue	Tragacanth may yield faint blue
Quince	Stringy Translucent	Blue	Above tests neg.	Quince is distinguished from starch and tragacanth by neg. reactions
Irish moss	Stringy	Brown (small blue particles)	Characteristic nodular structures with group reagent	Old prepns of this gum may fail to show characteristic structures
Group II.—Reagent: Alcoholic iodine soln (Let soln dry on mat, flush off with alcohol, and irrigate with H$_2$O)				
Agar	White Opaque	Opaque Blue-black	Stains with ruthenium red	Does not dissolve or lose shape when covered with H$_2$O
Irish moss	Stringy	Brown or lilac	Characteristic blue stain with alc. methylene blue	Reactions yielded by old as well as fresh prepns
Group III.—Reagent: Ruthenium red				
Karaya	Fine flocculent compact mass on centrfg	Swells considerably. Strongly stained pink gran. mass	Heat with HCl. Pink	Aq. methylene blue produces characteristic blue stain
Group IV.—Reagent: H$_2$SO$_4$ (Warm cautiously on steam bath)				
Carob bean	Stringy	Pink or red-brown	No satisfactory test	Alcohol ppt from carob bean gum resembles that from tragacanth
Acacia		Greenish brown	Ppt completely sol. in H$_2$O	Complete soln of acacia distinguishes it from most other gums

washings into filter as before. Repeat washing and kneading process with hot H$_2$O third time.

Dissolve residue in container in 10 ml warm alcohol and pour soln onto filter, collecting filtrate in weighed beaker or flask. Use enough hot alcohol in small portions to completely transfer soln of resin to filter and ensure thoro washing of filter. Evap. combined filtrate and washings to apparent dryness, add 1 ml absolute alcohol, and evap. solv., taking care to rotate container in inclined position as last portions of solv. are dissipated. Dry residue at 80° to constant wt.

36.506 Jalap (*178*)—Official Final Action

Proceed as in **36.505.**

Marihuana (Cannabis)
Duquenois-Levine Qualitative Test (179)—
Official Final Action

36.507   *Reagent*

Duquenois reagent.—Dissolve 12 drops acetaldehyde (fresh) and 1 g vanillin in 50 ml alcohol.

36.508   *Test*

Ext ca 100 mg sample with 25 ml pet ether, filter into white porcelain dish, and evap. to dryness on steam bath. Add 2 ml Duquenois reagent and stir to dissolve residue. Add 2 ml HCl, stir, and let stand 10 min. Note color, transfer soln to test tube, add 2 ml CHCl$_3$, and shake. Let sep. and note color in CHCl$_3$ layer; purple color is pos. test.

36.509 Menthol (*180*)—Official Final Action

Weigh 5 g menthol into 100 ml acetylation flask, and add 10 ml Ac$_2$O and 1 g powd anhyd. NaOAc. Gently boil mixt. 1 hr, cool, and disconnect flask from condenser, transferring mixt. to small separator. Rinse acetylation flask with three 5 ml portions warm H$_2$O and add rinsings to separator. After complete sepn, drain aq. layer, and wash remaining oil with successive 5 ml portions Na$_2$CO$_3$ soln (12.5 g in 200 ml H$_2$O) until mixt. is alk. to 2 drops phthln. Dry resulting oil with fused CaCl$_2$ and filter.

Transfer 4–5 ml dry acetylated oil to tared 100 ml erlenmeyer, note exact wt, W, add 50 ml $0.5N$ alc. KOH, connect flask to reflux condenser, and boil mixt. on H_2O bath 1 hr. Let cool, disconnect flask from condenser, and titr. excess alkali with $0.5N$ H_2SO_4, using 10 drops phthln as indicator. Calc. % menthol as follows: % total menthol = $X \times 7.813/[W - (X \times 0.021)]$, where X is result obtained by subtracting ml $0.5N$ H_2SO_4 required in titrn from ml $0.5N$ alc. KOH originally taken.

Podophyllum (*181*)—Official Final Action
36.510   Determination of Resin

Place 10 g sample, as "60-mesh" powder, in 250 ml erlenmeyer and add 35 ml alcohol. Fit flask with stopper thru which is inserted glass tube ca 1 m long to act as condenser, and gently heat mixt. on simmering steam bath 30 min, shaking occasionally. Transfer contents of flask to small percolator and percolate slowly with hot alcohol until ca 95 ml percolate collects. Collect ca 10 ml more percolate in sep. container. Cool first percolate to room temp. and dil. to 100 ml with portion of second percolate.

Place 50 ml alc. soln in tared beaker and add 2 ml H_2O. Evap. until percolate weighs 3 g. If wt is <3 g, add alcohol dropwise to make to 3 g. Slowly pour residue, with constant stirring, into second beaker contg 10 ml H_2O previously mixed with 1 ml $1N$ HCl and cooled to <10°. (Pellets of ice placed in beaker and renewed at intervals serve well.) Add 5 ml H_2O and few drops of HCl $(1+3)$ to tared beaker, stir well, and rub sides of container with glass rod. Add mixt. to second beaker and let stand overnight in refrigerator.

Decant supernatant into tared gooch and transfer ppt to crucible with small portions cold H_2O slightly acidulated with HCl. (If preferred, collect ppt on filter paper and, after washing, dissolve in hot alcohol, collecting soln in tared beaker.) Dry contents of crucible at 80° and weigh. If particles of resin adhere to either beaker, dissolve them in alcohol, evap. solv. in tared beaker, and dry residue at 80°. Cool, weigh, and add total net wt to wt contents of crucible.

Rutin (*182*)—Official Final Action
36.511   Reagents

(a) *Acid-alcohol reagent.*—Mix 550 ml alcohol with 50 ml HOAc and dil. to 1 L with H_2O.

(b) *Rutin std soln.*—0.02 mg/ml. Accurately weigh 100 mg rutin (obtainable from K&K Laboratories, Inc.) and dissolve in 50 ml acid-alcohol. Transfer to 250 ml vol. flask with small portions acid-alcohol. Dil. to vol. with reagent and mix well. Pipet 5 ml aliquot into 100 ml vol. flask and dil. to vol. with H_2O.

(c) *Quercetin std soln.*—0.01 mg/ml. Prep. as in (b), using 50 mg quercetin. Pure quercetin may be prepd as in J. Am. Pharm. Assoc., Sci. Ed. 42, 66(1953).

36.512   Apparatus

(a) *Spectrophotometer.*—Capable of isolating 338.5, 352.5, and 366.5 nm, with isolated spectrum not wider than 5 nm.

(b) *Absorption cells.*—Matched 1 cm.

(c) *Glass stirring rods.*—Of small enough diam. to dislodge material from tips of 50 ml conical centrf. tubes.

36.513   Preparation of Sample Solution

Weigh directly into 50 ml centrf. tube number of tablets required to give 0.05–0.50 g rutin ($\geqslant$5 tablets). Record number and wt. (If tablets are coated, dissolve coating with distd H_2O after weighing, discard aq. washings, and transfer rutin-contg core to centrf. tube.) Add 20 ml acid-alcohol reagent and break up tablets with stirring rod. After tablets are thoroly disintegrated, heat mixt. 10 min in H_2O bath held at 70–80°, resuspending material occasionally by stirring. Remove stirring rod, rinse with acid-alcohol reagent, and centrf. 15 min at ca 2000 rpm.

Decant supernatant into 250 ml vol. flask, using funnel and decanting with one smooth motion, and let tube drain ca 10 sec. While still inverted, rinse mouth of tube with acid-alcohol reagent. Ext twice more, starting with "Add 20 ml acid-alcohol reagent . . ." After third extn, dil. combined supernatants to 250 ml with acid-alcohol reagent. Any insol. material may be removed by filtration after diln if first 15–20 ml filtrate is discarded. Depending on original wt rutin taken, make diln with H_2O to give final concn of 0.01–0.03 g rutin/L. Ppts forming during aq. diln may be removed by filtration if first portion of filtrate is discarded to guard against concn changes due to adsorption.

36.514   Determination

Det. A_S of sample soln against H_2O blank at 338.5, 352.5, and 366.5 nm. Also det. A of std rutin soln, A_R, and std quercetin soln, A_Q, against H_2O blank at 352.5 and 366.5 nm. (In absence of std quercetin, values $A_{Q,352.5} = 0.553$ and $A_{Q,366.5} = 0.631$ may be used. Any error introduced by use of these predetd values should be of second order.) Calc. as follows:

$$R_1 = A_{S,\,338.5}/A_{S,\,352.5};$$

and

$$R_2 = A_{S,\,366.5}/A_{S,\,352.5}.$$

If $R_1 = 0.914 \pm .009$ and $R_2 = 0.842 \pm .013$, extd material can be considered pure rutin and wt rutin/tablet can be calcd from following equation:

mg Rutin/tablet
$$= A_{S,\,352.5} \times d \times W \times 0.02/A_{R,\,352.5} \times w,$$

where d = sample diln factor; W = av. wt/tablet; w = wt sample.

(Value of R_1 beyond its upper limit while R_2 remains within its range indicates interfering absorption which diminishes rapidly enough to be ineffective at 352.5 nm. Under this condition, A observed at 352.5 nm is accepted as correct, and rutin content is calcd as for pure rutin. Increase in R_2 while R_1 remains within or below its limits usually indicates presence of quercetin. Simultaneous increase or decrease of both ratios beyond their respective limits indicates invalidating condition.) Quantities of rutin and quercetin may be calcd by solution of following simultaneous equations:

$$A_{S, 352.5} = (A_{R, 352.5} \times r/0.02) +$$
$$(A_{Q, 352.5} \times q/0.01)$$
$$A_{S, 366.5} = (A_{R, 366.5} \times r/0.02) +$$
$$(A_{Q, 366.5} \times q/0.01)$$

where r = mg rutin/ml in sample soln, and q = mg quercetin/ml in sample soln.

Santonin in Mixtures—Official Final Action

36.515 ★ Langer Method ★
(Modified) (183)

(Caution: See 46.011, 46.039, 46.040, and 46.045.)

Weigh sample contg ca 0.15 g santonin, and ext with 10, 10, 10, 5, and 5 ml portions pet ether satd with santonin. (If sample is fat-free, this step may be omitted.) Filter each portion of solv. with aid of suction to complete dryness thru gooch provided with asbestos mat before following with another portion of fresh solv. Ext residue in soln flask and crucible with 15, 10, 5, and 5 ml hot benzene, filtering each portion as before. Evap. benzene ext in tared flask and dry residue to constant wt at 100°. Wt residue in flask = wt santonin in sample.

Dinitrophenylhydrazine Method (184)
36.516 Reagent

Dinitrophenylhydrazine sulfate soln.—Dissolve 1 g 2,4-dinitrophenylhydrazine in mixt. of 90 ml H_2O and 10 ml H_2SO_4 by warming; cool, and filter.

36.517 Determination

(Caution: See 46.011, 46.039, 46.040, and 46.045.)

Weigh 2.5 g ground sample into gooch and wash with ca 100 ml pet ether satd with santonin. Discard washings. Ext with ca 100 ml benzene, collecting filtrate in beaker. Evap. to dryness, warm residue with alcohol until dissolved, transfer to 100 ml vol. flask, cool, dil. to vol. at 20° with alcohol, and filter if necessary. To 25 ml of this soln add 50 ml dinitrophenylhydrazine sulfate soln and let stand 48 hr in dark. Collect ppt in gooch and wash with ca 150 ml alcohol (1 + 2). Dry residue 1 hr at 100°, cool, and weigh. Wt ppt × 0.5775 = wt santonin.

Ultraviolet Absorption Method (185)

(Applicable in presence of starch and calomel)
36.518 Reagent

Santonin std soln.—10 μg/ml. Weigh 50 mg santonin NF XI, transfer to 50 ml vol. flask, dissolve in alcohol, and dil. to vol. with alcohol. Pipet 2 ml aliquot into 200 ml vol. flask and dil. to vol. with alcohol.

36.519 Determination

Accurately weigh portion powd sample contg ca 35 mg santonin, transfer to 100 ml vol. flask, dil. to vol. with alcohol, and shake frequently during 15 min. Let settle ca 15 min, transfer 5 ml aliquot supernatant to 200 ml vol. flask, dil. to vol. with alcohol, and mix. Det. A of this soln and of std soln against alcohol at 240 nm.

Grains santonin/tablet = (wt std, mg) × A_{sample} × 4000 × tablet wt (mg)/A_{std} × mg sample × 64.8.

36.520 Identification

Ext portion of powd tablets with alcohol or use alc. soln from detn and evap. to dryness. Santonin gives white tabular crystals, mp 170–173°.

Infrared Method (186)—Official Final Action

(Applicable to tablets in presence of calomel)
36.521 Apparatus

Infrared spectrophotometer.—For operation in 2–15 μm region; equipped with 2 matched NaCl cells 1.0 mm thick, suitable for CS_2 solns. (Cells of shorter path length are not suitable because of low solubility of santonin.)

36.522 Determination

(Caution: See 46.011, 46.018, 46.039, 46.040, 46.048, and 46.056.)

Transfer 25 mg Santonin NF XI, accurately weighed, to 125 ml separator contg ca 15 ml H_2O. Ext as for sample.

Transfer accurately weighed portion powd tablets, contg ca 25 mg santonin, to 125 ml separator contg ca 15 ml H_2O. Make just ammoniacal with NH_4OH (1 + 9) (ca 1 drop) and ext with four 25 ml portions $CHCl_3$. Filter each ext thru cotton plug, moistened with $CHCl_3$, in long stem glass funnel into 250 ml beaker. Evap. combined $CHCl_3$ exts to ca 5 ml on steam bath with aid of air current. Transfer quant. to 25 ml g-s erlenmeyer with ca 10 ml $CHCl_3$ in 2 ml portions, and evap. to dryness. Wash down sides of flask with few ml anhyd. ether, repeating if necessary to form dry residue. Use caution to avoid loss of sample by spattering. Add 10 ml CS_2 from pipet, stopper flask, and mix by swirling. Filter any insol. material thru cotton, and immediately det. baseline A of sample and std solns relative to CS_2 at max. of 9.75 μm, drawing baseline between minima of 9.6

and 9.95 μm. Calc. % santonin in sample = $A \times$ mg std $\times$ 100/A_{std} $\times$ mg sample.

Record spectra of sample and std solns from 2 to 15 μm and compare for sample identity.

36.523 Santonin in Santonica (Levant Worm Seed) (*187*)—Official Final Action

(Caution: See **46.011, 46.039, 46.040, and 46.045.)**

Ext 3 g ground sample 3 hr with benzene in Soxhlet app. or automatic percolator, Fig. 36:4. Wash ext into separator with little benzene, add addnl benzene, if necessary, to make total ca 100 ml, and shake vigorously 5 min with 35 ml 8% Na₂CO₃ soln. After complete sepn, drain aq. layer into second separator. Wash benzene once with 10 ml H₂O and add washing to second separator. Shake combined aq. exts with 10 ml benzene, discard aq. layer, wash benzene with 5 ml H₂O, and combine with benzene in first separator. Filter benzene soln thru cotton and evap. filtrate to dryness.

Warm residue with 5 ml alcohol until mass disintegrates, and add 60 ml satd aq. Ba(OH)₂ soln while stirring. Heat mixt. to boiling, place on steam bath 10 min, filter into separator, and wash filter and beaker with two 10 ml portions hot Ba(OH)₂ soln. Add 6 ml HCl (2 + 1) to filtrate, cool, and ext with 25, 15, 10, 10, and 5 ml portions CHCl₃, filtering thru cotton pledget in stem of funnel. Evap. filtrate to dryness, dissolve residue in 25 ml alcohol by warming, mix soln with 50 ml dinitrophenylhydrazine sulfate soln, **36.516**, and

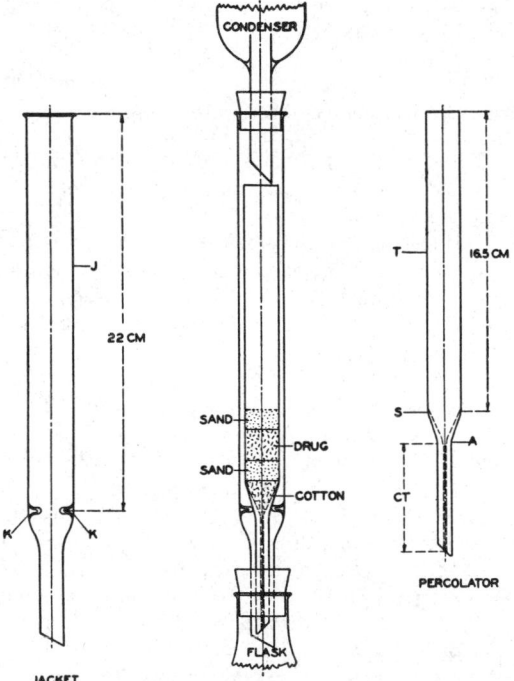

FIG. 36:4—Automatic percolator

proceed as in **36.517**, beginning "let stand 48 hr . . ."

36.524 Volatile Acidity of Tragacanth (*188*)—Official Final Action

Quantity of volatile (acetic) acidity developed in acid hydrolysis of gum tragacanth (*Astragalus gummifer* Lab.) affords valuable index of purity of this commodity when compared with results obtained by similar treatment of so-called "Indian gum" (*Cochlospermum gossypium* D. C. and *Sterculia urens* Roxb.).

Treat 1 g whole or powd sample in 700 ml r-b, long-neck flask in cold with 100 ml H₂O and 5 ml H₃PO₄ several hr, or until gum is completely swollen. Boil gently 2 hr under reflux condenser. Very small amt of cellulose substance remains undissolved. Tragacanth yields practically colorless soln. Indian gum gives pink or rose soln. This reaction may be used as preliminary test for detection of Indian gum.

Distill hydrolyzed product with steam, using scorching residue, do not conc. contents of distg condenser. Continue distn until distillate totals 600 ml and acid residue is ca 20 ml. To avoid scorching residue, do not conc. contents of distg flask to <20 ml. Titr. distillate with 0.1N NaOH, using 10 drops phthln. Correct result by blank detn and express as "volatile acidity," ml 0.1N NaOH required to neutze volatile (acetic) acid obtained.

MICROSCOPIC TESTS
Microchemical Tests
For Alkaloids and Related Amines—Official Final Action

### 36.525							*Reagents*

(a) *Ammoniacal silver nitrate soln.*—Mix 2.5 ml 4% AgNO₃ soln with 2.5 ml NH₄OH (1 + 5). Prep. fresh.

(b) *Ammonium hydroxide soln.*—10% NH₃ (2 + 3).

(c) *Ammonium thiocyanate soln.*—Dissolve 5 g NH₄CNS in 100 ml H₂O.

(d) *Bismuth iodide soln.*—(*1*) Prep. stock concd Bi(NO₃)₃ soln by dissolving 50 g Bi subnitrate in 70 ml HNO₃ (1 + 1) and dilg to 100 ml with H₂O. (*2*) Dissolve 1.25 g KI in 4.5 ml H₂O and add 0.5 ml stock concd Bi(NO₃)₃ soln. Prep. fresh when soln darkens appreciably.

(e) *Bismuth iodide in diluted sulfuric acid soln.*—Dissolve 1.25 g KI in 2.0 ml H₂O, and add 2.5 ml H₂SO₄ (1 + 3) and 0.5 ml stock concd Bi(NO₃)₃ soln, (d)(*1*). Prep. fresh daily.

(f) *Disodium phosphate soln.*—Dissolve 5 g Na₂HPO₄.12H₂O in 100 ml H₂O.

(g) *Gold bromide in hydrochloric acid soln.*—Dissolve 1 g HAuCl₄.3H₂O and 1.5 ml 40% HBr in 18 ml HCl. (Satd aq. NaBr soln may be substituted for the HBr.)

(h) *Gold chloride soln.*—Dissolve 1 g HAuCl₄.3H₂O in 20 ml H₂O.

(i) *Hydrochloric acid.*—5% (1 + 7).

(j) *Iodine-potassium iodide soln.*—Dissolve 1.27 g I and 2 g KI in 5 ml H₂O, and dil. to 100 ml.

(k) *Lead iodide soln.*—To aq. KOAc soln (1 + 3) add 1 drop Me red and HOAc until yellow changes to orange; then, while gently warming, sat. with PbI₂, cool, and filter.

(l) *Mercuric chloride soln.*—Dissolve 5 g HgCl₂ in 100 ml H₂O.

(m) *Mercuric chloride-sodium chloride soln.*—Dissolve 5 g HgCl₂ and 0.75 g NaCl in 100 ml H₂O.

(n) *Platinic chloride soln.*—Dissolve 5 g H₂PtCl₆.6H₂O in 100 ml H₂O.

(o) *Potassium cadmium iodide soln.*—Dissolve 3 g CdI₂ in 18 ml H₂O contg 6 g KI.

(p) *Potassium ferrocyanide soln.*—Dissolve 5 g K₄Fe(CN)₆.3H₂O in 100 ml H₂O.

(q) *Potassium hydroxide soln.*—Dissolve 5 g KOH in 100 ml H₂O.

(r) *Potassium iodide soln.*—Dissolve 5 g KI in 100 ml H₂O.

(s) *Potassium permanganate soln.*—Dissolve 1 g KMnO₄ in 100 ml H₂O.

(t) *Reinecke salt soln.*—Dissolve 0.1 g NH₄[Cr(NH₃)₂(CNS)₄].H₂O and 0.03 g NH₂OH.HCl in 10 ml alcohol. Filter, and store in refrigerator. (Reagent is stable ≥6 months.)

(u) *Sodium benzoate soln.*—Dissolve 5 g Na benzoate in 100 ml H₂O.

(v) *Sodium carbonate soln.*—Dissolve 5 g Na₂CO₃.H₂O in 100 ml H₂O.

(w) *Sodium iodide soln.*—Dissolve 5 g NaI in 100 ml H₂O.

(x) *Sodium nitroprusside.*—Na₂Fe(CN)₅NO.2H₂O crystals.

(y) *Zinc chloride soln.*—Dissolve 5 g ZnCl₂ in 100 ml H₂O.

(z) *Zinc potassium iodide soln.*—Dissolve 5 g Zn(OAc)₂.3H₂O and 20 g KI in 100 ml H₂O.

36.526   *Preparation of Samples*

(a) *Usual controls.*—Dissolve 0.4 or 0.2 mg pure alkaloid salt in 0.04 ml H₂O to make ca 1:100 or 1:200 soln.

(b) *Alkaloids in compounds.*—Sep. alkaloid in pure form by extg it from ammoniacal soln with suitable immiscible solv., and evap. solv. Dissolve little of residue in min. of 0.1N HCl and dil. with H₂O, if necessary, to ca alkaloid concn specified in (a) or in test.

(c) *Hypodermic tablets.*—Dissolve portion of tablet in drop of H₂O to ca same alkaloid concn specified in (a) or in test.

36.527   *Identification*

Place drop (ca 0.04 ml) of alkaloid soln on glass slide, add drop of reagent, and without stirring or covering, examine under microscope, using magnification of ca 100–150×. Note kind of crystals formed. Compare their characteristics with descriptions given, **36.528**, and with a control. Use polarizing microscope if available, and note characteristics such as birefringence and dichroism.

36.528   *Characteristics of Microchemical Tests for Alkaloids and Related Amines*

Alkaloid	Reagent	Description of Crystals
Aconitine (*189*)	Sodium carbonate	In 1:3000 soln heated to 50° in test tube. Small, transparent, hexagonal plates; also rods in contact.
Amylocaine (*190*) (Stovaine®)	1 drop HCl and 1 drop gold chloride	1:50. Dendritic crystals.
Apomorphine (*191*)	Potassium iodide	1:50. Small crystals that have sharp, clear-cut angles like those of diamond.
	Gold chloride	Red-brown, fine needles, in dense masses in all solns to 1:10,000.
	Hydrochloric acid	1:50. Small rods singly and in clusters.
Arecoline (*189*)	Bismuth iodide	Red, rhombic crystals.
Atropine (*192*)	Iodine potassium iodide	Small, dark rods and triangular plates form in great numbers, singly and in groups.
Benzylmorphine (*193*) (Peronine)	Potassium iodide	1:200. Dense rosettes of needles. Crystals are formed readily in dil. solns (1:1000) in form of sheaves of needles.
	Ammonium thiocyanate	1:200. Rosettes and sheaves of needles in acid or neut. soln.
	Hydrochloric acid	1:100. Rods, usually notched at ends and often in rosettes, are formed on stirring.
Berberine (*194*)	Hydrochloric acid	Satd soln; fine yellow needles. (Avoid excess reagent.)
Brucine (*195*)	Potassium iodide	Long masses of transparent, rectangular plates; also rosettes of thin plates.
	Mercuric chloride	Small, dense rosettes.

(Continued)

36.528   *Characteristics of Microchemical Tests for Alkaloids and Related Amines—Continued*

Alkaloid	Reagent	Description of Crystals
Choline (*196*)	Reinecke salt	Add 1 drop acetone to 1 drop H_2O soln of base. Stir, add 1 drop reagent, and stir again. 1:100. Thin, hexagonal plates and star-shaped forms. 1:1000–1:10,000. Six-sided, more coffin-shaped plates; sometimes rosette aggregates of plates on edge, resembling needles.
	Platinic chloride and sodium iodide	1:100 in H_2O. Add 1 drop H_2PtCl_6 soln, stir, and add small drop of NaI soln without stirring. Small black rectangular prisms and slender black rods.
Cinchonidine (*197*)	Sodium benzoate	Rosettes and sheaves of needles spreading to large size.
	Platinic chloride	Rosettes of transparent plates.
	Sodium carbonate	Spherical crystals, but not needles as in cinchonine.
Cinchonine (*197*)	Sodium carbonate	Dark rosettes, composed of radiating needles, form immediately.
	Disodium phosphate	Similar to crystals formed by Na_2CO_3, but more burr-shaped.
Cocaine (*198*)	Platinic chloride	Delicate, feathery crystals, later becoming heavier in structure.
Codeine (*198*)	Potassium cadmium iodide	Silvery, circular masses, crystg into dark rosettes of irregular outline.
	Iodine potassium iodide	Heavy, red-brown ppt; crystallizes very slowly in yellow blades extending in branches (never red).
Cotarnine (*194*)	Platinic chloride	1:200. Hair-like crystals, yellow and curving.
	Mercuric chloride	Colorless, long, branching needles.
	Potassium ferrocyanide	Acidify with 1 drop 5% HCl; globules that develop into dense, burr-shaped crystals; also amber-brown plates.
Dihydromorphinone (Dilaudid®) (*199*)	Sodium nitroprusside	To minute quantity (<1 mg) in 2 drops H_2O add minute fragment of reagent. Elongated 6-sided prisms; also in aggregates.
Ephedrine (*200*)	Bismuth iodide in dild sulfuric acid	1:200. Long, brownish-orange, radiating and interlacing needles and branching rods.
Ethylhydrocupreine (*201*) (Optochin®)	Ammonium thiocyanate	1:100 in 0.1N HCl. Long, straight needles.
Ethylmorphine (*193*) (Dionin®)	Iodine potassium iodide	1:200. Groups of yellow needles, branching later.
	Mercuric chloride	Transparent plates, often with notched ends; singly and in groups. Stir to start crystn.
Heroin (*202*) (Diacetylmorphine)	Platinic chloride	Spherical clusters of golden yellow needles form slowly around nucleus; cluster disintegrates on standing.
Homatropine (*203*)	Gold chloride	1:200. Green-gold blades, often with pointed ends and united in pairs; surfaces appear etched on long standing.
Hydrastine (*191*)	1 drop 5% HCl and 1 drop potassium ferrocyanide	1:100. Spheres of radiating crystals. Shake slide to start crystn. Avoid excess reagent.
Hydrastinine (*193*)	Potassium permanganate	1:500. Immediate red plates, often with serrated edges. In concd soln, great number of large red or brown plates with deeply cut edges.
	Mercuric chloride	1:500. Transparent needles forming branches rapidly in neut. and acidified solns.
	1 drop 5% HCl and 1 drop potassium ferrocyanide	1:200. Yellow rhombic plates and tree-like crystals.
Hyoscyamine (*203*)	Gold chloride	Thin, transparent, nearly colorless irregular plates, often curved. Crystals form slowly in 1:100 to 1:200 soln. Shaking slide aids crystn.
Morphine (*198*)	Potassium cadmium iodide	Silvery, gelatinous ppt, crystg in dense masses of fine needles.
	Iodine potassium iodide	Small drop of reagent produces heavy, red-brown ppt, slowly crystg in shining, red, overlapping plates extending in branches.

(Continued)

36.528   *Characteristics of Microchemical Tests for Alkaloids and Related Amines—Continued*

Alkaloid	Reagent	Description of Crystals
Narceine (194)	Iodine potassium iodide, or zinc potassium iodide	1:400. Blue, radiating needles, sometimes with yellow dichroism.
	Platinic chloride	Beautiful feathery rosettes develop in all solns.
Nicotine (204)	Mercuric chloride	Radiating, transparent blades form in presence of slight excess of H_2SO_4; feather-like blades form in presence of HCl.
	Mercuric chloride-sodium chloride	Radiating, transparent blades.
Noscapine (194) (l-Narcotine)	Potassium hydroxide or ammonium hydroxide	1:200. White, amorphous ppt that crystallizes slowly; dense rosettes of needles.
Papaverine (205)	Zinc chloride	Thin, rectangular plates in excess HCl.
Physostigmine (206)	Lead iodide	1:100. Radiating, serrated plates.
	Gold bromide in HCl	1 mg in 1 drop H_2O. Brown, dendritic aggregates.
Pilocarpine (192)	Platinic chloride	Crystals form slowly; layers of thin, yellow, triangular plates of delicate structure.
Procaine (205)	Platinic chloride	Spherical crystals of radiating branches.
	Gold chloride and HCl	Irregular, radiating branches.
Quinidine (197)	Potassium iodide	Small, triangular crystals in great numbers; best in 1:1000 diln; sol. in excess reagent.
Quinine (197)	Disodium phosphate	Silvery, sheaf-like crystals.
Racephedrine (207) (dl-Ephedrine)	Bismuth iodide in dild sulfuric acid	1:200. Large orange plates and red prisms and grains.
Scopolamine (203) (Hyoscine)	Gold chloride	Clusters of pale yellow, transparent blades, with coarse, saw-toothed edges form immediately on shaking slide. Crystals grow to large size in 1:200 soln.
Sparteine (204)	Gold chloride	Large numbers of blade-like crystals varying in size according to concn.
Strychnine (208)	Platinic chloride	Crystals form immediately in clusters and singly in small, wedge-shaped needles that move about field.
	Potassium cadmium iodide	Silvery masses, slowly forming rosettes.
Yohimbine (189)	Sodium carbonate	In 1:1000 soln heated to 50°. Fine needles in sheaf-like bundles and rosettes.

For Barbiturates (209)—Official Final Action
(*See also* **36.536.**)

36.529   *Reagent*

Iodine-potassium iodide soln.—Dissolve 5 g I and 80 g KI in enough H_2O (ca 78 ml) to make 100 ml. Dil. with 2 parts by vol. of H_3PO_4. Prep. dild reagent every 2–3 weeks.

36.530   *Identification*

Dissolve little barbiturate in drop H_2O on slide. If present as Na salt, it dissolves readily; if present as acid, add little droplet 1% NaOH on stirring rod and mix. Add 1 full drop reagent and let stand until crystn occurs (immediate with some compds, 0.5–1 hr with secobarbital). Free acid may ppt or crystallize. However, I reaction crystals are easily distinguished by their color, often coupled with strong dichroism. Det. birefringence with polarizing microscope. Cover glass is usually not needed but may be used for observation at high magnification and when slide stands >1 hr; on standing, KI may crystallize as square, colorless, isotropic crystals.

Note crystals formed and compare characteristics with description, **36.531**.

36.531   *See pages 712–713.*

For Sympathomimetics (207)—Official Final Action

36.532   *Reagents*

(a) *Bismuth iodide in diluted sulfuric acid soln.*—See **36.525(e)**.

(b) *Gold chloride in diluted phosphoric acid soln.*—Dissolve 1 g $HAuCl_4.3H_2O$ in 20 ml H_3PO_4 (1 + 2).

(c) *Platinic chloride in diluted phosphoric acid soln.*—Dissolve 1 g $H_2PtCl_6.6H_2O$ in 20 ml H_3PO_4 (1 + 3).

(d) *Sodium tetraphenylboron soln.*—Aq. soln (1 + 20).

Characteristics of Microchemical Tests for Barbiturates

36.531

Barbiturate	Crystal Form	Dichroism or Pleochroism	Remarks
Allylbarbital (5-Allyl-5-isobutyl-barbituric acid) "Itobarbital"	Immediate crystn in rods, splinters, and leaflike crystals with pointed ends.	Red to black dichroism.	Free acid may crystallize out.
5-Allyl-5-(2-cyclopenten-1-yl) barbituric acid (Cyclopal®)	Gradual crystn in dichroic straight-edged blades, brown-yellow to brown-orange.	—	Very bright birefringence; free acid as colorless rods, splinters, needles.
Amobarbital (5-Ethyl-5-isoamyl-barbituric acid)	Dil. soln: fairly large brown blades. Concd solns: multitudes of little pale-colored flakes.	—	Examine at 200×; sensitive test.
Aprobarbital (5-Allyl-5-isopro-pylbarbituric acid)	Light orange-brown rod-blades, birefringent.	Yellow to brown-orange dichroism.	—
Barbital (5,5-Diethylbarbituric acid)	Form very soon; fairly large, rectangular or splinter blades.	Extreme pleochroism by trans-mitted polarized light.	Beetle-green iridescence by re-flected light.
* Bemegride (4-Ethyl-4-methyl-2,6-piperidinedione)	Small light-colored dichroic rods or blades and flakes or plates, orangish-brown to colorless or yellowish.	—	Birefringence is bright and plates that are square or nearly so extin-guish diagonally.
Butabarbital Sodium (Sodium 5-sec-butyl-5-ethylbarbiturate)	Dil. soln: red-brown irregular plates. Concd soln: brown blades in clusters.	Slightly dichroic; dichroism yel-low to red-brown.	Free acid: colorless blades.
Butethal (5-Butyl-5-ethylbarbi-turic acid)	Small plate crystals, basically rhomboids. "Pro-peller-type" of elongate pointed blades.	Strong dichroism, light yellow to black.	—
Cyclobarbital (5-(1-Cyclohex-enyl)-5-ethylbarbituric acid)	Dil. soln: rosettes of little pointed crystals; larger are red-brown plates.	Red-brown plates of variable dichroism frequently four-bladed.	Sensitive test.
Diallyl barbituric acid (5,5-Diallyl-barbituric acid)	Crystallizes quickly in branching twigs, splinters, and blades.	Extreme black to "white" di-chroism by polarized light.	Golden-beetle iridescence by re-flected light.
Heptabarbital (5-(1-Cyclohepten-1-yl)-5-ethylbarbituric acid)	Little red-brown plates in great numbers, often 4-parted; good birefringence.	—	Sensitive.
Hexobarbital Sodium (Sodium 5-(1-cyclohexen-1-yl)-1,5-dimethyl-barbiturate	Dichroic blades and broad splinters in groups, varying to curving threads and needles in rosettes.	Very strong dichroism; black to light brownish-yellow.	Sensitive for I reaction crystals as well as for free acid.
Metharbital (5,5-Diethyl-1-methyl-barbituric acid)	Dark needles, small to large, and splintery narrow blades.	Dichroism black to brown.	Good birefringence with crossed nicols.
5-Methyl-5-phenylbarbituric acid (Rutonal®)	Red-brown irregular platy forms appear after free acid is pptd.	Gradually strongly dichroic rods or blades.	Test fairly sensitive for dil. soln.
Phenobarbital (5-Ethyl-5-phenyl-barbituric acid)	Soon crystallizes in little dark grains; also a few larger red blades and dark splinter-rods in clusters.	—	Free acid may also crystallize out.

(Continued)

36.531   Characteristics of Microchemical Tests for Barbiturates—Continued

Barbiturate	Crystal Form	Dichroism or Pleochroism	Remarks
Probarbital (5-Ethyl-5-isopropyl-barbituric acid)	Scattered iodine-reaction crystals form in various jagged shapes, color dark brown to black dichroism, or red-black with but little dichroism.		Free acid thrown out, forming long rods with pointed ends.
Secobarbital (5-Allyl-5-(1-methyl-butyl) barbituric acid)	Crystallizes in plates or elongate and rectangular but mostly distorted into any shape after 1 hr.	Light yellow to orange or red dichroism by polarized light.	Distinctly birefringent.
Sodium Pentobarbital (Sodium 5-ethyl-5-(1-methylbutyl) barbiturate)	Crystallizes quickly in great numbers of small red-brown plates.	Minute light-colored flakes exhibit dichroism; dark brown or black to yellow.	—
Talbutal (5-Allyl-5-sec-butylbar-bituric acid)	Amorphous ppt crystallizes in large needles and dichroic blades, lighter to deeper brown, in dendrites; then gray-black curled sheaves of threads.		Excellent test. Both types of crystals have good birefringence.
Vinbarbital (5-Ethyl-5-(1-methyl-1-butenyl) barbituric acid)	Multitudes of small dark crystals, tiny grains and rods with dichroism brown to black. In quite dil. soln possible to get good small crystals, little dark rods with dichroism red to black, and small plates tending to be square, generally appearing red but with same red to black dichroism, and with square extinction (not diagonal).		Very sensitive.

* This drug has barbiturate-type formula (although there is only one N) but is central nervous stimulant instead of depressant.

36.533   *Identification*

(a) *Direct test.*—Add drop of reagent to little of powd solid or crushed tablet and spread out on slide with little stirring. Do not stir to homogeneity as local concns and dilns will assist crystn. Let stand to evap. to higher acid concn if necessary for crystal formation.

(b) *Volatility test.*—Place small amt of substance or crushed tablet in depression of cavity slide, add drop 5% NaOH soln, and stir briefly. Place very small drop of reagent on thin slide, invert over cavity slide, and let stand. As crystals appear, examine with inverted slide in place. After observing crystals or after 1 hr or more exposure, if only few or no crystals form, reinvert thin slide with hanging drop, and let stand for gradual evapn of H_2O from reagent drop. Examine for crystals. Compare with descriptions, **36.534**.

36.534   *See page 714.*

For Synthetics—Official Final Action
36.535   *Reagents*

(a) *Acetic acid.*—Dil. 6 ml HOAc to 100 ml with H_2O.

(b) *Ammoniacal nickel acetate soln.*—Mix 1 vol. 5% $Ni(OAc)_2.4H_2O$ soln with 1 vol. NH_4OH (2 + 3). Use clear supernatant.

(c) *Ammoniacal silver nitrate soln.*—See **36.525(a)**.

(d) *Ammonium thiocyanate soln.*—See **36.525(c)**.

(e) *Barium hydroxide soln.*—Satd aq. soln.

(f) *Benzaldehyde.*—NF quality.

(g) *Bismuth iodide soln.*—See **36.525(d)**.

(h) *Bromide-bromate soln.*—Dissolve 0.3 g $KBrO_3$ and 1.2 g KBr in H_2O, and dil. to 100 ml.

(i) *Glycerol-alcohol mixture.*—(1 + 1).

(j) *Gold bromide in hydrochloric acid soln.*—See **36.525 (g)**.

(k) *Gold chloride soln.*—See **36.525(h)**.

(l) *Iodine-potassium iodide soln.*—See **36.525(j)**.

(m) *Lead acetate soln.*—Dissolve 5 g $Pb(OAc)_2$ .3H_2O in H_2O and dil. to 100 ml.

(n) *Lead triethanolamine soln.*—Add 1 ml triethanolamine (tech. 90% is satisfactory) to soln of 1 g $Pb(OAc)_2.3H_2O$ in 20 ml H_2O. Slight turbidity does not interfere.

(o) *Magnesia mixture.*—Dissolve 5.5 g $MgCl_2$ .6H_2O and 14.0 g NH_4Cl in H_2O. Add 13.05 ml NH_4OH and dil. to 100 ml with H_2O.

(p) *Mercuric chloride soln.*—See **36.525(l)**.

(q) *Mercurous nitrate soln.*—Dissolve 15 g $HgNO_3.H_2O$ in mixt. of 90 ml H_2O and 10 ml HNO_3 (1 + 9). Store in dark, amber bottle contg small globule of Hg.

(r) *Nitric acid.*—(1 + 1).

Sympathomimetic	Reagent	Test	Description of Crystals
Volatile Substances			
dl-Amphetamine	Gold chloride in dild phosphoric acid	direct or volatility	Very irregular plates, with irregular blade-arms especially after evapn; square if perfect.
	Platinic chloride in dild phosphoric acid	volatility	Irregular blades and needles, very low birefringence; after evapn, characteristic plates with narrow irregular arms of blades.
d-Amphetamine	Gold chloride in dild phosphoric acid	direct or volatility	Long yellow rods and blades; with evapn, some crystals as with *dl* may form.
	Platinic chloride in dild phosphoric acid	volatility	Long needles, often bent, very little birefringence; after some evapn, long rectangular blades. (*l*-Ephedrine in direct test gives similar crystals which are more sol.; it is less volatile and does not normally form crystals in hanging drop.)
Epinephrine	Sodium tetraphenyl-boron	volatility	MeNH$_2$ liberated; birefringent X's or 4-arm crystals; also thick blades with central rib, pointed ends, positive elongation.
Isoproterenol	Sodium tetraphenyl-boron	volatility	Isopropylamine liberated; plates tending to non-regular hexagons; no birefringence where plates lie flat but there are rods which are birefringent.
d- and *dl*-Methamphetamine (*d*- and *dl*-Desoxyephedrine)	Gold chloride in dild phosphoric acid	direct or volatility	Long blades and jointed crystals, fairly high birefringence.
	Platinic chloride in dild phosphoric acid	volatility	Grains with sharp edges which aggregate in chains and short prisms. Birefringent.
d-Methamphetamine	Bismuth iodide in dild sulfuric acid	volatility	Drops, long orange splinters, blades, needles; also deep red angular grains (red prisms only after evapn).
dl-Methamphetamine	Bismuth iodide in dild sulfuric acid	volatility	Drops, crystg in orange-red prisms with conspicuously slanting ends; inclined extinction ca 20°; also "mossy" formation of grains and some large deep red grains.
Slightly Volatile Substances			
dl-Ephedrine (racephedrine)	Gold chloride in dild phosphoric acid	direct or volatility	Irregular plates based on the square growing along diagonals in 4 arms; some birefringent, some not.
	Bismuth iodide in dild sulfuric acid	volatility	Orange rods or sticks, short and stubby, some plates; more irregular plates on evapn.
l-Ephedrine	Gold chloride in dild phosphoric acid	direct or volatility	Long needles or splinters and long jointed forms; strong birefringence.
	Bismuth iodide in dild sulfuric acid	volatility	Long brownish-orange needles, often branching or in sheaves; also, especially with evapn, orange irregular blades.
Pseudoephedrine	Gold chloride in dild phosphoric acid	direct or volatility (2 hr)	Thin branching sticks, many like combs; some broaden to blades or spear-head plates; very high birefringence.
Phenylpropanolamine	Gold chloride in dild phosphoric acid	direct	Plates and blades of extremely high birefringence, elongate hexagonal or diamonds, very bright colors. Branch into 4 or 6 irregular arms.
		volatility (2 hr)	After definite drying, pyramidal grains to blades and plates with irregular arms, very birefringent.
Phenmetrazine	Gold chloride in dild phosphoric acid	direct or volatility	Rectangular plates joined in jagged arms of strongly birefringent crystals, often in X forms, very characteristic.
	Bismuth iodide in dild sulfuric acid	volatility	Orange-red blades, usually pointed ends, often in rosettes; also with needles in branching aggregates; also red prisms.

(s) *Phosphotungstic acid soln.*—Dissolve 5 g $P_2O_5.24WO_3.xH_2O$ in 100 ml H_2O.

(t) *Picric acid.*—Crystals.

(u) *Picrolonic acid soln.*—Dissolve 250 mg 1-(*p*-nitrophenyl)-3-Me-4-nitropyrazolone in 25 ml alcohol.

(v) *Platinic chloride soln.*—See **36.525(n)**.

(w) *Potassium cadmium iodide soln.*—See **36.525(o)**.

(x) *Potassium ferrocyanide soln.*—See **36.525(p)**.

(y) *Silicotungstic acid soln.*—Dissolve 5 g $4H_2O$ $.SiO_2.12WO_3.22H_2O$ in 100 ml ca $6N$ H_2SO_4.

(z) *Silver nitrate soln.*—Dissolve 1 g $AgNO_3$ in 20 ml H_2O.

(aa) *Sodium nitrite soln.*—Dissolve 10 g $NaNO_2$ in H_2O and dil. to 100 ml.

(bb) *Zinc pyridine soln.*—Add 1 ml pyridine to soln of 1 g $Zn(OAc)_2.2H_2O$ in 20 ml H_2O.

36.536   *Characteristics of Microchemical Tests for Synthetics*

Synthetic	Solvent	Concentration of Synthetic	Reagent	Description of Tests and Crystals
Acetanilid (*210*)	HCl (1 + 3)	1:100	Phosphotungstic acid	Rosettes of prisms.
	HCl (1 + 3)	1:100	Bromide-bromate soln	Small prisms.
Acetophenetidin (*210*)		Approx. 1 mg powd material	HNO₃	Add 1 drop HNO₃, let stand few sec, then add 1 drop H₂O. Bright yellow, curving, branched crystals.
	HCl (1 + 3)	Satd soln	Iodine-potassium iodide	Large, irregular plates.
Acetylsalicylic acid (*211*)	2% triethanolamine	1:50	Silver nitrate	Fine, curling, hair-like crystals form first near edge of drop.
Aminopyrine (*212*)	H₂O	1:100	Mercuric chloride	Long, slender, radiating crystals, often curved.
			Potassium cadmium iodide	Groups of spiny branches.
Amobarbital (*201*) (Amytal®)	NH₄OH (1 + 9)	1:50	Acetic acid	Long, branching needles; some hexagonal plates in groups.
	NH₄OH (1 + 9)	1:25	Acetic acid	Groups of rectangular plates.
Antipyrine (*213*)	H₂O	1:100	Potassium ferrocyanide	Add 1 drop HCl (1 + 39). Acicular and prismatic crystals form.
Barbital (*201*)	—	Approx. 1 mg powder	Ammoniacal silver nitrate	Stir to aid soln and crystn. Very small, twinned crystals and larger tufts.
	NH₄OH (1 + 9)	1:50	Acetic acid	Dark burrs (stirring hastens crystn).
Benzoic acid (*211*)	—	Dry powder	Lead triethanolamine	Stir small amt of synthetic into 1 drop reagent. Stir thoroly to induce crystn. 4-sided plates, singly and in groups.
	—	Dry powder	Zinc pyridine	Stir small amt of synthetic into 1 drop reagent. Stir thoroly to induce crystn. Hexagonal crystals.
	2% triethanolamine	1:100 to 1:200	Silver nitrate	Rods or curving blades with irregular ends.
Cinchophen (*214*)	0.1N NaOH Add H₂O, and make slightly acid with HCl	1:1000	Gold chloride	Dark clusters of needles. Few short, rhombic crystals.
Diallylbarbituric acid (*215*)	—	Dry powder	Lead triethanolamine	Stir small amt of synthetic into 1 drop reagent. Rods singly and in clusters.
	—	Dry powder	Barium hydroxide	Stir small amt of synthetic into 1 drop reagent. Rods singly and in groups.
Dinitrophenol (*212*)	Small amt of 0.1N NaOH	1:100	HCl	Plates with 4 branches. In more dil. soln, single rectangular plates.

(Continued)

36.536   *Characteristics of Microchemical Tests for Synthetics—Continued*

Synthetic	Solvent	Concentration of Synthetic	Reagent	Description of Tests and Crystals
Diphenhydramine hydrochloride (Benadryl hydrochloride®) (216)	Glycerol-alcohol (1 + 1) or H_2O	Approx. 0.2 mg powder or tablet material or 1:1000	Platinic chloride	Aggregates of platy crystals form readily in glycerol-alcohol, gradually in H_2O. Plates with jagged edges, tendency to twin, forming X-shaped aggregates, hour-glass forms, and dendritic structures. First order gray polarization colors; symmetrical or parallel extinction. Plates show positive elongation.
Ethyl aminobenzoate (Benzocaine) (214)	0.1N HCl	1:100	Potassium ferrocyanide	Colorless, irregular plates and rods.
8-Hydroxyquinoline sulfate (Chinosol®, Oxyquinoline) (214)	Dissolve salt in H_2O. Dissolve free base in HCl (1 + 3), avoiding excess	1:500	Magnesia mixt.	Small, elliptical grains. Few burr-shaped crystals on standing.
Mandelic acid (215)	H_2O H_2O	1:100 1:100	Lead acetate Mercurous nitrate	Rosettes of thin, curving plates. Burr-shaped groups of needles.
Methenamine (213)	H_2O	1:500	Silicotungstic acid	Thin, transparent, rectangular crystals.
Neocinchophen (210)	HCl (1 + 3) HCl (1 + 3)	Satd soln Satd soln	Ammonium thiocyanate Platinic chloride	Rosettes of needles. (Gentle agitation by tipping slide back and forth hastens crystn.) Needles in clusters.
Pentylenetetrazol (217) (Metrazol®)	H_2O H_2O	— 1:100	Mercuric chloride (1:10) Silicotungstic acid	Rods, many almost needle-like; frequently in groups; also in radiating aggregates. Amorphous, changes to elongated prisms; also long needles.
Phenobarbital (201)	—	Approx. 1 mg powder	Ammoniacal nickel acetate	Stir to aid soln and crystn. Single rectangular crystals.
Phenazopyridine.HCl (Pyridium®; Mallophene®) (214)	Dissolve salt in H_2O. Dissolve free base in HCl (1 + 3) avoiding excess	1:1000	Ammonium thiocyanate	Small, red-brown, dense sheaves.
Pyrilamine maleate (Pyranisamine maleate) (216)	Glycerol-alcohol (1 + 1) or H_2O	1:1000 or ca 0.1 mg powder	Platinic chloride	Needles in rosette aggregates, sheaves, and singly. Needles show second order blue and green, and first order red and yellow polarization colors; parallel extinction and negative elongation.
Salicylic acid (211)	HCl (1 + 3) — 2% triethanolamine	Dry powder Dry powder 1:100 to 1:200	Bromide-bromate soln Lead triethanolamine Silver nitrate	Stir few crystals into 1 drop of the HCl. Add 1 drop reagent. Fine needles appear to grow from the crystals of salicylic acid. Stir few crystals into 1 drop reagent. Rods or needles grow from the crystals of salicylic acid. Small, irregular plates; few short rods.
Sulfadiazine (196)	H_2O	—	Gold bromide in HCl	Red, circular masses composed of fine needles.
Sulfanilamide (215)	— 0.1N NCl	Dry powder Satd soln	Benzaldehyde Sodium nitrite	Thoroly stir small quantity into 1 drop reagent. 4-sided plates. Yellow needles.
Sulfapyridine (199)	Acetone + H_2O	—	Gold chloride	Yellow rods or blades; also X-shaped aggregates.

(Continued)

36.536   *Characteristics of Microchemical Tests for Synthetics—Continued*

Synthetic	Solvent	Concentration of Synthetic	Reagent	Description of Tests and Crystals
Sodium sulfapyridine monohydrate (199)	H₂O	1:100	Gold chloride	Yellow rods in X-shaped aggregates.
Sulfathiazole (217)	50% alcohol	—	Picric acid	Long, fine, yellow needles, many curved, occur in dense rosettes; also short, stout rods in groups or singly.
	50% alcohol (or no solv.)	—	Picrolonic acid	Distinct rosettes of very fine needles; also single needles.
Triethanolamine (213)	H₂O	1:100	Bismuth iodide	Oily globules changing to large, red, hexagonal plates and prismatic crystals.
Tripelennamine hydrochloride (Pyribenzamine hydrochloride®) (216)	Glycerol-alcohol (1 + 1) or H₂O	1:1000 or ca 0.1 mg powder or tablet material	Platinic chloride	Small needles and bladed crystals in dense rosette aggregates and singly. Needles show first order white and yellow polarization colors, parallel extinction, and pos. elongation.

For Xanthine Group Alkaloids (207)— Official First Action

36.537   Reagents

(a) *Bismuth iodide soln.*—See **36.525**(d)(2).

(b) *Gold bromide in dilute hydrochloric acid.*—Dissolve 1 g $HAuCl_4.3H_2O$ in 1.5 ml 40% HBr and add HCl (1 + 3) to make 45 ml.

(c) *Iodine-potassium iodide soln (5–14).*—Dissolve 5 g I and 14 g KI in H₂O and dil. to 100 ml with H₂O.

36.538   General Test

(Murexide reaction)

To small amt of substance in small porcelain crucible add very small crystal KClO₃ and 1 drop HCl (1 + 1). Set on hot plate at ca 100°, or hot enough to boil off H₂O in short time. Soon after drying, residue becomes orange to red. Add 1 drop NH₄OH. Purple color is produced in presence of caffeine, theobromine, theophylline, and related xanthine derivatives.

36.539   Identification

(a) *Bismuth iodide soln.*—Add 1 drop reagent to little dry material on slide and cover.

(b) *Gold bromide in dilute hydrochloric acid.*—Place 1 drop reagent beside very small amt of dry substance on slide and apply cover glass so that reagent flows over substance.

(c) *Iodine-potassium iodide soln (5–14).*—In depression of cavity slide dissolve little of substance in small drop 1% NaOH soln and stir in excess NaHCO₃ (some undissolved). Add large drop reagent and stir slightly. Add several crystals KCl. Examine center and edge as soln evaps.

36.540

See page 718.

Optical-Crystallographic Examination of Crystalline Substances (218)—Official Final Action

(General knowledge of microscopy and crystallography is necessary for application of this technic. Some of std works on this subject are listed in Selected References (218). Optical-crystallographic properties of antihistamines, alkaloids, antibiotics, barbiturates, hallucinogens, steroids, sulfonamides, sympathomimetic amines and tranquilizers are given in Tables **47.027** and **47.028**.

36.541   Apparatus

(a) *Polarizing microscope.*—Fitted with polarizing prisms below and above rotating, graduated circular stage and with accessories (Bertrand lens or pinhole eyepiece, first order red or quartz wedge compensators) for observation of interference figures, optic sign, and sign of elongation.

(b) *Refractometer.*—For measuring refractive indices of liqs at 20° from 1.300 to 1.840 with accuracy of ±0.0005.

36.542   Reagents

Immersion media.—Ideally immersion media for refractive index detn should have same color and intensity of color as substance being examined and be chemically stable. Refractive indices should not vary perceptibly with ordinary changes of temp. with exception of special liqs used in index-variation methods. Permanent set of liqs covering range 1.430–1.790 in 0.005 intervals made with following mixts is useful for both inorg. and org. substances:

Mixture	n_D
Kerosene and mineral oil	1.435–1.480
Mineral oil and α-monochloronaphthalene	1.485–1.640
α-Monochloronaphthalene and methylene iodide	1.645–1.740
Methylene iodide and sulfur	1.740–1.790

Substances sol. in these liqs require prepg special set of liqs.

36.540   *Characteristics of Microchemical Tests for Xanthine Alkaloids*

Alkaloid	Reagent	Description of Crystals
Caffeine	Gold bromide in dil. HCl	Outer part: brownish needles with bright white birefringence. Inside part: small rods to sticks, little grains and plates with weak yellow birefringence.
	Bismuth iodide	Small brownish-orange rods or blades growing from sample or nearby in rosettes; also some orange grains.
	Iodine-potassium iodide (5–14)	Grains, dark red to black, sometimes yellow or orange-brown; generally square or cubical; birefringent with fairly strong light; some irregular dichroic blades.
Dyphylline	Gold bromide in dil. HCl	Needles, scattered and in rosettes; fairly bright birefringence.
	Bismuth iodide	Very small grains, flakes, blades in multitudes, birefringent.
	Iodine-potassium iodide (5–14)	Fuzzy brown dense rosettes thruout drop, birefringent around rims; excess reagent must be used; 5 min required to form crystals.
Theobromine	Gold bromide in dil. HCl	Grains or plates in dense groups; bright birefringence at edge of cluster.
	Bismuth iodide	Brown needles in rosettes.
	Iodine-potassium iodide (5–14)	Orange-brown chips; also rectangular plates with opposite sides incised; smaller crystals: grains, often lens shaped or diamonds; birefringent, somewhat dichroic.
Theophylline	Gold bromide in dil. HCl	Long needles in sheaves; fairly bright birefringence.
	Bismuth iodide	Grains and short prisms, often rectangular; brightly birefringent.
	Iodine-potassium iodide (5–14)	Black needles in rosettes around edge; birefringent; when larger, blades or rods, dichroic black vertically to yellow horizontally.

36.543   *Determinations*

Refractive indices.—Det. refractive indices by mounting cryst. material in suitable immersion liqs and observing Becke line. Successively suspend crystals or crystal fragments of substance in immersion liqs of known refractive indices. Greater the difference between refractive indices of crystal and liq., the more prominently one stands out in bold relief from other. By repeatedly mounting such crystals in oils of successively lower or higher index, ultimately zone of contact of crystal and liq. becomes practically invisible, demonstrating that refractive indices of liq. and solid have been matched.

In case of substances crystg in isometric (cubic) system, there is only 1 refractive index, designated by n. Such substances are not doubly refractive when examined with crossed nicols. Substances crystg in other systems, hexagonal, tetragonal, monoclinic, triclinic, and orthorhombic, in ideal cases, have more than 1 measureable refractive index. With uniaxial substances such as those crystg in hexagonal and tetragonal systems, 2 significant indices can be detd, designated as n_ϵ and n_ω. Substances crystg in monoclinic, triclinic, and orthorhombic systems, in ideal cases, have 3 refractive indices, designated as n_α, n_β, and n_γ.

Extinction and extinction angle of anisotropic substances.—Anisotropic crystals, when rotated through 360° on stage, become dark 4 times. Positions of darkness are known as extinction positions and correspond to positions in which vibrations of birefringent rays produced by crystal are mutually parallel to vibration directions of polarizer and analyzer indicated by cross hairs in eyepiece. If crystal extinguishes when crystal edge or face is parallel to one of cross hairs, extinction is *parallel*. If bisector of silhouette angle is parallel to one of cross hairs, extinction is *symmetrical*. Crystals showing extinction differing from these 2 have *inclined* extinction. Measure extinction angles on those crystals showing inclined extinction by rotating crystal so that crystal edge or face is parallel to 1 of cross hairs. Rotate stage until crystal extinguishes. Read on stage vernier extinction angle between face or edge at extinction and nearest cross hair. Express extinction angles with relationship to principal vibration directions of light and crystallographic axes.

Elongation.—Many crystals are frequently elongated in 1 direction. Relationship between direction of elongation and vibration directions of slow and fast rays of anisotropic crystal is sometimes of determinative value. If substance is length slow, *i.e.*, slow ray or higher refractive index is parallel to direction of elongation, sign of elongation is pos.; if substance is length fast, sign is neg.

Sign of elongation (+ or −) is detd with gypsum plate and crossed nicols. A long and narrow crystal, showing very little color with crossed nicols, is so oriented that its long dimension is parallel to direction "z" of plate (slow ray) which is inserted in slit of microscope tube. (Direction "z" is indicated by arrow on plate.) If crystal appears blue or other color of higher order than red-violet due to plate, elongation is +; if crystal appears yellow, white, or gray, *i.e.*, of lower order color than red-violet field, elongation is −.

Optic character and optic sign.—Det. optic character (uniaxial or biaxial) and optic sign (+ or —), using first order red or quartz wedge compensators in conjunction with interference figures. Obtain interference figures from conoscopic images of crystals suitably oriented. In absence of interference figures, det. these properties from relationship of principal refractive indices. When $(n_\beta - n_\alpha)$ is $< (n_\gamma - n_\beta)$, optic sign is +. When $(n_\beta - n_\alpha)$ is $> (n_\gamma - n_\beta)$, optic sign is —.

Optic axial angle (2V).—Calc. axial angle (2V) from values of 3 refractive indices (here designated α, β, and γ) according to formulas:

$$\text{Cos}^2\, V_\alpha = \frac{\gamma^2(\beta^2 - \alpha^2)}{\beta^2(\gamma^2 - \alpha^2)} \text{ (for } - \text{ optic sign), or}$$

$$\text{Cos}^2\, V_\gamma = \frac{\alpha^2(\gamma^2 - \beta^2)}{\beta^2(\gamma^2 - \alpha^2)} \text{ (for } + \text{ optic sign),}$$

where $2V_\alpha$ is axial angle about α, and $2V_\gamma$ is axial angle about γ. Alternatively, est. approx. value of 2V from curvature of isogyre referring to diagrams of substances with known angles. Angle ranges from small (0–25°, sharply curved) to medium (26–60°, moderately curved) to large (61–90°, nearly straight isogyre).

SELECTED REFERENCES

(1) JAOAC 10, 99(1927).

(2) JAOAC 25, 839(1942).

(3) JAOAC 44, 293(1961).

(4) JAOAC 44, 285(1961).

(5) JAOAC 42, 459(1959); 48, 607(1965).

(6) JAOAC 5, 154, 573(1921–1922); 7, 6(1923–(1924).

(7) JAOAC 50, 655(1967); 51, 494(1968).

(8) JAOAC 51, 1315(1968); 53, 603(1970).

(9) JAOAC 15, 402(1932).

(10) JAOAC 37, 685(1954).

(11) JAOAC 52, 507(1969).

(12) JAOAC 37, 685(1954).

(13) JAOAC 41, 504(1958).

(14) JAOAC 15, 83, 442(1932).

(15) JAOAC 51, 612(1968).

(16) JAOAC 51, 624(1968).

(17) JAOAC 25, 537(1942); 32, 548(1949); 33, 206(1950).

(18) JAOAC 12, 290(1929); 13, 329(1930); 14, 327(1931).

(19) JAOAC 14, 327(1931).

(20) JAOAC 30, 467(1947); 31, 528(1948).

(21) JAOAC 52, 854(1969); 53, 847(1970).

(22) JAOAC 43, 224(1960); 46, 634(1963).

(23) JAOAC 44, 288(1961).

(24) JAOAC 10, 359(1927); 11, 339(1928).

(25) JAOAC 51, 1318(1968).

(26) JAOAC 28, 711(1945); 31, 540(1948).

(27) JAOAC 42, 466(1959).

(28) JAOAC 25, 814(1942); 28, 686(1945).

(29) JAOAC 39, 639(1956).

(30) JAOAC 30, 476(1947).

(31) JAOAC 48, 579(1965).

(32) J. Pharm Sci. 52, 802(1963); JAOAC 52, 500(1969).

(33) JAOAC 53, 120(1970).

(34) JAOAC 48, 594(1965).

(35) JAOAC 40, 824(1957); 49, 237(1966).

(36) JAOAC 41, 499(1958).

(37) JAOAC 41, 509(1958).

(38) JAOAC 31, 526(1948); 32, 530(1949).

(39) JAOAC 5, 163, 589(1922).

(40) JAOAC 23, 776(1940).

(41) JAOAC 27, 354(1944); 31, 538(1948).

(42) JAOAC 53, 117(1970).

(43) JAOAC 25, 524(1942); 26, 238(1943).

(44) JAOAC 30, 464(1947).

(45) JAOAC 42, 455(1959).

(46) JAOAC 45, 595(1962).

(47) JAOAC 41, 488(1958).

(48) JAOAC 52, 113(1969).

(49) J. Am. Pharm. Assoc., Sci. Ed. 45, 708(1956); JAOAC 40, 64(1957).

(50) JAOAC 44, 303(1961).

(51) JAOAC 3, 379(1920); 4, 573(1921).

(52) JAOAC 19, 534(1936).

(53) JAOAC 21, 555(1938); 22, 729(1939).

(54) JAOAC 20, 577, 631(1937).

(55) JAOAC 53, 591(1970).

(56) JAOAC 2, 66(1916).

(57) JAOAC 2, 59(1916).

(58) JAOAC 2, 72(1916).

(59) JAOAC 2, 73(1916).

(60) JAOAC 2, 70(1916).

(61) JAOAC 8, 506(1925).

(62) JAOAC 22, 723(1939).

(63) JAOAC 43, 241(1960).

(64) JAOAC 23, 752(1940).

(65) JAOAC 24, 809(1941).

(66) JAOAC 25, 809(1942).

(67) JAOAC 2, 63(1916).

(68) JAOAC 2, 69(1916).

(69) JAOAC 5, 582(1922).

(70) JAOAC 8, 499(1925); 9, 278(1926).

(71) JAOAC 5, 583(1922).

(72) JAOAC 38, 635(1955).

(73) JAOAC 21, 560(1938); 22, 732(1939).

(74) JAOAC 7, 29(1923); 8, 40(1924); 8, 544 (1925).

(75) JAOAC 11, 51, 350(1928); 23, 60, 742(1940).

(76) JAOAC 41, 495(1958).

(77) JAOAC 2, 64(1916).

(78) JAOAC 21, 554(1938).

(79) JAOAC 20, 589(1937).

(80) JAOAC 13, 344(1930).

(81) JAOAC 43, 248(1960).

(82) JAOAC 46, 646(1963).

(83) JAOAC 48, 613(1965).

(84) J. Am. Pharm. Assoc., Sci. Ed. 35, 176 (1946); 39, 37, 544(1950); 42, 167(1953); JAOAC 34, 581(1951); 37, 702(1954).

(85) J. Pharm. Sci. 50, 550(1961); JAOAC 44, 317(1961).
(86) JAOAC 8, 48, 510(1924–1925); 25, 799 (1942); 26, 101(1943).
(87) JAOAC 19, 508(1936).
(88) JAOAC 38, 630(1955).
(89) JAOAC 38, 624 (1955).
(90) JAOAC 48, 582(1965).
(91) JAOAC 32, 533(1949); 34, 566(1951).
(92) JAOAC 51, 621(1968).
(93) JAOAC 34, 570(1951).
(94) JAOAC 51, 626(1968).
(95) JAOAC 27, 357(1944); 28, 708(1945).
(96) JAOAC 15, 426(1932); 16, 366(1933).
(97) JAOAC 10, 343(1927).
(98) JAOAC 11, 326(1928).
(99) JAOAC 9, 286(1926).
(100) JAOAC 15, 422(1932).
(101) JAOAC 42, 470(1959); 46, 150, 649(1963).
(102) JAOAC 49, 287(1966); 50, 787(1967).
(103) JAOAC 15, 456, 461(1932); 16, 379(1933); 17, 425(1934).
(104) JAOAC 32, 558(1949).
(105) JAOAC 21, 571(1938).
(106) JAOAC 24, 842(1941); 25, 847(1942).
(107) JAOAC 18, 525(1935); 19, 516(1936); 20, 555(1937); 21, 529(1938); 22, 712(1939).
(108) JAOAC 15, 419(1932); 32, 555(1949).
(109) JAOAC 24, 833(1941).
(110) JAOAC 40, 819(1957).
(111) JAOAC 17, 75, 432(1934).
(112) JAOAC 14, 312(1931).
(113) JAOAC 10, 367(1927); 11, 343(1928); 12, 280(1929).
(114) JAOAC 12, 280(1929).
(115) JAOAC 18, 520(1935).
(116) JAOAC 22, 743(1939).
(117) JAOAC 38, 651(1955).
(118) JAOAC 8, 551(1925); 9, 312(1926); 10, 374 (1927).
(119) JAOAC 50, 680(1967); 53, 382(1970).
(120) JAOAC 19, 535(1936); 21, 557(1938); 22, 730(1939).
(121) JAOAC 50, 669(1967).
(122) JAOAC 12, 264(1929); 14, 360(1931); 22, 761(1939).
(123) JAOAC 45, 616(1962).
(124) JAOAC 22, 739(1939).
(125) JAOAC 53, 834(1970).
(126) JAOAC 11, 360(1928); 12, 288(1929); 13, 326(1930); 16, 348(1933); 17, 440(1934); 18, 532(1935).
(127) JAOAC 28, 706(1945).
(128) JAOAC 14, 370(1931).
(129) JAOAC 15, 434(1932).
(130) JAOAC 15, 441(1932).
(131) JAOAC 22, 757(1939).
(132) JAOAC 41, 493(1958).
(133) JAOAC 51, 616(1968).
(134) JAOAC 3, 374(1920).
(135) JAOAC 43, 239(1960); 44, 152(1961).
(136) JAOAC 50, 674(1967).
(137) JAOAC 7, 20(1923).
(138) JAOAC 43, 259(1960).
(139) JAOAC 9, 316(1926); 10, 376(1927); 15, 140(1932); 20, 569(1937); 21, 541(1938).
(140) JAOAC 47, 469(1964).
(141) JAOAC 53, 594(1970).
(142) JAOAC 51, 631(1968).
(143) JAOAC 21, 552(1938).
(144) JAOAC 49, 857(1966); 50, 682(1967); 51, 273(1968).
(145) JAOAC 44, 312(1961).
(146) JAOAC 48, 590(1965).
(147) JAOAC 36, 734(1953).
(148) JAOAC 35, 572(1952).
(149) JAOAC 52, 111(1969).
(150) JAOAC 17, 451(1934); 18, 519(1935).
(151) JAOAC 31, 544(1948).
(152) JAOAC 32, 549(1949).
(153) JAOAC 10, 383(1927); 11, 362(1928).
(154) JAOAC 41, 496(1958).
(155) JAOAC 28, 723(1945); 31, 558(1948).
(156) JAOAC 50, 666(1967).
(157) JAOAC 18, 464(1935); 20, 592(1937).
(158) JAOAC 21, 543(1938); 22, 721(1939).
(159) JAOAC 16, 384(1933); 20, 564(1937).
(160) JAOAC 28, 699(1945); 29, 280(1946).
(161) JAOAC 31, 547(1948); 33, 203(1950).
(162) JAOAC 25, 843(1942); 26, 311(1943).
(163) JAOAC 7, 14(1923–1924).
(164) JAOAC 13, 364(1930); 14, 351(1931); 16, 364(1933).
(165) JAOAC 12, 296(1929); 14, 330(1931).
(166) JAOAC 13, 332(1930); 14, 330(1931); 15, 418(1932).
(167) JAOAC 47, 194, 474(1964).
(168) JAOAC 37, 697(1954).
(169) JAOAC 22, 748(1939).
(170) JAOAC 15, 407(1932).
(171) JAOAC 9, 52, 288(1926).
(172) JAOAC 28, 719(1945); 31, 535(1948).
(173) JAOAC 5, 587(1922).
(174) JAOAC 14, 63, 341(1931).
(175) J. Am. Pharm. Assoc., Sci. Ed. 43, 580 (1954); JAOAC 41, 487(1958).
(176) JAOAC 42, 453(1959).
(177) JAOAC 20, 588(1937); 22, 726(1939).
(178) JAOAC 15, 448(1932); 16, 375(1933).
(179) JAOAC 45, 597(1962).
(180) JAOAC 12, 300(1929); 14, 337(1931).
(181) JAOAC 16, 375(1933); 18, 555(1935).
(182) JAOAC 35, 566(1952); 36, 85, 699(1953).
(183) JAOAC 14, 321(1931).
(184) J. Pharm. Chim. 8th ser. 16, 49(1932); JAOAC 18, 526(1935).
(185) JAOAC 45, 593(1962).
(186) JAOAC 48, 592(1965).

(*187*) Quart. J. Pharmacol. **5**, 369(1932); JAOAC **18**, 526(1935); **19**, 517(1936).
(*188*) USDA Bur. Chem. Circ. **94**, p. 4; J. Ind. Eng. Chem. **4**, 374(1912); JAOAC **2**, 74 (1919).
(*189*) JAOAC **15**, 413(1932).
(*190*) JAOAC **23**, 746(1940).
(*191*) JAOAC **20**, 551(1937); **21**, 91(1938).
(*192*) JAOAC **11**, 353(1928); **14**, 316(1931); **18**, 521(1935).
(*193*) JAOAC **21**, 525(1938).
(*194*) JAOAC **22**, 706(1939).
(*195*) JAOAC **13**, 315(1930).
(*196*) JAOAC **26**, 96(1943).
(*197*) JAOAC **12**, 282(1929).
(*198*) JAOAC **10**, 370(1927); **11**, 353(1928).
(*199*) JAOAC **24**, 830(1941).
(*200*) JAOAC **14**, 316(1931).
(*201*) JAOAC **20**, 553(1937).
(*202*) JAOAC **5**, 154(1921); **10**, 370(1927).
(*203*) JAOAC **18**, 521(1935).
(*204*) JAOAC **16**, 345(1933).
(*205*) JAOAC **17**, 433(1934).
(*206*) JAOAC **23**, 746(1940); **24**, 830(1941).
(*207*) JAOAC **43**, 262(1960).
(*208*) JAOAC **11**, 353(1928).
(*209*) JAOAC **45**, 600(1962).
(*210*) JAOAC **19**, 514(1936).
(*211*) JAOAC **21**, 528(1938).
(*212*) JAOAC **18**, 523(1935).
(*213*) JAOAC **17**, 435(1934).
(*214*) JAOAC **16**, 391(1933).
(*215*) JAOAC **22**, 709(1939).
(*216*) JAOAC **35**, 576(1952).
(*217*) JAOAC **25**, 830(1942).
(*218*) Stewart and Stolman, editors, "Toxicology, Mechanisms and Analytical Methods," Vol. 1, pp. 660–713(1960); Hartshorne and Stuart, "Crystals and the Polarizing Microscope," 3rd ed., 1960; Chamot and Mason, "Handbook of Chemical Microscopy," Vol. 1, 1958; NF XIII, First Supplement; Bloss, "Introduction to the Methods of Optical Crystallography," 1961; Wahlstrom, "Optical Crystallography," 1969.

GENERAL REFERENCE

Banes, "Principles of Regulatory Drug Analysis," AOAC, Box 540 Benjamin Franklin Station, Washington, DC 20044 (1966).

37. Drugs and Feed Additives in Animal Tissues

ANOT (3-Amino-5-Nitro-o-Toluamide)
(1)—Official Final Action

37.001   *Principles*

ANOT, metabolite of zoalene, is liberated from ground tissue by enzymatic digestion with ficin. Digest is treated with $NaHCO_3$ and extd with acetone. $CHCl_3$ is added to sep. soln into 2 layers. Org. layer is concd and passed thru alumina column. Adsorbed ANOT is washed with $CHCl_3$ and eluted with 80% alcohol. Alcohol soln is passed thru cation exchange resin and ANOT is eluted with $4N$ HCl. Colored compd formed by diazotization and coupling with N-1-naphthylethylenediamine is measured at 540 nm.

37.002   *Apparatus*

(a) *Chromatographic tube.*—16 mm id × 600 mm.

(b) *Ion exchange columns for Dowex resin.*—11 mm id × 180 mm.

(c) *Multi-Mixer.*—Lourdes Model MM (Lourdes Instrument Corp., 148 Sweet Hollow Rd, Old Bethpage, NY 11804), or equiv.

(d) *Spectrophotometer.* — Beckman Instruments Model DU or equiv.

37.003   *Reagents*

(a) *Alumina.*—Activated, Alcoa grade F-20, 80–200 mesh.

(b) *3-Amino-5-nitro-o-toluamide.* — ANOT, analytical std. Available from Agricultural Dept., Dow Chemical Co.

(c) *Ammonium sulfamate soln.*—1.0%. Prep. fresh weekly.

(d) *Coupling reagent.*—0.25% aq. soln of N-1-naphthylethylenediamine.2HCl. Prep. fresh weekly and store in dark bottle.

(e) *Dowex 50W-X8 cation exchange resin.*—Hydrogen form, 200–400 mesh. J. T. Baker Chemical Co.

(f) *Ficin.*—Nutritional Biochemicals Corp. (*Caution:* Ficin is potent proteolytic enzyme which attacks living tissues. Avoid contact with skin and eyes and breathing dust.)

(g) *Sodium nitrite soln.*—0.25%. Prep. fresh daily.

37.004   *Preparation of Alumina Column*

Insert small plug of glass wool into chromatgc tube and compress in lower end of tube. Add 60 g alumina and pack by gently tapping tube on rubber stopper to ht of ca 30 cm. Add 100 ml $CHCl_3$ and drain to just above level of alumina. Do not drain $CHCl_3$ below level of alumina.

37.005   *Preparation of Ion Exchange Column*

Heat 100 g Dowex 50W-X8 on steam bath with 400 ml $6N$ HCl 2–3 hr. Filter on buchner and wash with H_2O until washings are acid-free. Wash resin with 100 ml 80% alcohol. Then mix resin with 250 ml 80% alcohol. Pour enough resin slurry into ion exchange column to give bed ht of ca 5 cm after settling. Wash resin with 25 ml 80% alcohol. Slight air pressure can be used to increase flow of liq. thru resin. Do not let liq. level drain below top of resin bed.

37.006   *Preparation of Standard Curve*

Accurately weigh 100 mg ANOT into 1 L vol. flask, dissolve in 50 ml acetone, and dil. to vol. with H_2O. Dil. 10 ml of this stock soln to 100 ml with H_2O to give working soln of 10 µg/ml. Pipet 0, 2, 4, 6, 8, and 10 ml aliquots of this soln into sep. 50 ml vol. flasks. Dil. each to ca 40 ml with $4N$ HCl. Proceed as in **37.007**, beginning "Add 1 ml 0.25% $NaNO_2$ ..." Plot A at 540 nm against µg ANOT.

37.007   *Determination*
(*Caution: See* **46.011, 46.040,** *and* **46.056.**)

Collect tissue, freeze with solid CO_2, and keep frozen until analyzed. Grind tissue while at least partially frozen and weigh 50 g into 1 qt Mason jar. Add 125 ml H_2O, 15 ml $1N$ HCl, and 5 g ficin, and mix with Multi-Mixer ca 5 min. Cover jar loosely and keep 24 hr at 30°. Then keep 30 min in bath at 70–80°, remove, and cool.

Weigh ca 10 g $NaHCO_3$ and slowly add to jar with stirring, taking care that sample does not foam over top of jar. When foaming has subsided, add 500 ml acetone and mix with Multi-Mixer 5 min.

Filter on buchner into 1 L filter flask, using 11 cm paper and ca 5 g Super-Cel as filter pad. Wash residue with 200 ml acetone, collecting washings in same flask. Transfer filtrate to 2 L separator and add 1 L $CHCl_3$. Shake ext in separator vigorously and let stand until layers sep. Drain $CHCl_3$ layer into 2 L beaker. Ext aq. layer with 200 ml $CHCl_3$ and combine $CHCl_3$ washing with original ext. Evap. $CHCl_3$ ext to ca 50 ml under heat lamp with air current. Add 100 ml $CHCl_3$ and again evap. to 50 ml. If soln is not clear, repeat addn and evapn of $CHCl_3$ to remove H_2O.

Add clear $CHCl_3$ soln to alumina column and drain to level of alumina. Wash with four 50 ml portions $CHCl_3$. Discard washings. Add 90 ml 80% alcohol to column to elute ANOT. Discard first 30 ml effluent and collect 60 ml in 100 ml beaker. Transfer this soln to column of Dowex 50W-X8. Slight air pressure may be used to increase flow of soln. After soln has drained to top of resin level, wash with 50 ml 80% alcohol followed by 50 ml H_2O. Discard washings. Add 45 ml $4N$ HCl and collect effluent in 50 ml vol. flask.

Add 1 ml 0.25% $NaNO_2$, mix, and let stand 5 min. Add 1 ml 1% NH_4 sulfamate, mix, and let stand 5 min. Add 1 ml coupling reagent, mix, dil. to vol. with $4N$ HCl, and mix thoroly. Let stand 15 min and read A at 540 nm, using 1 cm cells, against H_2O as ref.

37.008 Calculations

Correct A value of treated sample by subtracting av. A for untreated samples which are obtained from poultry not fed zoalene. Obtain μg of ANOT corresponding to corrected A from std curve.

ppm ANOT in sample = μg ANOT/g sample.

Ethoxyquin (1,2-Dihydro-6-ethoxy-2,2,4-trimethylquinoline) (2)—Official First Action

(Applicable to chicken tissues and eggs)

37.009 Apparatus

(a) *Photofluorometer.—(Caution: See 46.008.)* Instrument with primary filter passing only 365 nm Hg line and secondary filter passing light between 410 and 580 nm (but not below 410 nm). Photovolt Corp., 1115 Broadway, New York, NY 10010, Model 540 with BHgl primary filter and B470 secondary filter is suitable.

(b) *Separators.*—250 ml with Teflon stopcocks.

37.010 Reagents

(a) *Isooctane.*—Fluorescence <2% that of soln contg 0.020 μg quinine sulfate/ml $0.1N$ H_2SO_4. If necessary, purify isooctane by passing thru 30 × 2 cm activated alumina column.

(b) *Sulfuric acid-sodium sulfate soln.* — $0.3N$ H_2SO_4 contg 2% Na_2SO_4.

(c) *Ethoxyquin std solns.*—(1) *Stock soln.*—10 μg/ml. Place 10 mg com. grade ethoxyquin in 1 L vol. flask; dissolve and dil. to vol. with isooctane. Store in refrigerator. (2) *Working std solns.*—0.010, 0.020, 0.030, and 0.050 μg/ml. Transfer 1, 2, 3, and 5 ml aliquots stock soln to 1 L vol. flasks and dil. to vol. with isooctane. Prep. fresh on day of use.

37.011 Preparation of Standard Curve

Prep. std curve at time of analysis of final ethoxyquin exts. Read ethoxyquin stds with photofluorometer set at 0 with shutters closed and at 100 with most concd std. Plot instrument reading against μg ethoxyquin on linear graph paper.

37.012 Preparation of Sample and Extraction

All glassware must be free of stopcock grease.

(a) *Egg yolk.*—Carefully break egg to avoid rupturing yolk and sep. as much of egg white from yolk

as possible. Wash yolk in running H_2O to remove most of remaining egg white. Dry yolk on absorbent paper, break yolk sac, pour yolk into bottle, and stopper.

Weigh bottle contg yolk and pour ca 5 g yolk into mortar contg 25 g anhyd. granular Na_2SO_4 and 3 g anhyd. powd Na_2CO_3. Reweigh bottle and record wt yolk added. (Several samples may be prepd from same yolk.) Grind mixt. in mortar until uniform and dry 1 hr in desiccator contg Drierite.

Transfer dried mixt. to 4 oz screw-cap bottle and shake 30 min with 50 ml isooctane. Centrf. and filter supernatant thru Whatman No. 1 paper into 250 ml separator. Repeat extn with second 50 ml isooctane and add ext to separator.

Gently shake isooctane ext 1 min each with two 50 ml portions $0.3N$ H_2SO_4-Na_2SO_4 soln. Combine acid exts and add 10 ml $6N$ NaOH. Ext alk. soln with two 50 ml portions isooctane. Combine isooctane exts and dry 15 min over anhyd. Na_2SO_4; decant, and dil. to 100 ml with isooctane.

(b) *Tissue (muscle and liver).*—Accurately weigh ca 5 g muscle or 1 g liver and add to 15 g anhyd. Na_2SO_4 and 2 g anhyd. Na_2CO_3 in mortar. Grind until uniform and place in desiccator 1 hr.

Shake dried mixt. 30 min in 4 oz screw-cap bottle with 100 ml isooctane. Centrf., and filter into 250 ml separator. Continue as in (a), 4th par., beginning "Gently shake isooctane ext. . . ."

(c) *Fat.*—Accurately weigh ca 1 g frozen fat and add to 10 g granular, anhyd. Na_2SO_4 and 1 g anhyd. Na_2CO_3 in *glass* mortar. Grind mixt. thoroly. Add 20 ml isooctane and continue grinding several min. Decant isooctane into 4 oz screw-cap bottle. Repeat grinding with isooctane 3 times. Transfer isooctane ext to bottle, shake, and centrf.

Decant supernatant isooctane layer to 250 ml seprator and continue as in (a), 4th par., beginning "Gently shake isooctane ext. . . ."

37.013 Determination

Det. fluorescence of isooctane soln and calc. ethoxyquin content from std curve.

ppm Ethoxyquin = (μg/ml ethoxyquin) × (ml ext/g sample).

Nalidixic Acid (3)—Official First Action

(Applicable to chicken liver and muscle contg ≥100 ppb nalidixic acid)

37.014 Principle

Nalidixic acid is extd from aq. tissue homogenate with EtOAc. EtOAc is collected, concd, and passed thru Al_2O_3 column which retains nalidixic acid. Nalidixic acid is removed from column with borate buffer, acidified, and re-extd with $CHCl_3$. After $CHCl_3$ removal, residual nalidixic acid is made to fluoresce with H_2SO_4 and resultant fluorescence is measured with spectrofluorometer.

37.015 *Apparatus*

(a) *Spectrofluorometer.*—(*Caution: See* **46.008.**) Aminco-Bowman 4-8202, or equiv., with Xe lamp, IP 28 photomultiplier tube, and operated with manufacturer's slit arrangement No. 3. Precise wavelength settings for excitation and emission may vary slightly between instruments. Det. optimal wavelengths (ca 325 and 408 nm) after evapn of 2 ml working std soln (1 μg nalidixic acid) and soln of residue in 10 ml 21.5N H_2SO_4.

(b) *Chromatographic tubes.* — 11.5 $\times$ 160 mm (Kontes Glass Co. No. K-420000, or equiv.).

(c) *Shaker.* — Reciprocating (Sargent-Welch Scientific Co., No. S-74060, or equiv.).

37.016 *Reagents*

(a) *Phosphate buffer soln.*—pH 6.0. Weigh 28 g $NaH_2PO_4.H_2O$ into 1 L beaker, add ca 600 ml H_2O, and adjust pH electrometrically with aq. NaOH. Dil. to 1 L.

(b) *Borate buffer soln.*—pH 10.0. Dissolve 30 g H_3BO_3 in ca 600 ml H_2O and adjust pH electrometrically with aq. NaOH. Dil. to 1 L.

(c) *Dilute sulfuric acid.*—(*Caution: See* **46.030.**) (*1*) *21.5N.*—Measure 200 ml H_2O into 1 L flask and add gradually, with cooling, 300 ml H_2SO_4. Use soln at room temp. (*2*) *7N.*—Dil. 1 vol. (*1*) with 2 vols H_2O.

(d) *Alumina.*—Neut. (Fisher Scientific Co., No. A-950, or equiv.).

(e) *Nalidixic acid std solns.*—(*1*) *Stock soln.*—500 μg/ml. Dissolve 50.0 mg nalidixic acid (available from Sterling Winthrop Research Institute, Rensselaer, NY 12144) in 100 ml MeOH. (*2*) *Intermediate soln.*—5.0 μg/ml. Dil. 2.0 ml stock soln to 200 ml with MeOH. (*3*) *Working soln.*—0.5 μg/ml. Dil. 10.0 ml intermediate soln to 100 ml with MeOH.

37.017 *Determination*

(*Caution: See* **46.005, 46.039, 46.056,** and **46.057.**)

Transfer 10 g chicken liver or muscle to high-speed blender. Add 100 ml phosphate buffer and blend 2–3 min. Transfer homogenate to 500 ml g-s extn bottle and add 300 ml EtOAc.

Add 100 ml phosphate buffer to each of five 500 ml g-s extn bottles. Transfer 0, 1.0, 2.0, 3.0, and 4.0 ml working soln contg 0.0, 0.50, 1.0, 1.5, and 2.0 μg nalidixic acid, resp. Add 300 ml EtOAc to each. Mech. shake all bottles contg sample and std 10–15 min and centrf. ca 5 min at 2500 rpm. Withdraw 250 ml supernatant EtOAc from each and transfer to sep. 600 ml beakers. Evap. each under air current on steam bath to ca 60 ml.

Prep. adsorption column for sample and each std as follows: Place glass wool plug at bottom of chromatgc tube and add Al_2O_3 to depth of 3 cm (ca 3 g). Place another glass wool plug at top of column. Wash each column with 25 ml EtOAc. Transfer tis-

sue and std exts from beakers to respective columns. Rinse each beaker with 25 ml EtOAc followed by two 25 ml portions ether and two 25 ml portions MeOH. Transfer each solv. rinse to corresponding column and discard all eluates.

Add two 25 ml portions borate buffer and collect eluate in 50 ml graduate. Transfer eluate from graduate to 125 ml separator with Teflon stopcock. Ext with 25 ml ether and discard ether. Acidify aq. soln with 10 ml 7N H_2SO_4. Thoroly ext with 25 ml and 10 ml $CHCl_3$. Withdraw each $CHCl_3$ ext and combine in 100 ml beaker. (Do *not* introduce any aq. phase.) Evap. solv. just to dryness on steam bath.

Add 10.0 ml 21.5N H_2SO_4 to each beaker. Mix thoroly $\geq$ 10 min. Det. relative fluorescence (product of linear scale meter reading and meter multiplier setting) of processed blank, stds, and tissue sample in 1 cm cell at excitation 325 nm and emission 408 nm. Subtract relative fluorescence of reagent blank from relative fluorescence of all std and sample prepns.

Prep. std curve with reagent blank-corrected relative fluorescence values of processed stds as ordinate and corresponding μg nalidixic acid as abscissa. From std curve, det. amt nalidixic acid (x) which corresponds to reagent blank-corrected relative fluorescence of processed tissue sample.

$$\text{ppb Nalidixic acid} = (x \times 1000)/10 \text{ g (tissue wt)}$$

Zoalene (3,5-Dinitro-*o*-toluamide) (*1*)— Official Final Action

37.018 *Principles*

Ground tissue is extd with acetone, and benzene added to sep. soln into 2 layers. Org. layer is concd, and passed thru alumina column. Adsorbed zoalene is washed with $CHCl_3$ and eluted with 80% alcohol. Alc. soln is evapd just to dryness and residue dissolved in alc. DMF soln. Colored complex formed by addn of 1,3-diaminopropane is measured at 560 nm.

37.019 *Apparatus*

See **37.002**(a), (b), and (d).

37.020 *Reagents*

(a) *Acetone-benzene soln.*—Mix 35 parts acetone with 65 parts benzene.

(b) *Alumina.*—See **37.003**(a).

(c) *1,3-Diaminopropane.*—Union Carbide Corp.

(d) *Dimethylformamide-alcohol soln.*—Mix 4 parts DMF with 1 part absolute ethanol.

(e) *Zoalene.*—Analytical std. (Available from Agricultural Dept., Dow Chemical Co.)

37.021 *Preparation of Alumina Column*

See **37.004.**

37.022 *Preparation of Standard Curve*

Accurately weigh 100 mg zoalene into 1 L vol. flask, dissolve in 50 ml acetone, and dil. to vol. with H_2O. Dil. 10 ml of this stock soln to 100 ml with H_2O

to give working soln of 10 μg/ml. Pipet 0, 2, 4, 6, 8, and 10 ml aliquots working soln into sep. 100 ml beakers and evap. just to dryness under heat lamp. Add 5 ml alc. DMF soln to each beaker and stir 1–2 min. Add 5 ml 1,3-diaminopropane. After 10 min, measure A of soln at 560 nm, using 1 cm cells against H_2O as ref. Prep. std curve by plotting A against μg zoalene.

37.023   *Determination*
(*Caution: See* **46.004, 46.011, 46.039, 46.040, 46.045,** and **46.046.**)

Collect tissue, freeze with solid CO_2, and keep frozen until analyzed. Grind tissue while at least partially frozen and weigh 50 g into 1 qt Mason jar. Add 250 ml acetone and mix with Multi-Mixer ca 5 min. Filter on buchner into 1 L filter flask, using 11 cm paper and ca 5 g Super-Cel as filter pad. Wash residue with 100 ml acetone, collecting washings in same flask. Transfer filtrate to 1 L separator and add 500 ml benzene.

Shake ext in separator vigorously and let stand until layers sep. Swirl funnel and let stand again until layers sep. Drain aq. layer into 250 ml centrf. bottle. Transfer org. layer to 1 L beaker. Rinse separator with 100 ml acetone-benzene soln and add to centrf. bottle. Stopper, shake vigorously, and centrf. at ca 1700 rpm 20 min. Remove lower layer with suction tube and transfer org. layer to 1 L beaker.

Evap. to 10 ml under heat lamp with air current. Add 100 ml $CHCl_3$ and evap. to 50 ml. If soln is not clear, repeat addn and evapn of $CHCl_3$ to remove H_2O.

Add clear $CHCl_3$ soln to alumina column and drain to level of alumina. Wash with four 50 ml portions $CHCl_3$. Discard washings. Add 90 ml 80% alcohol to column to elute zoalene. Discard first 30 ml effluent and collect 60 ml in 100 ml beaker. Evap. soln under heat lamp with air current until residue no longer flows. Do not heat residue after beaker is dry.

Add 5 ml alc. DMF soln to beaker and warm with stirring to ca 45° to dissolve residue. When completely in soln, add 5 ml 1,3-diaminopropane to develop color. Filter thru small fluted paper. After 10 min, measure A of soln at 560 nm, using 1 cm cells against H_2O as ref.

37.024   *Calculations*

Correct A of treated sample by subtracting av. A for untreated samples which are obtained from poultry not fed zoalene. Obtain μg zoalene corresponding to corrected A from std curve.

ppm Zoalene in sample = μg zoalene/g sample.

SELECTED REFERENCES
(*1*) J. Agr. Food Chem. **9**, 201(1961); JAOAC **49**, 708(1966).
(*2*) JAOAC **50**, 844(1967); **51**, 453, 537(1968).
(*3*) JAOAC **53**, 464(1970).

38. Drugs in Feeds *

(Medicated feeds may deteriorate under improper storage conditions. When possible, use reasonably fresh samples, store them in the cold, and grind just before analysis.)

Total Arsenic (1)—Official Final Action

38.001 Reagents

(a) *Arsenic trioxide.*—NBS As$_2$O$_3$ Ref. Std or equiv.

(b) *Magnesium oxide-magnesium nitrate slurry.*—Suspend 75 g MgO and 105 g Mg(NO$_3$)$_2$.6H$_2$O in enough H$_2$O to make 1 L. Agitate vigorously before addn to sample. (Freshly prepd slurry gives ash which is easily disturbed by air currents.)

(c) *Stannous chloride soln.*—25.006(a). Effective as long as it discharges yellow color in sample ext.

(d) *Absorbing soln.*—Transfer with graduated cylinder 25 ml 1.5% HgCl$_2$ soln, and with pipet 3.75 ml 6N H$_2$SO$_4$ and 3.75 ml 0.03N KMnO$_4$, into 250 ml graduated cylinder. Dil. to 250 ml with H$_2$O and mix. Prep. fresh daily.

(e) *Ammonium molybdate reagent.*—Dissolve 1 g (NH$_4$)$_2$MoO$_4$ in 100 ml 5.4N H$_2$SO$_4$. Soln keeps several weeks. (Prep. 5.4N H$_2$SO$_4$ by dilg 6N (9 + 1).)

(f) *Hydrazine sulfate reagent.*—0.15%. Dissolve 0.15 g N$_2$H$_4$.H$_2$SO$_4$ in 100 ml H$_2$O. Soln keeps several weeks.

38.002 Apparatus

(Do not clean app. and glassware with detergents, as they interfere with color development. Haemo-Sol, available from Scientific Products, Inc., or equiv., is satisfactory.)

(a) *Evaporating dishes.*—70 ml capacity; Coors No. 430, size 00A, or equiv.

(b) *Arsine evolution apparatus.*—Bend 6 mm id glass tubing at 120° angle ca 4″ from one end and at 60° angle ca 6″ from other end. Plug shorter end with glass wool impregnated with satd Pb(OAc)$_2$ soln and insert in rubber stopper, placed in top of 125 ml erlenmeyer, so that end of tube projects just below stopper. Plug other end with unimpregnated glass wool and connect thru rubber tubing to glass tube, constricted at lower end, that reaches to bottom of 50 ml large neck vol. flask, or if preferred, 50 ml centrf. tube, marked exactly at 50 ml and approx. at 20 ml.

38.003 Preparation of Sample Solution

Weigh ground sample contg $\leq$50 µg As (unless aliquot is to be taken from digested soln) into 70 ml

---

ashing dish. If >2.5 g sample is used, increase amt of slurry and size of ashing dish. Add ca 10 ml well-mixed slurry, (b), and enough H$_2$O to permit thoro mixing with stirring rod. Rinse stirring rod, and dry sample at 100°. Ash 2–4 hr at 550–600°. (Slight C residue does not interfere. Use care to avoid loss of ash.)

Cool, and moisten residue with H$_2$O. Cover dish with watch glass and add ca 15 ml HCl (1 + 1). Let stand overnight, or heat on H$_2$O bath with agitation until ash dissolves. Filter thru Whatman No. 30 paper into 125 ml erlenmeyer. Rinse filter with enough hot H$_2$O, in several portions, to obtain ca 60 ml filtrate.

38.004 Preparation of Standard Curve

Dissolve 0.660 g As$_2$O$_3$ in 25 ml 10% NaOH soln, dil. to 1 L with H$_2$O, and mix. Dil. 10 ml aliquot to 1 L with H$_2$O (1 ml = 5 µg As). Transfer 0, 2, 4, 6, 8, 10, 12, and 14 ml aliquots from buret into 125 ml erlenmeyers. Dil. each to ca 60 ml with H$_2$O and proceed as in 38.005. Plot A against µg As.

38.005 Arsine Evolution

Add ca 10 ml HCl, 2 ml KI soln, 25.006(c), and 0.5 ml SnCl$_2$ soln, (c). Swirl, heat in H$_2$O bath 5 min, and cool. Have all parts of evolution app. ready for immediate assembly, with ca 20 ml absorbing soln, (d), in 50 ml vol. flask or centrf. tube marked at 50 ml. Add 5–6 g Zn, 25.006(b), to digested soln; quickly insert stopper contg glass tubing into erlenmeyer and place delivery tube against bottom of vol. flask or centrf. tube so that bubbles will be small. Use few drops of H$_2$O to test for leaks between rubber stopper and erlenmeyer. Connecting glass tube must be large enough so bubbles will not carry over Pb compds from impregnated glass wool plug into absorption flask.

38.006 Color Development

After 30 min disconnect rubber tubing, leaving delivery tube in receiving vessel so that any Hg arsenide on tube will be exposed to color-developing reagents. Add 1.0 ml NH$_4$ molybdate reagent, (e), and mix by forcing air thru delivery tube. Add 1.0 ml hydrazine sulfate reagent, (f), and again mix. Heat in boiling H$_2$O bath 20 min. Rinse delivery tube with H$_2$O and remove. Cool to room temp., dil. to 50 ml, and mix. Filter thru tight glass wool plug in funnel or centrf. (Do not use filter paper, as color will be adsorbed.) Read A against H$_2$O at 750 nm or above. Max. A is at 840 nm. Det. As content from

---

★ Methods so marked are surplus methods. *See* "Definitions of Terms and Explanatory Notes," item (29).

std curve. As × 2.90 = arsanilic acid; As × 2.24 = arsenosobenzene; As × 3.51 = 3-nitro-4-hydroxy-phenylarsonic acid; As × 3.3 = 4-nitrophenylarsonic acid; As × 3.47 = p-ureidobenzenearsonic acid.

2-Acetylamino-5-nitrothiazole (Cyzine®) (2)— Official Final Action

38.007 *Principle*

2-Acetylamino-5-nitrothiazole is extd from finished feeds by hot dimethylformamide (DMF). Aliquot of filtered ext is passed thru Al_2O_3 column. Impurities are removed by washing with DMF, and 2-acetyl-amino-5-nitrothiazole is eluted with acidified MeOH. A of yellow soln, developed by action of NaOH on compd, is detd spectrophtric at 410 nm.

38.008 *Apparatus*

(a) *Spectrophotometer.*—Beckman Instruments Model DU, or equiv.

(b) *Chromatographic tubes.*—10 (id) × 300 mm; Corning Glass Works No. 38450.

(c) *Filter grip.*—New York Laboratory Supply Co. No. 69641.

(d) *Filter disks.*—Glass fiber, 5.5 cm; Fisher Scientific Co. No. 9-873.

38.009 *Reagents*

(a) *2-Acetylamino-5-nitrothiazole.*—Purified compd available from American Cyanamid Co.

(b) *Acidified methanol.*—Add 2 ml 5N HCl to 100 ml MeOH.

(c) *Alcoholic sodium hydroxide soln.*—Add 2.5 ml 10N NaOH to 100 ml alcohol. Let stand 2 days for carbonates to settle.

(d) *Aluminum oxide.*—Alcoa F-20, for chromatgc adsorption. (Available from Fisher Scientific Co., as "Alumina, Adsorption, Fisher.") It is unsuitable for use as received and must be prepd as in **38.010(a)**.

38.010 *Preparation of Chromatographic Column*

(a) *Preparation of alumina.*—To 250 g alumina in 2 L beaker add 1.5 L H_2O, stir, let settle 10 min, and decant as much H_2O as possible. Add 1.5 L 1N HCl, stir well, and let stand ≥1 hr, stirring at 10–15 min intervals. Decant, including fines, and add 1.5 L H_2O. Stir, let settle, and decant H_2O, including fines. Continue washing and decanting to include fines with 1.5 L portions of H_2O *until pH of wash H_2O is same as that of H_2O being used for wash.* (Universal indicator paper is satisfactory for pH detn. When taking pH, H_2O should be essentially free from suspended fines.) Transfer alumina to buchner and air-dry ca 1 min, using gentle vac. Transfer alumina to wide, shallow dish and dry at 100–150° ≥16 hr, stirring several times during drying. Alumina should be free of lumps and should pour freely; if not, dry further. During drying, other materials must not be present in oven.

(b) *Preparation of column.*—Fit 0.25″ section of 0.25″ natural rubber tubing 0.5–1″ from end of stem of 75 mm glass funnel with ca 3 mm stem bore thruout length. Fit funnel into top of 10 × 300 mm chromatgc tube, forming tight seal. Fit 2″ piece of rubber tubing to end of tube and 3″ piece of tapered glass tubing or 3 mm bore glass stopcock to tubing. Control flow of liq. to ca 1 drop/sec by stopcock or pinch clamp.

Remove funnel and fill tube with DMF to ca 0.25″ above end of funnel stem after funnel is replaced. Make slurry of previously prepd alumina, using 3 vols DMF to 1 vol. alumina. Heat slurry on hot plate (do not boil) to expel adsorbed gases and cool to room temp. Prep. fresh before using; do not use slurry which has stood overnight. Swirl beaker to suspend alumina and add portions thru affixed funnel to tube until alumina is 275 mm high. After each addn, gently tap side of tube to disperse alumina evenly. Keep ca 0.5″ DMF over alumina until ready for use.

38.011 *Determination*

(*Caution: See* **46.018, 46.040,** and **46.053.**)

Weigh 20.0 g well-mixed, freshly ground feed and transfer to 250 ml beaker. To second 250 ml beaker, add 60 ml DMF from graduate, and bring to boil on hot plate under hood. Add boiling DMF to sample, boil 2 min, stirring constantly, and cool to room temp. Filter, using gentle suction, into 200 ml Kohlrausch flask by decanting thru 5.5 cm buchner fitted with glass fiber filter disk. (Adapt buchner to flask by means of filter grip.)

Repeat extn with 60 ml boiling DMF as above, transferring entire cooled contents of beaker to buchner. Rinse beaker with two 30 ml portions cold DMF, adding each to buchner. Cool flask to room temp. and dil. to vol. with DMF. Stopper and mix well.

Pipet 10 ml aliquot DMF ext thru funnel onto column and let it elute at ca 1 drop/sec. Just before ext reaches top of column, add 10 ml DMF and let it run thru. Repeat wash with two 10 ml portions DMF and discard all DMF eluates.

Pass four 10 ml portions acidified MeOH thru column to elute 2-acetylamino-5-nitrothiazole. Make each addn, including first, just before preceding one reaches top of column. Do not let column go dry at any time. Collect eluate in 50 ml g-s vol. flask until ca 2 ml of last acidified MeOH portion remains on top of column. To ca 40 ml eluate in vol. flask, add exactly 0.5 ml 5N HCl and mix. Soln should become distinctly lighter. Add MeOH to vol. and mix thoroly.

Pipet 20 ml aliquots into each of two 25 ml g-s vol. flasks. Dil. first to vol. with MeOH, stopper, and mix well (blank). To second flask add 5 ml alc. NaOH soln (sample soln). Prep. reagent blank by adding 5 ml alc. NaOH to third 25 ml vol. flask and dilg to vol. with MeOH. Det. A of blank and sample soln at 410 nm in 1 cm cell against reagent blank. Altho developed color is stable ca 0.5 hr, do not prep. sample solns until just before reading.

38.012   *Calculations*

% 2-Acetylamino-5-nitrothiazole =
[($A_{sample} - A_{blank}$) × 25 × 50 × 200 × 100]/
$\qquad$ (a × 100 × 20 × 10 × g sample)
= 1.25 × ($A_{sample} - A_{blank}$)/g sample,
$\qquad\qquad$ for a (1%, 1 cm) = 1000.

Det. a as follows: Accurately weigh ca 100 mg purified 2-acetylamino-5-nitrothiazole and transfer to 100 ml vol. flask with small portions DMF. Add total of ca 20 ml DMF and dissolve by warming on steam bath. After soln is complete, cool to room temp., dil. to vol. with DMF, stopper, and mix well. Dil. 5 ml aliquot to 200 ml with DMF, add 10 ml aliquot to prepd alumina column, **38.010**(b), and proceed as in detn.

a = (A_{std} × 25 × 50 × 200 × 1000)/
$\qquad\qquad$ (20 × 10 × 5 × mg sample)
= A_{std} × 250,000/mg sample.

Aklomide (2-Chloro-4-nitrobenzamide) (2,4-CNBA) (3)—Official First Action

(Applicable in presence of sulfanitran or roxarsone)

38.013   *Reagents*

(a) *Titanous chloride soln.*—4% aq. Prep. fresh on day of use from 20% soln or solid TiCl₃.

(b) *Sodium nitrite soln.*—0.1% aq. Prep. fresh on day of use.

(c) *Ammonium sulfamate soln.*—0.5% aq. Prep. fresh weekly.

(d) *Coupling reagent.*—0.1% aq. N-naphthyl-ethylenediamine.2HCl. Prep. fresh weekly and store in dark glass bottle in refrigerator.

(e) *Aklomide std solns.*—2-Chloro-4-nitrobenzamide, purified for std use, available from Salsbury Laboratories. (*1*) *Stock soln.*—1 mg/ml. Transfer 100 mg aklomide to 100 ml vol. flask, dissolve in ca 75 ml MeOH, dil. to vol. with MeOH, and mix well. (*2*) *Intermediate soln.*—10 μg/ml. Pipet 10 ml stock soln into 100 ml vol. flask, dil. to vol. with MeOH, and mix. Pipet 5 ml into 50 ml vol. flask. Evap. to dryness on H₂O bath with aid of gentle air stream and cool to room temp. Add ca 30 ml 0.15N HCl, shake 10 min intermittently, dil. to vol. with 0.15N HCl, and mix well. (*3*) *Working solns.*—0, 0.4, 0.8, 1.2, 1.6, and 2.0 μg/ml. Transfer 0, 1, 2, 3, 4, and 5 ml intermediate soln to sep. 25 ml vol. flasks and dil. to vol. with 0.15N HCl.

38.014   *Preparation of Standard Curve*

Transfer 4 ml aliquot from each working std soln to sep. colorimetric tubes and proceed with reduction, color development, and measurement as in **38.015**. Tubes contain 0, 1.6, 3.2, 4.8, 6.4, and 8.0 μg aklomide/tube, equiv. to 0, 0.008, 0.016, 0.024,

0.032, and 0.040% aklomide in feed when 5 g sample is taken. Plot spectrophtr reading against % aklomide.

38.015   *Determination*

Weigh 5 g sample contg ca 0.025% aklomide into 100 ml vol. flask, add 75 ml MeOH, and heat 30 min in 60° H₂O bath, shaking occasionally. Remove flask, cool to room temp., and dil. to vol. with MeOH. Mix thoroly and let stand 40 min to settle feed particles.

Pipet 5 ml clear supernatant into 50 ml vol. flask and dil. to vol. with 0.15N HCl. Mix well and filter thru Whatman No. 4 paper into 125 ml erlenmeyer. (If filtrate is cloudy, refilter.) Pipet 4 ml filtrate into each of 2 tubes, add 2 drops 4% TiCl₃ from dropper, mix, and let stand 2 min. Add 2 drops 10N NaOH from dropper, mix until white ppt persists, and acidify with 2.0 ml HCl. Mix and let stand until soln clears. Add 0.5 ml NaNO₂ to one tube and 0.5 ml H₂O to second tube as blank; mix. After 3 min, add 0.5 ml 0.5% NH₄ sulfamate to each tube and mix. After 2 min, add 0.5 ml coupling reagent to each, mix, and let color develop 15 min. Read A of soln at 545 nm in colorimeter or spectrophtr. Subtract reading of feed blank. Det. % aklomide in feed directly from std curve.

p-Aminobenzoic Acid (4)—Official Final Action

38.016   *Preparation of Standard Solution*

Transfer 0.100 g p-aminobenzoic acid (99+% purity, available from Nutritional Biochemicals Corp.) to 100 ml vol. flask, dissolve in 5 ml 1N NaOH, and dil. to vol. with H₂O. Dil. 5 ml aliquot to 200 ml with H₂O (1 ml = 25 μg). Place 2, 4, and 6 ml aliquots dild soln (50, 100, 150 μg) in 100 ml vol. flasks, add 3 ml HCl to each, dil. to vol. with H₂O, and mix.

38.017   *Determination*

Transfer 5 g freshly ground feed to 250 ml vol. flask, add 135 ml H₂O, making slurry of first 10 ml to wet sample completely, and then add 15 ml HCl. Mix, and place on steam bath 25 min, swirling occasionally until soln darkens. Cool, dil. to 250 ml with H₂O, and let feed particles settle. Pipet 50 ml into 100 ml vol. flask, dil. to vol. with H₂O, and mix thoroly. Pour soln into 250 ml beaker, add filter-aid, and filter thru 18.5 cm Whatman No. 2 paper, or equiv., discarding first 10–15 ml, if turbid.

Pipet two 10 ml aliquots into 50 ml beakers, add 5 ml H₂O and 2 ml *fresh 0.10% NaNO₂ soln*, mix, and let stand 3 min. Add 2 ml *0.50% NH₄ sulfamate soln*, mix, and let stand 2 min. Then add, to one beaker only, 1 ml coupling reagent, **38.013**(d), and to other 1 ml H₂O. Mix solns and wait 10 min. Det. A against H₂O at 545 nm in spectrophtr. (Avoid false readings due to N bubbles on cell walls.) Subtract blank A from sample A and calc. μg found by ref. to std curve.

% p-aminobenzoic acid in feed = μg found/1000.

K p-aminobenzoate = p-aminobenzoic acid × 1.278.

Prep. stds by treating 10 ml aliquots of three final std solns, representing 5, 10, and 15 μg, as in detn, beginning "add 5 ml H_2O ..." Plot A at 5, 10, and 15 μg and draw straight line.

38.018 Qualitative Tests

(To differentiate p-aminobenzoic acid, arsanilic acid, and sulfaquinoxaline)

Place 10 ml prepd sample filtrate in separator. Ext with 10 ml peroxide-free ether by vigorous shaking 30 sec. Let layers sep., and drain aq. layer into another separator. Re-ext with 10 ml ether and drain aq. layer into third separator for third extn with same vol. ether. After final extn, drain aq. layer into fourth separator, add 5 ml H_2O, mix, and couple soln as in **38.017**, second par. Wait 10 min, add 5 drops HCl and 10 ml isoamyl alcohol, and ext gently ca 30 sec. Let stand until layers sep. Red color in solv. is due to p-aminobenzoic acid; that in lower layer, to arsanilic acid. Drain as much aq. layer as possible and again ext with 10 ml solv. Arsanilic acid remains as distinct color in aq. layer, not as mere trace due to incomplete removal of p-aminobenzoic acid. Combine ether exts, wash with 5 ml H_2O, discard, and ext with 10 ml 1% Na_2CO_3 soln; acidify, and couple again to prove presence of sulfaquinoxaline.

2-Amino-5-Nitrothiazole (Enheptin®) (5)— Official Final Action

38.019 Reagents

(a) *Borate buffer.*—pH 9.0. Dil. 50.0 ml H_3BO_3-KCl soln, **45.010(c)**, and 21.40 ml 0.2M NaOH, **45.010(d)**, to 200 ml with H_2O.

(b) *Sodium hydrosulfite soln.*—Prep. 1% soln of Na hydrosulfite in borate buffer, (a), and use within 5 min of prepn.

(c) *Enheptin reference std.*—Available from American Cyanamid Co.

38.020 Determination

Transfer 2 g ground feed to 50 ml wide-mouth vol. flask, add 10 ml acetone, and let stand 2 min, swirling occasionally. Dil. to vol. with H_2O, mix, and filter immediately thru *coarse* paper. Transfer 25 ml aliquot to 50 ml vol. flask, add 15 ml 5% NH_4Cl soln, and mix. Dil. to vol. with H_2O, mix, and filter thru Whatman No. 42 paper (or equiv.), discarding first 10 ml filtrate.

Place 4 ml aliquot in each of 2 small beakers. To first, add 0.5 ml freshly prepd Na hydrosulfite soln. Dil. contents of both beakers to 10 ml and immediately read both solns on spectrophtr against H_2O at 388.5 nm. Subtract A of reduced soln from that of unreduced soln. From std curve read μg Enheptin corresponding to this difference.

μg Enheptin × 0.00125 = % Enheptin in sample.

38.021 Preparation of Standard Curve

Dissolve 100 mg 2-amino-5-nitrothiazole Ref. Std in 100 ml acetone and dil. to 1 L with H_2O. Transfer aliquots of 4, 8, 12, 16, and 20 ml to 100 ml vol. flasks and dil. to vol. with H_2O. Treat 5 ml aliquots of each diln as above, and read A of unreduced soln against reduced soln as blank, obtaining readings corresponding to 20, 40, 60, 80, and 100 μg.

Amprolium (1-(4-Amino-2-n-propyl-5-pyrimidinylmethyl)-2-picolinium chloride hydrochloride) (6)—Official Final Action

38.022 Principles

Amprolium is extd from feed with aq. MeOH. Ext is purified by chromatgy on Al_2O_3 and amprolium reacts with 2,7-naphthalenediol, $K_3Fe(CN)_6$, KCN, and NaOH in MeOH to form colored compd with absorption max. at 530 nm. There is no interference from usual components of com. feeds, vitamins, antibiotics, picolines, or pyrimidines. Nithiazide, Enheptin A, and nitrofurazone show some interference.

38.023 Reagents

(*Caution: See* **46.050**.)

(a) *Alcoholic sodium hydroxide soln.*—Dil. 15.0 ml aq. NaOH soln, (i), with anhyd. MeOH to 200 ml. Stopper, and mix well.

(b) *Aluminum oxide.*—Reagent grade suitable for chromatgy. Should pass following test: Vigorously shake 10 g Al_2O_3 with 100 ml H_2O in 250 ml g-s flask ≥ 2 min. Let settle, decant, and det. pH electrometrically. pH should be 9.5–10.5. (Aluminum Oxide Merck Reagent Chromatographic 71707 is suitable.)

(c) *Amprolium std soln.*—25 μg/ml. Weigh 25.0 mg Amprolium Ref. Std (available from Merck & Co.) into 50 ml vol. flask, dissolve in dil. MeOH, (e), dil. to vol., and mix. Dil. 5 ml to 100 ml in vol. flask with dil. MeOH. Soln is stable 1 week.

(d) *Color developing reagent.*—Add 5 ml $K_3Fe(CN)_6$ soln to 90 ml naphthalenediol soln in 250 ml g-s flask, and mix well. Add 5 ml KCN soln, stopper, mix well, and let stand 30–35 min. Add 100 ml alc. NaOH soln, (a), and mix. Use within 75 min, filtering thru medium porosity fritted glass filter just before use.

(e) *Dilute methyl alcohol.*—Mix 2 vols anhyd. MeOH with 1 vol. H_2O. Cool to room temp. before use.

(f) *Naphthalenediol soln.*—Dissolve 25 mg 2,7-naphthalenediol (Eastman Kodak Co.) in 1 L anhyd. MeOH.

(g) *Potassium cyanide soln.*—Dissolve 1.0 g KCN in 100 ml H_2O. Kept tightly stoppered, soln is stable 2 weeks.

(h) *Potassium ferricyanide soln.*—Dissolve 200 mg $K_3Fe(CN)_6$ in 100 ml H_2O. Kept tightly stoppered, soln is stable 2 weeks.

(i) *Sodium hydroxide soln.*—Dissolve 2.25 g NaOH in 200 ml H_2O.

38.024   Extraction

Accurately weigh quantity ground feed ($\leq$15 g) contg 1.5–2.5 mg amprolium and transfer to 250 ml g-s flask. Add 100.0 ml dil. MeOH, stopper, and stir magnetically or shake on mech. shaker 60 min. Filter thru Whatman No. 42 or equiv. paper and collect 25–40 ml clear filtrate, rejecting first 10–15 ml. Filtrate should be clear. Refilter if necessary thru fresh paper or centrf. until clear.

38.025   Chromatography

(a) *Preparation of aluminum oxide.*—Transfer 100 g Al_2O_3, (b), to suitable container, add 500 ml H_2O, and stir mech. 30 min. Filter slurry thru paper on buchner, wash with three 50 ml portions MeOH, and suck dry. Dry 2 hr at 100° in vac. oven. Prepd Al_2O_3 should be free flowing. Store in tightly stoppered bottle.

(b) *Preparation of column.*—Constrict end of 40 cm length of 9–10 mm id glass tubing by rotating in hot flame until opening is 4–5 mm. Insert small plug of Pyrex glass wool in lower end of tube and compress with glass rod to thickness ca 2–3 mm. Transfer 5.0 g prepd Al_2O_3 to dry tube and pack by gentle tapping of tube. Prep. sep. column for each sample.

(c) *Chromatography of feed extract.*—Pipet 25 ml clear ext onto column and let pass thru column by gravity. Reject first 1 ml eluate and collect next 5 ml for color development.

38.026   Determination

Mark 3 sep. 15 ml centrf. tubes as X, S, and B. To X add 4.00 ml clear eluate from column; to S add 4.00 ml amprolium std soln, and to B add 4.00 ml dil. MeOH as blank. Add 10.0 ml color developing reagent to each tube, stopper, mix, and let stand 20 min. Centrf. 2–3 min, decant into 1 cm cells, and cover. (If solns are not clear and free from suspended particles, decant into cells thru small plug of Pyrex glass wool.) Det. A of solns X and S in spectrophtr or colorimeter at 530 nm against soln B as ref. within 20–25 min after adding color developing reagent.

% Amprolium in feed = $(2.5A_x \times C)/(A_s \times W)$; where A_x and A_s refer to sample and std, resp., C = mg amprolium in final aliquot of std soln (0.100 mg), and W = wt original sample in g.

Fluorometric Method (7)—
Official Final Action

(Applicable in absence of antibiotics except procaine penicillin and chlortetracycline)

38.027   Reagents

(a) *Amprolium std solns.*—(1) *Stock soln.*—0.20 mg/ml. Weigh 20.0 mg Amprolium Ref. Std (available from Merck & Co.) and dissolve in enough TCA soln, (d), to make 100.0 ml. (2) *Working soln.*—1 μg/ ml. Dil. 5.00 ml stock soln to 100 ml with TCA soln and mix well. Further dil. 10 ml of this soln to 100 ml with H_2O, and mix well.

(b) *Potassium ferricyanide soln.*—Dissolve 2 g $K_3Fe(CN)_6$ in 100 ml H_2O.

(c) *Silver nitrate soln.*—Dissolve 5 g $AgNO_3$ in 100 ml H_2O.

(d) *Trichloroacetic acid (TCA) soln.*—Dissolve 5 g CCl_3COOH in 100 ml H_2O. Transfer 5.0 ml soln to 50 ml vol. flask, dil. to vol. with H_2O, and mix thoroly. Use as reagent blank and diluent.

38.028   Extraction

Grind feed sample to pass No. 20 sieve and mix thoroly. (High-speed blender grinds most feeds to desired fineness in ca 3 min.) Weigh quantity of sample contg ca 750 μg amprolium and transfer to 250 ml g-s flask. Add 100.0 ml TCA soln, stopper, and agitate 30 min on magnetic stirrer or mech. shaker.

Filter by gravity thru Whatman No. 42 paper, rejecting first 5 ml. Collect $\geq$10 ml clear filtrate. Transfer 5.00 ml clear ext to 50 ml vol. flask, dil. to 50.0 ml with H_2O, and mix well. This is dild sample ext.

38.029   Development of Fluorophor

Mark three 50 ml centrf. tubes X, Y, and Z. To tube X add 15.00 ml dild sample ext; to tube Y add 15.00 ml TCA blank soln; and to tube Z add 15.00 ml amprolium working std soln. To all tubes add 5.00 ml *NaOH soln* (3 + 10), stopper with polyethylene stoppers, and mix well. Immediately add 0.50 ml $AgNO_3$ soln to all tubes, stopper, and mix well. Let all tubes stand 2 min. Then to all tubes add 3.0 ml $K_3Fe(CN)_6$ soln, stopper, mix, and let stand 3.0 min.

During this 3 min wait, add 15 ml *n*-butanol to all tubes, as overlay, and stopper. After 3 min, vigorously shake all tubes 1.0 min, and centrf. 1 min. Transfer 10.0 ml aliquots of upper butanol layer from all tubes to test tubes. Add 1.00 ml absolute alcohol to each tube and mix well.

38.030   Measurement of Fluorescence
(Caution: See 46.008.)

(a) *For instruments designed to accommodate 10 × 10 mm cells and using monochromatic light for excitation (e.g., Aminco-Bowman).*—Set activation wavelength at 400 nm (uncorrected) and emission wavelength at 455 nm (uncorrected). Transfer ca 2.0 ml fluorophor butanol ext to cell and read.

(b) *For instruments designed to accommodate 10 × 40 mm cells and using filters to adjust wavelengths for excitation and emission (e.g., Pfaltz & Bauer).*—Use Corning Glass Works 5840 (CS-7-60) filter placed after source light to adjust excitation wavelength and Corning Glass Works 3385 (CS-3-71) filter placed behind cell to adjust emission wavelength. Transfer entire contents of test tube contg extd fluorophor to cell and read.

38.031 *Calculations*

% Amprolium in feed = $(X - Y) \times C/[150 \times (Z - Y) \times W]$, where X = fluorescence reading of sample; Y = fluorescence reading of reagent blank; Z = fluorescence reading of std; C = μg in 15 ml std soln (15.0); and W = g sample.

Arsanilic Acid (*p*-Aminobenzenearsonic Acid) (*8*)—Official Final Action

(Applicable in absence of sulfonamides)

38.032 *Determination*

Transfer 4.0 g freshly ground sample to 200 ml vol. flask, and add ca 80 ml H_2O and 4 ml $0.5N$ NaOH. Place flask on steam bath ca 5 min, swirling occasionally. Carefully add 20 ml HCl, mix, and cool to room temp. Dil. to vol. with H_2O, mix, pour into 250 ml beaker, add some Filter-Cel, or equiv., and filter thru Whatman No. 42 paper (or equiv.), discarding first 5 ml.

Pipet 5 ml aliquots of clear filtrate into each of two 20 $\times$ 175 mm test tubes. To each tube add 2 ml *0.1% $NaNO_2$ soln*, mix, and let stand 5 min. Add 2 ml *0.5% NH_4 sulfamate soln* and let stand 2 min. Then add, to 1 tube only, 1 ml coupling reagent, **38.013**(d), mix, and let stand 10 min before dilg both solns to vol. of 15 ml. Mix well, and det. A against H_2O at 538 nm in spectrophtr or with 540 nm filter in photometer. Subtract A of blank from sample A. Det. μg arsanilic acid in aliquot (equiv. to 100 mg sample) from std curve.

38.033 *Preparation of Standard Curve*

Transfer 0.100 g pure *arsanilic acid* to 100 ml vol. flask, add ca 20 ml H_2O and 2 ml $0.5N$ NaOH, and dissolve. Dil. to vol. with H_2O and mix well. Transfer 10 ml to 100 ml vol. flask, dil. to vol. with H_2O, and mix well. Dil. 5 ml of this soln to 250 ml with H_2O in vol. flask, and mix well (1 ml = 2 μg arsanilic acid). Pipet aliquots of 0, 2, 3, 5, and 8 ml of this std soln into 20 $\times$ 175 mm test tubes, add 1 ml HCl (1 + 1) to each tube, and continue as in **38.032**, beginning "To each tube add 2 ml *0.1% $NaNO_2$ ...*" Subtract blank A from A of stds and plot differences against 4, 6, 10, and 16 μg arsanilic acid in aliquots.

38.034   Bifuran—Official Final Action

See **38.064–38.065**.

★ **Bithionol (2,2'-Thiobis(4,6-dichloro-phenol)) (*9*)—Official Final Action** ★

38.035 *Reagents*

(a) *4-Aminoantipyrine soln.*—2% aq. soln. Stable $\geq$1 week. Development of yellow-green color does not affect usefulness of reagent. Reagent conforms to following specifications: mp, 105–109°, corrected; purity by HNO_2 titrn, $\geq$98%; sulfated ash, $\leq$0.25%; color, colorless, or not more than light tan. (Available from Winthrop Laboratories.)

(b) *Potassium ferricyanide soln.*—2% aq. soln. Stable $\geq$1 week.

(c) *Borax soln.*—Dissolve 50 g $Na_2B_4O_7 \cdot 10H_2O$ in H_2O and dil. to 1 L.

(d) *Methanolic hydrochloric acid.*—$0.1N$. To 100 ml $1.0N$ HCl add 900 ml absolute MeOH.

(e) *Bithionol std solns.*—(*1*) *Stock soln.*—Dissolve 50.0 mg pure bithionol (available from Hilton-Davis Chemical Co., 2235 Langdon Farm Rd, Cincinnati OH 45237) in 50.0 ml absolute MeOH. Discard after 1 week at room temp. (*2*) *Working soln.*—20 μg/ml. Dil. 2 ml stock soln to 100 ml with 5% borax soln. Use within 30 min of prepn.

38.036 *Preparation of Sample*

Grind 0.5–1.0 lb sample and mix thoroly.

38.037 *Determination*

Transfer 2.0 g prepd sample contg ca 1 mg bithionol to 250 ml g-s erlenmeyer. Pipet in 10 ml $0.1N$ HCl-MeOH, (d), and 200 ml *n*-hexane. Shake mech. 15 min; then add 10 ml H_2O by pipet and shake addnl 15 min. Let stand until layers are well sepd ($\leq$5–10 min is necessary). Pipet 50 ml hexane layer into 100 ml g-s graduated cylinder contg 10.0 ml $0.1N$ NaOH and shake 2 min. Clarify aq. soln by centrfg, and continue assay within 30 min.

To series of five 60 ml separators contg 20 ml H_2O add following in order listed: working bithionol std soln, 0, 1.0, 2.0, 3.0, 0 ml; centrfd alk. feed ext, 0, 0, 0, 0, 2.0 ml; $0.1N$ NaOH, 2.0, 2.0, 2.0, 2.0, 0 ml; $0.1N$ HCl, 2.0 ml to all; 5% borax soln, 3.0, 2.0, 1.0, 0.0, 3.0 ml; 2% aminoantipyrine soln, 0.4 ml to all; 2% $K_3Fe(CN)_6$ soln, 1.0 ml to all.

After swirling, add 15.0 ml 1-butanol to each separator. Stopper, and shake 1 min. Sep. and discard aq. layer. Swirl again and remove remaining H_2O. Decant 10 ml butanol ext into tube graduated accurately at 10 ml. Add 1.0 ml acetone to each tube to clarify solns and mix by swirling. Read T of solns in photometer, using ca 500 nm filter, and calc. % bithionol in sample = μg found/1000.

Buquinolate (Ethyl 4-hydroxy-6,7-diisobutoxy-3-quinolinecarboxylate) (*10*)— Official First Action

38.038 *Principle*

Buquinolate is extd from feed with $CHCl_3$ and concd to small known vol. Buquinolate is sepd from interfering substances by TLC utilizing 2 solv. systems. Buquinolate is eluted from substrate and detd fluorometrically.

38.039 *Reagents*

(a) *Alcohol, 80%.*—Dil. 84.3 ml alcohol to 100 ml with H_2O.

(b) *Developing solvent.*—Mix $CHCl_3$ with alcohol (10 + 1). Prep. fresh daily.

(c) *Buquinolate std solns.*—(*1*) *Stock soln.*—0.5 mg/ml. Dissolve 50.0 mg Buquinolate Ref. Std (available from Norwich Pharmacal Co., Norwich, NY 13815) in CHCl₃ to make 100 ml. Warm mixt. on steam bath as necessary. Soln is stable 1 month if protected from evapn. (*2*) *Working soln.*—100 μg/ml. Pipet 5.0 ml stock soln into 25 ml vol. flask, dil. to vol. with CHCl₃, and mix well. Prep. fresh daily.

38.040   *Apparatus*

(a) *Developing tanks.*—Line developing tanks (Brinkmann Instruments, Inc. No. 25-10-22, or equiv., for plates ≤200 × 200 mm) with Whatman 3 MM paper. Add 100 ml CHCl₃ to one tank; add 100 ml developing solv., (b), to second tank. Prep. each tank fresh daily.

(b) *Plates for TLC.*—Clean plates thoroly with alkyl benzene sulfonate-type detergent (Ajax, or equiv.) and brush; rinse plates with H₂O and then with acetone. Let plates air-dry. Slurry 60 g silica gel G (Brinkmann No. 68-00-26) with 120 ml H₂O. Pour into suitable applicator and spread 0.500 mm layer on 200 × 200 mm plates. Air-dry 15–30 min; then dry 2 hr at 110°. Cool and store plates in desiccator until used.

(c) *Fluorometer.*—Either spectrophotofluorometer or filter fluorometer may be used. (Suitable filters are: excitation, Baird Atomic, Inc. type A3 (UV Spectrum Filters, Cat. Nos. 14-08-7, 14-09-6); emission, Corning Glass Works 0–52 + 7–60.) (*Caution: See* 46.008.)

38.041   *Determination*

(*Caution: See* 46.016.)

Grind ca 100 g sample to pass No. 30 sieve and mix thoroly. Accurately weigh sample contg 1.25 mg buquinolate into 250 ml g-s erlenmeyer. Pipet 100 ml CHCl₃ into sample flask. Shake mixt. mech. 1 hr. Filter ext thru Whatman No. 54 paper on buchner with mild vac. (Take care to prevent solv. loss by evapn.) Transfer exactly 80 ml ext to 150 ml beaker and evap. almost to dryness on steam bath. Take up residue in small portion CHCl₃ and transfer to 10 ml vol. flask with small portions CHCl₃. Dil. to vol. with CHCl₃ and mix well.

Apply 250 μl sample ext and 250 μl working std soln to TLC plate. Place spots ca 25 mm from bottom of plate and 40 mm apart. (Do not touch needle to plate.) Develop plate in CHCl₃ developing tank, (a), until solv. front nearly reaches top of plate (ca 1 hr). Observe plate under short wavelength UV light: Buquinolate remains at origin; feed background migrates. Transfer air-dried (5–10 min) plate to tank contg developing solv., (b). Let plate develop until solv. front advances 12 cm. Air-dry 5–10 min. Examine plates under short wavelength UV light. Buquinolate migrates from origin (R_f, 0.4–0.6). With spatula, outline each buquinolate spot plus blank spot of equiv. area and R_f. Remove adsorbent from around buquinolate spots and discard. Quant. transfer each spot to sep. g-s 25 ml erlenmeyers. Pipet 10

ml 80% alcohol, (a), into each flask, shake mech. 20 min, and centrf.

Det. intensity of fluorescent radiation (*I*) of sample, std, and blank in 10 × 10 mm silica cells, at excitation and emission wavelengths of 265 and 375 nm, resp.

% Buquinolate = $[(I_{sample} - I_{blank})/(I_{std} - I_{blank})] × (0.125/g \; sample)$.

Cadmium Anthranilate (*11*)—
Official Final Action

38.042   *Reagents*

(a) *Cadmium std solns.*—(*1*) *Stock soln.*—Dissolve 100 mg pure Cd anthranilate (Ref. Std available from Feed Products Division, Hess & Clark Laboratories) in 5 ml HCl and dil. to 100 ml with H₂O. (*2*) *Working soln.*—10 μg Cd anthranilate/ml. Dil. 1.0 ml stock soln to 100 ml with H₂O.

(b) *Dithizone soln.*—Dissolve 8 mg dithizone in 1 L CHCl₃. (*A* of this soln against H₂O at 600 nm must be 1.0–1.5.) Store in amber bottle protected from light in refrigerator.

(c) *Sodium hydroxide-cyanide soln.*—Dissolve 40 g NaOH and 0.05 g KCN in H₂O and dil. to 100 ml. Store in polyethylene bottle.

38.043   *Determination*

Weigh 5 g sample into 250 ml erlenmeyer. Add exactly 100 ml 10% *trichloroacetic acid* (*Caution: See* 46.082), stopper, and shake vigorously 1 min. Filter thru medium paper. Pipet 1 ml filtrate into separator contg 25 ml *cold 2% tartaric acid*. Add 1 ml *5% hydroxylamine.HCl* and by pipet 15 ml dithizone soln. Mix, add 5 ml NaOH-KCN soln, and shake immediately 1 min. Keep time of contact of alkali with CHCl₃ to min. Filter CHCl₃ layer thru cotton plug in stem of separator into dry 1 cm cell. Read *A* of pink soln at 518 nm against H₂O.

To prep. std curve, pipet 0, 1, 2, 3, and 4 ml working soln into separator contg 25 ml cold 2% tartaric acid soln and proceed as above. Prep. std curve on same day as analyses.

% Cd anthranilate = μg Cd anthranilate found/500.

Decoquinate (Ethyl 6-*n*-decyloxy-7-ethoxy-4-hydroxy-3-quinolinecarboxylate) (*12*)—
Official First Action

38.044   *Principle*

Decoquinate is extd from feed with 1% CaCl₂-MeOH soln. After addn of H₂O and acid, the drug is extd into CHCl₃, then sepd from interfering materials by chromatgy on Florisil. Decoquinate is eluted from column with 1% CaCl₂-MeOH and detd by fluorometry against std treated similarly.

38.045   *Reagents*

(a) *Calcium chloride-methanol soln.*—1%. Dissolve 10 g anhyd. CaCl₂, reagent grade, in 1 L MeOH, spectral grade (Matheson Coleman & Bell) or equiv. redistd, reagent grade, anhyd. MeOH. Filter thru Whatman No. 2 paper.

(b) *Decoquinate std solns.—(1) Stock soln.*—300 μg/ml. Weigh 30 mg Decoquinate Ref. Std (available from Hess & Clark Laboratories). Dissolve and dil. to 100 ml with 1% CaCl₂-MeOH soln. Prep. fresh monthly. (2) *Working soln.*—6 μg/ml. Pipet 5 ml stock soln into 250 ml vol. flask and dil. to vol. with 1% CaCl₂-MeOH soln. Check *A* of this soln in 1 cm quartz cells at 265 nm against spectral grade MeOH (ca 0.660). Prep. fresh std when *A* is outside range 0.620–0.700. Soln is stable ≥1 week. (3) *Fluorescence reference soln.*—1.5 μg/ml. Pipet 25 ml working std into 100 ml vol. flask and dil. to vol. with spectral grade MeOH. Check *A* at 265 nm as above. Prep. fresh std when *A* is outside range 0.150–0.190.

(c) *Florisil.*—100–200 mesh (Fisher No. F-101).

38.046 *Apparatus*

(a) *Chromatographic columns.*—Draw 300 mm length of 9 mm tubing (7 mm id) to drip tip. Insert small glass wool plug to support adsorbent. Close drip end with short piece of tubing and pinchclamp. Add 5 ml CHCl₃ to column, then 0.5±0.01 g Florisil. Add 2 ml addnl CHCl₃ and stir with thin glass rod to settle adsorbent. Remove tubing and wash down sides of tube with CHCl₃. Prep. just before use.

(b) *Separators.*—125 or 250 ml with Teflon stopcocks.

(c) *Fluorometer.*—(*Caution: See* **46.008.**) Either spectrofluorometer or filter fluorometer may be used. Excitation filter: Baird Atomic, Inc. A-2 (UV Spectrum Filters Cat. No. 14-16-8, 325 nm); emission filter: Baird Atomic S/UV (UV Spectrum Filters Cat. No. 14-01-4, 390 nm).

38.047 *Determination*

Weigh 10 g sample into 125 ml erlenmeyer, add exactly 50 ml 1% CaCl₂-MeOH soln, stopper, and shake mech. 20 min. Decant soln into centrf. tube and centrf. 5 min at moderate speed. Pipet 10 ml clear supernatant into 125 ml separator. Prep. std by pipetting 10 ml working std soln into another separator. Add exactly (by pipet) 10 ml CHCl₃ to each funnel and swirl to mix. Add 100 ml dil. HCl (1 + 19) to each funnel. Shake gently by inverting 25 times; then allow 15 min for phases to sep. Drain CHCl₃ layer into centrf. tube and centrf. 5 min. Remove by aspiration any droplets of floating H₂O phase that seps.

Pipet 5 ml CHCl₃ sample soln onto Florisil column. Pipet 5 ml CHCl₃ std soln onto another column. Pipet 5 ml CHCl₃ onto third column (reagent blank). Pass two 10 ml portions anhyd. MeOH thru each column. Let MeOH drain to surface of Florisil and discard column effluent. Elute with 15 ml 1% CaCl₂-MeOH soln, collecting in tube marked at 15 ml. Mix

well, centrf. if not clear, and transfer to fluorometer cells. Set activation wavelength of fluorometer at 325 nm and emission wavelength at 390 nm. Set fluorometer sensitivity with fluorescence ref. std to give convenient scale reading (e.g., 100). Det. fluorescence of samples, std, and reagent blank. Subtract reagent blank correction, if any, from reading of std and samples.

% Decoquinate in feed = (0.003 × corrected fluorescence of sample)/corrected fluorescence of std.

Diethylstilbestrol (13)—Official First Action

38.048 *Reagent*

Diethylstilbestrol std soln.—55 μg/ml. Prep. stock soln contg 0.55 mg USP Ref. Std diethylstilbestrol/ ml CHCl₃. Dil. 10 ml of this stock soln to 100 ml with CHCl₃.

38.049 *Apparatus*

(a) *Lamp.*—Hanovia analytical model lamp, No. 7420, or SC-5010, or Hanovia Lethray J 24500 with 1-83-A-1 16″ Vycor lamp. (Engelhard Hanovia, Inc., 100 Chestnut St, Newark, NJ 07105, or equiv.) Wattage of lamp and distance from cell should be such that peak absorption results with min. rise in temp. of soln, preferably ≤1°. (*Caution: See* **46.016.**)

(b) *Spectrophotometer.* — Beckman DU, or equiv., with W lamp and matched 1 cm absorption cells. Cells must be silica or quartz, if used for irradiation.

(c) *Cells.*—Matched 1 cm quartz absorption cells or transparent quartz tubes, 16 × 150 mm for irradiation.

38.050 *Standardization*

Place quartz cells or tubes in suitable holder, rigidly fixed, so that cells or tubes are irradiated transversely and at fixed distance from lamp. (Do not irradiate from top.) Distance may be 6″ or whatever gives irradiation max. between ca 5–12 min. Cells or tubes must be clean and dry for each detn. Det. optimum irradiation time by irradiation in quartz cells of ca 3 ml HOAc contg diethylstilbestrol at time intervals of 1 min increments to find approx. irradiation max. Depending on source of irradiation, more exact irradiation time for max. *A* may result with shorter time intervals.

Pipet 1 ml std soln into 100 ml beaker, evap. in air current, add 10 ml HOAc, stir, and transfer ca 3 ml portions to each of 2 or 3 cells for irradiation. Cool if necessary, and det. *A* at 415 nm as in **38.051.** Alternatively, use mixt. of alcohol and 0.1M K₂HPO₄ (1 + 1) as solv.

Irradiation is critical and conditions must be carefully observed. Check frequently against std soln, and use exact same conditions for samples. Time of exposure may be longer with feed ext than with pure diethylstilbestrol soln.

38.051 *Determination*

Accurately weigh 20 g of "40-mesh" sample, add 2–3 g fine asbestos, or *Dicalite* or other diat. earth, mix well, transfer to extn thimble (33 × 94 mm), and place piece of absorbent cotton in top of thimble. Add to extn flask 140 ml solv. mixt. contg 7% v/v EtOH in CHCl₃, and ext 16 hr or overnight at rate of ≥100 drops/min in Soxhlet extractor. After extn, leave part of CHCl₃ in upper part of app. and transfer it to another flask. If insol. material is present in main ext, filter into 100 ml vol. flask (glass wool in funnel is suitable), rinse with rest of CHCl₃ from other flask, cool, dil. to vol. with CHCl₃, and mix.

Pipet 25 ml into 125 ml separator (aliquot *1*). Transfer another 25 ml into second 125 ml separator (aliquot *2*). Into second separator pipet 1.0 ml diethylstilbestrol std soln, contg 55 μg. Add 25 ml CHCl₃ and 25 ml 1N H₂SO₄ to each separator and wash by inverting funnel with rotary motion 6 times rather vigorously. Transfer lower CHCl₃ layer to another 125 ml separator, add 10 ml CHCl₃ to acid soln, and wash again as before. Combine CHCl₃ solns, discarding aq. soln.

Add 10 ml 1N NaOH and invert separator with rotary motion rather vigorously ca 12 times but not hard enough to cause serious emulsions. Drain CHCl₃ layer into another 125 ml separator. Again ext this CHCl₃ with 10 ml 1N NaOH in same way. Discard CHCl₃ layer and combine alk. exts in separator.

To combined alk. exts add 5 ml CHCl₃, shake few sec, discard lower CHCl₃ layer, and repeat 3 or 4 times in same way until CHCl₃ exts are colorless. Transfer washed alk. ext to 100 ml beaker. To this separator add 5 ml H₂O, shake, and add to combined alk. ext. Add 10 ml 2N H₃PO₄, cool to room temp., and adjust to pH 9.0±0.1 with 2N H₃PO₄. (*Caution:* Rinse separators that contained combined NaOH exts at least twice with H₂O to remove all alkalinity.)

Return pH-adjusted soln to original separator (alk.-free) from which it was taken, rinsing beakers with two 2 ml portions H₂O. Rinse beakers with 15 ml CHCl₃, shake 30–60 sec carefully to avoid emulsions, transfer lower CHCl₃ layer to clean, dry separator, and ext pH-adjusted soln twice more in same way with 15 ml portions CHCl₃. Combine all CHCl₃ exts, add 25 ml H₂O, and shake briefly. Filter CHCl₃ ext thru 30 ml fritted glass funnel (ca 20 × 100 mm), medium porosity, contg ¾" of anhyd. Na₂SO₄, into 50 ml vol. flask. Wash the H₂O with 2–5 ml portions CHCl₃ and use to rinse Na₂SO₄ and funnel. Continue to rinse funnel with CHCl₃ to 50 ml vol. Mix, and pipet 25 ml aliquot into 150 ml beaker previously rinsed with CHCl₃. Evap. just to dryness on steam bath with aid of air current (manifold arrangement works well on series of samples). Evap. last of CHCl₃ with air current only.

Pipet 10 ml HOAc, or alcohol-0.1M K₂HPO₄ (1 + 1), into the beaker. Stir with glass rod to ensure soln

of diethylstilbestrol. Transfer ca 3 ml into each of 2 or 3 matched quartz cells (1 cm thickness). Read *A* at 415 nm before irradiation. Immediately place cells in front of lamp, as in **38.050**, and irradiate under same conditions. Read *A*. If quartz tubes are used, readings before irradiation can be made on remaining 4 ml of soln for blank correction.

Calc. by increment method for each solv. where *A* refers to sample after irradiation; *A'*, before; *B* = *A* of sample plus added diethylstilbestrol after irradiation; *B'*, before.

$$\frac{A - A'}{(B - B') - (A - A')} \times 4.99$$

$$= \text{mg diethylstilbestrol/lb feed.}$$

Alternative calculations.—Prep. std curve from 27.5, 41.25, 55.0, 82.5, and 110 μg diethylstilbestrol. After correcting for blank, det. μg diethylstilbestrol from *A* reading.

μg × 0.1815 = mg diethylstilbestrol/lb feed.

1,2-Dimethyl-5-nitroimidazole (Dimetridazole) (*14*)—Official First Action

38.052 *Principle*

Dimetridazole is extd from feeds with MeOH, sepd from interfering substances by two Al₂O₃ chromatgc steps, and detd spectrophtric at its UV wavelength max. Nihydrazone, furazolidone, zoalene, 2-chloro-4-nitrobenzamide, tylosin, and large amts procaine (from procaine penicillin) interfere.

38.053 *Apparatus and Reagents*

(a) *Ultraviolet spectrophotometer.*—Beckman Instruments DK-2 ratio recording, Beckman DU, or equiv.

(b) *Chromatographic tubes.*—13 × 150 mm and 15 × 250 mm, constricted at bottom to hold glass wool plug and 6 mm od delivery tube.

(c) *Aluminum oxide.*—Suitable for chromatgy (Merck and Co. No. 71707, or equiv.). To det. suitability of Al₂O₃, perform detn on feed that does not contain dimetridazole or other imidazole drugs. If feed appears to contain >0.004% dimetridazole, use another batch of Al₂O₃.

(d) *1,2-Dimethyl-5-nitroimidazole (dimetridazole) std solns.*—(1) *Stock soln.*—0.1 mg/ml. Weigh 100 mg dimetridazole std (available from Salsbury Laboratories) into 100 ml vol. flask. Dissolve in H₂O by shaking frequently ca 20 min. Dil. to vol. with H₂O and mix. Pipet 20 ml into 200 ml vol. flask, dil. to vol. with H₂O, and mix. (2) *Working std solns.*—Pipet 5, 10, 20, 30, and 40 ml stock soln into sep. 100 ml vol. flasks. Add 5.0 ml 3N HCl to each, immediately dil. to vol. with H₂O, and mix. Pipet 5 ml each soln and 5 ml 0.10N NaOH into sep. 50 ml erlenmeyers. Stopper and mix. These solns contain 2.5, 5, 10, 15, and 20 μg dimetridazole/ml.

38.054 Preparation of Standard Curve

Proceed as in **38.057**, using working std solns and blank prepd by mixing 5 ml 0.15*N* HCl with 5 ml 0.10*N* NaOH.

Read *A* against blank as for recording or manual spectrophtrs. Construct std curve by plotting *A* against μg dimetridazole/ml.

38.055 Preparation of Sample

Weigh portion finely ground feed contg 0.5–2.0 mg dimetridazole (usually 5 g) into 100 ml vol. flask. Add 70–75 ml MeOH and place in constant temp. bath 30 min at 60°. Make certain that H_2O level covers flask to ca ⅛" below MeOH level. Swirl flask 2 or 3 times during first 5 min to heat evenly. Cool to room temp., dil. to vol. with MeOH, and mix. Let stand 5–10 min to let coarse feed particles settle.

38.056 Chromatography

Place small glass wool plug in bottom of 15 × 250 mm chromatgc tube and add 8 cm layer Al_2O_3; pack column tightly to prevent streaking. (If streaks enter effluent, pos. bias is introduced.) Decant methanolic ext onto column so that settled feed particles are not disturbed. Collect ca 30 ml eluate in 50 ml vol. flask. Stopper until ready for use.

(*Note:* Dimetridazole sublimes at temps >70°; manner of solv. removal is critical.) For feed contg 0.015% dimetridazole, pipet 15 ml effluent (4 ml if feed contains 0.06%; 3 ml if feed contains 0.10%) into 125 ml suction or r-b flask and evap. under reduced pressure from H_2O aspirator. If 15 ml is taken, use hot plate (low heat) or H_2O-bath to reduce to 3–4 ml. Shake to prevent bumping. When vol. approaches 3–4 ml remove flask from heat and remove last 3–4 ml only with heat from palm of hand. Continue shaking to prevent bumping. Do *not* attempt to attain complete dryness because part of the 2–3 drops of oily residue is dimetridazole.

Wash down walls of flask, beginning at base of neck, with 5.0 ml 0.10*N* NaOH. Swirl to wash walls. Let stand 5 min and add 5.0 ml 0.15*N* HCl. Swirl to mix and again wash flask walls. Stopper until ready for chromatgy.

38.057 Determination

Prep. second Al_2O_3 column by inserting small glass wool plug into bottom of 13 × 150 mm chromatgc tube, add 4 cm layer Al_2O_3, and tap gently to pack column lightly. Pour entire 10 ml soln onto column and let pass thru by gravity. Collect effluent in 50 ml erlenmeyer. Force out liq. adhering to column by applying air pressure with rubber bulb. Swirl flask to mix. Stopper until ready to read. Pass blank soln of 5 ml 0.15*N* HCl and 5 ml 0.10*N* NaOH thru sep. 4 cm Al_2O_3 column as above.

(a) *Using recording spectrophotometer.*—Fill matched pair silica cells with reagent blank and

with sample soln (always use same cell for blank) and scan from 330 to 310 nm. Read *A* at peak and obtain concn of soln in μg/ml from std curve. Calc. % dimetridazole = [(μg/ml from std curve) × diln factor × 100]/(g sample × 10⁶). Diln factor = 1.335×10^{-3} for feeds contg 0.015%; 5×10^{-3}, 0.06%; and 6.66×10^{-3}, 0.1%.

(b) *Using manual spectrophotometer.*—Locate peak *A* of sample soln (ca 318 nm), using matched pair silica cells, and set wavelength at peak. Read *A* of sample and blank solns and correct sample for blank. Obtain concn of soln in μg/ml from std curve, and calc. % in feed as above.

Ethopabate (Methyl 4-acetamido-2-ethoxy-benzoate) (*15*)—Official Final Action

38.058 Principle

Ethopabate is extd from feed by 50% MeOH at room temp. Clear filtrate is acidified with dil. HCl and extd with $CHCl_3$. Most interfering substances (amines, *p*-aminobenzoic acid, procaine) are sepd. $CHCl_3$ ext is washed with Na_2CO_3 soln to remove sulfaquinoxaline, acetyl-(*p*-nitrophenyl) sulfanilamide, and chlortetracycline. Ethopabate is converted to free amine by controlled acid hydrolysis. Free amine is diazotized and coupled; colored complex is extd with *n*-butanol and read at 550 nm.

38.059 Reagents

(a) *Dilute hydrochloric acid.*—0.3*N*. Dil. 25 ml HCl with H_2O to 1 L.

(b) *Sodium carbonate soln.*—Dissolve 40 g anhyd. Na_2CO_3 in H_2O and dil. to 1 L.

(c) *Coupling reagent (NED).*—Dissolve 50 mg N-(1-naphthyl)ethylenediamine.2HCl in 25 ml H_2O. Prep. fresh as needed.

(d) *Ethopabate std solns.*—(*1*) *Stock soln.*—0.400 mg/ml. Weigh 40.0 mg Ethopabate Ref. Std (available from Merck & Co.) into 100 ml vol. flask, dissolve in MeOH, and dil. to vol. (*2*) *Intermediate soln.*—40 μg/ml. Pipet 10.0 ml stock soln into 100 ml vol. flask, dil. to vol. with aq. MeOH (1 + 1), and mix well. Stored in tightly stoppered flasks, solns are stable ≥1 month. (*3*) *Working soln.*—16.0 μg/20.0 ml. Pipet 5.00 ml intermediate soln into 250 ml vol. flask, dil. to vol. with aq. MeOH (1 + 1), and mix well.

38.060 Extraction

Grind feed sample to pass No. 20 sieve and mix thoroly. (High-speed blender grinds most feeds to desired fineness in ca 3 min.) Accurately weigh sample contg ca 80 μg ethopabate (do not exceed 20 g). Transfer to 250 ml g-s flask. Add 100.0 ml aq. MeOH (1 + 1) and magnetic stirrer bar, stopper tightly, and agitate 1 hr. (Mech. shaker that provides vigorous agitation may be used instead of magnetic stirrer.) Centrf., or filter portion of ext thru fast paper. Collect only enough filtrate to supply aliquot for test. If necessary, store exts overnight at room temp. in tightly stoppered flasks.

38.061   *Removal of Interferences*

Pipet 20 ml clear ext into 50 ml centrf. tube. Add 5.0 ml dil. HCl (1 + 9) and 10 ml CHCl$_3$, stopper with polyethylene stopper, and shake vigorously 3 min on mech. shaker. Centrf., and carefully transfer bottom CHCl$_3$ layer into clean 50 ml centrf. tube, using syringe equipped with long needle. Repeat extn with two more 10 ml portions CHCl$_3$. Add 10 ml Na$_2$CO$_3$ soln to combined CHCl$_3$ exts, stopper, and shake 3 min. Centrf., and without disturbing interface, draw off most of top aq. layer, using syringe, and discard. Repeat washing with another 10 ml Na$_2$CO$_3$ soln, discarding washing. Add 10 ml H$_2$O to CHCl$_3$ ext, stopper, shake vigorously ca 1 min, and centrf. Draw off aq. layer and discard. Repeat with another 10 ml H$_2$O. (To avoid loss of drug and low results, do not disturb interface on CHCl$_3$, and complete extn and washings in shortest time possible. Prolonged contact with HCl and Na$_2$CO$_3$ may cause partial hydrolysis of ethopabate.)

Pipet 20 ml aq. MeOH (1 + 1) into 50 ml centrf. tube, add 5.0 ml dil. HCl (1 + 9), and proceed as for sample (reagent blank).

Pipet 20 ml (16.0 μg) ethopabate working std soln into 50 ml centrf. tube, add 5.0 ml dil. HCl (1 + 9), and proceed as for sample (std).

38.062   *Conversion of Ethopabate to Free Amine*

Quant. transfer washed CHCl$_3$ exts to sep. 100 ml beakers. Rinse each centrf. tube with two 3 ml portions aq. MeOH (1 + 1), adding rinsings to beaker. Place beaker on steam bath and evap. CHCl$_3$ to vol. of ca 2 ml. Add 5.0 ml aq. MeOH (1 + 1) and swirl beaker to dissolve completely.

Quant. transfer soln to r-b centrf. tube. Rinse beaker with 10, 10, and 5 ml portions 0.3N HCl. Immerse tube in boiling H$_2$O bath so that level of liq. in tube is just below level of H$_2$O bath. Heat 45 min. Remove tube from hot H$_2$O bath and cool to 10–15° in cold H$_2$O bath.

38.063   *Development and Measurement of Color*

Remove tubes from cold H$_2$O bath. Add 1.0 ml *freshly prepd 0.2% NaNO$_2$ soln* to each tube, mix, and let stand 2 min. Add 1.0 ml 1.0% NH$_4$ sulfamate soln, mix, and let stand 2 min. Add 1.0 ml NED soln, mix, and let stand 10 min. Add 5.0 g NaCl and 5.00 ml *n*-butanol, stopper, and shake vigorously until NaCl dissolves. Centrf., carefully transfer portion of clear, colored alc. layer to 1 cm cell, and read A at 555 nm against *n*-butanol. Correct for reagent blank.

% Ethopabate in feed = $0.008 \times (A - A_B)$ /$[(A' - A_B) \times W]$, where A refers to sample, A_B to reagent blank, A' to std, and W = g original sample.

Furazolidone (N-[5-nitro-2-furfurylidene]-3-amino-2-oxazolidone), Bifuran (Mixture of Furazolidone and Nitrofurazone), or Nitrofurazone (5-Nitro-2-furaldehyde semicarbazone) (16)—Official Final Action

38.064   *Reagents*

(a) *Phenylhydrazine hydrochloride soln.*—Dissolve 0.5 g phenylhydrazine.HCl in 50 ml H$_2$O. Prep. fresh daily. Mix equal vol. of this soln with HCl.

(b) *Furazolidone std solns.*—(1) *Stock soln.*—0.55 mg/ml. Weigh 55 mg furazolidone std (available from Hess & Clark, 7th and Orange Sts, Ashland, OH 44805) into 100 ml vol. flask, dil. to vol. with dimethylformamide (DMF), and mix. Soln is stable several months when protected from light. (2) *Working soln.*—Prep. working std corresponding to label declaration. For feeds contg 0.011% furazolidone, pipet 2 ml stock soln into 100 ml vol. flask, add 48 ml DMF, and dil. to vol. with H$_2$O. For feeds contg 0.00275% furazolidone, pipet 0.5 ml stock soln into 100 ml vol. flask, add 49.5 ml DMF, and dil. to vol. with H$_2$O.

(c) *Nitrofurazone std solns.*—(1) *Stock soln.*—0.56 mg/ml. Weigh 56 mg nitrofurazone std (available from Hess & Clark Laboratories) into 100 ml vol. flask, dil. to vol. with DMF, and mix. Soln is stable several months when protected from light. (2) *Working soln.*—Prep. working std corresponding to label declaration. For feeds contg 0.0056% nitrofurazone, pipet 1 ml stock soln into 100 ml vol. flask, add 49 ml DMF, and dil. to vol. with H$_2$O. For feeds contg 0.0112% nitrofurazone, pipet 2 ml stock soln into 100 ml vol. flask, add 48 ml DMF, and dil. to vol. with H$_2$O.

(d) *Bifuran std solns.*—(1) *Stock soln.*—0.1285 mg/ml. Pipet 20 ml nitrofurazone stock soln and 3 ml furazolidone stock soln into 100 ml vol. flask and dil. to vol. with DMF. (2) *Working soln.*—For feeds contg 0.0064% total nitrofurans, prep. working std by pipetting 5 ml bifuran stock soln into 100 ml vol. flask, adding 45 ml DMF, and dilg to vol. with H$_2$O.

(e) *Adsorbent.*—To 100 parts Merck Al$_2$O$_3$, chromatgc grade, in screw cap bottle, add 4 parts Mg(OH)$_2$, shake until thoroly mixed, then add 5 parts H$_2$O, and mix until all lumps disappear. Store in tightly sealed container.

38.065   *Determination*

(*Caution: See* **46.018, 46.040,** *and* **46.053.**)

Grind coarse or pelleted feeds to "20 mesh" thru cutting type mill such as Wiley Intermediate. Finer feeds need not be ground. Weigh 10 g sample into 125 ml erlenmeyer, add exactly 50 ml DMF, stopper loosely, and place in boiling H$_2$O bath 5 min. Shake on mech. shaker 10 min and filter thru rapid paper. To 25 ml filtrate add 25 ml H$_2$O and mix.

Prep. ca 20 mm diam. adsorption column, contg Al$_2$O$_3$-Mg(OH)$_2$ adsorbent, to ht of 5 cm. Pass the 50% DMF sample soln thru column, discarding first

3 ml eluate. (If column flow stops, break up gummy film at top of adsorbent, using long thin glass rod.) Pipet 5 ml aliquots of eluate into each of 2 numbered test tubes. Protect one tube from light. To other tube, add 3 drops *freshly prepd 2% soln of Na hydrosulfite* and let stand 20 min, shaking at ca 5 min intervals. Treat 5 ml aliquots of working std soln in exactly same manner.

Pipet 5 ml phenylhydrazine.HCl soln into each of the numbered test tubes contg samples and stds. Mix and place tubes in 70° H_2O bath 25 min; cool in 15° H_2O bath 5 min. Add exactly 10 ml toluene to each tube, stopper, and shake vigorously 40 times. Centrf. or filter toluene soln directly into absorption cell thru cotton wad inserted in stem of small funnel. Read A of solns at 440 nm.

$$[(A_{samp.} - A_{red.\ samp.}) \times 0.011\ (or\ 0.00275)]/$$
$$(A_{std} - A_{red.\ std}) = \%\ furazolidone.$$

$$[(A_{samp.} - A_{red.\ samp.}) \times 0.0064]/(A_{std} - A_{red.\ std})$$
$$= \%\ total\ nitrofurans\ (bifuran).$$

$$[(A_{samp.} - A_{red.\ samp.}) \times 0.0056\ (or\ 0.011)]/$$
$$(A_{std} - A_{red.\ std}) = \%\ nitrofurazone.$$

★ **Glycarbylamide (4,5-Imidazoledi-** ★
carboxamide) (17)—Official Final Action

38.066 *Principles*

Glycarbylamide is extd from feed with dimethylformamide (DMF). Ext is purified by chromatgy on Al_2O_3 and anion exchange resin, and traces of residual impurities are oxidized with Br. A of glycarbylamide is measured at 283 nm in alk. soln against portion of same soln from which glycarbylamide has been removed by adsorption on HgO.

38.067 *Reagents*

(a) *Dilute hydrochloric acid.*—Dil. 100 ml HCl to 1 L with H_2O.

(b) *Bromine soln.*—Dissolve 1.5 g $KBrO_3$ and 7.5 g KBr in H_2O and dil. to 250 ml.

(c) *Alkali soln.*—Dissolve 20 g Na metaborate ($NaBO_2.4H_2O$) and 45 g NaOH in enough H_2O to make 200 ml. Store in polyethylene bottle.

(d) *Sodium bisulfite soln.*—2% aq. soln. Prep. fresh.

(e) *Cyanide soln.*—Dissolve 1 g KCN in 100 ml 1N NaOH. *Poison: Handle with care.*

(f) *Aluminum oxide.*—See **38.023**(b).

(g) *Amberlite IRA-400.*—(Mallinckrodt Chemical Works No. 3336.) Regenerate resin before use as follows: Place ca 200 ml resin in large glass tube ca 2–3″ diam. and wash successively with ca 250 ml each of H_2O, 10% NaOH soln, H_2O, 10% HCl, H_2O, and 10% NaOH soln. Finally wash with H_2O until eluate is neut. to indicator paper. Store under H_2O in polyethylene bottles.

(h) *Mercuric oxide, red.*—Fine powder. Grind in mortar if necessary.

(i) *Glycarbylamide std solns.*—(1) *Stock soln.*— 0.320 mg/ml. Weigh 32.0 mg Glycarbylamide Ref.

Std (available from Merck & Co.) into 100 ml vol. flask and dil. to vol. with DMF. (2) *Working soln.*— 6.4 μg/ml. Dil. 5 ml stock soln to 250 ml with DMF.

38.068 *Columns for Chromatography*

(a) *Aluminum oxide column.*—Use 50 cm glass tube, 22 mm id, constricted at one end. Place glass wool plug in constricted end and add 15 g Al_2O_3. Pack by gentle tapping on side of tube. Wash column with 25 ml DMF and let solv. drain to 1–2 cm above bed level before adding sample to column. Prep. sep. column for each sample and std.

(b) *IRA-400 column.*—Prep. column from 24 cm glass tube, 9 mm id. Seal upper end to reservoir of 8 cm of 5 cm od tubing. Constrict lower end to hold glass wool plug and attach to piece of polyethylene tubing with screw clamp. Mark tube at 4″ above glass wool plug. Add H_2O slurry of resin to column until, after letting H_2O drain, resin level reaches mark. Backwash resin bed by attaching source of H_2O to bottom of column, washing resin into reservoir, and letting it settle into column with no flow thru column. Then let H_2O drain to ca 1 cm above top of resin bed, which should be at 4″ mark on column. Prep. sep. column for each sample and std.

38.069 *Extraction*

(*Caution: See* **46.040** *and* **46.053.**)

Accurately weigh quantity of ground feed (≤25 g) contg ca 1.2 mg glycarbylamide (20 g for 0.006%) and transfer to 500 ml g-s flask. Add 200.0 ml DMF and stopper. Stir vigorously 1 hr with magnetic stirrer. Transfer suspension to centrf. tube and centrf. 3–5 min. Alternatively, add 5–10 g Super-Cel or similar filter aid to suspension and filter thru Whatman No. 42 paper on buchner.

38.070 *Chromatography*

Pipet 100 ml clear filtrate onto Al_2O_3 column and let it pass thru column by gravity. Wash column with two 15 ml portions DMF followed by two 25 ml portions anhyd. MeOH. Discard washings.

Elute column with four 50 ml portions H_2O, letting H_2O pass thru column by gravity. Collect eluate in suitable container. Pass entire eluate thru Amberlite IRA-400 column at rate of 2–3 ml/min. Do not permit liq. level to drain into resin bed at any time. Wash column with 10, 20, and 20 ml portions H_2O, rinsing previous container, and drain at flow rate of 3 ml/min. Discard eluate and washings.

Elute column with 15 ml portions dil. HCl at ca 1–2 ml/min. (Do not exceed rate of 2 ml/min or low results may be obtained.) Reject first 3 ml of eluate and collect 50 ml in vol. flask. Stopper and mix thoroly.

38.071 *Determination*

Pipet 25 ml eluate into 50 ml g-s flask, add 1.0 ml Br soln, mix, and let stand 3 min. Add 1.0 ml 2%

NaHSO₃ soln, mix, and let stand 3 min. Finally add 5.0 ml alkali soln and mix carefully.

Pipet 10.0 ml of this soln into clean large test tube marked X. To remainder of soln add 1.0 g HgO, stopper, and shake vigorously 10 min, preferably mech. Transfer to centrf. tube and centrf. Transfer 10.0 ml clear supernatant to clean large test tube marked R. Add 1.0 ml KCN soln to each tube, X and R, and mix. Soln R should not be unnecessarily exposed to light and A measurement should be completed rapidly, preferably within 3 min after addn of KCN soln. Det. A of soln X against soln R in spectrophtr at 283 nm in 1 cm silica cell. Det. cell corrections, using ref. soln R in both cells.

Prep. std by transferring 100.0 ml working soln onto freshly prepd Al₂O₃ column and proceeding exactly as for sample.

% Glycarbylamide in feed = $1.28AC/A'W$, where A refers to sample, A' to std, C = mg glycarbylamide in final aliquot of std (0.100 mg), and W = wt original sample in g.

Nicarbazin (4,4′-Dinitrocarbanilide.2-hydroxy-4,6-dimethylpyrimidine) (18)—Official Final Action

(Presence of furazolidone, nitrofurazone, or nihydrazone may cause high results. Confirm presence of nicarbazin by Identification Test, **38.077**.)

38.072 *Reagents*

(a) *Dimethylformamide (DMF).*—Reagent grade.

(b) *Aluminum oxide.*—See **38.023(b)**.

(c) *Alcohol.*—Formulas SDA Nos. 2B, 3A, or 30 may be used.

(d) *Alcoholic sodium hydroxide soln.*—Dil. 2.0 ml clear 50% NaOH soln, **45.034(b)**, to 100 ml with alcohol. Centrf. in stoppered tube. Prep. fresh daily.

(e) *Nicarbazin std solns.*—(1) *Stock soln.*—Weigh 25.0 mg Nicarbazin Ref. Std (available from Merck & Co.) into 500 ml vol. flask, and dissolve in ca 150 ml DMF with aid of gentle heat. Cool, dil. to vol. with DMF, and mix well. Store protected from light. (2) *Working soln.*—12.5 µg/ml. Transfer 25.0 ml stock soln to 100 ml vol. flask and dil. to vol. with DMF. Mix well.

38.073 *Preparation of Column*

Use glass tube 22 mm id, ca 50 cm long, constricted at lower end. Place plug of glass wool in constricted end and add 30 g Al₂O₃ in 3 portions. Tamp down each portion with glass rod while applying gentle suction. Wash column with 25 ml DMF, draining to point 1–2 cm above bed level before adding sample to column. Prep. column for each sample and std.

Never let column run dry; keep head of liq. at all times.

38.074 *Preparation of Sample*

(*Caution:* See **46.011, 46.040,** and **46.053.**)

Weigh 10.0 g sample into 250 ml erlenmeyer and add 100.0 ml DMF. Heat *just to boiling* on hot plate in hood with intermittent stirring. Cool to room temp. by immersing in H₂O bath. Decant supernatant into centrf. tubes and centrf. 3 min.

38.075 *Determination*

(*Caution:* See **46.018, 46.040,** and **46.053.**)

Pipet 25.0 ml clear ext onto column and let pass thru column with aid of gentle suction. Wash column with three 10 ml portions DMF and reject washings. Elute with nine 5 ml portions alcohol, discarding first 15 ml eluate and collecting next 25 ml eluate in 1 × 8″ tube. Quant. transfer eluate into 50 ml vol. flask and dil. to vol. with alcohol. Mix well.

Pipet 25.0 ml working std soln onto another column and proceed as for sample.

Pipet two 15.0 ml portions sample soln into sep. 25 ml vol. flasks. To one add 5.0 ml alc. NaOH soln and adjust vol. of both solns to 25 ml with alcohol. Read A of yellow soln formed in first flask within 5 min in spectrophtr or colorimeter at 430 nm against second soln as blank. Calc. wt nicarbazin from std curve.

38.076 *Preparation of Standard Curve*

Pipet 10, 15, and 20 ml aliquots of chromatgd working std soln into sep. 25 ml vol. flasks, add 5 ml alc. NaOH, and dil. to vol. with alcohol. Mix well. Measure A within 5 min at 430 nm against alcohol.

Prep. std curve by plotting A against µg nicarbazin.

38.077 *Identification Test*

Place alcohol in 1 cm quartz cell and clear chromatgd sample soln in matched cell. Det. A at 2 nm intervals from 340 to 349 nm with Beckman Model DU spectrophtr (or equiv.) at min. slit width. Absorption max. at 344±4 nm confirms presence of nicarbazin.

Nicotine (19)—Official Final Action

(Applicable in the presence of phenothiazine, dibutyl tin dilaurate, and 2,2′-dihydroxy-5,5′-dichlorodiphenylmethane)

38.078 *Principle*

Nicotine is extd with alkali, steam distd, extd with CHCl₃, and detd spectrophtric in acidic soln.

38.079 *Reagents*

(a) *Dilute hydrochloric acid.*—0.05N. Dil. 4.1 ml HCl to 1 L with H₂O.

(b) *Nicotine std soln.*—0.012 mg/ml. Accurately weigh ca 100 mg nicotine and dil. to 100 ml in vol. flask with 0.05N HCl. Transfer 3.0 ml aliquot to 250 ml vol. flask and dil. to vol with 0.05N HCl. (*Caution:* Nicotine is very toxic.)

(c) *Antifoam.*—Antifoam A (Dow Corning Corp.) or equiv.

38.080 *Apparatus*

(a) *Distillation flask.*—250 ml r-b flask and Claisen distg head (Corning Glass Works No. 9300, or equiv.) or 250 ml Claisen flask.

(b) *Condenser.*—Graham coil type with 300 mm jacket (Corning No. 2500, or equiv.). Must be used in vertical position.

(c) *Ultraviolet recording spectrophotometer.*—Cary Model 11, or equiv.

38.081 **Determination**

(Detn can be interrupted at any step where soln is acidic.)

Accurately weigh representative portion of feed, ground thru No. 20 sieve, contg ca 3 mg nicotine and transfer to 250 ml centrf. bottle. Add 100 ml 0.5% NaOH soln, stopper (Neoprene or rubber), and shake vigorously 1 min. Centrf. ca 5 min at 1500 rpm. Decant free flowing and viscous liq. into 400–600 ml beaker. Rinse lip and centrf. bottle into beaker with few ml H_2O, being careful not to dislodge solid material. Repeat extn, centrfg, and rinsing twice, combining supernatants in beaker. Adjust soln to pH 2–3 with HCl and evap. on hot plate to ca 100 ml. Cool, adjust to pH 10–14 with NaOH (1 + 1), and transfer quant. to distn flask, using min. of H_2O. Vol. must be ≤125 ml. Add 10 drops antifoam to flask. Place tip of condenser below surface of 7 ml H_2SO_4 (1 + 5) in 500 ml flask or beaker (container must be tilted at first to obtain sufficient depth). Steam distill at rate of ≥8 ml/min. (It will be necessary to heat Claisen flask as distn proceeds to avoid condensation of steam in flask.) Collect ca 300 ml distillate. When distn is complete, rinse condenser into receiver with ca 5 ml H_2O.

Transfer distillate to 500 ml separator, rinse with H_2O, make distinctly alk. (pH 10–14) with NaOH (1 + 1), and ext with five 20 ml portions $CHCl_3$. Combine $CHCl_3$ exts in 250 ml separator. Ext nicotine from $CHCl_3$ with 20, 20, 15, 15, and 15 ml portions 0.05N HCl. Combine HCl exts in 125 ml separator and shake gently few sec with 15 ml pet ether to remove any remaining $CHCl_3$. Drain clear HCl layer into 250 ml vol. flask and wash pet ether with addnl 10 ml 0.05N HCl. Drain acid layer into vol. flask, dil. to vol. with 0.05N HCl, and record UV spectrum from 220 to 300 nm in 1 cm cell against 0.05N HCl in recording spectrophtr. Draw line tangent to 2 minima obtained (ca 226 and 280 nm), drop perpendicular from point of max. A (ca 259 nm) to tangent line, and det. net A. Similarly det. net A of std soln. Calc. as % nicotine in feed = (Net A of sample × mg nicotine in final std soln × 100)/ (Net A of std × g sample × 1000).

Nihydrazone (5-Nitro-2-furfuraldehyde acetylhydrazone) (20)—Official Final Action

38.082 **Reagents**

(a) *95% Dimethylformamide (DMF).*—Dil. 95 parts DMF (Eastman Kodak Co. No. 5870, or equiv.) with 5 parts H_2O.

(b) *Nihydrazone std solns.*—(1) *Stock soln.*—Weigh 110 mg cryst. nihydrazone (available from Hess & Clark Laboratories) into 100 ml vol. flask, dissolve in DMF, and dil. to vol. with DMF. Soln is stable several months when protected from light. (2) *Working soln.*—For feeds contg 0.011% nihydrazone, pipet 1 ml aliquot into 100 ml vol. flask, add 50 ml DMF, and dil. to vol. with H_2O.

38.083 **Determination**

Weigh 10 g sample into 125 ml erlenmeyer, add exactly 50 ml 95% DMF, stopper loosely, and place in boiling H_2O bath 5 min (or until temp. of solv. reaches 90°). Shake on mech. shaker 10 min and filter thru rapid paper. To 25 ml filtrate add 25 ml H_2O and mix. Let stand, protected from light, ≥30 min. (Some solids may sep.; standing for longer time is permissible.)

Prep. ca 20 mm diam. adsorption column contg adsorbent, **38.064**(e), to ht of 5 cm. (With highly colored feeds, use somewhat longer column.) Use plug of cotton or glass wool to support column, and similar plug or layer of washed sea sand on top. Pass the 50% DMF soln thru column, collecting ca 15 ml eluate. Pipet 5 ml aliquots into each of 2 tubes. Protect 1 tube from light; to other add 3 drops *freshly prepd 2% Na hydrosulfite soln*, mix, and let stand 5 min. Treat 5 ml aliquots dild std soln similarly.

Pipet 5 ml phenylhydrazine soln, **38.064**(a), into all test tubes, mix, and heat 20 min in H_2O bath at 40°. Cool by placing tubes in 15° H_2O bath 5 min. Add exactly 10 ml toluene to each tube, stopper, and shake vigorously 40 times. Sep. and centrf. toluene layer, and read A at 440 nm. [($A_{samp.} - A_{red.\ samp.}$) × 0.011]/($A_{std} - A_{red.\ std}$) = % nihydrazone.

Nithiazide (1-Ethyl-3-(5-nitro-2-thiazolyl) urea) (21)—Official Final Action

38.084 **Reagents**

(a) *Dimethylformamide (DMF).*—Reagent grade. If A of reagent blank as detd in **38.087** is >0.050, purify as follows: Add 1 g activated charcoal, NF XI/100 ml DMF. Shake ca 2 min, and filter. Refilter if not clear. (*Caution: See* **46.011, 46.018, 46.040,** and **46.053.**)

(b) *Aluminum oxide.*—See **38.023**(b).

(c) *Sodium hydroxide soln.*—1.0N aq. soln.

(d) *Procaine soln.*—Dissolve 100 mg procaine .HCl, USP, in 70 ml H_2O, add 20.0 ml HCl, mix well, cool to room temp., dil. to 100 ml with H_2O, and mix well.

(e) *Coupling reagent.*—See **38.013**(d). Prep. fresh daily.

(f) *Nithiazide std solns.*—(1) *Stock soln.*—0.400 mg/ml. Weigh 40.0 mg Nithiazide Ref. Std (available from Merck & Co.) into 100 ml vol. flask and dissolve in and dil. to vol. with DMF. Protected from light, soln is stable ca 6 weeks. (2) *Working soln.*—10 µg/ml. Pipet 5 ml std stock soln into 200 ml vol. flask, dil to vol. with DMF, and mix well.

38.085   *Extraction*

Accurately weigh quantity of ground sample (≤ 4 g) contg ca 0.5 mg nithiazide and transfer to 100 ml vol. flask. Add 50.00 ml DMF, stopper loosely, and heat 10 min at 60–75° (not >75°) in H_2O bath or on steam bath, swirling frequently. Remove flask and shake 15 min on shaking machine. Cool to room temp., transfer mixt. to 50 ml centrf. tube, and centrf.

38.086   *Chromatography*

(a) *Preparation of aluminum oxide.*—Transfer 200 g Al_2O_3 to 1 L beaker. Add 500 ml H_2O and agitate 5 min with mech. stirrer. Let settle 5 min and decant supernatant. Repeat washing with 2 addnl 500 ml portions H_2O and decant supernatant as completely as possible. Add 300 ml MeOH to Al_2O_3 and agitate ca 3 min. Filter thru buchner, continue to apply suction ca 5 min, and dry 4 hr at 110°. Store in tightly stoppered bottle.

(b) *Preparation of column.*—Prep. chromatgc tube as in **38.025**(b). Transfer 3.0 g prepd Al_2O_3 to tube in 2 equal portions. Lightly tamp each portion with glass rod while applying gentle suction. Wash column with 10.0 ml DMF and drain liq. to ca 5 mm above bed level prior to adding sample soln to column. Do not permit column to run dry; keep 5 mm head of liq. at all times. Prep. column for each sample, std, and reagent blank.

(c) *Chromatography of feed extract.*—Pipet 20 ml clear feed ext onto column and let it pass thru column by gravity. Do not let column run dry; keep 5 mm head of liq. Wash inner walls of tube and Al_2O_3 with three 4.0 ml portions DMF added from pipet. Let final DMF wash drain thru column until no further liq. appears at tip of column. Dry tip of column with filter paper.

Elute column by gravity with 4 ml portions H_2O. Collect first 1.0 ml eluate in graduated cylinder and reject; then collect eluate in 25 ml vol. flask until liq. level is just below mark. Adjust with H_2O to mark, stopper, and mix well. (Required time for elution should be ≤ 60 min; appreciably longer time indicates improper column prepn.)

38.087   *Determination*

Pipet 10 ml clear eluate into 25 ml vol. flask. Add 5.0 ml 1N NaOH, mix well, and let stand 10 min at 20–25°. Add 5.0 ml procaine soln, mix well, and let stand 2 min at 20–25°; then add enough coupling reagent to mark, stopper, mix, and let stand 15 min. (If colored soln is not clear, filter thru clean fritted glass funnel of medium or fine porosity.) Det. A of purple-red soln, in 1 cm cell in spectrophtr or colorimeter at 540 nm, against H_2O as ref.

Prep. reagent blank by transferring 20.0 ml DMF onto freshly prepd column and proceeding in exactly same manner as for sample.

Prep. std by transferring 20.0 ml nithiazide work-ing std onto freshly prepd column and proceeding in exactly same manner as for sample.

% Nithiazide in feed = $5C(A - A'')/8W(A' - A'')$, where A refers to sample, A' to std, A'' reagent blank, C = mg nithiazide in final aliquot of std (0.080 mg), and W = wt original sample in g.

Nitrodan (3-Methyl-5-(p-nitrophenyl-azo) rhodanine) (22)—Official Final Action

(Not applicable in presence of interfering nitro compds)

38.088   *Reagents*

(a) *N,N-Dimethylformamide (DMF) and alcohol solvent.*—(1 + 1). Mix equal vols DMF and alcohol (anhyd. or SDF 3A). Store in tightly closed container.

(b) *NaOH soln.*—2N. Dissolve 8 g NaOH in H_2O and dil. to 100 ml with H_2O.

(c) *Nitrodan std solns.*—(1) *Stock soln.*—200 µg/ml. Weigh exactly 50 mg nitrodan (available from Cooper Laboratories, 229 Cleveland Ave, Harrison, NJ 07029). Rinse into 250 ml vol. flask with DMF-alcohol solv., and dil. to ca 150 ml. Break up nitrodan particles with flattened stirring rod and shake to facilitate soln or dissolve, using magnetic stirrer. (Be sure all particles are dissolved.) Dil. to vol. and mix. (2) *Working soln.*—10 µg/ml. Pipet 5 ml stock soln into 100 ml vol. flask, dil. to vol. with DMF-alcohol solv., and mix.

Prep. all std solns same day as std curve.

38.089   *Preparation of Standard Curve*

Pipet 5, 10, 15, and 20 ml (50, 100, 150, and 200 µg nitrodan) working soln into four 50 ml vol. flasks. Dil. almost to vol. with DMF-alcohol solv. and mix. Just before reading, add 1 drop 2N NaOH to each flask, dil. to vol. with DMF-alcohol, and mix. Read A in 1 cm cells on Beckman Model DU spectrophtr, or equiv., at 575 nm against solv. Plot A against concn (µg/ml).

38.090   *Preparation of Sample*

(a) *Meals and pellets.*—Grind sample to pass thru sieve with 1 mm circular openings and mix thoroly.

(b) *Expanded dog food.*—Grind in high-speed blender ca 3 oz representative sample until chunks are broken (30–60 sec). Transfer to mixing jar and brush in fines that adhere to blender. Mix thoroly.

38.091   *Determination*

Weigh 2.0 g sample (or larger if necessary) and transfer to small glass mortar. Add ca 15 ml DMF-alcohol and grind with pestle to ensure complete contact of drug and solv. Quant. rinse sample and soln into medium porosity fritted glass funnel connected to 250 ml suction flask. Filter and wash with small portions of solv. until washings and residue are no longer violet. (Avoid unnecessary delay.) Transfer filtrate to vol. flask of vol. to yield final concn of 1–4 µg nitrodan/ml. Add 1 drop 2N NaOH just before reading, dil. to vol. with solv., and mix. Measure A within 10 min in 1 cm cell at 575 nm against solv.

% Nitrodan in sample = [(μg nitrodan/ml final soln) (from std curve) $\times$ 100]/(g sample/ml final soln) $\times$ 10^6.

38.092 Nitrofurazone—Official Final Action

See 38.064–38.065.

Nitromide (3,5-Dinitrobenzamide) (3,5-DNBA) (23)—Official Final Action

38.093 *Reagents*

(a) *Diethylamine reagent (DEA), aged.*—(1 year or older.) Fresh DEA may be artificially aged as follows: Place 1 L DEA in dry 2 L flask with 40 g Na or K fluosilicate. Connect flask to 24″ bulb reflux condenser and reflux on sand bath 2–3 days in hood. When reagent is sufficiently "aged," 2 ml clear DEA added to 8 ml dimethylsulfoxide contg 50 μg 3,5-dinitrobenzamide should develop max. color in ca 40 min. A as read on Beckman DU spectrophtr at 560 nm should be ca 0.375; on Klett-Summerson photoelec. colorimeter with No. 56 filter, ca 200. Reagent must be free from turbidity. Prep. new std curve for each batch of DEA.

(b) *3,5-Dinitrobenzamide (DNBA) std solns.*—(1) *Stock soln.*—1 mg/ml. Weigh 100 mg 3,5-DNBA into 100 ml flask and dil. to vol. with MeOH. (2) *Working soln.*—20 μg/ml. Transfer 2.0 ml aliquot stock soln to 100 ml vol. flask and dil. to vol. with MeOH.

38.094 *Preparation of Standard Curve*

Place 1.0, 2.0, 3.0, and 5.0 ml working soln contg 20, 40, 60, and 100 μg, resp., of 3,5-DNBA in 4 colorimeter tubes. Evap. to dryness in air current at 50°. Dissolve residue in 8 ml dimethylsulfoxide at 70°, cool, and add 2 ml DEA reagent. Place in dark at 20–25° and read after 60 min. Plot std curve, using A as ordinate and concn as abscissa.

38.095 *Preparation of Sample*

Weigh 5.0 g feed, contg 0.025% 3,5-DNBA, into 100 ml vol. flask and dil. to vol. with MeOH. Shake frequently 20 min and let stand 40 min to permit feed particles to settle.

If feed contains 0.075% 3,5-DNBA, use 2 g finely ground feed; if 0.15%, use 1 g in 100 ml or 5 g in 500 ml MeOH. Prep. premixes by weighing appropriate sample and serially dilg MeOH ext.

38.096 *Determination*

Pipet 4 ml aliquot of ext into g-s test tube. Place tube in H_2O bath at 50° and evap. to dryness with air current directed onto surface of MeOH. Add 8 ml dimethylsulfoxide and heat to 70° to hasten soln, cool, and add 2 ml DEA reagent. Place in dark at 20–25° for 60 min. Det A at 560 nm in Beckman DU spectrophtr, Klett-Summerson photoelec. colorim-

eter with No. 56 filter, or similar instrument, against dimethylsulfoxide as ref.

Det. amt of 3,5-DNBA in tube from std curve.

% 3,5-DNBA in feed
= μg 3,5-DNBA in tube $\times$ 25 $\times$ 100/5,000,000;
or μg 3,5-DNBA in tube $\times$ 5 = μg 3,5-DNBA/g of feed or ppm.

Nitrophenide (m,m′-Dinitrodiphenyldisulfide) (24)—Official Final Action

(Applicable in presence of arsanilic acid)

38.097 *Reagent*

(a) *Buffer soln.*—pH 6.6. Dissolve 41.29 g anhyd. Na_2HPO_4 in H_2O and dil. to 1 L. Dissolve 11.47 g citric acid.H_2O in H_2O and dil. to 1 L. Mix in equal proportions.

(b) *Nitrophenide reference std.*—Available from American Cyanamid Co.

38.098 *Determination*

Transfer 2 g ground sample to 300 ml erlenmeyer, add 0.5 g $Na_2S_2O_4$ and 50 ml buffer soln, and place in boiling H_2O bath 20 min. Remove flask, slowly add 10 ml HCl, and replace flask in boiling H_2O bath 5 min. (This heating destroys arsanilic acid and ppts colloidal S.) Remove flask, connect to compressed air or vac. manifold, and aerate vigorously 15 min. Transfer to 100 ml vol. flask, cool, dil. to vol. with H_2O, and mix. Filter thru Whatman No. 42 paper (or equiv.), discarding first 15 ml filtrate if turbid.

Pipet 5 ml portions of clear filtrate into each of two 50 ml beakers; to each add 2 ml *freshly prepd 0.1% NaNO_2 soln.* After 5 min, add 2 ml *0.50% aq. NH_4 sulfamate soln,* and let stand 2 min. Add 1 ml coupling reagent, 38.013(d), to first beaker and 1 ml H_2O to second. Thoroly mix solns after adding each reagent. After 10 min, add 15 ml H_2O to each beaker and mix. Read A of both solns against H_2O blank in spectrophtr at 545 nm. Subtract A of feed blank from sample A and det. quantity of nitrophenide from std curve. Divide by 1000 to obtain % nitrophenide.

38.099 *Preparation of Standard Curve*

Transfer 0.10 g pure nitrophenide to 100 ml vol. flask, dissolve in 50 ml acetone, and dil. to vol. with acetone. Pipet 10 ml aliquot into another 100 ml vol. flask and dil. to vol. with acetone. Pipet 2, 3, 4, 5, and 6 ml portions of this dild soln into sep. 100 ml vol. flasks and carefully evap. in gentle air stream. To each flask add 0.5 g $Na_2S_2O_4$ and 50 ml buffer soln, and proceed as in 38.098, aerating 20 min. Plot std curve representing 10, 15, 20, 25, and 30 μg nitrophenide against A.

Note: Detn may be performed in 100 ml vol. flasks, if care is taken to add HCl *slowly* and in *small portions* with constant swirling, after reduction, in order to avoid excessive foaming and loss of soln.

4-Nitrophenylarsonic Acid (Nitarsone)
(25)—Official First Action

38.100 *Principle*

Nitarsone is extd from feed with 50% dimethyl-sulfoxide (DMSO) and sepd from interferences by Al_2O_3 chromatgy. The nitro group is reduced with aq. 4% $TiCl_3$ and resulting amine assayed colorimetrically at 530 nm with Bratton-Marshall reaction. Arsanilic acid and carbarsone interfere.

38.101 *Reagents*

(a) *Nitarsone std solns.*—(1) *Stock soln.*—1 mg/ml. Weigh 100 mg nitarsone std (available from Salsbury Laboratories) into 100 ml vol. flask and dil. to vol. with 4% NaOH. (2) *Working soln.*—50 μg/ml. Dil. 10 ml stock soln to 200 ml with 4% NaOH.

(b) *Activated alumina.*—Alcoa grade F-20, 80–200 mesh (available from Fisher Scientific Co. as Alumina, adsorption, Fisher No. A-540). To det. suitability of Al_2O_3, perform entire detn on 100 μg nitarsone. Recovery should be >95%.

(c) *Dimethylsulfoxide (DMSO) soln.*—50%. Dil. with equal vol. H_2O. (*Caution:* DMSO can be harmful. Avoid skin contact by wearing heavy rubber gloves. Use effective fume removal device.)

(d) *Titanous chloride soln.*—4% aq. Prep. fresh daily from 20% soln open ≤3 months and kept refrigerated, or from solid $TiCl_3$. If >1 min required for color disappearance in detn, use fresh source of $TiCl_3$. (*Caution:* $TiCl_3$ is corrosive. Wear disposable plastic or rubber gloves. Avoid contact with eyes.)

(e) *Sodium nitrite soln.*—0.1% aq. Prep. weekly.

38.102 *Preparation of Standard Curve*

Pipet 0, 2, 5, 10, 15, 20, and 25 ml working soln into sep. 100 ml vol. flasks and dil. to vol. with 4% NaOH. Pipet 10 ml from each flask into sep. 50 ml vol. flasks, add 15 ml 4% NaOH, and dil. to vol. with H_2O. Pipet 4 ml from each flask into sep. test tubes and develop color as in **38.104,** beginning "... add 2 drops 4% $TiCl_3$ ..." Std concns correspond to 0, 0.004, 0.010, 0.020, 0.030, 0.040, and 0.050% nitarsone in feeds. Plot std curve of A against % drug in feed.

38.103 *Preparation of Sample*

Accurately weigh 5 g finely ground feed into 100 ml vol. flask. Add 75 ml 50% DMSO, place sample on wrist action mech. shaker, and shake at room temp. 30 min. Dil. to vol. with 50% DMSO and mix. Transfer 30–40 ml to 50 ml centrf. tube and centrf. 10 min at 2000 rpm.

38.104 *Determination*

(*Caution: See* **46.018.**)

Add Al_2O_3 to 20 × 400 mm chromatgc tube with fritted glass disk to depth of 7 cm. Tap tube wall to settle Al_2O_3; then add 1 cm layer of sand. Prewash column with 50 ml 50% DMSO before use.

Pipet 10 ml supernatant from prepn of sample onto prewashed column. For feeds contg >0.04% nitarsone, use smaller aliquot. Let sample enter column and then wash into column with several 5 ml portions H_2O. Wash column with 75 ml H_2O and discard eluate.

Elute nitarsone with 65 ml 4% NaOH, discarding first 15 ml. Collect remaining eluate in 100 ml vol. flask, letting column run dry. Nitarsone is eluted with ca 25–30 ml eluant. Dil. eluate to vol. with H_2O and mix.

Pipet 4 ml dild eluate into 2 test tubes, add 2 drops 4% $TiCl_3$ to each with mixing, and shake or mix on Vortex mixer until black color disappears. Add 2 ml HCl to each and mix thoroly. Add 0.5 ml 0.1% $NaNO_2$, (e), and mix. After 5 min, add 0.5 ml 0.5% NH_4 sulfamate, **38.013**(c), and mix. After 2 min, add 0.5 ml 0.1% coupling reagent, **38.013**(d), to one tube and 0.5 ml H_2O to second tube for blank. Let color develop 15 min; then read A of sample and blank at 530 nm on spectrophtr. Correct sample A for blank A and det. amt nitarsone in sample from std curve.

Phenothiazine (26)—Official Final Action

38.105 *Reagent*

Phenothiazine std soln.—Dissolve 10 mg recrystd (from 10% soln in toluene) phenothiazine in 50 ml alcohol and dil. to 100 ml with alcohol. For working stds, dil. with equal vol. of alcohol. (1 ml dild soln = 50 μg phenothiazine.) Use freshly prepd soln; alc. solns gradually develop rose tint within few hr.

38.106 *Determination*

Place 1 g ground sample in 100 ml vol. flask, add 50 ml alcohol, and heat on steam bath 15 min. Cool, dil. to vol. with alcohol, mix, and let settle (ca 15 min) until supernatant is clear.

Place 2 ml aliquot in 25 ml vol. flask and add 10 ml alcohol. To flask add, in order given, 1 ml *1% alc. p-aminobenzoic acid,* 1 ml *aq. 2% NaNO₂,* and 1 ml HCl (1 + 3). Dil. to vol. with alcohol. Read A of green soln at 600 nm in spectrophtr against reagent blank. Det. quantity phenothiazine from std curve. % phenothiazine = μg/200.

Prep. ref. curve, using 1, 2, and 3 ml dil. std soln, as above.

Piperazine (27)—Official Final Action

38.107 *Principle*

Piperazine or piperazine salt is quant. extd from feed into slightly acidic aq. soln. Dild filtrate is reacted with equal vol. benzoquinone at 80°. Colored complex formed is detd spectrophtric at 490 nm.

Applicable to detn of 0.05–0.5% piperazine, usually present as one of its salts, in animal feeds. Amines give similar color reaction. Alkalies produce increased color; pH adjustment in method overcomes interference of this kind.

38.108 *Apparatus*

(a) *Water bath.*—Approx. 10″ diam. with 6–8″ depth H_2O. Thermostatically controlled at $80\pm0.1°$. (Viscosity bath is satisfactory.)

(b) *Test tubes.*—Pyrex, 15 × 125 mm, with rubber stoppers and rack capable of supporting tubes when immersed in H_2O bath.

(c) *Spectrophotometer.* — Beckman Instruments Model B, or equiv.

38.109 *Reagents*

(a) *Quinone soln.*—Dissolve 0.5 g p-benzoquinone in 2.5 ml HOAc and little alcohol in dry 100 ml vol. flask and dil. to vol. with alcohol. Keep soln in ice bath or refrigerator. Prep. fresh daily. (*Note: p*-Benzoquinone is lachrymator; avoid breathing vapor and contact with skin and clothing.) If blanks are high or variable, purify p-benzoquinone by steam distn in hood.

(b) *Piperazine std solns.*—(1) *Stock soln.*—Dissolve exactly 185 mg pure piperazine.2HCl (equiv. to 100 mg piperazine) in H_2O and dil. to 250 ml. (2) *Working soln.*—20 µg/ml. Dil. 25.0 ml stock soln to vol. in 500 ml vol. flask.

38.110 *Preparation of Standard Curve*

Using working soln, add by microburet or pipets 20, 40, 60, 80, and 100 µg piperazine equiv. and intermediate values, if required, into test tubes. Dil. to 5 ml in each test tube with H_2O. Carry H_2O blank with each detn.

Add 5 ml quinone reagent to each std and blank. Stopper tubes and mix by inverting. Remove stoppers and immerse in H_2O bath at $80\pm0.1°$ exactly 10 min. (Bath temp. can be varied; use same temp. for samples and stds.) Immediately immerse tubes in ice bath 3 min. Let stand at room temp. 20 min, but $\leq$40 min. Read A at 490 nm in 1.0 cm cells, using reagent blank to zero instrument. Plot A of each std against µg piperazine.

38.111 *Determination*

Weigh 10.00 g well-mixed feed (grind pellets in mortar) into 16 oz wide-mouth, screw-cap bottle. Add exactly 200 ml H_2O from graduated cylinder and adjust to pH 4–5 (0.15 ml H_2SO_4 (1 + 2) is usually enough for 10 g feed). Cap or stopper bottle and place in wrist-action shaker, or equiv., 30 min. Add ca 5 g Celite as slurry to buchner contg 9.0 cm Whatman No. 3 paper and pull down under full vac. Wash pad with small portion feed ext and discard washing. Rapidly filter remaining feed ext and reserve filtrate for color development. (Do not delay; turbidity may form.)

Pipet 25.0 ml filtrate into 250 ml vol. flask and dil. to vol. with H_2O. Pipet 5 ml aliquot into test tube and immediately proceed with color development as in **38.110.** Carry H_2O blank with each detn.

Prep. sample color blank for each feed as follows: Pipet 5 ml aliquot dild ext into test tube and 5 ml H_2O into another test tube as ref. To each, add 5 ml soln contg 2.5 ml HOAc dild to 100 ml with alcohol. Mix by inverting and omit heating. Read A at same wavelength and subtract from sample reading. Run 1 or 2 stds with each detn to detect shift in std curve; adjust accordingly.

Calc. µg piperazine from std curve.

% Piperazine = (µg piperazine $\times 10^{-4}$)/g sample in aliquot.

Racephenicol (*dl*-Threo-2,2-dichloro-N-(β-hydroxy-α-(hydroxymethyl)-*p*-(methylsulfonyl) phenethyl] acetamide) —Official Final Action

Method I (28)

(Applicable to levels >0.002%)

38.112 *Principles*

Racephenicol is extd from feed samples with acetone, and the dichloroacetamido group is converted to amine compd by alk. hydrolysis. After cleanup, amine is oxidized with periodate to HCHO, methylamine, and p-methylsulfonylbenzaldehyde and latter detd by UV spectrophotometry. With blank correction, method will measure levels as low as 0.002%.

38.113 *Reagents*

(a) *Acetone.*—Test as follows: Evap. 20 ml to dryness in g-s flask. Take up any residue with 10 ml CH_2Cl_2 and measure A at 243 nm in 1 cm cell against CH_2Cl_2. A should be $\leq$0.03.

(b) *Methylene chloride.*—Spectral grade.

(c) *Sodium periodate soln.*—0.5%.

(d) *Racephenicol std soln.*—10 µg/ml. Dissolve 100.0 mg Racephenicol Ref. Std (available from Sterling-Winthrop Research Institute, Rensselaer, NY 12144) in 200.0 ml acetone. (Racephenicol dissolves slowly but completely.) Dil. 2.0 ml to 100 ml with acetone.

38.114 *Determination*

Accurately weigh ca 10 g sample into 250 ml g-s flask. Add 100 ml acetone by pipet, stopper, and shake vigorously 10 min. Filter ext thru Whatman No. 1 paper, or equiv., into dry flask. (Cover funnel with watch glass and take care to minimize solv. evapn.)

Transfer vol. filtrate contg ca 100 µg racephenicol to 100 ml beaker. If feed sample contains <0.005% but >0.002%, take identical vol. for feed blank detn. If feed blank is run, det. blank on all reagents carried thru entire detn.

Transfer 10.0 ml (100 µg) racephenicol std soln to 100 ml beaker. Evap. all beakers *just to dryness* on steam bath. No acetone odor should remain. Add 5 ml 0.4N NaOH to beakers, cover, and heat on steam bath 30 min, swirling occasionally. Do not evap. to dryness. Add 5 ml H_2O and transfer to individual

separators. Rinse beakers into separators with 5 ml
H₂O, 5 ml *1N HCl*, and then addnl 5 ml H₂O. Ext
with four 30 ml portions CHCl₃, shaking 30 sec each
time, and discard CHCl₃. Add 2–3 ml *10% Na₂CO₃*
soln to separators to adjust pH to 7.5–8.5 (indicator
paper; det. pH 30 sec after Na₂CO₃ addn and mixing). Add 5 ml 0.5% NaIO₄ soln to std, sample, and
reagent blank separators. *Do not add NaIO₄ to feed
blank sample.* Swirl, stopper separators, and let
stand 10 min.

Ext with three 10 ml portions CHCl₃. Filter exts
thru small CHCl₃-moistened cotton pledget, inserted
in stem of small funnel, into dry 50 ml ℥ flasks.
Evap. to ca 2 ml on steam bath under current of N.
Remove flasks from steam bath and displace last
traces of CHCl₃ with N (no odor). Pipet in 10 ml
CH₂Cl₂, stopper, and mix by swirling.

Transfer CH₂Cl₂ solns to 1 cm silica cells and det.
A at 243 nm against CH₂Cl₂.

38.115   *Calculations*

For level >0.005%; reagent and feed blanks not
used:

$$\% \text{ racephenicol} = \frac{(A_{\text{sample}}) \ (\text{mg std}) \ (0.1)}{(A_{\text{std}}) \ (\text{g sample in original acetone ext})}$$

For levels 0.002–0.005%; reagent and feed blanks
used:

$$\% \text{ racephenicol} = \frac{(A_{\text{sample}} - A_{\text{sample blank}}) \ (\text{mg std}) \ (0.1)}{(A_{\text{std}} - A_{\text{reagent blank}}) \ (\text{g sample in original acetone ext})}$$

Method II (29)

(Applicable to levels ≥0.0005%; *Caution: See
46.011, 46.018, 46.039, 46.040, and 46.043.*)

38.116   *Principles*

Feed samples are extd with hot CH₃CN. Fats are
selectively removed with hexane and CH₃CN is
volatilized. Nonvolatile material remaining is hydrolyzed to remove dichloracetamido group of racephenicol. Soln is cleaned up with CHCl₃ and oxidized
with periodate, converting residual amine compd to
p-methylsulfonylbenzaldehyde, which is measured
by UV spectrophotometry, using curvature inversion
technic.

38.117   *Apparatus*

(a) *Ratio recording ultraviolet spectrophotometer.*—
With 1.0 cm silica cells.

(b) *Centrifuge tubes.*—℥, 100 ml.

38.118   *Reagents*

(a) *Acetonitrile.*—Eastman Kodak Co., Spectro
Grade, or equiv.

(b) *Equilibrated acetonitrile and equilibrated n-
hexane.*—Shake 400 ml CH₃CN with 400 ml *n*-
hexane in 1 L separator 5 min. Filter lower equilibrated CH₃CN phase thru paper, det. wt of 100 ml

filtrate, and retain. Discard ca 15 ml lower portion
of hexane phase, pour remainder thru paper, and
retain. (These equilibrated solvs are to be used in
extn steps only and are not for use in spectrophtric
measurements.)

(c) *p-Methylsulfonylbenzaldehyde (p-MSBA) std
solns.*—(1) *Stock soln.*—500 μg/ml. Dissolve 50 mg
p-MSBA (available from Special Chemical Dept.,
Winthrop Laboratories) in 100 ml CH₃CN. (2) *Intermediate soln.*—10 μg/ml. Dil. 4 ml stock soln to 200
ml with CH₃CN. (3) *Working solns.*—4.0, 4.4, 4.8,
5.2, 5.6, 6.0, 6.4 μg/ml. Dil. 10, 11, 12, 13, 14, 15,
and 16 ml aliquots of intermediate soln to 25 ml.
Prep. working solns fresh weekly.

38.119   *Extraction*

Transfer feed sample contg 100 μg racephenicol to
250 ml ℥ flask. Record combined wt of flask and
sample. Add 70 ml equilibrated CH₃CN, and reflux
on hot plate 30 min, using H₂O-cooled condenser.
Remove flask from heat and let cool slowly to room
temp. Place flask and contents on balance. Add
equilibrated CH₃CN drop by drop until wt equals
wt of flask, sample, and predetd wt of 100 ml equilibrated CH₃CN. Stopper flask, mix, and decant ca 65
ml into 100 ml ℥ centrf. tube. Add 35 ml equilibrated
n-hexane, stopper, and shake vigorously. Centrf. ca
1–2 min, and aspirate hexane phase. Repeat addn of
35 ml equilibrated hexane, mixing, centrfg, and
hexane removal 3 times. After removal of last hexane
ext, transfer, by pipet, exactly 50 ml CH₃CN phase
to 100 ml beaker.

Evap. solv. to dryness over steam with aid of current of N. Add 5 ml 0.4N NaOH to beaker, place
watch glass over beaker, and continue heating over
steam 30 min. Do not permit to go to dryness.
Periodically, while heating, swirl gently. Add 5 ml
H₂O, transfer to 125 ml separator, and wash beaker
with addnl 5 ml H₂O and then with 5 ml 1N HCl.
Rinse beaker with 5 ml H₂O, and add to separator.
Ext with five 30 ml portions CHCl₃, shaking 30 sec
after each addn; let phases sep., and drain and discard CHCl₃.

Add 2–3 ml 10% Na₂CO₃ soln to acid-aq. phase
remaining in separator to adjust pH to 7.5–8.5. Det.
pH with indicator paper 30 sec after Na₂CO₃ addn
and mixing. If necessary, adjust again to pH 7.5–8.5.
Add 5 ml *0.5% NaIO₄ soln*, swirl, stopper, and let
separator stand 10 min. Add 5 ml 1N HCl and ext
with three 10 ml portions CHCl₃. Filter each ext thru
small CHCl₃-moistened pledget of cotton in top of
stem of glass filtering funnel. Collect filtrate in dry
50 ml ℥ flask. Evap. CHCl₃ to ca 3 ml on steam
bath with current of N. Remove flask from heat and
displace remainder of CHCl₃ with N. Add exactly 5
ml CH₃CN, stopper, and mix thoroly.

38.120   *Determination*

Transfer CH₃CN soln to 1 cm silica cell. Position
covered cell in sample cell compartment of spec-

trophtr. Transfer 4 μg/ml p-MSBA working std soln to second 1 cm silica cell and position covered cell in ref. cell compartment. Arrange wavelength scale expansion gears to produce ca 1 cm horizontal pen travel for each 25 nm wavelength change. With instrument set to record A, scan from 275 to 245 nm. Remove ref. cell, and discard contents. Rinse cell with two portions of 4.4 μg/ml p-MSBA std, fill cell with this std soln, and place cell in instrument. Reposition instrument at 275 nm, and repeat scan as for previous std soln. Continue process of replacing working std solns in ref. cell and rescanning until all stds have been run relative to sample soln. Det. concn of p-MSBA std that corresponds to point of curve inversion in vicinity of 250 nm. This is equiv. to concn of derived p-MSBA in sample soln (C).

% Racephenicol in feed =

$$\frac{C(\mu g/ml) \times 1.936 \times 5 \times 100 \times 100}{g\ sample \times 10^6 \times V}$$
$$= \frac{C(\mu g/ml) \times 9.68 \times 10^{-2}}{g\ sample \times V}$$

where V = vol. in ml of equilibrated CH_3CN evapd after hexane extn step.

Reserpine (30)—Official Final Action

(Applicable at 0.2–2.0 ppm level)

38.121 *Reagents*

(a) *Citric acid soln.*—Dissolve 2.0 g citric acid .H_2O in H_2O and dil. to 100 ml.

(b) *Sodium nitrite soln.*—Dissolve 0.1 g $NaNO_2$ in 50 ml H_2O and dil. to 100 ml with MeOH. Prep. fresh daily.

(c) *Sodium bicarbonate soln.*—Dissolve 1.0 g $NaHCO_3$ in H_2O and dil. to 100 ml.

(d) *Dilute sulfuric acid.*—Add 3.0 ml H_2SO_4 to ca 1 L H_2O and let cool to room temp.

(e) *Quinine sulfate soln.*—0.5 μg/ml. Dissolve 50 mg quinine sulfate in dil. H_2SO_4 and dil. to 100 ml with dil. H_2SO_4 (*Soln 1*). Dil. 2 ml *Soln 1* to 100 ml with dil. H_2SO_4 (*Soln 2*). Dil 5 ml *Soln 2* to 100 ml with dil. H_2SO_4 (*Soln 3*).

(f) *Reserpine std soln.*—2 μg/ml. Dissolve 50 mg reserpine in $CHCl_3$ and dil. to 50 ml (*Soln 1*). Dil. 4 ml *Soln 1* to 100 ml with $CHCl_3$ (*Soln 2*). Dil. 5 ml *Soln 2* to 100 ml with $CHCl_3$ (*Soln 3*). Prep. all solns fresh daily.

(g) *Desicote.*—Beckman Instruments No. 18772.

38.122 *Apparatus*

(a) *Photofluorometer.* — Coleman Instruments Model 12C with primary filter PC-6 (Corning Glass Works No. 7–51) and secondary filter PC-9A (Corning No. 3–71) or equiv. com. instrument with necessary sensitivity. Wavelengths of max. excitation and fluorescence of reserpine treated with HNO_2 are 390 and 510 nm, resp. (*Caution: See* **46.008.**)

(b) *Separators.*—500, 125, and 60 ml Squibb type with Teflon stopcocks. Coat 500 ml separators with Desicote as precaution to prevent adsorption of

reserpine by glass during n-hexane-citric acid extn. Adsorption is particularly significant in 8 μg std. Add 10–20 ml Desicote fluid to one 500 ml separator and shake until entire inner surface is wetted. Drain Desicote into other 500 ml separator and repeat. Dry separators by passing air current thru them. Remove any visible film by rinsing with CCl_4. Discard CCl_4 and air-dry separators as before. (*Caution:* Desicote may be harmful. Avoid contact with skin and eyes. Use effective fume removal device.)

(c) *Funnel.*—Buchner with fritted disk, coarse porosity, 60 ml capacity.

(d) *Filter bell.*—New York Laboratory Supply Co. No. 35070, or equiv.

38.123 *Extraction*

(All glassware must be scrupulously clean. Wash with $CHCl_3$ and/or MeOH and dry. Complete all assays in 1 day. Keep exposure of reserpine in $CHCl_3$ to light at min.)

Accurately weigh 2 ca 40 g samples. (Grind pelletized feed in high-speed blender ca 5 min.) Treat each sep. as follows: Press sample down firmly in funnel. Add 15–20 ml $CHCl_3$ (do not stir) to each funnel and collect filtrate in 100 ml vol. flask in filter bell with mild vac. Continue extns with 10–15 ml portions $CHCl_3$ until ca 100 ml collects; dil. to 100 ml with $CHCl_3$ and mix well.

(a) *For 2.0 ppm (0.0002%).*—Pipet 10 ml $CHCl_3$ ext of each sample and 30 ml $CHCl_3$ into sep. 500 ml separators.

(b) *For 1.0 ppm (0.0001%).*—Pipet 20 ml $CHCl_3$ ext of each sample and 20 ml $CHCl_3$ into sep. 500 ml separators.

(c) *For 0.2 ppm (0.00002%).*—Transfer 100 ml $CHCl_3$ ext to 500 ml r-b flask, rinsing with several small portions $CHCl_3$, and evap. to ca 20 ml under vac. at temp. ≤60° by means of rotating vac. evaporator. Transfer each concd ext to sep. 500 ml separators. Rinse flasks with two 10 ml portions $CHCl_3$ and add rinsings to separators.

Add 400 ml n-hexane to each separator and mix well. To each of 2 addnl 500 ml separators, add exactly 4 ml std reserpine *Soln 3*, 36 ml $CHCl_3$, and 400 ml n-hexane. Treat both samples and stds similarly and simultaneously. Ext with three 20 ml portions citric acid soln by shaking each ext *gently* for total of 5 min. (To avoid emulsions, shake 1 min and let sep.; repeat shaking twice for 2 min, and let sep. after each shaking.) Combine citric acid exts in 125 ml separator and ext with three 10 ml portions $CHCl_3$ by shaking *gently* ca 1 min for each extn. Combine $CHCl_3$ exts in 60 ml separator, add 5 ml $NaHCO_3$ soln, and shake gently 1 min. Let sep., and withdraw lower $CHCl_3$ layer into 50 ml vol. flask. Dil. to vol. with MeOH, and mix well.

38.124 *Development of Fluorescence*

Pipet two 15 ml portions of each feed ext and two 15 ml portions of each extd std into sep. 25 ml vol.

flasks (total of 8 flasks). To each add 0.5 ml HCl and swirl gently. To 1 flask from each feed extn and to 1 from each std, add 1.0 ml NaNO₂ soln from pipet and swirl gently (total of 4 flasks). To other flasks (blanks), add 1 ml dil. MeOH (1 + 1). Let stand 30 min, swirling occasionally, and dil. to vol. with MeOH.

Adjust photofluorometer to give galvanometer readings of 100 with quinine sulfate *Soln 3* and to 0 with dil. H₂SO₄. (With other suitable instruments, set 4.0 ml unextd std reserpine *Soln 3*, dild and developed as above for extd stds, to 60–80.) Det. fluorescence of std prepns, S; feed prepns, F; and respective blanks, S_0 and F_0.

38.125   *Calculations*

(a) For 2.0 ppm:

$$\% \text{ Reserpine} = (F - F_0)/[(S - S_0) \times 125 \times W].$$

(b) For 1.0 ppm:

$$\% \text{ Reserpine} = (F - F_0)/[(S - S_0) \times 250 \times W].$$

(c) For 0.2 ppm:

$$\% \text{ Reserpine} = (F - F_0)/[(S - S_0) \times 1{,}250 \times W],$$

where

$$W = \text{g feed sample.}$$

Ronnel (*O,O*-Dimethyl-*O*-(2,4,5-trichlorophenyl) phosphorothioate)
Gas Chromatographic Method (31)—Official First Action

38.126   *Principle*
Ronnel is extd from feed with acetone and dild with hexane for electron capture GLC detection.

38.127   *Apparatus*
Gas chromatograph.—With electron capture detector. Operating parameters: Column 4–6′ glass, 3–4 mm id packed with 5% (w/w) SF-96 silicone fluid on 60–80 mesh Chromosorb W; temps: column 195°, inlet 220°; carrier gas Ar-CH₄ (95 + 5), 60 ml/min; and attenuation to give ca 50% scale deflection with 1 ng ronnel. (Retention time for ronnel should be 5–10 min. Adjust column temp. if necessary.) Significant variations in replicate injections indicate instability of instrument or faulty injection and these should be rechecked.

38.128   *Reagents*
(a) *Hexane.*—Spectral grade.

(b) *Ronnel std solns.*—(*1*) *Stock soln.*—1 mg/ml. Dissolve 0.1000 g ronnel std sample (available from Dow Chemical Co., Sample Coordinator, Agricultural Products Dept.) in hexane and dil. to 100 ml. (*2*) *Intermediate soln.*—20 μg/ml. Dil. 2.0 ml stock soln to 100 ml with hexane. (*3*) *Working soln.*—1 ng/5 μl. Dil. 1.0 ml intermediate soln to 100 ml with hexane.

38.129   *Determination*
Weigh 10.0 g sample into 8 oz screw-cap extn bottle, or equiv. Add 200.0 ml acetone and shake 4 hr. Remove from shaker and centrf. portion 10 min. Pipet 1.0 ml into 100 ml vol. flask and dil. to vol. with hexane.

Inject 5 μl portions in following sequence: ronnel working std soln, dild sample ext, duplicate of dild sample ext, and ronnel working std soln. Record chromatogram of each.

Measure ronnel peak hts and calc. % ronnel as follows, using av. peak hts (PH) from std replicates and ext replicates for each detn:

$$\% \text{ Ronnel} = (\text{PH}_\text{sample}/\text{PH}_\text{std}) \times 0.04$$

Sample wt and aliquot specified are for feeds contg 0.04% ronnel. With feeds contg other levels of ronnel use 10.0 g sample but select aliquot or aliquots to give expected ronnel concn of 1 ng/5 μl final diln. Calc. % ronnel = (PH$_\text{sample}$/PH$_\text{std}$) × g ronnel in std injected × F × 100, where F = 1/[(g sample/ml in final diln) × (μl sample injected × 10⁻³)].

Ultraviolet Method (32)— Official Final Action
(For mineral feed mixts contg 1–40% ronnel)

38.130   *Principle*
Ronnel is extd from feed with MeOH, cleaned up with ion exchange resin, and detd by UV measurement.

38.131   *Reagents*
(a) *Methanol.*—Absolute. Coefficient C as detd in calibration with MeOH should be 0.0322–0.0330. If outside this range, adjust to this value by adding 5–15 drops HCl/L MeOH. Det. C on same day samples are analyzed.

(b) *Ronnel std solns.*—See **38.128**(b).

(c) *Ion exchange resin.*—Dowex 2-X8, 50–100 mesh. Obtainable in chloride form. Convert to acetate form as follows: Plug 10 × 300 mm chromatgc tube, equipped with Teflon stopcock, with glass wool. Fill with aq. slurry of resin to ht of ca 120 mm. Wash resin with ca 500 ml 10% aq. NaOAc soln until effluent gives only faint test for Cl with AgNO₃ after acidification with HNO₃. (Use ca 4 lb/sq in. N pressure to speed washing.) Keep resin covered with liq. during prepn, storage, and analysis. Extrude or wash resin into 100 ml beaker; wash 3 times with H₂O by decantation, then 3 times with MeOH. Pour MeOH slurry back into tube and wash with 50 ml HOAc-MeOH (1 + 4), followed by 50 ml MeOH. Keep resin column (now ready for use) covered with MeOH.

Resin can be used repeatedly unless samples contain considerable salt. Check activity periodically by passing 10 ml of soln of 50 mg trichlorophenol in 100 ml MeOH thru column, washing with three 10 ml portions MeOH, and dilg eluate to 100 ml with MeOH. If soln has noticeable peaks at 292 and 298 nm, discard resin. To prep. larger amts resin, use larger column. Store resin in closed container under MeOH. It is stable at least 1 month.

38.132 Calibration

Weigh 0.1000 g ronnel std into 100 ml vol. flask, dissolve in MeOH, dil. to vol., and mix. Dil. 10.0 ml to 100 ml with MeOH. Det A against MeOH in 1 cm Si cell at 302, 282, and 262 nm.

Calc. coefficient C (g ronnel/100 ml final soln/A unit) = 0.01/net A, where net A is $A_{282} - [(A_{302} + A_{262})/2]$. Coefficient C should be ca 0.0326.

38.133 Determination

(Caution: See 46.018 and 46.040.)

Weigh 10.0 g sample into 8 oz extn bottle, or equiv., add 100.0 ml MeOH, stopper, and shake vigorously 15 min on mech. shaker. Decant thru folded 18.5 cm Whatman No. 2V paper, or equiv., into 500 ml vol. flask. Repeat extn twice, shaking 3 min each time with 100 ml MeOH. Wash residue from bottle onto paper and wash thoroly with three 50 ml portions MeOH. Dil. to vol. with MeOH and mix. Pipet 20 ml aliquot onto ion exchange column, (c), and collect eluate in 250 ml vol. flask. Wash column with three 10 ml portions MeOH (do not let MeOH level drop below resin surface). Dil. to 250 ml with MeOH and mix. (If sample is reasonably fresh or if presence of 2,4,5-trichlorophenol is not suspected, ion exchange resin cleanup step may be omitted.) Det. net A against MeOH as in 38.132.

$$\% \text{ Ronnel} = (\text{net } A \times C \times 100)/\text{g sample}$$
$$\text{in 100 ml final soln}$$

Sample wt and aliquot specified are for mineral mixts contg 5% ronnel. With mineral mixts contg other levels of ronnel use 10.0 g sample but select aliquot to give expected ronnel concn of 0.01 g ronnel/100 ml of final diln. Calc. % ronnel from above formula.

38.134 Gas Chromatography

If GLC measurement of ronnel is desired, dil. 1.0 ml undild MeOH sample ext to 100 ml with hexane. (Dil. aliquot of MeOH ext with hexane same day to avoid hydrolysis of ronnel in MeOH.) Dil. 1.0 ml of this dild ext to 50 ml with hexane. Measure response from 5 μl injections of ronnel working std soln and final diln of ext as in 38.129. Calc. % ronnel = (PH$_{\text{sample}}$/PH$_{\text{std}}$) × 5.

Sample wt and aliquots specified are for mineral mixts contg 5% ronnel. With mineral mixts contg other levels of ronnel use 10.0 g sample but select aliquot to give expected ronnel concn of 1 ng/5 μl final diln. Calc. % ronnel by general formula shown in 38.129.

Sulfadimethoxine (2,5-Diamino-5-(4,5-dimethoxy)-methylbenzyl pyrimidine) (33)—Official First Action

38.135 Reagents and Apparatus

(a) *Ficin soln.*—0.2%. Disperse 500 mg ficin (Calbiochem, fig latex) in H$_2$O (preheated to 40°) and dil. to 250 ml. Use 10 ml of this warm soln in detn. (*Caution:* Ficin is very potent proteolytic enzyme which attacks living tissues. Avoid contact with skin and eyes and breathing dust.)

(b) *Petroleum ether.*—Bp 35–60°, purified on silica gel column.

(c) *Trichloroacetic acid soln.*—3%. Dissolve 30 g CCl$_3$COOH in H$_2$O and dil. to 1 L. (*Caution: See 46.082.*)

(d) *Sodium nitrite soln.*—0.1%. See 38.013(b).

(e) *Ammonium sulfamate soln.*—0.5%. Dissolve 500 mg NH$_4$SO$_3$NH$_2$ in H$_2$O and dil. to 100 ml.

(f) *N-(1-Naphthyl)ethylenediamine dihydrochloride soln (Bratton-Marshall reagent).*—0.1%. See 38.013(d).

(g) *Sulfadimethoxine std soln.*—Accurately weigh 125 mg sulfadimethoxine NF Ref. Std and transfer quant. into 100 ml vol. flask. Add ca 70 ml acetone and shake until completely dissolved. Dil. to vol. with acetone and mix. Pipet 20 ml soln into 200 ml vol. flask, dil. to vol. with acetone, and mix. Pipet 10 ml (or 5 ml if working at 0.00625% level) of last diln into 200 ml vol. flask contg 10 ml 0.2% ficin. Add ca 120 ml acetone and 2 ml 40% NaOH, and mix. Dil. to vol. with acetone and mix. Pipet 25 ml final diln into 50 ml g-s centrf. tube, evap. almost to dryness under N stream in 50° H$_2$O bath, and proceed as in 38.136, beginning "Pipet 15 ml pet ether into centrf. tube . . ." Resulting clear filtrate is std soln.

(h) *Reagent blank.*—Into 200 ml vol. flask pipet 10 ml 0.2% ficin and 2 ml 40% NaOH. Dil. to vol. with acetone and mix. Pipet 25 ml of this soln into 50 ml g-s centrf. tube, evap. almost to dryness under N stream in 50° H$_2$O bath, and proceed as in 38.136, beginning "Pipet 15 ml pet ether into centrf. tube . . ." Resulting clear filtrate is blank soln.

(i) *Spectrophotometer.*—With 5 cm cells, or Evelyn photoelec. colorimeter with 540 nm filter, or equiv.

38.136 Preparation of Sample

(Caution: See 46.004, 46.018, 46.039, and 46.046.)

Pipet 10 ml 0.2% ficin into high-speed blender. Accurately weigh 10 g sample into blender, spreading carefully on surface of liq. Let sample soak 10 min.

Add ca 120 ml acetone. Blend 2 min, adjusting speed with variable transformer, so that acetone does not wet screw cap. (*Caution:* To release pressure, stop blending after 3–4 sec and unscrew cap momentarily.) Blend 2 min and remove screw cap.

Push down into acetone all solid particles adhering to container wall, using rubber policeman. Replace screw cap and continue blending 1 min. Remove screw cap, pipet 2 ml 40% NaOH into container, and continue blending 2 min. Push down into acetone all solid particles adhering to wall of container, using rubber policeman.

Transfer blender contents quant. into 250 ml g-s graduate, using small portions acetone to total vol. of 200 ml. Stopper, mix well, and let liq. and solids sep. Wrap tip of 50 ml pipet with glass wool and transfer ca 40 ml ext into 50 ml g-s centrf. tube. Centrf. 5 min at 2000 rpm. Pipet 25 ml clear acetone ext into another centrf. tube and evap. almost to dryness (only few drops of oily, sirupy liq. left) under N stream in 50° H_2O bath. Pipet 15 ml pet ether into centrf. tube and dissolve or disperse residue in it.

Pipet 25 ml 0.2N NaOH into centrf. tube, stopper, and shake on mech. shaker 5 min. Centrf. tube at 2000 rpm 10 min. Transfer by pipet lower NaOH layer (ca 24 ml) into another centrf. tube and centrf. at 2000 rpm 10 min. Pipet 20 ml clear soln into 100 ml vol. flask. Dil. to vol. with 3% CCl_3COOH. Mix and let stand 10 min. Filter entire soln thru Whatman No. 42 paper, discarding first 10 ml filtrate. If turbid, filter thru second paper. Clear filtrate is sample soln.

38.137   *Determination*

(a) *Reading on spectrophotometer with 5 cm cells.*—Pipet following vols (ml) of indicated solns into 6 sep. labeled 25 ml vol. flasks:

Soln	Sample 1	Sample 2	Sample Blank	Std 1	Std 2	Reagent Blank
Sample	15	15	15	—	—	—
Std	—	—	—	15	15	—
Blank	—	—	—	—	—	15

Pipet 1 ml 0.1% $NaNO_2$ soln into each, mix, and let stand 3 min. Pipet 1 ml 0.5% NH_4 sulfamate soln into each, mix, and let stand 2 min. Pipet 1 ml 0.1% Bratton-Marshall reagent into all except sample blank, and 1 ml H_2O into sample blank. Mix and let stand 10 min in dark. Dil. each flask to vol. with H_2O and mix. Measure A of each soln at 540 nm in 5 cm cells against reagent blank in ref. cell.

(b) *Reading on Evelyn photoelectric colorimeter.*—Proceed as in (a) except do not dil. after standing, but read at existing vol.; 50 ml g-s centrf. tubes may be used in place of vol. flasks. Transfer solns from flasks or tubes into matched colorimeter tubes. Set instrument with 540 filter to 100% T (0 A) with tube contg reagent blank. Det. A (= 2 − log T) of each of other tubes contg samples, sample blank, and stds.

(c) *Calculation.*—Higher levels of sulfadimethoxine:

$$[(A_x - A_b) \times S]/(1000 \times A_s \times W) = \%$$
$$\text{sulfadimethoxine}$$

Lower levels of sulfadimethoxine:

$[(A_x - A_b) \times S]/2000 \times A_s \times W) = \%$ sulfadimethoxine, where A_x, A_b, and A_s refer to sample, reagent blank, and std, resp.; W = g original sample; and S = mg std weighed.

38.138   Sulfaguanidine (34)—Official First Action

Weigh 1 g ground sample into 250 ml vol. flask, and add 100 ml H_2O and 2.5 ml 0.50N NaOH. Heat in H_2O bath 15 min with occasional swirling, cool, dil. to vol., and mix well. Let material settle, pipet 25 ml into 100 ml vol. flask, add 10 ml *1.00% ZnSO_4* *.7H_2O soln*, dil. to vol., mix well, and let stand 1 min. Filter thru 18.5 cm Whatman No. 2 paper, discarding first 10 ml filtrate. (Filtrate must be free of turbidity.)

Pipet 2 ml clear filtrate into 25 ml vol. flask; add 2.5 ml 0.50N HCl and 2 ml *0.1% $NaNO_2$ soln (prepd fresh daily)*. Let stand 3 min. Add 2 ml *0.50% NH_4 sulfamate soln* and wait addnl 2 min. Add 2 ml coupling reagent, **38.013(d)**, and dil. to vol. Swirl flask after addn of each reagent. Prep. blank, using H_2O and same quantities of reagents dild to 25 ml. Shake vigorously. Measure A of colored soln in spectrophtr at 545 nm against reagent blank, and det. quantity of sulfaguanidine present by ref. to std curve. μg Sulfaguanidine × 0.05 = % sulfaguanidine in sample.

Prep. std curve as follows: Dissolve 0.010 g pure sulfaguanidine in 2.5 ml 0.50N NaOH and 100 ml H_2O in 250 ml vol. flask by heating 15 min in boiling H_2O bath. Cool, and dil. to vol. with H_2O. Pipet 25 ml of this soln into 100 ml vol. flask, add 10 ml of the $ZnSO_4$ soln, dil. to vol., and filter (1 ml = 10 μg sulfaguanidine). Pipet 1, 2, 3, and 4 ml portions of this dild soln (equiv. to 10, 20, 30, and 40 μg sulfaguanidine, resp.) into sep. 25 ml vol. flasks, dil. to 10 ml with H_2O, and proceed as in second par. beginning "add 2.5 ml 0.50N HCl . . ." Plot A against μg sulfaguanidine.

38.139   Sulfaquinoxaline (35)—Official Final Action

Weigh 5 g ground sample into 250 ml vol. flask, add 150 ml H_2O and 5 ml 0.5N NaOH, and place in boiling H_2O bath 15 min. Remove, cool, dil. to vol. with H_2O, mix, and let settle. Transfer 50 ml supernatant to 100 ml vol. flask, add 3 ml HCl, and dil. to vol. Mix, and filter thru 18.5 cm Whatman No. 2 paper (or equiv.), discarding first 15 ml filtrate if turbid.

To 10 ml filtrate in each of two 50 ml beakers add 2 ml *freshly prepd 0.1% $NaNO_2$ soln* and let stand 3 min. Add 2 ml *0.5% NH₄ sulfamate soln* and let stand 2 min. Add 1 ml coupling reagent, **38.013**(d), to first beaker and 1 ml H₂O to second beaker. Mix thoroly after adding each reagent. After 10 min, read *A* in spectrophtr at 545 nm. Subtract *A* of feed blank from sample *A* and det. quantity of sulfaquinoxaline from std curve. Divide by 1000 to obtain % sulfaquinoxaline.

Prep. std curve as follows: Dissolve 0.250 g pure sulfaquinoxaline in 5 ml 0.5*N* NaOH and 50 ml H₂O in 500 ml vol. flask, and dil. to vol. with H₂O. Pipet 5 ml aliquot of this soln into 100 ml vol. flask and dil. to vol. with H₂O. Pipet 2, 4, 6, 8, and 10 ml portions of this dild soln (equiv. to 50, 100, 150, 200, and 250 μg sulfaquinoxaline, resp.) into sep. 100 ml vol. flasks, add 3 ml HCl to each flask, and dil. to vol. with H₂O. Treat 10 ml aliquots of these final dilns as in second par. Det. *A* at 545 nm against H₂O blank, and plot *A* against μg sulfaquinoxaline.

Sulfaquinoxaline and Arsanilic Acid (*36*)— Official Final Action

38.140 *Preparation of Standard Curve*

Prep. sep. curves for sulfaquinoxaline and arsanilic acid as in **38.139**, third par., using 0.250 g of each.

38.141 *Determination*

(**a**) *Total absorbance.*—Det. *A* of sulfaquinoxaline and arsanilic acid as in **38.139**, par. 1 and 2. Let sample *A* − feed *A* = *x*.

(**b**) *Absorbance of arsanilic acid.*—Pipet 35 ml sample soln into separator; ext with three 50 ml portions ether, discarding ether exts. Transfer aq. layer to erlenmeyer and aerate 10 min to remove dissolved ether. Treat two 10 ml portions of this soln as in **38.139**, second par. Let *A* difference = *y*. From arsanilic acid std curve det. μg arsanilic acid corresponding to *y*. μg Arsanilic acid/1000 = % arsanilic acid in sample. Arsanilic acid × 1.101 = Na arsanilate (NH₂C₆H₄AsO(OH)ONa).

(**c**) *Absorbance of sulfaquinoxaline.*—Subtract *y* from *x*; from sulfaquinoxaline std curve det. μg sulfaquinoxaline corresponding to this difference. This value/1000 = % sulfaquinoxaline in sample.

Sulfamethazine (N-(4,6-Dimethyl-2-pyrimidinyl) sulfanilamide) (*37*)—Official First Action

(Applicable to feeds contg procaine penicillin)

38.142 *Reagents*

(**a**) *Sodium nitrite soln.*—0.1%. See **38.101**(e).

(**b**) *Sulfamethazine std.*—Available from American Cyanamid Co.

(**c**) *N-(1-Naphthyl)ethylenediamine dihydrochloride soln.*—0.1%. Prep. fresh daily.

(**d**) *Ammonium sulfamate soln.*—0.5%. Prep. fresh weekly.

(**e**) *50% Methanol soln.*—50% (v/v) aq. soln of MeOH.

(**f**) *Sulfamethazine std solns.*—(*1*) *Stock soln.*—Carefully weigh 0.100 g pure sulfamethazine into 100 ml vol. flask. Add 50 ml 50% MeOH soln and shake until dissolved. Dil. to vol. with 50% MeOH soln, (**e**). Soln is stable at least several weeks. (*2*) *Intermediate soln.*—Pipet 5 ml stock soln into 200 ml vol. flask, dil. to vol. with 50% MeOH, and mix well. Soln is also stable several weeks. (*3*) *Working soln.*—2.5 μg/ml. Pipet 10 ml intermediate soln into 100 ml vol. flask, add 1 ml HCl and 50 ml 50% MeOH, dil. to vol. with H₂O, and mix well. Soln is stable ca 2 weeks.

38.143 *Preparation of Sample*

Weigh 5.00 g sample into 250 ml g-s erlenmeyer. Add 100.0 ml 50% MeOH soln and shake well on mech. shaker 1 hr. Centrf. enough ext to give necessary aliquot size.

(**a**) *Samples containing 0.01% sulfamethazine.*—Pipet 25 ml centrfd 50% MeOH ext into 50 ml vol. flask. Add 0.5 ml HCl, 10 ml H₂O, and 5 ml 1% ZnSO₄ soln. Let stand 10 min; then dil. to vol. with H₂O and mix well.

(**b**) *Samples containing 0.04–0.05% sulfamethazine.*—Pipet 5.0 ml centrfd 50% MeOH ext into 50 ml vol. flask and proceed as in (**a**).

38.144 *Determination*

Filter portion of prepd soln thru Whatman No. 42 paper or equiv. into 250 ml flask. Filtrate should be clear. Pipet two 10 ml aliquots filtrate and 10 ml working std soln into sep. 50 ml centrf. tubes. To each tube add 1.0 ml 0.1% NaNO₂ soln; mix and let stand 3 min. Add 1.0 ml 0.5% NH₄ sulfamate soln; mix and let stand 2 min. Add 1.0 ml 0.1% N-(1-naphthyl)ethylenediamine.2HCl soln to one of sample solns and to std soln. To second sample soln add 1.0 ml H₂O (sample blank). Mix all solns well and let stand 10 min.

To sample, sample blank, and std soln add ca 10 ml CHCl₃, stopper, and shake *vigorously* 30 sec (30 sec is required to ensure complete removal of procaine dye). Add 0.8 ml 10*N* NaOH to sample, sample blank, and std soln. Stopper and shake vigorously ≥1 min to ensure complete removal of procaine dye. Centrf. solns at 2000 rpm 5 min or until aq. layer is completely clear. Remove 10.0 ml aq. phase with pipet and transfer to 50 ml erlenmeyer or 50 ml beaker. Add 1.0 ml HCl and remove fumes formed in flask with aspirator or air stream.

Read *A* of sample, sample blank, and std at 540 nm in spectrophtr, against H₂O blank. Correct *A* of sample by subtracting that of sample blank, and calc. % sulfamethazine = (corrected A_{sample}/A_{std}) × (2.5 μg/ml) × (50 ml/ml ext aliquot taken) × (100 ml/5 g) × (1 g/10⁶ μg) × 100.

Sulfanitran (Acetyl-(p-nitrophenyl)sulfanilamide; APNPS) (38)—Official Final Action

38.145　　　　　　　　　　Reagents

(a) *Sulfanitran std solns.*—(*1*) *Stock soln.*—100 μg/ml. Accurately weigh 100 mg pure APNPS (available from Salsbury Laboratories) into 1 L vol. flask, add enough 1N NaOH for complete soln, and dil. to vol. with H_2O. (*2*) *Working std soln.*—10 μg/ml. Dil. 10 ml stock soln to 100 ml with H_2O.

(b) *Coupling reagent.*—See **38.013**(d).

38.146　　　　Preparation of Standard Curve

Pipet 0, 4, 6, 8, and 10 ml aliquots working std soln into sep. 50 ml vol. flasks. Add 0.5 ml HCl and adjust vol. with H_2O to ca 15 ml. Place flasks in boiling H_2O bath 1 hr to deacetylate. Cool, and dil. to vol. Transfer 5 ml aliquot from each flask to sep. colorimeter tubes. Develop color by adding 0.5 ml *0.1% NaNO$_2$ soln* (not >5 days old, stored in refrigerator), 0.5 ml *0.5% NH$_4$ sulfamate soln*, and 0.5 ml *coupling reagent*, (b). Det. *A* at 540 nm against reagent blank (0 ml aliquot).

(To establish most reliable std curve, make detns on 3 sep. days and use av. values.)

38.147　　　　Extraction and Deacetylation

(For premixes, use proper dilns to give 5–10 μg APNPS in final aliquot, taking dilns into consideration in final calcn.)

Weigh 5.0 g sample into 100 ml vol. flask and add 80 ml MeOH. Place flask in 60° H_2O bath until MeOH is hot. Repeatedly remove and immerse flask during 20 min, shaking frequently. Cool to room temp., and dil. to vol. with MeOH. Shake thoroly, and let stand 40 min to permit particles to settle.

Pipet 25 ml aliquot MeOH ext into 50 ml vol. flask. Add 10 ml H_2O, 5 ml *1.0% ZnSO$_4$ soln*, and ca 3 drops 1N NaOH to improve flocculation. (Keep near neutrality.) Place flask in boiling H_2O bath 2 min to aid pptn; then cool to room temp., dil. to vol., mix thoroly, and filter thru Whatman No. 42 paper, or equiv. Discard first 5 ml filtrate.

Pipet 10 ml aliquot filtrate into 50 ml vol. flask contg 8.0 ml H_2O and 0.5 ml HCl. Place flask in boiling H_2O bath 1 hr to evap. off MeOH and deacetylate APNPS, shaking frequently during first 15 min. Cool to room temp. and dil. to vol. with H_2O. Centrf. if turbidity appears.

38.148　　　　　　　　Determination

Place 5.0 ml aliquot in each of 2 colorimeter tubes. To 1 tube (blank) add 1.0 ml H_2O and 0.5 ml coupling reagent, (b). To other tube add 0.5 ml 0.1% $NaNO_2$ soln; after 3 min, add 0.5 ml 0.5% NH_4 sulfamate soln, wait 2 min, and add 0.5 ml coupling reagent, (b). Close tube with thumb and invert immediately after adding each reagent. Let stand 10 min for color development and det. *A* of unknown and blank at 540 nm in spectrophtr or colorimeter against H_2O. Det. amt APNPS from std curve after subtracting *A* of blank.

% APNPS in sample = μg APNPS in tube × 200 × 100/5,000,000 (μg sample) = μg APNPS × 0.004.

Thiabendazole (2-(4-Thiazolyl)-benzimidazole) (39)—Official Final Action

Method I

(Applicable to all feeds)

38.149　　　　　　　　　　Principle

Thiabendazole is extd from feed with 0.1N HCl. Interferences are removed by adjusting ext to pH 5–6 with Na citrate and extg with $CHCl_3$. Thiabendazole is re-extd with 0.1N HCl and reduced with Zn slurry in 30% glycerol in presence of *p*-phenylenediamine. Oxidn with ferric iron yields blue complex which is extd with butanol and measured at 605 nm.

38.150　　　　　　　　　　Reagents

(a) *Zinc dust.*—Reagent grade. Crush fine lumps with spatula immediately before use.

(b) *Zinc slurry.*—Weigh 50 mg *p*-phenylenediamine.2HCl (*Caution: p*-phenylenediamine may be harmful; *see* **46.084**) and 2 g Zn dust into dry 100 ml g-s cylinder. Add 100 ml 30% (v/v) glycerol soln, stopper, and shake ca 30 sec to suspend Zn dust uniformly. (There must be no agglomeration of Zn.) Prep. just before use and use immediately.

(c) *Ferric soln.*—Dissolve 15.0 g $FeNH_4(SO_4)_2$ .12H_2O in 75 ml H_2O, add 10.0 ml 1N H_2SO_4, dil. to 100 ml, and mix.

(d) *Thiabendazole std solns.*—(*1*) *Stock soln.*—0.5 mg/ml. Dissolve 50.0 mg Thiabendazole Ref. Std (available from Merck & Co.) in 0.1N HCl and dil. to 100 ml. Soln is stable ≥1 month. (*2*) *Intermediate soln.*—50 μg/ml. Dil. 10 ml stock soln to 100 ml with 0.1N HCl. Soln is stable ≥1 month. (*3*) *Working soln.*—5 μg/ml. Dil. 20.0 ml intermediate soln to 200 ml with 0.1N HCl. (Use same 0.1N HCl as in extn of feed.)

38.151　　　　　　Preparation of Sample

Grind ca 100 g well-mixed sample to pass No. 30 sieve and mix. (3 min in high-speed blender should be sufficient.)

38.152　　　　　　　　　　Extraction

Weigh 2.000 g ground sample into 250 ml ᵮ 24/40 flat-bottom extn flask. (For feeds contg <0.025% thiabendazole, weigh 5.000 g.)

Add 100.0 ml 0.1N HCl to sample and add magnetic stirring bar. Connect flask to reflux condenser (Allihn, drip tip) and reflux gently on magnetic hot plate, while stirring, 30 min. Cool, transfer mixt. to centrf. tube, and centrf. ca 5 min. Dil. measured aliquot of supernatant to such vol. that each ml = 5 μg thiabendazole (serial dilns may be necessary). Such dilns det. "dilution factor," *DF*:

Declaration, %	Sample wt, g	Dilution(s)	DF
0.01	5	none	1
0.025	2	none	1
0.1	2	25–100	4
1.0	2	10–100; 25–100	40
6.0	2	10–100; 10–250	250

Mark series of 50 ml centrf. tubes 1, 2, 3, 4, etc. Place 20.0 ml 0.1N HCl in tube 1 and 20.0 ml (100 μg) working std soln in tubes 2 and 3. Place 20.0 ml aliquots sample solns in tubes 4, 5, etc. Add 3 g Na citrate, 3 g NaCl, and 20.0 ml CHCl₃ to each tube, stopper tightly with polyethylene stopper, and shake mech. 5 min. Centrf. ca 5 min and discard top layers. With pipet, transfer 10 ml CHCl₃ ext to dry, marked, centrf. tubes, add 25.0 ml 0.1N HCl to each, stopper, and shake 5 min. Centrf., and transfer, with pipet, 15 ml of top acid layer to another marked tube. (Because of timing, handle no more than 10 tubes at one time.)

With rapid delivery pipet, add 5 ml freshly prepd Zn slurry, (b), to each tube. (5 ml pipet with tip cut off to give delivery in ca 5 sec is suitable. Hold pipet directly over center of soln.) Do not shake tube but *immediately stopper* tightly and let stand 4 min. Start timing after delivery of slurry to first tube.

After 4 min, add 5.0 ml ferric soln, (c), to each tube with rapid pipet, stopper, and mix by inverting tube. Let stand 5 min; then shake vigorously and centrf. ca 3 min. With pipet, transfer 15 ml clear, colored soln to marked, dry, centrf. tubes. Let stand 45 min from addn of ferric soln. Then add 5.00 ml n-butanol and 3 g anhyd. Na₂SO₄ to each tube. Stopper, and immediately shake each tube ca 5 sec to avoid caking of Na₂SO₄; then shake all tubes ca 3 min or until Na₂SO₄ is completely dissolved. Centrf.

Transfer clear butanol soln (top layer) to dry 1 cm cell and read A at 605 nm against n-butanol as ref.

38.153   *Calculations*

% Thiabendazole in feed =
$(A_x - A_b)(C)(DF)/360(A_s - A_b)W$, where A_x refers to sample, A_b to reagent blank (tube 1), A_s to std, $C = $ μg thiabendazole std in final 15.0 ml colored soln = 18 μg, $DF = $ diln factor, and $W = $ g original sample.

Method II

(Applicable to cattle supplements and premixes contg >1% thiabendazole. Principle is same as 38.149 except that single extn at room temp. with 0.1N HCl is used.)

38.154   *Reagents*

See 38.150 except:

(a) *Thiabendazole working solution.*—Dil. 10.0 ml thiabendazole intermediate soln, 38.150(d)(2), to 250 ml with 0.1N HCl.

38.155   *Preparation of Sample*

See 38.151, except use ca 50 g representative sample.

38.156   *Extraction*

Weigh 2.000 g ground sample into 1 L vol. flask and add 750 ml 0.1N HCl. Add magnetic stirring bar, stopper, and mix vigorously on magnetic stirrer 1 hr at room temp. (Mech. shaker providing vigorous agitation may be used.) Remove and rinse bar, and dil. to vol. with 0.1N HCl. Mix, centrf., and dil. aliquots of clear ext to appropriate vol. with 0.1N HCl so that each ml = 2 μg thiabendazole. Diln factors, DF, are as follows (*see* 38.152):

Declaration, %	Dilution	DF
1.0	10–100	10
2.5	4.0–100	25
6.0	4.0–250	62.5

Develop color in exts as soon as possible after extn. (Acid exts of some feeds deteriorate upon standing.)

Mark series of 50 ml centrf. tubes (≤10) as in 38.152. Add 15.0 ml 0.1N HCl to tube 1, and 15.0 ml working soln, (a), to tubes 2 and 3. Add 15.0 ml sample exts to other tubes. Then with rapid delivery pipet, add 5.0 ml freshly prepd Zn slurry as in 38.152. Proceed as in 38.152 with addn of ferric soln, observing same technics and time precautions. Read final clear butanol ext, as above, in 1 cm cell at 605 nm.

38.157   *Calculations*

% Thiabendazole in feed =
$(A_x - A_b)(C)(DF)/90(A_s - A_b)W$, where symbols are as defined in 38.153.

Zoalene (3,5-Dinitro-o-toluamide) (40)— Official Final Action

(Not applicable in presence of furazolidone, nitrofurazone, and nihydrazone)

38.158   *Principles*

Zoalene is extd from feeds, premixes, and concs contg 0.004–25% with 85% acetonitrile. For mixes contg <1%, Al₂O₃ is added. After filtration and diln, zoalene is detd colorimetrically after reaction with ethylenediamine.

38.159   *Reagents*

(a) *Acetone.*—95%. Add 5 ml H₂O to 95 ml acetone.

(b) *Acetonitrile.*—85%. Add 850 ml practical grade CH₃CN to 150 ml H₂O (deionized or distd).

(c) *Activated alumina.*—Alcoa grade F 20, 80–200 mesh. (Available from Fisher Scientific Co. "Alumina, Adsorption, Fisher.")

(d) *Dimethylformamide (DMF).*—95%. Add 5 ml H₂O to 95 ml tech. DMF. Prep. fresh daily, since old solns may cause cloudiness.

(e) *Ethylenediamine.*—98–100%. Matheson Coleman & Bell.

(f) *Zoalene std soln.*—40 μg/ml. Weigh 40.0 mg Zoalene Ref. Std (available from Dow Chemical Co.) into 1 L vol. flask, dil. to vol. with 85% CH₃CN, and mix.

38.160 *Determination*

Weigh 10.0 g sample into 250 ml erlenmeyer and add 65 ml 85% CH₃CN. Warm on steam bath to 50±5°, swirling occasionally. Let cool to room temp. (ca 30 min). Add 20 g Al₂O₃ and swirl occasionally ca 3 min. (Addn of Al₂O₃ is unnecessary for concs contg ≥1% zoalene.) Filter with suction on medium or fine porosity 40 mm diam. fritted glass funnel, transferring as much solids as possible. Transfer remaining solids with min. vol. 85% CH₃CN, and suck dry. Suspend cake in funnel with min. vol. 85% CH₃CN, and slight stirring but without suction. Then filter with suction and repeat suspension and filtering, keeping total vol. <100 ml. Transfer combined filtrates to 100 ml vol. flask (or vol. flask may be used to collect filtrates directly), dil. to vol. with 85% CH₃CN, and mix.

Based on zoalene concn, make addnl dilns with 95% acetone and use aliquots indicated in Table 38:1.

Table 38:1—Dilution of Sample for Determination

% Zoalene in Sample	Addnl Diln	Aliquot Size, ml	Multiplication Factor *M*
0.004– 0.012	None	4	1
0.012– 0.025	None	2	2
0.025– 0.050	10 to 100	10	4
0.050– 0.10	10 to 100	5	8
0.10 – 0.25	10 to 100	2	20
0.25 – 0.5	1 to 100	10	40
0.5 – 1.0	1 to 100	5	80
1.0 – 2.5	1 to 100	2	200
2.5 – 5.0	1 to 1000	10	400
5.0 –10.0	1 to 1000	5	800
10.0 –25.0	1 to 1000	2	2000

Pipet indicated aliquots into three 50 ml beakers, X, Y, and Z, for concns <0.25%; omit X for samples >0.25%. Pipet 1 ml std soln into beaker Z and evap. all solns to dryness with air current. (Heat may be used but temp. must not exceed 60°.) Pipet 10 ml 95% DMF into X and 2 ml each into Y and Z. Swirl intermittently during 5 min to dissolve zoalene. Pipet 8 ml ethylenediamine into Y and Z and mix. If turbidity persists after 2 min, filter thru small Reeve Angel No. 804 or equiv. paper. Read *A* of solns against 95% DMF 5 min after addn of ethylenediamine at 560 nm in stoppered 1 cm cells. Keep cell compartment of spectrophtr at <30° to avoid rapid fading of color. If *A* is >1, reanalyze, using greater diln or smaller aliquot.

% Zoalene = $(A_Y - A_X) \times M/100(A_Z - A_Y)$.

Caution: CH₃CN and ethylenediamine are toxic. Handle in hood and avoid contact with skin.

ANTIBIOTICS

Microscopic Tests for Chlortetracycline and Oxytetracycline (41)—Official Final Action

38.161 *Apparatus*

Microscopes.—See **7.099.**

38.162 *Reagent*

Modified Sakaguchi reagent.—Dissolve 5 g H₃BO₃ in 150 ml H₂O and add 350 ml H₂SO₄. Store in g-s bottle in refrigerator. Use cold.

38.163 *Determination*

Grind sample as in **7.002.** Pipet ca 10 ml Sakaguchi reagent into 9 cm petri dish. Place No. 60 sieve over petri dish. With top of spatula, sprinkle ca 0.5 g sample on sieve, and gently tap it to obtain good distribution of particles over liq. surface. Place under stereoscopic microscope and examine with transmitted light at ca 15×. If substage illumination is not available, place petri dish on white surface and illuminate with blue light.

As particles of antibiotic slowly dissolve, diffusing chlortetracycline turns intense purple and oxytetracycline intense red. Colors fade in 5–10 min.

MICROBIOLOGICAL METHODS (42)

38.164 *Culture Media*

(a) *Agar medium A.*—Dissolve 6.0 g pancreatic digest of gelatin, 4.0 g pancreatic digest of casein, 3.0 g yeast ext, 1.5 g beef ext, 1.0 g anhyd. glucose, and 15 g agar in H₂O, and dil. to 1 L. Adjust with 1N NaOH or HCl (1 + 9) so that after sterilization for 30 min at 121°, pH is 6.5–6.6. (Difco Penassay Seed Agar and BBL Seed Agar have been found satisfactory.)

(b) *Agar medium B.*—Dissolve 6.0 g pancreatic digest of gelatin, 3.0 g yeast ext, 1.5 g beef ext, 1.0 g anhyd. glucose, and 15 g agar in H₂O, and dil. to 1 L. Adjust with 1N NaOH or HCl (1 + 9) so that after sterilization for 30 min at 121°, pH is 6.5–6.6. (Difco Yeast Beef Agar has been found satisfactory.)

(c) *Agar medium C.*—Dissolve 6.0 g pancreatic digest of gelatin, 3.0 g yeast ext, 1.5 g beef ext, and 15 g agar in H₂O, and dil. to 1 L. Adjust with 1N NaOH or HCl (1 + 9) so that after sterilization 30 min at 121°, pH is 6.5–6.6. (Difco Penassay Base Agar and BBL Base Agar have been found satisfactory.)

(d) *Agar medium D.*—Use agar medium C adjusted with 1N NaOH or HCl (1 + 9) so that final pH is 5.6–5.7.

(e) *Agar medium E.*—Use agar medium C adjusted with 1N NaOH so that final pH is 7.8–8.0. (Difco Streptomycin Assay Agar and BBL Streptomycin Assay Agar with Yeast Extract have been found satisfactory.)

(f) *Agar medium F.*—To each 100 ml melted agar medium E add 0.4–2.0 ml 1% sulfadiazine soln in

0.5N NaOH. Det. on trial plates optimum amt (usually 1.4 ml) sulfadiazine soln necessary to obtain largest, sharpest zones.

(g) *Agar medium G.*—Use agar medium A to which is added 300 mg MnSO$_4$.H$_2$O or 0.4 ml 1% MnCl$_2$ soln/L.

(h) *Agar medium H.*—Dil. 1 L agar medium A to 1.2 L and adjust to pH 8.1.

(i) *Agar medium I.*—Dissolve 9.4 g pancreatic digest of gelatin, 4.7 g yeast ext, 2.4 g beef ext, 10.0 g NaCl, 10.0 g anhyd. glucose, and 23.5 g agar in H$_2$O, and dil. to 1 L. Adjust with 1N NaOH or with HCl (1 + 11) so that after sterilization 30 min at 121° pH is 6.0–6.2. (BBL Nystatin Assay Agar has been found satisfactory.)

(j) *Agar medium J.*—Use agar medium A adjusted with 1N NaOH so that final pH is 7.9.

(k) *Agar medium K.*—Dissolve 6.0 g pancreatic digest of gelatin, 4.0 g pancreatic digest of casein, 3.0 g yeast ext, 1.5 g beef ext, 1.0 g anhyd. glucose, and 15 g agar in H$_2$O and dil. to 1 L. Adjust with 1N NaOH so that after 30 min sterilization at 121° pH is 7.9. (Difco and BBL neomycin assay agars have been found satisfactory.) To each L add 12.5 ml 2M CaCl$_2$ after autoclaving and just before pouring plates.

(l) *Broth medium A.*—Dissolve 5.0 g pancreatic digest of gelatin, 1.5 g yeast ext, 1.5 g beef ext, 3.5 g NaCl, 1.0 g anhyd. glucose, 3.68 g anhyd. K$_2$HPO$_4$, and 1.32 g anhyd. KH$_2$PO$_4$ in H$_2$O, and dil. to 1 L. Adjust with 1N NaOH or HCl (1 + 9) so that after sterilization 30 min at 121° pH is 6.95–7.05. (Difco Penassay Broth and BBL Antibiotic Assay Broth have been found satisfactory.)

(m) *Broth medium B.*—Dissolve 5.0 g pancreatic digest of casein, 5.0 g pancreatic digest of animal tissues, and 20 g anhyd. glucose in H$_2$O, and dil. to 1 L. Adjust with 1N NaOH or with HCl (1 + 11) so that after sterilization 30 min at 121° pH is 5.6–5.7. (BBL or Difco Sabouraud's broth has been found satisfactory.)

38.165 *Reagents*

(a) *Phosphate-bicarbonate buffer.*—pH 8. Dissolve 16.73 g anhyd. K$_2$HPO$_4$, 0.523 g anhyd. KH$_2$PO$_4$, and 20 g NaHCO$_3$ in H$_2$O and dil. to 1 L.

(b) *Phosphate buffer.*—pH 8. Dissolve 16.73 g anhyd. K$_2$HPO$_4$ and 0.523 g anhyd. KH$_2$PO$_4$ in H$_2$O and dil. to 1 L.

(c) *Phosphate buffer.*—pH 7.0. Dissolve 13.6 g anhyd. K$_2$HPO$_4$ and 4.0 g anhyd. KH$_2$PO$_4$ in H$_2$O and dil. to 1 L.

(d) *5% Phosphate buffer.*—pH 6.5. Dissolve 22.15 g anhyd. K$_2$HPO$_4$ and 27.85 g anhyd. KH$_2$PO$_4$ in H$_2$O and dil. to 1 L.

(e) *10% Phosphate buffer.*—pH 6. Dissolve 80 g anhyd. KH$_2$PO$_4$ and 20 g anhyd. K$_2$HPO$_4$ in H$_2$O and dil. to 1 L.

(f) *Phosphate buffer.*—pH 6. Dissolve 8.0 g anhyd. KH$_2$PO$_4$ and 2.0 g anhyd. K$_2$HPO$_4$ in H$_2$O and dil. to 1 L.

(g) *Phosphate buffer.*—pH 4.5. Dissolve 13.6 g anhyd. KH$_2$PO$_4$ in H$_2$O and dil. to 1 L.

(h) *Pyridine-buffer soln.*—Mix 9 vols pyridine and 31 vols pH 6.0 buffer, (f).

(i) *40% Pyridine-buffer soln.*—Mix 4 vols pyridine (2° boiling range), 3 vols 5% phosphate buffer, (d), and 3 vols H$_2$O.

(j) *Acid-acetone.*—Mix 1 vol. 4N HCl, 13 vols acetone, and 6 vols H$_2$O.

(k) *Acid-methanol.*—Mix 1 vol. HCl and 50 vols MeOH.

(l) *Ethyl acetate.*—99% undenatured grade.

(m) *Buffer-acetone extractant.*—Mix equal vols pH 6 buffer, (f), and acetone.

(n) *Tris buffer.*—pH 8.0, 0.05M. Dissolve 6.05 g tris(hydroxymethyl)aminomethane (THAM, primary std, available from Fisher Scientific Co.) in 900 ml H$_2$O, adjust pH to 8.0 with HCl, and dil. to 1 L.

(o) *Calcium chloride soln.*—2M. Dissolve 294.04 g CaCl$_2$.2H$_2$O and dil. to 1 L with H$_2$O.

(p) *Sodium chloride-calcium chloride soln.*—Dissolve 200 g NaCl in H$_2$O, add 10 ml 2M CaCl$_2$, and dil. to 1 L.

(q) *Sodium hypochlorite soln.*—5.25%. Use freshly opened bottle com. soln. (Clorox has been found satisfactory.) Store in dark at 2–10°.

(r) *Sterile isotonic saline soln.*—Dissolve 9.0 g NaCl in H$_2$O and dil. to 1 L. Autoclave 20 min at 121°.

(s) *Methanol.*—Anhyd.

38.166 *Apparatus*

(Mortars and pestles and high-speed blender jars, after disassembling, must be cleaned with great care to eliminate all traces of antibiotics. All app. which contacts sample and solns must be thoroly cleaned and be detergent-free before use; heat-treated, if possible, 2 hr at 200°.)

(a) *Cylinders.*—Polished open stainless steel cylinders, 8±0.1 mm od, 6±0.1 mm id, and 10±0.1 mm high (obtainable from S & L Metal Products Corp., 58–29 57th Drive, Maspeth, NY 11378). After use, tarnish may be removed or prevented by autoclaving with 2% citric acid soln 30 min at 121° or standing several days, and rinsing thoroly with H$_2$O.

(b) *Petri dishes (plates).*—Glass or plastic; 100 mm wide × 20 mm deep. Porcelain covers glazed on outside or cover lids with filter pad inserts are satisfactory for absorbing H$_2$O of syneresis. Glass or plastic covers may be used if they are raised slightly to allow escape of H$_2$O.

(c) *Cylinder dispenser.*—Cylinders, (a), may be placed on plates with Shaw Dispenser, available from E. C. Condit, PO Box 75, Middle Haddam, CT 06456.

(d) *Virtis homogenizer.*—With glass or stainless steel homogenizer cups.

(e) *Soxhlet extraction apparatus.*—145–200 ml capacity, with thimbles capable of holding 50 g feed.

(f) *Petri dish bottoms.*—90 mm wide × 20 mm deep with pour lips.

(g) *Centrifuge tube supports.*—Wood blocks with holes 2.5″ diam. and 2″ deep for supporting 50 ml r-b centrf. tubes.

(h) *Electric floor heating mat.*—Masonite, 20 × 24 × 5/16″ (available from Radiant Products, PO Box 1059, Monroe, NC 28110).

(i) *Aluminum air sparger.*—Construct from 110″ length of 0.25″ Al tubing. Make 3 semicircular bends 25, 52, and 79″ from short end and 70° bend 6.5″ from beginning of long end. Support sparger on 2 lengths of wood 17.5 × 1 × 0.5″; drill 16 holes with 1/16″ drill between supports 3.75″ apart and 8 other holes outside of supports so all holes will be centered over dishes they aerate. Connect both ends of sparger to glass Y-tube with Tygon tubing. Connect to air line supplying 40–50 lb/sq in. and equipped with H_2O trap.

38.167   Stock Cultures and Preparation of Test Organism Suspensions

For appropriate test organism designated below, prep. slant culture on 1 or more tubes of agar medium A. Incubate overnight at indicated temp. held constant to ±0.5°, and then store in dark at 2–10°. Do not use if >2 weeks old.

Prep. suspensions of test organisms as follows:

(a) *Micrococcus flavus.*—ATCC No. 10240. Incubate stock culture at 32–35°. Wash growth from stock culture with ca 3 ml broth medium A and transfer liq. to surface of 300 ml agar medium A in Roux bottle. Spread suspension evenly over entire surface, using sterile glass beads, and incubate overnight at 32–35°. Wash growth from agar surface with ca 25 ml sterile isotonic saline soln. Using photoelec. colorimeter and 18 mm diam. test tube as absorption cell, det. *T* of 1:50 diln of this bulk suspension at 650 nm, and, if necessary, adjust by diln so that 1:50 diln gives 75% *T*. (Adjusted bulk suspension, not 1:50 diln, is used in prepg seed layer.) Store adjusted bulk suspension at 2–10°. Use for bacitracin assay.

(b) *Sarcina subflava.*—ATCC No. 7468. Incubate stock culture at 32–35°. Prep. suspension as in (a) and use as alternative organism for bacitracin assay.

(c) *Bacillus cereus.*—ATCC No. 11778. Incubate stock culture at 30°. Wash growth from stock culture with ca 3 ml sterile H_2O, transfer to surface of 300 ml agar medium A, and incubate 7 days at 30°. Wash growth from agar surface with ca 25 ml H_2O and heat suspension 30 min at 65°. Centrf. and decant. Wash residual spores 3 times with sterile H_2O, centrfg and decanting each time. Discard wash H_2O. Heat residual spores 30 min at 65° and resuspend in sterile H_2O. Store this stock suspension at 2–10°. Use for chlortetracycline and oxytetracycline assays.

(d) *Bacillus subtilis.*—ATCC No. 6633. Incubate stock culture at 37°. Wash growth from stock culture with ca 3 ml sterile isotonic saline soln, transfer to surface of 300 ml agar medium G in Roux bottle, and incubate 7 days at 37°. Wash growth from agar surface with ca 50 ml sterile isotonic saline soln into centrf. bottle. Heat suspension 30 min in H_2O bath at 65° to destroy vegetative cells. Centrf., decant, and resuspend cells in ca 50 ml sterile isotonic saline soln. Repeat heating, centrfg, and suspending twice, or until supernatant is clear. Final suspension is stock spore suspension. Store at 2–10°. Use for hygromycin B and streptomycin assays.

(e) *Sarcina lutea.*—ATCC No. 9341. Incubate stock culture at 26–30°. Prep. organism suspension by one of following methods:

(1) *Roux bottle culture.*—Wash growth from 24 hr slant culture with ca 3 ml broth medium A, and transfer liq. to surface of 300 ml agar medium A in Roux bottle. Spread suspension evenly over entire surface, using sterile glass beads, and incubate 24 hr at 26–32°. Wash growth from agar surface with ca 15 ml sterile isotonic saline soln. Using photoelec. colorimeter and 18 mm diam. test tube as absorption cell, det. *T* of 1:10 diln of this bulk suspension at 650 nm, and, if necessary, adjust by diln so that 1:10 diln gives 10% *T*. Use adjusted bulk suspension (not 1:10 diln) in prepg seed layer. Store bulk suspension ≤2 weeks at 2–10°.

(2) *Broth culture.*—Wash growth from stock culture with ca 3 ml broth medium A, and transfer liq. to 100 ml broth medium A. Incubate 48 hr at 26–32° with continuous mech. agitation. This 48 hr culture is inoculum. Store ≤2 weeks at 2–10°.

Use for lincomycin, novobiocin feed supplement, oleandomycin, penicillin, and tylosin assays.

(f) *Staphylococcus epidermidis.*—ATCC 12228. Incubate stock culture at 32°. Inoculate 30 ml broth medium A in 300 ml flask with 1 loop from stock culture, and incubate overnight at 26–32°. Prep. daily. Use for neomycin and for novobiocin final feed assays.

(g) *Saccharomyces cerevisiae.*—ATCC No. 9763. Incubate stock culture on agar medium I at 37°. Prep. inoculum by one of following methods:

(1) *Broth culture.*—Inoculate 100 ml broth medium B with 1 loop from stock culture and incubate overnight at 37°. This culture is inoculum. Store ≤2 weeks at 2–10°.

(2) *Roux bottle culture.*—Wash growth from stock culture with ca 3 ml sterile isotonic saline soln, and transfer liq. to surface of 300 ml agar medium I in Roux bottle. Spread suspension evenly over entire surface, using sterile glass beads, and incubate 24 hr at 37°. Wash growth from agar surface with ca 15 ml sterile isotonic saline soln. Store ≤2 weeks at 2–10°.

Use for nystatin assay.

38.168   Preparation of Standard Response Line

Prep. std response line simultaneously with assay soln. Prep. concns of Ref. Std (described for each antibiotic). Use indicated concn as ref. concn.

Prep. plates with appropriate base agar layer and appropriate seed agar layer (described for each antibiotic). Place 6 cylinders on each plate at ca 60° intervals on 2.8 cm radius. Fill 3 alternate cylinders with ref. concn and other 3 cylinders with one of other concns of std. Use 3 plates for each concn required for std response line, except ref. concn. Incubate plates overnight at appropriate temp., and measure diams of zones of inhibition by means of mm ruler, calipers, or calibrated projection device. In each set of 3 plates average the 9 readings of ref. concn and the 9 readings of concn being tested. Av. of all 36 readings of ref. concn from 12 plates is correction point for response line. Correct av. value obtained for each concn to appropriate figure if ref. concn reading on that set of 3 plates was same as correction point.

For example, if in correcting second concn of std response line, av. of 36 readings of ref. concn is 20.0 mm, and av. of 9 readings of ref. concn of this set of 3 plates is 19.8 mm, correction is +0.2 mm. If av. reading of second concn on same 3 plates is 17.0 mm, corrected value is 17.2 mm. Plot corrected values, including correction point, on semilog graph paper, using logarithmic scale for concn and arithmetic scale for av. zone diams. Draw line of best fit by inspection or calc. as follows:

$$L = (3a + 2b + c - e)/5$$
$$H = (3e + 2d + c - a)/5$$

where L and H = calcd zone diams for low and high concns, resp., of std response line; a, b, c, d, and e = corrected av. zone diams for each concn on std response line.

Plot values for L and H and connect with straight line. Ref. point is zone size intercept on arithmetic scale for ref. concn with plotted response line.

38.169   *Determination*

Use 3 plates for each assay soln. On each plate fill 3 alternate cyclinders with ref. concn and fill other 3 cylinders with assay soln. Incubate plates overnight at appropriate temp. and measure diam. of zones of inhibition. Average the 9 readings of ref. concn and the 9 readings of assay soln. If assay soln gives larger av. than ref. concn, add difference between them to ref. point on std response line. If assay soln gives smaller value than ref. concn, subtract difference between them from ref. point on std response line. Using corrected value of assay soln, det. quantity of antibiotic from std response line.

Bacitracin—Official Final Action
For Feed Supplements (42)

38.170   *Standard Solutions*

(a) *Bacitracin stock soln.*—Dry ca 40 mg USP Zinc Bacitracin Ref. Std 3 hr at 60° in vac. oven at ≤5 mm pressure. Det. accurate dry wt and dissolve in 5 ml H_2O and 0.5 ml HCl (1 + 2.5). Add enough pH 6 buffer, **38.165(f)**, to give concn of exactly 100 units/

ml. Store in dark ≤5 days at 2–10°. (1 g bacitracin = 42,000 units.)

(b) *Std response line.*—Dil. appropriate aliquots of stock soln, (a), with enough pH 6 buffer, **38.165(f)**, to obtain concns of 0.05, 0.10, 0.20, 0.40, and 0.80 unit/ml. Ref. concn is 0.20 unit/ml.

38.171   *Plates*

(a) *Base layer.*—Add 10 ml melted agar medium C to sterile petri dishes, distribute evenly, and let harden on *perfectly level surface*.

(b) *Seed layer.*—Before assay, det. by prepn of trial plates optimum concn (usually 0.1–0.5%) of suspension of *M. flavus*, **38.167(a)**, or *S. subflava*, **38.167(b)**, to be added to agar medium A to obtain zones of inhibition of adequate size and sharpness. For actual assay add appropriate amt of suspension to agar medium A previously melted and cooled to 48°. Mix thoroly and add 4.0 ml to each of plates contg base layer. Distribute agar evenly by tilting plates from side to side with circular motion, and let harden. *Use plates same day prepd.*

38.172   *Assay Solution*

Place 2 g feed supplement conc. in 150 ml beaker, add 5 ml HCl (1 + 2.5), and stir 1 min. Check pH with test paper. If pH is >2, add more acid until pH 2 is reached. Add 45 ml pyridine buffer soln and transfer mixt. to centrf. tube. Shake well 5 min and centrf. ca 15 min at 2000 rpm. Dil. aliquot of clear soln with enough pH 6 buffer, **38.165(f)**, to obtain estd concn of 0.20 unit/ml. Designate soln obtained as assay soln.

38.173   *Assay*

Using bacitracin std response line, assay soln, and plates, proceed as in **38.168–38.169**, incubating at 32–35°.

For Mixed Feeds (43)—Official First Action
(Applicable to feeds contg ≥20 g bacitracin/ton)

38.174   *Standard Solutions*

(a) *Working soln.*—Dil. stock soln, **38.170(a)**, with enough pH 6.5 buffer, **38.165(d)**, to obtain concn of 10 units/ml. Prep. daily.

(b) *Std response line.*—Dil. appropriate aliquots of working soln, (a), with enough pH 6.5 buffer, **38.165(d)**, to obtain concns of 0.025, 0.05, 0.10, and 0.20 unit/ml. Ref. concn is 0.1 unit/ml.

38.175   *Plates*

Use single inoculated agar layer prepd as in **38.171(b)**, except add 10.0 ml to each plate and refrigerate ≥1 hr before use.

38.176   *Assay Solution*

Transfer 10.0 g mixed feed contg ≥20 g bacitracin/ton to 150 ml beaker. Add 20 ml acetone, stir, and let stand few min. Decant most of liq. into 50 ml r-b centrf. tube (guide stream with stirring rod).

Add 20 ml acetone to residue in beaker, stir, let stand few min, and decant again into centrf. tube. Centrf. 2–3 min at 1800 rpm, carefully decant, and discard supernatant acetone. Place centrf. tube in 37° incubator and dry sediment. Tilt beaker contg acetone-soaked solids and spread solids with stirring rod to hasten solv. evapn. Dry beaker and rod in 37° incubator (ca 1 hr).

Add 25 ml HCl (1 + 32) to dried residue in centrf. tube. Stir, and transfer acid to dry feed in beaker. Add 25 ml 40% pyridine buffer soln, 38.165(i), and stir. Pour contents of beaker back and forth from beaker to tube to combine and mix entire sample. Centrf. mixt. 5 min at 1800 rpm. Pipet 15 ml supernatant into 50 ml g-s cylinder and add MeOH to vol. of 30.0 ml. Stopper, shake, and let proteins settle few min. Transfer mixt. to 50 ml centrf. tube and centrf. 2–3 min at 1800 rpm. Carefully pipet 10 ml supernatant and transfer to petri dish with pour lip.

Center each dish on heating mat, 38.166(h), under corresponding hole in Al air sparger, 38.166(i). Slowly open air stopcock until open area ca 2–3″ diam. is formed in liq. Aerate until dry. Add 3 ml 5% buffer, 38.165(d), and loosen and stir residue with neoprene policeman. Transfer to 25 ml g-s graduated cylinder, guiding soln with diagonal edge of policeman. Wash dish and policeman with four 1 ml portions 5% buffer, 38.165(d), pouring each wash into cylinder. Add 1.0 ml 1N NaOH, stopper, and mix. Adjust to pH 6.50±0.05, using pH meter, returning portions used for checking pH to cylinder. Dil. to 10.0 ml (dil. 40 g/ton samples to 20.0 ml) with 5% buffer, 38.165(d). Transfer liq. to 15 ml centrf. tube and centrf. 5 min at 1800 rpm. Use clear supernatant as assay soln.

38.177   *Assay*

Using bacitracin std response line, 38.174(b), assay soln, 38.176, and plates, 38.175, proceed as in 38.168–38.169, except use 4 plates for each concn required for std response line (total of 12 plates) and for each assay soln. Incubate at 37°. Calc. *L* and *H* as follows:

$$L = (7a + 4b + c - 2d)/10$$
$$H = (7d + 4c + b - 2a)/10$$

38.178   *Calculation*

g/ton = (unit/ml assay soln) $\times$ (a/10) $\times$ (30/15) $\times$ (50/g sample) $\times$ (908,000/42,000), where

a = 10 for 20 g/ton and 20 for 40 g/ton samples; 10 = ml aliquot dried; 30 = vol. after addn of MeOH; 15 = vol. supernatant; 50 = vol. HCl and 40% pyridine buffer; 908,000 = number of g in ton; and 42,000 = number of units/g of bacitracin.

Chlortetracycline (CTC) Hydrochloride (44)—Official Final Action

38.179   *Standard Solutions*

(a) *Chlortetracycline stock soln.*—Accurately weigh ca 40 mg CTC.HCl NF Ref. Std and dissolve in enough 0.01N HCl to give concn of exactly 1000 µg/ml. Store in dark ≤5 days at 2–10°.

(b) *Std solns and response line for samples containing more than 50 ppm chlortetracycline.HCl.*—Dil. appropriate aliquots of stock soln, (a), with enough pH 4.5 buffer, 38.165(g), to obtain concns of 0.01, 0.02, 0.04, 0.08, and 0.16 µg/ml. Ref. concn is 0.04 µg/ml.

(c) *Std solns and response line for samples containing not more than 50 ppm chlortetracycline.HCl.*—Prep. as in (b), but dil. with inactivated diluent, (d), instead of buffer soln and include concns of 0, 0.005, and 0.32 µg CTC.HCl/ml. Draw best line of fit by inspection.

(d) *Inactivated diluent.*—To 10 ml acid-acetone feed ext (prepd from feed under test as in 38.181(b)) in 600 ml beaker, add 90 ml pH 4.5 phosphate buffer, 38.165(g), and adjust to pH 4.5–4.7 with 1N NaOH. Add 1.0 ml fresh 5.25% NaOCl soln, 38.165(q), and stir 1–2 min, rinsing sides of beaker. *Heat, stirring thoroly at 10 min intervals, in uncovered beaker in boiling H_2O bath 30 min.* Cool to room temp. under tap H_2O stream and transfer quant. to 100 ml vol. flask. Rinse beaker with 6 ml acetone, add rinsings to vol. flask, and dil. to vol. with pH 4.5 buffer. Transfer quant. to another flask and dil. with enough pH 4.5 buffer so that final concn of feed ext is same as that in assay soln.

38.180   *Plates*

(a) *Base layer.*—Add 6.0 ml melted agar medium D to sterile petri dishes, distribute evenly, and let harden on *perfectly level surface.*

(b) *Seed layer.*—Before assay, det. by prepn of trial plates optimum concn (usually 0.03–0.10%) of organism suspension of *B. cereus*, 38.167(c), to be added to agar medium D to obtain zones of inhibition with as little as 0.01 µg CTC.HCl/ml for assaying samples contg >50 ppm and 0.005 µg/ml for samples contg ≤50 ppm CTC.HCl. For actual assay add appropriate amt of suspension to agar medium D previously melted and cooled to 48°. Mix thoroly and add 4.0 ml to each of plates contg base layer. Distribute agar evenly by tilting plates from side to side with circular motion, and let harden. *Use plates same day prepd.*

38.181   *Preparation of Assay Solution*

(a) *Samples containing more than 50 ppm chlortetracycline.HCl.*—Place 2, 10, or 20 g sample, resp., contg CTC.HCl ≥10 g/lb (>2%), >400 ppm to 2%, or 50–400 ppm in 150 ml beaker and pipet in 40 ml acid-acetone soln, 38.165(j). Stir ca 2 min with glass rod, let stand 2 min, and stir. Adjust pH to 1.0–1.2 with HCl, if necessary, and note vol. HCl added. Transfer to 1 qt high-speed blender jar, using addnl 20 ml (minus vol. equiv. to HCl added in adjusting pH) acid-acetone to rinse beaker and pH meter electrodes. Cover jar and blend 3 min at high speed. Transfer mixt. to 100 ml centrf. tubes. Wash blender jar with 40 ml acid-acetone and combine washings with ext in centrf. tubes. Shake well 5 min. Centrf. ca 15 min at 2000 rpm. Combine and mix clarified exts. Adjust 10 ml aliquot to pH 4.5 with 1N NaOH. Dil. adjusted soln with enough pH 4.5 buffer, 38.165(g), to obtain estd concn of 0.04 μg/ml. Designate soln as assay soln.

(b) *Samples containing not more than 50 ppm chlortetracycline.HCl.*—Place 50 g sample in 250 ml beaker and pipet in 100 ml acid-acetone soln, 38.165(j). Stir, adjust pH, and blend as in (a), using 50 ml (less vol. equiv. to HCl added in adjusting pH) acid-acetone to transfer to blender jar. After blending, transfer quant. to 250 ml centrf. bottle, rinsing jar with 50 ml acid-acetone soln. Shake thoroly and centrf. ca 15 min at 2000 rpm. Pipet 5 ml clear supernatant into 50 ml beaker, add ca 40 ml pH 4.5 buffer, 38.165(g), mix, and adjust pH to 4.5–4.7 with 1N NaOH. Transfer quant. to flask, rinse beaker and pH meter electrodes with pH 4.5 buffer, and add rinsings to flask. Add enough pH 4.5 buffer to obtain estd concn of 0.04 μg/ml. Designate as assay soln.

38.182 *Assay*

Using CTC.HCl std response line, assay soln, and plates, proceed as in 38.168–38.169, incubating at 30°.

Hygromycin B (45)—Official Final Action
38.183 *Standard Solutions*

(a) *Hygromycin B stock soln.*—Accurately weigh amt of Hygromycin B Ref. Std (available from Microbiological Testing Dept., Eli Lilly and Co., Indianapolis, IN 46206) contg 50,000 units, transfer to 50 ml vol. flask, and dil. to vol. with pH 7 phosphate buffer, 38.165(c). Store in refrigerator ≤2 weeks.

(b) *Std response line.*—Dil. appropriate aliquots of stock soln daily with enough pH 7 buffer, 38.165(c), to obtain concns of 15, 25, 50, and 75 units/ml. Ref. concn is 25 units/ml.

38.184 *Plates*

(a) *Base layer.*—Add 10 ml melted agar medium E to sterile petri dishes, distribute evenly, and let harden *on perfectly level surface.*

(b) *Seed layer.*—Before assay det. by prepn of trial plates optimum concn (usually 0.2% of 1:10 diln) of spore suspension of *B. subtilis*, 38.167(d), to be added to agar medium E. For actual assay add appropriate amt of spore suspension to agar medium E which has been melted and cooled to 48°. Mix thoroly and add 4.0 ml to each plate contg base layer. Distribute agar evenly by tilting plates from side to side with circular motion, and let harden. Store plates at 2–10° until just before use. *Use same day prepd.*

38.185 *Assay Solution*

Preparation of ion exchange resin column.—Slurry ca 1 lb Amberlite IRC-50 ion exchange resin with 2 L 1N H₂SO₄ 3 hr. Wash until neut. with H₂O and gradually add solid LiOH with stirring until pH remains at 7–8. Let stand overnight and wash with H₂O ≥5 times. Neutze to pH 7.0 with 1N H₃PO₄. Store under H₂O in glass container.

Place glass wool plug at bottom of 6 mm id × 140 mm long tube fitted with valve to control flow and 50 ml reservoir at top. Fill tube with H₂O and add wet resin to within 20 mm of top of tube. Drain H₂O to within 5 mm of resin surface. Wash with 25 ml sterile H₂O immediately before use.

Weigh 50 g sample of feed contg 6000–12,000 units/lb (30 g for 18,000–24,000 units/lb, 20 g for >24,000) into jar of high-speed blender. Add 300 ml (500 for the higher potency feeds) pH 7 phosphate buffer, 38.165(c), and blend 5 min, operating blender from autotransformer set at 70. Centrf. 10 min at 2600 rpm. Adjust 125 ml supernatant to pH 5.0 with HCl (ca 0.5 ml). Add 50 ml CHCl₃ previously washed with pH 7.0 buffer, stopper, and shake thoroly. Centrf. mixt. 10 min at 2600 rpm. Remove aq. phase, adjust to pH 7.0 with 40% NaOH soln (ca 0.7 ml), and centrf.

Transfer 100 ml neutzd soln (75 ml if feed contains ≥42,000 units/lb) to ion exchange column and adjust flow rate to 40 drops/min. Wash column with four 20 ml portions sterile H₂O. Elute hygromycin B with 50 ml NH₄OH (1 + 9) into 100 ml Pyrex beaker. Evap. to 3–5 ml and adjust to pH 7.0 with 1N HCl. Transfer to 10 ml vol. flask, dil. to vol. with pH 7.0 phosphate buffer, and designate as assay soln. (Final concn should be ca 25 units/ml.)

38.186 *Assay*

Using hygromycin std response line, assay soln, and plates, proceed as in 38.168–38.169, except use 6 plates for each concn required for std response line (total of 18 plates) and for each assay soln. Equations for L and H cannot be used. Incubate at 37°.

38.187 *Calculation*

Units/lb = [1.1 × (units/ml assay soln) × 454 × ml pH 7 buffer (300 or 500) × 10 × (125 + ml HCl + ml 40% NaOH)]/[125 ml × g sample × ml neutzd soln put on column].

Lincomycin (46)—Official First Action
38.188 *Standard Solutions*

(a) *Lincomycin stock soln.*—Accurately weigh ca 40 mg USP Lincomycin.HCl Ref. Std and dissolve in enough pH 8 buffer, 38.165(b), to give concn of exactly 100 μg lincomycin base/ml. Store ≤30 days at 2–10°.

(b) *Std response line.*—Dil. aliquots stock soln, (a), with enough pH 8 phosphate buffer, 38.165(b), to obtain concns of 0.2, 0.4, 0.8, 1.6, and 3.2 μg lincomycin base/ml. Ref. concn is 0.8 μg/ml.

38.189 *Plates*

(a) *Base layer.*—Add 10 ml melted agar medium E to sterile petri dishes, distribute evenly, and let harden *on perfectly level surface.*

(b) *Seed layer.*—Before assay, det. by prepn of trial plates optimum concn of organism suspension of *S. lutea* (usually 0.02–0.05% of suspension prepd as in **38.167**(e)(*1*) or 0.2–1% as in **38.167**(e)(*2*)) to be added to agar medium J to obtain zones of inhibition of adequate size and sharpness. For assay, add appropriate amt of organism suspension to agar medium J previously melted and cooled to 48°. Mix thoroly and add 4.0 ml to each plate contg base layer. Distribute agar evenly by quickly swirling plates and let harden. *Use plates same day prepd.*

38.190 *Assay Solution*

Accurately weigh ca 10 g ground sample (thru 1 mm screen) and transfer to 250 ml g-s r-b flask, add 20 ml H_2O, and shake 10 min on wrist-action shaker. Add 50 ml 0.1N HCl-MeOH (1 + 4) and shake 10 min. Filter thru Whatman No. 4 paper, using 42 mm buchner and 500 ml flask. Repeat extn twice, using 50 ml HCl-MeOH each time. (Do *not* add more H_2O.) Alternatively, conduct extns in 250 ml centrf. bottle and centrf. to clarify.

Transfer combined filtrates to 500 ml r-b flask and evap. to 15–20 ml, using rotary evaporator to remove solvs. (Do *not* heat above 60°.) Transfer aq. ext to 125 ml separator. Rinse flask successively with 10 ml Skellysolve B, **3.025**(o), 7–8 ml phosphate buffer, **38.165**(b), and 10 ml Skellysolve B. Add all rinsings to separator, shake, and let sep. Drain aq. phase, ext. Skellysolve B twice with 7–8 ml buffer, and adjust combined exts to pH 8.0 with dil. NaOH soln. Adjust vol. with pH 8 buffer to 0.6–1.0 μg lincomycin base/ml.

38.191 *Assay*

Using lincomycin std response line and assay soln, proceed as in **38.168–38.169**, incubating at 32°.

Neomycin (47)—Official First Action

(Soybean content >40% reduces accuracy of method.)

38.192 *Standard Solutions*

(a) *Stock soln.*—Dry USP Neomycin Sulfate Ref. Std 3 hr in vac. oven at ≤5 mm. Accurately weigh enough dried std (10–50 mg) and dissolve in tris buffer, **38.165**(n), to give concn of 100 μg neomycin base/ml. (Neomycin sulfate equiv. to neomycin base is given on container.) Store ≤4 weeks at 2–10°.

(b) *Std response line.*—Dil. aliquots stock soln (a) with enough inactivated feed ext, **38.194**(b), to obtain 0.50, 0.75, 1.13, 1.69, and 2.53 μg neomycin base/ml. Prep. std response line for each feed sample.

33.193 *Plates*

(a) *Base layer.*—Add 10 ml melted agar medium K to petri dishes, distribute evenly, and let harden *on perfectly level surface.*

(b) *Seed layer.*—Add appropriate amt (usually 0.5–2%) broth culture of *S. epidermidis*, **38.167**(f), to agar medium K previously melted and cooled to 48°. Mix thoroly and add 4.0 ml to each plate contg base layer. Distribute agar evenly by tilting plates from side to side with circular motion and let harden. *Use plates same day prepd.*

38.194 *Assay Solution*

(a) *Preparation of sample.*—Weigh 20 g feed sample into 500 ml r-b flask. Add 100.0 ml NaCl-CaCl₂ soln, **38.165**(p), and shake 15 min on wrist-action shaker. Transfer contents to 250 ml centrf. bottle (*do not rinse*), centrf. 15 min at 1800–2000 rpm, and decant supernatant into beaker. Transfer 20 ml aliquot to 100 ml beaker and set aside to prep. std response line diluent. Using pH meter, adjust remaining portion with HCl to pH 2.0. Wait at least 5 min; then readjust to pH 8.0 with 10N NaOH. (High concns of acid and base are used to avoid significant changes in vol.) Centrf. 30–35 ml 15 min at 1800–2000 rpm. Dil. ext soln with tris buffer according to neomycin content in feed as in Table 38:2 (diln A).

Table 38:2—Dilution of Extract

Neomycin Base, g/ton	Sample Extract, Diln A	Neomycin Base, Final Concn, μg/ml	Inactivated Extract, Diln B
140	1 to 20	1.54	10 to 200
70	1 to 10	1.54	20 to 200
35	1 to 10	0.77	20 to 200

(b) *Preparation of std response line diluent.*—Inactivate the 20 ml aliquot from (a) by adjusting to pH 4.5–4.7 with 2N HCl. Add 1.5 ml fresh 5.25% NaOCl soln and heat 45 min in boiling H_2O bath, stirring thoroly at least every 10 min during heating period. Cool to room temp., adjust to pH 8.0 with 3.5N NaOH, and dil. to 20 ml with H_2O. Dil. inactivated ext with tris buffer, **38.165**(n), according to neomycin content in feed as in diln B column of Table 38:2.

Use dild soln to prep. std response line solns.

38.195 *Assay*

Using neomycin std response line, assay soln, and plates, proceed as in **38.168–38.169**, incubating at 32–35°.

Novobiocin (48)—Official Final Action

38.196 *Standard Solutions*

(a) *Novobiocin stock soln.*—Dry USP Novobiocin Ref. Std 3 hr at 60° in vac. oven at ≤5 mm. Accurately weigh ca 30 mg dried std, dissolve in 10 ml absolute alcohol, and dil. with enough pH 8 phosphate buffer, **38.165**(b), to give concn of 1 mg/ml. Store ≤3 weeks at 2–10°.

(b) *Std response line for feed supplements.*—Dil. aliquots of stock soln (a) with enough pH 6 buffer, **38.165**(f), to obtain concns of 1.9, 2.4, 3.0, 3.8, and 4.7 μg/ml. Ref. concn is 3.0 μg/ml.

(c) *Std response line for finished feed.*—Dil. aliquots of stock soln (a) with enough pH 6 buffer, **38.165**(f), to obtain concns of 0.128, 0.16, 0.20, 0.25, and 0.312 µg/ml. Ref. concn is 0.20 µg/ml.

38.197 *Plates*

(a) *For feed supplements.*—(1) *Base layer.*—Add 21 ml melted agar medium C to sterile petri dishes, distribute evenly, and let harden *on perfectly level surface.*

(2) *Seed layer.*—Before assay, det. by prepn of trial plates optimum concn of organism suspension of *S. lutea* (usually 0.2–0.5% of suspension prepd as in **38.167**(e)(1) or 2–5% as in **38.167**(e)(2)) to be added to agar medium C to obtain zones of inhibition of adequate size and sharpness. For actual assay, add appropriate amt of organism suspension to agar medium C, previously melted and cooled to 48°. Mix thoroly and add 5.0 ml to each plate contg base layer. Distribute agar evenly by tilting plates from side to side with circular motion, and let harden. *Use plates same day prepd.*

(b) *For final feed.*—(1) *Base layer.*—Prep. as in (a)(1), using 15 ml melted agar medium C.

(2) *Seed layer.*—Add appropriate amt (usually 0.5–2%) broth culture of *S. epidermidis*, **38.167**(f), to agar medium C previously melted and cooled to 48°. Mix thoroly and add 5 ml to each plate contg base layer. Distribute agar evenly by tilting plates from side to side with circular motion, and let harden. *Use plates same day prepd.*

38.198 *Assay Solution*

(a) *For feed supplements containing 50 mg/g.*—Accurately weigh suitable size sample and add enough absolute alcohol to give estd concn of 2 mg/ml. Let stand 30 min, shaking occasionally. Add equal vol. pH 8 phosphate buffer, **38.165**(b), and mix. Dil. to estd concn of 3 µg/ml with pH 6 buffer, **38.165**(f), and use as assay soln.

(b) *For final feed containing not less than 350 µg/g.*—Weigh 1.0 g feed into 50 ml g-s cylinder; ext twice with 20 ml EtOAc, shaking vigorously 2 min. Decant supernatant into second 50 ml g-s cylinder. Dil. to 50 ml with EtOAc. Transfer 2.0–4.0 ml aliquot to 100 ml vol. flask, add 5.0 ml pH 8 phosphate buffer, **38.165**(b), and mix thoroly. Dil. to vol. with pH 6 buffer, **38.165**(f), and shake vigorously to dissolve all EtOAc. Final concn of novobiocin should be 0.15–0.30 µg/ml.

38.199 *Assay*

Using proper novobiocin std response line, assay soln, and plates, proceed as in **38.168–38.169**, incubating at 32–35°.

Nystatin (49)—Official First Action

38.200 *Standard Solutions*

(a) *Nystatin stock soln.*—Dry ca 30 mg USP Nystatin Ref. Std 2 hr at 40° in vac. oven at ≤5 mm. Det. accurate dry wt and add enough MeOH to give concn of exactly 500 units/ml. Dissolve by shaking on mech. shaker 0.5 hr (soln may be slightly hazy). Prep. fresh daily. (1 g nystatin = 2,800,000 units.)

(b) *Std response line.*—To MeOH soln from **38.202**(c) add amt of nystatin std soln in MeOH equal to amt estd to be in 50 g original feed. Adjust vol. to 100 ml with MeOH and add to dried extd feed portion from **38.202**(c). Shake 1 hr on mech. shaker. Centrf., transfer 50 ml aliquot of clear supernatant and 20 ml H_2O to evapn flask, and evap. under vac. (ca 6 cm) in rotating evaporator in 37° H_2O bath. Transfer aq. residue to graduated cylinder, rinsing with several portions 10% pH 6 phosphate buffer, **38.165**(e), and combine solns so that final vol. is same as assay soln before addn of equilibrating fluid, **38.202**(d). Concn of nystatin std in this soln is 31.2 units/ml (62.5 units/ml if feed contains <40 ppm). Dil. aliquots of this soln with equilibrating fluid to obtain addnl concns of 12.8, 16.0, 20.0, and 25.0 units/ml (25.6, 32, 40, and 50 if feed contains <40 ppm). Ref. concn is 20.0 units/ml (40 if feed contains <40 ppm).

38.201 *Plates*

Seed agar.—Use single inoculated agar layer. Before assay, det. by prepn of trial plates optimum concn of organism suspension of *Sacch. cerevisiae* (usually 2% of suspension prepd as in **38.167**(g)(1) or 0.1% as in **38.167**(g)(2)) to be added to agar medium I to obtain zones of inhibition of adequate size and sharpness. For actual assay, add appropriate amt of organism suspension to agar medium I previously melted and cooled to 48°. Mix thoroly, and add 10 ml to each sterile petri dish. Distribute agar evenly by tilting plates from side to side with circular motion and let harden *on perfectly level surface. Use plates same day prepd.*

38.202 *Assay Solution*

(a) *Hexane wash.*—Place 50 g sample contg >20 g nystatin/ton in each of three 250 ml centrf. bottles. To each add 100 ml hexane and shake 20 min. Centrf., decant, and discard clear supernatant. Repeat washing, shaking, centrfg, and decanting with three 100 ml portions hexane. Air-dry the 3 washed feed portions.

(b) *Preparation of assay soln.*—To 1 portion of washed feed in 250 ml centrf. bottle, add 100 ml MeOH, and shake 1 hr on mech. shaker. Centrf., transfer 50 ml aliquot clear supernatant and 20 ml H_2O to evapn flask, and evap. under vac. (ca 6 cm) in rotating evaporator in 37° H_2O bath. Transfer aq. residue in flask to graduated cylinder. Rinse with several portions 10% pH 6 phosphate buffer, **38.165**(e), and add to cylinder. Dil. soln with addnl phosphate buffer to obtain estd concn of 31.2 units/ml (62.5 if feed contains <40 ppm). Dil. with enough equilibrating fluid, (d), below, to obtain estd concn of 20 units/ml (40 if feed contains <40 ppm). Designate vol. obtained as assay soln.

(c) *Extraction and inactivation of nystatin.*—Transfer 2 remaining portions hexane-washed feed to Soxhlet extn thimbles and ext each with ca 250 ml n-propanol 7–8 hr. Dry extd feed portions and save 1 for prepn of equilibrating fluid, (d), and 1 for prepn of std response line, **38.200(b)**. Add 10 ml NH₄OH (1 + 9) to each propanol ext and evap. to dryness under vac. (ca 6 cm) in rotating evaporator in 65° H₂O bath. Transfer each residue to 100 ml graduated cylinder with four 15 ml portions MeOH. Use one MeOH soln for prepn of equilibrating fluid and one for prepn of std response line.

(d) *Preparation of equilibrating fluid.*—Adjust vol. of one MeOH soln to 100 ml with MeOH and add to dried extd feed from (c) in 250 ml centrf. bottle. Shake 1 hr on mech. shaker. Centrf., transfer 50 ml aliquot clear supernatant and 20 ml H₂O to evapn flask, and evap. under vac. (ca 6 cm) in rotating evaporator in 37° H₂O bath. After removal of alcohol, transfer aq. residue in flask to graduated cylinder with several portions 10% pH 6 phosphate buffer, **38.165(e)**, and dil. with addnl phosphate buffer to obtain same vol. as assay soln before addn of equilibrating fluid.

38.203   *Assay*

Using nystatin std response line, assay soln, and plates, proceed as in **38.168–38.169**, incubating at 37°.

Oleandomycin (50)—Official Final Action

38.204   *Standard Solutions*

(a) *Heated feed extract.*—Distribute 20 g feed sample in 20 × 150 mm glass petri dish without cover and autoclave 90 min at 20 lb pressure. Add same amt of pH 8 phosphate-bicarbonate buffer, **38.165(a)**, as used in prepn of Assay Soln, **38.205**, shake 45 min, decant, and collect supernatant. If necessary, filter or centrf. to obtain clear soln.

(b) *Oleandomycin stock soln.*—Accurately weigh ca 40 mg Oleandomycin Chloroform Adduct Ref. Std (available from Brooklyn Quality Control, Chas. Pfizer & Co., 11 Bartlett St, Brooklyn, NY 11206) or NF Ref. Std. Dissolve in ca 5 ml MeOH and dil. with enough pH 8 phosphate-bicarbonate buffer, **38.165(a)**, to given concn of 125 μg/ml. Store in dark ≤3 days at 2–10°.

(c) *Std response line.*—Dil. appropriate aliquots of stock soln with enough heated feed ext to obtain concns of 0.045, 0.067, 0.10, 0.15, and 0.225 μg/ml. Ref. concn is 0.10 μg/ml.

38.205   *Assay Solutions*

To 20 g final feed sample contg 1–20 ppm oleandomycin, add enough pH 8 phosphate-bicarbonate buffer, **38.165(a)**, to give estd concn of 0.1 μg/ml. Shake mech. 45 min, let settle, decant, and collect supernatant as assay soln.

38.206   *Plates*

Use single inoculated agar layer. Before assay, det. by prepn of trial plates optimum concn of organism suspension of *S. lutea* (usually 0.03–0.1% of suspension prepd as in **38.167(e)(1)** or 0.3–1% as in **38.167 (e)(2)**) to be added to agar medium B to obtain zones of inhibition of adequate size and sharpness. For actual assay, add appropriate amt of organism suspension to agar medium B previously melted and cooled to 48°. Mix thoroly and add 10.0 ml to each petri dish. Distribute agar evenly by tilting plates from side to side with circular motion and let harden. *Use plates same day prepd.*

38.207   *Assay*

Using oleandomycin std response line, assay soln, and plates, proceed as in **38.168–38.169**, incubating at 37°.

Oxytetracycline (51)—Official Final Action

38.208   *Standard Solutions*

(a) *Oxytetracycline stock soln.*—Accurately weigh ca 40 mg oxytetracycline USP Ref. Std and dissolve in enough 0.1N HCl to give exact concn of 100 μg oxytetracycline/ml. (1 μg base is equiv. to 1.08 μg of the hydrochloride.) Store in dark ≤5 days at 2–10°.

(b) *Std response line.*—Dil. appropriate aliquots stock soln, (a), with enough pH 4.5 buffer, **38.165(g)**, to obtain concns of 0.05, 0.10, 0.20, 0.40, and 0.80 μg oxytetracycline/ml. Ref. concn is 0.20 μg/ml.

Method I
(Applicable to >220 mg/lb)

38.209   *Assay Solution*

Using mortar and pestle or high-speed blender, grind 2 g feed with 50 ml acid-MeOH, **38.165(k)**, and transfer mixt. to 100 ml centrf. tube. Wash mortar and pestle or blender jar with 50 ml acid-MeOH and combine washings with ext in centrf. tube. Shake well 5 min. Centrf. ca 15 min at 2000 rpm. Remove 10 ml clear soln and adjust to pH 4.5 with 1N NaOH. Dil. adjusted soln with enough pH 4.5 buffer, **33.165(g)**, to obtain estd concn of 0.20 μg/ml. Designate as assay soln.

38.210   *Assay*

Using oxytetracycline std response line and assay soln, and chlortetracycline plates, **38.180(b)**, proceed as in **38.168–38.169**, incubating at 30°.

Method II
(Applicable to ≤220 mg/lb)

38.211   *Plates*

Use single inoculated agar layer. Before assay, det. by prepn of trial plates optimum concn (usually 0.03–0.10%) of stock suspension of *B. cereus*, **38.167(c)**, to be added to agar medium D, **38.164(d)**, to obtain zones of inhibition with as little as 0.05 μg oxytetracycline/ml. For actual assay add appropriate amt of inoculum to agar medium D previously melted and cooled to 48°. Mix thoroly, and add 9.0 ml to each plate. Distribute agar evenly, and *let harden on perfectly level surface. Use plates same day prepd.*

38.212 *Assay Solution*

Accurately weigh 20 g ground finished feed into 250 ml extn flask, add 100 ml acid-MeOH, **38.165(k)**, stopper, and shake mech. 5 min. Centrf. ca 5 min at 2000 rpm. Remove 20 ml supernatant and adjust to pH 4.5 with 1N NaOH. Dil. adjusted soln with enough pH 4.5 buffer, **38.165(g)**, to obtain estd concn of 0.20 μg/ml and filter thru Whatman No. 2V paper, or equiv. Designate as assay soln.

38.213 *Assay*

Using oxytetracycline std response line, assay soln, **38.212**, and plates, proceed as in **38.168–38.169**, incubating at 28–30°. Calc. result as oxytetracycline .HCl by multiplying oxytetracycline base by 1.08.

Procaine Pencillin (52)—Official Final Action

38.214 *Standard Solutions*

(a) *Penicillin stock soln.*—Accurately weigh, in atm. of ≤50% relative humidity, ca 30 mg USP Sodium Penicillin G Ref. Std. Dissolve in enough pH 6 buffer, **38.165(f)**, to give known concn of 100–1000 units/ml. Store in dark ≤2 days at 2–10°.

(b) *Std response line.*—Dil. appropriate aliquots of stock soln, (a), with enough pH 6 buffer, **38.165(f)**, to obtain concns of 0.0125, 0.025, 0.05, 0.10, 0.20 unit/ml. Ref. concn is 0.05 unit/ml.

38.215 *Plates*

(a) *Base layer.*—Add 10 ml melted agar medium A to sterile petri dishes, distribute evenly, and let harden on *perfectly level surface.*

(b) *Seed layer.*—Before assay, det. by prepn of trial plates optimum concn of organism suspension of *S. lutea* (usually 0.2–0.5% of suspension prepd as in **38.167(e)(1)** or 2–5% as in **38.167(e)(2)**) to be added to agar medium B to obtain zones of inhibition of adequate size and sharpness.

For actual assay, add appropriate amt of organism suspension to agar medium B previously melted and cooled to 48°. Mix thoroly and add 4.0 ml to each plate contg base layer. Distribute agar evenly by tilting plates from side to side with circular motion, and let harden. *Use plates same day prepd.*

38.216 *Assay Solution*

Vary amts of feed sample and extractant according to penicillin content of feed as follows:

Penicillin Content	Sample Size, g	Vol. Extractant, ml
≥100 g/lb	1	100
1–100 g/lb	3	100
0.1–1 g/lb	10	100
<0.1 g/lb (200 g/ton)	50	200

Ext appropriate quantity of sample with pH 6 buffer-acetone extractant, **38.165(m)**, in suitable container, using either wrist-action or reciprocating mech. shaker 30 min or high-speed blender 2 min; let settle and decant supernatant. Centrf. if more than slightly turbid. Dil. aliquot of supernatant with enough pH 6 buffer, **38.165(f)**, to obtain estd concn of 0.05 unit/ml.

38.217 *Assay*

Using penicillin std response line, assay soln, and plates, proceed as in **38.168–38.169**, incubating at 26–32°. Calc. result in terms of units or wt (1 unit is antibiotic activity of 0.6 μg Na penicillin G; 1 mg = 1667 units).

38.218 *Identity*

To aliquot of supernatant assay soln, **38.216**, add enough *penicillinase soln* to inactivate penicillin activity by incubating mixt. 1 hr at 37°. Further dil. with enough pH 6 buffer, **38.165(f)**, to give same diln factor as in **38.216**. Assay as in **38.217**. Absence of zone of inhibition indicates that activity in sample is due to penicillin. (*See* **16.099**.)

Streptomycin (53)—Official First Action

38.219 *Standard Solutions*

(a) *Streptomycin stock soln.*—Dry ca 40 mg USP Streptomycin Sulfate Ref. Std 3 hr at 60° in vac. oven at ≤5 mm. Det. accurate dry wt and dissolve in enough H$_2$O to give concn of exactly 100 μg streptomycin base/ml. Store ≤30 days at 2–10°.

(b) *Std response line.*—(*1*) *Feed supplement assay.*—Dil. aliquots of stock soln, (a), with enough pH 8 buffer, **38.165(b)**, to obtain concns of 0.64, 0.80, 1.0, 1.25, and 1.56 μg streptomycin base/ml. Ref. concn is 1.0 μg/ml.

(*2*) *Final feed assay.*—Dil. aliquots stock soln, (a), with enough pH 8 buffer, **38.165(b)**, to obtain concns of 0.064, 0.08, 0.10, 0.125, and 0.156 μg streptomycin base/ml. Ref. concn is 0.10 μg/ml.

38.220 *Plates*

(a) *Base layer.*—(*1*) *For feed supplement assay.*—Add 12 ml melted agar medium E to sterile petri dishes. (*2*) *For final feed assay.*—Add 12 ml melted agar medium F to sterile petri dishes. Distribute agar evenly and let harden on *perfectly level surface.*

(b) *Seed layer.*—Before assay, det. by prepn of trial plates optimum concn (usually 0.05–0.2%) of spore suspension of *B. subtilis*, **38.167(d)**, to be added to agar medium E. For actual feed supplement assay, sharp zones of inhibition should be obtained with 0.64 μg streptomycin base/ml; for final feed assay, sharp zones should be obtained with 0.064 μg/ml. Add appropriate amt of spore suspension to agar medium E which has been melted and cooled to 48°. Mix thoroly and add 4.0 ml to each plate contg base layer. Evenly distribute agar by tilting plates from side to side with circular motion, and let harden. *Use plates same day prepd.*

38.221   *Assay Solution*

Using 10.0 g feed and 200 ml 0.5N HCl, shake 30 min with mech. shaker or blend 2 min in high-speed blender. Centrf. ca 15 min at 2000 rpm. Transfer aliquot of supernatant to beaker, add at least equal vol. pH 8 buffer, **38.165(b)**, and adjust to pH 8 with 5N and 1N NaOH. Transfer quant. to suitable vol. flask, dil. to vol. with pH 8 buffer, **38.165(b)**, and mix. Dil. aliquot with enough pH 8 phosphate buffer to obtain estd concn of 1.0 μg streptomycin base/ml (feed supplement assay) or 0.1 μg/ml (final feed assay). Remove any ppt by filtering or centrfg.

38.222   *Assay*

Using proper streptomycin std response line, assay soln, and plates, proceed as in **38.168–38.169**, incubating at 37°.

Tylosin (54)—Official Final Action

38.223   *Standard Solutions*

(a) *Tylosin stock soln.*—Dry Ref. Std Tylosin base (available from Eli Lilly & Co.) 4 hr at 70° and store in desiccator over fresh P_2O_5. Accurately weigh suitable quantity (10–50 mg) dried std and dissolve in 5 ml MeOH. Adjust vol. with pH 7 phosphate buffer, **38.165(c)**, to give concn of 1000 μg/ml. Store in refrigerator $\leq$2 weeks.

(b) *Std response line.*—Dil. appropriate aliquots of stock soln with mixt. of MeOH and pH 8 phosphate buffer, **38.165(b)**, (4 + 6), to obtain concns of 0.125, 0.25, 0.50, 1.0, and 2.0 μg/ml. Ref. concn is 0.50 μg/ml.

38.224   *Plates*

(a) *Base layer.*—Add 10 ml melted agar medium H to petri dishes, distribute evenly, and let harden on *perfectly level surface.*

(b) *Seed layer.*—Before assay, det. by prepn of trial plates optimum concn of organism suspension of *S. lutea* (usually 0.05–0.2% of suspension prepd as in **38.167(e)(1)** or 0.5–2% as in **33.167(e)(2)**) to be added to agar medium H to obtain zones of inhibition of adequate size and sharpness. For actual assay, add appropriate amt of organism suspension to agar medium H melted and cooled to 48°. Mix thoroly and add 5.0 ml to each plate contg base layer. Evenly distribute agar by tilting plates from side to side with circular motion, cover, and let harden. Refrigerate until just before application of assay solns.

38.225   *Assay Solution*

Accurately weigh 10 g feed premix or 20 g final feed (contg $\geq$10 g/ton) into 250 ml homogenizer cup or blender jar. Add 90 ml hot (70–80°) pH 8 phosphate buffer, **38.165(b)**, and place on steam bath 10 min. Blend 5 min, add 60 ml MeOH, and blend addnl

5 min. Centrf. or filter thru Whatman No. 1 paper and dil., if necessary, with mixt. of MeOH and pH 8 phosphate buffer, **38.165(b)**, (4 + 6), to concn of 0.5 μg tylosin/ml.

38.226   *Assay*

Simultaneously prep. std response line with assay soln.

Prep. 10 plates for std response line and 5 for each sample. Place 5 cylinders on each std response line plate at 72° intervals on 2.8 cm radius. Place 4 cylinders on each sample plate at 90° intervals. Fill cylinders on each of 10 std plates with each concn of std response line. On each sample plate fill 2 diagonally opposite cylinders with ref. concn and remaining 2 cylinders with assay soln. Incubate plates overnight at 30°. Measure zone of inhibition to nearest 0.1 mm. Record av. zone diam. for each concn of std on std plates and calc. line of best fit according to equations in **38.168**, where a, b, c, d, and e are av. zone diam. for each std concn. Plot values for L and H on semilog paper and connect with straight line. Ref. point is intercept of ordinate for 0.5 μg concn with plotted curve.

Average the 10 readings of ref. concn on sample plates and the 10 readings of assay soln. If assay soln gives larger av. than ref. concn, add difference between them to ref. point on std response line. If assay soln gives smaller value, subtract difference. Using corrected value of assay soln, det. concn tylosin in assay soln from std response line.

CHEMICAL METHODS

Griseofulvin (55)—Official First Action

(Applicable to concns $\geq$10 mg/oz. *Caution: See* **46.011, 46.040,** and **46.056.**)

38.227   *Reagents*

(a) *Activated alumina.*—Alcoa grade F-20.

(b) *Solvent mixture.*—Mix 65 parts pet ether with 35 parts CHCl₃ by vol.

(c) *Griseofulvin std soln.*—10 μg/ml. Accurately weigh ca 25 mg USP Griseofulvin Ref. Std into 250 ml vol. flask, dissolve, and dil. to vol. with solv. mixt. Dil. 10 ml of this soln to 100 ml in vol. flask.

38.228   *Apparatus*

(a) *Chromatographic tube.*—20 × 400 mm, with fritted disk and stopcock.

(b) *High-speed blender.*—Waring type, or equiv., 1 L capacity.

(c) *Spectrophotometer.*—Capable of accurate readings at 290 and 320 nm.

38.229   *Preparation of Sample*

Grind 250 g feed pellets or mash in high-speed blender 5 min. Accurately weigh ca 14 g finely powd feed into fat-free thimble and ext in Soxhlet app. 2 hr with 100 ml CHCl₃. Evap. ext to 10 ml on steam bath, dil. with 100 ml pet ether, and chromatograph.

38.230   *Preparation of*
                    Chromatographic Column

Place 50 ml solv. mixt., (b), in tube and add 45 ml activated alumina portionwise, with tapping to ensure uniform packing. Place small glass wool plug on top of alumina and drain solv. to just below top of plug.

38.231   *Determination*

Add $CHCl_3$-pet ether sample ext to column. As last of ext passes thru glass wool plug, rinse out sample flask with solv. mixt., add to column, and begin elution with solv. mixt. Adjust liq. head to give flow rate of 15–20 ml/min. Start collecting 25 ml fractions when green eluate first appears (discard yellow and almost colorless eluates which precede). When A of fractions at 290 nm exceeds A at 320 nm, stop fractionating, and collect next 700 ml eluate. Dil. eluate to vol. in 1 L vol. flask with solv. mixt. Det. A of this soln and of griseofulvin std soln at 290 and 320 nm against solv. mixt. blank.

38.232   *Calculations*

mg Griseofulvin/oz

$$= \frac{(A_{290} - A_{320})(W_s)(10)(28.35)}{(A'_{290} - A'_{320})(25)\text{ (g sample)}},$$

where A refers to sample eluate, A' to std soln, and W = mg ref. std griseofulvin used to prep. std soln.

SELECTED REFERENCES

(1) Ind. Eng. Chem., Anal. Ed. **15**, 408(1943); **24**, 1821(1952); Sandell, "Colorimetric Determination of Traces of Metals," 3rd ed., 1959; JAOAC **40**, 455(1957).
(2) JAOAC **44**, 26(1961); **46**, 463(1963).
(3) JAOAC **52**, 438(1969).
(4) JAOAC **47**, 214(1964).
(5) JAOAC **36**, 219(1953); **37**, 257(1954).
(6) JAOAC **44**, 5(1961).
(7) JAOAC **48**, 285(1965).
(8) JAOAC **37**, 257(1954); **40**, 452(1957).
(9) JAOAC **43**, 301(1960).
(10) JAOAC **50**, 264(1967).
(11) JAOAC **46**, 467(1963).
(12) JAOAC **51**, 1279(1968).
(13) JAOAC **39**, 327(1956); **40**, 459(1957); **41**, 316 (1958); **42**, 250(1959).
(14) JAOAC **48**, 301(1965); **53**, 646(1970).
(15) JAOAC **47**, 221(1964); **48**, 280(1965).
(16) JAOAC **40**, 463(1957); **41**, 333(1958); **43**, 310 (1960); **44**, 30(1961); **52**, 233, 421(1969).
(17) JAOAC **43**, 284(1960).
(18) JAOAC **39**, 321(1956); **40**, 469(1957); **41**, 326 (1958).
(19) JAOAC **47**, 226(1964).
(20) JAOAC **44**, 2(1961).
(21) JAOAC **43**, 295(1960).
(22) JAOAC **50**, 50, 261(1967).
(23) JAOAC **42**, 239(1959).
(24) JAOAC **35**, 552(1952); **36**, 219(1953); **39**, 307 (1956).
(25) JAOAC **53**, 641(1970).
(26) JAOAC **41**, 338(1958); **42**, 254(1959).
(27) JAOAC **50**, 268(1967).
(28) JAOAC **49**, 329(1966).
(29) JAOAC **51**, 752(1968).
(30) JAOAC **43**, 291(1960); **44**, 13(1961); **45**, 589 (1962); **46**, 448(1963).
(31) JAOAC **52**, 435(1969); **53**, 634(1970).
(32) JAOAC **49**, 241, 318(1966); **53**, 634(1970).
(33) JAOAC **53**, 638(1970).
(34) JAOAC **34**, 559(1951).
(35) JAOAC **33**, 156(1950); **38**, 229(1955); **39**, 307 (1956).
(36) JAOAC **39**, 307(1956).
(37) JAOAC **51**, 1282(1968); **52**, 423(1969).
(38) JAOAC **46**, 452(1963).
(39) JAOAC **49**, 312(1966).
(40) JAOAC **44**, 18(1961); **45**, 294(1962).
(41) JAOAC **51**, 750(1968).
(42) JAOAC **40**, 857(1957).
(43) JAOAC **48**, 256(1965).
(44) JAOAC **40**, 857(1957); **50**, 446(1967).
(45) JAOAC **43**, 213(1960).
(46) JAOAC **50**, 442(1967).
(47) JAOAC **53**, 60(1970).
(48) JAOAC **45**, 310(1962).
(49) JAOAC **46**, 438, 444(1963).
(50) JAOAC **43**, 211(1960).
(51) JAOAC **51**, 548(1968).
(52) JAOAC **50**, 450(1967).
(53) JAOAC **44**, 33(1961); **53**, 54(1970).
(54) JAOAC **45**, 317(1962).
(55) JAOAC **49**, 494(1966).

39. Vitamins and Other Nutrients *

CHEMICAL METHODS
Vitamin A in Margarine (1)—
Official First Action

39.001   *Principles*

Unsaponifiable portion of margarine is chromatgd on adsorption column consisting of 2 segments of activated and stdzd Al_2O_3 sepd by middle segment of alk. Al_2O_3. (If eluate fraction contg vitamin A is colored, it must be further chromatgd on column of MgO.) Top segment of Al_2O_3 column prevents caking and initiates sepn of vitamin A from carotene and other interfering substances. Middle section of alk. Al_2O_3 seps persistent interference that cannot be sepd by other adsorbents. Final portion of column is nonfluorescent and provides suitable background for observing vitamin A fluorescence on column, thus facilitating control of the chromatgy.

Carotene elutes from column first, second fraction of eluate is discarded, and third fraction contains vitamin A. Better control of chromatgy than is possible by observing colored and fluorescent bands on column is achieved by observing fluorescence in 1 ml portions from final parts of fluorescent and colored eluates. This technic achieves sepn of vitamin A from impurities that cause erroneously high values. Adequacy of sepn is detd from ratio of A of chromatgd vitamin A soln at 310 and 325 nm.

A of sample soln at 325 nm multiplied by factor 18.3 gives concn of vitamin A in units/ml.

39.002   *Apparatus*

(a) *Spectrophotometer and cells.*—UV spectrophtr with suitable source of UV light is required. (Incandescent lamp is *not* suitable source.) Spectrophtr (such as Beckman DU or equiv.) equipped with continuous spectrum source and reading to 200 nm is recommended. Matched quartz cells with 1.0 cm internal light path are preferable. If cells are not matched, suitable corrections must be made. Periodcally check wavelength and A scales of spectrophtr. (*See* Definitions of Terms and Explanatory Notes, item (22).)

(b) *Chromatographic tubes.*—(*1*) Tube 10 mm id and 9 cm long with funnel on upper end and stem on lower end 8 mm in diam. and 1.5″ long with sealed-in disk of medium porosity. (Available from Scientific Glass Apparatus Co.) (*2*) Tube 6 mm id and 25 cm long with lower 5 cm pulled out to form tapered constricted exit 2 mm id. Plug ca 1 cm of upper part of constricted section with glass wool. Fuse flared tube, 18 mm diam. and 14 cm long, to top of 6 mm section.

(c) *Vacuum gage with bleeder valve or pinchcock regulator.*—Use vac. micro bell jar large enough to hold 100 ml beaker or flask for applying vac. and collecting eluates. Control vac. from line or H_2O aspirator by gage and stopcock or screw clamp bleeder on T-tube.

(d) *Long wavelength ultraviolet lamp.*—Use lamp source of *weak* UV for observing fluorescent bands on chromatgc columns. Lamp should provide radiation in long (300 nm) wavelength region. Suitable lamp may be built or purchased (Fisher Scientific Co., 11-984-1, 3660 Å wavelength; or JAOAC **28,** 176(1945)). With com. lamps, narrow aperture or screen may be necessary to reduce amt of destructive radiation. (Vitamin A is readily destroyed by too intense UV light.)

39.003   *Reagents*

(a) *Potassium hydroxide soln.*—50% by wt (780 g/L).

(b) *Alcohol.*—Absolute and 95%. Shall not show $A > 0.05$ when measured at 300 nm in suitable spectrophtr in 1.0 cm quartz cell against H_2O. Isopropanol USP reagent of same spectral purity may be substituted for absolute alcohol in A measurements.

(c) *Ethyl ether.*—Peroxide-free. Use USP, freshly distilled, discarding first and last 10% of distillate; or use USP anesthesia grade in 0.5 lb cans. Must meet requirement for spectral purity described for alcohol, (b).

(d) *Petroleum ether.*—Bp 30–60°, ACS, free from fluorescence and with T at 300 nm $>85\%$ when measured against air in quartz spectrophtr fitted with 1 cm cell. This solv., available in 5 lb cans, should be suitable for chromatgc purposes. Also, in adsorbent activity test, eluant effect of 10 ml pet ether by itself must cause movement of visible color ≤ 1 cm below surface of column. To meet these requirements, purification by adsorption and/or distn may be necessary.

(e) *Eluting solns.*—(*1*) 16% redistd ether in pet ether; (*2*) 25% redistd ether in pet ether; (*3*) 10% absolute alcohol in pet ether. Dry (*1*) and (*2*) with anhyd. Na_2SO_4 and store over bright Cu strip or turnings to inhibit peroxide formation.

(f) *Sodium sulfate.*—Anhyd., granular; 10% soln must *not* be acid (red) to Me red. Must not adsorb vitamin A.

(g) *Alumina.*—Alcoa grade F-20 or Fisher "Alumina, Adsorption," Cat. No. A540. Before

---

★ Methods so marked are surplus methods. *See* "Definitions of Terms and Explanatory Notes," item (29).

working with alumina it is essential to det. that following specifications for particle size have been met: Not >50% of Al_2O_3 should pass No. 160 sieve; ca 50% should pass No. 100 sieve, but not No. 160 sieve. Remainder ($\leq$20%) which does not pass thru No. 100 sieve should pass No. 60 sieve. Blend thoroly before use.

(**h**) *Standardized alumina.*—Heat portion of Al_2O_3 3 hr in muffle at 600°, and after partial cooling, place in tightly closed screw-cap glass jar. Cool to room temp., pass thru No. 80 sieve, weigh, and place in tared screw-cap glass jar of such size that only $\frac{2}{3}$ of vol. is used. Add H_2O dropwise, with frequent shaking of capped bottle, until Al_2O_3 contains 3% by wt of added H_2O. (Proportion of H_2O required may vary from 2 to 4%; 3% is usually sufficient for new Al_2O_3 and 2% for rejuvenated material.) Continue shaking $\geq$15 min until no lumps remain and material is uniform. Transfer batch to several small, tightly capped jars.

Det. adsorption index as in **39.004**, after Al_2O_3 has remained in tightly capped jar overnight. (Since change in moisture content will affect adsorptivity of reagent, container must be kept tightly closed, except while removing portion of contents for use.) Adsorption index of stored material decreases with time and should be checked periodically. Al_2O_3 suitable for chromatgy has adsorption index of 30–40; extremely retentive Al_2O_3 with index >50 will not permit clean-cut sepns. When index is <10, adsorbent has lost most of its retentiveness. Decreased retentiveness may be due to excess H_2O content or to changed physical state caused by overheating.

(**i**) *Standardized alkaline alumina.*—Mix portion of Al_2O_3, (**g**), with equal wt of 10% (w/w) aq. KOH soln in evapg dish. Decant excess liq., and dry moist Al_2O_3 overnight at 100°. Pass dry material thru No. 60 sieve and place in capped bottle filled $\leq\frac{2}{3}$ full. Add H_2O dropwise with frequent shaking until Al_2O_3 contains 3% by wt of added H_2O. Det. adsorption index as in **39.004**. To be suitable for use, alk. Al_2O_3 should have index of 7–12. If desired adsorption index is not attained with 3% (w/w) H_2O, add addnl H_2O in 2% increments to index of 7–12. Store in tightly capped jars.

(**j**) *Standardized magnesium oxide.*—(Westvaco Sea Sorb 43, Fisher Scientific Co. No. S-120.) Heat portion of MgO 4 hr at 600°. After cooling, mix with equal portion of Hyflo Super-Cel (Celite), in $\frac{1}{2}$ full, tightly closed jar. Det. adsorption index as in **39.005**. To be suitable for use, the MgO-Celite mixt. should have index of 20–35.

(**k**) *Ext. D&C Yellow No. 10 soln.*—Dissolve 20 mg dye (Yellow OB; formerly FD&C Yellow No. 4; Colour Index No. 11390) in 1 L pet ether.

39.004   *Determination of Adsorption Index of Alumina*

Place adsorbent to be tested in chromatgc tube 6 mm id and 22 cm long, contg glass wool plug at bottom. Tap material into settled position, making column 10 cm high, and attach to vac. controlled bell jar. Add 1.0 ml Ext. D&C Yellow No. 10 soln to top of column. From accurately filled 50 ml graduated cylinder add small portions of eluting soln, 16% ether in pet ether. Apply slight vac. (5″ or 635 mm Hg pressure). Accurately det. vol. of eluant required to elute dye completely from column. This vol. in ml is adsorption index. For easier recognition of end point, collect eluate until all apparent color on column has been removed, and then collect 2 ml fractions in small beakers until colorless fraction is obtained.

39.005   *Determination of Adsorption Index of Magnesia*

Place MgO-Celite mixt. to be tested in chromatgc tube 10 mm id, 9 cm long, and fitted with sealed-in fritted glass disk. Apply 25″ vac. and, with aid of tamper of suitable diam., tightly pack column to ht of 1.5 cm. Release vac., and add 1.0 ml Ext. D&C Yellow No. 10 soln. From accurately filled 50 ml graduated cylinder add small (ca 2 ml) portions eluting soln, 10% absolute alcohol in pet ether. Apply 20″ of vac. and continue to add portions of eluant until most of color is eluted. Collect final eluates in 1.0 ml portions under 5″ of vac. Vol. in ml of eluant required to produce first colorless 1 ml fraction is adsorption index of MgO-Celite mixt. (Removal of individual fractions is easily accomplished at 5″ of vac. by slipping edge of micro bell jar over edge of its base plate.)

39.006   *Sampling*

Store sample in refrigerator. Remove outer layers from 1 lb prints and take sample from interior. Remove end slices from $\frac{1}{4}$ lb prints and take sample from remainder.

39.007   *Determination*

(*Caution: See* **46.011, 46.016, 46.039, 46.054,** and **46.073.**)

(**a**) *General precautions.*—Protect vitamin A from strong illumination by working in subdued light or by using nonactinic glassware. Avoid undue exposure of vitamin A solns to air. Perform chromatgc steps in completely darkened room to make possible adequate monitoring of chromatgc columns with UV light. Complete all steps as promptly as possible.

(**b**) *Saponification.*—Weigh 10±0.1 g sample into wide-mouth 500 ml erlenmeyer equipped with cold finger condenser, and add 75 ml 95% alcohol and 25 ml 50% KOH soln. Heat on elec. hot plate and stir so as to break up lumps and completely disperse sample. Maintain soln at vigorous boil 5 min. Remove heat and let stand at room temp. 20 min with occasional stirring. Avoid rapid cooling.

(**c**) *Extraction.*—Transfer soln to 500 ml separator. Rinse saponification flask with 100 ml H_2O in several portions and add rinsings to separator. Add 100 ml ether, shake vigorously, and let stand ca 2 min. Transfer aq. portion into another 500 ml separator and ext with four 50 ml portions ether. (In case of slow sepn, add 2–5 ml 95% alcohol and swirl gently.) Combine ether exts, pour two 100 ml portions H_2O into combined ether exts, swirl gently, and sep. Ext these 2 combined rinses with 2 consecutive 50 ml portions ether, adding ether to original ether exts. Pour two 100 ml portions H_2O thru combined ether exts and discard each washing without shaking. Add ca 10 ml 0.02N KOH, shake vigorously, and discard after sepn. Rinse with successive 50 ml portions H_2O, with gentle agitation, until rinse H_2O is alkali-free to phthln. Let ether soln stand 5 min, discard sepd H_2O, transfer with rinsing to 400–500 ml tall beaker, add 3–5 g anhyd. Na_2SO_4, and stir gently to remove traces of H_2O. Decant ether ext into another clean 400–500 ml beaker, and rinse Na_2SO_4 thoroly (ca 6 times) with small portions ether. Combine rinses with ext.

(**d**) *Preparation of soln for chromatography.*—Evap. ext on steam bath to vol. of ca 25 ml. Transfer to 50 ml beaker and continue evapn on steam bath until viscous oily residue forms which, when stirred with small rod, shows no indication of volatilizing liq. Heat ca 20 sec, but $\leq$2 min, until droplets of oil form. Remove from steam bath and immediately apply stream of *nitrogen* 1 min. Add 5 ml pet ether, transfer to 10 ml vol. flask, and dil. to vol. with pet ether. This is sample soln.

(**e**) *Alumina chromatography.*—Prep. chromatgc column (in 10 mm id $\times$ 9 cm tube), by packing each adsorbent by gravity and slightly tapping tube. Add stdzd Al_2O_3 to ht of 1 cm, then segment of alk. Al_2O_3 2 cm high, and another segment of stdzd Al_2O_3 4 cm high. Apply 5″ of vac., and add 5 ml pet ether, followed by 5 ml sample soln, then another 5 ml pet ether. As last of soln disappears into column, add 5 ml portions 16% ether eluant until all carotene elutes from column. Det. completeness of elution by collecting final part of eluate in 1 ml beakers and observing color against white background. Elution is complete when carotene color cannot be seen in last 1 ml fraction observed. Combine all carotene fractions and reserve for concn, below.

Continue elution with 5 ml portions 16% ether. Examine column regularly with UV lamp and observe progress of fluorescent vitamin A band. (Total time required to elute vitamin A should be $\leq$20 min. If it is desirable to accelerate movement of vitamin A down column, use 25% ether eluting solv. in 3 ml portions.) Discard eluate that collects after carotene fraction has been collected and before vitamin A band begins to elute. Collect all of vitamin A eluate in sep. beaker. Elution of vitamin A is complete when 1 ml portion of eluate collected in 1 ml beaker shows no vitamin A fluorescence when examined with UV lamp. Detn of cut-off point for collection of vitamin

A fraction is very important: If it goes too far, extraneous material absorbing at 325 nm will be present, giving erroneously high results; if chosen too early, vitamin A values will be low. Combine all vitamin A-contg fractions. (*Note:* Some food dyes may not be sepd from vitamin A by Al_2O_3 chromatgy. Whenever the fluorescent vitamin A eluate is colored, rechromatograph on MgO column as in (f).)

Treat carotene eluate and vitamin A eluate sep., maintaining identity of each soln.

Reduce vol. of carotene eluate and of vitamin A eluate to ca 2 ml by evapn on steam bath. Completely remove remaining solv. by evapn at temp. $\leq$40° under vac. or with stream of N. Dissolve carotene in 5 ml pet ether, transfer to 10 ml vol. flask, and dil. to vol. with pet ether. This is carotene soln for spectrophtric measurement.

If vitamin A eluate shows no indication of color, dissolve residue in 5 ml absolute alcohol, transfer to 10 ml vol. flask, and dil. to vol. with absolute alcohol. If vitamin A eluate is colored, dissolve residue in ca 2 ml pet ether and proceed with chromatgy on MgO-Celite.

(**f**) *Magnesium oxide chromatography.*—Add MgO-Celite mixt. to 10 mm id $\times$ 6.5 cm tube, apply full vac., and tamp lightly. Column should be 4 cm high. Add 5 ml pet ether and apply 15″ of vac. When pet ether disappears into column, add pet ether sample soln. Rinse container with three 2 ml portions pet ether and add each rinse to column. Elute vitamin A from column with 0.5% absolute alcohol in pet ether. Use technic of adding eluant, observing movement of vitamin A fluorescence, and collecting vitamin A eluate similar to that described for Al_2O_3 chromatgy. This sepn should take $\leq$10 min. Loss of vitamin A may result if this chromatgc step is too slow. Evap. solv. as before, dissolve residue in 5 ml absolute alcohol, transfer to 10 ml vol. flask, and dil. to vol. with absolute alcohol.

(**g**) *Spectrophotometric measurements and calculations.*—(*1*) *Carotene.*—Det. A of pet ether soln of carotene at 450 nm in 1 cm cell. Calc. μg carotene/lb of sample, or of carotene as units of vitamin A/lb of sample, using formulas:

$$\mu g \text{ carotene/lb} = A \times 4.17 \times 454/W;$$

carotene as units vitamin A/lb

$$= A \times 6.95 \times 454/W;$$

where W = g sample/ml soln.

(*2*) *Vitamin A.*—Det. A of absolute alcohol soln of vitamin A at 310 nm and at 325 nm in 1 cm cell. Calc. μg or units of vitamin A/lb, using formulas:

$$\mu g \text{ vitamin A/lb} = A_{325} \times 5.5 \times 454/W;$$

$$\text{units vitamin A/lb} = A_{325} \times 18.3 \times 454/W;$$

where $A_{325} = A$ at 325 nm and W = g sample/ml soln.

Det. ratio of A at 310 to 325 nm; this ratio is usually $\leq$1.

Vitamin A in Mixed Feeds (2)— Official Final Action

(Work in subdued light. Avoid high laboratory temps. Complete all steps of method as rapidly as consistent with careful following of directions.)

39.008 *Apparatus*

(a) *Photoelectric colorimeter.*—Evelyn or similar colorimeter or spectrophtr with direct-reading deflection-type galvanometer. Optical mechanism or filters to transmit light at 620 nm. (Instrument which provides for linearity between A and concn is preferable but not essential.) Use matched absorption tubes. For carotene detn, use 440 nm filter or wavelength setting.

(b) *Carr-Price reagent dispenser.*—9 or 10 ml, delivering vol. of reagent rapidly thru 3–4 mm diam. opening. Use all-glass app. Automatic pipet, hypodermic syringe, glass cylinder, or other types of app. may be used. App. must be clean and moisture-free.

(c) *Chromatographic tubes.*—18 × 200 mm (ca 12 mm id), sealed to tube 5 × 100 mm.

(d) *Eluate receiver.*—Corning Glass Works, special equipment, fraction collector No. 91200, or equiv.; or simple receiver consisting of 100 ml lipless graduated cylinder or 100 ml regular graduated cylinder with top cut off below lip and fitted with 2-hole stopper. Pass stem of chromatgc tube thru 1 hole and bent glass tube connected to source of vac. thru other. Ordinary H_2O aspirator may be used for vac.

(e) *Saponification apparatus.*—Any suitable ⑅ joint, H_2O-cooled, refluxing app. with 300–500 ml flask. Use boiling H_2O or steam for heat; or use special saponification and extn app. (Corning, special app., XA-4108, total capacity ca 500 ml).

(f) *Extraction apparatus (3).*—As above, or 500 ml separator, stopcock 4 mm, with device to push feed thru stopcock, if needed. To make device, use 2-hole stopper; thru 1 hole insert bent glass tube attached to rubber tube with glass mouthpiece. Thru other hole insert Fe or stainless steel wire with metal bead attached at ca midpoint so that when wire is raised bead will plug second hole and permit application of pressure; when wire is lowered, it will pass thru opened stopcock bore.

(g) *Ultraviolet light.*—Long wavelength, such as Mineralight model SL 5660 (Fisher Scientific Co. No. 11-984-20).

(h) *Evaporation assembly (3).*—To conc. exts after extn, if needed. Use H_2O aspirator and 60–65° H_2O bath (do not expose evapg soln and dry residue to atm.). Suitable assembly consists of Corning flask 4100 or 4320 of suitable size, connecting tube 8820 (⑅ 19/38–24/40), and male ⑅ 19/38 joint sealed to single arm of 2 mm bore, 3-way stopcock. One arm of stopcock is bent at 135° angle and attached to source of vac. thru trap; other arm is sealed to small reservoir made from test tube for adding solv. to dry residue as vac. is broken. For samples of high vitamin

A potency, aliquot may be evapd directly in colorimetric tubes attached to source of vac. thru stopper and Y-tube. Optionally, evapn may be under partial vac. and N.

39.009 *Reagents*

(a) *Adsorbent.*—Use Woelm Alumina, nonalk. (Alupharm Chemicals, PO Box 30628, New Orleans, LA 70130). Add 5% H_2O by placing measured amt of H_2O in small g-s bottle and distributing over walls; then add alumina and mix by shaking bottle until no lumps are observed. Let stand and cool ≥2 hr before use. Store in tightly closed bottle. (Woelm Alumina is heat-treated by manufacturer. Do not expose original or prepd alumina to air, since moisture content must be controlled carefully.)

(b) *Chloroform.*—Reagent grade. Purify if necessary by distn, discarding first and last 10%. (*Caution: See* **46.011, 46.040,** and **46.056.**)

(c) *Hexane.*—Skellysolve B or other good quality com. hexane. Redistill from all-glass app., using only 64–68° fraction. Solv. must be free from alcohols, esters, etc. (*Caution: See* **46.011, 46.039,** and **46.061.**)

(d) *Alcohol.*—95%. Aldehyde-free by Schiff's test.

(e) *Acetone in hexane soln.*—4% and 15%. Dil. reagent grade acetone with hexane.

(f) *Soln for removing antimony trichloride from tubes.*—Wash tubes with HCl, or let stand in 10% Rochelle salt soln to which detergent is added. Wash thoroly in hot detergent soln.

(g) *Potassium hydroxide soln.*—Dissolve 50 g reagent grade KOH in H_2O and dil. to 100 ml with H_2O. Mix thoroly.

(h) *Antimony trichloride (Carr-Price) reagent.*—(*Caution:* $SbCl_3$ is toxic and corrosive. Avoid contact with skin and eyes and breathing vapor.) To 200 g $SbCl_3$ crystals add enough $CHCl_3$ to make 1 L. Warm and shake to dissolve. Cool, and add 30 ml Ac_2O (*Caution: See* **46.022**). If soln is not clear, filter, centrf., or let settle and decant. Soln will keep in tightly stoppered brown bottle for several months. (Use fresh unopened bottle of reagent grade $SbCl_3$ crystals in ¼ or ½ lb g-s bottles with sealed stoppers. Crystals should be translucent; no fluids or colored decomposition products should be present. Crystals stored too long or in previously opened bottle often fail to meet conditions.)

(i) *Vitamin A reference soln.*—USP Ref. Std Soln of cryst. vitamin A acetate in cottonseed oil, encapsulated in gelatin. Potency 30 mg vitamin A alcohol/g oil or as stated at time of purchase. (30 mg vitamin A alcohol = 100,000 units.)

(j) *Carotene reference crystals.*—15% α-85% β carotene in sealed 100 mg or 200 mg vials, obtainable from General Biochemicals, 950 Laboratory Park, Chagrin Falls, OH 44022. Crystals should dissolve in hexane without residue and have characteristic spectrophtric curve. Det. concn, using spectrophtr, as in **39.017.**

39.010   *Preparation of Adsorption Column*

Place small pledget of cotton at bottom of chromatgc tube and pack with adsorbent mixt. added in several portions, tamping each lightly with blunt rod, to ht of 7 cm. Keep column under vac. during packing. Add 0.5 cm layer of powd anhyd. Na_2SO_4 on top of column, level, and pack lightly.

39.011   *Column Performance Test*
(*Caution: See* **46.016.**)

Check for recovery of vitamin A as follows: Saponify ca 0.1 g USP Vitamin A Ref. Std plus 2 g *fresh* cottonseed oil. Ext with hexane. Mix soln of ca 50–100 μg carotene and 30 μg of the saponified vitamin A. Dil. to 15 ml. Wash column with 20 ml hexane and adjust elution rate to ca 2 drops/sec. Before top of column runs dry, add vitamin A-carotene mixt. Elute carotene with 4% acetone in hexane. (Approx. 20–30 ml will be required.) Check for vitamin A band by brief inspection with UV light. Band should be $\leq$2 cm below top of alumina column.

Elute vitamin A with 15% acetone in hexane. (Approx. 30 ml should be enough.) Inspect last few ml of this eluate for vitamin A fluorescence, and if found, elute with few more ml of solv., until fluorescence no longer is observed in eluate. Evap. suitable aliquot of eluate to dryness under vac., add 1 ml $CHCl_3$, and det. vitamin A. Compare result with aliquot of saponified vitamin A in hexane not chromatographed.

39.012   *Preparation of Sample*

Collect 600–800 g bulk sample. Store in tightly closed glass containers at $\leq$0°. Just before analysis, grind $\geq$400 g portion bulk sample so that 95% passes No. 20 sieve. Mix, regrind, and remix by rolling on paper. Remove analytical samples. (Grinding is essential to fracture and help disperse high potency beadlet-type vitamin A products in sample. Avoid loss of fine particles. Feed supplements of >30 μg/g are best handled by diln with freshly ground cereal grain to contain $\leq$30 μg/g, grinding, and sampling as above.)

39.013   *Determination*

Det. blank on all reagents, including cottonseed oil. Blank *A* should be almost 0.

(a) *Preparation of std vitamin A curve.*—Cut tip from capsule of Std Ref. Soln and express appropriate amt of oil into small weighed beaker or watch glass. Weigh accurately. Transfer oil to vol. flask and dil. to vol. with reagent grade $CHCl_3$. Use soln as soon as possible, but never after 8 hr. Work in subdued light or use low-actinic glassware. Make series of dilns of vitamin A soln (5 or more) with $CHCl_3$ so that 1 ml aliquots treated as in (f) give *T* of 20–85%. Plot *A* against μg vitamin A. On most photometers plot will be straight line in this range and factor may be calcd for detg μg vitamin A. (*See* (f).)

(b) *Preparation of std carotene curve.*—Prep. series of dilns of α–β carotene in hexane. Plot *A* against μg carotene as in **39.017.** Use curve or factor for detg carotene content.

(c) *Determination of correction factor for yellow pigment in vitamin A eluate.*—Cryptoxanthin and similar pigments may elute with vitamin A alcohol. Correct for this pigment if present in more than mere traces. Suitable correction may be obtained by saponification and extn of sample of yellow corn as for sample. Chromatograph and save 15% acetone in hexane fraction. Det. concn of yellow pigment in this fraction by comparison to carotene calibration. Evap. solvs and dissolve residue in $CHCl_3$. Make series of dilns covering range of concns of yellow pigment of sample solns in the 1 ml $CHCl_3$ on which Carr-Price vitamin A color is read. Obtain factor for correcting for reaction of this pigment in Carr-Price detn of vitamin A, by plotting concn of yellow pigment in soln detd at 440 nm against concn of vitamin A detd from std vitamin A curve.

(d) *Saponification and extraction.*—(1) For products <4000 units/lb, weigh 40 g sample into 500 ml boiling flask; (2) for products 4000–20,000 units/lb, use 20–40 g samples; (3) for products >20,000 units /lb, use 10 g sample. When analyzing premixes or concs of low fat content, add 1 g *fresh* cottonseed oil to sample in boiling flask.

Add vol. (ml) alcohol 3 times wt (g) sample. *Swirl until all particles are thoroly wetted.* Add vol. KOH soln, **39.009**(g), equal to wt sample. Swirl again for thoro mixing. Reflux 30 min at rate of 2 drops/sec. Swirl and shake flask until all clumps are broken and particles are well dispersed $\geq$3 times during digestion. Repeat once prior to extn.

Cool to room temp. under running H_2O. Add vol. of H_2O 2 times wt of sample. Ext 3 times with hexane, first time using vol. of hexane 2–3 times wt of sample, and ca $\frac{2}{3}$ as much for subsequent extns. For high potency samples, use larger vol. hexane or addnl extns. (If considerable amts of carotenoid pigments are present, all are not removed in 3 extns, but those remaining in alc.-alk. layer are largely polyhydroxy and oxidized carotenoids.)

Combine all hexane exts in one separator. Pour 100 ml cool H_2O into separator and drain it when layers sep., retaining any emulsion in hexane layer. Repeat washing with successive 100 ml portions H_2O, with shaking, until washing is colorless to phthln. (If emulsions cause difficulty, use 10% alcohol-H_2O wash contg 0.1% HCl on third washing and follow with $\geq$2 H_2O washings.) Sep. final H_2O wash as completely as possible. Swirl separator, let soln stand 5 min, and drain any H_2O collecting in bottom. Carefully pour soln from top of separator thru small pledget of cotton into appropriate vol. flask. Rinse separator and cotton with small portions hexane, and dil. to vol. with hexane.

(e) *Chromatography.*—If possible, chromatograph aliquot contg ca 30 μg vitamin A, but preferably

≥20, in 10–15 ml hexane ext. If necessary, conc. portion of hexane ext under vac. to obtain enough vitamin A. Never chromatograph >25 ml soln.

Pack column as directed, wash with 20 ml hexane, and add ext contg vitamin A just before top of column runs dry. Elute at rate of 2 drops/sec. Sep. elute carotene and then vitamin A. Cryptoxanthin and similar pigments elute with vitamin A. Dil. carotene and also vitamin A eluate to vol. for colorimetry. Vol. of 50 ml of vitamin A eluate is convenient; 10 ml aliquot may be evapd for vitamin A detn.

(f) *Colorimetry.*—Det. concn of carotene in carotene eluate as in **39.017.**

Transfer 10 ml vitamin A eluate to colorimeter tube and read A of yellow soln as carotene. If this is more than trace, especially on low-potency samples, det. correction for yellow pigment as in (c).

Evap. solvs under vac. in hot (60–65°) H_2O bath. Dissolve residue in 1 ml $CHCl_3$. With 620 nm setting, adjust colorimeter to 100% T, using 1 ml $CHCl_3$ and measured vol. (9 or 10 ml) $SbCl_3$ reagent. Place tube contg 1 ml $CHCl_3$ soln in instrument and rapidly add $SbCl_3$ reagent. Take max. reading of galvanometer (work rapidly; color begins to fade in 3–5 sec). Examine tube within few sec. Soln should be blue and without turbidity; color should fade rapidly. Calc. wt vitamin A by ref. to std vitamin A curve. Det. recovery factor, R, for vitamin A in analysis by addns of known amts of vitamin A to duplicate samples or blank feeds in each series of similar samples analyzed.

Calc. vitamin A content of sample as follows:

Vitamin A $(\mu g/lb) = (C_u - C_k) \times 454/C_s \times R,$

where C_u = uncorrected concn of vitamin A in $\mu g/ml$ final diln; C_k = correction for yellow pigment expressed as μg vitamin A/ml final diln; C_s = g sample/ml final diln; and R = vitamin A recovery factor.

Carotenes in Fresh Plant Materials and Silages (4)—Official Final Action

(*Caution: See* **46.004, 46.011, 46.039, 46.046,** and **46.061.**)

39.014   Reagents

(a) *Acetone.*—Dry, alcohol-free. To dry, treat with anhyd. Na_2SO_4 and distill over granular ca "10 mesh" Zn.

(b) *Commercial hexane.*—Bp 60–70°; distilled over KOH.

(c) *Adsorbent.*—Activated magnesia (Sea Sorb 43; Fisher Scientific Co. No. S-120).

(d) *Diatomaceous earth.*—Hyflo Super-Cel.

39.015   Extraction

Cut material finely with scissors or knife, or grind in food chopper to assure representative sample. If analysis cannot be performed immediately, blanch in boiling H_2O 5–10 min and store in frozen condition. Place weighed sample, 2–5 g, in high-speed blender; add 40 ml acetone, 60 ml hexane, and 0.1 g $MgCO_3$,

and blend 5 min. Filter with suction or let residue settle and decant into separator, wash residue with two 25 ml portions acetone, then with 25 ml hexane, and combine exts. Wash acetone from ext with five 100 ml portions H_2O, transfer upper layer to 100 ml vol. flask contg 9 ml acetone, and dil. to vol. with hexane. If desired, alcohol may be used instead of acetone for extn. Use 80 ml alcohol and 60 ml hexane in blender; other quantities same as for acetone.

39.016   *Separation of Pigments*

Prep. chromatgc column with $1 + 1$ mixt. (wt basis) activated magnesia and diat. earth. (Suitable chromatgc tube can be made from Pyrex test tube 22 mm od and 175 mm long by sealing smaller tube (ca 10 mm od) to bottom.) To prep. column, place small glass wool or cotton plug inside tube, add loose adsorbent to 15 cm depth, attach tube to suction flask, and apply full vac. of H_2O pump. Use flat instrument (such as inverted cork mounted on rod or tamping rod) to gently press adsorbent and flatten surface (packed column should be ca 10 cm deep). Place 1 cm layer anhyd. Na_2SO_4 above adsorbent.

With vac. continuously applied to flask, pour ext into column. Use 50 ml acetone-hexane $(1 + 9)$, or slightly more, if necessary, to develop chromatogram and wash visible carotenes thru adsorbent. Keep top of column covered with layer of solv. during entire operation (conveniently done by clamping inverted vol. flask full of solv. above column with neck 1–2 cm above surface of adsorbent).

Collect entire eluate. (Carotenes pass rapidly thru column; bands of xanthophylls, carotene oxidn products, and chlorophylls should be present in column when operation is complete.) Transfer eluate, which has been reduced in vol. by loss of vapor thru H_2O pump, to 100 ml vol. flask, dil. to vol. with acetone-hexane $(1 + 9)$, and det. carotene content photometrically.

39.017   *Determination*

Det. A of soln as soon as possible with spectrophtr at 436 nm or with some other instrument provided with suitable filter system, such as Klett photometer with No. 44 filter, or Evelyn photoelec. colorimeter with 440 filter. Calibrate these instruments first with solns of high purity β-carotene as shown by characteristic absorption curve (J. Biol. Chem. **144,** 21(1942)). Prep. calibration chart and convert A of soln to be detd to carotene concn from chart.

When detns are made with properly calibrated spectrophtr at 436 nm, calc. from formula

$$C = (A \times 454)/(196 \times L \times W), \quad \text{where}$$

C = concn carotene (mg/lb) in original sample, L = cell length in cm, and W = g sample/ml final diln. Report results as mg β-carotene/lb. Multiply by 2.2 to give ppm or by 1667 to give International Units/lb.

Carotenes and Xanthophylls in Dried Plant Materials and Mixed Feeds (5)— Official First Action

(*Caution: See* 46.011, 46.018, 46.037, 46.039, and 46.046.)

39.018   *Apparatus*

(a) *Chromatographic tube.*—12.5 mm id × 30 cm, Pyrex, with bottom capillary tube 2 mm id × ca 10 cm to extend into neck of 25 ml vol. flask.

(b) *Vacuum filtration device.*—For collection of eluate in vol. flask (Fisher Scientific Co. "Filtrator," or equiv.). Attach rubber stopper to column to fit device.

39.019   *Reagents*

(a) *Acetone.*—Dry, alcohol-free. Distill over Zn (granular, ca 10 mesh).

(b) *Hexane.*—Com.; Phillips Petroleum Co. "high purity," or equiv.

(c) *Extractant.*—Hexane-acetone-absolute alcohol-toluene (10 + 7 + 6 + 7).

(d) *Adsorbent I.*—Mix in mech. blender 1–2 hr 1 + 1 (w/w) silica gel G (according to Stahl, Brinkmann Instruments, Inc.) and diat. earth (Hyflo Super-Cel, Fisher Scientific Co.).

(e) *Adsorbent II.*—Mix in mech. blender 1-2 hr 1 + 1 (w/w) activated magnesia (Sea Sorb 43, Fisher Scientific Co.) and diat. earth (Hyflo Super-Cel).

(f) *Methanolic potassium hydroxide.*—40%. Dissolve 40 g KOH in MeOH, cool, and dil. to 100 ml with MeOH.

(g) *Sodium sulfate soln.*—10%. Dissolve 10 g anhyd. Na_2SO_4 in 100 ml H_2O.

(h) *Eluants.* — (1) *Carotenes.* — Hexane-acetone (96 + 4). (2) *Monohydroxy pigments (MHP).*—Hexane-acetone (90 + 10). (3) *Dihydroxy pigments (DHP).*—Hexane-acetone (80 + 20). (4) *Total xanthophylls (TX).* — Hexane-acetone-MeOH (80 + 10 + 10).

(i) *1-(Phenylazo)-2-naphthol (C.I. Solvent Yellow 14; Sudan I) std solns.*—(1) *Stock soln.*—1.0 millimolar (*mM*). Recrystallize std (Aldrich Chemical Co., Milwaukee, WI 53210 or Matheson Coleman & Bell) from hot absolute alcohol. Dry crystals to constant wt in 70° vac. oven. Dissolve 0.1241 g in 500 ml acetone-isopropanol (1 + 1). (2) *Working soln.*—0.04*mM*. Dil. 20 ml stock soln to 500 ml with acetone-isopropanol (1 + 1). Store in dark.

39.020   *Preparation of Sample*

Grind sample to pass No. 40 sieve. Accurately weigh 2 g sample (1 g if total pigments are >200 mg/lb, 4 g if <50) into 100 ml vol. flask. Pipet 30 ml extractant into flask, stopper, and swirl 1 min.

(a) *Low moisture samples, e.g., dehydrated alfalfa or corn gluten.*—Pipet 1 ml H_2O/2 g sample into flask, stopper, swirl 1 min, and let stand in dark ca 16 hr. Pipet 2 ml 40% methanolic KOH into flask,

swirl 1 min, and let stand in dark 1 hr. Pipet 30 ml hexane into flask, swirl 1 min, dil. to vol. with 10% Na_2SO_4, and shake vigorously 1 min. Let stand in dark 1 hr before chromatgy. Upper phase is 50 ml.

(b) *High moisture (air-dried) samples.*—Let mixt. stand in dark ca 16 hr. Pipet 2 ml 40% methanolic KOH into flask and swirl 1 min; then pipet 1 ml H_2O/g sample, swirl 1 min, and let stand in dark 1 hr; then proceed with hexane addn as in (a).

39.021   *Chromatography*

With column on Filtrator, place absorbent cotton or glass wool plug in bottom and add ca 12 cm layer Adsorbent I. Apply full vac. and add more adsorbent to give 7 cm layer. Use flat instrument such as inverted cork on glass rod to press and flatten surface of adsorbent. Place 2 cm layer anhyd. Na_2SO_4 above adsorbent and press firmly.

(a) *Total carotenes.*—With 25 ml vol. flask in place to collect eluate, pipet 5 ml (or 10 ml if low pigment) of upper phase onto column and adjust vac. for flow of 2 or 3 drops/sec. Needle valve in vac. line helps control flow rate. Add carotene eluant as last of soln enters adsorbent and continue until carotene band is collected in flask. Keep adsorbent covered with solv. at all times. Release vac., place carotene soln in dark until it reaches room temp., and dil. to vol. with carotene eluant. Invert flask several times to mix; then det. *A* immediately, as in **39.022.**

Xanthophylls remain on column. For sepn of monohydroxy from dihydroxy pigments (both free from epoxy and polyoxy pigments), or for total xanthophylls, proceed as in (b) or (c).

(b) *Separation of xanthophylls.*—(1) With 25 ml vol. flask in Filtrator and vac. applied to column let eluant level approach adsorbent surface; then immediately add MHP eluant. Band of monohydroxy pigments (zeinoxanthin, cryptoxanthin) and any persistent mono- or di-esters should move down column ahead of other bands. When elution of MHP band is complete, place flask in dark to attain room temp. before dilg to vol. with MHP eluant and *A* detn. (2) Proceed as in (1), using DHP eluant to collect pigments of next band (lutein, zeaxanthin, and their isomers) in 25 (or 50 ml) vol. flask. Violaxanthin, neoxanthin, and other polyoxy pigments (POP) remain on column.

(c) *Total xanthophylls.*—If value for total xanthophylls is desired, pipet fresh aliquot from upper phase of original ext onto 7 cm column of Adsorbent II, and elute carotenes with hexane-acetone (90 + 10) and total xanthophylls with hexane-acetone-MeOH (80 + 10 + 10).

39.022   *Determination*

Measure *A* promptly to minimize isomerization and autoxidn losses. First, check calibration of spectrophtr by reading working std soln at 1 nm intervals between 469 and 479 nm. If max. value is not at 474 nm, recalibrate instrument. When instrument shows max. A at 474 nm and slit width is 0.03, working soln readings should be 0.561 (474) and 0.460 (436). Correct calcns from equations below, for instrument deviation factor. If instrument lacks controllable slit, est. concn by assuming that working std soln of dye, (i)(2), has same A as 2.35 mg carotenes/L at 436 nm and 2.38 mg xanthophylls/L at 474 nm.

Det. A of carotene fraction at 436 nm and MHP and DHP fractions at 474 nm. For highest accuracy, control soln vols to give A between 0.25 and 0.75.

39.023 *Calculations*

Following equations are applicable to A data obtained from calibrated spectrophtrs that operate with narrow slit width. Values 196 and 236 are a for *trans*-β-carotene and *trans*-lutein at prescribed wavelengths; b = cell length in cm; d = diln factor = (g sample $\times$ ml ext on column)/(50 ml upper phase $\times$ ml final diln); and f = instrument deviation factor = 0.460/observed A_{436} or 0.561/observed A_{474}. Carotene fraction concn (mg/lb) = $(A_{436} \times 454 \times f)/$ $(196 \times b \times d)$. MHP fraction concn (mg/lb), or DHP fraction concn (mg/lb), or total xanthophylls (mg/lb) = $(A_{474} \times 454 \times f)/(236 \times b \times d)$.

Thiamine (Vitamin B₁)

(Methods not applicable in presence of materials that adsorb thiamine or which contain extraneous materials which affect thiochrome fluorescence)

Fluorometric Method (6)—Official Final Action

39.024 *Reagents and Apparatus*

(a) *Double-normal sodium acetate.*—Dissolve 272 g NaOAc.3H₂O in enough H₂O to make 1 L.

(b) *Bromocresol green pH indicator.*—Dissolve 0.1 g indicator by triturating in agate mortar with 2.8 ml 0.05N NaOH, and dil. to 200 ml with H₂O.

(c) *Thymol blue pH indicator.*—Dissolve 0.1 g indicator by triturating in agate mortar with 4.3 ml 0.05N NaOH, and dil. to 200 ml with H₂O.

(d) *Enzyme soln.*—Prep., on day on which it is to be used, 10% aq. soln of enzyme prepn potent in diastatic and phosphorolytic activity. (Among enzymes available for this purpose are Mylase P (Wallerstein Co.), Clarase (Miles Laboratories, Inc.), and Takadiastase (Parke, Davis & Co., Joseph Campau Ave at the River, Detroit, MI 48232).

(e) *Base-exchange silicate.* — Purify artificially prepd silicate of base-exchange type, in form of granular powder of "50–80 mesh" size, as follows: Place convenient quantity (100–500 g) base-exchange silicate in suitable beaker, add enough hot 3% HOAc to cover material, and boil 10–15 min, stirring continuously. Let mixt. settle and decant supernatant. Repeat washing 3 times, then wash similarly 3 times with hot KCl soln (1 part by wt KCl/4 vols soln), and finally wash with boiling H₂O (*distilled* H₂O must be used) until last washing gives no reaction

for Cl. Dry material at ca 100° and store in well-closed container. (Purified base-exchange silicate may be purchased as "Thiochrome Decalso," Fisher Scientific Co. No. T-97.)

(f) *Chromatographic columns.*—Use glass chromatgc tubes (ca 275 mm overall length, with reservoir capacity ca 60 ml) consisting of 3 parts fused together with following approx. id: (*1*) reservoir at top, 95 mm long, 30 mm diam., converging into (*2*) adsorption tube, 145 mm long, 6 mm diam., and at lower end (*3*) tube is drawn into capillary 35 mm long and of such diam. that when tube is charged, rate of flow will be ≤1 ml/min. Prep. tubes for use as follows: Place over upper end of capillary, with aid of glass rod, pledget of fine glass wool. Add to adsorption tube H₂O suspension of 1.0–2.0 g purified base-exchange silicate, taking care to wash down all silicate from walls of reservoir. To keep air out of adsorption column, keep layer of liq. above surface of silicate during adsorption process. (Prevent tube from draining by placing rubber cap, filled with H₂O to avoid inclusion of air, over lower end of capillary.)

(g) *Neutral potassium chloride soln.*—Dissolve 250 g KCl in H₂O to make 1 L.

(h) *Acid potassium chloride soln.*—Add 8.5 ml HCl to 1 L of the neut. KCl soln.

(i) *Sodium hydroxide soln.*—15%. Dissolve 15 g NaOH in H₂O to make 100 ml.

(j) *Potassium ferricyanide soln.*—1%. Dissolve 1 g K₃Fe(CN)₆ in H₂O to make 100 ml. Prep. soln on day it is used.

(k) *Oxidizing reagent.*—Mix 4.0 ml of the 1% K₃Fe(CN)₆ soln with the 15% NaOH soln to make 100 ml. Use soln within 4 hr.

(l) *Isobutyl alcohol.*—Redistd in all-glass app. Use redistd product as anhyd. or H₂O-satd.

(m) *Quinine sulfate stock soln.*—Use quinine sulfate soln to govern reproducibility of fluorometer. Prep. stock soln of this reagent by dissolving 10 mg quinine sulfate in 0.1N H₂SO₄ to make 1 L. Store in light-resistant containers.

(n) *Quinine sulfate std soln.*—Dil. 1 vol. of the quinine sulfate stock soln with 39 vols 0.1N H₂SO₄. (Soln fluoresces to ca same degree as does isobutanol ext of thiochrome obtained from 1 μg thiamine .HCl.) Store soln in light-resistant containers.

(o) *Thiamine hydrochloride std solns.*—(*1*) *Stock soln.*—100 μg/ml. Accurately weigh 50–60 mg USP Thiamine Hydrochloride Ref. Std that has been dried to constant wt over P₂O₅ in desiccator. (Ref. std is hygroscopic; avoid absorption of moisture.) Dissolve in 20% alcohol adjusted to pH 3.5–4.3 with HCl, and dil. to 500 ml with the acidified alcohol. Add enough addnl acidified alcohol to make concn exactly 100 μg thiamine.HCl/ml. Store at ca 10° in g-s, light resistant bottle.

(*2*) *Intermediate soln.*—10 μg/ml. Dil. 100 ml stock soln to 1 L with 20% alcohol adjusted to pH 3.5–4.3 with HCl. Store at ca 10° in g-s, light resistant bottle.

(3) Working soln I.—1 µg/ml. To 10 ml intermediate soln, add ca 50 ml ca 0.1N HCl, digest or autoclave as in **39.025(a)(1)**, cool, and dil. to 100 ml with the 0.1N HCl. Prep. fresh soln for each assay.

(4) Working soln II.—0.2 µg/ml. For materials contg free thiamine, dil. 20 ml working soln I to 100 ml with 0.1N HCl. Designate as working std soln and proceed directly to oxidn, **39.028**.

For materials contg thiamine pyrophosphate, proceed as in **39.026** and **39.027**, using 20 ml working soln II. Designate final 25 ml vol. eluate (equiv. to 5 µg USP Thiamine.HCl Ref. Std) so obtained as working std soln and proceed as in **39.028**.

39.025   *Extraction*

(a) *For materials containing free thiamine (not applicable in presence of thiamine pyrophosphate).*— Place measured amt of sample in flask of suitable size, prep. sample by *(1)*, *(2)*, or *(3)*, and proceed directly to oxidn, **39.028**.

(1) For dry or semidry materials containing no appreciable quantity of basic substances.—Add vol. 0.1N HCl equal in ml to ≥10 times dry wt sample in g. Comminute and evenly disperse material in liq. if it is not readily sol. If lumping occurs, agitate vigorously so that all particles come in contact with liq.; then wash down sides of flask with 0.1N HCl. Digest 30 min at 95–100° in steam bath, or in boiling H₂O, with frequent mixing; or autoclave mixt. 30 min at 121–123°. Cool, and if lumping occurs, agitate mixt. until particles are evenly dispersed. Dil. with 0.1N HCl to measured vol. contg ca 0.2–5.0 µg thiamine/ml.

(2) For dry or semidry materials containing appreciable quantities of basic substances.—Add dil. HCl to adjust mixt. to ca pH 4.0. Add such amt of H₂O that total vol. liq. is equal in ml to ≥10 times dry wt sample in g. Add equiv. of 1 ml 10N HCl/100 ml liq. and proceed as in *(1)*, beginning with second sentence.

(3) For liquid materials.—Adjust material to ca pH 4.0 with dil. HCl, or, with vigorous agitation, NaOH soln, and proceed as in *(2)*, beginning with second sentence.

(b) *For materials containing thiamine pyrophosphate.*—Proceed as in **(a)(1)**, followed by enzyme hydrolysis and purification, **39.026–39.027**.

39.026   *Enzyme Hydrolysis*

Take aliquot contg ca 10–25 µg thiamine, dil. to ca 65 ml with 0.1N HCl, and adjust pH to 4.0–4.5 with ca 5 ml 2N NaOAc, using bromocresol green indicator on spot plate. Add 5 ml enzyme soln, mix, and incubate 3 hr at 45–50°. Cool, adjust to pH ca 3.5, dil. to 100 ml with H₂O, and filter thru paper known not to adsorb thiamine (ash-free papers have been found satisfactory).

39.027   *Purification*

Pass thru prepd chromatgc column aliquot of filtered soln contg ca 5 µg thiamine, and wash column with three 5 ml portions of almost boiling H₂O. Do not permit surface of liq. to fall below surface of base-exchange silicate.

Elute thiamine from base-exchange silicate by passing thru column five 4.0–4.5 ml portions almost boiling acid-KCl soln. Do not permit surface of liq. to fall below surface of silicate until final portion of acid-KCl soln has been added. Collect eluate in 25 ml vol. flask, cool, and dil. to vol. with acid-KCl soln. Designate this as Assay Soln.

39.028   *Oxidation of Thiamine*
to Thiochrome

To each of ≥4 ca 40 ml tubes (or reaction vessels) add ca 1.5 g NaCl or KCl and 5 ml working std soln. (*Precision and accuracy of results depend upon uniform technic in conducting following oxidn.* Protect soln from light which destroys thiochrome. Use pipet that delivers 3 ml in 1–2 sec for addn of oxidizing reagent.) Place tip of pipet contg oxidizing reagent in neck of tube and hold it so that stream of soln does not hit side of tube. Gently swirl tube to produce rotary motion in liq. and immediately add 3 ml oxidizing reagent. Remove pipet and swirl tube again to ensure adequate mixing. *Immediately* add 13 ml isobutanol, stopper, and shake tube vigorously ≥15 sec. Similarly treat ≥1 tube and treat each of ≥2 remaining tubes (std blanks) similarly except replace oxidizing reagent with 15% NaOH soln.

To each of ≥4 similar tubes add 5 ml Assay Soln. Treat these tubes in same manner as directed for tubes contg working std soln.

After isobutanol has been added to all tubes, shake again ca 2 min. (Tubes may be placed in shaker box for this addnl shaking.) Centrf. tubes at low speed until clear supernatant ext can be obtained from each. Pipet or decant ca 10 ml isobutanol ext (upper layer) from each tube into cell for thiochrome fluorescence measurement.

39.029   *Thiochrome Fluorescence*
Measurement

(Thiamine content of oxidized Assay Soln is detd by comparing intensity of fluorescence of ext of this soln with that from oxidized std soln. Intensity of fluorescence is proportional to quantity thiamine present and may be measured with suitable fluorometer. Input filter of narrow *T* range with max. ca 365 nm and output filter of narrow *T* range with max. ca 435 nm have been found satisfactory. Use quinine sulfate std soln to govern reproducibility of fluorometer. *Caution: See* **46.008**.)

Measure fluorescence of isobutanol ext from oxidized Assay Soln and call this reading *I*. Next measure fluorescence of ext from Assay Soln which has been treated with 3 ml 15% NaOH soln and call this reading (assay blank) *b*. Then measure fluorescence of ext from oxidized working std soln and call this reading *S*. Finally, measure fluorescence of ext from working std soln which has been treated with 3 ml of 15% NaOH soln and call this reading (std blank) *d*.

39.030 *Calculation*

Calc. as follows:

μg Thiamine.HCl in 5 ml Assay Soln = $(I - b)/(S - d)$.

Rapid Fluorometric Method
(7)—Official Final Action

(Applicable to detn of thiamine in enriched flour, farina, corn meal, macaroni, and noodle products, or where bound thiamine or thiamine pyrophosphate is not significant)

39.031 *Reagents*

See **39.024**(c), (i), (j), (k), (l), (m), (n), and (o).

39.032 *Preparation of Standard Solution*

Dil. 5 ml thiamine.HCl intermediate soln, **39.024**(o)(*2*), to 250 ml with ca 0.1N HCl (1 ml = 0.2 μg thiamine.HCl). Designate this as working std soln. If NaCl is to be added to sample for extn, add NaCl to working std soln, before final diln, to give final concn of ca 5% (w/v). Proceed as in **39.034**.

39.033 *Extraction*

Weigh enough sample to give final Assay Soln with thiamine concn of ca 0.2 μg/ml (*i.e.*, 4.54 g enriched flour for 100 ml or 9.07 g for 200 ml final vol.) and proceed by one of following methods:

(a) *95–100° Digestion.*—Place measured quantity of sample in bottle or flask of suitable size. (Addn of NaCl to give final concn of ca 5% (w/v) aids in subsequent sepn of sample soln. Thoroly mix flour and salt with stirring rod before adding 0.1N HCl.) Add in 2 portions, with vigorous stirring, vol. ca 0.1N HCl in proportion ca 15 ml acid to 1 g sample, using part of acid to wash down sides of vessel. Place vessel in H$_2$O bath previously heated to 95–100°. Stir at frequent intervals to keep solids in suspension during thickening stage (5–8 min) and occasionally during balance of total heating time of 30 min.

After hydrolysis has proceeded ca 10 min, place drop of soln on spot plate and test with thymol blue. Soln should be distinctly red (pH 1.0–1.2). If not acid enough (indicating presence of basic substances in sample), add ca 1N HCl in 1.0 ml amts until desired acidity is reached. Note amt of 1N acid required to supplement the 0.1N acid and *repeat digestion* with new sample wt and necessary mixt. of 1N and 0.1N acids. Cool, and dil. with 0.1N HCl to measured vol. contg ca 0.2 μg thiamine/ml.

Centrf. mixt. until supernatant is clear or practically so and/or filter thru paper known not to adsorb thiamine (ash-free papers have been found satisfactory), or filter thru fritted glass funnel, using suitable analytical filter-aid (ash-free filter pulp and Celite Analytical Filter-Aid have been found satisfactory). Discard first $\frac{1}{10}$ part of filtrate. Designate remainder of filtrate as Assay Soln.

(b) *Autoclaved digestion.*—Proceed as in (a) without addn of NaCl, except to autoclave 20 min at 5 lb

pressure (108–109°) with total heating time $\leq$35 min including 5–10 min to attain desired pressure and ca 5 min to reduce pressure. (It may be necessary to preheat autoclave to ca 100° before inserting samples.)

39.034 *Oxidation*

Proceed as in **39.028**, except add ca 2.5 g NaCl or KCl to each tube (or reaction vessel) before addn of 5 ml working std soln, **39.032**, or 5 ml Assay Soln, **39.033**. After addn of working std soln or Assay Soln, gently swirl each tube until most of salt is dissolved. Measure fluorescence of isobutanol exts as in **39.029**, and calc. thiamine.HCl content as in **39.030**.

Thiamine in Bread (*8*)—
Official Final Action

39.035 *Reagents and Apparatus*

Use reagents and app. as in **39.024** and following:

(a) *Thiamine hydrochloride working soln III.*—1 μg/ml. Pipet 20 ml thiamine.HCl intermediate soln, **39.024**(o)(*2*), into 200 ml vol. flask and dil. to vol. with ca 0.1N HCl. Prep. fresh daily.

(b) *Procedural std soln.*—Pipet 40 ml working soln III into one of the acid digestion containers, dil. to ca 150 ml with ca 0.1N HCl, and continue as under sample treatment (1 ml = 0.2 μg thiamine.HCl in final vol.). (To be used for recovery experiments to test efficiency of method.)

(c) *Direct std soln.*—0.2 μg/ml. Pipet 40 ml working soln III into 200 ml vol. flask, add ca 16 ml H$_2$O, and dil. to vol. with eluting reagent, **39.024**(h).

39.036 *Acid and Enzyme Digestions*

Weigh ($\pm$0.05 g) amt of air-dried bread, **14.099**, contg ca 40 μg thiamine and transfer to 250 ml digestion flask or centrf. bottle. Add 150 ml ca 0.1N HCl, stirring with glass rod to provide homogeneous mixt. with ca $\frac{1}{2}$ of acid and using remainder to wash down side of container. Digest 30 min in boiling H$_2$O bath. Stir enough to prevent lumping or clotting, especially during first 5–10 min. Cool to room temp. and adjust pH to 4.5 by adding 2N NaOAc, **39.024**(a), with pH meter control or with bromocresol green indicator, **39.024**(b), and spot plate; end point should be definitely on blue side of green-blue change. Alternatively, use constant amt of hydrolyzing acid and previously detd amt of NaOAc soln required to adjust to pH 4.5.

Add 5 ml enzyme soln, **39.024**(d), mix, warm to 45°, and digest in H$_2$O bath 1 hr at 45–50°. Stir at 10–15 min intervals. Cool, transfer, and dil. to vol. with 0.1N HCl in 200 ml vol. flask. Mix, and filter thru paper known not to adsorb thiamine. (Paper can be tested by comparing filtered and nonfiltered procedural std soln, **39.035**(b). Ash-free papers have been found satisfactory.) Check pH of filtrate (should be ca 3.5 for subsequent base exchange sepn) and purify as in **39.027**.

39.037
Oxidation of Thiamine to Thiochrome

Pipet duplicate 5 ml aliquots of direct std soln, **39.035**(c), and duplicate 5 ml aliquots of Assay Soln into ca 40 ml tubes or reaction vessels, and proceed as in **39.028**.

39.038
Thiochrome Fluorescence Measurement

(Caution: See 46.008.)

Thiamine content of oxidized Assay Soln is detd by comparing intensity of fluorescence of ext of this soln with that from oxidized direct std soln, **39.035** (c), correcting for blank fluorescence of each of these solns. Intensity of fluorescence is linear in range 0–2 µg thiamine and may be measured with fluorometer as in **39.029**.

mg Thiamine.HCl/lb (fresh basis)

$$= \frac{I}{B} \times \frac{40 \times 454 \times F}{W \times 1000},$$

if specified aliquots have been used, where $I =$ corrected reading of assay soln; $B =$ corrected reading of std soln; $W =$ g air-dried bread sample; and $F =$ air-dry wt: fresh wt ratio.

Riboflavin (Vitamin B₂) (9)
Fluorometric Method— Official Final Action

39.039
Apparatus

Photofluorometer.—Use fluorometer suitable for accurately measuring fluorescence of solns contg riboflavin in concns of 0.05–0.2 µg/ml. Input filter of narrow T range with max. ca 440 nm and output filter of narrow T range with max. ca 565 nm have been found satisfactory.

39.040
Reagents

(Do not shake std solns stored under toluene.)

(a) *Riboflavin std solns.*—(1) *Stock soln.*—100 µg/ml. Dissolve 50 mg USP Riboflavin Ref. Std, previously dried and stored in dark in desiccator over P_2O_5, in 0.02N HOAc to make 500 ml. (To facilitate soln, warm with ca 300 ml 0.02N HOAc on steam bath with constant stirring until dissolved, cool, and add 0.02N HOAc to make 500 ml.) Store under toluene at ca 10°

(2) *Intermediate soln.*—10 µg/ml. Dil. 100 ml stock soln to 1 L with 0.02N HOAc. Store under toluene at ca 10°.

(3) *Working soln I.*—1 µg/ml. Dil. 10 ml intermediate soln to 100 ml with H_2O. Prep fresh for each assay.

(4) *Working soln II.*—0.1 µg/ml. Dil. 10 ml intermediate soln to 1 L with H_2O. Prep. fresh for each assay.

(b) *Sodium hydrosulfite.*—High purity and stored to avoid undue exposure to light and air. Check suitability as follows: To each of ≥2 tubes add 10 ml H_2O and 1 ml std riboflavin soln contg 20 µg/ml, and proceed as in **39.042** with respect to addn of

HOAc, KMnO₄ soln, and H_2O_2 soln. Then when 8 mg $Na_2S_2O_4$ is added with mixing, riboflavin should be completely reduced in ≤5 sec.

(c) *Extraction soln.*—Mix 300 ml MeOH, 100 ml pyridine, 100 ml H_2O, and 10 ml HOAc. (Proportionate quantities may be prepd.)

39.041
Preparation of Sample Solution

(Thruout all stages of method protect solns from undue exposure to light and keep at pH < 7.0. Where directed to filter thru paper, use paper known not to adsorb riboflavin (ash-free papers have been found satisfactory).)

Place measured amt of sample in suitable size flask and proceed by one of following methods:

(a) *For dry or semidry materials containing no appreciable amount of basic substances.*—Add vol. 0.1N HCl equal in ml to ≥10 times dry wt sample in g; resulting soln must contain ≤0.1 mg riboflavin/ml. If material is not readily sol., comminute so that it may be evenly dispersed in liq. Then agitate vigorously and wash down sides of flask with 0.1N HCl.

Heat mixt. in autoclave at 121–123° (1.1–1.2 kg/sq cm) 30 min and cool. If lumping occurs, agitate mixt. until particles are evenly dispersed. Adjust, with vigorous agitation, to pH 6.0–6.5 with NaOH soln; then immediately add dil. HCl until no further pptn occurs (usually ca pH 4.5, isoelec. point of many proteins).

Dil. mixt. to measured vol. contg >0.1 µg riboflavin/ml and filter thru paper. (In case of mixt. difficult to filter, centrfg and/or filtering thru fritted glass, using suitable analytical filter-aid, may often be substituted for, or may precede, filtering thru paper. Ash-free filter paper pulp and Celite Analytical Filter-Aid have been found satisfactory.) Take aliquot of clear filtrate and check for dissolved protein by adding dropwise, first dil. HCl, and if no ppt forms, then, with vigorous agitation, NaOH soln, and proceed as follows:

(1) If no further pptn occurs, add, with vigorous agitation, NaOH soln to pH 6.8, dil. soln to final measured vol. contg ca 0.1 µg riboflavin/ml, and if cloudiness occurs, filter again.

(2) If further pptn occurs, adjust soln again to point of max. pptn, dil. to measured vol. contg >0.1 µg riboflavin/ml, and then filter. Take aliquot of clear filtrate and proceed as in (1).

If riboflavin content of sample is so low that these requirements cannot be met, conc. clear filtrate obtained at ca pH 4.5 to suitable vol. with heat under reduced pressure. Filter if necessary and proceed as in (1)

(b) *For dry or semidry materials containing appreciable quantities of basic substances.*—Adjust mixt. to pH 5.0–6.0 with dil. HCl. Add such amt of H_2O that total vol. liq. is equal in ml to ≥10 times dry wt sample in g. (Resulting soln must contain ≤0.1 mg riboflavin/ml.) Then add equiv. of 1.0 ml 10N HCl/100 ml liq. and proceed as in (a), beginning with second sentence.

(c) *For liquid materials.*—Adjust pH to 5.0–6.0 with dil. HCl or, with vigorous agitation, NaOH soln, and proceed as in (b), beginning with second sentence.

(d) *For concentrates, premixes, and multivitamin supplements (Official First Action).*—Place measured amt sample in flask and add vol. extn soln equal in ml to ≥ 10 times dry wt sample in g; resulting soln must contain ≤ 0.1 mg riboflavin/ml. If sample is not readily sol., comminute so that it may be dispersed evenly in liq. Then agitate vigorously and wash down sides of flask with extn soln.

Reflux mixt. 1 hr and cool. If lumping occurs, agitate mixt. until particles are dispersed evenly. Dil. mixt. to measured vol. with extn soln and let any undissolved particles settle, or filter or centrf., if necessary. Take aliquot of clear soln and dil. with H_2O to measured vol. contg ca 0.1 μg riboflavin/ml and filter if soln is not clear. Proceed with detn, **39.043**.

39.042 *Determination*

To each of ≥ 4 tubes (or reaction vessels) add 10 ml sample soln. (If fluorometer is type that requires tubular cuvets, all reactions may be carried out in matched set of these cuvets.) To each of ≥ 2 tubes add 1 ml std riboflavin working soln I and mix, and to each of ≥ 2 remaining tubes, add 1 ml H_2O and mix. To each tube add 1 ml HOAc and mix; add, with mixing, 0.5 ml 4.0% $KMnO_4$ soln (quantity may be increased for sample solns that contain excess of oxidizable material, but ≤ 0.5 ml in excess of that required to complete oxidn of foreign material should be added). Let stand 2 min; then to each tube add, with mixing, 0.5 ml 3.0% H_2O_2 soln; permanganate color must be destroyed within 10 sec. Shake vigorously until excess O is expelled. If gas bubbles remain on sides of tubes after foaming stops, remove by tipping tubes so that soln flows slowly from end to end.

In fluorometer, measure fluorescence of sample soln contg 1 ml added std riboflavin working soln I and call this reading X. Next, measure fluorescence of sample soln contg 1 ml added H_2O and call this reading B. Add, with mixing, 20 mg powd $Na_2S_2O_4$ to ≥ 2 tubes, measure fluorescence within 5 sec, and call reading C. Calc. on basis of aliquots taken as follows:

mg Riboflavin/ml final sample soln = $[(B - C)/(X - B)] \times 0.10 \times 0.001$. (Value of $(B - C)/(X - B)$ must be ≥ 0.66 and ≤ 1.5.)

Note: Quantity of $Na_2S_2O_4$ appreciably > 20 mg may reduce foreign pigments and/or foreign fluorescing substances, thereby causing erroneous results.

39.043 *Alternative Determination—Official First Action*
(Applicable to high potency samples)

Add 10 ml sample soln to ≥ 2 cuvets. Add 10 ml working std soln II to each of another set of ≥ 2 cuvets. Add 1 ml HOAc to each tube and mix.

Measure fluorescence of sample solns and std solns in fluorometer. Add, with mixing, 20 mg powd $Na_2S_2O_4$ to 1 tube each of std and sample and measure fluorescence within 5 sec. Calc. on basis of aliquots taken as follows: mg riboflavin/ml final sample soln = $[(I_u - Q_u)/(I_s - Q_s)] \times (0.1 \times 0.001)$, where I_u and I_s = fluorescence intensities of sample and std, resp., and Q_u and Q_s = fluorescences of sample and std, resp., after $Na_2S_2O_4$ addn.

Niacin (Nicotinic Acid) and Niacinamide (Nicotinamide) (*10*)—Official Final Action

39.044 *Reagents*

(a) *Niacin std solns.*—(*1*) *Stock soln.*—100 μg/ml. Dissolve 50 mg NF Niacin Ref. Std, previously dried and stored in dark in desiccator over P_2O_5, in 25% alcohol to make 500 ml. Store at ca 10°.

(*2*) *Working soln I.*—10 μg/ml. Remove small portion stock soln and let come to room temp. Dil. 10 ml to 100 ml with H_2O. Use as std soln in **39.045** (c).

(*3*) *Working soln II.*—4 μg/ml. Dil. 2 ml stock soln, allowed to come to room temp. as in (*2*), to 50 ml with H_2O. Use as std soln in **39.045**(b) and **39.046**(a).

(b) *Dilute ammonium hydroxide.*—Dil. 5 ml NH_4OH to 250 ml with H_2O.

(c) *Dilute hydrochloric acid.*—1 + 5.

(d) *Phosphate buffer soln.*—pH 8. Dissolve 60 g $Na_2HPO_4 \cdot 7H_2O$ and 10 g KH_2PO_4 in warm H_2O and dil. to 200 ml.

(e) *Cyanogen bromide soln.*—10%. Prep. under hood. Warm 370 ml H_2O to 40° in large flask and add 40 g CNBr. Shake until dissolved, cool, and dil. to 400 ml. Do not let CNBr or soln come in contact with skin. Store in refrigerator.

(f) *10% Sulfanilic acid soln.*—Add NH_4OH in 1 ml portions to mixt. of 20 g sulfanilic acid and 170 ml H_2O until acid dissolves. Adjust to pH 4.5 with HCl (1 + 1), using bromocresol green as outside indicator. Dil. to 200 ml. Soln should be almost colorless. Use in **39.046**(a).

(g) *55% Sulfanilic acid soln.*—Add 27 ml H_2O and 27 ml NH_4OH to 55 g sulfanilic acid and shake until dissolved, warming if necessary. Adjust to pH 7 with few drops NH_4OH or $5N$ HCl and dil. to 100 ml. Store in dark. Use in **39.046**(b).

39.045 *Preparation of Sample and Standards*

(a) *Pharmaceutical preparations.*—Disperse ≥ 5 tablets or capsules in small vol. H_2O with heat. Tablets may be ground first. Cool, transfer to vol. flask, and dil. to vol. Soln should contain 50–200 μg niacin/ml. Pipet 10 ml aliquot into 250 ml erlenmeyer and add 10 ml HCl. Evap. on hot plate to ca 2 ml, cool, add ca 25–50 ml H_2O, and adjust to pH 2.5–4.5 with 40% NaOH or KOH soln. Transfer to vol. flask of such size that soln contains ca 4 μg niacin/ml. Filter, if necessary, discarding first 10 ml filtrate. Proceed as in **39.046**(a).

(b) *Noncereal foods and feeds.*—Weigh 1 oz sample into 1 L erlenmeyer, add 200 ml $1N$ H_2SO_4, mix, and heat 30 min in autoclave at 15 lb pressure. Cool, adjust to pH 4.5 with $10N$ NaOH, using bromocresol green as outside indicator, dil. to 250 ml with H_2O, and filter. Weigh 17 g $(NH_4)_2SO_4$ into 50 ml vol. flask, pipet in 40 ml aliquot sample soln, dil. to vol. with H_2O, and shake vigorously. Filter, mix well, and use 1 ml aliquot for color development. In case of samples contg 16 mg niacin/lb, final soln contains 3.2 μg/ml.

Pipet 40 ml aliquot working soln II, **39.044(a)(3)**, into 17 g $(NH_4)_2SO_4$ in 50 ml vol. flask, and dil. to vol. with H_2O. This std contains 3.2 μg/ml. Proceed as in **39.046(a)**.

(c) *Cereal products.*—Run 1 reagent blank and 5 levels of working soln I, **39.044(a)(2)**, with samples thruout detn.

Place 1.5 g $Ca(OH)_2$ into each of six 250 ml erlenmeyers. From pipet add 0, 5, 10, 15, 20, and 25 ml working soln I, resp. Accurately weigh ca 2.5 g sample contg ca 100 μg niacin into another flask contg ca 1.5 g $Ca(OH)_2$. To all flasks add H_2O to ca 90 ml, shake to mix, and autoclave 2 hr at 15 lb pressure. Mix thoroly while still hot. Cool to ca 40°, transfer to 100 ml vol. flasks, and dil. to vol. (When necessary, sample may be stored in refrigerator few days.)

Transfer ca 50 ml supernatant from each vol. flask to sep. centrf. tubes and place in ice bath 15 min or in refrigerator ≥ 2 hr. Centrf. 15 min and pipet 20 ml supernatant from each tube into sep. centrf. tubes contg 8 g $(NH_4)_2SO_4$ and 2 ml phosphate buffer soln. Shake to dissolve and warm to 55–60°. Centrf. 5 min and filter thru Whatman No. 12 paper, or equiv., refiltering if necessary to obtain clear soln. Proceed as in **39.046(b)**.

39.046   *Determination*

(a) *For pharmaceutical preparations and noncereal foods and feeds.*—Add 10% sulfanilic acid soln, **39.044(f)**, and CNBr soln under hood from burets or pipets filled by mech. suction. *CNBr is toxic.* Use working soln II, **39.044(a)(3)**. Prep. tubes as follows:

Standard Blank	Sample Blank
1.0 ml std soln	1.0 ml sample soln
5.0 ml H_2O	5.0 ml H_2O
0.5 ml dil. NH_4OH	0.5 ml dil. NH_4OH
2.0 ml 10% sulfanilic acid	2.0 ml 10% sulfanilic acid
0.5 ml dil. HCl	0.5 ml dil. HCl

Standard Soln	Sample Soln
1.0 ml std soln	1.0 ml sample soln
0.5 ml dil. NH_4OH	0.5 ml dil. NH_4OH
5.0 ml CNBr	5.0 ml CNBr
2.0 ml 10% sulfanilic acid	2.0 ml 10% sulfanilic acid
0.5 ml H_2O	0.5 ml H_2O

Prep. sep. sample blank for each sample.

Pipet std soln and sample soln into respective tubes; add 5 ml H_2O for std blank and sample blank.

Add all subsequent solns to single tube and read color before proceeding with next tube. Starting with std blank, swirl tube to impart rotary motion in liq., immediately add dil. NH_4OH, swirl again, add sulfanilic acid, and swirl. Immediately add 0.5 ml dil. HCl, mix again, place in photoelec. colorimeter, and adjust instrument to 0 A at any specific wavelength between 430 and 450 nm within ca 30 sec after addn of sulfanilic acid soln. Treat std soln in same way as std blank with respect to addn of dil. NH_4OH. Immediately swirl tube, add CNBr soln, and swirl again. At 30 sec after addn of CNBr soln, swirl tube, add sulfanilic acid soln, and swirl again. Immediately add 0.5 ml H_2O, mix again, and stopper. With instrument set at 0 A for std blank, as above, read A of std soln at max. (Color reaches max. in ca 1.5 min after addn of sulfanilic acid soln, remains at peak ca 2 min, and then fades slowly.)

With sample blank set at 0 A, det. A of sample soln similarly. Niacin content is proportional to A if std and sample solns are ca same concn.

(b) *For cereal products.*—In each of 2 tubes place 5 ml std and in each of 2 addnl tubes place 5 ml sample soln. In addnl tube to be used as reagent blank, place 5 ml H_2O. To one std tube and one sample tube to be used as their resp. blanks, add 10 ml H_2O. Let all tubes stand 30 min in bath of finely crushed ice, preferably in refrigerator. To remaining sample and std tubes and to reagent blank, consecutively add 10 ml cold CNBr, followed in 30 sec by 1.0 ml 55% sulfanilic acid, **39.044(g)**. Mix immediately after addn of each reagent (most conveniently done by swirling), and stopper tubes contg CNBr. Replace all tubes in ice bath. To std and sample blank add 1.0 ml 55% sulfanilic acid soln.

Set colorimeter with 470 nm filter at 0 A with std blank, and read A of other tubes 12–15 min after addn of sulfanilic acid. Tubes must be cooled uniformly and each tube must be wiped dry just before placing in colorimeter. If tubes fog, dip momentarily in hot H_2O and wipe before reading.

Plot std curve of A of std minus that of reagent blank against niacin concn in μg/ml, drawing straight line of best fit. From this line read concn, C, corresponding to A of sample corrected for sample blank and reagent blank.

mg Niacin/100 g sample = $C/(10 \times$ g sample).

Niacinamide in Multivitamin Preparations (11)—Official Final Action

39.047   *Principle*

Niacinamide is extd in KH_2PO_4 soln at pH ca 4.5 and allowed to react with CNBr and barbituric acid. Reaction product is measured spectrophtric. Niacin does not interfere unless present at 3 times concn of amide.

39.048   *Reagents*

(a) *Cyanogen bromide soln.*—10%. See **39.044(e)**. Let come to room temp. before use.

(b) *Potassium dihydrogen phosphate solns.*—(1) 3%. Dissolve and dil. 30 g KH_2PO_4 to 1 L with H_2O. (2) *0.3%.*—Dil. soln (1) with H_2O (1 + 9).

(c) *Barbituric acid buffered soln.*—Prep. vol. required for each batch of assays by adding 2 g reagent grade barbituric acid to each 100 ml 3% KH_2PO_4. Stir mech. 1 hr and filter before use.

(d) *Niacinamide std solns.*—(1) *Stock soln.*—250 μg/ml. Dissolve and dil. 50 mg USP Niacinamide Ref. Std to 200 ml with 60% alcohol. Store at ca 10°. (2) *Working soln.*—5 μg/ml. Let small portion stock soln warm to room temp. Dil. 2 ml to 100 ml with 0.3% KH_2PO_4 soln.

39.049 Preparation of Samples

Take 5 tablets or capsules or appropriate vol. of liq. for each assay. Grind tablets to fine powder. Place accurately weighed sample in erlenmeyer (for capsules, add ca 2 ml ethylene chloride to aid dispersion). Add vol. 0.3% KH_2PO_4 soln equal in ml to at least twice mg niacinamide expected. If sample is not readily sol., shake to disperse and heat 15 min in boiling H_2O bath or in autoclave at 15 lb pressure. Dil. to ca 5 μg/ml with 0.3% KH_2PO_4 soln. Filter if necessary.

39.050 Determination

Prep. sep. sample blank for each sample by replacing CNBr with H_2O.

To 1 ml working std soln or assay soln in spectrophtr tube, add 0.5 ml CNBr soln, mix, stopper, and let stand 25–30 min. (To avoid standing >30 min when analyzing several samples, allow regular interval of 1–2 min between addns of CNBr.) Add 10 ml barbituric acid soln and swirl. (If barbituric acid soln cannot be added after 30 min, transfer tubes to crushed ice bath to stabilize CNBr reaction.)

Set spectrophtr to 0 A at 550 nm with appropriate blank in which CNBr is replaced by H_2O. Read A of reaction product at max. color development (ca 2–4 min after addn of barbituric acid soln; color remains stable ca 1 min, then fades slowly).

Calc. mg niacinamide in original wt sample taken = $(A_{sample} \times 5 \times diln\ factor)/(A_{std} \times 1000)$, where A_{sample} refers to sample soln, A_{std}, to std, and 5 = μg niacinamide/ml in working std soln. Report mg niacinamide/tablet, capsule, g or ml of liq.

Vitamin C (Ascorbic Acid)— Official Final Action

2,6-Dichloroindophenol Method (12)

(Applicable to detn of reduced ascorbic acid. Not applicable in presence of ferrous Fe, stannous Sn, cuprous Cu, SO_2, sulfite, or thiosulfate. *See Note.*)

39.051 Principles

Ascorbic acid reduces oxidn-reduction indicator dye, 2,6-dichloroindophenol, to colorless soln. At end point, excess unreduced dye is rose pink in acid soln. Vitamin is extd and titrn performed in presence of HPO_3-HOAc or HPO_3-HOAc-H_2SO_4 soln to main-

tain proper acidity for reaction and to avoid autoxidn of acid at high pH.

39.052 Reagents

(a) *Extracting solns.*—(1) *Metaphosphoric acid-acetic acid soln.*—Dissolve, with shaking, 15 g glacial HPO_3 pellets or freshly pulverized stick HPO_3 in 40 ml HOAc and 200 ml H_2O; dil. to ca 500 ml, and filter rapidly thru fluted paper into g-s bottle. (HPO_3 slowly changes to H_3PO_4, but if stored in refrigerator, soln remains satisfactory 7–10 days.) (2) *Metaphosphoric acid-acetic acid-sulfuric acid soln.*—Proceed as in (1), except use 0.3N H_2SO_4 in place of H_2O.

(b) *Ascorbic acid std soln.*—1 mg/ml. Accurately weigh 50 mg USP Ascorbic Acid Ref. Std that has been stored in desiccator away from direct sunlight. Transfer to 50 ml vol. flask. Dil. to vol. *immediately before use* with HPO_3-HOAc soln, (a)(1).

(c) *Indophenol std soln.*—Dissolve 50 mg 2,6-dichloroindophenol Na salt (Eastman Kodak Co. No. 3463), that has been stored in desiccator over soda lime, in 50 ml H_2O to which has been added 42 mg $NaHCO_3$; shake vigorously, and when dye dissolves, dil. to 200 ml with H_2O. Filter thru fluted paper into amber g-s bottle. Keep stoppered, out of direct sunlight, and store in refrigerator. (Decomposition products that make end point indistinct occur in some batches of dry indophenol and also develop with time in stock soln. Add 5.0 ml extg soln contg excess ascorbic acid to 15 ml dye reagent. If reduced soln is not practically colorless, discard, and prep. new stock soln. If dry dye is at fault, obtain new supply.)

Transfer three 2.0 ml aliquots ascorbic acid std soln to each of three 50 ml erlenmeyers contg 5.0 ml HPO_3-HOAc soln, (a)(1). Titr. rapidly with indophenol soln from 50 ml buret until light but distinct rose-pink persists ≥5 sec. (Each titrn should require ca 15 ml indophenol soln, and titrns should check within 0.1 ml.) Similarly titr. 3 blanks composed of 7.0 ml HPO_3-HOAc soln, (a)(1), plus vol. H_2O ca equiv. to vol. indophenol soln used in direct titrns. After subtracting av. blanks (usually ca 0.1 ml) from stdzn titrns, calc. and express concn of indophenol soln as mg ascorbic acid equiv. to 1.0 ml reagent. Stdze indophenol soln daily with freshly prepd ascorbic acid std soln.

(d) *Thymol blue pH indicator.*—0.04%. Dissolve 0.1 g indicator by triturating in agate mortar with 10.75 ml 0.02N NaOH and dil. to 250 ml with H_2O. Transition range: 1.2 (red)–2.8 (yellow). (Fisher Scientific Co. No. 5-985-B has been found satisfactory.)

39.053 Preliminary Test for Appreciable Quantity of Basic Substances

Grind representative sample or express contents from capsule and add ca 25 ml HPO_3-HOAc soln, (a)(1). Test pH by placing drop thymol blue pH indicator on pestle or by using spot plate. (pH >1.2

indicates appreciable amts of basic substances.) For liq. prepns, dil. representative sample ca two-fold with HPO₃-HOAc soln, (a)(*1*), before testing with indicator.

39.054   Preparation of Sample Assay Solution

(a) *For dry materials containing no appreciable quantity of basic substances.*—Pulverize sample by gentle grinding, add HPO₃-HOAc soln, (a)(*1*), and triturate until sample is in suspension. Dil. with HPO₃-HOAc soln, (a)(*1*), to measured vol. Designate this vol. as V ml.

(Use ca 10 ml extg soln/g dry sample. Final soln should contain 10–100 mg ascorbic acid/100 ml.)

(b) *For dry materials containing appreciable quantities of basic substances.*—Pulverize sample by gentle grinding, add HPO₃-HOAc-H₂SO₄ soln, (a)(*2*), to adjust pH to ca 1.2, and triturate until sample is in suspension. Dil. with HPO₃-HOAc soln, (a)(*1*), to measured vol. Designate this vol. as V ml.

(Use ca 10 ml extg soln/g dry sample. Final soln should contain 10–100 mg ascorbic acid/100 ml.)

(c) *For liquid materials.*—Take amt of sample contg ca 100 mg ascorbic acid. If appreciable amts of basic substances are present, adjust pH to ca 1.2 with HPO₃-HOAc-H₂SO₄ soln, (a)(*2*). Dil. with HPO₃-HOAc soln, (a)(*1*), to measured vol. contg 10–100 mg ascorbic acid/100 ml. Designate this vol. as V ml.

(d) *For fruit and vegetable juices.*—Prep. juice as in **22.003**(a). Add aliquots of ≥100 ml prepd juice to equal vols of HPO₃-HOAc soln, (a)(*1*). Designate total vol. as V ml. Mix, and filter thru rapid folded paper (Eaton-Dikeman No. 195, 18.5 cm, or equiv.).

39.055   Determination

Titr. 3 sample aliquots each contg ca 2 mg ascorbic acid and make blank detns for correction of titrns as in **39.052**(c), using proper vols of HPO₃-HOAc soln, (a)(*1*), and H₂O. If ca 2 mg ascorbic acid is contained in sample aliquot <7 ml, add HPO₃-HOAc soln to give 7 ml for titrn.

mg Ascorbic acid/g, tablet, ml, etc. $= (X - B) \times (F/E) \times (V/Y)$, where X = av. ml for sample titrn, B = av. ml for sample blank titrn, F = mg ascorbic acid equiv. to 1.0 ml indophenol std soln, E = number of g, tablets, ml, etc. assayed, V = initial assay soln vol., and Y = vol. sample aliquot titrated.

Note: Products contg ferrous Fe, stannous Sn, and cuprous Cu give values in excess of their actual ascorbic acid content by this method. Following are simple tests to det. whether these reducing ions are present in such amts as to invalidate test: Add 2 drops *0.05% aq. soln of methylene blue* to 10 ml freshly prepd mixt. (1 + 1) of juice and HPO₃-HOAc reagent and mix. Disappearance of methylene blue color in 5–10 sec indicates presence of interfering substances. Stannous Sn does not give this test and may be tested for as follows: To another 10 ml sample soln to which 10 ml HCl (1 + 3) has

been added, add 5 drops *0.05% aq. soln of indigo carmine* and mix. Disappearance of color in 5–10 sec indicates presence of stannous Sn or other interfering substance.

Microfluorometric Method (13)

39.056   Principles

Ascorbic acid is oxidized to dehydroascorbic acid in presence of Norit. Oxidized form is reacted with *o*-phenylenediamine to produce fluorophor having activation max. at ca 350 nm and fluorescence max. at ca 430 nm. Fluorescence intensity is proportional to concn.

Development of fluorescent derivative of vitamin is prevented by forming H₃BO₃-dehydroascorbic acid complex prior to addn of diamine soln. Any remaining fluorescence is due to extraneous materials. This serves as "blank."

Ascorbic plus dehydroascorbic acid is calcd by comparing corrected fluorescence reading for sample with that of std similarly oxidized and treated.

39.057   Reagents

(a) *Extracting solns.*—Prep.: (*1*) HPO₃-HOAc and (*2*) HPO₃-HOAc-H₂SO₄ solns as in **39.052**(a).

(b) *Ascorbic acid std soln.*—100 μg/ml. Dil. 10 ml ascorbic acid std soln, **39.052**(b), to 100 ml with HPO₃-HOAc soln, (a)(*1*).

(c) *o-Phenylenediamine soln.*—For each 100 ml soln required, weigh 20 mg *o*-phenylenediamine .2HCl (Eastman Kodak Co. No. 678). Dil. to vol. with H₂O immediately before use.

(d) *Thymol blue pH indicator.*—Prep. as in **39.052** (d).

(e) *Sodium acetate soln.*—Dissolve 500 g NaOAc .3H₂O in H₂O and dil. to 1 L.

(f) *Boric acid-sodium acetate soln.*—Dissolve 3 g H₃BO₃ in 100 ml NaOAc soln. Prep. fresh for each assay.

(g) *Acid-washed Norit.*—Add 1 L HCl (1 + 9) to 200 g Norit-A Neutral, Fisher Scientific Co. No. C-170, heat to boiling, and filter with vac. Remove cake to large beaker. Add 1 L H₂O, stir, and filter. Repeat washing with H₂O and filtering. Dry overnight at 110–120°.

39.058   Apparatus

(a) *Automatic pipetting machine.*—Brewer, BBL Div. of Bioquest, Greater Baltimore Ind. Park, Cockeysville, MD 21030, or equiv. Calibrate to deliver 5 ml aliquots.

(b) *Vortex mixer.*—Scientific Industries, Inc., 55 Madison Ave, Hempstead, NY 11550, or equiv.

(c) *Fluorometer.*—Aminco Fluoro-Microphotometer (American Instrument Co.) with lamp No. F4T4/BL and cuvet adapter B12-63019 to accept 18 × 150 mm test tubes, or equiv. Use as primary filter Corning Glass Works Nos. 7380 (C.S. No. 0-52) and 5860 (C.S. No. 7-37) and as secondary filter Corning Nos. 5113 (C.S. No. 5-58) and 3389 (C.S. No. 3-73). (*Caution: See* **46.008**.)

(d) *Fluorescence reading tubes.*—Stdzd 18 × 150 mm test tubes.

39.059 *Preliminary Test for Appreciable Quantity of Basic Substances*

Proceed as in **39.053.**

39.060 *Preparation of Sample Assay Solution*

(a) *For dry materials containing no appreciable quantity of basic substances.*—Proceed as in **39.054**(a). Dil. with HPO$_3$-HOAc soln, (a)(*1*), to ca 100 μg ascorbic acid/ml. Designate this vol. as V ml. Filter solns contg large amts of suspended solids thru Whatman No. 12 paper, or equiv. Designate as sample assay soln.

(b) *For dry materials containing appreciable quantities of basic substances.*—Proceed as in **39.054**(b). Then proceed as in (a), beginning "Dil. with ..."

(c) *For liquid materials.*—Proceed as in **39.054**(c). Then proceed as in (a), beginning "Dil. with ..."

(d) *For gelatin-encapsulated pharmaceutical products.*—Place sample in small beaker and heat gently with enough proper extg soln, (a)(*1*) or (*2*), to cover. If capsules do not disintegrate readily, crush with glass rod. Cool rapidly to room temp. If appreciable amts of basic substances are present, adjust pH to ca 1.2 with HPO$_3$-HOAc-H$_2$SO$_4$ soln, (a)(*2*). Proceed as in (a), beginning "Dil. with ..."

Note: For samples difficult to filter, proceed as in applicable section, (a), (b), (c), or (d), except dil. sample assay soln with HPO$_3$-HOAc soln to ca 50 μg ascorbic acid/ml. Compare with std soln prepd by dilg 5 ml ascorbic acid std soln, **39.052**(b), to 100 ml with HPO$_3$-HOAc soln. (1 ml = 50 μg ascorbic acid.)

39.061 *Determination*

Following steps must be performed consecutively without delay.

Transfer 100 ml std and sample assay solns to 300 ml erlenmeyers. Add 2 g acid-washed Norit, shake vigorously, and filter thru Whatman No. 12 paper, or equiv., discarding first few ml. Transfer 5 ml each filtrate to 100 ml vol. flask contg 5 ml H$_3$BO$_3$-NaOAc soln. Let stand 15 min, swirling occasionally. Designate as std or sample blank solns.

During 15 min period, transfer 5 ml of each filtrate to 100 ml vol. flask contg 5 ml NaOAc soln and ca 75 ml H$_2$O. Dil. to vol. with H$_2$O. Transfer 2 ml of each soln to each of 3 fluorescence reading tubes. Designate as std or sample tubes, resp.

At appropriate time, dil. blank solns to vol. with H$_2$O. Transfer 2 ml of these solns to each of 3 fluorescence reading tubes. Designate as std or sample blank tubes, resp.

Using automatic pipetting machine, add 5 ml *o*-phenylenediamine soln to all tubes. Use Vortex mixer to swirl tubes. Protect from light and let stand 35 min at room temp.

39.062 *Fluorometry*

Measure fluorescence of std tube (*C*), std blank tube (*B*), sample tube (*X*), and sample blank tube (*D*).

mg Ascorbic acid/g, tablet, ml, etc. = [(av. X − av. D)/(av. C − av. B)] × (20 × S × V/E), where V = initial assay soln vol., E = number of g, tablets, ml, etc., and S = concn of std in mg/ml added to reading tube.

Vitamin E (*14*)—Official First Action
(Applicable to pharmaceutical prepns)

39.063 *Apparatus*

(a) *Gas chromatograph.*—Equipped with either H flame or β-Ar ionization detector; capable of accepting glass column and glass-lined sample introduction system or on-column injection. Use following conditions for analysis: column temp. 270–285°; sample introduction system 295°; detector temp. 295°; N or Ar carrier gas flow adjusted so α-tocopheryl acetate peak appears 23–27 min after sample introduction; satisfactory recorder chart speed 0.33″/min; and β-Ar detector 900 v dc.

(b) *Filter assembly.*—Consisting of Millipore filter holder, No. XX 1004700, and microfiber glass pre-filter disk, No. AP 2004200 (Millipore Corp., Bedford, MA 01730); and Filtrator, Fisher Scientific Co. No. 9-788.

39.064 *Reagents*

(a) *n-Hexane.*—Pure grade, Phillips Petroleum Co.

(b) *d- or dl-α-Tocopherol.*—Eastman Kodak Co. No. 6340; or Hoffmann-La Roche, Inc. No. 60524.

(c) *d- or dl-α-Tocopheryl acetate.*—Eastman No. 6679; or Hoffmann-La Roche No. 60526.

(d) *d- or dl-α-Tocopheryl succinate.*—Eastman No. 6347; or Hoffmann-La Roche No. 60540.

Prep. primary stock solns of high purity stds of *d*- or *dl*-α-tocopherol, *d*- or *dl*-α-tocopheryl acetate, and *d*- or *dl*-α-tocopheryl succinate in *n*-hexane weekly. Dil. primary stock solns to 1 mg individual analog/ml for working stds. Refrigerate all stock and std solns in *amber* Pyrex vol. flasks under N.

39.065 *Preparation of Column*

Fill 8′ × 4 mm id (uniform bore) Pyrex column with 5% SE-30 on 100–120 mesh Gas-Chrom Q to within 4″ of injection point and 1″ of column exit. Vibrate column while filling. Insert glass wool plugs, one extending to top of carrier gas inlet arm at column injection end and another filling space between packing and septum at exit.

Condition column 24 hr at 285° and 80 ml/min carrier gas flow. Let column cool with gas flowing. Connect column outlet to detector; bring chromatograph to operating temp. and carrier gas flow rate. Record baseline to check instrument stability. Baseline drift should be ≤1% in 30 min.

(Pretested column available from Applied Science Labs.)

39.066　　　　　　　*Preparation of Samples*

Ext amt of sample, based on claimed vitamin E content, such that amt injected onto column in 3–4 μl is ca 3 μg or midpoint in calibration curve.

(a) *Tablets.*—Grind in mortar and ext with four 25 ml portions n-hexane. Filter ext thru filter assembly into receiver and dil. to such vol. that final concn is 1 mg vitamin E/ml.

(b) *Capsules.*—Dissolve in n-hexane under N, heating slightly if needed. If capsules do not disintegrate, cut open and remove contents with n-hexane. Open slip-capsules and place contents and capsule parts in n-hexane. Continue as in (a).

(c) *Injectables and liquids.*—Dil. with n-hexane so final concn is 1 mg vitamin E/ml. If product is not miscible in n-hexane, inject μl aliquots of product directly onto GLC column.

(d) *Other preparations.*—Samples not directly extractable with n-hexane may require dispersing with H_2O followed by dissolution with suitable solv.

39.067　　　　　　　*Injection Technic*

Use following injection technic with 10 μl Hamilton microsyringe: Draw 1 μl air into barrel, insert needle into sample, and draw desired amt into barrel; remove needle from soln, and draw 1 μl air into barrel. Check sample vol. between same μl range on calibration scale each time sample is obtained to ensure uniformity in vol.

Caution: Occasionally column is rendered unusable for 1–4 hr following direct injection. If this situation arises, either increase column temp. for short time to drive off sample contaminants or wait until baseline stabilizes at column operating temp.

39.068　　　　　　　*Performance Check*

Obtain GLC std curves of 2–5 μg of each analog daily. Construct calibration plot (y axis, response in area; x axis, μg injected) with ≥ 3 points in duplicate for each analog to be measured.

Monitor instrument and column performance by observing sepn of α-tocopherol and α-tocopheryl acetate peaks expressed as peak resolution.

Peak resolution $= 2D/(B + C)$, where $D =$ distance between analog peak maxima, $B = \alpha$-tocopheryl acetate peak base width, and $C = \alpha$-tocopherol peak base width.

Det. these values with mixt. of equal quantities α-tocopherol and α-tocopheryl acetate, using sample size so that ht of peaks is ca 50% full scale. If peak resolution is ≥ 1.0, column and instrument are satisfactory. All columns will show gradual loss in peak resolution; when value is < 1.0, install new column.

39.069　　　　　　　*Peak Identification*

Compare retention times of samples and stds. Distinguish α-tocopherol from α-tocopheryl succinate in sample exts (these vitamin E analogs have similar retention times) as follows: Obtain GLC analysis of ext. Add 1 ml Ac_2O-pyridine $(2 + 1)$ to ext, and shake 10 min. Evap. soln under N stream, dil. to original vol. with n-hexane, and obtain GLC analysis. If peak shifts to α-tocopheryl acetate position, sample contains alcohol; if it does not shift, sample contains α-tocopheryl succinate. Relative retention times are: α-tocopheryl acetate, 1.0; α-tocopherol, 0.9; α-tocopheryl succinate, 0.9.

39.070　　　　　　　*Determination*

Inject 2 μl sample ext. Det. area of each peak with electromech. or electronic integrator, or by triangulation, i.e., peak ht $\times$ peak width at half ht. Convert peak area to amt vitamin E analog, using specific calibration plot.

Calc. mg/tablet, capsule, or ml $= (X/N)(V/U)$, where $X = \mu$g read from calibration curve, $N = \mu$l injected (normally 2), $V =$ vol. total ext (ml), and $U =$ number tablets, capsules, or ml initially used.

If label claims are stated as International Units (IU), convert to wt, using following conversion factors:

1 mg dl-α-tocopheryl acetate = 1 IU; 1 mg dl-α-tocopherol = 1.1 IU; 1 mg d-α-tocopheryl acetate = 1.36 IU; 1 mg d-α-tocopherol = 1.49 IU; 1 mg d-α-tocopheryl succinate = 1.21 IU.

Calcium Pantothenate (15)—
Official First Action

(Applicable to pharmaceutical prepns. Method does not differentiate between d- and l-isomeric forms. Assuming that racemic Ca pantothenate is 50:50 mixt. of d- and l-isomeric forms, chemically detd values for total Ca pantothenate are reduced by ½ to give content of active d-Ca pantothenate. Similarly, vitamin products, in which isomeric form of pantothenate ingredient is not stated on label, would be reported as contg d-pantothenate equiv. to ½ that of detd value.)

39.071　　　　　　　*Principle*

Pantothenate molecule is cleaved with acid and resulting β-alanine is treated with chlorinating soln and then with KI. Free I is measured spectrophtric.

39.072　　　　　　　*Apparatus*

Chromatographic tubes.—Pyrex, 10 mm id $\times$ 300 mm long, with coarse fritted disks and tops tooled for rubber stoppers.

39.073　　　　　　　*Reagents*

(a) *Ion exchange resin.*—Dowex 50W-X4 (H^+ form); 100–200 mesh.

(b) *Florisil.*—60–100 mesh.

(c) *Borate buffer.*—0.05M. Dissolve 3.1 g reagent grade boric acid and 3.7 g KCl in ca 900 ml H_2O; adjust pH to precisely 10.5 with 2N NaOH and dil. to 1 L.

(d) *Chlorinating soln.*—Dil. 4–6% NaOCl soln 1 + 30 with 0.05M borate buffer; prep. daily and protect from light.

(e) *Acidified phenol soln.*—0.5% phenol in 0.1M HCl.

(f) *Potassium iodide.*—1% aq. soln. Prep. weekly and protect from light.

(g) *Phenolphthalein.*—0.02% in ethyl or iso-propyl alcohol.

(h) *Calcium pantothenate std soln.*—0.05 mg/ml. Dissolve 50.0 mg USP Ref. Std in 100.0 ml H_2O. Dil. 10.0 ml to 100.0 ml. Store at 10°.

39.074 *Preparation of Columns*

Wash Dowex and Florisil resins with H_2O to remove most of fines and store in H_2O until used. Use 2 columns for each sample to be assayed and one column for std. Add 5 cm Florisil to each tube, insert thin layer of glass wool, and add 5 cm Dowex 50W-X4. Wash resins with ca 15 ml $1M$ HCl and rinse with 150 ml H_2O. Prep. new columns before each assay.

39.075 *Determination*

Prep. aq. soln of sample contg 0.05 mg Ca pantothenate/ml based on label claim. Tablets and capsules may be heated in H_2O to facilitate extn. Remove colored outer coating of tablets by carefully washing with H_2O. It may be necessary to cut open and carefully remove contents of capsules with colored coatings.

Add 10 ml aliquots of sample and std to sep. columns and elute each with 70 ml H_2O into 200 ml erlenmeyer. Add 5 ml $2N$ HCl to both eluates and autoclave 30 min at 120°. Cool and dil. to 100 ml. Prep. sample blank by adding 10 ml aliquot of sample soln to sep. column and eluting with 70 ml H_2O. Dil. blank to 100 ml with H_2O. Transfer 10 ml aliquots of sample, sample blank, and std to sep. 50 ml g-s erlenmeyers. Add 2 drops 0.02% phthln soln to each. Titr. with $2N$ NaOH until red and then back-titr. with $0.1N$ HCl to colorless end point.

Add 1 ml chlorinating soln to each, mix, stopper, and let stand 15 min. Add 1 ml acidified phenol soln to decompose excess hypochlorite and swirl to rinse sides of flasks. Stopper and let stand 5 min. Add 1 ml KI soln and immediately add 20 ml absolute alcohol to each flask in turn. (Add immediately, as I color decreases rapidly in aq. soln.) Transfer solns to 50 ml vol. flasks. Dil. to vol. with absolute alcohol and mix. Let stand ≥10 min for max. color to develop. Det. *A* of solns at 358 nm on spectrophtr set at 0 *A* against reagent blank consisting of 10 ml H_2O and each of those reagents added at specified time intervals. Under these conditions I color is constant 24 hr.

Calc. concn Ca pantothenate in original sample = (A_{sample}/A_{std}) × declared potency.

MICROBIOLOGICAL METHODS
Vitamins—Official Final Action

(Thruout all stages, except where otherwise directed, protect solns from undue exposure to light.)

39.076 *Stock Solutions for Basal Media*

(Store all solns in dark at ca 10°. Store all solns except those contg alcohol under toluene. Proportionate quantities may be prepd.)

(a) *Acid-hydrolyzed casein soln.*—(*Caution: See* **46.011** *and* **46.015.**) Mix 400 g vitamin-free casein with 2 L constant-boiling HCl (ca $5N$) and either reflux 8–12 hr, or heat in autoclave 8–12 hr at 121–123°. Remove HCl from mixt. by distn under reduced pressure until thick paste remains. Redissolve paste in H_2O, adjust soln to pH 3.5±0.1 with ca 10% NaOH soln, and dil. with H_2O to 4 L. Add 80 g activated charcoal to soln, stir 1 hr, and filter. Repeat treatment with activated charcoal. Filter soln if ppt forms upon storage. (Some com. sources of vitamin-free acid-hydrolyzed casein have been found satisfactory.)

(b) *Adenine-guanine-uracil soln.*—Dissolve 0.7 g each of adenine sulfate, guanine.HCl, and uracil in 35 ml warm HCl (1 + 1), cool, and dil. with H_2O to 700 ml.

(c) *Asparagine soln.*—Dissolve 8 g L-asparagine .H_2O in H_2O and dil. to 800 ml.

(d) *Cystine soln.*—Suspend 2 g L-cystine in ca 750 ml H_2O, heat to 70–80°, and add HCl (1 + 1), drop-wise, with stirring, until solid dissolves. Cool, and dil. with H_2O to 1 L.

(e) *Cystine-tryptophan soln.*—Suspend 8 g L-cystine and 2 g L-tryptophan (or 4 g D,L-tryptophan) in ca 1.5 L H_2O, heat to 70–80°, and add HCl (1 + 1), dropwise, with stirring, until solids dissolve. Cool, and dil. with H_2O to 2 L.

(f) *Manganese sulfate soln.*—Dissolve 2 g $MnSO_4$ .H_2O in H_2O and dil. to 200 ml.

(g) *Photolyzed peptone soln.*—Dissolve 100 g peptone in 625 ml H_2O, add soln of 50 g NaOH in 625 ml H_2O, and mix in vessel (such as crystg dish) of such size that depth of soln is 1–2 cm. Place 100–500 watt bulb, fitted with reflector, ca 30–50 cm from soln, and expose soln, with occasional stirring, to light from bulb until riboflavin is destroyed (4–10 hr may be enough). Maintain soln at ≤25° during this treatment. Adjust soln to pH 6.0–6.5 with HOAc, add 18 g anhyd. NaOAc, stir until solid dissolves, dil. with H_2O to 2 L, and filter if soln is not clear.

(h) *Polysorbate 80 soln.*—Dissolve 25 g polysorbate 80 (polyoxyethylene sorbitan monooleate) in alcohol to make 250 ml.

(i) *Salt soln A.*—Dissolve 40 g anhyd. KH_2PO_4 and 40 g anhyd. K_2HPO_4 in H_2O, dil. to 800 ml, and add 8 drops HCl.

(j) *Salt soln B.*—Dissolve 20 g $MgSO_4.7H_2O$, 1 g NaCl, 1 g $FeSO_4.7H_2O$, and 1 g $MnSO_4.H_2O$ in H_2O, dil. to 1 L, and add 10 drops HCl.

(k) *Tryptophan soln.*—Suspend 2.0 g L-tryptophan (or 4.0 g D,L-tryptophan) in 700–800 ml H_2O, heat to 70–80°, and add HCl (1 + 1), dropwise, with stirring, until solid dissolves. Cool, and dil. with H_2O to 1 L.

(l) *Vitamin soln I.*—Dissolve 10 mg riboflavin, 10 mg thiamine.HCl, 0.1 mg biotin, and 20 mg niacin in $0.02N$ HOAc to make 400 ml.

(m) *Vitamin soln II.*—Dissolve 20 mg *p*-aminobenzoic acid, 10 mg Ca pantothenate, 40 mg pyridoxine.HCl, 40 mg pyridoxal.HCl, 8 mg pyridoxamine.2HCl, and 2 mg folic acid in 25% alcohol to make 400 ml.

(**n**) *Vitamin soln III.*—Dissolve 10 mg *p*-aminobenzoic acid, 40 mg pyridoxine.HCl, 4 mg thiamine.HCl, 8 mg Ca pantothenate, 8 mg niacin, and 0.2 mg biotin in ca 300 ml H_2O. Add 10 mg riboflavin dissolved in ca 200 ml $0.02N$ HOAc. Then add soln contg 1.9 g anhyd. NaOAc and 1.6 ml HOAc in ca 40 ml H_2O, and dil. with H_2O to 2 L.

(**o**) *Vitamin soln IV.*—Dissolve 8 mg riboflavin, 4 mg thiamine.HCl, and 0.016 mg biotin in $0.02N$ HOAc to make 400 ml.

(**p**) *Vitamin soln V.*—Dissolve 2 mg *p*-aminobenzoic acid, 4 mg Ca pantothenate, and 8 mg pyridoxine.HCl in 25% alcohol to make 200 ml.

(**q**) *Vitamin soln VI.*—Dissolve 2 mg *p*-aminobenzoic acid, 10 mg niacin, and 8 mg pyridoxine .HCl in 25% alcohol to make 200 ml.

(**r**) *Xanthine soln.*—Suspend 0.4 g xanthine in 60–80 ml H_2O, heat to ca 70°, add 12 ml NH_4OH $(2 + 3)$, and stir until solid dissolves. Cool, and dil. with H_2O to 400 ml.

(**s**) *Yeast supplement soln.*—Dissolve 20 g H_2O-sol. yeast ext in 100 ml H_2O, add soln of 30 g Pb subacetate in 100 ml H_2O (soln is turbid), and mix.

Filter, and adjust filtrate to pH 10 with NH_4OH $(1 + 2)$. Filter, and adjust filtrate to pH 6.5 with HOAc. Ppt excess Pb with H_2S, filter, and dil. filtrate with H_2O to 200 ml.

39.077   *See* bottom of page.

39.078   *Culture and Suspension Media*

(**a**) *Liquid culture medium.*—Dissolve 15 g peptonized milk, 5 g H_2O-sol. yeast ext, 10 g anhyd. glucose, and 2 g anhyd. KH_2PO_4 in ca 600 ml H_2O. Add 100 ml filtered tomato juice, and adjust to pH 6.5–6.8 with NaOH soln. Add, with mixing, 10 ml polysorbate 80 soln, **39.076**(**h**), and dil. with H_2O to 1 L. Add 10 ml portions soln to test tubes, plug with cotton, sterilize 15 min in autoclave at 121–123°, and cool tubes as rapidly as practicable to keep color formation at min. Store in dark at ca 10°. (Difco liq. culture medium for AOAC microbiological assays, Difco Laboratories, has been found satisfactory.)

(**b**) *Agar culture medium.*—To 500 ml liq. culture medium, (**a**), add 5.0–7.5 g agar, and heat with stirring on steam bath until agar dissolves. Add ca 10 ml portions hot soln to test tubes, plug with cotton, sterilize 15 min in autoclave at 121–123°, and cool

---

39.077   *Basal Media Stock Solutions for 250 ml (Proportionate Amounts May Be Prepared)[a]*

Ingredients (Stock Solutions, **39.076**)	(a) Cobalamin (Vitamin B_{12} Activity)	(b) Folic Acid (Pteroylglutamic Acid)	(c) Niacin and Niacinamide	(d) Pantothenic Acid	(e) Riboflavin (Vitamin B_2)
	ml	ml	ml	ml	ml
(**a**) Acid-hydrolyzed casein soln	25	25	25	25	
(**b**) Adenine-guanine-uracil soln	5	2.5	5	5	
(**c**) Asparagine soln	5	15			
(**d**) Cystine soln					25
(**e**) Cystine-tryptophan soln			25	25	
(**f**) Manganese sulfate soln		5			
(**g**) Photolyzed peptone soln					50
(**h**) Polysorbate 80 soln	5	0.25		0.25	
(**i**) Salt soln A	5		5	5	5
(**j**) Salt soln B	5	5	5	5	5
(**k**) Tryptophan soln		25			
(**l**) Vitamin soln I	10				
(**m**) Vitamin soln II	10				
(**n**) Vitamin soln III		50			
(**o**) Vitamin soln IV			5	5	
(**p**) Vitamin soln V			5		
(**q**) Vitamin soln VI				5	
(**r**) Xanthine soln	5	5			
(**s**) Yeast supplement soln					5
Solids	grams	grams	grams	grams	grams
Ascorbic acid	1				
L-Cysteine.HCl.H_2O		0.19			
L-Cystine	0.1				
Glucose, anhyd.	10	10	10	10	15
Glutathione		0.0013			
K_2HPO_4, anhyd.		1.6			
NaOAc, anhyd.	5		5	5	
Na citrate.$2H_2O$		13			
D,L-Tryptophan	0.1				

[a] Some com. sources of basal media have been found satisfactory.

tubes in upright position as rapidly as practicable to keep color formation at min. Store in dark at ca 10°. (Difco agar culture medium for AOAC microbiological assays (Lacto-bacilli Agar Loy) has been found satisfactory.)

(c) *Suspension medium.*—Dil. measured vol. appropriate basal medium stock soln, **39.077**, with equal vol. H₂O. Add 10 ml portions dild medium to test tubes, plug with cotton, sterilize 15 min in autoclave at 121–123°, and cool tubes as rapidly as practicable to keep color formation at min. Store in dark at ca 10°.

39.079 Stock Cultures of Test Organisms

For appropriate test organism, designated below, prep. stab culture in ≥1 tubes of *agar culture medium*, **39.078**(b). Incubate 6–24 hr at any selected temp. between 30 and 40° held constant to within ±0.5°, and finally store in dark at ca 10°. Before using new culture in assay, make several successive transfers of culture in 1–2 week period.

Prep. fresh stab culture ≥1 time weekly and do not use for prepg inoculum if >1 week old.

Activity of slow-growing culture may be increased by daily or twice-daily transfer of stab culture, and is considered satisfactory when definite turbidity in liq. inoculum can be observed 2–4 hr after inoculation. Slow-growing culture seldom gives suitable response curve and may cause erratic results.

(a) *Lactobacillus leichmannii.*—ATCC No. 7830. For use in assay of cobalamin.

(b) *Streptococcus faecalis.*—ATCC No. 8043. For use in assay of folic acid.

(c) *Lactobacillus plantarum.*—ATCC No. 8014. For use in assay of niacin and pantothenic acid.

(d) *Lactobacillus casei.*—ATCC No. 7469. For use in assay of riboflavin.

39.080 Assay Tubes

Meticulously cleanse by suitable means (Na lauryl sulfate USP has been found satisfactory as detergent), hard-glass test tubes, ca 20 × 150 mm, and other necessary glassware. (Test organisms are highly sensitive to minute amts of growth factors and to many cleansing agents. Therefore, it may be preferred to follow cleansing by heating 1–2 hr at ca 250°. This is of particular importance in cobalamin assay.)

Prep. tubes contg appropriate std soln as follows: To test tubes add, in duplicate (or replicate), 0.0 (for uninoculated blanks), 0.0 (for inoculated blanks), 1.0, 2.0, 3.0, 4.0, and 5.0 ml, resp., of std soln.

Prep. tubes contg appropriate assay soln as follows: To similar test tubes add, in duplicate (or replicate), 1.0, 2.0, 3.0, and 4.0 ml, resp., of assay soln.

To each tube of std soln and assay soln add H₂O to make 5.0 ml. Then add 5.0 ml appropriate basal medium stock soln, **39.077**, and mix. Cover tubes suitably to prevent bacterial contamination, and

sterilize (10 min for titrimetric method, **39.081**; or 5 min for turbidimetric method, **39.083**) in autoclave at 121–123°, reaching this temp. in ≤10 min. Cool as rapidly as practicable to keep color formation at min. Take precautions to keep sterilizing and cooling conditions uniform thruout assay. Too close packing of tubes in autoclave, or overloading of it, may cause variation in heating rate.

Aseptically inoculate each tube, except 1 set of duplicate (or replicate) tubes contg 0.0 ml std soln (uninoculated blanks), with 1 drop appropriate inoculum. Incubate for time period designated in titrimetric method, **39.081**, or turbidimetric method, **39.083**, at any selected temp. between 30 and 40° held constant to within ±0.5°. Contamination of assay tubes with any foreign organism invalidates assay.

Titrimetric Method
39.081 Determination

Incubate tubes 72 hr, and then titr. contents of each tube with 0.1N NaOH, using bromothymol blue indicator, or to pH 6.8 measured electrometrically.

Disregard results of assay if response at inoculated blank level is equiv. to titrn of >1.5 ml greater than that at uninoculated blank level. Response at 5.0 ml level of std soln should be equiv. to titrn of ca 8–12 ml.

Prep. std concn-response curve by plotting titrn values, expressed in ml 0.1N NaOH for each level of std soln used, against quantity of ref. std contained in respective tubes.

Det. quantity of vitamin for each level of assay soln by interpolation from std curve. Discard any observed titrn values equiv. to <0.5 ml or >4.5 ml, resp., of std soln. Proceed as in **39.084**.

Turbidimetric Method
(Not applicable in presence of extraneous turbidity or color in amt that interferes with turbidimetric measurements)

39.082 Calibration of Photometer

Using inoculum and std stock soln as prescribed for appropriate vitamin in following table, and using suspension medium **39.078**(c), proceed as directed below.

Vitamin	Inoculum	Std Stock Soln
Cobalamin	**39.087**[a]	**39.086**(a)
Folic acid	**39.095**	**39.094**(b)
Niacin	**39.107**	**39.102**(a)
Pantothenic acid	**39.116**	**39.111**(a)
Riboflavin	**39.125**	**39.120**(a)

[a] Proceed as in **39.087**, except replace fifth sentence with the following: "Dil. 0.2–1.0 ml aliquot of this suspension with 10 ml sterile suspension medium."

Aseptically add 1 ml inoculum to ca 300 ml sterile suspension medium contg 1.0 ml std stock soln, and incubate mixt. for same period and at same temp. to be employed in detn, **39.083**. After incubating, centrf. and wash cells 3 times with ca 50 ml portions 0.9% NaCl soln; then resuspend cells in the NaCl soln to make 25 ml.

Evap. 10 ml aliquot of cell suspension on steam bath, and dry to constant wt at 110° in vac. oven. Correcting for wt of NaCl, calc. dry wt of cells in mg/ml of suspension.

Dil. second measured aliquot of cell suspension with 0.9% NaCl soln so that each ml is equiv. to 0.5 mg dry cells. To test tubes add, in triplicate, 0.0 (for blanks), 0.5, 1.0, 1.5, 2.0, 2.5, 3.0, 4.0, and 5.0 ml, resp., of this dild cell suspension. To each tube add 0.9% NaCl soln to make 5.0 ml. Then add 5.0 ml appropriate basal medium stock soln, **39.077**, mix (1 drop of suitable *antifoam agent* may be added; 1–2% soln of Dow Corning Antifoam AF Emulsion or Antifoam B has been found satisfactory), and transfer to optical cell. With blanks set at 100% T, measure % T of contents of each tube under same conditions to be used in respective assay. Prep. curve by plotting % T readings for each level of dild cell suspension used against cell content (mg dry wt) of respective tubes.

Repeat appropriate calibration step at least twice more for photometer to be used in respective assay. Draw composite curve, best representing 3 or more individual curves, relating % T to mg dried cell wt for photometer under conditions of respective assay. Once appropriate curve for particular instrument is established, all subsequent relationships between % T and cell wt are detd directly from this curve. Respective assay limits expressed as mg dried cell wt/tube are so detd.

39.083   *Determination*

Incubate tubes 16–24 hr until max. turbidity is obtained, as demonstrated by lack of significant change during 2 hr addnl incubation period in tubes contg highest level of std soln.

Det. T of tubes as follows: Thoroly mix contents of each tube (1 drop of suitable antifoam agent soln may be added; 1–2% soln of Dow Corning Antifoam AF Emulsion or Antifoam B has been found satisfactory), and transfer to optical cell. Agitate contents, place cell in photometer set at any specific wavelength between 540 and 660 nm, and read % T when steady state is reached.

Steady state is observed few sec after agitation when galvanometer reading remains constant ≥30 sec. Allow ca same time interval for reading on each tube.

With T set at 100% for uninoculated blank level, read % T of inoculated blank level. If this reading corresponds to dried cell wt >0.6 mg/tube, disregard results of assay. Then with T reset at 100% for inoculated blank level, read % T for each of remaining tubes. Disregard results of assay if % T observed at 5.0 ml level of std soln (against inoculated blank) is equiv. to that for dried cell wt of <1.25 mg/tube.

Prep. std concn-response curve by plotting % T readings for each level of std soln used, against amt of ref. std contained in respective tubes.

Det. quantity of vitamin for each level of assay soln by interpolation from std curve. Discard any observed T values equiv. to <0.5 ml or >4.5 ml, resp., of std soln. Proceed as in **39.084**.

39.084   *Calculation for Both Titrimetric and Turbidimetric Methods*

For each level of assay soln used, calc. vitamin content/ml of assay soln. Calc. av. of values obtained from tubes that do not vary by >±10% from this av. If the number of acceptable values remaining is <⅔ of original number of tubes used in the 4 levels of assay soln, data are insufficient for calcg potency of sample. If number of acceptable values remaining is ≥⅔ of original number of tubes, calc. potency of sample from av. of them.

Cobalamin (Vitamin B₁₂ Activity) (*16*)

(Applicable to materials contg ca 0.1 μg (100 nanogram) or more of vitamin B₁₂ activity/g or ml)

39.085   *Basal Medium Stock Solution*

Using ingredients in amts prescribed for cobalamin, **39.077**(a), proceed as directed below.

Dissolve L-cystine and D,L-tryptophan in 10 ml 1N HCl. Using solns prepd as in **39.076**, add, with mixing, and in following order: adenine-guanine-uracil soln, (**b**); xanthine soln, (**r**); vitamin soln I, (**l**); vitamin soln II, (**m**); salt soln A, (**i**); salt soln B, (**j**); asparagine soln, (**c**); and acid-hydrolyzed casein soln, (**a**). Add ca 100 ml H₂O and add, with mixing, anhyd. glucose, anhyd. NaOAc, and ascorbic acid. When soln is complete, adjust to pH 6.0 with NaOH soln, add, with mixing, polysorbate 80 soln, (**h**), and dil. with H₂O to 250 ml.

Titrimetric Method

39.086   *Cyanocobalamin Standard Solutions*

(**a**) *Stock soln.*—100 nanograms/ml. Accurately weigh, in closed system, USP Cyanocobalamin Ref. Std equiv. to 50–60 μg cyanocobalamin, that has been dried to constant wt and stored in dark over P₂O₅ in desiccator. Dissolve in 25% alcohol, and dil. with addnl 25% alcohol to make cyanocobalamin concn exactly 100 nanograms/ml. Store in dark at ca 10°.

(**b**) *Intermediate soln.*—1 nanogram/ml. Dil. 10 ml stock soln, (**a**), with 25% alcohol to 1 L. Store in dark at ca 10°.

(**c**) *Working soln.*—Dil. suitable quantity of intermediate soln, (**b**), with H₂O to measured vol. such that after incubation as in **39.080** and **39.081**, response at 5.0 ml level of this soln is equiv. to titrn (as described in **39.081**) of ca 8–12 ml. Designate this as std soln. (This concn is usually 0.01–0.04 nanogram cyanocobalamin/ml std soln.) Prep. fresh std soln for each assay.

39.087 *Inoculum*

Make transfer of cells from stock culture of *Lactobacillus leichmannii*, **39.079(a)**, to sterile tube contg 10 ml liq. culture medium, **39.078(a)**. Incubate 6–24 hr at any selected temp. between 30 and 40° held constant to within ±0.5°. Under aseptic conditions, centrf. culture and decant supernatant. Suspend cells from culture in 10 ml sterile suspension medium, **39.078(c)**. Dil. aliquot with sterile suspension medium to give *T* equiv. to that for dried cell wt (as described in **39.082**) of 0.50–0.75 mg/tube when read against suspension medium set at 100% *T*. Cell suspension so obtained is inoculum.

39.088 *Assay Solution*

Prep. aq. extg soln just before use contg, in each 100 ml, 1.3 g anhyd. Na₂HPO₄, 1.2 g citric acid monohydrate, and 1.0 g *anhyd. Na metabisulfite*, Na₂S₂O₅. Place measured amt of sample in flask contg ≥25 ml extg soln for each g or ml sample taken. If sample is not readily sol., comminute to disperse it evenly in liq.; then agitate vigorously and wash down sides of flask with H₂O.

Autoclave mixt. 10 min at 121–123° and cool. If lumping occurs, agitate mixt. until particles are evenly dispersed. Dil. mixt to measured vol. with H₂O, and let any undissolved particles settle, or filter or centrf. if necessary. Take aliquot of clear soln, add H₂O, adjust to pH 6.0, and dil. with addnl H₂O to measured vol. contg, per ml, cobalamin activity ca equiv. to that of std soln, **39.086(c)**. Designate this as assay soln. Excess of bisulfite may affect test organism. Therefore, assay soln must contain ≤0.03 mg Na₂S₂O₅/ml.

39.089 *Assay*

Using std soln, **39.086(c)**, assay soln, **39.088**, basal medium stock soln, **39.085**, and inoculum, **39.087**, proceed as in **39.080**, **39.081**, and **39.084**.

Turbidimetric Method

39.090 *Cyanocobalamin Standard Solution*

Dil. suitable quantity of cyanocobalamin intermediate std soln, **39.086(b)**, with H₂O to measured vol. such that after incubation as in **39.080** and **39.083**, with inoculated blank set at 100% *T*, % *T* at 5.0 ml level of this soln is equiv. to that for dried cell wt (as described in **39.082**) of ≥1.25 mg. Designate this as std soln. (This concn is usually 0.01–0.04 nanogram cyanocobalamin/ml std soln.) Prep. fresh std soln for each assay.

39.091 *Assay Solution*

Proceed as in **39.088** except that where ref. is made to concn of cyanocobalamin activity ca equiv. to that of std soln, **39.086(c)**, replace by concn of cyanocobalamin activity ca equiv. to that of std soln, **39.090**. Designate soln so obtained as assay soln.

39.092 *Assay*

Using std soln, **39.090**, assay soln, **39.091**, basal medium stock soln, **39.085**, and inoculum, **39.087**, proceed as in **39.080**, **39.083**, and **39.084**.

Folic Acid (Pteroylglutamic Acid) (17)
(Applicable only to materials contg free forms of folic acid)

39.093 *Basal Medium Stock Solution*

Using ingredients in amts prescribed for folic acid, **39.077(b)**, proceed as directed below.

Using solns prepd as in **39.076** add, with mixing, and in following order: acid-hydrolyzed casein soln, (a); tryptophan soln, (k); adenine-guanine-uracil soln, (b); xanthine soln, (r); asparagine soln, (c); vitamin soln III, (n); and salt soln B, (j). Add ca 50 ml H₂O, and add, with mixing, cysteine, anhyd. glucose, Na citrate dihydrate, anhyd. K₂HPO₄, and glutathione. When soln is complete, adjust to pH 6.8 with NaOH soln, add, with mixing, polysorbate 80 soln, (h), and MnSO₄ soln, (f), and dil. with H₂O to 250 ml.

Titrimetric Method
39.094 *Folic Acid Standard Solutions*

(a) *Stock soln.*—100 μg/ml. Accurately weigh, in closed system, USP Folic Acid Ref. Std, equiv. to 50–60 mg folic acid, that has been dried to constant wt and stored in dark over P₂O₅ in desiccator. Dissolve in ca 30 ml 0.01*N* NaOH, add ca 300 ml H₂O, adjust to pH 7–8 with HCl soln, and dil. with addnl H₂O to make folic acid concn exactly 100 μg/ml. Store under toluene in dark at ca 10°.

(b) *Intermediate soln I.*—1 μg/ml. To 10 ml stock soln, (a), add ca 500 ml H₂O, adjust to pH 7–8, and dil. with addnl H₂O to 1 L. Store under toluene in dark at ca 10°.

(c) *Intermediate soln II.*—100 nanograms/ml. To 100 ml intermediate soln I, (b), add ca 500 ml H₂O, adjust to pH 7–8, and dil. with addnl H₂O to 1 L. Store under toluene in dark at ca 10°.

(d) *Working soln.*—Dil. suitable quantity of intermediate soln II, (c), with H₂O to measured vol. such that after incubation as in **39.080** and **39.081**, response at 5.0 ml level of this soln is equiv. to titrn (as described in **39.081**) of ca 8–12 ml. Designate this as std soln. (This concn is usually 1.0–4.0 nanograms folic acid/ml std soln.) Prep. fresh std soln for each assay.

39.095 *Inoculum*

Make transfer of cells from stock culture of *Streptococcus faecalis*, **39.079(b)**, to sterile tube contg 10 ml liq. culture medium, **39.078(a)**. Incubate 6–24 hr at any selected temp. between 30 and 40° held constant to within ±0.5°. Under aseptic conditions, centrf. culture and decant supernatant. Suspend cells from culture in 10 ml sterile suspension medium, **39.078(c)**. Cell suspension so obtained is inoculum.

39.096 *Assay Solution*

Place measured amt of sample in flask and add vol. H_2O equal in ml to ≥ 10 times dry wt sample in g; resulting soln must contain ≤ 1.0 mg folic acid/ml. Add equiv. of 2 ml NH_4OH $(2 + 3)/100$ ml liq. If sample is not readily sol., comminute to disperse it evenly in liq.; then agitate vigorously and wash down sides of flask with $0.1N$ NH_4OH.

Autoclave mixt. 15 min at 121–$123°$ and cool. If lumping occurs, agitate mixt. until particles are evenly dispersed. Dil. mixt. to measured vol. with H_2O, and let any undissolved particles settle, or filter or centrf. if necessary. Take aliquot of clear soln, add H_2O, adjust to pH 6.8, and dil. with addnl H_2O to measured vol. contg, per ml, folic acid ca equiv. to that of std soln, **39.094(d)**. Designate this as assay soln.

39.097 *Assay*

Using std soln, **39.094(d)**, assay soln, **39.096**, basal medium stock soln, **39.093**, and inoculum, **39.095**, proceed as in **39.080**, **39.081**, and **39.084**.

Turbidimetric Method
39.098 *Folic Acid Standard Solution*

Dil. suitable quantity of folic acid intermediate soln II, **39.094(c)**, with H_2O to measured vol. such that after incubation as in **39.080** and **39.083**, with inoculated blank set at 100% T, $\%$ T at 5.0 ml level of this soln is equiv. to that for dried cell wt (as described in **39.082**) of ≥ 1.25 mg. Designate this as std soln. (This concn is usually 0.5–2.0 nanograms folic acid/ml std soln.) Prep. fresh std soln for each assay.

39.099 *Assay Solution*

Proceed as in **39.096** except that where ref. is made to folic acid concn ca equiv. to that of std soln, **39.094(d)**, replace by folic acid concn ca equiv. to that of std soln, **39.098**. Designate soln so obtained as assay soln.

39.100 *Assay*

Using std soln, **39.098**, assay soln, **39.099**, basal medium stock soln, **39.093**, and inoculum, **39.095**, proceed as in **39.080**, **39.083**, and **39.084**.

Niacin and Niacinamide
(Nicotinic Acid and Nicotinamide) (*18*)
39.101 *Basal Medium Stock Solution*

Using ingredients in amts prescribed for niacin, **39.077(c)**, proceed as below.

Using solns prepd as in **39.076**, add, with mixing, and in following order: acid-hydrolyzed casein soln, (a); cystine-tryptophan soln, (e); adenine-guanine-uracil soln, (b); vitamin soln IV, (o); vitamin soln V, (p); salt soln A, (i); and salt soln B, (j). Add ca 100 ml H_2O, and add, with mixing, anhyd. glucose and anhyd. NaOAc. When soln is complete, adjust to pH 6.8 with NaOH soln, and dil. with H_2O to 250 ml.

Titrimetric Method
39.102 *Niacin Standard Solutions*

(a) *Stock soln.*—100 μg/ml. Accurately weigh, in closed system, 50–60 mg NF Niacin Ref. Std that has been dried to constant wt and stored in dark over P_2O_5 in desiccator. Dissolve in 25% alcohol, and dil. with addnl 25% alcohol to make niacin concn exactly 100 μg/ml. Store in dark at ca $10°$.

(b) *Intermediate soln I.*—10 μg/ml. Dil. 100 ml stock soln, (a), with 25% alcohol to 1 L. Store in dark at ca $10°$.

(c) *Working soln.*—Dil. suitable amt of intermediate soln, (b), with H_2O to measured vol. such that after incubation as in **39.080** and **39.081** response at 5.0 ml level of this soln is equiv. to titrn (as described in **39.081**) of ca 8–12 ml. Designate this as std soln. (This concn is usually 0.1–0.4 μg niacin/ml std soln.) Prep. fresh std soln for each assay.

39.103 *Inoculum*

(a) *Liquid culture medium.*—Dil. measured vol. basal medium stock soln, **39.101**, with equal vol. aq. soln contg 0.2 μg niacin/ml. Add 10 ml portions dild medium to test tubes, plug with cotton, sterilize 15 min in autoclave at 121–$123°$, and cool tubes as rapidly as practicable to avoid color formation from overheating. Store in dark at ca $10°$.

(b) *Inoculum.*—Make transfer of cells from stock culture of *Lactobacillus plantarum*, **39.079(c)**, to sterile tube contg 10 ml liq. culture medium, (a). Incubate 6–24 hr at any selected temp. between 30 and $40°$ held constant to within $\pm 0.5°$. Cell suspension so obtained is inoculum.

39.104 *Assay Solution*

Place measured amt of sample in flask and proceed as below. Designate final measured vol. so obtained as assay soln.

(a) *For dry or semidry materials containing no appreciable quantity of basic substances.*—Add vol. $1N$ H_2SO_4 equal in ml to ≥ 10 times dry wt sample in g; resulting soln must contain ≤ 5.0 mg niacin/ml. If sample is not readily sol., comminute to disperse it evenly in liq. Then agitate vigorously and wash down sides of flask with $1N$ H_2SO_4.

Autoclave mixt. 30 min at 121–$123°$ and cool. If lumping occurs, agitate mixt. until particles are evenly dispersed. If dissolved protein is not present, adjust mixt. to pH 6.8 with NaOH soln, dil. with H_2O to final measured vol. contg, per ml, niacin ca equiv. to that of std soln, **39.102(c)**, and filter if soln is not clear.

If dissolved protein is present, adjust mixt., with vigorous agitation, to pH 6.0–6.5 with NaOH soln; then immediately add dil. HCl until no further pptn occurs (usually ca pH 4.5, isoelectric point of many proteins). Dil. mixt. to measured vol. with H_2O, and filter. (In case of mixt. difficult to filter, centrfg and/or filtering thru fritted glass, using suitable analytical filter-aid, may often be substituted for, or may precede, filtering thru paper. Ash-free filter paper pulp and Celite Analytical Filter-Aid have been found satisfactory.) Take aliquot of clear filtrate and check for dissolved protein by adding dropwise, first dil. HCl, and if no ppt forms, then, with vigorous agitation, NaOH soln, and proceed as follows with this aliquot:

(1) If no further pptn occurs, add, with vigorous agitation, NaOH soln to pH 6.8, and dil. with H_2O to final measured vol. contg, per ml, niacin ca equiv. to that of std soln, 39.102(c). If cloudiness occurs, refilter.

(2) If further pptn occurs, adjust mixt. again to point of max. pptn, dil. with H_2O to measured vol., and then filter. Take aliquot of clear filtrate and proceed as in (1).

(b) *For dry or semidry materials containing appreciable quantities of basic substances.*—Adjust mixt. to pH 5.0–6.0 with dil. H_2SO_4. Add vol. H_2O equal in ml to ≥ 10 times dry wt sample in g; resulting soln must contain ≤ 5.0 mg niacin/ml. Then add equiv. of 10 ml $10N$ H_2SO_4/100 ml liq. and proceed as in (a), beginning with second sentence, "If sample is not readily sol., ..."

(c) *For liquid materials.*—Adjust mixt. to pH 5.0–6.0 with H_2SO_4 soln or NaOH soln and proceed as in (b), beginning with second sentence, "Add vol. H_2O ..."

39.105 Assay

Using std soln, 39.102(c), assay soln, 39.104, basal medium stock soln, 39.101, and inoculum, 39.103(b), proceed as in 39.080, 39.081, and 39.084. Value so obtained is potency of sample expressed as niacin equiv. Multiply this value by 0.992 if potency is to be expressed as niacinamide equiv.

Turbidimetric Method

39.106 Niacin Standard Solutions

(a) *Intermediate soln II.*—1.0 µg/ml. Dil. 10 ml niacin std stock soln I, 39.102(a), with 25% alcohol to 1 L. Store in dark at ca 10°.

(b) *Working soln.*—Dil. suitable amt of intermediate soln II, (a), with H_2O to measured vol. such that after incubation as in 39.080 and 39.083, with inoculated blank set at 100% T, % T at 5.0 ml level of this soln is equiv. to that for dried cell wt (as described in 39.082) of ≥ 1.25 mg. Designate this as std soln. (This concn is usually 0.01–0.04 µg niacin/ml std soln.) Prep. fresh std soln for each assay.

39.107 Inoculum

Proceed as in 39.103(b). Then under aseptic conditions, centrf. culture so obtained and decant supernatant. Suspend cells from culture in 10 ml sterile suspension medium, 39.078(c). Cell suspension so obtained is inoculum.

39.108 Assay Solution

Proceed as in 39.104 except that where ref. is made to niacin concn ca equiv. to that of std soln, 39.102 (c), replace by niacin concn ca equiv. to that of std soln, 39.106(b). Designate soln so obtained as assay soln.

39.109 Assay

Using std soln, 39.106(b), assay soln, 39.108, basal medium stock soln, 39.101, and inoculum, 39.107, proceed as in 39.080, 39.083, and 39.084. Value so obtained is potency of sample expressed as niacin equiv. Multiply this value by 0.992 if potency is to be expressed as niacinamide equiv.

Pantothenic Acid (19)

(Applicable only to materials contg Ca pantothenate or other free forms of pantothenic acid)

39.110 Basal Medium Stock Solution

Using ingredients in amts prescribed for pantothenic acid, 39.077(d), proceed as below.

Using solns prepd as in 39.076, add, with mixing, and in following order: acid-hydrolyzed casein soln, (a); cystine-tryptophan soln, (e); adenine-guanine-uracil soln, (b); vitamin soln IV, (o); vitamin soln VI, (q); salt soln A, (i); and salt soln B, (j). Add ca 100 ml H_2O and add, with mixing, anhyd. glucose and anhyd. NaOAc. When soln is complete, adjust to pH 6.8 with NaOH soln, add, with mixing, polysorbate 80 soln, (h), and dil. with H_2O to 250 ml.

Titrimetric Method

39.111 Pantothenic Acid Standard Solutions

(a) *Stock soln.*—40 µg/ml. Accurately weigh, in closed system, 45–55 mg USP Calcium Pantothenate Ref. Std that has been dried to constant wt and stored in dark over P_2O_5 in desiccator. Dissolve in ca 500 ml H_2O, add 10 ml $0.2N$ HOAc and 100 ml $0.2N$ NaOAc, and dil. with addnl H_2O to make Ca pantothenate concn exactly 43.47 µg/ml (40 µg pantothenic acid/ml.) Store under toluene in dark at ca 10°.

(b) *Intermediate soln.*—1.0 µg/ml. To 25 ml stock soln, (a), add ca 500 ml H_2O, 10 ml $0.2N$ HOAc, and 100 ml $0.2N$ NaOAc, and dil. with addnl H_2O to 1 L. Store under toluene in dark at ca 10°.

(c) *Working soln.*—Dil. suitable amt of intermediate soln, (b), with H_2O to measured vol. such that after incubation as in 39.080 and 39.081, response at 5.0 ml level of this soln is equiv. to titrn (as described in 39.081) of ca 8–12 ml. Designate this as std soln. (This concn is usually 0.005–0.020 µg pantothenic acid/ml std soln.) Prep. fresh std soln for each assay.

39.112 Inoculum

(a) *Liquid culture medium.*—Dil. measured vol. basal medium stock soln, 39.110, with equal vol. aq. soln contg 0.04 µg pantothenic acid/ml. Add 10 ml portions dild medium to test tubes, plug with cotton, sterilize 15 min in autoclave at 121–123°, and cool tubes as rapidly as practicable to avoid color formation from overheating. Store in dark at ca 10°.

(b) Make transfer of cells from stock culture of *Lactobacillus plantarum*, **39.079**(c), to sterile tube contg 10 ml liq. culture medium, (a). Incubate 6–24 hr at any selected temp. between 30 and 40° held constant to within ±0.5°. Cell suspension so obtained is inoculum.

39.113   *Assay Solution*

(Thruout all stages, keep soln below pH 7.0 to prevent loss of pantothenic acid.)

Place measured amt of sample in flask and proceed as below. (Where directed to filter thru paper, use paper known not to adsorb pantothenic acid. Ashfree papers have been found satisfactory.) Designate final measured vol. so obtained as assay soln.

(a) *For dry or semidry materials containing no appreciable quantity of basic substances.*—Add vol. H_2O equal in ml to ≥10 times dry wt sample in g; resulting soln must contain ≤5 mg pantothenic acid/ml. Adjust mixt. to pH 5.65±0.05 with HOAc soln or NaOAc soln. If sample is not readily sol., comminute so that it may be evenly dispersed in liq. Then agitate vigorously and wash down sides of flask with aq. soln contg in each liter 10 ml 0.2N HOAc and 100 ml 0.2N NaOAc.

Autoclave mixt. 5–7 min at 121–123° and cool. Then proceed as in **39.104**(a), beginning with second sentence in second par., "If lumping occurs . . ." except where ref. is made to niacin concn ca equiv. to that of std soln, **39.102**(c), replace by pantothenic acid concn ca equiv. to that of std soln, **39.111**(c).

(b) *For dry or semidry materials containing appreciable quantities of basic substances.*—Adjust mixt. to pH 5.0–6.0 with HOAc soln. Add vol. H_2O equal in ml ≥10 times dry wt sample in g; resulting soln must contain ≤5 mg pantothenic acid/ml. Then proceed as in (a) beginning with second sentence: "Adjust mixt. to pH 5.65±0.05 . . ."

(c) *For liquid materials.*—Adjust mixt. to pH 5.0–6.0 with HOAc soln or NaOAc soln and proceed as in (b), beginning with second sentence: "Add vol. H_2O . . ."

39.114   *Assay*

Using std soln, **39.111**(c), assay soln, **39.113**, basal medium stock soln, **39.110**, and inoculum, **39.112**(b), proceed as in **39.080**, **39.081**, and **39.084**. Value so obtained is potency of sample expressed as D-pantothenic acid equiv. Multiply this value by 1.087 if potency is to be expressed as Ca D-pantothenate equiv.

Turbidimetric Method

39.115   *Pantothenic Acid Standard Solution*

Dil. suitable amt of pantothenic acid intermediate soln, **39.111**(b), with H_2O to measured vol. such that

after incubation as in **39.080** and **39.083**, with inoculated blank set at 100% T, % T at 5.0 ml level of this soln is equiv. to that for dried cell wt (as described in **39.082**) of ≥1.25 mg. Designate this as std soln. (This concn is usually 0.003–0.012 μg pantothenic acid/ml std soln.) Prep. fresh std soln for each assay.

39.116   *Inoculum*

Proceed as in **39.112**(b). Then under aseptic conditions, centrf. culture so obtained and decant supernatant. Suspend cells from culture in 10 ml sterile suspension medium, **39.078**(c). Cell suspension so obtained is inoculum.

39.117   *Assay Solution*

Proceed as in **39.113** except that where ref. is made to pantothenic acid concn ca equiv. to that of std soln, **39.111**(c), replace by pantothenic acid concn ca equiv. to that of std soln, **39.115**. Designate soln so obtained as assay soln.

39.118   *Assay*

Using std soln, **39.115**, assay soln, **39.117**, basal medium stock soln, **39.110**, and inoculum, **39.116**, proceed as in **39.080**, **39.083**, and **39.084**. Value so obtained is potency of sample expressed as D-pantothenic acid equiv. Multiply this value by 1.087 if potency is to be expressed as Ca D-pantothenate equiv.

Riboflavin (Vitamin B₂) (20)

(Not applicable in presence of materials which adsorb riboflavin)

39.119   *Basal Medium Stock Solution*

Using ingredients in amts prescribed for riboflavin, **39.077**(e), proceed as below.

Using solns prepd as in **39.076**, add, with mixing, and in following order: photolyzed peptone soln, (g); cystine soln, (d); yeast supplement soln, (s); salt soln A, (i); and salt soln B, (j). Add ca 100 ml H_2O, and add, with mixing, anhyd. glucose. When soln is complete, adjust to pH 6.8 with NaOH soln, and dil. with H_2O to 250 ml.

Titrimetric Method

39.120   *Riboflavin Standard Solutions*

(Do not shake std solns stored under toluene.)

(a) *Stock soln.*—100 μg/ml. Accurately weigh, in closed system, 50–60 mg USP Riboflavin Ref. Std that has been dried to constant wt and stored in dark over P_2O_5 in desiccator. Suspend in ca 300 ml 0.02N HOAc and warm on steam bath, with stirring, until solid dissolves. Cool, and dil. with 0.02N HOAc to make riboflavin concn exactly 100 μg/ml. Store under toluene in dark at ca 10°.

(b) *Intermediate soln I.*—10 μg/ml. Dil. 100 ml stock soln, (a), with 0.02N HOAc to 1 L. Store under toluene in dark at ca 10°.

(c) *Working soln.*—Dil. suitable amt of intermediate soln, (b), with H_2O to measured vol. such that after incubation as in **39.080** and **39.081**, response at 5.0 ml level of this soln is equiv. to titrn (as described in **39.081**) of ca 8–12 ml. Designate this as std soln. (This concn is usually 0.05–0.20 μg riboflavin/ml std soln.) Prep. fresh std soln for each assay.

39.121   Inoculum

(a) *Liquid culture medium.*—Dil. measured vol. basal medium stock soln, **39.119**, with equal vol. aq. soln contg 0.1 μg riboflavin/ml. Add 10 ml portions dild medium to test tubes, plug with cotton, sterilize 15 min in autoclave at 121–123°, and cool tubes as rapidly as practicable to avoid color formation from overheating. Store in dark at ca 10°.

(b) Make transfer of cells from stock culture of *Lactobacillus casei*, **39.079**(d), to sterile tube contg 10 ml liq. culture medium, (a). Incubate 6–24 hr at any selected temp. between 30 and 40° held constant to within ±0.5°. Cell suspension so obtained is inoculum.

39.122   Assay Solution

(Thruout all stages, keep solution below pH 7.0 to prevent loss of riboflavin.)

Place measured amt of sample in flask and proceed as below. (Where directed to filter thru paper, use paper known not to adsorb riboflavin. Ash-free papers have been found satisfactory.) Designate final measured vol. so obtained as assay soln.

(a) *For dry or semidry materials containing no appreciable quantity of basic substances.*—Add vol. $0.1N$ HCl equal in ml to ≥10 times dry wt sample in g; resulting soln must contain ≤0.1 mg riboflavin/ml. If sample is not readily sol., comminute so that it may be evenly dispersed in liq. Then agitate vigorously and wash down sides of flask with $0.1N$ HCl.

Then proceed as in **39.104**(a), beginning with second par., "Autoclave mixt. 30 min . . ." except that where ref. is made to niacin concn ca equiv. to that of std soln, **39.102**(c), replace by riboflavin concn ca equiv. to that of std soln, **39.120**(c).

If riboflavin content of sample is so low that these requirements cannot be met, conc. clear filtrate obtained at ca pH 4.5 to suitable vol. with heat under reduced pressure. Filter if necessary, and proceed as in **39.104**(a)(1).

(b) *For dry or semidry materials containing appreciable quantities of basic substances.*—Adjust mixt. to pH 5.0–6.0 with dil. HCl. Add vol. H_2O equal in ml to ≥10 times dry wt sample in g; resulting soln must contain ≤0.1 mg riboflavin/ml. Then add equiv. of 1.0 ml $10N$ HCl/100 ml liq. and proceed as in (a), beginning with second sentence, "If sample is not readily sol. . . ."

(c) *For liquid materials.*—Adjust mixt. to pH 5.0–6.0 with dil. HCl, or with vigorous agitation, NaOH soln, and proceed as in (b), beginning with second sentence, "Add vol. H_2O . . ."

39.123   Assay

Using std soln, **39.120**(c), assay soln, **39.122**, basal medium stock soln, **39.119**, and inoculum, **39.121**(b), proceed as in **39.080**, **39.081**, and **39.084**.

Turbidimetric Method

39.124   Riboflavin Standard Solutions

(Do not shake std solns stored under toluene.)

(a) *Intermediate soln II.*—1.0 μg/ml. Dil. 10 ml riboflavin stock soln, **39.120**(a), with $0.02N$ HOAc to 1 L. Store under toluene in dark at ca 10°.

(b) *Std soln.*—Dil. suitable quantity of intermediate soln II, (a), with H_2O to measured vol. such that after incubation as in **39.080** and **39.083**, with inoculated blank set at 100% T, % T at 5.0 ml level of this soln is equiv. to that for dried cell wt (as described in **39.082**) of ≥1.25 mg. Designate this as std soln. (This concn is usually 0.01–0.04 μg riboflavin/ml std soln.) Prep. fresh std soln for each assay.

39.125   Inoculum

Proceed as in **39.121**(b). Then under aseptic conditions, centrf. culture so obtained and decant supernatant. Suspend cells from culture in 10 ml sterile suspension medium, **39.078**(c). Cell suspension so obtained is inoculum.

39.126   Assay Solution

Proceed as in **39.122** except that where ref. is made to riboflavin concn ca equiv. to that of std soln, **39.120**(c), replace by riboflavin concn ca equiv. to that of std soln, **39.124**(b). Designate soln so obtained as assay soln.

39.127   Assay

Using std soln, **39.124**(b), assay soln, **39.126**, basal medium stock soln, **39.119**, and inoculum, **39.125**, proceed as in **39.080**, **39.083**, and **39.084**.

Amino Acids (21)—Official First Action

(Applicable only to materials contg free forms of amino acids in absence of appreciable quantity of protein)

39.128   Stock Solutions for Basal Media

(Store all solns under toluene; in addn, store vitamin and amino acid solns in dark at ca 10°.)

(a) *Amino acid soln.*—Prep. stock soln of each amino acid as in table, **39.129**. Use amino acids of highest purity available. (DL form may be preferred since it is less likely to be contaminated with other amino acids.) If DL form is used, double wt given in table. Dissolve amino acid with heat, if necessary, and dil. to indicated vol. with H_2O. Where special solvs are indicated, dissolve amino acid in vol. initial solv. specified, and dil. to final vol. with H_2O.

(b) *Adenine-guanine-uracil soln.*—See **39.076**(b).

(c) *Salt soln A.*—Dissolve 50 g anhyd. K_2HPO_4 and 50 g anhyd. KH_2PO_4 in H_2O, dil. to 500 ml, and add 5 drops HCl.

(d) *Salt soln B.*—Dissolve 20 g $MgSO_4.7H_2O$, 1 g NaCl, 1 g $FeSO_4.7H_2O$, and 1 g $MnSO_4.H_2O$ in H_2O, dil. to 500 ml, and add 5 drops HCl.

(e) *Vitamin soln I.*—Dissolve 25 mg riboflavin, 25 mg thiamine.HCl, 50 mg niacin, and 0.15 mg biotin in $0.02N$ HOAc to make 1 L.

(f) *Vitamin soln II.*—Dissolve 50 mg pyridoxal, 50 mg pyridoxamine.HCl, 25 mg Ca pantothenate, 5 mg *p*-aminobenzoic acid, and 0.25 mg folic acid in 25% alcohol to make 1 L.

plug with cotton (or screw cap tubes may be used), sterilize 15 min in autoclave at 121–123°, and cool tubes as rapidly as practicable to keep color formation at min. Store in dark at ca 10°.

(c) *Liquid suspension medium.*—Dil. measured vol. appropriate basal medium (without amino acid being assayed), **39.130**, with equal vol. H_2O. Add 10 ml portions to test tubes, plug with cotton, sterilize 15 min at 121–123°, and cool as rapidly as practica-

39.129   Amino Acid Stock Solns

	Amino Acid	Weight	Initial Solvent	Final Volume	Final Concn
		g	ml	ml	mg/ml
(a)	L-Alanine	5.000	900 H_2O	1000	5
(b)	L-Arginine.HCl	12.095	400 H_2O	500	20
(c)	L-Asparagine	5.000	400 H_2O	500	10
(d)	L-Aspartic acid	10.000	100 $1N$ NaOH	1000	10
(e)	L-Cysteine.HCl	5.000	100 $2N$ HCl	1000	5
(f)	L-Cystine	5.000	100 $2N$ HCl	1000	5
(g)	L-Glutamic acid	10.000	100 $1N$ NaOH	1000	10
(h)	Glycine	10.000	400 H_2O	500	20
(i)	L-Histidine.HCl	12.351	400 H_2O	500	20
(j)	L-Hydroxyproline	5.000	150 H_2O	250	20
(k)	L-Isoleucine	5.000	900 H_2O	1000	5
(l)	L-Leucine	10.000	900 H_2O	1000	10
(m)	L-Lysine.HCl	6.248	400 H_2O	500	10
(n)	L-Methionine	5.000	900 H_2O	1000	5
(o)	L-Norleucine	5.000	100 $2N$ HCl	1000	5
(p)	L-Phenylalanine	5.000	900 H_2O	1000	5
(q)	L-Proline	5.000	150 H_2O	250	20
(r)	L-Serine	5.000	900 H_2O	1000	5
(s)	L-Threonine	5.000	900 H_2O	1000	5
(t)	L-Tryptophan	5.000	50 $1N$ NaOH	500	10
(u)	L-Tyrosine	5.000	50 $1N$ NaOH	500	10
(v)	L-Valine	5.000	900 H_2O	1000	5

39.130   Basal Medium

Complete assay medium is given in table, **39.131**. In prepg medium for given assay, omit particular amino acid to be assayed from medium. Concn of all ingredients in basal medium is twice what it will be in assay tube after addn of sample or std soln and H_2O. Table lists amts of ingredients required for 50, 100, 150, and 200 tubes. Prep. fresh for each assay.

To combined solns add glucose and NaOAc with mixing. When soln is complete, adjust to pH 6.8 and dil. to vol. (*Note:* Quantities of glucose and NaOAc depend upon organism used in assay.)

39.131   *See* top of next page.

39.132   Culture and Suspension Media

(a) *Agar culture medium.*—See **39.078**(b). (Available from Difco Laboratories as Lactobacilli Agar Loy.)

(b) *Liquid culture medium.*—Dil. measured vol. of complete amino acid basal medium, **39.130**, with equal vol. H_2O. Add 10 ml portions to test tubes,

ble to keep color formation at min. Store in dark at ca 10°.

39.133   Stock Cultures of Test Organisms

Prep. and test cultures as in **39.079**. Use following organisms:

(a) *Streptococcus faecalis.*—ATCC No. 9790. For use in assay of isoleucine, leucine, threonine, tryptophan, valine, arginine, and histidine.

(b) *Lactobacillus plantarum.*—ATCC No. 8014. For use in assay of isoleucine, leucine, methionine, phenylalanine, tryptophan, and valine.

(c) *Pediococcus cerevisiae.*—ATCC No. 8042. For use in assay of lysine, methionine, phenylalanine, tyrosine, cystine, and histidine.

39.134   Inoculum

Make transfer of cells from fresh stock culture of appropriate organism to sterile tube contg 10 ml liq. culture medium, **39.132**(b). Incubate 16–24 hr at $34 \pm 0.5°$. Under aseptic conditions centrf. and decant supernatant. Suspend cells in 10 ml appropriate sterile suspension medium, **39.132**(c).

39.131 *Composition of Basal Medium*

Ingredients (Stock solns, **39.128**)	250 ml	500 ml	750 ml	1 L
	ml	ml	ml	ml
(a) Amino Acid Solns:				
L-Alanine	10	20	30	40
L-Arginine.HCl	5	10	15	20
L-Asparagine	5	10	15	20
L-Aspartic acid	5	10	15	20
L-Cysteine.HCl	5	10	15	20
L-Cystine	5	10	15	20
L-Glutamic acid[a]	25	50	75	100
Glycine	5	10	15	20
L-Histidine.HCl	5	10	15	20
L-Hydroxyproline	2.5	5	7.5	10
L-Isoleucine	10	20	30	40
L-Leucine	5	10	15	20
L-Lysine.HCl	5	10	15	20
L-Methionine	10	20	30	40
L-Norleucine	10	20	30	40
L-Phenylalanine	10	20	30	40
L-Proline	2.5	5	7.5	10
L-Serine	10	20	30	40
L-Threonine	10	20	30	40
L-Tryptophan	5	10	15	20
L-Tyrosine	10	20	30	40
L-Valine	10	20	30	40
(b) Adenine-guanine-uracil	5	10	15	20
(e) Vitamin Soln I	10	20	30	40
(f) Vitamin Soln II	10	20	30	40
(c) Salt Soln A	2.5	5.0	7.5	10
(d) Salt Soln B	2.5	5.0	7.5	10
Glucose, anhyd.				
with *S. faecalis*	5 g	10 g	15 g	20 g
with *L. plantarum* or *P. cerevisiae*	10 g	20 g	30 g	40 g
NaOAc, anhyd.				
with *S. faecalis*	3 g	6 g	9 g	12 g
with *L. plantarum* or *P. cerevisiae*	6 g	12 g	18 g	24 g

[a] For methionine assay use DL-glutamic acid since L-glutamic acid often contains methionine.

39.135 *Reference Standard Solutions of Amino Acids*

Dry stdzd amino acids (available from Nutritional Biochemicals Corp.) to constant wt over P_2O_5 and store in desiccator over P_2O_5. Prep. stock soln of each amino acid by accurately weighing amt designated in **39.136** in closed system and dil. to final vol. with H_2O. Prep. std working soln by dilg aliquot std stock soln to designated vol. with H_2O. Store std stock solns under toluene in dark at ca 10°. Prep. std working solns fresh for each assay.

39.136 *See* top of next page.

39.137 *Calibration of Photometer*

Using inoculum, **39.134**, and std stock solns, **39.136**, proceed as in **39.082**, incubating 16–24 hr at 34±0.5°. In measurement, use basal medium, **39.130**, for dilg.

39.138 *Preparation of Sample*

(a) *Liquids containing free amino acids.*—Dil. with H_2O to concn required to obtain assay soln.

(b) *Dry or semidry materials.*—Add H_2O equal in ml to ≥ 10 times dry wt in g of sample. Heat 10 min in autoclave at 121–123°. Cool, dil. to vol., and filter if necessary to obtain assay soln.

39.139 *Assay*

Proceed as in **39.080** (disregard ref. to titrimetric method), using working std solns, **39.136**, assay soln, **39.138**, and basal medium, **39.131** (omitting amino acid being assayed). Incubate 16–24 hr at 34±0.5°.

39.140 *Determination*

Proceed as in **39.083**.

39.141 *Calculation*

Proceed as in **39.084**.

Vitamin B₆ (Pyridoxine, Pyridoxal, Pyridoxamine) in Food Extracts (22)—Official First Action

39.142 *Reagents*

(Work in subdued light with all solns contg vitamin B₆.)

(a) *Potassium acetate buffers.*—(1) *0.01M, pH 4.5.*—Dissolve 0.981 g KOAc in H_2O and dil. to 1

39.136   *Preparation of Reference Stock and Standard Amino Acid Solutions*

Amino Acid	Std Stock Soln			Std Working Soln		
	mg	final vol. ml	concn µg/ml	aliquot ml	final vol. ml	concn µg/ml
L-Arginine.HCl	121	500	200	5	200	5
L-Cystine (dissolve in 100 ml 1N HCl)	100	1000	100	15	500	3
L-Histidine.HCl.H₂O	135	1000	100	15	500	3
L-Isoleucine	100	1000	100	5	100	5
L-Leucine	100	1000	100			
(with *L. plantarum*)				5	100	5
(with *S. faecalis*)				10	100	10
L-Lysine.HCl	251	1000	200	15	200	15
L-Methionine	50	1000	50	10	250	2
L-Phenylalanine	100	1000	100	5	100	5
L-Threonine	100	1000	100	5	100	5
L-Tryptophan (dissolve in 100 ml 0.1N NaOH)	40	1000	40	5	250	0.8
L-Tyrosine (dissolve in 100 ml 0.1N NaOH)	100	1000	100			
(with *L. plantarum*)				5	250	2
(with *P. cerevisiae*)				10	250	4
L-Valine	100	1000	100			
(with *L. plantarum*)				10	200	5
(with *S. faecalis*)				10	100	10

L. Adjust pH with HOAc. *(2) 0.02M, pH 5.5.*— Dissolve 1.96 g KOAc in H₂O and dil. to 1 L. Adjust pH with HOAc. *(3) 0.04M, pH 6.0.*—Dissolve 3.92 g KOAc in H₂O and dil. to 1 L. Adjust pH with HOAc. *(4) 0.1M, pH 7.0.*—Dissolve 9.815 g KOAc in H₂O and dil. to 1 L. Adjust pH with HOAc or KOH soln.

(b) *Potassium chloride-phosphate buffer.*—pH 8.0. Dissolve 74.6 g KCl and 17.4 g K₂HPO₄ in 800 ml H₂O and adjust pH with HOAc. Dil. to 1 L.

(c) *Ion exchange resin.*—Dowex AG 50W-X8, 100–200 mesh.

(d) *Acid-hydrolyzed casein soln.* — 100 mg/ml. *(Caution: See* **46.011** *and* **46.015**.) Mix 100 g vitamin-free casein with 500 ml constant-boiling HCl (ca 5N HCl, 208 ml HCl dild to 500 ml with H₂O) and reflux 8 hr. Remove HCl from mixt. by distn under vac. until very thick sirup remains, keeping H₂O bath temp. <80°. Dissolve sirup in H₂O and conc. again in same manner. Redissolve sirup in H₂O.

Adjust to pH 4 with 40% NaOH, add H₂O to ca 600 ml, add 40 g activated C, stir 4 hr, and filter with vac. thru buchner with thin pad of HCl-washed Filter-Cel. Continue following activated C treatments only if soln is not clear and colorless: Add 20 g activated C to filtrate, stir 1 hr, and re-filter. Repeat with fresh 10 g portion activated C and filter. When soln is clear and colorless, dil. to 1 L with H₂O. (Before soln is dild to vol., 2–3 ml 6N HCl may be added to extend time before microbial growth occurs.) Store in refrigerator.

(e) *Vitamin soln I.*—Dissolve 10 mg thiamine and 1 g inositol in ca 200 ml H₂O and dil. to 1 L. Store in refrigerator. (1 ml = 10 µg thiamine and 1 mg inositol.)

(f) *Vitamin soln II.*—Dissolve 10 mg biotin in 100 ml 50% alcohol. Store in refrigerator. (1 ml = 100 µg biotin.) Dissolve 200 mg Ca pantothenate and 200 mg niacin in ca 200 ml H₂O; add 8 ml biotin soln and dil. to 1 L with H₂O. Store in refrigerator. (1 ml = 200 µg each Ca pantothenate and niacin and 0.8 µg biotin.)

(g) *Salt soln I.*—Dissolve 17 g KCl, 10.3 g MgSO₄.7H₂O, 100 mg FeCl₃.6H₂O, and 100 mg MnSO₄.H₂O in ca 800 ml H₂O. Add 2 ml HCl. Dissolve 5 g CaCl₂.2H₂O in ca 100 ml H₂O, add to first soln, and dil. to 1 L with H₂O. Store in refrigerator. (1 ml = 17 mg KCl, 10.3 mg MgSO₄.7H₂O, 100 µg FeCl₃.6H₂O, 100 µg MnSO₄.H₂O, and 5 mg CaCl₂.2H₂O.)

(h) *Salt soln II.*—Dissolve 22 g KH₂PO₄ and 40 g (NH₄)₂HPO₄ in H₂O and dil. to 1 L. Store in refrigerator. (1 ml = 22 mg KH₂PO₄ and 40 mg (NH₄)₂HPO₄.)

(i) *Polysorbate 80 soln.*—Weigh 2.5 g polysorbate 80 (Tween 80) in small beaker. Transfer with warm (45°) H₂O and dil. to 500 ml. Store in refrigerator. (1 ml = 5 mg polysorbate 80.)

(j) *Citric acid soln.*—(1 + 1). Dissolve 50 g citric acid in 50 ml H₂O. Store at room temp. in bottle with plastic stopper.

(k) *Ammonium phosphate soln.*—(1 + 2). Dissolve 25 g (NH₄)₂HPO₄ in 50 ml H₂O. Store at room temp. in bottle with plastic stopper.

(l) *Pyridoxine, pyridoxal, and pyridoxamine std solns.*—Prep. sep. solns for each as follows: *(1) Stock soln.*—10.0 µg/ml. Dissolve 12.16 mg pyridoxine .HCl, 12.18 mg pyridoxal.HCl, and 14.34 mg pyridoxamine.HCl, resp., in 1N HCl and dil. to 1 L with 1N HCl. Store in g-s bottles in refrigerator.

(2) Intermediate soln.—1.0 µg/ml. Dil. 10 ml stock soln to 100 ml with H₂O.

(3) Working soln.—1.0 ng/ml. Dil. 5 ml intermediate soln to 500 ml with H₂O and mix. Dil. 10 ml to 100 ml with H₂O. Prep. fresh for each assay.

(m) *Mixed pyridoxine, pyridoxal, pyridoxamine solns (for liquid broth culture).*—Pipet 2 ml of each intermediate soln (1.0 μg/ml) into 1 L vol. flask and dil. to vol. with H_2O.

(n) *Citrate buffer soln.*—Dissolve 100 g K citrate and 20 g citric acid in H_2O and dil. to 1 L. Store in refrigerator. (1 ml = 100 mg K citrate and 20 mg citric acid.)

(o) *Basal medium stock soln (for 200 tubes).*—To make 1 L medium, add to ca 400 ml H_2O: 100 ml citrate buffer, 100 ml hydrolyzed casein soln, 50 ml vitamin soln I, 25 ml vitamin soln II, 50 ml salt soln I, and 50 ml salt soln II. Dissolve 100 g glucose in this soln. Dissolve 22 mg DL-tryptophan, 27 mg L-histidine.HCl, 100 mg DL-methionine, 216 mg DL-isoleucine, and 256 mg DL-valine in 10 ml 10% HCl in small beaker and add to above. Add 20 ml polysorbate 80 soln. Adjust to pH 4.5 with citric acid (1 + 1) or $(NH_4)_2HPO_4$ (1 + 2) solns. Dil. to 1 L with H_2O. Store in Pyrex bottle plugged with cotton in refrigerator. Prep. $\leq$24 hr before use. When ready, steam 10 min and cool.

(p) *Test organism.*—*Saccharomyces carlsbergensis* (ATCC No. 9080). Maintain by weekly transfers on wort agar slants (q). Incubate these freshly seeded agar slants 24 hr at 30° and refrigerate.

(q) *Agar culture medium.*—Suspend 25 g Bacto-wort agar in ca 400 ml H_2O in marked 500 ml wide-mouth erlenmeyer. Plug with cotton, steam ca 10 min to dissolve agar, and adjust vol. to 500 ml. Pipet hot agar in ca 10 ml amts into 20 × 150 mm test tubes, plug with absorbent cotton, and autoclave 15 min at 121°. Since this medium has acid reaction, avoid overheating which results in softer medium. Tilt hot agar tubes to form slants and cool in this position.

(r) *Liquid culture medium.*—Pipet 5 ml mixed soln, (m), into 16 × 150 mm test tubes contg two 4 mm glass beads, plug with absorbent cotton, and autoclave 10 min at 121°. Add 5 ml steamed vitamin B_6-free basal medium, (o), under aseptic conditions. Store tubes in refrigerator.

(s) *Inoculum rinse.*—Pipet 5 ml H_2O into test tubes, plug with absorbent cotton, and autoclave 10 min at 121°. Add 5 ml steamed vitamin B_6-free basal medium, (o), under aseptic conditions. Store tubes in refrigerator.

39.143 *Assay Inoculum*
(Caution: See 46.005.)

Incubate cells for inoculum on agar 24 hr at 30° before use. Transfer these cells under aseptic condition to liq. broth culture tubes. Plug with absorbent cotton held on with masking tape and place tubes on shaker 20 hr in 30° room. Replace cotton plugs aseptically with sterile rubber stoppers; centrf. 1.5 min at 2500 rpm. Decant liq. and resuspend in 10 ml inoculum rinse. Sep. by centrfg 1.5 min at 2500 rpm. Decant liq., resuspend in second 10 ml sterile inoculum rinse, centrf. 1.5 min, and decant. Cells suspended in third 10 ml inoculum rinse are assay inoculum.

39.144 *Preparation of Exchange Resin and Column*

To 250 g Dowex AG 50W-X8 (100–200 mesh) in H form add excess 6N KOH until supernatant is blue to litmus. Let settle, decant, and rinse resin with H_2O until supernatant is clear. Add ca 600 ml 3N HCl, stir, and heat 0.5 hr in boiling H_2O bath. Decant and repeat treatment with 3N HCl twice. Rinse resin until rinse H_2O is neut. Add 6N KOH until pH is strongly basic and stir 1 hr. Rinse with H_2O until rinse H_2O is neut. Suspend in 2M KOAc and store in refrigerator until needed. Just before use, wash resin with H_2O until H_2O is green to bromothymol blue. Resin can be regenerated, beginning with 3N HCl treatment.

Prep. tubes by sealing capillary stopcock, 1.5 mm bore and 5 cm side arms, to 19 mm id glass tube $\geq$40 cm long. Pour 5–10 ml H_2O onto tube. Place glass wool plug in bottom of tube and remove bubbles from capillary and glass wool. Rinse measured 30 ml prepd resin, settled out of H_2O suspension, into tube with H_2O. After resin settles in tube, place glass wool plug on top of resin. Rinse column with 50 ml hot H_2O followed by two 50 ml portions hot 0.01M KOAc (pH 4.5). pH of last buffer rinse from column should be 4.5; otherwise, more rinsing with buffer is required. Do not permit liq. level on column to fall below top glass wool plug at any time.

39.145 *Preparation of Sample*

Weigh 1–2 g dry product into 500 ml erlenmeyer. For plant products, add 200 ml 0.44N HCl and for animal products, add 200 ml 0.055N HCl. Autoclave plant soln 2 hr at 121°, and animal soln 5 hr at 121°. Cool to room temp., adjust to pH 4.5 with 6N or satd KOH, and dil. to 250 ml with H_2O in vol. flask. Filter thru Whatman No. 40 paper. Take 40–200 ml filtered aliquot for chromatgy.

39.146 *Chromatography*

Place desired amt filtered ext on ion exchange column in ca 50 ml portions and let pass completely thru with no flow regulation. Wash beaker and column 3 times with ca 5 ml portions hot 0.02M KOAc (pH 5.5), followed by similar washing to column sides. Wash column with same soln until total of 100 ml 0.02M KOAc (pH 5.5) soln is used. Elute pyridoxal with two 50 ml portions boiling 0.04M KOAc (pH 6.0), using 100 ml vol. flask as receiver. Elute pyridoxine with two 50 ml portions boiling 0.1M KOAc (pH 7.0), using 100 ml vol. flask as receiver. Elute pyridoxamine with two 50 ml portions boiling KCl-K_2HPO_4 (pH 8.0) soln, using 250 ml beaker as receiver. Adjust pH to 4.5. Dil. pyridoxine and pyridoxal eluates to 100 ml and pyridoxamine eluate to 200 ml with H_2O unless otherwise desired.

For std pyridoxine, pyridoxal, and pyridoxamine, mix 10 ml each intermediate soln, neutze with KOH, and adjust to pH 4.5 with HOAc. Put this soln on column, wash, and elute fractions as above. Dil. eluted pyridoxine and pyridoxal stds to 100 ml and dil. eluted pyridoxamine, after pH is adjusted to 4.5, to 200 ml with H_2O. Dil. eluted stds to 1.0 ng/ml with H_2O.

39.147   *Assay*

Heat clean tubes and glass beads 2 hr at 260°. Place two 4 mm glass beads in each 16 × 150 mm screw-cap glass culture tube. For std curve, pipet into triplicate tubes appropriate freshly prepd std working solns to give 0.0, 0.0, 1.0, 2.0, 3.0, 4.0, and 5.0 ng pyridoxine, pyridoxal, or pyridoxamine/tube. Similarly prep. set of tubes for eluted stds, omitting blanks. Dil. sample eluates from chromatgc column to contain ca 1 ng vitamin B_6 component/ml. Pipet 1, 2, 3, 4, and 5 ml dild eluates into triplicate tubes. Pipet H_2O into all tubes to bring vol. to 5 ml/tube. Cap tubes with plastic caps with ⅛″ hole thru top. Autoclave entire set 10 min at 121°. Cool tubes to room temp. Using automatic pipet with sterilized delivery attachments, pipet 5 ml steamed medium, (o), thru hole in cap. Cover tubes with sterile cheesecloth and place in refrigerator. Remove from refrigerator 1 hr before inoculation. Aseptically inoculate thru cap of each tube, except first set of 0.0 level for std curves, with 1 drop assay inoculum of *S. carlsbergensis* suspended cells. Take care to maintain uniform cell suspension, since they may settle out during inoculation step. Incubate tubes on constant rotary shaker 22 hr in temp.-regulated room (30°). Steam tubes in autoclave 5 min, cool, and remove caps. Read % *T* at 550 nm on spectrophtr. Set 100% *T* with H_2O to read uninoculated blank. Set 100% *T* with uninoculated blank to read inoculated blank. Mix 9 inoculated blank tubes, and with this mixt. set at 100% *T* on instrument, read all other tubes.

Average readings of triplicate tubes and plot % *T* against ng eluted std pyridoxine, pyridoxal, or pyridoxamine/tube on semilog paper. Det. amt pyridoxine, pyridoxal, or pyridoxamine/sample tube by interpolation. Report µg pyridoxine, pyridoxal, and pyridoxamine/g sample.

BIOASSAY METHODS

Thiamine Hydrochloride (Vitamin B₁) (23)

39.148 ★ *Growth Method—Official Final* ★ *Action*

See 39.108–39.115, 10th ed.

Vitamin D (24)—Official Final Action

(Not applicable to products offered for poultry feeding)

39.149   *Definitions*

Assay group means group of rats to which assay sample (vitamin D sample) is administered during assay period. *Assay sample* means sample under ex-

amination for vitamin D potency. *Assay soln* means soln of sample in oil prepd for feeding after saponification procedure. *Assay period* means interval in life of rat between last day of depletion period and eighth or eleventh day thereafter. *Assemble* means procedure by which rats are selected and assigned to groups for purposes of feeding, care, and observation. *Daily* means each of first 6 or 8 days of assay period. *Depletion period* means interval in life of rat between last day of preliminary period and first day of assay period. *Dose* means quantity of ref. oil or of assay milk or other supplement to be fed daily to rat during assay period. *Feed* means make readily available to rat or administer to rat by mouth. *Group* means 7 or more rats maintained on same required dietary regimen during assay period. *Preliminary period* means interval in life of rat between seventh day after birth and first day of depletion period.

39.150   *Reagents*

(a) *Ground gluten.*—Clean, sound product made from wheat flour by almost complete removal of starch, contg ≤10% H_2O and, calcd on H_2O-free basis, ≥14.2% N, ≤15% N-free ext (using protein factor 5.7), and ≤5.5% starch (detd by diastase method, **7.061**).

(b) *Reference oil.*—USP Vitamin D Capsules Ref. Std.

(c) *Cottonseed oil.*—USP grade meeting following addnl requirements: Saponify 10 g oil as in **39.154**, and dissolve unsaponifiable residue in 10 ml pet ether. In sep. container place 0.4 ml $FeCl_3$ soln (1 + 1000) and 12 ml soln of α,α-dipyridyl in absolute alcohol (1 + 6000), mix, and 5 min later read *A* in 1.0 cm cell at 520 nm, using suitable spectrophtr, against absolute alcohol. Then add 0.2 ml soln of unsaponifiable residue in pet ether to entire colored soln, and after 5 min read *A*. Difference between first and second *A* values is ≥0.125.

(d) *Rachitogenic diet.*—Mix 76% whole yellow corn, ground to pass No. 30 sieve; 20% gluten, ground to pass No. 30 sieve; 3% $CaCO_3$; and 1% NaCl.

39.151   *Preservation of Sample*

Store samples so as to minimize exposure to heat, light, and air. Milk samples must be delivered in original container immediately after collection or be stored under refrigeration in iced container until delivered. After delivery to assayer, milk must be preserved in its homogeneous state by refrigeration at temp. ≤10° for ≤10 days, or be preserved for ≤30 days by addn of 2 drops 10% HCHO soln to 1 qt milk in addn to refrigeration at temp. ≤10°. Evapd and reconstituted milk must be preserved in same manner as fluid milk. Soured or curdled sample is unsuitable for assay purposes. Sample of dried milk, after being opened by assayer, must be preserved by refrigeration at temp. ≤10°.

39.152 *Sample*

Sample shall consist of ≥10 g food, 10 capsules or tablets, or sufficient vol. of liqs to satisfy needs of entire assay.

If amt of vitamin D in sample is such that aliquot to be fed contains <5 mg P, sample may be fed directly. If aliquot contains >5 mg P, sample must be saponified.

All manipulations and dilns of vitamin sample must be made with materials known to be free of vitamin D.

39.153 *Preparation of Sample for Direct Feeding*

(a) *Feed concentrates and tablets.*—Thoroly grind weighed sample. Promptly weigh aliquot of ground powder and grind it again with equal wt of edible vegetable oil. To this add such quantity of powd sucrose that assay dose will be contained in 1–2 g. Mix thoroly by grinding again and proceed as in assay period, **39.159**.

(b) *Capsules.*—Open weighed capsules and transfer contents as completely as possible into container. Thoroly mix combined contents and promptly weigh aliquot. Proceed as in (a). Obtain sample wt by subtracting wt empty ether-washed capsules from total wt capsules.

(c) *Oils.*—Add amt of edible vegetable oil that will produce diln contg assay dose in vol. equal to vol. ref. diln.

(d) *Water-miscible liquids.*—Dil. as for oils, using H₂O, glycerol, or propylene glycol to facilitate feeding.

39.154 *Preparation of Sample by Saponification*

(*Caution: See* **46.011, 46.039,** *and* **46.054.**)

Weigh sample and transfer to saponification flask. (For milk, see **39.155**.)

In case of capsules or tablets, place ≥10 in small reflux flask, add 10 ml H₂O, and heat on steam bath ca 10 min. Crush each capsule or tablet with blunt glass rod and warm 5 min more. Add 2 ml cottonseed oil and vol. of KOH (50% w/w) soln representing 2.5 ml for each g total wt of sample plus cottonseed oil, but ≥15 ml. Add 50 ml alcohol and reflux vigorously 30 min in 100° bath. Cool soln and transfer to Squibb-type separator, using 50 ml H₂O. Ext with four 30 ml portions peroxide-free ether (USP anesthesia ether is suitable), using more H₂O or small portions alcohol to break any emulsions that may form. Wash combined ether exts 4 times with H₂O as follows: (*1*) 100 ml with very gentle swirling; (*2*) 100 ml with gentle swirling; (*3*) 50 ml with gentle shaking; (*4*) 50 ml with vigorous shaking. Dry ether ext with two 75 ml portions satd NaCl soln, shaking vigorously both times. Transfer ether ext to beaker and evap. on steam bath to convenient vol. If H₂O is present, dry with 3–5 g anhyd. Na₂SO₄. Decant into weighed container, rinse beaker and Na₂SO₄ with 3–5 addnl portions ether, and combine all washings in weighed container. Evap. ether on steam bath until no ether odor is detectable, and weigh fat. Multiply by 1.10 to det. vol., and add amt of edible vegetable oil that will produce convenient final diln for feeding. Mix thoroly (magnetic stirrer is desirable).

39.155 *Preparation of Milk Samples*

Proceed as in **39.154** with following special modifications: Use 50–100 ml alcohol and 10 g KOH pellets per 100 ml sample. Swirl until all KOH dissolves. Reflux 40–60 min. (To minimize bumping and scorching of sample, place several short pieces of glass stirring rod in saponification flask and use oil or H₂O bath at 100°.) Use 50–100 ml ether for first extn. Only small part of butterfat is saponified, but fat may be fed without affecting results. Where unusually large amt (>0.5 g) of fat would have to be fed in every dose, ext from which ether has been evapd may be resaponified as in **39.154**.

39.156 *Preliminary Period*

Thruout preliminary period each rat must be raised under immediate supervision of, or according to directions specified by, assayer. Thruout preliminary period, keep rats on dietary regimen that provides for normal development in all respects, except to limit supply of vitamin D to such degree that rats, weighing 40–60 g at age of 21–30 days, and subsisting 18–25 days on suitable rachitogenic diet, show evidence of severe rickets.

39.157 *Depletion Period*

Rat is suitable for depletion period when its age is ≤30 days, and its body wt is >44 g but ≤60 g, provided it shows no evidence of injury, disease, or anatomical abnormality that might hinder growth and development. Thruout depletion period provide each rat with rachitogenic diet, and H₂O or USP H₂O *ad libitum*, and permit no other dietary supplement to be available.

39.158 *Assembling Rats into Groups for Assay Period*

Assemble rats that are suitable for assay period into groups. For each sample provide one or more assay groups. In assay of one sample at least one ref. group must be provided, but this ref. group may be used for concurrent assay of more than one assay sample. (Where 2 ref. groups are desired, dose levels must be selected so that ratio of higher to lower dose is not <1.5 or >2.5. Dosage levels for samples based upon single assumed potency for each sample may be equiv. to ref. levels or at mid-level equal to square root of product of the 2 dosage levels of the ref.) On any one day during interval of assembling rats into groups, total number of rats assigned to make up any one group must not exceed by >2 the number of rats that have been assigned to make up any other group. When assembling of all groups is completed, total number of rats in each group must be same. Assign not >3 rats from 1 litter to assay group unless equal number of rats from same litter is assigned to ref. group. There must be enough animals in each group to meet requirements specified in **39.162.**

39.159 Assay Period

Rat is suitable for assay period provided depletion period is >18 days but ≤25 days, and provided rat shows evidence of rickets characterized by distinctive wobbly rachitic gait and enlarged joints. Presence of rickets may also be established by examination of leg bone of one member of litter by "line test," **39.160,** or by X-ray examination of animals selected for assay. Keep each rat in individual cage, provided with rachitogenic diet and H_2O *ad libitum.* On any calendar day of assay period, assay and ref. groups must receive rachitogenic diet compounded from same lots of ingredients.

Following optional methods of feeding ref. oil soln and sample soln are permissible, but both ref. oil soln and sample soln must be fed according to same method in any 1 assay. Supplements may be fed on first day of assay period, or in equal portions on first, third, and fifth days, or on first and third days, or on first and fourth days of 7 day or 10 day assay period, or on first 6 days of 7 day assay period, or on first 8 days of 10 day assay period; supplements may be fed admixed with quantity of basal ration that will be consumed within first 5 days of 7 day assay period or within first 8 days of 10 day assay period. In each case make unsupplemented ration available during remainder of assay period.

Feed quantity of ref. oil found by experience to cause extent and degree of calcification of rachitic metaphysis equiv. to 4 on line test chart. Feed that quantity of sample soln which is calcd to contain, on basis of claimed or assumed potency, same number of units of vitamin D as contained in quantity of ref. oil fed.

After assay period kill each rat and examine one or more leg bones for healing of rachitic metaphysis according to "line test," **39.160.**

Ref. oil may be dild with edible vegetable oil free from vitamins A and D before being fed. Dild oil must be stored in dark at temp. ≤10° for ≤30 days. Do not feed >0.2 ml of dild oil as daily dose. During assay period keep all conditions of environment (particularly physiologically active radiations) as uniform as possible with respect to assay and ref. groups.

39.160 Line Test

Make line test on proximal end of tibia or distal end of radius or ulna. Remove end of desired bone from animal and clean off adhering tissue. Make longitudinal median section thru end of bone with clean, sharp blade to expose plane surface thru junc-

tion of epiphysis and diaphysis. In any one assay use same bone of all animals and section thru same plane. Rinse both sections of bone in H_2O and immerse in 2% $AgNO_3$ soln 1 min. Then rinse sections in H_2O and expose sectioned surfaces in H_2O to daylight or other source of actinic light until calcified areas have developed clearly defined stains without marked discoloration of uncalcified areas. Immediately record extent and degree of calcification of rachitic metaphysis of every section.

Staining procedure may be modified to differentiate more clearly between calcified and uncalcified areas. Suitable alternative procedure is to take freshly sectioned bone and proceed as follows: (*1*) Soak in ether-acetone mixt. $(3 + 1)$ ≥5 min (at this stage, after bone sections are dry, they may be mounted for convenience and ease of handling on std microscope slides with aid of rubber cement and remainder of procedure performed in Coplin staining jars); (*2*) soak in alcohol 10 min; (*3*) soak in acetone 10 min; (*4*) soak 40 min in H_2O which is completely changed after 1, 10, 20, and 30 min; (*5*) stain with 2% $AgNO_3$ soln 60 sec; and (*6*) wash 40 min with H_2O in dark with complete changes after 1, 10, 20, and 30 min. Expose stained sections in H_2O to daylight or other source of actinic light until stains have developed.

Score degree of calcification of rachitic metaphysis in each rat according to scale shown in Fig. 39:1. Because lines pictured in chart differ somewhat from line of healing being scored, it is necessary to visualize calcification as if it were compact and continuous in comparing it with appropriate figure in chart. Use of chart is illustrated by accompanying photographs of actual sections of radii, Fig. 39:2.

39.161 Recording of Data

On day beginning assay period and on seventh or tenth day thereafter, depending on duration of assay period, record body wt of each rat. Keep record of quantity of rachitogenic diet consumed/rat during assay period. Assign numerical values to extent and degree of calcification of rachitic metaphyses of bones examined by line test by comparison with line test chart so that it is possible to average performance of each group.

39.162 Potency of Assay Sample

Consider data from rat valid for establishing vitamin D potency of assay sample only when wt of rat at termination of assay period equals or exceeds wt of rat on beginning day of assay period, and only when rat has consumed each prescribed dose of assay sample within 24 hr from time it was fed.

Consider data from ref. group valid for establishing vitamin D potency of assay sample when ≥⅔ but not <7 rats in ref. groups that meet wt criteria show degree of calcification of rachitic metaphysis ≥0.5 and ≤8.0 on line test chart.

Consider data from assay group valid for establishing vitamin D potency of assay sample when ≥ 7 rats in assay group meet wt criteria.

When av. response of assay group equals or exceeds av. response of ref. group, consider that vitamin D content of sample fed during assay period equals or exceeds vitamin D content of ref. oil fed during assay period. When av. response of assay group is less than av. response of ref. group, and $< \frac{1}{2}$ of rats in assay group show degree of calcification of rachitic metaphysis ≥ 0.5 on line test chart, consider vitamin D content of sample fed during assay period to be less than vitamin D content of ref. oil fed during assay period. When av. response of assay group (A) is less than av. response of ref. group (R) and if $\geq \frac{1}{2}$ rats in assay group show degree of calcification of rachitic metaphysis ≥ 0.5 on line test chart, and:

(1) *Rats in assay and reference groups are unpaired by litter mates, then:*

$$t^2 = C_u(\overline{Y}_R - \overline{Y}_A)^2/S_u^2,$$

where:

$$C_u = n_A n_R/(n_A + n_R),$$
$$S_u^2 = (\Sigma Y^2 - n_R \overline{Y}_R^2 - n_A \overline{Y}_A^2)/(n_A + n - 2)$$

$\overline{Y}_R$ = av. score for ref. group, $\overline{Y}_A$ = av. score for assay group, ΣY^2 = sum of squares of all individual scores, n_A = number of rats in assay group, and n_R = number of rats in ref. group. Find t^2 in table, where d.f. = degrees of freedom = $n_A + n_R - 2$. Or:

(2) *Rats in assay and reference groups are paired by litter mates,* subtract each response in assay group from associated litter mate response in ref. group. Maintain sign of difference. Then:

$$t^2 = n_P \overline{D}^2/S_D^2,$$

where: n_P = number of pairs, $\overline{D}^2$ = square of av. difference, $\overline{D}$ = av. of differences, S_D^2 = variance of differences = $(\Sigma D^2 - n_P \overline{D}^2)/(n_P - 1)$, and ΣD^2 = sum of squares of differences. Find t^2 in Table 39:1, where d.f. = $n_P - 1$.

If calcd t^2 exceeds t^2 in table, consider vitamin D content of sample fed during assay period to be less than vitamin D content of ref. oil fed during assay period; otherwise consider that vitamin D content of sample equals or exceeds vitamin D content of ref. oil, provided S_u is < 1.5, or S_D^2 is < 2.5. If S_u^2 or S_D^2 is > 1.5 or 2.5, resp., data of this assay are inadequate to establish potency of assay sample. (Assay must then be extended or repeated.)

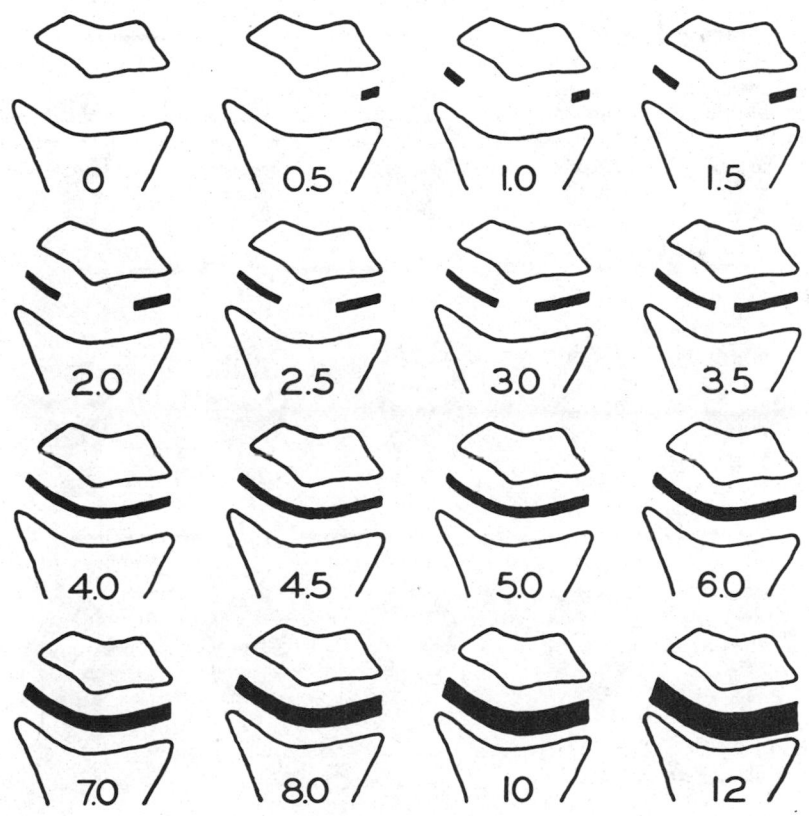

FIG. 39:1—Line test chart

Calcn of t^2 and S^2 is illustrated as follows:

(1) *For unpaired data:*

Healing Scores	
Reference	Assay
3.62	4.00
3.12	4.37
6.00	2.37
5.50	2.00
4.25	3.75
5.50	2.50
4.75	4.00
Average = $\bar{Y}$ = 4.68	3.28

$\Sigma Y^2 = 240.9901$

$$C_u = (n_A \times n_R)/(n_A + n_R)$$
$$= (7 \times 7)/(7 + 7) = 3.5$$

$$S_u^2 = (\Sigma Y^2 - n_R \bar{Y}_R^2 - n_A \bar{Y}_A^2)/(n_A + n_R - 2)$$
$$= [240.9901 - 7(4.68)^2 - 7(3.28)^2]/12$$
$$= 1.0304$$

$$t^2 = (C_u/S_u^2)(\bar{Y}_R - \bar{Y}_A)^2$$
$$= (3.5/1.0304)(4.68 - 3.28)^2 = 6.658$$

d.f. $= n_R + n_A - 2 = 12$

Tabular t^2 for d.f. = 12 is 3.176

Calcd t^2 (6.658) exceeds value in table for d.f. = 12 (3.176); therefore, vitamin D content of assay sample is less than vitamin D content of ref. oil. Since S_u^2 (1.0304) is <1.50, assay is valid.

Table 39:1—t^2 Values

d.f.	t^2	d.f.	t^2	d.f.	t^2
6	3.775	14	3.101	22	2.948
7	3.591	15	3.073	23	2.938
8	3.460	16	3.049	24	2.928
9	3.360	17	3.028	25	2.917
10	3.283	18	3.007	26	2.910
11	3.226	19	2.989	27	2.900
12	3.176	20	2.976	28	2.893
13	3.136	21	2.962	29	2.887
				30	2.880

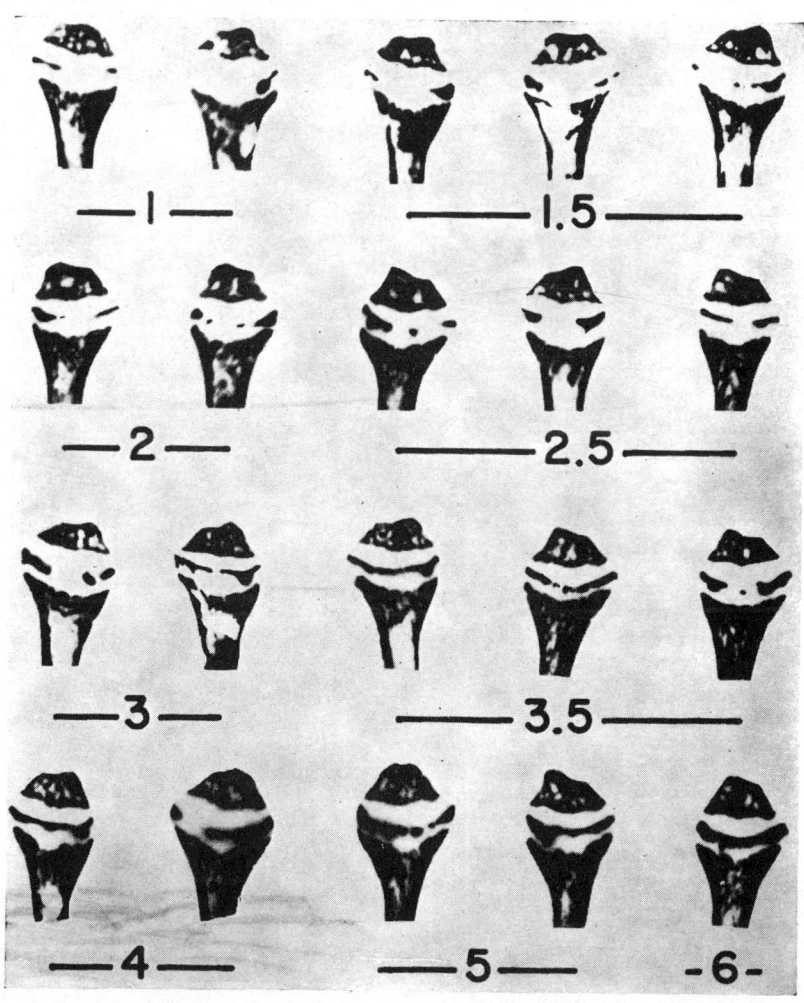

FIG. 39:2—Photographs of radii sections scored according to line test chart.
For illustrative purposes only; should *not* be used as scoring scale

(2) *For paired data:*

Litter	Healing Scores Reference	Assay	Difference
1	4.02	4.40	− .38
2	3.52	4.77	− 1.25
3	6.40	2.77	+ 3.63
4	5.90	2.40	+ 3.50
5	4.65	4.15	+ .50
6	5.90	2.90	+ 3.00
7	5.15	4.40	+ .75

Average $= \overline{D}$ $= 1.39$

ΣD^2 $= 36.9463$

$$S_D^2 = (\Sigma D^2 - n_P \overline{D}^2)/(n_P - 1)$$
$$= [36.9463 - 7(1.39)^2]/6 = 3.9036$$
$$t^2 = (n_P \overline{D}^2)/(S_D^2)$$
$$= 7(1.39)^2/3.9036 = 3.4647$$
$$\text{d.f.} = n_P - 1 = 6$$

Tabular t^2 for d.f. $= 6$ is 3.775

Altho calcd value of t^2, 3.4647, is less than tabular value for d.f. $= 6$ of 3.755, indicating that vitamin D content of assay sample equals or exceeds vitamin D content of ref. oil, *assay must be repeated* since value for S_D^2 of 3.9036 is >2.5. Available data are inadequate to establish potency of sample.

(If desired, potency of vitamin D_2 may be calcd from multiple level assays by statistical procedure of USP XVIII, p. 873.)

Vitamin D in Poultry Feed Supplements (25)—Official Final Action

(Applicable to fish and fish liver oils and their exts, and to materials used for supplementing vitamin D content of feeds. Not applicable to irradiated ergosterol products or to irradiated yeast unless recommended for poultry. This assay is comparison, under conditions specified, of efficacy of product under assay with that of USP Vitamin D Oil Ref. Std in controlling ash content of bones of growing chicks.)

39.163 Basal Rachitic Ration

The basal ration is uniform mixt. in proportions designated of following ingredients, which have been finely ground:

	per cent
Yellow corn, ground	58
Wheat flour middlings or wheat gray shorts	25
Casein, crude, domestic, acid pptd	12
Calcium phosphate, tribasic	2
Salt, iodized (0.02% KI)	1
Yeast, non-irradiated (7% min. N)	2

To each kg of above mixt. add 0.2 g $MnSO_4.4H_2O$.

39.164 Determination

Provide cages with screen bottoms and keep chicks away from sunshine or other source of actinic light that may influence calcification. Keep cages in rooms in which wide variations in temp. are prevented (constant temp. preferred). Unless temp. of room is adequately controlled, provide each cage with suitable elec. heating device. Start all birds to be used in one assay on same day and keep all conditions of environment uniform for all groups in assay.

Make assay on groups of 1- or 2-day-old White Leghorn chicks as specified below. Provide for one or more neg. control groups that receive no vitamin D, three or more pos. control groups that receive graduated levels of vitamin D from USP Vitamin D Ref. Std, and one or more assay groups for each product to be assayed. Have pos. control and assay groups consist of ≥ 20 birds each, and neg. control consist of ≥ 10 birds.

Prep. rations for all groups in assay from one batch of basal ration. Add Ref. Std to basal ration in such quantities as to produce measurable increase in % bone ash above that obtained in neg. control group (it is not possible to make comparisons if max. bone ash is obtained). Add assay product to basal ration in such quantities as to permit direct comparison in response of assay and pos. control groups.

To basal ration of neg. control group add corn oil equal in quantity to max. quantity of oil fed to any group in assay, and add corn oil to rations of other groups until total quantity of corn oil and oil contg vitamin D is equal to quantity of corn oil added to ration of neg. control group.

Feed chicks in respective groups prescribed ration and H_2O (natural or distd) *ad libitum* 21 days. Discard all chicks that show abnormality or disease not related to vitamin D deficiency. At least 15 chicks must remain in each ref. or assay group used in calcg vitamin D potency of assay product.

Thruout any one assay, consistently use the specific method, (a) or (b), adopted for extg, drying, and ashing of bones.

(a) Kill chicks; remove left tibia of each bird and clean off adhering tissue. (To facilitate removal of adhering tissue, bones may be placed in boiling H_2O ≤ 2 min. Bones may be preserved in alcohol for extn.) Completely ext bones with suitable fat solv. or solvs (20 hr with hot alcohol followed by 20 hr with ether is suitable, and bones should be crushed to facilitate extn). Dry extd bones to constant wt at 95–100° under pressure <100 mm Hg (ca 5 hr), cool in desiccator, and weigh. Ash H_2O- and fat-free bones from each group of birds in muffle furnace to constant wt at any given temp. between 450 and 550°, or if preferred, 1 hr at ca 850°. (Ash detn may be made on individual bones if desired.)

(b) Alternatively, use toe ash measurement of response to vitamin D: Excise middle toe from each foot by cutting thru joint between second and third tarsal bones from distal end. Use entire toe for sample. Remove any dirt, but not tissue, and do not ext with solv. Composite samples of group, dry 8 hr at 100° in air oven, and ash 4 hr at 600° in furnace.

39.165 Interpretation of Results

One international chick unit of vitamin D is equal in biological activity to one unit vitamin D in USP Vitamin D Ref. Std in this method of assay. Product under assay meets its declared vitamin potency in international chick units of vitamin D if % ash in H_2O- and fat-free bone produced in assay groups by given number of units of vitamin D is equal to or is greater than % ash produced by same number of units of vitamin D from USP Ref. Std.

Biological Evaluation of Protein Quality
(26)—Official Final Action

(Applicable to materials contg >1.80% N)

39.166   *Reagents*

(a) *ANRC reference casein.*—Available from Sheffield Chemical, 2400 Morris Ave, Union, NJ 07083.

(b) *Salt mixture USP.*—Either USP salt mixt. or salt mixt. having essentially same proportions of the elements. Prep. USP XVIII (p. 885) salt mixt. as follows: Grind in mortar portion of 139.3 g NaCl with 0.79 g KI. Similarly grind together remainder of the NaCl with 389.0 g KH_2PO_4, 57.3 g $MgSO_4$ anhyd., 381.4 g $CaCO_3$, 27.0 g $FeSO_4.7H_2O$, 4.01 g $MnSO_4.H_2O$, 0.548 g $ZnSO_4.7H_2O$, 0.477 g $CuSO_4$.$5H_2O$, and 0.023 g $CoCl_2.6H_2O$, finally adding the NaCl-KI mixt. Reduce entire mixt. to fine powder.

(c) *Vitamin mixture.*—

	mg/100 g ration
Vitamin A (dry, stabilized)	2000 (IU)
Vitamin D (dry, stabilized)	200 (IU)
Vitamin E (dry, stabilized)	10 (IU)
Menadione	0.5
Choline	200
p-Aminobenzoic acid	10
Inositol	10
Niacin	4
Ca D-pantothenate	4
Riboflavin	0.8
Thiamine.HCl	0.5
Pyridoxine.HCl	0.5
Folic acid	0.2
Biotin	0.04
Vitamin B_{12}	0.003
Glucose, to make	1000

(d) *Cottonseed oil.*

(e) *Cellulose.*—Cellu Flour, Solka Floc, or equiv.

(f) *Protein evaluation basal diet.*—

Sample	$X*$
Cottonseed oil	$8 - \dfrac{X \times \% \text{ ether extract}}{100}$
Salt mixture USP	$5 - \dfrac{X \times \% \text{ ash}}{100}$
Vitamin mixture	1
Cellulose	$1 - \dfrac{X \times \% \text{ crude fiber}}{100}$
Water	$5 - \dfrac{X \times \% \text{ moisture}}{100}$

Sucrose or corn starch, to make 100

$$*X = \frac{1.44 \times 100}{\% \text{ N of Sample}}$$

All % figures refer to sample. Proximate analysis is needed to adjust diet so that all comparisons between samples and ref. material shall be made with diets having same content of N, fat, ash, moisture, and crude fiber. These suggested levels of fat, ash, moisture, and crude fiber are desirable whenever proximate analysis of sample permits.

39.167   *Experimental Animals*

Laboratory rats, males, shall be from same colony, and maintained during period before weaning upon diet and under environmental conditions that will provide for normal development in all respects; weaned; ≥21 days of age but ≤28 days of age; range of individual rat wts among animals used shall be ≤10 g. When animals are transported from breeding colony to test laboratory, acclimation period of ≥3 days but <7 should precede test.

39.168   *Assay Groups*

Assemble groups of ≥10 rats. In assay of each material provide 1 group that will receive ANRC ref. casein. One ref. casein group may be used for concurrent assay of >1 assay material. When assembling of all groups is complete, total number of rats in each group must be the same, and av. wt of rats in any 1 group on day beginning assay period must not exceed by >5 g av. wt of rats in any other group.

39.169   *Assay Period*

Thruout assay period keep each rat in individual cage and provide with appropriate assay diet and H_2O *ad libitum.* During assay period maintain all conditions of environment as uniform as possible with respect to each of groups being compared to ANRC reference casein. Record body wt of each rat on beginning day of assay period and body wt and food intake of each rat at regular intervals, not >7 days, and on 28th day after beginning of assay period.

39.170   *Calculation and Tabulation*
                                                        of Results

Calc. av. 28 day wt gain and protein (N × 6.25) intake per rat for each group. Calc. Protein Efficiency Ratio (PER) (wt gain/protein intake) for each group. Det. ratio × 100 of PER for each assay group to PER for ANRC casein ref. group. Tabulate 28 day wt gains, protein intake, PER, and ratio × 100 of sample PER to ANRC Ref. Casein PER for each assay group. Report protein quality of sample as ratio × 100 of sample PER to ANRC Ref. Casein PER.

SELECTED REFERENCES

(1) JAOAC **43**, 6(1960); **45**, 442(1962).

(2) JAOAC **33**, 615(1950); **34**, 370(1951); **35**, 706 (1952); **36**, 812(1953); **37**, 742(1954); **38**, 692,

695(1955); **39**, 126(1956); **40**, 865(1957); **41**, 593(1958); **42**, 422, 520(1959); **43**, 30(1960); **49**, 250(1966); Analyst **89**, 7(1964).

(*3*) JAOAC **39**, 126(1956).

(*4*) Ind. Eng. Chem., Anal. Ed. **13**, 600(1941); **15**, 18(1943); **16**, 513(1944); **19**, 170(1947); J. Biol. Chem. **164**, 2(1946); JAOAC **25**, 573, 886 (1942); **26**, 77(1943); **27**, 542(1944); **28**, 563 (1945); **29**, 18(1946); **30**, 412(1947); **31**, 459, 621, 623, 633, 776(1948); **32**, 480, 766, 775, 804 (1949); **33**, 647(1950); **34**, 387, 460(1951); **35**, 736, 826(1952); **36**, 857(1953); **37**, 753, 756, 880, 887, 894(1954); **38**, 694(1955); **39**, 139 (1956); **40**, 865(1957); **41**, 600(1958); **42**, 528 (1959); **45**, 219(1962); **53**, 181, 186(1970).

(*5*) JAOAC **53**, 181, 186(1970).

(*6*) JAOAC **25**, 456(1942); **27**, 534(1944); **28**, 554 (1945); **31**, 455(1948); **43**, 45, 55(1960).

(*7*) JAOAC **36**, 837(1953); **37**, 122, 757(1954); **38**, 722(1955).

(*8*) JAOAC **40**, 843(1957); **41**, 603(1958); **43**, 47 (1960).

(*9*) JAOAC **23**, 346(1940); **24**, 413(1941); **25**, 459 (1942); **26**, 81(1943); **27**, 540(1944); **30**, 392 (1947); **31**, 701(1948); **32**, 108, 461(1949); **33**, 88, 632(1950); **37**, 770(1954); **43**, 42(1960); **53**, 542(1970).

(*10*) Anal. Chem. **23**, 983(1951); JAOAC **34**, 380 (1951); **36**, 1018(1953); **42**, 625(1959); **44**, 431 (1961); **45**, 449(1962); **51**, 506, 828(1968).

(*11*) J. Pharm. Sci. **50**, 926(1961); JAOAC **51**, 828 (1968).

(*12*) J. Biol. Chem. **103**, 687(1933); **112**, 625(1936); **116**, 409, 563(1936); **126**, 771(1938); Biochem. J. **27**, 580(1933); **30**, 2273(1936); **36**, 115(1942); Physiol. Rev. **16**, 238(1936); J. Am. Med. Assoc. **111**, 1290(1938); Biochem. Z. **301**, 229 (1939); JAOAC **27**, 537(1944); **28**, 559(1945); **29**, 69(1946); **30**, 673(1947); **32**, 479(1949); **34**, 380(1951); **36**, 1127(1953); **38**, 514(1955); **50**, 798(1967).

(*13*) JAOAC **48**, 1248(1965); **50**, 798(1967).

(*14*) JAOAC **50**, 809(1967); **52**, 442(1969).

(*15*) JAOAC **48**, 1217(1965); **52**, 448(1969).

(*16*) JAOAC **35**, 161, 169, 726(1952); **36**, 846(1953); **37**, 781(1954); **38**, 711(1955); **39**, 167, 172 (1956); **40**, 856(1957); **41**, 61, 587(1958); **42**, 529(1959).

(*17*) Science **100**, 295(1944); J. Biol. Chem. **157**, 303 (1945); **163**, 447, 449(1946); Ann. N.Y. Acad. Sci. **48**, 261(1946); Analyst **72**, 84(1947); JAOAC **31**, 466(1948); **32**, 464(1949); **33**, 633 (1950); **39**, 172(1956); **40**, 855, 856(1957); **41**, 61, 587, 591(1958); **42**, 529(1959); **51**, 591 (1968).

(*18*) JAOAC **27**, 105(1944); **30**, 82(1947); **32**, 110, 479(1949); **39**, 172(1956); **40**, 856(1957); **41**, 61, 587(1958); **42**, 529(1959).

(*19*) JAOAC **28**, 567(1945); **35**, 103, 722(1952); **37**, 779(1954); **38**, 710(1955); **39**, 172(1956); **40**, 853, 856(1957); **41**, 61, 587, 739(1958); **42**, 525, 529(1959); J. Biol. Chem. **192**, 181(1951).

(*20*) JAOAC **23**, 346(1940); **24**, 413(1941); **25**, 459 (1942); **26**, 81(1943); **27**, 540(1944); **28**, 560 (1945); **29**, 25(1946); **30**, 79, 391(1947); **31**, 701 (1948); **32**, 105, 461(1949); **33**, 88, 631(1950); **37**, 770(1954); **39**, 172(1956); **40**, 856(1957); **41**, 61, 587(1958); **42**, 529(1959).

(*21*) JAOAC **41**, 420, 679(1958); **43**, 34(1960).

(*22*) JAOAC **44**, 426(1961); **47**, 750(1964); **53**, 546 (1970).

(*23*) JAOAC **21**, 305, 622(1938); **22**, 662(1939); **23**, 653(1940); **24**, 147, 403(1941); **25**, 456(1942); **27**, 534(1944).

(*24*) JAOAC **19**, 248(1936); **20**, 213(1937); **21**, 243 (1938); **22**, 468(1939); **23**, 341(1940); **32**, 480, 801(1949); **38**, 165(1955); **39**, 141(1956); **41**, 588(1958); **43**, 59(1960); **45**, 22(1962); **46**, 160 (1963); Anal. Chem. **24**, 1841(1952).

(*25*) JAOAC **15**, 222, 660(1932); **16**, 184(1933); **17**, 180(1934); **18**, 341, 357, 471(1935); **19**, 628, 637, 647(1936); **20**, 438, 450(1937); **21**, 607 (1938); **22**, 445, 656(1939); **23**, 648, 665(1940); **24**, 190, 432, 858, 961(1941); **25**, 213, 459, 518 (1942); **26**, 263, 516(1943); **27**, 283, 289(1944); **29**, 396(1946); **30**, 190(1947); **32**, 801(1949); **33**, 645(1950); **35**, 27, 715(1952).

(*26*) JAOAC **43**, 38(1960).

40. Extraneous Materials: Isolation★

GENERAL

40.001 Definition of Terms

(a) *Extraneous materials.*—Any foreign matter in product associated with objectionable conditions or practices in production, storage, or distribution; included are filth (see (b)–(f)), decomposed material (decayed tissues due to parasitic or nonparasitic causes), and miscellaneous matter such as sand and soil, glass, rust, or other foreign substances. Excluded are bacterial counts.

(b) *Filth.*—Any objectionable matter contributed by animal contamination of product such as rodent, insect, or bird matter; or any other objectionable matter contributed by insanitary conditions.

(c) *Suggested format for reporting identified filth.*—
Method(s): AOAC XI method(s) used for analysis of product.
Code(s): Manufacturer's or distributor's identification marks.
Subdivision numbers: Use inspector's subdivision number when given.
Amount of subdivision examined: Amt of sample portion analyzed.
Findings: Use *only* those captions that apply to findings.

(*1*) Whole insects or equiv. (total no.). Give identity of insects if known, and state whether alive or dead. Give size.
   (a) Adults including flies
   (b) Pupae
   (c) Maggots
   (d) Larvae, other than maggots
   (e) Adult heads
   (f) Larval heads
   (g) Pupal cast skins
   (h) Larval cast skins
   (i) Larval head capsules

(*2*) No. insect fragments, identified. Give size range and identity.

(*3*) No. insect fragments, unidentified. Give size range.

(*4*) No. insect eggs (give kind).

(*5*) No. aphids, thrips, psocids, spiders, scale insects, mites, etc.
   Fragments of above.

(*6*) No. setae (if fly, state).

(*7*) No. insect excreta pellets (identify as to insect order if known).

(*8*) No. rat or mouse excreta pellets (state which or give length; give wt if from condimental seeds and spices).

(*9*) No. rat or mouse excreta pellet fragments.

(*10*) No. rat or mouse hairs and hair fragments (give sizes or range).

(*11*) No. other hairs (give size and kind if known).

(*12*) No. feather fragments (give size).

(*13*) Other extraneous materials (describe).

(*14*) Rodent urine on bagging or food beneath (give dimensions of stain).

(*15*) Bird excreta on bagging or food beneath.

Except where total is called for, there should be no duplication in various elements. For example, setae are insect fragments but report only under setae. Similarly where fragments can be identified as from mites, aphids, thrips, and scale insects, report under that heading, not under insect fragments. It is important to report whether or not infestation is due to live insects and whether or not sample was fumigated before shipment or upon receipt at laboratory.

(d) *Heavy filth.*—Heavier filth material sepd from product by sedimentation based on different densities of filth, food particles, and immersion liqs such as CHCl₃, CCl₄, etc. Examples of such filth are insect and rodent excreta pellets and pellet fragments, sand, and soil.

(e) *Light filth.*—Lighter filth particles that are oleophilic and are sepd from product by floating them in an oil-aq. liq. mixt. Examples are insect fragments, rodent hairs, and feather barbules.

(f) *Sieved filth.*—Filth particles of specific size ranges sepd quant. from product by use of selected sieve mesh sizes.

40.002 Apparatus

(a) *Aerator, water.*—Fisher Scientific Co. No. 14-551, Arthur H. Thomas Co. No. 5059, or equiv., with lower screen removed.

(b) *Autoclave.*—(*1*) *Slow exhaust type.*—Set "slow exh" to lower pressure from 15 to 0 psi in 15–20 min. (*2*) *Non-slow exhaust.*—Let cool to 0 psi before opening or venting.

(c) *Blood counting cell.*—Depth 0.1 mm, preferably ruled in the Thoma or old Neubauer system. Cell with "improved" Neubauer system, equipped with optically worked cover glass, may also be used.

(d) *Bolting cloth.*—Silk cloth woven to std size opening and thickness which is used in flour mills. Number of silk specifies number of mesh/linear in. "X," "XX," or "XXX" after number refers to

---

★ Methods so marked are surplus methods. *See* "Definitions of Terms and Explanatory Notes," item (29).

thickness of thread from which cloth is woven; this also affects size of opening in cloth. Therefore, follow designation exactly as to both number and "X" of bolting cloth.

Prep. disks by boiling large squares of silk before cutting them into circles. Circles cut from unboiled silk shrink and become misshapen. Make rulings ca 5–7 mm apart with India ink or other permanent marking material, using fine pen, on boiled and pressed cloth marked off in circles ca 85 mm diam.

(e) *Butter stirrer.*—See Fig. 40:1.

(f) *Compound microscope.*—See (n)(1).

(g) *Cyclone.*—Laboratory cyclone or pulper consists of cylindrical perforated metal screen in which revolves paddle which forces soft material from food product out thru openings in screen. Tough materials such as seeds, skins, and stems are moved along and out opening in end of cylinder. Use as power source ¼ horsepower, 110 v, 1725 rpm elec. motor. Screen is 22 gage material, 400 holes/sq in., each 0.027″ diam. Screen is 2.5″ id and length of effective screen is 3″. Paddle has 2 fins, each $^{25}/_{32}$″ wide, set alternately and extending $1^{3}/_{16}$″ from center of shaft. Pulper is fed thru hopper which leads into basin 3.5″ long and 2.5″ id. Portion of paddle with fins inserted

at 30° angle forces material from basin into screening compartment. Cyclone is so constructed that waste opening may be closed, as needed. Sieved material is caught in shield and delivered thru spout to container. Machine may be readily disassembled for washing. (Blueprints available from Div. Microbiology, Food and Drug Administration, Washington, DC 20204.)

(h) *Extraction vessels.*—(1) *Kilborn funnel.*—1 L 3.5″ od by 9.5″ high, 8 mm opening at tip. (Scientific Products, Inc. No. F 7979). Rubber tubing $^{3}/_{8}$″ id and pinch clamp provides convenient cut-off.

(2) *Percolator.*—2 L, Corning Glass Works No. 7040, or equiv., conforming to following general size and shape: 115 mm id × 300 mm length, ca 90 mm id at 200 mm down from top, with 8–9 mm bore tip, with cut-off as in (1).

(3) *Trap flask (Wildman).*—Consists of 1 or 2 L erlenmeyer into which is inserted close-fitting rubber stopper supported on stiff metal rod $^{3}/_{16}$″ diam. and ca 4″ longer than ht of flask. (Rod of greater diam. is not desirable because of its greater displacement of liq.) Rod is threaded (#10–32) at lower end and furnished with nuts and washers to hold it in place on stopper. Countersink lower nut and washer in the rubber to prevent striking flask. *See* Fig. 40:2 and **40.004(a)**.

(i) *Filter paper.*—Use smooth, high wet-strength, rapid-acting filter paper ruled with oil-, alcohol-, and water-proof lines 5 mm apart. S&S No. 8 is satisfactory.

(j) *Funnels for filtration with suction.*—Use funnels with filter papers or bolting cloth cupped up on sides to eliminate loss of solids. Use rapid filter paper for filtration thru Hirsch funnel.

Use of wire screen or bolting cloth between perforated funnel plate and filter paper accelerates filtration and gives more uniform distribution of solids.

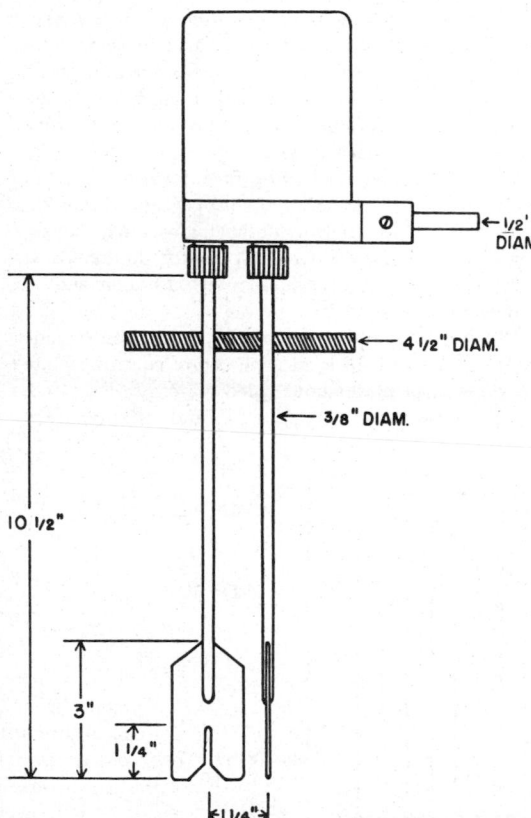

FIG. 40:1—Mechanical butter stirrer

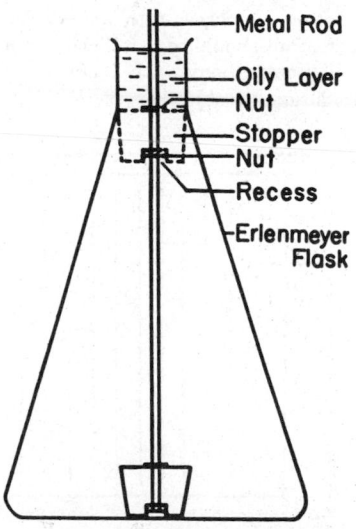

FIG. 40:2—Wildman trap flask

(k) *Greenough-type (widefield stereoscopic) microscope for filth examination.*—See (n)(2).

(l) *Illuminators for widefield stereoscopic microscopes.*—(1) *Filth examination.*—Illuminator for this purpose should have: Compactness and flexibility; transformer or resistor to vary light intensity; focusing adjustment to give uniformly lighted field of view; blue-white color from cool low-voltage source. (2) *Rot fragment counting.*—Use small substage illuminator fitted with daylight or blue ground-glass filter and 15 watt bulb.

(m) *Howard mold-counting apparatus.*—(1) *Howard mold-counting slide.*—Glass slide of one-piece construction with flat plane circle ca 19 mm diam. or rectangle 20 × 15 mm surrounded by moat and flanked on each side by shoulders 0.1 mm higher than plane surface. Cover glass is supported on shoulders and leaves depth of 0.1 mm between underside of cover glass and plane surface. Central plane, shoulders, and cover glass have optically worked surfaces. To facilitate calibration of microscope, newer slides are engraved with circle 1.382 mm diam. or with 2 fine parallel lines 1.382 mm apart.

(2) *Accessory disk for mold counting.*—Glass disk that fits into microscope eyepiece, ruled into squares each side of which is equal to ⅙ of diam. of field. Since limiting diaphragm is eyepiece field stop, rulings equal ⅙ of this diaphragm opening. Field viewed on slide with mold-counting microscope has diam. of 1.382 mm at magnification of 90–125×.

(3) *Method of illumination of compound microscope for mold counting.*—Unless microscope has built-in light source, fasten lamp and microscope securely to baseboard so that they are used and maintained as unit (*e.g.*, Bausch and Lomb baseboard No. 31-50-54). Adjust mirror pivot so that it is not easily moved, and hold microscope in place by screws or cleats.

(n) *Microscopes.*—(1) *Compound microscope.*—For mold counting and other filth and decomposition work, microscope should have following min. specifications: Binocular body with inclined oculars; 4 parfocal achromatic objectives of ca 5, 10, 20, and 40×; revolving 4-place nosepiece; achromatic condenser with N.A. of 1.40 in centerable mount; 10× Huygenian eyepieces; fine adjustment; mech. stage preferably with adjusting buttons at sides of stage (if photomicrographs are to be made, revolving stage is more satisfactory); stdzd field of view of 1.382 mm diam. at 90–125×; equipped with drop-in ocular disk ruled in squares, each of which is ⅙ of field diam.

(2) *Widefield stereoscopic microscope for filth and rot fragment examination.*—Microscope should have following min. specifications: Binocular body with inclined oculars; sliding or revolving nosepiece to accommodate 3 objectives; 3 parfocal objectives 1×, 3×, and 6 or 7.5×; paired 10× and paired 15× widefield oculars; mounted on base and capable of illumination by transmitted or reflected light. 30× is ordinarily used for routine examination of filter papers. Verification at higher magnification may be required.

(o) *Petri dishes.*—Use to hold filter papers, bolting cloths, etc., for microscopic examination; low-edge (10 mm high) type.

(p) *Rot fragment counting plate and cover preparation.*—Glass plate; 55 mm × 100 mm, 1.5–4.0 mm thick with cover 50 mm × 85 mm, ca 1.5 mm thick. Carefully paint on coat of resist over the entire surface, avoiding pinholes. Asphaltum varnish makes excellent resist; paraffin wax may also be used. Carefully scribe crosswise parallel lines, 4.5 mm apart with 15 mm space at each end, thru resist. If asphaltum varnish is used, lines may be scribed with new steel-wheel glass cutter.

Place coated scribed slides face down over HF in polyethylene container. Det. proper acid fume exposure by trial and error. Following etching, remove resist by placing slide in H_2O contg detergent. If resist is not easily scrubbed off, use benzene or toluene for cleanup.

Fasten ½ of square cover slip, ca 22 mm on side and ca 0.25 mm thick, at each end of counting plate to raise cover plate above ruled plate. See Fig. 40:3.

(q) *Sieves.*—See Definitions and Explanatory

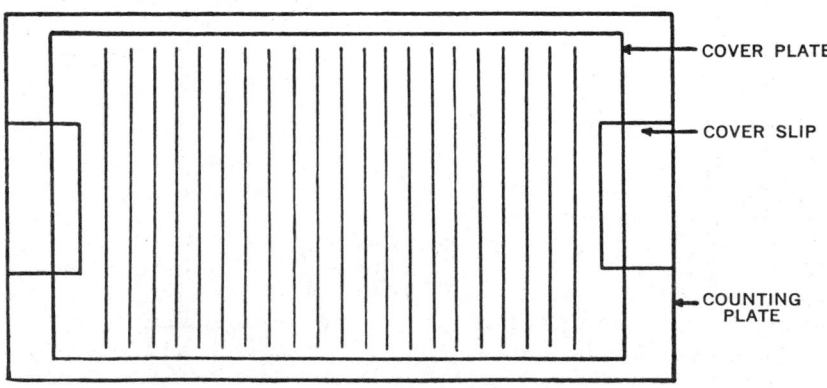

FIG. 40:3—Rot fragment counting slide

Notes, item (15). Sieves of No. 100 or finer should be "plain (not twill) weave" of stainless steel. Plain weave is woven with one wire alternately over and under next.

(r) *Stirrer-magnetic hot plate.*—Independent heat and speed controls continuously variable; Arthur H. Thomas Co. No. 9236-H45 or 9236-P, or equiv.

(s) *Stirring bars for magnetic stirring.*—Teflon covered bars ca 1⅛″ long × ca ⅜″ diam., either round or octagonal. Scientific Glass Apparatus Co. No. S-6936 item D, or equiv.

(t) *Beakers, funnels, etc.*—Do not use polyethylene containers, as insect fragments and rodent hairs adhere to app. made from this material.

40.003 *Reagents*

(a) *Acetic acid.*—Practical glacial HOAc is satisfactory.

(b) *Acetone.*—Practical acetone is suitable unless otherwise specified.

(c) *Alcohol.*—95% com. ethanol (not denatured) unless otherwise specified. Make all dilns by vol.

(d) *Algin soln for rot fragment determination.*—Proceed as for stabilizer solns, (ee); then adjust final mixt. to pH 7.0–7.5 with NaOH soln.

(e) *Antifoam soln.*—1 g Dow Corning Antifoam A compd dild with 20 ml EtOAc. Use supernatant and keep tightly closed.

(f) *Borax.*—Household borax is satisfactory. This is usually $Na_2B_4O_7 \cdot 10H_2O$, which is not very sol. in cold H_2O. If >5% borax soln is desired, it must be kept hot.

(g) *Calgon.*—Na hexametaphosphate (obtainable from Calgon Corp., PO Box 1346, Pittsburgh, PA 15230).

(h) *Carbon tetrachloride.*—Tech. grade is suitable unless otherwise specified.

(i) *Carob bean soln.*—Blend 0.75% carob bean gum in H_2O. Boil 2 min and cool to 20–25°. Add 2 ml HCHO/100 ml and stir gently. Let settle and use clear supernatant.

(j) *Castor oil.*—USP.

(k) *Chloral hydrate.*—Aq. soln (1 + 1) or *see* Hertwig's soln.

(l) *Chloroform.*—Tech. grade is suitable unless otherwise specified. Mixt. of pet ether and CCl_4 adjusted to sp gr of $CHCl_3$, 1.5, may be used instead of $CHCl_3$.

(m) *Chloroplatinic acid soln.*—Dissolve 5 g H_2PtCl_6 in 100 ml H_2O.

(n) *Crystal violet soln.*—Dissolve 10 g dye (Colour Index 42555) in 100 ml alcohol and filter.

(o) *Detergent soln.*—Prep. aq. Na lauryl sulfate soln as required.

(p) *Formaldehyde soln.*—Use USP reagent soln. Strength is expressed as % by vol. of USP soln.

(q) *Heptane.*—Com. *n*-heptane contg <8% toluene.

(r) *Hertwig's soln.*—Useful for clearing plant and insect materials; action continues on standing. Use only for temporary mounts, not for permanent slides. Mix 19 ml HCl, 150 ml H_2O, 60 ml glycerol, and 270 g chloral hydrate.

(s) *Emulsifier.*—Nonionic H_2O-sol. surfactant, nonylphenoxypoly(ethyleneoxy)ethanol, Igepal CO-730 (GAF Corp.), or equiv.

(t) *Emulsifier.*—Nonionic H_2O-sol. surfactant, dialkylphenoxypoly(ethyleneoxy)ethanol, Igepal DM-710 (GAF Corp.), or equiv.

(u) *Isopropanol saturated with heptane.*—To 600 ml isopropanol add 45 ml heptane and 430 ml H_2O, mix, and let stand overnight. Siphon from below interface.

(v) *Kerosene, deodorized.*—Refinol No. 9 (Standard Oil of Indiana), Dispersol (Shell Oil Co.), or equiv. insecticide grade.

(w) *Mineral oil.*—Paraffin oil, white, light, 125/135 Saybolt Universal Viscosity (38°), sp gr 0.840–0.860 (24°). Fisher Scientific Co. No. 0-119, or equiv.

(x) *Pancreatin soln.*—Use NF or sol. pancreatin kept refrigerated at 10°. Use fresh soln. Mix at rate of 5 g/100 ml H_2O at ≤40°. Use special soln for cheese, 10 g/100 ml. Stir with malted milk unit or blender 10 min, or let stand 30 min with frequent shaking. Centrf. at 1500 rpm and filter supernatant thru S&S No. 8 paper, or equiv. Alternatively, filter thru cotton pads 4–5″ thick and then thru rapid No. 8 paper in Hirsch funnel with suction.

(y) *Phosphoric acid.*—Tech. grade.

(z) *Sodium carbonate.*—Tech. grade. If hydrated salt is used, calc. to anhyd. basis.

(aa) *Sodium chloride.*—Tech. grade.

(bb) *Sodium oleate.*—Tech. grade.

(cc) *Sodium phosphate soln.*—Tech. grade Na_3PO_4. Prep. 5% soln.

(dd) *Sodium sulfite.*—Tech. grade. If hydrated salt is used, calc. to anhyd. basis.

(ee) *Stabilizer solns.*—0.5% Na carboxymethylcellulose preferred (Cellulose Gum CMC-7H3SF, Hercules Inc., Cellulose and Protein Products Dept., Wilmington, DE 19899). Place 500 ml boiling H_2O in high-speed blender and cover. With blender running, add 2.5 g Cellulose Gum and 10 ml HCHO, and blend ca 1 min. Alternatives: 3–5% pectin or 1% algin. Add required quantity of stabilizer directly to H_2O while agitating in high-speed blender. Treat soln with vac. or heat to remove air bubbles. Add 2 ml HCHO/100 ml soln as preservative. (If blender is not available, mix dry stabilizer with alcohol to facilitate incorporation with H_2O.) Adjust to pH 7.0–7.5.

(ff) *Tween 80–60% alcohol soln.*—To 40 ml polysorbate 80 (Atlas Chemical Industries, Inc.) add 210 ml 60% alcohol, mix, and filter. (Proportionate reagent quantities may be prepd.)

(gg) *Tetrasodium EDTA soln.*—Dissolve 5 g Na_4EDTA in 100 ml H_2O, add 150 ml alcohol, mix, and filter. (Proportionate quantities may be prepd.)

40.004   *Special Technics*

(a) *Operation of Wildman trap flask.*—Unless otherwise directed in specific method, cool mixt. in flask to room temp. Bring vol. of liq. to ca 900 ml in 2 L flask and to ca 600 ml in 1 L flask. Add down stirring rod amt of flotation liq. as stated in method. Tilt flask ca 45° from vertical and mix 1 min at rate of 200–250 strokes/min with brisk rotary motion so that liq. is brought to a roll. Avoid splashing thru surface of liq. with rubber stopper. Add enough liq. to bring flotation liq. well into neck of flask.

Unless otherwise stated, let mixt. stand 30 min, intermittently stirring bottom layer every 3–6 min during first 20 min of standing. Spin stopper to remove sediment and trap off by raising stopper as far as possible into neck of flask, being sure that oil layer and ≥1 cm of liq. below interface are above stopper. Hold stopper in place and pour off liq. into beaker. Rinse out material on rod and in neck of flask with liq. extn medium in which flotation was performed and add to beaker.

Do not wash out neck of flask with 95% alcohol or other liq. which may interfere with surface relationships of the 2 phases; this will cause loss in recovery in subsequent trappings.

Filter trapped material and rinsings with suction thru rapid paper in Hirsch funnel. Add flotation liq. as specified to trap flask and stir vigorously. Add enough liq. extn medium to bring flotation liq. into neck of flask. Trap off again, rinse, and filter as above.

(b) *Operation of magnetic stirrer.*—To disperse flotation liq. thru sample. Dil. liq. extn medium to vol. specified in method and bring to proper temp. Add stirring bar, **40.002(s)**, and proper vol. of flotation liq. Slowly bring unit to max. speed that does not produce visible or audible splashing (central portion of stirring bar is usually just visible at bottom of vortex) and stir for time stated in method. Time stirring interval after achieving proper speed and vortex.

(c) *Tween 80-Na₄EDTA extraction.*—Add 300 ml 60% alcohol to sample in 2 L trap flask. Successively, without interruption, add 250 ml Tween 80–60% alcohol soln, **40.003(ff)**; mix and quickly add 250 ml EDTA-60% alcohol soln, **40.003(gg)**, followed by 70 ml heptane, **40.003(q)**. Mix 1 min as in (a), and rapidly fill flask with 60% alcohol.

During first 20 min of standing, gently stir settled material occasionally. After 20 min, rotate rod to remove debris from stopper surface and clamp unrinsed rod so that stopper is above level of settled material. Let stand undisturbed 1 addnl hr. Trap off as in (a), without disturbing interface while manipulating rod. Rinse with 60% alcohol. Add 40 ml heptane, let stand 1.5 hr, and perform second trapping.

(d) *Filtration technic.*—(Treatment of trapped-off material.) If material trapped off in beaker contains appreciable starchy debris, add enough HCl to make soln 1–2% of HCl (1 + 99–49), bring to boil, and

filter while hot. If fats or colloidal material retard filtration, hasten by playing stream of hot H₂O over paper during filtration.

(e) *Clearing of plant materials.*—With sedimentation or flotation procedures some food material may be trapped off with filth particles. By proper clearing, filth may be made to stand out in contrast with white background of filter paper by one of following technics:

(*1*) For heavy filth, moisten paper with H₂O or 50% alcohol. (This method does not clear material completely, but it leaves rodent pellets and other filth soft and pliable.)

(*2*) For light filth examination, wet paper with glycerol-alcohol (1 + 1) immediately after filtering. Place enough liq. on paper to fill fibers but not enough to cause flowing of extd materials. This clearing agent does not harden filth material on paper, as do many oils which might be used as clearing agents.

(*3*) Clove oil can be used for clearing plant materials. This oil has high refractive index and clears more completely than does alcohol-glycerol soln.

(f) *Illumination for the widefield stereoscopic microscope.*—(*1*) *By direct light.*—Focus and adjust light to strike paper at ca 70° angle from horizontal. Light may come from right or left.

(*2*) *By transmitted light.*—In cases where transmitted light is necessary, use mirror on microscope stand. Mirror with white surface instead of conventional silvered mirror is particularly useful.

In counting rot fragments, remove mirror and metal contrast plate and replace with box-type substage lamp. Place lamp, **40.002(l)(2)**, so that center of glass filter is directly below objective and within 2 cm of glass microscope plate.

(g) *Microscopic examination of filter papers.*—Make examination at 30× (unless otherwise specified), using widefield stereoscopic microscope, on properly cleared paper. Continually tease and probe particles while observing thru microscope. Turn over all large pieces of material such as bran which might obscure filth elements. Examine all doubtful pieces of material at 60–75×. At least twice magnification used in original examination is necessary to show new details not observable at lower power. If doubt still remains, mount piece, clear thoroly, and examine under compd microscope. *Thoro knowledge of appearance of authentic materials is assumed.*

BEVERAGES AND BEVERAGE MATERIALS

Cocoa, Chocolate, and Press Cake

Light Filth (*1*)—Official First Action

40.005   *Apparatus and Reagents*

(a) *Hirsch porcelain funnel with plug.*—Size 0, fitted with fixed perforated filtering plate. Diam. at top, 94 mm; diam. of plate, 56 mm. Fit stem end of funnel with rubber tubing ca 4″ long which can be plugged with plastic or cork stopper.

(b) *Sodium hypochlorite soln.*—Approx. 0.25%.

Dil. 5 ml com. NaOCl soln, 5.25% by wt, with 95 ml H_2O. Prep. fresh daily.

40.006 *Determination*

(a) *Cocoa.*—Mix 50 g cocoa into 500 ml hot (55–70°) 2% detergent soln, **40.003**(o). Pour portion-wise onto No. 230 sieve, **40.002**(q), and wash with forcible stream of 55–70° tap H_2O, using aerator, **40.002**(a). Remove fat by tilting sieve ca 20° and play H_2O thru liq. which collects at side. When fat and fine material have washed thru and foam is gone, transfer residue to 2 L trap flask, **40.002**(h)(*3*), with H_2O. (Use only glass funnels and beakers; insect fragments stick to polyethylene.) Add ca 500 ml H_2O and boil 10 min. Cool to room temp. and add H_2O to total vol. of 1 L. Pour 50 ml heptane, **40.003**(q), down stirring rod. Lower magnetic stir-ring bar, **40.002**(s), into flask on stirring rod stopper. Raise rod above liq. and secure with clamp. Stir magnetically, **40.004**(b), 5 min. After stirring, fill flask with H_2O. Let stand 30 min, gently stirring bottom layer every 4–5 min with stirring bar for first 20 min. Trap off heptane. Add 35 ml more heptane, stir gently 1 min, let stand 15 min, and again trap off. Filter combined trappings, using the Hirsch funnel. Remove paper and examine micro-scopically for hairs. Return paper to Hirsch funnel in suction flask. Wash thoroly with H_2O. (If paper contains alcohol and glycerol from examination for hairs, wash first with alcohol and then with H_2O.) Apply vac. until paper appears dry, turn off vac., and plug rubber tubing with stopper. Cover paper with ca ⅛″ (5–7 ml) NaOCl soln and let stand until bleaching of cocoa tissue is complete, but <30 min. Maintain level of soln entire period and do not let soln flow over rim of paper. Turn on vac., which will remove stopper. Wash paper with H_2O. Examine microscopically for insect fragments and other ex-traneous materials.

(b) *Chocolate.*—Use 100 g finely shaven chocolate and proceed as in (a).

(c) *Press cake.*—Heat sample (usually very hard lumps) 2–3 hr at 60–70° and break into 0.5″ or smaller pieces. Mix 50 g into 500 ml hot 2% deter-gent soln, **40.003**(o), in 800 ml beaker. Stir with butter stirrer, **40.002**(e), at low speed 2–3 hr until completely dispersed, or let soak overnight. Stir thoroly, pour portionwise onto No. 230 sieve, **40.002**(q), and proceed as in (a).

Ground Coffee and Coffee Substitutes

(*Caution: See* **46.011, 46.040,** and **46.056.**)

40.007 Filth—Official First Action

(a) *Heavy filth, sand, and soil.*—Weigh 100 g in 600 ml beaker, add 350 ml $CHCl_3$, and boil 15 min, stir-ring occasionally. Wash down sides of beaker with $CHCl_3$. Let mixt. cool and settle 15 min with oc-casional stirring of top layer. Carefully decant $CHCl_3$ and floating tissue onto smooth ca 15 cm filter

paper in buchner without disturbing heavy residue on bottom of beaker. Repeat decanting with small amts of $CHCl_3$ until practically no plant tissue re-mains with residue on bottom of beaker. (Sp gr of $CHCl_3$ may be increased by addn of CCl_4, if neces-sary to float plant tissue. Do not add CCl_4 beyond 1 part CCl_4 to 1 part $CHCl_3$.) Transfer residue from beaker to ashless filter paper and examine for filth. If residue is appreciable, ignite filter and det. wt sand, soil, etc.

(b) *Light filth.*—Air-dry decanted material on paper overnight or for 1 hr in oven at ca 80°, trans-fer dried material to 2 L trap flask, and add 400 ml hot H_2O. Boil 15 min and, if necessary, add small amts cold H_2O intermittently to prevent foaming. Cool mixt. to <20°. Trap off twice, using 35 ml and 25 ml portions heptane, **40.003**(q), resp. In first trapping, after stirring heptane, let stand 5 min be-fore filling flask. Filter and examine microscopically.

Aphids in Hops
Light Filth (2)—Official First Action
(AOAC–ASBC Method)

40.008 *Reagents and Apparatus*

(a) *Flotation soln.*—Satd $Na_2B_4O_7$ soln, 100 g borax/L H_2O.

(b) *Iodine stain.*—Dissolve 0.5 g I and 1.5 g KI in 25 ml H_2O.

(c) *Blender.*—"Intensifier" Twin Shell Blender, Patterson-Kelly Co., East Stroudsburg, PA 18301, or equiv.

40.009 *Preparation of Sample*

Place sample in blender, using 4 qt size shell for small samples or 8 qt size shell for large samples. Activate blender and "intensifier" for 1 min inter-vals until blending and breakage of strigs are com-plete. Draw off 10 g samples from bottom plate.

40.010 *Determination*

Mix 10 g representative sample in 100 ml satd borax soln in 2 L Wildman trap flask. Bring to *slow* boil. Keep mixt. from boiling onto sides of flask by keeping boiling to min. and by washing down sides with H_2O. Boil 1.5 hr, and cool to room temp. Fill flask to 1600 ml with H_2O, and 35 ml heptane, **40.003**(q), and stir vigorously 10 sec. Fill flask with H_2O, let stand 30 min, and trap off. Perform second trapping, using 25 ml heptane, stirring 10 sec, and letting flask stand 15 min. Wash neck of flask with isopropanol. Pour trappings onto ruled paper(s), add 10–12 drops I stain, and examine microscopically. If excess plant tissue is present in trappings, pour trap-pings thru 5″ No. 10 sieve held over paper. Wash plant tissue on sieve with alcohol onto filter paper to remove any adhering insects.

Count as aphid any whole aphid or part contg head. Count individually aphid cast skins and other insects.

40.011   Gross Contamination

See **40.105.**

40.012   Heavy and Light Filth

See **40.106.**

DAIRY PRODUCTS

Sediment Test on Milk (3)—
Official Final Action

40.013   *Apparatus and Materials*

(a) *Tester.*—Simply constructed, easily cleaned, and adjustable between samplings to permit sanitary removal of used disk and replacement with clean disk. Before using, check tester for reproducibility as in **40.014.** Milk or sediment must not by-pass disk. Select type according to method of sampling:

(1) *For mixed sample method.*—Pressure, gravity, or vac. type: (a) For 1 gal. sample use any suitable device that will filter sample thru disk with exposed area 1⅛″ diam. (b) For 1 pt sample, equip single-unit, off-bottom tester with special head (available from Sediment Testing Supply Co., 20 E. Jackson Blvd, Chicago, IL 60604) having filtering area 0.40″ diam., or use any suitable device having filtering area 0.40″ diam.

(2) *For off-bottom method.*—Single-unit type for intake of 1 pt on upstroke of plunger and discharge thru disk on down stroke, or 2-unit type, contg 1 unit for removal of 1 pt milk from bottom of can and another for filtering sample. Use sampling device long enough to permit reaching bottom of milk can, with filtering area 1⅛″ diam.

(b) *Cotton sediment disks.*—Std lintine cotton disks or pads, 1¼″ diam., for use over flat wire screen in tester to expose filtration area 1⅛″ diam. Disk must not contain phenolic resins or other chemicals that may contaminate milk.

Test sediment disks as follows: Filter 12 mg std sediment mixt. (60 ml aliquot (d)) thru pad, using clean flask to catch filtrate. Transfer filtrate to beaker, rinse flask 3 times with H_2O, and add rinsings to beaker. Filter filtrate thru 7 or 9 cm S&S White Ribbon paper (or equiv.) that has been washed with ca 200 ml H_2O, dried to constant wt at 100°, and cooled in covered dish in desiccator before weighing. Thoroly rinse beaker and paper with H_2O and dry to constant wt as above. Test ≥3 disks; av. wt sediment passing thru each disk should be ≤2.8 mg. In addn, std disk prepd from fine mixt. should not appear to have sediment buried beneath surface.

(c) *Sediment filtering apparatus.*—(1) *For 1⅛″ diameter stds.*—App. must hold 1¼″ sediment disk and have effective filtering area 1⅛″ diam. This 1⅛″ area must be unobstructed except for wire screen or wire screen and perforated plate support for filter disk. App. should be supported in filter flask so vac. can be used for rapid filtration or flask air outlet can be closed to stop filtration. App. should have ca 80°

funnel with min. capacity of 80 ml and max. capacity of 450 ml. Test app. by filtering H_2O suspension of C thru std disk. Disk should have clean, sharply defined border. When sediment suspension is filtered, sediment should be evenly distributed over disk with no pattern formation. Figs 40:4 and 40:5 show suitable app.

(2) *For 0.40″ diameter stds.*—Vac. type that holds 1¼″ sediment disk and uses only 0.40″ diam. filtering area. Test app. as in (1).

(d) *Preparation of coarse std sediment disks.*—Prep. uniform mixt. of oven-dried (100°) materials which meet following screening specifications. Grind all materials by hand with mortar and pestle.

	Per cent
Cow manure, thru No. 40	53
Cow manure, thru No. 20, retained on No. 40	2
Garden soil, thru No. 40	27
Charcoal, thru No. 40	14
Charcoal, thru No. 20, retained on No. 40	4

Place 2.00 g above mixt. in 100 ml vol. flask, thoroly wet with 4–6 ml *0.1% Aerosol OT soln* (prep. 1–2% soln in acetone and dil. with H_2O) or other suitable wetting agent, add 46 ml 0.75% carob bean gum soln prepd as in **40.003(ee),** and bring level of liq. just into neck of flask by adding 50% (by wt) sucrose soln. Let stand ≥30 min, add few drops alcohol, and dil. to vol. with the sucrose soln. Mix thoroly, pour into 250 ml beaker or other suitable container, and stir with mech. or magnetic stirrer at speed (ca 200–300 rpm) such that mixt. is thoroly agitated but very little air is whipped into suspension. Observe with bright reflected light to see that suspension is uniformly stirred.

Transfer, while stirring, 10 ml portion (200 mg std sediment) with large-tip, graduated pipet to 1 L vol. flask, and dil. to vol. with the 50% by wt sucrose soln. When thoroly mixed, each ml contains 0.2 mg sediment. Mix, pour into 1.5 L beaker, and stir with mech. stirrer as above. If particles accumulate on side of beaker, wash down with portions of sediment suspension or push under with tip of pipet. While stirring, pipet definite vols of sediment mixt. and add to ¾ pt filtered sweet skim milk. Mix thoroly and pass mixt. thru std sediment disk in filtering app., (c)(1). Gently pour milk down side of filtering app. and filter with very little or no suction. Wash container promptly with ¼ pt filtered skim milk. Let last portion of milk flow thru pad with no suction applied. If sediment does not appear to be evenly distributed over pad, add 15 or 20 ml skim milk and let it filter thru without suction. Repeat addn until sediment appears evenly distributed. Suck air thru disk ca 1 min to remove excess skim milk.

For permanent record, mount and spray disks with 40% HCHO soln or with alc. soln contg 2.5 g each of menthol and thymol in 100 ml. Alternatively, if most of milk is removed by thoro aspiration, no preservative is needed. Dried pads may be coated with colorless plastic cement dild with 1–3 vols acetone so that mixt. is thin enough to pour easily. If acetone dissolves pigment from paper and stains pads, place pads on flat glass plate for treating with dild cement. Move pads while drying to prevent sticking to glass. When pads are almost dry, place light wt (*e.g.*, petri dish) directly on them to prevent curling. Pads may be mounted with plastic cement. (Std disks made from manure contg large amt of chlorophyll cannot be coated with plastic cement, as solv. exts chlorophyll and stains pad green. Use this method of preserving pads only if there is no leaching of pigment from sediment on addn of dild plastic cement.)

Following above method, prep. series of disks contg sediment remaining from 0.0, 0.2, 0.5, 1.0, 2.0, 3.0, 4.0, 5.0, 6.0, 7.0, 8.0, 9.0, 10.0, 12.0, and 14.0 mg std mixt. Mark disks to show quantity of sediment (mg) used to prep. each pad. Do not use as std any pad on which sediment is not evenly distributed.

For comparison with tests on samples, entire series of disks may be used, but usually it is more convenient to select few disks denoting variations in grade that are applicable to particular investiga-

tions being made. If grading charts are prepd and reports made, indicate on chart and report whether mixed or off-bottom sample was used. If stds are to be handled or used for appreciable length of time, place them under glass, transparent plastic sheets, or other suitable materials. In using stds, use either of following methods: (*1*) Grade sediment disk to nearest std disk regardless of whether actual quantity of sediment is above or below std; or (*2*) grade sediment disk of sample as "more than __mg" or "less than __ mg." Choose stds· to fit method of grading. When grading disks, disregard gross pieces of material (whole flies, hairs, large chunks of dirt or manure, etc.) but if such matter is present, list each sep. on report.

(**e**) *Preparation of fine std sediment disks.*—(*1*) 1⅛″ *diameter stds.*—Grind oven-dried (100°) cow manure, garden soil, and wood charcoal (not powd) in impact mill, Wiley mill, or other suitable type, using fine screen in mill. Pass cow manure thru Wiley mill or similar type 2 or 3 times. Sift materials sep. in max. batches of 50 g as follows: Dry 25–50 g at 100° for 3–4 hr. While still warm place in 8″ No. 140 sieve nested over No. 230. Add cover and receiver. Shake

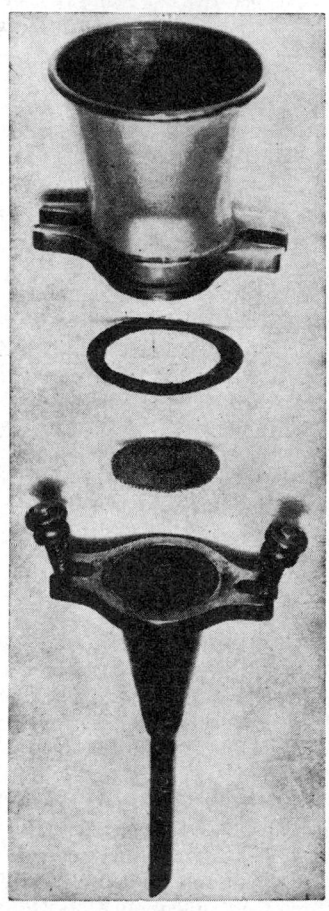

FIG. 40:4—Sediment filtering apparatus, unassembled

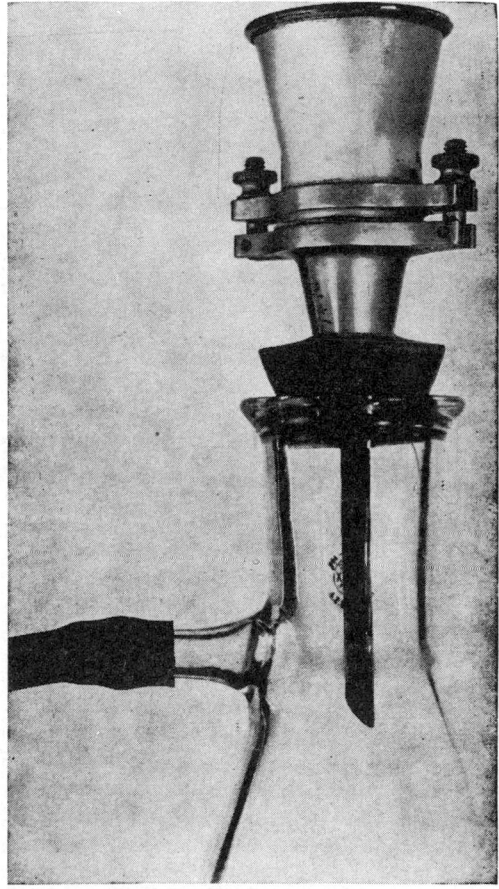

FIG. 40:5—Sediment filtering apparatus, assembled

nested sieves by hand 5 min at ca 120 strokes/min. Sep. sieves and brush off material adhering to underside of No. 230 and discard before emptying sieve. Dry material retained on No. 230 ca 2 hr (max. batch 20 g) and resift 5 min as above. Sep. sieves and brush off material adhering to underside of No. 230 before emptying. Use "on 230" fractions from second siftings and mix uniformly in following proportions: Cow manure 66%, garden soil 28%, and charcoal 6%.

Combine above 2 "on 140" fractions of each of the 3 materials and resift as above, except use No. 120 sieve nested over No. 140. Resift new "on 140" fraction, retaining "on 140" fraction from second sifting. (Dry before each sifting and brush material from underside of No. 140 sieve before emptying.) Mix manure, soil, and charcoal in above proportions.

Place 1.80 g mixt. from "on 230" fractions and 0.20 g mixt. from "on 140" fractions in 100 ml vol. flask. Proceed as in (d), beginning "...thoroly wet with 4–6 ml *0.1% Aerosol OT soln*..." except use H_2O instead of 50% sucrose for dilg 10 ml aliquot to 1 L.

Where (d) states "While stirring, pipet definite vols..." proceed as follows: Det. approx. funnel capacity of filtering app., (c)(*1*), by pouring H_2O into assembled app. with filter flask air outlet closed. Include H_2O that filters thru as part of funnel capacity. While stirring, pipet aliquots of sediment suspension into beakers. Add H_2O to make total vol. 20–50 ml less than funnel capacity, using min. total vol. of 60 ml and max. of 400 ml.

With filter flask air outlet closed to prevent filtration, mix dild aliquot and pour into app., (c)(*1*), fitted with wet std disk, (b). (Use alcohol or wetting agent if necessary to wet disk.) Add 20–50 ml H_2O to beaker and rinse by swirling. Pour into funnel, keeping lip of beaker touching surface of H_2O if possible. (Rinse H_2O should nearly fill funnel if capacity is ≤450 ml.) Open flask air outlet. After H_2O has filtered thru pad, apply vac. and aspirate disk for ca 1 min. Remove pad and let dry in covered dish. If sediment is not evenly distributed, discard pad. After some practice, ca 75% of pads prepd should be acceptable. No preservative is required. Pads may be coated with dild plastic cement and used as in (d).

(*2*) *0.40″ diameter stds.*—While stirring, pipet 100 ml above dild fine suspension into suitable container and dil. to 800 ml with H_2O. Each ml contains 0.025 mg sediment and when filtered thru 0.40″ diam. area is equiv. to 0.2 mg filtered thru 1⅛″ diam. area. Prep. series of stds by filtering suitable aliquots thru disks in app., (c)(*2*). Dil. each aliquot to 50–60 ml and filter with min. suction. Rinse beaker with small vol. H_2O and add to funnel. Carefully rinse side of funnel with small vol. H_2O. Use min. suction necessary to remove excess H_2O from disk. Designate 0.40″ diam. stds as "___mg equiv." and use in grading 1 pt mixed sample test disks in same manner as 1⅛″ diam. stds are used.

(f) *Photographic stds.*—Photographic stds (obtainable from Photography Div., Office of Information, US Dept. of Agriculture, Washington, DC 20250) may be used as guide in grading sediment pads, but it is preferable to use actual disks prepd as in (d) or (e). Stds that more nearly resemble disk being graded should be used in each case. Do not use photographs that have become faded, stained, soiled, or otherwise damaged.

40.014   Checking Sediment Testers

To check sediment testing devices, proceed as follows: Measure actual quantity of milk delivered to assure that 1 pt is withdrawn and passes thru disk. Transfer 10 ml 2% sediment suspension in sucrose soln, **40.013**(d), using large-tip, graduated pipet, to 10 gal. clean filtered H_2O in clean milk can. After thoroly agitating mixt., remove 1 pt with clean pt measure and filter thru 1⅛″ diam. area of sediment disk, **40.013**(b), mounted on suitable funnel of correct size, *e.g.*, **40.013**(c)(*1*). After thoro agitation of contents of milk can, again remove pt sample with the sediment testing device and pass thru sediment disk in exactly same manner as for testing milk. Repeat this operation with the tester several times to det. whether all disks so obtained give same sediment as disk obtained by filtering thru funnel, **40.013**(c)(*1*).

40.015   Collection of Sample

(a) *Mixed sample method.*—For retail containers, 5 to 10 gal. cans, and storage tanks, use 1 pt or 1 gal. samples. Before mixing milk, transfer with small strainer any floating extraneous matter, such as flies, hairs, large chunks of debris, etc., to mounted disk, **40.016**(a), or mount on sep. disk, properly identified. Thoroly mix milk in container before removing test portion. Avoid contamination of sample with foreign matter on stirrers or by any other means. For retail containers take 1 pt from mixed container or composite sufficient number to make 1 gal. Proceed as in **40.016**(a).

(b) *Off-bottom method.*—For 5 to 10 gal. cans take pt sample with either type of off-bottom tester from unstirred can of milk. Before withdrawing sample, remove with small strainer any floating extraneous matter as in (a). Take sample ≤¼″ off bottom of unstirred can of milk by inserting sampler and, during upstroke of plunger, drawing head of instrument once across diam. of can bottom or around circumference if can has high center. Expel milk with gun in can and then with short stroke remove excess fluid from pad. Proceed as in **40.016**(b).

40.016   Determination

(a) *Mixed samples.*—Pass sample thru properly adjusted disk, **40.013**(b), held in correct position in tester. Warm 1-pt sample to 90–100°F and filter thru restricted area 0.40″ diam., **40.013**(a)(*1*). If single-unit off-bottom tester with special head is used, warm sample larger than 1 pt to 90–100°F and withdraw 1 pt with tester while stirring, or draw 1 pt into tester and warm milk by holding tester under running hot H_2O before discharging milk thru disk.

Warm 1 gal. sample to 80–90°F or filter cold thru $1\frac{1}{8}''$ diam. area of disk, **40.013(b)**. If milk is filtered at temp. <90°F, rinse disk by filtering ca $\frac{1}{2}$ pt sediment-free warm (90–100°F) H_2O thru disk before removing from tester. If milk is to be salvaged, do not dil. with H_2O. (Milk varies in its rate of flow thru disks; pasteurized milk may be more difficult to filter than raw milk. Other factors influencing rate of flow are temp., fat content, degree of clumping of fat globules, stage of lactation, presence of mastitic milk, and amt of sediment in sample.)

Remove disk from tester and mount on special sized paper or store in individual transparent waxed envelope. (If disk is placed on paper or in envelope while still moist, drying milk acts as adhesive.) Grade by comparison with std disks, **40.013(d)** or **(e)**, and indicate on report whether pad was graded wet or dry. (Character of sediment may be detd by microscopic examination.)

To prevent decomposition on storage, disk may be sprayed with HCHO soln or alc. menthol-thymol soln as in **40.013(d)**. Do not use glue to affix disk to paper; if disk becomes detached, moisten with few drops H_2O and remount. Protect from contamination.

(b) *Off-bottom samples.*—Remove disk from tester, **40.015(b)**, and proceed as in **(a)**, third par., beginning "mount on special sized paper..."

Filth in Butter, Cheese, Cheese Products, Dried Milk Products, and Dairy Products in General—Official First Action

Use following methods independently or in various combinations. Weigh 225 g, except in **40.021**, into suitable container and use S&S ruled No. 8 paper for filtration. Cut hard cheese into small pieces.

40.017 *Butter*

Place container in H_2O bath or oven at ca 80°. When fat seps, filter directly thru paper with suction, retaining most of curd and H_2O in container. After fat passes thru, filter remaining material. To facilitate filtration of curd, wash paper with near boiling H_2O during filtration. (For butter not filterable by this process, use **40.019**.) Examine paper microscopically.

40.018 *Evaporated Milk, Condensed Milk, Sweet Cream, Spray-Dried Whole or Skim Milk*

Reconstitute dried or concd products. Dil. reconstituted product with equal vol. hot H_2O, hot 3% $Na_2C_2O_4$ soln, or hot 2% Na_2CO_3 soln, and filter with suction. During filtration, continually wash paper with stream of near boiling H_2O to prevent accumulation of layer of particles which clog paper. Examine paper microscopically.

40.019 *Soft and Semi-soft Cheese and Sour Cream; Some Dried Whole and Skim Milks; and Butter that Cannot Be Filtered by 40.017*

Heat sample in 1.5–2 L beaker with 800–1000 ml H_3PO_4 (1 + 40) with continuous stirring with slow speed mech. stirrer, **40.002(e)**, until mixt. is boiling, or add cheese to boiling H_3PO_4 soln, and continue boiling up to 20 min to disperse. Filter, without letting mixt. accumulate on paper, continually washing filter with stream of near boiling H_2O to prevent clogging. When filtration is impeded, add H_2O, dil. (1–5%) alkali, dil. H_3PO_4 soln, or hot alcohol until paper clears; then resume addn of sample suspension and H_2O. Examine paper microscopically.

40.020 *Hard Cheeses, Hard Skim, Part Skim Milk Cheeses (Romano, Ricotta, Feta, Pecorino, Sardo, Goats' Milk Cheeses, Sbrinz, Goya, Whey Cheeses, etc.) (4)*

(Not applicable to cheeses contg herbs, spices, or molds thruout)

Prep. cheese for sampling by trimming and discarding thin layers to remove all "old" cut surfaces and to keep paraffin coating and mold out of sample. Cut and break up 225 g trimmed cheese into 4 L beaker. Add ca 700 ml ca 55° filtered H_2O. Set beaker under mech. stirrer, **40.002(e)**, and stir 15 min, maintaining mixt. at 55°. Add 100 ml 20% aq. Na_4EDTA soln, stir, and adjust mixt. to pH 8 with NH_4OH or dil. HCl (1 + 2). Rinse sides of beaker free of adhering cheese particles with ca 60° H_2O. Maintain pH 8 by addn of NH_4OH and keep adding ca 60° H_2O to dil. cheese mixt. to ca 3 L. If foaming occurs, place wet vegetable parchment Patapar paper (available from Patterson Paper Co., Bristol, PA 19007), split to accommodate stirrer blades, over top of beaker to break foam. Continue stirring until cheese becomes finely dispersed.

Cool dispersion to 40° and adjust to pH 8 with NH_4OH or HCl (1 + 2). Add 300 ml pancreatin soln, **40.003(x)**, (except use 600 ml pancreatin soln for ricotta). Let mixt. digest at ≤40° with continued stirring ca 1.5 hr. Maintain pH 8 by addn of NH_4OH.

After digestion, place beaker on hot plate and heat to 65–68°, continuing mech. stirring. Adjust to pH 6.0±0.2 with HCl (1 + 2). Carefully adjust stirrer blades close to bottom of beaker to pick up any cheese particles which settle. Continue stirring 15 min or until cheese appears completely solubilized. Rinse inside of beaker, stirrer blades, etc., with ca 65° H_2O and filter thru ruled paper, using ca 65° H_2O and later alcohol to rinse beaker. If filtration becomes slow (e.g., cream cheese), let paper clear, wash with alcohol, and use addnl paper. Mixt. will filter more easily if No. 60 screen (ca 5 cm diam.) is placed under paper and small amt of mixt. is allowed to suck dry before filtering is continued. Examine paper microscopically.

40.021   *Casein (5)*

Weigh 50 g sample into 1 L beaker. Slowly stir in 170 ml 20% Na$_4$EDTA soln until well mixed with sample. With constant stirring, bring vol. to 1 L with hot tap H$_2$O (55–70°). Wet sieve on No. 230 sieve, **40.002(q)**, with forcible spray of hot tap H$_2$O until foam subsides. Wash sieve retainings into beaker and pour onto ruled filter paper. Examine papers microscopically.

40.022   *Cheese Containing Mold,*
Plant Tissues, and Spices

Disperse cheese by **40.019** or first par. of **40.020**. Pour thru No. 140 sieve, **40.002(q)**, washing thoroly with forcible stream of H$_2$O. Transfer material retained on sieve to beaker. Add 200 ml 2% H$_3$PO$_4$, boil until lumpy residue dissolves, and pour again thru No. 140 sieve, washing thoroly with forcible stream of hot H$_2$O. Transfer material on sieve with ca 200 ml 60% alcohol to trap flask and cool. Trap off, using heptane, **40.003(q)**, and H$_2$O, filter, and examine microscopically.

40.023   Sediment in Cream, Butter, Cheese, Cheese Products, Dried Milk Products, and Dairy Products in General— Official First Action

(a) *Rapid method for sweet cream and cream in which curd is easy to disperse and in absence of mold.*— Place 1 pt sample in beaker or pan of convenient size, ca 2 L, and add ca 1 pt hot H$_2$O (70–90°). More or less H$_2$O may be added so that mixt. when ready for filtration is at 45–60°. Remove whole flies or other large filth particles which float to surface and which would be broken up by stirrer. Place these on sediment pad when completed. Place pan under malted milk stirrer, and add, while stirring, 25 ml 40% Calgon soln, **40.003(g)**; if necessary, add more Calgon soln to make mixt. alk. to litmus. Stir 30–60 sec or until curd is broken up. Filter with vac. thru std sediment disk, **40.013(b)**. If pad clogs, filter remaining portion thru fresh disk. Rinse pan and funnel with hot H$_2$O onto sediment disk.

(b) *Other dairy products.*—Proceed as in **40.019** or **40.020**, and filter thru std sediment disk, **40.013(b)**. Violent mech. agitation, such as is provided by malted milk stirrer, may be used to faciliate dispersion of product.

Compare with std sediment disks, **40.013(d)**, **(e)(1)**, or **(f)**.

40.024   ★   Mold in Butter (6)—   ★
Official Final Action

(a) Carefully examine surface of sample and note any visible mold growth. To eliminate possibility of contamination by surface mold, scrape off and discard ⅛″ of surface. Weigh, in 50 ml beaker, 1 g butter obtained from exposed surface. Add 7 g hot (50–60°) stabilizer soln, **40.003(ee)**. Stir until mixt. is uniform and fat globules are 0.1–0.2 mm diam.

Mount portion of mixt. on Howard cell, **40.002(m)(1)**, and est. mold as in **40.085**. Consider fields pos. when single filament or combined length of 2 longest filaments exceeds ⅙ diam. of field.

(b) *Alternative procedure (staining).*—Add 1 or 2 drops 5% aq. crystal violet soln to stabilizer-butter mixt. after butter is melted. Mix prepn thoroly and prep. slide as above.

NUTS AND NUT PRODUCTS
Shelled Nuts (Except Pecans)
Light Filth (7)—Official First Action
40.025   *Apparatus and Reagents*

(a) *Buchner funnel.*—100 mm plate diam., Coors No. 3, or equiv.

(b) *Filter paper.*—S&S No. 588; 24 and 32 cm, folded, or equiv.

(c) *60% Alcohol-calcium chloride soln.*—To each 3 L 60% alcohol (amt for 1 analysis) add 200 g anhyd. CaCl$_2$. Stir well until salt dissolves. Cloudiness from traces of CaCO$_3$ will clear up during analysis when soln is acidified.

40.026   *Nutmeats, All Sizes, Except Pecans*
(*Caution: See* **46.039, 46.040, 46.055,**
and **46.056.**)

Weigh 100 g sample into 1.5 L beaker. Add 600 ml CHCl$_3$; boil 15 min. Prep. 24 cm paper in buchner by moistening with H$_2$O and forming around base of 1 L beaker. Place 7 cm disk of bolting cloth, **40.002(d)**, (mesh size not critical) in funnel, insert paper, apply vac., and press moistened paper until good seal is obtained. Rinse paper with isopropanol. Quant. transfer nutmeats and CHCl$_3$ onto previously prepd paper. Maintain suction on nutmeats in buchner 5 min after visible dripping ceases. Quant. transfer nutmeats on paper to 2 L trap flask, **40.002(h)(3)**. Scrape all fines from paper with spatula and finally rinse paper clean with 60% alcohol-CaCl$_2$ soln. Bring vol. to 1 L with 60% alcohol-CaCl$_2$ soln and add 50 ml HCl. Add magnetic stirring bar, **40.002(s)**, to flask. Place flask on magnetic stirring hot plate, **40.002(r)**, and heat to *full boil* with gentle stirring. Immediately transfer flask to cool stirring unit and add 40 ml mineral oil, **40.003(w)**, by pouring down stirring rod. Stir magnetically, **40.004(b)**, 2 min.

Fill with 60% alcohol-CaCl$_2$ soln and gently stir 5–10 sec with stirring rod. Let stand 2 min and trap off. Add 25 ml mineral oil, hand stir gently 30 sec, and let stand 10 min. Repeat trapping. Wash flask neck thoroly with isopropanol, and transfer washings to beaker with trappings. Filter onto ruled paper and examine microscopically.

Pecans, All Sizes—Official First Action
40.027   Light Filth (7)
(*Caution: See* **46.040** and **46.056.**)

Prep. 32 cm filter paper by forming around base of 1 L beaker. Place paper into 1.5 L beaker and weigh

100 g sample into filter paper cup. Add 400 ml $CHCl_3$ and boil 5 min. After few min cooling, lift paper and drain. Repeat 5 min boil and drain with two addnl 400 ml portions $CHCl_3$. Proceed as in **40.026**, beginning "Place 7 cm disk of bolting cloth . . ."

40.028 Heavy Filth

(*Caution: See* **46.011, 46.039,** *and* **46.073.**)

Weigh 100 g sample into 600 ml beaker. Add ca 350 ml pet ether and boil gently 30 min, adding pet ether to maintain original vol. Decant solv., taking care not to lose any coarse nut tissue, and discard. Add ca 300 ml $CHCl_3$ to beaker and let settle 10–15 min. Pour off floating nutmeats and ca ⅔ of the $CHCl_3$ thru 15 cm (or larger) paper in buchner, without disturbing residue in bottom of beaker. Repeat sepn with smaller quantities of mixt. of $CHCl_3$ and CCl_4 (1 + 1) until residue in beaker is relatively free of nutmeat particles. Transfer residue in beaker to ashless paper and examine for heavy filth. If appreciable amt of sand and soil is present, ignite paper in weighed crucible at ca 500° and weigh.

40.029 Curculio Larvae in Pecan Pieces (8)

Weigh 115 g (ca ¼ lb) sample into 1.5 L beaker and add magnetic stirring bar, **40.002(s)**. Add 300 ml undild isopropanol and stir on magnetic stirrer, **40.002(r)**, 5–10 sec. Add H_2O (200 ml for midget pieces and 300 ml for small, small medium, medium, and mixed pieces) and stir 5–10 sec on stirrer. After few sec, gently agitate settled nutmeats with stirring rod to release any entrapped curculio. Remove all floating material and examine for curculio larvae. Reclaim flotation soln by pouring thru No. 12 sieve and use for one addnl sample.

Shredded Coconut

40.030 Filth—Official First Action

(a) *Heavy filth.*—Proceed as in **40.049**, using 100 g sample in 800 ml beaker.

(b) *Light filth.*—Weigh 100 g sample into 2 L beaker. Add 1 L hot 5% borax soln, boil 10–15 min, pour thru 8″ No. 140 sieve, **40.002(q)**, and wash well with hot H_2O. Using wide aperture funnel, transfer coconut to 2 L trap flask, **40.002(h)(3)**, with ca 700 ml 60% alcohol. Wash sieve with forcible stream of hot H_2O, collecting final residue at one edge of screen and transferring to trap flask with stream of 60% alcohol. Add 50 ml heptane, **40.003(q)**, to trap flask and mix thoroly. Fill flask with 60% alcohol. Let stand 30 min with occasional gentle beating and lifting of coconut material to free any rodent hairs adhering to it. Trap off heptane layer, using 60% alcohol as rinse, and filter thru ruled paper. Add 25 ml heptane to trap flask and make second extn. After 30 min, trap off, and filter on second paper. Examine papers microscopically.

Peanut Butter

40.031 ★ Preparation of Sample— ★ Official First Action

Examine individually at least 3, and preferably 6, jars. If jars contain <1 lb each, make 3–6 composites of ≥2 jars each so that composite samples will be ca 1 lb. Remove contents of each jar and mix thoroly, preferably in evapg dishes of convenient size, using heavy table fork or spatula. Peanut butter after warming may also be mixed in the jar by means of mixer, **40.002(e)**, equipped with stiff paddles. If large number of jars is to be examined, make composite samples by thoroly mixing contents of 3–6 jars of equal size.

40.032 ★ Water-Insoluble Inorganic ★ Residue ("WIIR") and Excreta— Official First Action

(*Caution: See* **46.011, 46.039, 46.040, 46.056,** *and* **46.073.**)

Weigh 100 g sample into 250 ml beaker (hooked-lip type), add ca 10 ml pet ether, and mix thoroly. Continue to add pet ether, mixing thoroly until ca 150 ml has been added. Cover, let settle 25 min, and decant 100 ml pet ether layer and floating light tissue without losing any coarse peanut tissue. Add ca 125 ml pet ether to residue and mix, let settle 15 min, and decant 100 ml as before. Repeat with third ca 125 ml addn of pet ether, stir, wash down sides of beaker with stream of pet ether, let settle 10 min, and decant 100 ml. Discard all decanted portions of pet ether.

Evap. remainder of pet ether from residue in beaker; gentle heat may be used. Add 150 ml $CHCl_3$ to residue and mix thoroly; cover beaker and let settle 20 min. Stir top layer several times during this period. Carefully decant $CHCl_3$ and floating peanut tissue onto 15 cm paper in buchner without disturbing heavy residue in bottom of beaker.

Repeat extn with small amts of $CHCl_3$, rinsing all particles from sides of beaker. At this point watch for fragments of rodent excreta pellets on top of NaCl in bottom of beaker; do not decant them. (If sample contains considerable peanut skin, it may be necessary to use mixt. of $CHCl_3$ and just enough CCl_4 to float skin particles away from heavy residue of NaCl, sand, etc.) Dry residue in air.

Add 50 ml HCl (1 + 35) to residue in beaker; then add 90 ml boiling H_2O and let stand 30 min with occasional stirring to dissolve any phosphate, carbonate, or anhydrite ($CaSO_4$) included with the NaCl. Decant liq. thru ashless filter in 60° glass funnel and finally transfer residue with hot H_2O. Test filtrate for sulfate by adding 5 ml satd $BaCl_2$ soln. Wash residue on filter several times with hot H_2O.

If test for sulfate in filtrate was pos., test residue on filter by placing clean beaker or test tube under funnel and treating residue with 25 ml HCl (1 + 35), adding little at time. Test filtrate with 20 drops satd $BaCl_2$ soln (fine white ppt of $BaSO_4$ indicates presence of anhydrite in residue on filter; allow 5 min for ppt to appear). Wash residue on filter with hot H_2O until all HCl is removed.

Examine residue microscopically for fragments of rodent excreta pellets (identified by presence of rodent hair fragments in mass), insect excreta pellets, and other filth. Ignite paper in weighed crucible over medium Bunsen flame or in furnace at ca 500°. Cool, and weigh crucible and contents to nearest 0.5 mg. If "WIIR" is excessive and application of above test indicates that all $CaSO_4$ has not been removed, make quant. detn of either Ca or sulfate in "WIIR" in crucible, as in **33.053** or **33.052**. Calc. this wt to $CaSO_4$ and correct wt of "WIIR."

Light Filth (9)—Official First Action

40.033 *Reagent*

Detergent soln.—Dissolve sep. 20 g USP Na lauryl sulfate and 10 g tech. $Na_2B_7O_4 . 10H_2O$ in H_2O, combine, and dil. to 1 L.

40.034 *Determination*

Weigh 100 g sample into 1.5 L beaker and heat on steam bath until softened. Add 1 L filtered hot detergent soln, and stir well. Heat 10 min *in* steam bath. Stir well, pour portionwise onto No. 230 sieve, **40.002(q)**, and wash with forcible stream of 55–70° tap H_2O, using aerator, **40.002(a)**. When foam is gone, transfer material on sieve to 2 L trap flask, **40.002(h)(3)**, with 55% alcohol (or 40% isopropanol) and bring vol. to 1 L. Add 50 ml HCl. Lower magnetic stirring bar, **40.002(s)**, into flask on stirring rod stopper. Heat to boiling and boil 10 min while slowly stirring on magnetic stirring hot plate, **40.002(r)**, with stirring bar.

Transfer flask to unheated stirring unit and immediately add 40 ml mineral oil, **40.003(w)**, by pouring down stirring rod. Stir magnetically, **40.004(b)**, 2 min. Fill with deaerated 55% alcohol (or 40% isopropanol) and gently stir 5–10 sec with stoppered rod. Let stand 5 min. Trap off. Add 25 ml mineral oil, hand stir gently 30 sec, and let stand 5 min. Repeat trapping. Wash flask neck thoroly with isopropanol. Filter onto ruled paper and examine microscopically.

40.035 ★ **Rocks and Decomposed** ★ **Peanuts in Coarse Peanut Butter—Official First Action**

(*Caution: See* **46.040** *and* **46.049**.)

Remove entire contents of jar to 1.5 L beaker or other suitable container. Add ca 700 ml CCl_4 and mix thoroly, using mixer, **40.002(e)**, if convenient. Rinse jar with CCl_4 and add rinsings to beaker. Let mixt. stand ≥15 min with occasional stirring. Decant ca ⅔ of mixt. and add ca 200 ml CCl_4. Let stand 5 min and decant. Wash down sides of beaker with CCl_4 and repeat decantation until residue is free from peanut tissue. Save all decanted material.

Dry residue in beaker and wash out salt with hot H_2O. If large amt of sand is present, wash residue to remove salt, phosphate, carbonate, and anhydrite as in **40.032**, fourth par. Transfer residue to ashless filter paper and examine under low-power microscope. Report number and approx. size of rocks and other extraneous material. If much sand is present, ignite filter and weigh residue, including rocks, reporting result in mg/100 g peanut butter.

Pour decanted CCl_4-peanut mixt. thru No. 14 sieve and examine residue for gross filth, stems, other extraneous material, and decomposed peanut tissue.

40.036 ★ **Glass—Procedure** ★

Take precautions to avoid picking up glass particles when removing contents from glass container and during analysis. Use only stainless steel, Al, plastic, or other nonglass laboratory ware. Filter reagents.

Loosen jar tops and warm jars of peanut butter several hr at ca 50° in oven.

Add 10 g household detergent powder, such as alkyl aryl sulfonate, to 2 L ca 70° H_2O. Mix thoroly and filter thru folded filter into 3–4 L stainless steel beaker. Place beaker in ca 70° H_2O bath and set beaker with bath under paddle type stirrer, **40.002(e)**. While stirring detergent soln, add entire contents of 12 oz jars, or composite contents of two 6 oz jars, or subdivided 12 oz sample portions of larger containers. Rinse jar and top portionwise with ca 100 ml kerosene and finally with detergent H_2O, and add washings to mixt. Continue stirring ca 3 min. Stop stirrer, scrape bottom and sides of beaker with metal spatula, and manually mix any residual peanut butter. Replace paddle and stir again ca 3 min until peanut material is completely dispersed. Stop stirrer, rinse paddle blades over beaker with H_2O, and promptly begin decantation procedure.

In decanting, let mixt. settle full 15 sec each time after beaker is refilled with 55–70° H_2O, with beaker in upright position, or leaning up to 45°. Pour off *smoothly*, after indicated standing period, ≤80% of beaker contents. Repeat as necessary until coarser particulate matter with small amt of clear H_2O is left. Carefully pour off as much of this clear H_2O as possible, still leaving particulate matter in beaker. Thoroly rinse down sides of beaker with alcohol from plastic wash bottle, and continue decantations after standing 15 sec as above, finally pouring off all possible alcohol without losing particles. Rinse sides of beaker with ca 250 ml $CHCl_3$. If plant particles tend to aggregate, add more alcohol down sides of beaker until particles are freely mobile. After 20 sec standing, decant, agitating plant particles to free any mech. entrapped glass. Be careful that glass from beaker pocket is not picked up by plant material as it sweeps forward from "back" side of beaker during decantation. Remove as much plant material as practical by $CHCl_3$ decantations, after 20 sec standing, with preceding precautions. Transfer beaker contents to filter paper (preferably black) on buchner.

Invert beaker over filter and scrupulously rinse sides and bottom of beaker with jet streams of alcohol and warm H_2O alternately from plastic wash bottles.

Examine microscopically at $30\times$ for glass particles, using only H_2O as moistening agent.

CEREAL FOODS
Rye, Whole Wheat, and High Bran Content Breads and Baked Goods with Fruit and Nut Tissues
Light Filth—Official First Action
40.037   *Pancreatin Digestion Method*

Post milling contamination.—Weigh 225 g sample into 2 L beaker, add enough hot H_2O to soften and sat. material, and proceed as in (a). If lumps persist or if H_2O is not immediately absorbed uniformly thru entire mass, proceed as in (b).

(a) Adjust mixt. to pH 7–8 with ca 5% Na_3PO_4 soln. Stir and break up material as much as possible. Cool to 40° and add 100 ml pancreatin soln, **40.003(x)**. Stir thoroly and readjust to pH 7–8. Let stand 30 min, stir, and readjust pH.

(b) Est. vol. of mixt. and add HCl to ca $1 + 49$ concn. Boil until solids become finely divided and so digested that mixt. will not froth over when covered during boiling. Neutze to ca pH 6 with NaOH soln; then add Na_3PO_4 soln to pH 8 and continue as in (a).

For white flour products, add 0.2 ml or 4 drops HCHO and digest overnight. For products made from whole wheat and rye flours and from similar materials of high bran content, digest only 2–3 hr.

Pour digested material thru 5″ or 8″ No. 140 sieve, **40.002(q)**. While pouring, play forcible stream of hot H_2O from tap on this material. Wash well with large stream of hot H_2O. After complete washing (no starchy material visible unattached to bran), wash twice alternately with alcohol and $CHCl_3$ in that order, and then rinse thoroly with alcohol and finally with H_2O.

Transfer material to filter paper if little residue remains or to 1 or 2 L trap flask, **40.002(h)(3)**, if large amt remains. Transfer bulk of material with spoon. Rinse residue from screen with 60% alcohol from wash bottle. Wash screen with forcible stream of hot H_2O, collecting final residue at one edge of screen and transferring to trap flask with stream of 60% alcohol as above. Add 400 or 900 ml 60% alcohol, depending on size of trap flask.

Boil 20 min. Cool to $<20°$ and add 20 or 40 ml heptane, **40.003(q)**; fill flask with 60% alcohol, and trap off as usual. Trap off second time. Use care in stirring and adding alcohol to prevent emulsions or inclusion of air. If residue in flask tends to rise, stir material down 2 or 3 times. Filter trapped-off material and examine microscopically.

40.038   *Acid Hydrolysis Method (10)*
(Rapid method; also applicable to flours)

Post milling contamination.—Add 225 g to 2 L beaker contg ca 1 L H_2O and 30 ml HCl. Wet product

completely and, for flour, stir until slurry is practically lump-free. Add antifoam, cover with watch glass, and heat 15–20 min in autoclave at 121°. Let pressure fall to 0 before opening vent valve. Transfer digest in small portions to 5 or 8″ No. 140 sieve, **40.002(q)**, washing thoroly between addns with needle spray with H_2O pressure adjusted for min. splashing. After all sample has been transferred, continue washing until there is no further reduction in amt of residue. Proceed as in **40.037(b)**, par. 3, beginning "After complete washing..."

Spray head may be made by removing screens from faucet aerator and inserting short length of $\frac{3}{8}″$ pipe into top opening to serve as hose connector.

40.039   *Pre- and Post-Milling Contamination*

Direct trapping.—To 1 L boiling HCl $(1 + 49)$ add 225 g sample, and continue heating 30–40 min, or until mixt. becomes finely divided mass that will not froth over when covered. Cool somewhat, partially neutze with NaOH soln, adjust to pH 7–8 with Na_3PO_4 soln, cool to 35–40°, and digest with pancreatin as in **40.037**. Bring to boil, cool, transfer to 2 L trap flask, **40.002(h)(3)**, ext, and examine microscopically.

Baked Products
(Other Than Those in 40.037–40.039)
40.040   **Light Filth (11)—Official First Action**

Add 1 L hot (55–70°) tap H_2O to 2 L beaker. Add 20 ml DM-710, **40.003(t)**, and 5 ml CO-730, **40.003(s)**, and mix well. Add 225 g sample, breaking any crust to <1 sq in. Stir well. Proceed with either autoclave, (a), or steam bath, (b).

(a) *Autoclave.*—Add 30 ml HCl with stirring. Add 1 ml antifoam soln, **40.003(e)**. Autoclave as in **40.002(b)(1)** or **(b)(2)**.

(b) *Steam bath.*—Add 90 ml HCl with stirring. Heat in steam bath for 10 min. Add 1 ml antifoam soln. Boil 15 min on stirring hot plate, keeping beaker covered with watch glass.

Wet sieve on No. 230 plain weave sieve, **40.002(q)**, with hot H_2O (55–70°). Sieve until effluent is clear and foam is gone. Transfer sieve retainings to original beaker. (*Caution:* Do not allow sample in beaker or sieve to cool.) Add 30 ml HCl and dil. to 1 L with H_2O. Stir on stirring hot plate, **40.002(r)**, and bring to boil. Boil 6 min, add 50 ml mineral oil, **40.003(w)**, and continue heating until boiling resumes. Transfer beaker to cool stirring plate, **40.002(r)**. Stir magnetically, **40.004(b)**, 3 min.

Promptly transfer beaker contents to percolator, **40.002(h)(2)**, contg ca 250 ml H_2O. Rinse beaker into percolator and bring vol. to 1700 ml mark with H_2O. After 1 min, stir percolator contents with glass rod. Place rod in beaker and set aside to receive final oil drain. Let stand 2 min. Drain oil to 250 ml mark and discard drainings. Refill percolator with H_2O. Continue drain and refill cycles until lower aq. phase is almost clear. Drain oil to 250 ml mark. Drain oil into original beaker. Wash percolator sides with min. of 50 ml H_2O and alcohol or isopropanol. If sides do not appear clean, follow with H_2O and 5% detergent wash, **40.003(o)**. Filter onto ruled paper and examine microscopically.

Alimentary Pastes

40.041   Light Filth (12)—Official First Action

Weigh 225 g sample into 1.5–2.0 L beaker. Add 1 L HCl (30.0 + 970) and 0.3 ml antifoam soln, **40.003(e)**. (For spaghetti, break into lengths that will *not* lie flat on bottom of beaker.) Autoclave 30 min at 121° in either **40.002(b)**(*1*) or (*2*).

Wet sieve on No. 230 plain weave sieve, **40.002(q)**, with hot tap H_2O (50–70°) to remove all original liq. and major portion of fine material.

Return sieve retainings to original beaker with hot H_2O (60–100°), dilg to ca 1 L. Add 30 ml HCl, magnetic stirring bar, **40.002(s)**, and 50 ml mineral oil, **40.003(w)**.

Stir magnetically, **40.004(b)**, 6 min. Promptly transfer to percolator, **40.002(h)**(*2*), contg ca 250 ml H_2O. Rinse beaker into percolator with hot tap H_2O to bring to 1700 ml. After 3 min, drain oil interface to 250 ml. Discard drainings and refill by pouring hot tap H_2O down percolator sides to loosen adhering material and refill to 1700 ml mark. After 2–3 min, drain and refill for 2 more cycles. (Lower layer should be almost free of suspended material after last refill; if not, continue thru 1 or more recycles.) Finally, drain oil-H_2O interface to 250 ml mark, change to original beaker and drain. Promptly wash down sides successively with ≥50 ml portions hot tap H_2O, isopropanol or alcohol, and hot tap H_2O. Use 5% detergent soln, **40.003(o)**, if necessary.

Transfer beaker contents to ruled filter paper with min. of 50 ml washes of hot H_2O, alcohol or isopropanol, and H_2O or detergent, using rubber policeman if necessary to clean sides of beaker.

Breakfast Cereals, Corn and Rice, Ready-to-Eat and Corn Chip Products

40.042   Light Filth (13)—Official First Action

(*Caution: See* **46.039.**)

(**a**) *Cereals and food products containing no fats or oils.*—(Check ingredient label.) To 1–1.5 L beaker (depending on bulk of product), add 50 g sample, 500 ml hot (55–70°) tap H_2O, and 40 ml HCl. Bring mixt. to full boil on hot plate-magnetic stirrer, **40.002(r)**, using slow stirring speed. Boil 20 min and wet sieve immediately on No. 230 plain weave sieve, **40.002(q)**, with forceful hot (55–70°) H_2O spray until residue no longer passes thru sieve and H_2O is clear. Wash sieve retainings *either* into 2 L Wildman trap flask, **40.002(h)**(*3*), or back into original beaker if Kilborn separator, **40.002(h)**(*1*), is to be used, using 40% isopropanol.

(*1*) *Trap flask.*—Bring vol. to 800 ml with 40% isopropanol and add 30 ml HCl. Raise stirring rod

plunger and secure above liq. with clamp. Add stirring bar, **40.002(s)**, and stir at slow speed while bringing mixt. to boil. Boil 5 min. Add 50 ml mineral oil, **40.003(w)**, and stir magnetically, **40.004(b)**, 3 min.

Remove from heat and fill with 40% isopropanol. Let stand 10 min and trap off, rinsing neck of flask and rod with isopropanol or alcohol. Filter trappings thru ruled paper.

(*2*) *Kilborn separator.*—Bring vol. in original beaker to 600 ml with 40% isopropanol and add 25 ml HCl. Bring to boil with slow stirring, boil 5 min, add 50 ml mineral oil, and stir magnetically 3 min.

Transfer from beaker to 1 L Kilborn separator, rinsing beaker into Kilborn with 40% isopropanol. If residue in Kilborn is heavy, resuspend with glass rod. Rinse rod into Kilborn.

Let stand 3 min and drain contents to within 1″ of bottom of oil layer. Refill with hot (55–70°) tap H_2O. Repeat drain and refill steps with 3 min intervals, until H_2O phase is free of plant material. Discard drainings. Drain oil layer into original beaker, rinsing sides of Kilborn alternately with isopropanol or hot H_2O and alcohol, using rubber policeman to clean sides. Filter contents of beaker thru ruled paper.

(**b**) *Cereals and food products containing natural and synthetic fats or vegetable oils.*—Proceed as in (**a**), beginning "500 ml hot (55–70°) tap H_2O ..." but also add to this mixt. 20 ml DM-710, **40.003(t)**; then proceed as in (**a**) with no further changes.

Wheat Germ, Raw or Processed
Light Filth (14)—Official First Action

(*Caution: See* **46.040** and **46.056.**)

40.043   *Apparatus and Reagent*

(**a**) *Filter paper.*—S&S No. 588, 32 cm folded, or equiv.

(**b**) *Antifoam A compound.*—Aerosol formula. Use as needed.

(**c**) *Alcohol.*—55% alcohol or 40% isopropanol. Use same alcohol thruout trapping.

40.044   *Determination*

Open folded 32 cm filter paper. Center paper over top of 400 ml beaker, place 250 ml beaker in middle of paper, and press into larger beaker. Remove 250 ml beaker. Tare 400 ml beaker and paper, weigh 50 g sample into filter paper in beaker, and add ca 150 ml $CHCl_3$. Boil on steam bath 5 min, occasionally rinsing down sides of filter paper with $CHCl_3$ to maintain original level. Remove sample from heat. Carefully lift paper contg sample from beaker so as to prevent any loss of sample. Let most of $CHCl_3$ drain into beaker; then discard drainings. Continue above operation 2 addnl times beginning "add ca 150 ml $CHCl_3$." After last $CHCl_3$ defatting, place filter paper contg sample in buchner. Apply vac.

until draining slows to drip. Rinse sides of paper and sample with undild isopropanol and apply vac. until draining has ceased. Turn off vac. Add ca 50–60 ml undild isopropanol to sample. Let stand 2 min; then apply vac. until dripping ceases and sample appears dry. Transfer sample from filter paper into 1 L beaker with hot tap H_2O (55–70°). Fold filter paper in half and rub together; then wash with hot tap H_2O into beaker. Repeat several times until filter paper appears clean. Discard paper and bring vol. of hot H_2O to 600 ml. Add 30 ml HCl and 1 ml antifoam, 40.003(e). Boil on hot plate, 40.002(r), 10 min with constant stirring; then remove from heat. Pour contents of beaker onto No. 230 plain weave sieve, 40.002(q), and wash with forcible hot H_2O spray (55–70°), 40.002(a), until all starchy material has passed thru and only bran remains (color of sample will change from light tan to dark brown). Transfer material from sieve to 2 L trap flask with alcohol, (c), dil. to ca 1 L, and add 50 ml HCl. Heat to 60–70° on hot plate (do *not* boil), remove flask from heat, and add 50 ml mineral oil, 40.003(w). Stir magnetically, 40.004(b), 3 min. Fill flask with alcohol, (c), stir gently by hand 1 min, let flask stand 10 min, and trap off, rinsing neck of flask with alcohol. Perform second extn, using 25 ml mineral oil. Stir gently by hand 1 min, let stand 15 min, and trap off. Rinse neck of flask with undild isopropanol or alcohol. Filter trappings thru ruled paper and examine microscopically.

Flours (White, Wheat, and Corn)

Light and Heavy Filth—Official First Action
40.045   Pancreatin Digestion Method

(a) *Light filth.*—Weigh 50 g flour into 600 ml beaker; stir into smooth slurry with 50 ml pancreatin soln, 40.003(x), dild with 100 ml H_2O. Dil. with H_2O to total vol. of ca 400 ml, and adjust to pH 8 with Na_3PO_4 soln. Readjust pH after ca 15 min and again in ca 45 min. Add, with stirring, 3 drops HCHO soln and digest 16–18 hr at room temp. or ≤40°. Transfer to 2 L trap flask and ext as in 40.004(a), using 30 and 20 ml deodorized kerosene, 40.003(v), and H_2O as solvs. Combine trappings and rinsings in beaker, transfer to 2 L trap flask, and trap off as above. If considerable starchy material is in ext, hydrolyze with HCl as in 40.004(d). Examine papers microscopically.

(b) *Rodent excreta.*—Proceed as in 40.049.

40.046   Acid Hydrolysis Method (15)

Light filth.—Disperse 50 g flour in 1 L beaker with ca 400 ml HCl (5 + 95) and 20 ml mineral oil, 40.003(w). Place on hot plate, bring to rolling boil with stirring, and boil 10 min. Remove from heat and transfer quant. to extn vessel, 40.002(h)(1) or (2). Rinse beaker and rod with ≤50 ml hot H_2O, transfer rinsings to extn vessel, and retain beaker and rod. Fill extn vessel with cold H_2O to ca 1″ from top. Let

settle 30 min, and drain carefully without forming vortex, until upper layer is ca 2″ from bottom. Add 25 ml kerosene, 40.003(v), to extn vessel and drain oil layer into retained beaker. If excessive starchy material has sepd with oil layer, hydrolyze with 100–200 ml HCl (5 + 95) before continuing. Wash sides of extn vessel with 5% detergent soln, 40.003(o), in wash bottle, and collect washings in retained beaker. Filter entire contents of beaker thru ruled paper, 40.002(i), in Hirsch funnel. Rinse beaker with 5% detergent soln, and filter. Examine microscopically at 30×.

40.047   Insect Eggs (16)—Official First Action

Transfer 50 g flour to No. 100 sieve (if >ca 0.1 g residue is obtained, No. 60 or No. 80 sieve should be used to prevent slow filtration after digestion) and sift gently until no more flour passes thru. Transfer residue on sieve to 250 ml beaker and wet with 2–3 ml alcohol. Add 30 ml H_2SO_4 (1 + 19), cover beaker, and heat on steam bath 10 min. Filter thru paper on suction funnel, using min. suction necessary to filter. Keep beaker partially inverted over funnel and rinse with H_2O. Turn off suction. Add 15–20 ml ca 0.1N I to paper in funnel. Allow 10–15 sec for I to stain contents. Apply gentle suction. After I passes thru filter, wash paper with 25–30 ml 1% H_2SO_4, followed by several small H_2O washes. Transfer paper to petri dish and examine at once under 20× magnification.

40.048   Insect Excreta (17)—
Official First Action

(a) *Optional for 1–4 samples.*—Weigh 0.20 g flour on weighed flat glass disk 7–7.5 cm diam. Add clove oil and spread mixt. into thin uniform layer. (Enough oil should be present to clear flour and present smooth surface of oil, but not so much that mixt. flows off disk.) Place wire grid over disk and examine microscopically with dark background and intense reflected light. Depending upon size of plate, larger amts of flour and ruled glass plate can be used and oil-flour mount covered with glass, *e.g.*, use 0.5 g flour on tomato rot count plate, 40.002(p). Weigh flour in counterbalanced scoop or directly on plate. Thoroly sat. flour on counting plate, cover with glass, and count insect excreta. To move or turn suspected particles, gently apply pressure or move cover slightly while observing thru microscope.

(b) *Optional in multiple-sample schedule.*—Tare 2–8 small numbered vials on each balance pan and weigh by shifting weights from one side to other. (If desired, larger portion may be weighed in beaker and some of flour floated off in $CHCl_3$-ether or $CHCl_3$-toluene mixt., sp gr 1.40, before transferring to filter paper.) Rinse contents of each vial onto smooth-surface, ruled paper in Hirsch funnel with $CHCl_3$ or CCl_4. Transfer paper to petri dish, flood with clove oil, and examine with dark background and intense reflected light.

Whole and Degerminated Corn Meal (for Rodent Excreta Only), Corn Grits, Rye Meal, Wheat Meal, Whole Wheat Flour, Farina, and Semolina

40.049   Rodent Excreta (18)—Official First Action

(*Caution: See* 46.040, 46.049, *and* 46.056.)

Weigh 50 g sample in 250 ml hooked-lip beaker. Add $CHCl_3$ to within ca 1 cm of top, mix thoroly, and let settle at least 30 min, stirring surface layer occasionally. Carefully decant $CHCl_3$ and float tissue onto buchner, without disturbing heavy residue in bottom of beaker. Before decanting, take care that floating layer has not become so compact as to render this operation difficult. Add amt of CCl_4 equal to amt of $CHCl_3$ and tissue left in beaker, let settle again, and decant as before. Repeat this process with mixt. of equal parts $CHCl_3$ and CCl_4 until very little tissue remains in beaker. Do not decant any rodent excreta fragments that may be present. Wash residue in beaker onto 7 cm ruled paper with stream of $CHCl_3$ or CCl_4 and examine microscopically.

40.050   Light Filth—Official First Action

(Not applicable to whole and degerminated corn meal)

Draw air thru material in buchner, 40.049, until liq. evaps. Air-dry overnight, or dry in oven at ca 80°. (*Caution:* In oven drying phosgene is liberated and adequate ventilation must be provided.) Transfer residue to 1 L trap flask, 40.002(h)(3). Add 100 ml 60% isopropanol satd with heptane, 40.003(u), and mix thoroly. Wash down sides of flask with isopropanol-heptane soln until ca 400 ml is added, and soak 30 min. Trap off twice with 20–30 ml heptane, 40.003(q), for each trapping and 60% isopropanol satd with heptane as liq. extn medium. In first trapping, let stand 5 min after stirring in heptane before filling flask. Filter and examine both trappings microscopically.

Cornmeal, Whole and Degerminated

40.051   Light Filth (19)—Official First Action

If rodent excreta, 40.049, is detd first, draw air thru residue in buchner until liq. evaps, and air-dry overnight, or dry in oven 1 hr at 80° with precautions as in 40.050. Quant. transfer material with HCl (7 + 93) into 1.5 L beaker and proceed as below, beginning "...add 600 ml HCl..."

If rodent excreta is not to be detd, weigh 50 g corn meal into 1.5 L beaker and add 600 ml HCl (7 + 93). Mix to smooth slurry. Add 30 ml mineral oil, 40.003(w). Place on hot plate and bring to *rolling boil;* hold at *rolling boil* ca 10 min. Transfer quant. to Kilborn funnel, 40.002(h)(1); retain beaker and stirring rod for rinsing. Fill separator to ca 0.5" from top with cold H_2O.

After 1.5–2 min, gently stir contents of separator; let oil layer sep. again ca 1.5–2 min, and slowly drain

and discard lower layer until interface is ca 2" above constriction. Fill separator with cold H_2O to ca 0.5" from top; let oil sep. 1.5–2 min, and slowly drain and discard lower aq. layer until interface is ca 2" above constriction. Repeat H_2O wash until lower layer is clear.

Filter mineral oil and H_2O retained in separator thru ruled paper, 40.002(i), using Hirsch funnel. After mineral oil layer has passed thru paper, rinse all glassware thoroly with alcohol, followed by H_2O, then 5% detergent soln, 40.003(o), and cold H_2O. Filter each rinse sep. thru same paper. Examine paper at 30×.

Rye Flour

40.052   Light Filth (20)—Official First Action

Weigh 50 g flour into 2 L trap flask, 40.002(h)(3), add 300 ml 60% alcohol, mix, and let stand 10 min. Add 250 ml Tween 80–60% alcohol soln, 40.003(ff), and mix. Quickly add 250 ml Na_4EDTA-60% alcohol soln, 40.003(gg), and ca 70 ml heptane, 40.003(q). Stir immediately 1 min in usual manner. Fill flask with 60% alcohol. (Add reagents, mix heptane, and fill flask with 60% alcohol without interruption. Operate only 1 flask at time for these 3 steps.) Stir occasionally during first 20 min after flask is filled.

After 20 min, rotate plunger to remove flour which settled on top surface. Raise rod so that plunger is above mass of flour at bottom of flask. Clamp unrinsed rod in place (clothes pin is convenient) so that plunger is held above flour mass to minimize flour settling on it. Let flask stand *undisturbed* addnl hr. Trap off, without disturbing interface, rinse neck of flask with 60% alcohol, and filter. Repeat extn, using 40 ml heptane and 1.5 hr standing. Examine papers microscopically.

Soy Bean Flour

40.053   Light Filth—Procedure

(*Caution: See* 46.011, 46.039, *and* 46.073.)

Weigh 50 g sample into 600 ml beaker, add 150 ml pet ether, and mix thoroly. Let settle 5 min and decant ca 100 ml solv. and any floating light tissue, avoiding loss of any heavier flour materials. Replenish pet ether and mix with residue. Let settle 5 min and decant as before. Discard decanted portions. Evap. pet ether from residue with gentle heat, stirring as residue dries to avoid formation of lumps. Dry until no pet ether remains and proceed as in 40.045(a), beginning "...stir into smooth slurry..."

Cereal Grains

40.054   Internal Insect Infestation—Official First Action

Mix grain by passing 6 times thru Jones sampler, recombining sepns before each pass. Sep. slightly >100 g and weigh 100 g. Transfer weighed sample, small amt at time, to 5" or 8" No. 12 sieve, and with stiff bristle brush, work insects thru sieve as completely as possible.

Grind screened sample in Labconco mill (Laboratory Construction Co., 8811 Prospect Ave, Kansas City, MO 64132, or equiv.) set at 0.061″. (Dry damp or tempered grain in forced-draft oven 1 hr at 70–80° or 2 hr in oven without draft.) Transfer cracked grain, including any residue in mill, to 2 L trap flask, 40.002(h)(3), trap as in 40.004(a), using 60% isopropanol satd with heptane, 40.003(u), and heptane, 40.003(q), as solvs, and filter on 10XX bolting cloth, 40.002(d). If considerable starchy material is in ext, hydrolyze with HCl as in 40.004(d). Examine as in 40.004(g) except use 15 × as lower limit of magnification. Count only whole insects, insect heads, cast skins, and head capsules.

Unpopped Popcorn, Cereal Grains, Peas, Beans, Etc.

40.055 External Light Filth—Procedure

Transfer 225 g sample to 2 L trap flask, 40.002(h) (3). Add 600 ml 40% alcohol and boil gently, with frequent stirring, 5 min. Cool, trap off, using heptane, 40.003(q), and 40% alcohol, filter, and examine microscopically.

Starch

40.056 Filth—Official First Action

Weigh 225 g starch into 1.5 L beaker. Add, with stirring, 1200 ml cold H_2O (15–20°). Stir out lumps and pour thru 5–8″ No. 140 sieve, 40.002(q). Wash with cold running H_2O. Rinse particles from sieve onto filter paper, first using H_2O and then 60% alcohol. Examine paper microscopically.

Brewer's Grits

40.057 Rodent Excreta—Procedure— See 40.049

40.058 Light Filth—Official First Action— See 40.050

Popped Popcorn

40.059 Filth—Procedure

Weigh 50 g corn into 2 L trap flask. Add 500 ml hot H_2O, boil 15 min, and cool to room temp. Add 35 ml heptane, 40.003(q), mix, and let stand 5 min. Fill with H_2O, trap off, filter, and examine microscopically.

EGGS AND EGG PRODUCTS (21)— OFFICIAL FIRST ACTION

(Eggs may be contaminated with chicken excrement, dirt, sand, metal fragments, hairs, and feathers, depending upon condition of the eggs, method of manufacture, and storage conditions. Method of isolation of contaminants depends upon nature of product (whole, whites, or yolks) and physical state (fresh, frozen, or dried).)

40.060 Reagents

(a) *Anionic surfactant.*—Na N-methyl-N-tall oil acid taurate, Igepon TK-32 (GAF Corp.), or equiv.

(b) *Phenolphthalein soln.*—Prep. 5% soln in alcohol, dil. with equal vol. H_2O, and filter.

(c) *Disodium phosphate soln.*—Filtered satd soln (ca 100 g anhyd. salt/L), and filtered 6% (anhyd. basis) aq. soln.

(d) *Trisodium phosphate soln.*—Filtered satd soln.

(e) *Tetrasodium EDTA soln.*—10% filtered aq. soln of Na_4EDTA.

40.061 Light and Heavy Filth and Other Extraneous Materials

(a) *Whole eggs or yolks.*—Thaw frozen sample at room temp. or in cold running H_2O. Weigh 100 g thawed sample into 250 ml centrf. bottle. Add 30 ml 6% Na_2HPO_4 and stir. Shake vigorously 1.5–2.0 min, add addnl 30 ml 6% Na_2HPO_4, and shake ca 2 min. Dil. with 6% reagent to fill bottle and centrf. whole eggs 5 min at 1500 rpm and yolks 5 min at 800 rpm. Decant ca ⅔ liq. into 1.5 or 2.0 L beaker and isolate light filth as in (b). Add ca equal vol. 6% Na_2HPO_4 to residue in bottle, shake well, and recentrf. Decant closely. To sediment in bottle add ca ½ vol. H_3PO_4 and warm on steam bath. Transfer to 250 ml beaker, boil 3–5 min, and filter while boiling. Examine at 30 × for metal and glass fragments, and chicken excrement. Check amorphous white material for uric acid as in 40.140.

(b) *Egg whites.*—Use decanted whole egg or yolk material from (a) or weigh 100 g thawed whites into 1.5 or 2.0 L beaker and add ca 300 ml 6% Na_2HPO_4 in small portions with thoro stirring. Add 16 ml Na_4EDTA soln, (e), then 12 ml phthln, (b). Let stand 10 min; then adjust to pH 7.6–8.0, using H_3PO_4 (1 + 9) or Na_3PO_4 soln as needed. Add 2 ml surfactant, (a), and readjust to pH 7.6–8.0, using short range pH paper. Add 200 ml pancreatin soln, 40.003(x), and readjust to pH 7.6–8.0.

Place in 37–38° H_2O bath to ca depth of digestion mixt.; stir, and adjust to pH 7.6–8.0 at ca 15 min intervals for ca 2 hr. Add 2 ml surfactant and dil. to 1.0–1.2 L with H_2O. Adjust to pH 8.0 and place in incubator at 37° overnight. Readjust to pH 8.0 and let stand 15–20 min without stirring. Decant in small portions onto ruled paper, using full suction, while washing paper with hot tap H_2O. Examine paper microscopically.

(c) *Dried egg yolks.*—Defat egg yolks as follows: Weigh 25 g sample into 150 ml tall-form beaker, add 50 ml pet ether, and stir thoroly (until smooth). While stirring, add solv. to almost fill beaker. Stir top again after 1 min, let stand 1 min, and decant solv. into larger beaker. Repeat defatting step twice more with pet ether. Filter combined washes thru smooth textured paper, air-dry paper thoroly, and hold for pancreatin digestion. Discard solv. (*Caution: See 46.011.*) Place 150 ml beaker on steam bath and remove solv. completely from residue with continuous stirring to prevent bumping. Transfer dried residue in beaker and dried residue on paper, using spatula, to 600 ml beaker and proceed as in (d).

(d) *Dried whole eggs.*—Weigh 25 g sample into 600 ml beaker, or continue with dried yolk residue from (c). Add mixt. of 90 ml satd soln of Na_2HPO_4 and 10 ml alcohol in small portions with stirring. (Suspension must be smooth and finely divided at this point.) With stirring, add 12 ml Na_4EDTA soln, (e), then 5 ml phthln, (b). If intense red develops, discharge with H_3PO_4 (1 + 9). Adjust to pH 7.6–8.0 with satd Na_3PO_4 soln, using short range indicator paper. Add 200 ml pancreatin soln, **40.003(x)**, to suspension. Continue as in (b), beginning "Place in 37–38° H_2O bath ..." Examine papers microscopically.

(e) *Dried whites.*—Weigh 25 g sample into 250 or 400 ml beaker. Dil. 4.5 ml surfactant, (a), to 35 ml with H_2O and add to beaker in portions of 5 ml, rotating and shaking beaker until sample absorbs each portion. Let soak 10–15 min; then add 20 ml H_2O in 4–5 portions with thoro stirring after each addn. Stir to smooth slurry. (Material must be finely dispersed before proceeding.) Add 7 ml Na_4EDTA soln, (e), then 3 ml phthln, (b). Transfer to 1.5 or 2 L beaker and dil. with H_2O to 700–800 ml. Adjust to pH 7.2–7.6 and add 200 ml pancreatin soln, **40.003(x)**. Continue as in (b), beginning "Place in 37–38° H_2O bath ..." Examine papers microscopically.

40.062 Sedimentation Method for Chicken Excrement and Heavy Filth

(a) *Frozen whole eggs or yolks.*—Examine by **40.061(a)**.

(b) *Dried egg yolk.*—Add 25 g sample in small portions with continuous stirring to mixt. of 75 ml H_3PO_4 (1 + 9) and 5 ml surfactant in 150 ml tall-form beaker. Stir to smooth paste and add H_3PO_4, few ml at time, to fill beaker while stirring. Stir top layer 1 min and let stand 5 min. Decant ca $2/3$ vol. into 250 ml beaker and add H_3PO_4 (1 + 9) to both beakers equal to vol. present. Stir contents of both beakers 1 min and let stand 5 min. Again stir top layers 1 min and slowly add H_3PO_4 with stirring to fill both beakers. Let stand 5 min and repeat stirring and standing. Decant both beakers closely into 1 L beaker.

Dil. material in 1 L beaker with H_2O, stirring continuously, until full. Stir top layer 1 min and let stand 5 min and repeat stirring and standing. Decant closely, discarding supernatants. Composite all residues in 250 ml beaker by transferring with H_3PO_4 (1 + 9) from wash bottle. Decant acid and floating egg material and transfer residue to ruled paper with H_2O, using min. suction. Wash residue with two 30 ml portions H_2O, using min. suction. Examine microscopically, keeping paper moist. Check amorphous white material for uric acid as in **40.140**.

POULTRY, MEAT, AND FISH AND OTHER MARINE PRODUCTS

40.063 ★ Filth and Sand in Chicken ★ Giblet Paste—Procedure

(*Caution: See* **46.011, 46.040,** and **46.056.**)

Weigh 100 g sample into 400 ml lipped beaker. Add $CHCl_3$ to within 1" of top of beaker, mix thoroly, and let settle ca 30 min, stirring top layer occasionally. Make opening in floating layer and decant most of $CHCl_3$. Add, stir, and decant $CHCl_3$ 3 times. Retain decanted $CHCl_3$ and filter thru 10XX bolting cloth, **40.002(d)**. Examine microscopically. After third extn, decant paste layer into 2 L trap flask, **40.002(h)(3)**. Evap. most of $CHCl_3$ from material in flask.

Add ca 50 ml hot H_2O to residue in beaker. Decant and wash residue thru ashless paper in 60° funnel. Wash with warm H_2O. Transfer filter to petri dish and examine for rodent excreta, sand, etc. To weigh sand, etc., fold paper, dry in weighed crucible, ignite, and weigh to nearest 0.5 mg.

To paste in trap flask add 200 ml hot H_2O and heat on steam bath 15 min. Cool to room temp. Add 35 ml heptane, **40.003(q)**, mix, and let stand 10 min, stirring several times. Trap off with H_2O, filter, and examine microscopically.

40.064 Light Filth in Canned Fish—Procedure

If can contains 1 lb or less, transfer total contents to 2 L trap flask, **40.002(h)(3)**. Reduce larger portions to 1 lb. Avoid breaking fish into small particles. Cover fish with hot H_2O and rinse can and lid with 25 ml kerosene, **40.003(v)**, letting rinsings enter trap flask. Mix, and fill flask with warm H_2O. Trap off, filter, and examine. Trap off second time, using 20 ml kerosene, filter, and examine microscopically.

40.065 ★ Glass in Meat Scraps— ★ Procedure

(*Caution: See* **46.040** and **46.049.**)

Weigh 50 g well-mixed sample into 400 ml beaker, add ca 350 ml CCl_4, and mix contents thoroly. Let stand 30 min with occasional stirring. Decant and discard CCl_4 and floating org. matter, leaving bone and heavy matter in beaker. Add more solv. and again decant if necessary. Wash out adhering CCl_4 with one rinse of ca 100 ml alcohol and then one rinse of 350 ml H_2O, decanting slowly after each addn of alcohol or H_2O to prevent loss of heavy matter. Add 50 ml HCl and heat on steam bath ca 1 hr.

Wash residue with 3–6 portions H_2O, using 350 ml each time; rinse once with ca 50 ml alcohol and then 2 or 3 times with CCl_4; decant after each addn and finish with rinse of $CHCl_3$. Let heavy residue dry thoroly and weigh to nearest mg. Pass dry residue thru No. 40 and No. 60 sieves, and weigh total residue on each sieve and also material passing thru the No. 60 sieve. With aid of Greenough-type microscope pick out and weigh glass from fraction retained on No. 40 sieve. Est. % glass in each portion passing thru No. 40 sieve.

Notes: Check all particles of glass with polarizing microscope since particles of clear quartz may be mistaken for glass unless examined with polarized light. Since glass is isotropic in character it shows complete extinction of transmitted light when examined between crossed nicols, while quartz, which is double refracting, exhibits polarization colors.

The estn of % glass may be made by detg % glass particles from microscopic examination of min. of 200 random particles from each portion, using polarized light.

40.066 Shell in Canned Crabmeat, Clams, and Oysters (*22*)—Official First Action

(**a**) *Crabmeat.*—Weigh 57 g (2 oz) representative sample into 400 ml beaker. Add 150 ml 1.5% NaOH soln and stir to break up lumps. Add 10 drops *1% aq. Alizarin Red S* indicator. Heat until meat has been digested (10 min at ca 80°), stirring 3 or 4 times. Pour on No. 12 sieve nested in No. 60 sieve, and wash with H_2O. Wash shell from both sieves onto weighed paper, dry at 100°, and cool to room temp. Weigh and count shell. Report shell as number of pieces and wt/lb.

(**b**) *Clams and oysters.*—Weigh 57 g (2 oz) representative sample into 600 ml beaker. Continue as above except digest by boiling ca 15 min.

FRUIT AND FRUIT PRODUCTS
Apple Butter
40.067 Rot—Official Final Action
Make mold count as in **40.085.**

40.068 Insect and Rodent Filth—Official First Action

Weigh 100 g sample into 400 ml beaker, add enough hot H_2O to obtain uniform dispersion, and pour into 2 L trap flask, **40.002**(h)(*3*). Rinse beaker with hot H_2O and add rinse H_2O to flask. Add 25–35 ml castor oil and mix thoroly. Add enough hot H_2O to bring oil layer into neck of flask. Stir vigorously with vertical motion while adding H_2O. Let stand 30 min, trap off, filter, and examine paper microscopically.

★ *Dried Apple Chops* ★
40.069 Heavy Filth—Official First Action
Place 50 g sample in 1 L beaker or other suitable container. Add enough tap H_2O to cover apples and shake or stir 5 min. Empty contents into No. 6 or No. 8 sieve, recovering H_2O in beaker. Wash out container and add rinse H_2O to that in beaker. Rinse off pieces of apple with fine stream of tap H_2O delivered with as much force as possible. Catch this rinse H_2O in beaker also, transfer to 2 L separator, and let stand 15 min, with occasional gentle rotary shaking. Open stopcock, and draw off heavy particles and small amt of liq. Filter drained material and examine microscopically.

40.070 ★ Insects and Light Filth— ★ Official First Action

Place 50 g sample in beaker, cover with H_2O, and boil 15 min. Empty apples onto No. 6 or No. 8 sieve, recovering H_2O in beaker. Rinse beaker. Rinse apples with strong stream of hot H_2O. Place all H_2O in 2 L trap flask, **40.002**(h)(*3*), add 20 ml castor oil, mix well, and add enough hot tap H_2O to fill flask. Let stand 30 min with occasional stirring. Trap off oil layer, add H_2O to flask, stir, and trap off again in 10 min. Filter trapped-off portion thru rapid paper. Examine microscopically.

Blackberries, Blueberries, Loganberries, Raspberries, and Cherries, Fresh, Canned, and Frozen

40.071 Rot in Blackberries, Raspberries, and Other Drupelet Berries—Official First Action

(**a**) *Frozen with or without sugar.*—Pulp berries thru cyclone, **40.002**(g), and mix thoroly. Mix 25 g pulp with 50 ml stabilizer soln, **40.003**(ee). Make mold count as in **40.085.**

(**b**) *Frozen in sirup, canned in sirup or water.*—Drain berries 2 min on No. 20 sieve. Pulp, dil., and make mold count as in (**a**).

40.072 Maggots in Blueberries and Cherries—Procedure

Weigh 567 g (20 oz) fresh fruit or use No. 2 can of processed fruit. Add 100 ml H_2O to fresh or frozen fruit and boil 5 min, with frequent stirring. (Omit this step with canned fruit.) Transfer ½″ layer of fruit to No. 6 sieve immersed in pan of H_2O. Shake loose maggots and debris thru sieve. Carefully mash fruit under H_2O to rub any remaining maggots thru sieve. Rinse and discard any pulp and seeds. Repeat above process with another portion of fruit.

After all fruit is screened, transfer mixt. to black-bottom pan. (With cherries, transfer first to No. 6 sieve resting in ca 1″ H_2O, shake sieve until maggots drop thru, and discard pulp on sieve.) Slowly decant H_2O and pulp from pan. Add more H_2O and repeat decantation. Pick out and count maggots by examination of contents of pan. Transfer contents of this pan to white-bottom pan and count maggots in pan.

Citrus and Pineapple Juices, Canned, Single Strength
40.073 Mold Count—Official First Action
Pour contents of can into beaker and mix thoroly by pouring back and forth between beaker and can ≥12 times. After mixing, transfer 50 ml juice to graduated 50 ml conical-bottom centrf. tube. Centrf. 10 min at 2200 rpm, using International type SB, size 1 centrf., with 8-place No. 240 head (distance

from center of centrf. head to center of cups (at rest) is 5¼″), or other centrf. giving equiv. centrifugal force as computed by following formula: $N_1{}^2r_1 = N_2{}^2r_2$, where N = rpm, and r = radius of centrf. arm. Check speed with tachometer, since rheostat does not necessarily indicate speed in rpm.

Gradually let centrf. come to complete stop before removing tubes and read vol. sediment in centrf. tube. Remove tube and decant supernatant without disturbing sediment. With pineapple juice, add 0.5 ml HCl (to dissolve oxalate crystals). Add H_2O to tube to bring level to 10 ml mark and then add 5 ml stabilizer soln, 40.003(ee). Thoroly mix sediment, H_2O, and stabilizer soln and pour into small beaker. Mix by pouring back and forth between beaker and tube ≥6 times. Stir mixt. thoroly in beaker and proceed as in 40.085. In addn to checking microscopic fields, indicate those fields positive due to *Geotrichum candidum*.

40.074 Fly Eggs and Maggots— Official First Action

Filter 250 ml thoroly mixed sample thru buchner fitted with 10XX bolting cloth, 40.002(d) (wire mesh screen under bolting cloth facilitates filtration). Pour juice slowly to avoid accumulation of excess pulp on cloth (2 or 3 cloths may be necessary). Examine filters microscopically.

40.075 Insect Fragments and Rodent Contamination—Official First Action

To 250 ml juice in 2 L trap flask add 15 ml castor oil, 40.003(j), and fill with enough hot H_2O (ca 70°), stirring vigorously, to bring oil layer into neck of flask. Let stand 30 min. Trap off, filter, and examine.

Cranberry Sauce
40.076 Mold—Official First Action

(a) *Strained sauce.*—Immerse unopened can of sauce in boiling H_2O bath 30–45 min to facilitate breaking gel. Remove can from bath and open carefully to avoid loss of sauce thru sudden release of pressure. Transfer contents into suitable beaker (1 L beaker for No. 2 can). Stir sauce to break gel. (Slow-speed elec. mixer (350–450 rpm) may be used.) Thoroly mix 50 g stirred sauce with 50 g stabilizer soln, 40.003(ee). Make mold count of mixt. as in 40.085.

(b) *Whole sauce (seeds and skins included).*—Pulp contents of container (if considerably >1 lb, such as No. 10 can, remove well-mixed aliquot of 1 lb) thru cyclone to remove skins and seeds, and prep. homogeneous pulp. Mix 50 g of this pulp with 50 g stabilizer soln, 40.003(ee). Make mold count as in 40.085.

Fig and Fruit Paste
40.077 Light and Heavy Filth (23)— Official First Action

(a) *Light filth.*—Weigh 100 g paste into 1 L beaker. Add 400 ml boiling H_2O and magnetic stirring bar,

40.002(s). Boil on magnetic stirring hot plate, 40.002(r), until all lumps are disintegrated. Wet sieve mixt. on 8″ No. 140 sieve, 40.002(q), with hot tap H_2O to remove fine and sol. material. Transfer residue from sieve to 2 L trap flask, 40.002(h)(3), with H_2O. Add H_2O to bring vol. to ca 900 ml, add 35 ml kerosene, 40.003(v), and ext as in 40.004(a). Make second extn with 25 ml kerosene. Examine papers microscopically as in 40.004(f)(1) and (g).

(b) *Heavy filth.*—Empty remaining trap flask contents and rinsings onto 8″ No. 140 sieve. Wet sieve with hot tap H_2O to remove kerosene as completely as possible. Transfer material from sieve to 1 L beaker and add hot H_2O to ca 400 ml. Heat to boiling and boil 15 min. Add 10% Na_4EDTA soln to keep pH ca 8. Transfer hot mixt. to 8″ No. 140 sieve. Wet sieve until seeds are completely sepd from fig tissue. Return residue on sieve to the 1 L beaker. Add H_2O to ca 300 ml, swirl, and quickly decant suspended fig tissue and filth elements onto ruled paper in Hirsch funnel, retaining seeds in beaker. Add H_2O and repeat decanting, changing paper as necessary. Examine papers for heavy filth elements at ca 30×.

Jam and Jelly
40.078 Insect and Rodent Filth— Official First Action

(a) *Jam.*—Empty contents of jar into dish and mix thoroly. Weigh 100 g into beaker, add 200 ml H_2O (ca 50°), transfer to 1 L trap flask, 40.002(h)(3), add 10 ml HCl, and boil ca 5 min. Cool to room temp., add 25 ml heptane, 40.003(q), and stir thoroly. Trap off, filter, and examine microscopically.

(b) *Jelly.*—Empty contents of jar into dish and mix thoroly. Weigh 100 g into beaker and add 300–400 ml hot H_2O; warm beaker, with stirring, until jelly dissolves, filter, and examine microscopically.

When so-called "jellies" contg small quantities of fruit tissue will not filter thru paper, proceed as in (a).

Raisins
40.079 Light Filth (24)—Official First Action
(Caution: See 46.040 and 46.056.)

Add 500 ml $CHCl_3$ to 225 g sample in 1 L beaker and boil on steam bath 10 min, keeping $CHCl_3$ vol. at ca 500 ml. Decant $CHCl_3$, holding back raisins with glass rod, onto 7.5 cm ruled filter paper in Hirsch funnel. Retain paper. Repeat 10 min $CHCl_3$ boil and decant. Wash filter retainings from paper back into beaker contg raisin tissue with H_2O. Bring vol. in beaker to 700 ml with hot H_2O (55–70°) and rehydrate *in steam bath* 30 min. Sieve portionwise onto 8″ No. 8 sieve nested in 8″ No. 140 sieve, 40.002(q). Thoroly wash each portion with stream of hot H_2O while gently rubbing raisins over sieve with fingers. Microscopically examine any decomposed raisins for fly eggs and maggots.

Wet retainings on No. 140 sieve with 25% isopropanol, transfer to 2 L trap flask, **40.002**(h)(*3*), with 25% isopropanol, and bring vol. to 1 L. Add 70 ml HCl and magnetic stirring bar to flask, heat to boiling, and continue for 10 min, slowly stirring on magnetic stirring hot plate, **40.002**(r), with stirring bar, **40.002**(s). Cool to <25° in cold H$_2$O bath. Add 40 ml flotation oil (mix kerosene, **40.003**(v), and mineral oil, **40.003**(w), (1 + 2)) and stir magnetically, **40.004**(b), 5 min. Let stand 1 min after gentle 10–15 sec stir with stoppered rod (*see* **40.004**(a)). Fill with deaerated 25% isopropanol by slowly running alcohol down rod onto top of stopper maintained ca ⅛″ above liq.-air interface. Let stand 15 min, gently stirring mixt. 2–3 times during first 10 min. Trap; filter first and second extns sep. Add 25 ml flotation oil and gently hand stir 1 min. Let stand 1 min; gently disturb oil-alcohol interface with several up and down strokes of stoppered rod to cause fine plant material to settle. Let stand 10 min. Perform second trapping. Thoroly wash flask neck with isopropanol. Pour trappings onto ruled filter paper and examine at 30×. If second extn is difficult to filter, pour onto No. 230 sieve, **40.002**(q), and wash twice alternately with undild isopropanol and hot H$_2$O. Wash sieve retainings into 400 ml beaker with hot H$_2$O and add 7 ml HCl/100 ml H$_2$O. Boil 10 min and pour onto ruled filter paper.

Strawberries (Frozen)

40.080 Mold—Official Final Action

Pulp thawed berries thru cyclone and mix thoroly. (Pour juice thru cyclone last.) If necessary, remove air bubbles with suction or by mixing ca 100 g pulp with 3–5 drops *capryl alcohol*. Again mix thoroly and make mold count as in **40.085**.

SUGAR AND SUGAR PRODUCTS
Candy

40.081 Filth—Official First Action

(a) *In hard candy, gum drops, gum, starch, or pectin-base candies.*—Dissolve in boiling HCl (1 + 70), filter thru rapid paper on Hirsch funnel, and examine microscopically.

(b) *In hard candy difficult to filter by* (a) (*e.g., licorice candy*).—Proceed as in (c) except to substitute HCl (1 + 70) for borax soln.

(c) *In chocolate candy with or without fruit or nuts, fruity candy, etc.*—Weigh 225 g sample into 2 L beaker, add 1 L 5–10% Na$_2$B$_4$O$_7$.10H$_2$O soln, simmer 10–15 min, and pour thru 5–8″ No. 140 screen. While pouring, play forcible stream of hot H$_2$O onto material. Wash well with large stream of hot H$_2$O; wash twice alternately with alcohol and CHCl$_3$ in that order; finally rinse with alcohol and hot H$_2$O. Transfer material to filter paper if little residue remains or to 1–2 L trap flask, **40.002**(h)(*3*), if amt of residue is large.

In latter case, transfer bulk of material with spoon;

then wash screen with forcible stream of hot H$_2$O so as to collect final residue at one edge of screen, and finally transfer residue to trap flask with stream of 60% alcohol from wash bottle. Add 600 or 900 ml 60% alcohol, depending on size of trap flask, boil 20 min, cool to <20°, add 20 or 40 ml heptane, **40.003**(q), and mix thoroly. Fill flask with 60% alcohol and trap off as usual. Add heptane and trap off second time. Filter and examine. If large quantity of peanut testa or similar material floats into neck of flask, pour trapped-off material thru No. 8 or No. 10 sieve, rinse thoroly, filter liq. portion, and examine microscopically.

(d) *In chocolate candy coating.*—Heat 400 ml heptane in 800 ml beaker to 40–50° and keep at this temp. Place portion of candy in wire basket (ca 3¼″ diam. × 1″ high) made from No. 8 screen and with wire handles. Move basket up and down thru heptane until chocolate coating dissolves. Rinse each candy center with fine stream of heptane from wash bottle and save center. Repeat with balance of sample. Stir heptane-chocolate suspension and pour thru No. 140 sieve. Transfer residue from sieve to filter paper and examine microscopically. Examine candy centers by appropriate method, (a), (b), or (c).

Chewing Gum

40.082 ★ Filth—Procedure ★
(*Caution: See* **46.039, 46.040, 46.046, 46.049,** and **46.056**.)

Add 100 g gum to 300–600 ml H$_2$O or 150–600 ml HCl (1 + 17), bring to boil, and boil 10–12 min. To avoid excessive caramelization, do not boil longer than necessary to obtain fine dispersion of gum particles in liq. Treat dispersed gum by one of following procedures to dissolve or soften chicle:

(a) Let mixt. cool to ca 55°, add 150 ml acetone, and stir; then add 150 ml CHCl$_3$. Bring to boil and boil until mixt. is dispersed evenly. While hot, pour thru 10XX bolting cloth, **40.002**(d), in Hirsch funnel, and examine microscopically.

(b) Cool to ca 80° (if CCl$_4$ is to be used) or ca 63° (if CHCl$_3$ is to be used); add ca 150 ml CCl$_4$ or CHCl$_3$ and simmer 5–10 min or until chicle dissolves. While hot, filter thru 10XX bolting cloth in Hirsch funnel, and examine microscopically.

Caution: As these mixts tend to foam and boil over, take adequate precautions against fire or hazardous prolonged breathing of vapors from org. solvs. Stir all mixts while adding liqs and while heating to boiling. When transferring to new container, take care to rinse old container with hot H$_2$O and appropriate org. solv. Filtering funnel may be greased to prevent the cooling gum from sticking to it.

Sirups, Molasses, and Honey

40.083 Filth—Official First Action

(a) Mix sample thoroly and dissolve 200 g in 200 ml hot H$_2$O acidified with 5 ml HNO$_3$. Filter at once thru rapid paper in Hirsch funnel. Wash with min. amt of hot H_2O and examine microscopically.

(b) *Alternative procedure.*—Dissolve 200 g in 500 ml hot H_2O. Filter at once thru 10XX bolting cloth in Hirsch funnel. Wash with min. amt of hot H_2O and examine microscopically.

Sugars

40.084 Filth—Official First Action

Dissolve 100 g sample in ca 200 ml hot H_2O. Boil, and filter at once thru rapid paper in Hirsch funnel. Examine microscopically.

VEGETABLES AND VEGETABLE PRODUCTS

Tomato Products (Not Dehydrated)

40.085 Molds (25)—Official Final Action

In making mold counts of tomato products, use juice as it comes from container. For catsup, place 50 ml stabilizer soln, **40.003(ee)**, in 100 ml graduated cylinder, add 50 ml well mixed catsup sample by displacement, and mix thoroly. In case of puree and paste add H_2O to make mixt. with total tomato solids content that gives refractive index of 1.3438–1.3445 at 25°.

Clean Howard cell, **40.002(m)(1)**, so that Newton's rings are produced between slide and cover glass. Remove cover and with knife blade or scalpel place portion of well-mixed sample upon central disk; with same instrument, spread evenly over disk, and cover with glass so as to give uniform distribution. Use only enough sample to bring material to edge of disk. (It is of utmost importance that portion be taken from thoroly mixed sample and spread evenly over slide disk. Otherwise, when cover slip is put in place, insol. material, and consequently molds, may be more abundant at center of mount.) Discard any mount showing uneven distribution or absence of Newton's rings, or liq. that has been drawn across moat and between cover glass and shoulder.

Place slide under microscope and examine with such adjustment that each field of view covers 1.5 sq mm. (This area, which is essential, may frequently be obtained by so adjusting draw-tube that diam. of field becomes 1.382 mm. When such adjustment is not possible, make accessory drop-in ocular diaphragm with aperture accurately cut to necessary size. Diam. of area of field of view can be detd by use of stage micrometer. When instrument is properly adjusted, quantity of liq. examined per field is 0.15 cu. mm.) Use magnification of 90–125×. In those instances where identifying characteristics of mold filaments are not clearly discernible in std field, use magnification of ca 200× (8 mm objective) to confirm identity of mold filaments previously observed in std field. *See* Figs. 40:6–40:8.

From each of ≥ 2 mounts examine ≥ 25 fields taken in such manner as to be representative of all sections of mount. Observe each field, noting presence or absence of mold filaments and recording results as pos. when aggregate length of ≤ 3 filaments present exceeds $\frac{1}{6}$ of diam. of field. Calc. proportion of pos. fields from results of examination of all observed fields and report as % fields contg mold filaments.

40.086 ★ Yeasts and Spores— ★ Official Final Action

Fill graduated cylinder with H_2O to 20 ml mark and add sample until mixt. reaches 30 ml mark, to obtain diln of $1 + 2$. Close graduate, or pour contents into erlenmeyer, and shake vigorously 15–20 sec. To assure thoro mixing, mixt. should fill $\leq \frac{3}{4}$ of erlenmeyer. For tomato sauce or paste, or for products running high in number of organisms, or of heavy consistency, use diln that permits ready counting.

Pour mixt. into beaker. Thoroly clean blood-counting cell, **40.002(c)**, to obtain good Newton's rings. Thoroly stir contents of beaker with scalpel or knife blade and after it stands 3–5 sec, remove small portion, place it upon central disk of blood-counting cell, and cover immediately with cover glass. Discard any mount showing uneven distribution, absence of Newton's rings, or liq. that has been drawn across moat and between cover glass and shoulder. Let slide stand ≥ 10 min before beginning to make count. Use magnification of 300–400×. Count number of yeasts and spores in either whole counting area (1.0 sq mm), which represents vol. of 0.1 cu. mm, or portion thereof. If less than whole vol. is counted, choose representative areas for counting. Calc. number of yeasts and spores/ml or g of original products.

Example: If 25 spores were observed in $\frac{1}{2}$ of 1.0 sq mm area, and diln of 2 parts H_2O with 1 part product was made originally, then total number of organisms $= 25 \times 2 \times 10 \times 1000 \times 3 = 1,500,000$, where $25 =$ no. of organisms observed; $2 =$ factor to det. organisms/0.1 cu. mm; $10 =$ factor to det. organisms/1.0 cu. mm; $1000 =$ factor to det. organisms/ 1.0 ml; and $3 =$ factor representing diln.

40.087 Rot in Canned Tomatoes— Official First Action

Drain contents of can 2 min on No. 2 sieve. For containers of <3 lb net wt, use 8″ diam. sieve; for containers of ≥ 3 lb net wt, use 12″ sieve. Examine drained tomatoes and record number and size of any rotten portions present. Pass drained tomatoes thru laboratory cyclone, **40.002(g)**. Make mold counts on both drained juice and pulped tomatoes as in **40.085**.

40.088 Rot Fragments in Comminuted Tomato Products (26)— Official First Action

Weigh 10 g juice or 5 g catsup or sauce, and transfer with 100 ml H_2O to 400 ml beaker. In case of puree or paste add H_2O to make mixt. of total tomato solids content that gives refractive index of 1.3438–1.3445 at 25°. Use 5 g mixt. for sample.

Add 10 drops crystal violet soln, **40.003(n)**, stir and let stain 3 min. Add 200 ml H_2O and spread evenly over surface of 3″ No. 60 sieve. Rinse beaker with 200 ml H_2O, and pour H_2O evenly over tomato tissue on sieve. Tilt sieve to ca 30° angle and wash tissue to lower edge with H_2O. Let tissue drain, and transfer with spatula to bottom of graduated tube ca 12 × 3 cm. Transfer remaining tissue by washing down with H_2O from dropper and immediately tak-

ing up tissue in wash H_2O before it has run thru sieve. Make vol. of H_2O and tissue to 10 ml with H_2O. Add stabilizer soln, **40.003(ee)**, to bring vol. to 20 ml and mix well. Pipet 2 sep. 0.5 ml portions and spread evenly over 2 counting slides, **40.002(p)**. (Satisfactory measuring device is 1 ml pipet with 3 mm bore (±0.5 mm) cut off at 1 ml mark. In pipet-ting, draw material slightly above 0.5 ml mark and let it drop slowly to mark. Let material flow slowly onto slide, spreading uniformly in center of slide to cover area ca 6 × 2 cm. Touch lower end of pipet

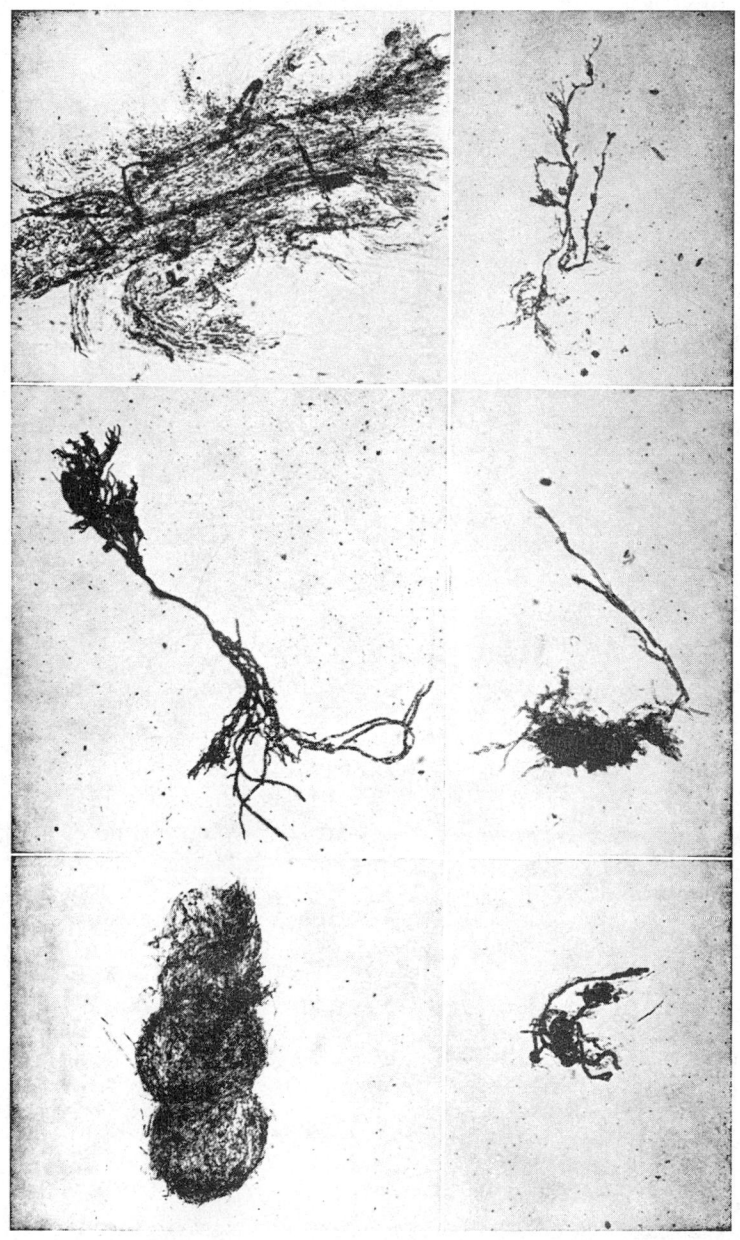

FIG. 40:6—Rot fragments from tomato puree. 40×

to slide several times to ensure complete removal of material. Blow out last drop if necessary.) Examine each slide at 30–45 ×, using transmitted light. Count number of rot fragments on each of the 2 slides, add results, and multiply by 2 (for 10 g sample) or 4 (for 5 g sample) to obtain number of rot fragments per g juice, catsup, sauce, or dild puree or paste. Rot fragment is defined as particle of tomato cellular material with one or more mold filaments attached. Some may appear as almost solid masses of mold. *See* Figs. 40:6–40:8.

40.089   Fly Eggs and Maggots— Official First Action

(a) *Comminuted products.*—Thoroly mix sample and transfer 100 g to 2 L separator. Add 20–30 ml heptane and shake thoroly, releasing pressure as necessary. Fill separator with H_2O in such manner as to produce max. agitation. Place separator in ring stand and let settle; at 15 min intervals during 1 hr, drain 15–20 ml from separator, and gently shake separator with rotary motion to facilitate settling out of fly eggs and maggots. If drained liq. contains

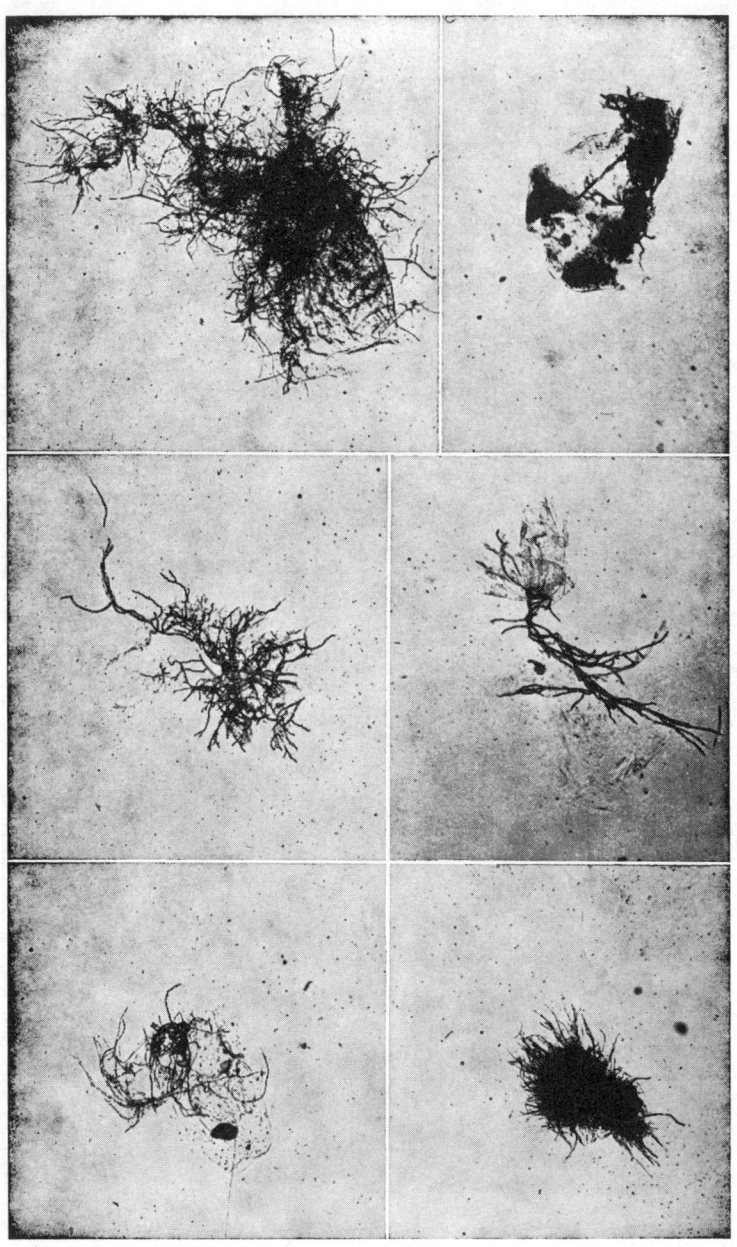

FIG. 40:7—Rot fragments from tomato puree. 40 ×

seeds, pass it thru No. 10 sieve, and thoroly rinse seeds and sieve, recovering both liq. portion and rinse H_2O in beaker. Filter thru 10XX bolting cloth in Hirsch funnel. (Pretreat cloth as in **40.002(d)**. Dissolve 0.05 g FD&C Blue No. 1 in 1 L H_2O, add 2.5 ml HOAc, warm to 80°, add ruled cloth, and hold at 80–85° ca 15 min with stirring. Rinse well in flowing H_2O. Store dry out of light.) Examine for eggs and maggots at ca 10×. If fly eggs or maggots are found in this examination, continue sepg and draining as above addnl hr.

(b) *Canned tomatoes.*—Pulp entire contents of can in such way that min. number of eggs and maggots are crushed or broken. (This may be done by passing material thru No. 6 or No. 8 sieve and adding seeds and residue remaining on sieve to pulp.)

Place 500 g of the well-mixed pulped tomatoes in 6 L separator. Add 125–150 ml heptane, **40.003(q)**, and ca 1 L H_2O and shake vigorously, releasing pressure as necessary. Fill separator with H_2O. Place separator in ring stand and let layers sep. At 15 min intervals during 1 hr, drain 25–30 ml from bottom

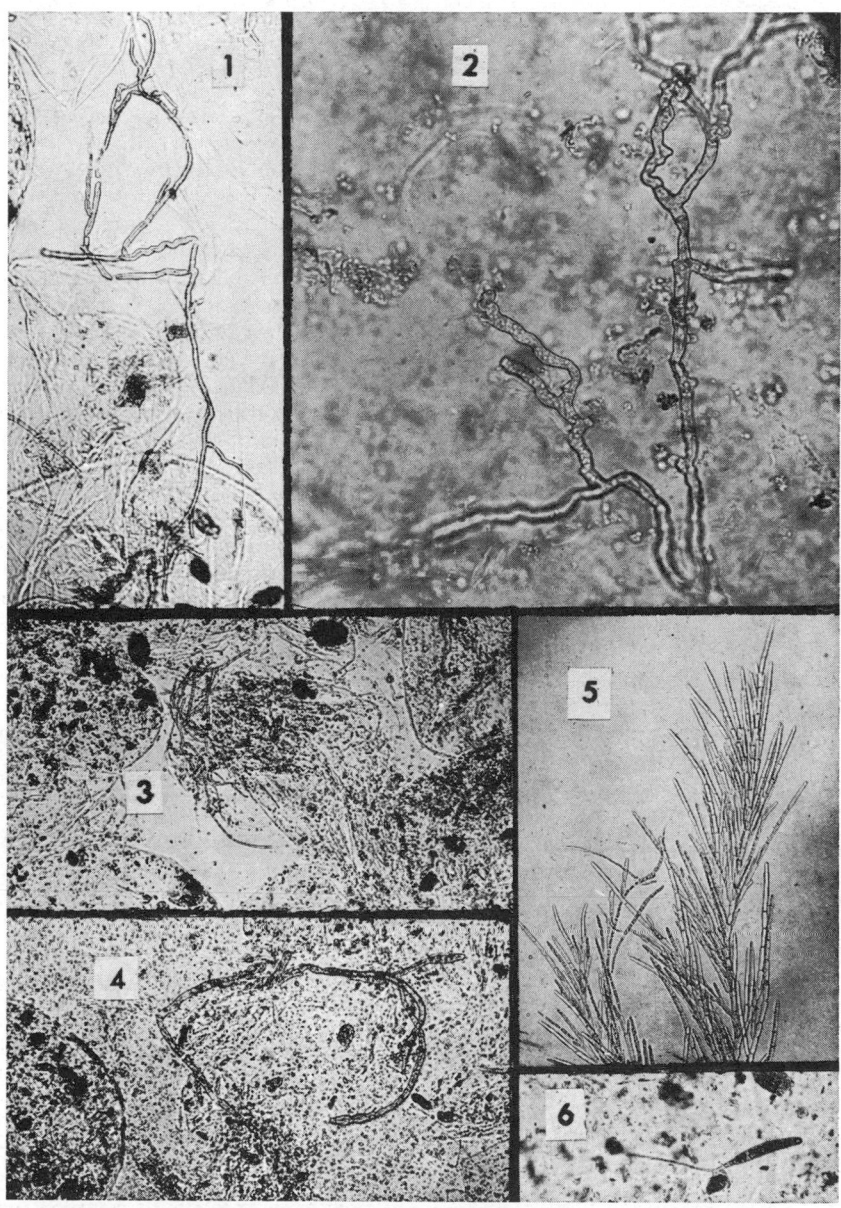

FIG. 40:8—Mold filaments in tomato products (100×). 1, branching mold and tomato cells. 2, coarse mold showing nonparallel and parallel walls, branching, granulation, and blunt tips. 3, very fine mold. 4, mold showing beginning of sporulation at end of hypha. 5, *Geotrichum* mold showing cross walls and feathery appearance characteristic of slimy machinery. 6, *Alternaria* spore with attached hypha.

of separator, and gently shake separator with rotary motion to facilitate settling of fly eggs and maggots. Each portion may be examined at once or combined with subsequent portions. Pass drained portions thru No. 10 sieve and thoroly rinse seeds and sieve, recovering both liq. portion and rinse H_2O in beaker. Filter thru 10XX bolting cloth in Hirsch funnel. Examine cloth for eggs and maggots at ca $10\times$. If fly eggs or maggots are found in this examination, continue sepg and draining as above addnl hr.

40.090   Light Filth

(a) *Comminuted products (Official First Action).*— Place 200 g of any tomato product except paste (where 100 g is used) in trap flask, **40.002**(h)(*3*), with 20 ml castor oil and mix well. Add enough hot tap H_2O (ca $70°$) to fill flask. (At first, bubbles of air tend to bring up tomato tissues, but after several stirrings these begin to settle out, leaving H_2O layer near oil fairly clear.) Let stand with occasional gentle stirring 30 min; then trap off into beaker. Wash out neck of flask with heptane to remove adhering castor oil. Add little more hot H_2O to flask, stir, let stand 10 min, and then trap off again. (Occasionally it may be necessary to transfer trapped-off material to another trap flask and rewash to eliminate tomato tissue.) Filter trapped-off portion; thoroly wash beaker, sides of funnel, and paper with heptane to dissolve oil and speed filtration. Examine paper at $20–30\times$.

(b) *Canned tomatoes (Procedure).*—Drain entire can on No. 6 sieve, saving drained juice. (For cans contg <3 lb use 8″ sieve; use larger sieve for larger cans or drain and rinse portionwise.) Rinse portion on sieve with hot H_2O (ca $70°$) from wash bottle and transfer drained juice, fragments, and washings to 1 or more 2 L Wildman trap flasks (max. 900 ml/ flask; No. 10 cans require $\geq$2). Bring vol. in flasks to ca 900 ml with H_2O ($70°$) and add 20–25 ml castor oil. Tilt flask to ca $45°$ and mix 1 min with brisk rotary motion (200–250 strokes/min). Avoid splashing thru surface with stopper. Add hot H_2O to bring oil layer into neck and let stand 30 min with occasional stirring. Trap off into beaker oil-H_2O layer and any debris that rises. Wash out oil in neck with heptane. Add ca 10 ml hot H_2O to flask, stir, let stand 10 min, and trap into same beaker. Add 25–30 ml heptane to beaker and stir to dissolve oil. Filter thru paper (use hot H_2O or heptane if necessary) and examine paper microscopically.

Tomato Soup, Canned Spaghetti, Pork and Beans, and Other Similar Products Containing Tomato Sauce

40.091   Mold—Official First Action

(a) *Tomato soup.*—Place unopened can in hot H_2O and heat until contents are thoroly warmed;

then open. Transfer 10 ml thoroly mixed soup to 50 ml centrf. tube and add 3 ml NaOH soln (1 + 1). If starch is absent, omit the NaOH. Stir until starch dissolves and tissues clear. Add enough H_2O to fill tube, and centrf. (Time required to centrf. sample varies greatly. With centrf. arm length of $5\frac{1}{4}″$ and speed of ca 1600 rpm, ca 20 min is required for av. sample. In heavy soups, gelatinizing of much starch sometimes interferes with proper settling out of solids during centrfg. If liq. remains cloudy, it may be necessary to discard sample and start again by adding 3 ml NaOH soln to only 5 ml soup.) When supernatant is clear, pour off; if not entirely clear, check supernatant for mold before discarding. Add enough H_2O to residue in tube to bring to original vol. of soup, mix, and count mold as in **40.085**.

(b) *Tomato sauce in pork and beans, spaghetti, ravioli, chili con carne, tamales, etc.*—Place unopened can in hot H_2O and heat until contents are thoroly warmed. Open can and transfer contents onto No. 6 sieve. Drain until major portion of liq. passes thru. (With some products, sauce runs thru at once, but in case of some beans and spaghetti 10 min or more may be required.) Mix sauce thoroly, place 10 ml in centrf. tube, and proceed as in (a). Use care in counting products contg meat so as not to confuse mold filaments and muscle fibers that superficially resemble each other; muscle fibers are usually much thicker and striations are often visible.

(c) *Tomato sauce packing medium on fish.*—Place unopened can in hot H_2O (ca $90–95°$) until contents are thoroly warmed. Open can and drain contents on No. 6 sieve until major portion of sauce and oil passes thru. Mix liq., place up to 50 ml in 50 ml centrf. tube, and centrf. as in (a). Record vol. of lower oil-free sauce layer and discard oil and part of sauce layer. Add H_2O to bring to recorded vol., mix, and count mold as in **40.085**, removing bits of fish tissue from slide, if necessary, before counting.

Pureed Infant Food

40.092   Molds—Official First Action

Proceed as in **40.085**. Add ca 0.2 g NaOH to ca 6 g product before counting, and stir thoroly until NaOH is dissolved.

40.093   Light Filth—Official First Action

Utilize oil-in-H_2O extn principle as carried out in trap flask, **40.002**(h)(*3*). Analyze all foods in similar manner, except to vary temp. and type of oil used as indicated in table.

Transfer contents of 2 cans or jars of food to 1 L trap flask previously rinsed with H_2O. Thoroly mix in ca 20 ml of the oil. Fill with deaerated H_2O either at room temp. or at $50–70°$. Let mixt. stand 30 min, stirring 4–6 times during this period to release filth from layer of food. Trap off and examine microscopically.

Use type of oil and temp. indicated in following table:

Food	Oil	Temp.
All fruits Asparagus Beets Carrots Green beans Peas	Light mineral oil	Room
Spinach	Light mineral oil	50–70°
Squash	Castor oil	50–70°

40.094 Fly Eggs and Maggots— Official First Action

Transfer residue in the trap flask, 40.093, to 2 L separator. Add ca 100 ml heptane, 40.003(q), and shake vigorously. Let material settle ca 2 hr, occasionally stirring surface layer to permit any eggs and maggots to settle out. Withdraw ca 200 ml from bottom of separator and filter this material thru 10XX bolting cloth, 40.002(d), using several cloths if there is large accumulation of sediment. Examine microscopically at 15–20×.

Peas and Beans
40.095 Weevils—Official First Action

Microscopic examination.—If peas or beans are canned and of normal texture, pour on No. 8 sieve in pan filled with enough H_2O to stand 2–3 cm above mesh of sieve. Mash peas thru sieve with fingers. After as much as possible of material has been worked thru, remove sieve from pan and shake excess H_2O back into pan. Transfer material retained on sieve to 2 L beaker. Pour material that passed thru No. 8 sieve onto No. 40 sieve, discarding that which passes thru. Let material on sieve drain few min, and shake lightly to remove free H_2O from solid material. (If peas are unusually hard, or have tough skins, pass contents of can thru meat or food chopper directly onto No. 40 sieve.) Discard any excess H_2O passing thru this sieve. Cook dried or frozen peas before maceration.

Add material retained on the No. 40 sieve to the beaker. Add ca 130 ml heptane, 40.003(q), to this material and mix thoroly with large spoon. Rinse any material remaining on sieve into can with H_2O. Stir material in can and pick out any insects that may rise to top of H_2O layer. Repeat stirring and searching several times until no more larvae are recovered.

Add enough H_2O to bring contents of beaker to within 1–2 cm of top. Pick out any larvae visible at surface. Stir again, and let mixt. stand ca 5 min; then skim off heptane and upper part of H_2O layer with spoon and place in trap flask, 40.002(h)(3), previously filled ca ¼ full of H_2O. Add 90–100 ml heptane to material remaining in beaker, and stir vigorously. After standing ca 5 addnl min, skim off heptane and upper part of H_2O layer as before and add to material already in trap flask.

Fill flask with H_2O. Trap off as much heptane as possible and filter into Hirsch funnel. Lower stopper into flask, and, to rinse sides of trap flask, apply vac. ca 5 min by fitting large rubber stopper and glass tube over mouth of flask. (As ordinary erlenmeyer collapses under vac. of 20″ of Hg, use either less vac. or heavy-wall flask.) Release vac., add H_2O, and trap off. Add trapped-off portion to that already on filter. Examine microscopically.

Potato Chips
40.096 Filth—Official First Action

Weigh 100 g sample into 1.5 L beaker. Crush chips into small pieces and cover with pet ether. Let stand ca 5 min and decant thru filter. Add pet ether and decant again thru filter. Let pet ether evap. from chips. Transfer to 2 L trap flask, add 500 ml 60% alcohol, and boil ca 30 min, replacing alcohol lost by evapn. Cool, add 35 ml heptane, 40.003(q), mix, let stand ca 5 min, and fill with 60% alcohol. Let stand, trap off twice, and filter as usual. Examine papers microscopically.

Canned Greens and Broccoli
40.097 Insects—Official First Action

Transfer contents of can to pan of suitable size and chop up leaves into pieces 1–2″ long. Weigh 100 g well-mixed sample into 1 L beaker. Add 500–600 ml H_2O and boil 5 min. Pour H_2O and sample into 2 L trap flask, 40.002(h)(3). Add 35 ml heptane, 40.003(q), and stir mixt. thoroly to ensure contact between heptane and all portions of leaves. Fill flask with deaerated H_2O, let stand 30 min, trap off heptane layer, filter, and examine microscopically. Add 40 ml heptane to flask and repeat extn.

If plant tissue rises to interface, place No. 8 sieve, 6–8″ diam., in suitable size evapg dish contg enough H_2O to cover screen ca ½″. Pour entrapped heptane from trap flask onto sieve as it is held under the H_2O. Move sieve gently up and down to let insects pass thru into the H_2O. Remove screen and filter contents of dish. Repeat washing to free any insects left on greens on screen, and filter washings. Examine papers microscopically.

40.098 Aphids and Thrips— Official First Action

Det. drained wt of contents of canned greens as in 40.087, reserving drained liquor. Chop drained leaves into pieces 1–2″ long and weigh 100 g well-mixed sample into 1 L beaker. Add H_2O to cover adequately, followed by 25 g neut. $Pb(OAc)_2 \cdot 3H_2O$ crystals (or equiv. soln of $Pb(OAc)_2$) and 10 ml HOAc. Boil on hot plate 5–10 min, cool, and transfer to 2 L trap flask, 40.002(h)(3). Add 35 ml heptane, 40.003(q), and mix thoroly to assure contact between heptane and all portions of leaves. Fill flask with deaerated H_2O. Let settle few min for most of vegetable matter to sink to bottom. To force any tissue that rises (probably held by entrapped globules of heptane) to sink, pivot lower end of trap-rod on bottom of flask, and rotate upper part of rod around neck of flask to knock globules from vegetable tissue without at same time breaking interface and thus rewetting tissue with heptane. Again let flask stand, trap off heptane layer, and filter.

Re-ext with 20 ml heptane, trap off, and filter (usually possible on same paper). Det. total number of aphids or other light filth in entire liquor drained from can by subjecting it to heptane flotation as usual. (Normally liquor does not present any difficulty and use of Pb(OAc)$_2$ is unnecessary.) Count total number of aphids and thrips including parts contg heads. Count cast skins and other insects sep. Calc. on basis of wt of drained material.

40.099   Heavy Filth—Official First Action

Recover heavy filth such as soil, maggots (especially those of spinach leaf miner), and rodent excreta, that sink to bottom of trap flask, as follows: Transfer contents of trap flask, **40.097** or **40.098,** by rinsing with H$_2$O into 4–6 qt pail. Add H$_2$O to pail until ca full. Stir, let stand short time, and decant ca half pail contents. Refill pail with H$_2$O and repeat operation until most of floating greens are removed. Wash the heavy filth left in pail into black shallow pan and examine visually for larvae, stones, and other debris, picking material out with forceps.

Sauerkraut
40.100   Filth—Official First Action

Use entire contents of container of <2 lb. Use 24 oz well mixed sample from larger containers. Wash small portion at time on nested 8″ Nos. 8, 20, and 140 sieves, **40.002**(q). Wash material remaining on No. 20 sieve with washings passing thru No. 140 sieve. Transfer material on No. 20 sieve to paper and examine at ca 10× for whole insects or large body parts. Transfer material remaining on No. 140 sieve to paper and examine microscopically.

Mushrooms
Canned, Fresh, and Frozen (27)— Official First Action
(For maggots, mites, etc.)

40.101   *Reagents and Apparatus*

(a) *Crystal violet.*—Satd aq. soln.

(b) *Sodium hypochlorite soln.*—Com. product contg ca 5.25%.

(c) *High-speed blender.*—To measure speed, attach 1-hole No. 8 rubber stopper to square rotor shaft and insert tachometer. Det. variable transformer setting for 3000–3500 rpm. (Attachment of blender jar does not alter speed significantly.)

(d) *Variable transformer.*—Output voltage 0–140; ≥7.5 amp.

40.102   *Determination*

Pour contents of can evenly over weighed No. 8 sieve. Use 8″ sieve, for containers of net wt <3 lb and 12″ sieve for larger containers. Drain 2 min, and reweigh sieve and mushrooms to det. drained wt mushrooms.

Rinse container, and use rinsings and several addnl portions H$_2$O to rinse mushrooms on sieve (ca 500 ml total). Combine drained liq. with rinsings and filter thru ruled paper. Examine residue on paper microscopically and det. total number of maggots in liq.

Place 100 g drained mushrooms in high speed blender (*see* (c)). Add 300 ml H$_2$O and blend 30–45 sec at 3000–3500 rpm. Attain proper speed quickly by boosting setting to 1.5–2× desired setting on variable transformer for few sec at start. Fragments of mushrooms after blending should be ≤3–5 mm long. Pour mixt. into nested set of 8″ Nos. 20, 40, and 140 sieves, **40.002**(q). Rinse tissue 2–3 min with spray of tap H$_2$O from aerator. Discard material on No. 20 sieve. Transfer residue from No. 40 sieve to 600 ml beaker with H$_2$O and bring total vol. to ca 100 ml. Add 5 ml crystal violet soln and heat to boiling. Pour stained mixt. into No. 40 sieve. Wash mushroom tissue, and maggots, if any, to edge of sieve and remove excess stain with tap H$_2$O from aerator. Using wash bottle contg NaOCl soln, (b), and gentle spray of tap H$_2$O from aerator, **40.002**(a), alternately spray tissue with H$_2$O and NaOCl soln until stain has been removed from mushroom tissue. Wash tissue into 600 ml beaker and transfer to ruled paper, using vac. Avoid obscuring maggots with mushroom tissues. (Not more than 2–3 papers should be necessary.)

Transfer residue from No. 140 sieve to 600 ml beaker with H$_2$O and repeat staining, bleaching, and filtering as above.

Examine papers for maggots and other extraneous materials at 10–30×. Maggots are stained dark violet. Det. number of maggots in 100 g drained mushrooms and add to this value the number in proportionate amt of drained liq. calcd as follows:

(100/total g drained mushrooms) × total number of maggots in liq.

Dried (Not Powdered)
40.103   Light and Heavy Filth—Procedure

Thoroly mix sample and weigh 100 g portion. Transfer mushrooms to trap flask, **40.002**(h)(*3*), add H$_2$O, and let soak several hr, preferably overnight on steam bath, or boil 30 min. Cool to room temp., add 30 ml heptane, **40.003**(q), and churn contents by hard, rapid pounding of mushrooms against bottom of flask, using vertical movement of rubber plunger. Trap off twice, filter, and examine microscopically.

Pour remaining liq. and mushrooms in flask onto No. 8 sieve in dishpan and add enough H$_2$O to partially immerse sieve. Rub mushrooms over sieve to release any insects, such as maggots, that may have remained in tunnels in mushrooms, letting them drop thru sieve. Filter thru 10XX bolting cloth and examine microscopically.

Sweet Corn

40.104 Filth—Official First Action

(a) *Microscopic examination.*—Place 200 g well-mixed sample in 2 L trap flask, 40.002(h)(*3*), add 20 ml castor oil, and mix well. Add enough hot tap H_2O (ca 50°) to fill flask. Let stand 30 min with occasional gentle stirring; then trap off, into beaker, oil and H_2O layer and any corn debris that rises into neck of trap flask. To dissolve adhering oil, wash out neck of flask with hot alcohol. Add ca 10 ml more hot H_2O to flask, stir, let stand 10 min, and trap off again into same beaker.

Add ca 25–30 ml heptane to trapped-off portion and stir well to dissolve castor oil. Transfer contents of beaker into No. 6 or No. 8 sieve held in 400 ml beaker. Thoroly wash corn debris on sieve with hot alcohol, and filter material that passes thru sieve, thoroly washing beaker, sides of funnel, and paper with hot alcohol. Examine paper microscopically.

(b) *Macroscopic examination.*—Empty residue of corn remaining on bottom of flask when trapping is completed, (a), onto 5″ or 8″ No. 20 sieve. Place remainder of corn from can on sieve, portionwise if necessary, and wash under tap to remove starch and fine particles. Place residue on sieve in pan and examine under H_2O for worm-eaten or rotten kernels and whole worms, heads, or large fragments.

SPICES AND OTHER CONDIMENTS

Ground Allspice, Anise, Caraway, Cardamom, Celery Seed, Cloves, Coriander, Cumin, Curry Powder, Dill Seed, Fennel, Fenugreek, Ginger, Mace, Marjoram, Mustard, Nutmeg, Oregano, Poppy Seed, Rosemary, Sage, Savory, Thyme, and Condiments

40.105 Gross Contamination— Official First Action

Sift 200–400 g ground spice thru No. 20 sieve. Transfer any insects or other filth retained on sieve to suitable dish and examine with Greenough microscope.

40.106 Heavy and Light Filth— Official First Action

(*Caution: See* 46.011, 46.039, 46.040, 46.056, *and* 46.073.)

(a) *Heavy filth and sand.*—Weigh 10 g sample into 250 ml beaker. Add 150 ml pet ether and boil gently 15 min on steam bath in hood. Occasionally add pet ether to keep vol. constant. Decant pet ether onto smooth 7 cm paper in buchner. Add 150 ml $CHCl_3$ to beaker and let stand 30 min with occasional stirring. Decant spice and $CHCl_3$ onto funnel, leaving heavy residue of sand and soil, if any, in beaker. If appreciable spice tissue remains on bottom of beaker, add

successive portions of $CHCl_3$ mixed with CCl_4 to give increasingly higher sp gr until practically all spice tissue is floated off. Transfer residue from beaker to ashless paper and examine microscopically. If there is appreciable quantity of residue, place paper in weighed crucible, ignite, and weigh sand and soil.

(b) *Light filth.*—Thoroly dry material in buchner and transfer, including fine material that must be scraped from paper, to 1 L trap flask, 40.002(h)(*3*). Add ca 150 ml H_2O, heat to boiling, and simmer 15 min, with stirring; wash down inside of flask with H_2O; and cool to <20°. Add 25 ml heptane, 40.003(q), mix thoroly, and let stand 5 min; then fill flask with H_2O and let stand 30 min. Stir every 5 min, trap off, and filter. Add ca 15 ml heptane to flask and mix thoroly; trap off and filter second time after 15 min. If second extn yields appreciable amt of filth, decant most of liq. from flask, add 15 ml heptane, and make third extn. Examine papers microscopically.

Ground Cinnamon

40.107 Heavy and Light Filth— Official First Action

(a) *Heavy filth and sand.*—Weigh 2 g sample into 50 ml centrf. tube and add ca 45 ml CCl_4. Centrf. 5 min at 800 rpm in International size I, type SB, centrf., using No. 240 head with arm length of 5.25″, or equiv. Stir layer at top of liq. and repeat centrfg. Decant ca $2/3$ of liq. and floating layer, and add fresh CCl_4 up to 45 ml. Mix thoroly and again centrf. Decant as much of liq. and floating layer as possible without disturbing residue in centrf. tube. Wash residue onto 11 cm ashless paper with CCl_4. Examine under low-power microscope for filth. If there is appreciable residue, place paper in weighed crucible, ignite, and weigh sand and soil.

(b) *Light filth* (*28*).—(Where alcohol and 60% alcohol are specified, isopropanol and 40% isopropanol, resp., may be substituted. Use same alcohol thruout method.) Weigh 50 g sample into 800 ml beaker. Add 500 ml hot (55–70°) tap H_2O and 50 ml HCl. Stir several min with stirring bar at high speed on magnetic stirring hot plate, holding temp. without boiling until gel is dispersed (suspension will become less viscous and vortex will become more pronounced). Sieve portionwise onto No. 230 sieve, 40.002(q), with forceful stream of hot tap H_2O, using aerator, 40.002(a). After fine material has passed thru sieve, wash residue alternately with alcohol and hot tap H_2O until most foam and color have passed thru. Transfer residue to 1.5 L beaker with 60% alcohol, using spoon to transfer bulk of material. Dil. to 1 L with 60% alcohol. Add 50 ml HCl and heat (do *not* boil) while stirring with magnetic stirrer, 40.002(r), to prevent charring. When mixt. is hot (ca 55°), add 50 ml mineral oil, 40.003(w), and stir magnetically, 40.004(b), 4 min. Transfer beaker contents to 2 L percolator, 40.002(h)(*2*), rinse beaker well with 60% alcohol, and add rinsings to percolator. Bring vol. in percolator to ca 1.7 L with 60% alcohol. Resuspend material in percolator by vigorously stirring with glass rod, and rinse rod into percolator with 60% alcohol. Let settle 3 min, and immediately drain material in percolator to within several cm of bottom of mineral oil layer. Refill percolator with hot tap H_2O, adding H_2O rapidly to thoroly resuspend material in percolator. Let settle 3 min, and drain again. Repeat hot H_2O rinses until aq. medium is practically free of suspended matter with max. of 7 rinses. Discard hot H_2O rinses. Drain mineral oil layer into 800 ml beaker and rinse down sides of percolator with alternate rinses of 95% alcohol and hot (55–70°) tap H_2O (use rubber policeman if necessary). Pour mineral oil and final rinses onto ruled paper and examine microscopically.

Ground Turmeric

40.108   Light Filth—Official First Action

(Caution: See **46.040, 46.049,** *and* **46.056.***)*

Weigh 25 g sample into 400 ml beaker. Add 300 ml $CHCl_3$-CCl_4 mixt. $(1 + 1)$, stir thoroly, and let stand 15 min with occasional stirring. Transfer mixt. onto 15 cm paper in buchner and rinse with solv. Dry overnight or in oven 1 hr at 80°. Transfer dry residue to 600 ml beaker. Add 300–400 ml H_2O, stir until smooth, add filtered aq. ext from 5 g pancreatin, **40.003(x)**, and mix. Adjust to pH 8 with Na_3PO_4 soln. Readjust pH after ca 15 min and again after ca 45 min. Add 5 drops HCHO and digest overnight at 37–40°. Cool, transfer digested material to 2 L trap flask, **40.002(h)(3)**, and add H_2O to 800 ml. Trap off twice with 25 and 15 ml heptane, **40.003(q)**, resp., as in **40.004(a)**. Combine trappings in beaker, transfer to trap flask, and fill with H_2O. Stir, and after 30 min, trap off into beaker and filter. Examine microscopically.

Ground Black and White Pepper

40.109   Heavy and Light Filth—Official First Action

(Caution: See **46.040** *and* **46.049.***)*

(a) *Heavy filth and sand.*—Weigh 50 g sample into 600 ml beaker. Add 400 ml CCl_4 and let beaker stand ≥ 1 hr with occasional stirring. Decant pepper and solv. onto 15 cm paper in buchner, leaving heavy residue of sand and soil in beaker. Repeat decantation with CCl_4 if necessary to secure practically complete sepn of spice materials from any heavy residue. Transfer residue from beaker to ashless paper and examine for filth. If there is appreciable residue, place paper in weighed crucible, ignite, and weigh sand and soil.

(b) *Light filth.*—Wash spice material in buchner, (a), with $CHCl_3$ and dry overnight or in oven 1 hr at 80°. Transfer dry residue to 600 ml beaker and proceed as in **40.108,** beginning "Add 300–400 ml H_2O, ..."

Ground Onion and Garlic Powder

40.110   Heavy and Light Filth—Official First Action

(Caution: See **46.040** *and* **46.049.***)*

(a) *Heavy filth and sand.*—Weigh 50 g sample into 250 ml hook-lip beaker. Add 200 ml CCl_4, stir thoroly, and let stand 30 min with occasional stirring. Decant plant tissue onto 15 cm paper in buchner, add 100 ml CCl_4, and repeat decantation until practically no plant tissue remains with sand and soil on bottom of beaker. Transfer residue in beaker to ashless paper with stream of CCl_4 from wash bottle and examine for filth. If there is appreciable residue, place paper in weighed crucible, ignite, and weigh sand and soil.

(b) *Light filth.*—Dry residue of plant tissue from buchner, (a), overnight or in oven 1 hr at 80°, and transfer to 2 L trap flask, **40.002(h)(3)**. Add 250 ml Tween 80–60% alcohol soln, **40.003(ff)**, mix well, and let stand 15–30 min. Add 60% alcohol to 800 ml and trap off twice in 60% alcohol with 75 and 35 ml heptane, **40.003(q)**, resp., as in **40.004(a)**. Let stand 1–1.5 hr for each extn and avoid stirring except for few circular upward strokes immediately after filling flask with 60% alcohol. Filter, and examine microscopically.

Ground Capsicums (Red and Cayenne Pepper, Chili Powder, etc.)

40.111   Heavy and Light Filth—Official First Action

(Caution: See **46.040** *and* **46.049.***)*

(a) *Heavy filth and sand.*—Isolate gross filth such as large larvae, adult insects, clumps of webbing, and insect and rodent excreta pellets by sifting pepper thru No. 10 sieve.

Weigh 50 g sifted sample into 600 ml beaker and add 400 ml pet ether. Boil gently 30 min, occasionally adding pet ether to keep vol. constant. Decant pet ether onto smooth 15 cm paper in buchner. Add 400 ml CCl_4 and let stand 30 min with occasional stirring. Decant pepper and solv. onto same 15 cm paper in buchner, leaving heavy residue of sand and soil in beaker. Repeat decantation with CCl_4 if necessary to secure practically complete sepn of spice materials from heavy residue. Transfer residue from beaker to ashless paper and examine for filth. If there is appreciable residue, place paper in weighed crucible, ignite, and det. sand and soil.

(b) *Light filth.*—Wash spice material in buchner, (a), with $CHCl_3$ and dry overnight or in oven 1 hr at 80°. Transfer dry residue to 600 ml beaker and add 300–400 ml H_2O, stirring until smooth. Add filtered aq. ext from 5 g pancreatin, **40.003(x)**, and mix. Adjust to pH 8 with Na_3PO_4 after ca 15 min, and again after ca 45 min. Add 5 drops HCHO and digest overnight at 37–40°. Transfer digested material to 2 L trap flask, **40.002(h)(3)**, cautiously boil ca 10 min until foaming partially subsides, and cool to 20°.

Add H$_2$O to ca 800 ml and trap off twice with 25 and 15 ml heptane, **40.003(q)**, resp., as in **40.004(a)**. Combine trappings in beaker, transfer to trap flask, and fill with H$_2$O. Stir, and after 30 min, trap off into beaker and filter. Examine microscopically.

40.112 Rot (Based on Mold Count)—
Official First Action

Weigh 10 g thoroly mixed sample of ground capsicum and transfer to high-speed blender. Add 200 ml 1% NaOH soln in 3 or 4 successive portions, stirring after each addn, washing down with final portion any material that may stick to walls of blender. Agitate mixt. in blender 1 min. With rubber policeman rub down into mixt. any material sticking to walls and repeat blending 2 min longer. Add 2 or 3 drops *capryl alcohol* to break foam. Mix 100 g of this mixt. with 50 g stabilizer soln, **40.003(ee)**, and count with Howard mold-counting slide, **40.002(m)(1)**, as in **40.085**.

Occasionally blended mixt. contains particles of seed tissue that make it difficult to obtain Newton's rings in prepg slide for mold counting. Clamp devised for holding cover slip in place to obviate this difficulty consists of metal plate with circular opening, 2.5 cm diam., in center of plate; 2 clips attached to edge of plate hold cover slip in position when slide is placed on plate.

Paprika—Official First Action
40.113 Gross Contamination
See **40.105**.

40.114 Light Filth (*29*)

Add 25 g sample to 500 ml 1% aq. Na lauryl sulfate soln. Heat on steam bath 10 min. Wash on No. 230 sieve, **40.002(q)**, with forcible stream of hot H$_2$O (55–70°), using aerator, **40.002(a)**. (If H$_2$O temp. is <55°, complete wet sieving, and wash sieve residue with 2 L boiling H$_2$O, adding 200–250 ml at time to residue, shaking each portion thru sieve before adding next portion. Continue as below, beginning "... transfer to 2 L trap flask with 60% alcohol.")

When foam disappears, transfer to 2 L trap flask with 60% alcohol. Rinse sides of flask with 60% alcohol, and dil. to 900–1000 ml with 60% alcohol. Pour 60 ml heptane, **40.003(q)**, down stirring rod. Stir magnetically, **40.004(b)**, 6 min. Let stand 2–3 min. Mix 50 ml Tween soln, **40.003(ff)**, 50 ml Na$_4$-EDTA soln, **40.003(gg)**, and 200 ml 60% alcohol. Pour mixt. down stirring rod, with top of disk or rubber stirring stopper held just below surface of liq. Mix 1 min by gently swirling with stirring rod just beneath surface of liq. Pour 60% alcohol down stirring rod. Raise rod and clamp so stopper is held above layer of settled plant material. Let stand 5 min. Rotate stopper to free settled plant debris. Let stand 25 min and trap off. Decant free liq. onto ruled paper. Add 10 ml acetone to settled material in beaker, swirl, and decant free liq. Repeat acetone

decantation step 2 more times. Complete transfer of beaker contents to paper with 95% alcohol. Perform second trapping with 30 ml heptane and add enough H$_2$O (ca 30 ml) to refill flask. Transfer second trapping to sep. paper, decanting with acetone as before. Examine papers microscopically at 30×.

★ *Whole Spices* ★
40.115 Filth by Flotation—
Official First Action

Crack whole spice into small pieces to facilitate extn and proceed as in **40.106**, using 100 g sample with appropriate changes in app. size and reagent vols.

Whole Marjoram, Savory, and Thyme
40.116 Filth—Official First Action

Weigh 25 g sample into 400 ml beaker and proceed as in **40.106(a)** and **(b)**, except use more reagent, and where necessary, 2 L trap flask, and add 400 ml hot H$_2$O + 20 ml HCl; also use 35 ml heptane, **40.003(q)**, instead of 25 ml.

Whole, Cracked, or Pieces of Allspice, Anise, Bay Leaves, Caraway, Celery Seed, Cloves, Coriander, Cumin, Dill Seed, Fennel Seed, Fenugreek, Ginger, Mace, Mixed Pickling Spice, Mustard, Nutmeg, Black Pepper, White Pepper, Poppy Seed, Rosemary, Sage, and Turmeric
40.117 Filth—Official First Action

Weigh 25 g sample and proceed as in **40.106(a)** and **(b)**, using larger beaker and more reagent if necessary.

Unground Cinnamon, Crude and Reconditioned
40.118 Light Filth (*30*)—Official First Action

If sample is reconditioned or if pieces are not rolled and are <3″ long, weigh 100 g sample directly into 1.5 L beaker. If sample consists of quills, break open quills into lengths of ≤3″ and transfer broken pieces, including dust and small particles, to 1.5 L beaker. Add 1 L hot tap H$_2$O and 50 ml HCl. Heat on hot plate to ca 60°. Pour portionwise onto No. 6 over No. 230 sieve, **40.002(q)**, and rinse well with forcible stream of hot tap H$_2$O, using aerator, **40.002(a)**, while turning larger pieces with glass rod. Discard material on No. 6 sieve and transfer residue on No. 230 sieve to 2 L trap flask, **40.002(h)(3)**, with hot tap H$_2$O, using spoon if necessary. Fill trap flask to 1 L with H$_2$O and add 50 ml HCl. Heat with stirring to ca 60–70°. Add 50 ml mineral oil, **40.003(w)**, and stir magnetically, **40.004(b)**, 2 min. Fill with H$_2$O, let stand 5 min, and trap. Add 25 ml mineral oil, gently stir with stopper 1 min, let stand 5 min, and again trap. Rinse neck of flask with alcohol or isopropanol. Filter trappings onto ruled filter paper and examine for insects and other arthropods, hairs, excreta, etc.

Unground Oregano

Light Filth (*31*)—Official First Action

40.119 *Reagents*

(a) *Polysorbate 80-tetrasodium EDTA mixture* (*1 + 1*).—Prep. from Tween 80–60% alcohol soln, **40.003(ff)**, and Na₄EDTA–60% alcohol soln, **40.003(gg)**.

(b) *15% Alcohol.*—Prep. ca 1700 ml/sample prior to analysis.

40.120 *Determination*

Weigh 10 g sample into 2 L trap flask, **40.002(h)(3)**, add 400 ml 60% alcohol, and boil gently 10 min, occasionally swirling flask gently and/or using plunger to prevent material from accumulating on wall of flask above surface of liq. Immediately add 100 ml Tween 80-Na₄EDTA mixt., and swirl few sec, again using plunger to clear material from wall of flask. Let stand 10 min. Dil. to 800 ml with 15% alcohol. Add 50 ml mineral oil, **40.003(w)**, and stir magnetically, **40.004(b)**, 2 min. Fill with 15% alcohol and hand stir every 2–3 min for 20 min. Clamp stirring rod in place so that plunger is held above mass of material at bottom of flask. Leave flask undisturbed 10 min. Trap, filter onto ruled paper, and examine microscopically.

★ Unground Fermented Crushed Peppers ★

40.121 Light and Heavy Filth—Official First Action

(a) *Light filth.*—Mix 100 g sample in beaker with 100 ml heptane, **40.003(q)**. Thin mixt. with little H₂O if necessary for mixing. Pour mixt. into cylindrical, white enamel pan ca 8″ high × 10″ diam. that has been almost filled with H₂O, and stir gently. Most of pepper particles sink or remain suspended in the H₂O; light filth and some debris come to surface with the heptane. Decant top layer of heptane and part of H₂O layer (ca 1.5 L in all) into 2 L trap flask, **40.002(h)(3)**, thru glass funnel. Rinse funnel and fill trap flask with H₂O. Stir, and let settle 30 min. Trap off, filter, and examine microscopically.

(b) *Heavy filth.*—Gently stir material in pan, (a), and let settle ca 30 sec. Decant pepper skin fragments. Add more H₂O and repeat operation until quantity of seeds and pepper fragments does not seriously interfere with examination of paper for heavy filth. Do not try to get paper entirely free from pepper skin and seeds, because filth will also be decanted. Transfer heavy residue to ruled paper and examine microscopically.

★ Pepper Sauce ★

40.122 Light and Heavy Filth—Official First Action

(a) *Light filth.*—Mix 100 g sauce with 100 ml H₂O and 35 ml heptane, **40.003(q)**, in 2 L trap flask,

40.002(h)(3). Fill flask with H₂O, stir, and let settle 30 min. Trap off, filter, and examine microscopically.

(b) *Heavy filth.*—Transfer remainder of material from (a) in trap flask to white enamel pan. Treat by sedimentation method as in **40.121(b)**.

Prepared Mustard

40.123 Light Filth (*32*)—Official First Action

Weigh 100 g well mixed sample into 1 L beaker, and slowly add 400 ml HCl (3 + 97) and 20 ml mineral oil, **40.003(w)**, with constant stirring until smooth slurry forms. Proceed as in **40.051,** beginning "Place on hot plate . . ." Rinse final papers with enough alcohol to remove yellow color.

Condimental Seeds

40.124 Rodent and Insect Excreta—Official First Action

Prep. liq. with sp gr of 1.16–1.19 by mixing CHCl₃ or CCl₄ with alcohol or pet ether. Mix 200 g of the seed with 500–700 ml of the liq. in 1 qt drug percolator. Let mixt. stand 30 min, stirring at ca 5 min intervals. Trap sediment in lower end of percolator with cork plug and remove lower cork so as to deliver all sediment into beaker. Lift upper cork slightly and rinse tube and cork by letting small amt of liq. pass. After stirring top layer, make 2 more sepns at 5 min intervals. Transfer contents of beaker to filter paper, drain liq., and examine. Sep. rodent excreta and insect excreta, air dry, and weigh each sep. to nearest mg.

★ Whole Tamarind Pulp ★

40.125 Light Filth—Official First Action

Mix sample thoroly and weigh 500 g into 1.5 L beaker. Add hot H₂O to within 1″ of top of beaker and simmer 15–20 min, stirring occasionally to break up mass of material. Pour contents of beaker thru No. 2 sieve, catching filtrate in convenient receptacle.

Break up material on sieve and wash thoroly with hot H₂O to remove all small adhering particles (filth, etc.). Discard material retained on No. 2 sieve, pour material passing thru sieve onto No. 140 sieve, **40.002(q)**, and wash thoroly with hot H₂O.

Transfer material retained on No. 140 sieve to 2 L trap flask, **40.002(h)(3)**, with cold H₂O. Mix in 35 ml heptane, **40.003(q)**, and let stand 5 min. Fill flask with H₂O and let settle 30 min, stirring every 5 min. (Pulp rising in neck of flask may be worked down by stirring gently with rubber stopper.) Trap off, and filter thru 10XX bolting cloth, **40.002(d)**. Add ca 20 ml heptane to flask and mix thoroly; trap off and filter second time after 15 min. If second extn yields appreciable amt of filth, decant most of liq. from flask, add 15 ml heptane, and make third extn. Examine papers microscopically.

Whole Pickles

40.126 Filth—Official First Action

Pour entire contents of jar onto No. 8 sieve nested in No. 140 sieve, **40.002(q)**. Wash jar thoroly to remove any filth adhering to sides, and pour washings thru sieves. Wash pickles thoroly with stream of hot H_2O, turning from time to time. Transfer material on No. 140 sieve directly to ruled paper and examine microscopically. If only small quantity of debris is washed from pickles, wash directly onto filter paper. State which method was used.

Chopped Pickles and Relish

40.127 Filth—Official First Action

Add 200 ml H_2O to 100 g sample in trap flask or beaker, boil 15 min, and cool. If boiling is done in beaker, transfer to trap flask, **40.002(h)(3)**. Trap off twice, using 25 and 15 ml heptane, **40.003(q)**. Filter, and examine microscopically.

Dressings for Food

40.128 Filth—Official First Action

Weigh 200 g sample into 800 ml beaker, stir in 50 ml H_3PO_4, and mix thoroly. Thin with ca 600 ml H_2O, and again mix thoroly. If possible, filter thru No. 8 ruled paper with suction, otherwise thru No. 140 sieve, **40.002(q)**, and transfer to ruled paper. Examine papers microscopically.

ANIMAL EXCRETIONS

Urine Stains on Foods and Containers (33)— Official First Action

40.129 Preliminary Examination with Ultraviolet Light

(*Caution: See 46.016.*)

Examine suspected stains in dark room under UV light. (Dried urine on textiles usually fluoresces blue-white, but color varies somewhat, depending upon natural color of textile and type of lamp and filter used.) Run check patches with known types of urine. For microchemical analysis, outline stained area with pencil under the UV light. When odor of urine is detected, report this finding.

40.130 Urease Test for Urea

Cut out portion of stained area and transfer 1 or 2 threads to 5 ml crucible or beaker. Save balance of cloth for **40.133**. Leach 10 min in just enough warm H_2O to cover material. Remove threads and squeeze out as much fluid as possible with clean, flat-tip forceps.

Transfer 2 or 3 drops to microculture slide with deep cylindrical depression. Add small drop *urease mixt.* (suspension of $\frac{1}{4}$ of 25 mg urease tablet in 0.5–0.7 ml H_2O). Place small drop *10% H_2PtCl_6 soln* on cover slip and invert over the depression, with hanging drop at center of depression opening. (Cover slip may be sealed on with petrolatum if only minute quantities of urea are suspected.)

With evolution of NH_3, brilliant, highly refractive, octahedral crystals of $(NH_4)_2PtCl_6$ are formed in hanging drop. Time required for crystals to form varies from few sec to 30 min, or even longer in some instances, according to conditions. Crystals may be visible to naked eye and are readily detected under microscope at $100\times$. Certain org. compds that are volatile and H_2O-sol. may yield crystals in the hanging drop, and if reagent soln is too concd, H_2PtCl_6 may crystallize. However, crystal habits of these substances are different from those of $(NH_4)_2PtCl_6$. (Stained patches of the food material can be tested by method similar to above.)

Urease-Bromothymol Blue Test Paper Test for Urea (34)—Official First Action

(Applicable to cloth or sack fibers, whole or ground cereal grains, whole or chopped nuts, spices, neut. solns, etc.)

40.131   Reagents

(a) *Urease soln.*—Wet 0.2 g urease powder with small amt of H_2O, stir into paste, and dil. to 10 ml with H_2O.

(b) *Bromothymol blue soln.*—Rub 0.15 g indicator powder in mortar with 2.4 ml $0.1N$ NaOH soln. After indicator dissolves, wash mortar and pestle with H_2O, and dil. to 50 ml with H_2O. Soln should be green; pH ca 7.0.

(c) *Test paper A.*—Mix 10 ml indicator soln, (b), with 10 ml urease soln, (a). Pour mixt. into watch glass. Using clean tweezers, dip pieces of heavy filter paper (Whatman No. 5, S&S No. 598, or 589 green ribbon have been found satisfactory) in soln. (To avoid uneven distribution of indicator and enzyme, wet entire paper at once by laying it on surface of soln.) Hang paper to dry in place free from NH_3 fumes, strong air currents, or heat. Paper should be orange when dry. Store dry paper in well-stoppered, dark glass bottle in cool place.

(d) *Test paper B.*—Dil. indicator soln, (b), with equal portion of H_2O. Dip pieces of filter paper (same kind as used for test paper A) in indicator soln and hang to dry as in (c).

40.132   Qualitative Test

Test neut. solns for urea by placing drop on dry test paper A. Appearance of blue or green spot after few min incubation at room temp. indicates urea.

For detection of urea in very small, dry particles, dip pieces of both test papers, A and B, of appropriate size into H_2O, using clean tweezers. Wet each entire paper at once by laying it on surface of H_2O (indicator flows unevenly if paper is wet with drops). Shake papers to remove excess H_2O and place on clean, flat piece of glass. (If paper on glass has shiny appearance, too much H_2O has been added. Let dry slightly before using.) Place sample on papers, cover with another clean, flat piece of glass, and press down gently.

Immediate development of blue spot on both papers A and B indicates alk. particles. If alk. particles are extremely small, color development is delayed 10–30 sec, but develops on both papers. Blue spots which develop on test paper A alone indicate urea. Reaction usually requires 30–60 sec to give detectable color, time varying inversely with urea concn. Spots continue to develop and enlarge for 10–20 min and then fade gradually.

Larger particles may be tested similarly, altho it may not be practical to cover them with glass plate. Papers must be protected from NH_3 fumes and from drafts that would remove liberated NH_3 from the urea.

40.133 Xanthydrol Test for Urea (35)— Official First Action

(Not applicable in presence of dried skim milk)

Place portion of stained cloth, ca ⅛″ square (stain located by fluorescence) on microscope slide. Add drop of HOAc (2 + 1) and stir. (Or instead of cutting out a patch of cloth, rinse stained material with H_2O or other suitable solv. such as HOAc, acetone, or hot alcohol, evap. soln to dryness, dissolve residue in little HOAc (2 + 1), and place drop on slide.)

Transfer droplet with stirring rod to another place on slide and dil. with drop of HOAc (2 + 1). To both drops add very small amt of *xanthydrol* and stir into soln. If urea is present, crystals of dixanthylurea form very shortly. Examine with magnification of ca 100–120× (higher power may be used for closer examination if crystals formed are quite small). Use of polarizing microscope is desirable but not essential.

Crystals may be either or both of 2 kinds, depending on concn of urea present: (*a*) most prevalent are clusters of narrow feather-blades of low birefringence which form thruout soln at ca 1:200 to 1:25,000 concn (under low power they may appear to be needles or threads); (*b*) straight needles, often in sheaves or clusters, of much greater birefringence, forming chiefly at or near edge as drop evaps, at concns from 1:50 to 1:1,000. Both kinds have neg. elongation (observed with polarizing microscope, using red plate). Crystals should be noted before drop dries, but remain when it dries. Response is given by fresh urine solids content of ca 2 mg to 4 μg in drop. Test material from portion of sample other than fluorescent spot as blank.

Urine in Grain (36)—Official First Action
40.134   *Principles*

Grain is sprayed with Mg uranyl acetate soln. If rodent urine is present, its Na content reacts to cause greenish fluorescence on kernel when sample is viewed under short-wave UV light.

40.135   *Reagents*

(a) *Magnesium uranyl acetate soln.*—Prep. reagents **3.023**(a) and (b) in ⅒ quantities, mix, add 22 ml glycerol, mix, and filter thru washed, dried paper.

(b) *Urease-bromothymol blue test paper A.*—Prep. as in **40.131**(c).

(c) *Xanthydrol.*—Eastman Kodak Co. No. 1559, crystals.

40.136   *Apparatus*

(a) *Ultraviolet lamp.*—Short wave, 2537 Å, with filters to eliminate most visible light. ("Chromato-Vue" Ultra-Violet Products, Inc., or equiv.)

(b) *Chromatographic sprayer.*—250 ml, to deliver fine spray from air supply (Kontes Glass Co., K-422500, or equiv.). Hand-operated atomizer is satisfactory if it delivers fine spray.

40.137   *Ultraviolet Test*

Spread 50 g grain in shallow tray, or on sheet of waxed paper on tray. Place in hood or well ventilated area, and spray evenly with Mg uranyl acetate reagent, making several sweeps horizontally and vertically across sample. Let stand 1–3 min, and examine under short-wave UV light. With clean tweezers, transfer kernels showing greenish fluorescent areas to spot plate. (Avoid prolonged exposure to UV light and do not touch grains with bare fingers (use gloves). Perspiration may cause false fluorescence.)

Use as blanks 1 or 2 kernels showing no green fluorescence under UV light.

40.138   *Urease-Bromothymol Blue Test*

Add 1–4 drops H_2O to each suspect kernel on spot plate. Let stand 3–5 min. Place strip of test paper A on glass microscope slide, transfer drop of ext to paper with stirring rod, and cover with second slide. Blue spots, slowly developing over 2–4 min, indicate urea. (As reagent is slightly acid, color may not appear for several min, depending on how heavily grain was sprayed.)

40.139   *Confirmatory Test*

Transfer 1–2 drops aq. ext of suspect kernels to microscope slide and evap. to dryness. Add drop of HOAc (2 + 1) and very small amt of xanthydrol crystals. If urea is present, characteristic crystals of dixanthylurea form quickly, and are visible at 60× or lower with wide-field stereoscopic microscope.

Bird Excrement in Food and Containers (37)— Official Final Action
40.140   *Test for Uric Acid*

(Not suitable for minute residues from suspect areas of food containers)

Transfer white, amorphous, grainy particles to depression of spot plate preheated to ca 100° on hot plate or in oven. Add small drop of HNO_3 (1 + 1) to sides of depression so that it will run down to wet particles; then evap. to dryness in 0.5–1.0 min. Heat 1–3 min. If particles turn orange-red to deep red with heat, uric acid and/or its salts may be present.

To confirm: Cool plate until there is no perceptible

heat to back of hand; then streak across colored area with small glass rod wetted with 50% NaOH soln. Intense purple will develop almost immediately.

Modification for particles less than 1 mg.—Position microscope or strong magnifying glass to observe 18 mm No. 2 cover glass placed on metal surface heated to ca 110–120°. Place suspect particle on glass, add 5–10 μl HNO_3, evap. to dryness, and heat in oven 5–7 min at 135–140°. Remove to cool white surface under magnifier and observe baked reaction residue. Pos. reaction shows yellow-orange to orange-red ring.

To confirm: With 1 mm glass rod place small drop 50% NaOH on edge of cover glass. Wipe rod and transfer small portion of drop to edge of baked residue. *Do not flood.* Purple-violet color develops promptly with uric acid or its salts.

Uric Acid in Flour (38)—Official Final Action
(Applicable to levels $\geq$4 mg/100 g)

40.141 Apparatus

(a) *Spectrophotometer.* — Beckman Instruments Model DU, or equiv.

(b) *Centrifuge.*—Desk centrf. with multiple head to hold 15 ml polyethylene test tubes.

(c) *Incubator or water bath.*—Capable of maintaining temp. of 37±1°.

40.142 Reagents

(a) *Uric acid std soln.*—100 μg/ml. Dissolve 100 mg uric acid in 1 L 5% NaOAc soln. (If necessary, warm in H_2O bath at 60–70°.) Filter and store in brown bottle; discard after 1 week. (Do *not* use com. uric acid std solns, as they may contain uricase inhibitors.)

(b) *Sodium borate buffer.*—0.01M, pH 9.2. Dissolve 3.8 g $Na_2B_4O_7.10H_2O$ in H_2O and dil. to 1 L.

(c) *Sodium acetate soln.*—5%. Dissolve 100 g anhyd. NaOAc in H_2O and dil. to 2 L. If necessary, adjust pH to 8.8–9.2 with HOAc or NaOH.

(d) *Glutathione soln.*—10 mg/ml in H_2O. Use within 30 min.

(e) *Uricase soln.*—Prep. suspension of 10 mg dried uricase in 50 ml 0.01M Na borate buffer. Use within 1 hr. (Clean all glassware that comes in contact with uricase enzyme with chromic acid soln; adsorbed uricase on glass surface produces low results.)

40.143 Preliminary Tests

(a) *Test for purity of reagents.*—Dil. 5.0 ml uric acid std soln to 25 ml with 5% NaOAc soln. Place 5 ml in each of 3 test tubes. To 1 tube add 5 ml Na borate buffer, invert several times, and measure A at 292 nm. A should be $\geq$0.72, which corresponds to 0.072 A units/μg uric acid/ml final soln. Test std uric acid soln daily.

(b) *Test for efficiency of uricase soln.*—Label remaining 2 tubes in (a) as No. 1 and No. 2; label a third test tube No. 3. Add 5 ml uricase soln to tubes No. 1 and No. 3. Close mouth of tube No. 1 with

piece of cellophane paper under thumb and invert. Stopper all 3 tubes with clean rubber stoppers and incubate 2 hr at 37°. After incubation, mix contents of tubes No. 2 and No. 3 by repeatedly pouring (6 times) from one tube to other, and immediately (within 60 sec) read A of combined solns at 292 nm, using soln in tube No. 1 as blank. A should be $\geq$0.648 for $\geq$90% of theoretical efficiency of uricase. If efficiency is <90%, incubate 4 hr. If increased incubation does not increase efficiency to 90%, discard uricase sample.

40.144 Preparation of Standard Curve

Pipet 2.5, 5.0, 10.0, and 15.0 ml uric acid std soln into 5 beakers (corresponds to 1.0, 2.0, 4.0, and 6.0 μg uric acid/ml in final soln, resp.), and carry out all steps as in **40.145**, except omit flour.

40.145 Determination

Add 25 ml 1N HCl and 5 ml glutathione soln to 4 g flour in 250 ml beaker. Mix well with glass rod and let stand overnight ($\geq$16 hr). Add 25 ml 1N NaOH (with stirring) and adjust pH to 9.0–9.3 with 1N NaOH or 1N HCl. Transfer to 100 ml g-s graduate, carefully scraping all material sticking to sides of beaker with glass rod. Rinse beaker with 6 small portions 5% NaOAc and dil. to 100 ml with 5% NaOAc. Shake *gently* by inverting graduate several times every 10 min for 1 hr. (Vigorous shaking tends to produce turbid soln.) Transfer aliquot to 15 ml polyethylene test tube and centrf. 30 min at 3000 rpm. Decant supernatant into small erlenmeyer, mix well, and pipet 4 ml into each of 2 test tubes, No. 1 and No. 2. To each tube, add 1 ml Na borate buffer and mix by rotating between palms of hands. (Mix soln with Na borate buffer within 15 min to avoid turbid soln.) Label third tube as No. 3. Add 5 ml uricase soln to tubes No. 1 and No. 3. Mix contents of tube No. 1 as in **40.143**(b). Stopper all 3 tubes with rubber stoppers and incubate 2 hr at 37°. Combine solns in tubes No. 2 and No. 3, as in **40.143**(b), and read A immediately (within 60 sec) at 292 nm against soln No. 1 (blank). (If flour ext appears very turbid after centrfg, dil. centrfd ext 1 + 4 with Na borate buffer and pipet 5.0 ml into each of 2 test tubes, No. 1 and No. 2. Add 5 ml uricase to each tube (No. 1 and No. 3) and proceed with detn as above.)

Reading, A, corresponds to amt of uric acid present in 4 ml portions of centrfd soln; amt of uric acid obtained from std curve × diln factor = amt of uric acid in sample.

MISCELLANEOUS
Plant Gums, Crude
40.146 Light Filth (39)—Official First Action

(If av. particle is $\leq$5 mm, proceed with method. If particle size is >5 mm, break into pieces by hand or by dropping small amts at a time into high-speed blender until desired size is reached. Where 95% and 40% alcohol are specified, isopropanol and 30% isopropanol, resp., can be substituted.)

Weigh 50 g sample into 2 L beaker, add 1200 ml H_2O and 15 ml HCl, and stir well. Autoclave 1 hr at 121°. Slow vent. (Arabic and guar gums will completely dissolve in 15–30 min in 1200 ml H_2O + 25 ml HCl when placed on stirring hot plate or in steam bath.) Sieve portionwise on No. 230 sieve, **40.002**(q), using forcible stream of hot (55–70°) tap H_2O from aerator, **40.002**(a), until all gum has passed thru. Transfer directly to ruled filter paper if negligible amts of plant tissue remain on sieve. If large amts of plant debris remain on sieve, transfer to 1 L trap flask with 40% alcohol. Bring vol. to 500 ml with 40% alcohol and add 25 ml HCl. Heat to ca 60° on magnetic hot plate while stirring with magnetic stirring bar. Add 25 ml mineral oil; stir magnetically, **40.004**(b), 2 min. Fill flask with 40% alcohol and gently swirl contents with stopper. Let stand 10 min and perform first trapping. Add 25 ml mineral oil, and gently stir with stopper 1 min. Let stand 5 min and perform second trapping. Rinse neck of flask with 95% alcohol and pour trappings onto ruled filter paper. Examine under 30×.

Leafy Crude Drugs

40.147   Gross Contamination
  See **40.105**.

40.148   Heavy and Light Filth
  See **40.106**.

SELECTED REFERENCES

(1) JAOAC **48**, 543(1965); **50**, 496(1967).
(2) JAOAC **50**, 499, 520(1967).
(3) JAOAC **35**, 340(1952); **36**, 310(1953); **37**, 117 (1954); **48**, 559(1965); Am. J. Pub. Health **37**, 728(1947).
(4) JAOAC **50**, 501(1967).
(5) JAOAC **53**, 552(1970).
(6) JAOAC **20**, 93(1937); **22**, 495(1939); **23**, 468, 693(1940); **24**, 183, 550(1941); **25**, 609(1942); Food Inds. **7**, 441(1935).
(7) JAOAC **53**, 553(1970).
(8) JAOAC **53**, 550(1970).
(9) JAOAC **51**, 531(1968).
(10) JAOAC **45**, 660(1962).
(11) JAOAC **53**, 562(1970).
(12) JAOAC **52**, 463(1969).
(13) JAOAC **53**, 558(1970).
(14) JAOAC **53**, 560(1970).
(15) JAOAC **48**, 554(1965).
(16) Food Inds. **12**, 36(1940).
(17) JAOAC **26**, 257(1943).
(18) Cereal Chem. **18**, 655(1941).
(19) JAOAC **51**, 522(1968).
(20) JAOAC **38**, 264(1955).
(21) JAOAC **43**, 565(1960).
(22) JAOAC **51**, 504(1968).
(23) JAOAC **47**, 897(1964).
(24) JAOAC **52**, 19(1969).
(25) Bur. Chem. Circ. **68** (1911); Food and Drug Adm. Leaflet, July 1942; Natl. Canners Assoc. Bull. 27L Rev. (July 1950); Am. Can Co. Bull. (1954); JAOAC **49**, 572(1966).
(26) JAOAC **35**, 337(1952).
(27) JAOAC **49**, 576(1966); **50**, 514(1967).
(28) JAOAC **51**, 518(1968).
(29) JAOAC **51**, 525(1968).
(30) JAOAC **52**, 469(1969).
(31) JAOAC **52**, 21(1969).
(32) JAOAC **51**, 522(1968).
(33) JAOAC **25**, 772(1942).
(34) JAOAC **35**, 544(1962).
(35) JAOAC **42**, 473(1959).
(36) JAOAC **46**, 685(1963).
(37) JAOAC **45**, 659(1962); **47**, 516(1964).
(38) JAOAC **49**, 899(1966); **50**, 776(1967); **52**, 833 (1969).
(39) JAOAC **52**, 17(1969).

GENERAL REFERENCES

(1) Microscopic-Analytical Methods in Food and Drug Control. Food and Drug Tech. Bull. No. 1. (Out of print.)
(2) Annotated Bibliography of Methods for Examination of Foods. JAOAC **29**, 420(1946); JAOAC **38**, 1016(1955).
(3) Insect Contaminants of Foods. JAOAC **33**, 898 (1950).
(4) Insect Setae. JAOAC **37**, 960(1954).
(5) Radiographic Applications. JAOAC **37**, 148 (1954).
(6) "Identification of Stored Products by the Micromorphology of the Exoskeleton." A series published in JAOAC (reprints are no longer available): Elytral patterns **38**, 776(1955); Adult antennas **39**, 879(1956); Larval fragments **39**, 990(1956); Adult legs **40**, 973(1957); Adult and larval beetle mandibles **41**, 460(1958); Adult labral characteristics **41**, 472(1958); Head, thorax, abdomen **41**, 828(1958); Adult moths **43**, 444(1960); Larvae of moths **41**, 704(1958); Cockroach fragments **41**, 886(1958); Miscellaneous insects **41**, 206(1958).
(7) "Micro-Analytical Entomology for Food Sanitation Control." AOAC, PO Box 540, Benjamin Franklin Station, Washington, DC 20044 (1962).
(8) Winton, A. L. and Winton, K. B., "The Structure and Composition of Foods." John Wiley & Sons (4 Vols: 1932–1939).
(9) "Food Microscopy." A series published in Food **25**(1956)–**28**(1959).

41. Microbiological Methods

Cross Reference Tables

41.001   *Methods for Examination of Foods*

Eggs and Egg products
Coliform organisms	41.009
Direct microscopic count	41.012
Fungi	41.011
Plate counts	41.008
Salmonella	41.024–41.040
Staphylococci, hemolytic	41.010
Streptococci	41.010

Foods, chilled, frozen, precooked, or prepared
Aerobic plate count	41.015
Coliform organisms	41.016
Escherichia coli	41.016
Staphylococcus aureus, coagulase positive	41.018

Foods, outbreak
Clostridium perfringens	41.019–41.023

Milk products, dried
Salmonella	41.024–41.040

Nut meats, tree
Aerobic plate count	41.015
Coliform organisms	41.016
Escherichia coli	41.016

41.002   *Methods for Examination for Organisms*

Clostridium perfringens
Foods, chilled, frozen, precooked, or prepared	41.019–41.023

Coliform organisms
Eggs and egg products	41.009
Foods, chilled, frozen, precooked, or prepared	41.016
Nut meats, tree	41.016

Escherichia coli
Foods, chilled, frozen, precooked, or prepared	41.016
Nut meats, tree	41.016

Fungi
Eggs and egg products	41.011

Salmonella
Eggs and egg products	41.024–41.040
Milk products, dried	41.024–41.040

Staphylococci, hemolytic
Eggs and egg products	41.010

Staphylococcus aureus, coagulase positive
Foods, chilled, frozen, precooked, or prepared	41.018

Streptococci
Eggs and egg products	41.010

EXAMINATION OF EGGS AND EGG PRODUCTS (*1*)

("Manual of Microbiological Methods," by The Committee on Bacteriological Technic, 1957, McGraw-Hill Book Co., 330 W. 42nd St, New York, NY 10036, should be used as guide for further study of microorganisms obtained in culturing procedures described.)

Sampling—Official Final Action

41.003   *Equipment*

(a) *Liquid eggs.*—Sampling tube or dipper, sterile sample containers with tight closures (pt Mason jars or friction top cans are most practical), alcohol, alcohol lamp or other burner, absorbent cotton, clean cloth or towel, and H_2O pail.

(b) *Frozen eggs.*—Elec. (high speed) or hand drill with $1 \times 16''$ auger, hammer and steel strip ($12 \times 2 \times 0.25''$), or other tool for opening cans; tablespoon, hatchet or chisel, precooled sterile containers, etc., as in (a).

(c) *Dried eggs.*—Grain trier long enough to reach to bottom of containers to be sampled. Clean sample containers with tight closures (pt Mason jars or paperboard cartons), clean cloth or towel, and tablespoon.

41.004   *Methods*

Take samples from representative number of containers in lot, **17.001.** Sterilize sampling tube or dipper, auger, spoon, and hatchet by wiping with alcohol-soaked cotton and flaming over alcohol lamp or other burner. Between samplings, thoroly wash instruments, dry, and resterilize. Open and sample all containers under as nearly aseptic conditions as possible.

(a) *Liquid eggs.*—Thoroly mix contents of container with sterile sample tube or dipper, and transfer ca ¾ pt to sterile sample container. Keep samples at $<5°$ but avoid freezing. Observe and record odor of each container sampled as normal, abnormal, reject, or musty.

(b) *Frozen eggs.*—Remove top layer of egg with sterilized hatchet or chisel. Drill 3 cores from top to bottom of container: first core in center, second core midway between center and periphery, and third core near edge of container. Transfer drillings from container to sample container with sterile spoon. Examine product organoleptically by smelling at opening of fourth drill-hole made after removal of bacteriological sample. (Heat produced by elec. drill intensifies odor of egg material, thus facilitating organoleptic examination.) Record odors as normal, abnormal, reject, or musty. Refrigerate samples with solid CO_2 or other suitable refrigerant if analysis is to be delayed or sampling point is at some distance from laboratory.

(c) *Dried eggs.*—For small packages, take entire parcel or parcels for sample. For boxes and barrels, remove top layer with sterile spoon or other sterile instrument, and with sterile trier remove ≥ 3 cores as in (b). (Samples should consist of ca $\frac{3}{4}$ pt.) Aseptically transfer core to sample container with sterile spoon or other suitable instrument. Store samples under refrigeration or in cool place.

Culture Media—Official Final Action
41.005   *Standard Methods Media*

(a) *Dilution water.*—To prep. stock soln, dissolve 34 g KH_2PO_4 in 500 ml H_2O, adjust to pH 7.2 with $1N$ NaOH (ca 175 ml), and dil. to 1 L with H_2O. To prep. buffered H_2O for dilns, dil. 1.25 ml stock soln to 1 L with boiled and cooled H_2O. Autoclave 15 min at 121°.

(b) *Buffered glucose broth (MR-VP medium).*—For Me red-Voges Proskauer (MR-VP) tests. Dissolve 5.0 g proteose peptone, 5.0 g glucose, and 5.0 g K_2HPO_4 in ca 800 ml H_2O with gentle heat and occasional stirring. Filter, cool to 20°, and dil. to 1 L. Dispense 10 ml portions into test tubes and autoclave 12–15 min at 121°. Max. exposure to heat should be ≤ 30 min. Final pH, 6.9±0.1.

(c) *Endo medium.*—Suspend 3.5 g K_2HPO_4, 10.0 g peptone, 20.0 g agar, and 10 g lactose in 1 L H_2O. Boil to dissolve, add H_2O to original vol., and clarify if necessary. Dispense in 100 ml portions and autoclave 15 min at 121°. Final pH, 7.4±0.1. Before use, add 0.25 g Na_2SO_3 and 1.0 ml filtered 5% alc. soln basic fuchsin.

(d) *Eosin methylene blue agar (Levine).*—Dissolve 10.0 g peptone, 2.0 g K_2HPO_4, and 20.0 g agar in 1 L H_2O. Boil to dissolve and add H_2O to original vol. Dispense in 100 or 200 ml portions and autoclave 15 min at 121°. Final pH, 7.1±0.1. Before use, melt and to each 100 ml add 5 ml sterile 20% lactose soln, 2.0 ml aq. 2% Eosin Y soln, and 1.3 ml 0.5% aq. methylene blue soln.

(e) *Koser's citrate broth.*—Dissolve 1.5 g $NaNH_4$-$HPO_4.4H_2O$, 1.0 g K_2HPO_4, 0.2 g $MgSO_4.7H_2O$, and 3.0 g Na citrate.$2H_2O$ in 1 L H_2O. Dispense in 10 ml portions into test tubes and autoclave 15 min at 121°. Final pH 6.7±0.1.

(f) *Lactose broth.*—Dissolve on H_2O bath, with stirring, 3.0 g beef ext and 5.0 g polypeptone or peptone in 1 L H_2O. Add 5.0 g lactose. Dispense into fermentation tubes and autoclave 15 min at 121°. Max. exposure to heat should be ≤ 30 min. Final pH 6.9±0.1.

(g) *Plate count agar (tryptone glucose yeast agar).*—Suspend 5.0 g peptone-tryptone (pancreatic digest of casein), 2.5 g yeast ext, 1.0 g glucose, and 15.0 g agar in 1 L H_2O. Heat to boiling until all ingredients are dissolved. Autoclave 15 min at 121°. Final pH, 7.0±0.1.

(h) *Tryptophane broth.*—Dissolve by heating, with stirring, 10.0 g tryptone or trypticase in 1 L H_2O. Dispense in 5 ml portions into test tubes and autoclave 15 min at 121°.

41.006   *Other Media*

(a) *Malt agar.*—Dissolve by boiling 30 g malt ext (Difco) and 15.0 g agar in 1 L H_2O. Autoclave 15 min at 121°. Just before use, melt malt agar and acidify with 85% lactic acid to pH 3.5. Do not reheat medium after addn of acid.

(b) *Milk protein hydrolysate glucose agar.*—BBL dehydrated, or prep. from 9.0 g milk protein hydrolysate, 1 g glucose, 15 agar, and 1 L H_2O; adjust to pH 7.0.

(c) *Physiological salt soln.*—Dissolve 8.5 g NaCl in 1 L H_2O. Autoclave 15 min at 121° and cool to room temp.

(d) *Veal infusion agar.*—Mix 500 g ground lean veal and 1 L H_2O. Infuse overnight in refrigerator and strain thru cheesecloth without pressure. Dil. to original vol. with H_2O and skim off any fat. Steam in Arnold sterilizer 30 min and filter thru paper. Add 10.0 g peptone (Difco), 5.0 g NaCl, and 15.0 g agar.

Steam in Arnold sterilizer to dissolve ingredients. Adjust to pH 7.6 and steam in Arnold sterilizer 15 min. Filter thru buchner with paper pulp mat, with suction. (Use egg albumen for clarification when necessary. Add fresh white of 1 egg previously beaten with 50 ml medium or its equiv. in desiccated egg white (1.5 g) to each L of medium before adjusting pH and after cooling to 50°. Shake thoroly to ensure soln of egg white. Let stand 20 min. Heat in Arnold sterilizer 15 min to coagulate egg white. Shake vigorously and reheat. Filter, adjust to pH 7.6, steam in Arnold sterilizer 15 min, and filter.)

Place 10 ml portions in test tubes or 80 ml quantities into bottles. Autoclave 20 min at 121°; final pH 7.4.

For hemolytic tests, cool melted agar to 45° and add 5% defibrinated horse, sheep, or rabbit blood prior to pouring plates (0.5 ml blood/10 ml medium).

Operating Technic (2)
41.007   *Preparation of Sample—*
                                      Official Final Action

(a) *Liquid eggs.*—Thoroly mix sample with sterile spoon or sterile elec. stirrer and prep. 1:10 diln by aseptically weighing 11 g egg material into sterile wide-mouth g-s or screw-cap bottle; add 99 g sterile diln H_2O, **41.005**(a), or sterile physiological salt soln, **41.006**(c), and 1 tablespoonful sterile glass shot. Thoroly agitate 1:10 diln to ensure complete soln or distribution of egg material in diluent by shaking each container rapidly 25 times, each shake being up-and-down movement of ca 1′, time interval not exceeding 7 sec. Let bubbles escape. Transfer representative portion from 1:10 diln for higher serial dilns as needed. Proceed as in **41.008–41.012**(a). Pour all plates and inoculate other media within 15 min after prepn of first diln to prevent growth or death of microorganisms.

(b) *Frozen eggs.*—Thaw frozen egg material as rapidly as possible to prevent increase in number of microorganisms present and at temp. low enough to prevent destruction of the microorganisms ($\leq 45°$ for ≤ 15 min). (Frequent rotary shaking of sample container aids in thawing frozen material. Thawing temp. may be maintained by use of H_2O bath or bacteriological incubator.) Proceed as in (a).

(c) *Dried eggs.*—Thoroly mix sample with sterile spoon or spatula. Prep. 1:10 diln as in (a). If material is relatively insol. (stored samples), use $0.1N$ LiOH as diluent. Prep. serial dilns as in (a) and proceed as in **41.008–41.012**(b).

41.008 Plate Counts—Official Final Action

Inoculate one set of petri plates with 1 ml portion of each suitable diln. Pour plates with tryptone glucose yeast agar or milk protein hydrolysate glucose agar previously cooled to $42-45°$. Incubate inoculated plates 3 days at $32°$. Count plates with aid of Quebec colony counter, if available. Express final results as number of viable microorganisms/g egg material.

41.009 Incidence of Coliform Group— Official Final Action

(a) Inoculate 1.0 ml portions from suitable dilns of egg material into fermentation tubes of lactose broth. Incubate 24–48 hr at $35°$. Streak eosin methylene blue or Endo medium plates from all lactose broth cultures showing gas production. Incubate plates 24–48 hr at $35°$. Examine plates of differential media for colonies of microorganisms of coliform group. Record number of coliform bacteria/g egg material as reciprocal of highest diln showing pos. confirmation on differential media.

(b) *Biochemical reaction (optional).*—Inoculate from colonies of coliform types of bacteria appearing on differential agar plates to agar slants, **41.005**(g) or **41.006**(b). Incubate 24 hr at $35°$. Purify cultures for further study. Obtain IMViC biochemical reactions of purified cultures by following tests:

Kovac test (indole production);
Acid production in Me red indicator;
Acetylmethylcarbinol production;

Koser sodium citrate test (utilization of Na citrate as sole source of C).

Note: Follow methods for biochemical reactions recommended in "Standard Methods for Examination of Water and Waste Water," 12th ed., 1965, American Public Health Association, 1790 Broadway, New York, NY 10019.

41.010 Incidence of Hemolytic Staphylococci and Streptococci—Procedure

Inoculate petri plates with 1 ml portions of suitable dilns. Pour plates with veal-infusion agar contg 5% defibrinated horse, sheep, or rabbit blood (0.5 ml blood/10 ml medium). Cool agar to $45°$ and add blood just prior to pouring plates. Incubate plates 24 hr at $35°$. Confirm presence of coccus types of microorganisms by microscopic examination of smears taken from representative colonies and stained by Gram method. Express final results as number/g.

41.011 Tests for Fungi—Procedure

Inoculate petri plates with 1 ml portions of suitable dilns. Pour inoculated plates with malt agar, **41.006**(a), previously cooled to $42-45°$. Incubate plates 5 days at $20°$ or at room temp., if $20°$ incubator is not available. Express final results as number of fungi/g egg material. Confirm yeast colonies by microscopic examination of smears stained by Gram method.

41.012 Direct Microscopic Counts— Official Final Action

North aniline oil-methylene blue stain.—Mix 3.0 ml aniline oil with 10.0 ml alcohol, and slowly add 1.5 ml HCl with constant agitation. Add 30.0 ml satd alc. methylene blue soln, dil. to 100.0 ml with H_2O, and filter.

(a) *Liquid and frozen eggs.*—Place 0.01 ml undild egg material on clean, dry microscopic slide and spread over area of 2 sq cm (circular area with diam. of 1.6 cm suggested). Let film prepn dry on level surface at $35-40°$. Immerse in xylene ≤ 1 min; then immerse in alcohol ≤ 1 min. Stain ≤ 45 sec in North aniline oil-methylene blue stain (10–20 min preferred; exposure up to 2 hr does not overstain). Wash slide by repeated immersions in H_2O and dry thoroly before examination. Observe subsequent operations and precaution as in "Standard Methods for Examination of Dairy Products," 12th ed., 1967, American Public Health Association. Express final result as number of bacteria/g egg material (double microscopic factor, since 2 sq cm area is used).

(b) *Dried eggs.*—Place 0.01 ml of 1:10 or 1:100 diln of dried egg material on clean, dry microscopic slide and spread over 2 sq cm.

Note: $0.1N$ LiOH may be used as diluent and is preferred for samples that are relatively insol. Circular area with diam. of 1.6 cm is preferable. Addn of drop of H_2O to each film facilitates uniform spreading.

Proceed as in (**a**). Double microscopic factor, since area of 2 sq cm is used, and multiply count by 10 or 100, depending on whether film was prepd from 1:10 or 1:100 diln.

EXAMINATION OF FROZEN, CHILLED, PRECOOKED, OR PREPARED FOODS
(3)—OFFICIAL FIRST ACTION

(For the detn of aerobic plate count, most probable number of coliform bacteria and *Escherichia coli*, and staphylococcus in products such as frozen cooked meat, poultry, and vegetable products; cooked and/or breaded seafood; bakery products; salads; tree nut meats; and ingredients of food samples collected during sanitation inspections of food producing establishments, unless specific directions are given for that product)

41.013   *Media and Reagents*
(Use anhyd. salts unless otherwise specified.)

Ingredients and reagents used to prep. following media may be product of any manufacturer if comparative tests show that satisfactory results are obtained. Use pure carbohydrates suitable for biological use; ACS reagent grade inorg. chemicals; dyes certified by "Biological Stain Commission" for use in media. Use distd H_2O in all prepns.

For convenience, dehydrated media of any brand equiv. to formulation may be used. Test each lot of medium for sterility and growth-promoting qualities of suitable organisms (e.g., inoculate media contg lactose with coliform bacteria, staphylococcus media with staphylococcus, etc.).

Det. pH before autoclaving with pH meter stdzd against std buffers, **45.007**. Adjust pH, when necessary, by adding $1N$ NaOH or $1N$ HCl so that stated final pH results after autoclaving.

Use std sterile glass or plastic, 100×15 mm, petri dishes.

(**a**) *Plate count agar.*—See **41.005**(**g**).

(**b**) *Lauryl tryptose broth.*—Dissolve 20.0 g trypticase or tryptose (pancreatic digest of casein), 5.0 g NaCl, 5.0 g lactose, 2.75 g K_2HPO_4, 2.75 g KH_2PO_4, and 0.1 g Na lauryl sulfate in 1 L H_2O with gentle heat, if necessary. Dispense 10 ml portions into 20×150 mm test tubes contg inverted fermentation tubes 10×75 mm. Autoclave 15 min at 121°. Final pH, 6.8 ± 0.1.

(**c**) *Brilliant green lactose bile (BGLB) broth.*—Dissolve 10.0 g peptone and 10.0 g lactose in ca 500 ml H_2O. Add soln (pH 7.0–7.5) of 20 g dehydrated oxgall or oxbile in 200 ml H_2O. Dil. to 975 ml and adjust pH to 7.4. Add 13.3 ml 0.1% soln of brilliant green, and dil. to 1 L with H_2O. Filter thru cotton and dispense 10 ml portions in 20×150 mm test tubes contg inverted 10×75 mm fermentation tubes. Autoclave 15 min at 121°. Final pH 7.2 ± 0.1.

(**d**) *Eosin methylene blue agar (Levine).*—See **41.005**(**d**).

(**e**) *Vogel-Johnson (V-J) agar (tellurite glycine red agar base).*—Suspend 10.0 g trypticase or tryptose

(pancreatic digest of casein), 5.0 g yeast ext, 10.0 g D-mannitol, 5.0 g K_2HPO_4, 5.0 g $LiCl.6H_2O$, 10.0 g glycine, 16.0 g agar, and 0.025 g phenol red in H_2O, dil. to 1 L, and mix thoroly. Heat with frequent agitation and boil 1 min. Dispense in 100 ml portions and autoclave 15 min at 121°. Cool to 45–50°. To each 100 ml add 2 ml 1% K tellurite soln which has been autoclaved sep. 15 min at 121°. Mix gently. Pour 15–18 ml into petri dishes. Final pH 7.2 ± 0.2.

(**f**) *Trypticase (tryptic) soy broth with 10% sodium chloride.*—Add 95 g NaCl to 1 L of soln of 17.0 g trypticase or tryptose (pancreatic digest of casein), 3.0 g phytone (papaic digest of soya meal), 5.0 g NaCl, 2.5 g K_2HPO_4, and 2.5 g glucose. Heat gently if necessary. Dispense into 16–20 mm diam. tubes to depth of 5–8 cm. Autoclave 15 min at 121°. Final pH, 7.3 ± 0.1.

(**g**) *EC broth.*—Dissolve 20.0 g trypticase or tryptose (pancreatic digest of casein), 1.5 g Bacto bile salt No. 3 or bile salt mixt., 5.0 g lactose, 4.0 g K_2HPO_4, 1.5 g KH_2PO_4, and 5.0 g NaCl in 1 L H_2O. Dispense 8 ml into 16×150 mm test tubes contg inverted 10×75 mm fermentation tube. Autoclave 15 min at 121°. Final pH 6.9 ± 0.1.

(**h**) *Brain-heart infusion.*—Dissolve infusion from 200 g calf brain and from 250 g beef heart, 10.0 g proteose peptone or Gelysate, 5.0 g NaCl, 2.5 g $Na_2HPO_4.12H_2O$, and 2.0 g glucose in 1 L H_2O, heating gently if necessary. Dispense into bottles or tubes for storage and autoclave 15 min at 121°. Final pH, 7.4 ± 0.1.

(**i**) *Desiccated coagulase plasma (rabbit) with EDTA.*—Reconstitute according to manufacturer's directions. If not available, reconstitute *Desiccated coagulase plasma (rabbit)* and add Na_2H_2EDTA to final concn of 0.1% in reconstituted plasma.

(**j**) *Tryptophane broth.*—See **41.005**(**h**) but dispense in 10 ml portions.

(**k**) *Buffered glucose broth.*—See **41.005**(**b**). Baltimore Biological Laboratories, PO Box 175, Cockeysville, MD 21030, or Difco dehydrated medium may be used.

(**l**) *Koser's citrate broth.*—See **41.005**(**e**).

(**m**) *Butterfield's buffered phosphate diluent.*—(*1*) *Stock soln.*—Dissolve 34.0 g KH_2PO_4 in 500 ml H_2O, adjust to pH 7.2 with ca 175 ml $1N$ NaOH, and dil. to 1 L. Store in refrigerator. (*2*) *Diluent.*—Dil. 1.25 ml stock soln to 1 L with H_2O. Prep. diln blanks with this soln, dispensing enough to allow for losses during autoclaving. Autoclave 15 min at 121°.

41.014   *Preparation of Sample*
(Prep. all decimal dilns with 90 ml sterile diluent plus 10 ml previous diln unless otherwise specified. Shake all dilns 25 times in 1' arc.
Pipets must accurately deliver required vol. Do not use to deliver <10% of their total vol. For example, to deliver 1 ml, do not use pipet >10 ml; to deliver 0.1 ml, do not use pipet >1 ml.)

(**a**) *Frozen and/or prepared foods.*—Use balance with capacity of ≥ 2 kg and sensitivity of 0.1 g to aseptically weigh 50 g unthawed (if frozen) sample into sterile high-speed blender jar. Add 450 ml diluent, (m)(2), and blend 2 min. (If necessary to temper frozen sample to remove 50 g portion, hold ≤18 hr at 2–5°.) Not >15 min should elapse from time sample is blended until all dilns are in appropriate media.

If entire sample consists of <50 g, weigh portion equiv. to ½ sample and add amt of sterile diluent required to make 1:10 diln. Total vol. in blender jar must completely cover blades.

(b) *Tree nut meat halves and larger pieces.*—Aseptically weigh 50 g sample into sterile jar. Add 50 ml diluent, (m)(2), and shake vigorously (50 times thru 1′ arc) to obtain 10^0 diln. Let stand 3–5 min and shake just before making serial dilns and inoculations.

(c) *Nut meal.*—Aseptically weigh 10 g sample into sterile jar. Add 90 ml diluent, (m)(2), to obtain 10^{-1} diln.

41.015 Aerobic Plate Count
(Not applicable to tree nut meats)

Seed duplicate petri dishes in dilns of 1:10, 1:100, 1:1000, etc., using plate count agar, (a). Ordinarily 1:100 thru 1:10,000 are satisfactory. Place 1 ml appropriate diln in each plate, and add molten agar (cooled to 42–45°) within 15 min from time of original diln. Incubate 48±2 hr at 35° and count duplicate plates in suitable range (30–300 colonies). If plates do not contain 30–300 colonies, record diln counted and note number of colonies found. Average counts obtained and report as aerobic plate count/g.

41.016 Coliform Group and E. coli

Seed 3-tube most probable number (MPN) series into lauryl sulfate tryptose broth, (b), using 1 ml inocula of 1:10, 1:100, and 1:1000 dilns, using triplicate tubes at each diln. (For nut meats (halves and larger pieces), begin MPN detn with 10^0 diln; for nut meal, begin with 10^{-1} diln.) Incubate 48±2 hr at 35° for gas formation as evidenced by displacement of liq. in insert tube or by vigorous effervescence when tubes are shaken *gently*. Examine tubes for gas formation at 24 and 48 hr intervals. Transfer, using 3 mm loop, from gassing tubes to BGLB, (c) (omit this transfer for tree nuts), and EC broth, (g), at time gas formation is noted.

Incubate BGLB broth 48±2 hr at 35°. Using MPN table, 41.017, compute MPN on basis of number of tubes of BGLB broth producing gas by end of incubation period. Report as MPN of coliform bacteria/g.

Incubate EC broth 48±2 hr at 45.5±0.05° in covered H₂O bath. Submerge broth tubes in bath so that H₂O level is above highest level of medium. Examine tubes for gas formation at 24 or 48 hr intervals. Streak gas-pos. tubes on Levine's eosine methylene blue agar plates, (d), and incubate plates 24±2 hr at 35°.

Pick 2 or more well isolated typical colonies from Levine's eosine methylene blue agar plates and transfer to agar slants prepd from agar medium, (a). Incubate 18–24 hr at 35°. If typical colonies are not present, pick 2 or more colonies most likely to be *E. coli*. Pick ≥2 from every plate.

Transfer growth from plate count agar slants into following broths for identification by biochemical tests:

(a) *Trytophane broth, (j).*—Incubate 24±2 hr at 35° and test for indole by adding 0.2–0.3 ml Kovac's reagent, 41.025(a), to 24 hr culture. Test is pos. if upper layer turns red.

(b) *MR-VP medium, (k).*—Incubate 48±2 hr at 35°. Aseptically transfer 0.7 ml culture to porcelain spot plate to test for acetylmethylcarbinol. Add 0.1 ml 5% alc. α-naphthol soln, 0.1 ml KOH soln (4 + 10), and few crystals of creatine. Let stand 2 hr. Test is pos. if eosine pink develops. Alternatively, *see* 41.033(c)(1).

Incubate remainder of MR-VP medium for addnl 48 hr and test for Me red reaction by adding 5 drops Me red soln to culture. Test is pos. if culture turns red; neg., if yellow. (Prep. Me red soln by dissolving 0.1 g Me red in 300 ml 90% alcohol and dilg to 500 ml with H₂O.)

(c) *Koser citrate broth, (l).*—Incubate 96 hr at 35° and record growth as + or −.

(d) *Lauryl sulfate tryptose broth, (b).*—Incubate 48±2 hr at 35°. Examine tubes for gas formation.

(e) *Gram stain.*—Perform Gram stain on 18 hr agar slant (Standard Methods for the Examination of Water and Waste Water, 12th ed.). Coliform organisms will stain red (neg.); Gram-pos. organisms will stain blue-black.

(f) *Classification.*—Classify biochemical types as follows:

Indole	MR	VP	Citrate	Type
+	+	−	−	Typical *E. coli*
−	+	−	−	Atypical *E. coli*
+	+	−	+	Typical Intermediate
−	+	−	+	Atypical Intermediate
−	−	+	+	Typical *A. aerogenes*
+	−	+	+	Atypical *A. aerogenes*

Other groupings may appear; in such cases cultures are usually mixed. Restreak to det. their purity.

Compute MPN of *E. coli*/g, considering Gram neg., nonspore-forming rods producing gas in lactose and producing + + − − or − + − − IMViC patterns as *E. coli*.

41.017 See top of next page.

41.018 Coagulase-Positive Staphylococci
(Not applicable to tree nut meats)

Inoculate 3 tubes of trypticase soy broth with 10% NaCl, (f), at each test diln with 1 ml aliquots of decimal dilns of sample. Max. diln of sample must be

41.017   Most Probable Numbers (MPN) per 1 g of sample, using 3 tubes
with each of 0.1, 0.01, and 0.001 g portions

Positive Tubes				Positive Tubes				Positive Tubes				Positive Tubes			
0.1	0.01	0.001	MPN	0.1	0.01	0.001	MPN	0.1	0.01	0.001	MPN	0.1	0.01	0.001	MPN
0	0	0	<3.	1	0	0	3.6	2	0	0	9.1	3	0	0	23.
0	0	1	3.	1	0	1	7.2	2	0	1	14.	3	0	1	39.
0	0	2	6.	1	0	2	11.	2	0	2	20.	3	0	2	64.
0	0	3	9.	1	0	3	15.	2	0	3	26.	3	0	3	95.
0	1	0	3.	1	1	0	7.3	2	1	0	15.	3	1	0	43.
0	1	1	6.1	1	1	1	11.	2	1	1	20.	3	1	1	75.
0	1	2	9.2	1	1	2	15.	2	1	2	27.	3	1	2	120.
0	1	3	12.	1	1	3	19.	2	1	3	34.	3	1	3	160.
0	2	0	6.2	1	2	0	11.	2	2	0	21.	3	2	0	93.
0	2	1	9.3	1	2	1	15.	2	2	1	28.	3	2	1	150.
0	2	2	12.	1	2	2	20.	2	2	2	35.	3	2	2	210.
0	2	3	16.	1	2	3	24.	2	2	3	42.	3	2	3	290.
0	3	0	9.4	1	3	0	16.	2	3	0	29.	3	3	0	240.
0	3	1	13.	1	3	1	20.	2	3	1	36.	3	3	1	460.
0	3	2	16.	1	3	2	24.	2	3	2	44.	3	3	2	1100.
0	3	3	19.	1	3	3	29.	2	3	3	53.	3	3	3	>1100.

high enough to yield neg. end point. Incubate 48 hr at 35–37°.

Using 3 mm loop, transfer one loopful from each inoculated tube to previously prepd Vogel-Johnson agar plates, and streak in such manner as to give isolated colonies. Incubate plates 48±2 hr at 35–37°.

Pick ≥1 of each visibly different colony type, which has reduced tellurite, from all sample dilns tested, and transfer to agar slants prepd from plate count agar medium, (a). Incubate slants at 35–37° long enough to give visible growth. Microscopically examine cultured organisms and discard noncoccal forms.

Inoculate tubes contg 0.2 ml brain heart infusion broth with *small* amt of growth from plate count agar slant. Do not transfer large clumps of growth. Incubate 18–24 hr at 35–37°. Add 0.5 ml reconstituted coagulase plasma with EDTA, (i), and mix thoroly. Place tubes in 37° H₂O bath and examine periodically over 4 hr interval for clot formation. Doubtful coagulase test results should be rechecked on brain heart infusion cultures which have been incubated at 35–37° for >18 hr but ≤48 hr.

Test pos. and neg. controls simultaneously with unknown cultures.

Report coagulase-pos. staphylococci Most Probable Number (MPN)/g from tables of MPN values, **41.017.**

Clostridium perfringens
(4)—Official First Action

(Applicable to examination of outbreak foods in in which relatively large numbers of vegetative cells are expected to be present)

41.019   *Apparatus*

(a) *Pipets.*—American Public Health Association (APHA) milk diln specifications: 1.1 ml with 0.1 and 1 ml graduations, and 11 ml with 1.0 ml graduations.

(b) *Colony counter.*—Quebec, or equiv., dark field model.

(c) *High-speed blender.*—Waring Blendor, or equiv., 2-speed std model, with low speed operation at 8,000 rpm, equipped with 1 L glass or metal jars with covers. One jar is required for each sample.

41.020   *Reagents*

(a) *Phosphate stock buffer soln.*—See **4.023(e).**

(b) *Phosphate buffer dilution water.*—See **4.023(f).**

(c) *Nitrite test reagents.*—(1) *Reagent A:* Dissolve 8 g sulfanilic acid in 1 L 5N HOAc (2 + 5). (2) *Reagent B:* Dissolve 5 g α-naphthylamine in 1 L 5N HOAc.

(d) *Sulfite-polymyxin-sulfadiazine (SPS) agar.*— 15.0 g tryptone, 15.0 g agar, 10.0 g yeast ext, and 0.5 g Fe citrate dild to 1 L with H₂O. (BBL-01-705 is satisfactory.) Adjust to pH 7.0 and sterilize 15 min at 121°. Aseptically add following Seitz-filtered solns to each 1 L sterile medium: 5.0 ml freshly prepd 10% Na₂SO₃.7H₂O soln, 10 ml 0.1% polymyxin B sulfate soln, and 10 ml Na sulfadiazine soln contg 12 mg/ml. (Recommended sterilization of BBL-SPS is 15 min at 118°; if inconvenient, 10 min at 121° is satisfactory for vols ≤200 ml.)

(e) *Motility-nitrate medium.* — (Difco B268 + 0.3% agar.) 3.0 g beef ext, 5.0 g peptone, 1.0 g KNO₃, and 3.0 g agar dild to 1 L with H₂O. Adjust pH to 7.0, dispense in 10 ml portions in 150 × 16 mm screw-capped tubes, and sterilize 15 min at 121°. Prep. fresh for each use.

(f) *Sporulation broth.*—20.0 g trypticase, 20.0 g vitamin-free casamino acids, and 1.0 g Na thioglycolate dild to 1 L with H₂O. Dispense in 10 ml portions into 150 × 16 mm screw-capped tubes. Sterilize 15 min at 121°. Just before use, add to each tube 1 ml Seitz-filtered stock soln contg 10 μg thiamine.HCl/ml.

(g) *Fluid thioglycolate medium.*—(BBL-01-140, Difco B256, Oxoid CM173.) Dispense 10 ml portions into 150 × 16 mm screw-capped tubes. Sterilize 15 min at 121°, and cool quickly. Just before use, heat in flowing steam 10 min to dispel O, and cool rapidly in tap H_2O. Final pH is 7.1.

41.021 Preparation of Food Homogenate

Using aseptic technic, weigh 50 g food sample into 250 ml beaker sterilized with Al cover. Transfer to sterile blender jar, using portion of 450 ml phosphate buffer diln H_2O to rinse any adhering food from the beaker into blender jar. Add remaining diln H_2O to jar and blend 2 min at low speed (8,000 rpm). Use this 1:10 diln to prep. series of decimal dilns from 10^{-1} to 10^{-5} by transferring 11 ml 1:10 diln to a 99 ml diln blank, vigorously shaking 25 times, and proceeding in same manner until 10^{-5} diln is reached.

41.022 Plate Count Technic

Aseptically pipet 1 ml of each diln of homogenate to marked, duplicate culture dishes. Pour 15 ml SPS agar into each plate, rotate to mix inoculum and agar, and let solidify; then overlay with addnl 4–5 ml SPS agar.

Invert plates and place in anaerobic jar. Produce anaerobic conditions. Place jar in 35° incubator and incubate 24 hr. (*Note:* It is better to stack plastic petri dishes in alternate columns one above another; this prevents formation of seal tight enough so that anaerobiosis will not be obtained within plates.) After incubation, remove plates from jar and observe macroscopically for growth and black colony production. Select plates showing estd 30–300 black colonies. Using Quebec colony counter with piece of white tissue paper over counting area, count colonies and calc. number of *Clostridia* sp./g food.

41.023 Confirmation Technic

Select 10 colonies from countable plates (30–300 colonies), inoculate tube of fluid thioglycolate medium with each, and incubate 4 hr at 46° or overnight at 35°. Check fluid thioglycolate cultures for purity by making Gram-stained smear. If pure, stab-inoculate nitrate-motility medium, using small loop instead of straight wire, and inoculate sporulation broth with 2 ml portion. Incubate both media ca 18–24 hr at 35°. Examine tubes of nitrate-motility medium by transmitted light for type of growth along stab. Nonmotile organisms produce growth only in and along line of stab. Motile organisms produce diffuse growth out into medium away from stab. Make smear for Gram stain from growth in tube.

Test nitrate-motility medium for presence of nitrite by adding 5 drops each of nitrite Reagents A and B. Pink or red color denotes presence of nitrites. If no color develops, mix reagents with upper third of medium by jabbing down into medium with sterile loop; if no color develops, add few grains of powd Zn metal, and let stand few min. Neg. test after addn of Zn indicates that nitrates are completely reduced;

pos. test indicates that organism is incapable of reducing nitrates.

Make smear of material in sporulation medium, air-dry, and heat-fix. Stain 10 min with satd aq. malachite green (ca 7.6%) without heat, rinse with tap H_2O ca 10 sec, stain 15 sec with 0.25% aq. safranin, rinse with tap H_2O, blot, dry, and examine microscopically. Spores will be stained green; vegetative cells, red.

Pipet 2 ml sporulation broth into sterile test tube and heat 10 min in 80° H_2O bath. Transfer to ice bath; when broth is cool, add 1 ml to tube of fluid thioglycolate medium. Incubate 18–24 hr in 37° H_2O bath. Examine fluid thioglycolate medium for evidence of growth, and observe microscopically for typical Gram-pos. rods. If growth is present, record that sporulation broth contained spores. If no growth is seen, reincubate 24 hr and examine; if no growth is again evident, sporulation broth contains no spores.

Production of H_2S in SPS agar and reduction of nitrate by nonmotile, Gram-pos., spore-forming bacillus yield provisional identification as *C. perfringens*. Calc. number of *C. perfringens* in sample on basis of % colonies picked that confirm as *C. perfringens*. (*Example:* If av. plate count of 10^{-4} diln was 85, and 8 of 10 colonies picked were confirmed as *C. perfringens*, number of *C. perfringens*/g food is $85 \times (8/10) \times 10,000 = 680,000$.)

Salmonella (5)

(Applicable to the detection and identification of *Salmonella* from dried whole egg, dried egg yolk, and dried egg white (official final action) and to nonfat dry milk and dry whole milk (official first action))

Method described is minimal. Depending upon history of sample, addnl types of examinations may be applied. Use *Identification of Enterobacteriaceae*, P. R. Edwards and W. H. Ewing, Burgess Publishing Co., Minneapolis, MN 55415, 2nd Ed., 1962, as guide for further study of isolated microorganisms.

41.024 Culture Media

(*See* introduction, **41.013.** Sizes of culture media containers (test tubes, flasks, and petri dishes) are specified in prepn of each medium. Different size containers may be used if they give identical results. All media containers must have covers, caps, or plugs which prevent contamination but maintain aerobic conditions unless otherwise directed.)

(a) *Lactose broth.*—See **41.005(f).** Dispense 225 ml portions in 500 ml screw-cap bottles or flasks.

(b)(1) *Selenite cystine broth.*—Suspend 5.0 g tryptone or polypeptone, 4.0 g lactose, 10.0 g anhyd. Na_2HPO_4, 4.0 g $NaHSeO_3$, and 0.01 g L-cystine in 1 L H_2O and mix thoroly. Heat with frequent agitation. Dispense 10 ml portions in sterile 16 × 150 mm test tubes. Heat 10 min in flowing steam. *Do not autoclave.* Final pH, 7.0±0.1. Medium is not sterile. Use same day as prepd.

(2) *Selenite cystine broth (North and Bartram).*—Prep. as in (1), using 5.0 g polypeptone or 4.0 g tryptone, 4.0 g lactose, 4.0 g $NaHSeO_3$, 5.5 g anhyd.

Na_2HPO_4, 4.5 g anhyd. KH_2PO_4, and 1 ml 1% L-cystine (10 mg) soln prepd by dissolving 1.0 g L-cystine in 15 ml 1*N* NaOH and dilg to 100 ml with sterile H_2O.

(c) *Tetrathionate broth (with iodine and brilliant green).*—Suspend 5.0 g polypeptone, 1.0 g bile salts, 10 g $CaCO_3$, and 30 g $Na_2S_2O_3.5H_2O$ in 1 L H_2O, mix thoroly, and heat to boiling. (Ppt will not dissolve completely.) Cool to <45° and store at 5–8°. Prep. I-KI soln by dissolving 5 g KI in 5 ml sterile H_2O, adding 6 g resublimed I, dissolving, and dilg to 20 ml with sterile H_2O. Prep. brilliant green soln by dissolving 0.1 g dye in sterile H_2O and dilg to 100 ml. On day medium is used, add 20 ml I-KI soln and 10 ml brilliant green soln per 1 L basal broth. Resuspend ppt by gentle agitation and aseptically dispense 10 ml portions in 20 × 150 or 16 × 150 mm sterile test tubes. *Do not heat medium after addn of I-KI and dye solns.*

(d) *Brilliant green agar.*—Use com. dehydrated medium contg 3.0 g yeast ext, 10 g proteose peptone No. 3 or polypeptone, 5.0 g NaCl, 10 g lactose, 10 g sucrose, 0.08 g phenol red, 5 ml 0.25% brilliant green (12.5 mg) soln, and 20 g agar. Suspend medium in 1 L H_2O, mix thoroly, and heat with occasional agitation. Boil 1 min to dissolve. Autoclave 1 L portions 12 min at 121°. (Addnl heating decreases selectivity of medium; less heating increases selectivity.) Cool to 45–50° and pour 20 ml portions into 15 × 100 mm petri dishes. Let dry ca 2 hr with covers partially removed; then close plates. Final pH, 6.9±0.1.

(e) *Salmonella-Shigella agar.*—Suspend 5.0 g beef ext, 5.0 g polypeptone or proteose peptone, 10 g lactose, 8.5 g bile salts mixt., 8.5 g Na citrate.$2H_2O$, 8.5 g $Na_2S_2O_3.5H_2O$, 1.0 g ferric citrate, 13.5 g agar, 0.33 ml 0.1% brilliant green (0.33 mg) soln, and 2.5 ml 1% neutral red (25 mg) soln in 1 L H_2O, and mix thoroly until homogeneous. Heat with occasional agitation and boil 1–2 min until ingredients dissolve. Cool to 45–50° and pour 20 ml portions into 15 × 100 mm petri dishes. Let dry ca 2 hr with covers partially removed; then close plates. Final pH, 7.0±0.1. *Do not autoclave.*

(f) *Bismuth sulfite agar (Wilson and Blair).*—Suspend 10 g polypeptone or peptone, 5.0 g beef ext, 5.0 g glucose, 4.0 g $Na_2HPO_4.12H_2O$, 0.3 g $FeSO_4$.$7H_2O$, 8.0 g $Bi_2(SO_3)_3$ indicator, 0.025 g brilliant green, and 20 g agar in 1 L H_2O, mix thoroly, and heat with occasional agitation. Boil ca 1 min to obtain uniform suspension. (Ppt will not dissolve.) Cool to 45–50°. Suspend ppt by gentle agitation and pour 20 ml portions into 15 × 100 mm petri dishes. Let dry ca 2 hr with covers partially removed; then close plates. Final pH, 7.6±0.1. *Do not autoclave.* Selectivity of plates decreases 48 hr after prepn.

(g) *Triple sugar iron agar (TSI agar).*—Suspend ingredients (*1*) or (*2*) in 1 L H_2O, mix thoroly, and heat with occasional agitation. Boil ca 1 min until ingredients dissolve. Fill 16 × 150 mm tubes ⅓ full and cap or plug so that aerobic conditions are maintained during use. Autoclave 12 min at 121°. Before medium solidifies, place tubes in slanted position so that deep butts (ca 1¼″) and adequate slants (ca 2″) are formed on solidification.

(*1*) 20 g polypeptone, 5.0 g NaCl, 10 g lactose, 10 g sucrose, 1 g glucose, 0.2 g $Fe(NH_4)_2(SO_4)_2.6H_2O$, 0.2 g $Na_2S_2O_3$, 0.025 g phenol red, and 13 g agar. Final pH, 7.3±0.1.

(*2*) 3.0 g beef ext, 3.0 g yeast ext, 15 g peptone, 5.0 g proteose-peptone, 1.0 g glucose, 10 g lactose, 10 g sucrose, 0.2 g $FeSO_4.7H_2O$, 5.0 g NaCl, 0.3 g $Na_2S_2O_3$, 0.024 g phenol red, and 12 g agar. Final pH, 7.4±0.1.

(h) *Tryptophane broth.*—See **41.005**(h). Use 16 or 20 × 150 mm test tubes.

(i) *Buffered glucose broth (MR-VP medium).*—See **41.005**(b). Use 16 or 20 × 150 mm test tubes.

(j) *Simmon's citrate agar.*—Dissolve 2.0 g Na citrate, 5.0 g NaCl, 1.0 g K_2HPO_4, 1.0 g $NH_4H_2PO_4$, 0.2 g $MgSO_4$, 0.08 g bromothymol blue, and 15 g agar in 1 L H_2O, and heat gently with occasional agitation. Boil 1–2 min until ingredients dissolve. Fill 13 or 16 × 150 mm test tubes ⅓ full and cap or plug so that aerobic conditions are maintained during use. Autoclave 15 min at 121°. Before medium solidifies, place tubes in slanted position so that deep butts (ca ¾ or 1¼″, resp.) and adequate slants (ca 1½ or 2″, resp.) are formed on solidification.

(k)(*1*) *Urea broth.*—Dissolve 20 g urea, 0.1 g yeast ext, 9.1 g KH_2PO_4, 9.5 g Na_2HPO_4, and 4.0 ml 0.25% phenol red (10 mg) soln in 1 L H_2O. *Do not heat.* Sterilize by filtration and aseptically dispense 1.5–3 ml portions in 13 × 100 mm sterile test tubes. Final pH, 6.8±0.1.

(*2*) *Rapid urea broth.*—Prep. as in (*1*), using 0.091 and 0.095 g phosphate salts, resp.

(l) *Malonate broth.*—Dissolve 1.0 g yeast ext, 2.0 g $(NH_4)_2SO_4$, 0.6 g K_2HPO_4, 0.4 g KH_2PO_4, 2.0 g NaCl, 3.0 g Na malonate, 0.25 g glucose, and 0.025 g bromothymol blue in 1 L H_2O, heating if necessary until dissolved. Dispense 3 ml portions in 13 × 100 mm test tubes and autoclave 15 min at 121°. Final pH, 6.7±0.1.

(m)(*1*) *Lysine iron agar (Edwards and Fife).*—Dissolve 5.0 g gelysate or peptone, 3.0 g yeast ext, 1.0 g glucose, 10 g L-lysine, 0.5 g ferric ammonium citrate, 0.04 g anhyd. $Na_2S_2O_3$, 0.02 g bromocresol purple, and 15 g agar in 1 L H_2O, heating until dissolved. Dispense 4 ml portions in 13 × 100 ml test tubes and cap or plug so that aerobic conditions are maintained during use. Autoclave 12 min at 121°. Before medium solidifies, place tubes in slanted position so that 1½″ butts and 1″ slants are formed on solidification. Final pH, 6.7±0.1.

(*2*) *Lysine decarboxylase broth (Falkow).*—Dissolve 5.0 g gelysate or peptone, 3.0 g yeast ext, 1.0 g glucose, 5.0 g L-lysine, and 0.02 g bromocresol purple in 1 L H_2O, heating until dissolved. Dispense 5 ml portions in 16 × 125 mm screw-cap test tubes. Autoclave, loosely capped, 15 min at 121°. Screw caps on tightly for storage and after inoculation. Final pH, 6.5–6.8.

(**n**) *Motility test medium (semisolid medium).*— Dissolve 3.0 g beef ext, 10 g peptone or gelysate, 5.0 g NaCl, and 4.0 g agar in 1 L H_2O and heat gently with occasional agitation. Boil 1–2 min to dissolve. If medium is to be stored, dispense 20 ml portions into screw-cap containers, replacing caps loosely. Autoclave 15 min at 121°. Cool to 45°. To store, screw caps on tightly and refrigerate at 5–8°. To use, remelt in boiling H_2O or flowing steam and cool to 45°. Aseptically dispense 20 ml portions in 15 × 100 mm petri dishes and let solidify with dish completely covered. Use plates same day as prepd. Final pH, 7.4±0.1.

(**o**) *Potassium cyanide (KCN) broth.*—Dissolve 3.0 g proteose peptone No. 3 or polypeptone, 5.0 g NaCl, 0.225 g KH_2PO_4, and 5.64 g Na_2HPO_4 in 1 L H_2O. Autoclave 15 min at 121°. Cool and refrigerate at 5–8°. Final pH, 7.6±0.1. Dissolve 0.5 g KCN in 100 ml cold (5–8°) sterile H_2O. Using sterile bulb pipet or sterile syringe (*do not pipet by mouth*), aseptically add 15 ml cold KCN soln per L cold, sterile basal broth. Mix thoroly with gentle agitation and aseptically dispense 1–1.5 ml portions in sterile 13 × 100 mm test tubes. Using aseptic technic, immediately stopper tubes with No. 2 corks impregnated with paraffin. Prep. corks by boiling in paraffin ca 5 min. Place corks in tubes so that paraffin does not flow into broth but forms good seal between rim of tube and cork. Medium stored at 5–8° is usually stable ca 2 weeks.

(**p**)(*1*) *Phenol red carbohydrate broth.*—Dissolve 10 g trypticase or proteose peptone No. 3, 5.0 g NaCl, 1.0 g beef ext (optional), and 7.2 ml 0.25% phenol red (18 mg) soln in 1 L H_2O and heat with gentle agitation until dissolved. Dissolve 5 g dulcitol, 10 g lactose, or 10 g sucrose (as specified in title of test) in this basal broth. Dispense 2.5 ml portions in 13 × 100 mm test tubes contg inverted 6 × 50 mm fermentation tubes. Autoclave 10 min at 118° (12 psi). Final pH, 7.3±0.1. Alternatively, dissolve ingredients, omitting carbohydrate, in 800 ml H_2O with heat and occasional agitation. Dispense 2.0 ml portions in 13 × 100 mm test tubes contg inverted fermentation tubes. Autoclave 15 min at 118° and let cool. Dissolve carbohydrate in 200 ml H_2O and sterilize by passing soln thru bacteria-retaining filter. Aseptically add 0.5 ml sterile filtrate to each tube of sterilized broth after cooling to <45°. Shake gently to mix. Final pH, 7.4±0.1.

(*2*) *Purple carbohydrate broth.*—Prep. as in (*1*), using as basal broth 10 g proteose peptone No. 3 or gelysate, 5.0 g NaCl, and 0.015 or 0.020 g bromocresol purple. Final pH, 6.8±0.1.

(**q**) *MacConkey agar.*—Suspend 3.0 g proteose peptone or polypeptone, 17 g peptone or gelysate, 10 g lactose, 1.5 g bile salts No. 3 or bile salts mixt., 5.0 g NaCl, 3.0 ml 1% neutral red (30 mg) soln, 1 ml 0.1% crystal violet (1.0 mg) soln, and 13.5 g agar in

1 L H_2O and mix thoroly until homogeneous. Heat, with occasional agitation, and boil 1–2 min until ingredients dissolve. Autoclave 15 min at 121°. Cool to 45–50° and pour 20 ml portions into 15 × 100 mm petri dishes. Let dry ≥2 hr with plates covered. Do not use wet plates. Final pH, 7.1±0.1.

(**r**) *Brain heart infusion broth.*—See **41.013**(h), dispensing 5 ml portions in 16 × 150 mm test tubes.

41.025   *Diagnostic Reagents*

(**a**) *Kovac's reagent for indole test.*—Dissolve 5 g *p*-dimethylaminobenzaldehyde in 75 ml amyl alcohol and slowly add 25 ml HCl.

(**b**) *Voges-Proskauer (VP) test reagents.*—(*1*) *Alpha-naphthol soln.*—5%. Dissolve 5.0 g α-naphthol in 100 ml absolute alcohol.

(*2*) *Potassium hydroxide soln.*—40%. Dissolve 40 g KOH in H_2O and dil. to 100 ml.

(**c**) *Sodium hydroxide soln.*—1N. Dissolve 42.11 g 95% reagent NaOH in sterile H_2O and dil. to 1 L.

(**d**) *Hydrochloric acid soln.*—1N. Dil. 89 ml to 1 L with sterile H_2O.

(**e**) *Methyl red indicator.*—Dissolve 0.10 g Me red in 300 ml alcohol and dil. to 500 ml with H_2O.

(**f**) *Sterile physiological saline soln.*—See **41.006**(c).

(**g**) *Formalized physiological saline soln.*—Add 6 ml HCHO soln (36–38%) to sterile saline soln, (**f**), mix, and store in tightly stoppered containers.

(**h**) *Salmonella polyvalent somatic (O) antiserum.*— ("Serological Identification of the *Salmonella* Serotypes," No. 0168, Difco Laboratories, July 1970, p. 4, or equiv.) Contains agglutinins for at least somatic (O) antigens 1, 2, 3, 4, 5, 6, 7, 8, 9, 10, 11, 12, 13, 14, 15, 16, 19, 22, 23, 24, 25, 34, and Vi. They are agglutinins for somatic (O) groups: A, B, C_1, C_2, D, E_1, E_2, E_3, E_4, F, G, H, I, and Vi.

(**i**) *Salmonella individual somatic (O) antisera.*— (*See* ref. in (**h**).) For at least each of the somatic (O) groups listed in (**h**).

(**j**) *Salmonella polyvalent flagellar (H) antiserum Poly a-z.*—(*See* p. 5 of ref. in (**h**).) Contains agglutinins for at least the following flagellar (H) antigens: a, b, c, d, e, f, g, h, i, k, l, m, n, p, q, r, s, t, u, v, w, x, y, z, z_4, z_6, z_{10}, z_{13}, z_{15}, z_{23}, z_{24}, z_{28}, z_{29}, z_{32}, z_{40}, 1, 2, 5, 6, 7.

(**k**) *Salmonella "Spicer-Edwards" flagellar (H) antisera.*—(From p. 10 of ref. in (**h**).) Consists of 7 pooled or polyvalent antisera which react as in Table 41:1.

(**l**) *pH Test paper.*—Min. range 6.0–7.6 with max. gradations of 0.4 pH for each color change.

(**m**) *Sterile distilled water.*—Dispense 1 L H_2O into 2 L wide-mouth flask or wide-mouth jar; plug or cap loosely. Autoclave 20 min at 121°.

(**n**) *Brilliant green dye soln.*—1%. Dissolve 1 g in sterile H_2O and dil. to 100 ml. (Since some batches of dye are unusually toxic, test all batches of dye before use and use only those producing satisfactory results when tested with known pos. and neg. test organisms.)

Table 41:1—Salmonella H Antisera Spicer-Edwards and H Antigens with Which Each Reacts

H Antigens	Salmonella H Antisera Spicer-Edwards			
	1	2	3	4
a	+	+	+	−
b	+	+	−	+
c	+	+	−	−
d	+	−	+	+
eh	+	−	+	−
G Complex[a]	+	−	−	+
i	+	−	−	−
k	−	+	+	+
r	−	+	−	+
y	−	+	−	−
z	−	−	+	+
z_4 Complex[b]	−	−	+	−
z_{10}	−	−	−	+
z_{29}	−	+	+	−

H Antigens	Salmonella H Antisera
enx, enz$_{15}$	EN complex
lv, lw, lz$_{13}$, lz$_{28}$	L complex
1, 2; 1, 5; 1, 6; 1, 7	1 complex

[a] The G complex component of Salmonella H antisera Spicer-Edwards 1 and 4 reacts with antigens f, g, m, p, q, s, t, and u.

[b] The z_4 complex component reacts with z_4, z_{23}, z_{24}, and z_{32}.

(From Difco Laboratories)

Detection

41.026 — Preparation of Sample

(a) *Dried whole egg, dried egg yolk, and dried egg white.*—Aseptically open sample container and aseptically weigh 25 g sample into sterile, empty, wide-mouth, screw-cap pt jar. Add ca 15 ml sterile lactose broth, **41.024(a)**. Stir with sterile glass rod, sterile spoon, or sterile tongue depressor to smooth suspension. Add 3 addnl portions lactose broth, 10, 10, and 190 ml for total of 225 ml. Stir after each addn until sample is suspended without lumps. Cap jar securely and let stand at room temp. 60 min. Mix well by shaking, and det. pH with test paper, **41.025** (l). Adjust pH, if necessary, to 6.8±0.2 with sterile 1N NaOH or HCl, **41.025(c)** or (d), capping jar securely and mixing well before detg final pH. Loosen jar cap ca ¼ turn and incubate 24±2 hr at 35°.

(b) *Nonfat dry milk and dry whole milk.*—Aseptically weigh 100 g sample into sterile 2 L flask (or wide-mouth screw-cap 2 qt jar). Add 1 L H$_2$O and mix well. Det. pH with test paper, **41.025(l)**. (If pH is <6.6, adjust to 6.8±0.2 with 1N NaOH.) Add 2 ml 1% aq. brilliant green and mix well. Incubate 24±2 hr at 35°.

41.027 — Isolation

(a) *Growth on selective media.*—Gently shake incubated sample mixt., **41.026**, and transfer 1 ml to 10 ml selenite cystine broth, **41.024(b)(1)** or (2), and addnl 1 ml to 10 ml tetrathionate broth, **41.024(c)**. Incubate 24±2 hr at 35°.

Streak 3 mm loopful of incubated selenite cystine broth on selective media plates of brilliant green agar, **41.024(d)**, *Salmonella-Shigella* agar, **41.024(e)**, and Bi$_2$(SO$_3$)$_3$ agar, **41.024(f)**. Repeat with 3 mm loopful of incubated tetrathionate broth. Incubate plates 24±2 hr at 35°.

(b) *Appearance of typical Salmonella colonies.*— (1) *On brilliant green agar.*—Colorless, pink to fuchsia, translucent to opaque, with surrounding medium pink to red. Some *Salmonella* appear as transparent green colonies if surrounded by lactose- or sucrose-fermenting organisms which produce colonies that are yellow-green or green.

(2) *On Salmonella-Shigella agar.*—Uncolored to pale pink, opaque, transparent or translucent, but some strains produce black-centered colonies.

(3) *On bismuth sulfite agar.*—Brown, gray to black, sometimes with metallic sheen. Surrounding medium is usually brown at first, turning black with increasing incubation time. Some strains produce green colonies with little or no darkening of surrounding medium.

If plates do not have typical or suspicious colonies or do not contain growth, incubate addnl 24 hr.

41.028 — Treatment of Typical or Suspicious Colonies

(a) *Inoculation of triple sugar iron (TSI) agar.*— Pick with needle 2 or more typical or suspicious colonies, if present, from each brilliant green, *Salmonella-Shigella*, and Bi$_2$(SO$_3$)$_3$ agar plates having growth. Inoculate TSI agar slant, **41.024(g)**, with portion of each colony by streaking slant and stabbing butt. Store picked selective plates at 5–8° or at room temp. (ca 26°).

(b) *Presumptive positive reactions.*—Incubate TSI slants 24±2 hr at 35°. Presumptive pos. *Salmonella* cultures have alk. (red) slants and acid (yellow) butts, with or without H$_2$S (blackening of agar). (H$_2$S-neg. TSI cultures which otherwise appear to be salmonellae cannot be excluded from further examination.)

If TSI fails to give a typical *Salmonella* reaction, pick addnl suspicious colonies from selective medium plate not giving presumptive pos. culture and inoculate TSI slant as in (a).

To detect lactose- or sucrose-fermenting *Salmonella* or lactose-fermenting Arizona organisms, use lysine iron agar, **41.024(m)(1)**, as in **41.031(a)**, to test: (1) all H$_2$S-pos. TSI agar cultures (including yellow slants) isolated from any selective agar plate, and (2) all TSI agar cultures (including yellow slants) isolated from bismuth sulfite agar colonies. Further test lysine decarboxylase-pos. cultures to det. if they are *Salmonella* sp., **41.033(f)(1)**, or Arizona organisms, **41.033(f)(2)**.

(c) *Selection for identification.*—Apply biochemical and serological identification tests to 3 presumptive pos. TSI agar cultures picked from selective agar plates streaked from selenite cystine broth and to 3 presumptive pos. TSI agar cultures picked from selective agar plates streaked from tetrathionate broth.

If 3 presumptive pos. TSI agar cultures are not isolated from 1 set of selective agar plates, test other presumptive pos. TSI agar cultures, if isolated, by biochemical and serological tests. A min. of 6 TSI cultures are examined for each 25 g sample tested.

Identification
41.029 *Cultures*

Pure cultures on TSI agar are required for inoculation of biochemical test media.

(a) *Pure cultures.*—Proceed to **41.030.**

(b) *Mixed cultures.*—Streak any culture that appears to be mixed on MacConkey's agar, **41.024(q),** or brilliant green agar, **41.024(d).** Incubate 24±2 hr at 35°.

(c) *Appearance of Salmonella colonies.*—(*1*) *On MacConkey's agar.*—Typical colonies appear transparent and colorless, sometimes with dark centers. *Salmonella* will clear areas of pptd bile caused by other organisms sometimes present in medium.

(*2*) *On brilliant green agar.*—See **41.027(b)(1).**

Pick with needle ≥2 typical or suspicious colonies and inoculate TSI slants by streaking the slant and stabbing the butt as in **41.028(a).** Retest purified cultures as in **41.028(b),** and proceed with identification.

41.030 *Subcultures*

(a) *Urease test.*—Subculture two 3 mm loopfuls of presumptive pos. TSI agar culture to urea broth, **41.024(k)(1),** and incubate 24±2 hr at 35° or inoculate rapid urea broth, **41.024(k)(2),** and incubate 2 hr in H_2O bath at 37±0.5°. Discard all cultures that give pos. test (purple-red color). Salmonellae are urease neg. (no change in orange color of medium).

(b) *Serological flagellar (H) screening test.*—To reduce number of presumptive pos. TSI agar cultures carried thru identification tests, perform serological flagellar (H) screening test by transferring one 3 mm loopful of each urease-neg. TSI agar culture to either:

(*1*) Brain heart infusion broth, **41.024(r),** (for test on same day) and incubate at 35° until visible growth occurs (ca 4–6 hr); or

(*2*) Tryptophane broth, **41.024(h),** (for test on following day) and incubate 24±2 hr at 35°.

To 5 ml of each of the 6 broth cultures add ca 2.5 ml formalized physiological saline soln, **41.025(g).** Select 2 formalized broth cultures and test with *Salmonella* flagellar (H) antisera, **41.025(j)** or **(k),** as in **41.039** or **41.040.**

If selected formalized broth cultures are pos., perform addnl tests on these cultures, beginning with **41.031,** except step **41.031(c)(4)** may be omitted.

If both formalized broth cultures are not pos., perform test on the 4 remaining other broth cultures **(41.030(b)(1)** or **(2))** to obtain, if possible, 2 pos. cultures for addnl testing, **41.031.**

If all urease-neg. TSI cultures from sample are *Salmonella* serological flagellar (H) test neg., then perform addnl tests, beginning with **41.031,** on all cultures.

41.031 *Testing Urease-Negative Cultures*

Transfer 1 loopful of presumptive pos. TSI agar culture to each of following media:

(a) *Lysine iron agar,* **41.024(m)(1).**—Streak slant and stab butt. Replace tube cap *loosely* and incubate 48±2 hr at 35°. Examine at least every 24 hr. Salmonellae give alk. reaction of purple color thruout medium (final color is slightly darker than original purple color of medium). If H_2S is produced, butt of medium is blackened. Neg. test is purple or red slant and yellow butt.

If liq. medium is preferred, inoculate tube of lysine decarboxylase broth, **41.024(m)(2).** Close tube cap *tightly* after inoculation and incubate 96±2 hr at 35°. Examine at least every 24 hr. Salmonellae give alk. reaction of purple color thruout broth (final color is slightly darker than original purple color of medium). Sometimes tubes which have yellow color after 8–12 hr of incubation change to purple later. Neg. test is permanent yellow color thruout broth.

(Lysine iron agar is incubated loosely capped so that aerobic conditions are maintained, while lysine decarboxylase broth is incubated tightly closed to exclude air.)

(b) *Phenol red dulcitol broth,* **41.024(p)(1).**—Incubate 48±2 hr at 35°. Examine at least every 24 hr. Most salmonellae give pos. test indicated by gas formation (displacement of liq. in inverted tube) and acid reaction (yellow). Neg. test is alk. reaction (red) and no gas formation.

(Purple broth base with dulcitol, **41.024(p)(2),** may be substituted. Pos. test is acid reaction (yellow) and gas. Neg. test is alk. reaction (purple).)

(c) *Tryptophane broth,* **41.024(h).**—Incubate 24±2 hr at 35° and test as follows:

(*1*) Transfer 3 mm loopful, excluding all solid particles, to KCN broth, **41.024(o).** Heat rim of tube to form good seal when restoppered. Incubate 48±2 hr at 35°. Salmonellae do not grow in this broth as shown by lack of turbidity (neg. test).

(*2*) Transfer 3 mm loopful to malonate broth, **41.024(l),** and incubate 48±2 hr at 35°. Salmonellae give neg. test as shown by green color (unchanged). Pos. test (alk. reaction) is shown by blue color.

(*3*) Transfer 5 ml to empty test tube and add 0.2–0.3 ml Kovac's reagent, **41.025(a).** Pos. test for indole is shown by deep red color in reagent on surface of broth. Most salmonellae are indole neg.

(*4*) To remainder of 24-hr tryptophane broth culture (ca 5 ml) add ca 2.5 ml formalized physiological saline soln, **41.025(g).** Refrigerate formalized broth at 5–8° if test is to be performed on another day. Perform *Salmonella* serological flagellar (H) test, **41.039,** or "Spicer-Edwards" flagellar (H) test tube test, **41.040,** using formalized broth culture as flagellar (H) antigen to be tested.

(d) *Tests indicating absence of Salmonella.*—Discard, as not *Salmonella,* cultures that show either:

(*1*) Pos. indole test (red) and neg. *Salmonella* serological flagellar (H) test.

(*2*) Pos. KCN broth test (growth) and neg. lysine decarboxylase test (yellow).

(e) *Testing of TSI agar cultures.*—Use *Salmonella* serological somatic (O) test, **41.037.**

(f) *Classification.*—Classify as *Salmonella* sp. cultures that have all characteristics shown in table, **41.032.** If 1 TSI culture from 25 g sample is classified as *Salmonella* sp., further testing of other TSI cultures from same 25 g sample is unnecessary.

(g) *Special cases.*—Cultures that contain demonstrable *Salmonella* antigens as shown by pos. *Salmonella* serological somatic (O) test and pos. flagellar (H) test but do not have biochemical characteristics of salmonellae should be purified as in **41.029(b)** and retested, beginning with **41.030.**

41.032　　*Characteristics of Salmonella*

Test or Substrate	Results
Urease, **41.030(a)**	Negative (orange-red)
Lysine decarboxylase, **41.031(a)**	Positive (alk.; purple thruout medium)
Phenol red dulcitol broth, **41.031(b)**	Positive (yellow and gas)
KCN broth, **41.031(c)(*1*)**	Negative (no growth)
Malonate broth, **41.031(c)(*2*)**	Negative (unchanged green)
Indole test, **41.031(c)(*3*)**	Negative (no red color)
Polyvalent flagellar test, **41.030(b), 41.031(c)(*4*)**	Positive (visible agglutination)
Polyvalent somatic test, **41.031(e)**	Positive (visible agglutination)

41.033　　*Additional Biochemical Tests*

Perform addnl tests on cultures that do not give identical test results as in **41.032** and do not classify as *Salmonella* sp. Transfer 1 loopful of culture from each unclassified TSI agar slant to each of following media:

(a) *Phenol red lactose broth,* **41.024(p)(*1*).**—Incubate 48±2 hr at 35°. Examine inoculated broth at least every 24 hr. Pos. test is shown by gas formation (displacement of liq. in inverted tube) and acid reaction (yellow). Most salmonellae give neg. test shown by alk. reaction (red) and no gas formation.

Discard, as not *Salmonella,* cultures that give pos. phenol red lactose broth test, except: (*1*) Cultures described in **41.028(b),** and (*2*) cultures that also give pos. malonate broth test. Cultures that are phenol red lactose broth pos. or neg. and malonate broth pos. are tested further to det. if they are *Arizona* sp., **41.033(e)(*2*).**

(Purple lactose broth, **41.024(p)(*2*),** may be substituted. Pos. test is acid reaction (yellow) and gas. Neg. test is alk. reaction (purple) and no gas formation.)

(b) *Phenol red sucrose broth,* **41.024(p)(*1*).**—Incubate and read as in (a) above. Discard, as not *Salmonella,* cultures that give pos. test, except cultures described in **41.028(b).** (Purple sucrose broth may be substituted and read as in (a) above.)

(c) *Buffered glucose broth (MR-VP medium,* **41.024** (i)).—Incubate 48±2 hr at 35°.

(*1*) Perform Voges-Proskauer (VP) test at room temp. by transferring 1 ml 48-hr culture to test tube and adding 0.6 ml α-naphthol soln, **41.025(b)(*1*),** and 0.2 ml 40% KOH soln, **41.025(b)(*2*).** Shake after each addn. To intensify and speed reaction, add few creatine crystals to test medium. Read results 4 hr after adding reagents. Pos. VP test is development of eosin pink color. Salmonellae give neg. test.

(*2*) Incubate remainder of MR-VP medium addnl 48±2 hr at 35°. Perform Me red test by transferring 5 ml culture to test tube and adding 5-6 drops Me red soln, **41.025(e),** and read results immediately. Salmonellae give pos. test (red). Neg. test is indicated by yellow color.

(d) *Simmon's citrate agar,* **41.024(j).**—Inoculate by streaking slant and stabbing butt. Incubate 96±2 hr at 35°. Salmonellae usually give pos. test shown by growth and color change from green to blue (alk.). Color change usually appears first on slant and then spreads thru medium. Neg. test is indicated by no or very little growth and no change in color of medium.

(e) *Classification.*—Classify cultures according to results listed in Table **41.034.** If 1 TSI culture from 25 g sample is classified as *Salmonella* sp., further testing of other TSI cultures from same 25 g sample is unnecessary.

(*1*) *Salmonella* sp.—Cultures that have reaction patterns of Table **41.034,** column A or B.

(*2*) *Arizona* sp.—Cultures that have reaction pattern of Table **41.034,** column C.

(*3*) *Non-Salmonella* sp.—Discard, as not *Salmonella,* cultures that give results listed in any 1 subdivision of Table **41.035.** (*See* p. 851.)

(f) *Tests indicating absence of Salmonella.*—Discard, as not *Salmonella,* cultures that give the following 3 results:

(*1*) Pos. KCN broth test (growth),

(*2*) Pos. Voges-Proskauer test (red), and

(*3*) Neg. Me red test (yellow).

41.034 **41.035** }　*See* page 851.

41.036　　*Summary of Classification of Non-Salmonella Cultures*

Classify, by performing addnl tests described in *Identification of Enterobacteriaceae,* any culture that is not clearly identified as *Salmonella* sp. or *Arizona* sp. by classification schemes in Tables **41.032** and **41.034** or not eliminated from these groups by test reactions listed in Table **41.035.**

If neither of 2 TSI cultures carried thru biochemi-

41.034   *Characteristics of Salmonella and Arizona*

| Test or Substrate | Classification[a] | | |
| | Salmonella sp. | | Arizona sp. |
	A	B	C
Urease test, **41.030(a)**	–	–	–
Lysine decarboxylase, **41.031(a)**	alk.	alk.	alk.
Phenol red dulcitol broth, **41.031(b)**	AG	AG or A or –	–
KCN broth, **41.031(c)(***1***)**	NGr	NGr	NGr
Malonate broth, **41.031(c)(***2***)**	–	–	+
Indole test, **41.031(c)(***3***)**	–	–	–
Polyvalent flagellar test, **41.030(b)**, **41.031(c)(***4***)** or Spicer-Edwards flagellar (H) test, **41.040**	+	+	+ or –
Polyvalent somatic test, **41.031(e)**	+ or –	+	+ or –
Phenol red lactose broth, **41.033(a)**	–[b]	–[b]	AG or A or –
Phenol red sucrose broth, **41.033(b)**	–[b]	–[b]	–
Voges-Proskauer test, **41.033(c)(***1***)**	–	–	–
Methyl red test, **41.033(c)(***2***)**	+	+	+
Simmon's citrate, **41.033(d)**	+	+ or –	+

[a] NGr = no growth; + = pos. test; – = neg. test or no acid or gas; A = acid; AG = acid and gas; alk. = alkaline.
[b] Majority of strains give neg. test, but atypical strains giving pos. test have been reported.

41.035   *Characteristics of Non-Salmonella Cultures*

Test(s) or Substrate(s)	Results
(a) Urease test, **41.030(a)**	Positive (purple-red)
(b) Indole test, **41,031(c)(***3***)** Polyvalent flagellar test, **41.030(b)**, **41.031(c)(***4***)** or Spicer-Edwards flagellar (H) test, **41.040**	Positive (red) Negative (no agglutination)
(c) Lysine decarboxylase test, **41.031(a)** KCN broth, **41.031(c)(***1***)**	Negative (yellow) Positive (growth)
(d) Phenol red lactose broth[a], **41.033(a)**	Positive (gas and acid)[b]
(e) Phenol red sucrose broth, **41.033(b)**	Positive (gas and acid)[b]
(f) KCN broth, **41.031(c)(***1***)** Voges-Proskauer test, **41.033(c)(***1***)** Methyl red test, **41.033(c)(***2***)**	Positive (growth) Positive (red) Negative (yellow)

[a] Malonate broth positive cultures are tested further to det. if they are *Arizona* sp., **41.033(e)(***2***)**.
[b] Do not discard pos. broth cultures subcultured from H₂S-pos. TSI slants or bismuth sulfite agar colonies; test further to det. if they are *Salmonella* sp.

cal tests, **41.031–41.035**, confirms as *Salmonella*, perform biochemical tests, beginning with **41.031**, on all other urease-neg. TSI cultures from same 25 g sample.

Salmonella Serological Tests

Dil. and pretest all *Salmonella* serological antisera with known test cultures to insure reliability of results with unknown cultures. *Caution:* Handle viable cultures carefully to prevent contaminating environment.

41.037   *Polyvalent Somatic (O) Slide or Plate Test*

Using wax pencil, mark off 2 sections ca 1 × 2 cm on inside of glass or plastic petri dish. Place ½ of 3 mm loopful of culture from 24- or 48-hr TSI agar slant on dish in upper part of each marked section. Add 1 drop saline soln, **41.025(f)**, to lower part of each marked section. With clean, sterile transfer loop or needle, emulsify culture in saline soln for 1 section and repeat for other section. Add 1 drop *Salmonella* polyvalent somatic (O) antiserum, **41.025(h)**, to a section of emulsified culture and mix with clean, sterile transfer loop or needle. Tilt mixt. in both sections back and forth 1 min and observe against dark background. Any degree of agglutination is pos. reaction.

Classify polyvalent somatic (O) test as:

(a) *Positive.* — Agglutination in culture-saline-serum mixt. and no agglutination in culture-saline mixt.

(b) *Negative.*—No agglutination in culture-saline-serum mixt. (Polyvalent somatic antisera do not contain agglutinins for antigens of some salmonellae isolated from foods. Neg. somatic reactions occur with salmonellae serotypes whose corresponding agglutinins are not contained in the antisera, i.e., *S. cerro*, group K(18); *S. minnesota*, group L(21); *S. alachua*, group O(35).)

(c) *Non-specific.*—Both mixts agglutinate. Requires addnl testing as in *Identification of Enterobacteriaceae.*

41.038   *Determination of Somatic Grouping (Optional)*

Perform serological somatic (O) test on culture as in **41.037**, using individual group somatic (O) antiserum (including Vi), **41.025(i)**, instead of *Salmonella* polyvalent somatic (O) antiserum. Repeat test, using each group somatic antiserum or until culture reacts with specific group antiserum.

Suspend cultures pos. with Vi antiserum by emulsifying growth from slant surface in 1 ml physiological saline soln, 41.025(f), to make heavy suspension. Heat in boiling H_2O 20–30 min and let cool. Retest heated suspension, using somatic group D, C_1, and Vi antisera. Vi-pos. cultures which react with somatic group D antiserum are probably *Salmonella typhi*, and Vi-pos. cultures which react with somatic group C_1 antiserum are probably *Salmonella paratyphi C*. For these cultures to be classified as *Salmonella* sp., they must have characteristics of salmonellae as in Table **41.032** or **41.034**. Heated Vi-pos. cultures which do not react with any individual somatic serum but continue to react with Vi antiserum probably belong to *Citrobacter* group and are not *Salmonella*. Confirm conclusion by biochemical tests listed in Table **41.034**.

Cultures that give pos. somatic (O) test with any individual somatic (O) antiserum are recorded as pos. for that somatic (O) group; cultures that do not react with any individual somatic (O) antiserum are recorded as neg. for individual group somatic (O) test.

41.039 Polyvalent Flagellar (H) Test Tube Test

Place 0.5 ml appropriately dild *Salmonella* polyvalent flagellar (H) antiserum, **41.025(j)**, in 10 × 75 or 13 × 100 mm serological test tube and add 0.5 ml antigen to be tested: formalized brain-heart infusion broth, **41.030(b)**(*1*), or 0.5 ml formalized tryptophane broth culture, **41.030(b)**(*2*) or **41.031(c)**(*4*). If formalized culture contains granular particles, pellicles, or sediment, also prep. saline control by mixing 0.5 ml formalized saline soln, **41.025(g)**, with 0.5 ml formalized tryptophane broth culture in same size serological test tube. Incubate mixts 1 hr in H_2O bath at 50°. Observe preliminary results at 15 min intervals and read final results at 1 hr.

Classify polyvalent flagellar (H) test as:

(**a**) *Positive*.—Agglutination in culture-formalized saline-serum mixt. and no agglutination in culture-formalized saline mixt.

(**b**) *Negative*.—No agglutination in culture-formalized saline-serum mixt. (Polyvalent flagellar antiserum does not contain agglutinins for antigens of some salmonellae isolated from foods. Neg. flagellar reactions occur with *Salmonella* serotypes whose corresponding agglutinins are not contained in the antisera (i.e., *S. simsbury*, z_{27}; *S. chittagong*, z_{35})).

(**c**) *Non-specific*.—Both mixts agglutinate. Requires addnl testing as in *Identification of Enterobacteriaceae*.

Cultures that give typical biochemical results as salmonellae but do not agglutinate in *Salmonella* flagellar (H) antisera must be tested to det. if sufficient flagellar (H) antigens are present. Test motility of culture as follows:

Inoculate petri dish contg motility test medium, **41.024(n)**, with 3 mm loopful TSI culture by stabbing medium once, 10 mm from edge of plate to depth of 2–3 mm. (Do not stab to bottom of plate with inoculum.) Do not inoculate any other portion of plate. Incubate 24 hr at 35°. When organism has migrated 40 mm or more toward other side of plate, it is sufficiently motile to retest.

Transfer 3 mm loopful of growth which migrated farthest from inoculation point into tube of tryptophane broth, **41.024(h)**. Incubate 24±2 hr at 35°. Retest this culture by adding ½ vol. formalized physiological saline soln, **41.025(g)**, and repeat *Salmonella* serological flagellar (H) test, **41.039** or **41.040**.

Incubate cultures that are not motile after first 24 hr incubation for addnl 24 hr at 35°. If still neg., incubate 5 days at 25° before classifying as non-motile (flagellar (H) antigen not detected).

Cultures that are non-motile or cultures that are *Salmonella* serological flagellar (H) test-neg., when retested, are classified according to results of other tests in *Identification of Enterobacteriaceae*.

41.040 "Spicer-Edwards" Flagellar (H) Test Tube Test

(Alternative to polyvalent flagellar (H) test tube test, **41.039**, to det. presence or absence of flagellar (H) antigens)

Test each culture, using each of the 7 "Spicer-Edwards" flagellar (H) antisera, **41.025(k)**. Perform test as in **41.039**, using 1 of the 7 "Spicer-Edwards" (H) antisera for each test instead of *Salmonella* polyvalent flagellar (H) antiserum. Since there are 7 "Spicer-Edwards" antisera, each culture must be tested 7 times.

Pos. agglutination indicates presence of flagellar (H) antigen. Identify by comparing pattern of agglutination reactions obtained with agglutinins known to be present in each of the 7 "Spicer-Edwards" (H) antisera. Results of these reactions are shown in Table 41:1, page 848.

If culture produces pos. agglutination when tested with each of the 4 "Spicer-Edwards" antisera 1, 2, 3 and 4 (4 plus pattern), then results indicate presence of non-specific antigen other than *Salmonella* antigen or presence of more than single *Salmonella* H antigen which cannot be identified with this antisera until antigens are sepd.

SELECTED REFERENCES

(*1*) JAOAC **22**, 625(1939).

(*2*) JAOAC **36**, 91, 316(1953).

(*3*) JAOAC **49**, 270, 276(1966); **51**, 865, 867(1968).

(*4*) Appl. Microbiol. **10**, 193(1962); JAOAC **51**, 1338(1968).

(*5*) JAOAC **50**, 753(1967); **51**, 870(1968); **52**, 455 (1969).

42. Microchemical Methods[★]

Molecular Weight (*1*)—Official First Action

Thermoelectric-Vapor Pressure Method

(Applicable to materials with molecular wts <500.)

42.001   *Apparatus and Reagents*

(**a**) *Molecular weight apparatus.*—Vapor pressure osmometer, Hewlett-Packard; molecular wt app., Hitachi Perkin-Elmer; isothermal distn app., Arthur H. Thomas Co.; or equiv. equipment using vapor pressure equilibrium technic. Instrument must use sensitive bridge system to measure temp. difference between solv. and test soln drops suspended on thermistors in constant temp. cell whose atm. is satd with solv. vapor.

(**b**) *Standards.*—Benzil, molecular wt 210.23, mp 94.5–95.5°, and C and H analyses within 0.2% of theoretical values (C, 79.99; H, 4.79). Recrystallize from EtOAc, acetone, or CHCl₃, if necessary.

If sample is ionizable salt sol. in H₂O, use reagent grade KCl as std. If sample is not a salt and sol. only in H₂O, use sucrose as std.

(**c**) *Solvents.*—Use reagent grade solv. from same lot and preferably from same bottle to sat. cell and to prep. sample and std solns. Solv. must completely dissolve sample, preferably without heating. (Proper choice of solv. and std is critical.) Preferred solvs are (number indicates order of choice):

	Nature of Sample				
Solvent	Un-known	Neu-tral	Acidic	Basic	Salt
Acetone	2	1	1	–	–
Ethyl acetate	1	2	2	1	–
Chloroform	3	3	–	2	–
Water	–	–	–	–	1

For samples not sol. in solvs listed, test solubility in H₂O (if thermistor wiring is completely encased in glass or plastic), *n*-heptane, and benzene. Other solvs that may be used are: alcohol, CCl₄, methylethyl ketone, dioxane, cyclohexane, CH₂Cl₂, dimethyl formamide, toluene, and acetonitrile. Use solvs such as esters, ketones, or alcohols for samples which tend to form dimers thru H bonding, e.g., org. acids.

42.002   *Determination*

Follow manufacturer's instructions including recommended concn range for solns, instrument operation, and reading of ΔR response.

[★] Methods so marked are surplus methods. *See* "Definitions of Terms and Explanatory Notes," item (29).

Adjust cell temp. so vapor pressure of solv. is 150–350 mm, preferably 200–300 mm. If instrument is not equipped to cool cell, cell temp. must be enough above ambient (ca 5°) so thermostatic control maintains constant cell temp.

Construct calibration curve with std and solv. to be used in analysis. Det. ΔR response at 4 std concns in recommended range and plot ΔR against mole fraction (MF). Prep. sample soln in recommended range and obtain 3 ΔR readings. Use median ΔR value to calc. molecular wt. If calibration curve is straight line, calc. molecular wt (MW) of sample by:

MW = (g solute)(MW solv.)(K − ΔR)/(ΔR)(g solv.), where K = (ΔR std)/(MF std) and MF std = [(g std)/(MW std)]/[(g std/MW std) + (g solv./MW solv.)]

If ΔR–MF plot yields curved line, interpolate MF of sample from calibration curve and calc. molecular wt by:

MW = (g solute)(MW solv.)(1 − MF)/(MF)(g solv.)

Bromine, Chlorine, and Iodine

Carius Combustion Method (2)—Official Final Action

(Do not alter combustion conditions such as temp., size of sample, vol. of acid, etc. Variations from specified conditions present dangerous explosion hazard.)

42.003   *Reagents*

(**a**) *Fuming nitric acid.*—Reagent grade, halogen-free, sp gr 1.50.

(**b**) *Silver nitrate.*—Reagent grade, powd.

42.004   *Apparatus (3)*

(**a**) *Combustion tubes.*—Fig. 42:1. Use clean, heavy- or std-wall Pyrex tubes, free from flaws, with round seal at bottom, and with following specifications. (Vol. HNO₃ and temp. depend on combustion tube used.)

Dimensions	Heavy Wall	Std Wall
Wall thickness, mm	2.3±0.3	1.2±0.2
Outside diam., mm	13±0.8	13±0.7
Length, mm	210±10	240±10
Length of sealed tube between bottom and start of taper at shoulder, mm	150–175	180–210
Vol. HNO₃ (sp gr 60°F, ca 1.5), ml	0.5	0.3
Temp., °C	250	300

853

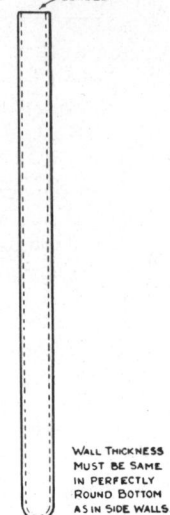

FIG. 42:1—Combustion tube

(b) *Furnace.*—Elec., to hold 4 or more tubes at ca 45° angle. Must maintain temp. of 250±10° or 300 ±10° for 5 hr or more, with ≤5° difference between any 2 points on a tube or 5° difference between similar points on any 2 tubes. Must have variable resistor or other device to adjust furnace to desired temp. Open end of furnace wells must have safety device to retain glass in furnace in case tube explodes, and device must be provided for removing individual tubes from wells (*2*).

(c) *Filter tubes.*—Micro 3 ml filter tube with medium-coarse porosity fritted disk (av. pore diam. 15–25 μm) (*3*).

(d) *Siphon.*—Make from 3 mm od glass tubing, with parallel arms, one 50 and other 250 mm long, and with 110 mm connecting section rising with 13° slope to longer arm (*3*).

42.005   *Sample*

Using microchemical balance, weigh 5–20 mg sample contg min. of 1.5 mg Cl, 2.5 mg Br, or 3.2 mg I; or using semimicrochemical balance, weigh 10–20 mg sample contg min. of 2.5 mg Cl, 4.5 mg Br, or 5.7 mg I.

(a) *Solid samples.*—Weigh by difference in weighing tube (*3*).

(b) *Viscous liquids or gummy solids.*—Weigh in porcelain boat.

(c) *Volatile liquids.*—Weigh in 5 cm sealed glass tube, 1–2 mm id with capillary tip. Break off tip of capillary before placing in combustion tube, sealed end down.

42.006   *Determination*

Place weighed sample in combustion tube, add powd AgNO₃ 100% in excess of amt estd to be necessary, and add 0.5±0.05 or 0.3±0.03 ml fuming HNO₃, depending on type of combustion tube, **42.004**(a). Using blast lamp and holding at 30–40° angle, slowly rotate tube in flame until wall thickens, pull out, and seal off narrow neck of tube. Wall of seal should be ≥¾ of thickness of tube wall and sealed tube should have length shown in table. (If sample and HNO₃ react at room temp., immediately cool bottom of tube in ice-H₂O or solid CO₂-acetone bath, remove, and seal at once.) Immediately place tube in furnace and heat 5 hr at 250 or 300±10°, according to tube size.

Observe following precautions before and during opening of combustion tubes: (*a*) Place asbestos glove on hand used to hold small burner or hand torch; (*b*) protect face by transparent face mask or work behind safety shield; (*c*) be certain tube has cooled to room temp., (*d*) force tip of tube ca 2″ out of furnace well; (*e*) gently flame end to drive all acid from tip and upper walls; and (*f*) soften tip with small hot flame until pressure in tube is released by blowing out softened glass.

Remove vented tube from furnace and cut off constricted end by scratching tube with file ca ½″ from shoulder of open end, moistening scratch, and touching with tip of very hot glass rod. Remove end of tube with care and fire polish to avoid contaminating ppt with glass splinters.

Rinse walls of tube with H₂O until tube is ca ¾ full, place in steam or boiling H₂O bath, protected from light, and digest until ppt coagulates (ca 30 min). Longer digestion is required for I than for Br or Cl since eutectic mixt. of AgNO₃ and AgI is formed, which melts below temp. of steam bath and persists as heavy yellow oil on bottom of tube. Stirring with glass rod speeds up soln of AgNO₃ and greatly reduces digestion time, which *must* be continued until ppt is in form of *fine powder*. If excessive amts of AgNO₃ have been used, greater dilns than specified are required for complete pptn. Therefore, after digestion appears complete, pipet few drops of clear supernatant aq. soln into test tube contg several ml H₂O. If turbidity occurs, entire supernatant must be dild with H₂O until pptn stops, and digestion to coagulate ppt must be repeated. If no turbidity occurs on diln, pipetted portion may be discarded.

Place previously washed, dried, and weighed filter tube in 1-hole stopper in suction flask, connect short arm of siphon to filter tube thru small rubber stopper, and adjust tube so that long arm of siphon almost touches ppt. Transfer ppt to filter tube by suction. Rinse tube and ppt alternately with 1% HNO₃ and alcohol, using 2 or 3 ml portions for each rinse.

Remove siphon, rinse tip and stopper with alcohol, and rinse filter tube and ppt first with the acid, then with alcohol. Wipe outside of filter tube with moist chamois (or cheesecloth) and dry 30 min at 125° in air oven or 30 min at 80° in vac. oven; cool to room temp. (ca 30 min) and weigh. Handle dry tube with chamois finger cots or tweezers. Make blank detn and subtract any correction from wt sample ppt.

$$(\text{wt ppt} - \text{blank}) \times \frac{Cl}{AgCl} \times \frac{100}{\text{wt sample}} = \% \; Cl$$

$$(\text{wt ppt} - \text{blank}) \times \frac{Br}{AgBr} \times \frac{100}{\text{wt sample}} = \% \; Br$$

$$(\text{wt ppt} - \text{blank}) \times \frac{I}{AgI} \times \frac{100}{\text{wt sample}} = \% \; I.$$

Carbon and Hydrogen (4)—Official Final Action

42.007   *Reagents*

(a) *Copper oxide.*—Wire form, ca 1 mm diam. and 3–4 mm long; discard material finer than "20-mesh." Ignite 1 hr at 800–900° before placing in combustion tube.

(b) *Platinum gauze, 52 mesh.*—From three 3×5 cm sections, make 3 rolls, each 30 mm long $\times$ 7 mm od. Boil 15 min in HNO_3 $(1 + 1)$ and ignite in non-luminous Bunsen flame.

(c) *Asbestos.*—Gooch asbestos; ignite 30 min at 800–900° and store in wide-mouth bottle.

(d) *Silver.*—Fine wire or ribbon; if tarnished, reduce in stream of H at 350–450°. (*Note:* H ignites explosively in O. Flush reduction app. with CO_2 or N before and after H use. Vent exhaust gas into effective fume removal device. Perform reduction behind safety barrier.)

(e) *Lead dioxide.*—Pellets, 1–2 mm diam., special grade for microanalysis; or prep. by digesting com. grade powder 2 hr in HNO_3, let stand 1 hr, decant, wash with H_2O until acid-free, evap. to dryness, and cut into 2 mm cubes. Roll cubes in jar to round corners and sieve out powder.

(f) *Glass wool.*—Pyrex, pliable.

(g) *Dehydrite or Anhydrone.*—$(Mg(ClO_4)_2$, anhyd.) Break pieces to <3 mm long; discard portion passing thru No. 40 sieve.

(h) *Ascarite.*—(NaOH on asbestos.) Use com. prepn of "8–20 mesh."

42.008   *Apparatus (See Fig. 42:2)*

(a) *Oxygen.*—Cylinder with pressure regulator adjustable from 0 to 10 lb pressure on low-pressure side and with needle-valve control.

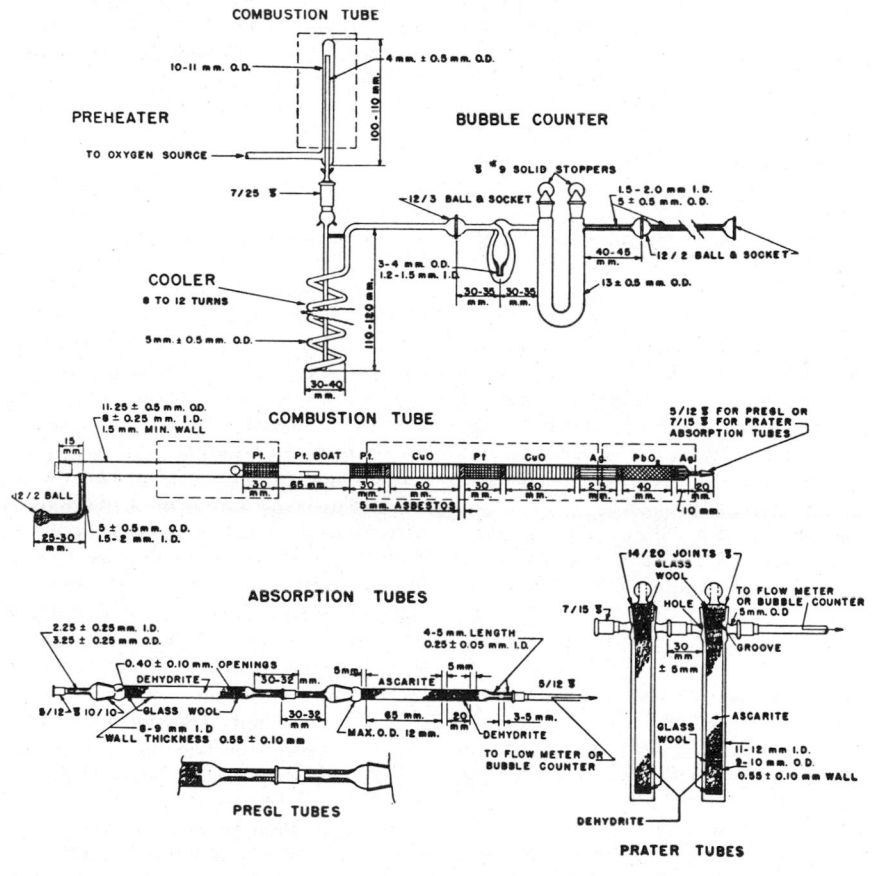

FIG. 42:2—Carbon and hydrogen apparatus

(b) *Preheater.*—Specifications as recommended by Committee on Microchemical Apparatus, Div. Anal. Chem. (ACS) (*3*), except with 12/2 ball joint. Rubber connectors may be used.

(c) *Bubble counter and U-tube.*—According to recommended specifications (*3*) except with ball joints. Rubber connectors may be used.

(d) *Combustion tube.*—Fused quartz (or Vycor) glass, dimensions according to recommended specifications but with 12/2 ball joint on side arm and 5/12 or 7/15 inner joint on exit end. Rubber connectors may be used. (Pyrex tubes may be used but furnace temps should be $\leq 725°$.)

(e) *Absorption tubes.*—Pregl type, according to recommended specifications (*3*) but with 5/12 joints; alternatively, Prater type, semimicro size with 7/15 joints. Rubber connectors may be used.

(f) *Bubble counter or flowmeter.*—Any convenient arrangement to measure 10–30 ml/min gas flow from exit end of second absorption tube.

(g) *Preheater furnace.*—Elec., 12–14 mm id $\times$ 5″ long, maintained at $600\pm25°$. Gas heaters may be used for all furnaces but specified temps should be maintained. Temps of furnaces are measured at center of furnace inside empty combustion tube with one end stoppered.

(h) *Burning furnace.*—Elec., 13–14 mm id $\times$ 4″ long. Furnace should reach 600–700° in 5 min, ca 800° in 15 min, with max. of 850° in 30 min. *See* (g).

(i) *Long furnace.*—Elec., 13–14 mm id $\times$ 8″ long; maintained at 775–800°. *See* (g).

(j) *Constant temperature mortar.*—Elec., 13–14 mm id $\times$ 3″ long, thermostatically controlled at $177\pm2°$. *See* (g).

42.009   *Preparation of Apparatus*

(a) *Preheater.*—Place CuO in preheater tube, connect spiral cooling coil, immerse coil in beaker of H_2O, and support assembly by suitable clamps and stand. Place furnace over preheater tube and maintain at ca 600°. Connect side arm of combustion unit to needle valve of O pressure regulator by suitable tubing, rubber or Tygon.

(b) *Bubble counter-U-tube.*—Fill bubble counter and U-tube by placing glass wool plug at bottom of U, fill side next to bubble counter with Dehydrite to within 12 mm of side arm, and cap with another glass wool plug. Place Ascarite layer in other side to within 38 mm of side arm; then insert glass wool plug, ca 25 mm of Dehydrite, and finally second plug. Cement in stoppers with glass cement or paraffin; then with medicine dropper add H_2SO_4 to bubbler until level is 3–4 mm above bubbler tip. Connect to preheater with pressure clamp.

(c) *Combustion tube.*—Clean and dry combustion tube. Place 10 mm roll of Ag in exit end with 1 or 2 strands reaching to open end of ground joint. Insert loose asbestos plug (not choking plug), 40 mm PbO_2, asbestos plug, and second Ag roll 25 mm long, which should extend into long furnace ca 12 mm. Insert as-bestos plug, 60 mm CuO, asbestos plug, 30 mm Pt gauze roll, asbestos plug, 60 mm CuO, asbestos plug, and finally 30 mm Pt gauze, which should extend about 10 mm beyond end of long furnace. Place prepd tube in furnaces with exit end protruding far enough beyond constant-temp. mortar to permit connecting absorption tubes. Connect side arm to bubble counter-U-tube.

(d) *Absorption tube.*—Place glass wool plug in end of H_2O absorption tube, fill tube to within 12 mm of other end with Dehydrite or Anhydrone, and cap with second glass wool plug. If Pregl tubes are used, seal ground-glass joint with enough glass cement to give clear seal, and remove any excess on outer surface of tube with cotton dipped in benzene or other solv. If Prater tubes are used, lubricate lower $\frac{2}{3}$ of inner joint with min. of light stopcock grease and insert in outer tube.

Prep. CO_2 absorption tube by placing glass wool plug in end and fill tube to ca 38 mm of other end with Ascarite. Insert 6 mm glass wool plug, add 20 mm layer of Dehydrite, and cap filling with another glass wool plug. Complete assembly of absorption tube as for H_2O absorption tube. Connect absorption tubes to combustion tube with ground joints (use no lubricant) or with special impregnated rubber tubing.

Attach calibrated bubble counter or flowmeter to exit end of CO_2 absorption tube.

42.010   *Determination*

(a) *Conditioning apparatus.*—Condition prepd and assembled app. by heating combustion tube 3–4 hr with long furnace at 775–800° and with O flowing thru app. at rate of 15–20 ml/min. Use 3–4 lb O pressure on low pressure side of regulator. At the same time, make 2 simulated sample burnings, without sample, with burning furnace at 825–850°. (Temp. must be ca 100° lower if Pyrex combustion tubes are used.)

Burn unweighed 10–15 mg sample to condition combustion and absorption tubes. With absorption tubes connected, adjust needle valve on regulator so that O flow is 15–20 ml/min and place burning furnace ca 75 mm from long furnace. Place micro Pt boat contg sample in combustion tube ca 50 mm from long furnace. Insert third Pt roll 25 mm from boat, and stopper tube. Turn on burning furnace and let it reach ca 600° before starting sample combustion by moving furnace over sample at rate of 25 mm in 6–8 min. Move burning furnace across sample only once, taking 18–24 min for full travel of furnace. Turn off burning furnace 5 min after it reaches long furnace but continue to sweep O thru tube for addnl 15 min before disconnecting absorption tubes.

Remove absorption tubes and place by balance to equilibrate. Handle tubes only with clean chamois finger cots. If Prater tubes are used, turn joints $\frac{1}{4}$ turn to seal. If rubber connections are used, wipe only tips of tubes with moist, then dry, chamois before placing them by balance. Wait 10 min if ground joints were used or 15 min if rubber connections were made; then weigh CO_2 absorption tube first and H_2O absorption tube next, using glass tare with vol. and surface ca equal to that of absorption tubes. Record wts of tubes and reconnect to combustion tube for subsequent analysis.

(b) *Proving the apparatus.*—Replace boat with one contg 10–15 mg sample of std compd such as NBS microchemical std, weighed to nearest 0.01 mg. Repeat combustion and weighing as in (a). Calc. % C and H in std sample from increase in wt of CO_2 and H_2O absorption tubes. Repeat analysis until results from 2 consecutive runs are within 0.30% of theoretical values and means of C and H results are within 0.20% of theoretical value for the std compd. (Humidity conditions of room may make it necessary to correct apparent wt of H_2O by subtracting a blank value.)

When app. meets this test, analyses of samples are made as above.

Fluorine (5)—Official Final Action

42.011   *Reagents*

(a) *Sodium alizarin sulfonate indicator.*—(Alizarin red S) 0.035% aq. soln.

(b) *Sodium fluoride std soln.*—0.01N. Dissolve 0.4200 g NaF in H_2O and dil. to 1 L.

(c) *Thorium nitrate std soln.*—0.01N. Dissolve 1.38 g $Th(NO_3)_4.4H_2O$ in H_2O and dil. to 1 L. Stdze by titrg against 0.01N NaF, using 1, 2, 3, 4, 5, 6, 7, 8, 9, and 10 ml portions and plotting curve.

42.012   *Apparatus*

(a) *Schöniger combustion flask.*—500 ml with filter paper carriers.

(b) *Distillation apparatus.*—See Fig. 42:3. Attach to steam generator. Steam enters thru joint. J_1, passes thru 2 concentric tubes, IT_1 and ET_1, and enters distn flask, D, thru 2 openings. Vapors enter condenser, C, which consists of 3 concentric tubes. In IT_2 and ET_2 vapors are condensed; in ET_3, cooling H_2O is circulated. Distillate drains off on right thru descending tube. Ground joint, J_2, serves as opening for addn of soln and as seat for thermometer which records temp. of liq., L. Elec. heating jacket, H, surrounds section of distn flask contg liq. and is prepd from 600 cm Nichrome wire, W, of 2.120 ohms/foot, 420 cm of which is wound on 48 mm diam. glass cylinder covered with Al foil and asbestos, then covered with insulating cement, asbestos, and another layer of cement. Jacket is held in place with ring, R, and temp. is controlled with 7.5 amp variable transformer.

42.013   *Determination*

(a) *In absence of arsenic, mercury, and phosphorus.* —Place sample contg 0.5–0.7 mg F on filter paper carrier. (Weigh liq. samples in gelatin or Me cellulose capsules and place closed capsule on paper carrier.)

Add ca 15–20 mg Na_2O_2, wrap mixt. in filter paper, and place in Pt basket carrier in stopper of Schöniger flask. Place 20 ml H_2O in flask, introduce O several min, ignite sample, and immediately insert into flask. (*Note:* Use safety barrier and reinforced gloves. Remote control igniting device is also available.) After combustion is complete, shake vigorously until cloudiness disappears, and let flask stand undisturbed ca 15 min to ensure complete absorption of oxidn products. (If enough I is present to give yellow soln, warm on steam bath to dispel color.) Wash soln into titrg vessel, adjust to pH 3.0±0.05 with 1N and 0.1N HCl and 0.1N NaOH, using pH meter, and add 2 ml Na alizarin sulfonate indicator. (pH adjustment is critical since alizarin sulfonate is also acid-base indicator.) Titr. with std $Th(NO_3)_4$ soln to pink end point, preferably using photoelec. photometer with 520 nm filter, using entire soln rather than aliquot. If visual titrn is used, compare color with controls in fluorescent light. Det. mg F from std curve and calc. %F = mg F × 100/mg sample.

(b) *In presence of arsenic, mercury, and phosphorus.*—Burn sample as in (a) and transfer soln to distn app. thru joint J_2 with as little H_2O as possible. Add 20 ml 70–72% $HClO_4$, 1 ml 25% $AgClO_4$, and ca 12 glass beads. Heat mixt. by means of jacket, and as temp. rises, start steam generation. Maintain temp. of mixt. at 135±2° after raising temp. to this

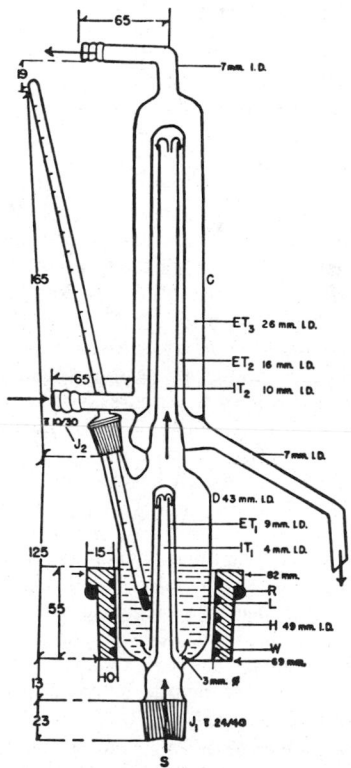

FIG. 42:3—Upper section of distilling apparatus. From Anal. Chem. 29, 141(1957)

point as quickly as possible by adjusting transformer. Collect distillate in 250 ml. vol flask. (Practice is required for successful manipulation of distn. To avoid sucking back of soln, keep vol. in flask at min. and keep steam generation constant. Addn of phthln and small amt of $0.1N$ NaOH to generator provides means of detg if suck-back has occurred.) (Clean distn app. between detns by replacing steam generator with bottle or flask connected to suction and immersing distillate delivery tube in F-free H_2O, which is sucked thru entire system.)

Transfer distillate to titrg vessel, adjust to pH 3.0 ± 0.05, add 2 ml Na alizarin sulfonate indicator, and titr. as in (a).

Nitrogen (6)

Micro-Kjeldahl Method—Official Final Action
(Not applicable to material contg N–N
or N–O linkages)

42.014   **Reagents**

(a) *Sulfuric acid.*—Sp gr 1.84, N-free.

(b) *Mercuric oxide.*—N-free.

(c) *Potassium sulfate.*—N-free.

(d) *Sodium hydroxide-sodium thiosulfate soln.*— Dissolve 60 g NaOH and 5 g $Na_2S_2O_3.5H_2O$ in H_2O and dil. to 100 ml or add 25 ml 25% $Na_2S_2O_3.5H_2O$ to 100 ml 50% NaOH soln.

(e) *Boric acid soln.*—Satd soln.

(f) *Indicator soln.*—(1) *Methyl red-methylene blue.* —Mix 2 parts 0.2% alc. Me red soln with 1 part 0.2% alc. methylene blue soln; or (2) *Methyl red-bromocresol green soln.*—Mix 1 part 0.2% alc. Me red soln with 5 parts 0.2% alc. bromocresol green soln.

(g) *Hydrochloric acid.*—$0.02N$. Prep. as in **45.012** and stdze as in **45.016** or **45.018**.

42.015   *Apparatus (7)*

(a) *Digestion rack.*—Use rack with either gas or elec. heaters which will supply enough heat to 30 ml flask to cause 15 ml H_2O at 25° to come to rolling boil in ≥ 2 but <3 min.

(b) *Distillation apparatus.*—Use one-piece or Parnas-Wagner distn app. recommended by Committee on Microchemical Apparatus, ACS (7).

(c) *Digestion flasks.*—Use 30 ml regular Kjeldahl or Solty's type flasks (7). For small samples, 10 ml Kjeldahl flasks may be used.

42.016   *Determination*

Weigh sample requiring 3–10 ml 0.01 or $0.02N$ HCl and transfer to 30 ml digestion flask. If sample wt is <10 mg, use micro balance. (Wt should be ≤ 100 mg dry org. matter.) Use charging tube for dry solids, porcelain boat for sticky solids or nonvolatile liqs, and capillary or capsule for volatile liqs. Add 1.9 ± 0.1 g K_2SO_4, 40 ± 10 mg HgO, and 2.0 ± 0.1 ml H_2SO_4. If sample wt is >15 mg, add addnl 0.1 ml H_2SO_4 for each 10 mg dry org. matter >15 mg. Make certain that acid has sp gr of at least 1.84 if sample contains nitriles. (10 ml flasks and ½ quan-

tities of reagents may be used for samples <7 mg.) Add boiling chips which pass No. 10 sieve. If boiling time for digestion rack heaters is 2–2.5 min, digest 1 hr after all H_2O is distilled and acid comes to true boil; if boiling time is 2.5–3 min, digest 1.5 hr. (Digest 0.5 hr if sample is known to contain no refractory ring N.)

Cool, add min. quantity of H_2O to dissolve solids, cool, and place thin film of Vaseline on rim of flask. Transfer digest and boiling chips to distn app. and rinse flask 5 or 6 times with 1–2 ml portions H_2O. Place 125 ml Phillips beaker or erlenmeyer contg 5 ml satd H_3BO_3 soln and 2–4 drops indicator under condenser with tip extending below surface of soln. Add 8–10 ml NaOH-$Na_2S_2O_3$ soln to still, collect ca 15 ml distillate, and dil. to ca 50 ml. (Use 2.5 ml H_3BO_3 and 1–2 drops indicator, and dil. to ca 25 ml if $0.01N$ HCl is to be used.) Titr. to gray end point or first appearance of violet. Make blank detn and calc. % N = [(ml HCl − ml blank) × normality × 14.007 × 100]/mg sample.

Oxygen (8)—Official Final Action

42.017   *Principles*

Org. O compds are thermally decomposed in inert atm. to H_2O, CO, and CO_2. At 1120° following reactions are complete: $C + CO_2 \rightarrow 2CO$; $H_2O + C \rightarrow H_2 + CO$. The CO is converted to CO_2 by reaction with CuO and CO_2 is detd gravimetrically.

42.018   *Reagents*

(a) *Copper oxide.*—See **42.007**(a).

(b) *Ascarite.*—See **42.007**(h).

(c) *Dehydrite or Anhydrone.*—See **42.007**(g).

(d) *Nitrogen.*—Purify high purity N by passing thru series of scrubbing bottles contg different solid desiccants ($CaCl_2$, anhyd. $Mg(ClO_4)_2$, and P_2O_5), then thru tube contg closely packed reduced Cu turnings at 600°, thru Anhydrone, and finally thru bubble counter and U-tube.

(e) *Carbon.*—Wyex Compact Black, J. M. Huber, Inc., or equiv., 30–80 mesh, available from Arthur H. Thomas Co. Purify by digesting with HCl. Add large quantity H_2O, stir mech., let C settle, and decant H_2O. Repeat until H_2O wash is Cl-free. Dry C, place in quartz tube, and heat in slow stream of N, (d), several hr, increasing temp. gradually to 550°.

(f) *Quartz chips.*—Clean chips with HF, rinse with H_2O, and dry in oven.

42.019   *Apparatus (See Figs. 42:4 and 42:5)*

(a) *Long stationary furnace, 675°.*—**42.008**(i) except maintained at $675\pm5°$; (A).

(b) *Long stationary furnace, 1120°.*—See (c); (B).

(c) *Short movable furnace, 1120°.*—This furnace (C), and that in (b) may be available as unit.

(d) *Nitrogen purification train.*—Preheater furnace (D), **42.008**(g), with section of combustion

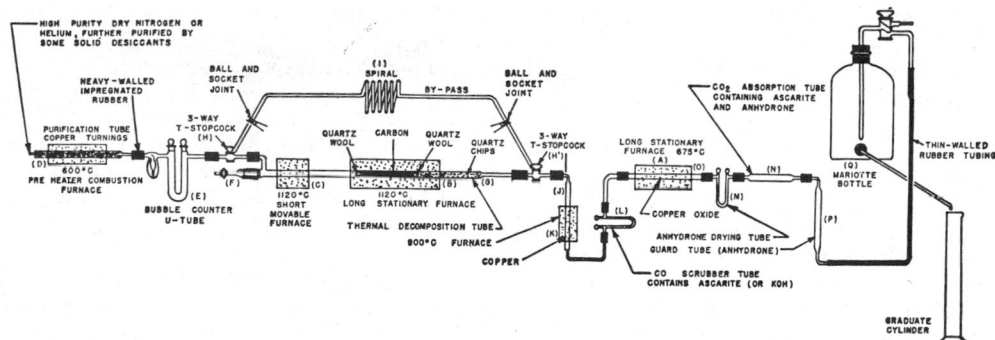

FIG. 42:4—Gravimetric setup for oxygen determination. (Note: (1) All rubber connections made of heavy-walled impregnated rubber except Mariotte bottle. (2) Tubes marked (M) and (L) may be replaced with regulation absorption tubes)

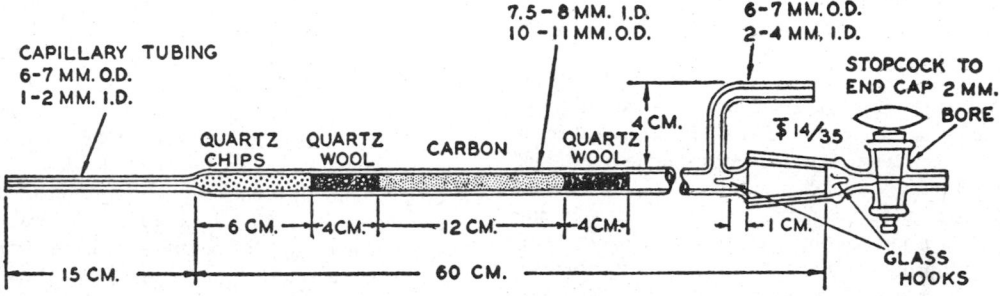

FIG. 42:5—Quartz reaction tube and filling for oxygen determination

tubing, Pyrex glass No. 1720 or equiv., packed with ca 10 cm reduced Cu turnings.

(**e**) *Bubble counter and U-tube.*—See **42.008**(c) and **42.009**(b).

(**f**) *Cap.*—⨍ 14/35 cap with 2 mm stopcock; (*F*).

(**g**) *Thermal decomposition tube.*—Clear fused quartz, solar radiation grade, 7.5–8 mm id, 10–11 mm od, and 60 cm long, exclusive of capillary tube; (*G*). At one end is ⨍ 14/35 male joint. About 1 cm from joint is bent side arm, 6–7 mm od and 2–4 mm id. At other end is 15 cm capillary tube 6–7 mm od and 1–2 mm id. Wash tube with HF and H_2O, and dry.

Fill tube as shown in Fig. 42:5, with repeated tapping to avoid channeling. The C must *at all times* be in section of furnace that is at 1120°.

(**h**) *By-pass stopcocks.*—3 way T-type with ⨍ ball joint on side arm; (*H*) and (*H′*).

(**i**) *Spiral by-pass tube.*—Glass tube (*I*), contg spiral, for flexibility, and ⨍ socket joints on each end. Length should be sufficient to connect to ⨍ ball joints on ⨍ stopcocks, (*H*) and (*H′*).

(**j**) *Quartz tube.*—Filled with reduced Cu; (*J*).

(**k**) *Short stationary furnace, 900°.*—**42.008**(h), except capable of maintaining 900°; (*K*).

(**l**) *Scrubber tube.*—Any type of drying tube fitted with crushed KOH pellets or Ascarite, (*L*), for removing halogens and S.

(**m**) *Drying tube.*—See **42.008**(e), or use U-tube. Fill with Anhydrone only, as in **42.009**(d); (*M*).

(**n**) *Carbon dioxide absorption tube.*—Fill with Ascarite and Anhydrone as in **42.009**(d); (*N*).

(**o**) *Oxidation tube.*—Tube, 30–40 cm, exclusive of tip, similar to that in (**d**) except packed with ca 25 cm CuO wire. Let 5 cm extend beyond furnace. Maintain at 675±5° to oxidize CO to CO_2; (*O*).

(**p**) *Guard tube.*—Glass tube 110–120 mm × 10–12 mm od, 1 mm wall, contg Anhydrone; (*P*).

(**q**) *Mariotte bottle.*—Glass 2 L bottle. Place 1-hole rubber stopper in top of bottle. Insert glass tube to 7–10 cm of bottom of bottle. Attach 3-way stopcock to top of tube. In bottom opening insert 1-hole rubber stopper contg drain tube to 1 L graduate. Fill bottle with H_2O; (*Q*).

(**r**) *Safety trap.*—Gas washing bottle, 125 ml, Drechsel tall form, Kimble Products No. 15060 or equiv. Connect T-tube to top of center tube. Fill bottle ca ⅓ with Hg and connect by T-tube between preheater and N supply. (Gas pressure valve, Friedrich, or other regulator may also be used.)

(**s**) *Nitrogen tank.*—Use tank of high purity N equipped with pressure reducing valve, and safety valve to blow off at set pressure.

42.020   *Assembling Apparatus*

Assemble as in Fig. 42:4, starting with N tank (**s**), not shown, and connecting as follows, using ground glass joints and paraffin-impregnated heavy-wall tubing: Safety trap (**r**), not shown; purification train (*D*); bubble counter and U-tube (*E*); thermal decomposition tube (*G*); spiral by-pass tube (*I*); quartz tube (*J*); U-tube (*L*); oxidn tube (*O*); drying tube (*M*); CO_2 absorption tube (*N*); guard tube (*P*); and Mariotte bottle (*Q*).

42.021   *Conditioning Apparatus*

Assemble app. up to CO_2 absorption tube; set various furnaces in place. Pass slow stream of N (10 ml/min) thru system 1–2 hr at *room temp.* Heat all units to specified temps and continue N stream 2 days. Attach remainder of app. with arm of Mariotte bottle slightly below horizontal, and adjust ht of Hg in safety trap (**r**) to obtain 10 ml N/min thru system with all parts at operating temp. Record rates of bubble flow thru bubble counter and Mariotte bottle.

C in thermal decomposition tube (**g**) must be at 1120°. Best results are obtained by keeping furnaces at specified temp. at all times, even when not in use.

42.022   *Determination*

Adjust N flow to 10 ml/min with all furnaces heated to specified temp. Cool short movable furnace (*C*) to room temp. Weigh enough sample to produce 1.0–1.3 mg O; if solid, weigh directly in Pt boat; if liq., weigh in capillary tube, preferably quartz, and insert in Coombs-Alber Pt sleeve or long Pt boat. Turn stopcocks (*H*) and (*H′*) and open stopcock on cap (*F*) to let N flow in reverse direction thru tube (*G*). Remove cap (*F*), and insert Pt boat contg sample to within ca 7 cm of long furnace (*B*) with aid of Pt hook on end of glass rod. Immediately replace cap (*F*) with its stopcock open and let reverse flow of N continue ca 20 min to expel all air.

Weigh CO_2 absorption tube (*N*) as in **42.010** and attach in position. Close stopcock on cap (*F*) and turn stopcocks (*H*) and (*H′*) so N flows forward thru decomposition tube (*G*). Open stopcock on Mariotte bottle (*Q*) and let N flow thru entire system at 10 ml/min. Heat movable furnace (*C*) to ca 1120°, move to within ca 3 cm of sample, and turn on automatic drive to pyrolyze sample slowly. About 25–30 min is required for furnace (*C*) to reach furnace (*B*). Move furnace forward and heat parts of tube insulated by walls of furnaces 5–10 min to pyrolyze any material condensed in cooler portions of tube. Return furnaces to original positions. Let furnace (*C*) cool. Continue flow of N until ca 700 ml has passed thru from beginning of pyrolysis, using exactly same amt in detn and blank. Remove CO_2 absorption tube *N*, and reweigh as in **42.010.**

Perform blank detn with empty Pt boat and subtract wt CO_2 of blank from that of detn. (Well-functioning app. gives zero blank.)

$$\% \ O = Wt \ CO_2 \times 0.3635 \times 100/wt \ sample.$$

42.023   *Cleaning Reaction Tube*

When visibility becomes poor on thermal decomposition tube from deposited C, remove as follows: With entire app. assembled (with absorption tube

and Mariotte bottle attached), close stopcock (*H*) to both (*G*) and (*I*). Turn stopcock (*H′*) to connect (*G*) to (*J*). Open cap stopcock (*F*), lower arm of Mariotte bottle, and suck air thru reaction tube. Heat movable furnace to 1120° and move it over against long furnace. C will be burned off in few min. Close stopcock of cap (*F*), and turn stopcock (*H*) to connect reaction tube (*G*) with N supply. Pass N thru system overnight to remove air.

Phosphorus (9)—Official Final Action

42.024   *Reagents*

(**a**) *Nitric-sulfuric acid mixture.*—Slowly pour 420 ml HNO_3 into 580 ml H_2O; then slowly add 30 ml H_2SO_4.

(**b**) *Ammonium nitrate soln.*—2%. Prep. 2% soln of NH_4NO_3 in H_2O, add 2 drops HNO_3, and store in g-s bottle. Filter immediately before use.

(**c**) *Molybdate reagent.*—Dissolve 150 g powd NH_4 molybdate in 400 ml H_2O and cool under tap. Place 50 g $(NH_4)_2SO_4$ in 1 L vol. flask, dissolve in mixt. of 105 ml H_2O and 395 ml HNO_3, and cool under tap. Pour cooled molybdate soln slowly into $(NH_4)_2SO_4$ soln with constant stirring and cooling under tap. Dil. soln to 1 L, store in refrigerator 3 days, filter, and store in .paraffin-lined, g-s, brown bottle in refrigerator. Filter reagent immediately before use and check by periodically analyzing std sample.

42.025   *Apparatus*

(**a**) *Kjeldahl digestion flasks (30 ml), rack, and manifold.*—See **42.015**(a) and (c).

(**b**) *Filter tubes and filtration assembly.*—See **42.004**(c) and (d).

(**c**) *Rubber stoppers.*—Two or three small, solid rubber stoppers to loosen ppt from walls of flask.

42.026   *Determination*

Weigh 3–20 mg sample, depending on P content and whether micro or semimicro balance is used (max. wt ppt = 50 mg). Weigh in charging tube, if possible, and transfer to Kjeldahl flask. Use porcelain boat for sticky solids and viscous liqs, and glass capillary for volatile liqs.

Add 0.5 ml H_2SO_4 followed by 4–5 drops HNO_3. Heat on digestion rack to white SO_3 fumes and cool under tap. Add 4–5 drops HNO_3, repeat digestion, and cool under tap. Add 4–5 drops HNO_3 and again digest to SO_3 fumes. Cool to room temp.; add 2 ml acid mixt., (**a**), and 12.5 ml H_2O, rinsing down neck of flask. (If porcelain boat was used to add sample, remove boat with Pt wire; if glass capillary was used, filter digestion mixt. to remove capillary. Rinse filter and boat or capillary with 12.5 ml H_2O used to dil. sample.)

Place flask on steam bath 15 min to convert P to H_3PO_4. Remove from steam bath and pipet 15 ml molybdate reagent, (**c**), into center of digest, not down walls of flask. Let stand 2–3 min; then gently swirl to mix contents, being careful to prevent reagents from splashing on neck of flask. Cover flask and set in dark place overnight.

Condition filter tube as described below and weigh empty tube. Connect tared filter tube to filtration assembly and transfer ppt to filter thru siphon tube. Wash flask alternately with 1–2 ml portions of the NH_4NO_3 soln and alcohol. Add 2–3 small rubber stoppers to digestion flask, shake to loosen any ppt, and transfer with the NH_4NO_3 soln and alcohol. Disconnect siphon tube; rinse ppt from tip and stopper into filter tube with the NH_4NO_3 soln and alcohol. Wash ppt with more NH_4NO_3 soln, alcohol, and finally with acetone, and suck dry. Wipe filter tube with chamois skin, place in vertical position in vac. desiccator contg no desiccant, and evacuate to 1 mm for 30 min with mech. vac. pump in continuous operation. Release vac. and weigh *immediately* to nearest 0.1 mg. (Rapid weighing is essential because of hygroscopic nature of ppt.)

mg ppt $\times$ 0.014524 $\times$ 100/mg sample = %P.

Sulfur

Titrimetric Carius Combustion Method (10)—Official Final Action

(Not applicable in presence of P)

42.027   **Reagents**

(a) *Fuming nitric acid.*—Reagent grade, sp gr 1.50.

(b) *Sodium chloride.*—Reagent grade, fine crystals.

(c) *Barium choride soln.*—Approx. 0.02N. Stdze by titrg 5–7 mg freshly dried K_2SO_4, ACS (weighed to nearest 0.01 mg), by method used for sample titrn. Correct titrn for indicator error by blank detn.

(d) *Potassium sulfate.*—ACS, powd and dried.

(e) *Phenolphthalein soln.*—0.5% soln in 50% alcohol.

(f) *Sulfate indicator.*—"THQ" sulfate indicator (Betz Labs, Inc., 4636 Somerton Rd, Trevose, PA 19047) or mix 0.1 g K rhodizonate with 15 g sucrose by grinding in mortar.

42.028   **Apparatus**

(a) *Combustion tubes and furnace.*—See 42.004(a) and (b).

(b) *Titration assembly.*—5 ml buret graduated in 0.01 ml; rectangular titrn cell ca 2 $\times$ 4 $\times$ 5 cm with min. capacity of 50 ml; and std orange-red glass color filter (Corning Glass Works No. 3482, lantern shade yellow) selected to have 37% T at 550 nm. Place cell and filter side by side on milk glass window illuminated from below, preferably by fluorescent light. Mask light source so that only cells and filter are illuminated.

42.029   **Sample**

Using microchemical balance, weigh 5–20 mg sample contg $\geq$0.75 mg S, or using semimicrochem-

ical balance, weigh 10–20 mg sample contg $\geq$0.75 mg S (1.5 mg for gravimetric detn). Weigh samples as in 42.005.

42.030   **Determination**

Place weighed sample in combustion tube, add NaCl 100% in excess of amt equiv. to S in sample, and proceed as in 42.006, beginning "and add ... fuming HNO_3 ..." thru end of third par. "... with glass splinters."

Transfer contents of tube to 50 ml beaker, rinsing tube 4–6 times with 3–5 ml portions H_2O. Evap. to dryness on steam bath.

Dissolve residue in 10 ml H_2O, pour soln into titrn cell, add 1 drop phthln, and make just alk. with ca 0.1N NaOH, then acid with ca 0.02N HCl, adding 1 drop excess. Add ca 0.15 g of the sulfate indicator, stir to dissolve, and rinse beaker 2 or 3 times, using enough alcohol so that final soln contains ca 50%. Titr. with std $BaCl_2$ soln from 5 ml buret until stable color of soln immediately after stirring matches std glass color filter. Make certain end point taken is real and not pseudo end point which fades on standing 1–2 min. Det. blank on reagents and correct titrn.

$$(ml\ BaCl_2 - ml\ blank) \times normality \times 16.032$$
$$\times 100/wt\ sample\ (mg) = \% S$$

Gravimetric Carius Combustion Method (11)—Official Final Action

(Applicable in presence of P)

42.031   **Apparatus (3)**

Crucible and filter stick.—Porcelain crucible, ca 15 ml capacity, with black inside glaze, wt ca 10 g; with porcelain filter stick, with unglazed bottom, wt ca 2 g.

42.032   **Determination**

Dissolve residue, 42.030, in 3 ml H_2O, pour into previously ignited and weighed (with filter stick) porcelain crucible, and rinse beaker with four 2 ml portions H_2O. Place crucible on steam bath until soln is near bp. If vol. exceeds 10–11 ml, evap. to this vol. Add dropwise 0.5 ml 10% $BaCl_2$ soln (1 ml for samples contg >5 mg S), digest at least 15 min, and cool 15 min.

Connect porcelain filter, previously ignited and weighed with crucible, to arm of siphon with rubber tubing. Connect other arm of siphon to suction flask thru rubber stopper. Lower filter into crucible, slowly draw off soln, and rinse ppt, walls of crucible, and filter with five or six 3 ml portions HCl (1 + 300), drawing off as much liq. as possible. Carefully detach filter, place in crucible, wipe outside of crucible and end of filter with moist chamois or cheesecloth, and handle thereafter with crucible tongs. Place crucible and filter in larger crucible and dry in oven 10 min at ca 110°. Ignite in muffle 10 min at 700–750° (ppt may also be ignited by heating larger crucible contg crucible and filter to dull red heat with Meker burner), cool on metal block 30 min or in desiccator 1 hr, and weigh. Det. blank on reagents.

(wt BaSO$_4$ − blank) × 0.1374

$$× 100/\text{wt sample} = \% \text{ S}$$

42.033 ★ Titrimetric Catalytic Combustion Method (10)— Official Final Action ★

See 38.031–38.034, 10th ed.

42.034 ★ Gravimetric Catalytic Combustion Method (11)— Official Final Action ★

See 38.035, 10th ed.

Alkoxyl Groups (12)—Official Final Action
42.035   Reagents

(a) *Acetic acid-potassium acetate-bromine soln.*— Dissolve 10 g KOAc in enough HOAc to make 100 ml, and add 3 ml Br.

(b) *Sodium acetate soln.*—Dissolve 25 g NaOAc .3H$_2$O in enough H$_2$O to make 100 ml.

(c) *Starch indicator.*—Mix ca 2 g finely powd potato starch with cold H$_2$O to thin paste; add ca 200 ml boiling H$_2$O, stirring constantly. Add ca 1 ml Hg, shake, and let soln stand over the Hg.

(d) *Sodium thiosulfate std soln.*—0.02N. Prep. daily by dilg 0.1N soln, 45.038–45.039.

(e) *Hydriodic acid.*—Place 250 ml constant boiling (57%) HI (sp gr 1.7) in 500 ml r-b flask connected by ⌐̄ joint to air condenser, and reflux 2 hr while stream of CO$_2$ or N bubbles thru from glass tube extending to bottom. Do not let acid vapors come in contact with org. material. As soon as refluxing stops, discontinue gas flow. Cool, and store in g-s bottle.

42.036   Apparatus

Use modified Clark app., Figs. 42:6 and 42:7.

42.037   Determination

Fill scrubber half way with NaOAc soln, and fill receiver ⅔ full with freshly prepd KOAc-Br soln. Weigh enough sample in Pt boat to require ca 8 ml Na$_2$S$_2$O$_3$ soln in detn, and place in bottom of boiling flask. Add 2.5 ml melted *phenol* from wide-tip pipet and 5 ml of the HI, and connect boiling flask. Pass CO$_2$ thru app. from side arm of flask at uniform rate of 15 ml/min. Let reaction mixt. remain at room temp. 30 min. With manteled micro burner, boil liq. at such rate that vapors of boiling liq. rise into condenser, but not more than half way; continue boiling 60 min (first 30 min with H$_2$O circulating thru condenser and last 30 min with H$_2$O drained from condenser). Disconnect flask, remove receiver, and rinse delivery tube and contents of receiver into 125 ml

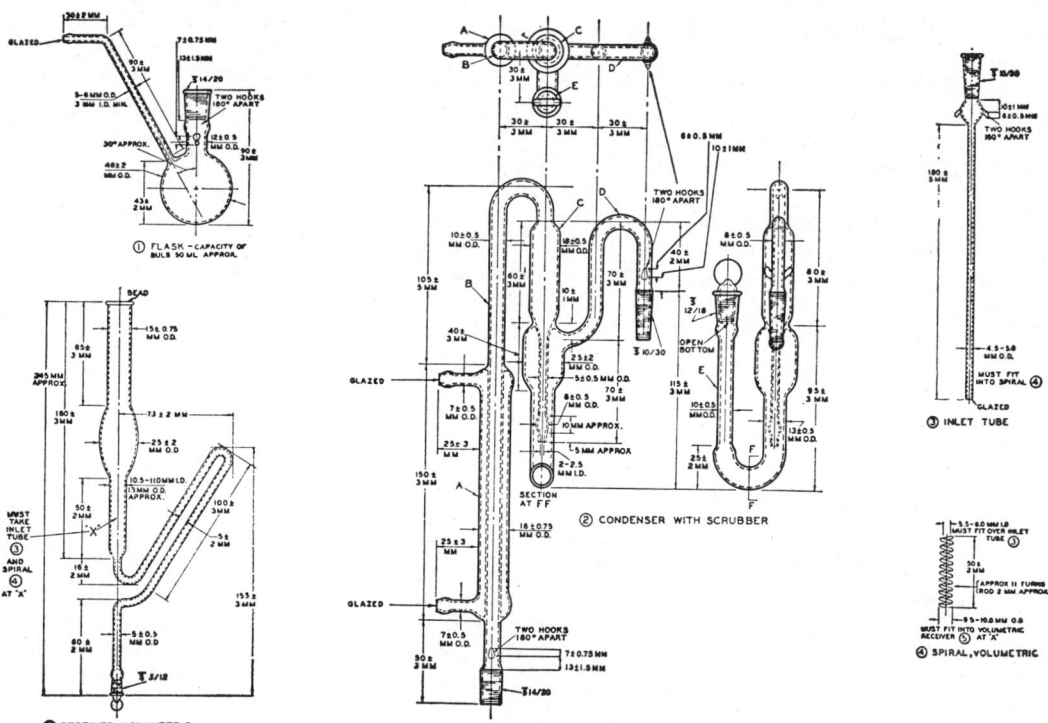

FIG. 42:6—Details of modified Clark apparatus

erlenmeyer contg 5 ml NaOAc soln. Adjust vol. to ca 50 ml and add *formic acid* dropwise until excess Br is destroyed.

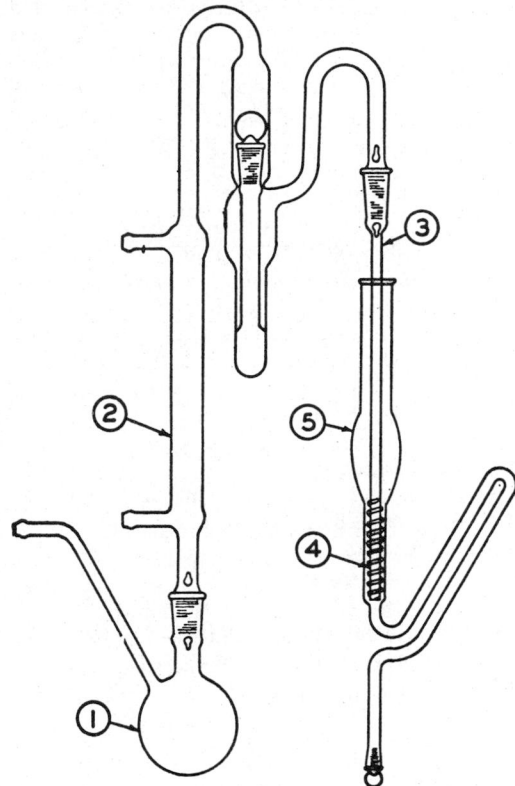

FIG. 42:7—Modified Clark apparatus

Remove any Br vapors by blowing air over liq.; then add 0.5 g KI and 5 ml 10% H_2SO_4. Swirl soln to dissolve KI and mix contents; then titr. liberated I with the $Na_2S_2O_3$ soln, using starch indicator as in stdzn.

Det. blank on all reagents by making detn without sample and calc. % alkoxyl group as follows:

(ml in detn − ml in blank) × normality × equiv.
wt × 100/sample wt in mg = % alkoxyl group

Equiv. wt: methoxyl = 5.17; ethoxyl = 7.51.

SELECTED REFERENCES

(*1*) JAOAC **51,** 1231(1968); **52,** 430(1969).
(*2*) JAOAC **35,** 291(1952); **36,** 91, 319(1953); **40,** 381(1957); **41,** 297(1958); Anal. Chem. **23,** 1689(1951).
(*3*) Anal. Chem. **21,** 1555(1949).
(*4*) JAOAC **32,** 561(1949); **34,** 94, 607(1951); Anal. Chem. **23,** 911(1951).
(*5*) JAOAC **44,** 258(1961).
(*6*) JAOAC **32,** 561(1949); **33,** 179(1950); **43,** 689 (1960).
(*7*) Anal. Chem. **23,** 523(1951).
(*8*) Steyermark, A., "Quantitative Organic Microanalysis," 2nd Ed., Academic Press, New York (1961); JAOAC **46,** 559(1963).
(*9*) JAOAC **40,** 386(1957).
(*10*) JAOAC **35,** 305(1952); **36,** 91, 335(1953).
(*11*) JAOAC **38,** 377(1955).
(*12*) JAOAC **39,** 108, 401(1956).

43. Radioactivity*

43.001 ★ Qualitative Test— ★
Official Final Action
(Applicable to solids)
See **40.001,** 10th ed. (alpha ray electroscope).

Quantitative Methods

43.002 ★ *Emanation or Radon Method* ★
(1)—Official Final Action
(Applicable only to Ra in quantities $<10^{-9}$ g. Limit is arbitrary, depending on particular equipment used and accuracy required.)
See **40.002–40.005,** 10th ed. (*Caution: See* **46.011** and **46.025.**)

43.003 ★ *Gamma Ray Method Using* ★
Electroscope (2)—Official Final Action
(Applicable only to Ra in quantities $>10^{-5}$ g. Limit is arbitrary, depending on particular equipment used and accuracy required.)
See **40.006–40.010,** 10th ed.

43.004 ★ *Gamma Ray Method Using* ★
Geiger-Muller Counter (3)—Official Final Action
(Applicable only to Ra in quantities $>10^{-7}$ g. Limit is arbitrary, depending on particular equipment used and accuracy required.)
See **40.011–40.015,** 10th ed.

Tritium in Water (4)—Official First Action

43.005 *Principle*

Sample is distd to remove quenching materials and nonvolatile radioactive materials. Distn is to dryness to ensure complete transfer of ^{3}H to distillate. Aliquot of distillate is mixed with scintillation soln and counted in liq. scintillation spectrometer (coincidence-type). Std ^{3}H and background samples are prepd and counted alternately to nullify errors produced by aging of scintillation medium or instrument drift.

43.006 *Apparatus*

(a) *Liquid scintillation spectrometer.* — Coincidence-type. Available from Nuclear-Chicago Corp., 333 E. Howard Ave, Des Plaines, IL 60018, Packard Instrument Co., 2200 Warrenville Rd, Downers Grove, IL 60515, and others.

(b) *Liquid scintillation vial.*—20 ml; low-K glass,

polyethylene, nylon, or equiv. bottles, available from manufacturers under (**a**).

43.007 *Reagents*

(a) *Scintillation soln.*—Thoroly mix 4 g PPO (2,5-diphenyloxazole), 0.05 g POPOP (1,4-di-2-(5-phenyloxazolyl) benzene), and 120 g solid naphthalene in 1 L spectral grade 1,4-dioxane. (Available from manufacturers under **43.006**(**a**).) Store in dark bottles. Soln is stable 2 months.

(b) *Tritium std soln.*—Pipet 4 ml H$_2$O of known ^{3}H activity and 16 ml scintillation soln into scintillation vial, cover vial tightly with screw cap, and mix thoroly by shaking.

(c) *Background soln.*—Mix 4 ml distd H$_2$O (free of ^{3}H activity to be measured in samples) with 16 ml scintillation soln as in (**b**).

43.008 *Preparation of Sample*

Distill 20–30 ml sample to dryness. Mix 4 ml sample distillate with 16 ml scintillation soln as in **43.007**(**b**).

43.009 *Determination*

Dark-adapt and cool sample, background, and std solns ca 3 hr in instrument freezer at $>2°$ (to prevent solidification of soln with time), or at ambient temp. if ambient temp. liq. scintillation spectrometer is used, prior to counting. Count solns for total of 200,000 counts or 100 min, whichever is sooner.

43.010 *Calculation*

Counting efficiency, $E = (S - B)/D$; ^{3}H, pCi (picocuries)/ml $= (C - B)/(E \times 4 \times 2.22)$, where S = gross cpm (counts/min) of std, B = cpm background, D = dpm (disintegrations/min) of ^{3}H activity in std, and C = gross cpm for sample.

Radioactive Contamination—Procedure
Emergency Level Procedure (5)

43.011 *Apparatus*

(a) *Portable count-rate meter.*—Consists of: (*1*) *Self-quenching glass Geiger-Müller tube,* side wall ≤ 32 mg/cm^2, mounted in slide opening metal shield; threshold ca 800 v, operated at ca midpoint of voltage plateau, slope of which is $\leq 10\%$, connected with coaxial cable to (*2*) *Suitable power supply and electronic amplifier unit* with meter calibrated in milliroentgens (mr)/hr, connected thru sensitivity switch providing 3 ranges of scale reading, *e.g.*, 0–20, 0–2, and 0–0.2 mr/hr; linear response within each range.

(b) *Comparison std.*—Induces meter response

★ Methods so marked are surplus methods. *See* "Definitions of Terms and Explanatory Notes," item (29).

identical to that from surface of H_2O contaminated with fission products decaying at rate of 2×10^5 dpm/ml (emergency tolerance level for H_2O to be consumed for ≤ 10 day period). Construct such std as follows: Uniformly suspend suitable quantity "60-mesh" $UO_2(OAc)_2 \cdot 2H_2O$ (ca 3 g, adjusted by trial; *Caution: See* **46.083** and **46.084**) in 5 g liq. casting plastic, level, and solidify in shallow container, such as lid of ointment tin, ca 80 mm diam. and side wall 15 mm deeper than layer of plastic. Base of ointment tin, fitted with indented ring 15 mm below its edge, serves as container for liqs and finely divided solids to be tested, and to protect comparison std when not in use. Supplementary std of ½ this activity may be prepd similarly for monitoring supplies to be consumed over 30 day period.

43.012   *Determination*

With selectivity switch set for highest range (*e.g.*, 0–20 mr/hr), and with shield open, place G-M tube diametrically across std in contact with edge of container at 2 points. Adjust meter pointer to convenient value ca midway of scale with calibration screw and record reading as av. of fluctuations over 1–2 min. Duplicate reading should check within ±5%. Avoid extraneous radiation, such as that from luminous dial watch.

Fill sample container with liq. or finely divided solid to level of indented ring and obtain duplicate readings. Sample readings within ±100% of std reading are of practical quant. significance for monitoring under emergency conditions.

SELECTED REFERENCES

(*1*) Rev. Sci. Instrum. **4**, 216(1933); **6**, 99(1935); Phys. Rev. **55**, 931(1939).
(*2*) JAOAC **19**, 101(1936).
(*3*) JAOAC **25**, 103, 618(1942).
(*4*) JAOAC **52**, 90(1969).
(*5*) JAOAC **38**, 678(1955).

44. Spectroscopic Methods[*]

EMISSION SPECTROGRAPHIC METHODS —OFFICIAL FIRST ACTION

Aluminum, Boron, Calcium, Copper, Iron, Magnesium, Manganese, Phosphorus, Potassium, Sodium, and Zinc in Plants (1)

44.001 *Principles*

Methods described cover detn of major and micronutrient elements in plants, which can be detd simultaneously. However, basic instrumental technics described are not limited to plant analysis. With appropriate modifications of sample prepn and details of stds, both methods may be adapted to many analytical problems involving other agricultural and biological materials.

Descriptions illustrate wide latitude permissible between methods capable of satisfactory performance. Two entirely different instrumental technics are described which may be combined with any of the photometric methods. Points in both methods may be helpful and suggestive in instances where available equipment does not permit complete adherence to details of either method. In such cases *"General Recommendations,"* **44.002,** are helpful.

Direct current arc excitation method involves comparison of samples and stds of closely similar composition. Spectra are prepd by dc arc excitation under chemically buffered conditions. Spark excitation method employs internal std technic, spark excitation, and correction system for matrix differences. It permits some leeway in composition between sample and std, and is advantageous for batches of samples of varying composition.

Substitutions in app. for either method may be made if based on approx. equiv. performance.

44.002 *General Recommendations*

(a) *Instrumental technic.*—If, because of equipment limitations, neither of described methods can be followed in detail, or if particular analytical problem involves detn of other elements, following procedure is recommended: Det. experimentally, to limits of facilities available, potentials of various electrode prepns and excitation conditions with relation to element detectability and general concn requirements. If set of conditions shows promise, make preliminary check for replicability of line indices.

For detn of very minute amts of some elements in plants, preliminary chemical sepn and concn may be necessary. (Satisfactory procedure using 8-hydroxyquinoline is described by Mitchell ("The Spectrochemical Analysis of Soils, Plants, and Related Materials," 1964).) Trace element conc. so obtained may be combined with suitable matrix, and subsequent treatment adapted to regular instrumental technic.

Selection of analysis lines on basis of desirable intensity and freedom from spectral interference by other elements is facilitated by prepg spectrum of each component element at av. concn level at which it occurs in material to be analyzed. Align spectra collectively for comparison, preferably by exposure on same film or plate.

(b) *Precision.*—Stdze all conditions of technic and det. reproducibility of results by making ca 20 successive exposures on sample of representative composition. For each element, calc. std deviation of single exposure and divide by square root of number of individual exposures that will be averaged in practice to constitute one detn. From this est. of std deviation of single detn, calc. coefficient of variation for each element. Following upper limits for precision error of spectrographic detns in analysis of plant material are suggested as being satisfactory in relation to other routine methods, or to practical requirements: Coefficients of variation for K, Ca, and P, 5.0%; Mg, Mn, Fe, Al, Na, and Cu, 10.0; B, 15.0. Where only semiquant. results are required, an overall coefficient of variation of 30% can be obtained.

(c) *Accuracy.*—Precise technic is essential, but is by no means only factor involved in ultimate accuracy. Reliability and appropriateness of stds and judgment used in ref. procedure are of utmost importance. Failure in any of these respects can result in serious calibration error for otherwise satisfactory method.

Carefully prep. synthetic stds from highest grade H_2O-free analyzed chemicals, collectively blanked for minor and trace elements. Preferably confirm values assigned natural stds by results of more than one laboratory.

Necessity for matrix similarity between stds and samples, or for closely controlled correction system for matrix differences, is stressed in methods and is again emphasized. Check correction scales frequently against stds which closely match particular types of plant materials being analyzed.

[*] All methods in this chapter are surplus. *See* "Definitions of Terms and Explanatory Notes," item (29).

Precision error of technic applies to ref. exposures as well as to samples. For this reason, base fiducial adjustments on as many ref. exposures as may feasibly be included in each series of samples.

★ *Direct Current Arc Excitation Method* ★

44.003 *Apparatus*

(a) *Self-maintaining dc discharge.*

(b) *Large Littrow prism spectrograph.*—Equipped with custom built device for magnetically rotating arc envelope.

(c) *Photographic plates.*—Eastman Kodak No. 3.

(d) *Facilities for controlled processing of photographic plates.*

(e) *Lathe.*—For machining electrodes.

(f) *Comparator microphotometer.*

(g) *Lower electrodes.*—Cut std grade $\frac{5}{16}''$ diam. spectrographic C rods into $\frac{7}{8}''$ segments. In one end of each segment drill tapered hole for mounting on pedestal for burning; in other end drill crater 7 mm diam. × 4 mm deep; machine wall thickness to 0.4 mm. Purify these electrodes by preburning with ca 2.5 mg buffer, **44.004**(a), until buffer is consumed.

(h) *Upper electrodes.*—Use high purity C rods, $\frac{1}{8}''$ diam.

44.004 *Reagents*

(a) *Buffer.*—Mix equal parts, by wt, of Li_2SO_4 and pure spectrographic graphite powder.

(b) *Std solns.*—Make exploratory analysis of particular batch of samples to be analyzed. On basis of this analysis, prep. stock mixt. from individual pure chloride solns of respective elements, adjusting concns in mixt. so that they are equiv. to 0.1 of highest concn of each element in samples. Adjust acidity to 1 ml HCl/100 ml. Make successive dilns, each 40% or 50% of previous concn, to produce series of element concns covering indicated sample ranges. Use HCl (1 + 100) in prepg dilns. (It is important that major element levels be in ca same ratios to each other in these stds as they are in samples.)

(c) *Paraffin soln.*—Dissolve 12 g paraffin in enough kerosene to make 100 ml.

44.005 *Preparation of Samples*

Grind dried plant material in Wiley mill fitted with No. 40 stainless steel sieve. Dry ground sample in oven and transfer accurately weighed 10 mg portions of dried sample to electrode craters, **44.003**(g). Insert charged electrodes in holes drilled in Transite block, and ash by placing block in cold muffle furnace and heating slowly to 500°. Remove from oven, and let cool. Waterproof electrodes contg ash by dropping 4 drops of the lukewarm paraffin soln, **44.004**(c), around each crater edge and letting air-dry. Add 1 drop H_2O and 2 drops HCl (1 + 30) to each crater to convert salts to chlorides. Dry treated electrodes at 100°.

Transfer accurately measured 0.1 ml portions of std solns, **44.004**(b), to electrode craters which have been waterproofed with the paraffin soln, and dry in oven at 100°.

44.006 *Determination*

Add 4 mg buffer, **44.004**(a), to each of electrodes contg residues from samples and stds, **44.005**, align electrodes in holders, and burn to completion with current of 150 v and 24 amp. During burning period, magnetically rotate gaseous envelope of arc to increase homogeneity, and maintain electrode alignment by periodic adjustment. Place stepped sector in light beam to permit simultaneous detn of Al, B, Ca, Cu, Fe, Mg, Mn, Na, and P. Replicate series of exposures 3 or 4 times on different plates.

Process photographic plates, **44.003**(c), under controlled conditions, as in **44.013**. Use following analysis lines: Ca, 2997.3; Mg, 2779.8; P, 2553.3; Mn, 2801.1 or 3054.4; Fe, 3020.6; Al, 3082.2; Na, 3302.3; Cu, 3247.5 or 3274.0; and B, 2496.8 or 2497.7 Å.

Det. element concn by photometry either semiquant., **44.016**(b), or quant., **44.015** and **44.016**(a).

★ *Alternating Current Spark* ★
Excitation Method

44.007 *Apparatus*

(a) *Spark excitation source.*

(b) *Spectrograph.*—Applied Research Laboratories 1.5 m grating spectrograph, with enclosed spark stand.

(c) *Photographic film.*—Eastman Kodak Spec. Anal. No. 1.

(d) *Film-processing equipment.*

(e) *Electrode drill.*

(f) *Calculating board and comparator microphotometer.*

(g) *Lower electrodes.*—Purify std grade spectrographic C rods, $\frac{1}{4}''$ diam., by successive hot digestions with HCl (1 + 1), HNO_3 (1 + 1), and H_2O. Dry in oven. Cut purified rods into 2″ lengths. In one end of each 2″ rod, drill crater 5 mm diam. × 6 mm deep, and pack crater with portion of C removed in drilling.

(h) *Upper electrodes.*—Point appropriate lengths of purified rod, (g), in pencil sharpener equipped with pin-stop to produce $\frac{1}{16}''$ diam. flat tip.

44.008 *Reagents*

(a) *Hydrochloric acid-cobalt dissolving soln.*—Dil. 20 ml 2% Co soln and 300 ml HCl to 2 L.

(b) *Element soln.*—Prep. stock soln of each element from pure salt. Following concns are convenient: K, 5.0% and 0.5%; Ca, 3.0% and 0.3%; Mg and P, 1.0% and 0.1%; Mn, Fe, Al, Zn, and Na, 0.5%, 0.05%, and 0.005%; Cu and B, 0.05%, 0.005%, and 0.0005% (5 ppm); and Co, 2.0%.

(c) *Stock mixt.*—Prep. by combining following quantities of element solns and dilg to 500 ml.

Element	Concn of Stock Soln %	Quantity ml	Equiv. to Sample Percentage of
K	5.0	50	0.5
Ca	3.0	50	0.3
Mg	1.0	35	0.07
P	1.0	35	0.07
Na	0.5	20	0.02
Fe	0.5	5	0.005 (50 ppm)
Al	0.5	5	0.005 (50 ppm)
Zn	0.5	5	0.005 (50 ppm)
Mn	0.5	2	0.002 (20 ppm)
Cu	0.05	5	0.0005 (5 ppm)
B	0.05	5	0.0005 (5 ppm)

Relation between stds and samples in fourth column is based on Cl residue from 1 g sample dissolved in 5 ml of the HCl-Co dissolving soln, (a). For each ml of the stock mixt. evapd and so dissolved, resulting std corresponds to listed percentage of the respective element.

44.009   *Preparation of Standards*

(Procedure is designed to cover analysis of miscellaneous plant material of various composition. Ref. stds used, therefore, are of general nature. If requirements are confined to analysis of specific reasonably uniform types of plant material, stdzn procedure may be simplified to satisfy only variations involved. In such cases, adjust suggested proportional composition and concns of stds to approx. match material to be analyzed. In practice, spectra of 10 samples and duplicates of 2 ref. stds are recorded on one film, and series of exposures is duplicated on another film. Avs of ratio values for the two films should be used in all cases.)

(a) *Stds for K, Mg, Fe, Al, Zn, Mn, Cu, and B curves.*—Prep. series of stds by evapg 1, 2, 4, 7, and 10 ml aliquots of stock mixt., **44.008**(c), with 2 ml HCl and dissolving each residue in 5 ml of the HCl-Co dissolving soln, **44.008**(a). (P and Ca are affected by progressive increase in concn of matrix elements in these stds.)

(b) *Stds for P curve.*—Make 5 mixts from element solns, **44.008**(b), each contg sample equivs of 2.5% K, 1.5% Ca, and 0.3% Mg. Add to these mixts 1, 2, 4, 6, and 8 ml, resp., of 0.1% P soln. Add 2 ml HCl to each mixt., evap., and dissolve in 5 ml HCl-Co dissolving soln as in (a). (Because different K and Ca levels affect fiducial point rather than slope of P curve, 0.4% P present in all Ca stds serves to indicate relative fiducial adjustments necessary for various quantities of K and Ca present.)

(c) *Stds for Ca curve.*—To mixts, each contg sample equivs of 1.0% K, 0.3% Mg, and 0.4% P, add 1, 2, 4, 8, and 12 ml, resp., of the 0.3% Ca soln. Evap. and dissolve as in (b). (These stds represent 0.3%, 0.6%, etc., of Ca, and are used to obtain Ca

curve for K level of 1%.) Prep. 3 more sets of Ca stds similarly, raising K levels in these sets to 2.0%, 3.5%, and 5.0%, resp.

(d) *Stds for routine reference.*—Prep. low, medium, and high stds, from 2.5, 5, and 10 ml portions of the stock mixt., **44.008**(c), treated as in (a). (Addnl stds to match composition of unusual samples may be prepd from the element solns, **44.008**(b).)

44.010   *Preparation of Samples*

Weigh quantity of dry, ground material that will produce ash weighing preferably between 0.06 and 0.10 g. (1 g av. plant material meets this requirement.) Ash at 550°. Digest ash with excess HCl (1 + 1) and evap. to dryness on hot plate. Treat residue with 5 ml HCl-Co dissolving soln, **44.008**(a), and warm until salts dissolve. If any insol. material remains, let it settle out or remove by filtering thru small, dry filter.

Add, drop by drop, ca 0.1 ml sample or std soln to packed electrode, **44.007**(g), and let sink in. Dry treated electrodes 2 hr at 130° and keep in desiccator until sparked. (Rapidity with which soln soaks into electrode influences general density of spectrum. Individual electrodes, although prepd as nearly identically as possible, may vary considerably in this respect. Where absorption is very rapid, add addnl drop soln, so that some will remain on top of electrode several min before being absorbed. If surface of electrode is glazed in packing operation, no soln will penetrate; in this case discard electrode.)

44.011   *Determination*

(a) *Excitation.*—Align and space electrodes 3 mm apart in holders with jig, and spark 25 sec. (This period is usually enough to empty crater; disregard any remaining material.) Set source parameters to give either uniform breakdown voltage at tandem air gap or to have the voltage at analytical gap in damped region for Applied Research Laboratories type source. Use 40 μm slit width and aperture which permits 14 exposures and clear strip for densitometer settings on film. Adjust gates so that total background, in general, is slight. Use no lens or filter. Make no background correction.

(b) *Emulsion calibration.*—Prep. emulsion calibration curves in 3000 and 4000 Å regions as in **44.015**(a).

(c) *Film processing.*—Process photographic film, **44.007**(c), under controlled conditions as in **44.013.**

(d) *Photometry.*—Use following analysis lines: K, 4044 or 4047; Ca, 2997; Mg, 2781 or 3337; P, 2553 or 2555; Mn, 2949, 2933, or 3460; Fe, 3020.6 or 3021.1; Al, 3082; Zn, 3345; Na, 3302; Cu, 3274; B, 2498; and Co (ref. line), 3044 Å.

Det. log intensity ratios, **44.016**(a), for all elements except K from 3000 Å emulsion calibration curve and those for K from 4000 Å emulsion calibration curve.

(While spectral density level equiv. to 25–30% T for Co ref. line is desirable from standpoint of uniform element range coverage, density range between 20% and 50% T for this line does not affect validity of element/Co ratios. For this reason, density differences encountered between duplicate exposures provide excellent addnl check on emulsion calibration.)

Plot resp. ratios against known percentages of elements in stds and draw analysis curves. Ratios from sample spectra may be referred directly to these curves, if desired, to obtain analysis values. Due to considerable number of curves involved in analysis of miscellaneous plant materials, however, it is more convenient to arrange data obtained from these curves as percentage scales for each element.

Mount blank cardboard strip parallel to horizontal logarithmic scale on calcg board, which is allowed to represent log I ratios. Mark complete range of percentage points on this strip in alignment with corresponding ratios on logarithmic scale. Fiducial relationship is adjustable by sliding strip in its mounting.

On Ca strip, place the several scales corresponding to different level of K. On P strip, place series of replicas of P scale in fiducial alignment relative to different levels of combined K and Ca (Anal. Chem. **25**, 946(1953)).

Correlate all analysis strips with low, medium, and high general stds and mark percentage levels of these stds on the strips as fiducial ref. points. Make fiducial adjustment for each set of duplicate films by aligning these ref. points with resp. av. ratios for stds thereon. Refer accompanying samples to these settings.

In practice, det. K first. With K percentage known, proper scale to be used for Ca is indicated. With both K and Ca contents known, correct scale for P is indicated. Make no correction for matrix variation for other elements.

Photographic Processing

44.012   *Apparatus and Reagents*

(a) *Equipment.*—Developing machine; washer; dryer; large, easily read elec. timer; safelight; storage refrigerator; and water cooler.

(b) *Developer.*—Eastman Kodak D-19 or D-8.

(c) *Stop bath.*—2% HOAc.

(d) *Fixer.*—Eastman Kodak F-5 or Eastman rapid liq.

44.013   *Technic*

Store films or plates in refrigerator and remove 24 hr before opening to equilibrate to laboratory atm. Use safelights appropriate to emulsion being processed. Carefully control time of each operation.

(a) *Developing.*—Place film or plate in developing machine contg developer and agitate 3–5 min at constant temp. of 18–21°. Maintain same time and temp. for all films or plates of particular series. Im-

merse in stop bath of 2% HOAc for 30 sec immediately after development.

(b) *Fixing.*—After plate or film is cleared in fixer, **44.012**(d), fix at least 1 min (longer for indefinite preservation of negative). Wash 3 min in running H_2O at 18–21°, rinse in distd H_2O, and dry in 32° air in dryer.

Photometry

44.014   *Apparatus*

(a) *Microphotometer.*

(b) *Seidel scale and calculating board.*

(c) *All-iron globule arc.*

(d) *Step sector or step filter.*

44.015   *Emulsion Calibration Curves* (2)

Select emulsion with finest grain that line sensitivity will permit. Use all-Fe globule arc, run at very low amperage, as light source. Align spectrograph optics to give max. uniformity of line intensity and check for synchronism and scattered light within spectrograph. Adjust microphotometer to focus sharply, with min. T for given line. Set scanning element and spectrogram line parallel. Set microphotometer scale at 100% T on clear area and zero T for complete blackening. Frequently check scale range, and at least each time wavelength of spectrogram is changed. Det. response of emulsion to light by 2-step, step sector, 2 line, or line group method. Each method uses sep. system to measure variable quantities of light falling on emulsion. Step sector and 2-step method vary amt of light in each line of spectrogram, whereas line and line group method rely on constant intensity differences between suitable lines of spectrum.

(a) *Line group method.*—Make spectrogram, using all-Fe globule arc as light source and power source, spectrograph, and microphotometer that will be used in analytical work. Use no sector or filter. Measure T of selected lines in microphotometer and transform readings to Seidel function, **44.014**(b). Plot Seidel functions against known relative intensities of selected lines to obtain emulsion calibration curve. Intensities are listed in (2), but since observed, relative intensities are affected by source conditions and instrumental characteristics, check their scale validities by 2-step or step sector method. Where emulsion response varies with wavelength, draw calibration curves for each wavelength region used.

(b) *Two-step method.*—Make spectrogram, using all-Fe globule arc as light source and power source, spectrograph, and microphotometer that will be used in analytical work. Use 2-step sector or step filter to give 2-step spectrogram. Measure T of group of closely neighboring lines and transform to Seidel function, **44.014**(b). Prep. preliminary curve by plotting weak step of a line against strong step of same line for each line measured. Prep. preliminary curve table of values for weak and strong line steps, beginning at high point strong line value and reading off values for weak line as next value for strong line (2). Plot emulsion calibration curve, using this table and intervals equal to log of step ratio of sector or filter used. Make sep. emulsion calibration curves for each wavelength region used.

44.016   *Analytical Curve*

Analytical curve is plot of log of concn of element in std versus either log intensity ratio or T of line from that std. Intensity ratio curve is corrected for plate response and excitation variation and gives more precise results than T curve. Latter gives adequate semiquant. or comparative results.

(a) *Intensity ratio curve.*—Prep. std spectrograms contg increasing quantities of each of elements to be analyzed and same quantity of internal std. Measure T of lines, using only values in straight line portion of calibration curve, and transform to Seidel values.

From calibration curve, **44.015**, read intensity value corresponding to Seidel value. Calc. intensity ratio of line of variable constituent to line of internal std. Plot log of intensity ratio against log of known concn. Where necessary, correct for background (2). Use calcg board, **44.014(b)**, to perform mech. operations of obtaining analytical curve.

(b) *Transmittance curve.*—Prep. std spectrograms as in **44.016(a)**, measure T of each line, and obtain quadruplicate values for each std. Use no internal std. Plot log of mean value against log of std concn. Run each replicate on different film or plate on different days. Treat samples for analysis in like manner.

SELECTED REFERENCES

(*1*) JAOAC **36**, 411(1953); **37,** 721(1954).
(*2*) ASTM, "Methods for Emission Spectrographic Analysis," 5th Ed., 1968.

45. Standard Solutions and Materials

45.001 General Directions (1)

Accurately calibrated equipment, which meets NBS specifications, should be used. Because alk. and other corrosive solns dissolve glass, to avoid vol. errors such solns should not be stored in calibrated app., and burets used continuously should be recalibrated periodically.

Working temp. of std soln should approximate that of its temp. during stdzn. If temp. corrections are necessary, sufficient accuracy may be obtained by use of following table:

45.003 Preparation of Standard Solution

Prep. ca $0.1N$ soln from reagent that shows no Cl, using 7.612 g NH_4CNS or 9.718 g KCNS/L.

45.004 Standardization

Accurately weigh, on tared watch glass, enough purified $AgNO_3$ to give titrn of ca 40 ml (ca 0.7 g for $0.1N$ soln) and transfer with H_2O thru glass funnel to 250 ml g-s erlenmeyer. Dissolve in ca 75 ml H_2O (halogen-free), and add 5 ml HNO_3 (1 + 1) and 2 ml Fe alum soln, 45.031(a). Titr. with thiocyanate

Vol. Std Soln	Correction in Milliliters at—												
	6°	8°	10°	12°	14°	16°	18°	20°	22°	24°	26°	28°	30°
ml													
10	0.01	0.01	0.01	0.01	0.01	0.01	0.00	0.00	0.00	0.00	−0.01	−0.02	−0.02
20	0.03	0.03	0.03	0.02	0.02	0.01	0.01	0.00	−0.01	−0.02	−0.03	−0.03	−0.03
25	0.04	0.03	0.03	0.03	0.02	0.02	0.01	0.00	−0.01	−0.02	−0.03	−0.04	−0.05
30	0.04	0.04	0.04	0.03	0.03	0.02	0.01	0.00	−0.01	−0.02	−0.04	−0.05	−0.07
40	0.06	0.06	0.05	0.04	0.04	0.03	0.01	0.00	−0.02	−0.03	−0.05	−0.07	−0.09
50	0.07	0.07	0.06	0.06	0.05	0.03	0.02	0.00	−0.02	−0.04	−0.06	−0.09	−0.12

Ammonium and Potassium Thiocyanates (2)—Official Final Action

45.002 Reagents

(a) *Purified silver nitrate.*—Dissolve 50 g $AgNO_3$ in 20 ml boiling H_2O contg ca 5 drops HNO_3. Heat to dissolve, filter while still hot thru fritted glass filter, using suction, and collect filtrate in clean Pyrex beaker. Wash beaker and filter with ca 5 ml hot H_2O, adding washings to filtrate. Cool in ice bath, stirring to induce crystn, and place in refrigerator at ca 10° until equilibrium is reached. Decant liq. thru fritted glass filter and transfer crystals to filter. Cover filter with watch glass and draw air thru filter to remove adhering liq. Transfer crystals to small, clean Pyrex beaker. Cover beaker with watch glass and place inside larger covered Pyrex beaker. Dry at 105° and fuse at 220–250° (mp 208°), holding at this temp. ca 15 min after crystals are melted. Protect from dust during prepn. Cool in desiccator, remove product from beaker, powder in mortar, dry 0.5 hr at 105°, and store in brown g-s bottle in dark over good desiccant.

(b) *Reference soln.*—To mixt. of 5 ml HNO_3 (1 + 1), 2 ml Fe alum soln, 45.031(a), and 115 ml H_2O, add ca 0.02 ml $0.1N$ thiocyanate, 45.003, noting exact quantity used.

soln until soln has reddish-brown color, which remains after shaking vigorously 1 min. Record buret reading and set flask aside 5 min, shaking occasionally and maintaining end point color by addn of thiocyanate soln as required. Then add addnl thiocyanate soln, if necessary, to produce permanent end point color, matching with color of ref. soln, 45.002(b). From total vol. thiocyanate soln used in titrn subtract quantity contained in ref. soln.

$$\text{Normality} = \frac{\text{g } AgNO_3 \times 1000}{\text{ml titer} \times 169.87}.$$

Arsenious Oxide (3)—Official Final Action

45.005 Reagent

Arsenious oxide.—Use NBS Std Sample 83. Dry 1 hr at 105° immediately before using.

45.006 Preparation of Standard Solution

Accurately weigh As_2O_3 by difference from small g-s weighing bottle (use ca 4.95 g/L for $0.1N$). Dissolve in $1N$ NaOH (50 ml/5 g As_2O_3) in flask or beaker by heating on steam bath. Add ca same quantity of $1N$ H_2SO_4. Cool, quant. transfer mixt. to vol. flask, and dil. to vol. (Soln must be neut. to litmus, not alk.)

$$\text{Normality} = \frac{\text{g } As_2O_3 \times 4000}{\text{ml final vol} \times 197.84}.$$

Buffer Solutions for Calibration of pH Equipment (4)—Official Final Action

45.007   Preparation of Standard Buffer Solutions

Use H_2O with pH of ≥ 6.5 but ≤ 7.5, obtained by boiling H_2O 15 min and cooling under CO_2-free conditions. Store std buffer solns except $Ca(OH)_2$ in bottles of chemically resistant glass. Protect phosphate, borax, and $Ca(OH)_2$ buffers from contamination with CO_2.

(a) *Potassium tetroxalate buffer soln.*—$0.0496M$; $0.05m$. Transfer 12.61 g $KHC_2O_4.H_2C_2O_4.2H_2O$ (air wt) (NBS Std Sample 189) to 1 L vol. flask, dil. to vol. with H_2O, and mix thoroly. (It is not necessary to remove dissolved CO_2 from the H_2O or to dry salt before weighing.) Prep. fresh every 2 months.

(b) *Potassium hydrogen tartrate buffer soln.*—Satd soln at 25°, $0.034M$. Add excess (ca 100%) of $KHC_4H_4O_6$ (NBS Std Sample 188) to H_2O in g-s bottle or flask, and shake vigorously; few min shaking is enough for satn (100 ml H_2O at 25° dissolves ca 0.7 g $KHC_4H_4O_6$). Adjust to 25°, let solid settle, and decant clear soln, or filter if necessary. Discard when mold appears. Few crystals of thymol added during prepn will retard mold growth, and will alter pH by <0.01 unit. For accuracy of ±0.01 pH unit, temp. of soln at satn must be between 20 and 30°.

(c) *Acid potassium phthalate buffer soln.*—$0.0496M$; $0.05m$. Dissolve 10.12 g dried (1 hr at 105°) $HKC_8H_4O_4$ (NBS Std Sample 185) in H_2O and dil. to 1 L. (Elaborate precautions for exclusion of atm. CO_2 are unnecessary, altho soln should be protected against evapn and contamination with molds. Replace soln if mold appears).

(d) *Phosphate buffer soln.*—$0.0249M$; $0.025m$. Dissolve 3.388 g KH_2PO_4 and 3.533 g Na_2HPO_4 (NBS Std Samples 186-I and II) in H_2O and dil. to 1 L. (Dry salts 2 hr at 130° before use.)

(e) *Phosphate buffer soln.* — $0.008663M$, $0.008695m$ KH_2PO_4 and $0.03030M$, $0.03043m$ Na_2HPO_4. Dissolve 1.179 g KH_2PO_4 and 4.302 g Na_2HPO_4 (NBS Std Samples 186-I and II) in H_2O and dil. to 1 L. (Dry salts 2 hr at 130° before use.)

(f) *Borax buffer soln.*—$0.00996M$; $0.01m$. Dissolve 3.80 g $Na_2B_4O_7.10H_2O$ (NBS Std Sample 187) in H_2O and dil. to 1 L. (Salt must not be dried in oven before use.) To avoid contamination with CO_2, stopper bottle except when in use or protect with soda-lime tube. Use buffer soln within 10 min after removal from bottle.

(g) *Sodium bicarbonate-carbonate buffer soln.*—$0.0249M$; $0.025m$ (each). Transfer 2.092 g $NaHCO_3$ (NBS std sample 191; do not heat) and 2.640 g Na_2CO_3 (NBS std sample 192; dry 2 hr at 275°) to 1 L vol. flask. Dissolve and dil. to vol. with CO_2-free H_2O.

(h) *Calcium hydroxide buffer soln.*—Satd soln at 25°, $0.02025M$. Slowly heat finely granular, ACS Reagent $CaCO_3$, Low in Alkalies, to 1000° in Pt dish and maintain at this temp. 45–60 min. Cool in desiccator, and add to H_2O with stirring. Heat to boiling with continuous stirring. Cool, and filter on medium fritted glass filter. Dry at 110°, cool, and crush to fine, granular powder.

Place crushed CaO in polyethylene bottle, add H_2O, shake vigorously, let settle, and record temp. (Keep large excess of $Ca(OH)_2$ in bottle.) For use, filter soln thru medium fritted glass filter. Use at same temp. at which satn took place, and discard filtered soln if it becomes turbid. When more buffer soln is needed, add addnl H_2O to suspension, re-sat., and filter as above.

45.008   pH Values for Standard Buffer Solutions

pH values of std buffer solns as function of temp. are given in following table:

Temperature	0.05m Potassium Tetroxalate	Satd Potassium Hydrogen Tartrate	0.05m Acid Potassium Phthalate	0.025m Phosphate	0.008695m and 0.03043m Phosphate	0.01m Borax	0.025m NaHCO₃ and 0.025m Na₂CO₃	Satd Calcium Hydroxide
°C	pH	pH	pH	pH	pH	pH	pH	pH
0	1.666	—	4.012	6.981	7.531	9.464	10.321	13.423
5	1.668	—	4.005	6.948	7.497	9.395	10.248	13.207
10	1.670	—	4.002	6.920	7.469	9.332	10.181	13.003
15	1.672	—	4.001	6.897	7.445	9.276	10.120	12.810
20	1.675	—	4.003	6.878	7.426	9.225	10.064	12.627
25	1.679	3.557	4.008	6.862	7.410	9.180	10.014	12.454
30	1.683	3.552	4.014	6.850	7.397	9.139	9.968	12.289
35	1.688	3.549	4.023	6.841	7.386	9.102	9.928	12.133
38	1.691	3.548	4.030	6.837	7.381	9.081	—	12.043
40	1.694	3.547	4.033	6.835	7.377	9.068	9.891	11.984
45	1.700	3.547	4.045	6.831	7.370	9.038	9.859	11.841
50	1.707	3.549	4.058	6.830	7.364	9.011	9.831	11.705
55	1.715	3.554	4.073	6.832	—	8.985	—	11.574
60	1.723	3.560	4.089	6.836	—	8.962	—	11.449

Standard Buffers and Indicators for Colorimetric pH Comparisons (5)— Official Final Action

45.009 Preparation of Sulfonphthalein Indicators

	A	pH
Bromocresol green	14.3	3.8–5.4
Chlorophenol red	23.6	4.8–6.4
Bromothymol blue	16.0	6.0–7.6
Phenol red	28.2	6.8–8.4

A = ml $0.01N$ NaOH/0.1 g indicator required to form mono-Na salt. Dil. to 250 ml for 0.04% reagent.

45.010 Preparation of Stock Solutions

Use recently boiled and cooled H_2O.

(a) *Acid potassium phthalate soln.*—$0.2M$. Dry to constant wt at 110–115°. Dissolve 40.836 g in H_2O and dil. to 1 L.

(b) *Monopotassium phosphate soln.*—$0.2M$. Dry KH_2PO_4 to constant wt at 110–115°. Dissolve 27.232 g in H_2O and dil. to 1 L. Soln should be distinctly red with Me red, and distinctly blue with bromophenol blue.

(c) *Boric acid-potassium chloride soln.*—$0.2M$. Dry H_3BO_3 to constant wt in desiccator over $CaCl_2$. Dry KCl 2 days in oven at 115–120°. Dissolve 12.405 g H_3BO_3 and 14.912 g KCl in H_2O, and dil. to 1 L.

(d) *Sodium hydroxide std soln.*—$0.2M$. Prep. and stdze as in 45.033–45.036; 0.04084 g $KHC_8H_4O_4$ = 1 ml $0.2M$ NaOH. It is preferable to use factor with soln rather than try to adjust to exactly $0.2M$.

45.011 Preparation of Buffer Solutions

Prep. std buffer solns from designated amts stock solns, 45.010, and dil. to 200 ml. For use as colorimetric std, mix 20 ml buffer soln with 0.5 ml indicator soln, 45.009.

Phthalate-NaOH Mixtures

pH	0.2M KH Phthalate (ml)	0.2M NaOH (ml)
5.0	50	23.65
5.2	50	29.75
5.4	50	35.25
5.6	50	39.70
5.8	50	43.10
6.0	50	45.40
6.2	50	47.00

KH2PO4-NaOH Mixtures

pH	0.2M KH2PO4 (ml)	0.2M NaOH (ml)
5.8	50	3.66
6.0	50	5.64
6.2	50	8.55
6.4	50	12.60
6.6	50	17.74
6.8	50	23.60
7.0	50	29.54
7.2	50	34.90
7.4	50	39.34
7.6	50	42.74
7.8	50	45.17
8.0	50	46.85

H3BO3-KCl-NaOH Mixtures

pH	0.2M H3BO3, KCl (ml)	0.2M NaOH (ml)
7.8	50	2.65
8.0	50	4.00
8.2	50	5.90
8.4	50	8.55
8.6	50	12.00

Hydrochloric Acid—Official Final Action

45.012 Preparation of Standard Solutions

Following table gives approx. quantities of HCl (reagent quality, 35–37% HCl) required to make 10 L std solns:

Approx. normality	ml HCl to be dild to 10 L
0.01	8.9
0.02	17.8
0.10	89.0
0.50	445.0
1.0	890.0

45.013 Standard Sodium Hydroxide Method (6)

Titr. 40 ml against std alkali soln, 45.035–45.037, of ca same concn as acid being stdzd in 300 ml flask that has been swept free from CO_2, using CO_2-free H_2O and 3 drops phthln.

Normality
= (ml std alkali × normality of alkali)/ml HCl.

If more concd than desired, dil. soln to required normality value by following formula:

$$V_1 = V_2 \times N_2/N_1,$$

where N_2 and V_2 represent normality and vol. of stock soln, resp., and V_1 represents vol. to which stock soln should be dild to obtain desired normality, N_1.

Check exact concn of final soln by titrn as above. Normality will be exact only if same indicator is used in detn as in stdzn. Restdze if indicators other than phthln are to be used.

45.014 Constant Boiling Method (7)

Dil. 850 ml HCl (35–37% HCl) with 750 ml H_2O. Check sp gr with spindle and adjust to 1.10. Place 1.5 L in 2 L flat-bottom distg flask, add ca 10 SiC grains (ca "20 mesh"), and connect to long, straight inner-tube condenser. Heat on elec. hot plate and distill at rate of 5–10 ml/min, keeping end of condenser open to air. When 1125 ml has distd, change receivers and catch next 225 ml, which is constant boiling HCl, in erlenmeyer with end of condenser inserted into flask, but above surface of liq. Read barometer to nearest mm at beginning and end of collection of 225 ml portion and note barometer temp. Average readings.

Calc. air wt in g (G) of this constant boiling HCl required to give one equiv. wt of HCl from one of following equations:

For $P_0 = 540$–669 mm Hg:
$$G = 162.255 + 0.02415 \, P_0$$

For $P_0 = 670$–780 mm Hg:
$$G = 164.673 + 0.02039 \, P_0$$

P_0 = barometric pressure in mm Hg corrected to 0°C for expansion of Hg and of barometer scale. For brass scale barometer, following correction is accurate enough: $P_0 = P_t(1 - 0.000162t)$, where t = barometer temp. in °C.

Weigh required quantity of constant boiling HCl in tared, stoppered flask with accuracy of at least one part in 10,000. Dil. immediately, and finally dil. to vol. with CO_2-free H_2O at desired temp.

Standard Borax Method (8)

45.015   *Reagents*

(a) *Methyl red indicator.*—Dissolve 100 mg Me red in 60 ml alcohol and dil. with H_2O to 100 ml.

(b) *Reference soln.*—Prep. ref. soln of H_3BO_3, NaCl, and indicator corresponding to composition and vol. of soln at equivalence point. For use in detn of end point of titrn with $0.1N$ HCl, ref. soln should be $0.1M$ in H_3BO_3 and $0.05M$ in NaCl.

(c) *Std borax.*—Sat. 300 ml H_2O at 55° (not higher) with $Na_2B_4O_7.10H_2O$ (ACS) (ca 45 g). Filter at this temp. thru folded paper into 500 ml erlenmeyer. Cool filtrate to ca 10°, with continuous agitation during crystn. Decant supernatant, rinse ppt once with 25 ml cold H_2O, and dissolve crystals in just enough H_2O at 55° to ensure complete soln (ca 200 ml). Recrystallize by cooling to ca 10°, agitating flask during crystn.

Filter crystals onto small buchner with suction, wash ppt once with 25 ml ice-cold H_2O, and dry crystals by washing with two 20 ml portions alcohol, drying after each washing with suction. Follow with two 20 ml portions ether. (Just before use, free alcohol and ether from any possible reacting acids by vigorously shaking each with 2–3 g of the pure, dry $Na_2B_4O_7.10H_2O$ and then filtering.) Spread crystals on watch glass, immediately place dried $Na_2B_4O_7$.$10H_2O$ in closed container over soln satd with respect to both sucrose and NaCl, and let it remain at least 24 hr before using. Then transfer the pure $Na_2B_4O_7.10H_2O$ to g-s container and store in closed container over soln satd with respect to both sucrose and NaCl when not in use (stable under these conditions 1 year).

45.016   *Standardization*

Accurately weigh enough std $Na_2B_4O_7.10H_2O$ to titr. ca 40 ml and transfer to 300 ml flask. Add 40 ml CO_2-free H_2O and stopper flask. Swirl gently until sample dissolves. Add 4 drops Me red and titr. with soln that is being stdzd to equivalence point as indicated by ref. soln.

$$\text{Normality} = \frac{\text{g } Na_2B_4O_7.10H_2O \times 1000}{\text{ml acid} \times 190.69}.$$

Standard Sodium Carbonate Method (8)

45.017   *Reagents*

(a) *Methyl orange indicator.*—0.1% in H_2O.

(b) *Reference soln.*—80 ml CO_2-free H_2O contg 3 or 4 drops Me orange.

(c) *Anhydrous sodium carbonate (9).*—Heat 250 ml H_2O to 80° and add $NaHCO_3$ (ACS), stirring until no more dissolves. Then filter soln thru folded paper (use of hot H_2O funnel is desirable) into erlenmeyer. Cool filtrate to ca 10°, swirling constantly during crystn. Fine crystals of trona that sep. out have approx. composition: $Na_2CO_3.NaHCO_3.2H_2O$. Decant supernatant, drain crystals by suction, and wash once with cold H_2O.

Transfer ppt, being careful not to include any paper fibers, to large flat-bottom Pt dish. Heat 1 hr at 290° in elec. oven or furnace with pyrometer control. Stir contents occasionally with Pt wire. After heating, cool in desiccator. Place the anhyd. Na_2CO_3 in g-s container and store in desiccator contg efficient desiccant. Dry at 120° just before using.

45.018   *Standardization*

Accurately weigh enough anhyd. Na_2CO_3 to titr. ca 40 ml, transfer to 300 ml erlenmeyer, and dissolve in 40 ml H_2O. Add 3 drops Me orange and titr. until color begins to deviate from H_2O tint (ref. soln). (Equivalence point has not been reached.) Boil soln gently 2 min, and cool. Titr. until color is barely different from H_2O tint of indicator.

$$\text{Normality} = \frac{\text{g } Na_2CO_3 \times 1000}{\text{ml acid} \times 52.994}.$$

Iodine (3)—Official Final Action

45.019   *Preparation of Standard Solution*

Dissolve weighed quantities of I (12.7 g/L for $0.1N$ soln) and KI, in proportion of 20 g KI to 13 g I, in 50 ml H_2O. When I dissolves, transfer soln to g-s vol. flask. Dil. to vol. with H_2O and mix thoroly. Keep soln in dark brown g-s bottle away from light and restdze as frequently as necessary.

45.020   *Standardization*

Transfer accurately measured portion of std As_2O_3 soln, **45.006**, (40–50 ml ca $0.1N$ soln for $0.1N$ I soln) to erlenmeyer. Acidify slightly with H_2SO_4 $(1 + 10)$, neutze with solid $NaHCO_3$, and add ca 2 g excess. Titr. with I soln, using ca 0.2% starch soln (5 ml/100 ml) as indicator. Sat. soln with CO_2 at end of titrn by adding 1 ml H_2SO_4 $(1 + 10)$ just before end point is reached.

$$\text{Normality} = \frac{\text{ml } As_2O_3 \times \text{normality } As_2O_3}{\text{ml I}}.$$

Potassium Bromide-Bromate (10)—Official Final Action

45.021   *Preparation of Standard Solution*

Dissolve ca 2.8 g $KBrO_3$ and 12 g KBr in boiled H_2O and dil. to 1 L with boiled H_2O for ca $0.1N$ soln.

45.022 *Standardization*

Measure 40 ml std As_2O_3 soln, **45.006,** from buret into 300 ml erlenmeyer. Add 10 ml HCl and 3 drops Me orange, **45.017**(a). Titr. with $KBr-KBrO_3$ soln until 1 drop, or less, causes color of Me orange to fade completely. Swirl soln constantly and add last ml dropwise with swirling between drops.

$$Normality = \frac{ml\ As_2O_3 \times normality\ As_2O_3}{ml\ KBr-KBrO_3}.$$

Potassium Dichromate (11)— Official Final Action

45.023 *Reagent*

Starch soln.—Mix ca 1 g arrowroot starch with 10 ml H_2O and pour slowly, with constant stirring, into 200 ml boiling H_2O. Boil until thin, translucent fluid is obtained. Let settle and use clear supernatant. Preserve with Hg.

45.024 *Assay of Stock Potassium Dichromate*

If $K_2Cr_2O_7$ is in small crystals, composite it by shaking thoroly in large, clean jar; if it is in lumps, grind representative sample until it passes thru No. 60 sieve, and then composite by shaking. Dry portion for weighings 2 hr at 100°.

Weigh, into each of 3 g-s erlenmeyers, enough NBS Std Sample $K_2Cr_2O_7$ 136 to give titer of 100.5–102.0 ml $0.1N$ $Na_2S_2O_3$, **45.038** (0.4928–0.5001 g for $0.1N$ soln). Completely dissolve in 100 ml H_2O, add 4.0 g KI, and swirl mixt. until dissolved. With buret, add 4.0 ml HCl, stopper flask, mix by swirling, and let stand in dark 10 min. Cool flask ca 1 min in ice-H_2O.

While swirling flask, pipet in 100 ml $Na_2S_2O_3$ soln. Add 5 ml starch soln and complete titrn with $Na_2S_2O_3$ soln added from 10 ml microburet (graduated in 0.05 ml). End point is from bluish-green to clear green; change takes place within 0.01 ml. Record titer to nearest 0.01 ml. Calc. apparent normality of $Na_2S_2O_3$ soln for each of the 3 titrns, and average. Designate this av. as N_{NBS}.

Similarly titr. 3 portions of stock $K_2Cr_2O_7$ and calc. the 3 apparent normalities. Designate each of these results as N_{stock}. Calc. % purity of stock $K_2Cr_2O_7 = (N_{NBS} \times 100)/N_{stock}$.

Take av. of the 3 results as % purity of stock $K_2Cr_2O_7$.

45.025 *Preparation of Standard Solution*

Dissolve theoretical quantity of NBS Std Sample $K_2Cr_2O_7$ 136 (4.9032 g for $0.1N$ soln), or quantity stock $K_2Cr_2O_7$, **45.024,** found to have oxidimetric value 99.95–100.05% of NBS Std Sample, in enough H_2O to make 1 L. (Dry $K_2Cr_2O_7$ 2 hr at 100° before weighing.)

Potassium Permanganate (12)— Official Final Action

45.026 *Preparation of Standard Solution*

Dissolve slightly more than desired equiv. wt (3.2 g for $0.1N$) of $KMnO_4$ in 1 L H_2O. Boil soln 1

hr. Protect from dust and let stand overnight. Thoroly clean 15 cm glass funnel, perforated porcelain plate from Caldwell crucible, and g-s bottle (preferably of brown glass) with warm H_2SO_4-$K_2Cr_2O_7$ soln. Digest asbestos for use in gooches on steam bath 1 hr with ca $0.1N$ $KMnO_4$ that has been acidified with few drops H_2SO_4 (1 + 3). Let settle, decant, and replace with H_2O. To prep. glass funnel, place porcelain plate in apex, make pad of asbestos ca 3 mm thick on plate, and wash acid-free. (Pad should not be too tightly packed and only moderate suction should be applied.) Insert stem of funnel into neck of bottle and filter $KMnO_4$ soln directly into bottle without aid of suction.

45.027 *Standardization*

For $0.1N$ soln, transfer 0.3 g dried (1 hr at 105°) NBS Std Sample Na oxalate 40 to 600 ml beaker. Add 250 ml H_2SO_4 (5 + 95) previously boiled 10–15 min and then cooled to $27 \pm 3°$.

Stir until $Na_2C_2O_4$ dissolves. Add 39–40 ml $KMnO_4$ soln at rate of 25–35 ml/min, stirring slowly. Let stand until pink disappears (ca 45 sec). If pink should persist because $KMnO_4$ soln is too concd, discard and begin again, adding few ml less of $KMnO_4$ soln. Heat to 55–60°, and complete titrn by adding $KMnO_4$ soln until faint pink persists 30 sec. Add last 0.5–1 ml dropwise with particular care to let each drop decolorize before adding next.

Det. excess of $KMnO_4$ soln required to turn soln pink by matching with color obtained by adding $KMnO_4$ soln to same vol. of boiled and cooled dil. H_2SO_4 at 55–60°. This correction is usually 0.03–0.05 ml. From net vol. $KMnO_4$, calc. normality:

$$Normality = \frac{g\ Na_2C_2O_4 \times 1000}{ml\ KMnO_4 \times 66.999}.$$

Silver Nitrate (13)—Official Final Action

45.028 *Preparation of Standard Solution*

Dissolve slightly more than theoretical quantity of $AgNO_3$ (equiv. wt, 169.87) in halogen-free H_2O and dil. to vol. Thoroly clean glassware, avoid contact with dust, and keep prepd soln in amber g-s bottles away from light.

Mohr Method

45.029 *Reagents*

(a) *Potassium chloride.*—Recrystallize KCl 3 times with H_2O, dry at 110°, and then heat at ca 500° to constant wt. Equiv. wt KCl = 74.555.

(b) *Potassium chromate soln.*—5% soln of K_2CrO_4 in H_2O.

45.030 *Standardization*

Accurately weigh enough KCl to yield titrn of ca 40 ml (ca 0.3 g for $0.1N$ soln), and transfer to 250 ml g-s erlenmeyer with 40 ml H_2O. Add 1 ml K_2CrO_4 soln and titr. with $AgNO_3$ soln until first perceptible pale red-brown appears. From titrn vol. subtract ml of the $AgNO_3$ soln required to produce end point color in 75 ml H_2O contg 1 ml K_2CrO_4 soln. From net vol. $AgNO_3$, calc. normality:

$$\text{Normality} = \frac{g \ KCl \times 1000}{ml \ AgNO_3 \times 74.555}.$$

Volhard Method

45.031   *Reagents*

(a) *Ferric alum indicator soln.*—Satd soln of $FeNH_4(SO_4)_2.12H_2O$ in H_2O.

(b) *Potassium or ammonium thiocyanate std soln.*—Prep. ca $0.1N$ soln, **45.003**. Det. working titer by accurately measuring 40–50 ml std $AgNO_3$ soln, adding 2 ml Fe alum soln and 5 ml HNO_3 $(1 + 1)$, and titrg with the thiocyanate soln until soln appears pale rose after vigorous shaking.

45.032   *Standardization*

Accurately weigh enough KCl, **45.029(a)**, to yield titrn of ca 40 ml (ca 0.3 g for $0.1N$ soln) and transfer to 250 ml g-s erlenmeyer with 40 ml H_2O. Add 5 ml HNO_3 $(1 + 1)$ and add excess $AgNO_3$ soln. Mix, and let stand few min protected from light. Filter thru gooch prepd with medium pad of asbestos previously rinsed with 2% HNO_3. Wash flask and ppt with several small portions of 2% HNO_3, passing washings thru crucible until filtrate and washings measure ca 150 ml. Add 2 ml Fe alum soln and titr. residual $AgNO_3$ with thiocyanate soln. From titrn, together with ratio of the 2 solns, calc. net vol. $AgNO_3$ soln. (Errors of blank are compensating and may be disregarded.) From net vol. $AgNO_3$, calc. normality as in **45.030**.

Sodium Hydroxide—Official Final Action

Standard Potassium Hydrogen Phthalate Method (14)

45.033   *Apparatus*

Use buret and pipet calibrated by NBS or by analyst. Protect exits to air of automatic burets from CO_2 contamination by suitable guard tubes contg soda-lime. Use containers of alkali-resistant glass.

45.034   *Reagents*

(a) *Carbonate-free water.*—Prep. by one of following methods: (*1*) Boil H_2O 20 min and cool with soda-lime protection; (*2*) bubble air, freed from CO_2 by passing thru tower of soda-lime, thru H_2O 12 hr.

(b) *Sodium hydroxide soln.*—$(1 + 1)$. To 1 part NaOH (reagent quality contg $<5\%$ Na_2CO_3) in flask add 1 part H_2O and swirl until soln is complete. Close with rubber stopper. Set aside until Na_2CO_3 has settled, leaving perfectly clear liq. (ca 10 days).

(c) *Acid potassium phthalate.*—NBS Std Sample for Acidimetry 84. Crush to pass No. 100 sieve. Dry 2 hr at 120°. Cool in desiccator contg H_2SO_4.

45.035   *Preparation of Standard Solution*

Following table gives approx. quantities of NaOH soln $(1 + 1)$ necessary to make 10 L of std solns:

Approx. normality	ml NaOH to be dild to 10 L
0.01	5.4
0.02	10.8
0.10	54.0
0.50	270.0
1.0	540.0

Add required quantity of NaOH soln $(1 + 1)$ to 10 L CO_2-free H_2O. Check normality, which should be slightly high, as in **45.036**, and adjust to desired concn by following formula: $V_1 = V_2 \times N_2/N_1$, where N_2 and V_2 represent normality and vol. stock soln, resp., and V_1, vol. to which stock soln should be dild to obtain desired normality, N_1. Stdze final soln as in **45.036** or **45.037**.

45.036   *Standardization*

Accurately weigh enough dried $KHC_8H_4O_4$ to titr. ca 40 ml and transfer to 300 ml flask that has been swept free from CO_2. Add 50 ml cool CO_2-free H_2O. Stopper flask and swirl gently until sample dissolves. Titr. to pH 8.6 with soln being stdzd, taking precautions to exclude CO_2 and using as indicator either glass-electrode pH meter or 3 drops phthln. In latter case, det. end point by comparison with pH 8.6 buffer soln, **45.011**, contg 3 drops phthln. Det. vol. NaOH required to produce end point of blank by matching color in another flask contg 3 drops phthln and same vol. CO_2-free H_2O. Subtract vol. required from that used in first titrn and calc. normality.

$$\text{Normality} = \frac{g \ KHC_8H_4O_4 \times 1000}{ml \ NaOH \times 204.229}.$$

45.037   *Constant Boiling Hydrochloric Acid Method (7)*

Accurately weigh from weighing buret enough constant boiling HCl, **45.014**, to titr. ca 40 ml, into erlenmeyer previously swept free from CO_2. Add ca 40 ml CO_2-free H_2O, then 3–5 drops desired indicator, and titr. with soln being stdzd.

$$\text{Normality} = \frac{g \ HCl \times 1000}{ml \ titer \times G},$$

where G has value given in **45.014**.

Sodium Thiosulfate (15)—Official Final Action

45.038   *Preparation of Standard Solution*

Dissolve ca 25 g $Na_2S_2O_3.5H_2O$ in 1 L H_2O. Boil gently 5 min and transfer while hot to storage bottle previously cleaned with hot H_2SO_4-$K_2Cr_2O_7$ soln and rinsed with warm boiled H_2O. (Temper bottle, if not heat-resistant, before adding hot soln.) Store soln in dark, cool place; do not return unused portions to stock bottle. If solns less concd than $0.1N$ are desired, prep. by diln with boiled H_2O. (More dil. solns are less stable and should be prepd just before use.)

45.039 *Standardization*

Accurately weigh 0.20–0.23 g $K_2Cr_2O_7$ (NBS Std Sample 136 dried 2 hr at 100°) and place in g-s I flask (or g-s flask). Dissolve in 80 ml Cl-free H_2O contg 2 g KI. Add, with swirling, 20 ml ca $1N$ HCl and immediately place in dark 10 min. Titr. with $Na_2S_2O_3$ soln, **45.038**, adding starch soln after most of I has been consumed.

$$\text{Normality} = \frac{\text{g } K_2Cr_2O_7 \times 1000}{\text{ml } Na_2S_2O_3 \times 49.032}.$$

Sulfuric Acid—Official Final Action

45.040 *Preparation of Standard Solution*

Following table gives approx. quantities of H_2SO_4 (ca 94% H_2SO_4) necessary to make 10 L std solns:

Approx. normality	ml H_2SO_4 to be dild to 10 L
0.01	2.8
0.02	5.7
0.10	28.4
0.50	141.8
1.0	283.5

Standard Borax Method (8)

45.041 *Standardization—See 45.016*

45.042 *Specific Gravity Method (16)*

Dil. H_2SO_4 with enough H_2O to make convenient quantity of ca 70% H_2SO_4 by wt. Det. sp gr in air at convenient temp. (0–40°) as in **9.011** (or sp gr may be detd with Sprengel pycnometer), protecting soln from contact with air. Calc. exact % H_2SO_4 from equation:

$$P = S(85.87 + 0.05T - 0.0004t^2) - 69.82,$$

where $P = \%$ H_2SO_4 by wt and $S = $ sp gr (in air) at $T°$, compared with H_2O at $t°$.

Weigh exactly W g prepd acid contg $P\%$ H_2SO_4 and dil. to n L to make required soln contg G g H_2SO_4/L. W may be calcd by equation:

$$W = nG \times 100/P.$$

Titanium Trichloride (17)— Official Final Action

45.043 *Preparation of Standard Solution*

To 200 ml com. 15% $TiCl_3$ soln add 150 ml HCl and dil. to 2 L. Make soln ca $0.1N$, place in container with H atm. provision (JAOAC 5, 207(1921), and let stand 2 days for absorption of residual O.

45.044 *Standardization*

Weigh 3 g $FeSO_4(NH_4)_2SO_4 \cdot 6H_2O$ and transfer to 500 ml flask. Introduce stream of CO_2 and add 50 ml recently boiled H_2O and 25 ml 40% (by wt) H_2SO_4. Then, without interrupting current of CO_2, rapidly add 40 ml $0.1N$ $K_2Cr_2O_7$, **45.025**. Add $TiCl_3$ soln until near calcd end point. Then quickly add 5 g NH_4CNS, and complete titrn. Det. blank on 3 g $FeSO_4(NH_4)_2SO_4 \cdot 6H_2O$, using same quantities of H_2O, H_2SO_4, and NH_4CNS, and current of CO_2. From net vol. $TiCl_3$, calc. normality:

$$\text{Normality} = \frac{\text{ml } K_2Cr_2O_7 \times \text{normality } K_2Cr_2O_7}{\text{ml } TiCl_3}.$$

SELECTED REFERENCES

(1) JAOAC **25**, 650(1942).

(2) JAOAC **25**, 661(1942); **30**, 105, 496(1947).

(3) JAOAC **22**, 568(1939); **24**, 100, 639(1941).

(4) NBS Certificates for Standard Samples 185, 186, 187a, 188, 189, 191, and 192; JAOAC **33**, 223(1950); **41**, 302(1958); **47**, 43(1964).

(5) JAOAC **24**, 583(1941); Clark, "Determination of Hydrogen-ions," 3rd Ed., pp. 91, 94, 192–202.

(6) JAOAC **19**, 107, 194(1936); **49**, 250(1966); Kolthoff & Stenger, "Volumetric Analysis," II, 52(1947).

(7) JAOAC **25**, 653(1942); **36**, 96, 354(1953); **37**, 122, 462(1954).

(8) JAOAC **22**, 102, 563(1939).

(9) Kolthoff & Stenger, "Volumetric Analysis," II, 80(1947); Ind. Eng. Chem., Anal. Ed. **9**, 141(1937); JAOAC **22**, 563(1939).

(10) JAOAC **30**, 502(1947); **31**, 119, 572(1948).

(11) JAOAC **32**, 587(1949); **33**, 225(1950).

(12) JAOAC **23**, 543(1940); **31**, 568(1948); J. Research NBS **15**, 493(1935); Research Paper No. 843.

(13) JAOAC **24**, 100, 631(1941).

(14) JAOAC **19**, 107, 194(1936); NBS Certificate for Standard Sample 84.

(15) JAOAC **25**, 659(1942); **27**, 557(1944); **28**, 594(1945); **38**, 382(1955); **47**, 43, 46(1964); **48**, 103(1965).

(16) J. Chem. Soc. Trans. **57**, 64(1890); J. Soc. Chem. Ind. (1899), 1091; JAOAC **24**, 636 (1941).

(17) JAOAC **31**, 573(1948); **32**, 589(1949).

46. Laboratory Safety

General Instructions

Thruout this book, appropriate refs are made to sections in this chapter to identify hazards and means for avoiding or protecting against them. Special hazards carry cautionary statement in method in which they occur. These statements are in addn to special precautionary practices observed in your laboratories. Also there are special regulations governing use of radioisotopes which are not described herein.

Nature and amt of each chemical and its prescribed use were criteria used in detg if cautionary statement for method was indicated.

Safety hazard was considered to exist when nature, amt, and use of chemical or equipment specified in method appeared probable of producing any of following:

(a) Concn of vapors from flammable liq. exceeding 25% of lower flammability limit of that liq. described by National Fire Protection Association, Boston, MA.

(b) Contact between analyst and quantities of material highly active physiologically or toxic to man in excess of Threshold Limit Values published by American Conference of Governmental Environmental Hygienists, Cincinnati, OH.

(c) Contact between analyst and quantities of highly corrosive material sufficient to produce serious injury.

(d) Contact between analyst and radiations which could be harmful.

(e) Explosion or violent reaction.

(f) Injury to analyst by hazards in equipment or processes which are not readily detectable by analyst.

When in doubt about possible hazards not covered in this chapter, consult refs at end of chapter or other sources of information such as hazard warnings on labels and manufacturers' data sheets.

Equipment

Avoid use of equipment for purposes other than intended. This practice results in unforeseen accidents. Some common hazards associated with equipment specified in this book are described below (7, 9).

46.001 *Refrigerators*

Should be explosion proof or explosion resistant when used for storage of ether and other highly volatile, flammable liqs. They can be made explosion resistant by removing light switch, receptacle, and associated wiring and placing thermoregulation controls on outside of refrigerator.

46.002 *Glass*

Dispose of chipped or broken glassware in special containers; minor chips may be fire-polished and glassware retained. If glassware is to be repaired, mark defective area plainly and store in special location until repairs are completed.

46.003 *Fire Extinguishers*

Class B and C dry chemical fire extinguishers (for flammable liq. and elec. fires) should be conveniently available to each laboratory room. Carbon dioxide fire extinguishers should be used on fires in electronic equipment.

Become familiar with their location and methods for effective use.

46.004 *Blenders*

Motor on high-speed blenders used to mix flammable solv. with other materials should be explosion proof. Perform blending of toxic or flammable liqs with effective fume removal device.

46.005 *Centrifuges*

Carefully adjust all tubes to equal wt before loading them into centrf. Make certain that stoppers of tubes placed in pivot-type head will clear center when tubes swing to horizontal. Do not open centrf. cover until machine stops completely. Before removing tubes, turn elec. switch to "off" instead of relying on zero-set rheostat. Use only tubes specially designed for centrfg. Safe speed for various tube materials (glass, cellulose nitrate, polyethylene, etc.) recommended by tube manufacturer should not be exceeded. Cellulose nitrate tubes may explode if autoclaved. Heating cellulose nitrate tubes > 60° may cause them to produce harmful nitrogen oxide fumes.

46.006 *Atomic Absorption Spectrophotometer*

Use effective fume removal device to remove gaseous effluents from burner. This is especially important when N_2O is used as fuel oxidant. If instrument has drain trap, check to ensure it is filled with H_2O prior to igniting burner. Explosions of fuel gas accumulating thru this drain line have been reported.

46.007 *Flame Photometer*

Use effective fume removal device to remove gaseous burner effluents.

46.008 *Photofluorometer*

Considerable amts of O_3 are formed by UV light radiated by quartz lamp. Ozone is toxic even in low concns; remove thru effective fume removal device placed near quartz lamp.

46.009 *Monitoring Equipment*

Some methods in this book require extns or refluxing operations which must proceed >8 hr. It is common for such processes to run overnight unattended. To avoid possibility of fire from overheating or loss of solv. by evapn, monitor these processes by appropriate equipment which will automatically shut down process in event of overheating, loss of cooling H_2O, or other occurrence. Ref *9* at end of this chapter describes several types of automatic process shut-down equipment designs.

46.010 *Compressed Gas Cylinders*

Identify by name(s) of gas(es) contents of compressed gas cylinders on attached decal, stencil, or tag, instead of by color codes. Secure cylinders in upright position by means of strap, chain, or non-tip base. Use only correct pressure gages, pressure regulator, and flow regulator for each size of gas cylinder and type of gas as specified by supplier. Use toxic gases only in effective fume removal device. When burning gas, use back flow prevention device in gas line to prevent flame being sucked back into cylinder from burning app. to help avoid possible explosions.

46.011 *Distillation, Extraction, and Evaporations*

(a) *Flammable liquids.*—Perform behind safety barrier with hot H_2O, steam, or elec. mantle heating. Use effective fume removal device to remove flammable vapors as produced. Set up app. on firm supports and secure all connections. Leave ample headroom in flask and add boiling chips before heating is begun. All controls, unless vapor sealed, should be located outside vapor area. Dispose of waste flammable solvs by evapn as above unless other provisions for safe disposal are available.

(b) *Toxic liquids.*—Use effective fume removal device to remove toxic vapors as produced. Avoid contact with skin. Set up app. on firm supports and secure all connections. Dispose of waste toxic solvs by evapn, using effective fume removal device unless other provisions for safe disposal are available.

46.012 *Electrical Equipment*

Accidents involving elec. equipment may result in *mech. injury*, e.g., fingers being caught in chopping mill knives; *elec. shock*, which may be due to lack of, or improper grounding, defective equipment, exposed wiring, or inadequate maintenance; and *fire* thru ignition of flammable vapors by electrically produced spark. Ground all elec. equipment to avoid accidental shock. Installation, maintenance, and repair operations should be performed by qualified electricians.

46.013 *Parr Bomb*

Follow manufacturer's directions closely to avoid explosion.

46.014 *Pressure*

Do not conduct pressure operations with std glassware. In certain circumstances, glassware specifically designed to withstand pressure may be used. Observe manufacturer's recommended safeguards when using pressure app. such as calorimeter bomb, hydrogenator, etc.

46.015 *Vacuum*

Tape or shield with safety barrier containers or app. to be used under vac. to minimize effects of possible implosion. Vac. pump drive belts must have effective guards.

46.016 *Hazardous Radiations*

UV radiation is encountered in atomic absorption spectrophotometry, fluorometry, UV spectrophotometry, germicidal lamps, and both long and short wave UV lamps used to monitor chromatgc sepns. Never expose unprotected eyes to UV light from any source either direct or reflected (e.g., flames in flame photometer, lamps, elec. arcs, etc.). Always wear appropriate eye protection such as goggles having uranium oxide lenses, welder's goggles, etc., when such radiations are present and unshielded. Keep skin exposure to UV radiations to min.

Technics and Practices
46.017 *Spraying Chromatograms*

When strong corrosive and toxic reagents are sprayed on chromatograms, use gloves, face shields, respiratory protection, and appropriate fume removal device to protect skin, eyes, and respiratory tract against mists or fumes generated by spraying device.

46.018 *Pipets*

Do not pipet hazardous liqs by using mouth suction to fill pipet. Use pipettor or rubber tubing connected thru trap to vac. line for this purpose.

46.019 *Wet Oxidation*

This technic is among most hazardous uses of acids but can be performed safely. Observe precautions in this chapter for particular acids used and rigorously follow directions given in specific method being used.

46.020 *Hazardous or After Hours Work*

Anyone working alone after hours or on hazardous procedures should arrange for someone to contact him periodically as safety measure.

46.021 *Glass Tubing*

Protect hands with heavy towel or gloves when inserting glass tubing into cork or rubber stopper. Fire polish all raw glass cuts.

Acids

Use effective *acid resistant* fume removal device whenever heating acids or performing reactions which liberate acid fumes. In dilg, always add acid to H_2O unless otherwise directed in method. Keep acids off skin and protect eyes from spattering. If acids are spilled on skin, wash immediately with large amts of H_2O.

46.022 *Acetic Acid and Acetic Anhydride*

React vigorously or explosively with CrO_3 and other strong oxidizers. Wear face shield and heavy rubber gloves when using.

46.023 *Chromic and Perchromic Acids*

Can react explosively with Ac_2O, HOAc, EtOAc, isoamyl alcohol, and benzaldehyde. Less hazardous with ethylene glycol, furfural, glycerol, and MeOH. Conduct reactions behind safety barrier. Wear face shield and heavy rubber gloves.

46.024 *Formic and Performic Acids*

Strong reducing agents; react vigorously or explosively with oxidizing agents. Irritating to skin, forming blisters. Performic acid (formyl hydroperoxide) has detonated for no apparent reason while being poured. Wear face shield and heavy rubber gloves when using.

46.025 *Hydrofluoric Acid*

Very hazardous with NH_3. It can cause painful sores on skin and is extremely irritating to eyes. Use effective removal device. Wear eye goggles and acid-resistant gloves.

46.026 *Nitric Acid*

Reacts vigorously or explosively with aniline, H_2S, flammable solvs, hydrazine, and metal powders (especially Zn, Al, and Mg). Gaseous nitrogen oxides from HNO_3 can cause severe lung damage. Copious fumes are evolved when concd HNO_3 and concd HCl are mixed. Avoid premixing. Use effective fume removal device when fumes are generated.

46.027 *Oxalic Acid*

Forms explosive compd with Ag and Hg. Oxalates are toxic. Avoid skin contact and ingestion.

46.028 *Perchloric Acid*

Contact with oxidizable or combustible materials or with dehydrating or reducing agents may result in fire or explosion. Persons using this acid should be thoroly familiar with its hazards. Safety practices should include following:

(a) Remove spilled $HClO_4$ by immediate and thoro washing with large amts of H_2O.

(b) Hoods, ducts, and other devices for removing $HClO_4$ vapor should be made of chemically inert materials and so designed that they can be thoroly washed with H_2O. Exhaust systems should discharge in safe location and fan should be accessible for cleaning.

(c) Avoid use of org. chemicals in hoods or other fume removal devices employed for $HClO_4$ digestions.

(d) Use goggles, barrier shields, and other devices as may be necessary for personal protection.

(e) In wet combustions with $HClO_4$, treat sample first with HNO_3 to destroy easily oxidizable org. matter unless otherwise specified. *Do not evap. to dryness.*

(f) Contact of $HClO_4$ soln with strong dehydrating agents such as P_2O_5 or concd H_2SO_4 may result in formation of explosive anhyd. $HClO_4$. Exercise special care in performing analyses requiring use of $HClO_4$ with such agents. Extremely sensitive to shock and heat when concn is >72%.

(g) Also observe precautions outlined in (1) "Perchloric Acid Solution," Chemical Safety Data Sheet SD-11 (1947), Manufacturing Chemists Association of the US, 1825 Connecticut Ave, NW, Washington, DC 20009; (2) "Applied Inorganic Analysis," W. F. Hillebrand, G. E. F. Lundell, H. A. Bright, and J. I. Hoffman, 2nd ed., (1953), pp. 39–40, John Wiley and Sons, Inc., New York, NY; (3) "Notes on Perchloric Acid and Its Handling in Analytical Work," Analyst **84**, 214–216(1959); (4) "Perchlorates," ACS Monograph No. 146, J. C. Schumacher, ed., Reinhold (1960). *See also* refs at end of this chapter.

46.029 *Picric Acid*

Highly sensitive to shock when in dry state. In contact with metals and NH_3, it produces picrates which are more sensitive to shock than picric acid. Readily absorbed thru skin and irritating to eyes. Wear heavy rubber gloves and eye protection.

46.030 *Sulfuric Acid*

Always add H_2SO_4 to H_2O. Wear face shield and heavy rubber gloves to protect against splashes.

46.031 *Fuming Acids*

Prep. and use with effective fume removal device. Wear acid resistant gloves and eye protection.

Alkalies

Alkalies can burn skin, eyes, and respiratory tract severely. Wear heavy rubber gloves and face shield to protect against concd alkali liqs. Use effective fume removal device or gas mask to protect respiratory tract against alkali dusts or vapors.

46.032 *Ammonia*

Extremely caustic liq. and gas. Wear skin, eye, and respiratory protection when handling in anhyd. liq. or gaseous state. NH_3 vapors are flammable. Reacts violently with strong oxidizing agents, halogens, and strong acids.

46.033 *Ammonium Hydroxide*

Caustic liq. Forms explosive compds with many heavy metals such as Ag, Pb, Zn, and their salts, especially halide salts.

46.034 *Sodium, Potassium, Lithium, Calcium Metals*

Violently reactive with H_2O or moisture, CO_2, halogens, strong acids, and chlorinated hydrocarbons. Emit corrosive fumes when burned. Can cause severe burns. Wear skin and eye protection when handling. Use only dry alcohol when preparing Na alcoholate and add metal directly to alcohol, one small piece at a time. Avoid adding metallic Na to reaction thru condenser.

46.035 *Sodium Peroxide*

Less caustic than Na and K hydroxides but reacts violently with H_2O, org. matter, charcoal, glycerol, Et_2O, or P. Wear skin, eye, and respiratory protection when handling multigram quantities.

46.036 *Calcium Oxide (Burnt Lime)*

Strongly caustic! Reacts violently with H_2O. Protect skin, eyes, and respiratory tract against contact with dust.

46.037 *Sodium and Potassium Hydroxides*

Extremely caustic. Can cause severe burns. Protect skin and eyes when working with these alkalies as solids or concd solns.

46.038 *Sodium Biphenyl, Sodium Methylate, and Sodium Ethylate*

Less caustic than NaOH but can be injurious. React vigorously with H_2O. Protect skin and eyes when handling.

Organic Solvents

46.039 *Flammable Solvents*

Do not let vapors conc. to flammable level in work area, since it is nearly impossible to eliminate all chance of sparks from static electricity even tho elec. equipment is grounded. Use effective fume removal device to remove these vapors when released.

46.040 *Toxic Solvents*

Vapors from some volatile solvs are highly toxic (1–3, 9, 10). Several of these solvs are readily absorbed thru skin. Use effective fume removal device to remove vapors of these solvs as they are liberated.

Special Chemical Hazards

46.041 *Pesticides*

Many pesticide chemicals are extremely toxic. These chemicals include org. Cl, carbamate, and org. P insecticides, mercurials, arsenicals, cyanides, nicotine, and other chemicals (1, 6). Observe following min. precautions at all times. Consult safety data sheets or labels for addnl information.

(a) Do all laboratory sampling, mixing, weighing, etc., under effective fume removal device in area having good forced ventilation of nonrecirculated air, or wear gas mask of proper type. If mask is used, replace cartridges as recommended, since using contaminated mask may be worse than no mask.

(b) Keep off skin. Wear clean protective clothing and nonpermeable gloves (such as polyethylene gloves) as necessary. Wash thoroly with soap and water to avoid contaminating food and smoking materials.

(c) Label all sample containers with name and approx. content of all pesticides.

(d) Have readily available and study information on symptoms of poisoning and first aid treatment for each type of pesticide being handled (1, 6).

(e) Consult physician about preventive measures and antidotes for use in emergencies when pesticide poisoning is suspected.

(f) Follow your organization's procedures when disposing of waste pesticides. The manufacturer can be contacted for advice on disposal problems.

(g) Do not enter pesticide *residue* or other laboratories after handling pesticide formulations until protective clothing and gloves have been removed and face and hands thoroly washed with soap and water.

46.042 *Aniline*

Toxic. Avoid contact with skin and eyes. Use effective fume removal device. Ignites in presence of fuming HNO_3. Forms explosive with O_3.

46.043 *Acetonitrile*

Toxic. Avoid contact with skin and eyes. Use effective fume removal device. HCN is liberated on contact with acid.

46.044 *Ammoniacal Silver Nitrate*

Use soon after prepn and do not allow to stand for long periods of time.

46.045 *Benzene*

Toxic. Highly flammable. Avoid contact with skin and breathing vapors. Use effective fume removal device. Decomposes violently in presence of strong oxidizing agents. Reacts violently with Cl.

46.046 *Acetone*

Highly flammable. Forms explosive peroxides with oxidizing agents. Use effective fume removal device.

46.047   *Bromine and Chlorine*

Hazardous with NH_3, H, petroleum gases, turpentine, benzene, and metal powders. Extremely corrosive. Use effective fume removal device. Protect skin against exposure.

46.048   *Carbon Disulfide*

Extremely flammable with low ignition temp. Toxic. Use effective fume removal device. Can react vigorously to violently with strong oxidizing agents, azides, and Zn. Avoid static electricity.

46.049   *Carbon Tetrachloride*

Reacts violently with alkali metals. Toxic. Fumes may decompose to phosgene when heated strongly. Use effective fume removal device.

46.050   *Cyanides*

Cyanides react with acids to form highly toxic HCN gas. Use only in effective fume removal device.

46.051   *Cyclohexane*

Highly flammable. Use effective fume removal device. Can react vigorously with strong oxidizing agents.

46.052   *Di- and Triethylamine*

Flammable. Toxic. Corrosive to skin and eyes. Use effective fume removal device. Can react vigorously with oxidizing materials.

46.053   *Dimethylformamide*

Toxic. Flammable. Avoid contact with skin and eyes. Use effective fume removal device. Can react vigorously with oxidizing agents, halogenated hydrocarbons, and inorg. nitrates.

46.054   *Diethyl Ether*

Extremely flammable. Unstable peroxides can form upon long standing or exposure to sunlight in bottles. Can react explosively when in contact with Cl, O_3, $LiAlH_4$, or strong oxidizing agents. Use effective fume removal device. Avoid static electricity. See also **46.070(b)**.

46.055   *Ethanol*

Flammable. Use effective fume removal device when heating or evapg.

46.056   *Chloroform*

Can be harmful if inhaled. Forms phosgene when heated to decomposition. Use effective fume removal device. Can react explosively with Al, Li, Mg, Na, K, disilane, N_2O_4, and NaOH plus MeOH.

46.057   *Ethyl Acetate*

Flammable, especially when being evapd. Irritating to eyes and respiratory tract. Use effective fume removal device.

46.058   *Formaldehyde*

Exposure to high concns may cause skin irritation and inflammation of mucous membranes, eyes, and respiratory tract. Use skin protection and effective fume removal device.

46.059   *Hydrogen Sulfide*

Hazardous with oxidizing gases, fuming HNO_3, and Na_2O_2. Forms explosive mixts with air. Toxic. Use effective fume removal device.

46.060   *Hypophosphorus Acid*

Reacts violently with oxiding agents. On decomposition, it emits highly toxic fumes (phosphine) and may explode. Use effective fume removal device.

46.061   *Hexane*

Highly flammable. Use effective fume removal device.

46.062   *Isooctane*

Highly flammable. Use effective fume removal device.

46.063   *Magnesium*

When finely divided, liberates H in contact with H_2O. Burns in air when exposed to flame. Can be explosive in contact with $CHCl_3$ or CH_3Cl.

46.064   *Magnesium Perchlorate*

Explodes on contact with acids and reducing materials. Use as drying agent on inorg. gases and materials only.

46.065   *Mercury*

Hazardous in contact with NH_3, halogens, and alkali. Vapors are extremely toxic and cumulative. Regard spills on hot surfaces as extremely hazardous and clean up promptly. Powd S sprinkled over spilled Hg can assist in cleaning up spills. High degree of personal cleanliness is necessary for persons who use Hg. Handle only in locations where any spill can be readily and thoroly cleaned up. When Hg evapn is necessary, use effective fume removal device.

To avoid environmental contamination, dil. liq. remaining in Kjeldahl distn flask $1+1$ with H_2O and filter out insol. Hg salts. Reserve ppt in closed labeled container for recovery of Hg or disposal appropriate for Hg.

46.066   *Methanol*

Flammable. Toxic. Avoid contact with eyes and breathing vapors. Use effective fume removal device. Can react vigorously with NaOH plus $CHCl_3$, and KOH plus $CHCl_3$ or $HClO_4$.

46.067   *Methyl Cellosolve*

Vapors can be harmful. Use effective fume removal device.

46.068 *Nitrobenzene and Other Nitroaromatics*

Readily absorbed thru skin. Symptoms of intoxication are sense of well-being and bluish tint on tongue, lips, and fingernails. Wear resistant rubber gloves when handling. To heat or evap., use effective fume removal device.

46.069 *Oxidizers*

(Perchlorates, peroxides, permanganates, persulfates, perborates, nitrates, chlorates, chlorites, bromates, iodates, concd H_2SO_4, concd HNO_3, CrO_3)

Can react violently with most metal powders, NH_3, and ammonium salts, P, many finely divided org. compds, flammable liquids, acids, and S. Use exactly as specified in method. Handle in effective fume removal device from behind explosion resistant barrier. Use face shield.

46.070 *Peroxides*

(a) *Hydrogen peroxide.*—30% strength is hazardous; can cause severe burns. Drying H_2O_2 on org. material such as paper or cloth can lead to spontaneous combustion. Cu, Fe, Cr, other metals, and their salts cause rapid catalytic decomposition of H_2O_2. Hazardous with flammable liqs, aniline, and nitrobenzene. Since it slowly decomposes with evolution of O, provide stored H_2O_2 with vent caps. Wear gloves and eye protection when handling.

(b) *Ether peroxides.*—These peroxides form in Et_2O, dioxane, and other ethers during storage. They are explosive and must be destroyed chemically before distn or evapn. Exposure to light influences peroxide formation in ethers. Filtration thru activated alumina is reported to be effective in removing peroxides. Store over Na ribbon to retard peroxide formation.

46.071 *Phosphotungstic Acid*

Emits highly toxic fumes when heated to decomposition or in strong alkali.

46.072 *Pyridine*

Toxic. Flammable. Use effective fume removal device. Releases toxic cyanides when heated to decomposition.

46.073 *Petroleum Ether*

Extremely flammable. Use effective fume removal device. Avoid static electricity.

46.074 *Pentane*

Extremely flammable. Use effective fume removal device. Avoid static electricity.

46.075 *Radioactive Chemicals*

Consult National Bureau of Standards Handbook #42, "Safe Handling of Radioactive Isotopes," before handling these materials.

46.076 *Silver Nitrate*

Powerful oxidizing agent; strongly corrosive. Dust or solid form is hazardous to eyes. Handle as in **46.069.**

46.077 *Silver Iodate*

Powerful oxidizing agent. Can initiate combustion in contact with org. material (e.g., paper or cloth). Can react vigorously with reducing agents. Handle as in **46.069.**

46.078 *Arsenic Trioxide*

Toxic. Forms toxic volatile halides in contact with halide acids. Forms volatile, highly toxic arsine when reduced in acid soln. Protect skin and respiratory tract when handling. Use effective fume removal device when arsine or arsenic trihalide is formed.

46.079 *Mercury Salts*

Mercuric salts are quite toxic and mostly H_2O-sol. Use skin and respiratory protection when dry mercuric salts are to be used. Use skin protection when concd aq. solns of mercuric salts are used. Mercurous salts are generally less toxic than mercuric salts. Use of personal protection is advisable when handling these salts and their concd solns.

See also **46.065.**

46.080 *Permanganates*

Moderately toxic. Readily sol. in H_2O. Strong oxidizing agent. May form explosive mixt. with H_2SO_4 or $HClO_4$. When using with strong acids to destroy org. matter, perform reaction behind safety barrier.

46.081 *Sulfur Dioxide*

Toxic gas. Forms H_2SO_3 in contact with moisture. Use effective fume removal device to remove SO_2 vapors released by reaction or from gas cylinder. Avoid contact with skin, eyes, and respiratory tract.

46.082 *Di- and Trichloroacetic Acids*

Protein precipitants. Can cause severe burns to skin and respiratory tract. Use rubber gloves, eye protection, and effective fume removal device to remove vapors generated.

46.083 *Uranyl Acetate*

Highly toxic. Avoid skin contact and breathing dusts.

46.084 *Toxic Dusts*

Use goggles and gloves to avoid contact with skin and eyes. Use effective fume removal device or other respiratory protection.

SELECTED REFERENCES

(1) Gleason, Gosselin and Hodge, "Clinical Toxicology of Commercial Products (Home and Farm)" (1963); The Williams & Wilkins Co., Baltimore, MD 21202.

(2) American Conference of Governmental Industrial Hygienists, "Threshold Limit Values"; 1014 Broadway, Cincinnati, OH 45202.

(3) Sax, "Dangerous Properties of Industrial Materials." 2nd Ed. (1963); Reinhold Publishing Corp., New York, NY 10022.

(4) National Fire Protection Association, "Fire Protection Guide on Hazardous Materials," 2nd Ed. (1967); 60 Batterymarch St, Boston, MA 02110.

(5) C. Marsden, "Solvents Guide" (1963); Interscience Publishers, New York, NY 10016.

(6) Brown, "Pesticides in Clinical Practice: Identification, Pharmacology and Therapeutics" (1966); C. C. Thomas, Springfield, IL 62703.

(7) National Institutes of Health, Handbook No. 3, "Chemical and Biological Safety Guide", Bethesda, MD 20014.

(8) Ind. Eng. Chem., Anal. Ed. 18, 52(1946).

(9) N. V. Steere, "Handbook of Laboratory Safety" (1967); The Chemical Rubber Company, Cleveland, OH 44128.

(10) Journal of the American Society of Safety Engineers, 7, Feb. 1964.

47. Reference Tables

★ Tables so marked are surplus. *See* "Definitions of Terms and Explanatory Notes," item (29).

ADDITIONAL SURPLUS TABLES

47.001 Table of atomic weights 1969; from Commission on Atomic Weights, International Union of Pure and Applied Chemistry

(Based on assigned relative atomic mass of $^{12}C = 12$)

Values apply to elements as they exist in materials of terrestrial origin and to certain artificial elements. When used with the footnotes, they are reliable to ± 1 in the last digit, or ± 3 if that digit is in bold type.

Name	Symbol	Atomic Number	Atomic Weight	Name	Symbol	Atomic Number	Atomic Weight
Actinium	Ac	89	—	Mercury	Hg	80	200.59
Aluminum	Al	13	26.9815[a]	Molybdenum	Mo	42	95.94
Americium	Am	95	—	Neodymium	Nd	60	144.24
Antimony	Sb	51	121.75	Neon	Ne	10	20.179[c]
Argon	Ar	18	39.948[b, c, d, g]	Neptunium	Np	93	237.0482[b]
Arsenic	As	33	74.9216[a]	Nickel	Ni	28	58.71
Astatine	At	85	—	Niobium	Nb	41	92.9064[a]
Barium	Ba	56	137.34	Nitrogen	N	7	14.0067[b, c]
Berkelium	Bk	97	—	Nobelium	No	102	—
Beryllium	Be	4	9.01218[a]	Osmium	Os	76	190.2
Bismuth	Bi	83	208.9806[a]	Oxygen	O	8	15.9994[b, c, d]
Boron	B	5	10.81[c, d, e]	Palladium	Pd	46	106.4
Bromine	Br	35	79.904[c]	Phosphorus	P	15	30.9738[a]
Cadmium	Cd	48	112.40	Platinum	Pt	78	195.09
Calcium	Ca	20	40.08	Plutonium	Pu	94	—
Californium	Cf	98	—	Polonium	Po	84	—
Carbon	C	6	12.011[b, d]	Potassium	K	19	39.102
Cerium	Ce	58	140.12	Praseodymium	Pr	59	140.0977[a]
Cesium	Cs	55	132.9055[a]	Promethium	Pm	61	—
Chlorine	Cl	17	35.453[c]	Protactinium	Pa	91	231.0359[a]
Chromium	Cr	24	51.996[c]	Radium	Ra	88	226.0254[a, f, g]
Cobalt	Co	27	58.9332[a]	Radon	Rn	86	—
Copper	Cu	29	63.546[c, d]	Rhenium	Re	75	186.2
Curium	Cm	96	—	Rhodium	Rh	45	102.9055[a]
Dysprosium	Dy	66	162.50	Rubidium	Rb	37	85.4678[c]
Einsteinium	Es	99	—	Ruthenium	Ru	44	101.07
Erbium	Er	68	167.26	Samarium	Sm	62	150.4
Europium	Eu	63	151.96	Scandium	Sc	21	44.9559[a]
Fermium	Fm	100	—	Selenium	Se	34	78.96
Fluorine	F	9	18.9984[a]	Silicon	Si	14	28.086[d]
Francium	Fr	87	—	Silver	Ag	47	107.868[c]
Gadolinium	Gd	64	157.25	Sodium	Na	11	22.9898[a]
Gallium	Ga	31	69.72	Strontium	Sr	38	87.62[g]
Germanium	Ge	32	72.59	Sulfur	S	16	32.06[d]
Gold	Au	79	196.9665[a]	Tantalum	Ta	73	180.9479[b]
Hafnium	Hf	72	178.49	Technetium	Tc	43	98.9062[f]
Helium	He	2	4.00260[b, c]	Tellurium	Te	52	127.60
Holmium	Ho	67	164.9303[a]	Terbium	Tb	65	158.9254[a]
Hydrogen	H	1	1.0080[b, d]	Thallium	Tl	81	204.37
Indium	In	49	114.82	Thorium	Th	90	232.0381[a]
Iodine	I	53	126.9045[a]	Thulium	Tm	69	168.9342[a]
Iridium	Ir	77	192.22	Tin	Sn	50	118.69
Iron	Fe	26	55.847	Titanium	Ti	22	47.90
Krypton	Kr	36	83.80	Tungsten	W	74	183.85
Lanthanum	La	57	138.9055[b]	Uranium	U	92	238.029[b, c, e]
Lawrencium	Lr	103	—	Vanadium	V	23	50.9414[b, c]
Lead	Pb	82	207.2[d, g]	Wolfram	W	74	183.85
Lithium	Li	3	6.941[c, d, e]	Xenon	Xe	54	131.30
Lutetium	Lu	71	174.97	Ytterbium	Yb	70	173.04
Magnesium	Mg	12	24.305[c]	Yttrium	Y	39	88.9059[a]
Manganese	Mn	25	54.9380[a]	Zinc	Zn	30	65.37
Mendelevium	Md	101	—	Zirconium	Zr	40	91.22

[a] Mononuclidic element.

[b] One predominant isotope (about 99–100% abundance).

[c] Atomic wt is based on calibrated measurements.

[d] Variation in isotopic abundance in terrestrial samples limits precision of atomic wt given.

[e] Users are cautioned against possibility of large variations in atomic wt due to inadvertent or undisclosed artificial isotopic sepn in com. available materials.

[f] Most commonly available long-lived isotope.

[g] In some geological specimens this element has a highly anomalous isotopic composition, corresponding to an atomic wt significantly different from that given.

47.002   Various strength solutions of the common acids, alkalies, and alcohol[a]

(a) *Ammonia solns:* Specification requires $\geq 28-\leq 30\%$ NH_3 by wt. Sp gr of 28.0% NH_3 soln = 0.9 at 15°. Mix and dil. to 1 L.

NH₃ Strength Desired	Reagent NH₃ Required	
g/L	g	ml
5	17.86	19.8
10	35.71	39.7
15	53.57	59.5
20	71.43	79.4
25	89.29	99.2
50	178.57	198.4
75	267.86	297.6
100	357.14	396.8
150	535.71	595.2
200	714.29	793.7

(b) *Sodium hydroxide solns:* Specification requires $\geq 97\%$ NaOH in sticks or pellets of caustic soda. Dissolve and dil. to 1 L.

NaOH Strength Desired	NaOH Required	
g/L	g	
12.5	12.89	For crude fiber
30	30.93	
40	41.24	1N soln
50	51.55	
75	77.32	
100	103.09	
150	154.64	
200	206.19	
250	257.73	
300	309.28	

(c) *Hydrochloric acid solns:* Specification requires $\geq 36.5-\leq 38.0\%$ HCl by wt. Sp gr of 37.2% HCl soln = 1.19 at 15°. Mix with H_2O and dil. to 1 L.

HCl Strength Desired	HCl Required		
g/L	g	ml	
5	13.44	11.29	
10	26.88	22.59	
15	40.32	33.88	
20	53.77	45.18	
36.46	98.01	82.36	1N soln
50	134.41	112.95	
100	268.82	225.90	
150	403.23	338.85	
200	537.63	451.79	
222.6	598.39	502.85	Constant boiling
278.4	748.39	628.90	Sp gr 1.125
300	806.45	677.69	

(d) *Nitric acid solns:* Specification requires $\geq 69.0-\leq 71.0\%$ HNO_3 by wt. Sp gr of 70.4% HNO_3 soln = 1.42 at 15°. 1 ml concd HNO_3 contains ca 1.00 g HNO_3. Mix with H_2O and dil. to 1 L.

HNO₃ Strength Desired	HNO₃ Required		
g/L	g	ml	
5	7.10	5.0	
10	14.20	10.0	
20	28.41	20.0	
30	42.61	30.0	
40	56.82	40.0	
50	71.02	50.0	
63	89.49	63.0	1N soln
70	99.43	70.0	
100	142.05	100.0	
150	213.07	150.0	
200	284.09	200.1	
300	426.14	300.1	

(e) *Sulfuric acid solns:* Specification requires $\geq 95.0-\leq 98.0\%$ H_2SO_4 by wt. Sp gr of 96.0% soln = 1.84 at 15°. Pour acid into excess of H_2O and dil. to 1 L.

H₂SO₄ Strength Desired	H₂SO₄ Required		
g/L	g	ml	
5	5.21	2.8	
12.5	13.02	7.1	For crude fiber
20	20.83	11.3	
30	31.25	17.0	
40	41.67	22.6	
49	51.04	27.7	1N soln
100	104.17	56.6	
150	156.25	84.9	
250	260.42	141.5	
300	312.50	169.8	
400	416.67	226.5	

(f) *Alcoholic solns:*[b] Specification requires 95% C_2H_5OH by vol. Sp gr = 0.810 at 25°. Mix and dil. to 1 L.

Alcohol Strength Desired	Alcohol Required	
ml/L	g	ml
50	42.63	52.6
100	85.26	105.3
150	127.89	157.9
200	170.52	210.5
250	213.16	263.2
300	255.78	315.9
400	341.04	421.1
500	426.32 (proof)	526.3
700	596.84	736.8

[a] Prepd by G. C. Spencer and H. J. Fisher, 1935 and updated by W. D. Hubbard, 1970.

[b] Alcohol of any desired strength may be obtained by taking number of ml 95% alcohol equiv. to desired strength and dilg soln to 95 ml; e.g., to obtain soln of 70% alcohol, take 70 ml 95% alcohol and dil. to 95 ml.

47.003   Percentages by volume at 15.56°C (60°F) of ethyl alcohol corresponding to apparent specific gravity at various temperatures[a]

Apparent Specific Gravity	15.56 ——— 15.56	20/20	22/22	24/24	25/25	26/26	28/28	30/30	32/32	34/34	35/35	36/36
1.0000	0.00	0.00	0.00	0.00	0.00	0.00	0.00	0.00	0.00	0.00	0.00	0.00
0.9999	.07	.07	.07	.07	.07	.07	.07	.07	.07	.07	.07	.07
98	.13	.13	.13	.13	.13	.13	.13	.13	.13	.13	.13	.13
97	.20	.20	.20	.20	.20	.20	.20	.20	.20	.20	.20	.20
96	.27	.26	.26	.26	.26	.26	.26	.26	.26	.26	.26	.26
95	.33	.33	.33	.33	.33	.33	.33	.33	.33	.33	.33	.33
94	.40	.40	.40	.40	.40	.40	.40	.40	.40	.40	.40	.40
93	.47	.46	.46	.46	.46	.46	.46	.46	.46	.46	.46	.46
92	.53	.53	.53	.53	.53	.53	.53	.53	.53	.53	.53	.53
91	.60	.60	.60	.60	.60	.60	.60	.60	.60	.60	.60	.60
90	.67	.66	.66	.66	.66	.66	.66	.66	.66	.66	.66	.66
89	.73	.73	.73	.73	.73	.73	.73	.73	.73	.73	.73	.73
88	.80	.80	.80	.80	.80	.80	.79	.79	.79	.79	.79	.79
87	.87	.87	.87	.87	.87	.87	.86	.86	.86	.86	.86	.86
86	.93	.93	.93	.93	.93	.93	.93	.93	.93	.93	.93	.93
85	1.00	1.00	1.00	1.00	1.00	1.00	.99	.99	.99	.99	.99	.99
84	.07	.07	.07	.07	.07	.07	1.06	1.06	1.06	1.06	1.06	1.06
83	.14	.14	.14	.13	.13	.13	.13	.13	.13	.13	.13	.13
82	.20	.20	.20	.20	.20	.20	.20	.19	.19	.19	.19	.19
81	.27	.27	.27	.27	.27	.27	.26	.26	.26	.26	.26	.26
80	.34	.34	.34	.34	.34	.33	.33	.32	.32	.32	.32	.32
79	.41	.41	.41	.40	.40	.40	.40	.39	.39	.39	.39	.39
78	.48	.48	.48	.47	.47	.47	.47	.46	.46	.46	.46	.46
77	.54	.54	.54	.54	.54	.53	.53	.53	.53	.53	.52	.52
76	.61	.61	.61	.60	.60	.60	.60	.59	.59	.59	.59	.59
75	.68	.68	.68	.67	.67	.67	.67	.66	.66	.66	.66	.66
74	.75	.75	.75	.74	.74	.73	.73	.73	.73	.72	.72	.72
73	.82	.81	.81	.81	.81	.80	.80	.80	.80	.79	.79	.79
72	.88	.88	.88	.87	.87	.87	.86	.86	.86	.85	.85	.85
71	.95	.95	.95	.94	.94	.94	.93	.93	.93	.92	.92	.92
70	2.02	2.02	2.02	2.01	2.01	2.01	2.00	2.00	2.00	.99	.99	.99
69	.09	.09	.09	.08	.08	.08	.07	.07	.06	2.05	2.05	2.05
68	.16	.15	.15	.14	.14	.14	.14	.14	.13	.12	.12	.12
67	.23	.22	.22	.21	.21	.21	.20	.20	.20	.19	.19	.19
66	.30	.29	.29	.28	.28	.28	.27	.27	.27	.26	.26	.26
65	.37	.36	.36	.35	.35	.35	.34	.34	.33	.32	.32	.32
64	.43	.43	.43	.42	.42	.42	.41	.41	.40	.39	.39	.39
63	.50	.50	.50	.49	.49	.49	.48	.48	.47	.46	.46	.46
62	.57	.57	.57	.56	.56	.56	.55	.54	.54	.53	.53	.53
61	.64	.64	.64	.63	.63	.63	.62	.61	.60	.60	.59	.59
60	.71	.70	.70	.70	.70	.70	.69	.68	.67	.67	.66	.66
59	.78	.77	.77	.77	.77	.77	.76	.75	.74	.74	.73	.73
58	.85	.84	.84	.83	.83	.83	.82	.82	.81	.81	.80	.80
57	.92	.91	.91	.90	.90	.90	.89	.88	.87	.87	.86	.86
56	.99	.98	.98	.97	.97	.97	.96	.95	.94	.94	.93	.93
55	3.06	3.05	3.05	3.04	3.04	3.04	3.03	3.02	3.01	3.01	3.00	3.00
54	.13	.12	.12	.11	.11	.11	.10	.09	.08	.08	.07	.07
53	.20	.19	.19	.18	.18	.18	.17	.16	.15	.15	.14	.14
52	.27	.26	.26	.25	.25	.25	.24	.23	.22	.22	.21	.21
51	.34	.33	.33	.32	.32	.32	.31	.30	.29	.28	.27	.27
50	.41	.40	.40	.39	.39	.39	.38	.37	.36	.35	.34	.34
49	.49	.47	.47	.46	.46	.46	.45	.44	.43	.42	.41	.41
48	.56	.54	.54	.53	.53	.53	.52	.51	.50	.49	.48	.48
47	.63	.61	.61	.60	.60	.60	.59	.58	.57	.56	.55	.55
46	.70	.68	.68	.67	.67	.67	.66	.65	.64	.63	.62	.62
45	.77	.76	.75	.74	.74	.74	.73	.72	.70	.69	.68	.68
44	.84	.83	.82	.81	.81	.81	.79	.78	.77	.76	.75	.75
43	.91	.90	.89	.88	.88	.88	.86	.85	.84	.83	.82	.82
42	.99	.97	.96	.95	.95	.95	.93	.92	.91	.90	.89	.89
41	4.06	4.04	4.03	4.02	4.02	4.02	4.00	.99	.98	.97	.96	.96
40	.13	.11	.10	.10	.09	.09	.07	4.06	4.05	4.04	4.03	4.03
39	.20	.18	.17	.17	.16	.16	.14	.13	.12	.11	.10	.10
38	.28	.26	.25	.25	.24	.23	.21	.20	.19	.18	.17	.17
37	.35	.33	.32	.32	.31	.30	.28	.27	.26	.25	.24	.24
36	.42	.40	.39	.39	.38	.37	.36	.35	.33	.32	.31	.30
35	.50	.48	.47	.46	.45	.44	.43	.42	.40	.39	.38	.37
34	.57	.55	.54	.53	.52	.51	.50	.49	.47	.46	.45	.44
33	.64	.62	.61	.60	.59	.58	.57	.56	.54	.53	.52	.51
32	.71	.69	.68	.67	.66	.65	.64	.63	.61	.60	.59	.58
31	.79	.77	.76	.75	.74	.73	.72	.70	.68	.67	.66	.65

(Continued)

[a] Compiled at National Bureau of Standards. Table is based on data published in *Bull. Natl. Bur. Std.* **9**(3) (1913), (Sci. Paper No. 197).

47.003 Percentages by volume at 15.56°C (60°F) of ethyl alcohol corresponding to apparent specific gravity at various temperatures[a]—Continued.

Apparent Specific Gravity	15.56/15.56	20/20	22/22	24/24	25/25	26/26	28/28	30/30	32/32	34/34	35/35	36/36
0.9930	4.86	4.84	4.83	4.82	4.81	4.80	4.79	4.77	4.75	4.74	4.73	4.72
29	.93	.91	.90	.89	.88	.87	.86	.84	.82	.81	.80	.79
28	5.01	.98	.97	.96	.95	.94	.93	.91	.89	.88	.87	.86
27	.08	5.06	5.04	5.03	5.02	5.01	5.00	.98	.96	.95	.94	.93
26	.16	.13	.12	.11	.10	.09	.07	5.05	5.03	5.02	5.01	5.00
25	.23	.21	.19	.18	.17	.16	.14	.12	.10	.09	.08	.07
24	.31	.28	.26	.25	.24	.23	.21	.20	.18	.16	.15	.14
23	.39	.36	.34	.33	.32	.31	.29	.27	.25	.23	.22	.21
22	.46	.43	.41	.40	.39	.38	.36	.34	.32	.30	.29	.28
21	.54	.51	.49	.48	.47	.46	.44	.42	.40	.38	.37	.36
20	.61	.58	.56	.55	.54	.53	.51	.49	.47	.45	.44	.43
19	.69	.66	.64	.62	.61	.60	.58	.56	.54	.52	.51	.50
18	.77	.73	.71	.70	.69	.68	.66	.64	.62	.59	.58	.57
17	.84	.81	.79	.77	.76	.75	.73	.71	.69	.66	.65	.64
16	.92	.88	.86	.85	.84	.83	.80	.78	.76	.74	.73	.72
15	.99	.96	.94	.92	.91	.90	.87	.85	.83	.81	.80	.79
14	6.07	6.03	6.01	6.00	.99	.98	.95	.93	.91	.88	.87	.86
13	.15	.11	.09	.07	6.06	6.05	6.02	6.00	.98	.95	.94	.93
12	.23	.18	.16	.15	.14	.13	.10	.08	6.05	6.02	6.01	6.00
11	.30	.26	.24	.22	.21	.20	.17	.15	.12	.10	.09	.08
10	.38	.34	.32	.30	.29	.28	.25	.23	.20	.17	.16	.15
09	.46	.41	.39	.37	.36	.35	.32	.30	.28	.25	.24	.23
08	.54	.49	.47	.45	.44	.43	.40	.38	.35	.32	.31	.30
07	.62	.57	.55	.53	.52	.51	.48	.45	.42	.39	.38	.37
06	.70	.65	.63	.60	.59	.58	.55	.53	.50	.47	.46	.45
05	.77	.73	.71	.68	.67	.66	.63	.60	.57	.54	.53	.52
04	.85	.80	.78	.75	.74	.73	.70	.68	.65	.62	.60	.59
03	.93	.88	.86	.83	.82	.81	.78	.75	.72	.69	.68	.67
02	7.01	.96	.93	.90	.89	.88	.85	.83	.80	.77	.75	.74
01	.09	7.04	7.01	.98	.97	.95	.92	.90	.87	.84	.82	.81
00	.17	.12	.09	7.06	7.05	7.03	7.00	.98	.94	.91	.90	.88
0.9899	.25	.19	.16	.13	.12	.10	.07	7.05	7.01	.98	.97	.95
98	.33	.27	.24	.21	.20	.18	.15	.13	.09	7.06	7.04	7.02
97	.41	.35	.32	.29	.28	.26	.23	.21	.17	.14	.12	.10
96	.50	.43	.40	.37	.36	.34	.31	.28	.24	.21	.19	.17
95	.58	.51	.48	.45	.44	.42	.39	.36	.32	.29	.27	.25
94	.66	.59	.56	.53	.52	.50	.47	.44	.40	.36	.34	.32
93	.74	.67	.64	.60	.59	.57	.54	.51	.47	.44	.42	.40
92	.82	.75	.72	.68	.67	.65	.62	.59	.55	.51	.49	.47
91	.90	.82	.79	.76	.75	.73	.70	.66	.62	.59	.57	.55
90	.98	.90	.87	.84	.83	.81	.78	.74	.70	.66	.64	.62
89	8.07	.98	.95	.92	.91	.89	.86	.82	.78	.74	.72	.70
88	.15	8.06	8.03	8.00	.98	.96	.93	.89	.85	.81	.79	.77
87	.23	.15	.11	.08	8.06	8.04	8.01	.97	.93	.89	.87	.85
86	.32	.23	.19	.16	.14	.12	.09	8.05	8.01	.96	.94	.92
85	.40	.31	.27	.24	.22	.20	.16	.12	.08	8.04	8.02	8.00
84	.48	.39	.35	.32	.30	.28	.24	.20	.16	.11	.09	.07
83	.57	.47	.43	.40	.38	.36	.32	.27	.23	.19	.17	.15
82	.65	.55	.51	.48	.46	.44	.40	.35	.31	.26	.24	.22
81	.73	.63	.59	.56	.54	.52	.48	.43	.39	.34	.32	.30
80	.82	.71	.67	.63	.61	.59	.55	.50	.46	.41	.39	.37
79	.90	.79	.75	.71	.69	.67	.63	.58	.54	.49	.47	.45
78	.98	.88	.84	.79	.77	.75	.71	.66	.61	.56	.54	.52
77	9.07	.96	.92	.87	.85	.83	.78	.73	.69	.64	.62	.60
76	.15	9.04	9.00	.95	.93	.91	.86	.81	.76	.71	.69	.67
75	.24	.13	.08	9.03	9.01	.99	.94	.89	.84	.79	.77	.75
74	.32	.21	.16	.11	.09	9.07	9.02	.96	.91	.86	.84	.82
73	.40	.29	.24	.19	.17	.15	.10	9.04	.99	.94	.92	.90
72	.49	.38	.33	.27	.25	.23	.18	.12	9.07	9.02	.99	.97
71	.57	.46	.41	.35	.33	.31	.26	.20	.15	.10	9.07	9.05
70	.66	.54	.49	.43	.41	.38	.33	.27	.22	.17	.14	.12
69	.74	.62	.57	.51	.49	.46	.41	.35	.30	.25	.22	.19
68	.82	.70	.65	.59	.57	.54	.49	.43	.37	.32	.29	.26
67	.91	.79	.74	.68	.65	.62	.57	.51	.45	.40	.37	.34
66	.99	.87	.82	.76	.73	.70	.65	.59	.53	.47	.44	.41
65	10.08	.95	.90	.84	.81	.78	.72	.66	.60	.54	.51	.48
64	.16	10.03	.98	.92	.89	.86	.80	.74	.68	.62	.59	.56
63	.25	.11	10.06	10.00	.97	.94	.88	.82	.76	.69	.66	.63
62	.33	.20	.14	.08	10.05	10.02	.96	.90	.84	.77	.74	.71
61	.42	.28	.22	.16	.13	.10	10.04	.98	.91	.84	.81	.78

(Continued)

47.003 **Percentages by volume at 15.56°C (60°F) of ethyl alcohol corresponding to apparent specific gravity at various temperatures[a]—Continued.**

Apparent Specific Gravity	15.56/15.56	20/20	22/22	24/24	25/25	26/26	28/28	30/30	32/32	34/34	35/35	36/36
0.9860	10.50	10.36	10.30	10.24	10.21	10.18	10.11	10.05	9.99	9.92	9.89	9.86
59	.59	.44	.38	.32	.29	.26	.19	.13	10.06	.99	.96	.93
58	.68	.53	.47	.40	.37	.34	.27	.21	.14	10.07	10.04	10.00
57	.76	.61	.55	.48	.44	.41	.34	.28	.21	.14	.11	.07
56	.85	.69	.63	.56	.52	.49	.42	.36	.29	.22	.19	.15
55	.93	.78	.71	.64	.60	.57	.50	.44	.37	.30	.26	.23
54	11.02	.86	.79	.72	.68	.65	.58	.52	.45	.38	.34	.31
53	.11	.94	.87	.80	.76	.73	.66	.59	.52	.45	.41	.38
52	.19	11.03	.96	.88	.84	.81	.74	.67	.60	.53	.49	.45
51	.28	.11	11.04	.96	.92	.89	.82	.75	.67	.60	.56	.52
50	.37	.19	.12	11.04	11.00	.96	.89	.82	.74	.67	.63	.59
49	.46	.28	.20	.12	.08	11.04	.97	.90	.82	.75	.71	.67
48	.54	.36	.28	.20	.16	.12	11.05	.98	.90	.82	.78	.74
47	.63	.45	.36	.28	.24	.20	.13	11.05	.97	.90	.86	.82
46	.72	.53	.45	.37	.33	.29	.21	.13	11.05	.97	.93	.89
45	.81	.61	.53	.45	.41	.37	.29	.21	.13	11.05	11.01	.97
44	.89	.70	.62	.53	.49	.45	.37	.29	.21	.12	.08	11.04
43	.98	.78	.70	.61	.57	.53	.44	.36	.28	.20	.16	.12
42	12.07	.87	.78	.69	.65	.61	.52	.44	.36	.27	.23	.19
41	.16	.95	.86	.78	.73	.69	.60	.52	.44	.35	.31	.27
40	.25	12.04	.95	.86	.81	.77	.68	.60	.51	.42	.38	.34
39	.34	.12	12.03	.94	.89	.85	.76	.67	.58	.50	.46	.42
38	.43	.21	.12	12.03	.98	.93	.84	.75	.66	.57	.53	.49
37	.52	.29	.20	.11	12.06	12.01	.92	.83	.74	.65	.61	.57
36	.61	.38	.28	.19	.14	.09	12.00	.91	.82	.73	.68	.64
35	.70	.47	.37	.27	.22	.17	.07	.98	.89	.80	.76	.72
34	.79	.55	.45	.35	.30	.25	.15	12.06	.97	.88	.83	.79
33	.88	.64	.54	.44	.39	.34	.24	.14	12.05	.96	.91	.86
32	.97	.73	.63	.52	.47	.42	.32	.22	.12	12.03	.98	.93
31	13.06	.81	.71	.60	.55	.50	.40	.30	.20	.11	12.06	12.01
30	.16	.90	.79	.68	.63	.58	.48	.38	.28	.19	.14	.09
29	.25	.99	.88	.77	.71	.66	.56	.46	.36	.26	.21	.16
28	.34	13.07	.96	.85	.80	.74	.64	.54	.44	.34	.29	.24
27	.43	.16	13.05	.93	.88	.82	.72	.62	.52	.42	.37	.32
26	.52	.25	.13	13.01	.96	.90	.80	.70	.59	.49	.44	.39
25	.61	.34	.22	.10	13.04	.99	.88	.78	.67	.57	.52	.47
24	.71	.43	.31	.19	.13	13.08	.97	.86	.75	.65	.60	.55
23	.80	.51	.39	.27	.21	.16	13.05	.94	.83	.72	.67	.62
22	.89	.60	.47	.35	.29	.24	.13	13.02	.91	.80	.75	.70
21	.98	.68	.56	.44	.38	.33	.22	.10	.99	.88	.82	.77
20	14.08	.77	.64	.52	.46	.40	.29	.18	13.06	.95	.90	.85
19	.17	.86	.73	.61	.55	.49	.37	.26	.15	13.04	.98	.93
18	.26	.95	.82	.69	.63	.57	.45	.34	.22	.11	13.05	13.00
17	.36	14.04	.91	.78	.72	.66	.54	.42	.30	.19	.13	.08
16	.45	.13	14.00	.87	.80	.74	.62	.50	.38	.27	.21	.16
15	.55	.22	.08	.95	.88	.82	.70	.58	.46	.34	.28	.23
14	.64	.30	.17	14.04	.97	.91	.78	.66	.54	.42	.36	.30
13	.74	.39	.25	.12	14.05	.99	.86	.74	.62	.50	.44	.38
12	.83	.48	.34	.20	.13	14.07	.94	.82	.70	.58	.52	.46
11	.92	.57	.43	.29	.22	.16	14.03	.90	.77	.65	.59	.53
10	15.02	.66	.51	.37	.30	.24	.11	.98	.85	.73	.67	.61
09	.11	.75	.60	.46	.39	.32	.19	14.06	.93	.81	.75	.69
08	.21	.84	.69	.54	.47	.40	.27	.14	14.01	.88	.82	.76
07	.30	.93	.77	.62	.55	.48	.35	.22	.09	.96	.90	.84
06	.40	15.02	.86	.71	.64	.57	.43	.30	.17	14.04	.98	.92
05	.49	.11	.95	.79	.72	.65	.51	.38	.25	.12	14.05	.99
04	.58	.20	15.04	.88	.81	.74	.60	.46	.33	.20	.13	14.07
03	.67	.28	.12	.96	.89	.82	.68	.54	.41	.28	.21	.15
02	.77	.37	.21	15.05	.97	.90	.76	.62	.49	.36	.29	.23
01	.87	.46	.30	.14	15.06	.99	.84	.70	.56	.43	.36	.30
00	.96	.55	.39	.23	.15	15.07	.92	.78	.64	.51	.44	.38
0.9799	16.06	.64	.48	.32	.24	.16	15.01	.86	.72	.59	.52	.46
98	.15	.73	.57	.40	.32	.24	.09	.94	.80	.67	.60	.54
97	.25	.82	.65	.49	.41	.33	.17	15.02	.88	.74	.67	.61
96	.35	.91	.74	.57	.49	.41	.26	.11	.96	.82	.75	.68
95	.44	16.00	.83	.66	.58	.50	.34	.19	15.04	.90	.83	.76
94	.54	.10	.92	.75	.66	.59	.43	.27	.12	.98	.91	.84
93	.63	.19	16.01	.84	.75	.67	.51	.35	.20	15.05	.98	.91
92	.73	.28	.10	.93	.84	.76	.59	.43	.28	.13	15.06	.99
91	.83	.37	.19	16.01	.92	.84	.67	.51	.36	.21	.14	15.07

(Continued)

47.003   Percentages by volume at 15.56°C (60°F) of ethyl alcohol corresponding to apparent specific gravity at various temperatures[a]—Continued.

Apparent Specific Gravity	15.56/15.56	20/20	22/22	24/24	25/25	26/26	28/28	30/30	32/32	34/34	35/35	36/36
0.9790	16.92	16.46	16.27	16.09	16.00	15.92	15.75	15.59	15.44	15.29	15.22	15.15
89	17.02	.55	.26	.18	.09	16.01	.84	.67	.52	.37	.30	.23
88	.12	.64	.45	.27	.18	.10	.93	.76	.61	.45	.38	.31
87	.22	.73	.54	.36	.27	.18	16.01	.84	.68	.52	.45	.38
86	.32	.83	.63	.44	.35	.26	.09	.92	.76	.60	.53	.46
85	.42	.92	.72	.53	.44	.35	.17	16.00	.84	.68	.61	.53
84	.51	17.01	.81	.62	.53	.44	.26	.08	.92	.76	.69	.61
83	.61	.10	.90	.70	.61	.52	.34	.17	.10	.84	.77	.69
82	.71	.20	.99	.79	.70	.61	.43	.25	16.08	.92	.84	.76
81	.81	.29	17.08	.88	.78	.69	.51	.33	.16	16.00	.92	.84
80	.91	.38	.17	.97	.87	.78	.59	.41	.24	.08	16.00	.92
79	18.01	.47	.26	17.06	.96	.87	.68	.50	.33	.16	.08	16.00
78	.11	.57	.35	.14	17.04	.95	.76	.58	.41	.24	.16	.08
77	.21	.66	.44	.23	.13	17.04	.85	.66	.49	.32	.24	.16
76	.31	.75	.53	.32	.22	.12	.93	.74	.57	.40	.32	.24
75	.41	.84	.62	.40	.30	.20	17.01	.83	.65	.48	.40	.32
74	.51	.94	.72	.50	.39	.29	.10	.91	.73	.56	.48	.40
73	.61	18.03	.81	.59	.48	.38	.18	.99	.81	.64	.56	.48
72	.71	.12	.90	.68	.57	.47	.27	17.07	.89	.72	.63	.55
71	.81	.22	.99	.76	.65	.55	.35	.16	.97	.80	.71	.63
70	.91	.31	18.08	.85	.74	.63	.43	.24	17.05	.88	.79	.71
69	19.01	.40	.16	.94	.83	.72	.52	.32	.14	.96	.87	.79
68	.11	.50	.25	18.02	.91	.80	.60	.40	.22	17.04	.95	.86
67	.21	.59	.34	.11	18.00	.89	.69	.49	.30	.12	17.03	.94
66	.32	.69	.44	.20	.09	.98	.78	.57	.38	.20	.11	17.02
65	.42	.78	.53	.29	.18	18.07	.86	.65	.46	.28	.19	.10
64	.52	.88	.63	.38	.27	.16	.95	.74	.55	.36	.27	.17
63	.62	.97	.71	.47	.35	.24	18.03	.82	.62	.43	.35	.25
62	.72	19.07	.81	.56	.44	.33	.11	.90	.70	.51	.43	.33
61	.83	.16	.90	.65	.53	.42	.20	.98	.78	.59	.50	.41
60	.93	.26	.99	.74	.62	.50	.28	18.07	.87	.67	.58	.49
59	20.03	.35	19.08	.83	.71	.60	.37	.15	.95	.75	.66	.56
58	.13	.45	.18	.92	.80	.69	.46	.23	18.03	.83	.74	.64
57	.23	.54	.27	19.01	.88	.77	.54	.32	.11	.91	.82	.72
56	.33	.64	.36	.10	.97	.86	.62	.40	.19	.99	.90	.80
55	.43	.73	.45	.19	19.06	.94	.70	.48	.27	18.07	.98	.88
54	.53	.83	.55	.28	.15	19.03	.79	.57	.36	.15	18.06	.96
53	.63	.92	.64	.37	.24	.12	.88	.65	.44	.23	.13	18.04
52	.73	20.02	.73	.46	.33	.21	.96	.73	.52	.31	.21	.12
51	.83	.11	.82	.55	.42	.30	19.05	.82	.60	.39	.29	.19
50	.93	.20	.91	.64	.50	.38	.13	.90	.68	.47	.37	.27
49	21.03	.30	20.01	.73	.59	.47	.22	.98	.76	.55	.45	.35
48	.13	.39	.10	.82	.68	.56	.31	19.07	.85	.64	.53	.43
47	.23	.48	.19	.91	.77	.65	.39	.15	.93	.72	.61	.51
46	.33	.58	.28	20.00	.86	.74	.48	.24	19.01	.80	.69	.59
45	.43	.67	.37	.09	.95	.82	.56	.32	.09	.88	.77	.67
44	.52	.76	.46	.17	20.03	.90	.64	.40	.17	.96	.85	.75
43	.62	.86	.55	.26	.12	.99	.73	.49	.26	19.04	.93	.83
42	.72	.95	.64	.35	.21	20.08	.82	.57	.34	.12	19.01	.91
41	.82	21.04	.73	.44	.30	.17	.91	.66	.42	.20	.09	.98
40	.92	.14	.82	.53	.38	.25	.99	.74	.50	.28	.17	19.06
39	22.02	.23	.91	.62	.47	.34	20.07	.82	.58	.35	.24	.23
38	.12	.32	21.00	.71	.56	.43	.16	.90	.66	.43	.32	.31
37	.22	.41	.09	.79	.64	.51	.24	.98	.74	.51	.40	.29
36	.31	.50	.18	.88	.73	.59	.32	20.06	.82	.59	.48	.37
35	.41	.60	.27	.97	.82	.68	.41	.15	.90	.67	.56	.45
34	.51	.69	.36	21.05	.90	.77	.50	.24	.99	.75	.64	.53
33	.61	.78	.45	.14	.99	.85	.58	.32	20.07	.83	.72	.61
32	.71	.87	.54	.23	21.08	.94	.66	.40	.15	.91	.80	.68
31	.80	.96	.63	.32	.16	21.02	.74	.48	.23	.99	.87	.76
30	.90	22.05	.72	.41	.25	.11	.83	.56	.31	20.07	.95	.84
29	23.00	.14	.81	.50	.34	.20	.91	.64	.39	.15	20.03	.92
28	.10	.24	.90	.58	.42	.28	.99	.72	.47	.23	.11	20.00
27	.19	.33	.99	.67	.51	.36	21.07	.80	.55	.31	.19	.08
26	.29	.42	22.08	.76	.59	.45	.16	.89	.63	.39	.27	.16
25	.38	.51	.17	.84	.68	.53	.24	.97	.71	.46	.34	.23
24	.48	.60	.26	.93	.77	.62	.33	21.05	.79	.54	.42	.30
23	.58	.69	.34	22.01	.85	.70	.41	.13	.87	.62	.50	.38
22	.67	.78	.43	.10	.94	.78	.49	.21	.95	.70	.58	.46
21	.77	.87	.52	.19	22.03	.87	.58	.30	21.03	.78	.66	.54

(Continued)

47.003 **Percentages by volume at 15.56°C (60°F) of ethyl alcohol corresponding to apparent specific gravity at various temperatures**[a]—*Continued.*

Apparent Specific Gravity	15.56 / 15.56	20/20	22/22	24/24	25/25	26/26	28/28	30/30	32/32	34/34	35/35	36/36
0.9720	23.87	22.96	22.61	22.27	22.11	21.96	21.66	21.38	20.11	20.86	20.73	20.61
19	.96	23.06	.70	.36	.19	22.04	.74	.46	.19	.94	.81	.69
18	24.06	.15	.79	.45	.28	.12	.82	.54	.27	21.02	.89	.77
17	.15	.24	.88	.54	.36	.21	.91	.62	.35	.10	.97	.85
16	.25	.33	.96	.62	.45	.30	.99	.70	.43	.17	21.05	.92
15	.34	.42	23.05	.70	.53	.38	22.08	.79	.51	.24	.12	.99
14	.43	.51	.14	.79	.62	.46	.16	.87	.59	.33	.20	21.08
13	.53	.60	.22	.87	.70	.54	.24	.95	.67	.40	.27	.15
12	.62	.69	.31	.96	.79	.63	.32	22.03	.75	.88	.35	.22
11	.72	.78	.40	23.04	.87	.71	.40	.11	.83	.56	.43	.30
10	.81	.87	.49	.13	.96	.81	.49	.19	.91	.64	.50	.37
09	.91	.95	.57	.21	23.04	.88	.57	.27	.99	.72	.58	.45
08	25.00	24.04	.66	.30	.13	.97	.65	.35	22.07	.80	.66	.53
07	.09	.13	.74	.38	.21	23.05	.73	.43	.14	.87	.73	.60
06	.19	.22	.83	.47	.29	.13	.81	.51	.22	.95	.81	.68
05	.28	.31	.92	.56	.38	.22	.90	.59	.30	22.03	.89	.76
04	.38	.40	24.00	.64	.46	.30	.98	.67	.38	.10	.96	.83
03	.47	.49	.09	.73	.55	.38	23.06	.75	.46	.18	22.04	.91
02	.57	.58	.18	.81	.63	.46	.14	.83	.53	.25	.11	.98
01	.66	.66	.26	.89	.71	.54	.21	.90	.61	.33	.19	22.06
00	.75	.75	.35	.98	.80	.63	.30	.98	.69	.41	.27	.14
0.9699	.85	.84	.44	24.06	.88	.72	.38	23.06	.77	.48	.34	.21
98	.94	.93	.53	.15	.97	.80	.46	.14	.84	.55	.42	.28
97	26.04	25.01	.61	.23	24.05	.88	.54	.22	.92	.63	.49	.35
96	.13	.10	.69	.31	.13	.96	.62	.30	23.00	.71	.57	.43
95	.22	.19	.78	.40	.22	24.05	.70	.38	.08	.78	.64	.50
94	.31	.28	.86	.48	.30	.13	.78	.45	.15	.86	.72	.58
93	.41	.36	.95	.57	.38	.21	.86	.53	.23	.94	.80	.66
92	.50	.45	25.04	.65	.47	.29	.94	.61	.31	23.01	.87	.74
91	.59	.54	.13	.74	.55	.37	24.02	.69	.38	.08	.95	.81
90	.69	.62	.21	.82	.63	.45	.10	.77	.46	.16	23.02	.88
89	.78	.71	.29	.90	.72	.53	.18	.84	.53	.23	.10	.96
88	.87	.80	.38	.98	.80	.61	.26	.92	.61	.31	.17	23.03
87	.96	.89	.46	25.07	.88	.69	.34	24.00	.68	.38	.24	.10
86	27.05	.98	.55	.15	.97	.77	.42	.08	.76	.46	.32	.18
85	.15	26.06	.63	.23	25.05	.85	.50	.16	.84	.53	.39	.25
84	.24	.15	.72	.32	.13	.94	.58	.23	.92	.61	.47	.33
83	.33	.24	.80	.40	.21	25.02	.66	.31	.99	.68	.54	.40
82	.42	.33	.89	.48	.29	.10	.74	.39	24.06	.75	.61	.47
81	.51	.41	.97	.57	.37	.18	.81	.47	.14	.83	.69	.54
80	.60	.50	26.06	.65	.45	.26	.89	.54	.21	.90	.76	.61
79	.69	.59	.14	.73	.53	.34	.97	.62	.30	.98	.84	.69
78	.78	.67	.22	.81	.61	.42	25.05	.70	.37	24.06	.91	.77
77	.87	.76	.31	.89	.69	.50	.13	.78	.45	.14	.99	.84
76	.96	.84	.39	.97	.77	.58	.21	.85	.52	.21	24.06	.91
75	28.05	.93	.47	26.05	.85	.66	.29	.93	.60	.29	.13	.99
74	.14	27.01	.56	.14	.94	.74	.37	25.01	.68	.36	.21	24.06
73	.23	.10	.64	.22	26.02	.82	.45	.09	.75	.43	.28	.13
72	.32	.19	.73	.30	.10	.90	.53	.16	.83	.51	.36	.20
71	.41	.27	.81	.38	.18	.98	.60	.24	.90	.58	.43	.28
70	.50	.36	.89	.46	.26	26.06	.68	.32	.98	.66	.50	.35
69	.59	.44	.97	.54	.34	.14	.76	.40	25.06	.73	.58	.42
68	.68	.52	27.05	.63	.42	.22	.84	.47	.13	.81	.65	.50
67	.77	.61	.14	.71	.50	.30	.92	.55	.20	.88	.73	.57
66	.86	.69	.22	.79	.58	.38	.99	.63	.28	.95	.80	.64
65	.95	.77	.30	.87	.66	.46	26.07	.70	.36	25.03	.87	.72
64	29.04	.86	.39	.95	.74	.54	.15	.78	.44	.11	.95	.79
63	.12	.94	.47	27.03	.82	.62	.23	.86	.51	.18	25.02	.86
62	.21	28.02	.55	.11	.90	.70	.31	.94	.59	.25	.09	.93
61	.30	.11	.64	.19	.98	.77	.38	26.02	.66	.33	.17	25.01
60	.39	.19	.72	.27	27.06	.85	.46	.09	.74	.40	.24	.08
59	.47	.28	.81	.35	.13	.93	.54	.17	.82	.48	.31	.15
58	.56	.36	.89	.43	.21	27.01	.61	.24	.89	.56	.39	.23
57	.65	.44	.97	.51	.29	.09	.69	.32	.97	.63	.46	.30
56	.74	.53	28.05	.59	.37	.17	.77	.39	26.04	.70	.53	.37
55	.82	.61	.13	.67	.45	.25	.85	.47	.11	.77	.61	.45
54	.91	.69	.21	.75	.53	.33	.93	.55	.19	.85	.68	.52
53	30.00	.78	.29	.83	.61	.41	27.00	.62	.26	.92	.75	.59
52	.09	.86	.37	.91	.69	.49	.08	.70	.34	.99	.82	.66
51	.17	.94	.45	.99	.77	.56	.16	.78	.41	26.06	.90	.74

(Continued)

47.003   Percentages by volume at 15.56°C (60°F) of ethyl alcohol corresponding to apparent specific gravity at various temperatures[a]—Continued.

Apparent Specific Gravity	15.56/15.56	20/20	22/22	24/24	25/25	26/26	28/28	30/30	32/32	34/34	35/35	36/36
0.9650	30.26	29.03	28.53	28.07	27.85	27.64	27.23	26.85	26.49	26.14	25.97	25.81
49	.34	.11	.61	.15	.93	.72	.31	.92	.56	.21	26.04	.89
48	.43	.19	.69	.23	28.01	.79	.38	27.00	.64	.29	.11	.96
47	.52	.27	.73	.31	.09	.87	.46	.07	.71	.36	.19	26.03
46	.60	.35	.85	.39	.16	.95	.53	.15	.78	.43	.26	.10
45	.69	.44	.93	.47	.24	28.03	.61	.22	.85	.51	.33	.17
44	.78	.52	29.02	.55	.32	.10	.69	.30	.93	.58	.40	.24
43	.86	.60	.10	.63	.40	.18	.76	.37	27.00	.65	.47	.31
42	.95	.68	.18	.71	.47	.26	.84	.44	.07	.72	.54	.38
41	31.03	.76	.26	.79	.55	.34	.91	.52	.14	.79	.61	.45
40	.11	.85	.34	.86	.63	.41	.99	.59	.22	.86	.69	.52
39	.20	.93	.42	.93	.71	.49	28.06	.67	.29	.93	.76	.59
38	.28	30.01	.50	29.01	.78	.56	.14	.74	.37	27.01	.83	.66
37	.36	.09	.58	.09	.86	.64	.21	.81	.44	.08	.90	.73
36	.44	.17	.66	.17	.94	.72	.29	.89	.51	.15	.97	.80
35	.52	.25	.74	.25	29.02	.80	.37	.96	.58	.22	27.04	.87
34	.61	.34	.82	.33	.09	.87	.44	28.04	.66	.29	.11	.94
33	.69	.42	.90	.41	.17	.95	.52	.11	.73	.36	.18	27.01
32	.77	.50	.98	.49	.25	29.03	.60	.19	.80	.43	.25	.08
31	.85	.58	30.06	.57	.33	.11	.67	.26	.87	.50	.32	.15
30	.93	.66	.13	.64	.40	.18	.74	.33	.95	.58	.39	.22
29	32.02	.74	.21	.72	.48	.26	.82	.41	28.02	.65	.46	.29
28	.09	.82	.29	.79	.56	.33	.89	.48	.09	.72	.54	.36
27	.17	.89	.36	.87	.64	.41	.97	.56	.17	.79	.61	.43
26	.25	.97	.44	.95	.71	.48	29.04	.63	.24	.86	.68	.50
25	.33	31.05	.52	30.03	.79	.56	.12	.70	.31	.93	.75	.57
24	.41	.13	.60	.10	.87	.64	.20	.78	.38	28.00	.82	.64
23	.49	.20	.67	.17	.95	.71	.27	.85	.45	.07	.89	.71
22	.57	.28	.75	.25	30.02	.79	.35	.93	.52	.14	.96	.78
21	.65	.36	.83	.33	.10	.86	.42	29.00	.59	.21	28.03	.85
20	.72	.44	.91	.41	.17	.94	.50	.07	.67	.29	.10	.92
19	.80	.52			.25	30.01	.57	.14	.74	.36	.17	.99
18	.88	.59			.32	.09	.65	.22	.82	.43	.24	28.06
17	.96	.67			.40	.16	.72	.29	.89	.50	.31	.13
16	33.04	.75			.47	.24	.79	.36	.96	.57	.38	.20
15	.12	.82			.54	.31	.86	.43	29.03	.64	.45	.27
14	.19	.90			.62	.39	.94	.51	.10	.71	.52	.34
13	.27	.98			.69	.46	30.01	.58	.17	.78	.59	.41
12	.35	32.05			.77	.53	.08	.65	.24	.85	.66	.48
11	.43	.13			.84	.61	.15	.72	.31	.92	.73	.55
10	.50	.21			.92	.68	.23	.80	.39	.99	.80	.62
09	.58	.28			.99	.75	.30	.87	.46	29.06	.87	.69
08	.66	.36			31.07	.83	.38	.94	.53	.13	.94	.76
07	.74	.43			.13	.90	.45	30.01	.60	.20	29.01	.83
06	.81	.51			.21	.98	.52	.09	.67	.27	.08	.90
05	.89	.58			.29	31.05	.59	.16	.74	.34	.15	.97
04	.97	.66			.36	.13	.66	.23	.81	.41	.22	29.04
03	34.05	.73			.43	.20	.73	.30	.88	.48	.29	.11
02	.12	.81			.51	.28	.80	.37	.95	.55	.36	.18
01	.20	.88			.58	.35	.88	.44	30.02	.62	.43	.25
00	.27	.96			.65	.42	.95	.51	.09	.69	.50	.31
0.9599	.35	33.03			.73			.58	.16	.76	.57	.38
98	.42	.10			.80			.65	.23	.83	.63	.45
97	.50	.18			.87			.72	.30	.90	.70	.51
96	.57	.25			.95			.79	.37	.97	.77	.58
95	.65	.32			32.02			.87	.44	30.04	.84	.65
94	.72	.40			.09			.94	.51	.11	.91	.72
93	.80	.47			.16			31.01	.58	.18	.98	.79
92	.87	.54			.23			.08	.65	.25	30.05	.86
91	.95	.62			.30			.15	.72	.32	.12	.93
90	35.02	.69			.37			.22	.79	.38	.18	.99
89	.09	.76			.44			.29			.25	30.06
88	.17	.84			.51			.35			.32	.13
87	.24	.91			.58			.42			.39	.20
86	.31	.98			.65			.49			.46	.27
85	.38	34.05			.73			.56			.52	.33
84	.46	.12			.80			.63			.59	.40
83	.53	.20			.87			.70			.66	.47
82	.60	.27			.94			.77			.73	.54
81	.67	.34			33.01			.84			.80	.61

(Continued)

47.003 **Percentages by volume at 15.56°C (60°F) of ethyl alcohol corresponding to apparent specific gravity at various temperatures[a]—Continued.**

Apparent Specific Gravity	15.56/15.56	20/20	25/25	30/30	35/35	Apparent Specific Gravity	15.56/15.56	20/20	25/25	30/30	35/35
0.9580	35.75	34.41	33.08	31.91	30.86	0.9510	40.46	39.10	37.71	36.47	35.34
79	.82	.48	.15	.98	.93	09	.52	.16	.78	.53	.40
78	.89	.56	.22	32.05	31.00	08	.58	.23	.84	.59	.46
77	.96	.63	.29	.11	.07	07	.65	.29	.90	.65	.52
76	36.04	.70	.36	.18	.13	06	.71	.35	.96	.72	.58
75	.11	.77	.43	.25	.20	05	.77	.41	38.02	.78	.64
74	.18	.84	.50	.32	.26	04	.84	.48	.09	.84	.71
73	.25	.91	.57	.38	.33	03	.90	.54	.15	.90	.77
72	.32	.98	.64	.45	.39	02	.96	.60	.21	.96	.83
71	.39	35.05	.71	.52	.46	01	41.02	.67	.27	37.02	.89
70	.46	.12	.78	.58	.53	00	.09	.73	.33	.09	.95
69	.53	.19	.85	.65	.59	0.9499	.15	.79	.40	.15	36.01
68	.60	.26	.92	.72	.66	98	.21	.85	.46	.21	.07
67	.67	.33	.99	.79	.72	97	.27	.91	.52	.27	.13
66	.74	.40	34.05	.85	.79	96	.33	.98	.58	.33	.19
65	.81	.47	.12	.92	.86	95	.40	40.04	.64	.39	.25
64	.88	.54	.19	.99	.92	94	.46	.10	.70	.45	.31
63	.95	.61	.26	33.05	.99	93	.52	.16	.77	.51	.37
62	37.02	.68	.32	.12	32.05	92	.58	.22	.83	.57	.43
61	.09	.75	.39	.19	.12	91	.64	.29	.89	.63	.49
60	.16	.82	.46	.25	.18	90	.70	.35	.95	.70	.55
59	.22	.88	.53	.32	.25	89	.77	.41	39.01	.76	.61
58	.29	.95	.59	.39	.31	88	.83	.47	.07	.82	.67
57	.36	36.02	.66	.45	.37	87	.89	.53	.13	.88	.73
56	.43	.09	.73	.52	.44	86	.95	.59	.20	.94	.79
55	.50	.15	.80	.59	.50	85	42.01	.65	.26	38.00	.85
54	.56	.22	.86	.65	.57	84	.07	.71	.32	.06	.91
53	.63	.29	.93	.72	.63	83	.13	.78	.38	.12	.97
52	.70	.36	35.00	.79	.70	82	.19	.84	.44	.18	37.03
51	.77	.42	.07	.85	.76	81	.25	.90	.50	.24	.09
50	.84	.49	.13	.92	.83	80	.31	.96	.56	.30	.15
49	.90	.56	.20	.99	.89	79	.37	41.02	.62	.36	.21
48	.97	.63	.26	34.05	.95	78	.43	.08	.68	.42	.26
47	38.04	.69	.33	.12	33.02	77	.49	.14	.74	.48	.32
46	.11	.76	.39	.18	.08	76	.55	.20	.80	.54	.38
45	.17	.83	.46	.25	.15	75	.61	.26	.87	.60	.44
44	.24	.89	.53	.31	.21	74	.67	.32	.93	.66	.50
43	.31	.96	.59	.38	.27	73	.73	.38	.99	.72	.56
42	.37	37.03	.66	.44	.34	72	.80	.44	40.05	.78	.62
41	.44	.09	.72	.51	.40	71	.86	.50	.11	.84	.68
40	.51	.16	.79	.57	.46	70	.92	.56	.17	.90	.74
39	.57	.23	.86	.64	.53	69	.98	.62	.22	.96	.79
38	.64	.29	.92	.70	.59	68	43.04	.68	.28	39.02	.85
37	.71	.36	.99	.77	.66	67	.09	.74	.34	.08	.91
36	.77	.42	36.05	.83	.72	66	.15	.80	.40	.13	.97
35	.84	.49	.12	.90	.78	65	.21	.86	.46	.19	38.03
34	.91	.56	.18	.96	.85	64	.27	.92	.52	.25	.09
33	.97	.62	.25	35.03	.91	63	.33	.98	.58	.31	.15
32	39.04	.69	.31	.09	.97	62	.39	42.04	.64	.37	.20
31	.10	.75	.38	.15	34.04	61	.45	.09	.70	.43	.26
30	.17	.82	.44	.22	.10	60	.51	.15	.76	.49	.32
29	.23	.88	.51	.28	.16	59	.57	.21	.82	.54	.38
28	.30	.95	.57	.34	.22	58	.63	.27	.88	.60	.44
27	.36	38.01	.64	.41	.29	57	.69	.33	.93	.66	.49
26	.43	.07	.70	.47	.35	56	.75	.39	.99	.72	.55
25	.49	.14	.77	.53	.41	55	.80	.45	41.05	.78	.61
24	.56	.20	.83	.59	.47	54	.86	.51	.11	.84	.67
23	.62	.27	.90	.66	.53	53	.92	.57	.17	.89	.73
22	.69	.33	.96	.72	.60	52	.98	.63	.23	.95	.78
21	.75	.39	37.02	.78	.66	51	44.04	.69	.28	40.01	.84
20	.82	.46	.09	.85	.72	50	.10	.74	.34	.07	.90
19	.88	.52	.15	.91	.78	49	.16	.80	.40	.13	.96
18	.95	.59	.21	.97	.84	48	.21	.86	.46	.18	39.02
17	40.01	.65	.28	36.04	.91	47	.27	.92	.51	.24	.07
16	.08	.72	.34	.10	.97	46	.33	.98	.57	.30	.13
15	.14	.78	.40	.16	35.04	45	.39	43.04	.63	.35	.19
14	.20	.84	.46	.22	.10	44	.45	.09	.69	.41	.24
13	.27	.91	.52	.28	.16	43	.50	.15	.75	.47	.30
12	.33	.97	.59	.35	.22	42	.56	.21	.80	.53	.36
11	.39	39.04	.65	.41	.28	41	.62	.27	.86	.58	.41

(Continued)

47.003   **Percentages by volume at 15.56°C (60°F) of ethyl alcohol corresponding to apparent specific gravity at various temperatures[a]—Continued.**

Apparent Specific Gravity	15.56 / 15.56	20/20	25/25	30/30	35/35	Apparent Specific Gravity	15.56 / 15.56	20/20	25/25	30/30	35/35
0.9440	44.68	43.33	41.92	40.64	39.47	0.9370	48.53	47.20	45.81	44.52	43.33
39	.73	.39	.98	.70	.53	69	.58	.26	.86	.58	.38
38	.79	.44	42.03	.75	.59	68	.63	.31	.91	.63	.43
37	.85	.50	.09	.81	.64	67	.69	.36	.97	.68	.49
36	.91	.56	.15	.87	.70	66	.74	.42	46.02	.74	.54
35	.97	.62	.21	.93	.76	65	.79	.47	.07	.79	.59
34	45.02	.67	.26	.98	.81	64	.85	.52	.13	.84	.65
33	.08	.73	.32	41.04	.87	63	.90	.58	.18	.90	.70
32	.14	.78	.38	.10	.93	62	.95	.63	.23	.95	.75
31	.19	.85	.43	.15	.98	61	49.01	.68	.29	45.01	.81
30	.25	.90	.49	.21	40.04	60	.06	.73	.34	.06	.86
29	.31	.96	.55	.27	.09	59	.11	.79	.39	.11	.91
28	.36	44.02	.61	.32	.15	58	.16	.84	.45	.16	.97
27	.42	.07	.66	.38	.21	57	.21	.89	.50	.22	44.02
26	.47	.13	.72	.44	.26	56	.26	.94	.55	.27	.07
25	.53	.18	.78	.49	.32	55	.32	48.00	.61	.32	.13
24	.59	.24	.83	.55	.37	54	.37	.05	.66	.37	.18
23	.64	.30	.89	.60	.43	53	.42	.10	.71	.43	.23
22	.70	.35	.95	.66	.48	52	.47	.15	.77	.48	.28
21	.76	.41	43.01	.72	.54	51	.52	.21	.82	.53	.34
20	.81	.46	.06	.77	.59	50	.58	.26	.87	.58	.39
19	.87	.52	.12	.83	.65	49	.63	.31	.93	.64	.44
18	.93	.58	.17	.89	.71	48	.68	.36	.98	.69	.49
17	.98	.63	.23	.94	.76	47	.73	.41	47.03	.74	.54
16	46.04	.69	.29	42.00	.82	46	.78	.47	.08	.79	.60
15	.09	.74	.34	.06	.87	45	.83	.52	.14	.85	.65
14	.15	.80	.40	.11	.93	44	.89	.57	.19	.90	.70
13	.20	.86	.46	.17	.98	43	.94	.62	.24	.95	.75
12	.26	.91	.51	.22	41.04	42	.99	.68	.29	46.01	.81
11	.31	.97	.57	.28	.09	41	50.04	.73	.34	.06	.86
10	.37	45.03	.62	.33	.15	40	.09	.78	.40	.11	.91
09	.43	.08	.68	.39	.20	39	.14	.83	.45	.16	.96
08	.48	.14	.74	.44	.26	38	.19	.88	.50	.21	45.02
07	.54	.19	.79	.50	.31	37	.24	.94	.55	.27	.07
06	.59	.25	.85	.56	.37	36	.30	.99	.60	.32	.12
05	.65	.30	.90	.61	.42	35	.35	49.04	.66	.37	.17
04	.70	.36	.96	.67	.48	34	.40	.09	.71	.42	.22
03	.76	.42	44.02	.72	.53	33	.45	.14	.76	.47	.27
02	.81	.47	.07	.78	.59	32	.50	.19	.81	.53	.33
01	.87	.53	.13	.83	.64	31	.55	.25	.86	.58	.38
00	.92	.58	.18	.89	.70	30	.60	.30	.92	.63	.43
0.9399	.98	.64	.23	.94	.75	29	.65	.35	.97	.68	.48
98	47.03	.69	.29	43.00	.81	28	.70	.40	48.02	.73	.53
97	.09	.74	.34	.05	.86	27	.75	.45	.07	.79	.59
96	.14	.80	.40	.11	.92	26	.81	.50	.12	.84	.64
95	.19	.85	.45	.16	.97	25	.86	.55	.17	.89	.69
94	.25	.91	.51	.22	42.03	24	.91	.60	.22	.94	.74
93	.30	.96	.56	.27	.08	23	.96	.65	.28	.99	.79
92	.35	46.01	.62	.33	.14	22	51.01	.70	.33	47.05	.84
91	.41	.07	.67	.38	.19	21	.06	.75	.38	.10	.90
90	.46	.12	.73	.44	.24	20	.11	.80	.43	.15	.95
89	.52	.18	.78	.49	.30	19	.16	.85	.48	.20	46.00
88	.57	.23	.84	.55	.35	18	.21	.90	.53	.25	.05
87	.62	.29	.89	.60	.41	17	.26	.95	.58	.30	.10
86	.68	.34	.95	.66	.46	16	.31	50.00	.63	.35	.15
85	.73	.39	45.00	.71	.52	15	.36	.05	.68	.40	.20
84	.78	.45	.05	.77	.57	14	.41	.10	.73	.45	.26
83	.84	.50	.11	.82	.63	13	.46	.16	.79	.50	.31
82	.89	.56	.16	.87	.68	12	.51	.21	.84	.55	.36
81	.95	.61	.22	.93	.73	11	.56	.26	.89	.60	.41
80	48.00	.67	.27	.98	.79	10	.61	.31	.94	.65	.46
79	.05	.72	.32	44.04	.84	09	.66	.36	.99	.71	.51
78	.11	.77	.38	.09	.90	08	.71	.41	49.04	.76	.56
77	.16	.83	.43	.15	.95	07	.76	.46	.09	.81	.61
76	.21	.88	.48	.20	43.01	06	.81	.51	.14	.86	.66
75	.26	.94	.54	.25	.06	05	.86	.56	.19	.91	.71
74	.32	.99	.59	.31	.11	04	.91	.61	.24	.96	.77
73	.37	47.04	.65	.36	.17	03	.96	.66	.29	48.01	.82
72	.42	.10	.70	.41	.22	02	52.01	.71	.34	.06	.87
71	.48	.15	.75	.47	.27	01	.06	.76	.39	.11	.92

(Continued)

47.003 Percentages by volume at 15.56°C (60°F) of ethyl alcohol corresponding to apparent specific gravity at various temperatures[a]—*Continued*.

Apparent Specific Gravity	15.56/15.56	20/20	25/25	30/30	35/35	Apparent Specific Gravity	15.56/15.56	20/20	25/25	30/30	35/35
0.9300	52.11	50.81	49.44	48.16	46.97	0.9230	55.52	54.24	52.88	51.61	50.41
0.9299	.16	.86	.49	.21	47.02	29	.57	.29	.93	.66	.46
98	.21	.91	.54	.26	.07	28	.62	.33	.98	.71	.51
97	.26	.96	.59	.31	.12	27	.67	.38	53.03	.75	.56
96	.31	51.01	.64	.36	.17	26	.71	.43	.08	.80	.60
95	.36	.06	.69	.41	.22	25	.76	.48	.12	.85	.65
94	.41	.11	.74	.46	.27	24	.81	.53	.17	.90	.70
93	.46	.16	.79	.51	.32	23	.86	.57	.22	.95	.75
92	.51	.21	.84	.56	.37	22	.90	.62	.27	52.00	.80
91	.56	.26	.89	.61	.42	21	.95	.67	.31	.04	.85
90	.61	.31	.94	.66	.47	20	56.00	.72	.36	.09	.89
89	.66	.36	.99	.71	.52	19	.05	.77	.41	.14	.94
88	.71	.41	50.04	.76	.57	18	.09	.81	.46	.19	.99
87	.76	.46	.09	.81	.62	17	.14	.86	.50	.23	51.04
86	.81	.50	.14	.86	.67	16	.19	.91	.55	.28	.09
85	.86	.55	.19	.91	.72	15	.24	.96	.60	.33	.13
84	.91	.60	.24	.96	.77	14	.28	55.00	.65	.38	.18
83	.96	.65	.29	49.01	.82	13	.33	.05	.70	.43	.23
82	53.00	.70	.34	.06	.87	12	.38	.10	.74	.47	.27
81	.05	.75	.39	.11	.92	11	.43	.15	.79	.52	.32
80	.10	.80	.44	.16	.97	10	.47	.19	.84	.57	.37
79	.15	.85	.49	.21	48.02	09	.52	.24	.89	.62	.42
78	.20	.90	.54	.26	.07	08	.57	.29	.93	.67	.46
77	.25	.95	.59	.31	.12	07	.62	.34	.98	.71	.51
76	.30	52.00	.64	.36	.17	06	.66	.38	54.03	.76	.56
75	.35	.05	.68	.41	.22	05	.71	.43	.08	.81	.61
74	.40	.10	.73	.46	.27	04	.76	.48	.12	.86	.65
73	.45	.15	.78	.51	.32	03	.81	.53	.17	.90	.70
72	.50	.20	.83	.56	.37	02	.85	.57	.22	.95	.75
71	.54	.25	.88	.61	.42	01	.90	.62	.26	53.00	.80
70	.59	.29	.93	.66	.47	00	.95	.67	.31	.05	.84
69	.64	.34	.98	.71	.52	0.9199	57.00	.71	.36	.09	.89
68	.69	.39	51.03	.76	.57	98	.04	.76	.41	.14	.94
67	.74	.44	.08	.81	.62	97	.09	.81	.45	.19	.99
66	.79	.49	.13	.86	.67	96	.13	.86	.50	.23	52.03
65	.84	.54	.18	.91	.71	95	.18	.90	.55	.28	.08
64	.89	.59	.23	.96	.76	94	.23	.95	.59	.33	.13
63	.94	.64	.27	50.00	.81	93	.27	56.00	.64	.37	.17
62	.99	.69	.32	.05	.86	92	.32	.04	.69	.42	.22
61	54.03	.74	.37	.10	.91	91	.37	.09	.74	.47	.27
60	.08	.79	.42	.15	.96	90	.41	.14	.78	.51	.32
59	.13	.84	.47	.20	49.01	89	.46	.18	.83	.56	.36
58	.18	.89	.52	.25	.06	88	.51	.23	.88	.61	.41
57	.23	.93	.57	.30	.11	87	.55	.28	.92	.65	.46
56	.28	.98	.62	.35	.15	86	.60	.32	.97	.70	.50
55	.32	53.03	.67	.40	.20	85	.65	.37	55.02	.75	.55
54	.37	.08	.72	.44	.25	84	.69	.42	.07	.79	.60
53	.42	.13	.76	.49	.30	83	.74	.46	.11	.84	.65
52	.47	.18	.81	.54	.35	82	.79	.51	.16	.89	.69
51	.52	.22	.86	.59	.40	81	.83	.56	.21	.93	.74
50	.57	.27	.91	.64	.44	80	.88	.60	.25	.98	.79
49	.61	.32	.96	.69	.49	79	.93	.65	.30	54.03	.83
48	.66	.37	52.01	.74	.54	78	.97	.70	.35	.07	.88
47	.71	.42	.06	.79	.59	77	58.02	.74	.39	.12	.93
46	.76	.47	.11	.83	.64	76	.06	.79	.44	.17	.98
45	.81	.52	.16	.88	.69	75	.11	.84	.49	.21	53.02
44	.86	.56	.20	.93	.73	74	.16	.88	.53	.26	.07
43	.90	.61	.25	.98	.78	73	.20	.93	.58	.31	.12
42	.95	.66	.30	51.03	.83	72	.25	.97	.63	.36	.16
41	55.00	.71	.35	.08	.88	71	.29	57.02	.67	.40	.21
40	.05	.76	.40	.13	.93	70	.34	.07	.72	.45	.26
39	.10	.81	.45	.17	.98	69	.38	.11	.77	.50	.30
38	.14	.85	.50	.22	50.02	68	.43	.16	.81	.54	.35
37	.19	.90	.54	.27	.07	67	.47	.21	.86	.59	.40
36	.24	.95	.59	.32	.12	66	.52	.25	.91	.64	.44
35	.29	54.00	.64	.37	.17	65	.57	.30	.95	.68	.49
34	.33	.05	.69	.42	.22	64	.61	.35	56.00	.73	.53
33	.38	.09	.74	.46	.27	63	.66	.39	.05	.78	.58
32	.43	.14	.79	.51	.31	62	.70	.44	.09	.82	.63
31	.48	.19	.83	.56	.36	61	.75	.48	.14	.87	.67

(Continued)

47.003   **Percentages by volume at 15.56°C (60°F) of ethyl alcohol corresponding to apparent specific gravity at various temperatures**[a]—*Continued.*

Apparent Specific Gravity	15.56 / 15.56	20/20	25/25	30/30	35/35	Apparent Specific Gravity	15.56 / 15.56	20/20	25/25	30/30	35/35
0.9160	58.79	57.53	56.18	54.92	53.72	0.9090	61.92	60.68	59.36	58.11	56.93
59	.84	.58	.23	.96	.77	89	.96	.72	.40	.15	.97
58	.89	.62	.28	55.01	.81	88	62.01	.77	.45	.20	57.02
57	.93	.67	.32	.06	.86	87	.05	.81	.49	.24	.06
56	.98	.71	.37	.10	.91	86	.10	.86	.53	.29	.11
55	59.02	.76	.41	.15	.95	85	.14	.90	.58	.33	.15
54	.07	.81	.46	.19	54.00	84	.18	.94	.63	.38	.19
53	.11	.85	.51	.24	.05	83	.23	.99	.67	.42	.24
52	.16	.90	.55	.29	.09	82	.27	61.03	.71	.46	.28
51	.20	.94	.60	.33	.14	81	.31	.08	.76	.51	.33
50	.25	.99	.65	.38	.18	80	.36	.12	.80	.55	.37
49	.29	58.03	.69	.42	.23	79	.40	.17	.85	.60	.42
48	.34	.08	.74	.47	.28	78	.45	.21	.89	.64	.46
47	.38	.13	.78	.52	.32	77	.49	.25	.94	.69	.50
46	.43	.17	.83	.56	.37	76	.53	.30	.98	.73	.55
45	.47	.22	.88	.61	.41	75	.58	.34	60.03	.77	.59
44	.52	.26	.92	.65	.46	74	.62	.39	.07	.82	.64
43	.56	.31	.97	.70	.51	73	.66	.43	.11	.86	.68
42	.61	.35	57.01	.75	.55	72	.71	.47	.16	.91	.73
41	.65	.40	.06	.79	.60	71	.75	.52	.20	.95	.77
40	.70	.44	.10	.84	.65	70	.79	.56	.25	59.00	.81
39	.74	.49	.15	.88	.69	69	.84	.60	.29	.04	.86
38	.79	.53	.20	.93	.74	68	.88	.65	.33	.08	.90
37	.83	.58	.24	.98	.78	67	.93	.69	.38	.13	.95
36	.88	.62	.29	56.02	.83	66	.97	.74	.42	.17	.99
35	.92	.67	.33	.07	.88	65	63.01	.78	.46	.21	58.04
34	.97	.71	.38	.11	.92	64	.06	.82	.51	.26	.08
33	60.01	.76	.42	.16	.97	63	.10	.87	.55	.30	.12
32	.06	.80	.47	.21	55.01	62	.14	.91	.60	.35	.17
31	.10	.85	.51	.25	.06	61	.19	.96	.64	.39	.21
30	.15	.89	.56	.30	.11	60	.23	62.00	.68	.43	.26
29	.19	.94	.60	.34	.15	59	.27	.04	.73	.48	.30
28	.24	.98	.65	.39	.20	58	.32	.09	.77	.52	.34
27	.28	59.03	.70	.44	.24	57	.36	.13	.82	.57	.39
26	.33	.07	.74	.48	.29	56	.40	.17	.86	.61	.43
25	.37	.12	.79	.53	.33	55	.45	.22	.90	.65	.48
24	.42	.16	.83	.57	.38	54	.49	.26	.95	.70	.52
23	.46	.21	.88	.62	.42	53	.53	.30	.99	.74	.56
22	.50	.25	.92	.67	.47	52	.58	.35	61.03	.79	.61
21	.55	.30	.97	.71	.52	51	.62	.39	.08	.83	.65
20	.59	.34	58.01	.76	.56	50	.66	.43	.12	.87	.70
19	.64	.39	.06	.80	.61	49	.71	.48	.16	.92	.74
18	.68	.43	.10	.85	.65	48	.75	.52	.21	.96	.78
17	.73	.48	.15	.89	.70	47	.79	.56	.25	60.00	.83
16	.77	.52	.19	.94	.74	46	.84	.60	.29	.05	.87
15	.82	.57	.24	.99	.79	45	.88	.65	.34	.09	.92
14	.86	.61	.28	57.03	.84	44	.92	.69	.38	.14	.96
13	.91	.66	.33	.08	.88	43	.97	.73	.42	.18	59.00
12	.95	.70	.37	.12	.93	42	64.01	.78	.47	.22	.05
11	61.00	.75	.42	.17	.97	41	.05	.82	.51	.27	.09
10	.04	.79	.46	.21	56.02	40	.09	.86	.55	.31	.13
09	.08	.84	.51	.26	.06	39	.14	.91	.60	.35	.18
08	.13	.88	.55	.30	.11	38	.18	.95	.64	.40	.22
07	.17	.92	.60	.35	.15	37	.22	.99	.68	.44	.27
06	.22	.97	.64	.39	.20	36	.27	63.04	.73	.48	.31
05	.26	60.01	.69	.44	.25	35	.31	.08	.77	.53	.35
04	.30	.06	.73	.48	.29	34	.35	.12	.81	.57	.40
03	.35	.10	.78	.53	.34	33	.40	.17	.86	.62	.44
02	.39	.15	.82	.57	.38	32	.44	.21	.90	.66	.48
01	.44	.19	.87	.62	.43	31	.48	.25	.94	.70	.53
00	.48	.24	.91	.66	.47	30	.53	.30	.99	.75	.57
0.9099	.52	.28	.96	.71	.52	29	.57	.34	62.03	.79	.61
98	.57	.33	59.00	.75	.56	28	.61	.38	.07	.83	.66
97	.61	.37	.04	.80	.61	27	.66	.43	.12	.88	.70
96	.66	.41	.09	.84	.65	26	.70	.47	.16	.92	.74
95	.70	.46	.13	.89	.70	25	.74	.51	.20	.97	.79
94	.74	.50	.18	.93	.75	24	.78	.56	.24	61.01	.83
93	.79	.55	.22	.98	.79	23	.83	.60	.29	.05	.87
92	.83	.59	.27	58.02	.84	22	.87	.64	.23	.09	.92
91	.88	.64	.31	.07	.88	21	.91	.69	.37	.14	.96

(Continued)

47.003   Percentages by volume at 15.56°C (60°F) of ethyl alcohol corresponding to apparent specific gravity at various temperatures[a]—Continued.

Apparent Specific Gravity	15.56 / 15.56	20/20	25/25	30/30	35/35	Apparent Specific Gravity	15.56 / 15.56	20/20	25/25	30/30	35/35
0.9020	64.96	63.73	62.42	61.18	60.00	0.8950	67.90	66.69	65.39	64.16	62.99
19	65.00	.77	.46	.22	.05	49	.94	.73	.44	.21	63.03
18	.04	.82	.50	.27	.09	48	.98	.77	.48	.25	.08
17	.09	.86	.55	.31	.13	47	68.02	.81	.52	.29	.12
16	.13	.90	.59	.35	.18	46	.07	.85	.56	.33	.16
15	.17	.94	.63	.40	.22	45	.11	.90	.60	.37	.20
14	.21	.99	.67	.44	.26	44	.15	.94	.64	.42	.24
13	.26	64.03	.72	.48	.30	43	.19	.98	.69	.46	.28
12	.30	.07	.76	.53	.35	42	.23	67.02	.73	.50	.33
11	.34	.11	.80	.57	.39	41	.27	.06	.77	.54	.37
10	.38	.16	.85	.61	.43	40	.31	.10	.81	.58	.41
09	.43	.20	.89	.66	.48	39	.35	.15	.85	.63	.45
08	.47	.24	.93	.70	.52	38	.39	.19	.90	.67	.49
07	.51	.28	.97	.74	.56	37	.43	.23	.94	.71	.54
06	.55	.33	63.02	.78	.61	36	.48	.27	.98	.75	.58
05	.60	.37	.06	.83	.65	35	.52	.31	66.02	.79	.62
04	.64	.41	.10	.87	.69	34	.56	.35	.06	.84	.66
03	.68	.45	.15	.91	.73	33	.60	.39	.10	.88	.70
02	.72	.50	.19	.96	.78	32	.64	.43	.15	.92	.74
01	.77	.54	.23	62.00	.82	31	.68	.47	.19	.96	.79
00	.81	.58	.27	.04	.86	30	.72	.52	.23	65.00	.83
0.8999	.85	.62	.32	.09	.91	29	.76	.56	.27	.05	.87
98	.89	.67	.36	.13	.95	28	.80	.60	.31	.09	.91
97	.94	.71	.40	.17	.99	27	.84	.64	.35	.13	.95
96	.98	.75	.44	.21	61.03	26	.89	.68	.39	.17	64.00
95	66.02	.79	.49	.26	.08	25	.93	.72	.44	.21	.04
94	.06	.84	.53	.30	.12	24	.97	.76	.48	.25	.08
93	.10	.88	.57	.34	.16	23	69.01	.80	.52	.29	.12
92	.15	.92	.62	.38	.21	22	.05	.84	.56	.34	.16
91	.19	.96	.66	.43	.25	21	.09	.89	.60	.38	.21
90	.23	65.01	.70	.47	.29	20	.13	.93	.64	.42	.25
89	.27	.05	.74	.51	.33	19	.17	.97	.68	.46	.29
88	.31	.09	.79	.55	.38	18	.21	68.01	.73	.50	.33
87	.36	.13	.83	.60	.42	17	.25	.05	.77	.54	.37
86	.40	.18	.87	.64	.46	16	.29	.09	.81	.59	.41
85	.44	.22	.91	.68	.50	15	.33	.13	.85	.63	.46
84	.48	.26	.96	.72	.55	14	.37	.17	.89	.67	.50
83	.52	.30	64.00	.77	.59	13	.41	.21	.93	.71	.54
82	.56	.35	.04	.81	.63	12	.46	.26	.98	.75	.58
81	.61	.39	.08	.85	.68	11	.50	.30	67.02	.79	.62
80	.65	.43	.13	.89	.72	10	.54	.34	.06	.83	.67
79	.69	.47	.17	.94	.76	09	.58	.38	.10	.88	.71
78	.73	.51	.21	.98	.80	08	.62	.42	.14	.92	.75
77	.77	.56	.25	63.02	.85	07	.66	.46	.18	.96	.79
76	.82	.60	.30	.06	.89	06	.70	.50	.22	66.00	.83
75	.86	.64	.34	.11	.93	05	.74	.54	.26	.04	.87
74	.90	.68	.38	.15	.97	04	.78	.58	.30	.08	.92
73	.94	.72	.42	.19	62.02	03	.82	.62	.34	.12	.96
72	.98	.77	.47	.23	.06	02	.86	.67	.39	.17	65.00
71	67.03	.81	.51	.28	.10	01	.90	.71	.43	.21	.04
70	.07	.85	.55	.32	.14	00	.94	.75	.47	.25	.08
69	.11	.89	.59	.36	.19	0.8899	.98	.79	.51	.29	.12
68	.15	.94	.64	.40	.23	98	70.02	.83	.55	.33	.17
67	.19	.98	.68	.44	.27	97	.06	.87	.59	.37	.21
66	.23	66.02	.72	.49	.31	96	.10	.91	.63	.41	.25
65	.28	.06	.76	.53	.36	95	.14	.95	.67	.45	.29
64	.32	.10	.81	.57	.40	94	.18	.99	.71	.50	.33
63	.36	.15	.85	.61	.44	93	.22	69.03	.75	.54	.37
62	.40	.19	.89	.66	.48	92	.27	.07	.80	.58	.41
61	.44	.23	.93	.70	.53	91	.31	.11	.84	.62	.45
60	.48	.27	.97	.74	.57	90	.35	.15	.88	.66	.50
59	.53	.31	65.02	.78	.61	89	.39	.19	.92	.70	.54
58	.57	.36	.06	.83	.65	88	.43	.23	.96	.74	.58
57	.61	.40	.10	.87	.69	87	.47	.27	68.00	.79	.62
56	.65	.44	.14	.91	.74	86	.51	.32	.04	.83	.66
55	.69	.48	.18	.95	.78	85	.55	.36	.08	.87	.70
54	.73	.52	.23	64.00	.82	84	.59	.40	.12	.91	.74
53	.78	.56	.27	.04	.86	83	.63	.44	.16	.95	.79
52	.82	.60	.31	.08	.91	82	.67	.48	.20	.99	.83
51	.86	.65	.35	.12	.95	81	.71	.52	.24	67.03	.87

(Continued)

47.003　　**Percentages by volume at 15.56°C (60°F) of ethyl alcohol corresponding to apparent specific gravity at various temperatures[a]—Continued.**

Apparent Specific Gravity	15.56 / 15.56	20/20	25/25	30/30	35/35	Apparent Specific Gravity	15.56 / 15.56	20/20	25/25	30/30	35/35
0.8880	70.75	69.56	68.28	67.07	65.91	0.8810	73.50	72.34	71.09	69.89	68.74
79	.79	.60	.33	.11	.95	09	.54	.38	.13	.93	.78
78	.83	.64	.37	.15	.99	08	.58	.42	.16	.97	.82
77	.87	.68	.41	.20	66.03	07	.62	.46	.20	70.01	.86
76	.91	.72	.45	.24	.07	06	.66	.50	.24	.05	.90
75	.95	.76	.49	.28	.11	05	.70	.53	.28	.09	.94
74	.99	.80	.53	.32	.16	04	.74	.57	.32	.13	.98
73	71.03	.84	.57	.36	.20	03	.78	.61	.36	.17	69.02
72	.07	.88	.61	.40	.24	02	.81	.65	.40	.21	.06
71	.11	.92	.65	.44	.28	01	.85	.69	.44	.25	.10
70	.15	.96	.69	.48	.32	00	.89	.73	.48	.29	.14
69	.19	70.00	.73	.52	.36	0.8799	.93	.77	.52	.33	.18
68	.23	.04	.77	.56	.40	98	.97	.81	.56	.37	.22
67	.27	.08	.81	.60	.44	97	74.01	.85	.60	.41	.26
66	.31	.12	.85	.64	.48	96	.05	.88	.64	.44	.30
65	.35	.16	.89	.68	.52	95	.08	.92	.67	.48	.34
64	.38	.20	.93	.72	.56	94	.12	.96	.71	.52	.38
63	.42	.24	.98	.76	.60	93	.16	73.00	.75	.56	.42
62	.46	.28	69.02	.80	.64	92	.20	.04	.79	.60	.45
61	.50	.32	.06	.85	.69	91	.24	.08	.83	.64	.49
60	.54	.36	.10	.89	.73	90	.28	.12	.87	.68	.53
59	.58	.40	.14	.93	.77	89	.32	.16	.91	.72	.57
58	.62	.44	.18	.97	.81	88	.36	.19	.95	.76	.61
57	.66	.48	.22	68.01	.85	87	.39	.23	.99	.80	.65
56	.70	.52	.26	.05	.89	86	.43	.27	72.03	.84	.69
55	.74	.56	.30	.09	.93	85	.47	.31	.07	.88	.73
54	.78	.60	.34	.13	.97	84	.51	.35	.11	.92	.77
53	.82	.64	.38	.17	67.01	83	.55	.39	.14	.96	.81
52	.86	.68	.42	.21	.05	82	.59	.43	.18	71.00	.85
51	.90	.72	.46	.25	.09	81	.63	.47	.22	.04	.89
50	.94	.76	.50	.29	.13	80	.66	.50	.26	.07	.93
49	.98	.80	.54	.33	.17	79	.70	.54	.30	.11	.97
48	72.02	.84	.58	.37	.21	78	.74	.58	.34	.15	70.01
47	.06	.88	.62	.41	.25	77	.78	.62	.38	.19	.05
46	.10	.92	.66	.45	.29	76	.82	.66	.42	.23	.09
45	.14	.96	.70	.49	.33	75	.86	.70	.46	.27	.13
44	.18	71.00	.74	.53	.38	74	.90	.74	.49	.31	.16
43	.22	.04	.78	.57	.42	73	.93	.78	.53	.35	.20
42	.25	.08	.82	.61	.46	72	.97	.81	.57	.39	.24
41	.29	.12	.86	.65	.50	71	75.01	.85	.61	.42	.28
40	.33	.16	.90	.69	.54	70	.05	.89	.65	.46	.32
39	.37	.20	.94	.73	.58	69	.09	.93	.69	.50	.36
38	.41	.24	.98	.77	.62	68	.13	.97	.73	.54	.40
37	.45	.27	70.02	.81	.66	67	.16	74.01	.77	.58	.44
36	.49	.31	.06	.85	.70	66	.20	.05	.81	.62	.48
35	.53	.35	.10	.89	.74	65	.24	.08	.84	.66	.52
34	.57	.39	.13	.93	.78	64	.28	.12	.88	.70	.56
33	.61	.43	.17	.97	.82	63	.32	.16	.92	.74	.60
32	.65	.47	.21	69.01	.86	62	.35	.20	.96	.77	.64
31	.69	.51	.25	.05	.90	61	.39	.24	73.00	.81	.67
30	.73	.55	.29	.09	.94	60	.43	.28	.04	.85	.71
29	.76	.59	.33	.13	.98	59	.47	.32	.08	.89	.75
28	.80	.63	.37	.17	68.02	58	.51	.35	.12	.93	.79
27	.84	.67	.41	.21	.06	57	.54	.39	.15	.97	.83
26	.88	.71	.45	.25	.10	56	.58	.43	.19	72.01	.87
25	.92	.75	.49	.29	.14	55	.62	.47	.23	.05	.91
24	.96	.79	.53	.33	.18	54	.66	.51	.27	.08	.95
23	73.00	.83	.57	.37	.22	53	.70	.55	.31	.12	.99
22	.04	.87	.61	.41	.26	52	.73	.58	.35	.16	71.03
21	.08	.91	.65	.45	.30	51	.77	.62	.38	.20	.07
20	.12	.95	.69	.49	.34	50	.81	.66	.42	.24	.10
19	.16	.99	.73	.53	.38	49	.85	.70	.46	.28	.14
18	.19	72.03	.77	.57	.42	48	.89	.74	.50	.32	.18
17	.23	.07	.81	.61	.46	47	.92	.77	.54	.36	.22
16	.27	.10	.85	.65	.50	46	.96	.81	.58	.39	.26
15	.31	.14	.89	.69	.54	45	76.00	.85	.62	.43	.30
14	.35	.18	.93	.73	.58	44	.04	.89	.65	.47	.34
13	.39	.22	.97	.77	.62	43	.07	.93	.69	.51	.38
12	.43	.26	71.01	.81	.66	42	.11	.97	.73	.55	.41
11	.47	.30	.05	.85	.70	41	.15	75.00	.77	.59	.45

(Continued)

47.003 Percentages by volume at 15.56°C (60°F) of ethyl alcohol corresponding to apparent specific gravity at various temperatures[a]—Continued.

Apparent Specific Gravity	15.56 / 15.56	20/20	25/25	30/30	35/35	Apparent Specific Gravity	15.56 / 15.56	20/20	25/25	30/30	35/35
0.8740	76.19	75.04	73.81	72.63	71.49	0.8670	78.78	77.66	76.45	75.29	74.17
39	.22	.08	.85	.66	.53	69	.82	.70	.49	.33	.21
38	.26	.12	.88	.70	.57	68	.85	.73	.53	.37	.24
37	.30	.16	.92	.74	.61	67	.89	.77	.56	.40	.28
36	.34	.19	.96	.78	.65	66	.93	.81	.60	.44	.32
35	.37	.23	74.00	.82	.69	65	.96	.84	.64	.48	.36
34	.41	.27	.04	.86	.72	64	79.00	.88	.68	.51	.39
33	.45	.31	.08	.90	.76	63	.04	.92	.71	.55	.43
32	.49	.35	.11	.93	.80	62	.07	.96	.75	.59	.47
31	.52	.38	.15	.97	.84	61	.11	.99	.79	.63	.51
30	.56	.42	.19	73.01	.88	60	.14	78.03	.82	.66	.55
29	.60	.46	.23	.05	.92	59	.18	.07	.86	.70	.58
28	.64	.50	.27	.09	.96	58	.22	.10	.90	.74	.62
27	.67	.54	.31	.13	72.00	57	.25	.14	.94	.78	.66
26	.71	.57	.34	.16	.03	56	.29	.17	.97	.81	.70
25	.75	.61	.38	.20	.07	55	.32	.21	77.01	.85	.73
24	.79	.65	.42	.24	.11	54	.36	.25	.05	.89	.77
23	.82	.69	.46	.28	.15	53	.40	.28	.08	.93	.81
22	.86	.73	.50	.32	.19	52	.43	.32	.12	.96	.85
21	.90	.76	.53	.35	.23	51	.47	.36	.16	76.00	.88
20	.94	.80	.57	.39	.27	50	.51	.39	.19	.04	.92
19	.97	.84	.61	.43	.30	49	.54	.43	.23	.07	.96
18	77.01	.88	.65	.47	.34	48	.58	.47	.27	.11	75.00
17	.05	.91	.69	.51	.38	47	.61	.50	.30	.15	.03
16	.09	.95	.73	.55	.42	46	.65	.54	.34	.19	.07
15	.12	.99	.76	.58	.46	45	.69	.57	.38	.22	.11
14	.16	76.03	.80	.62	.50	44	.72	.61	.41	.26	.15
13	.20	.06	.84	.66	.53	43	.76	.65	.45	.30	.18
12	.23	.10	.88	.70	.57	42	.79	.68	.49	.33	.22
11	.27	.14	.92	.74	.61	41	.83	.72	.52	.37	.26
10	.31	.18	.95	.77	.65	40	.87	.76	.56	.41	.29
09	.34	.22	.99	.81	.69	39	.90	.79	.60	.44	.33
08	.38	.25	75.03	.85	.73	38	.94	.83	.63	.48	.37
07	.42	.29	.07	.89	.77	37	.97	.86	.67	.52	.41
06	.46	.33	.10	.93	.80	36	80.01	.90	.71	.56	.44
05	.49	.37	.14	.97	.84	35	.05	.94	.74	.59	.48
04	.53	.40	.18	74.00	.88	34	.08	.97	.78	.63	.52
03	.57	.44	.22	.04	.92	33	.12	79.01	.82	.67	.56
02	.60	.48	.25	.08	.96	32	.15	.05	.85	.70	.59
01	.64	.52	.29	.12	73.00	31	.19	.08	.89	.74	.63
00	.68	.55	.33	.16	.03	30	.22	.12	.93	.78	.67
0.8699	.71	.59	.37	.19	.07	29	.26	.16	.96	.81	.71
98	.75	.63	.40	.23	.11	28	.30	.19	78.00	.85	.74
97	.79	.66	.44	.27	.15	27	.33	.23	.04	.89	.78
96	.83	.70	.48	.31	.19	26	.37	.26	.07	.93	.82
95	.86	.74	.52	.35	.22	25	.40	.30	.11	.96	.85
94	.90	.78	.55	.38	.26	24	.44	.34	.14	77.00	.89
93	.94	.81	.59	.42	.30	23	.47	.37	.18	.04	.93
92	.97	.85	.63	.46	.34	22	.51	.41	.22	.07	.97
91	78.01	.89	.67	.50	.38	21	.55	.45	.25	.11	76.00
90	.05	.92	.70	.54	.41	20	.58	.48	.29	.15	.04
89	.08	.96	.74	.57	.45	19	.62	.52	.33	.18	.08
88	.12	77.00	.78	.61	.49	18	.65	.55	.36	.22	.11
87	.16	.03	.82	.65	.53	17	.69	.59	.40	.26	.15
86	.19	.07	.85	.69	.56	16	.72	.63	.43	.29	.19
85	.23	.11	.89	.73	.60	15	.76	.66	.47	.33	.23
84	.27	.14	.93	.76	.64	14	.80	.70	.51	.36	.26
83	.30	.18	.97	.80	.68	13	.83	.73	.54	.40	.30
82	.34	.22	76.00	.84	.72	12	.87	.77	.58	.44	.34
81	.38	.26	.04	.88	.75	11	.90	.80	.62	.47	.37
80	.41	.29	.08	.92	.79	10	.94	.84	.65	.51	.41
79	.45	.33	.12	.95	.83	09	.97	.88	.69	.55	.45
78	.49	.37	.15	.99	.87	08	81.01	.91	.72	.58	.48
77	.52	.40	.19	75.03	.91	07	.05	.95	.76	.62	.52
76	.56	.44	.23	.07	.94	06	.08	.98	.80	.66	.56
75	.60	.48	.26	.10	.98	05	.12	80.02	.83	.69	.59
74	.63	.51	.30	.14	74.02	04	.15	.05	.87	.73	.63
73	.67	.55	.34	.18	.06	03	.19	.09	.91	.77	.67
72	.71	.59	.38	.22	.09	02	.22	.13	.94	.80	.70
71	.74	.62	.41	.25	.13	01	.26	.16	.98	.84	.74

(Continued)

902   47. Reference Tables

47.003   Percentages by volume at 15.56°C (60°F) of ethyl alcohol corresponding to apparent specific gravity at various temperatures[a]—Continued.

Apparent Specific Gravity	15.56/15.56	20/20	25/25	30/30	35/35
0.8600	81.29	80.20	79.01	77.88	76.78
0.8599	.33	.23	.05	.91	.82
98	.36	.27	.09	.95	.85
97	.40	.30	.12	.99	.89
96	.43	.34	.16	78.02	.93
95	.47	.38	.19	.06	.96
94	.51	.41	.23	.09	77.00
93	.54	.45	.27	.13	.04
92	.58	.48	.30	.17	.07
91	.61	.52	.34	.20	.11
90	.65	.55	.37	.24	.14
89	.68	.59	.41	.27	.18
88	.72	.62	.44	.31	.22
87	.75	.66	.48	.35	.25
86	.79	.69	.52	.38	.29
85	.82	.73	.55	.42	.33
84	.86	.77	.59	.45	.36
83	.89	.80	.62	.49	.40
82	.93	.84	.66	.53	.43
81	.96	.87	.70	.56	.47
80	82.00	.91	.73	.60	.51
79	.03	.94	.77	.64	.54
78	.07	.98	.80	.67	.58
77	.10	81.01	.84	.71	.62
76	.14	.05	.87	.74	.65
75	.17	.08	.91	.78	.69
74	.21	.12	.95	.82	.72
73	.24	.16	.98	.85	.76
72	.28	.19	80.02	.89	.80
71	.31	.23	.05	.92	.83
70	.35	.26	.09	.96	.87
69	.38	.30	.12	79.00	.91
68	.42	.33	.16	.03	.94
67	.45	.37	.20	.07	.98
66	.49	.40	.23	.10	78.01
65	.52	.44	.27	.14	.05
64	.56	.47	.30	.17	.09
63	.59	.51	.34	.21	.12
62	.63	.54	.37	.25	.16
61	.66	.58	.41	.28	.19
60	.70	.61	.44	.32	.23
59	.73	.65	.48	.35	.27
58	.77	.68	.51	.39	.30
57	.80	.72	.55	.42	.34
56	.84	.75	.59	.46	.37
55	.87	.79	.62	.49	.41
54	.91	.82	.66	.53	.45
53	.94	.86	.69	.57	.48
52	.98	.89	.73	.60	.52
51	83.01	.93	.76	.64	.55
50	.04	.96	.80	.67	.59
49	.08	82.00	.83	.71	.63
48	.11	.03	.87	.74	.66
47	.15	.07	.90	.78	.70
46	.18	.10	.94	.81	.73
45	.22	.14	.98	.85	.77
44	.25	.17	81.01	.89	.81
43	.29	.21	.05	.92	.84
42	.32	.24	.08	.96	.88
41	.35	.28	.12	.99	.91
40	.39	.31	.15	80.03	.95
39	.42	.35	.19	.06	.99
38	.46	.38	.22	.10	79.02
37	.49	.42	.26	.13	.06
36	.53	.45	.29	.17	.09
35	.56	.49	.30	.20	.13
34	.59	.52	.36	.24	.16
33	.63	.55	.40	.28	.20
32	.66	.59	.43	.31	.23
31	.70	.62	.47	.35	.27

Apparent Specific Gravity	15.56/15.56	20/20	25/25	30/30	35/35
0.8530	83.73	82.66	81.50	80.38	79.30
29	.77	.69	.54	.42	.34
28	.80	.73	.57	.45	.38
27	.84	.76	.61	.49	.41
26	.87	.80	.64	.52	.45
25	.90	.83	.68	.56	.48
24	.94	.87	.71	.59	.52
23	.97	.90	.75	.63	.55
22	84.01	.94	.78	.66	.59
21	.04	.97	.82	.70	.62
20	.07	83.01	.85	.73	.66
19	.11	.04	.89	.77	.70
18	.14	.07	.92	.81	.73
17	.18	.11	.96	.84	.77
16	.21	.14	.99	.88	.80
15	.24	.18	82.03	.91	.84
14	.28	.21	.06	.95	.87
13	.31	.25	.10	.98	.91
12	.34	.28	.13	81.02	.94
11	.38	.32	.16	.05	.98
10	.41	.35	.20	.09	80.01
09	.45	.39	.23	.12	.05
08	.48	.42	.27	.16	.08
07	.51	.45	.30	.19	.12
06	.55	.49	.34	.23	.15
05	.58	.52	.37	.26	.19
04	.61	.56	.41	.30	.23
03	.65	.59	.44	.33	.26
02	.68	.62	.47	.37	.30
01	.72	.66	.51	.40	.33
00	.75	.69	.54	.44	.37
0.8499	.78	.73	.58	.47	.40
98	.82	.76	.61	.51	.44
97	.85	.79	.65	.54	.47
96	.89	.83	.68	.57	.51
95	.92	.86	.71	.61	.54
94	.95	.90	.75	.64	.58
93	.99	.93	.78	.68	.61
92	85.02	.97	.82	.71	.65
91	.05	84.00	.85	.75	.68
90	.09	.03	.89	.78	.72
89	.12	.07	.92	.82	.75
88	.15	.10	.96	.85	.79
87	.18	.14	.99	.89	.82
86	.22	.17	83.02	.92	.86
85	.25	.20	.06	.96	.89
84	.28	.24	.09	.99	.93
83	.32	.27	.13	82.03	.96
82	.35	.31	.16	.06	81.00
81	.38	.34	.20	.10	.03
80	.42	.37	.23	.13	.07
79	.45	.41	.26	.17	.10
78	.48	.44	.30	.20	.14
77	.51	.47	.33	.24	.17
76	.55	.51	.37	.27	.21
75	.58	.54	.40	.30	.24
74	.61	.57	.43	.34	.28
73	.65	.61	.47	.37	.31
72	.68	.64	.50	.41	.35
71	.71	.67	.54	.44	.38
70	.75	.71	.57	.48	.42
69	.78	.74	.61	.51	.45
68	.81	.78	.64	.55	.49
67	.84	.81	.67	.58	.52
66	.88	.84	.71	.62	.56
65	.91	.88	.74	.65	.59
64	.94	.91	.78	.69	.63
63	.98	.94	.81	.72	.66
62	86.01	.98	.85	.75	.70
61	.04	85.01	.88	.79	.73

(Continued)

47.003 Percentages by volume at 15.56°C (60°F) of ethyl alcohol corresponding to apparent specific gravity at various temperatures[a]—Continued.

Apparent Specific Gravity	15.56 / 15.56	20/20	25/25	30/30	35/35	Apparent Specific Gravity	15.56 / 15.56	20/20	25/25	30/30	35/35
0.8460	86.08	85.04	83.91	82.82	81.77	0.8390	88.33	87.33	86.24	85.18	84.16
59	.11	.08	.95	.86	.80	89	.36	.36	.28	.22	.19
58	.14	.11	.98	.89	.84	88	.39	.39	.31	.25	.22
57	.17	.14	84.02	.93	.87	87	.43	.43	.34	.28	.26
56	.21	.18	.05	.96	.91	86	.46	.46	.37	.31	.29
55	.24	.21	.08	83.00	.94	85	.49	.49	.40	.35	.32
54	.27	.24	.12	.03	.98	84	.52	.52	.44	.38	.36
53	.30	.28	.15	.06	82.01	83	.55	.55	.47	.41	.39
52	.34	.31	.18	.10	.04	82	.58	.58	.50	.45	.42
51	.37	.34	.22	.13	.08	81	.61	.62	.53	.48	.46
50	.40	.38	.25	.17	.11	80	.65	.65	.57	.51	.49
49	.43	.41	.29	.20	.15	79	.68	.68	.60	.54	.52
48	.47	.44	.32	.23	.18	78	.71	.71	.63	.58	.55
47	.50	.48	.35	.27	.22	77	.74	.74	.66	.61	.59
46	.53	.51	.39	.30	.25	76	.77	.78	.70	.64	.62
45	.57	.54	.42	.34	.28	75	.80	.81	.73	.68	.65
44	.60	.57	.45	.37	.32	74	.83	.84	.76	.71	.69
43	.63	.61	.49	.40	.35	73	.87	.87	.79	.74	.72
42	.66	.64	.52	.44	.39	72	.90	.90	.83	.77	.75
41	.70	.67	.55	.47	.42	71	.93	.94	.86	.81	.79
40	.73	.71	.59	.51	.46	70	.96	.97	.89	.84	.82
39	.76	.74	.62	.54	.49	69	.99	88.00	.92	.87	.85
38	.79	.77	.65	.57	.52	68	89.02	.03	.95	.90	.89
37	.83	.80	.69	.61	.56	67	.05	.06	.99	.94	.92
36	.86	.84	.72	.64	.59	66	.08	.09	87.02	.97	.95
35	.89	.87	.76	.68	.63	65	.11	.13	.05	86.00	.99
34	.92	.90	.79	.71	.66	64	.14	.16	.08	.04	85.02
33	.96	.94	.82	.74	.70	63	.18	.19	.11	.07	.05
32	.99	.97	.86	.78	.73	62	.21	.22	.15	.10	.08
31	87.02	86.00	.89	.81	.76	61	.24	.25	.18	.13	.12
30	.05	.03	.92	.85	.80	60	.27	.29	.21	.16	.15
29	.09	.07	.96	.88	.83	59	.30	.32	.24	.20	.18
28	.12	.10	.99	.91	.87	58	.33	.35	.27	.23	.22
27	.15	.13	85.02	.95	.90	57	.36	.38	.31	.26	.25
26	.18	.16	.06	.98	.93	56	.39	.41	.34	.29	.28
25	.22	.20	.09	84.02	.97	55	.42	.44	.37	.33	.31
24	.25	.23	.12	.05	83.00	54	.45	.47	.40	.36	.35
23	.28	.26	.16	.08	.04	53	.48	.50	.43	.39	.38
22	.31	.30	.19	.12	.07	52	.51	.54	.46	.42	.41
21	.34	.33	.22	.15	.11	51	.54	.57	.50	.45	.44
20	.38	.36	.25	.18	.14	50	.58	.60	.53	.49	.48
19	.41	.39	.29	.22	.17	49	.61	.63	.56	.52	.51
18	.44	.43	.32	.25	.21	48	.64	.66	.59	.55	.54
17	.47	.46	.35	.28	.24	47	.67	.69	.62	.58	.58
16	.50	.49	.39	.32	.28	46	.70	.72	.66	.62	.61
15	.54	.52	.42	.35	.31	45	.73	.75	.69	.65	.64
14	.57	.56	.45	.38	.34	44	.76	.79	.72	.68	.67
13	.60	.59	.49	.42	.38	43	.79	.82	.75	.71	.71
12	.63	.62	.52	.45	.41	42	.82	.85	.78	.75	.74
11	.67	.65	.55	.48	.45	41	.85	.88	.82	.78	.77
10	.70	.68	.59	.52	.48	40	.88	.91	.85	.81	.80
09	.73	.72	.62	.55	.51	39	.91	.94	.88	.84	.84
08	.76	.75	.65	.59	.55	38	.94	.97	.91	.87	.87
07	.79	.78	.69	.62	.58	37	.98	89.00	.94	.91	.90
06	.83	.81	.72	.65	.62	36	90.01	.04	.97	.94	.93
05	.86	.85	.75	.69	.65	35	.04	.07	88.01	.97	.97
04	.89	.88	.78	.72	.68	34	.07	.10	.04	87.00	86.00
03	.92	.91	.82	.75	.72	33	.10	.13	.07	.04	.03
02	.95	.94	.85	.79	.75	32	.13	.16	.10	.07	.06
01	.99	.98	.88	.82	.79	31	.16	.19	.13	.10	.10
00	88.02	87.01	.92	.85	.82	30	.19	.22	.16	.13	.13
0.8399	.05	.04	.95	.89	.85	29	.22	.25	.19	.16	.16
98	.08	.07	.98	.92	.89	28	.25	.28	.23	.19	.19
97	.11	.10	86.02	.95	.92	27	.28	.31	.26	.23	.23
96	.14	.14	.05	.99	.96	26	.31	.35	.29	.26	.26
95	.18	.17	.08	85.02	.99	25	.34	.38	.32	.29	.29
94	.21	.20	.11	.05	84.02	24	.37	.41	.35	.32	.32
93	.24	.23	.15	.09	.06	23	.40	.44	.38	.35	.35
92	.27	.27	.18	.12	.09	22	.43	.47	.41	.39	.39
91	.30	.30	.21	.15	.12	21	.46	.50	.45	.42	.42

(Continued)

47.003   **Percentages by volume at 15.56°C (60°F) of ethyl alcohol corresponding to apparent specific gravity at various temperatures**[a]—*Continued.*

Apparent Specific Gravity	15.56 / 15.56	20/20	25/25	30/30	35/35	Apparent Specific Gravity	15.56 / 15.56	20/20	25/25	30/30	35/35
0.8320	90.49	89.53	88.48	87.45	86.45	0.8250	92.53	91.62	90.61	89.64	88.67
19	.51	.56	.51	.48	.48	49	.55	.64	.64	.67	.70
18	.54	.59	.54	.51	.52	48	.58	.67	.67	.70	.73
17	.57	.62	.57	.54	.55	47	.61	.70	.70	.73	.76
16	.60	.65	.60	.58	.58	46	.64	.73	.73	.76	.79
15	.63	.68	.64	.61	.61	45	.66	.76	.76	.79	.83
14	.66	.71	.67	.64	.65	44	.69	.79	.79	.82	.86
13	.69	.74	.70	.67	.68	43	.72	.82	.82	.85	.89
12	.72	.77	.73	.70	.71	42	.75	.85	.85	.88	.92
11	.75	.80	.76	.74	.74	41	.78	.87	.88	.91	.95
10	.78	.83	.79	.77	.77	40	.80	.90	.91	.94	.98
09	.81	.86	.82	.80	.81	39	.83	.93	.94	.97	89.01
08	.84	.89	.85	.83	.84	38	.86	.96	.97	90.00	.04
07	.87	.93	.88	.86	.87	37	.89	.99	91.00	.03	.07
06	.90	.96	.92	.89	.90	36	.92	92.02	.03	.06	.10
05	.93	.99	.95	.93	.94	35	.94	.05	.06	.09	.13
04	.96	90.02	.98	.96	.97	34	.97	.08	.09	.12	.16
03	.99	.05	89.01	.99	87.00	33	93.00	.10	.12	.15	.20
02	91.02	.08	.04	88.02	.03	32	.03	.13	.15	.18	.23
01	.05	.11	.07	.05	.06	31	.05	.16	.18	.21	.26
00	.08	.14	.10	.08	.10	30	.08	.19	.21	.24	.29
0.8299	.11	.17	.13	.12	.13	29	.11	.22	.23	.27	.32
98	.14	.20	.16	.15	.16	28	.14	.25	.26	.30	.35
97	.17	.23	.19	.18	.19	27	.16	.28	.29	.33	.38
96	.20	.26	.22	.21	.22	26	.19	.31	.32	.36	.41
95	.23	.29	.25	.24	.25	25	.22	.33	.35	.39	.44
94	.26	.32	.28	.27	.29	24	.25	.36	.38	.42	.47
93	.28	.35	.31	.30	.32	23	.27	.39	.41	.45	.50
92	.31	.38	.35	.34	.35	22	.30	.42	.44	.48	.53
91	.34	.41	.38	.37	.38	21	.33	.45	.47	.51	.56
90	.37	.44	.41	.40	.41	20	.36	.48	.50	.54	.59
89	.40	.47	.44	.43	.44	19	.38	.50	.52	.57	.62
88	.43	.50	.47	.46	.48	18	.41	.53	.55	.60	.65
87	.46	.53	.50	.49	.51	17	.44	.56	.58	.63	.68
86	.49	.56	.53	.52	.54	16	.47	.59	.61	.66	.71
85	.52	.59	.56	.55	.57	15	.49	.62	.64	.69	.74
84	.55	.62	.59	.59	.60	14	.52	.65	.67	.72	.77
83	.58	.65	.62	.62	.63	13	.55	.67	.70	.75	.80
82	.60	.67	.65	.65	.67	12	.58	.70	.73	.78	.84
81	.63	.70	.68	.68	.70	11	.60	.73	.76	.81	.87
80	.66	.73	.71	.71	.73	10	.63	.76	.79	.84	.90
79	.69	.76	.74	.74	.76	09	.66	.79	.81	.87	.93
78	.72	.79	.77	.77	.79	08	.68	.81	.84	.90	.96
77	.75	.82	.80	.81	.83	07	.71	.84	.87	.93	.99
76	.78	.85	.83	.84	.86	06	.74	.87	.90	.96	90.02
75	.81	.88	.87	.87	.89	05	.76	.90	.93	.99	.05
74	.84	.91	.90	.90	.92	04	.79	.92	.96	91.01	.08
73	.87	.94	.93	.93	.95	03	.82	.95	.99	.04	.11
72	.90	.97	.96	.96	.98	02	.84	.98	92.02	.07	.14
71	.92	91.00	.99	.99	88.02	01	.87	93.01	.05	.10	.17
70	.95	.03	90.02	89.02	.05	00	.90	.04	.07	.13	.20
69	.98	.06	.05	.06	.08	0.8199	.92	.06	.10	.16	.23
68	92.01	.09	.08	.09	.11	98	.95	.09	.13	.19	.26
67	.04	.12	.11	.12	.14	97	.98	.12	.16	.22	.29
66	.07	.15	.14	.15	.17	96	94.01	.14	.19	.25	.32
65	.10	.18	.17	.18	.20	95	.03	.17	.22	.27	.35
64	.13	.21	.20	.21	.23	94	.06	.20	.24	.30	.38
63	.15	.24	.23	.24	.26	93	.08	.23	.27	.33	.40
62	.18	.27	.26	.27	.30	92	.11	.25	.30	.36	.43
61	.21	.29	.29	.30	.33	91	.14	.28	.33	.39	.46
60	.24	.32	.32	.33	.36	90	.16	.31	.36	.42	.49
59	.27	.35	.35	.36	.39	89	.19	.34	.39	.45	.52
58	.30	.38	.38	.39	.42	88	.22	.36	.41	.48	.55
57	.33	.41	.41	.42	.45	87	.24	.39	.44	.51	.58
56	.35	.44	.44	.45	.48	86	.27	.42	.47	.53	.61
55	.38	.47	.47	.48	.51	85	.30	.44	.50	.56	.64
54	.41	.50	.50	.51	.55	84	.32	.47	.53	.59	.67
53	.44	.53	.53	.54	.58	83	.35	.50	.56	.62	.70
52	.47	.56	.56	.57	.61	82	.38	.53	.58	.65	.73
51	.50	.59	.59	.61	.64	81	.40	.55	.61	.68	.76

(Continued)

47.003 Percentages by volume at 15.56°C (60°F) of ethyl alcohol corresponding to apparent specific gravity at various temperatures[a]—Continued.

Apparent Specific Gravity	15.56 / 15.56	20/20	25/25	30/30	35/35	Apparent Specific Gravity	15.56 / 15.56	20/20	25/25	30/30	35/35
0.8180	94.43	93.58	92.64	91.71	90.79	0.8110	96.20	95.42	94.53	93.67	92.80
79	.46	.61	.67	.74	.82	09	.23	.44	.56	.69	.83
78	.48	.64	.70	.77	.85	08	.25	.47	.59	.72	.86
77	.51	.66	.72	.79	.88	07	.28	.49	.61	.75	.89
76	.53	.69	.75	.82	.91	06	.30	.52	.64	.77	.92
75	.56	.72	.78	.85	.94	05	.32	.54	.65	.80	.94
74	.59	.74	.81	.88	.97	04	.35	.57	.69	.83	.97
73	.61	.77	.84	.91	91.00	03	.37	.59	.72	.85	93.00
72	.64	.80	.86	.94	.03	02	.40	.62	.74	.88	.03
71	.66	.82	.89	.97	.06	01	.42	.64	.77	.91	.05
70	.69	.85	.92	92.00	.09	00	.45	.67	.79	.94	.08
69	.72	.88	.95	.03	.12	0.8099	.47	.69	.82	.96	.11
68	.74	.90	.97	.05	.14	98	.50	.72	.85	.99	.14
67	.77	.93	93.00	.08	.17	97	.52	.74	.87	94.02	.16
66	.79	.96	.03	.11	.20	96	.54	.77	.90	.04	.19
65	.82	.98	.06	.14	.23	95	.57	.79	.92	.07	.22
64	.84	94.01	.09	.17	.26	94	.59	.82	.95	.10	.25
63	.87	.04	.11	.20	.29	93	.61	.84	.98	.12	.27
62	.90	.06	.14	.22	.32	92	.64	.87	95.00	.15	.30
61	.92	.09	.17	.25	.35	91	.66	.89	.03	.17	.33
60	.95	.12	.20	.28	.38	90	.69	.92	.05	.20	.36
59	.97	.14	.22	.31	.40	89	.71	.94	.08	.23	.38
58	95.00	.17	.25	.34	.43	88	.73	.97	.10	.25	.41
57	.03	.20	.28	.36	.46	87	.76	.99	.13	.28	.44
56	.05	.22	.30	.39	.49	86	.78	96.02	.16	.31	.46
55	.08	.25	.33	.42	.52	85	.81	.04	.18	.33	.49
54	.10	.28	.36	.45	.55	84	.83	.07	.21	.36	.52
53	.13	.30	.39	.48	.58	83	.85	.09	.23	.39	.55
52	.15	.33	.41	.51	.61	82	.88	.11	.26	.41	.57
51	.18	.36	.44	.54	.64	81	.90	.14	.28	.44	.60
50	.20	.38	.47	.56	.66	80	.93	.16	.31	.47	.63
49	.23	.41	.50	.59	.69	79	.95	.19	.33	.49	.65
48	.25	.44	.52	.62	.72	78	.97	.21	.36	.52	.68
47	.28	.46	.55	.65	.75	77	97.00	.24	.39	.54	.71
46	.30	.49	.58	.68	.78	76	.02	.26	.41	.57	.73
45	.33	.51	.60	.70	.81	75	.04	.29	.44	.60	.76
44	.36	.54	.63	.73	.84	74	.07	.31	.46	.62	.79
43	.38	.57	.66	.76	.87	73	.09	.33	.49	.65	.81
42	.41	.59	.69	.79	.90	72	.11	.36	.51	.67	.84
41	.43	.62	.71	.82	.92	71	.14	.38	.54	.70	.87
40	.46	.64	.74	.84	.95	70	.16	.41	.56	.73	.90
39	.48	.67	.77	.87	.98	69	.18	.43	.59	.75	.92
38	.51	.70	.79	.90	92.01	68	.21	.46	.61	.78	.95
37	.53	.72	.82	.93	.04	67	.23	.48	.64	.80	.98
36	.56	.75	.85	.96	.07	66	.25	.50	.66	.83	94.00
35	.58	.77	.87	.98	.10	65	.28	.53	.69	.86	.03
34	.61	.80	.90	93.01	.13	64	.30	.55	.71	.88	.06
33	.63	.83	.93	.04	.15	63	.32	.58	.74	.91	.08
32	.66	.85	.95	.07	.18	62	.35	.60	.76	.93	.11
31	.68	.88	.98	.09	.21	61	.37	.63	.79	.96	.14
30	.71	.90	94.01	.12	.24	60	.39	.65	.81	.99	.16
29	.73	.93	.03	.15	.27	59	.42	.67	.84	95.01	.19
28	.76	.95	.06	.18	.30	58	.44	.70	.86	.04	.22
27	.78	.98	.09	.20	.33	57	.46	.72	.89	.06	.24
26	.81	95.01	.11	.23	.35	56	.49	.75	.91	.09	.27
25	.83	.03	.14	.26	.38	55	.51	.77	.94	.11	.30
24	.86	.06	.17	.29	.41	54	.53	.79	.96	.14	.32
23	.88	.08	.19	.31	.44	53	.55	.82	.99	.17	.35
22	.91	.11	.22	.34	.47	52	.58	.84	96.01	.19	.38
21	.93	.14	.24	.37	.50	51	.60	.86	.04	.22	.40
20	.96	.16	.27	.40	.53	50	.62	.89	.06	.24	.43
19	.98	.19	.30	.42	.55	49	.64	.91	.09	.27	.45
18	96.01	.21	.32	.45	.58	48	.67	.94	.11	.29	.48
17	.03	.24	.35	.48	.61	47	.69	.96	.14	.32	.51
16	.06	.26	.38	.51	.64	46	.71	.98	.16	.34	.53
15	.08	.29	.40	.53	.66	45	.73	97.01	.19	.37	.56
14	.10	.32	.43	.56	.69	44	.76	.03	.21	.40	.59
13	.13	.34	.46	.59	.72	43	.78	.05	.24	.42	.61
12	.15	.37	.48	.61	.75	42	.80	.08	.26	.45	.64
11	.18	.39	.51	.64	.78	41	.82	.10	.28	.47	.66

(Continued)

47.003   Percentages by volume at 15.56°C (60°F) of ethyl alcohol corresponding to apparent specific gravity at various temperatures[a]—Continued.

Apparent Specific Gravity	15.56 / 15.56	20/20	25/25	30/30	35/35
0.8040	97.85	97.12	96.31	95.50	94.69
39	.87	.15	.33	.52	.72
38	.89	.17	.36	.55	.74
37	.91	.19	.38	.57	.77
36	.94	.22	.41	.60	.79
35	.96	.24	.43	.62	.82
34	.98	.26	.46	.65	.85
33	98.00	.29	.48	.67	.87
32	.03	.31	.50	.70	.90
31	.05	.33	.53	.72	.92
30	.07	.36	.55	.75	.95
29	.09	.38	.58	.77	.98
28	.11	.40	.60	.80	95.00
27	.14	.43	.62	.82	.03
26	.16	.45	.65	.85	.05
25	.18	.47	.67	.87	.08
24	.20	.49	.70	.90	.11
23	.22	.52	.72	.92	.13
22	.25	.54	.74	.95	.16
21	.27	.56	.77	.97	.18
20	.29	.59	.79	96.00	.21
19	.31	.61	.82	.02	.23
18	.33	.63	.84	.05	.26
17	.35	.66	.86	.07	.28
16	.38	.68	.89	.10	.31
15	.40	.70	.91	.12	.34
14	.42	.72	.94	.15	.36
13	.44	.75	.96	.17	.39
12	.46	.77	.98	.20	.41
11	.48	.79	97.01	.22	.44
10	.50	.81	.03	.25	.46
09	.53	.84	.05	.27	.49
08	.55	.86	.08	.29	.52
07	.57	.88	.10	.32	.54
06	.59	.90	.12	.34	.57
05	.61	.92	.15	.37	.59
04	.63	.95	.17	.39	.62
03	.65	.97	.19	.42	.64
02	.67	.99	.22	.44	.67
01	.70	98.01	.24	.47	.69
00	.72	.03	.26	.49	.72
0.7999	.74	.06	.29	.51	.74
98	.76	.08	.31	.54	.77
97	.78	.10	.33	.56	.79
96	.80	.12	.36	.59	.82
95	.82	.14	.38	.61	.84
94	.84	.17	.40	.63	.87
93	.86	.19	.43	.66	.89
92	.88	.21	.45	.68	.92
91	.90	.23	.47	.71	.94
90	.92	.26	.50	.73	.97
89	.95	.28	.52	.75	.99
88	.97	.30	.54	.78	96.02
87	.99	.32	.57	.80	.04
86	99.01	.34	.59	.83	.07
85	.03	.36	.61	.85	.09
84	.05	.39	.63	.87	.12
83	.07	.41	.66	.90	.14
82	.09	.43	.68	.92	.16
81	.11	.45	.70	.95	.19
80	.13	.47	.72	.97	.21
79	.15	.49	.75	97.00	.24
78	.17	.51	.77	.02	.26
77	.19	.54	.79	.04	.29
76	.21	.56	.81	.07	.31
75	.23	.58	.84	.09	.34
74	.25	.60	.86	.11	.36
73	.27	.62	.88	.14	.38
72	.29	.64	.90	.16	.41
71	.31	.66	.93	.18	.43

Apparent Specific Gravity	15.56 / 15.56	20/20	25/25	30/30	35/35
0.7970	99.33	98.68	97.95	97.21	96.46
69	.35	.70	.97	.23	.48
68	.37	.72	.99	.25	.51
67	.39	.75	98.02	.28	.53
66	.42	.77	.04	.30	.56
65	.44	.79	.06	.32	.58
64	.46	.81	.08	.35	.60
63	.48	.83	.10	.37	.63
62	.50	.85	.12	.39	.65
61	.52	.87	.15	.42	.68
60	.54	.89	.17	.44	.70
59	.56	.91	.19	.46	.72
58	.58	.93	.21	.49	.75
57	.60	.95	.23	.51	.77
56	.61	.97	.26	.53	.80
55	.63	99.00	.28	.56	.82
54	.65	.02	.30	.58	.84
53	.67	.04	.32	.60	.87
52	.69	.06	.34	.62	.89
51	.71	.08	.36	.65	.92
50	.73	.10	.39	.67	.94
49	.75	.12	.41	.69	.96
48	.77	.14	.43	.71	.99
47	.79	.16	.45	.74	97.01
46	.81	.18	.47	.76	.04
45	.83	.20	.49	.78	.06
44	.85	.22	.51	.80	.08
43	.87	.24	.54	.83	.11
42	.89	.26	.56	.85	.13
41	.91	.28	.58	.87	.15
40	.93	.30	.60	.89	.18
39	.95	.32	.62	.92	.20
38	.97	.34	.64	.94	.22
37	.99	.36	.66	.96	.25
36	100.00	.38	.68	.98	.27
35		.40	.70	98.01	.29
34		.42	.73	.03	.32
33		.44	.75	.05	.34
32		.46	.77	.07	.36
31		.48	.79	.09	.39
30		.50	.81	.12	.41
29		.52	.83	.14	.43
28		.54	.85	.16	.46
27		.56	.87	.18	.48
26		.58	.89	.20	.50
25		.60	.91	.23	.52
24		.62	.93	.25	.55
23		.64	.96	.27	.57
22		.66	.98	.29	.59
21		.68	99.00	.31	.62
20		.70	.02	.33	.64
19		.72	.04	.36	.66
18		.74	.06	.38	.68
17		.76	.08	.40	.71
16		.78	.10	.42	.73
15		.80	.12	.44	.75
14		.82	.14	.46	.77
13		.84	.16	.48	.80
12		.86	.18	.51	.82
11		.88	.20	.53	.84
10		.90	.22	.55	.86
09		.92	.24	.57	.89
08		.94	.27	.59	.91
07		.96	.29	.61	.93
06		.98	.31	.63	.95
05		100.00	.33	.66	.98
04			.35	.68	98.00
03			.37	.70	.02
02			.39	.72	.04
01			.41	.74	.07

(Continued)

47.003   Percentages by volume at 15.56°C (60°F) of ethyl alcohol corresponding to apparent specific gravity at various temperatures[a]—Concluded.

Apparent Specific Gravity	25/25	30/30	35/35	Apparent Specific Gravity	35/35
0.7900	99.43	98.76	98.09	0.7830	99.56
.7899	.45	.78	.11	29	.58
98	.47	.80	.13	28	.60
97	.49	.82	.15	27	.62
96	.51	.84	.18	26	.64
95	.53	.87	.20	25	.66
94	.55	.89	.22	24	.68
93	.57	.91	.24	23	.70
92	.59	.93	.26	22	.72
91	.61	.95	.29	21	.74
90	.63	.97	.31	20	.76
89	.65	.99	.33	19	.78
88	.67	99.01	.35	18	.80
87	.69	.03	.37	17	.82
86	.71	.05	.40	16	.84
85	.73	.07	.42	15	.86
84	.75	.09	.44	14	.88
83	.77	.12	.46	13	.90
82	.79	.14	.48	12	.92
81	.81	.16	.50	11	.94
80	.83	.18	.53	10	.96
79	.85	.20	.55	09	.98
78	.86	.22	.57	08	100.00
77	.88	.24	.59		
76	.90	.26	.61		
75	.92	.28	.63		
74	.94	.30	.65		
73	.96	.32	.67		
72	.98	.34	.70		
71	100.00	.36	.72		
70		.38	.74		
69		.40	.76		
68		.42	.78		
67		.44	.80		
66		.46	.82		
65		.48	.84		
64		.50	.86		
63		.52	.89		
62		.54	.91		
61		.56	.93		
60		.58	.95		
59		.60	.97		
58		.62	.99		
57		.64	99.01		
56		.66	.03		
55		.68	.05		
54		.70	.07		
53		.72	.09		
52		.74	.12		
51		.76	.14		
50		.78	.16		
49		.80	.18		
48		.82	.20		
47		.84	.22		
46		.86	.24		
45		.88	.26		
44		.90	.28		
43		.92	.30		
42		.94	.32		
41		.96	.34		
40		.98	.36		
39		100.00	.38		
38			.40		
37			.42		
36			.44		
35			.46		
34			.48		
33			.50		
32			.52		
31			.54		

47.004 Alcohol table for calculating percentages of alcohol by volume at 15.56°C (60°F) in mixtures of ethyl alcohol and water from the Zeiss immersion refractometer readings and refractive indices at 17.5–25°C[a]

Scale Reading[b]	Refractive Index	Temp., °C								
		17.5	18	19	20	21	22	23	24	25
13.2	1.33250									0.00
.4	3257									0.18
.6	3265								0.14	0.35
.8	3273							0.10	0.31	0.53
14.0	3281						0.08	0.28	0.49	0.70
.2	3288					0.04	0.24	0.45	0.67	0.88
.4	3296					0.21	0.41	0.63	0.84	1.06
.6	3304				0.16	0.38	0.59	0.80	1.02	1.24
.8	3312			0.14	0.34	0.55	0.77	0.98	1.19	1.40
15.0	3319	0.00	0.10	0.31	0.52	0.73	0.94	1.16	1.36	1.55
.2	3327	0.17	0.27	0.48	0.69	0.91	1.12	1.32	1.51	1.71
.4	3335	0.34	0.44	0.65	0.85	1.07	1.29	1.47	1.66	1.86
.6	3343	0.51	0.60	0.82	1.03	1.24	1.44	1.62	1.82	2.01
.8	3350	0.68	0.78	0.99	1.21	1.40	1.60	1.77	1.97	2.17
16.0	3358	0.84	0.94	1.17	1.36	1.55	1.75	1.92	2.12	2.33
.2	3366	1.02	1.12	1.32	1.51	1.70	1.90	2.08	2.27	2.48
.4	3374	1.18	1.29	1.47	1.66	1.85	2.05	2.24	2.43	2.62
.6	3381	1.34	1.43	1.62	1.81	2.00	2.20	2.39	2.57	2.77
.8	3389	1.49	1.57	1.77	1.96	2.15	2.35	2.53	2.72	2.92
17.0	3397	1.63	1.72	1.92	2.11	2.30	2.50	2.69	2.87	3.06
.2	3405	1.77	1.87	2.06	2.26	2.45	2.65	2.82	3.02	3.21
.4	3412	1.92	2.01	2.21	2.41	2.59	2.79	2.97	3.17	3.36
.6	3420	2.07	2.16	2.36	2.56	2.74	2.94	3.12	3.32	3.51
.8	3428	2.21	2.31	2.51	2.70	2.89	3.09	3.27	3.46	3.66
18.0	3435	2.36	2.45	2.66	2.85	3.04	3.23	3.42	3.61	3.81
.2	3443	2.50	2.60	2.81	3.00	3.19	3.37	3.57	3.76	3.96
.4	3451	2.65	2.75	2.96	3.15	3.34	3.52	3.71	3.91	4.11
.6	3459	2.80	2.90	3.10	3.30	3.48	3.66	3.86	4.06	4.26
.8	3466	2.95	3.05	3.25	3.45	3.63	3.81	4.01	4.21	4.41
19.0	3474	3.10	3.19	3.40	3.59	3.77	3.96	4.16	4.36	4.56
.2	3482	3.25	3.34	3.55	3.73	3.92	4.11	4.31	4.51	4.70
.4	3489	3.39	3.48	3.70	3.88	4.07	4.26	4.46	4.65	4.85
.6	3497	3.53	3.63	3.84	4.03	4.22	4.41	4.61	4.80	5.00
.8	3505	3.68	3.78	3.98	4.17	4.37	4.56	4.75	4.95	5.15
20.0	3513	3.83	3.93	4.13	4.32	4.52	4.72	4.90	5.10	5.29
.2	3520	3.97	4.07	4.27	4.47	4.66	4.87	5.05	5.24	5.44
.4	3528	4.12	4.22	4.42	4.61	4.82	5.01	5.20	5.38	5.58
.6	3536	4.26	4.36	4.56	4.75	4.96	5.15	5.34	5.52	5.72
.8	3543	4.41	4.51	4.70	4.90	5.10	5.29	5.48	5.67	5.87
21.0	3551	4.56	4.65	4.85	5.04	5.24	5.44	5.62	5.82	6.02
.2	3559	4.70	4.80	4.99	5.19	5.39	5.58	5.77	5.96	6.16
.4	3566	4.84	4.94	5.14	5.33	5.53	5.72	5.91	6.11	6.30
.6	3574	4.99	5.09	5.28	5.47	5.67	5.87	6.06	6.25	6.44
.8	3582	5.13	5.23	5.43	5.61	5.82	6.01	6.20	6.39	6.59
22.0	1.33590	5.27	5.37	5.57	5.76	5.96	6.15	6.34	6.54	6.73
.2	3597	5.41	5.51	5.71	5.90	6.11	6.29	6.49	6.68	6.87
.4	3605	5.56	5.65	5.85	6.05	6.25	6.43	6.63	6.82	7.01
.6	3613	5.70	5.80	6.00	6.19	6.39	6.57	6.77	6.96	7.16
.8	3620	5.85	5.94	6.14	6.33	6.53	6.71	6.91	7.10	7.31

(Continued)

[a] Rearranged from table of B. H. St. John, which is based upon data of Doroschevskii and Dvorzhanchik, *J. Russ. Phys. Chem. Soc.* **40**, 101(1908). Scale readings were converted into refractive indices by using $n_D = 1.327338 + 0.00039347X - 0.00000020446X^2$.

[b] Scale readings refer only to scale of arbitrary units proposed by Pulfrich, *Z. Angew. Chem.* 1168(1899). According to this scale, 14.5 = 1.33300, 50.0 = 1.34650, and 100.0 = 1.36464. If immersion refractometer used is calibrated to another arbitrary scale, readings must be converted into refractive indices before table is used to determine per cent alcohol.

47.004 Alcohol table for calculating percentages of alcohol by volume at 15.56°C (60°F) in mixtures of ethyl alcohol and water from the Zeiss immersion refractometer readings and refractive indices at 17.5–25°C[a]—Continued.

Scale Reading[b]	Refractive Index	Temp., °C								
		17.5	18	19	20	21	22	23	24	25
23.0	1.33628	5.99	6.08	6.28	6.47	6.67	6.86	7.06	7.24	7.45
.2	3636	6.13	6.22	6.42	6.61	6.81	7.00	7.20	7.39	7.59
.4	3643	6.27	6.36	6.56	6.75	6.95	7.14	7.34	7.53	7.73
.6	3651	6.41	6.50	6.70	6.90	7.09	7.28	7.48	7.67	7.87
.8	3659	6.55	6.64	6.85	7.04	7.23	7.42	7.62	7.81	8.00
24.0	3666	6.69	6.78	6.99	7.18	7.38	7.56	7.76	7.95	8.14
.2	3674	6.83	6.92	7.13	7.32	7.52	7.70	7.90	8.09	8.28
.4	3682	6.97	7.06	7.27	7.46	7.66	7.84	8.04	8.23	8.42
.6	3689	7.11	7.20	7.41	7.60	7.80	7.98	8.17	8.37	8.55
.8	3697	7.25	7.35	7.55	7.74	7.93	8.12	8.31	8.51	8.69
25.0	3705	7.39	7.49	7.68	7.88	8.06	8.26	8.45	8.64	8.84
.2	3712	7.53	7.63	7.82	8.01	8.20	8.40	8.59	8.78	8.98
.4	3720	7.66	7.76	7.95	8.14	8.34	8.54	8.73	8.92	9.12
.6	3728	7.80	7.90	8.09	8.28	8.48	8.68	8.86	9.06	9.26
.8	3735	7.94	8.03	8.22	8.42	8.62	8.82	9.00	9.20	9.39
26.0	3743	8.07	8.16	8.36	8.55	8.75	8.95	9.14	9.34	9.53
.2	3751	8.21	8.30	8.50	8.69	8.89	9.09	9.28	9.48	9.67
.4	3758	8.34	8.44	8.63	8.82	9.03	9.22	9.42	9.61	9.81
.6	3766	8.48	8.57	8.77	8.96	9.16	9.36	9.55	9.75	9.95
.8	3774	8.62	8.71	8.91	9.10	9.30	9.49	9.69	9.89	10.09
27.0	3781	8.75	8.85	9.05	9.23	9.44	9.63	9.83	10.03	10.23
.2	3789	8.89	8.98	9.18	9.37	9.58	9.76	9.97	10.17	10.37
.4	3796	9.02	9.12	9.32	9.51	9.71	9.90	10.10	10.31	10.51
.6	3804	9.16	9.26	9.45	9.65	9.85	10.03	10.24	10.45	10.65
.8	3812	9.29	9.39	9.59	9.79	9.98	10.17	10.38	10.58	10.79
28.0	3820	9.43	9.53	9.72	9.92	10.12	10.31	10.51	10.72	10.93
.2	3827	9.57	9.66	9.86	10.06	10.25	10.45	10.65	10.86	11.06
.4	3835	9.70	9.80	9.99	10.19	10.39	10.59	10.79	11.00	11.20
.6	3842	9.84	9.93	10.13	10.32	10.52	10.72	10.93	11.13	11.33
.8	3850	9.97	10.07	10.26	10.46	10.66	10.86	11.06	11.27	11.47
29.0	3858	10.10	10.19	10.40	10.59	10.79	11.00	11.20	11.40	11.61
.2	3865	10.24	10.33	10.52	10.73	10.93	11.13	11.33	11.54	11.75
.4	3873	10.36	10.46	10.66	10.86	11.06	11.27	11.47	11.67	11.88
.6	3881	10.50	10.59	10.79	10.99	11.20	11.39	11.60	11.81	12.01
.8	3888	10.63	10.72	10.93	11.12	11.33	11.53	11.74	11.94	12.15
30.0	3896	10.76	10.86	11.05	11.26	11.46	11.66	11.87	12.08	12.29
.2	3904	10.89	10.99	11.18	11.38	11.59	11.79	12.00	12.21	12.42
.4	3911	11.02	11.12	11.31	11.51	11.72	11.93	12.13	12.34	12.56
.6	3919	11.15	11.25	11.44	11.64	11.85	12.06	12.27	12.48	12.70
.8	3926	11.28	11.38	11.58	11.78	11.99	12.19	12.40	12.61	12.84
31.0	3934	11.41	11.51	11.71	11.91	12.12	12.32	12.54	12.75	12.97
.2	3942	11.54	11.64	11.84	12.04	12.25	12.46	12.67	12.89	13.11
.4	3949	11.66	11.77	11.97	12.17	12.38	12.59	12.81	13.02	13.24
.6	3957	11.79	11.90	12.10	12.30	12.51	12.72	12.94	13.15	13.37
.8	3964	11.92	12.03	12.23	12.43	12.64	12.85	13.07	13.29	13.51
32.0	3972	12.05	12.15	12.36	12.57	12.78	12.99	13.20	13.42	13.64
.2	3980	12.18	12.28	12.49	12.70	12.91	13.12	13.34	13.55	13.77
.4	3987	12.31	12.40	12.62	12.83	13.04	13.25	13.47	13.69	13.91
.6	3995	12.43	12.54	12.75	12.96	13.17	13.38	13.60	13.82	14.04
.8	4002	12.56	12.67	12.88	13.09	13.30	13.51	13.73	13.95	14.17
33.0	4010	12.69	12.79	13.01	13.22	13.43	13.64	13.86	14.09	14.31
.2	4018	12.82	12.92	13.13	13.35	13.56	13.78	13.99	14.22	14.44
.4	4025	12.95	13.05	13.26	13.48	13.69	13.91	14.13	14.35	14.58
.6	4033	13.08	13.18	13.39	13.61	13.82	14.04	14.26	14.48	14.71
.8	4040	13.20	13.30	13.52	13.74	13.95	14.17	14.39	14.62	14.85

(Continued)

47.004 Alcohol table for calculating percentages of alcohol by volume at 15.56°C (60°F) in mixtures of ethyl alcohol and water from the Zeiss immersion refractometer readings and refractive indices at 17.5–25°C[a]—*Continued.*

Scale Reading[b]	Refractive Index	Temp., °C								
		17.5	18	19	20	21	22	23	24	25
34.0	1.34048	13.33	13.43	13.64	13.86	14.08	14.30	14.52	14.75	14.98
.2	4056	13.45	13.56	13.77	13.99	14.21	14.43	14.65	14.88	15.11
.4	4063	13.58	13.68	13.90	14.12	14.34	14.57	14.78	15.01	15.25
.6	4071	13.70	13.81	14.02	14.25	14.47	14.70	14.91	15.14	15.38
.8	4078	13.83	13.94	14.14	14.37	14.59	14.83	15.05	15.28	15.51
35.0	4086	13.96	14.06	14.27	14.50	14.72	14.96	15.18	15.41	15.65
.2	4094	14.08	14.19	14.39	14.62	14.85	15.09	15.31	15.54	15.78
.4	4101	14.21	14.31	14.52	14.75	14.97	15.22	15.44	15.67	15.91
.6	4109	14.33	14.44	14.65	14.87	15.10	15.34	15.56	15.80	16.05
.8	4116	14.46	14.56	14.78	15.00	15.23	15.47	15.69	15.93	16.18
36.0	4124	14.58	14.69	14.90	15.13	15.35	15.59	15.82	16.06	16.31
.2	4131	14.71	14.81	15.03	15.25	15.48	15.72	15.95	16.19	16.44
.4	4139	14.83	14.94	15.16	15.38	15.61	15.85	16.08	16.32	16.56
.6	4146	14.96	15.06	15.28	15.51	15.73	15.97	16.21	16.45	16.69
.8	4154	15.08	15.19	15.41	15.63	15.86	16.10	16.34	16.58	16.82
37.0	4162	15.20	15.31	15.53	15.76	15.99	16.23	16.47	16.71	16.95
.2	4169	15.33	15.44	15.66	15.89	16.11	16.35	16.60	16.84	17.08
.4	4177	15.45	15.56	15.79	16.01	16.24	16.48	16.72	16.97	17.21
.6	4184	15.57	15.69	15.91	16.14	16.37	16.61	16.85	17.09	17.34
.8	4192	15.70	15.81	16.04	16.26	16.49	16.73	16.98	17.22	17.46
38.0	4199	15.82	15.94	16.16	16.39	16.62	16.86	17.11	17.35	17.59
.2	4207	15.94	16.06	16.29	16.51	16.75	16.99	17.23	17.47	17.72
.4	4215	16.07	16.18	16.41	16.64	16.87	17.11	17.36	17.60	17.85
.6	4222	16.19	16.31	16.53	16.76	17.00	17.24	17.48	17.73	17.97
.8	4230	16.31	16.43	16.66	16.89	17.13	17.36	17.61	17.85	18.10
39.0	4237	16.44	16.55	16.78	17.01	17.25	17.49	17.74	17.98	18.23
.2	4245	16.56	16.67	16.91	17.14	17.38	17.62	17.86	18.11	18.35
.4	4252	16.68	16.80	17.03	17.26	17.50	17.74	17.99	18.23	18.48
.6	4260	16.80	16.92	17.15	17.39	17.63	17.87	18.11	18.36	18.61
.8	4267	16.93	17.04	17.28	17.51	17.75	17.99	18.24	18.48	18.73
40.0	4275	17.05	17.16	17.40	17.63	17.88	18.12	18.36	18.61	18.86
.2	4282	17.17	17.29	17.52	17.76	18.00	18.24	18.49	18.74	18.99
.4	4290	17.29	17.41	17.64	17.88	18.12	18.37	18.61	18.86	19.11
.6	4298	17.41	17.53	17.77	18.01	18.25	18.49	18.74	18.99	19.24
.8	4305	17.54	17.65	17.89	18.13	18.37	18.61	18.86	19.11	19.37
41.0	4313	17.66	17.77	18.01	18.25	18.49	18.74	18.99	19.24	19.49
.2	4320	17.78	17.90	18.13	18.37	18.62	18.86	19.11	19.36	19.62
.4	4328	17.90	18.03	18.26	18.50	18.74	18.99	19.24	19.49	19.75
.6	4335	18.02	18.14	18.38	18.62	18.86	19.11	19.36	19.61	19.87
.8	4343	18.14	18.26	18.50	18.74	18.99	19.23	19.48	19.74	20.00
42.0	4350	18.27	18.38	18.62	18.87	19.11	19.36	19.61	19.86	20.13
.2	4358	18.39	18.50	18.74	18.99	19.23	19.48	19.73	19.99	20.25
.4	4365	18.51	18.62	18.87	19.11	19.36	19.60	19.86	20.11	20.38
.6	4373	18.63	18.75	18.99	19.23	19.48	19.72	19.98	20.24	20.50
.8	4380	18.75	18.87	19.11	19.36	19.60	19.85	20.10	20.36	20.63
43.0	4388	18.87	18.99	19.23	19.48	19.72	19.97	20.23	20.49	20.75
.2	4395	18.99	19.11	19.35	19.60	19.85	20.09	20.35	20.61	20.88
.4	4403	19.11	19.23	19.47	19.72	19.97	20.21	20.47	20.74	21.01
.6	4410	19.23	19.35	19.59	19.85	20.09	20.34	20.60	20.86	21.13
.8	4418	19.35	19.47	19.72	19.97	20.21	20.46	20.72	20.99	21.25
44.0	4426	19.46	19.59	19.84	20.09	20.34	20.58	20.84	21.11	21.38
.2	4433	19.58	19.71	19.96	20.21	20.46	20.71	20.96	21.23	21.50
.4	4440	19.70	19.83	20.08	20.33	20.58	20.83	21.09	21.36	21.63
.6	4448	19.82	19.95	20.20	20.45	20.70	20.95	21.21	21.48	21.75
.8	4456	19.94	20.07	20.32	20.58	20.82	21.07	21.33	21.60	21.88

(Continued)

47.004   **Alcohol table for calculating percentages of alcohol by volume at 15.56°C (60°F) in mixtures of ethyl alcohol and water from the Zeiss immersion refractometer readings and refractive indices at 17.5–25°C[a]—Continued.**

Scale Reading[b]	Refractive Index	Temp., °C								
		17.5	18	19	20	21	22	23	24	25
45.0	1.34463	20.06	20.18	20.44	20.70	20.95	21.19	21.45	21.73	22.00
.2	4470	20.18	20.30	20.56	20.82	21.07	21.31	21.58	21.85	22.13
.4	4478	20.29	20.42	20.68	20.94	21.19	21.43	21.70	21.98	22.25
.6	4486	20.41	20.54	20.80	21.06	21.31	21.55	21.82	22.10	22.38
.8	4493	20.53	20.66	20.92	21.18	21.43	21.67	21.94	22.23	22.51
46.0	4500	20.65	20.78	21.04	21.30	21.54	21.79	22.07	22.35	22.64
.2	4508	20.76	20.89	21.16	21.42	21.66	21.91	22.19	22.48	22.76
.4	4516	20.88	21.01	21.28	21.54	21.78	22.03	22.32	22.61	22.89
.6	4523	21.00	21.13	21.40	21.66	21.90	22.16	22.44	22.73	23.02
.8	4530	21.12	21.25	21.52	21.78	22.02	22.28	22.57	22.86	23.15
47.0	4538	21.24	21.37	21.64	21.90	22.15	22.41	22.69	22.99	23.28
.2	4545	21.36	21.49	21.76	22.02	22.27	22.53	22.82	23.12	23.41
.4	4553	21.48	21.61	21.88	22.15	22.39	22.66	22.94	23.24	23.54
.6	4560	21.60	21.73	22.00	22.27	22.51	22.78	23.07	23.37	23.67
.8	4568	21.72	21.85	22.12	22.39	22.64	22.91	23.20	23.50	23.80
48.0	4575	21.84	21.97	22.24	22.51	22.76	23.03	23.32	23.63	23.93
.2	4583	21.96	22.09	22.36	22.63	22.88	23.16	23.45	23.76	24.06
.4	4590	22.08	22.21	22.48	22.75	23.01	23.28	23.58	23.89	24.19
.6	4598	22.20	22.33	22.60	22.87	23.13	23.41	23.71	24.02	24.32
.8	4605	22.32	22.45	22.72	22.99	23.26	23.54	23.83	24.14	24.45
49.0	4613	22.44	22.57	22.84	23.12	23.38	23.66	23.96	24.27	24.59
.2	4620	22.56	22.69	22.96	23.24	23.51	23.79	24.09	24.40	24.72
.4	4628	22.68	22.81	23.08	23.36	23.63	23.92	24.22	24.53	24.85
.6	4635	22.80	22.93	23.21	23.48	23.76	24.04	24.35	24.66	24.98
.8	4643	22.92	23.05	23.33	23.61	23.88	24.17	24.48	24.79	25.11
50.0	4650	23.04	23.17	23.45	23.73	24.01	24.30	24.61	24.92	25.25
.2	4658	23.16	23.30	23.57	23.85	24.13	24.43	24.74	25.05	25.38
.4	4665	23.28	23.42	23.69	23.98	24.26	24.56	24.86	25.18	25.51
.6	4672	23.40	23.54	23.81	24.10	24.38	24.69	24.99	25.32	25.65
.8	4680	23.51	23.66	23.93	24.22	24.51	24.81	25.12	25.45	25.78
51.0	4687	23.63	23.78	24.05	24.35	24.64	24.94	25.25	25.58	25.91
.2	4695	23.75	23.90	24.18	24.47	24.76	25.07	25.38	25.71	26.05
.4	4702	23.87	24.02	24.30	24.59	24.89	25.20	25.51	25.84	26.18
.6	4710	23.99	24.14	24.42	24.72	25.01	25.33	25.64	25.97	26.32
.8	4717	24.11	24.26	24.54	24.84	25.14	25.46	25.77	26.11	26.45
52.0	4724	24.23	24.38	24.66	24.96	25.27	25.58	25.90	26.24	26.59
.2	4732	24.36	24.50	24.79	25.09	25.39	25.71	26.03	26.37	26.72
.4	4740	24.48	24.62	24.91	25.21	25.52	25.84	26.16	26.51	26.86
.6	4747	24.60	24.74	25.03	25.34	25.65	25.97	26.29	26.64	26.99
.8	4754	24.72	24.86	25.15	25.46	25.77	26.10	26.42	26.77	27.13
53.0	4762	24.84	24.98	25.28	25.59	25.90	26.23	26.56	26.91	27.27
.2	4769	24.96	25.10	25.40	25.71	26.03	26.35	26.69	27.04	27.40
.4	4777	25.08	25.23	25.52	25.84	26.15	26.48	26.82	27.17	27.54
.6	4784	25.20	25.35	25.65	25.96	26.28	26.61	26.95	27.31	27.67
.8	4792	25.32	25.47	25.77	26.09	26.41	26.74	27.08	27.44	27.81
54.0	4799	25.44	25.59	25.90	26.22	26.54	26.87	27.21	27.58	27.95
.2	4806	25.56	25.71	26.02	26.34	26.67	27.00	27.35	27.71	28.08
.4	4814	25.68	25.84	26.14	26.47	26.79	27.13	27.48	27.85	28.22
.6	4821	25.81	25.96	26.27	26.59	26.92	27.26	27.61	27.98	28.36
.8	4829	25.93	26.08	26.39	26.72	27.05	27.39	27.75	28.11	28.49
55.0	4836	26.05	26.20	26.52	26.85	27.18	27.52	27.88	28.25	28.63
.2	4844	26.17	26.32	26.64	26.97	27.31	27.65	28.01	28.38	28.77
.4	4851	26.29	26.45	26.76	27.10	27.43	27.78	28.15	28.52	28.90
.6	4858	26.41	26.57	26.89	27.23	27.55	27.92	28.28	28.65	29.04
.8	4866	26.53	26.69	27.01	27.35	27.69	28.05	28.41	28.78	29.18

(Continued)

47.004   Alcohol table for calculating percentages of alcohol by volume at 15.56°C (60°F) in mixtures of ethyl alcohol and water from the Zeiss immersion refractometer readings and refractive indices at 17.5–25°C[a]—*Continued.*

Scale Reading[b]	Refractive Index	Temp., °C								
		17.5	18	19	20	21	22	23	24	25
56.0	1.34873	26.65	26.81	27.14	27.48	27.82	28.18	28.54	28.92	29.31
.2	4880	26.78	26.93	27.26	27.60	27.94	28.31	28.68	29.05	29.45
.4	4888	26.90	27.05	27.38	27.73	28.07	28.44	28.81	29.19	29.58
.6	4895	27.02	27.18	27.51	27.85	28.20	28.56	28.94	29.32	29.72
.8	4903	27.14	27.30	27.63	27.98	28.33	28.69	29.07	29.46	29.86
57.0	4910	27.26	27.42	27.75	28.10	28.46	28.82	29.20	29.59	29.99
.2	4918	27.38	27.54	27.88	28.23	28.59	28.95	29.34	29.73	30.13
.4	4925	27.50	27.66	28.00	28.35	28.72	29.08	29.47	29.86	30.27
.6	4932	27.62	27.79	28.13	28.48	28.85	29.21	29.60	30.00	30.41
.8	4940	27.75	27.91	28.25	28.60	28.97	29.34	29.73	30.14	30.55
58.0	4947	27.87	28.03	28.38	28.73	29.10	29.47	29.87	30.27	30.69
.2	4954	27.99	28.15	28.50	28.86	29.23	29.60	29.99	30.41	30.83
.4	4962	28.11	28.28	28.62	28.98	29.36	29.73	30.13	30.54	30.97
.6	4969	28.23	28.40	28.75	29.11	29.48	29.86	30.26	30.68	31.11
.8	4977	28.35	28.52	28.88	29.23	29.61	29.99	30.40	30.82	31.25
59.0	4984	28.47	28.64	29.00	29.36	29.74	30.13	30.53	30.95	31.40
.2	4991	28.59	28.77	29.12	29.49	29.87	30.26	30.67	31.09	31.54
.4	4999	28.71	28.89	29.25	29.61	29.99	30.39	30.81	31.23	31.68
.6	5006	28.84	29.01	29.37	29.74	30.13	30.53	30.94	31.38	31.83
.8	5014	28.96	29.13	29.50	29.87	30.26	30.66	31.08	31.52	31.97
60.0	5021	29.08	29.26	29.62	29.99	30.39	30.79	31.22	31.66	32.12
.2	5028	29.20	29.38	29.74	30.12	30.52	30.93	31.36	31.80	32.27
.4	5036	29.32	29.50	29.87	30.25	30.65	31.06	31.50	31.94	32.41
.6	5043	29.45	29.63	29.99	30.38	30.78	31.20	31.64	32.09	32.56
.8	5050	29.57	29.75	30.12	30.51	30.91	31.33	31.78	32.23	32.71
61.0	5058	29.69	29.87	30.25	30.64	31.05	31.47	31.92	32.38	32.86
.2	5065	29.81	29.99	30.38	30.77	31.18	31.61	32.06	32.52	33.01
.4	5073	29.93	30.12	30.50	30.90	31.32	31.74	32.20	32.67	33.16
.6	5080	30.06	30.25	30.63	31.03	31.45	31.88	32.34	32.81	33.31
.8	5087	30.18	30.37	30.76	31.16	31.59	32.01	32.49	32.96	33.46
62.0	5095	30.31	30.50	30.89	31.29	31.72	32.16	32.63	33.10	33.60
.2	5102	30.43	30.63	31.01	31.43	31.86	32.30	32.77	33.25	33.75
.4	5110	30.56	30.75	31.14	31.56	31.99	32.44	32.91	33.40	33.90
.6	5117	30.69	30.88	31.28	31.69	32.13	32.58	33.06	33.55	34.05
.8	5124	30.81	31.01	31.41	31.83	32.27	32.72	33.20	33.70	34.21
63.0	5132	30.94	31.14	31.54	31.96	32.41	32.87	33.35	33.84	34.36
.2	5139	31.06	31.26	31.67	32.10	32.55	33.01	33.50	33.99	34.52
.4	5146	31.19	31.39	31.80	32.23	32.69	33.15	33.64	34.15	34.67
.6	5154	31.32	31.52	31.93	32.37	32.83	33.30	33.79	34.30	34.83
.8	5161	31.45	31.65	32.07	32.51	32.97	33.44	33.93	34.45	34.98
64.0	5168	31.58	31.78	32.20	32.65	33.11	33.59	34.08	34.61	35.15
.2	5176	31.70	31.91	32.34	32.79	33.25	33.73	34.23	34.76	35.31
.4	5183	31.83	32.04	32.47	32.92	33.39	33.88	34.39	34.92	35.48
.6	5190	31.96	32.17	32.60	33.06	33.53	34.02	34.54	35.07	35.64
.8	5198	32.09	32.30	32.74	33.20	33.67	34.17	34.69	35.23	35.80
65.0	5205	32.22	32.43	32.87	33.34	33.82	34.32	34.84	35.39	35.97
.2	5212	32.35	32.57	33.01	33.48	33.96	34.47	34.99	35.55	36.13
.4	5220	32.48	32.70	33.15	33.62	34.10	34.61	35.15	35.71	36.30
.6	5227	32.61	32.83	33.28	33.76	34.25	34.76	35.30	35.87	36.46
.8	5234	32.75	32.96	33.42	33.90	34.40	34.91	35.46	36.02	36.63
66.0	5242	32.88	33.10	33.56	34.04	34.54	35.06	35.62	36.19	36.79
.2	5249	33.01	33.23	33.70	34.18	34.69	35.22	35.77	36.35	36.96
.4	5256	33.14	33.37	33.84	34.33	34.84	35.38	35.93	36.52	37.13
.6	5264	33.28	33.51	33.98	34.47	34.99	35.53	36.09	36.68	37.30
.8	5271	33.41	33.65	34.12	34.62	35.14	35.69	36.25	36.84	37.48
67.0	5278	33.55	33.79	34.26	34.76	35.29	35.84	36.41	37.01	37.65
.2	5286	33.69	33.92	34.41	34.91	35.44	36.00	36.57	37.18	37.83
.4	5293	33.82	34.06	34.55	35.05	35.60	36.16	36.73	37.35	38.00
.6	5300	33.96	34.20	34.69	35.20	35.75	36.32	36.90	37.52	38.18
.8	5308	34.09	34.34	34.84	35.35	35.90	36.48	37.06	37.69	38.35

(Continued)

47.004 **Alcohol table for calculating percentages of alcohol by volume at 15.56°C (60°F) in mixtures of ethyl alcohol and water from the Zeiss immersion refractometer readings and refractive indices at 17.5–25°C[a]—Concluded.**

Scale Reading[b]	Refractive Index	Temp., °C								
		17.5	18	19	20	21	22	23	24	25
68.0	1.35315	34.23	34.48	34.98	35.50	36.05	36.63	37.23	37.86	38.53
.2	5322	34.36	34.62	35.13	35.65	36.21	36.79	37.39	38.03	38.70
.4	5329	34.50	34.76	35.27	35.80	36.37	36.95	37.56	38.21	38.88
.6	5337	34.64	34.90	35.42	35.95	36.52	37.12	37.73	38.38	39.06
.8	5344	34.77	35.04	35.57	36.10	36.68	37.28	37.90	38.56	39.24
69.0	5351	34.91	35.19	35.71	36.25	36.84	37.45	38.07	38.73	39.43
.2	5359	35.04	35.33	35.86	36.41	36.99	37.61	38.24	38.90	39.61
.4	5366	35.19	35.47	36.01	36.56	37.15	37.78	38.41	39.08	39.80
.6	5373	35.34	35.62	36.16	36.72	37.32	37.94	38.58	39.26	39.98
.8	5381	35.49	35.76	36.31	36.87	37.48	38.11	38.75	39.45	40.17
70.0	5388	35.64	35.91	36.46	37.02	37.64	38.28	38.92	39.63	40.35
.2	5395	35.78	36.05	36.61	37.19	37.80	38.45	39.10	39.81	40.53
.4	5402	35.93	36.20	36.76	37.35	37.97	38.61	39.28	39.99	40.72
.6	5410	36.08	36.35	36.92	37.51	38.13	38.78	39.46	40.17	40.90
.8	5417	36.23	36.50	37.07	37.67	38.30	38.95	39.64	40.35	41.08
71.0	5424	36.38	36.65	37.23	37.83	38.47	39.12	39.82	40.54	41.27
.2	5432	36.53	36.80	37.39	37.99	38.63	39.30	40.00	40.72	41.46
.4	5439	36.68	36.95	37.55	38.16	38.80	39.48	40.18	40.90	41.64
.6	5446	36.83	37.11	37.71	38.32	38.97	39.65	40.36	41.08	41.83
.8	5454	36.98	37.27	37.87	38.49	39.14	39.83	40.54	41.27	42.02
72.0	5461	37.13	37.42	38.02	38.65	39.31	40.01	40.72	41.45	42.21
.2	5468	37.29	37.58	38.19	38.82	39.49	40.18	40.90	41.64	42.40
.4	5475	37.44	37.73	38.35	38.98	39.66	40.36	41.08	41.82	42.58
.6	5483	37.60	37.89	38.51	39.16	39.83	40.54	41.26	42.01	42.77
.8	5490	37.75	38.05	38.67	39.33	40.01	40.71	41.45	42.19	42.96
73.0	5497	37.91	38.21	38.84	39.50	40.18	40.88	41.63	42.38	43.15
.2	5504	38.06	38.37	39.00	39.67	40.36	41.06	41.81	42.56	43.33
.4	5512	38.22	38.53	39.17	39.84	40.53	41.24	41.99	42.75	43.52
.6	5519	38.38	38.69	39.34	40.02	40.70	41.42	42.17	42.93	43.70
.8	5526	38.54	38.85	39.50	40.19	40.88	41.60	42.36	43.12	43.89
74.0	5533	38.70	39.01	39.67	40.36	41.05	41.78	42.54	43.31	44.08
.2	5541	38.86	39.18	39.84	40.53	41.23	41.96	42.72	43.49	44.28
.4	5548	39.02	39.34	40.01	40.71	41.41	42.15	42.91	43.68	44.48
.6	5555	39.18	39.51	40.18	40.88	41.59	42.33	43.09	43.86	44.67
.8	5563	39.35	39.68	40.35	41.05	41.77	42.51	43.28	44.05	44.87
75.0	5570	39.51	39.84	40.53	41.23	41.95	42.70	43.46	44.25	45.07
.2	5577	39.68	40.01	40.70	41.41	42.13	42.88	43.65	44.44	45.29
.4	5584	39.84	40.18	40.87	41.58	42.31	43.07	43.83	44.63	45.50
.6	5592	40.01	40.35	41.04	41.76	42.49	43.25	44.02	44.83	45.71
.8	5599	40.18	40.53	41.22	41.94	42.67	43.44	44.21	45.03	45.92
76.0	5606	40.35	40.70	41.40	42.12	42.85	43.63	44.41	45.24	46.12
.2	5613	40.53	40.87	41.57	42.30	43.04	43.81	44.60	45.44	46.34
.4	5621	40.70	41.04	41.75	42.48	43.22	44.00	44.80	45.65	46.56
.6	5628	40.87	41.22	41.92	42.66	43.41	44.19	44.99	45.86	46.78
.8	5635	41.04	41.39	42.10	42.84	43.60	44.38	45.19	46.07	47.00
77.0	5642	41.22	41.57	42.28	43.02	43.79	44.57	45.40	46.29	47.23
.2	5650	41.39	41.74	42.46	43.20	43.97	44.76	45.60	46.51	47.45
.4	5657	41.57	41.91	42.63	43.39	44.16	44.95	45.81	46.73	47.68
.6	5664	41.75	42.09	42.81	43.57	44.35	45.15	46.01	46.95	47.91
.8	5671	41.92	42.26	42.99	43.76	44.54	45.35	46.23	47.17	48.14
78.0	5678	42.09	42.43	43.17	43.94	44.73	45.56	46.45	47.40	48.37
.2	5686	42.26	42.61	43.36	44.13	44.92	45.76	46.67	47.63	48.60
.4	5693	42.44	42.78	43.54	44.32	45.12	45.96	46.89	47.85	48.84
.6	5700	42.61	42.96	43.72	44.51	45.32	46.17	47.11	48.08	49.07
.8	5707	42.78	43.14	43.91	44.70	45.52	46.39	47.34	48.31	49.31
79.0	5715	42.95	43.32	44.09	44.89	45.72	46.61	47.56	48.53	49.54
.2	5722	43.13	43.50	44.28	45.08	45.92	46.83	47.79	48.76	49.77
.4	5729	43.31	43.68	44.47	45.28	46.13	47.04	48.01	48.99	50.01
.6	5736	43.49	43.86	44.65	45.48	46.34	47.26	48.23	49.22	50.24
.8	5744	43.67	44.05	44.84	45.68	46.56	47.48	48.46	49.45	50.48
80.0	5751	43.85	44.24	45.04	45.88	46.77	47.70	48.68	49.68	50.71

47.005 **Percentages by weight corresponding to various percentages by volume at 15.56°C (60°F) in mixtures of ethyl alcohol and water**[a]

by Vol.	% Alcohol by Wt	Difference	by Vol.	% Alcohol by Wt	Difference
0	0.000		50	42.487	
1	0.795	0.795	51	43.428	0.941
2	1.593	.798	52	44.374	.946
3	2.392	.799	53	45.326	.952
4	3.194	.802	54	46.283	.957
		.804			.962
5	3.998		55	47.245	
6	4.804	.806	56	48.214	.969
7	5.612	.808	57	49.187	.973
8	6.422	.810	58	50.167	.980
9	7.234	.812	59	51.154	.987
		.813			.993
10	8.047		60	52.147	
11	8.862	.815	61	53.146	.999
12	9.679	.817	62	54.152	1.006
13	10.497	.818	63	55.165	.013
14	11.317	.820	64	56.184	.019
		.821			.024
15	12.138		65	57.208	
16	12.961	.823	66	58.241	.033
17	13.786	.825	67	59.279	.038
18	14.612	.826	68	60.325	.046
19	15.440	.828	69	61.379	.054
		.829			.062
20	16.269		70	62.441	
21	17.100	.831	71	63.511	.070
22	17.933	.833	72	64.588	.077
23	18.768	.835	73	65.674	.086
24	19.604	.836	74	66.768	.094
		.839			.102
25	20.443		75	67.870	
26	21.285	.842	76	68.982	.112
27	22.127	.842	77	70.102	.120
28	22.973	.846	78	71.234	.132
29	23.820	.847	79	72.375	.141
		.850			.151
30	24.670		80	73.526	
31	25.524	.854	81	74.686	.160
32	26.382	.858	82	75.858	.172
33	27.242	.860	83	77.039	.181
34	28.104	.862	84	78.233	.194
		.867			.208
35	28.971		85	79.441	
36	29.842	.871	86	80.662	.221
37	30.717	.875	87	81.897	.235
38	31.596	.879	88	83.144	.247
39	32.478	.882	89	84.408	.264
		.886			.281
40	33.364		90	85.689	
41	34.254	.890	91	86.989	.300
42	35.150	.896	92	88.310	.321
43	36.050	.900	93	89.652	.342
44	36.955	.905	94	91.025	.373
		.910			.398
45	37.865		95	92.423	
46	38.778	.913	96	93.851	.428
47	39.697	.919	97	95.315	.464
48	40.622	.925	98	96.820	.505
49	41.551	.929	99	98.381	.561
		.936			1.619
50	42.487		100	100.000	

[a] *Natl. Bur. Std.* Circ. 19, p. 18 (1924).

47.006   Density of carbon dioxide (Parr)[a]

(Wt in mg of 1 ml CO_2 at 700–770 mm pressure and 10–30°C. Corrected for aq. vapor and barometer readings on glass scale. Calcd from 1.976 equals wt of 1 L CO_2 at 0°C, 760 mm pressure, and 41° latitude.)

mm	10°	11°	12°	13°	14°	15°	16°	17°	18°	19°	inches
700	1.7288	1.7201	1.7113	1.7020	1.6927	1.6863	1.6799	1.6716	1.6632	1.6547	27.56
702	338	252	164	072	980	914	848	765	680	595	27.64
704	388	302	215	124	.7033	965	897	813	729	644	27.72
706	438	353	266	176	086	.7016	946	862	778	692	27.80
708	488	403	317	228	139	067	995	911	826	741	27.87
710	538	453	368	280	192	118	.7044	960	874	789	27.95
712	588	504	419	332	245	169	092	.7008	922	837	28.03
714	638	555	470	384	298	220	141	057	970	886	28.11
716	688	605	521	436	351	271	190	106	.7019	934	28.19
718	738	656	572	488	404	322	239	154	068	983	28.27
720	788	706	623	540	457	373	288	203	117	.7031	28.35
722	838	756	673	590	506	422	337	252	166	079	28.43
724	888	806	723	639	555	471	386	301	215	128	28.50
726	938	856	773	689	605	520	435	349	263	176	28.58
728	988	905	822	738	654	569	484	398	312	225	28.66
730	.8038	955	872	788	703	618	533	447	360	273	28.74
732	089	.8005	921	837	752	667	582	496	409	321	28.82
734	139	055	971	887	802	717	631	545	458	370	28.90
736	189	105	.8021	936	851	766	680	593	506	418	28.98
738	239	155	071	986	901	815	729	642	555	467	29.06
740	288	204	120	.8035	950	864	778	691	603	515	29.13
742	338	254	170	085	999	913	827	740	652	564	29.21
744	388	304	219	134	.8048	962	875	788	700	612	29.29
746	439	354	269	184	098	.8011	924	837	749	661	29.37
748	489	404	319	233	147	060	973	886	798	709	29.45
750	539	454	368	282	196	109	.8022	934	846	757	29.53
752	589	504	418	332	246	159	072	984	895	806	29.61
754	639	554	468	382	295	208	120	.8032	944	854	29.69
756	689	603	517	431	344	257	169	081	992	902	29.76
758	739	653	567	481	394	306	218	130	.8041	951	29.84
760	789	703	617	530	443	355	267	178	089	999	29.92
762	839	753	667	580	492	404	316	227	138	.8048	30.00
764	890	803	716	629	541	453	365	276	187	096	30.08
766	940	853	766	679	591	503	414	325	235	144	30.16
768	990	903	816	728	640	552	463	374	284	193	30.24
770	.9040	953	865	777	689	601	512	422	332	241	30.31

mm	20°	21°	22°	23°	24°	25°	26°	27°	28°	29°	30°	inches
700	1.6462	1.6370	1.6278	1.6195	1.6112	1.6021	1.5930	1.5837	1.5744	1.5649	1.5554	27.56
702	510	419	327	243	160	068	977	884	791	696	600	27.64
704	558	467	376	292	207	116	.6025	931	838	742	647	27.72
706	607	516	425	340	254	163	072	979	885	789	693	27.80
708	655	564	474	388	302	211	119	.6026	932	836	740	27.87
710	703	613	522	436	350	258	166	073	978	882	786	27.95
712	751	662	571	485	397	305	214	120	.6025	929	832	28.03
714	799	710	620	533	444	353	261	167	072	976	879	28.11
716	848	759	670	581	492	400	308	215	119	.6023	925	28.19
718	896	807	718	629	540	448	356	262	166	069	972	28.27
720	944	856	767	678	587	495	403	309	213	116	.6018	28.35
722	992	904	815	726	635	543	450	356	.6260	163	065	28.43
724	.7041	953	863	773	682	590	497	403	307	210	.6111	28.50
726	089	.7001	911	821	730	638	544	450	354	256	157	28.58
728	137	049	959	869	778	685	591	497	401	303	204	28.66
730	185	097	.7007	917	825	732	638	544	448	350	251	28.74
732	233	145	055	964	872	779	685	591	494	396	297	28.82
734	282	193	103	.7012	920	827	733	638	541	443	343	28.90
736	330	241	151	060	968	875	780	685	588	490	390	28.98
738	378	289	199	107	.7015	922	827	732	635	537	437	29.06
740	426	337	247	155	063	969	874	778	681	583	483	29.13
742	475	385	295	203	111	.7017	922	826	729	630	530	29.12
744	523	433	342	250	158	064	969	873	776	677	577	29.29
746	571	481	390	298	206	112	.7016	920	822	723	623	29.37
748	619	529	438	346	253	159	063	967	869	770	670	29.45
750	667	577	486	394	301	206	110	.7014	916	817	716	29.53
752	716	625	534	441	348	254	158	061	963	864	763	29.61
754	764	673	582	489	396	301	205	108	.7010	910	809	29.69
756	812	721	630	537	443	348	252	155	057	957	856	29.76
758	861	770	678	585	491	396	300	202	104	.7004	903	29.84
760	909	818	725	632	538	443	347	249	150	050	949	29.92
762	957	866	773	680	586	490	394	296	197	097	996	30.00
764	.8005	914	821	728	633	538	441	343	244	144	.7042	30.08
766	053	962	869	776	681	585	488	390	291	191	089	30.16
768	102	.8010	917	823	728	633	535	437	338	237	135	30.24
770	150	058	965	871	776	680	582	484	385	284	182	30.31

[a] *J. Am. Chem. Soc.* **31**, 237(1909). Values of 700–718 mm were calcd by formula given by Parr.

47.007   Correction factors for gasometric determination of carbon dioxide[a]

(Based on sample weighing 1.7000 g)

(Multiply number of ml gas evolved from 1.7000 g sample by factor that corresponds with existing atmospheric conditions and divide by 10 to obtain % CO_2 by wt in sample.)

mm	15.0°C 59.0°F	15.5°C 59.9°F	16.0°C 60.8°F	16.5°C 61.7°F	17.0°C 62.6°F	17.5°C 63.5°F	18.0°C 64.4°F	18.5°C 65.3°F	19.0°C 66.2°F	19.5°C 67.1°F	inches
700	0.99194	0.99006	0.98818	0.98573	0.98329	0.98082	0.97835	0.97585	0.97335	0.97085	27.56
702	0.99494	0.99300	0.99106	0.98862	0.98618	0.98368	0.98118	0.97868	0.97618	0.97368	27.64
704	0.99794	0.99544	0.99394	0.99147	0.98900	0.98653	0.98406	0.98156	0.97906	0.97653	27.72
706	1.00094	0.99886	0.99682	0.99435	0.99188	0.98941	0.98694	0.98406	0.98188	0.97938	27.80
708	1.00394	1.00183	0.99971	0.99723	0.99476	0.99226	0.98976	0.98726	0.98476	0.98224	27.87
710	1.00694	1.00477	1.00259	1.00012	0.99765	0.99512	0.99259	0.99009	0.98759	0.98506	27.95
712	1.00994	1.00767	1.00541	1.00294	1.00047	0.99795	0.99541	0.99291	0.99041	0.98788	28.03
714	1.01294	1.01061	1.00829	1.00582	1.00335	1.00080	1.99824	0.99576	0.99329	0.99073	28.11
716	1.01594	1.01356	1.01118	1.00871	1.00624	1.00368	1.00112	0.99861	0.99612	0.99358	28.19
718	1.01894	1.01650	1.01406	1.01156	1.00906	1.00653	1.00400	1.00150	0.99900	0.99644	28.27
720	1.02194	1.01949	1.01694	1.01444	1.01194	1.00941	1.00688	1.00435	1.00182	0.99925	28.35
722	1.02482	1.02232	1.01982	1.01732	1.01482	1.01229	1.00976	1.00720	1.00465	1.00209	28.43
724	1.02771	1.02521	1.02271	1.02021	1.01771	1.01518	1.01265	1.01009	1.00753	1.00497	28.50
726	1.03059	1.02809	1.02559	1.02306	1.02053	1.01800	1.01547	1.01291	1.01035	1.00779	28.58
728	1.03347	1.03097	1.02847	1.02594	1.02341	1.02088	1.01835	1.01580	1.01324	1.01065	28.66
730	1.03635	1.03385	1.03135	1.02882	1.02629	1.02374	1.02118	1.01862	1.01606	1.01347	28.74
732	1.03924	1.03674	1.03424	1.03171	1.02918	1.02662	1.02406	1.02147	1.01888	1.01629	28.82
734	1.04218	1.03915	1.03712	1.03459	1.03206	1.02950	1.02694	1.02435	1.02176	1.01919	28.90
736	1.04506	1.04253	1.04000	1.03744	1.03488	1.03232	1.02976	1.02718	1.02459	1.02200	28.98
738	1.04794	1.04541	1.04288	1.04037	1.03776	1.03521	1.03265	1.03006	1.02747	1.02486	29.06
740	1.05082	1.04829	1.04576	1.04321	1.04065	1.03806	1.03547	1.03288	1.03029	1.02768	29.13
742	1.05371	1.05118	1.04865	1.04609	1.04353	1.04094	1.03835	1.03577	1.03318	1.03056	29.21
744	1.05659	1.05403	1.05147	1.04991	1.04635	1.04377	1.04118	1.03859	1.03600	1.03338	29.29
746	1.05947	1.05691	1.05435	1.05180	1.04924	1.04665	1.04406	1.04147	1.03888	1.03624	29.37
748	1.06235	1.05929	1.05724	1.05418	1.05212	1.04953	1.04694	1.04433	1.04171	1.03906	29.45
750	1.06524	1.06218	1.06012	1.05748	1.05494	1.05235	1.04976	1.04715	1.04453	1.04189	29.53
752	1.06818	1.06512	1.06306	1.06047	1.05788	1.05527	1.05265	1.05003	1.04741	1.04477	29.61
754	1.07106	1.06847	1.06588	1.06330	1.06071	1.05812	1.05553	1.05289	1.05024	1.04759	29.69
756	1.07394	1.07135	1.06876	1.06618	1.06359	1.06197	1.05835	1.05571	1.05306	1.05041	29.76
758	1.07682	1.07423	1.07165	1.06906	1.06647	1.06386	1.06124	1.05859	1.05594	1.05330	29.84
760	1.07971	1.07712	1.07453	1.07191	1.06929	1.06668	1.06406	1.06141	1.05876	1.05612	29.92
762	1.08259	1.08050	1.07741	1.07480	1.07218	1.06956	1.06694	1.06430	1.06165	1.05897	30.00
764	1.08547	1.08288	1.08029	1.07768	1.07506	1.07244	1.06982	1.06715	1.06447	1.06179	30.08
766	1.08841	1.08580	1.08318	1.08056	1.07794	1.07530	1.07265	1.06997	1.06729	1.06462	30.16
768	1.09129	1.08868	1.08606	1.08344	1.08082	1.07818	1.07553	1.07285	1.07018	1.06750	30.24
770	1.09418	1.09156	1.08894	1.08630	1.08365	1.08100	1.07835	1.07567	1.07300	1.07032	30.31

mm	20.0°C 68.0°F	20.5°C 68.9°F	21.0°C 69.8°F	21.5°C 70.7°F	22.0°C 71.6°F	22.0°C 72.5°F	23.0°C 73.4°F	23.5°C 74.3°F	24.0°C 75.2°F	24.5°C 76.1°F	inches
700	0.96835	0.96564	0.96294	0.96023	0.95753	0.95509	0.95265	0.95020	0.94776	0.94508	27.56
702	0.97118	0.96850	0.96582	0.96311	0.96041	0.95794	0.95547	0.95303	0.95059	0.94788	27.64
704	0.97400	0.97132	0.96865	0.96597	0.96329	0.96082	0.95835	0.95585	0.95335	0.95067	27.72
706	0.97688	0.97420	0.97153	0.96888	0.96624	0.96371	0.96118	0.95865	0.95612	0.95344	27.80
708	0.97971	0.97703	0.97435	0.97173	0.96912	0.96656	0.96400	0.96147	0.95894	0.95626	27.87
710	0.98253	0.97988	0.97724	0.97459	0.97195	0.96938	0.96682	0.96429	0.96176	0.95905	27.95
712	0.98535	0.98273	0.98012	0.97747	0.97483	0.97227	0.96971	0.96712	0.96453	0.96182	28.03
714	0.98818	0.98556	0.98294	0.98032	0.97771	0.97512	0.97253	0.96991	0.96729	0.96461	28.11
716	0.99106	0.98844	0.98582	0.98323	0.98065	0.97800	0.97535	0.97273	0.97012	0.96741	28.19
718	0.99388	0.99126	0.98865	0.98606	0.98348	0.98083	0.97818	0.97556	0.97294	0.97023	28.27
720	0.99671	0.99412	0.99153	0.98894	0.98636	0.98371	0.98106	0.97838	0.97571	0.97300	28.35
722	0.99953	0.99694	0.99435	0.99176	0.98918	0.98653	0.98388	0.98120	0.97853	0.97582	28.43
724	1.00241	0.99982	0.99724	0.99462	0.99200	0.98932	0.98665	0.98397	0.98129	0.97858	28.50
726	1.00524	1.00265	1.00006	0.99746	0.99483	0.99215	0.98947	0.98679	0.98412	0.98141	28.58
728	1.00806	1.00547	1.00288	1.00027	0.99765	0.99497	0.99229	0.98961	0.98694	0.98420	28.66
730	1.01088	1.00829	1.00571	1.00306	1.00041	1.99781	0.99512	0.99241	0.98971	0.98697	28.74
732	1.01371	1.01112	1.00853	1.00588	1.00324	1.00056	0.99788	0.99517	0.99247	0.98973	28.82
734	1.01659	1.01497	1.01135	1.00870	1.00606	1.00338	1.00071	0.99799	0.99529	0.99255	28.90
736	1.01941	1.01679	1.01418	1.01153	1.00888	1.00620	1.00353	1.00083	0.99812	0.99538	28.98
738	1.02224	1.01962	1.01700	1.01435	1.01171	1.00900	1.00629	1.00359	1.00088	0.99815	29.06
740	1.02506	1.02244	1.01982	1.01717	1.01453	1.01182	1.00912	1.00643	1.00371	1.00095	29.13
742	1.02794	1.02529	1.02265	1.02000	1.01735	1.01464	1.01194	1.00923	1.00653	1.00377	29.21
744	1.03076	1.02811	1.02547	1.02279	1.02212	1.01752	1.01471	1.01200	1.00929	1.00643	29.29
746	1.03359	1.03094	1.02829	1.02561	1.02294	1.02024	1.01753	1.01482	1.01212	1.00936	29.37
748	1.03641	1.03376	1.03112	1.02844	1.02576	1.02306	1.02035	1.01762	1.01488	1.01212	29.45
750	1.03924	1.03659	1.03394	1.03126	1.02859	1.02589	1.02318	1.02045	1.01771	1.01492	29.53
752	1.04212	1.03944	1.03676	1.03408	1.03141	1.02868	1.02594	1.02321	1.02047	1.01771	29.61
754	1.04494	1.04226	1.03959	1.03691	1.03424	1.03150	1.02876	1.02603	1.02339	1.02050	29.69
756	1.04776	1.04508	1.04241	1.03973	1.03706	1.03433	1.03159	1.02883	1.02606	1.02326	29.76
758	1.05065	1.04797	1.04529	1.04259	1.03988	1.03715	1.03441	1.03165	1.02888	1.02608	29.84
760	1.05347	1.05079	1.04812	1.04539	1.04265	1.03992	1.03718	1.03442	1.03165	1.02886	29.92
762	1.05629	1.05361	1.05094	1.04821	1.04547	1.04274	1.04000	1.03724	1.03447	1.03164	30.00
764	1.05912	1.05644	1.05376	1.05103	1.04829	1.04556	1.04282	1.04003	1.03723	1.03444	30.08
766	1.06194	1.05926	1.05659	1.05386	1.05112	1.04839	1.04565	1.04285	1.04005	1.03723	30.16
768	1.06482	1.06212	1.05941	1.05668	1.05394	1.05118	1.04841	1.04562	1.04282	1.04003	30.24
770	1.06765	1.06424	1.06224	1.05950	1.05676	1.05400	1.05123	1.04844	1.04564	1.04282	30.31

(Continued)

[a] Calcd from 1.976 = wt 1 L CO_2 at 0°C, 760 mm pressure, and 41° latitude. Formula given by W. Parr, *J. Am. Chem. Soc.* **31**, 237(1909).

47.007   Correction factors for gasometric determination of carbon dioxide[a]**—Concluded.**

(Based on sample weighing 1.7000 g)

(Multiply number of ml gas evolved from 1.7000 g sample by factor that corresponds with existing atmospheric conditions and divide by 10 to obtain % CO_2 by wt in sample.)

mm	25.0°C 77.0°F	25.5°C 77.9°F	26.0°C 78.8°F	26.5°C 79.7°F	27.0°C 80.6°F	27.5°C 81.5°F	28.0°C 82.4°F	28.5°C 83.3°F	29.0°C 84.2°F	29.5°C 85.1°F	inches
700	0.94241	0.93973	0.93706	0.93432	0.93159	0.92885	0.92612	0.92332	0.92053	0.91773	27.56
702	0.94518	0.94250	0.93982	0.93708	0.93435	0.92161	0.92888	0.92608	0.92329	0.92047	27.64
704	0.94800	0.94532	0.94256	0.93988	0.93712	0.93438	0.93165	0.92882	0.92600	0.92320	27.72
706	0.95076	0.94808	0.94541	0.94267	0.93994	0.93717	0.93441	0.93158	0.92876	0.92594	27.80
708	0.95359	0.95088	0.94818	0.94544	0.94271	0.93994	0.93718	0.93435	0.93153	0.92870	27.87
710	0.95635	0.95364	0.95094	0.94820	0.94547	0.94267	0.93988	0.93706	0.93424	0.93141	27.95
712	0.95812	0.95644	0.95376	0.95100	0.94824	0.94544	0.94265	0.93982	0.93700	0.93414	28.03
714	0.96194	0.95923	0.95653	0.95376	0.95100	0.94820	0.94541	0.94258	0.93976	0.93691	28.11
716	0.96471	0.96200	0.95929	0.95655	0.95382	0.95100	0.94818	0.94535	0.94253	0.93964	28.19
718	0.96753	0.96482	0.96212	0.95935	0.95659	0.95376	0.95094	0.94809	0.94524	0.94238	28.27
720	0.97029	0.96758	0.96488	0.96213	0.95939	0.95655	0.95371	0.95085	0.94800	0.94512	28.35
722	0.97312	0.97038	0.96765	0.69488	0.96212	0.95929	0.95647	0.95361	0.95076	0.94788	28.43
724	0.97588	0.97314	0.97041	0.96764	0.96488	0.96206	0.95924	0.95638	0.95353	0.95062	28.50
726	0.97871	0.97594	0.97318	0.97041	0.96765	0.96482	0.96200	0.95912	0.95624	0.95332	28.58
728	0.98147	0.97870	0.97594	0.97319	0.97041	0.96758	0.96476	0.96188	0.95900	0.95609	28.66
730	0.98424	0.98147	0.97871	0.97594	0.97318	0.97036	0.96753	0.96464	0.96176	0.95885	28.74
732	0.98700	0.98423	0.98147	0.97871	0.97594	0.97309	0.97024	0.96735	0.96447	0.96156	28.82
734	0.98982	0.98705	0.98429	0.98165	0.97871	0.97585	0.97300	0.97012	0.96724	0.96429	28.90
736	0.99265	0.98985	0.98706	0.98426	0.98147	0.97861	0.97576	0.97288	0.97000	0.96706	28.98
738	0.99541	0.99261	0.98982	0.98703	0.98424	0.98138	0.97835	0.97564	0.97276	0.96982	29.06
740	0.99818	0.99538	0.99259	0.98976	0.98694	0.98409	0.98124	0.97835	0.97547	0.97253	29.13
742	1.00100	0.99820	0.99541	0.99258	0.98976	0.98691	0.98406	0.98115	0.97824	0.97529	29.21
744	1.00376	1.00097	0.99818	0.99535	0.99253	0.98967	0.98682	0.98391	0.98100	0.97806	29.29
746	1.00659	1.00376	1.00094	0.99809	0.99529	0.99241	0.98953	0.98662	0.98371	0.98076	29.37
748	1.00935	1.00653	1.00371	1.00088	0.99806	0.99517	0.99229	0.98938	0.98647	0.98353	29.45
750	1.01212	1.00936	1.00659	1.00370	1.00082	0.99796	0.99506	0.99215	0.98924	0.98626	29.53
752	1.01494	1.01211	1.00929	1.00644	1.00359	1.00071	0.99782	0.99491	0.99200	0.98903	29.61
754	1.01771	1.01483	1.01206	1.00921	1.00635	1.00342	1.00059	0.99738	0.99471	0.99173	29.69
756	1.02047	1.01764	1.01482	1.01197	1.00912	1.00624	1.00335	1.00041	0.99747	0.99450	29.76
758	1.02329	1.02047	1.01765	1.01477	1.01188	1.00900	1.00612	1.00318	1.00024	0.99724	29.84
760	1.02606	1.02323	1.02041	1.01753	1.01465	1.01174	1.00882	1.00588	1.00294	0.99995	29.92
762	1.02882	1.02600	1.02318	1.02030	1.01741	1.01450	1.01159	1.00865	1.00571	1.00274	30.00
764	1.03165	1.02880	1.02594	1.02306	1.02018	1.01727	1.01435	1.01141	1.00847	1.00547	30.08
766	1.03441	1.03156	1.02871	1.02583	1.02294	1.02003	1.01712	1.01418	1.01124	1.00824	30.16
768	1.03724	1.03435	1.03147	1.02859	1.02571	1.02280	1.01988	1.01611	1.01394	1.01094	30.24
770	1.04000	1.03712	1.03424	1.03136	1.02847	1.02556	1.02265	1.01968	1.01671	1.01371	30.31

mm	30.0°C 86.0°F	30.5°C 86.9°F	31.0°C 87.8°F	31.5°C 88.7°F	32.0°C 89.6°F	32.5°C 90.5°F	33.0°C 91.4°F	33.5°C 92.3°F	34.0°C 93.2°F	34.5°C 94.1°F	35.0°C 95.0°F	inches
700	0.91494	0.91203	0.90912	0.90620	0.90329	0.90082	0.89735	0.89432	0.89129	0.88821	0.88512	27.56
702	0.91765	0.91476	0.91188	0.90894	0.90600	0.90303	0.90006	0.89703	0.89400	0.89091	0.88782	27.64
704	0.92041	0.91750	0.91459	0.91165	0.90871	0.90576	0.90282	0.89976	0.89671	0.89362	0.89053	27.72
706	0.92312	0.92024	0.91735	0.91441	0.91147	0.90847	0.90547	0.90241	0.89935	0.89627	0.89318	27.80
708	0.92588	0.92297	0.92006	0.91712	0.91418	0.91118	0.90818	0.90512	0.90206	0.89897	0.89588	27.87
710	0.92859	0.92567	0.92276	0.91982	0.91688	0.91388	0.91088	0.90782	0.90476	0.90168	0.89859	27.95
712	0.93129	0.92841	0.92553	0.92256	0.91959	0.91659	0.91359	0.91053	0.90747	0.90438	0.90129	28.03
714	0.93406	0.93115	0.92824	0.92529	0.92235	0.91932	0.91629	0.91323	0.91018	0.90706	0.90394	28.11
716	0.93676	0.93388	0.93100	0.92803	0.92506	0.92203	0.91900	0.91594	0.91288	0.90976	0.90665	28.19
718	0.93953	0.93662	0.93371	0.93078	0.92776	0.92474	0.92171	0.91865	0.91559	0.91247	0.90935	28.27
720	0.94224	0.93932	0.93641	0.93344	0.93047	0.92744	0.92441	0.92135	0.91829	0.91517	0.91206	28.35
722	0.94500	0.94209	0.93918	0.93618	0.93318	0.93015	0.92712	0.92412	0.92100	0.91785	0.91471	28.43
724	0.94771	0.94479	0.94188	0.93897	0.93606	0.93294	0.92982	0.92676	0.92371	0.92056	0.91741	28.50
726	0.95041	0.94750	0.94459	0.94159	0.93859	0.93556	0.93253	0.92944	0.92635	0.92323	0.92012	28.58
728	0.95318	0.95026	0.94735	0.94435	0.94135	0.93830	0.93544	0.93215	0.92906	0.92591	0.92276	28.66
730	0.95594	0.95300	0.95006	0.94706	0.94406	0.94103	0.93800	0.93488	0.93176	0.92861	0.92547	28.74
732	0.85865	0.95578	0.95282	0.94979	0.94676	0.94373	0.94071	0.93759	0.93447	0.93132	0.92818	28.82
734	0.96135	0.95844	0.95553	0.95250	0.94947	0.94644	0.94341	0.94034	0.93718	0.93403	0.93088	28.90
736	0.96412	0.96118	0.95824	0.95521	0.95218	0.94915	0.94612	0.94300	0.93088	0.93670	0.93353	28.98
738	0.96688	0.96394	0.96100	0.95797	0.95494	0.95188	0.94882	0.94570	0.94259	0.93941	0.93624	29.06
740	0.96959	0.96665	0.96371	0.96068	0.95765	0.95459	0.95153	0.94841	0.94529	0.94211	0.93894	29.13
742	0.97235	0.96941	0.96647	0.96341	0.96035	0.95730	0.95424	0.95112	0.94800	0.94482	0.94165	29.21
744	0.97512	0.97215	0.96918	0.96615	0.96312	0.96003	0.95694	0.95382	0.95071	0.94750	0.94429	29.29
746	0.97782	0.97485	0.97188	0.96885	0.96582	0.96273	0.95965	0.95653	0.95341	0.95020	0.94700	29.37
748	0.98059	0.97762	0.97465	0.97159	0.96853	0.96544	0.96235	0.95925	0.95606	0.95288	0.94971	29.45
750	0.98329	0.98032	0.97735	0.97429	0.97124	0.96815	0.96506	0.96191	0.95876	0.95558	0.94251	29.53
752	0.98606	0.98306	0.98006	0.97703	0.97400	0.97088	0.96776	0.96461	0.96147	0.95826	0.95506	29.61
754	0.98876	0.98579	0.98282	0.97976	0.97671	0.97359	0.97047	0.96732	0.96418	0.96097	0.95776	29.69
756	0.99153	0.98853	0.98553	0.98247	0.97941	0.97629	0.97318	0.97003	0.96688	0.96367	0.96047	29.76
758	0.99429	0.99129	0.98829	0.98521	0.98212	0.97900	0.97588	0.97273	0.96959	0.96638	0.96318	29.84
760	0.99700	0.99400	0.99100	0.98794	0.98488	0.98176	0.97865	0.97547	0.97229	0.96908	0.96588	29.92
762	0.99976	0.99673	0.99371	0.99065	0.98759	0.98443	0.98135	0.97817	0.97500	0.97176	0.96853	30.00
764	1.00247	0.99948	0.99647	0.99338	0.99029	0.98717	0.98406	0.98088	0.97771	0.97447	0.97124	30.08
766	1.00524	1.00221	0.99918	0.99609	0.99300	0.98988	0.98676	0.98356	0.98053	0.97714	0.97394	30.16
768	1.00794	1.00491	1.00188	0.99880	0.99571	0.99259	0.98947	0.98629	0.98312	0.97986	0.97659	30.24
770	1.01071	1.00768	1.00465	1.00156	0.99847	0.99532	0.99218	0.98897	0.98576	0.98252	0.97929	30.31

47.008   Degrees Brix, specific gravity, and degrees Baumé of sugar solutions (Plato Table)[a]

°Brix or % by Wt of Sucrose	Specific Gravity at:		°Baumé (Modulus 145)	°Brix or % by Wt of Sucrose	Specific Gravity at:		°Baumé (Modulus 145)
	20/20°	20/4°			20/20°	20/4°	
0.0	1.00000	0.998234	0.00	9.0	1.03586	1.034029	5.02
.2	078	9010	.11	.2	668	4850	.13
.4	155	9786	.22	.4	750	5671	.24
.6	233	1.000563	.34	.6	833	6494	.35
.8	311	1342	.45	.8	915	7318	.46
1.0	389	2120	.56	10.0	998	8143	.57
.2	467	2897	.67	.2	4081	8970	.68
.4	545	3675	.79	.4	164	9797	.80
.6	623	4453	.90	.6	247	40626	.91
.8	701	5234	1.01	.8	330	1456	6.02
2.0	779	6015	.12	11.0	413	2288	.13
.2	858	6796	.23	.2	497	3121	.24
.4	936	7580	.34	.4	580	3954	.35
.6	1015	8363	.46	.6	664	4788	.46
.8	093	9148	.57	.8	747	5625	.57
3.0	172	9934	.68	12.0	831	6462	.68
.2	251	10721	.79	.2	915	7300	.79
.4	330	1510	.90	.4	999	8140	.90
.6	409	2298	2.02	.6	5084	8980	7.02
.8	488	3089	.13	.8	168	9822	.13
4.0	567	3881	.24	13.0	252	50665	.24
.2	647	4673	.35	.2	337	1510	.35
.4	726	5467	.46	.4	422	2356	.46
.6	806	6261	.57	.6	506	3202	.57
.8	886	7058	.68	.8	591	4050	.68
5.0	965	7854	.79	14.0	677	4900	.79
.2	2045	8652	.91	.2	762	5751	.90
.4	125	9451	3.02	.4	847	6602	8.01
.6	206	20251	.13	.6	933	7455	.12
.8	286	1053	.24	.8	6018	8310	.23
6.0	366	1855	.35	15.0	104	9165	.34
.2	447	2659	.46	.2	190	60022	.45
.4	527	3463	.57	.4	276	0880	.56
.6	608	4270	.69	.6	362	1738	.67
.8	689	5077	.80	.8	448	2598	.78
7.0	770	5885	.91	16.0	534	3460	.89
.2	851	6694	4.02	.2	621	4324	9.00
.4	932	7504	.13	.4	707	5188	.11
.6	3013	8316	.24	.6	794	6054	.22
.8	095	9128	.35	.8	881	6921	.33
8.0	176	9942	.46	17.0	968	7789	.45
.2	258	30757	.58	.2	7055	8658	.56
.4	340	1573	.69	.4	142	9529	.67
.6	422	2391	.80	.6	229	70400	.78
.8	504	3209	.91	.8	317	1273	.89

(Continued)

[a] *Natl. Bur. Std. Circ.* C440, pp. 614, 626(1942). Based upon figures prepared by Kaiserliche Normal-Eichungs-Kommission and accepted by International Commission for Uniform Methods of Sugar Analysis.

47.008   Degrees Brix, specific gravity, and degrees Baumé of sugar solutions (Plato Table)[a]—Continued.

°Brix or % by Wt of Sucrose	Specific Gravity at:		°Baumé (Modulus 145)	°Brix or % by Wt of Sucrose	Specific Gravity at:		°Baumé (Modulus 145)
	20/20°	20/4°			20/20°	20/4°	
18.0	1.07404	1.072147	10.00	27.0	1.11480	1.112828	14.93
.2	492	3023	.11	.2	573	3763	15.04
.4	580	3900	.22	.4	667	4697	.15
.6	668	4777	.33	.6	761	5635	.26
.8	756	5657	.44	.8	855	6572	.37
19.0	844	6537	.55	28.0	949	7512	.48
.2	932	7419	.66	.2	2043	8453	.59
.4	8021	8302	.77	.4	138	9395	.69
.6	110	9187	.88	.6	232	20339	.80
.8	198	80072	.99	.8	327	1284	.91
20.0	287	0959	11.10	29.0	422	2231	16.02
.2	376	1848	.21	.2	517	3179	.13
.4	465	2737	.32	.4	612	4128	.24
.6	554	3628	.43	.6	707	5079	.35
.8	644	4520	.54	.8	802	6030	.46
21.0	733	5414	.65	30.0	898	6984	.57
.2	823	6309	.76	.2	993	7939	.67
.4	913	7205	.87	.4	3089	8896	.78
.6	9003	8101	.98	.6	185	9853	.89
.8	093	9000	12.09	.8	281	30812	17.00
22.0	183	9900	.20	31.0	378	1773	.11
.2	273	90802	.31	.2	474	2735	.22
.4	364	1704	.42	.4	570	3698	.33
.6	454	2607	.52	.6	667	4663	.43
.8	545	3513	.63	.8	764	5628	.54
23.0	636	4420	.74	32.0	861	6596	.65
.2	727	5328	.85	.2	958	7565	.76
.4	818	6236	.96	.4	4055	8534	.87
.6	909	7147	13.07	.6	152	9506	.98
.8	.10000	8058	.18	.8	250	40479	18.08
24.0	092	8971	.29	33.0	347	1453	.19
.2	183	9886	.40	.2	445	2429	.30
.4	275	.100802	.51	.4	543	3405	.41
.6	367	1718	.62	.6	641	4384	.52
.8	459	2637	.73	.8	739	5363	.63
25.0	551	3557	.84	34.0	837	6345	.73
.2	643	4478	.95	.2	936	7328	.84
.4	736	5400	14.06	.4	5034	8313	.95
.6	828	6324	.17	.6	133	9298	19.06
.8	921	7248	.28	.8	232	50286	.17
26.0	1014	8175	.39	35.0	331	1275	.28
.2	106	9103	.49	.2	430	2265	.38
.4	200	10033	.60	.4	530	3256	.49
.6	293	0963	.71	.6	629	4249	.60
.8	386	1895	.82	.8	729	5242	.71

(Continued)

47.008   Degrees Brix, specific gravity, and degrees Baumé of sugar solutions (Plato Table)[a]—Continued.

°Brix or % by Wt of Sucrose	Specific Gravity at:		°Baumé (Modulus 145)	°Brix or % by Wt of Sucrose	Specific Gravity at:		°Baumé (Modulus 145)
	20/20°	20/4°			20/20°	20/4°	
36.0	1.15828	1.156238	19.81	45.0	1.20467	1.202540	24.63
.2	928	7235	.92	.2	573	3603	.74
.4	6028	8233	20.03	.4	680	4668	.85
.6	128	9233	.14	.6	787	5733	.95
.8	228	60233	.25	.8	894	6801	25.06
37.0	329	1236	.35	46.0	1001	7870	.17
.2	430	2240	.46	.2	108	8940	.27
.4	530	3245	.57	.4	215	10013	.38
.6	631	4252	.68	.6	323	1086	.48
.8	732	5259	.78	.8	431	2162	.59
38.0	833	6269	.89	47.0	538	3238	.70
.2	934	7281	21.00	.2	646	4317	.80
.4	7036	8293	.11	.4	755	5395	.91
.6	138	9307	.21	.6	863	6476	26.01
.8	239	70322	.32	.8	971	7559	.12
39.0	341	1340	.43	48.0	2080	8643	.23
.2	443	2359	.54	.2	189	9729	.33
.4	545	3379	.64	.4	298	20815	.44
.6	648	4400	.75	.6	406	1904	.54
.8	750	5423	.86	.8	516	2995	.65
40.0	853	6447	.97	49.0	625	4086	.75
.2	956	7473	22.07	.2	735	5180	.86
.4	8058	8501	.18	.4	844	6274	.96
.6	162	9527	.29	.6	954	7371	27.07
.8	265	80560	.39	.8	3064	8469	.18
41.0	368	1592	.50	50.0	174	9567	.28
.2	472	2625	.61	.2	284	30668	.39
.4	575	3660	.72	.4	395	1770	.49
.6	679	4696	.82	.6	506	2874	.60
.8	783	5734	.93	.8	616	3979	.70
42.0	887	6773	23.04	51.0	727	5085	.81
.2	992	7814	.14	.2	838	6194	.91
.4	9096	8856	.25	.4	949	7303	28.02
.6	201	9901	.36	.6	4060	8414	.12
.8	305	90946	.46	.8	172	9527	.23
43.0	410	1993	.57	52.0	284	40641	.33
.2	515	3041	.68	.2	395	1757	.44
.4	620	4090	.78	.4	507	2873	.54
.6	726	5141	.89	.6	619	3992	.65
.8	831	6193	24.00	.8	731	5113	.75
44.0	936	7247	.10	53.0	844	6234	.86
.2	.20042	8303	.21	.2	956	7358	.96
.4	148	9360	.32	.4	5069	8482	29.06
.6	254	.200420	.42	.6	182	9609	.17
.8	360	1480	.53	.8	295	50737	.27

(Continued)

47.008   Degrees Brix, specific gravity, and degrees Baumé of sugar solutions (Plato Table)[a]—Continued.

°Brix or % by Wt of Sucrose	Specific Gravity at:		°Baumé (Modulus 145)	°Brix or % by Wt of Sucrose	Specific Gravity at:		°Baumé (Modulus 145)
	20/20°	20/4°			20/20°	20/4°	
54.0	1.25408	1.251866	29.38	63.0	1.30657	1.304267	34.02
.2	521	2997	.48	.2	778	5467	.12
.4	635	4129	.59	.4	898	6669	.23
.6	748	5264	.69	.6	1019	7872	.33
.8	862	6400	.80	.8	139	9077	.43
55.0	976	7535	.90	64.0	260	10282	.53
.2	6090	8674	30.00	.2	381	1489	.63
.4	204	9815	.11	.4	502	2699	.74
.6	319	60955	.21	.6	623	3909	.84
.8	433	2099	.32	.8	745	5121	.94
56.0	548	3243	.42	65.0	866	6334	35.04
.2	663	4390	.52	.2	988	7549	.14
.4	778	5537	.63	.4	2110	8766	.24
.6	893	6686	.73	.6	232	9983	.34
.8	7008	7837	.83	.8	354	21203	.45
57.0	123	8989	.94	66.0	476	2425	.55
.2	239	70143	31.04	.2	599	3648	.65
.4	355	1299	.15	.4	722	4872	.75
.6	471	2455	.25	.6	844	6097	.85
.8	587	3614	.35	.8	967	7325	.95
58.0	703	4774	.46	67.0	3090	8554	36.05
.2	819	5936	.56	.2	214	9785	.15
.4	936	7098	.66	.4	337	31017	.25
.6	8052	8262	.76	.6	460	2250	.35
.8	169	9428	.87	.8	584	3485	.45
59.0	286	80595	.97	68.0	708	4722	.55
.2	404	1764	32.07	.2	832	5961	.66
.4	520	2935	.18	.4	957	7200	.76
.6	638	4107	.28	.6	4081	8441	.86
.8	755	5281	.38	.8	205	9684	.96
60.0	873	6456	.49	69.0	330	40928	37.06
.2	991	7633	.59	.2	455	2174	.16
.4	9109	8811	.69	.4	580	3421	.26
.6	227	9991	.79	.6	705	4671	.36
.8	346	91172	.90	.8	830	5922	.46
61.0	464	2354	33.00	70.0	956	7174	.56
.2	583	3539	.10	.2	5081	8427	.66
.4	701	4725	.20	.4	207	9682	.76
.6	820	5911	.31	.6	333	50939	.86
.8	940	7100	.41	.8	459	2197	.96
62.0	.30059	8291	33.51	71.0	585	3456	38.06
.2	178	9483	.61	.2	711	4717	.16
.4	298	.300677	.72	.4	838	5980	.26
.6	418	1871	.82	.6	964	7245	.35
.8	537	3068	.92	.8	6091	8511	.45

(Continued)

47.008   Degrees Brix, specific gravity, and degrees Baumé of sugar solutions (Plato Table)[a]—*Continued.*

°Brix or % by Wt of Sucrose	Specific Gravity at:		°Baumé (Modulus 145)	°Brix or % by Wt of Sucrose	Specific Gravity at:		°Baumé (Modulus 145)
	20/20°	20/4°			20/20°	20/4°	
72.0	1.36218	1.359778	38.55	81.0	1.42088	1.418374	42.95
.2	346	61047	.65	.2	222	9711	43.05
.4	473	2317	.75	.4	356	21049	.14
.6	600	3590	.85	.6	490	2390	.24
.8	728	4864	.95	.8	625	3730	.33
73.0	856	6139	39.05	82.0	759	5072	.43
.2	983	7415	.15	.2	894	6416	.53
.4	7111	8693	.25	.4	3029	7761	.62
.6	240	9973	.35	.6	164	9109	.72
.8	368	71254	.44	.8	298	30457	.81
74.0	496	2536	.54	83.0	434	1807	.91
.2	625	3820	.64	.2	569	3158	44.00
.4	754	5105	.74	.4	705	4511	.10
.6	883	6392	.84	.6	841	5866	.19
.8	8012	7680	.94	.8	976	7222	.29
75.0	141	8971	40.03	84.0	4112	8579	.38
.2	270	80262	.13	.2	249	9938	.48
.4	400	1555	.23	.4	385	41299	.57
.6	530	2851	.33	.6	521	2661	.67
.8	660	4148	.43	.8	658	4024	.76
76.0	790	5446	.53	85.0	794	5388	.86
.2	920	6745	.62	.2	931	6754	.95
.4	9050	8045	.72	.4	5068	8121	45.05
.6	180	9347	.82	.6	205	9491	.14
.8	311	90651	.92	.8	343	50860	.24
77.0	442	1956	41.01	86.0	480	2232	.33
.2	573	3263	.11	.2	618	3605	.42
.4	704	4571	.21	.4	755	4980	.52
.6	835	5881	.31	.6	893	6357	.61
.8	966	7192	.40	.8	6031	7735	.71
78.0	.40098	8505	.50	87.0	170	9114	.80
.2	230	9819	.60	.2	308	60495	.89
.4	361	.401134	.70	.4	446	1877	.99
.6	493	2452	.79	.6	585	3260	46.08
.8	625	3771	.89	.8	724	4645	.17
79.0	758	5091	.99	88.0	862	6032	.27
.2	890	6412	42.08	.2	7002	7420	.36
.4	1023	7735	.18	.4	141	8810	.45
.6	155	9061	.28	.6	280	70200	.55
.8	288	10387	.37	.8	420	1592	.64
80.0	421	1715	.47	89.0	559	2986	.73
.2	554	3044	.57	.2	699	4381	.83
.4	688	4374	.66	.4	839	5779	.92
.6	821	5706	.76	.6	979	7176	47.01
.8	955	7039	.85	.8	8119	8575	.11

(Continued)

47.008   **Degrees Brix, specific gravity, and degrees Baumé of sugar solutions (Plato Table)**[a]—*Concluded.*

°Brix or % by Wt of Sucrose	Specific Gravity at:		°Baumé (Modulus 145)	°Brix or % by Wt of Sucrose	Specific Gravity at:		°Baumé (Modulus 145)
	20/20°	20/4°			20/20°	20/4°	
90.0	1.48259	1.479976	47.20	95.0	1.51814	1.515455	49.49
.2	400	81378	.29	.2	958	6893	.58
.4	540	2782	.38	.4	2102	8332	.67
.6	681	4187	.48	.6	246	9771	.76
.8	822	5593	.57	.8	390	21212	.85
91.0	963	7002	.66	96.0	535	2656	.94
.2	9104	8411	.75	.2	680	4100	50.03
.4	246	9823	.84	.4	824	5546	.12
.6	387	91234	.94	.6	969	6993	.21
.8	529	2647	48.03	.8	3114	8441	.30
92.0	671	4063	.12	97.0	260	9891	.39
.2	812	5479	.21	.2	405	31342	.48
.4	954	6897	.30	.4	551	2794	.57
.6	.50097	8316	.40	.6	696	4248	.66
.8	239	9736	.49	.8	842	5704	.75
93.0	381	.501158	.58	98.0	988	7161	.84
.2	524	2582	.67	.2	4134	8618	.93
.4	667	4006	.76	.4	280	40076	51.02
.6	810	5432	.85	.6	426	1536	.10
.8	952	6859	.94	.8	573	2998	.19
94.0	1096	8289	49.03	99.0	719	4462	.28
.2	239	9720	.12	.2	866	5926	.37
.4	382	11151	.22	.4	5013	7392	.46
.6	526	2585	.31	.6	160	8861	.55
.8	670	4019	.40	.8	307	50329	.64
				100.0	454	1800	.73

47.009   Specific gravity and degrees Plato of sugar solutions or per cent extract by weight[a]

Specific Gravity at 20/20°	g Extract in 100 g Soln	Specific Gravity at 20/20°	g Extract in 100 g Soln	Specific Gravity at 20/20°	g Extract in 100 g Soln	Specific Gravity at 20/20°	g Extract in 100 g Soln	Specific Gravity at 20/20°	g Extract in 100 g Soln
1.00000	0.000	1.00300	0.770	1.00600	1.539	1.00900	2.305	1.01200	3.067
05	13	05	83	05	52	05	17	05	80
10	26	10	96	10	65	10	30	10	93
15	39	15	.808	15	78	15	43	15	.105
20	52	20	21	20	90	20	56	20	18
25	64	25	34	25	.603	25	69	25	31
30	77	30	47	30	16	30	81	30	43
35	90	35	59	35	29	35	94	35	56
40	.103	40	72	40	41	40	.407	40	69
45	16	45	85	45	54	45	19	45	81
1.00050	29	1.00350	98	1.00650	67	1.00950	32	1.01250	94
55	41	55	.911	55	80	55	45	55	.207
60	54	60	24	60	93	60	58	60	19
65	67	65	37	65	.705	65	70	65	32
70	80	70	49	70	18	70	83	70	45
75	93	75	62	75	31	75	96	75	57
80	.206	80	75	80	44	80	.508	80	70
85	19	85	88	85	57	85	21	85	82
90	31	90	1.001	90	69	90	34	90	95
95	44	95	14	95	82	95	47	95	.308
1.00100	57	1.00400	26	1.00700	95	1.01000	60	1.01300	21
05	70	05	39	05	.807	05	72	05	33
10	83	10	52	10	20	10	85	10	46
15	96	15	65	15	33	15	98	15	58
20	.309	20	78	20	46	20	.610	20	71
25	21	25	90	25	59	25	23	25	84
30	34	30	.103	30	72	30	36	30	96
35	47	35	16	35	84	35	49	35	.409
40	60	40	29	40	97	40	61	40	21
45	73	45	42	45	.910	45	74	45	34
1.00150	86	1.00450	55	1.00750	23	1.01050	87	1.01350	47
55	98	55	68	55	35	55	99	55	59
60	.411	60	80	60	48	60	.712	60	72
65	24	65	93	65	61	65	25	65	85
70	37	70	.206	70	73	70	38	70	97
75	50	75	19	75	86	75	50	75	.510
80	63	80	32	80	99	80	63	80	23
85	76	85	44	85	2.012	85	76	85	35
90	88	90	57	90	25	90	78	90	48
95	.501	95	70	95	38	95	.801	95	61
1.00200	14	1.00500	83	1.00800	53	1.01100	14	1.01400	73
05	27	05	96	05	65	05	26	05	86
10	40	10	.308	10	78	10	39	10	98
15	52	15	21	15	91	15	52	14	.611
20	65	20	34	20	.101	20	64	20	24
25	78	25	47	25	14	25	77	25	36
30	91	30	60	30	27	30	90	30	49
35	.604	35	72	35	39	35	.903	35	62
40	16	40	85	40	52	40	15	40	74
45	29	45	98	45	65	45	28	45	87
1.00250	42	1.00550	.411	1.00850	78	1.01150	40	1.01450	99
55	55	55	24	55	91	55	53	55	.712
60	68	60	37	60	.203	60	66	60	25
65	80	65	50	65	16	65	79	65	37
70	93	70	62	70	29	70	91	70	50
75	.706	75	75	75	41	75	3.004	75	62
80	19	80	88	80	54	80	17	80	75
85	32	85	.501	85	67	85	29	85	88
90	45	90	14	90	80	90	42	90	.800
95	57	95	26	95	.292	95	55	95	13

[a] From the American Society of Brewing Chemists.   (Continued)

47.009   **Specific gravity and degrees Plato of sugar solutions or per cent extract by weight**[a]—*Continued.*

Specific Gravity at 20/20°	g Extract in 100 g Soln	Specific Gravity at 20/20°	g Extract in 100 g Soln	Specific Gravity at 20/20°	g Extract in 100 g Soln	Specific Gravity at 20/20°	g Extract in 100 g Soln	Specific Gravity at 20/20°	g Extract in 100 g Soln
1.01500	3.826	1.01800	4.580	1.02100	5.330	1.02400	6.077	1.02700	6.819
05	38	05	92	05	43	05	89	05	31
10	51	10	.605	10	55	10	.101	10	44
15	63	15	17	15	67	15	14	15	56
20	76	20	30	20	80	20	26	20	68
25	88	25	42	25	92	25	39	25	81
30	.901	30	55	30	.405	30	51	30	93
35	14	35	68	35	18	35	63	35	.905
40	26	40	80	40	30	40	76	40	18
45	39	45	92	45	43	45	88	45	30
1.01550	51	1.01850	.705	1.02150	55	1.02450	.200	1.02750	43
55	64	55	18	55	67	55	13	55	55
60	77	60	30	60	80	60	25	60	67
65	89	65	43	65	92	65	38	65	79
70	4.002	70	55	70	.505	70	50	70	92
75	14	75	68	75	17	75	63	75	7.004
80	27	80	80	80	30	80	75	80	17
85	39	85	92	85	42	85	87	85	29
90	52	90	.805	90	55	90	.300	90	41
95	65	95	18	95	67	95	12	95	53
1.01600	77	1.01900	30	1.02200	80	1.02500	25	1.02800	66
05	90	05	43	05	92	05	37	05	78
10	.102	10	55	10	.605	10	50	10	91
15	15	15	68	15	17	15	62	15	.103
20	28	20	80	20	29	20	74	20	15
25	40	25	93	25	42	25	87	25	27
30	53	30	.905	30	54	30	99	30	40
35	65	35	18	35	67	35	.411	35	52
40	78	40	30	40	79	40	24	40	64
45	90	45	43	45	92	45	36	45	77
1.01650	.203	1.01950	55	1.02250	.704	1.02550	49	1.02850	89
55	16	55	68	55	16	55	61	55	.201
60	28	60	80	60	29	60	73	60	14
65	41	65	93	65	41	65	85	65	26
70	53	70	5.006	70	54	70	98	70	38
75	66	75	18	75	66	75	.510	75	51
80	78	80	30	80	79	80	23	80	63
85	91	85	43	85	91	85	35	85	75
90	.304	90	55	90	.803	90	47	90	87
95	16	95	68	95	16	95	60	95	.300
1.01700	29	1.02000	80	1.02300	28	1.02600	72	1.02900	12
05	41	05	93	05	41	05	84	05	24
10	54	10	.106	10	53	10	97	10	37
15	66	15	18	15	65	15	.609	15	49
20	79	20	30	20	78	20	21	20	61
25	91	25	43	25	90	25	34	25	74
30	.404	30	55	30	.903	30	46	30	86
35	17	35	68	35	15	35	59	35	98
40	29	40	80	40	28	40	71	40	.411
45	42	45	93	45	40	45	83	45	23
1.01750	54	1.02050	.205	1.02350	52	1.02650	96	1.02950	35
55	67	55	18	55	65	55	.708	55	47
60	79	60	30	60	77	60	20	60	60
65	92	65	43	65	90	65	33	65	72
70	.505	70	55	70	6.002	70	45	70	84
75	17	75	68	75	15	75	57	75	97
80	29	80	80	80	27	80	70	80	.509
85	42	85	93	85	39	85	82	85	21
90	55	90	.305	90	52	90	94	90	33
95	67	95	18	95	64	95	.807	95	46

(Continued)

47.009   Specific gravity and degrees Plato of sugar solutions or per cent extract by weight[a]—Continued.

Specific Gravity at 20/20°	g Extract in 100 g Soln	Specific Gravity at 20/20°	g Extract in 100 g Soln	Specific Gravity at 20/20°	g Extract in 100 g Soln	Specific Gravity at 20/20°	g Extract in 100 g Soln	Specific Gravity at 20/20°	g Extract in 100 g Soln
1.03000	7.558	1.03300	8.293	1.03600	9.024	1.03900	9.751	1.04200	10.475
05	70	05	.305	05	36	05	64	05	87
10	83	10	17	10	48	10	76	10	99
15	95	15	30	15	60	15	88	15	.511
20	.607	20	42	20	73	20	.800	20	23
25	19	25	54	25	85	25	12	25	36
30	32	30	66	30	97	30	24	30	48
35	44	35	78	35	.109	35	36	35	59
40	56	40	91	40	21	40	48	40	71
45	68	45	.403	45	33	45	60	45	84
1.03050	81	1.03350	15	1.03650	45	1.03950	73	1.04250	96
55	93	55	27	55	58	55	85	55	.608
60	.705	60	39	60	70	60	97	60	20
65	17	65	52	65	82	65	.909	65	32
70	30	70	64	70	94	70	21	70	44
75	42	75	76	75	.206	75	33	75	56
80	54	80	88	80	18	80	45	80	68
85	67	85	.500	85	30	85	57	85	80
90	79	90	13	90	43	90	69	90	92
95	91	95	25	95	55	95	81	95	.704
1.03100	.803	1.03400	37	1.03700	67	1.04000	93	1.04300	16
05	16	05	49	05	79	05	10.005	05	28
10	28	10	61	10	91	10	17	10	40
15	40	15	74	15	.303	15	30	15	52
20	53	20	86	20	16	20	42	20	64
25	65	25	98	25	28	25	54	25	76
30	77	30	.610	30	40	30	66	30	88
35	89	35	22	35	52	35	78	35	.800
40	.901	40	34	40	64	40	90	40	12
45	14	45	47	45	76	45	.102	45	24
1.03150	26	1.03450	59	1.03750	88	1.04050	14	1.04350	36
55	38	55	71	55	.400	55	26	55	48
60	50	60	83	60	13	60	38	60	60
65	63	65	95	65	25	65	50	65	72
70	75	70	.708	70	37	70	62	70	84
75	87	75	20	75	49	75	74	75	96
80	8.000	80	32	80	61	80	86	80	.908
85	12	85	44	85	73	85	98	85	20
90	24	90	56	90	85	90	.210	90	32
95	36	95	68	95	98	95	23	95	44
1.03200	48	1.03500	81	1.03800	.509	1.04100	34	1.04400	56
05	61	05	93	05	22	05	46	05	68
10	73	10	.805	10	34	10	59	10	80
15	85	15	17	15	46	15	71	15	92
20	98	20	30	20	58	20	83	20	11.004
25	.110	25	42	25	70	25	95	25	16
30	22	30	54	30	82	30	.307	30	27
35	34	35	66	35	94	35	19	35	39
40	46	40	78	40	.606	40	31	40	51
45	59	45	90	45	18	45	43	45	63
1.03250	71	1.03550	.902	1.03850	31	1.04150	55	1.04450	75
55	83	55	15	55	43	55	67	55	87
60	95	60	27	60	55	60	79	60	.100
65	.207	65	39	65	67	65	91	65	12
70	20	70	51	70	79	70	.403	70	23
75	32	75	63	75	91	75	15	75	35
80	44	80	75	80	.703	80	27	80	47
85	56	85	88	85	15	85	39	85	59
90	69	90	9.000	90	27	90	51	90	71
95	81	95	12	95	40	95	63	95	83

(Continued)

47.009   Specific gravity and degrees Plato of sugar solutions or per cent extract by weight[a]—*Continued*.

Specific Gravity at 20/20°	g Extract in 100 g Soln	Specific Gravity at 20/20°	g Extract in 100 g Soln	Specific Gravity at 20/20°	g Extract in 100 g Soln	Specific Gravity at 20/20°	g Extract in 100 g Soln	Specific Gravity at 20/20°	g Extract in 100 g Soln
1.04500	11.195	1.04800	11.912	1.05100	12.624	1.05400	13.333	1.05700	14.039
05	.207	05	23	05	36	05	45	05	51
10	19	10	35	10	48	10	57	10	62
15	31	15	47	15	60	15	69	15	74
20	43	20	59	20	72	20	80	20	86
25	55	25	71	25	84	25	92	25	97
30	67	30	83	30	95	30	.404	30	.109
35	79	35	95	35	.707	35	16	35	21
40	91	40	12.007	40	19	40	28	40	33
45	.303	45	19	45	31	45	39	45	44
1.04550	15	1.04850	31	1.05150	43	1.05450	51	1.05750	56
55	27	55	42	55	55	55	63	55	68
60	39	60	54	60	67	60	75	60	79
65	51	65	66	65	78	65	87	65	91
70	63	70	78	70	90	70	99	70	.203
75	75	75	90	75	.802	75	.510	75	15
80	87	80	.102	80	14	80	22	80	26
85	99	85	14	85	26	85	34	85	38
90	.411	90	26	90	38	90	46	90	50
95	23	95	38	95	49	95	57	95	61
1.04600	35	1.04900	50	1.05200	61	1.05500	69	1.05800	73
05	46	05	62	05	73	05	81	05	85
10	58	10	73	10	85	10	93	10	97
15	70	15	85	15	97	15	.604	15	.308
20	82	20	97	20	.909	20	16	20	20
25	94	25	.209	25	20	25	28	25	32
30	.506	30	21	30	32	30	40	30	43
35	18	35	33	35	44	35	51	35	55
40	30	40	45	40	56	40	63	40	67
45	42	45	56	45	68	45	75	45	79
1.04650	54	1.04950	68	1.05250	79	1.05550	87	1.05850	90
55	66	55	80	55	91	55	98	55	.402
60	78	60	92	60	13.003	60	.710	60	14
65	90	65	.304	65	15	65	22	65	25
70	.602	70	16	70	27	70	34	70	37
75	14	75	28	75	39	75	46	75	49
80	26	80	40	80	50	80	57	80	60
85	38	85	51	85	62	85	69	85	72
90	50	90	63	90	74	90	81	90	84
95	61	95	75	95	86	95	92	95	95
1.04700	73	1.05000	87	1.05300	98	1.05600	.804	1.05900	.507
05	85	05	99	05	.109	05	16	05	19
10	97	10	.411	10	21	10	28	10	31
15	.709	15	23	15	33	15	39	15	42
20	21	20	35	20	45	20	51	20	54
25	33	25	47	25	57	25	63	25	65
30	45	30	58	30	68	30	75	30	77
35	57	35	70	35	80	35	86	35	89
40	68	40	82	40	92	40	98	40	.601
45	80	45	94	45	.204	45	.910	45	12
1.04750	92	1.05050	.506	1.05350	15	1.05650	21	1.05950	24
55	.804	55	18	55	27	55	33	55	36
60	16	60	30	60	39	60	45	60	47
65	28	65	42	65	51	65	57	65	59
70	40	70	53	70	63	70	68	70	71
75	52	75	65	75	74	75	80	75	82
80	64	80	77	80	86	80	92	80	94
85	76	85	89	85	98	85	14.004	85	.706
90	88	90	.601	90	.310	90	15	90	17
95	.900	95	13	95	22	95	27	95	29

(Continued)

47.009   Specific gravity and degrees Plato of sugar solutions or per cent extract by weight[a]—*Concluded.*

Specific Gravity at 20/20°	g Extract in 100 g Soln	Specific Gravity at 20/20°	g Extract in 100 g Soln	Specific Gravity at 20/20°	g Extract in 100 g Soln	Specific Gravity at 20/20°	g Extract in 100 g Soln	Specific Gravity at 20/20°	g Extract in 100 g Soln
1.06000	14.741	1.06200	15.207	1.06400	15.671	1.06600	16.134	1.06800	16.595
05	52	05	18	05	83	05	45	05	.606
10	64	10	30	10	94	10	57	10	18
15	76	15	41	15	.706	15	69	15	30
20	87	20	53	20	17	20	80	20	41
25	99	25	65	25	29	25	91	25	52
30	.811	30	76	30	41	30	.203	30	64
35	22	35	88	35	52	35	15	35	76
40	34	40	.300	40	64	40	26	40	87
45	46	45	11	45	76	45	38	45	99
1.06050	57	1.06250	23	1.06450	87	1.06650	49	1.06850	.710
55	69	55	34	55	99	55	61	55	22
60	81	60	46	60	.810	60	72	60	33
65	92	65	58	65	22	65	84	65	44
70	.904	70	69	70	33	70	95	70	56
75	16	75	81	75	45	75	.307	75	68
80	27	80	93	80	57	80	19	80	79
85	39	85	.404	85	68	85	30	85	91
90	50	90	16	90	80	90	41	90	.802
95	62	95	27	95	91	95	53	95	13
1.06100	74	1.06300	39	1.06500	.903	1.06700	65	1.06900	25
05	86	05	51	05	14	05	76	05	36
10	97	10	62	10	26	10	88	10	48
15	15.009	15	74	15	38	15	99	15	59
20	20	20	86	20	49	20	.411	20	71
25	32	25	97	25	61	25	22	25	82
30	44	30	.509	30	72	30	34	30	94
35	55	35	20	35	84	35	45	35	.905
40	67	40	32	40	95	40	57	40	17
45	79	45	44	45	16.007	45	68	45	28
1.06150	90	1.06350	55	1.06550	19	1.06750	80	1.06950	40
55	.102	55	67	55	30	55	91	55	51
60	14	60	78	60	41	60	.503	60	63
65	25	65	90	65	53	65	14	65	74
70	37	70	.602	70	65	70	26	70	86
75	48	75	13	75	76	75	37	75	97
80	60	80	25	80	88	80	49	80	17.009
85	72	85	37	85	99	85	61	85	20
90	83	90	48	90	.111	90	72	90	32
95	95	95	60	95	22	95	83	95	43

47.010   Temperature corrections for readings of saccharometers (standard at 20°C)

(Calcd from data on thermal expansion of sugar solns by Plato[a] and assumed that instrument is of Jena 16[111] glass. Table should be used with caution and only for approx. results when temp. differs much from standard temp. or from temp. of surrounding air.)

Temp., °C	Observed Percentage of Sugar													
	0	5	10	15	20	25	30	35	40	45	50	55	60	70
	Subtract from Per Cent Sugar													
0	0.30	0.49	0.65	0.77	0.89	0.99	1.08	1.16	1.24	1.31	1.37	1.41	1.44	1.49
5	.36	.47	.56	.65	.73	.80	0.86	0.91	0.97	1.01	1.05	1.08	1.10	1.14
10	.32	.38	.43	.48	.52	.57	.60	.64	.67	0.70	0.72	0.74	0.75	0.77
11	.31	.35	.40	.44	.48	.51	.55	.58	.60	.63	.65	.66	.68	.70
12	.29	.32	.36	.40	.43	.46	.50	.52	.54	.56	.58	.59	.60	.62
13	.26	.29	.32	.35	.38	.41	.44	.46	.48	.49	.51	.52	.53	.55
14	.24	.26	.29	.31	.34	.36	.38	.40	.41	.42	.44	.45	.46	.47
15	.20	.22	.24	.26	.28	.30	.32	.33	.34	.36	.36	.37	.38	.39
16	.17	.18	.20	.22	.23	.25	.26	.27	.28	.28	.29	.30	.31	.32
17	.13	.14	.15	.16	.18	.19	.20	.20	.21	.21	.22	.23	.23	.24
18	.09	.10	.10	.11	.12	.13	.13	.14	.14	.14	.15	.15	.15	.16
19	.05	.05	.05	.06	.06	.06	.07	.07	.07	.07	.08	.08	.08	.08
17.5	.11	.12	.12	.14	.15	.16	.16	.17	.17	.18	.18	.19	.19	.20
15.56 (60°F)	.18	.20	.22	.24	.26	.28	.29	.30	.30	.32	.33	.33	.34	.34
	Add to Per Cent Sugar													
21	0.04	0.05	0.06	0.06	0.06	0.07	0.07	0.07	0.07	0.08	0.08	0.08	0.08	0.09
22	.10	.10	.11	.12	.12	.13	.14	.14	.15	.15	.16	.16	.16	.16
23	.16	.16	.17	.17	.19	.20	.21	.21	.22	.23	.24	.24	.24	.24
24	.21	.22	.23	.24	.26	.27	.28	.29	.30	.31	.32	.32	.32	.32
25	.27	.28	.30	.31	.32	.34	.35	.36	.38	.38	.39	.39	.40	.39
26	.33	.34	.36	.37	.40	.40	.42	.44	.46	.47	.47	.48	.48	.48
27	.40	.41	.42	.44	.46	.48	.50	.52	.54	.54	.55	.56	.56	.56
28	.46	.47	.49	.51	.54	.56	.58	.60	.61	.62	.63	.64	.64	.64
29	.54	.55	.56	.59	.61	.63	.66	.68	.70	.70	.71	.72	.72	.72
30	.61	.62	.63	.66	.68	.71	.73	.76	.78	.78	.79	.80	.80	.81
35	.99	1.01	1.02	1.06	1.10	1.13	1.16	1.18	1.20	1.21	1.22	1.22	1.23	1.22
40	1.42	1.45	1.47	1.51	1.54	1.57	1.60	1.62	1.64	1.65	1.65	1.65	1.66	1.65
45	1.91	1.94	1.96	2.00	2.03	2.05	2.07	2.09	2.10	2.10	2.10	2.10	2.10	2.08
50	2.46	2.48	2.50	2.53	2.56	2.57	2.58	2.59	2.59	2.58	2.58	2.57	2.56	2.52
55	3.05	3.07	3.09	3.12	3.12	3.12	3.12	3.11	3.10	3.08	3.07	3.05	3.03	2.97
60	3.69	3.72	3.73	3.73	3.72	3.70	3.67	3.65	3.62	3.60	3.57	3.54	3.50	3.43
27.5	0.43	0.44	0.46	0.48	0.50	0.52	0.54	0.56	0.58	0.58	0.59	0.60	0.60	0.60

[a] Charlottenberg. Physikalisch-technische reichsanstalt. Wiss. Abhandl. Kaiserliche Norm.-Eichungs-Komm., **2**, 140(1900).

47.011   Jackson-Mathews table of densities of fructose solutions and mean density and expansion coefficients between 20 and 25°C[a]

(All wts corrected to vac.)

Fructose, %	D_4^{20}	D_4^{25}	$-\Delta D/\Delta t$	$\Delta v/\Delta t$	Fructose, %	D_4^{20}	D_4^{25}	$-\Delta D/\Delta t$	$\Delta v/\Delta t$
			$\times 10^{-6}$	$\times 10^{-6}$				$\times 10^{-5}$	$\times 10^{-5}$
0	0.99823	0.99708	231	231	36	1.1568	1.1544	48	42
1	.00214	.00095	238	237	37	618	593	49	42
2	0607	0484	245	243	38	668	643	50	43
3	1003	0877	252	249	39	718	693	50	43
4	1402	1272	259	255	40	769	7435	51	43
5	1803	1670	266	261	41	820	794	52	44
6	2207	2071	273	267	42	872	845	53	44
7	2614	2475	280	273	43	923	897	53	45
8	3024	2881	287	278	44	975	9485	54	45
					45	.2028	.20005	55	45
9	3437	3290	294	284					
10	3853	3702	301	290	46	0805	053	55	46
11	4271	4118	308	295	47	134	106	56	46
12	4692	4535	315	300	48	187	159	57	46
					49	241	212	57	47
13	5116	4955	323	307	50	295	266	58	47
14	5543	5378	330	313					
15	5972	5804	337	318	51	349	320	59	47
16	6405	6233	345	324	52	404	374	59	48
					53	459	429	60	48
17	6840	6664	352	329	54	514	484	60	48
18	7278	7098	360	336	55	570	539	61	49
19	7719	7535	367	341					
20	8162	7975	375	347	56	626	595	62	49
			$\times 10^{-5}$	$\times 10^{-5}$	57	682	651	62	49
21	8606	842	38	35	58	739	707	63	50
22	9055	886	38	35	59	796	764	64	50
23	9507	931	39	36					
24	9962	976	40	36	60	853	821	64	50
25	.10420	.1022	41	37	61	911	878	65	50
					62	969	936	66	51
26	088	0675	41	37	63	.3027	994	66	51
27	1345	1135	42	38					
28	181	160	43	38	64	086	.3052	67	51
29	229	207	43	39	65	145	111	67	51
30	276	254	44	39	66	204	170	68	51
					67	263	229	69	52
31	324	3015	45	40	68	323	289	69	52
32	372	349	46	40	69	384	349	70	52
33	4205	397	46	40	70	444	409	70	52
34	469	446	47	41	71	505	470	71	53
35	5185	495	48	41					

[a] *J. Res. Natl. Bur. Std.* **8**, 437(1932), RP 426; Natl. Bur. Std. Circ. 440(1942).

47.012   Refractive indices (n) of sucrose solutions at 20°C[a]

(International Scale, 1936)[b]

n, 20°	Sucrose, %	n, 20°	Sucrose, %	n, 20°	Sucrose, %	n, 20°	Sucrose, %	n, 20°	Sucrose, %
1.33299	0.0	1.34629	9.0	1.36053	18.0	1.3758	27.0	1.3920	36.0
328	.2	660	.2	086	.2	61	.2	24	.2
357	.4	691	.4	119	.4	65	.4	28	.4
385	.6	721	.6	152	.6	68	.6	31	.6
414	.8	752	.8	185	.8	72	.8	35	.8
443	1.0	783	10.0	218	19.0	75	28.0	39	37.0
472	.2	814	.2	251	.2	79	.2	43	.2
501	.4	845	.4	284	.4	82	.4	47	.4
530	.6	875	.6	318	.6	86	.6	50	.6
559	.8	906	.8	351	.8	89	.8	54	.8
588	2.0	937	11.0	384	20.0	93	29.0	58	38.0
617	.2	968	.2	417	.2	97	.2	62	.2
646	.4	999	.4	451	.4	800	.4	66	.4
675	.6	5031	.6	484	.6	04	.6	70	.6˙
704	.8	062	.8	518	.8	07	.8	74	.8
733	3.0	093	12.0	551	21.0	11	30.0	78	39.0
762	.2	124	.2	585	.2	15	.2	82	.2
792	.4	156	.4	618	.4	18	.4	86	.4
821	.6	187	.6	652	.6	22	.6	89	.6
851	.8	219	.8	685	.8	25	.8	93	.8
880	4.0	250	13.0	719	22.0	29	31.0	97	40.0
909	.2	282	.2	753	.2	33	.2	.4001	.2
939	.4	313	.4	787	.4	36	.4	05	.4
968	.6	345	.6	820	.6	40	.6	08	.6
998	.8	376	.8	854	.8	43	.8	12	.8
4027	5.0	408	14.0	888	23.0	47	32.0	16	41.0
057	.2	440	.2	922	.2	51	.2	20	.2
087	.4	472	.4	956	.4	54	.4	24	.4
116	.6	503	.6	991	.6	58	.6	28	.6
146	.8	535	.8	7025	.8	61	.8	32	.8
176	6.0	567	15.0	059	24.0	65	33.0	36	42.0
206	.2	599	.2	09	.2	69	.2	40	.2
236	.4	631	.4	13	.4	72	.4	44	.4
266	.6	664	.6	16	.6	76	.6	48	.6
296	.8	696	.8	20	.8	79	.8	52	.8
326	7.0	728	16.0	23	25.0	83	34.0	56	43.0
356	.2	760	.2	26	.2	87	.2	60	.2
386	.4	793	.4	30	.4	91	.4	64	.4
417	.6	825	.6	33	.6	94	.6	68	.6
447	.8	858	.8	37	.8	98	.8	72	.8
477	8.0	890	17.0	40	26.0	902	35.0	76	44.0
507	.2	923	.2	44	.2	06	.2	80	.2
538	.4	955	.4	47	.4	09	.4	84	.4
568	.6	988	.6	51	.6	13	.6	88	.6
599	.8	6020	.8	54	.8	16	.8	92	.8

(Continued)

[a] Values in this table for range 0 to 49.8% sucrose are in accordance with International Scale of Refractive Indices of Sucrose at 20°C, 1936, adopted as official at 1938 meeting of the AOAC. Values of indices for range 0–24% sucrose are given to five decimal places, those 24.2 to 49.8% to four decimal places. Values for range 50 to 85% are those adopted as official at 1959 meeting and are given to five decimal places.

[b] *Intern. Sugar J.* **39**, 225(1937).

47.012   Refractive indices (n) of sucrose solutions at 20°C[a]—Concluded.

(International Scale, 1936)[b]

n, 20°	Sucrose, %	n, 20°	Sucrose, %	n, 20°	Sucrose, %	n, 20°	Sucrose, %	n, 20°	Sucrose, %
1.4096	45.0	1.42646	53.0	1.44420	61.0	1.46299	69.0	1.48288	77.0
4100	.2	689	.2	465	.2	347	.2	339	.2
04	.4	733	.4	511	.4	396	.4	390	.4
09	.6	776	.6	557	.6	444	.6	442	.6
13	.8	819	.8	603	.8	493	.8	493	.8
17	46.0	862	54.0	649	62.0	541	70.0	544	78.0
21	.2	906	.2	695	.2	590	.2	596	.2
25	.4	949	.4	741	.4	639	.4	648	.4
29	.6	993	.6	787	.6	688	.6	699	.6
33	.8	3036	.8	833	.8	737	.8	751	.8
37	47.0	080	55.0	879	63.0	786	71.0	803	79.0
41	.2	124	.2	926	.2	835	.2	855	.2
45	.4	168	.4	972	.4	884	.4	907	.4
50	.6	211	.6	5019	.6	933	.6	959	.6
54	.8	255	.8	065	.8	982	.8	9011	.8
58	48.0	299	56.0	112	64.0	7032	72.0	063	80.0
62	.2	343	.2	158	.2	081	.2	115	.2
66	.4	387	.4	205	.4	131	.4	167	.4
71	.6	432	.6	252	.6	180	.6	220	.6
75	.8	476	.8	299	.8	230	.8	272	.8
79	49.0	520	57.0	346	65.0	279	73.0	325	81.0
83	.2	564	.2	393	.2	329	.2	377	.2
87	.4	609	.4	440	.4	379	.4	430	.4
92	.6	653	.6	487	.6	429	.6	483	.6
96	.8	698	.8	534	.8	479	.8	536	.8
2008	50.0	742	58.0	581	66.0	529	74.0	589	82.0
050	.2	787	.2	629	.2	579	.2	641	.2
092	.4	832	.4	676	.4	629	.4	695	.4
135	.6	877	.6	724	.6	679	.6	748	.6
177	.8	922	.8	771	.8	730	.8	801	.8
219	51.0	966	59.0	819	67.0	780	75.0	854	83.0
261	.2	4011	.2	867	.2	831	.2	907	.2
304	.4	057	.4	914	.4	881	.4	961	.4
347	.6	102	.6	962	.6	932	.6	.50014	.6
389	.8	147	.8	6010	.8	982	.8	068	.8
432	52.0	192	60.0	058	68.0	8033	76.0	121	84.0
475	.2	238	.2	106	.2	084	.2	175	.2
517	.4	283	.4	154	.4	135	.4	229	.4
560	.6	328	.6	202	.6	186	.6	283	.6
603	.8	374	.8	251	.8	237	.8	337	.8
								391	85.0

47.013 Table for determining per cent sucrose in sugar solutions from readings of Zeiss immersion refractometer at 20°C[a]

Reading[b] at 20°	n_D^{20}	Sucrose, %	Reading[b] at 20°	n_D^{20}	Sucrose, %	Reading[b] at 20°	n_D^{20}	Sucrose, %
14.47	1.33299	0	45	1.34463	7.91	76	1.35606	15.24
15	3320	0.15	46	4500	8.15	77	5642	15.47
16	3358	0.41	47	4537	8.39	78	5678	15.69
17	3397	0.68	48	4575	8.64	79	5714	15.91
18	3435	0.94	49	4612	8.89			
19	3474	1.21				80	5750	16.14
			50	4650	9.13	81	5786	16.36
20	3513	1.48	51	4687	9.38	82	5822	16.58
21	3551	1.74	52	4724	9.62	83	5858	16.81
22	3590	2.01	53	4761	9.86	84	5894	17.03
23	3628	2.27	54	4798	10.10	85	5930	17.25
24	3667	2.54	55	4836	10.34	86	5966	17.47
25	3705	2.80	56	4873	10.58	87	6002	17.69
26	3743	3.07	57	4910	10.82	88	6038	17.91
27	3781	3.33	58	4947	11.06	89	6074	18.12
28	3820	3.59	59	4984	11.30			
29	3858	3.85				90	6109	18.34
			60	5021	11.54	91	6145	18.56
30	3896	4.11	61	5058	11.78	92	6181	18.78
31	3934	4.36	62	5095	12.01	93	6217	19.00
32	3972	4.62	63	5132	12.25	94	6252	19.21
33	4010	4.88	64	5169	12.48	95	6287	19.42
34	4048	5.14	65	5205	12.72	96	6323	19.63
35	4086	5.40	66	5242	12.95	97	6359	19.85
36	4124	5.65	67	5279	13.18	98	6394	20.06
37	4162	5.91	68	5316	13.41	99	6429	20.27
38	4199	6.16	69	5352	13.64			
39	4237	6.41				100	6464	20.48
			70	5388	13.87	101	6500	20.69
40	4275	6.66	71	5425	14.10	102	6535	20.90
41	4313	6.91	72	5461	14.33	103	6570	21.11
42	4350	7.16	73	5497	14.56	104	6605	21.32
43	4388	7.41	74	5533	14.79	105	6640	21.53
44	4426	7.66	75	5569	15.01			

[a] Values in this table were calcd by J. A. Mathews from five-place indices of Schönrock as given by Landt, *Z. Ver. Deut. Zucker-Ind.* **83**, 692(1933).

[b] Scale readings refer only to scale of arbitrary units proposed by Pulfrich, *Z. Angew. Chem.* 1168(1899). According to this scale 14.5 = 1.33300, 50.0 = 1.34650, and 100.0 = 1.36464. If immersion refractometer used is calibrated according to another arbitrary scale, readings must be converted into refractive indices before this table is used to determine per cent sugar.

47.014   Refractive indices of glucose, fructose, invert sugar, and raffinose hydrate solutions at 20°C

% by Wt in Air	Refractive Index				% by Wt in Air	Refractive Index		
	Glucose[a]	Fructose	Invert Sugar[a]	Raffinose Hydrate[b]		Glucose[a]	Fructose	Invert Sugar[a]
0	1.33299	1.33299	1.33299	1.33299	50	1.41826	1.41819	1.41827
1	3442	3441	3441	3422	51	2029	2022	2031
2	3586	3583	3583	3546	52	2233	2228	2236
3	3731	3727	3727	3671	53	2439	2434	2443
4	3877	3872	3872	3797	54	2646	2642	2650
5	4024	4017	4018	3924	55	2855	2851	2860
6	4173	4164	4165	4052	56	3065	3062	3070
7	4322	4312	4313	4181	57	3276	3273	3283
8	4472	4461	4462	4311	58	3488	3487	3496
9	4623	4611	4612	4443	59	3702	3701	3711
10	4775	4762	4764	4576	60	3918	3917	3928
11	4928	4914	4916	4709	61	4135	4135	4146
12	5082	5067	5070	4844	62	4354	4353	4365
13	5237	5221	5225	4979	63	4574	4573	4586
14	5393	5377	5381	5116	64	4796	4794	4808
15	5551	5534	5538	5253	65	5019	5017	5032
16	5710	5692	5696	5391	66	5244	5241	5257
17	5870	5851	5856	5530	67	5470	5466	5484
18	6031	6011	6016	5670	68	5697	5693	5712
19	6193	6172	6178	5811	69	5926	5921	5941
20	6356	6335	6341	5953	70	6156	6150	6172
21	6520	6499	6506	6096	71	6388	6380	6405
22	6685	6664	6671	6239	72	6621	6612	6639
23	6852	6830	6838	6384	73	6856	6845	6874
24	7020	6998	7006	6529	74	7092	7079	7111
25	7189	7167	7175	6676	75	7330	7315	7350
26	7359	7337	7345	6824	76	7569	7551	7590
27	7530	7508	7517	6972	77	7810	7789	7831
28	7702	7681	7690	7121	78	8052	8028	8074
29	7876	7855	7864	7272	79	8296	8269	8319
30	8051	8030	8040	7424	80	8542	8510	8564
31	8228	8207	8217	7577	81		8753	
32	8406	8385	8395	7730	82		8997	
33	8585	8564	8574	7884	83		9242	
34	8765	8745	8755	8040	84		9488	
35	8946	8927	8937	8197	85		9735	
36	9129	9110	9120	8356	86		9984	
37	9313	9295	9305	8516	87		.50233	
38	9498	9481	9491	8677	88		0484	
39	9684	9668	9678	8840	89		0736	
40	9872	9857	9866	9004	90		0988	
41	.40061	.40047	.40056					
42	0251	0238	0248					
43	0443	0431	0440					
44	0636	0625	0634					
45	0831	0821	0830					
46	1028	1018	1026					
47	1226	1216	1225					
48	1425	1415	1424					
49	1625	1616	1625					

[a] Zerban and Martin, *JAOAC* **27**, 295(1944). Glucose values graphically smoothed, Young and Jones, *JAOAC* **37**, 932 (1954).
[b] Zerban and Martin, *JAOAC* **34**, 808(1951).

47.015 Temperature corrections for readings of per cent sucrose in sugar solutions by either Abbé or immersion refractometer at temperatures other than 20°C[a]

(International Temperature Correction Table, 1936)[a]

Temp., °C	Per Cent Sucrose										
	0	5	10	15	20	25	30	40	50	60	70
	Subtract from Per Cent Sucrose										
10	0.50	0.54	0.58	0.61	0.64	0.66	0.68	0.72	0.74	0.76	0.79
11	.46	.49	.53	.55	.58	.60	.62	.65	.67	.69	.71
12	.42	.45	.48	.50	.52	.54	.56	.58	.60	.61	.63
13	.37	.40	.42	.44	.46	.48	.49	.51	.53	.54	.55
14	.33	.35	.37	.39	.40	.41	.42	.44	.45	.46	.48
15	.27	.29	.31	.33	.34	.34	.35	.37	.38	.39	.40
16	.22	.24	.25	.26	.27	.28	.28	.30	.30	.31	.32
17	.17	.18	.19	.20	.21	.21	.21	.22	.23	.23	.24
18	.12	.13	.13	.14	.14	.14	.14	.15	.15	.16	.16
19	.06	.06	.06	.07	.07	.07	.07	.08	.08	.08	.08
	Add to Per Cent Sucrose										
21	0.06	0.07	0.07	0.07	0.07	0.08	0.08	0.08	0.08	0.08	0.08
22	.13	.13	.14	.14	.15	.15	.15	.15	.16	.16	.16
23	.19	.20	.21	.22	.22	.23	.23	.23	.24	.24	.24
24	.26	.27	.28	.29	.30	.30	.31	.31	.31	.32	.32
25	.33	.35	.36	.37	.38	.38	.39	.40	.40	.40	.40
26	.40	.42	.43	.44	.45	.46	.47	.48	.48	.48	.48
27	.48	.50	.52	.53	.54	.55	.55	.56	.56	.56	.56
28	.56	.57	.60	.61	.62	.63	.63	.64	.64	.64	.64
29	.64	.66	.68	.69	.71	.72	.72	.73	.73	.73	.73
30	.72	.74	.77	.78	.79	.80	.80	.81	.81	.81	.81

[a] *Intern. Sugar J.* **39**, 24s (1937).

47.016   ★   Corrections to be subtracted from iodine titer to obtain mg invert sugar by Ofner method[a]   ★

See **43.014**, 10th ed.

[a] *JAOAC* **26**, 470 (1943).

★ Tables so marked are surplus tables. *See* "Definitions of Terms and Explanatory Notes," item (29).

47.017   **Total reducing sugar required for complete reduction of 10 ml Soxhlet solution to be used in conjunction with Lane-Eynon general volumetric method**

Titer	Invert Sugar, No Sucrose	g Sucrose/100 ml Invert Sugar				Glu-cose	Fruc-tose	Maltose		Lactose	
		1	5	10	25			Anhyd.	$C_{12}H_{22}O_{11}.H_2O$	Anhyd.	$C_{12}H_{22}O_{11}.H_2O$
					Required for Reduction of 10 ml Soxhlet Soln						
15	50.5	49.9	47.6	46.1	43.4	49.1	52.2	77.2	81.3	64.9	68.3
16	.6	50.0	.6	.1	.4	.2	.3	.1	.2	.8	.2
17	.7	.1	.6	.1	.4	.3	.3	.0	.1	.8	.2
18	.8	.1	.6	.1	.3	.3	.4	.0	.0	.7	.1
19	.8	.2	.6	.1	.3	.4	.5	76.9	80.9	.7	.1
20	.9	.2	.6	.1	.2	.5	.5	.8	.8	.6	.0
21	51.0	.2	.6	.1	.2	.5	.6	.7	.7	.6	.0
22	.0	.3	.6	.1	.1	.6	.7	.6	.6	.6	.0
23	.1	.3	.6	.1	.0	.7	.7	.5	.5	.5	67.9
24	.2	.3	.6	.1	.9	.8	.8	.4	.4	.5	.9
25	.2	.4	.6	.0	.8	.8	.8	.4	.4	.5	.9
26	.3	.4	.6	.0	.8	.9	.9	.3	.3	.5	.9
27	.4	.4	.6	.0	.7	.9	.9	.2	.2	.4	.8
28	.4	.5	47.7	.0	.7	50.0	53.0	.1	.1	.4	.8
29	.5	.5	.7	.0	.6	.0	.1	.0	.0	.4	.8
30	.5	.5	.7	.0	.5	.1	.2	.0	.0	.4	.8
31	.6	.6	.7	45.9	.5	.2	.2	75.9	79.9	.4	.8
32	.6	.6	.7	.9	.4	.2	.3	.9	.9	.4	.8
33	.7	.6	.7	.9	.3	.3	.3	.8	.8	.4	.8
34	.7	.6	.7	.8	.2	.3	.4	.8	.8	.4	.9
35	.8	.7	.7	.8	.2	.4	.4	.7	.7	.5	.9
36	.8	.7	.7	.8	.1	.4	.5	.6	.6	.5	.9
37	.9	.7	.7	.7	.0	.5	.5	.6	.6	.5	.9
38	.9	.7	.7	.7	.0	.5	.6	.5	.5	.5	.9
39	52.0	.8	.7	.7	41.9	.6	.6	.5	.5	.5	.9
40	.0	.8	.7	.6	.8	.6	.6	.4	.4	.5	.9
41	.1	.8	.7	.6	.8	.7	.7	.4	.4	.6	68.0
42	.1	.8	.7	.6	.7	.7	.7	.3	.3	.6	.0
43	.2	.8	.7	.5	.6	.8	.8	.3	.3	.6	.0
44	.2	.9	.7	.5	.5	.8	.8	.2	.2	.6	.0
45	.3	.9	.7	.4	.4	.9	.9	.2	.2	.7	.1
46	.3	.9	.7	.4	.4	.9	.9	.1	.1	.7	.1
47	.4	.9	.7	.3	.3	51.0	.9	.1	.1	.8	.2
48	.4	.9	.7	.3	.2	.0	54.0	.1	.1	.8	.2
49	.5	.0	.7	.2	.1	.0	.0	.0	.0	.8	.2
50	.5	.0	.7	.2	.0	.1	.0	.0	.0	.9	.3

47.018 Total reducing sugar required for complete reduction of 25 ml Soxhlet solution to be used in conjunction with Lane-Eynon general volumetric method

Titer	Invert Sugar, No Sucrose	1 g Sucrose/ 100 ml Invert Sugar	Glu-cose	Fruc-tose	Maltose		Lactose	
					Anhyd.	$C_{12}H_{22}O_{11}.H_2O$	Anhyd.	$C_{12}H_{22}O_{11}.H_2O$
				Required for Reduction of 25 ml Soxhlet Soln				
15	123.6	122.6	120.2	127.4	197.8	208.2	163.9	172.5
16	.6	.7	.2	.4	.4	207.8	.5	.1
17	.6	.7	.2	.5	.0	.4	.1	171.7
18	.7	.7	.2	.5	196.7	.1	162.8	.4
19	.7	.8	.3	.6	.5	206.8	.5	.1
20	.8	.8	.3	.6	.2	.5	.3	170.9
21	.8	.8	.3	.7	195.8	.1	.0	.6
22	.9	.9	.4	.7	.5	205.8	161.8	.4
23	.9	.9	.4	.8	.1	.4	.6	.2
24	124.0	.9	.5	.8	194.8	.1	.5	.0
25	.0	123.0	.5	.9	.5	204.8	.4	169.9
26	.1	.0	.6	.9	.2	.4	.2	.7
27	.1	.0	.6	128.0	193.9	.1	.0	.5
28	.2	.1	.7	.0	.6	203.8	160.8	.3
29	.2	.1	.7	.1	.3	.5	.7	.2
30	.3	.1	.8	.1	.0	.2	.6	.0
31	.3	.2	.8	.1	192.8	202.9	.5	168.9
32	.4	.2	.8	.2	.5	.6	.4	.8
33	.4	.2	.9	.2	.2	.3	.2	.6
34	.5	.3	.9	.3	191.9	.0	.1	.5
35	.5	.3	121.0	.3	.7	201.8	.0	.4
36	.6	.3	.0	.4	.4	.5	159.8	.2
37	.6	.4	.1	.4	.2	.2	.7	.1
38	.7	.4	.2	.5	.0	.0	.6	.0
39	.7	.4	.2	.5	190.8	200.8	.5	167.9
40	.8	.4	.2	.6	.5	.5	.4	.8
41	.8	.5	.3	.6	.3	.3	.3	.7
42	.9	.5	.4	.6	.1	.1	.2	.6
43	.9	.5	.4	.7	189.8	199.8	.2	.6
44	125.0	.6	.5	.7	.6	.6	.1	.5
45	.0	.6	.5	.8	.4	.4	.0	.4
46	.1	.6	.6	.8	.2	.2	.0	.4
47	.1	.7	.6	.9	.0	.0	158.9	.3
48	.2	.7	.7	.9	188.9	198.9	.8	.2
49	.2	.7	.7	129.0	.8	.7	.8	.2
50	.3	.8	.8	.0	.7	.6	.7	.1

47.019   Hammond table for calculating glucose, fructose, and invert sugar and lactose alone and in the presence of sucrose[a], with values for maltose from the Munson and Walker table[b]; values expressed as mg

Cu[c]	Cu₂O[c]	Glucose	Fructose	Invert Sugar	Invert Sugar and Sucrose			Lactose .H₂O	Lactose.H₂O and Sucrose		Cu₂O[d]	Maltose .H₂O
					0.3 g Total Sugar	0.4 g Total Sugar	2.0 g Total Sugar		1 Lactose 4 Sucrose	1 Lactose 12 Sucrose		
10	11.3	4.6	5.1	5.2	3.2	2.9		7.7	7.7	6.6	10	6.2
11	12.4	5.1	5.6	5.7	3.7	3.4		8.5	8.5	7.3		
12	13.5	5.6	6.1	6.2	4.2	3.9		9.3	9.2	8.0	12	7.9
13	14.6	6.0	6.7	6.7	4.8	4.4		10.0	10.0	8.7		
14	15.8	6.5	7.2	7.2	5.3	4.9		10.8	10.7	9.4	14	9.5
15	16.9	7.0	7.7	7.7	5.8	5.4		11.5	11.5	10.1		
16	18.0	7.5	8.3	8.2	6.3	5.9		12.3	12.2	10.8	16	11.2
17	19.1	8.0	8.8	8.7	6.8	6.4		13.1	12.9	11.5		
18	20.3	8.5	9.3	9.2	7.3	6.9		13.8	13.7	12.2	18	12.9
19	21.4	8.9	9.9	9.7	7.8	7.4		14.6	14.4	12.9		
20	22.5	9.4	10.4	10.2	8.3	7.9	1.9	15.4	15.2	13.6	20	14.6
21	23.6	9.9	10.9	10.7	8.8	8.4	2.4	16.1	15.9	14.4		
22	24.8	10.4	11.5	11.2	9.3	8.9	2.9	16.9	16.7	15.1	22	16.2
23	25.9	10.9	12.0	11.7	9.9	9.5	3.4	17.7	17.4	15.8		
24	27.0	11.4	12.5	12.3	10.4	10.0	3.9	18.4	18.2	16.5	24	17.9
25	28.1	11.9	13.1	12.8	10.9	10.5	4.4	19.2	18.9	17.2		
26	29.3	12.3	13.6	13.3	11.4	11.0	4.9	19.9	19.7	17.9	26	19.6
27	30.4	12.8	14.2	13.8	11.9	11.5	5.5	20.7	20.4	18.6		
28	31.5	13.3	14.7	14.3	12.4	12.0	6.0	21.5	21.1	19.3	28	21.2
29	32.6	13.8	15.2	14.8	12.9	12.5	6.5	22.2	21.9	20.0		
30	33.8	14.3	15.8	15.3	13.4	13.0	7.0	23.0	22.6	20.7	30	22.9
31	34.9	14.8	16.3	15.8	14.0	13.5	7.5	23.8	23.4	21.4		
32	36.0	15.3	16.8	16.3	14.5	14.1	8.0	24.5	24.1	22.2	32	24.6
33	37.2	15.7	17.4	16.8	15.0	14.6	8.5	25.3	24.9	22.9		
34	38.3	16.2	17.9	17.3	15.5	15.1	9.0	26.1	25.6	23.6	34	26.2
35	39.4	16.7	18.4	17.8	16.0	15.6	9.5	26.8	26.4	24.3		
36	40.5	17.2	19.0	18.3	16.5	16.1	10.1	27.6	27.1	25.0	36	27.9
37	41.7	17.7	19.5	18.9	17.0	16.6	10.6	28.4	27.9	25.7		
38	42.8	18.2	20.1	19.4	17.6	17.1	11.1	29.1	28.6	26.4	38	29.6
39	43.9	18.7	20.6	19.9	18.1	17.6	11.6	29.9	29.4	27.1		
40	45.0	19.2	21.1	20.4	18.6	18.2	12.1	30.6	30.1	27.8	40	31.3
41	46.2	19.7	21.7	20.9	19.1	18.7	12.6	31.4	30.8	28.6		
42	47.3	20.1	22.2	21.4	19.6	19.2	13.1	32.2	31.6	29.3	42	32.9
43	48.4	20.6	22.8	21.9	20.1	19.7	13.7	32.9	32.3	30.0		
44	49.5	21.1	23.3	22.4	20.7	20.2	14.2	33.7	33.1	30.7	44	34.6
45	50.7	21.6	23.8	22.9	21.2	20.7	14.7	34.5	33.8	31.4		
46	51.8	22.1	24.4	23.5	21.7	21.3	15.2	35.2	34.6	32.1	46	36.3
47	52.9	22.6	24.9	24.0	22.2	21.8	15.7	36.0	35.3	32.8		
48	54.0	23.1	25.4	24.5	22.7	22.3	16.2	36.8	36.1	33.5	48	37.9
49	55.2	23.6	26.0	25.0	23.2	22.8	16.8	37.5	36.8	34.3		
50	56.3	24.1	26.5	25.5	23.8	23.3	17.3	38.3	37.6	35.0	50	39.6
51	57.4	24.6	27.1	26.0	24.3	23.8	17.8	39.1	38.3	35.7		
52	58.5	25.1	27.6	26.5	24.8	24.3	18.3	39.8	39.1	36.4	52	41.3
53	59.7	25.6	28.2	27.0	25.3	24.9	18.8	40.6	39.8	37.1		
54	60.8	26.1	28.7	27.6	25.8	25.4	19.3	41.4	40.6	37.8	54	42.9
55	61.9	26.5	29.2	28.1	26.3	25.9	19.9	42.1	41.3	38.5		
56	63.0	27.0	29.8	28.6	26.9	26.4	20.4	42.9	42.1	39.3	56	44.6
57	64.2	27.5	30.3	29.1	27.4	26.9	20.9	43.7	42.8	40.0		
58	65.3	28.0	30.9	29.6	27.9	27.5	21.4	44.4	43.6	40.7	58	46.3
59	66.4	28.5	31.4	30.1	28.4	28.0	21.9	45.2	44.3	41.4		

[a] *J. Res. Natl. Bur. Std.* **24**, 589–596(1940); **41**, 217–220(1948).
[b] **43.012,** *Official Methods of Analysis,* 10th Ed. (Cu₂O = Cu × 1.1259).
[c] Applicable to all sugars except maltose.
[d] Applicable only to maltose.

(Continued)

47.019 Hammond table for calculating glucose, fructose, and invert sugar and lactose alone and in the presence of sucrose[a], with values for maltose from the Munson and Walker table[b]; values expressed as mg —*Continued.*

Cu[c]	Cu₂O[c]	Glu-cose	Fruc-tose	Invert Sugar	0.3 g Total Sugar	0.4 g Total Sugar	2.0 g Total Sugar	Lactose .H₂O	1 Lactose 4 Su-crose	1 Lactose 12 Su-crose	Cu₂O[d]	Maltose .H₂O
					Invert Sugar and Sucrose				Lactose.H₂O and Sucrose			
60	67.6	29.0	31.9	30.6	28.9	28.5	22.5	46.0	45.1	42.1	60	48.0
61	68.7	29.5	32.5	31.2	29.5	29.0	23.0	46.7	45.8	42.8		
62	69.8	30.0	33.0	31.7	30.0	29.5	23.5	47.5	46.5	43.6	62	49.6
63	70.9	30.5	33.6	32.2	30.5	30.1	24.0	48.3	47.3	44.3		
64	72.1	31.0	34.1	32.7	31.0	30.6	24.5	49.0	48.0	45.0	64	51.3
65	73.2	31.5	34.7	33.2	31.6	31.1	25.1	49.8	48.8	45.7		
66	74.3	32.0	35.2	33.7	32.1	31.6	25.6	50.6	49.5	46.4	66	53.0
67	75.4	32.5	35.8	34.3	32.6	32.1	26.1	51.3	50.3	47.1		
68	76.6	33.0	36.3	34.8	33.1	32.7	26.6	52.1	51.0	47.9	68	54.6
69	77.7	33.5	36.8	35.3	33.6	33.2	27.1	52.9	51.8	48.6		
70	78.8	34.0	37.4	35.8	34.2	33.7	27.7	53.6	52.5	49.3	70	56.3
71	79.9	34.5	37.9	36.3	34.7	34.2	28.2	54.4	53.3	50.0		
72	81.1	35.0	38.5	36.8	35.2	34.7	28.7	55.2	54.0	50.7	72	58.0
73	82.2	35.5	39.0	37.4	35.7	35.3	29.2	55.9	54.8	51.4		
74	83.3	36.0	39.6	37.9	36.3	35.8	29.8	56.7	55.5	52.2	74	59.6
75	84.4	36.5	40.1	38.4	36.8	36.3	30.3	57.5	56.3	52.9		
76	85.6	37.0	40.7	38.9	37.3	36.8	30.8	58.2	57.0	53.6	76	61.3
77	86.7	37.5	41.2	39.4	37.8	37.4	31.3	59.0	57.8	54.3		
78	87.8	38.0	41.7	40.0	38.4	37.9	31.9	59.8	58.5	55.0	78	63.0
79	88.9	38.5	42.3	40.5	38.9	38.4	32.4	60.5	59.3	55.7		
80	90.1	39.0	42.8	41.0	39.4	38.9	32.9	61.3	60.0	56.5	80	64.6
81	91.2	39.5	43.4	41.5	39.9	39.5	33.4	62.1	60.8	57.2		
82	92.3	40.0	43.9	42.0	40.5	40.0	34.0	62.8	61.6	57.9	82	66.3
83	93.4	40.5	44.5	42.6	41.0	40.5	34.5	63.6	62.3	58.6		
84	94.6	41.0	45.0	43.1	41.5	41.0	35.0	64.4	63.1	59.3	84	68.0
85	95.7	41.5	45.6	43.6	42.0	41.6	35.5	65.1	63.8	60.1		
86	96.8	42.0	46.1	44.1	42.6	42.1	36.1	65.9	64.6	60.8	86	69.7
87	97.9	42.5	46.7	44.7	43.1	42.6	36.6	66.7	65.3	61.5		
88	99.1	43.0	47.2	45.2	43.6	43.1	37.1	67.4	66.1	62.2	88	71.3
89	100.2	43.5	47.8	45.7	44.1	43.7	37.6	68.2	66.8	62.9		
90	101.3	44.0	48.3	46.2	44.7	44.2	38.2	69.0	67.6	63.7	90	73.0
91	102.5	44.5	48.9	46.7	45.2	44.7	38.7	69.7	68.3	64.4		
92	103.6	45.0	49.4	47.3	45.7	45.2	39.2	70.5	69.1	65.1	92	74.7
93	104.7	45.5	50.0	47.8	46.3	45.8	39.8	71.3	69.8	65.8		
94	105.8	46.0	50.5	48.3	46.8	46.3	40.3	72.1	70.6	66.5	94	76.3
95	107.0	46.5	51.1	48.8	47.3	46.8	40.8	72.8	71.3	67.3		
96	108.1	47.0	51.6	49.4	47.8	47.4	41.3	73.6	72.1	68.0	96	78.0
97	109.2	47.5	52.2	49.9	48.4	47.9	41.9	74.4	72.8	68.7		
98	110.3	48.0	52.7	50.4	48.9	48.4	42.4	75.1	73.6	69.4	98	79.7
99	111.5	48.5	53.3	50.9	49.4	48.9	42.9	75.9	74.3	70.2		
100	112.6	49.0	53.8	51.5	50.0	49.5	43.5	76.7	75.1	70.9	100	81.3
101	113.7	49.5	54.4	52.0	50.5	50.0	44.0	77.4	75.8	71.6		
102	114.8	50.0	54.9	52.5	51.0	50.5	44.5	78.2	76.6	72.3	102	83.0
103	116.0	50.6	55.5	53.0	51.6	51.1	45.1	79.0	77.3	73.1		
104	117.1	51.1	56.0	53.6	52.1	51.6	45.6	79.7	78.1	73.8	104	84.7
105	118.2	51.6	56.6	54.1	52.6	52.1	46.1	80.5	78.8	74.5		
106	119.3	52.1	57.1	54.6	53.1	52.7	46.7	81.3	79.6	75.2	106	86.3
107	120.5	52.6	57.7	55.2	53.7	53.2	47.2	82.1	80.4	76.0		
108	121.6	53.1	58.2	55.7	54.2	53.7	47.7	82.8	81.1	76.7	108	88.0
109	122.7	53.6	58.8	56.2	54.7	54.2	48.3	83.6	81.9	77.4		

(Continued)

47.019 Hammond table for calculating glucose, fructose, and invert sugar and lactose alone and in the presence of sucrose[a], with values for maltose from the Munson and Walker table[b]; values expressed as mg —Continued.

Cu[c]	Cu$_2$O[c]	Glucose	Fructose	Invert Sugar	Invert Sugar and Sucrose 0.3 g Total Sugar	0.4 g Total Sugar	2.0 g Total Sugar	Lactose .H$_2$O	Lactose.H$_2$O and Sucrose 1 Lactose 4 Sucrose	1 Lactose 12 Sucrose	Cu$_2$O[d]	Maltose .H$_2$O
110	123.8	54.1	59.3	56.7	55.3	54.8	48.8	84.4	82.6	78.1	110	89.7
111	125.0	54.6	59.9	57.3	55.8	55.3	49.3	85.1	83.4	78.9		
112	126.1	55.1	60.4	57.8	56.3	55.8	49.9	85.9	84.1	79.6	112	91.3
113	127.2	55.6	61.0	58.3	56.9	56.4	50.4	86.7	84.9	80.3		
114	128.3	56.1	61.6	58.9	57.4	56.9	50.9	87.4	85.6	81.0	114	93.0
115	129.5	56.7	62.1	59.4	57.9	57.4	51.5	88.2	86.4	81.8		
116	130.6	57.2	62.7	59.9	58.5	58.0	52.0	89.0	87.1	82.5	116	94.7
117	131.7	57.7	63.2	60.4	59.0	58.5	52.5	89.8	87.9	83.2		
118	132.8	58.2	63.8	61.0	59.5	59.0	53.1	90.5	88.6	84.0	118	96.4
119	134.0	58.7	64.3	61.5	60.1	59.6	53.6	91.3	89.4	84.7		
120	135.1	59.2	64.9	62.0	60.6	60.1	54.1	92.1	90.2	85.4	120	98.0
121	136.2	59.7	65.4	62.6	61.2	60.7	54.7	92.8	90.9	86.1		
122	137.4	60.2	66.0	63.1	61.7	61.2	55.2	93.6	91.7	86.9	122	99.7
123	138.5	60.7	66.5	63.6	62.2	61.7	55.8	94.4	92.4	87.6		
124	139.6	61.3	67.1	64.2	62.8	62.3	56.3	95.2	93.2	88.3	124	101.4
125	140.7	61.8	67.7	64.7	63.3	62.8	56.8	95.9	93.9	89.0		
126	141.9	62.3	68.2	65.2	63.8	63.3	57.4	96.7	94.7	89.8	126	103.0
127	143.0	62.8	68.8	65.8	64.4	63.9	57.9	97.5	95.5	90.5		
128	144.1	63.3	69.3	66.3	64.9	64.4	58.4	98.2	96.2	91.2	128	104.7
129	145.2	63.8	69.9	66.8	65.4	64.9	59.0	99.0	97.0	92.0		
130	146.4	64.3	70.4	67.4	66.0	65.5	59.5	99.8	97.7	92.7	130	106.4
131	147.5	64.9	71.0	67.9	66.5	66.0	60.1	100.6	98.5	93.4		
132	148.6	65.4	71.6	68.4	67.1	66.6	60.6	101.3	99.2	94.1	132	108.0
133	149.7	65.9	72.1	69.0	67.6	67.1	61.1	102.1	100.0	94.9		
134	150.9	66.4	72.7	69.5	68.1	67.6	61.7	102.9	100.7	95.6	134	109.7
135	152.0	66.9	73.2	70.0	68.7	68.2	62.2	103.6	101.5	96.3		
136	153.1	67.4	73.8	70.6	69.2	68.7	62.8	104.4	102.3	97.1	136	111.4
137	154.2	68.0	74.3	71.1	69.8	69.3	63.3	105.2	103.0	97.8		
138	155.4	68.5	74.9	71.6	70.3	69.8	63.9	106.0	103.8	98.5	138	113.0
139	156.5	69.0	75.5	72.2	70.8	70.3	64.4	106.7	104.5	99.3		
140	157.6	69.5	76.0	72.7	71.4	70.9	64.9	107.5	105.3	100.0	140	114.7
141	158.7	70.0	76.6	73.2	71.9	71.4	65.5	108.3	106.0	100.7		
142	159.9	70.5	77.1	73.8	72.5	72.0	66.0	109.0	106.8	101.4	142	116.4
143	161.0	71.1	77.7	74.3	73.0	72.5	66.6	109.8	107.5	102.2		
144	162.1	71.6	78.3	74.9	73.5	73.0	67.1	110.6	108.3	102.9	144	118.0
145	163.2	72.1	78.8	75.4	74.1	73.6	67.7	111.4	109.1	103.6		
146	164.4	72.6	79.4	75.9	74.6	74.1	68.2	112.1	109.8	104.4	146	119.7
147	165.5	73.1	80.0	76.5	75.2	74.7	68.7	112.9	110.6	105.1		
148	166.6	73.7	80.5	77.0	75.7	75.2	69.3	113.7	111.3	105.8	148	121.4
149	167.8	74.2	81.1	77.6	76.3	75.7	69.8	114.4	112.1	106.6		
150	168.9	74.7	81.6	78.1	76.8	76.3	70.4	115.2	112.8	107.3	150	123.0
151	170.0	75.2	82.2	78.6	77.3	76.8	70.9	116.0	113.6	108.0		
152	171.1	75.7	82.8	79.2	77.9	77.4	71.5	116.8	114.4	108.8	152	124.7
153	172.3	76.3	83.3	79.7	78.4	77.9	72.0	117.5	115.1	109.5		
154	173.4	76.8	83.9	80.3	79.0	78.5	72.6	118.3	115.9	110.2	154	126.4
155	174.5	77.3	84.4	80.8	79.5	79.0	73.1	119.1	116.6	111.0		
156	175.6	77.8	85.0	81.3	80.1	79.6	73.7	119.9	117.4	111.7	156	128.0
157	176.8	78.3	85.6	81.9	80.6	80.1	74.2	120.6	118.2	112.4		
158	177.9	78.9	86.1	82.4	81.2	80.6	74.8	121.4	118.9	113.2	158	129.7
159	179.0	79.4	86.7	83.0	81.7	81.2	75.3	122.2	119.7	113.9		

(Continued)

47.019 Hammond table for calculating glucose, fructose, and invert sugar and lactose alone and in the presence of sucrose[a], with values for maltose from the Munson and Walker table[b]; values expressed as mg —*Continued*.

Cu[c]	Cu₂O[c]	Glu- cose	Fruc- tose	Invert Sugar	Invert Sugar and Sucrose 0.3 g Total Sugar	0.4 g Total Sugar	2.0 g Total Sugar	Lactose .H₂O	Lactose.H₂O and Sucrose 1 Lactose 4 Su- crose	1 Lactose 12 Su- crose	Cu₂O[d]	Maltose .H₂O
160	180.1	79.9	87.3	83.5	82.2	81.7	75.9	122.9	120.4	114.6	160	131.4
161	181.3	80.4	87.8	84.0	82.8	82.3	76.4	123.7	121.2	115.4		
162	182.4	81.0	88.4	84.6	83.3	82.8	77.0	124.5	121.9	116.1	162	133.0
163	183.5	81.5	89.0	85.1	83.9	83.4	77.5	125.3	122.7	116.8		
164	184.6	82.0	89.5	85.7	84.4	83.9	78.1	126.0	123.5	117.6	164	134.7
165	185.8	82.5	90.1	86.2	85.0	84.5	78.6	126.8	124.2	118.3		
166	186.9	83.1	90.6	86.8	85.5	85.0	79.2	127.6	125.0	119.1	166	136.4
167	188.0	83.6	91.2	87.3	86.1	85.6	79.7	128.4	125.7	119.8		
168	189.1	84.1	91.8	87.8	86.6	86.1	80.3	129.1	126.5	120.5	168	138.0
169	190.3	84.6	92.3	88.4	87.2	86.7	80.8	129.9	127.3	121.3		
170	191.4	85.2	92.9	88.9	87.7	87.2	81.4	130.7	128.0	122.0	170	139.7
171	192.5	85.7	93.5	89.5	88.3	87.8	81.9	131.5	128.8	122.7		
172	193.6	86.2	94.0	90.0	88.8	88.3	82.5	132.2	129.5	123.5	172	141.4
173	194.8	86.7	94.6	90.6	89.4	88.9	83.0	133.0	130.3	124.2		
174	195.9	87.3	95.2	91.1	89.9	89.4	83.6	133.8	131.1	124.9	174	143.0
175	197.0	87.8	95.7	91.7	90.5	90.0	84.1	134.6	131.8	125.7		
176	198.1	88.3	96.3	92.2	91.0	90.5	84.7	135.3	132.6	126.4	176	144.7
177	199.3	88.9	96.9	92.8	91.6	91.1	85.2	136.1	133.4	127.2		
178	200.4	89.4	97.4	93.3	92.1	91.6	85.8	136.9	134.1	127.9	178	146.4
179	201.5	89.9	98.0	93.8	92.7	92.2	86.3	137.7	134.9	128.6		
180	202.7	90.4	98.6	94.4	93.2	92.7	86.9	138.4	135.6	129.4	180	148.0
181	203.8	91.0	99.2	94.9	93.8	93.3	87.4	139.2	136.4	130.1		
182	204.9	91.5	99.7	95.5	94.3	93.8	88.0	140.0	137.2	130.8	182	149.7
183	206.0	92.0	100.3	96.0	94.9	94.4	88.6	140.8	137.9	131.6		
184	207.2	92.6	100.9	96.6	95.4	94.9	89.1	141.5	138.7	132.3	184	151.4
185	208.3	93.1	101.4	97.1	96.0	95.5	89.7	142.3	139.4	133.1		
186	209.4	93.6	102.0	97.7	96.5	96.0	90.2	143.1	140.2	133.8	186	153.0
187	210.5	94.2	102.6	98.2	97.1	96.6	90.8	143.9	141.0	134.5		
188	211.7	94.7	103.1	98.8	97.6	97.1	91.3	144.6	141.7	135.3	188	154.7
189	212.8	95.2	103.7	99.3	98.2	97.7	91.9	145.4	142.5	136.0		
190	213.9	95.7	104.3	99.9	98.7	98.2	92.4	146.2	143.3	136.8	190	156.4
191	215.0	96.3	104.8	100.4	99.3	98.8	93.0	147.0	144.0	137.5		
192	216.2	96.8	105.4	101.0	99.9	99.4	93.6	147.7	144.8	138.2	192	158.0
193	217.3	97.3	106.0	101.5	100.4	99.9	94.1	148.5	145.5	139.0		
194	218.4	97.9	106.6	102.1	101.0	100.5	94.7	149.3	146.3	139.7	194	159.7
195	219.5	98.4	107.1	102.6	101.5	101.0	95.2	150.1	147.1	140.5		
196	220.7	98.9	107.7	103.2	102.1	101.6	95.8	150.8	147.8	141.2	196	161.4
197	221.8	99.5	108.3	103.7	102.6	102.1	96.4	151.6	148.6	142.0		
198	222.9	100.0	108.8	104.3	103.2	102.7	96.9	152.4	149.3	142.7	198	163.0
199	224.0	100.5	109.4	104.8	103.7	103.2	97.5	153.2	150.1	143.4		
200	225.2	101.1	110.0	105.4	104.3	103.8	98.0	153.9	150.9	144.2	200	164.7
201	226.3	101.6	110.6	106.0	104.9	104.4	98.6	154.7	151.6	144.9		
202	227.4	102.2	111.1	106.5	105.4	104.9	99.2	155.5	152.4	145.7	202	166.4
203	228.5	102.7	111.7	107.1	106.0	105.5	99.7	156.3	153.2	146.4		
204	229.7	103.2	112.3	107.6	106.5	106.0	100.3	157.0	153.9	147.1	204	168.0
205	230.8	103.8	112.9	108.2	107.1	106.6	100.9	157.8	154.7	147.9		
206	231.9	104.3	113.4	108.7	107.6	107.2	101.4	158.6	155.5	148.6	206	169.7
207	233.1	104.8	114.0	109.3	108.2	107.7	102.0	159.4	156.2	149.4		
208	234.2	105.4	114.6	109.8	108.8	108.3	102.5	160.2	157.0	150.1	208	171.4
209	235.3	105.9	115.2	110.4	109.3	108.8	103.1	160.9	157.7	150.9		

(Continued)

47. REFERENCE TABLES

47.019 Hammond table for calculating glucose, fructose, and invert sugar and lactose alone and in the presence of sucrose[a], with values for maltose from the Munson and Walker table[b]; values expressed as mg —*Continued.*

Cu[c]	Cu$_2$O[c]	Glu-cose	Fruc-tose	Invert Sugar	Invert Sugar and Sucrose			Lactose .H$_2$O	Lactose.H$_2$O and Sucrose		Cu$_2$O[d]	Maltose .H$_2$O
					0.3 g Total Sugar	0.4 g Total Sugar	2.0 g Total Sugar		1 Lactose 4 Su-crose	1 Lactose 12 Su-crose		
210	236.4	106.5	115.7	110.9	109.9	109.4	103.7	161.7	158.5	151.6	210	173.0
211	237.6	107.0	116.3	111.5	110.4	110.0	104.2	162.5	159.3	152.4		
212	238.7	107.5	116.9	112.1	111.0	110.5	104.8	163.3	160.0	153.1	212	174.7
213	239.8	108.1	117.5	112.6	111.6	111.1	105.4	164.0	160.8	153.8		
214	240.9	108.6	118.0	113.2	112.1	111.6	105.9	164.8	161.6	154.6	214	176.4
215	242.1	109.2	118.6	113.7	112.7	112.2	106.5	165.6	162.3	155.3		
216	243.1	109.7	119.2	114.3	113.2	112.8	107.1	166.4	163.1	156.1	216	178.0
217	244.3	110.2	119.8	114.9	113.8	113.3	107.7	167.1	163.9	156.8		
218	245.4	110.8	120.3	115.4	114.4	113.9	108.2	167.9	164.6	157.6	218	179.7
219	246.6	111.3	120.9	116.0	114.9	114.4	108.8	168.7	165.4	158.3		
220	247.7	111.9	121.5	116.5	115.5	115.0	109.3	169.5	166.2	159.1	220	181.4
221	248.8	112.4	122.1	117.1	116.1	115.6	109.9	170.3	166.9	159.8		
222	249.9	112.9	122.6	117.6	116.6	116.1	110.5	171.0	167.7	160.6	222	183.0
223	251.1	113.5	123.2	118.2	117.2	116.7	111.0	171.8	168.5	161.3		
224	252.2	114.0	123.8	118.8	117.7	117.3	111.6	172.6	169.2	162.1	224	184.7
225	253.3	114.6	124.4	119.3	118.3	117.8	112.2	173.4	170.0	162.8		
226	254.4	115.1	125.0	119.9	118.9	118.4	112.7	174.2	170.8	163.6	226	186.4
227	255.6	115.7	125.5	120.4	119.4	119.0	113.3	174.9	171.5	164.3		
228	256.7	116.2	126.1	121.0	120.0	119.5	113.9	175.7	172.3	165.1	228	188.0
229	257.8	116.7	126.7	121.6	120.6	120.1	114.4	176.5	173.1	165.8		
230	258.9	117.3	127.3	122.1	121.1	120.7	115.0	177.3	173.8	166.5	230	189.7
231	260.1	117.8	127.9	122.7	121.7	121.2	115.6	178.1	174.6	167.3		
232	261.2	118.4	128.4	123.3	122.3	121.8	116.2	178.8	175.3	168.0	232	191.3
233	262.3	118.9	129.0	123.8	122.8	122.4	116.7	179.6	176.1	168.8		
234	263.4	119.5	129.6	124.4	123.4	122.9	117.3	180.4	176.9	169.5	234	193.0
235	264.6	120.0	130.2	124.9	124.0	123.5	117.9	181.2	177.6	170.3		
236	265.7	120.6	130.8	125.5	124.5	124.1	118.4	181.9	178.4	171.0	236	194.7
237	266.8	121.1	131.3	126.1	125.1	124.6	119.0	182.7	179.2	171.8		
238	268.0	121.7	131.9	126.6	125.7	125.2	119.6	183.5	180.0	172.5	238	196.3
239	269.1	122.2	132.5	127.2	126.2	125.8	120.2	184.3	180.7	173.3		
240	270.2	122.7	133.1	127.8	126.8	126.3	120.7	185.1	181.5	174.0	240	198.0
241	271.3	123.3	133.7	128.3	127.4	126.9	121.3	185.8	182.3	174.8		
242	272.5	123.8	134.2	128.9	127.9	127.5	121.9	186.6	183.0	175.5	242	199.7
243	273.6	124.4	134.8	129.5	128.5	128.0	122.5	187.4	183.8	176.3		
244	274.7	124.9	135.4	130.0	129.1	128.6	123.0	188.2	184.6	177.0	244	201.3
245	275.8	125.5	136.0	130.6	129.6	129.2	123.6	189.0	185.3	177.8		
246	277.0	126.0	136.6	131.2	130.2	129.8	124.2	189.7	186.1	178.5	246	203.0
247	278.1	126.6	137.2	131.7	130.8	130.3	124.8	190.5	186.9	179.3		
248	279.2	127.1	137.7	132.3	131.3	130.9	125.3	191.3	187.6	180.1	248	204.7
249	280.3	127.7	138.3	132.9	131.9	131.5	125.9	192.1	188.4	180.8		
250	281.5	128.2	138.9	133.4	132.5	132.0	126.5	192.9	189.2	181.6	250	206.3
251	282.6	128.8	139.5	134.0	133.1	132.6	127.1	193.6	189.9	182.3		
252	283.7	129.3	140.1	134.6	133.6	133.2	127.6	194.4	190.7	183.1	252	208.0
253	284.8	129.9	140.7	135.1	134.2	133.8	128.2	195.2	191.5	183.8		
254	286.0	130.4	141.3	135.7	134.8	134.3	128.8	196.0	192.2	184.6	254	209.7
255	287.1	131.0	141.8	136.3	135.3	134.9	129.4	196.8	193.0	185.3		
256	288.2	131.6	142.4	136.8	135.9	135.5	130.0	197.5	193.8	186.1	256	211.3
257	289.3	132.1	143.0	137.4	136.5	136.0	130.5	198.3	194.6	186.8		
258	290.5	132.7	143.6	138.0	137.1	136.6	131.1	199.1	195.3	187.6	258	213.0
259	291.6	133.2	144.2	138.6	137.6	137.2	131.7	199.9	196.1	188.3		

(Continued)

47.019   Hammond table for calculating glucose, fructose, and invert sugar and lactose alone and in the presence of sucrose[a], with values for maltose from the Munson and Walker table[b]; values expressed as mg
—*Continued*.

Cu[c]	Cu$_2$O[c]	Glu-cose	Fruc-tose	Invert Sugar	Invert Sugar and Sucrose 0.3 g Total Sugar	0.4 g Total Sugar	2.0 g Total Sugar	Lactose .H$_2$O	Lactose.H$_2$O and Sucrose 1 Lactose 4 Su-crose	1 Lactose 12 Su-crose	Cu$_2$O[d]	Maltose .H$_2$O
260	292.7	133.8	144.8	139.1	138.2	137.8	132.3	200.7	196.9	189.1	260	214.7
261	293.8	134.3	145.4	139.7	138.8	138.3	132.9	201.4	197.6	189.8		
262	295.0	134.9	145.9	140.3	139.4	138.9	133.4	202.2	198.4	190.6	262	216.3
263	296.1	135.4	146.5	140.8	139.9	139.5	134.0	203.0	199.2	191.4		
264	297.2	136.0	147.1	141.4	140.5	140.1	134.6	203.8	199.9	192.1	264	218.0
265	298.3	136.5	147.7	142.0	141.1	140.7	135.2	204.6	200.7	192.9		
266	299.5	137.1	148.3	142.6	141.7	141.2	135.8	205.3	201.5	193.6	266	219.7
267	300.6	137.7	148.9	143.1	142.2	141.8	136.3	206.1	202.2	194.4		
268	301.7	138.2	149.5	143.7	142.8	142.4	136.9	206.9	203.0	195.1	268	221.3
269	302.9	138.8	150.1	144.3	143.4	143.0	137.5	207.7	203.8	195.9		
270	304.0	139.3	150.6	144.8	144.0	143.5	138.1	208.5	204.6	196.7	270	223.0
271	305.1	139.9	151.2	145.4	144.5	144.1	138.7	209.2	205.3	197.4		
272	306.2	140.4	151.8	146.0	145.1	144.7	139.3	210.0	206.1	198.2	272	224.6
273	307.4	141.0	152.4	146.6	145.7	145.3	139.8	210.8	206.9	198.9		
274	308.5	141.6	153.0	147.1	146.3	145.9	140.4	211.6	207.6	199.7	274	226.3
275	309.6	142.1	153.6	147.7	146.8	146.4	141.0	212.4	208.4	200.4		
276	310.7	142.7	154.2	148.3	147.4	147.0	141.6	213.2	209.2	201.2	276	228.0
277	311.9	143.2	154.8	148.9	148.0	147.6	142.2	214.0	210.0	202.0		
278	313.0	143.8	155.4	149.4	148.6	148.2	142.8	214.7	210.7	202.7	278	229.6
279	314.1	144.4	156.0	150.0	149.2	148.8	143.4	215.5	211.5	203.5		
280	315.2	144.9	156.5	150.6	149.7	149.3	143.9	216.3	212.3	204.2	280	231.3
281	316.4	145.5	157.1	151.2	150.3	149.9	144.5	217.1	213.0	205.0		
282	317.5	146.0	157.7	151.8	150.9	150.5	145.1	217.9	213.8	205.7	282	233.0
283	318.6	146.6	158.3	152.3	151.5	151.1	145.7	218.7	214.6	206.5		
284	319.7	147.2	158.9	152.9	152.1	151.7	146.3	219.4	215.4	207.3	284	234.6
285	320.9	147.7	159.5	153.5	152.6	152.2	146.9	220.2	216.1	208.0		
286	322.0	148.3	160.1	154.1	153.2	152.8	147.5	221.0	216.9	208.8	286	236.3
287	323.1	148.8	160.7	154.6	153.8	153.4	148.1	221.8	217.7	209.5		
288	324.2	149.4	161.3	155.2	154.4	154.0	148.6	222.6	218.4	210.3	288	238.0
289	325.4	150.0	161.9	155.8	155.0	154.6	149.2	223.3	219.2	211.1		
290	326.5	150.5	162.5	156.4	155.5	155.2	149.8	224.1	220.0	211.8	290	239.6
291	327.6	151.1	163.1	157.0	156.1	155.7	150.4	224.9	220.8	212.6		
292	328.7	151.7	163.7	157.5	156.7	156.3	151.0	225.7	221.5	213.4	292	241.3
293	329.9	152.2	164.3	158.1	157.3	156.9	151.6	226.5	222.3	214.1		
294	331.0	152.8	164.9	158.7	157.9	157.5	152.2	227.3	223.1	214.9	294	242.9
295	332.1	153.4	165.4	159.3	158.5	158.1	152.8	228.0	223.9	215.6		
296	333.3	153.9	166.0	159.9	159.0	158.7	153.4	228.8	224.6	216.4	296	244.6
297	334.4	154.5	166.6	160.5	159.6	159.3	154.0	229.6	225.4	217.2		
298	335.5	155.1	167.2	161.0	160.2	159.9	154.6	230.4	226.2	217.9	298	246.3
299	336.6	155.6	167.8	161.6	160.8	160.4	155.2	231.2	227.0	218.7		
300	337.8	156.2	168.4	162.2	161.4	161.0	155.7	232.0	227.7	219.5	300	247.9
301	338.9	156.8	169.0	162.8	162.0	161.6	156.3	232.7	228.5	220.2		
302	340.0	157.3	169.6	163.4	162.5	162.2	156.9	233.5	229.3	221.0	302	249.6
303	341.1	157.9	170.2	164.0	163.1	162.8	157.5	234.3	230.1	221.7		
304	342.3	158.5	170.8	164.5	163.7	163.4	158.1	235.1	230.8	222.5	304	251.3
305	343.4	159.0	171.4	165.1	164.3	164.0	158.7	235.9	231.6	223.3		
306	344.5	159.6	172.0	165.7	164.9	164.6	159.3	236.7	232.4	224.0	306	252.9
307	345.6	160.2	172.6	166.3	165.5	165.1	159.9	237.4	233.1	224.8		
308	346.8	160.7	173.2	166.9	166.1	165.7	160.5	238.2	233.9	225.6	308	254.6
309	347.9	161.3	173.8	167.5	166.7	166.3	161.1	239.0	234.7	226.3		

(Continued)

47.019   **Hammond table for calculating glucose, fructose, and invert sugar and lactose alone and in the presence of sucrose[a], with values for maltose from the Munson and Walker table[b]; values expressed as mg** —*Continued.*

Cu[c]	Cu$_2$O[c]	Glu-cose	Fruc-tose	Invert Sugar	Invert Sugar and Sucrose			Lactose .H$_2$O	Lactose.H$_2$O and Sucrose		Cu$_2$O[d]	Maltose .H$_2$O
					0.3 g Total Sugar	0.4 g Total Sugar	2.0 g Total Sugar		1 Lactose 4 Su-crose	1 Lactose 12 Su-crose		
310	349.0	161.9	174.4	168.0	167.2	166.9	161.7	239.8	235.5	227.1	310	256.3
311	350.1	162.5	175.0	168.6	167.8	167.5	162.3	240.6	236.3	227.9		
312	351.3	163.0	175.6	169.2	168.4	168.1	162.9	241.4	237.0	228.6	312	257.9
313	352.4	163.6	176.2	169.8	169.0	168.7	163.5	242.2	237.8	229.4		
314	353.5	164.2	176.8	170.4	169.6	169.3	164.1	243.0	238.6	230.2	314	259.6
315	354.6	164.7	177.4	171.0	170.2	169.9	164.7	243.7	239.4	230.9		
316	355.8	165.3	178.0	171.6	170.8	170.5	165.3	244.5	240.1	231.7	316	261.2
317	356.9	165.9	178.6	172.2	171.4	171.1	165.9	245.3	240.9	232.5		
318	358.0	166.5	179.2	172.8	172.0	171.7	166.5	246.1	241.7	233.2	318	262.9
319	359.1	167.0	179.8	173.3	172.6	172.2	167.1	246.9	242.5	234.0		
320	360.3	167.6	180.4	173.9	173.1	172.8	167.7	247.7	243.2	234.8	320	264.6
321	361.4	168.2	181.0	174.5	173.7	173.4	168.3	248.5	244.0	235.5		
322	362.5	168.8	181.6	175.1	174.3	174.0	168.9	249.2	244.8	236.3	322	266.2
323	363.6	169.3	182.2	175.7	174.9	174.6	169.5	250.0	245.6	237.1		
324	364.8	169.9	182.8	176.3	175.5	175.2	170.1	250.8	246.3	237.8	324	267.9
325	365.9	170.5	183.4	176.9	176.1	175.8	170.7	251.6	247.1	238.6		
326	367.0	171.1	184.0	177.5	176.7	176.4	171.3	252.4	247.9	239.4	326	269.6
327	368.2	171.6	184.6	178.1	177.3	177.0	171.9	253.2	248.7	240.1		
328	369.3	172.2	185.2	178.7	177.9	177.6	172.5	253.9	249.5	240.9	328	271.2
329	370.4	172.8	185.8	179.2	178.5	178.2	173.1	254.7	250.2	241.7		
330	371.5	173.4	186.4	179.8	179.1	178.8	173.7	255.5	251.0	242.4	330	272.9
331	372.7	173.9	187.0	180.4	179.7	179.4	174.3	256.3	251.8	243.2		
332	373.8	174.5	187.6	181.0	180.3	180.0	174.9	257.1	252.6	244.0	332	274.6
333	374.9	175.1	188.2	181.6	180.9	180.6	175.5	257.9	253.3	244.8		
334	376.0	175.7	188.8	182.2	181.5	181.2	176.1	258.7	254.1	245.5	334	276.2
335	377.2	176.3	189.4	182.8	182.1	181.8	176.7	259.4	254.9	246.3		
336	378.3	176.8	190.1	183.4	182.6	182.4	177.3	260.2	255.7	247.1	336	277.9
337	379.4	177.4	190.7	184.0	183.2	183.0	178.0	261.0	256.5	247.8		
338	380.5	178.0	191.3	184.6	183.8	183.6	178.6	261.8	257.2	248.6	338	279.5
339	381.7	178.6	191.9	185.2	184.4	184.2	179.2	262.6	258.0	249.4		
340	382.8	179.2	192.5	185.8	185.0	184.8	179.8	263.4	258.8	250.2	340	281.2
341	383.9	179.7	193.1	186.4	185.6	185.4	180.4	264.2	259.6	250.9		
342	385.0	180.3	193.7	187.0	186.2	186.0	181.0	265.0	260.4	251.7	342	282.9
343	386.2	180.9	194.3	187.6	186.8	186.6	181.6	265.8	261.1	252.5		
344	387.3	181.5	194.9	188.2	187.4	187.2	182.2	266.6	261.9	253.3	344	284.5
345	388.4	182.1	195.5	188.8	188.0	187.8	182.8	267.4	262.7	254.0		
346	389.5	182.7	196.1	189.4	188.6	188.4	183.4	268.1	263.5	254.8	346	286.2
347	390.7	183.2	196.7	190.0	189.2	189.0	184.0	268.9	264.2	255.6		
348	391.8	183.8	197.3	190.6	189.8	189.6	184.6	269.7	265.0	256.4	348	287.9
349	392.9	184.4	197.9	191.2	190.4	190.2	185.3	270.5	265.8	257.1		
350	394.0	185.0	198.5	191.8	191.0	190.8	185.9	271.3	266.6	257.9	350	289.5
351	395.2	185.6	199.2	192.4	191.6	191.4	186.5	272.1	267.4	258.7		
352	396.3	186.2	199.8	193.0	192.2	192.0	187.1	272.9	268.2	259.4	352	291.2
353	397.4	186.8	200.4	193.6	192.8	192.6	187.7	273.7	268.9	260.2		
354	398.5	187.3	201.0	194.2	193.4	193.2	188.3	274.4	269.7	261.0	354	292.8
355	399.7	187.9	201.6	194.8	194.0	193.8	188.9	275.2	270.5	261.8		
356	400.8	188.5	202.2	195.4	194.6	194.4	189.5	276.0	271.3	262.6	356	294.5
357	401.9	189.1	202.8	196.0	195.2	195.0	190.2	276.8	272.1	263.3		
358	403.1	189.7	203.4	196.6	195.8	195.7	190.8	277.6	272.8	264.1	358	296.2
359	404.2	190.3	204.0	197.2	196.4	196.3	191.4	278.4	273.6	264.9		

(Continued)

47.019 **Hammond table for calculating glucose, fructose, and invert sugar and lactose alone and in the presence of sucrose[a], with values for maltose from the Munson and Walker table[b]; values expressed as mg** —*Continued.*

Cu[c]	Cu₂O[c]	Glu-cose	Fruc-tose	Invert Sugar	Invert Sugar and Sucrose			Lactose .H₂O	Lactose.H₂O and Sucrose		Cu₂O[d]	Maltose .H₂O
					0.3 g Total Sugar	0.4 g Total Sugar	2.0 g Total Sugar		1 Lactose 4 Su-crose	1 Lactose 12 Su-crose		
360	405.3	190.9	204.7	197.8	197.1	196.9	192.0	279.2	274.4	265.7	360	297.8
361	406.4	191.5	205.3	198.4	197.7	197.5	192.6	280.0	275.2	266.4		
362	407.6	192.0	205.9	199.0	198.3	198.1	193.2	280.8	276.0	267.2	362	299.5
363	408.7	192.6	206.5	199.6	198.9	198.7	193.9	281.6	276.8	268.0		
364	409.8	193.2	207.1	200.2	199.5	199.3	194.5	282.4	277.5	268.8	364	301.2
365	410.9	193.8	207.7	200.8	200.1	199.9	195.1	283.2	278.3	269.6		
366	412.1	194.4	208.3	201.4	200.7	200.5	195.7	284.0	279.1	270.3	366	302.8
367	413.2	195.0	209.0	202.0	201.3	201.1	196.3	284.8	279.9	271.1		
368	414.3	195.6	209.6	202.6	201.9	201.7	196.9	285.6	280.7	271.9	368	304.5
369	415.4	196.2	210.2	203.2	202.5	202.4	197.6	286.3	281.5	272.7		
370	416.6	196.8	210.8	203.8	203.1	203.0	198.2	287.1	282.2	273.5	370	306.1
371	417.7	197.4	211.4	204.4	203.7	203.6	198.8	287.9	283.0	274.2		
372	418.8	198.0	212.0	205.0	204.3	204.2	199.4	288.7	283.8	275.0	372	307.8
373	419.9	198.5	212.6	205.7	204.9	204.8	200.0	289.5	284.6	275.8		
374	421.1	199.1	213.3	206.3	205.6	205.4	200.7	290.3	285.4	276.6	374	309.5
375	422.2	199.7	213.9	206.9	206.2	206.0	201.3	291.1	286.2	277.4		
376	423.3	200.3	214.5	207.5	206.8	206.6	201.9	291.9	286.9	278.2	376	311.1
377	424.4	200.9	215.1	208.1	207.4	207.3	202.5	292.7	287.7	278.9		
378	425.6	201.5	215.7	208.7	208.0	207.9	203.1	293.5	288.5	279.7	378	312.8
379	426.7	202.1	216.3	209.3	208.6	208.5	203.8	294.3	289.3	280.5		
380	427.8	202.7	217.0	209.9	209.2	209.1	204.4	295.0	290.1	281.3	380	314.5
381	428.9	203.3	217.6	210.5	209.8	209.7	205.0	295.8	290.9	282.1		
382	430.1	203.9	218.2	211.1	210.4	210.3	205.6	296.6	291.7	282.9	382	316.1
383	431.2	204.5	218.8	211.8	211.1	211.0	206.3	297.4	292.4	283.6		
384	432.3	205.1	219.5	212.4	211.7	211.6	206.9	298.2	293.2	284.4	384	317.8
385	433.5	205.7	220.1	213.0	212.3	212.2	207.5	299.0	294.0	285.2		
386	434.6	206.3	220.7	213.6	212.9	212.8	208.1	299.8	294.8	286.0	386	319.4
387	435.7	206.9	221.3	214.2	213.5	213.4	208.8	300.6	295.6	286.8		
388	436.8	207.5	221.9	214.8	214.1	214.0	209.4	301.4	296.4	287.6	388	321.1
389	438.0	208.1	222.6	215.4	214.7	214.7	210.0	302.2	297.2	288.4		
390	439.1	208.7	223.2	216.0	215.4	215.3	210.6	303.0	298.0	289.2	390	322.8
391	440.2	209.3	223.8	216.7	216.0	215.9	211.3	303.8	298.8	290.0		
392	441.3	209.9	224.4	217.3	216.6	216.5	211.9	304.6	299.5	290.7	392	324.4
393	442.5	210.5	225.1	217.9	217.2	217.1	212.5	305.4	300.3	291.5		
394	443.6	211.1	225.7	218.5	217.8	217.8	213.2	306.2	301.1	292.3	394	326.1
395	444.7	211.7	226.3	219.1	218.5	218.4	213.8	307.0	301.9	293.1		
396	445.8	212.3	226.9	219.8	219.1	219.0	214.4	307.8	302.7	293.9	396	327.7
397	447.0	212.9	227.6	220.4	219.7	219.6	215.1	308.6	303.5	294.7		
398	448.1	213.5	228.2	221.0	220.3	220.3	215.7	309.4	304.3	295.5	398	329.4
399	449.2	214.1	228.8	221.6	220.9	220.9	216.3	310.2	305.1	296.3		
400	450.3	214.7	229.4	222.2	221.5	221.5	217.0	311.0	305.9	297.1	400	331.1
401	451.5	215.3	230.1	222.9	222.2	222.1	217.6	311.8	306.7	297.9		
402	452.6	215.9	230.7	223.5	222.8	222.8	218.2	312.6	307.5	298.7	402	332.7
403	453.7	216.5	231.3	224.1	223.4	223.4	218.9	313.4	308.3	299.5		
404	454.8	217.1	232.0	224.7	224.0	224.0	219.5	314.2	309.1	300.3	404	334.4
405	456.0	217.8	232.6	225.4	224.7	224.7	220.1	315.0	309.9	301.1		
406	457.1	218.4	233.2	226.0	225.3	225.3	220.8	315.9	310.7	301.9	406	336.0
407	458.2	219.0	233.9	226.6	225.9	225.9	221.4	316.7	311.5	302.7		
408	459.3	219.6	234.5	227.2	226.6	226.5	222.0	317.5	312.3	303.5	408	337.7
409	460.5	220.2	235.1	227.9	227.2	227.2	222.7	318.3	313.1	304.3		

(Continued)

47.019   Hammond table for calculating glucose, fructose, and invert sugar and lactose alone and in the presence of sucrose[a], with values for maltose from the Munson and Walker table[b]; values expressed as mg
—*Concluded.*

Cu[c]	Cu$_2$O[c]	Glu-cose	Fruc-tose	Invert Sugar	Invert Sugar and Sucrose			Lactose .H$_2$O	Lactose.H$_2$O and Sucrose		Cu$_2$O[d]	Maltose .H$_2$O
					0.3 g Total Sugar	0.4 g Total Sugar	2.0 g Total Sugar		1 Lactose 4 Su-crose	1 Lactose 12 Su-crose		
410	461.6	220.8	235.8	228.5	227.8	227.8	223.3	319.1	313.9	305.1	410	339.4
411	462.7	221.4	236.4	229.1	228.4	228.4	224.0	319.9	314.7	305.9		
412	463.8	222.0	237.1	229.7	229.1	229.1	224.6	320.7	315.5	306.7	412	341.0
413	465.0	222.6	237.7	230.4	229.7	229.7	225.3	321.6	316.3	307.6		
414	466.1	223.3	238.4	231.0	230.4	230.4	225.9	322.4	317.1	308.4	414	342.7
415	467.2	223.9	239.0	231.7	231.0	231.0	226.6	323.2	317.9	309.2		
416	468.4	224.5	239.7	232.3	231.6	231.7	227.2	324.0	318.7	310.0	416	344.4
417	469.5	225.1	240.3	232.9	232.3	232.3	227.8	324.9	319.5	310.8		
418	470.6	225.7	241.0	233.6	232.9	232.9	228.5	325.7	320.3	311.7	418	346.0
419	471.7	226.3	241.6	234.2	233.5	233.6	229.1	326.5	321.2	312.5		
420	472.9	227.0	242.2	234.8	234.2	234.2	229.8	327.4	322.0	313.4	420	347.7
421	474.0	227.6	242.9	235.5	234.8	234.9	230.4	328.2	322.8	314.2		
422	475.1	228.2	243.6	236.1	235.5	235.5	231.1	329.1	323.6	315.0	422	349.3
423	476.2	228.8	244.3	236.8	236.2	236.2	231.8	329.9	324.5	315.9		
424	477.4	229.5	244.9	237.5	236.8	236.9	232.4	330.8	325.3	316.8	424	351.0
425	478.5	230.1	245.6	238.1	237.5	237.5	233.1	331.7	326.2	317.6		
426	479.6	230.7	246.3	238.8	238.2	238.2	233.8	332.6	327.0	318.5	426	352.7
427	480.7	231.4	247.0	239.5	238.8	238.9	234.5	333.5	327.9	319.4		
428	481.9	232.0	247.8	240.2	239.5	239.6	235.1	334.4	328.8	320.4	428	354.3
429	483.0	232.7	248.5	240.8	240.2	240.3	235.8	335.3	329.7	321.3		
430	484.1	233.3	249.2	241.5	240.9	241.0	236.5	336.3	330.6	322.3	430	356.0
431	485.2	234.0	250.0	242.3	241.7	241.7	237.2	337.3	331.5	323.3		
432	486.4	234.7	250.8	243.0	242.4	242.5	238.0	338.3	332.5	324.4	432	357.6
433	487.5	235.3	251.6	243.8	243.2	243.3	238.7	339.4	333.5	325.5		
434	488.6	236.1	252.7	244.7	244.1	244.2	239.6	340.7	334.6	326.7	434	359.3
435	489.7	236.9	253.7	245.6	245.1	245.1	240.4	342.0	335.8	328.1		
											436	361.0
											438	362.6
											440	364.3
											442	365.9
											444	367.6
											446	369.3
											448	370.9
											450	372.6
											452	374.2
											454	375.9
											456	377.6
											458	379.2
											460	380.9
											462	382.5
											464	384.2
											466	385.9
											468	387.5
											470	389.2
											472	390.8
											474	392.5
											476	394.2
											478	395.8
											480	397.5
											482	399.1
											484	400.8
											486	402.4
											488	404.1
											490	405.8

47.020   Density of sucrose solutions at 0–100°C and 0–70%, in mg/ml[a]

% Sugar	Temperature, °C										
	0[b]	10[b]	20[b]	30	40	50	60	70	80	90	100[c]
0	0.99987	0.99973	0.99823	0.99567	0.99224	0.98807	0.98324	0.97781	0.97183	0.96534	0.95838
10	1.04135	1.04016	1.03814	1.03529	1.03156	1.02713	1.02207	1.01648	1.01039	1.00381	0.9968
20	1.08546	1.08353	1.08096	1.07766	1.07366	1.06898	1.06365	1.05790	1.05169	1.04503	1.0379
30	1.13274	1.13014	1.12698	1.12325	1.11888	1.11395	1.10847	1.10257	1.09626	1.08956	1.0825
40	1.18349	1.18020	1.17645	1.17231	1.16758	1.16238	1.15675	1.15073	1.14432	1 13746	1 1301
50	1 23775	1 23382	1 22957	1 22501	1 21996	1 21455	1.20875	1.20260	1.19615	1.18939	1.1823
60	1.29560	1.29117	1.28646	1.28149	1.27616	1.27035	1.26464	1.25844	1.25191	1.24511	1.2378
70	1.35719	1.35230	1.34717	1.34185	1.33635	1.33056	1.32454	1.31834	1.31190	1.30527	

[a] Schneider, Schliephake, and Klimmek, *Zucker Beih.* **4**(2), 72–76(1962).
[b] Values taken from Plato *et al.*, Charlottenberg. Physikalisch-technische reichsanstalt. Wiss. Abhandl. Kaiserliche Norm.-Eichungs-komm., No. 2, and *Z. Ver. Deut. Zuckerind.* **50**, 982 and 1079(1900).
[c] Extrapolated.

47.021   Volume factors for thermal expansion of sucrose solutions up to 100°C[a]; volumes at 20°C = 1.0000

% Sugar	Temperature, °C										
	0	10	20	30	40	50	60	70	80	90	100
0	0.9984	0.9985	1.0000	1.0026	1.0060	1.0102	1.0152	1.0209	1.0274	1.0342	1.0411
10	0.9969	0.9981	1.0000	1.0027	1.0064	1.0107	1.0157	1.0213	1.0274	1.0342	1.0416
20	0.9958	0.9976	1.0000	1.0030	1.0068	1.0112	1.0163	1.0218	1.0278	1.0344	1.0416
30	0.9949	0.9972	1.0000	1.0033	1.0072	1.0117	1.0167	1.0221	1.0280	1.0343	1.0411
40	0.9941	0.9969	1.0000	1.0036	1.0076	1.0121	1.0170	1.0224	1.0280	1.0343	1.0410
50	0.9934	0.9966	1.0000	1.0038	1.0079	1.0123	1.0172	1.0224	1.0279	1.0338	1.0400
60	0.9929	0.9963	1.0000	1.0039	1.0081	1.0125	1.0173	1.0223	1.0276	1.0332	1.0391

[a] Schneider, Schliephake, and Klimmek, *Zucker Beih.* **4**(2), 72–76 (1962).

47.022   ★ Meissl and Hiller factors for determining invert sugar in materials in which, of total sugars ★ present, more than 1.5% is invert sugar and less than 98.5% is sucrose

See **43.015**, 10th ed.

47.023   ★ Wein table for determining maltose ★

See **43.016**, 10th ed.

★ Tables so marked are surplus tables. *See* "Definitions of Terms and Explanatory Notes," item (29).

47.024 ★ **Quisumbing and Thomas table for calculating glucose, fructose, invert sugar, lactose, and ★
maltose; values expressed in mg**

					Lactose		Maltose	
Cu	Cu_2O	d-Glucose	d-Fructose	Invert Sugar	$C_{12}H_{22}O_{11}$	$C_{12}H_{22}O_{11}$ .H_2O	$C_{12}H_{22}O_{11}$	$C_{12}H_{22}O_{11}.H_2O$
10	11.1	4.8	5.3	5.0	7.7	8.1	9.4	9.9
20	22.5	9.5	10.5	10.1	15.5	16.3	18.8	19.8
30	33.8	14.3	15.8	15.2	23.2	24.4	28.2	29.7
40	45.0	19.1	21.2	20.3	30.9	32.5	37.6	39.6
50	56.3	24.0	26.5	25.4	38.7	40.7	47.0	49.5
60	67.6	28.9	31.9	30.6	46.4	48.8	56.4	59.4
70	78.8	33.7	37.2	35.7	54.0	56.9	65.8	69.3
80	90.1	38.7	42.6	40.9	61.7	65.0	75.2	79.2
90	101.3	43.6	48.0	46.1	69.5	73.2	84.6	89.1
100	112.6	48.6	53.4	51.3	77.2	81.3	94.0	99.0
110	123.8	53.5	58.8	56.5	85.0	89.5	103.4	108.9
120	135.1	58.5	64.3	61.8	92.7	97.6	112.8	118.8
130	146.4	63.5	69.7	67.0	100.4	105.7	122.2	128.7
140	157.6	68.6	75.2	72.3	108.2	113.9	131.6	138.6
150	168.9	73.7	80.7	77.6	116.0	122.0	141.0	148.5
160	180.1	78.8	86.2	82.9	123.7	130.1	150.4	158.4
170	191.4	83.9	91.7	88.3	131.4	138.3	159.8	168.3
180	202.6	89.1	97.2	93.7	139.1	146.4	169.2	178.2
190	213.9	94.2	102.8	99.1	146.9	154.6	178.8	188.1
200	225.2	99.4	108.4	104.4	154.6	162.7	188.2	198.0
210	236.4	104.6	114.0	109.8	162.3	170.9	197.6	207.9
220	247.7	109.9	119.6	115.2	170.0	179.0	207.0	217.8
230	258.9	115.1	125.2	120.6	177.8	187.2	216.4	227.7
240	270.2	120.4	130.8	126.1	185.5	195.3	225.8	237.6
250	281.5	125.7	136.4	131.6	193.2	203.4	235.2	247.5
260	292.7	131.0	142.1	137.1	201.0	211.6	244.6	257.4
270	304.0	136.4	147.8	142.6	208.8	219.8	254.0	267.3
280	315.2	141.7	153.5	148.2	216.5	227.9	263.4	277.2
290	326.5	147.1	159.2	153.7	224.2	236.0	272.8	287.1
300	337.8	152.6	165.0	159.3	232.0	244.2	282.2	297.0
310	349.0	158.0	170.7	164.9	239.7	252.3	291.6	306.9
320	360.3	163.5	176.5	170.5	247.5	260.5	301.0	316.8
330	371.5	168.9	182.3	176.1	255.3	268.7	310.4	326.7
340	382.8	174.5	188.1	181.8	263.0	276.8	319.8	336.6
350	394.0	180.0	193.9	187.4	270.7	285.0	329.2	346.5
360	405.3	185.5	199.7	193.1	278.4	293.1	338.6	356.4
370	416.6	191.1	205.5	198.8	286.2	301.3	348.0	366.3
380	427.8	196.7	211.4	204.5	293.9	309.4	357.4	376.2
390	439.1	202.3	217.3	210.2	301.6	317.5	366.8	386.1
400	450.3	208.0	223.2	216.0	309.4	325.7	376.2	396.0
410	461.6	213.7	229.1	221.8	317.1	333.8	385.6	405.9
420	472.9	219.4	235.0	227.6	324.9	342.0	395.0	415.8
430	484.1	225.1	240.9	233.4	332.6	350.1	404.4	425.7
440	495.4	230.8	246.9	239.2	340.4	358.3	413.8	435.6
450	506.6	236.6	252.9	245.0	348.1	366.4	423.2	445.5
460	517.9	242.4	258.9	250.9	355.9	374.6	423.6	455.4
470	529.1	248.1	264.9	256.8	363.6	382.7	442.0	465.3
480	540.4	254.8	270.9	262.7	371.3	390.9	451.4	475.2

★ Tables so marked are surplus tables. *See* "Definitions of Terms and Explanatory Notes," item (29).

47.025 **Table for determining total solids in milk from any given specific gravity and percentage of fat (Shaw and Eckles); results expressed as per cent total solids**

% Fat	Lactometer Reading at 60°F (Quévenne Degrees)										
	26	27	28	29	30	31	32	33	34	35	36
2.00	8.90	9.15	9.40	9.65	9.90	10.15	10.40	10.66	10.91	11.16	11.41
.05	.96	.21	.46	.71	.96	.21	.46	.72	.97	.22	.47
.10	9.02	.27	.52	.77	10.02	.27	.52	.78	11.03	.28	.53
.15	.08	.33	.58	.83	.08	.33	.58	.84	.09	.34	.59
.20	.14	.39	.64	.89	.14	.39	.64	.90	.15	.40	.65
.25	.20	.45	.70	.95	.20	.45	.70	.96	.21	.46	.71
.30	.26	.51	.76	10.01	.26	.51	.76	11.02	.27	.52	.77
.35	.32	.57	.82	.07	.32	.57	.82	.08	.33	.58	.83
.40	.38	.63	.88	.13	.38	.63	.88	.14	.39	.64	.89
.45	.44	.69	.94	.19	.44	.69	.94	.20	.45	.70	.95
.50	.50	.75	10.00	.25	.50	.75	11.00	.26	.51	.76	12.01
.55	.56	.81	.06	.31	.56	.81	.06	.32	.57	.82	.07
.60	.62	.87	.12	.37	.62	.87	.12	.38	.63	.88	.13
.65	.68	.93	.18	.43	.68	.93	.18	.44	.69	.94	.19
.70	.74	.99	.24	.49	.74	.99	.24	.50	.75	12.00	.25
.75	.80	10.05	.30	.55	.80	11.05	.31	.56	.81	.06	.31
.80	.86	.11	.36	.61	.86	.11	.37	.62	.87	.12	.37
.85	.92	.17	.42	.67	.92	.17	.43	.68	.93	.18	.43
.90	.98	.23	.48	.73	.98	.23	.49	.74	.99	.24	.49
.95	10.04	.29	.54	.79	11.04	.30	.55	.80	12.05	.30	.55
3.00	.10	.35	.60	.85	.10	.36	.61	.86	.11	.36	.61
.05	.16	.41	.66	.91	.17	.42	.67	.92	.17	.42	.68
.10	.22	.47	.72	.97	.23	.48	.73	.98	.23	.48	.74
.15	.28	.53	.78	11.03	.29	.54	.79	12.04	.29	.55	.80
.20	.34	.59	.84	.09	.35	.60	.85	.10	.35	.61	.86
.25	.40	.65	.90	.16	.41	.66	.91	.16	.42	.67	.92
.30	.46	.71	.96	.22	.47	.72	.97	.22	.48	.73	.98
.35	.52	.77	11.03	.28	.53	.78	12.03	.28	.54	.79	13.04
.40	.58	.83	.09	.34	.59	.84	.09	.34	.60	.85	.10
.45	.64	.89	.15	.40	.65	.90	.15	.40	.66	.91	.16
.50	.70	.95	.21	.46	.71	.96	.21	.46	.72	.97	.22
.55	.76	11.02	.27	.52	.77	12.02	.27	.52	.78	13.03	.28
.60	.82	.08	.33	.58	.83	.08	.33	.58	.84	.09	.34
.65	.88	.14	.39	.64	.89	.14	.39	.64	.90	.15	.40
.70	.94	.20	.45	.70	.95	.20	.45	.70	.96	.21	.46
.75	11.00	.26	.51	.76	12.01	.26	.51	.76	13.02	.27	.52
.80	.06	.32	.57	.82	.07	.32	.57	.82	.08	.33	.58
.85	.12	.38	.63	.88	.13	.38	.63	.88	.14	.39	.64
.90	.18	.44	.69	.94	.19	.44	.69	.94	.20	.45	.70
.95	.24	.50	.75	12.00	.25	.50	.75	13.00	.26	.51	.77
4.00	.30	.56	.81	.06	.31	.56	.81	.06	.32	.57	.83
.05	.36	.62	.87	.12	.37	.62	.87	.12	.38	.63	.89
.10	.42	.68	.93	.18	.43	.68	.93	.18	.44	.69	.95
.15	.48	.74	.99	.24	.49	.74	.99	.25	.50	.76	14.01
.20	.54	.80	12.05	.30	.55	.80	13.05	.31	.56	.82	.07
.25	.60	.86	.11	.36	.61	.86	.12	.37	.62	.88	.13
.30	.66	.92	.17	.42	.67	.92	.18	.43	.68	.94	.19
.35	.72	.98	.23	.48	.73	.98	.24	.49	.74	14.00	.25
.40	.78	12.04	.29	.54	.79	13.04	.30	.55	.80	.06	.31
.45	.84	.10	.35	.60	.85	.10	.36	.61	.86	.12	.37
.50	.90	.16	.41	.66	.91	.16	.42	.67	.92	.18	.43
.55	.97	.22	.47	.72	.97	.22	.48	73	98	.24	.49
.60	12.03	.28	.53	.78	13.03	.28	.54	.79	14.04	.30	.55
.65	.09	.34	.59	.84	.09	.34	.60	.85	.10	.36	.61
.70	.15	.40	.65	.90	.15	.40	.66	.91	.16	.42	.67
.75	.21	.46	.71	.96	.21	.46	.72	.97	.22	.48	.73
.80	.27	.52	.77	13.02	.27	.52	.78	14.03	.28	.54	.79
.85	.33	.58	.83	.08	.33	.58	.84	.09	.34	.60	.85
.90	.39	.64	.89	.14	.39	.64	.90	.15	.40	.66	.91
.95	.45	.70	.95	.20	.45	.70	.96	.21	.46	.72	.97

(Continued)

47.025 Table for determining total solids in milk from any given specific gravity and percentage of fat (Shaw and Eckles); results expressed as per cent total solids—*Concluded.*

% Fat	\multicolumn{11}{c}{Lactometer Reading at 60°F (Quévenne Degrees)}
	26	27	28	29	30	31	32	33	34	35	36
5.00	12.51	12.76	13.01	13.26	13.51	13.76	14.02	14.27	14.52	14.78	15.03
.05	.57	.82	.07	.32	.57	.83	.08	.33	.58	.84	.09
.10	.63	.88	.13	.38	.63	.89	.14	.39	.64	.90	.15
.15	.69	.94	.19	.44	.69	.95	.20	.45	.70	.96	.21
.20	.75	13.00	.25	.50	.75	14.01	.26	.51	.76	15.02	.27
.25	.81	.06	.31	.56	.81	.07	.32	.57	.82	.08	.33
.30	.87	.12	.37	.62	.87	.13	.38	.63	.88	.14	.39
.35	.93	.18	.43	.68	.93	.19	.44	.70	.95	.20	.45
.40	.99	.24	.49	.74	14.00	.25	.50	.76	15.01	.26	.51
.45	13.05	.30	.55	.80	.06	.31	.56	.82	.07	.32	.57
.50	.11	.36	.61	.86	.12	.37	.62	.88	.13	.38	.63
.55	.17	.42	.67	.93	.18	.43	.69	.94	.19	.44	.69
.60	.23	.48	.73	.99	.24	.49	.75	15.00	.25	.50	.75
.65	.29	.54	.79	14.05	.30	.55	.81	.06	.31	.56	.81
.70	.35	.60	.85	.11	.36	.61	.87	.12	.37	.62	.87
.75	.41	.66	.91	.17	.42	.68	.93	.18	.43	.68	.93
.80	.47	.72	.97	.23	.48	.74	.99	.24	.49	.74	.99
.85	.53	.78	14.04	.29	.54	.80	15.05	.30	.55	.80	16.06
.90	.59	.84	.10	.35	.60	.86	.11	.36	.61	.86	.12
.95	.65	.90	.16	.41	.66	.92	.17	.42	.67	.92	.18
6.00	.71	.96	.22	.47	.72	.98	.23	.48	.73	.98	.24
.05	.77	14.02	.28	.53	.78	15.04	.29	.54	.79	16.04	.30
.10	.83	.08	.34	.59	.84	.10	.35	.60	.85	.10	.35
.15	.89	.14	.40	.65	.90	.16	.41	.66	.91	.16	.42
.20	.95	.20	.46	.71	.96	.22	.47	.72	.97	.22	.48
.25	14.01	.26	.52	.77	15.02	.28	.53	.78	16.03	.28	.54
.30	.07	.32	.58	.83	.08	.34	.59	.84	.09	.34	.60
.35	.13	.38	.64	.90	.14	.40	.65	.90	.15	.40	.66
.40	.19	.44	.70	.96	.20	.46	.71	.96	.21	.46	.72
.45	.25	.50	.76	15.02	.26	.52	.77	16.02	.27	.52	.78
.50	.31	.56	.82	.08	.32	.58	.83	.08	.33	.58	.84
.55	.37	.62	.88	.14	.38	.64	.89	.14	.39	.64	.90
.60	.43	.68	.94	.20	.44	.70	.95	.20	.45	.70	.96
.65	.49	.74	15.00	.26	.50	.76	16.01	.26	.51	.76	17.02
.70	.55	.80	.06	.32	.56	.82	.07	.32	.57	.82	.08
.75	.61	.86	.12	.38	.62	.88	.13	.38	.63	.88	.14
.80	.67	.92	.18	.44	.68	.94	.19	.44	.69	.94	.20
.85	.73	.98	.24	.50	.74	16.00	.25	.50	.75	17.00	.26
.90	.79	15.04	.30	.56	.80	.06	.31	.56	.81	.06	.32
.95	.85	.10	.36	.62	.86	.12	.37	.62	.87	.12	.38

Proportional Parts

Lactometer Fraction	Fraction to Be Added to Total Solids	Lactometer Fraction	Fraction to Be Added to Total Solids	Lactometer Fraction	Fraction to Be Added to Total Solids
0.1	0.03	0.4	0.10	0.7	0.18
.2	.05	.5	.13	.8	.20
.3	.08	.6	.15	.9	.23

Table giving proportional parts shows amount to be added when lactometer readings are in whole numbers and decimals.

47.026   Correction table for specific gravity of milk (Quévenne lactometer)[a]

	Temperature (°F)									
Lactometer	51	52	53	54	55	56	57	58	59	60
20	19.3	19.4	19.4	19.5	19.6	19.7	19.8	19.9	19.9	20.0
21	20.3	20.3	20.4	20.5	20.6	20.7	20.8	20.9	20.9	21.0
22	21.3	21.3	21.4	21.5	21.6	21.7	21.8	21.9	21.9	22.0
23	22.3	22.3	22.4	22.5	22.6	22.7	22.8	22.8	22.9	23.0
24	23.3	23.3	23.4	23.5	23.6	23.6	23.7	23.8	23.9	24.0
25	24.2	24.3	24.4	24.5	24.6	24.6	24.7	24.8	24.9	25.0
26	25.2	25.2	25.3	25.4	25.5	25.6	25.7	25.8	25.9	26.0
27	26.2	26.2	26.3	26.4	26.5	26.6	26.7	26.8	26.9	27.0
28	27.1	27.2	27.3	27.4	27.5	27.6	27.7	27.8	27.9	28.0
29	28.1	28.2	28.3	28.4	28.5	28.6	28.7	28.8	28.9	29.0
30	29.1	29.1	29.2	29.3	29.4	29.6	29.7	29.8	29.9	30.0
31	30.0	30.1	30.2	30.3	30.4	30.5	30.6	30.8	30.9	31.0
32	31.0	31.1	31.2	31.3	31.4	31.5	31.6	31.7	31.9	32.0
33	31.9	32.0	32.1	32.3	32.4	32.5	32.6	32.7	32.9	33.0
34	32.9	33.0	33.1	33.2	33.3	33.5	33.6	33.7	33.9	34.0
35	33.8	33.9	34.0	34.2	34.3	34.5	34.6	34.7	34.9	35.0

	Temperature (°F)									
Lactometer	61	62	63	64	65	66	67	68	69	70
20	20.1	20.2	20.2	20.3	20.4	20.5	20.6	20.7	20.9	21.0
21	21.1	21.2	21.3	21.4	21.5	21.6	21.7	21.8	22.0	22.1
22	22.1	22.2	22.3	22.4	22.5	22.6	22.7	22.8	23.0	23.1
23	23.1	23.2	23.3	23.4	23.5	23.6	23.7	23.8	24.0	24.1
24	24.1	24.2	24.3	24.4	24.5	24.6	24.7	24.9	25.0	25.1
25	25.1	25.2	25.3	25.4	25.5	25.6	25.7	25.9	26.0	26.1
26	26.1	26.2	26.3	26.5	26.6	26.7	26.8	27.0	27.1	27.2
27	27.1	27.3	27.4	27.5	27.6	27.7	27.8	28.0	28.1	28.2
28	28.1	28.3	28.4	28.5	28.6	28.7	28.8	29.0	29.1	29.2
29	29.1	29.3	29.4	29.5	29.6	29.7	29.9	30.1	30.2	30.3
30	30.1	30.3	30.4	30.5	30.7	30.8	30.9	31.1	31.2	31.3
31	31.2	31.3	31.4	31.5	31.7	31.8	31.9	32.1	32.2	32.4
32	32.2	32.3	32.5	32.6	32.7	32.9	33.0	33.2	33.3	33.4
33	33.2	33.3	33.5	33.6	33.8	33.9	34.0	34.2	34.3	34.5
34	34.2	34.3	34.5	34.6	34.8	34.9	35.0	35.2	35.3	35.5
35	35.2	35.3	35.5	35.6	35.8	36.9	36.1	36.2	36.4	36.5

[a] Paul G. Heineman, *Milk*, W. B. Saunders Co., Philadelphia, 1921, p. 144.

47.027 Optical crystallographic properties of some crystalline drugs[a]

Alkaloids and Related Amines

Compound	α	β	γ	Optic Sign	Extinction	Elongation	2V	Remarks
Aconitine	1.560	—	1.575	+		—	36°	
Alphaprodine.HCl	1.499	1.572	1.597	—	p, i		63°	
Apomorphine.HCl	1.638	1.658	1.701	+				
Arecoline.HBr	1.555	1.590	1.655	+	p			
Atropine	1.550	1.583	1.595	—				n_α very common
Atropine sulfate	1.555	—	1.60					
Benzethonium chloride	1.560	1.565	1.589	+			48°	Most fragments do not extinguish completely
Berberine	1.490	1.701	>1.734	—	p	—		Yellow needles and rods
Berberine.HCl.2H$_2$O	1.500	1.535	>1.733	+	p			
Brucine	1.562	—	>1.65		p			
Brucine sulfate	1.512	1.595	1.688	+	p	+	88°	6-sided plates and rods
Cetylpyridinium chloride	1.509	1.566	1.613	—	—	++++	59°	Op. ax. fig. common $r>v$ weak
Cinchonidine	1.610	1.625	1.675	+	p	+++		
Cinchonidine sulfate	1.562	1.604	1.660	+	p	++	21°	Plates and rods
Cinchonine	1.570	1.685	1.690	—			large	
Cinchonine.HCl.2H$_2$O	1.545	1.617	1.661	—				
Cocaine.HCl	1.570	1.596	1.618	—				
Codeine	1.543	1.636	1.684	+	p		53°	
Codeine.HCl	1.559	1.580	1.676	—	p	—		Rods
Codeine sulfate	1.561	1.642	1.661	+				Uniaxial
Diacetylmorphine.HCl.H$_2$O	1.578$_\beta$	—	1.613$_\varepsilon$		p			
Diphenylhydantoin	1.600	—	1.635	—	p	— —		
l-Ephedrine.HCl	1.530	1.603	1.638		p	— —	70°	Prisms and rods
Ethoheptazine citrate	1.537	—	1.556					
Ethylhydrocupreine.HCl	1.513	—	1.619					
Hydrastine	1.550	1.734	>1.734					n_α common
Hyoscyamine	1.562	—	1.581					
Isobucaine.HCl	1.522	1.574	1.612	—	p, i	++	82°	
Levallorphan tartrate	1.545	1.595	1.653	++	p, i	-+	86°	
Meperidine.HCl	1.545	1.581	1.618	+	p	+	33°	
Methscopolamine bromide	1.580	1.615	1.617	—				
Methylphenidate.HCl	1.558	1.581	1.585	—			43°	
Morphine.H$_2$O	1.580	1.625	1.645	—	p	-+		
Morphine.HCl.3H$_2$O	1.540	n_i1.590	1.635	—	p	— —		Orthorhombic n_α common
Morphine sulfate.5H$_2$O	1.545	1.620	1.632	—	p	— —		
Papaverine	1.625	1.690	>1.690			— —	large	
Papaverine.HCl	1.555	n_i1.733	>1.733		p	— —		

[a] Abbreviations: p = parallel; s = symmetrical; i = inclined; n = index; n_i = intermediate index; Bx.ac. = acute bisectrix; Bx.ob. = obtuse bisectrix; Op.ax. = optic axis; fig. = figure; sl = slightly; r = red; v = violet.

(Continued)

47.027 Optical crystallographic properties of some crystalline drugs[a]—Continued.

Compound	α	β	γ	Optic Sign	Extinction	Elongation	2V	Remarks
Alkaloids and Related Amines—Continued								
Phenmetrazine.HCl	1.508	1.516	1.628	+			very large	
Phensuximide	1.536	1.617	>1.673		p, i			
Phenylbutazone	1.600	—	1.620	+	p	−	55°	
Quinidine	1.580	1.665	1.690	+	p	+		
Quinidine sulfate	1.565	1.607	1.670	+	p	+		
Quinine	1.620	1.625	1.630	−	p	−	very large	
Quinine.HCl	1.590	1.610	1.669	+	p	+	61°	r > v
Racephedrine.HCl	1.570	1.608	1.630	−				Irregular fragments; op. ax. figs. occasional
Scopolamine.HBr	1.567	1.585	1.623	+	p		medium	Rods and prisms
Strychnine	1.617	1.660	>1.690	+	p	+	large	
Strychnine.HCl.2H2O	1.610	1.626	1.668	+		−	large	
Syrosingopine	1.529	1.538	1.646	+	p	−	34°	
Yohimbine	1.548	1.563	1.688	+			42°	
Yohimbine.HCl	1.57	1.61	1.69	+				
Antibiotics								
Carbomycin	1.474	1.484	1.513	+	p	±	70–80°	
Chloramphenicol	1.523	1.608	1.659	−	p	−		
Chloramphenicol palmitate	1.527	—	1.569		p, s	∓	59°	Rod-shaped aggregates
Chlortetracycline.HCl	1.635	1.706	1.730	−				
Cycloserine	1.583	—	1.630	−				
Dihydrostreptomycin.3HCl	1.522	1.548	1.566	−	p	+	80°	
Dihydrostreptomycin sulfate	1.552	1.558	1.566	+	p, i		89°	Ext. angle = 18°
Erythromycin estolate	1.483	1.488	1.515	+	p		52°	
Erythromycin ethylcarbonate	1.496	1.506	1.510	−	p	+		Op. ax. figs. common
Erythromycin ethylsuccinate	1.490	1.515	1.567	+	p	+	medium	n_γ rare
Erythromycin gluceptate	1.506	—	1.528	+	p	+	75°	
Erythromycin.HI.H2O	1.528	1.536	1.550	−	p	+	84°	
Erythromycin.2H2O	1.512	1.523	1.532	−	p		60°	
Erythromycin oxalate.2H2O	1.484	1.492	1.516	+	p	+		
Erythromycin stearate	1.498	1.507	1.563	+	p, i	∓	small	n_γ rare
Fumagillin	1.518	ca 1.572	>1.780				small	
Gramicidin	1.541	ca 1.553	1.573					
Neomycin sulfate	n 1.541							Isotropic

(Continued)

47.027 Optical crystallographic properties of some crystalline drugs[a]—Continued.

Compound	α	β	γ	Optic Sign	Extinction	Elongation	2V	Remarks
Antibiotics—Continued								
Novobiocin acid, form 2	1.608	1.638	1.654	–			71°	$r > v$
Novobiocin sodium	1.565	–	1.629			–		Tiny needles
Nystatin	1.512	1.583	1.682	+	p	–		Small, pale yellow rods
Oxytetracycline.2H$_2$O	1.634	1.646	>1.700	+	p		28°	Op. ax. figs. common
Oxytetracycline.HCl	1.546	1.635	1.730	+	p, i	+	very large	
Penicillin G benzathine	1.523	1.622	1.630	–	p	+	very small	n_α and n_γ common
Penicillin G dibenzylamine	1.567	–	1.613		p	+		
Penicillin G *l*-ephedrine	1.575	–	1.610		p	–		
Penicillin G *l*-ephenamine	1.583	1.590	1.648	+	i		small	Bx. ac. figs.
Penicillin G hydrabamine	1.556	ca 1.590	1.619		p, i	–	medium	Elongated rectangular plates
Penicillin G.HI diethylaminoethyl ester	1.601	1.608	1.632	+	p	–		
Penicillin G potassium	1.550		1.603	–		+		n_β common
Penicillin G procaine	1.545	1.570	1.685	+	p, i	+		n_β common
Penicillin G sodium	1.550	1.609	1.620	–	p	+	large	
Penicillin O chloroprocaine	1.541	1.585	1.656	+	p	+	large	
Penicillin O potassium	1.545	–	1.593		p			
Tetracycline.HCl	1.603	1.685	1.714	–	p		large	Bx. ac. and op. ax. figs.
Tetracycline.3H$_2$O	1.538	1.646	sl >1.787	+	p, i	+	large	Occasional op. ax. figs.
Tyrocidine.HCl	1.553	–	1.584		p			
Antihistamines								
Anthallan®.HCl	1.505	1.585	1.617	–	p	–		Small rods & irregular fragments; no figs.
Bromothen.HCl	1.617	1.654	1.734	+	i	+		Very small rods
Chlorcyclizine.HCl	1.590	1.610	1.665	+				Thin platy fragments; op. ax. figs. common
Chlorcyclizine.2HCl	1.610	1.660	1.665	–	p		very small	Short rods & thin 6-sided plates; op. ax. figs. common
Chlorothen citrate	1.583	1.603	1.645					Minute plates & shreds; op. ax. figs. rare
Chlorothen.HCl	1.553	1.625	>1.734					Massive fragments, some rectangular; op. ax. figs. occasional
Chlorpheniramine maleate	1.533	n_i1.668	sl <1.734					Box-like prisms & irregular fragments; figs. infrequent
Cyproheptadine.HCl	1.620	1.647	1.738	+	p		60°	
Dexchlorpheniramine maleate	1.509	1.564	1.683	+	p		70°	

(Continued)

47.027 Optical crystallographic properties of some crystalline drugs[a]—Continued.

Compound	α	β	γ	Optic Sign	Extinction	Elongation	2V	Remarks
Antihistamines—Continued								
Dimenhydrinate (unsatisfactory for optical crystallographic study)								Platy material & rods
Diphenhydramine.HCl	1.602	1.625	1.630	−	p	−		6-sided plates
Doxylamine succinate	ca 1.525	1.563	1.598	−	p	−	86°	Rods & square plates; op. ax. figs. occasional
p-Fluorotripelennamine.HCl	1.585	1.600	1.668	+			large	Elongated 6-sided rods with obtuse ends; op. ax. figs. frequent
Methaphenilene.HCl	1.604	1.675	1.733	−				Thick hexagonal plates
Methapyrilene.HCl	1.588	1.654	>1.695– <1.734	−	p, i	±		Elongated 6-sided & irregular fragments; figs. rare
2-(4-Morpholinyl) ethyl benzhydryl ether.HCl (Linadryl.HCl)	1.577	1.631	1.672	−				Short prisms
Phenbenzamine.HCl	1.587	1.635	1.734	+	p	+	small	Rods & plates
Pheniramine maleate	1.548	1.574	1.665	+			small	Massive prisms; elongated or short & stubby
Promethazine.HBr	1.667	1.675	>1.733	+	p	+		Rods & irregular fragments
Promethazine.HCl	1.617	1.691	1.733	−				Stout prismatic forms; no figs.
Pyrathiazine.HCl	1.690	—	1.737	−				Rods & irregular fragments
Pyrilamine maleate (unsatisfactory for optical crystallographic study)								
Pyrrobutamine phosphate	1.566	1.614	1.653	−	p	+	82°	Square plates & stubby prisms
Thenyldiamine.HCl	1.590	—	1.680	−			large	Rods & platy material
Thonzylamine.HCl	1.612	1.679	1.691	−				Rectangular plates & prisms from water; op. ax. figs. common
Tripelennamine.HCl	1.580	1.655	1.705	+	p	+		
Barbiturates								
Allobarbital	1.516	1.572	1.625	−	s		large	Op. ax. fig. common
Alphenal (5-allyl-5-phenylbarbituric acid)	1.551	1.578	1.645	+	p	−	67°	Op. ax. fig. common
Amobarbital	1.467	1.533	1.560	−	p	+		
Amobarbital sodium	n 1.505				i			Isotropic
Aprobarbital	1.520	1.581	1.600	−			medium	Rods
Barbital	1.445	1.548	1.580					All n's common
Barbital sodium	1.512	1.532	1.615				40°	
Butabarbital sodium	1.465	1.529	1.532	−	p	+	very small	
Butalbital	1.508	n 1.521	1.577	+	p	+	medium	Rods and plates

(Continued)

76.027   Optical crystallographic properties of some crystalline drugs^a—Continued.

Compound	α	β	γ	Optic Sign	Extinction	Elongation	2V	Remarks
Barbiturates—Continued								
Butallylonal	1.524	1.577	1.603	−	p	+	medium	Rosettes of tiny rods and blades; bx. ac. figs. occasional
Butethal	1.454	1.518	1.556	−	i		large	Rods & needles; op. ax. and bx. ac. figs. common
Cyclobarbital	1.515	1.546	1.621	+		±	69°	Bx. ac. & bx. ob. figs. common
Cyclopal® (5-allyl-5-(2-cyclopenten-1-yl) barbituric acid)	1.520	1.575	1.626	−		−	85°	Bx. ac. fig. common
Hexethal (5-ethyl-5-n-hexylbarbituric acid)	1.473	1.519	1.549	−		−	76°	
Hexobarbital	1.546	1.608	1.634	−	p	+	64°	Bx. ac. & op. ax. figs. common
Mephobarbital	1.594	1.610	1.651	+	p	−	65°	Bx. ac. fig. common
Pentobarbital	1.465	—	1.565	−	i		very large	
Pentobarbital sodium	1.477	—	1.523					
Phenobarbital	1.557	1.620	1.667	−	p	−		β very common
Phenobarbital sodium (unstable)								
Probarbital	1.477	1.573	1.624	−	i	++	73°	Rods
Probarbital sodium	1.532	—	1.629		p	++		Rods & needles
Secobarbital	1.487	1.557	1.563	−	p		31°	
Secobarbital sodium	1.490	n_i1.500	1.525					
Sigmodal® (5-(2-bromoallyl)-5-(1-methyl-butyl) barbituric acid)	1.519	1.583	1.634	−		+	80°	
Thiopental	1.534	1.634	—	−	i		40–45°	Lamellar
Vinbarbital	1.506	1.544	1.672	+	p	−	61°	
Hallucinogens								
d-Lysergic acid diethylamide tartrate (LSD-25)	1.540	1.596	1.676	+	i		83°	
4-Methyl-2,5-dimethoxyamphetamine.HCl ("STP".HCl) (DOM®)	1.518	1.622	1.632	−			33°	Bx. ob. figs. common
Phencyclidine.HCl	1.572	1.618	1.654	−			80°	
Psilocybin	1.527	1.554	1.672	+			55°	n_β and n_γ common
Steroids								
Betamethasone	1.554	—	1.667		p	+		Very small rods
Cholesterol	1.520	1.532	1.566		p	++	60°	Elongated plates
Cortisone	1.552	1.572	1.625		p	+	medium	n_α and n_β most common

(Continued)

47.027 Optical crystallographic properties of some crystalline drugs[a]—Continued.

Compound	α	β	γ	Optic Sign	Extinction	Elongation	2V	Remarks
Steroids—Continued								
Cortisone acetate	1.512	1.552	1.621	+	p	±	medium	
Dehydrocholic acid	1.510	1.542	1.572	−	p, i	±	80°	r > v
Desoxycorticosterone acetate	1.529	1.550	1.630	+			54°	Bx. ac. common
Dexamethasone	1.553	1.572	1.648	+	p	−	52°	Orthorhombic system
Diethylstilbestrol, trans	1.594	1.611	1.73	+	p			Plates
Equilin	1.534	1.677	1.705	−		−	40°	
Estradiol benzoate	1.586	1.603	1.633	+	p	−	large	
Estradiol dipropionate	1.506	—	1.598	−	i			2E = 46°
Estrone, phase 1	1.520	1.642	1.692	−			60°	Ext. angle = 12°; r>v
Estrone, phase 2	1.511	1.621	1.697	−			75°	r>v weak
Estrone, phase 3	1.594	1.628	1.647	−	p		73°	Metastable crystals, 6-sided plates
Ethisterone	1.576	1.625	1.645	−			67°	2E = 127°
Fluorometholone	1.562	1.568	1.704	+			26°	r > v strong
Hydrocortisone	1.531	1.550	1.638	+	p, i	n	83°	Tiny rods & plates
Hydrocortisone acetate	1.543	1.589	1.627	−			83°	Monoclinic; r>v
Methylprednisolone acetate	1.562	1.575	1.700	+	p, i	±	38°	v > r
Methylprednisolone sodium succinate	1.552	—	1.561	+		−	very small	
Methyltestosterone	1.555	ca 1.565	1.620	+	p		medium	
Prednisone	1.587	1.590	1.651	+	p		very small	Bx. ac. common
Progesterone, alpha	1.542	1.554	1.663	+		−	40°	Platy fragments with brilliant interference colors
Progesterone, beta	1.529	1.575	1.676	+	p	−	68°	Crystals acicular
Testosterone	1.548	1.565	1.670	−	p	−	medium	
Triamcinolone acetonide	1.546_e		1.595_ω	−				
Triamcinolone diacetate	1.517	1.567	1.592	−	p, i	±	69°	
Sulfonamides								
Succinylsulfathiazole	1.578	1.676	1.710	−	i		58°	Rods
Sulfacetamide	1.559	1.564	1.727	+	s		21°	
Sulfadiazine	1.596	1.675	1.830	+	p, i		76°	
Sulfadiazine[b]	1.615	1.663	>1.734		p	±		Rods
Sulfaguanidine	1.606	1.663	1.734			±		
Sulfaguanidine·H₂O	1.586	1.649	1.731	+	p, i	±	86°	Op. ax. fig.

[b] The second set of optical properties in each case represents intermediate data which are quite commonly found in some commercial samples. They probably represent an anhydrous form or merely a different common orientation of the crystal.

(Continued)

47.027　Optical crystallographic properties of some crystalline drugs[a]—Continued.

Compound	α	β	γ	Optic Sign	Extinction	Elongation	2V	Remarks
Sulfonamides—Continued								
Sulfallantoin® (sulfanilamide+allantoin-addition product)	1.513	1.590	>1.690, <1.733					Op. ax. fig.
Sulfamerazine	1.568	1.657	1.687	−		±	58°	
Sulfamerazine[b]	1.587	—	1.675					Rods
Sulfamethazine	1.584	1.623	>1.778		p	−		Bx. ac. fig.
Sulfamidazole® (sulfanilamide+sulfa-thiazole-double crystal)[c]	1.661	1.678	>1.733	+	p	−	small	
Sulfanilamide phase B (anhyd.)	1.555	1.672	1.85	+	p	−		Stable form coml prepns
Sulfanilamide.HCl	1.540	1.655	1.690		p	−		Rods
Sulfapyridine[b]	1.680	1.733	>1.733					Op. ax. fig.
Sulfapyridine, phase I	1.670	1.736	1.813	+	p, i	±	88°	Tabular to equant; stable form coml prepns
Sulfapyridine sodium.H₂O	1.590	—	1.700	+	p	−		
Sulfathiazole, phase I	1.674	1.685	>1.733	+		±	small	α & β common
Sulfathiazole, phase II	1.598	1.741	1.780	−	p, i		52°	Lath shaped
Sulfathiazole[b]	1.695	n₁ 1.733	>1.733					
Sulfathiazole sodium.1½H₂O	1.596	—	1.621					
Sulfisoxazole	1.605	1.642	1.697	+	p	±	large	Plates & rods
Sympathomimetic Amines								
dl-Amphetamine.HCl	1.508	1.582	1.611	+	p	−	large	Rods and plates
dl-Amphetamine phosphate, dibasic	1.549	1.589	1.665	+		−		Small platy crystals; bx. ac. figs. common
dl-Amphetamine sulfate	1.520	1.531	1.614	+	p, i	±	very small	
Dextroamphetamine.HCl	1.560	1.592	1.622	+	p	±	very large	Large plates & rods; op. ax. figs. occasional
Dextroamphetamine phosphate, dibasic	1.546	1.583	1.664	+		±	medium	Plates with truncated corners
Dextroamphetamine sulfate	1.501	1.545	1.603	+	p	−	small	6-8-sided plates
l-Ephedrine.HCl	1.530	1.603	1.638	−	p	−	70°	Elongated prisms & rods
l-Ephedrine sulfate	1.540	1.565	1.587		p	−	large	6-sided plates & rods
Epinephrine	1.548	1.597	>1.735	+	p	−	medium	Thin, blade-like, 6-sided crystals in rosettes; bx. ac. figs. common
Hydroxyamphetamine.HBr	1.560	1.680	1.734	−				Irregular fragments
p-Hydroxyephedrine.HCl	1.507	1.604	1.668	−	p	±		Rectangular rods; bx. ob. figs. common
p-Hydroxymethamphetamine sulfate	1.516	1.552	1.645	+	s	+		Rhombohedral or 6-sided plates
Isoxsuprine.HCl	1.508	1.648	1.670	−	p, i		40°	
Levamfetamine succinate	1.572	1.587	1.650	+	p, i		52°	Bx. ac. figs. common

[c] Equimolecular proportions.

(Continued)

47.027 Optical crystallographic properties of some crystalline drugs[a]—Concluded.

Compound	α	β	γ	Optic Sign	Extinction	Elongation	2V	Remarks
Sympathomimetic Amines—Continued								
Mephentermine sulfate	1.530	1.585	1.596	−	p, i	—	46°	Irregular fragments; op. ax. figs. frequent
Methamphetamine.HCl	1.530	1.537	1.615	+	p			Small 6-sided platy or rod-like crystals; no figs.
dl-Methamphetamine.HCl	1.535	1.540	1.620	+	p	−	small	
Naphazoline nitrate	1.560	1.619	>1.740	+	s, i			6-sided plates & irregular fragments; bx. ac. figs. common
Phenylpropanolamine.HCl	1.563	1.618	1.650	−			large	
Phenylpropylmethylamine.HCl	1.577	—	1.603		p			Small rod-like fragments; no figs.
Pseudoephedrine.HCl	1.543	—	1.632	−	p	−		
Racephedrine.HCl	1.570	1.608	1.630			−		Irregular fragments; op. ax. figs. occasional
dl-Synephrine base (Desoxyepinephrine)	1.546	1.604	ca 1.725	+	s, i		large	Platy crystals, often diamond-shaped; op. ax. figs. common
Synephrine.HCl	1.549	1.605	1.664	+	p, i		large	Large plates; bx. ac. figs. frequent
dl-Synephrine (+) tartrate (neutral salt)	1.516	n_i1.620	1.689	+	i	+	large	Rods & plates; partial op. ax. figs. common
Tolazoline.HCl	1.586	1.604	1.703	+	i			6-sided plates; inclined op. ax. figs. common
Tuaminoheptane sulfate	1.458$_\omega$		1.468$_\varepsilon$	+	p			Irregular-shaped plates & fibrous flakes; figs. frequent
Tranquilizers								
Azacyclonol.HCl	1.638	1.647	1.674	+			medium	6-sided prisms; n_β rare
Chlordiazepoxide.HCl	1.634	ca 1.710	>1.780	+			large	
Chlorpromazine.HCl	1.584	—	>1.735	+	i			Recrystallized from dil. alcohol
Ethinamate	1.530	1.536	1.546	−			76°	6-sided rods and plates
Glutethimide	1.572	1.585	1.590		p, i	+	large	Fibers and irregular thin platy fragments with wavy extinction
Meprobamate	ca 1.515	—	ca 1.544		p	+ +		Irregular platy fragments
Thiopropazate.2HCl	1.589	1.609	1.700					

47.028   Table of refractive indices for drugs, arranged according to ascending value of the lowest index[a]

α	β	γ	Compound
		Alkaloids and Related Amines	
1.490	1.701	>1.734	Berberine
1.499	1.572	1.597	Alphaprodine.HCl
1.500	1.535	>1.733	Berberine.HCl.2H$_2$O
1.508	1.516	1.628	Phenmetrazine.HCl
1.509	1.566	1.613	Cetylpyridinium chloride
1.512	1.595	1.688	Brucine sulfate
1.513	—	1.619	Ethylhydrocupreine.HCl
1.522	1.574	1.612	Isobucaine.HCl
1.529	1.538	1.646	Syrosingopine
1.530	1.603	1.638	l-Ephedrine.HCl
1.536	1.617	>1.673	Phensuximide
1.537	—	1.556	Ethoheptazine citrate
1.540	1.590	1.635	Morphine.HCl.H$_2$O
1.543	1.636	1.684	Codeine
1.545	1.581	1.618	Meperidine.HCl
1.545	1.595	1.653	Levallorphan tartrate
1.545	1.617	1.661	Cinchonine.HCl.2H$_2$O
1.545	1.620	1.632	Morphine sulfate.5H$_2$O
1.548	1.563	1.688	Yohimbine
1.550	1.583	1.595	Atropine
1.550	1.734	>1.734	Hydrastine
1.555	—	1.60	Atropine sulfate
1.555	1.590	1.655	Arecoline.HBr
1.555	n$_i$1.733	>1.733	Papaverine.HCl
1.558	1.581	1.585	Methylphenidate.HCl
1.559	1.580	1.676	Codeine.HCl
1.560	—	1.575	Aconitine
1.560	1.565	1.589	Benzethonium chloride
1.561	1.642	1.661	Codeine sulfate
1.562	—	1.581	Hyoscyamine
1.562	—	>1.65	Brucine
1.562	1.604	1.660	Cinchonidine sulfate
1.565	1.607	1.670	Quinidine sulfate
1.567	1.585	1.623	Scopolamine.HBr
1.57	1.61	1.69	Yohimbine.HCl
1.570	1.596	1.618	Cocaine.HCl
1.570	1.608	1.630	Racephedrine.HCl
1.570	1.685	1.690	Cinchonine
1.578$_\omega$		1.613$_\epsilon$	Diacetylmorphine.HCl.H$_2$O
1.580	1.615	1.617	Methscopolamine bromide
1.580	1.625	1.645	Morphine.H$_2$O
1.580	1.665	1.690	Quinidine
1.590	1.610	1.669	Quinine.HCl
1.600	—	1.620	Phenylbutazone
1.600	—	1.635	Diphenylhydantoin
1.610	1.625	1.675	Cinchonidine
1.610	1.626	1.668	Strychnine.HCl.2H$_2$O
1.617	1.660	>1.690	Strychnine
1.620	1.625	1.630	Quinine
1.625	1.690	>1.690	Papaverine
1.638	1.658	1.701	Apomorphine.HCl
		Antibiotics	
1.474	1.484	1.513	Carbomycin
1.483	1.488	1.515	Erythromycin estolate
1.484	1.492	1.516	Erythromycin oxalate.2H$_2$O
1.490	1.515	1.567	Erythromycin ethylsuccinate
1.496	1.506	1.510	Erythromycin ethylcarbonate
1.498	1.507	1.563	Erythromycin stearate
1.506	—	1.528	Erythromycin gluceptate
1.512	1.523	1.532	Erythromycin.2H$_2$O
1.512	1.583	1.682	Nystatin
1.518	ca 1.572	>1.780	Fumagillin
1.522	1.548	1.566	Dihydrostreptomycin.3HCl
1.523	1.608	1.659	Chloramphenicol
1.523	1.622	1.630	Penicillin G benzathine

[a] See **47.027** for symbols.

(Continued)

47.028 **Table of refractive indices for drugs, arranged according to ascending value of the lowest index**[a] —*Continued.*

α	β	γ	Compound
			Antibiotics—*Continued*
1.527	—	1.569	Chloramphenicol palmitate
1.528	1.536	1.550	Erythromycin.HI.H_2O
1.538	1.646	sl >1.787	Tetracycline.$3H_2O$
n 1.541			Neomycin sulfate
1.541	ca 1.553	1.573	Gramicidin
1.541	1.585	1.656	Penicillin O chloroprocaine
1.545	—	1.593	Penicillin O potassium
1.545	1.570	1.685	Penicillin G procaine
1.546	1.635	1.730	Oxytetracycline.HCl
1.550	—	1.603	Penicillin G potassium
1.550	1.609	1.620	Penicillin G sodium
1.552	1.558	1.566	Dihydrostreptomycin sulfate
1.553	—	1.584	Tyrocidine.HCl
1.556	ca 1.590	1.619	Penicillin G hydrabamine
1.565	—	1.629	Novobiocin sodium
1.567	—	1.613	Penicillin G dibenzylamine
1.575	—	1.610	Penicillin G *l*-ephedrine
1.583	—	1.630	Cycloserine
1.583	1.590	1.648	Penicillin G *l*-ephenamine
1.601	1.608	1.632	Penicillin G.HI diethylaminoethyl ester
1.603	1.685	1.714	Tetracycline.HCl
1.608	1.638	1.654	Novobiocin acid, form 2
1.634	1.646	>1.700	Oxytetracycline.$2H_2O$
1.635	1.706	1.730	Chlortetracycline.HCl
			Antihistamines
1.505	1.585	1.617	Anthallan®.HCl
1.509	1.564	1.683	Dexchlorpheniramine maleate
ca 1.525	1.563	1.598	Doxylamine succinate
1.533	n_i1.668	sl <1.734	Chlorpheniramine maleate
1.548	1.574	1.665	Pheniramine maleate
1.553	1.625	>1.734	Chlorothen.HCl
1.566	1.614	1.653	Pyrrobutamine phosphate
1.577	1.631	1.672	2(4-Morpholinyl) ethyl benzhydryl ether.HCl
1.580	1.655	1.705	Tripelennamine.HCl
1.583	1.603	1.645	Chlorothen citrate
1.585	1.600	1.668	*p*-Fluorotripelennamine.HCl
1.587	1.635	1.734	Phenbenzamine.HCl
1.588	1.654	>1.695–<1.734	Methapyrilene.HCl
1.590	—	1.680	Thenyldiamine.HCl
1.590	1.610	1.665	Chlorcyclizine.HCl
1.602	1.625	1.630	Diphenhydramine.HCl
1.604	1.675	1.733	Methaphenilene.HCl
1.610	1.660	1.665	Chlorcyclizine.2HCl
1.612	1.679	1.691	Thonzylamine.HCl
1.617	1.654	1.734	Bromothen.HCl
1.617	1.691	1.733	Promethazine.HCl
1.620	1.647	1.738	Cyproheptadine.HCl
1.667	1.675	>1.733	Promethazine.HBr
1.690	—	1.737	Pyrathiazine.HCl
			Barbiturates
1.445	1.548	1.580	Barbital
1.454	1.518	1.556	Butethal
1.465	—	1.565	Pentobarbital
1.465	1.529	1.532	Butabarbital sodium
1.467	1.533	1.560	Amobarbital
1.473	1.519	1.549	Hexethal
1.477	—	1.523	Pentobarbital sodium
1.477	1.573	1.624	Probarbital
1.487	1.557	1.563	Secobarbital
1.490	n_i1.500	1.525	Secobarbital sodium
n 1.505			Amobarbital sodium
1.506	1.544	1.672	Vinbarbital

(Continued)

47.028   **Table of refractive indices for drugs, arranged according to ascending value of the lowest index**[a]
—*Continued.*

α	β	γ	Compound
			Barbiturates—*Continued*
1.508	n_i1.521	1.577	Butalbital
1.512	1.532	1.615	Barbital sodium
1.515	1.546	1.621	Cyclobarbital
1.516	1.572	1.625	Allobarbital
1.519	1.583	1.634	Sigmodal®
1.520	1.575	1.626	Cyclopal®
1.520	1.581	1.600	Aprobarbital
1.524	1.577	1.603	Butallylonal
1.532	—	1.629	Probarbital sodium
1.534	1.634	—	Thiopental
1.546	1.608	1.634	Hexobarbital
1.551	1.578	1.645	Alphenal
1.557	1.620	1.667	Phenobarbital
1.594	1.610	1.651	Mephobarbital
			Hallucinogens
1.518	1.622	1.632	4-Methyl-2,5-dimethoxyamphetamine.HCl
1.527	1.554	1.672	Psilocybin
1.540	1.596	1.676	*d*-Lysergic acid diethylamide tartrate
1.572	1.618	1.654	Phencyclidine.HCl
			Steroids
1.506	—	1.598	Estradiol dipropionate
1.510	1.542	1.572	Dehydrocholic acid
1.511	1.621	1.697	Estrone, phase 2
1.512	1.552	1.621	Cortisone acetate
1.517	1.567	1.592	Triamcinolone diacetate
1.520	1.532	1.566	Cholesterol
1.520	1.642	1.692	Estrone, phase 1
1.529	1.550	1.630	Desoxycorticosterone acetate
1.529	1.575	1.676	Progesterone, beta
1.531	1.550	1.638	Hydrocortisone
1.534	1.677	1.705	Equilin
1.542	1.554	1.663	Progesterone, alpha
1.543	1.589	1.627	Hydrocortisone acetate
1.546$_\epsilon$		1.595$_\omega$	Triamcinolone acetonide
1.548	1.565	1.670	Testosterone
1.552	—	1.561	Methylprednisolone sodium succinate
1.552	1.572	1.625	Cortisone
1.553	1.572	1.648	Dexamethasone
1.554	—	1.667	Betamethasone
1.555	ca 1.565	1.620	Methyltestosterone
1.562	1.575	1.700	Methylprednisolone acetate
1.562	1.568	1.704	Fluorometholone
1.576	1.625	1.645	Ethisterone
1.586	1.603	1.633	Estradiol benzoate
1.587	1.590	1.651	Prednisone
1.594	1.611	1.73	Diethylstilbestrol, trans
1.594	1.628	1.647	Estrone, phase 3
			Sulfonamides
1.513	1.590	>1.690–<1.733	Sulfallantoin®
1.540	1.655	1.690	Sulfanilamide.HCl
1.555	1.672	1.85	Sulfanilamide, phase B (anhyd.)
1.559	1.564	1.727	Sulfacetamide
1.568	1.657	1.687	Sulfamerazine
1.578	1.676	1.710	Succinylsulfathiazole
1.584	1.623	>1.778	Sulfamethazine
1.586	1.649	1.731	Sulfaguanidine.H_2O
1.587	—	1.675	Sulfamerazine[b]
1.590	—	1.700	Sulfapyridine sodium.H_2O

(Continued)

[b] The second set of optical properties in each case represents intermediate data which are commonly found in some com. samples. They probably represent an anhyd. form or merely a different common orientation of the crystal.

47.028 **Table of refractive indices for drugs, arranged according to ascending value of the lowest index**[a] *—Concluded.*

α	β	γ	Compound
			Sulfonamides—*Continued*
1.596	—	1.621	Sulfathiazole sodium.$1\frac{1}{2}H_2O$
1.596	1.675	1.830	Sulfadiazine
1.598	1.741	1.780	Sulfathiazole, phase II
1.605	1.642	1.697	Sulfisoxazole
1.606	1.663	1.734	Sulfaguanidine
1.615	1.663	>1.734	Sulfadiazine[b]
1.661	1.678	>1.733	Sulfamidazole®
1.670	1.736	1.813	Sulfapyridine, phase I
1.674	1.685	>1.733	Sulfathiazole, phase I
1.680	1.733	>1.733	Sulfapyridine[b]
1.695	$n_i 1.733$	>1.733	Sulfathiazole[b]
			Sympathomimetic Amines
1.458_ω		1.468_ϵ	Tuaminoheptane sulfate
1.501	1.545	1.603	Dextroamphetamine sulfate
1.507	1.604	1.668	p-Hydroxyephedrine.HCl
1.508	1.582	1.611	dl-Amphetamine.HCl
1.508	1.648	1.670	Isoxsuprine.HCl
1.516	1.552	1.645	p-Hydroxymethamphetamine sulfate
1.516	$n_i 1.620$	1.689	dl-Synephrine (+) tartrate (neutral salt)
1.520	1.531	1.614	dl-Amphetamine sulfate
1.530	1.537	1.615	Methamphetamine.HCl
1.530	1.585	1.596	Mephentermine sulfate
1.530	1.603	1.638	l-Ephedrine.HCl
1.535	1.540	1.620	dl-Methamphetamine.HCl
1.540	1.565	1.587	l-Ephedrine sulfate
1.543	—	1.632	Pseudoephedrine.HCl
1.546	1.583	1.664	Dextroamphetamine phosphate, dibasic
1.546	1.604	ca 1.725	dl-Synephrine base
1.548	1.597	>1.735	Epinephrine
1.549	1.589	1.665	dl-Amphetamine phosphate, dibasic
1.549	1.605	1.664	Synephrine.HCl
1.560	1.592	1.622	Dextroamphetamine.HCl
1.560	1.619	>1.740	Naphazoline nitrate
1.560	1.680	1.734	Hydroxyamphetamine.HBr
1.563	1.618	1.650	Phenylpropanolamine.HCl
1.570	1.608	1.630	Racephedrine.HCl
1.572	1.587	1.650	Levamfetamine succinate
1.577	—	1.603	Phenylpropylmethylamine.HCl
1.586	1.604	1.703	Tolazoline.HCl
			Tranquilizers
ca 1.515	—	ca 1.544	Meprobamate
1.530	1.536	1.546	Ethinamate
1.572	1.585	1.590	Glutethimide
1.584	—	>1.735	Chlorpromazine.HCl
1.589	1.609	1.700	Thiopropazate.2HCl
1.634	ca 1.710	>1.780	Chlordiazepoxide.HCl
1.638	1.647	1.674	Azacyclonol.HCl

47.029   Nomograph relating absorbance, concentration, and absorptivity (1 cm cell)

(A straight edge placed at known values on two appropriate axes (i.e., absorbance and absorptivity) will intersect the corresponding value on the third axis (i.e., concentration).)

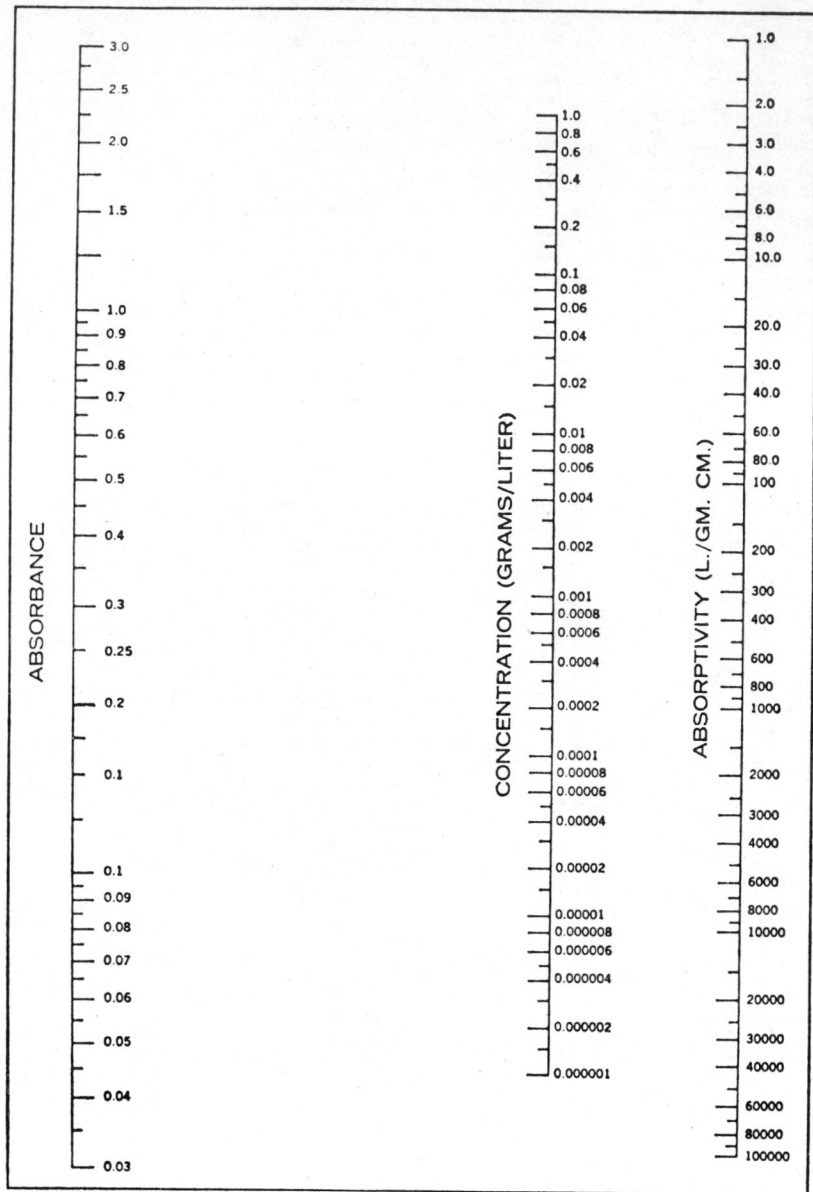

Reprinted from *The Analyzer* **4**, No. 2 (1963)
Beckman Instruments, Inc., Fullerton, Calif.

Index

Entries usually will be found under the constituent sought rather than under the product in which it is to be determined, *e.g.*, the determination of potassium in fruits will be found under potassium rather than under fruits. Commodities and products may often be located more easily through the Table of Contents.

Secondary determinations, (*e.g.*, water-soluble ash) have been included with the primary determination (ash). Negative prefixes (*e.g.*, *non*sugar, *un*fermentable) are usually not indexed when there is a corresponding positive entry for the same determination.

Ordinary reagents are not indexed unless they are "named" (*e.g.*, Keller-Kiliani reagent) or are likely to be useful in other methods (*e.g.*, coupling reagent). Buffer solutions are indexed only if a specific pH is given in the description.

The number in brackets at the end of a line listing a chemical is the *Chemical Abstracts Service* registry number. If two compounds are listed on the same line, the entry refers to the first.

In placing entries, positional prefixes are ignored (*e.g.*, numerals, Greek letters unless spelled out, *o-*, *m-*, *p-*, atomic symbols, etc.). The hyphen is considered a space unless this will separate related compounds.

Acidity (*Contd.*)

cordials and liqueurs, 155
dressings for food, 517
ether extract, of eggs and egg products, 288
fat of grain products, 222
fat of wheat flour, 214
fruits and fruit products, 377
gelatin dessert powders, 390
grain and stock feeds, 132
honey, 548
mayonnaise and salad dressing, 517
milk, 245
nonalcoholic beverages and concentrates, 192
prepared mustard, 576
roasted coffee, 238
starch conversion products, 555
tragacanth, 708
vinegar, 520
wines, 187
wort, 179

Acidity, titratable, in fruits and fruit products, 377
in milk, 245

Acidity, volatile, in fruits, 377
in wines, 187

Acids, in beer, 160
in bread, 225, 226
butter, 268–271
canned vegetable products, 561
color additives, 605
cordials and liqueurs, 155
cream, 263
crude and refined oils, 446
eggs and egg products, 288–292
fish and other marine products, 297–302
fruit and fruit products, 377–385
honey, 548
hops, 176
nonalcoholic beverages and concentrates, 192
oils, fats, and waxes, 446–457
spirits, 150
vinegars, 520
wines, 187–188

Acids, alpha and beta, in hops, 176

Acids, common, various strength solutions, table, 888
safety aspects, 880

Acids, fatty, in face powder, 611
in oils, fats, and waxes, 449, 455
isolated trans isomers, 453
separation, 226

Acids, fatty, free, in crude and refined oils, 446

Acids, fatty, methyl esters of, in oils, fats, and waxes, 454, 455

Acids, fatty, volatile, in eggs and egg products, 290
in fish and other marine products, 297, 300

Acids, fatty, water-insoluble, in butter, 269–271
in cream, 263
eggs and egg products, 292

Acids, fixed, in spirits, 150

Acids, free fatty, in fats and oils, 446

Acids, organic, foreign, in fruits, 384

Acids, polyunstaurated, 450–453

Acids, soluble, in fats and oils, 446

Acids, volatile, in beer, 160
in bread, separation, 226
butter, 271
cream, 263

nonalcoholic beverages and concentrates, 193
oils, fats, and waxes, 446
spirits, 150
vinegar, 520
wine, 187

Acidulants, 330

Aconitine, in aconite root, 624   [1 353 704]
microchemical test, 709
optical properties, 952, 960

Acrospire, length of, malt, 166

Active. *See also* specific constituent

Active chlorine, in chloramine T, 98

Activity index, nitrogen, of urea-formaldehyde compounds, 19

Adamkiewicz test, for proteins, 123

Added. *See* specific constituent

Additives, color, 575–605
analysis, 582–588

Additives, flavoring, in vanilla extracts, 317

Additives, food, direct, 330–360
indirect, 361–366

Adrenalin. *See* Epinephrine

Adsorption column for sugars, 545

Adsorption index, for alumina and magnesia, 765

Aerobic plate count, of foods, 843

Aerosol OT solution, standard, 346

Aflatoxins, 426–438
bioassay, 436–438

Agar, in meats and meat products,   [PM9 002 180] 396
test for, 705

Agar media. *See* specific test

Agricultural liming materials, 1–7

AI. *See* Activity index

Aklomide, in feeds, 728   [3 011 890]

Alba Red, analysis, 586   [6 371 557]

Albumin, in evaporated milk, 265   [PM9 006 502]
in milk, 249

Albumin nitrogen, in liquid eggs, 284

Albuminoid nitrogen, in feeds, 125

Alcohol, aldehyde-free, 322, 563   [64 175]
by hydrometer, 146
oxidation, 183
refraction, 146
specific gravity, 145
Williams field test, 146
for spectrophotometry, 764
safety aspects, 882
tables: immersion refractometer readings corresponding to specific gravity, 154
various strength solutions, 888
volume from specific gravity, 889
volume from immersion refractometer readings and refractive indices, 908
weight corresponding to volume, 914

Alcohol, in almond extract, 325
in beer, 158, 159
cassia, cinnamon, and clove extracts, 326
cordials and liqueurs, 154
cosmetics, 606
drugs, 619
fruit and fruit products, 369
ginger extract, 326
lemon, orange, and lime extracts and flavors, 320
nonalcoholic beverages and concentrates, 192